Jane's
FIGHTING SHIPS

Edited by Captain Richard Sharpe OBE RN

Ninety-seventh edition
1994-95

Founded in 1897 by Fred T Jane

Copyright © 1994 by Jane's Information Group Limited, Sentinel House, 163 Brighton Road, Coulsdon, Surrey CR5 2NH, UK

In the USA and its dependencies
Jane's Information Group Inc, 1340 Braddock Place, Suite 300, Alexandria, VA 22314-1651, USA

British Library Cataloguing-in-Publication Data.
A catalogue record for this book is available from the British Library.

Printed and bound in Great Britain by Butler and Tanner Limited, Frome and London

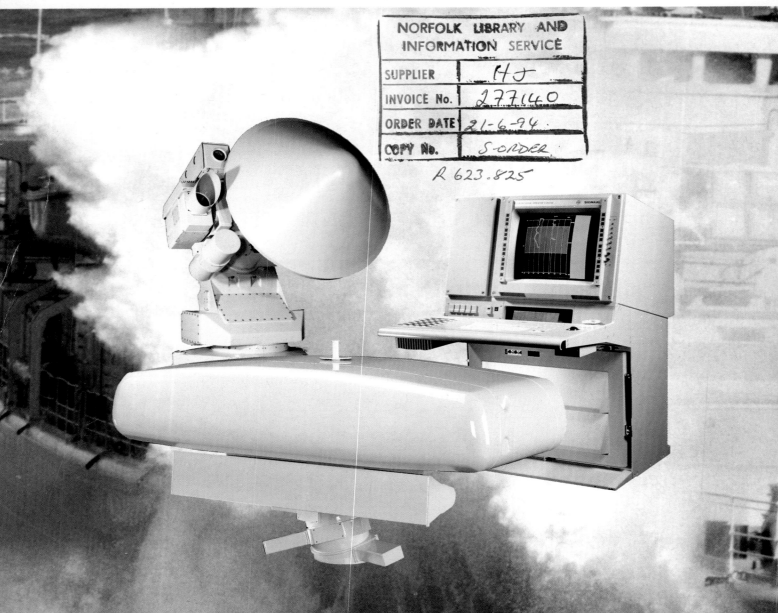

DIFFERENT SHAPES, SAME PERFECTION

An unparalleled combination for small to medium patrol craft

Developed from the same high tech designs as SIGNAAL's blue water fleet versions, compact, lightweight, state-of-the-art systems such as TACTICOS, STING and VARIANT are perfectly suited to guard Exclusive Economic Zones (EEZ's) and to protect valuable sea lanes.

Integrated into a Fully Distributed architecture, SIGNAAL's latest SEWACO FD configuration provides a technical solution today for the requirements of tomorrow. Reduced manpower, commonality of components and corresponding low cost make this integrated system as impressive as some ocean waves.

The core of the SEWACO FD system is the TACTICOS Command & Control system. A variable number of Multifunction Operator Consoles (MOC) with excellent high definition full-colour presentation,

fabulous processing power and Ada programming, make TACTICOS a flexible system.

Using advanced processing techniques, the STING dual-band gun and missile fire control director acquires and tracks very small and fast manoeuvring targets automatically. A TV/IR camera permits passive operations.

The VARIANT surveillance and target indication radar combines a dual-band pulse doppler main radar and a single-band Low Probability of Intercept CW radar to provide Air/Surveillance target detection and tracking. Meticulous surface target tracking (TWS) provides superior gun-fire targeting accuracy.

Different shapes, same perfection and increased performance supplied by SIGNAAL.

Hollandse Signaalapparaten B.V.   P.O. Box 42   7550 GD Hengelo Ov   The Netherlands   Telephone +31.74.488111   Fax +31.74.425936

SIGNAAL   SPECIALISTS IN NAVAL COMBAT SYSTEMS

F46E

FIRST SIGHT.

FIRST STRIKE.

Dusk. The constant surveillance of a nation's maritime frontiers goes on. Watches change, but the equipment remains on continuous alert.

The watchful eyes of the nation.

A supreme responsibility that demands the supreme vision of Pilkington Optronics – manufacturers of the most advanced submarine periscope and mast systems – from midget to nuclear – to 14 of today's navies.

Pilkington Optronics non-hull penetrating sensor systems keep them at the leading edge of technology.

The far-seeing naval forces of tomorrow.

PILKINGTON
OPTRONICS

Barr & Stroud Limited
1 Linthouse Road, Govan, Glasgow G51 4BZ
Telephone: 041-440 4000
Fax: 041-440 4001

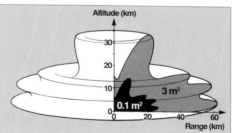 

Contents

ADMINISTRATION

Publishing Director: Robert Hutchinson

Managing Editor: Keith Faulkner

Yearbook Editorial Production Manager: Ruth Simmance

Senior Production Editor: Diana Burns

Marketing Manager: Ruth Jowett

EDITORIAL OFFICES

Jane's Information Group Limited, Sentinel House,
163 Brighton Road, Coulsdon, Surrey CR5 2NH, United Kingdom

Tel: 081 763 1030 International +44 81 763 1030
Telex: 916907 Janes G
Fax: 081 763 1006 International +44 81 763 1006

SALES OFFICES

Send enquiries to:
Fabiana Angelini, International Sales Manager,
Jane's Information Group Limited, UK address as above

Send USA enquiries to:
Joe McHale, Senior Vice-President Product Sales,
Jane's Information Group Inc, 1340 Braddock Place, Suite 300,
Alexandria, VA 22314-1651

Tel: +1 703 683 3700
Telex: 6819193
Fax: +1 703 836 0029

ADVERTISEMENT SALES OFFICES

Advertisement Sales Manager: Sandie Palmer

Australia: Brendan Gullifer, Havre & Gullifer (PTY) Ltd, 253
Richardson Street, Middle Park, Victoria 3206

Tel: +61 3 6960288
Fax: +61 3 6966951

Brazil: L Bilyk, Brazmedia International S/C Ltda, Alameda Gabriel
Monteiro da Silva, 366 CEP, 01442, São Paulo

Tel: +55 11 853 4133
Telex: 32836 BMED BR
Fax: +55 11 852 6485

France: Patrice Février, Jane's Information Group – France,
BP 418, 35 avenue MacMahon, F-75824 Paris

Tel: +33 1 45 72 33 11
Fax: +33 1 45 72 17 95

Germany and Austria: Rainer Vogel, Media Services International,
Schwabenbergstrasse 12, D-82275 Emmering, Germany

Tel: +49 8141 42534
Fax: +49 8141 6706

Hong Kong: Jeremy Miller, Major Media Ltd, Room 142, 14F Capitol
Centre, 5-19 Jardine's Bazaar, Causeway Bay

Tel: +852 890 3110
Fax: +852 576 3397

Israel: Oreet Ben-Yaacov, Oreet International Media, 15 Kineret
Street, 51201 Bene-Berak

Tel: +972 3 570 6527
Fax: +972 3 570 6526

Italy and Switzerland: Ediconsult Internazionale Srl, Piazza Fontane
Marose 3, I-16123 Genoa, Italy

Tel: +39 10 583684
Telex: 281197 EDINT I
Fax: +39 10 566578

Korea: Young Seoh Chinn, JES Media International, 6th Floor,
Donghye Bldg, 47-16 Myungit Dong, Kangdong-gu, Seoul 134-070,
Korea

Tel: +82 2 481 3411
Fax: +82 2 481 3414

Scandinavia: Gillian Thompson, First Call International,
11 Chardmore Road, London N16 6JA, UK.

Tel: +44 81 806 2301/3538
Fax: + 44 81 806 8137

Singapore, Indonesia, Malaysia, Philippines, Taiwan and Thailand:
Hoo Siew Sai, Major Media (Singapore) Pte Ltd, 6th Floor, 52 Chin
Swee Road, Singapore 0316

Tel: +65 738 0122
Telex: RS 43370 AMPLS
Fax: +65 738 2108

Spain: Jesus Moran Iglesias, Varex SA, Modesto Lafuente 4,
E-28010 Madrid

Tel: +34 1 448 7622
Fax: +34 1 446 0198

United States and Canada: Kimberly S Hanson, Director of
Advertising Sales and Marketing, Jane's Information Group Inc, 1340
Braddock Place, Suite 300, Alexandria, VA 22314-1651

Tel: +1 703 683 3700
Telex: 6819193
Fax: +1 703 836 0029

USA Mid-Atlantic: Jennifer Felix, Regional Representative
(address as above)

United States and Canada: Maureen Nute, Advertising Production
Manager
(see United States and Canada)

USA South Eastern – Regional Manager: Kristin Schulze
(see United States and Canada)

USA and Canada – Northeastern Regional Manager: Melissa C
Gunning
(see United States and Canada)

USA and Canada – Western Regional Manager: Anne Marie St.
John-Brooks, Jane's Information Group, 1523 Rollins Road,
Burlingame, CA 94010

Tel: +1 415 259 9982
Fax: +1 415 259 9751

United Kingdom/Rest of World: Sandie Palmer, Jane's Information
Group, Sentinel House, 163 Brighton Road, Coulsdon, Surrey
CR5 2NH

Tel: 081 763 1030 International +44 81 763 1030
Telex: 916907 Janes G
Fax: 081 763 1006 International +44 81 763 0643

Administration: Tara Betts, Jane's Information Group
(see United Kingdom)

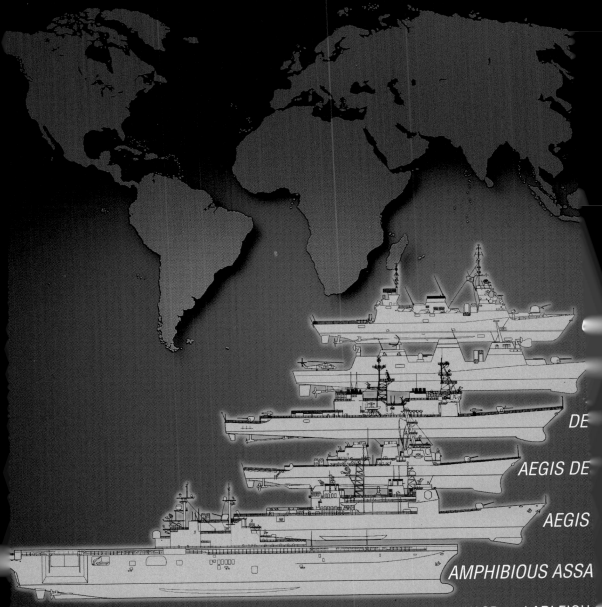

Alphabetical list of advertisers

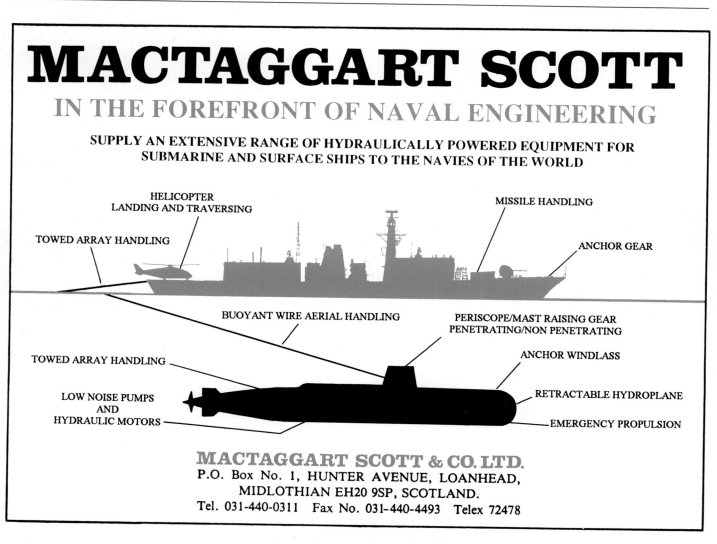

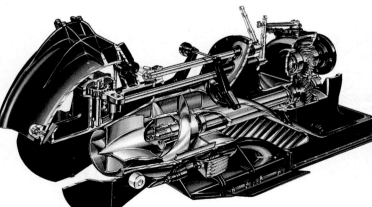

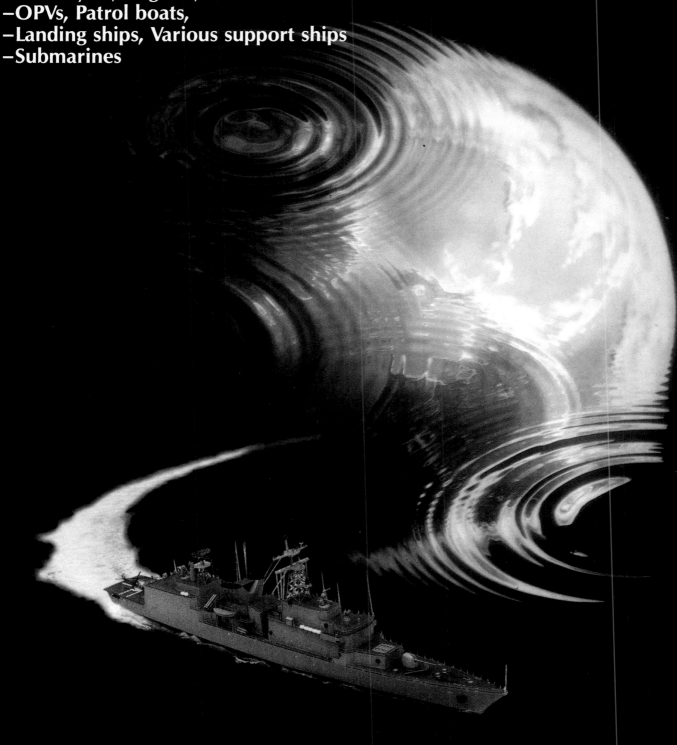

Classified list of advertisers

The companies advertising in this publication have informed us that they are involved in the fields of manufacture indicated below:

Acoustic range equipment
Safare-Crouzet

Acoustic transducers
Safare-Crouzet

Action information systems
Hollandse Signaalapparaten

Air cushion vehicles
Hyundai Heavy Industries
Korea Tacoma Marine
Royal Schelde

Air independent propulsion systems
NEVESBU

Aircraft arresting gear
MacTaggart Scott

Aircraft carriers
C. I. S. DEG
Empresa Nacional Bazan
Sperry Marine

Air-sea rescue launches
FR Lürssen Werft

Ammunition fuzes
Matra Défense

Ammunition hoists
MacTaggart Scott

Amphibious ships
Chantiers de l'Atlantique
Hyundai Heavy Industries
Ingalls Shipbuilding
Korea Tacoma Marine
NEVESBU
Wärtsilä Diesel
Yarrow Shipbuilders

Antennas
Elettronica
Hollandse Signaalapparaten
Sperry Marine

Anti-aircraft weapon systems
Matra Défense

Anti-ship weapon systems
Hollandse Signaalapparaten
Matra Défense

Anti-submarine weapon systems
Loral Librascope
Matra Défense

Artificial intelligence
Hollandse Signaalapparaten
Wärtsilä Diesel

Assault vessels
Chantiers de l'Atlantique
Crestitalia
Daewoo Shipbuilding & Heavy
  Machinery
Empresa Nacional Bazan
FR Lürssen Werft
Hyundai Heavy Industries
Ingalls Shipbuilding
Wärtsilä Diesel

Automatic control systems
Empresa Nacional Bazan
Riva Calzoni
Safare-Crouzet

Auxiliary machinery
Cincinnati Gear Company
Empresa Nacional Bazan
Fincantieri
Wärtsilä Diesel

Auxiliary propulsion systems
Empresa Nacional Bazan
Leroux et Lotz Naval
MacTaggart Scott
MagneTek
Riva Calzoni
Wärtsilä Diesel

Auxiliary vessels
Chantiers de l'Atlantique
Daewoo Shipbuilding & Heavy
  Machinery
Empresa Nacional Bazan
Fincantieri
FR Lürssen Werft
Hyundai Heavy Industries
Leroux et Lotz Naval
Wärtsilä Diesel
Yarrow Shipbuilders

Boilers
Daewoo Shipbuilding & Heavy
  Machinery
Hyundai Heavy Industries

Bulk carriers
Chantiers de l'Atlantique
Daewoo Shipbuilding & Heavy
  Machinery
Fincantieri
Hyundai Heavy Industries
NEVESBU

Sperry Marine
Wärtsilä Diesel

Cable-laying vessels
Daewoo Shipbuilding & Heavy
  Machinery
Fincantieri
Hyundai Heavy Industries
Wärtsilä Diesel

Car ferries
Chantiers de l'Atlantique
Daewoo Shipbuilding & Heavy
  Machinery
Empresa Nacional Bazan
Fincantieri
Hyundai Heavy Industries
Leroux et Lotz Naval
NEVESBU
Royal Schelde
Sperry Marine
Wärtsilä Diesel

Cargo handling equipment
Hyundai Heavy Industries

Cargo ships
Chantiers de l'Atlantique
Daewoo Shipbuilding & Heavy
  Machinery
Fincantieri
Leroux et Lotz Naval
NEVESBU
Royal Schelde
Sperry Marine
Wärtsilä Diesel

**Catamarans, multi-role, high-speed
  and workboats**
Crestitalia
Daewoo Shipbuilding & Heavy
  Machinery
Empresa Nacional Bazan
Fincantieri
Hyundai Heavy Industries
Intermarine
Royal Schelde
Sperry Marine
Wärtsilä Diesel

Centralised & automatic control
Empresa Nacional Bazan
Riva Calzoni
Safare-Crouzet

Chaff systems
Loral Hycor
Matra Défense

[12]

ALENIA ELSAG SISTEMI NAVALI. ADVANCED ELECTRONICS FOR SAILING IN SAFE WATERS.

Alenia Elsag Sistemi Navali has specialized for more than 30 years in advanced electronic systems. The Company, which is coordinated by Alenia, operates producing search radars, command and control systems, surface-to-air missile systems, radar and electro-optical tracking systems, sonar systems for surface and underwater units, all operational with the Italian Navy and with those of many other countries. These reliable high technology systems guarantee the safety and defense of those who work at sea. Alenia Elsag Sistemi Navali makes sailing in safe waters a reality.

Alenia Elsag
Sistemi Navali

A   F I N M E C C A N I C A   C O M P A N Y

[13]

CLASSIFIED LIST OF ADVERTISERS

Coast guards
Crestitalia
Daewoo Shipbuilding & Heavy
    Machinery
Empresa Nacional Bazan
Fincantieri
FR Lürssen Werft
Hyundai Heavy Industries
Intermarine
Korea Tacoma Marine
Leroux et Lotz Naval
Safare-Crouzet
Sperry Marine
Wärtsilä Diesel

Coastal and inshore minesweepers
Crestitalia
Empresa Nacional Bazan
FR Lürssen Werft
Intermarine
Wärtsilä Diesel
Yarrow Shipbuilders

Combat support boats
C. I. S. DEG
Crestitalia
Daewoo Shipbuilding & Heavy
    Machinery
Empresa Nacional Bazan
FR Lürssen Werft
Hyundai Heavy Industries

Combat systems engineering
C. I. S. DEG
Empresa Nacional Bazan
Hollandse Signaalapparaten
Ingalls Shipbuilding
Loral Librascope
Safare-Crouzet
Yarrow Shipbuilders

Computers
Hollandse Signaalapparaten

**Construction, extension and
    modernisation**
Empresa Nacional Bazan
Hyundai Heavy Industries
Wärtsilä Diesel

Container ships
Chantiers de l'Atlantique
Daewoo Shipbuilding & Heavy
    Machinery
Fincantieri
Hyundai Heavy Industries
NEVESBU
Sperry Marine
Wärtsilä Diesel

Corvettes
C. I. S. DEG
Chantiers de l'Atlantique
Daewoo Shipbuilding & Heavy
    Machinery
Empresa Nacional Bazan
Eurocorvette

FR Lürssen Werft
Hyundai Heavy Industries
Ingalls Shipbuilding
Korea Tacoma Marine
NEVESBU
Royal Schelde
Sperry Marine
Wärtsilä Diesel
Yarrow Shipbuilders

Countermeasures
Elettronica
Loral Hycor
Loral Librascope
MacTaggart Scott
Matra Défense
Safare-Crouzet
Sperry Marine

Craneships
Daewoo Shipbuilding & Heavy
    Machinery
Fincantieri
Hyundai Heavy Industries
NEVESBU
Sperry Marine
Wärtsilä Diesel

Cruisers
C. I. S. DEG
Chantiers de l'Atlantique
Fincantieri
Ingalls Shipbuilding
Sperry Marine
Wärtsilä Diesel

Customs
Crestitalia
Daewoo Shipbuilding & Heavy
    Machinery
Leroux et Lotz Naval

Data links
Empresa Nacional Bazan
Hollandse Signaalapparaten
Sperry Marine

Data recording systems
Empresa Nacional Bazan
Hollandse Signaalapparaten
Wärtsilä Diesel

Deck machinery
Hyundai Heavy Industries
MacTaggart Scott
Riva Calzoni

Decoy systems
Loral Hycor
Safare-Crouzet

Deep ocean survey
Safare-Crouzet

Defence contractors
C. I. S. DEG
Elettronica

Hollandse Signaalapparaten
MagneTek
Safare-Crouzet
Wärtsilä Diesel

Degaussing systems
MagneTek

Design of warships
Daewoo Shipbuilding & Heavy
    Machinery
Empresa Nacional Bazan
Hyundai Heavy Industries
Ingalls Shipbuilding
FR Lürssen Werft
Korea Tacoma Marine
NEVESBU
Royal Schelde
Yarrow Shipbuilders

Destroyers
C. I. S. DEG
Chantiers de l'Atlantique
Empresa Nacional Bazan
Fincantieri
Hyundai Heavy Industries
Ingalls Shipbuilding
Korea Tacoma Marine
NEVESBU
Sperry Marine
Wärtsilä Diesel
Yarrow Shipbuilers

Diesel engines
Empresa Nacional Bazan
Hyundai Heavy Industries
SEMT Pielstick
Wärtsilä Diesel

Digital databus systems, shipborne
Alenia Elsag Sistemi Navali
Empresa Nacional Bazan
Hollandse Signaalapparaten

Display systems
Hollandse Signaalapparaten
Sperry Marine
Wärtsilä Diesel

Diving equipment
Safare-Crouzet

Diving systems
Safare-Crouzet

Diving vessels
Daewoo Shipbuilding & Heavy
    Machinery
Hyundai Heavy Industries
Korea Tacoma Marine
Leroux et Lotz Naval
Wärtsilä Diesel

Dredgers
Chantiers de l'Atlantique
Daewoo Shipbuilding & Heavy
    Machinery
Hyundai Heavy Industries

HYUNDAI
TELLS WARSHIP TECHNOLOGY

The leading shipbuilder, HYUNDAI, has shown its excellence in building sophisticated naval & auxiliary ships with good performance record.

We know what advanced navies in the world require to reinforce defense system. HYUNDAI always aims to take initiative in complying with those requirements with top Quality and Cost Efficiency.

HYUNDAI
HEAVY INDUSTRIES CO., LTD.
Special & Naval Shipbuilding Division

1,Cheonha-dong,Ulsan,Korea Telex:K52452 Tel:Ulsan 30-2840/2080 Seoul 746-4671 Fax:(522)30-3491

Sperry Marine
Wärtsilä Diesel

Dry cargo vessel
Chantiers de l'Atlantique
Daewoo Shipbuilding & Heavy
  Machinery
Fincantieri
Hyundai Heavy Industries
Ingalls Shipbuilding
NEVESBU
Sperry Marine
Wärtsilä Diesel

Dynamic positioning
Riva Calzoni

Early warning systems
Ericsson Radar
Hollandse Signaalapparaten

Echo sounders
Safare-Crouzet

Electrical equipment
MagneTek

Electrohydraulic auxiliaries
Hyundai Heavy Industries
Riva Calzoni

Electro-optics
Elettronica
Ericsson Radar
Hollandse Signaalapparaten
Pilkington Optronics

Electronic countermeasure
Elettronica
Empresa Nacional Bazan
Loral Hycor
Loral Librascope
Matra Défense
Pilkington Optronics
Safare-Crouzet
Sperry Marine

Electronic equipment
Empresa Nacional Bazan
MagneTek
Matra Défense
Riva Calzoni
Safare-Crouzet
Sperry Marine
Wärtsilä Diesel

Electronic warfare
Elettronica
Ericsson Radar
Safare-Crouzet

Engines, diesel
Empresa Nacional Bazan
Fincantieri
Hyundai Heavy Industries
SEMT Pielstick
Wärtsilä Diesel

Engines, gas-turbine
Empresa Nacional Bazan
Hyundai Heavy Industries

Engines, steam turbine
Empresa Nacional Bazan

Equipment protection
MagneTek

Fast attack craft
C. I. S. DEG
Crestitalia
Daewoo Shipbuilding & Heavy
  Machinery
Empresa Nacional Bazan
Fincantieri
FR Lürssen Werft
Hyundai Heavy Industries
Ingalls Shipbuilding
Royal Schelde
Wärtsilä Diesel
Yarrow Shipbuilders

Fast patrol craft
Crestitalia
Daewoo Shipbuilding & Heavy
  Machinery
Empresa Nacional Bazan
Fincantieri
Hyundai Heavy Industries
Ingalls Shipbuilding
Intermarine
Korea Tacoma Marine
Leroux et Lotz Naval
Royal Schelde
Sperry Marine
Wärtsilä Diesel
Yarrow Shipbuilders

Fast strike craft
Crestitalia
Daewoo Shipbuilding & Heavy
  Machinery
Empresa Nacional Bazan
FR Lürssen Werft
Ingalls Shipbuilding
Royal Schelde
Wärtsilä Diesel
Yarrow Shipbuilders

Fast offshore patrol and attack craft
Crestitalia
Daewoo Shipbuilding & Heavy
  Machinery
Empresa Nacional Bazan
Fincantieri
FR Lürssen Werft
Ingalls Shipbuilding
Intermarine
Korea Tacoma Marine
NEVESBU
Royal Schelde
Wärtsilä Diesel
Yarrow Shipbuilders

Fast warship design service
Daewoo Shipbuilding & Heavy
  Machinery
Empresa Nacional Bazan
FR Lürssen Werft
Ingalls Shipbuilding
Korea Tacoma Marine
NEVESBU
Royal Schelde

Ferries
Chantiers de l'Atlantique
Daewoo Shipbuilding & Heavy
  Machinery
Empresa Nacional Bazan
Fincantieri
FR Lürssen Werft
Korea Tacoma Marine
Leroux et Lotz Naval
NEVESBU
Royal Schelde
Sperry Marine
Wärtsilä Diesel

**Fibreglass vessels and other
  products**
Crestitalia
Intermarine
Leroux et Lotz Naval

Fibre optics
Hollandse Signaalapparaten
Safare-Crouzet
Sperry Marine

Fire-control systems
Empresa Nacional Bazan
Ericsson Radar
Hollandse Signaalapparaten
Loral Librascope
Pilkington Optronics

Firefighting ships
Daewoo Shipbuilding & Heavy
  Machinery
FR Lürssen Werft
Korea Tacoma Marine
Leroux et Lotz Naval
Wärtsilä Diesel

Fishery protection
FR Lürssen Werft
Leroux et Lotz Naval

Flares
Loral Hycor

Frigates
C. I. S. DEG
Chantiers de l'Atlantique
Daewoo Shipbuilding & Heavy
  Machinery
Empresa Nacional Bazan
Fincantieri
Hyundai Heavy Industries
Ingalls Shipbuilding
Korea Tacoma Marine

[17]

NEVESBU
Royal Schelde
Sperry Marine
Wärtsilä Diesel
Yarrow Shipbuilders

Gas-turbines
Empresa Nacional Bazan

Generators, diesel
Empresa Nacional Bazan
SEMT Pielstick
Wärtsilä Diesel

Glassfibre vessels and other products
FR Lürssen Werft
Wärtsilä Diesel
Yarrow Shipbuilders

Guided missile systems
FR Lürssen Werft
Matra Défense
NEVESBU
Royal Schelde
Wärtsilä Diesel

Guided missile ships
Chantiers de l'Atlantique
Daewoo Shipbuilding & Heavy
 Machinery
Ingalls Shipbuilding
Matra Défense
Yarrow Shipbuilding

Harbour defence vessels
Crestitalia
Daewoo Shipbuilding & Heavy
 Machinery
FR Lürssen Werft
Ingalls Shipbuilding
Wärtsilä Diesel

Helicopters
Riva Calzoni

High energy laser systems
Pilkington Optronics

Hydraulic equipment
MacTaggart Scott
Riva Calzoni

Hydrofoils
C. I. S. DEG
Fincantieri
Hyundai Heavy Industries
Safare-Crouzet
Sperry Marine

Hydraulic survey equipment/vessels
Daewoo Shipbuilding & Heavy
 Machinery
FR Lürssen Werft
Hyundai Heavy Industries

Hydrographic survey equipment/ vessels
Crestitalia
Daewoo Shipbuilding & Heavy
 Machinery
Empresa Nacional Bazan
Leroux et Lotz Naval
NEVESBU
Wärtsilä Diesel
Yarrow Shipbuilders

Icebreakers
Sperry Marine
Wärtsilä Diesel

IFF radar
Ericsson Radar

Infra-red systems
Elettronica
Ericsson Radar
Hollandse Signaalapparaten
Pilkington Optronics

Instruments
Hollandse Signaalapparaten
Safare-Crouzet
Sperry Marine

Integrated communications systems
Empresa Nacional Bazan
Safare-Crouzet
Sperry Marine

Integrated logistic support
C. I. S. DEG
Elettronica
Empresa Nacional Bazan
Hollandse Signaalapparaten
Ingalls Shipbuilding
MagneTek
Pilkington Optronics
Safare-Crouzet
Sperry Marine
Wärtsilä Diesel

Intercommunications systems
Safare-Crouzet
Sperry Marine

Integrated logistic support
Empresa Nacional Bazan
Yarrow Shipbuilders

Interior design and furnishing for ships
Empresa Nacional Bazan

Landing craft
Daewoo Shipbuilding & Heavy
 Machinery
Empresa Nacional Bazan
Fincantieri
FR Lürssen Werft
Hyundai Heavy Industries
Korea Tacoma Marine

Leroux et Lotz Naval
Wärtsilä Diesel

Landing ships
Chantiers de l'Atlantique
Daewoo Shipbuilding & Heavy
 Machinery
Empresa Nacional Bazan
FR Lürssen Werft
Hyundai Heavy Industries
Ingalls Shipbuilding
Korea Tacoma Marine
Leroux et Lotz Naval
NEVESBU
Yarrow Shipbuilders
Wärtsilä Diesel

Laser systems
Ericsson Radar
Pilkington Optronics

Launches, rescue
Leroux et Lotz Naval
Wärtsilä Diesel

Lifeboats/rescue
Crestitalia
Fincantieri
Leroux et Lotz Naval

Lifts, hydraulic
MacTaggart Scott

Logistics
C. I. S. DEG
Empresa Nacional Bazan
Hollandse Signaalapparaten
Safare-Crouzet

Logistics support vessels
C. I. S. DEG
Chantiers de l'Atlantique
Daewoo Shipbuilding & Heavy
 Machinery
Empresa Nacional Bazan
Hyundai Heavy Industries
Ingalls Shipbuilding
Korea Tacoma Marine
Leroux et Lotz Naval
NEVESBU
Royal Schelde
Sperry Marine
Yarrow Shipbuilders
Wärtsilä Diesel

Magnetic measurements facilities
MagneTek

Maintenance and repair ships
Empresa Nacional Bazan
Ingalls Shipbuilding
Wärtsilä Diesel

Management services
Hollandse Signaalapparaten
Ingalls Shipbuilding

c.i.s. DEG

00161 Rome - Via Morgagni, 30/E - Telefax 4403723 - Tel.: 06/4403722 - 4403729 - 4403682 - 4403731 - 4403725

- AESN — Rome
- ALENIA — Rome
- ELETTRONICA — Rome
- ELMER — Pomezia
- OTO MELARA — La Spezia
- S.M.A. — Florence

ENGINEERING CONSORTIUM C.I.S.DEG A TOP LEVEL TECHNICAL ORGANIZATION SINCE 1974 THE MAJOR CONTRACTOR OF THE ITALIAN NAVY FOR DESIGN INTEGRATION, INSTALLATION OF COMBACT SYSTEMS ON FIGHTING UNITS

STUDIO EFFE '76 - Roma

Log meter for mercantile ship, French make and design, beginning of 20th century.

Failing ship standard compass, design by G.W. Lyth, Stockholm; end of 19th century.

Torpedo-boat Zenith clock with second and rewind indicator; beginning of 20th century.

Walker three face log with incorporated meter; end of 19th century.

Sextant, design by F.M. Jones, London; beginning of 20th century.

C.I.S.DEG ACTIVITIES

- **ADVANCED DESIGN AND ENGINEERING**
- **INTEGRATION EQUIPMENT AND SYSTEM DESIGN**
- **INSTALLATION AND SEA ACCEPTANCE TRIALS**
- **CONFIGURATION CONTROL**
- **HIGH LEVEL QUALITY CONTROL**
- **INTEGRATED LOGISTICS SUPPORT**
- **MILITARY STANDARD HANDBOOKS**

CLASSIFIED LIST OF ADVERTISERS

Marine architects
Daewoo Shipbuilding & Heavy
 Machinery
Empresa Nacional Bazan
Ingalls Shipbuilding
NEVESBU

Marine consultants
Daewoo Shipbuilding & Heavy
 Machinery
NEVESBU
Safare-Crouzet

Marine electronic equipment
Safare-Crouzet
Sperry Marine
Wärtsilä Diesel

**Marine engine monitoring and data
 recording systems**
Empresa Nacional Bazan
Safare-Crouzet
Wärtsilä Diesel

Merchant ships
Chantiers de l'Atlantique
Daewoo Shipbuilding & Heavy
 Machinery
Fincantieri
Hyundai Heavy Industries
Ingalls Shipbuilding
NEVESBU
Royal Schelde
Sperry Marine
Wärtsilä Diesel

Microwave systems
Elettronica
Hollandse Signaalapparaten

Mine countermeasure vessels
Crestitalia
FR Lürssen Werft
Intermarine
Wärtsilä Diesel
Yarrow Shipbuilders

Mine countermeasures
FR Lürssen Werft
Intermarine
MacTaggart Scott

Minehunters
C. I. S. DEG
Crestitalia
Empresa Nacional Bazan
Fincantieri
FR Lürssen Werft
Intermarine
Wärtsilä Diesel
Yarrow Shipbuilders

**Minehunting support and training
 systems**
FR Lürssen Werft
Riva Calzoni

Minelayers
Empresa Nacional Bazan
Fincantieri
FR Lürssen Werft
Hyundai Heavy Industries
Intermarine
Wärtsilä Diesel

Minesweepers
Crestitalia
Empresa Nacional Bazan
FR Lürssen Werft
Intermarine
Wärtsilä Diesel

Minesweeping equipment
MacTaggart Scott
Safare-Crouzet

Missile control systems
Ericsson Radar
Matra Défense

Missile launching systems
Loral Librascope
Matra Défense
Riva Calzoni

Missile ships
Chantiers de l'Atlantique
Crestitalia
Daewoo Shipbuilding & Heavy
 Machinery
FR Lürssen Werft
Hyundai Heavy Industries
Ingalls Shipbuilding
Matra Défense
Royal Schelde
Wärtsilä Diesel
Yarrow Shipbuilders

Motors, hydraulic
Hyundai Heavy Industries
MacTaggart Scott
Riva Calzoni

Motor Torpedo boats
FR Lürssen Werft

Naval architects
Empresa Nacional Bazan
Hyundai Heavy Industries
Ingalls Shipbuilding
NEVESBU
Yarrow Shipbuilders

Naval-based design
Daewoo Shipbuilding & Heavy
 Machinery
FR Lürssen Werft
Ingalls Shipbuilding
NEVESBU

Naval guns
Empresa Nacional Bazan

Naval patrol vessels
Crestitalia

Daewoo Shipbuilding & Heavy
 Machinery
Empresa Nacional Bazan
Eurocorvette
Fincantieri
FR Lürssen Werft
Hyundai Heavy Industries
Ingalls Shipbuilding
Intermarine
Korea Tacoma Marine
Leroux et Lotz Naval
NEVESBU
Sperry Marine
Royal Schelde
Wärtsilä Diesel
Yarrow Shipbuilders

Naval radar
Ericsson Radar
Hollandse Signaalapparaten
Sperry Marine

Naval systems, installation
C. I. S. DEG
Empresa Nacional Bazan
Hollandse Signaalapparaten
Hyundai Heavy Industries
Ingalls Shipbuilding
Safare-Crouzet
Sperry Marine

**Naval systems, planning and
 integration**
C. I. S. DEG
Hollandse Signaalapparaten
Ingalls Shipbuilding
Riva Calzoni
Safare-Crouzet
Sperry Marine

Navigations aids
Sperry Marine

Night vision systems
Elettronica
Hollandse Signaalapparaten
Pilkington Optronics

Non-hull penetrating masts
MacTaggart Scott
Pilkington Optronics
Riva Calzoni
Sperry Marine

Non-magnetic minesweepers
FR Lürssen Werft
Wärtsilä Diesel
Yarrow Shipbuilders

Oceanographic survey ships
Chantiers de l'Atlantique
Crestitalia
Daewoo Shipbuilding & Heavy
 Machinery
Empresa Nacional Bazan
FR Lürssen Werft
Hyundai Heavy Industries

[20]

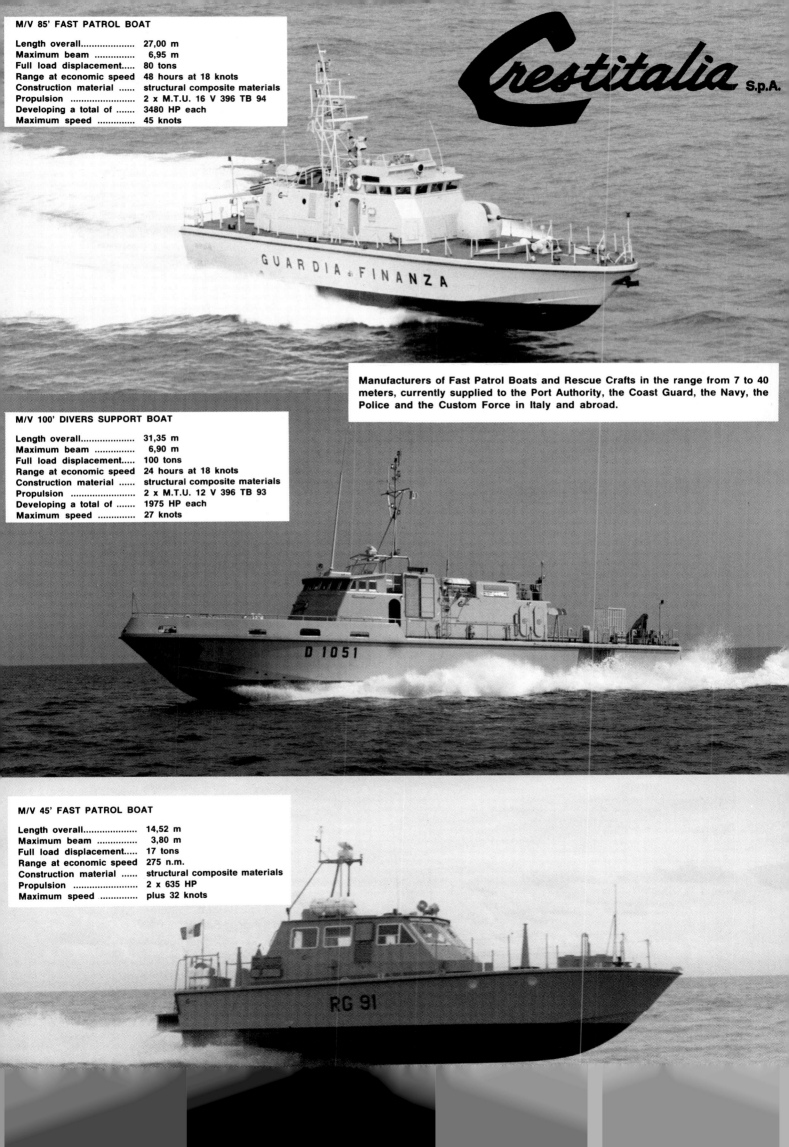

M/V 85' FAST PATROL BOAT

Length overall.....................	27,00 m
Maximum beam	6,95 m
Full load displacement.....	80 tons
Range at economic speed	48 hours at 18 knots
Construction material	structural composite materials
Propulsion	2 x M.T.U. 16 V 396 TB 94
Developing a total of	3480 HP each
Maximum speed	45 knots

Crestitalia S.p.A.

Manufacturers of Fast Patrol Boats and Rescue Crafts in the range from 7 to 40 meters, currently supplied to the Port Authority, the Coast Guard, the Navy, the Police and the Custom Force in Italy and abroad.

M/V 100' DIVERS SUPPORT BOAT

Length overall....................	31,35 m
Maximum beam	6,90 m
Full load displacement.....	100 tons
Range at economic speed	24 hours at 18 knots
Construction material	structural composite materials
Propulsion	2 x M.T.U. 12 V 396 TB 93
Developing a total of	1975 HP each
Maximum speed	27 knots

M/V 45' FAST PATROL BOAT

Length overall....................	14,52 m
Maximum beam	3,80 m
Full load displacement.....	17 tons
Range at economic speed	275 n.m.
Construction material	structural composite materials
Propulsion	2 x 635 HP
Maximum speed	plus 32 knots

Intermarine
Korea Tacoma Marine
Leroux et Lotz Naval
NEVESBU
Wärtsilä Diesel
Yarrow Shipbuilders

Offshore patrol vessels
Chantiers de l'Atlantique
Daewoo Shipbuilding & Heavy
 Machinery
Empresa Nacional Bazan
Fincantieri
FR Lürssen Werft
Hyundai Heavy Industries
Ingalls Shipbuilding
Intermarine
Korea Tacoma Marine
Leroux et Lotz Naval
NEVESBU
Royal Schelde
Sperry Marine
Wärtsilä Diesel
Yarrow Shipbuilders

Oil drilling rigs
Chantiers de l'Atlantique
Daewoo Shipbuilding & Heavy
 Machinery
Hyundai Heavy Industries
Sperry Marine
Wärtsilä Diesel

Oil pollution control vessels
Daewoo Shipbuilding & Heavy
 Machinery
FR Lürssen Werft
Hyundai Heavy Industries
Sperry Marine

Oil rig supply vessels and work boats
Daewoo Shipbuilding & Heavy
 Machinery
Fincantieri
Hyundai Heavy Industries
Wärtsilä Diesel

Optical equipment
Hollandse Signaalapparaten

Optronics
Hollandse Signaalapparaten
Matra Défense
Pilkington Optronics
Sperry Marine

Ordnance
Empresa Nacional Bazan

Parts for diesel engines
Empresa Nacional Bazan
Wärtsilä Diesel

Patrol boats
Crestitalia
Daewoo Shipbuilding & Heavy
 Machinery
Empresa Nacional Bazan

Fincantieri
FR Lürssen Werft
Hyundai Heavy Industries
Intermarine
Leroux et Lotz Naval
Royal Schelde
Sperry Marine
Wärtsilä Diesel

Periscopes
Pilkington Optronics
Sperry Marine

Pilot boats
Crestitalia
Hyundai Heavy Industries
Leroux et Lotz Naval
Wärtsilä Diesel

Plotting and tracking systems
Hollandse Signaalapparaten
Sperry Marine

Power supplies
Hollandse Signaalapparaten
MagneTek

Pressure vessels
Cincinnati Gear Company
Daewoo Shipbuilding & Heavy
 Machinery
Hyundai Heavy Industries
Wärtsilä Diesel

Propellers, ships
Hyundai Heavy Industries
Wärtsilä Diesel

Propulsion systems
Cincinnati Gear Company
Empresa Nacional Bazan
Fincantieri
MacTaggart Scott
SEMT Pielstick
Wärtsilä Diesel

Pumps
MacTaggart Scott

Radar antennas
Ericsson Radar
Hollandse Signaalapparaten
Sperry Marine

Radar countermeasure
Elettronica
Sperry Marine

Radar for fire-control
Ericsson Radar
Hollandse Signaalapparaten

Radar transponders
Hollandse Signaalapparaten

Radio equipment
Hollandse Signaalapparaten
Sperry Marine

Reduction gears
Cincinnati Gear Company
Royal Schelde
Wärtsilä Diesel

**Re-equipment, modernisation of
 naval vessels**
Empresa Nacional Bazan
Hollandse Signaalapparaten
Leroux et Lotz Naval
Wärtsilä Diesel

Remote power control systems
Wärtsilä Diesel

Research ships
Crestitalia
Daewoo Shipbuilding & Heavy
 Machinery
Empresa Nacional Bazan
FR Lürssen Werft
Hyundai Heavy Industries
Leroux et Lotz Naval
NEVESBU
Royal Schelde
Wärtsilä Diesel

Rocket launchers
Matra Défense

Salvage vessels
Crestitalia
Daewoo Shipbuilding & Heavy
 Machinery
Empresa Nacional Bazan
Hyundai Heavy Industries
Korea Tacoma Marine
Leroux et Lotz Naval
Wärtsilä Diesel

Search and rescue vessels
Crestitalia
Daewoo Shipbuilding & Heavy
 Machinery
Empresa Nacional Bazan
Hyundai Heavy Industries
Leroux et Lotz Naval
Royal Schelde
Wärtsilä Diesel

Ship and submarine design
Daewoo Shipbuilding & Heavy
 Machinery
Empresa Nacional Bazan
Fincantieri
Ingalls Shipbuilding
NEVESBU

Ship defence systems
Empresa Nacional Bazan
Ericsson Radar
Hollandse Signaalapparaten
Loral Hycor
Pilkington Optronics

Ship machinery
Empresa Nacional Bazan

FINCANTIERI
IS BUILDING FOR THE SEA

D 560

L 9892

 IRI GRUPPO

FINCANTIERI
Cantieri Navali Italiani S.p.A.

NAVAL SHIPBUILDING DIVISION
16129 Genova/Italy Via Cipro 11
Tel. (0) 10 59951 Tlx 270168 FINCGE I
Fax (0) 10 5995379

Riva Calzoni
SEMT Pielstick
Wärtsilä Diesel

Ship repair/refit
Daewoo Shipbuilding & Heavy
  Machinery
Empresa Nacional Bazan
Fincantieri
Ingalls Shipbuilding
Leroux et Lotz Naval

Ship systems engineering
C. I. S. DEG
Empresa Nacional Bazan
Hollandse Signaalapparaten
Ingalls Shipbuilding
MacTaggart Scott
NEVESBU
Wärtsilä Diesel

Simulators
Elettronica
Hollandse Signaalapparaten
Riva Calzoni

Software services
Empresa Nacional Bazan
Hollandse Signaalapparaten

Sonar decoys
Safare-Crouzet

Sonar equipment
Hollandse Signaalapparaten
Safare-Crouzet

**Sonar ranges (design and
  installation)**
Safare-Crouzet

Sonobuoys
Safare-Crouzet

Speed boats
Crestitalia
Daewoo Shipbuilding & Heavy
  Machinery
Hyundai Heavy Industries
Korea Tacoma Marine
Mathiesen's Badebyggeri

Stabilising equipment
Sperry Marine

Steam-raising plant, conventional
Empresa Nacional Bazan

Steam-raising plant, nuclear
Empresa Nacional Bazan

Steam turbines
Empresa Nacional Bazan
Hyundai Heavy Industries

Steering gear
Empresa Nacional Bazan
MacTaggart Scott

Submarine control systems
Loral Librascope
Riva Calzoni
Safare-Crouzet

Submarine-fire control
Loral Librascope

Submarine hull equipment
Riva Calzoni

Submarine mast actuation
MacTaggart Scott
Riva Calzoni

Submarine snorkels
Riva Calzoni

**Submarine control and attack
  trainers**
Loral Librascope

Submarine winches
MacTaggart Scott
Riva Calzoni

Submarines
C. I. S. DEG
Daewoo Shipbuilding & Heavy
  Machinery
Empresa Nacional Bazan
Fincantieri
Korea Tacoma Marine
NEVESBU

Submersibles
Riva Calzoni

Supply ships
Chantiers de l'Atlantique
Daewoo Shipbuilding & Heavy
  Machinery
Empresa Nacional Bazan
Fincantieri
Hyundai Heavy Industries
Leroux et Lotz Naval
NEVESBU
Royal Schelde
Wärtsilä Diesel

Support services
Daewoo Shipbuilding & Heavy
  Machinery
Hollandse Signaalapparaten
Wärtsilä Diesel
Yarrow Shipbuilders

Support service vessels
Chantiers de l'Atlantique
Empresa Nacional Bazan
Hyundai Heavy Industries
Royal Schelde
Wärtsilä Diesel

Surface effect ships
Empresa Nacional Bazan
FR Lürssen Werft

Hyundai Heavy Industries
Royal Schelde

Surveillance craft
Daewoo Shipbuilding & Heavy
  Machinery
Empresa Nacional Bazan
FR Lürssen Werft
Leroux et Lotz Naval
Wärtsilä Diesel

Tactical training simulators
Elettronica
Hollandse Signaalapparaten

Tankers
Daewoo Shipbuilding & Heavy
  Machinery
Fincantieri
Hyundai Heavy Industries
Korea Tacoma Marine
NEVESBU
Sperry Marine
Wärtsilä Diesel

Technical co-operation
C. I. S. DEG
Daewoo Shipbuilding & Heavy
  Machinery
Empresa Nacional Bazan
Hollandse Signaalapparaten
Leroux et Lotz Naval
Wärtsilä Diesel

Technical publications
C. I. S. DEG
Hollandse Signaalapparaten
Wärtsilä Diesel

Telecommunications equipment
Hollandse Signaalapparaten
Safare-Crouzet
Sperry Marine

Tenders
Chantiers de l'Atlantique
Crestitalia
Daewoo Shipbuilding & Heavy
  Machinery
FR Lürssen Werft
Hyundai Heavy Industries

Test equipment
Hollandse Signaalapparaten
Pilkington Optronics

Thermal imaging systems
Elettronica
Ericsson Radar
Hollandse Signaalapparaten
Pilkington Optronics

Throughwater communications
Safare-Crouzet

Thrusters
Wärtsilä Diesel

Torpedo control systems
Hollandse Signaalapparaten
Loral Librascope
Safare-Crouzet

Torpedo decoys
Loral Librascope
Safare-Crouzet

Torpedo handling systems
Riva Calzoni

Torpedo launching systems
Loral Librascope

Torpedo recovery vessels
Crestitalia

Towed Array Systems
MacTaggart Scott

Training equipment
C. I. S. DEG
Empresa Nacional Bazan
Hollandse Signaalapparaten
Wärtsilä Diesel

Training programmes
C. I. S. DEG
Empresa Nacional Bazan
Hollandse Signaalapparaten
Ingalls Shipbuilding
Sperry Marine
Wärtsilä Diesel

Training services
C. I. S. DEG
Empresa Nacional Bazan
Hollandse Signaalapparaten
Ingalls Shipbuilding
Sperry Marine
Wärtsilä Diesel

Transducers
Safare-Crouzet

Trawlers
Leroux et Lotz Naval

Mathiesen's Badebyggeri
Wärtsilä Diesel

Troop ships
Chantiers de l'Atlantique
Crestitalia
Empresa Nacional Bazan
Korea Tacoma Marine
Leroux et Lotz Naval
Royal Schelde
Sperry Marine
Wärtsilä Diesel

Tugs
Empresa Nacional Bazan
Daewoo Shipbuilding & Heavy
  Machinery
Hyundai Heavy Industries
Korea Tacoma Marine
Sperry Marine
Wärtsilä Diesel

Turbine gears
Cincinnati Gear Company
Empresa Nacional Bazan

Turbines
Empresa Nacional Bazan

Turbines, gas marine
Empresa Nacional Bazan
Hyundai Heavy Industries

Turbines, steam marine
Empresa Nacional Bazan
Hyundai Heavy Industries

Ultra-fast attack boats
FR Lürssen Werft
Ingalls Shipbuilding

Ultra-fast patrol boats
FR Lürssen Werft
Ingalls Shipbuilding

Underwater acoustic systems
Safare-Crouzet

Underwater communications
Safare-Crouzet

Underwater television equipment
Safare-Crouzet

Underwater warning systems
Safare-Crouzet

Warships
C. I. S. DEG
Chantiers de l'Atlantique
Daewoo Shipbuilding & Heavy
  Machinery
Empresa Nacional Bazan
Fincantieri
FR Lürssen Werft
Hyundai Heavy Industries
Ingalls Shipbuilding
Korea Tacoma Marine
NEVESBU
Royal Schelde
Yarrow Shipbuilders

Waterjet propulsion systems
Castoldi
Cincinnati Gear Company
Riva Calzoni

Weapon control systems
Empresa Nacional Bazan
Ericsson Radar
Hollandse Signaalapparaten
Loral Librascope
Matra Défense
Safare-Crouzet

Weapon systems
Empresa Nacional Bazan
Loral Librascope
Matra Défense
Safare-Crouzet

Yachts, training and royal
Chantiers de l'Atlantique
Crestitalia

Underwater acoustics and communication

- **U/RDT - 1 A** passive sonar for torpedo detection : improvement of all existing sonars on surface ships by adding detection and classification of torpedoes.
- **VELOX - M 7 :** sonar intercept.

- **QSUA - 4 A :** self noise detection.
- **TUUM - 4 A/B :** multichannel underwater telephone.
- **Internal communication systems** for surface ships and submarines.

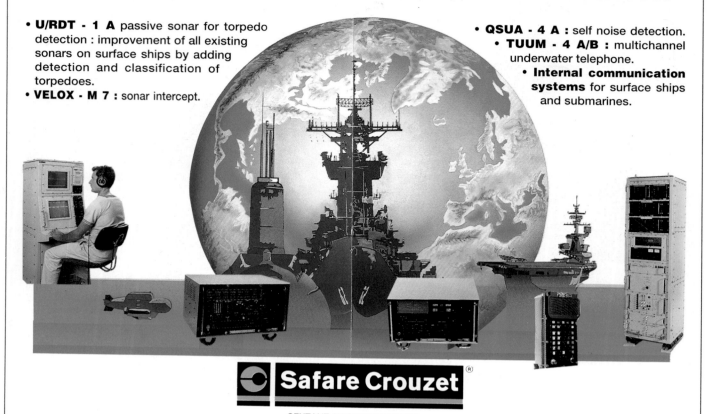

Safare Crouzet ®

SEXTANT AVIONIQUE GROUP

An important guide to the technologies and systems required to equip modern submarines to perform a wider role than currently.

Jane's Underwater Warfare Systems 1994-1995

CONTENTS

ANTI-SUBMARINE WARFARE: Command & Control/Weapons & Control Systems; Sonar Systems; Countermeasures; Communications; Electro-Optical Systems.

UNDERWATER WEAPONS: Torpedoes; Guided Weapons; Rockets; Depth Charges; Mines.

MINE WARFARE: Command & Control/Weapons & Control Systems; Sonar Systems; Mine Disposal Vehicles; Minesweeping Systems; Diver Systems

ASSOCIATED UNDERWATER WARFARE SYSTEMS: Acoustic Systems (management); Oceanography Systems; Hydrographic Survey Systems; Signature Management Training & Simulation Systems; Navigational Trainers; Radar Systems; Mission Recorder Systems; Consoles & Displays; Transducers & Transponders; Signal Processors; Weapons Test Ranges

REFER TO ORDER FORM FOR PRICE DETAILS

PATROL VESSELS

EUROCORVETTE

A naval European venture of
Bremer Vulkan, Germany
Chantiers de l'Atlantique, France

Head Office : 38, avenue Kléber - 75116 Paris - France
Tel : (33-1) 47 55 27 70 - Fax (33-1) 47 55 28 48

SSBNs have spare capacity for sub-strategic and conventional warheads.

Jane's

FIGHTING SHIPS

1994-95

Jane's Information Group Limited, Sentinel House, 163 Brighton Road, Coulsdon, Surrey CR5 2NH, UK
Jane's Information Group Inc, 1340 Braddock Place, Suite 300, Alexandria, VA 22314-1651, USA

SCHELDE SHIPBUILDING

For coastal states naval defence is of key importance. So is their selection of naval vessels, which must be reliable and technologically advanced to meet all threats. Schelde Shipbuilding, with many years of proven,

successful experience in building the most advanced naval vessels is well qualified to provide vessels designed to meet a wide range of defence criteria. Frigates, corvettes, high-speed patrol boats and fleet auxilliary support vessels: whatever the requirement, our know-how serves to fulfill your needs. Modern vessels, with compact powerful and integrated combat systems, served by a total integrated logistical support system, as required for the 21st century. When you have defined your requirements, discuss them with us. We turn your ideas into practical realities.

"OUR KNOW-HOW TURNS IDEAS INTO PRACTICAL REALITIES"

SCHELDE SHIPBUILDING
P.O. Box 16, 4380 AA Vlissingen, Holland.
Telephone (31) 1184 82118. Telefax (31) 1184 85010. Telex 37815 kms nl.

ROYAL SCHELDE

Foreword

"Soldiers are not as other men . . . View with extreme suspicion all theories and representations of war that equate it with any other activity in human affairs''. An unremarkable comment by the military historian John Keegan, but one which seems to be particularly relevant in the context of what is currently happening to those who serve in many contemporary navies.

One of the few beneficial effects of regular major wars in the first half of this century was the forced indoctrination of much of the young male population into some form of military service. Beneficial in the sense that when subsequently they reached positions of influence, whether in government, industry or the media, they had first hand knowledge that war, and training for war, was not like other activities.

Such men are now a dying breed, and those still of working age who have had military experience in the hundreds of minor campaigns since the Second World War are by comparison a very small minority. Understandably, these few have less and less influence over the majority who see Defence as just another spending department absorbing chunks of a national income, with few results that match their narrow conception of political, industrial or social cost benefits.

This process was under way long before the fall of the Berlin Wall, which signalled the end of that particular phase of the lasting confrontation between opposing forms of government, but inevitably has been much accelerated in the last four years, when the simplistic short-term case for defence spending has been harder to define. This is particularly so in Europe, whether you live east or west of the old Iron Curtain, although it has noticeably had less effect on those countries that have a tradition of lengthy national service.

Of the fighting services most affected by this growing lack of comprehension in places of influence, it is not difficult to make a case that those who go to sea are amongst the worst off. Even people who have not had military training have some feel for the concept of land/air warfare, although they might be unable to define what makes one air squadron or infantry battalion better than another.

The canvas on which the maritime battle is fought is more complex. There is a third dimension of sub-surface warfare to add to those of surface and air. In addition there is an interface with the land itself, for amphibious operations, for shore bombardment whether by ballistic or cruise missiles, seaborne aircraft or gun, and for reinforcement and resupply of land forces. Perhaps the greatest difference in terms of civilian perception is that aircraft, armoured vehicles and ground troops regularly engage in one to one combat worldwide, an activity which projects simple televisual images. Ships are no longer seen to do this, and if submarines are practising the art under water, they have not fired at each other for years, and even if they had, CNN would not have been there to record it.

The point though is not to emphasize the difference in these various forms of warfare, it is to highlight the lifestyle of the people involved and why their organisation and conditions of service need to remain responsive to some basic requirements if quality people are to be recruited and retained.

The first requirement is a sense of purpose and a sense of worth. To leave home voluntarily on a six month deployment, of which the major part will be spent in what is effectively a prison regime on the high seas, requires a solid belief in what you are doing and the certainty that others think it is worthwhile.

The second requirement is confidence in your equipment, the knowledge that it is at least as good as that of any potential enemy, that it can be relied upon to be available when required, and that the logistic backup is adequate for routine maintenance and repair.

The third necessity is belief in your own training and that of the people around you, on whose actions ultimately your survival may depend. This mutual trust is an absolute prerequisite for the running of an efficient warship.

The final requirement is that you and your family will be sufficiently rewarded to have a secure, if not affluent, future whether you survive or not.

Confidence in the politico military command and control system under which your ship is operating is an additional bonus, but any study of history will have convinced you that traditionally you have had to survive with this as an uncertain variable. Today's polyglot command and control organisations may be justifiable as a political necessity, but they do not inspire military confidence.

It is not overstating the case to say that in many navies almost every one of these conditions is being undermined.

A military sense of purpose requires an objective and an enemy. In an unstable world, those who study conflict have no difficulty in establishing that even if their country is not directly threatened today, it will be tomorrow. These experts also know that deterrence through strength comes cheaper in money and lives than fighting from weakness, and that economic and other national interests are better protected at a safe distance from the home base. This is mere sophistry to many of those who have had no military experience of any kind and can see no further than the boundaries of here and now.

As an example, a normally perceptive and intelligent journalist for a middle of the road newspaper wrote in a review of a recent television documentary on marine commandos, "Why do we need these people? What is the point in their training now that the cold war is over?" Subsequently at least half the letters commenting on the review supported the sentiment.

In the UK the Parliamentary Defence Committee in a report last year concluded that "In the event of full scale war the Royal Navy would be incapable of defending our sea routes on which we depend for our trade and the movement of our Armed Forces. It is our view that this shortcoming poses a serious and potentially fatal threat to the long term security of this country." Far from galvanising the nation, this self-evident truth was treated with a yawn of indifference by the Government and the media.

There are similar stories coming out of every democratic country with a maritime tradition, including until recently Russia, which at least for this short period in its history can be legitimately adjudged a democracy.

Submarine-launched weapons are a major threat   *H M Steele*

In such a climate, any naval hierarchy has got a tough job instilling a sense of purpose and worth into its impressionable recruits.

The second requirement for the man at sea is confidence in his equipment. If the soldier is faced by overwhelming odds he can usually retreat, or at least go to ground. Similarly, the airman can light up the after burner and may be able to survive to fight another day. Once engaged by modern weapons the surface sailor can neither run nor hide.

In the mid-1990s, the most likely form of attack against surface ships is the air flight missile. To the variety of air, surface and sub-surface missile launch platforms has been added the coastal battery. The first successful attack on a ship from a shore-based missile was in 1982 when an Argentine weapon fired from East Falkland Island hit a British destroyer which was carrying out a gunnery bombardment from close inshore. In recent years a whole range of coastal batteries has been deployed in Scandinavia, the southern and eastern shores of the Mediterranean, the Adriatic, the Red Sea, the Gulf of Aden, most of the Persian Gulf and the southern coastline of Iran. Many of these missiles are of Chinese and North Korean origin, and inevitably they are spreading along some of the coastlines of the China Seas. The proliferation of data link systems even in third world countries means that the launch platform does not itself have to be in contact with the target. Targeting can be done, although not easily, by aircraft or by another vessel in the vicinity, which itself may even appear to be a non-combatant.

Defence against missile attack involves several layers, the first of which is to attack the firing platform either at its base or in transit to the firing position. But to be certain of survival, the target ship or its escort must be able to deploy a whole range of hard and soft kill defensive weapons and decoys against the growing sophistication of the homing warhead. Any attempt to save money by equipping with second best in this area is about as suicidal a policy as it is possible to imagine. Defences are keeping up with the problem, not least in stealth design during construction, and in the use of a whole range of complex decoys and jammers, but this is one area of spending which must be sacrosanct if the confidence of those at sea is to be maintained.

Depending on the nature of the enemy, an even more serious threat to the surface ship is the submarine-launched torpedo. Submarines can also fire anti-ship missiles. Any relaxation in effort put into anti-submarine warfare is therefore likely to prove very expensive at some time in the future, even though the submarine's weapons are neither as cheap nor as easy to fire as the ship or aircraft-launched air flight missile. Although some would add mines to the serious threat category, these are essentially static weapons to be avoided rather than defended against.

Although missiles and submarines are the major preoccupations of the surface ship defences, the whole range of shipborne high technology equipment suffers unless adequate spares are available. A recent tendency to try and take short cuts to save money on logistic backup is certain to undermine morale. The ship's maintainers will work all hours to keep propulsion and weapon systems operational, but if a replacement part is needed it must be available without subjecting the users to the restrictive practices of a civilian style accountancy system.

The third requirement for a successful warship is mutual trust and confidence in the competence of those with whom you are working. Training and selection are key elements as they are in any industry, but the difference here is that you cannot hire and fire in mid-ocean, nor can you advertise in the open market for people to drive your ships. Those you train you have to keep in adequate numbers, and they have to be prepared to stay at work 24 hours a day. Necessarily this particular place of work functions with a culture and a set of rules not always compatible with either civilian fashions or expectations.

The culture is not inflexible, and evolves slowly of its own volition, but does not take kindly to having new ideas forced upon it. It has also traditionally been all male and the introduction of women into this environment represents more of a fundamental change than may have first been appreciated, even by its strongest advocates within the service.

The rest of this Foreword could easily be devoted to a precis of what has already been written on this subject. Rationally, the change to a sea-going equal status for women reflects an evolution in the western world which has already been accepted, introduces more civilised standards of behaviour and language than would normally be expected from an all male ship's company and, as a generalisation, provides greater application skills when operating such things as radar and communications equipment. If you ask the Captain of a ship whether he approves of this change he will invariably say yes, because these advantages are self-evident and because naval officers are programmed to make positive responses to new ideas.

At the peer group level, where emotions cut more ice than official policy, there is much less certainty. In most navies which have introduced women in warships at sea, the mistake has been made of placing them in a small minority, which puts the women under unnecessary emotional pressures. Amongst the men, the most common complaint is that they

are no longer competing for promotion on a level playing field, and there is genuine concern that when it comes to fires, floods and damage control, the women will not be able to pull their weight.

The US Navy has only just started to introduce women into frontline warships and statistics from other navies are not widely available. In the UK it has been reported that despite an initial surge of female volunteers, applications have dropped steeply after the first experience, and accommodation modifications in some ships have now been cancelled. One explanation is that the sea-going culture has been forced to change too quickly and has resisted by showing overt disapproval. Few people want to work where they feel unwanted.

The issue of homosexuality has been handled with some insensitivity by people with no knowledge of warship life. The traditional all male enclave of the fighting services has always been an attractive prospect for the sexually ambivalent, most of whom know that they will be tolerated, and even accepted, as long as they do their professional work well and keep their sexual preference well concealed. Any attempt to relax this rule will never be accepted by the majority of sailors. At sea your professional life IS your private life. The people you work with are always with you and mutual respect and trust are essential. Threatening or non-conformal behaviour of any kind always causes an antagonistic reaction from the majority. This reaction is unresponsive to remote authority or standards imposed from outside.

The last requirement is that of being adequately rewarded for an often uncomfortable and sometimes dangerous life, which involves long separations from your family and has few points of contact with the normal everyday existence of the civilian who goes home after work.

Few sailors want to spend their whole working lives at sea, but while serving they expect their disrupted existence to have some compensations. Although pay is high on anyone's list, no one expects to get rich by going to sea, and just as important to morale is an understanding organisation ashore which looks after their interests, helps their families in a crisis and provides some stability in a basically uncertain existence. Sailors acknowledge that the programme of their ship is liable to change on occasions, but will be the first to resent arbitrary or badly explained disruptions.

For most people the important priorities are: job security within defined limits which are not constantly being changed, a promotion system which is seen to favour those who deserve it, shore leave to compensate for time spent away from home and a fair job assignment system which gives each sailor an equal share of the popular and unpopular billets.

In times of naval contraction or drawdown none of this is easy to achieve and if handled without sympathy or understanding creates a residue of disaffection and bitterness which undermines operational effectiveness.

United States

In his annual statement to Congress, the outgoing Chief of Naval Operations was brave enough this year to publish the Fleet operational disposition on 1 February 1994. Deployed worldwide were the following:

	Atlantic	Pacific	Indian Ocean	Mediterranean
Aircraft carriers	3	—	1	1
Submarines	17	13	1	4
Surface combatants	25	14	9	8
Helo carriers	2	2	2	—
Amphibious ships	15	10	6	—
Auxiliaries	17	15	6	6

These ships were underway on this day and, together with seven other vessels on anti-narcotics patrols in the Caribbean, represented some 42 per cent of the total US naval force available in early 1994. This is a powerful example of the *Pax Americana* at sea, and an unambiguous revelation of the United States' superpower status, which has been used so successfully to maintain the security of international waters and shipping routes. Attached to the amphibious ships were four Marine Expeditionary Units, and the various Fleets were conducting 12 exercises with 14 different countries as well as meeting UN, NATO and national operational commitments.

The bravery involved in publishing these figures is that they invite repetition at the same time next year, when the effect of the current drawdown to a Fleet of 373 battle force ships will be starkly revealed. During this financial year 65 major surface warships, 13 nuclear submarines and 23 frontline air squadrons are being decommissioned. Naval personnel numbers are scheduled to drop below 500 000 by the end of the year, for the first time since 1951. No one has said what happens next year except that the agenda now includes a possible further reduction to 331 ships.

The present medium term aim is for a naval strength of 394 000 by the end of the decade, manning 11 aircraft carriers, 55 SSNs and 114 surface

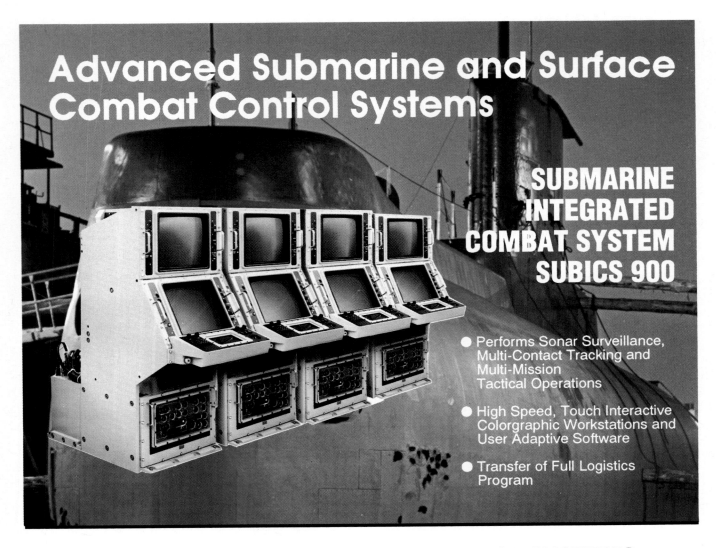

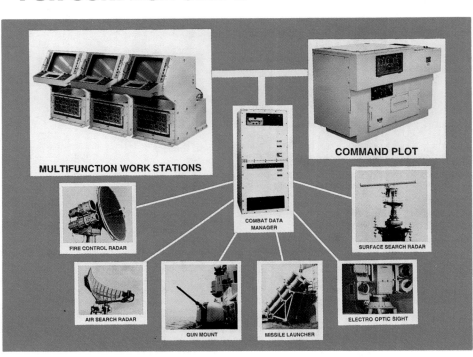
[36]

combatants. The same document also sets out the priorities for managing the defence cutbacks following on from the 1993 Bottom-Up review of the USA Armed Forces. These are placed in order: people, operational readiness, efficient use of resources and new technology. By any standards this is enlightened leadership as long as it is carried through at every level. The danger is that it will be forced off the rails by heavy-weight vested interests, which tend to protect the inefficient use of resources by such things as keeping open redundant bases, and by putting forward unproven technology as the all-consuming answer to every military problem. In fact, the setting out of these priorities as guiding principles has obviously been done as a form of pre-emptive defence. The authors know that a struggle will continue between those who want to maintain an effective navy and those who are more interested in the political benefits of dipping into the defence spending barrel.

On the new equipment side, naval priorities include the new attack submarine, strike and marine lift aircraft and precision weapons. On the submarine and aircraft front there appears to be tremendous background activity but not a lot of visible progress up front. Without a new deep strike aircraft the future of carrier battle groups is in jeopardy, because however you dress it up that is the primary offensive role of the fixed-wing carrier, particularly in littoral warfare.

A new deep strike aircraft is essential for the future of the carriers
A Sheldon Duplaix

For those who have to make decisions on the final design of the new attack submarine, it is possible to have much sympathy. As well as being the primary ASW weapon system in a maritime world where the submarine remains potentially the most damaging threat, the SSN is the only class of ship which has a natural form of stealth technology which is the envy of all surface ship and aircraft designers. And yet for some reason the 'acceptable' standards of vulnerability are set tens of times higher than for any other land/air or sea/air platform. This puts unit costs through the roof, and is a mind-set that needs to be broken, or at least forced to find a better compromise than one which makes the perfect submarine too expensive to build. A few less dubious scientific projections for the future, a better perspective on those isolated operational incidents and set piece trials where invulnerability has been proved to be less than total, and an application of commonsense based on the realities of free play warfare might help break the log jam.

Ship self-defence is moving up the priority list for reasons explained in the introduction to this Foreword. The intended aim is to give all principal major surface combatants an automated sensor/weapon response to missile attack. A major co-operative demonstration is planned for a carrier battle group in mid-1994. Full automation will be an expensive business in responses to false alarms, and no doubt manufacturers of expendable decoys are anticipating some good times ahead.

Perhaps the most innovative of all naval programmes is the development of the Trident missile, and the SSBNs that carry it, away from the former rigid adherence to the operational dogma of Strategic Deterrence, and into sub-strategic or even conventional warfare. The design of a kinetic energy warhead and precision mid-course guidance would open up a whole new involvement in littoral warfare for these virtually invulnerable submarines.

A trial firing from *Nebraska* (SSBN 739) last October included three re-entry vehicles equipped with GPS receivers. This was to test the feasibility of receiving target location data from the satellite constellation and transmitting it to a ground station. The trial also included deployment of an experimental warhead to simulate a kinetic energy weapon.

In the days of the cold war, fear of triggering an automatic response to

the firing of a ballistic weapon was a major inhibiting factor in developing new roles for the SSBN. If the more relaxed atmosphere between the countries capable of firing these weapons is maintained, there is no reason why the Trident system should not diversify into a precision-guided conventional weapon of the sort that could penetrate an underground command bunker, or even deep under the surface of the sea.

The Navy is also determined to continue to press its claim for the upgrading of the Standard missile as a primary defence against ballistic weapons. The target date for deployment is 1996, with the initial aim of providing protection to both ships and adjacent land targets by short-range missiles. A new seeker, fuse and warhead are needed, but the upgraded Block IVA weapon has already been flown to Mach 5.6, and further tests are scheduled later this year, if sufficient funding is available. Following on would be an 'upper tier' system, extending defences against long range ballistic weapons and making use of space-based target indication.

Operationally, the Navy took part in six major crisis responses in the last 12 months. This is a level of commitment undiminished since the break-up of the Soviet Union, and one which cannot be maintained by a smaller navy without subjecting its people to greater stress.

In submarine warfare, a much greater emphasis is being placed on shallow water operations and the development of UUVs. Improved communications are allowing tactical control to be taken by surface task group commanders as a matter of course. The 'silent' service is learning to talk.

An interesting experiment was carried out in the carrier *Theodore Roosevelt* in a six-month deployment to the Mediterranean and Gulf, which included embarking 600 Marines and 10 support helicopters for the whole period. Although this was part of the adaptive joint force package to bring more flexibility to Navy/Marine operations, it was not deemed a success. The carrier had to sacrifice some of its normal complement of F14 fighters, and the Marine force was not considered large enough to be able to carry out autonomous operations ashore for sufficient time to make an unsupported landing worthwhile.

In a book recently published on American strategy after the Cold War, a senior Marine Corps General comments that ''. . . in the ranking of the world's militaries, the US is not only in the first place, the next dozen or so places are not even occupied.''

Those who doubt this might like to consider the fact that this year the USN is laying off more major warships than any other single country has in its total operational inventory, with the sole exception of Russia.

Russia

Just about the only certainty on the state of this navy is that every western commentator now knows the shipbuilding project numbers of the various classes of ships and submarines, and most also know the Russian class names. As NATO-allocated names have been the popular currency for decades, this merely causes irritation to occasional readers who can instantly summon up the image of a Delta IV SSBN but have not the least idea of what is meant by a Delfin Project 667 BDRM.

If that seems a trivial comment on what is still the only navy that can challenge the United States maritime supremacy, it does have a more serious point. Because of the Russian drive for exports, there is much more technical data available on naval weapon systems, and to some extent shipbuilding programmes can also now be analysed without the help of intelligence disseminated in Washington. In addition, there is a newly published Fleet Plan for the next decade (although it already shows signs of ageing) and a proliferation of publicly reported comments by Russian commanders.

What is missing is any clear indication as to what is happening politically, as the lifeblood of the Russian experiment with democracy and partial openness drains slowly into the sands. If the military industrial complex has regained control of the country with the aim of reconstituting the old empire, then the naval highlights of the last 12 months are not only historical, but could be largely irrelevant. The menacing undertones of the President's state of the nation address in early 1994 was unambiguous in its indication of a return to some of the former Soviet values, both in the restoration of internal law and order, and in its attitude to those countries which for nearly 45 years provided the outer ring of Russia's defences.

From the low point of 1992, the Navy is slowly recovering its poise as well as some of its shipbuilding and maintenance budget. There is no doubt that the chaos of the early 1990s has done damage, and some major warships which in former years would have been repaired, are now being scrapped so that money can be spent on more recent priorities.

In shipbuilding terms these include completing the last of the Kirov class battle cruisers, building a new generation of nuclear attack submarines, improving the Kilo class diesel submarine design and concentrating on developing Sovremenny and Neustrashimy class destroyers and

The Only Proven
Ring Laser Gyro Navigator
with Demonstrated Performance

The MK-49 Ring Laser Gyro Navigator (RLGN) has been chosen by six navies as the navigator of choice for new construction and backfit submarines and surface ships.

The MK-49 is the most accurate, reliable and cost effective navigation system available. As the vital ship navigation reference, the MK-49 provides precise position, velocity, attitude and attitude rates in digital and analog formats.

The MK-49 has been in full production since 1990 and is available for submarine and surface ships today.

MK-49
RLGN
Ring Laser Gyro Navigator

For further information on this and other Sperry Marine products contact:

frigates. The second Kuznetsov class aircraft carrier *Varyag* is still wanted, if a way can be found of getting the Ukrainian shipyard at Niko-layev to complete it.

Anyone who doubts the commitment to carrier aviation by the Navy is ignoring the evidence of the extensive trials carried out by *Kuznetsov* at the end of 1993 and the development of the Flanker aircraft as a carrier-embarked air defence fighter. Paying off the older Kiev class ships, all of which had serious propulsion problems, is clearing the way for the expertise to be focused on the two (or three) newest vessels. A serious fire in the single modified Kiev class *Gorshkov* in February this year has not been helpful to this new policy but does give added impetus to the need to complete *Varyag*.

Operational submarine activity was the least affected part of the naval cutbacks, and the capability of the Russian SSBN force remains as formidable as ever. Agreements not to target NATO countries owe more to political theatre than military reality, as the resetting of target co-ordinates is not a lengthy procedure. SSBN numbers are being reduced, but the residual capability is still more than enough to destroy most of the world's centres of population.

In 1993 there was a marked increase in surface ship deployments, with well-armed ships enjoying the hospitality of many nations. This constant exposure to other navies, both in harbour and in UN-mandated activities at sea, has convinced the Russian hierarchy that its over-whelming failure has been in the treatment of its people. There are signs of a new approach to training and an awareness that meeting personnel concerns is not just an irritating distraction, but the key to a competent ship.

Reducing the Navy to a manageable size consistent with its resources is a task being tackled with vigour and conviction in the Northern and Baltic Fleets. The problems in the Pacific are more intractable, because of the length of the logistic supply lines, and there is no doubt that this Fleet has suffered most in terms of damage caused by lack of mainten-ance and insufficient fuel to go to sea.

In the Black Sea, few now doubt Russia's intention, one way or another, to hold on to Sevastopol as the main base, or of its growing ascendency over the Ukrainian economy. Ukraine is slowly generating its own navy, and this is listed in the relevant section of the book. None-theless there is no certainty that a separate navy has a long-term future unless common cause is made with the Russians.

The expression "leaner, fitter and meaner" when applied to western navies is usually a euphemism intended to mark serious cutbacks in already overstretched operational and equipment programmes. When applied to the Russian Fleets it can be taken much more at face value. By 1989 the old Soviet Navy had gorged on shipbuilding programmes which had outgrown the Union's capacity to support either the ships, the

technology or to train its people effectively. A further severe disadvan-tage was the isolation of its officers from the progress and standards of other major navies, and a reliance on conscripted sailors, many of whom did not even share a common language.

It will take some years to change the standards, but an impressive start has been made to match the Russian sea-going Fleet to its new and rationalised infrastructure, to instil initiative into its officers and to attract the right quality of volunteers to serve in the lower ranks. A smaller Fleet is emerging, but it is only small by comparison with what it had become in the Soviet era. By any other yardstick this is still a very large navy, with adequate numbers of modern surface ships to defend its intended sphere of influence, backed up by naval air-power, much of which is based ashore. The nuclear attack submarine Flotilla may be out of sight; it should never be out of any military planner's mind.

In 1994 the stated primary objectives are to complete the last Kirov class battle cruiser and several delayed destroyers and frigates, to carry out intensive flying training from *Kuznetsov*, to concentrate on building the next generation of SSN, the first of which has already been laid down, and to finalise the design of a new maritime patrol aircraft.

In terms of deployments, the aim is to go on contributing to UN sanc-tions operations, and to exercise with other navies to improve liaison procedures for this task.

The hidden agenda depends on political developments.

United Kingdom

After nearly five years of paying off ships and auxiliaries in the ratio of 12 to every new one ordered, the Royal Navy is being forced to project its future mainly as a contributor to European operations. In fact, as NATO has been the primary official rationale for UK defence spending for over two decades, this is in some ways not a new departure; nonethe-less it represents one example amongst many of the steady loss of British sovereignty to Europe without public debate.

The rationale of the new approach is that as most of the maritime countries of NATO Europe have surface escorts and diesel submarines in large numbers, the British can afford to concentrate on providing SSNs, aircraft carriers and large amphibious ships. The result of this 'policy' is already evident with the paying off of the last four diesel sub-marines, all of which are newly built, and the failure to order new escorts in numbers which would even maintain the existing force, already down to 35 hulls. In the longer term the present shipbuilding programme will sustain about 25.

The basic principle when haggling with uncomprehending Treasury officials over defence spending is not to give up anything in exchange for a considered judgement that by so doing you protect something else. The concession is gratefully received, and cost cutting is then re-focused

A marked increase in surface ship deployments   *A Sheldon Duplaix*

on the next project, which may well be the one you were trying to preserve.

In spite of the financial climate, a single helicopter carrier has been ordered in the last 12 months, the only new ship of any kind to reach the building contract stage. The absence of such a vessel during operations in the Adriatic has caused problems evident even to the most casual observer. In theory, new LPDs and new generation SSNs are still being funded, with the LPDs out to tender later this year and the SSNs in 1995. As these two programmes were originally scheduled for building contracts in 1990 and 1991 respectively, and the European Fighter Aircraft is hoovering up all spare defence equipment funds for the late 1990s, no one is sure when these commitments will be met. A submarine-borne strategic deterrent without the back-up of modern SSNs is absurd, and the last Trafalgar class commissioned in 1991. There is already a minimum gap of 13 years before the first of a follow-on class could be operational. Tenders are again out for new Sandown class minehunters, which is a repeat of the cancelled 1990 contracts.

It would be nice to comment in a more positive vein about the next generation escort, which is a rigidly structured collaborative project with France and Italy to produce a new air defence ship to replace the Type 42s. Unfortunately, inevitable and legitimate disagreements about the surveillance and target indication radar are only the tip of a number of divergent equipment requirements being suppressed by political directives to 'make the project work'. The result is inevitable delays, and cost escalation will follow just as it has with the Eurofighter aircraft. A better way of achieving some of the advantages of collaboration without the need for so much compromise is being followed by Germany, the Netherlands and Spain, who are combining only on aspects where they find commonality, and seem to have made better use of the lessons learned from the aborted NATO frigate project.

For the first time for several years the Navy again has three aircraft carriers at sea. In early 1994 one of the two operational ships is permanently on station in the Adriatic in support of British forces in Bosnia, and the third is working up after a three-year modernisation programme. In 1993 an SSN deployed for seven months, including lengthy periods spent in and around the Gulf to test the feasibility of operations in that area, now that diesel submarines will no longer be available by 1995. It would be interesting to know if European partners are willing to contribute to the Armilla Patrol with conventional submarines.

The SSN is capable of supporting commando type operations in shallow water. The trouble is that the shallower the water, the more intense the mining threat, and it makes little sense to risk losing a multi-million dollar submarine to a five hundred dollar mine, if the same job can be done, at less risk, by a smaller cheaper vessel. Also, basic ASW training needs diesel submarine targets. Typical of the measures that are having to be faced by the naval hierarchy, is a plan to run on one of the Upholder class as a partially operational training boat, on similar terms to those used for target-towing aircraft with civilian pilots. Although imaginative and cheap to implement, the project seems unlikely to succeed because of the political embarrassment it could generate. These submarines cost £225 million each to build and £2 million each per year to operate, according to the Defence Estimates. The difference between the cost of using the investment and laying them up is negligible by comparison with some of the extravagant MoD infrastructure costs which do nothing to enhance frontline capability.

In the Fleet Air Arm, the uprated FRS 2 Sea Harrier is a marked improvement on its predecessor, and the new Merlin helicopter is making progress towards the long-term aim of acceptance as a multi-role aircraft.

As in the United States Navy, the self-imposed limitation on Trident missile re-entry vehicles and warheads has thrown up spare capacity in the system, which could be filled by the development of sub-strategic or conventional hyper-velocity kinetic energy weapons. The Navy is to take over the sub-strategic role from the Air Force within the next 10 years, but no official announcements have yet been made about how this is to be achieved.

There is also a very strong case for fitting US Tomahawk cruise missiles in all classes of submarines. The weapon can be fired from normal torpedo tubes, and the improved submerged-launch version has a range of 900 kms (487 nm), an adjustable flight profile and has demonstrated its accuracy against Iraqi targets. Submarine-launched Tomahawk also has political advantages in not putting at risk either the firing platform or innocent civilians living adjacent to military targets. It can be fired with very little disruption to whatever other task the submarine is engaged in at the time. There are no other weapon systems that have so many obvious advantages as an existing force multiplier, and Tomahawk could be acquired at minimal cost by comparison with other methods of achieving the same capability.

For the first time for over 30 years this edition has no entry in the UK section for the Valiant, Oberon, Leander, Type 21 and Ton classes.

Valete to some distinguished designs, all of which, except Valiant, live on in other navies.

There is no reduction in the commitment to maintaining peace in the Gulf

Europe

As the European Union expands, possibly soon to include most of the Nordic countries, so the political pressure grows for a common European defence force. This has always been one of the objectives of the federalist lobby within the old European Community and its proponents argue that such a process merely recognises what is happening in the Adriatic and Bosnia, where international forces combine and co-operate under UN and NATO Commanders drawn from a number of different countries. Furthermore, France, Italy and Spain are already using the Western European Union (WEU) to co-ordinate their naval deployments and plans for dealing with emergencies in the Mediterranean. If you add to that the international nature of much of Europe's major defence industries and the political drive towards collaborative projects, there is a form of logic in taking the process to its natural conclusion as enshrined in the Maastricht Treaty, which charged the WEU with developing a genuine European defence identity.

To quote Palmerston: "Nations have no permanent allies or enemies, only permanent interests." Therefore, for a federal defence force to emerge successfully, the Europe of the European Union has to arrive at a point in its political development where it is effectively one nation, or at least there must be an accepted belief that its permanent interests are common to each country within the Union. Put like that, the idea is nonsense and yet that is the path down which defence forces are being driven, because Europe's richer nations have for some time not been prepared to pay the premium for adequate individual defence forces. At the same time, they are also unwilling to put together a shared command, control, communication and intelligence structure that can function effectively without the operational intelligence and politico/military leadership of the United States.

Where navies are concerned, the result is unilateral disarmament, in which the order rates for new ships are inadequate even to maintain existing naval capabilities. The penalty for all this will ultimately depend on the form of the next threat. The complacency of western Europe is revealed in a recent survey in which only 32 per cent of Germans are concerned about military threats, whereas in Poland the figure rises to nearly two thirds of the population. These are countries with a shared border, so the discrepancy can only be explained by different perceptions based on the experience of the last few decades.

In the Baltic, Russian antagonism to suggestions that some of the for-

mer USSR satellites might join NATO, has not prevented multilateral agreements going ahead for naval exercises involving Poland, Germany and Denmark. Poland and the Netherlands have gone even further, signing a protocol to allow an exchange of personnel and joint training. Later this year, the Polish Navy is to take part in a NATO exercise as a result of the 'Partnership for Peace' initiative between NATO and eastern European countries. Of all the nations of the former Warsaw Pact, Poland is the most anxious to join NATO.

Scandinavia still retains a lively interest in autonomous defences and Sweden is leading the way amongst European navies in the development of sea control in its archipelago. Existing programmes include modern submarines fitted with AIP, advanced stealth designs for surface craft based on the SES technology demonstrator *Smyge*, controllable sea mines, harbour surveillance sonars and shore-based anti-ship missiles. Sweden sees the SES design as having a distinct maximum effective tonnage, above which it is better to revert to a traditional monohull.

The Baltic States are slowly building up their own Coast Guards, with help from Sweden, Finland and Germany. Progress is well documented in this edition.

Norway has also been strengthening its coastline with modernised coastal torpedo batteries and controllable minefields. Trials with the SES design *Oksøy* minehunter are now well under way after some initial delays, and a similar hull design demonstrator is running trials to evaluate a new class of fast attack craft.

Germany has been amongst the leaders in vigorously pruning its defence budget. Apart from four new frigates of the Brandenburg class, of which the first is on trials, and the tail end of a new minehunter class, the shipbuilding programme is bare. New AIP submarines are projected, as is a class of four new air defence ships, but Bonn is in no hurry to place orders.

The Netherlands has nearly completed the Karel Doorman class frigates and Walrus class submarines, and will then only have a combat support ship and an LPD under construction, until work starts on new air defence command ships in collaboration with Germany and Spain. Meanwhile, older submarines and frigates are being paid off or sold before the end of their useful lives, and a new minehunter project has been shelved in favour of modernising some existing ships and acquiring some remote-controlled drones. This Navy is very active in crisis intervention operations and is being reorganised with that as the main priority.

In France, all major naval equipment programmes have been drawn out; a dubious method of saving money in the longer term, but one which so far has prevented any cancellations.

A white paper released in March this year projected a navy of almost 100 warships including aircraft carriers and submarines, but because of the state of the economy ''Some choices may have to be made between major projects to maintain a credible defence.'' In fact, alone amongst Western nations, France has tried to maintain its defence budget with an increase of 3.6 per cent in 1994, a reflection of a national/European policy which intends to draw closer to NATO without returning totally to the alliance. The annual 'Loi de Programmation' follows the white paper this Summer and may be more specific about where the axe is to fall.

A carrier group in the Adriatic in support of UN operations   *French Navy*

Like Britain, France has maintained a carrier group in the Adriatic for much of the last year in support of its UN peacekeeping contingent in Bosnia. So seriously is this role taken, that the second period of deck landing trials of the Rafale M aircraft were interrupted in February to allow *Foch* to resume operational patrols. Marines and amphibious ships have also been deployed to the area.

Spain has managed to halt three years of decline in defence funding after the Chiefs of Staff had declared openly that training and reserves of equipment had already been reduced to the minimum if operational requirements were to be met. In the Navy, sea time has been curtailed and there has been a drastic reduction of some 71 patrol craft, which have all been paid off, although a few have transferred to other government agencies dealing with smuggling and anti-illegal immigration problems. Ship construction programmes, which virtually halted for a time, have now picked up again.

Mediterranean

In the Mediterranean, the Adriatic Sea has been the focus of most attention, although political events in Egypt and Algeria continue to cause concern. US, British, French and Italian navies have maintained national task groups in contingency deployments off the coasts of Croatia and Montenegro. At the same time, UN sanctions in the southern Adriatic and Straits of Otranto have been enforced since 15 June 1993 by the combined naval forces provided by the WEU and by NATO, through STANAVFORLANT and STANAVFORMED. This is a sensible rationalisation of the earlier confusion caused by competing NATO and WEU forces, in which some of the same ships transferred between one and the other. Code-named SHARP GUARD, the integrated operational forces number up to 20 warships divided between three groups under the Commanders of the three contributing organisations. Each group rotates between the two main operational areas, going off station for training, port visits and maintenance periods.

The main task is to keep under surveillance all merchant vessels in the areas, boarding them where necessary to establish types of cargoes and destinations, and to prevent breaches of the UN trade embargo against Serbia and Montenegro. Command is exercised by NATO through COMNAVSOUTH and the Italians have provided much of the essential host nation support.

As a method of gaining experience in multinational operations whether under NATO command, or by multinational co-operation of forces under national commands, these operations are helping to train all participating navies in joint operations of a particular type. There is a danger of becoming too pleased with the results of this exercise, bearing in mind the weakness of the rump of the former Yugoslav Navy, which has lost most of its bases to Croatia, and would need a strong suicidal tendency to try and take on some of the West's most modern warships and submarines, as well as some formidable carrier-based air power. Experts quietly shudder at the prospect of this combination of national and international command and control being exercised in a setting where the enemy had some real fire power. Nonetheless the potential submarine and missile threat, however small, cannot be ignored, and this provides more realistic training than many traditional peacetime exercises.

The Italian Navy may have been in the thick of all this operational activity, but a year of partial political paralysis has made decisions on defence funding and future equipment programmes even more difficult to achieve than in Europe's other retreating defence industries.

At least so far Europe has been spared the Balkans conflict spilling over into Greece and Turkey. Given the even-handed way in which the US is handing over Knox class frigates to as many as five different Mediterranean navies, (Spain, Greece, Turkey, Egypt and possibly Morocco), confusion over IFF could become intense should any of these countries decide not to stay on the same side.

Some commentators now believe that the balance of naval power in the Aegean has moved steadily in favour of Greece, which has a marginal advantage over Turkey in terms of numbers of modern frigates and submarines, in spite of considerable financial problems in the two warship yards in recent years. The return of the Panhellenic Socialist Party at the end of last year resurrected memories of its antagonism to the US when last in power four years ago.

One of the first laws passed by the new government permitted the recall from retirement of general officers, whereupon virtually all the serving Greek Admirals resigned in protest, to be replaced not by others promoted in their place, but by those who had already been retired. A further development last February was the declaration of a joint area of defence between Greece and Cyprus.

Turkey has a vibrant submarine and surface ship building programme as well as recent second hand acquisitions from the US and Germany, so any perceived Greek advantage is likely to be short-lived.

The eastern Mediterranean also plays host to an Israeli Navy which has three US-built ocean-going missile corvettes about to be delivered, and two German-built submarines under construction, as well as an Egyptian Fleet which, in addition to its Knox class frigates, is also upgrading submarine and minehunter capabilities with US assistance. As

the Palestinian peace accord seems to be unstable and the Egyptians are having growing problems with Muslim fanatics fuelled by Iran and Libya, the eastern Mediterranean remains a volatile and turbulent cockpit.

The Russian Black Sea Fleet is still quiescent, although for a time in early Summer 1993 the Russian Mediterranean Squadron was re-established with ships from the Northern and Baltic Fleets coming under the tactical control of a cruiser from the Black Sea. For the first time, the Bulgarian and Turkish Navies have been co-operating in low level exercises at sea.

Events in Algeria are causing concern in Europe   *Diego Quevedo*

Along the north African littoral, European concern currently centres on Algeria. The fear is that if Islamic revolutionary violence cannot be contained by the military government in Algiers, it will spread to Europe. The prospect of NATO navies having to turn back hordes of would-be illegal immigrants to southern Europe is bad enough, but there is also the danger of attracting converts from the underprivileged community of Algerians already living in France. Not only is there a threat of a right wing reaction to further immigrants, there is also the foundation of a terrorist force already domiciled in Europe. Given their internal problems, money for the Navy is not Algeria's highest priority, although one of the Kilo class submarines has returned to St Petersburg for a refit. It was said to be in poor condition on arrival, which arguably could have been the reason it was sent.

Indian Ocean and Gulf
At the western end of the Indian Ocean the navies of Ethiopia and Eritrea are slowly beginning to get back on an operational footing, with Eritrea offering basing rights at Aseb. The Yemen is another country with an uncertain future, with four years of notional unity seeming to have weakened rather than strengthened the country. Some naval units are in good condition, but most of their time is spent alongside in Aden. Another civil war may be imminent.

Most of the Gulf countries remain active in the naval equipment market, with enthusiasm curbed only by the low price of oil. It has to be admitted that there are more statements of intention than actual orders for new ships. Fear of Iran is the driving force, in particular the threat to seaborne trade from coastal missile batteries, shore-based aircraft, flotillas of small craft and, more recently, two Kilo class submarines and the purchase of Chinese rising mines. The US naval presence, supported by its allies, remains the pre-condition for an uneasy peace in the area.

After the delivery of the second submarine to Iran, Russia is reported to have cancelled the third, but this order could easily be resurrected in due course. Early this year Iranian naval forces carried out their first ever exercises with another navy, joining up with Pakistan at the northern end of the Arabian Sea.

The ubiquitous Knox class frigates may well have found another customer in Oman. If the transfer goes ahead, it represents a major step forward in the evolution of this efficient and expanding navy.

Iraq has now handed back to Kuwait all the remaining vessels captured in 1990, and not destroyed in Desert Storm. All are wrecked beyond repair. Iraq maintains her two corvettes and one tanker embargoed in Italian and Egyptian ports. All three ships have skeleton crews, but seem unlikely to be released in the foreseeable future.

The Pakistan Navy is suffering from the withdrawal of eight US frigates leased for five years in 1988/89, but has compensated by acquiring all six of the UK Amazon class. There are plans to update these ships with SSMs, CIWS and EW systems in Karachi, but the frigates are sailing from the UK with only limited equipment fitted. The last pair is scheduled to arrive later on this year. Pakistan has a competent naval special service group, which has replaced its older midget submarines with three 110 ton boats armed with torpedo tubes, and capable of minelaying as well as underwater swimmer operations.

This year India has halted a seven-year decline in military spending, in order to prevent a possible crisis caused by its dependency on unreliable Russian suppliers. Progress on new construction destroyers and frigates has remained inordinately slow because of the Russian connection, in marked contrast to the building of a new indigenous amphibious ship, which is rushing ahead. The operational Fleet has been hosting both US and Russian visits, and has been assured that Russia still considers the Navy to be a high priority market. The last years seem to have brought no visible progress on the next generation aircraft carrier or submarine programmes.

Bangladesh is still looking towards Britain for more frigates, having recently acquired an Island class patrol vessel as a training ship, while Burma continues to grow closer to China with more attack craft transferred, continued rumours of second-hand frigates and Chinese instructors on secondment to the Navy. China has denied any formal link with Burma's new SIGINT base on Great Coco Island adjacent to the Indian-held Andaman Islands, but no-one doubts that the information gained is being relayed to Peking.

Pacific Asia and the China Seas
With infinite caution the South East Asian nations (ASEAN), comprising Malaysia, Singapore, Thailand, Philippines, Brunei and Indonesia, are creeping towards some kind of regional security co-operation. An ASEAN-sponsored forum including the US, Canada, Japan, South Korea, Australia, New Zealand, China, Russia, Vietnam, Cambodia, Laos, Papua New Guinea and the UK is to meet for the first time this Summer for talks about talks, so as better to understand each other's concerns.

ASEAN itself still shies away from any formal defence co-operation, not least because of the territorial disputes between most of the member nations. As these countries become richer and US intervention on their behalf becomes less likely, so inevitably defence spending will grow.

Singapore has become the latest country to express interest in the acquisition of a submarine force, and Thailand, which has been blowing hot and cold on this issue for some years now, is again looking like joining the market. Thailand is also to acquire the lease on a couple of Knox class frigates (having been offered four) to go with her latest Chinese-built ships, and is aiming to gain VSTOL experience with some ex-Spanish Matador aircraft before the new aircraft carrier completes in three years' time.

Malaysia is being courted by every warship builder because of her requirement for large numbers of offshore patrol vessels. A collaborative project with Australia would make much sense politically, but might drive the Australians into the early acquisition of a helicopter-carrying mini corvette which could have adverse implications for its other naval programmes.

In Cambodia the United Nations force (UNTAC) finally left in November, having done much to restore the riverine navy to some semblance of operational effectiveness. Most of the larger craft of USSR origin are now working again and have resumed their former colours, having painted over the white of the UN and the 'Peace in Cambodia' slogans daubed on the ships' sides.

China continues to strengthen the South Seas Fleet, and makes no secret of her intention to dominate the East and South China Seas. The latest indicator for the future is the demand on the Hong Kong Government to build a far larger naval base than is required for existing types of patrol craft. The new base is on the mainland side of the harbour and replaces the old naval establishment on a prime waterfront site in the centre of the city, which has been taken over for civilian development. Specifically, China's requirement is for a base of nearly 500 m in waterfront length, which could of course harbour several frigates.

International views on China's maritime ambitions are diverse. There are those who argue that only a fool would disrupt the region's economic growth by starting a war, and anyhow China's Fleet is a paper tiger which needs at least another decade to bring weapon systems technology and operational standards up to acceptable levels, even if there were enough people of the right quality to man the ships, which at the moment there are not.

On the hawkish side of the fence are those who point to the potential prize of an estimated 50 billion tons of oil and mineral deposits offshore, the aggressive claims for increased territorial waters, the behaviour over the negotiations for greater democratic government in Hong Kong, and

The UN peacekeeping force left Cambodia at the end of last year

the numerous incidents of unarmed merchant ships, including those of Russia and Japan, being attacked or arrested either by Chinese militia craft or occasionally by the Navy itself.

The stated intention is to have two 48 000 ton aircraft carriers leading two task Fleets by 2005. As of now, there are new submarines (including the Russian Kilo class), destroyer, frigate and amphibious shipbuilding programmes. One new indicator of a serious intention to modernise has been the formal paying off in the last 12 months of several of the more obsolete frigates, which have hung around the order of battle in various states of partial reserve for many years. As the Russians have recently discovered, preserving ships long past their sell-by date is an unnecessary drain on maintenance and training budgets, which are far better concentrated on newer vessels.

China continues to export a range of ships and weapon systems at very competitive prices. The technology is improving with Russian assistance, and with a much reduced threat to her land borders the Navy is receiving more attention, more funds, and is attracting better quality recruits. All nations put their own interests first, but none seems to pursue them with quite such naked disregard for international sensitivities as the current Chinese Government. It makes for an uncomfortable neighbour.

Whatever anyone else may think about China's long-term intentions, Taiwan's defence minister is certain that the military build-up on the mainland is "An attempt to lay the foundations of a regional superpower." He is also concerned that because of growing social and economic developments between the two countries, "There is danger of complacency and lack of support for strong national defence in Taiwan."

No sign of that so far, as $10 billion is currently invested in building frigates of the modified Oliver Perry and French La Fayette classes and acquiring ships of the ex-US Knox class, plus a vigorous search to find some European diesel submarine shipyard whose government is prepared to risk China's wrath. As previous sales to Taiwan and South Africa have shown, it is possible to dress up some ships as commercial vessels, but submarines are a little harder to disguise. Selling them in sections for Taiwan to assemble seems to be the most promising approach.

At the northern end of the region Russian warships visited the South Korean port of Pusan for the first time in August last year, as a mark of the growing ties between the two countries. South Korea has also started to take a broader look at regional stability issues, and has contributed to UN peacekeeping operations.

The submarine programme is going well with a projected total of nine hulls so far, but the new destroyer is still progressing very slowly due to charges of corruption in the selection of some of the weapon systems. More minehunters have entered service in the last year. The growing emphasis on amphibious and ocean-going support ships is also an indication of South Korea's wider maritime intentions.

Reports of North Korea receiving up to 40 Russian submarines for scrap at the end of last year sent a shiver of anxiety through the international community. These were reported as being decommissioned diesel boats of the Golf, Foxtrot, Romeo and Whiskey classes, which have been decaying at Pacific Fleet anchorages for a number of years. The Japanese company acting as an intermediary for the deal was

adamant that the submarines were being broken up on arrival, but no one has any doubt that North Korea's obsolescent Romeo class could be the beneficiaries of spare parts taken from the scrapyard. The Golf class was capable of firing ballistic missiles, and the last one only decommissioned some four years ago. It is therefore possible that the missile tubes may be adaptable for other weapons.

A couple of North Korean ships made an unusual excursion into the Sea of Japan in support of a test firing of a ground-based ballistic missile in mid-1993. Apart from confirmation of the age of most of the ship's armament, one picture appeared to show vegetation growing on the upper deck. The strength of this navy remains in its ability to carry out clandestine inshore operations with midget submarines and low profile attack craft. Optronic detection technology is helping to counter this type of threat, but the potential effectiveness of this force should not be underestimated.

Japan, Indonesia and to a much lesser extent the Philippines are the other major players in this dynamic and potentially dangerous part of the world.

Indonesia is receiving 39 warships and auxiliaries from Germany   R Kramer

Indonesia is in the process of absorbing and finding crews for the 39 warships and auxiliaries on their way from the former East Germany. This would be a considerable challenge for any of the world's major navies, and is stretching Indonesia's resources to the limit. Some of these ships are expected to be put straight into a limited operational status, but all are being formally commissioned first. As the contract includes refurbishment in German shipyards prior to transfer, they are also arriving in good condition in spite of their age.

Last year links continued to be forged with Australia through combined naval operations including MCMV, replenishment at sea and control of shipping exercises.

This year's section on the Philippine Navy indicates the steady progress made to rejuvenate the Fleet and pay off the older ships. The more ambitious plans for corvettes and large attack craft are still in need of adequate funding, but the arrival of two new LSL support ships is a major step forward in regaining control of the internal waters of the archipelago.

Japan's defence expenditure is three times that of the two Koreas combined, and four times that of the total spent by the six ASEAN countries. It is also probably greater than China's but only because personnel costs are several times higher. Naval recruitment remains a major problem and the JMSDF is planning to disperse its ships to a wider range of home ports, to encourage a regional recruitment policy. The problem is particularly acute in the Yokosuka area which houses about one third of the Navy, and where some ships are short of a full complement.

A year ago it was possible to forecast an impending relaxation of the constitutional straitjacket which largely confines the Navy to home waters. Minehunter deployments to the Gulf had been successfully concluded and participation in more UN operations seemed likely. Unfortunately the Defence Minister moved too fast for public opinion by openly advocating more flexibility or even amendments to the constitution. This presumption of change cost him his job at the end of last year.

The key territorial issue of sovereignty over the Kurile Islands remains deadlocked, in spite of heads of government discussions with Russia. Neutral observers believe that a compromise in which the two southern islands are returned to Japan would have been better than no

agreement at all, and depending on what happens next in Moscow, an opportunity may have been lost.

In spite of some reining back of defence spending, the Navy got pretty well what it asked for in the FY 1994 shipbuilding programme, except for one hydrofoil attack craft postponed for another year. Japan's first Aegis-equipped destroyer is close to being fully operational, and because of North Korea's ballistic missiles, much interest is being taken in the US development of the Standard SAM to defend against these weapons. The acquisition of Tomahawk would also be a logical extension of existing weapon capabilities.

Southern Hemisphere

In Australia there is considerable naval activity, and a few problems. Moving the main submarine operating base from Sydney to Perth is one of the problems. The new facilities may be excellent but is it where sailors settled at the other end of the country want to live? Not surprisingly the retention of trained men has become more difficult, although there may be a few going spare as Britain pays off its last diesel boats. *Collins*, the lead ship of a new class, is being held up because of combat system software delays, a problem which has a ring familiar to most western navies.

Two major decisions imminent are the new minehunters, where the trade-off between cost and capability requires experienced naval judgement unhindered by interference from any lobby group, and possible replacement patrol vessels in collaboration with Malaysia. A collaborative project fits neatly into the recently published revised defence strategy which puts more emphasis on co-operation with ASEAN countries. The original plan was to refurbish the existing patrol craft, and therefore bringing forward orders for new craft may impact adversely on the FFG update and new destroyer programmes also projected during the next few years. The defence review notes that East Asia strategic issues have a heavy maritime focus and resurrects the concept of sea control in the context of the secure passage of maritime trade. For this the larger ships will be essential.

The acquisition of two ex-US LSTs has resolved for a time the problems of training and military support ships and, if there are no second thoughts, will soon release *Jervis Bay* to the scrapyard and *Tobruk* possibly to New Zealand to solve its military sealift ship requirement.

There seems also to have been a change of plan on shipborne helicopters. The previous concept of one type for all requirements has given way to the need for a lighter aircraft of the Lynx type to augment the Seahawks, and to be fitted in OPVs and projected survey ships.

The thrill of a collaborative project is a heady mixture difficult for politicians to resist, even though it may generate as many problems as it resolves. If there is not already a handbook on the history of bilateral or multi-national naval equipment projects, it is time someone wrote one.

It seems a shame to have to continue to dismiss central African navies in a few dismal lines, but progress is not easy to find as the continent's mounting international debt is a major deterrent to any serious procurement activity.

The genesis of South Africa's River class minehunters has now been acknowledged. The first two were built in Germany and assembled in South Africa for the Department of Transport, and the second pair were constructed in South Africa. All four were operated by the Navy from 1981 as research ships, until finally hoisting the South African ensign and 'coming out' in 1988.

The two large support ships, one of which was acquired as a replacement last year, have been active in carrying supplies to a number of countries including Bangladesh, Mozambique, Madagascar and Kenya. One of those vessels has also been to the eastern Mediterranean, Black Sea and the Gulf. These and other visits are part of a policy of renewing international relations, and former links have also been revived by western navies visiting South African ports.

The Navy badly wants new corvettes as a first priority, but it seems likely that any orders will have to wait until the advent of a new administration able to run a stable government.

Nigeria, once again back under military rule, is talking about building a new class of patrol vessels but may find it difficult to fund the project.

In South America, Brazil's navy has had a better year than last, recommissioning the aircraft carrier after a lengthy refit and launching the first submarine to be built in a local shipyard. The first of a new class of patrol craft was also accepted into service, but shipyard problems have caused the Navy to transfer the contract for two ships to Germany. Knox class frigates have been offered but may not be taken up.

Argentina's shipbuilding programme has virtually been halted, but the Navy has been active operationally with deck landings on the Brazilian carrier, and submarine excursions to the vicinity of the Falkland Islands. A Special Forces command has been created to oversee the activities of the Navy's frogmen and the Army's amphibious commandos. Both are élite groups trained in covert infiltration of military targets.

Chile is modernising her naval forces

New photographs of Chilean destroyers and frigates indicate considerable progress in updating weapon systems and helicopter facilities, and new combat data systems are also being installed. Plans to acquire more Leander class frigates have been postponed through lack of funds.

Peru has had a clear-out of elderly destroyers, but not the cruiser *Almirante Grau* which is still in commission and visited Costa Rica earlier this year. Venezuela has been offered a pair of Knox class frigates which seems odd as the Navy is still trying to fund the projected update of its Lupo class ships.

Central America and Canada

The Mexican Navy has grown to a strength of nearly 40 000 people. As well as having active newbuild gunship and conversion programmes, the Navy acquired two former US Bronstein class frigates at the end of last year. Forces are split between the Atlantic and Pacific coasts and Mexico is still searching to find the ideal organisation to maintain the integrity of its long coastlines. Most of the ships' names and pennant numbers were changed at the beginning of this year, which is likely to cause recognition problems for those operating in this part of the world without this year's copy of *Jane's Fighting Ships*.

Haiti has seen the gathering of yet another international naval task group enforcing UN sanctions against an illegal regime. Countries that have sent ships include Canada, US, UK, France, Netherlands and Argentina.

The Canadian Navy needs new helicopters

Although one of the most successful contributors to the international scene, Canada's defence forces are in further confusion as a result of a government which made election promises to scrap new equipment without first thinking through the alternatives. Military equipment projects in all industrialised nations have to go through a series of elaborate hoops before a contract is even contemplated, let alone placed. Once the decision has been made, there is an assumption of a real requirement, even if the method of meeting it can still be questioned. The Navy's frigates need new helicopters. Cancelling the type that had been ordered blows a hole in the rationale for much associated expenditure, some of which has already been made, and therefore still leaves a requirement unless there are also doubts over the future of the frigates.

LEROUX & LOTZ
NAVAL

■ **A COMPLETE RANGE OF OFFSHORE PATROL VESSELS**

OPV 54 delivered to the Mauritanian Navy and ordered by the French Navy

OPV 64 ordered by the Moroccan Navy

OTHER MILITARY VESSELS AVAILABLE:

■ **HYDROGRAPHIC SHIPS**

■ **LANDING SHIPS (LSC – LCT)**

■ **TRAINING SHIPS**

■ **CLEARANCE DIVING VESSELS**

■ **REGIONAL SUPPORT VESSELS**

■ **TUGS AND SUPPLY VESSELS**

■ **30 YEARS OF CLOSE COLLABORATION WITH THE FRENCH NAVY AND OF INTERNATIONAL EXPERIENCE**

LEROUX & LOTZ
a diversified industrial group
with 1400 employees

10, rue des Usines – 44100 NANTES – Tél.: 40.95.96.97 – Fax: 40.46.52.06

Furthermore, the cancellation charges for the helicopters, the loss to Canadian industry of offset technology agreements, the need for urgent refurbishment of the old types still in service, the expense of their growing unreliability and the eventual cost of replacement in a few short years, is likely to render the whole exercise ultimately as expensive as the original contract.

Piling on the agony came the defence budget in February which seeks to claw back another billion and a half Canadian dollars in the next three years. This must put a further question mark over replacement submarines and new patrol vessels, will certainly add to the list of base closures and, in the words of one Admiral, may lead to new frigates being "tied up because there is no money to send them to sea." Some ships may have to accept that not all defects can be fixed, and task groups will take longer to be put together. What sort of sailors do politicians think will put up with this?

Finally, replacing the Chief of Defence Staff by his predecessor suggests a government with little confidence in the serving higher echelons. In this Ottawa has something in common with the new administration in Athens.

In Conclusion

Reviewing the trends around the world's navies, some general conclusions are apparent, few of them contentious.

(1) The single strategic deterrent role of SSBN operations is changing as, for a time, is the tempo and urgency of their operational cycle.

(2) The most potent force at sea remains the SSN. Diesel submarines and mines are widespread. There should be no relaxation in efforts to improve anti-submarine warfare or mine countermeasures.

(3) In the context of the support of amphibious and land forces in littoral warfare, a nation does not have "Much of a Navy without aircraft carriers and seaborne aircraft", to quote a former US CNO.

(4) Surface warships must have adequate hard and soft-kill defences against sea-skimming missiles, which are proliferating, not least in coastal sites.

(5) The continued security of the bulk of international trade depends on the worldwide deployment of the US Navy, supported by its allies. The decline in numbers of operational warships continues in most western navies, but is most marked in the US and the UK.

(6) The build-up of maritime forces in South East Asia is accelerating and matches the economic growth of the countries in the region.

(7) As its free economy falters and crime becomes widespread, the re-establishment of military/industrial power in Russia is well advanced.

The supremacy of western navies is based on the quality and experience of their sailors and an acceptance of an uncomfortable and often unattractive way of life. Standards are being compromised because the effect of many cost-cutting measures is being calculated in civilian accountancy terms.

Start treating those who go to sea with their unusual lifestyle as though they are a business commodity, and the chances rapidly diminish of attracting and retaining the people that are needed. Such is the complexity of the modern warship that once the expertise has been allowed to wither, it will not be possible to resurrect it in a crisis. This is particularly true for those nations that are neglecting their Merchant Marine and running down much of their naval reserves.

Before reducing your naval services too far, you had better be sure that an inability to control or influence what happens at sea is not going to threaten your military or economic survival for the foreseeable future. Seaborne trade is currently running at over 4000 million tons a year, some 12 times greater than in 1950, and is still rising. The ships that carry it are increasingly vulnerable. For maritime nations, upon the safety of that trade "Does the wellbeing of the state depend."

Richard Sharpe   **April 1994**

Celebrating the 50th anniversary of the Battle of the Atlantic - a Partnership for Peace?

Acknowledgements

The most important change this year has been the introduction of a free Information Update service to those who buy the book on subscription. This means that for the first time in the long history of *Jane's Fighting Ships* we can use the book's format to keep subscribers abreast of some of the major changes throughout the year. The Updates provide up to the minute news, as well as additional and rewritten entries to be pinned to the appropriate pages.

Those readers who have not worked in a Ministry of Defence headquarters may wonder if the rate of change justifies the effort. Those whose daily work involves the management of change in navies will have no such doubts. Ask any staff officer about a new ship or weapon system programme, or plans for modifying or paying off older vessels, and he will usually 'know' the answer but 'not for another month or so'. Even using the most modern publishing technology, a new book will always be out of date on distribution, some sections more so than others, depending on the date of the last information received. Also, for the editor, there are some difficult decisions as to what to include. For example, a projected transfer of a second-hand ship on lease may be inserted, and if the transfer is not confirmed it is an incorrect addition, even if the small print identified the original uncertainty. If it is left out and the lease goes ahead, there may be a gap of as much as a year before the omission can be corrected. With a regular updating news sheet, these sort of problems are easily resolved. At the same time, the annual major revision will continue to replace many of the photographs and to record the literally thousands of detailed changes which are the lifeblood of any serious book of reference.

All of which makes our regular contributors even more important, particularly those who are in constant touch sending both information and photographs. In the top flight of these are the naval attachés in London, naval headquarters worldwide and the shipbuilding industries. Information for the world's most powerful navy is largely provided by Captain Vince Thomas, editor of the US Navy League's Seapower Almanac, who this year celebrated his tenth annual contribution to *Jane's Fighting Ships*. Another invaluable member of the team is Ian Sturton, who now has the distinction of being the artist for each of the line drawings published in the book. Flags and Ensigns have been updated by the Flag Institute, Chester, and W Maitland Thornton continues to expand the Officer Rank and Insignia section. The only change amongst this group is Mike Forder, a former colleague, who has taken over the Index and Pennant List. Apart from needing the professional skills of the indexer, this job requires detailed knowledge of naval nomenclature and maritime jargon.

Another innovation this year will be *Jane's Fighting Ships Recognition Handbook*, which is due out in the Autumn. This will draw on the text and line drawings of the parent publication, and is being put together by Keith Faulkner.

The backbone of *Jane's Fighting Ships* remains the individual contributors, who provide expert information and large numbers of photographs. Those who wish to be acknowledged include: Cdr Massimo Annati, Dr Giorgio Arra, Signor Erminio Bagnasco, Monsieur Guy de Bakker, Mr Paul Beaver, Lt Cdr E M Bentley, Mr K Brett, Herr Siegfried Breyer, Mr J L M van der Burg, Señor Camil Busquets i Vilanova, Señor Albert Campanera i Rovira, Señor Diego Quevedo Carmona, Senhor Mario Roberto Vaz Carneiro, Herr Harald Carstens, Lt Chun, Dr Chien Chung, Senhor Sergio Baptista da Costa, Mr D A Cromby, Mr Gary Davies, Herr Horst Dehnst, Mr Desmond Dempsey, Mr Demetrios Dervissis, Herr Hartmut Ehlers, Mr Selçuk Emre, Mr Marko Enqvist, Cdr Duncan Fergusson, Cdr Aldo Fraccaroli, Signora Marina Fraccaroli, Señor Francisco Gamez Balcazar, Signor Giorgio Ghiglione, Signor Giorgio Giorgerini, Mr Leo van Ginderen, Lt Col Werner Globke, Cdr James Goldrick, Mr David Graham, Cdr A W Grazebrook, Mr G Gyssels, Capt Hans Harboe-Hansen, Mr P Humphries, Mr Vic Jeffery, Mr Ziro Kimata, Herr G Koop, Mr Per Kornefeldt, Mr Michael Lechnar, Mr Boris Lemachko, Vice Admiral Sergio Loperena Garcia, Flight Lt I M McKenzie, Mr C Douglas Maginley, Mr Erik Laursen, Mr Michael Laursen, Signor Aureliano Molinari, Mr Julio Montes, Captain J E Moore, Señor Antonio Morena Garcia, Mr John Mortimer, Mr Hachiro Nakai, Rear Admiral Chart Navavichit, Herr Michael Nitz, Mr Nixon, Mr P O'Keeffe, Mr Robert Pabst, Cdr N Perry, Signor L Poggiali, Mr S Poynton, Mr D Radmore, Mr C Redlich, Mr A J R Risseeuw, Cdr L Robbins, Monsieur J Y Robert, Mr F Sadek, Mr Selim San, Signor Alessandro Sancin, Mr Walter Sartori, Lt J Sears, Monsieur A Sheldon Duplaix, Herr N A Sifferlinger, Mr Adam Smigielski, Mr H M Steele, Mr J Straczek, Mr B Sullivan, Señor X I Taibo, Mr Toshio Tamura, Herr S Terzibaschitsch, Mr Guy Toremans, Mr Marek Twardowski, Mr Maurice Voss, Dr Milan Vego, Mr David Warren, Dr Andre Wessels, Messrs Wright & Logan, Mr Cem D Yaylali, Señor Luis Oscar Zunino.

Jane's comprehensive library of books and CD-ROM tapes are the principal source of aircraft and weapon systems details, and particularly important are *Jane's All the World's Aircraft, Jane's High-Speed Marine Craft, Jane's Strategic Weapon Systems, Jane's Naval Weapon Systems, Jane's Radar and EW Systems* and *Jane's Underwater Warfare Systems*. Jane's magazines, including *International Defense Review, Jane's Intelligence Review* and *Jane's Defence Weekly* provide much useful information, as does *Ships of the World*, a Japanese monthly magazine.

This year we were particularly fortunate in having no changes of personnel at Coulsdon where the production work is done. Ruth Simmance goes from strength to strength as the presiding genius of the editorial department, while the detailed work is done with care and accuracy by Diana Burns, Sarah Erskine and Kathryn Jones. There is a particular skill in composing a full page from a number of different entry styles used in *Jane's Fighting Ships*, while maintaining the traditional clarity of layout, so that entries don't spill over from page to page. Jack Brenchley and Keith Biller are the masters of this art, while Chrissie Richards runs the production schedule and Alan Ricketts transposes all of it into CD-ROM.

The editorial and production teams handle most of the Jane's yearbook output, and not the least of their accomplishments is the tactful handling of editors' overblown egos. At least in the office my wife Joanna only has to deal with one of these, while processing the huge amount of correspondence which the annual update entails.

The regular Information Updates mean that we can now make use of selected information almost as soon as it comes in, but the 1995 book schedule remains the same as in previous years. Because of the volume of change, major contributors are asked to respond in October, with supplementary information to follow up to the end of March. This helps to spread the updating load evenly over the major revision period.

Information from anyone with an interest in navies and warships is very welcome, and it is always a pleasure to hear from those at sea.

My address is:

Captain Richard Sharpe
Foundry House
Kingsley
Bordon
Hampshire GU35 9LY
United Kingdom

Fax number (UK) 0420 477833

Note: No illustration from this book may be reproduced without the publisher's permission, but the Press may reproduce information and governmental photographs provided that *Jane's Fighting Ships* is acknowledged as the source. Photographs credited to other than official organisations must not be reproduced without permission from the originator.

Biographical note: The Editor
In 34 years in the Royal Navy the editor travelled all over the world. He has commanded nuclear and conventional submarines as well as a guided missile destroyer which was for some of the time the Flagship of NATO's Standing Naval Force Atlantic. He has also served in several appointments at the Ministry of Defence in London, including one in Naval Intelligence, and has been the Submarine Operations Officer on the staff of the UK Commander-in-Chief Fleet. In his last job before taking over as editor of Jane's Fighting Ships he was responsible for the selection of RN officers.

Proven power

With over 1000 engines on active duty with the world's navies, the Wärtsilä Diesel Group is a leader in high and medium speed marine propulsion, auxiliary engines and propulsion systems.

Installations range from fast patrol craft through mine sweeper hunters, corvettes and multipurpose frigates to landing ships, underway replenishment ships and maritime prepositioning ships; all deliver the absolute reliability, availability and superior performance navies and coastal defence forces demand.

The Wärtsilä Diesel Group's engines offer fast load-change characteristics, shock durability, fuel economy, long overhaul intervals and ease of maintenance. Back-up is provided by a round-the-clock global service network. No matter how special the vessel, the Wärtsilä Diesel Group has the resources and experience to provide the custom-made solution.

Wärtsilä Diesel Oy, P.O.Box 244, FIN-65101 Vaasa, Finland, Telephone +358-61-3270, Telefax +358-61-3171 906   **Wärtsilä Diesel AB**, P.O.Box 920, S-46129 Trollhättan, Sweden, Telephone +46-520-22 600, Telefax +46-520-22 850   **Wartsila SACM Diesel S.A.**, Usine de la Combe, B.P. 115, F-17700 Surgeres, France, Telephone +33-46-303 150, Telefax +33-46-303 159

Glossary

(see also Type abbreviations at head of Pennant List)

AAW	Anti-air warfare
ACDS	Advanced combat direction system
ACV	Air cushion vehicle
AEW	Airborne early warning
AIP	Air independent propulsion
ANV	Advanced naval vehicle
ARM	Anti-radiation missile
A/S, ASW	Anti-submarine (warfare)
ASM	Air-to-surface missile
BPDMS	Base point defence missile system
Cal	Calibre — the diameter of a gun barrel; also used for measuring length of the barrel eg a 6 in gun 50 calibres long (6 in/50) would be 25 ft long
CIWS	Close in weapon system
COD	Carrier onboard delivery
CODAG, CODOG, CODLAG, COGAG, COGOG, COSAG	Descriptions of mixed propulsion systems: combined diesel and gas turbine, diesel-electric and gas turbine, diesel or gas turbine, gas turbine and gas turbine, gas turbine or gas turbine, steam and gas turbine
CONAS	Combined nuclear and steam
cp	Controllable pitch (propellers)
DC	Depth charge
DCT	Depth charge thrower
DP	Dual purpose (gun) for surface or AA use
Displacement	Basically the weight of water displaced by a ship's hull when floating: (a) Light: without fuel, water or ammunition (b) Normal: used for Japanese MSA ships. Similar to 'standard' (c) Standard: as defined by Washington Naval Conference 1922 — fully manned and stored but without fuel or reserve feed-water (d) Full load: fully laden with all stores, ammunition, fuel and water
DSRV	Deep submergence recovery vessel
dwt	Deadweight tonnage
ECM	Electronic countermeasures eg jamming
ECCM	Electronic counter-countermeasures
EEZ	Exclusive economic zone
EHF	Extreme high frequency
ELF	Extreme low frequency radio
ELINT	Electronic intelligence eg recording radar, W/T etc
ESM	Electronic support measures eg intercept
EW	Electronic warfare
FAC	Fast attack craft
FLIR	Forward looking infra-red radar
FRAM	Fleet rehabilitation and modernisation programme
GFCS	Gun fire control system
GMLS	Guided missile launch system
GPS	Geographical positioning system
grt	Gross registered tonnage
GWS	Guided weapon system
HF	High frequency

Horsepower (hp) or (hp(m))	Power developed or applied:
	(a) bhp: brake horsepower = power available at the crankshaft
	(b) shp: shaft horsepower = power delivered to the propeller shaft
	(c) ihp: indicated horsepower = power produced by expansion of gases in the cylinders of reciprocating steam engines
	(d) 1 kW = 1.341 hp = 1.360 metric hp
	     1 hp = 0.746 kW = 1.014 metric hp
	     1 metric hp = 0.735 kW = 0.968 hp
	(e) Sustained horsepower may be different for similar engines in different conditions

IFF	Identification friend/foe
kT	Kiloton
kW	Kilowatt
LAMPS	Light airborne multi-purpose system
LCM	Landing craft, mechanised
LCU	Landing craft, utility
LCVP/LCP	Landing craft, vehicles/personnel
Length	Expressed in various ways: (a) oa: overall = length between extremities (b) pp: between perpendiculars = between fore side of the stem and after side of the rudderpost (c) wl: water-line = between extremities on the water-line
LF	Low frequency
LMCR	Liquid metal cooled reactor
LRMP	Long-range maritime patrol
LSM	Landing ship, medium
MAD	Magnetic Anomaly Detector — for anti-submarine detection identifying a steel body in the earth's magnetic field
MAP	US Military Assistance Programme
MCMV	Mine countermeasures vessel
MDF	Maritime defence force
Measurement	See Tonnage
MF	Medium frequency
MFCS	Missile fire control system
MG	Machine gun
MIRV	Multiple, independently targetable re-entry vehicle
MRV	Multiple re-entry vehicle
MSA	Maritime safety agency
MSC	US Military Sealift Command
MSC	Coastal minesweeper
MSH	Minehunter
MW	Megawatt
NBC	Nuclear, biological and chemical (warfare)
net	Net registered tonnage
nm	Nautical miles
NTDS	Naval tactical direction system
NTU	New Threat Upgrade
oa	Overall length
OPV	Offshore patrol vessel
OTC	Officer in Tactical Command
PDMS	Point defence missile system
PUFFS	Passive underwater fire control system
PWR	Pressurised water reactor
RAM	Radar absorbent material
RAS	Replenishment at sea
RBU	Anti-submarine rocket launcher
RIB	Rigid inflatable boat
Ro-ro	Roll-on/roll-off
ROV	Remote operated vehicle
rpm	Revolutions per minute of engines, propellers, radar aerials etc
SAM	Surface-to-air missile
SAR	Search and rescue
SATCOM	Satellite communications
SES	Surface effect ship
SHF	Super high frequency
SINS	Ship's inertial navigation system
SLBM	Submarine-launched ballistic missile
SLCM	Ship-launched cruise missile
SLEP	Service Life Extension Program
SNLE	Nuclear-powered ballistic missile submarine (French)
SRBOC	Super rapid blooming offboard chaff
SS	Attack submarine
SSAN	Auxiliary nuclear-powered submarine
SSBN	Nuclear-powered ballistic missile submarine
SSDE	Submerged signal and decoy ejector
SSG	Guided missile submarine
SSGN	Nuclear-powered guided missile submarine
SSM	Surface-to-surface missile
SSN	Nuclear-powered attack submarine
STIR	Surveillance Target Indicator Radar
Subroc/Asroc	Rocket-assisted torpedo part of whose range is in the air
SURTASS	Surface Towed Array Surveillance System
SUWN-1	Surface-to-underwater missile launcher
SWATH	Small waterplane area twin hull
TACAN	Tactical air navigation beacon
TACTASS	Tactical Towed Acoustic Sensor System
TAS	Target Acquisition System
TASS	Towed Array Surveillance System
Tonnage	Measurement tons, computed on capacity of a ship's hull rather than its 'displacement' (see above): (a) Gross: the internal volume of all spaces within the hull and all permanently enclosed spaces above decks that are available for cargo, stores and accommodation. The result in cubic feet divided by 100 = gross tonnage (b) Net: gross minus all those spaces used for machinery, accommodation etc ('non-earning' spaces) (c) Deadweight (dwt): the amount of cargo, bunkers, stores etc that a ship can carry at her load draught
Tonnes	One ton equals 1.016 tonnes
UHF	Ultra-high frequency
VDS	Variable depth sonar which is lowered to best listening depth. Known as dunking sonar in helicopters.
Vertrep	Vertical replenishment
VLF	Very low frequency radio
VLS	Vertical launch system
VSTOL	Vertical or short take-off/landing
VTOL	Vertical take off/landing
WIG	Wing-in-ground effect
wl	Waterline length

Ensigns and Flags of the World's Navies

The following pictorial representations show each country's ensign where it has one or its national flag. In cases where countries do not have ensigns their warships normally fly the national flag.

Albania
National Flag

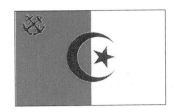

Algeria
Ensign

Angola
National Flag

Anguilla
Ensign

Antigua
National Flag

Argentina
National Flag and Ensign

Australia
Ensign

Austria
Ensign

Azerbaijan
National Flag

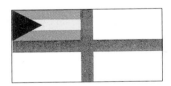

Bahamas
Ensign

Bahrain
National Flag

Bangladesh
National Flag

Barbados
Ensign

Belgium
Ensign

Belize
National Flag

Benin
National Flag

Bermuda
National Flag

Bolivia
Ensign

Brazil
National Flag

Brunei
Ensign

Bulgaria
Ensign

Burma
National Flag

Cambodia
National Flag

Cameroon
National Flag

Canada
National Flag and Ensign

Cape Verde
National Flag

Chile
National Flag and Ensign

China, People's Republic
Ensign

Colombia
Ensign

Comoro Islands
National Flag

Congo
National Flag

Cook Islands
National Flag

Costa Rica
Ensign and Government Flag

Croatia
National Flag

Cuba
National Flag and Ensign

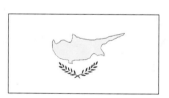

Cyprus, Republic
National Flag

Cyprus, Turkish Republic
(Not recognised by United Nations)
National Flag

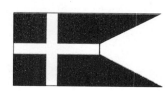

Denmark
Ensign

Djibouti
National Flag

Dominica
National Flag

Dominican Republic
Ensign

Ecuador
National Flag and Ensign

Egypt
Ensign

El Salvador
National Flag and Ensign

[58]

Equatorial Guinea
National Flag

Estonia
National Flag

Ethiopia
National Flag

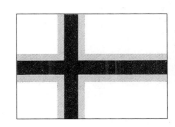

Faroes
The Islands Flag

Falkland Islands
Falkland Islands Flag

Fiji
Ensign

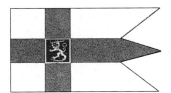

Finland
Ensign

France
Ensign

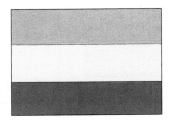

Gabon
National Flag

Gambia
National Flag

Georgia
National Flag

Germany
Ensign

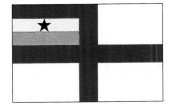

Ghana
Ensign

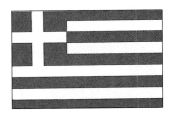

Greece
National Flag and Ensign

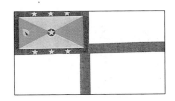

Grenada
Ensign

Guatemala
National Flag and Ensign

Guinea
National Flag

Guinea-Bissau
National Flag

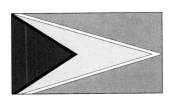

Guyana
National Flag

Haiti
State Flag and Ensign

Honduras
Ensign

Hong Kong
Hong Kong Flag

Hungary
National Flag

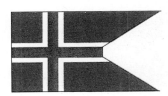

Iceland
Ensign

India
Ensign

Indonesia
National Flag and Ensign

Iran
National Flag

Iraq
National Flag

Ireland
National Flag and Ensign

Israel
Ensign

Italy
Ensign

Ivory Coast
National Flag

Jamaica
Ensign

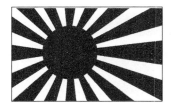

Japan
Ensign

Jordan
Ensign

Kenya
Ensign

**Korea, Democratic
People's Republic (North)**
National Flag

Korea, Republic (South)
Ensign

Kuwait
National Flag

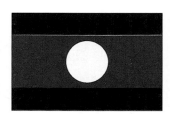

Laos
National Flag

Latvia
Ensign

Lebanon
National Flag

Liberia
National Flag and Ensign

Libya
National Flag

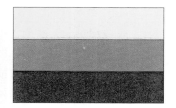

Lithuania
National Flag

Madagascar
National Flag

Malawi
National Flag

Malaysia
Ensign

Maldives
National Flag

Mali
National Flag

Malta
National Flag

Mauritania
National Flag

Mauritius
Ensign

Mexico
National Flag and Ensign

Monserrat
National Flag

Morocco
Ensign

Mozambique
National Flag

NATO
*Flag of the North Atlantic
Treaty Organization*

Netherlands
National Flag and Ensign

New Zealand
Ensign

Nicaragua
National Flag and Ensign

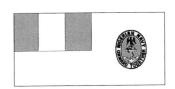

Nigeria
Ensign

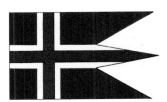

Norway
Ensign

Oman
Ensign

Pakistan
Ensign

Panama
National Flag and Ensign

Papua New Guinea
Ensign

Paraguay
National Flag and Ensign

Paraguay
*National Flag and Ensign
(reverse)*

Peru
Ensign

Philippines
National Flag

Poland
Ensign

Portugal
National Flag and Ensign

Qatar
National Flag

Romania
National Flag and Ensign

Russia
Ensign

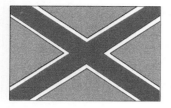

Russia
Border Guard Ensign

Russia & Ukraine
(Black Sea Fleet)
Ensign

St Kitts-Nevis
National Flag

St Lucia
National Flag

St Vincent
National Flag

Saudi Arabia
Ensign

Senegal
National Flag

Seychelles
National Flag

Sierre Leone
Ensign

Singapore
Ensign

Solomon Islands
National Flag

Somalia
National Flag

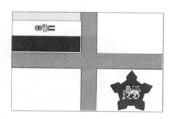

South Africa
Naval Ensign

Spain
National Flag and Ensign

Sri Lanka
Ensign

Sudan
National Flag

Surinam
National Flag

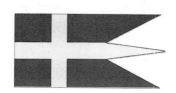

Sweden
Ensign and Jack

Switzerland
National Flag

Syria
National Flag

Taiwan
National Flag and Ensign

Tanzania
Ensign

Thailand
Ensign

Togo
National Flag

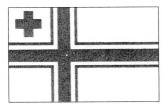

Tonga
Ensign

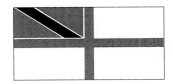

Trinidad and Tobago
Ensign

Tunisia
National Flag

Turkey
National Flag and Ensign

Turks and Caicos
National Flag

Uganda
National Flag

Ukraine
National Flag

Union of Soviet Socialist Republics (former)
Ensign

United Arab Emirates
National Flag

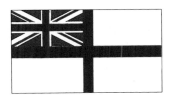

United Kingdom
Ensign

United States of America
National Flag and Ensign

Uruguay
National Flag and Ensign

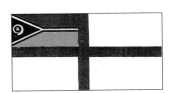

Vanuatu
Ensign

Venezuela
National Flag and Ensign

Vietnam
National Flag

Virgin Islands
National Flag

Western Samoa
National Flag

Yemen
National Flag

Yugoslavia
National Flag

Zaire
National Flag

Save trees, buy a disc!

Too much paper and storage are two common problems for most libraries, and not least for most offices! But not any longer. Jane's can now give you instant access to the most comprehensive open source defence and aerospace information library available - **Jane's Electronic Information System (EIS)**, and there's not a single sheet of paper to be found! In fact, if you have spare space amounting to about half the size of this advertisement, you are well on the way to having your own defence and aerospace information library at your fingertips.

Jane's EIS can give you all that information across 1, 2 or any number of Jane's yearbooks in just seconds, all on just one compact disc.

Jane's EIS is a product designed to satisfy many of the contemporary information requirements for defence and military intelligence professionals and operates across a broad range of _UNIX_ platforms.

Isolate, retrieve and incorporate Jane's valuable open source information and graphics into your own studies and reports. For more information contact the Jane's EIS Helpline in the UK on +44 (0) 81 763 9945, fax +44 (0) 81 763 1006. In the USA/Canada, call +1 (703) 683 3700, fax +1 (703) 836 0029.

Jane's EIS - over 20 yearbooks on 1 disc.

Ranks and Insignia of the World's Navies

Where possible, the rank titles are shown in the language of the relevant country followed by the equivalent ranks in English.

The sleeves are drawn to one scale and the shoulder insignia to another allowing respective comparisons of size to be made. The exception to this is Croatia where badges worn on the right breast of the uniforms are depicted.

Albania

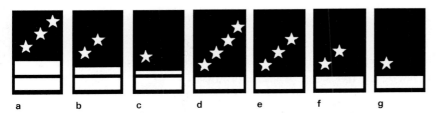

a b c d e f g

a: *Colonel*, Captain   **b**: *Lieutenant Colonel*, Commander   **c**: *Major*, Lieutenant Commander
d: *Captain*, Lieutenant   **e**: *Senior Lieutenant*, Senior Lieutenant   **f**: *Lieutenant*, Sub Lieutenant
g: *Junior Lieutenant*, Acting Sub Lieutenant

Silver stars and gold braid on black.

Algeria (Algerian Marine)

a b c d e f

a: *'Aqid*, Captain   **b**: *Muqaddam*, Commander   **c**: *Ra'id*, Lieutenant
Commander   **d**: *Naqib*, Lieutenant   **e**: *Mulazim Awwal*, Sub Lieutenant
f: *Mulazim*, Acting Sub Lieutenant

Gold on navy blue.

Angola (Marinha di Duerra)

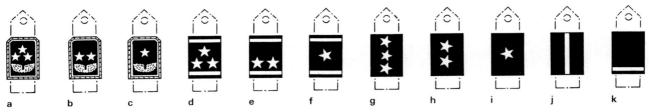

a b c d e f g h i j k

a: *Almirante*, Admiral   **b**: *Vice-Almirante*, Vice Admiral   **c**: *Contra-Almirante*, Rear Admiral   **d**: *Capitão-de-Mar-e-Guerra*, Captain   **e**: *Capitão-de-Fragata*,
Commander   **f**: *Capitão-de-Corveta*, Lieutenant Commander   **g**: *Tenente-de-Navio*, Lieutenant   **h**: *Tenente-de-Fragata*, Sub Lieutenant   **i**: *Tenente-de-
Corveta*, Acting Sub Lieutenant   **j**: *Alférez*, Midshipman   **k**: *Aspirante*, Cadet

Admiral to Lieutenant Commander, gold on navy blue. Lieutenant to Sub Lieutenant, silver on navy blue. Midshipman and Cadet, light blue on navy blue.

Argentina Navy (Armada Argentina)

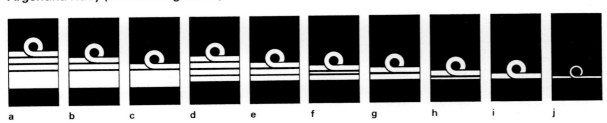

a b c d e f g h i j

a: *Almirante*, Admiral   **b**: *Vicealmirante*, Vice Admiral   **c**: *Contraalmirante*, Rear Admiral   **d**: *Capitán de Navío*, Captain   **e**: *Capitán de
Fragata*, Commander   **f**: *Capitán de Corbeta*, Lieutenant Commander   **g**: *Teniente de Navío*, Lieutenant   **h**: *Teniente de Fragata*, Sub
Lieutenant   **i**: *Teniente de Corbeta*, Acting Lieutenant   **j**: *Guardiamarina*, Midshipman

Gold on navy blue.

Argentina (Coast Guard) (Prefectura Naval Argentina)

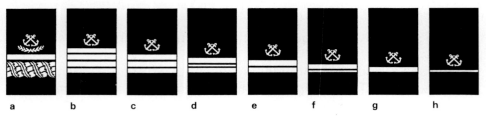

a: *Prefecto General*, Rear Admiral   b: *Prefecto Mayor*, Captain   c: *Prefecto Principal*, Commander   d: *Prefecto*, Lieutenant Commander   e: *Subprefecto*, Lieutenant   f: *Oficial Principal*, Sub Lieutenant   g: *Oficial Auxiliar*, Acting Sub Lieutenant   h: *Oficial Ayudante*, Midshipman

Gold on navy blue.

Australia

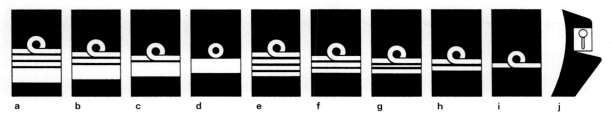

a: Admiral   b: Vice Admiral   c: Rear Admiral   d: Commodore   e: Captain   f: Commander   g: Lieutenant Commander
h: Lieutenant   i: Sub Lieutenant   j: Midshipman

Gold on navy blue.

Australia (Customs Service)

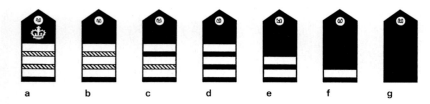

a: Customs Officer Band 6   b: Customs Officer Band 5   c: Customs Officer Band 4
d: Customs Officer Band 3   e: Customs Officer Band 2   f: Customs Officer Band 1
g: Assistant Customs Officer

Gold buttons, stripes and crown with red cushions on navy blue.

Bahamas (Royal Bahamas Defence Force (Naval Division))

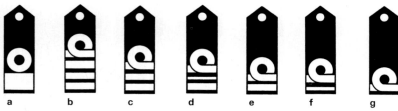

a: Commodore   b: Captain   c: Commander   d: Lieutenant Commander   e: Lieutenant
f: Junior Lieutenant   g: Sub Lieutenant

Gold on black.

Bahrain Coast Guard

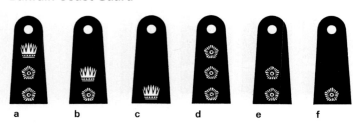

a: *'Aqid*, Colonel   b: *Muqaddam*, Lieutenant Colonel   c: *Ra'id*, Major
d: *Naqib*, Captain   e: *Mulazim Awwal*, Lieutenant   f: *Mulazim Thani*, Second Lieutenant

Gold and red on navy blue.

Bangladesh

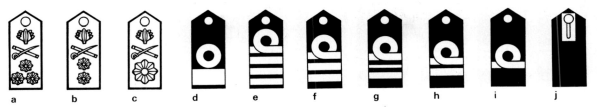

a: Admiral   b: Vice Admiral   c: Rear Admiral   d: Commodore   e: Captain   f: Commander   g: Lieutenant Commander
h: Lieutenant   i: Sub Lieutenant   j: Midshipman

Gold on navy blue. Flag ranks, gold edged blue, silver devices. White patch on midshipman's shoulder strap.

Barbados (Barbados Coast Guard)

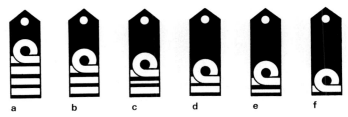

a: Captain   b: Commander   c: Lieutenant Commander   d: Lieutenant
e: Junior Lieutenant   f: Sub Lieutenant

Gold on black.

Belgium (Zeemacht/La Force Naval)

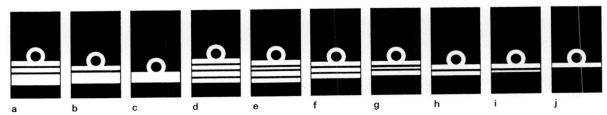

a: *Vice-Admiraal/Vice Amiral*, Vice Admiral   b: *Divisie-Admiraal/Amiral de Division*, Rear Admiral   c: *Commodore/Commodore*, Commodore
d: *Kapitein-ter-Zee/Capitaine de Vaisseau*, Captain   e: *Fregatkapitein/Capitaine de Frégate*, Commander   f: *Corvetkapitein/Capitaine de Corvette*, Lieutenant Commander   g: *Luitenant-ter-Zee 1ste Klasse/Lieutenant de Vaisseau 1re Classe*, Senior Lieutenant   h: *Luitenant-ter-Zee/ Lieutenant de Vaisseau*, Lieutenant   i: *Vaandrig-ter-Zee/Enseigne de Vaisseau*, Sub Lieutenant   j: *Vaandrig-ter-Zee 2e Klasse/Enseigne de Vaisseau 2e Classe*, Acting Sub Lieutenant

Ranks given in Flemish, French and English. Gold on navy blue.

Belize (Belize Defence Force (Marine Wing))

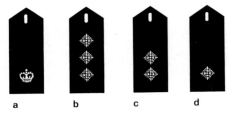

a: *Major*, Lieutenant Commander   b: *Captain*, Lieutenant
c: *Lieutenant*, Sub Lieutenant   d: *2nd Lieutenant*, Acting Sub Lieutenant

Gold on light khaki or olive drab.

Bermuda (Police - Marine Division)

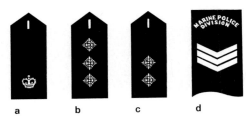

a: Superintendent   b: Chief Inspector   c: Inspector   d: Sergeant

White on black.

Bolivia

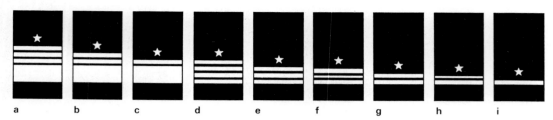

a: *Almirante*, Admiral   b: *Vicealmirante*, Vice Admiral   c: *Contraalmirante*, Rear Admiral   d: *Capitán de Navío*, Captain
e: *Capitán de Fragata*, Commander   f: *Capitán de Corbeta*, Lieutenant Commander   g: *Teniente de Navío*, Lieutenant
h: *Teniente de Fragata*, Sub Lieutenant   i: *Alférez*, Acting Sub Lieutenant

Gold on navy blue.

Brazil (Marinha do Brasil)

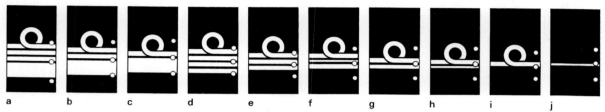

a: *Almirante*, Admiral   b: *Vice-Almirante*, Vice Admiral   c: *Contra-Almirante*, Rear Admiral   d: *Capitão-de-Mar-e-Guerra*, Captain
e: *Capitão-de-Fragata*, Commander   f: *Capitão-de-Corveta*, Lieutenant Commander   g: *Capitão-de-Tenente*, Lieutenant   h: *Primeiro-Tenente*,
Sub Lieutenant   i: *Segundo-Tenente*, Acting Sub Lieutenant   j: *Guarda-Marinha*, Midshipman

Gold on dark blue.

British Virgin Islands (Police - Marine Branch)

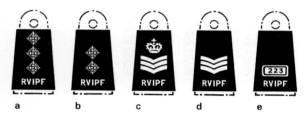

a: Chief Inspector   b: Inspector   c: Station Sergeant   d: Sergeant   e: Constable

Silver on black.

Burma

a: Admiral   b: Vice Admiral   c: Rear Admiral   d: Commodore   e: Captain   f: Commander   g: Lieutenant Commander   h: Lieutenant
i: Sub Lieutenant   j: Acting Sub Lieutenant

Gold on dark blue. All three services have same rank insignia based on the army.

Cameroon (Marine Nationale République du Cameroun)

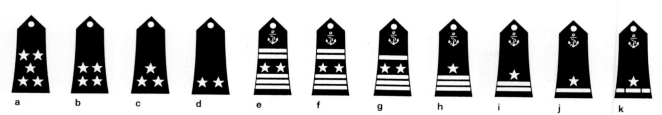

a: *Amiral d'Escadre*, Admiral of the Fleet   b: *Vice-Amiral d'Escadre*, Admiral   c: *Vice-Amiral*, Vice Admiral   d: *Contre-Amiral*, Rear Admiral   e: *Capitaine de Vaisseau*,
Captain   f: *Capitaine de Frégate*, Commander   g: *Capitaine de Corvette*, Lieutenant Commander   h: *Lieutenant de Vaisseau*, Lieutenant   i: *Enseigne de Vaisseau 1re
Classe*, Sub Lieutenant   j: *Enseigne de Vaisseau 2e Class*, Acting Sub Lieutenant   k: *Aspirant*, Midshipman

Gold on navy blue. Top two stripes for Commander, silver.

Canada (Maritime Command)

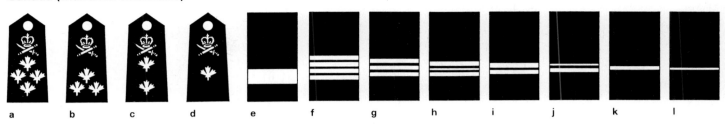

a: Admiral   b: Vice Admiral   c: Rear Admiral   d: Commodore   e: All Flag Ranks   f: Captain   g: Commander   h: Lieutenant Commander   i: Lieutenant   j: Sub Lieutenant   k: Acting Sub Lieutenant   l: Officer Cadet

Gold on black.

Canada (Coast Guard)

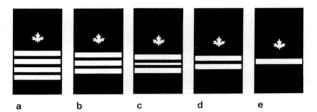

a: Commanding Officer   b: Chief Officer   c: First Officer
d: Second Officer   e: Third Officer
Rank structure for large ships only.

Gold on navy blue.

Chile (Armada de Chile)

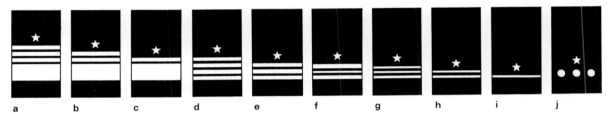

a: *Almirante*, Admiral   b: *Vicealmirante*, Vice Admiral   c: *Contraalmirante*, Rear Admiral   d: *Capitán de Navío*, Captain   e: *Capitán de Fragata*, Commander   f: *Capitán de Corbeta*, Lieutenant Commander   g: *Teniente Primero*, Lieutenant   h: *Teniente Segundo*, Junior Lieutenant   i: *Sub Teniente*, Sub Lieutenant   j: *Guardia Marina*, Midshipman

Gold on black.

China (People's Liberation Army Navy)

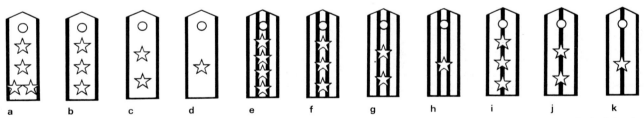

a: *Senior General*, Admiral of the Fleet   b: *General*, Admiral   c: *Lieutenant General*, Vice Admiral   d: *Major General*, Rear Admiral   e: *Senior Colonel*, Commodore   f: *Colonel*, Captain   g: *Lieutenant Colonel*, Commander   h: *Major Colonel*, Lieutenant Commander   i: *Captain*, Lieutenant   j: *Lieutenant*, Sub Lieutenant   k: *Second Lieutenant*, Acting Sub Lieutenant

Generals, gold edged dark blue. Gold button. Silver stars. Senior Colonel to Major Colonel two dark blue stripes. Captain to Second Lieutenant one dark blue stripe.

Colombia (Armada de la Republica de Colombia)

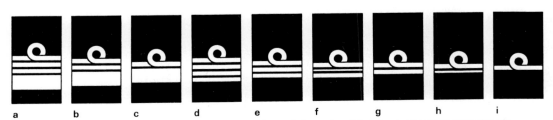

a: *Almirante*, Admiral   b: *Vicealmirante*, Vice Admiral   c: *Contraalmirante*, Rear Admiral   d: *Capitán de Navío*, Captain
e: *Capitán de Fragata*, Commander   f: *Capitán de Corbeta*, Lieutenant Commander   g: *Teniente de Navío*, Lieutenant
h: *Teniente de Fragata*, Sub Lieutenant   i: *Teniente de Corbeta*, Acting Sub Lieutenant

Gold on black.

Congo

a b c d e f

a: *Capitaine de Vaisseau*, Captain   **b:** *Capitaine de Frégate*, Commander
c: *Capitaine de Corvette*, Lieutenant Commander   **d:** *Lieutenant de Vaisseau*,
Lieutenant   **e:** *Enseigne de Vaisseau 1re Classe*, Sub Lieutenant   **f:** *Enseigne de Vaisseau 2e Classe*, Acting Sub Lieutenant

Captain three red stars, Commander one gold over two red stars, Lieutenant Commander one red star, remainder gold stars, all on black.

Croatia (Hrvatska Ratna Mornarica)

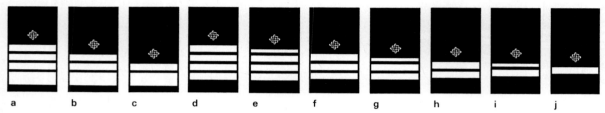

a b c d e f g h i j

a: *Admiral*, Admiral   **b:** *Viceadmiral*, Vice Admiral   **c:** *Kontraadmiral*, Rear Admiral   **d:** *Kapetan Bojnog*, Captain   **e:** *Kapetan Fregate*, Commander   **f:** *Kapetan Korvete*, Lieutenant Commander   **g:** *Poručnik Bojnog*, Lieutenant   **h:** *Poručnik Fregate*, Sub Lieutenant   **i:** *Poručnik Korvete*, Acting Sub Lieutenant   **j:** *Zastavnik*, Midshipman

Gold on black.

Cuba (Marinha de Guerra Revolucionaria)

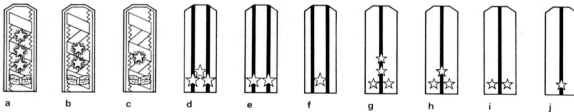

a b c d e f g h i j

a: *Almirante*, Admiral   **b:** *Vicealmirante*, Vice Admiral   **c:** *Contraalmirante*, Rear Admiral   **d:** *Capitán de Navío*, Captain   **e:** *Capitán de Fregata*, Commander   **f:** *Capitán de Corbeta*, Lieutenant Commander   **g:** *Teniente de Navío*, Senior Lieutenant   **h:** *Teniente de Fregata*, Lieutenant   **i:** *Teniente de Corbeta*, Sub Lieutenant   **j:** *Alférez*, Acting Sub Lieutenant

Black stripes. Admirals, gold stars on blue design.

Cyprus

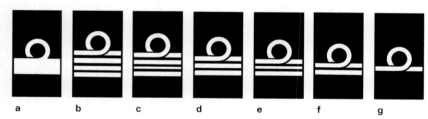

a b c d e f g

a: *Captain First in Command*, Commodore   **b:** *Captain*, Captain   **c:** *Commander*, Commander
d: *Lieutenant Commander*, Lieutenant Commander   **e:** *Lieutenant*, Lieutenant   **f:** *Sub Lieutenant*, Sub Lieutenant   **g:** *Ensign*, Acting Sub Lieutenant

Gold on navy blue.

Cyprus (Port and Marine Police)

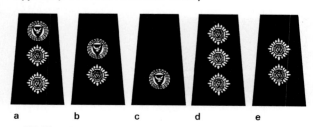

a b c d e

a: Chief Superintendent   **b:** Superintendent A   **c:** Superintendent B
d: Chief Inspector   **e:** Inspector

Silver wreath and stars, blue enamel shield and white dove on black.

Denmark (Søvaernet)

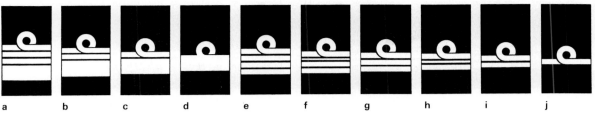

a   b   c   d   e   f   g   h   i   j

a: *Admiral*, Admiral   **b:** *Viceadmiral*, Vice Admiral   **c:** *Kontreadmiral*, Rear Admiral   **d:** *Flotilleadmiral*, Commodore   **e:** *Kommandør*, Captain
f: *Kommandørkaptajn*, Senior Commander   **g:** *Orlogskaptajn*, Commander   **h:** *Kaptajnløjtnant*, Lieutenant Commander   **i:** *Premierløjtnant*,
Lieutenant   **j:** *Løjtnant*, Junior Grade Lieutenant

Gold on black.

Dominican Republic (Marinha de Guerra)

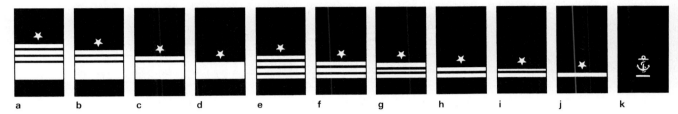

a   b   c   d   e   f   g   h   i   j   k

a: *Almirante*, Admiral   **b:** *Vicealmirante*, Vice Admiral   **c:** *Contraalmirante*, Rear Admiral   **d:** *Comodoro*, Commodore   **e:** *Capitán de Navío*, Captain
f: *Capitán de Fragata*, Commander   **g:** *Capitán de Corbeta*, Lieutenant Commander   **h:** *Teniente de Navío*, Lieutenant   **i:** *Alférez de Navío*, Sub Lieutenant
j: *Alférez de Fragata*, Acting Sub Lieutenant   **k:** *Guariamarina*, Midshipman

Gold on black.

Ecuador (Armada de Guerra)

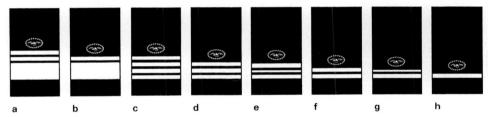

a   b   c   d   e   f   g   h

a: *Vicealmirante*, Vice Admiral   **b:** *Contraalmirante*, Rear Admiral   **c:** *Capitán de Navío*, Captain   **d:** *Capitán de*
Fragata, Commander   **e:** *Capitán de Corbeta*, Lieutenant Commander   **f:** *Teniente de Fragata*, Lieutenant
g: *Alférez de Navío*, Sub Lieutenant   **h:** *Alférez de Fragata*, Acting Sub Lieutenant

Gold on black.

Egypt

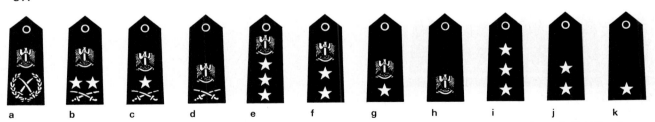

a   b   c   d   e   f   g   h   i   j   k

a: *Mushir*, Admiral of the Fleet   **b:** *Fariq Awwal*, Admiral   **c:** *Fariq*, Vice Admiral   **d:** *Liwa'*, Rear Admiral   **e:** *'Amid*, Commodore   **f:** *'Aqid*, Captain
g: *Muqaddam*, Commander   **h:** *Ra'id*, Lieutenant Commander   **i:** *Naqib*, Lieutenant   **j:** *Mulazim Awwal*, Sub Lieutenant   **k:** *Mulazim*, Acting Sub
Lieutenant

Gold on black. Shield on eagle's breast black, white and red.

El Salvador

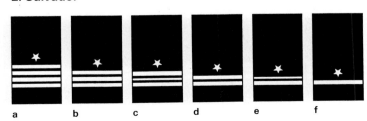

a   b   c   d   e   f

a: *Coronel*, Captain   **b:** *Teniente Coronel*, Commander   **c:** *Mayor*, Lieutenant
Commander   **d:** *Capitán*, Lieutenant   **e:** *Teniente*, Sub Lieutenant   **f:** *Sub Teniente*,
Acting Sub Lieutenant

Gold on navy blue.

Finland (Suomen Merivoimat)

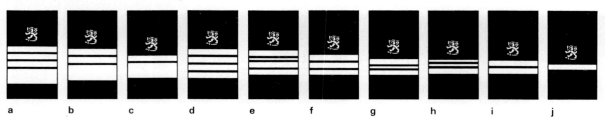

a: *Amiraali*, Admiral **b:** *Vara-amiraali*, Vice Admiral **c:** *Kontra-amiraali*, Rear Admiral **d:** *Kommodori*, Captain **e:** *Komentaja*, Commander **f:** *Komentajakapteeni*, Lieutenant Commander **g:** *Kapteeniluutnantti*, Senior Lieutenant **h:** *Yliluutnantti*, Lieutenant **i:** *Luutnantti*, Junior Lieutenant **j:** *Aliluutnantti*, Sub Lieutenant

Gold on black.

France (Marine Nationale)

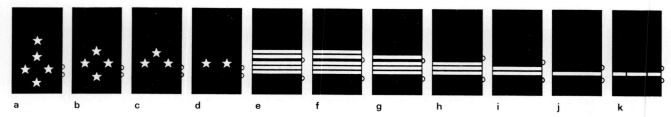

a: *Amiral*, Admiral of the Fleet **b:** *Vice-Amiral d'Escadre*, Admiral **c:** *Vice-Amiral*, Vice Admiral **d:** *Contre-Amiral*, Rear Admiral **e:** *Capitaine de Vaisseau*, Captain **f:** *Capitaine de Frégate*, Commander **g:** *Capitaine de Corvette*, Lieutenant Commander **h:** *Lieutenant de Vaisseau*, Lieutenant **i:** *Enseigne de Vaisseau de 1re Classe*, Sub Lieutenant **j:** *Enseigne de Vaisseau de 2e Classe*, Acting Sub Lieutenant **k:** *Aspirant*, Midshipman

Flag ranks, silver stars. Captain, gold. Commander, three gold two silver. Lieutenant Commander to Midshipman, gold. Vertical stripes on Midshipman's lace, mid blue. All on dark blue.

France (Gendarmerie Maritime)

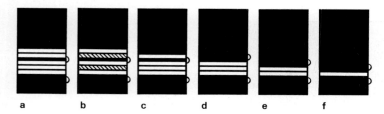

a: *Officier én Chef de 1re Classe*, Captain **b:** *Officier én Chef de 2e Classe*, Commander **c:** *Officier Principal*, Lieutenant Commander **d:** *Officier de 1re Classe*, Lieutenant **e:** *Officier de 2e Classe*, Sub Lieutenant **f:** *Officier de 3e Classe*, Acting Sub Lieutenant

Silver on blue. Commander, gold and silver on blue.

Gabon (Marine Gabonaise)

a: *Capitaine de Vaisseau*, Captain (also Commodore) **b:** *Capitaine de Frégate*, Commander **c:** *Capitaine de Corvette*, Lieutenant Commander **d:** *Lieutenant de Vaisseau*, Lieutenant **e:** *Enseigne de Vaisseau 1re Classe*, Sub Lieutenant **f:** *Enseigne de Vaisseau 2e Classe*, Acting Sub Lieutenant

Gold on black. Commander, silver and gold on black.

Germany

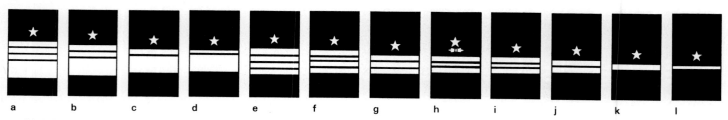

a: *Admiral*, Admiral **b:** *Viceadmiral*, Vice Admiral **c:** *Konteradmiral*, Rear Admiral **d:** *Flottillenadmiral*, Commodore **e:** *Kapitan zur See*, Captain **f:** *Fregattenkapitan*, Commander **g:** *Korvettenkapitan*, Lieutenant Commander **h:** *Stabskapitanleutnant*, Senior Lieutenant **i:** *Kapitanleutnant*, Lieutenant **j:** *Oberleutnant zur See*, Sub Lieutenant **k:** *Leutnant zur See*, Acting Sub Lieutenant **l:** *Oberfahnrich zur See*, Midshipman

Gold on navy blue.

Germany Coast Guard (Bundesgrenzschutz See)

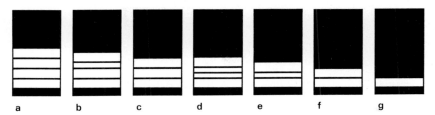

a b c d e f g

a: *Polizeidirektor im BGS*, Captain **b:** *Polizeioberrat im BGS*, Commander **c:** *Polizeirat im BGS*, Lieutenant Commander **d:** *Erster Polizeihauptkommissar im BGS*, Senior Lieutenant **e:** *Polizeihauptkommissar im BGS*, Lieutenant **f:** *Polizeioberkommissar im BGS*, Sub Lieutenant **g:** *Polizeikommissar im BGS*, Acting Sub Lieutenant

Gold on navy blue.

Ghana

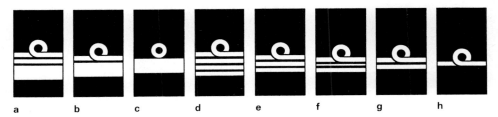

a b c d e f g h

a: Vice Admiral **b:** Rear Admiral **c:** Commodore **d:** Captain **e:** Commander **f:** Lieutenant Commander **g:** Lieutenant **h:** Sub Lieutenant

Gold on navy blue.

Greece (Hellenic Navy)

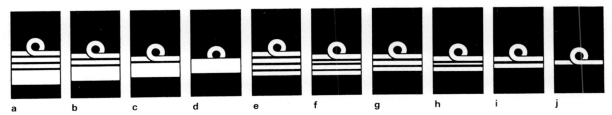

a b c d e f g h i j

a: *Navarchos*, Admiral **b:** *Antinavarchos*, Vice Admiral **c:** *Yponavarchos*, Rear Admiral **d:** *Archipiarchos*, Commodore **e:** *Pliarchos*, Captain **f:** *Antipliarchos*, Commander **g:** *Plotarchos*, Lieutenant Commander **h:** *Ypopliarchos*, Lieutenant **i:** *Anthypopliarchos*, Sub Lieutenant **j:** *Simaioforos*, Acting Sub Lieutenant

Gold on navy blue.

Greece Coast Guard (Hellenic Coast Guard)

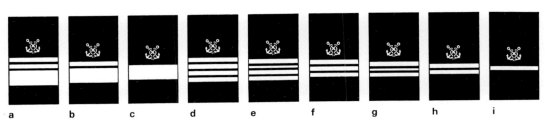

a b c d e f g h i

a: *Antinavarchos*, Vice Admiral **b:** *Yponavarchos*, Rear Admiral **c:** *Archipiarchos*, Commodore **d:** *Pliarchos*, Captain **e:** *Antipliarchos*, Commander **f:** *Plotarchos*, Lieutenant Commander **g:** *Ypopliarchos*, Lieutenant **h:** *Anthypopliarchos*, Sub Lieutenant **i:** *Simaioforos*, Acting Sub Lieutenant

Gold on navy blue.

Guatemala (Marina de Guatemala)

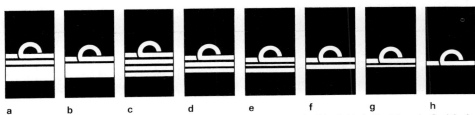

a b c d e f g h

a: *Vicealmirante*, Vice Admiral **b:** *Contraalmirante*, Rear Admiral **c:** *Capitán de Navío*, Captain **d:** *Capitán de Fragata*, Commander **e:** *Capitán de Corbeta*, Lieutenant Commander **f:** *Teniente de Navío*, Lieutenant **g:** *Teniente de Fragata*, Sub Lieutenant **h:** *Teniente de Corbeta*, Acting Sub Lieutenant

Gold on navy blue.

Guinea

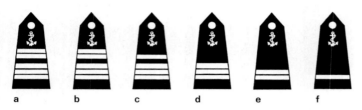

a   b   c   d   e   f

a: *Capitaine de Vaisseau*, Captain   **b**: *Capitaine de Frégate*, Commander
c: *Capitaine de Corvette*, Lieutenant Commander   **d**: *Lieutenant de Vaisseau*,
Lieutenant   **e**: *Enseigne de Vaisseau 1re Classe*, Sub Lieutenant   **f**: *Enseigne
de Vaisseau 2e Classe*, Acting Sub Lieutenant

Gold on black. Commander, three gold two silver stripes.

Haiti (Marine de Haiti)

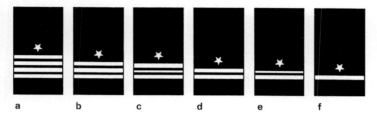

a   b   c   d   e   f

a: *Capitaine de Vaisseau*, Captain   **b**: *Commandant*, Commander   **c**: *Lieutenant
Commandant*, Lieutenant Commander   **d**: *Lieutenant de Vaisseau*, Lieutenant
e: *Sous Lieutenant de Vaisseau*, Sub Lieutenant   **f**: *Enseigne de Vaisseau*, Acting
Sub Lieutenant

Gold on navy blue.

Honduras (Fuerza Naval Republica de Honduras)

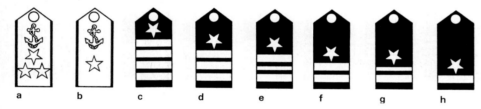

a   b   c   d   e   f   g   h

a: *Almirante*, Vice Admiral   **b**: *Contralmirante*, Rear Admiral   **c**: *Capitán de Navío*, Captain   **d**: *Capitán de
Fragata*, Commander   **e**: *Capitán de Corbeta*, Lieutenant Commander   **f**: *Teniente de Navío*, Lieutenant
g: *Teniente de Fragata*, Sub Lieutenant   **h**: *Alférez de Fragata*, Acting Sub Lieutenant

Gold on navy blue. Flag ranks, gold shoulder boards edged blue, silver devices.

Hong Kong (Royal Hong Kong Police - Marine Branch)

a   b   c   d   e   f   g   h

a: Assistant Commissioner of Police (Marine Branch Commander)   **b**: Chief Superintendent (Deputy Marine Branch
Commander)   **c**: Senior Superintendent   **d**: Superintendent   **e**: Chief Inspector   **f**: Senior Inspector   **g**: Inspector
h: Probationary Inspector

Silver on navy blue

Iceland (Coast Guard)

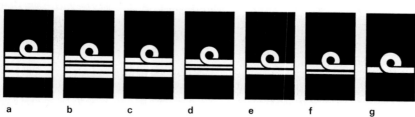

a   b   c   d   e   f   g

a: *Director General*, Captain   **b**: *Chief of Operations*, Senior Commander   **c**: *Captain and Chief Engineer*, Commander   **d**: *Chief
Mate and First Engineer*, Lieutenant Commander   **e**: *First Mate and Second Engineer*, Lieutenant   **f**: *Second Mate and officers
with less than 6 years' service*, Sub Lieutenant   **g**: *Officers with less than 2 years' service*, Acting Sub Lieutenant

Gold on navy blue.

India

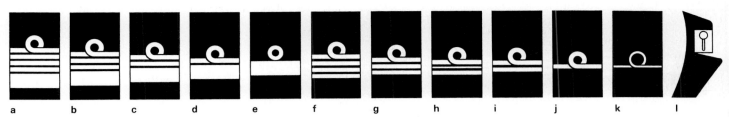

a: *Admiral of the Fleet*,   b: *Admiral*,   c: *Vice Admiral*,   d: *Rear Admiral*,   e: *Commodore*,   f: *Captain*,   g: *Commander*,   h: *Lieutenant Commander*,
i: *Lieutenant*,   j: *Sub Lieutenant*,   k: *Commissioned Officer*,   l: *Midshipman (Lapel)*
Gold on navy blue.

India (Coast Guard)

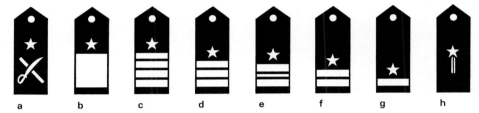

a: *Inspector General*, Rear Admiral   b: *Deputy Inspector General with 3 years' seniority and plus*, Commodore
c: *Deputy Inspector General*, Captain   d: *d: Commandant*, Commander   e: *Deputy Commandant*, Lieutenant
Commander   f: *Assistant Commandant*, Lieutenant   g: *Undertrainee Assistant Commandant after completion of
Phase III afloat training and during sub courses*, Acting Lieutenant   h: *Undertrainee Assistant Commandant after
Phase II afloat training*, Midshipman
Gold on navy blue.

Indonesia (Tentara Nasional Indonesia Angkatan Laut)

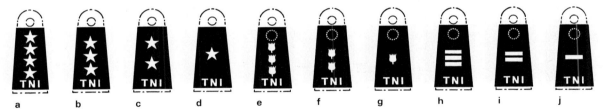

a: *Laksamana*, Admiral   b: *Laksdya*, Vice Admiral   c: *Laksda*, Rear Admiral   d: *Laksma*, Commodore   e: *Kolonel*, Captain   f: *Letnan Kolonel*, Commander
g: *Mayor*, Lieutenant Commander   h: *Kapten*, Lieutenant   i: *Letnan Satu*, Sub Lieutenant   j: *Letnan Dua*, Acting Sub Lieutenant
Gold on medium blue.

Iran

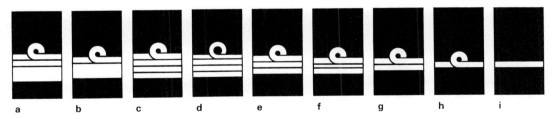

a: *Daryaban*, Vice Admiral   b: *Daryadar*, Rear Admiral   c: *Nakhoda Yekom*, Captain   d: *Nakhoda Dovom*, Commander
e: *Nakhoda Sevom*, Lieutenant Commander   f: *Navsarvan*, Lieutenant   g: *Navban Yekom*, Junior Lieutenant   h: *Navban
Dovom*, Sub Lieutenant   i: *Navban Sevom*, Midshipman
Gold on navy blue.

Iraq

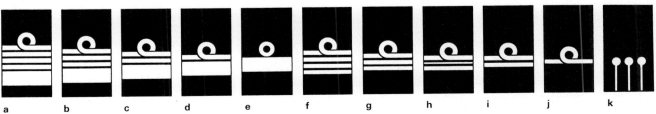

a: *Mushir*, Admiral of the Fleet   b: *Fariq Awwal*, Admiral   c: *Fariq*, Vice Admiral   d: *Liwa'*, Rear Admiral   e: *'Amid*, Commodore   f: *'Aqid*, Captain   g: *Muqaddam*,
Commander   h: *Ra'id*, Lieutenant Commander   i: *Naqib*, Lieutenant   j: *Mulazim Awwal*, Sub Lieutenant   k: *Mulazim*, Midshipman
Gold on navy blue.

Ireland (An Serghis Chablaigh)

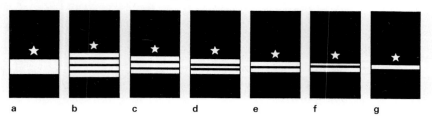

a   b   c   d   e   f   g

a: Commodore   **b:** Captain   **c:** Commander   **d:** Lieutenant Commander   **e:** Lieutenant
f: Sub Lieutenant   **g:** Ensign

Gold on navy blue.

Israel

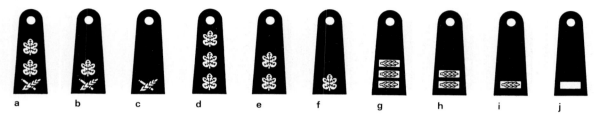

a   b   c   d   e   f   g   h   i   j

a: *General (Rav-Aluf)*, Vice Admiral   **b:** *Major General (Aluf)*, Rear Admiral   **c:** *Brigadier (Tat-Aluf)*, Commodore   **d:** *Colonel (Alut-Mishneh)*, Captain
e: *Lieutenant Colonel (Sgan-Aluf)*, Commander   **f:** *Major (Rav-Seren)*, Lieutenant Commander   **g:** *Captain (Seren)*, Lieutenant   **h:** *First Lieutenant (Segen)*,
Sub Lieutenant   **i:** *Second Lieutenant (Segen-Mishneh)*, Acting Sub Lieutenant   **j:** *Officer Aspirant (Mamak)*, Officer Candidate

Bright brass or gold generally on dark blue or black. Officer Candidate, white bar.

Italy (Marine Militare)

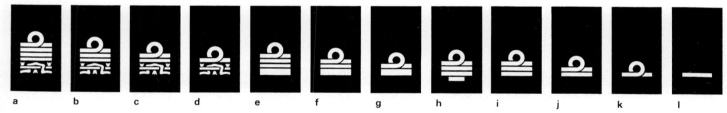

a   b   c   d   e   f   g   h   i   j   k   l

a: *Ammiraglio di Squadra*, Admiral Commanding Navy   **b:** *Ammiraglio di Squadra*, Admiral   **c:** *Ammiraglio di Divisione*, Vice Admiral   **d:** *Contrammiraglio*, Rear Admiral
e: *Capitano di Vascello*, Captain   **f:** *Capitano di Fregata*, Commander   **g:** *Capitano di Corvetta*, Lieutenant Commander   **h:** *1° Tenente di Vascello*, First Lieutenant
i: *Tenente di Vascello*, Lieutenant   **j:** *Sottotenente di Vascello*, Sub Lieutenant   **k:** *Guardiamarina*, Midshipman   **l:** *Aspirante Guardiamarina*, (Officer Candidate)

Gold on dark blue.

Ivory Coast (Marine Ivoirienne)

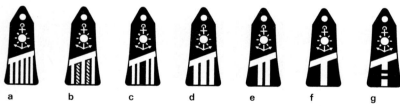

a   b   c   d   e   f   g

a: *Capitaine de Vaisseau*, Captain   **b:** *Capitaine de Frégate*, Commander   **c:** *Capitaine de Corvette*,
Lieutenant Commander   **d:** *Lieutenant de Vaisseau*, Lieutenant   **e:** *Enseigne de Vaisseau de 1re Classe*,
Sub Lieutenant   **f:** *Enseigne de Vaisseau de 2e Classe*, Acting Sub Lieutenant   **g:** *Aspirant*, Midshipman

Gold on black. Commander   **h:** *gold and silver on black.*

Jamaica (Jamaica Defence Force Coast Guard)

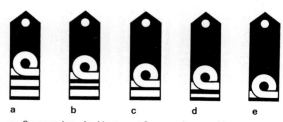

a   b   c   d   e

a: Commander   **b:** Lieutenant Commander   **c:** Lieutenant
d: Junior Lieutenant   **e:** Ensign

Gold on black.

[76]

Japan (Maritime Self Defence Force)

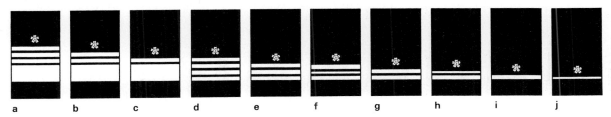

a: Admiral   b: Vice Admiral   c: Rear Admiral   d: Captain   e: Commander   f: Lieutenant Commander   g: Lieutenant   h: Sub Lieutenant
i: Acting Sub Lieutenant   j: Warrant Officer

Gold on navy blue.

Japan (Maritime Safety Agency)

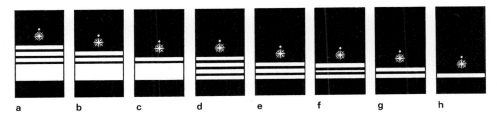

a: Commandant   b: Vice Commandant   c: Maritime Safety Superintendent First Grade   d: Maritime Safety
Superintendent Second Grade   e: Maritime Safety Superintendent Third Grade   f: Maritime Safety Officer First
Grade   g: Maritime Safety Officer Second Grade   h: Maritime Safety Officer Third grade

Gold on navy blue.

Kenya

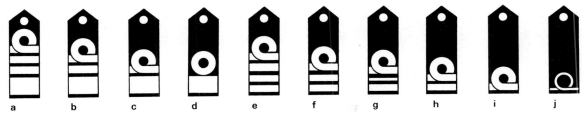

a: *General*, Admiral   b: *Lieutenant General*, Vice Admiral   c: *Major General*, Rear Admiral   d: *Brigadier*, Commodore   e: *Colonel*, Captain
f: *Lieutenant Colonel*, Commander   g: *Major*, Lieutenant Commander   h: *Captain*, Lieutenant   i: *Lieutenant*, Sub Lieutenant   j: *Second
Lieutenant*, Acting Sub Lieutenant

Gold on black.

Korea, Democratic People's Republic (North)

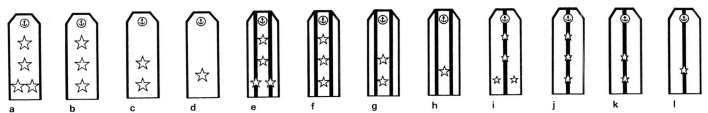

a: Admiral of the Fleet   b: Admiral   c: Vice Admiral   d: Rear Admiral   e: Commodore   f: Captain   g: Commander   h: Lieutenant Commander
i: Senior Lieutenant   j: Lieutenant   k: Sub Lieutenant   l: Acting Sub Lieutenant

Black stripes, silver stars on gold.

Korea, People's Republic (South)

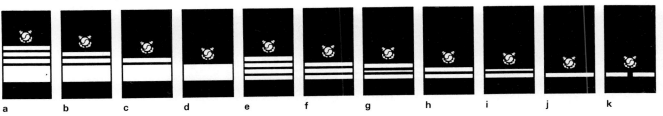

a: Admiral   b: Vice Admiral   c: Rear Admiral   d: Commodore   e: Captain   f: Commander   g: Lieutenant Commander   h: Lieutenant   i: Sub Lieutenant
j: Acting Sub Lieutenant   k: Warrant Officer

Gold on navy blue.

Kuwait

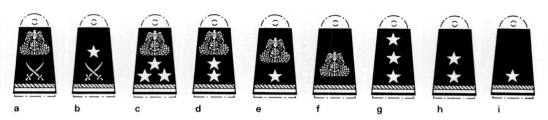

a: *Fariq*, Vice Admiral **b**: *Liwa'*, Rear Admiral **c**: *'Amid*, Commodore **d**: *'Aqid*, Captain **e**: *Muqaddam*, Commander
f: *Ra'id*, Lieutenant Commander **g**: *Naqib*, Lieutenant **h**: *Mulazim Awwal*, Sub Lieutenant **i**: *Mulazim*, Acting Sub Lieutenant
Usually gold on tan. Can be gold on dark green or dark blue.

Laos

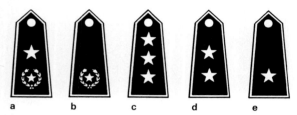

a: *Phavatho*, Commander **b**: *Phavatri*, Lieutenant Commander
c: *Ruaek*, Lieutenant **d**: *Ruatho*, Sub Lieutenant **e**: *Ruatri*, Acting
Sub Lieutenant
Gold on dark blue.

Lebanon

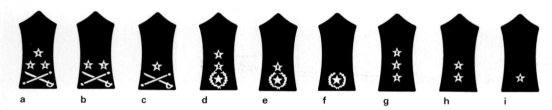

a: *'Imad*, Vice Admiral **b**: *Liwa'*, Rear Admiral **c**: *'Amid*, Commodore **d**: *'Aqid*, Captain **e**: *Muqaddam*, Commander
f: *Ra'id*, Lieutenant Commander **g**: *Ra'is*, Lieutenant **h**: *Mulazim Awwal*, Sub Lieutenant **i**: *Mulazim*, Acting Sub Lieutenant
Gold on black.

Liberia (Liberian National Coast Guard)

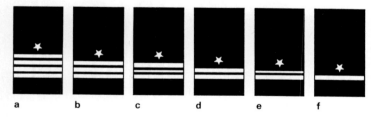

a: Captain **b**: Commander **c**: Lieutenant Commander **d**: Lieutenant
e: Lieutenant Junior Grade **f**: Ensign
Gold on black.

Libya

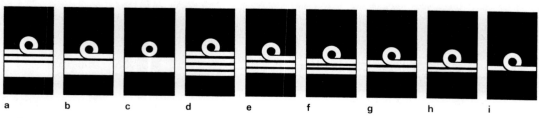

a: *Fariq*, Vice Admiral **b**: *Liwa'*, Rear Admiral **c**: *'Amid*, Commodore **d**: *'Aqid*, Captain **e**: *Muqaddam*, Commander
f: *Ra'id*, Lieutenant Commander **g**: *Naqib*, Lieutenant **h**: *Mulazim Awwal*, Sub Lieutenant **i**: *Mulazim*, Acting Sub Lieutenant
Gold on navy blue.

[78]

Lithuania (Kariniu Juru)

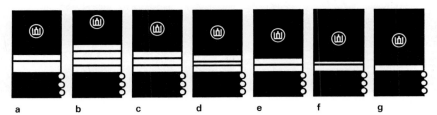

a: *Komandoras*, Commodore   b: *Komandoras-Leitenantas*, Captain   c: *Jūru Kapitonas*, Commander
d: *Kapitonas-Leitenantas*, Lieutenant Commander   e: *Jūru Vyresnysis Leitenantas*, Lieutenant
f: *Jūru Leitenantas*, Sub Lieutenant   g: *Jūru Jaunesnysis Leitenantas*, Acting Sub Lieutenant

Gold on black.

Madagascar (Malagasy Republic Marine)

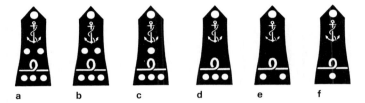

a: *Capitaine de Vaisseau*, Captain   b: *Capitaine de Frégate*, Commander   c: *Capitaine de Corvette*, Lieutenant Commander   d: *Lieutenant de Vaisseau*, Lieutenant   e: *Enseigne de Vaisseau 1re Classe*, Sub Lieutenant   f: *Enseigne de Vaisseau 2e Classe*, Acting Sub Lieutenant

Gold on black. Commander, top two discs silver.

Malaysia (Tentera Laut)

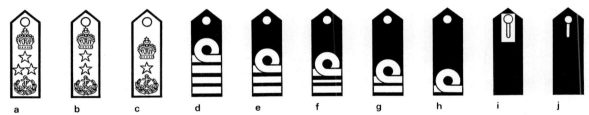

a: *Laksamana Madya*, Vice Admiral   b: *Laksamana Muda*, Rear Admiral   c: *Laksamana Pertama*, Commodore   d: *Kapetan*, Captain
e: *Komander*, Commander   f: *Leftenan Komander*, Lieutenant Commander   g: *Leftenan*, Lieutenant   h: *Leftenan Madya and Leftenan Muda*, Sub Lieutenant and Acting Sub Lieutenant   i: *Kadet Kanan*, Midshipman   j: *Kadet*, Cadet

Vice Admiral to Commodore, silver on gold. Remainder gold on navy blue, plus midshipman's white patch.

Mauritania (Marine Mauritanienne)

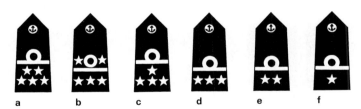

a: *Colonel*, Captain   b: *Lieutenant Colonel*, Commander   c: *Major*, Lieutenant Commander   d: *Captain*, Lieutenant   e: *Lieutenant*, Sub Lieutenant   f: *2nd Lieutenant*, Acting Sub Lieutenant

Gold on blue or green. Exception is two silver stars above lace for commander.

Mexico (Armada de Mexico)

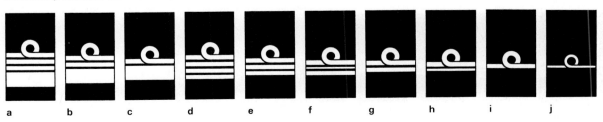

a: *Almirante*, Admiral   b: *Vicealmirante*, Vice Admiral   c: *Contraalmirante*, Rear Admiral   d: *Capitán de Navío*, Captain   e: *Capitán de Fragata*, Commander   f: *Capitán de Corbeta*, Lieutenant Commander   g: *Teniente de Navío*, Lieutenant   h: *Teniente de Fragata*, Sub Lieutenant
i: *Teniente de Corbeta*, Acting Sub Lieutenant   j: *Guardiamarina*, Midshipman

Gold on navy blue.

Morocco

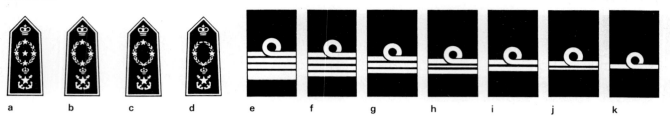

a: *Amiral*, Admiral of the Fleet   b: *Amiral d'Escadre*, Admiral   c: *Vice Amiral*, Vice Admiral   d: *Contre Amiral*, Rear Admiral   e: *Capitaine de Vaisseau Major*, Commodore   f: *Capitaine de Vaisseau*, Captain   g: *Capitaine de Frégate*, Commander   h: *Capitaine de Corvette*, Lieutenant Commander   i: *Lieutenant de Vaisseau*, Lieutenant   j: *Enseigne de Vaisseau 1re Classe*, Sub Lieutenant   k: *Enseigne de Vaisseau 2e Classe*, Acting Sub Lieutenant

Gold on black. Flag ranks silver stars.

Mozambique

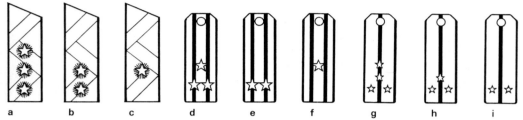

a: *Almirante*, Admiral   b: *Vice-Almirante*, Vice Admiral   c: *Contra-Almirante*, Rear Admiral   d: *Capitão-de-Mar-e-Guerra*, Captain
e: *Capitão-de-Fregate*, Commander   f: *Capitão-Tenente*, Lieutenant Commander   g: *Primeiro-Tenente*, Lieutenant   h: *Segundo-Tenente*, Sub Lieutenant   i: *Guarda-Marinha*, Midshipman

Black rays, edging and stripes, silver stars. All on gold.

Netherlands (Koninklijke Marine)

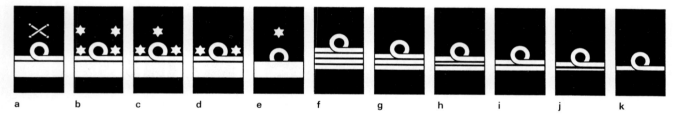

a: *Admiraal*, Admiral of the Fleet   b: *Luitenant-Admiraal*, Admiral   c: *Vice-Admiraal*, Vice Admiral   d: *Schout-bij-nacht*, Rear Admiral   e: *Commandeur*, Commodore
f: *Kapitein ter zee*, Captain   g: *Kapitein-luitenant ter zee*, Commander   h: *Luitenant ter zee der eerste klasse*, Lieutenant Commander   i: *Luitenant ter zee der tweede klasse oudste categorie*, Lieutenant   j: *Luitenant ter zee der tweede klasse*, Sub Lieutenant   k: *Luitenant ter zee der derde klasse*, Acting Sub Lieutenant

Gold on navy blue. Stars and crossed batons, silver.

New Zealand

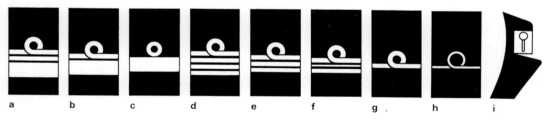

a: Vice Admiral   b: Rear Admiral   c: Commodore   d: Captain   e: Commander   f: Lieutenant Commander
g: Sub Lieutenant   h: Ensign   i: Midshipman

Gold on navy blue.

Nigeria

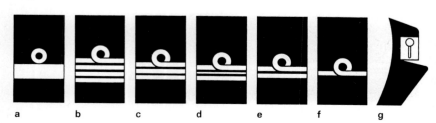

a: *Brigadier*, Commodore   b: *Colonel*, Captain   c: *Lieutenant Colonel*, Commander
d: *Major*, Lieutenant Commander   e: *Captain*, Lieutenant   f: *Lieutenant*, Sub Lieutenant
g: *Second Lieutenant*, Midshipman

Gold on navy blue.

Norway (Sjoforsvaret)

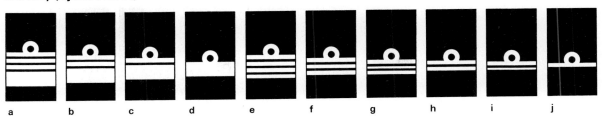

a: *Admiral*, Admiral   **b:** *Viseadmiral*, Vice Admiral   **c:** *Kontreadmiral*, Rear Admiral   **d:** *Kommandør*, Commodore   **e:** *Kommandør Kaptein*, Captain
f: *Orlogskaptein*, Commander   **g:** *Kapteinløytnant*, Lieutenant Commander   **h:** *Løytnant*, Lieutenant   **i:** *Fenrik*, Sub Lieutenant   **j:** *Ustskrevet*, Acting Sub Lieutenant

Gold on navy blue.

Oman

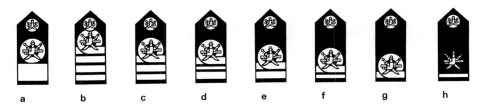

a: *'Amid Bahriyya*, Commodore   **b:** *'Aqid Bahriyya*, Captain   **c:** *Muqaddam Bahriyya*, Commander   **d:** *Ra'id Bahriyya*, Lieutenant Commander   **e:** *Naqib Bahriyya*, Lieutenant   **f:** *Mulazim Awwal Bahriyya*, Sub Lieutenant
g: *Mulazim Tanin Bahriyya*, Acting Sub Lieutenant   **h:** *Dabit Murashshah*, Midshipman

Gold on navy blue. White stripe, midshipman.

Pakistan

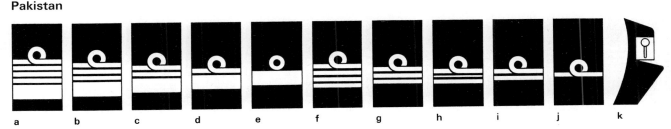

a: Admiral of the Fleet   **b:** Admiral   **c:** Vice Admiral   **d:** Rear Admiral   **e:** Commodore   **f:** Captain   **g:** Commander   **h:** Lieutenant Commander
i: Lieutenant   **j:** Sub Lieutenant   **k:** Midshipman

Gold on navy blue.

Paraguay (Armada Nacional)

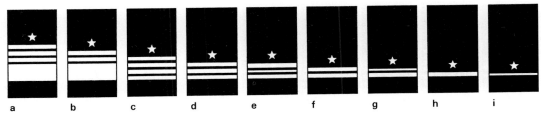

a: *Vicealmirante*, Vice Admiral   **b:** *Contralmirante*, Rear Admiral   **c:** *Capitán de Navío*, Captain   **d:** *Capitán de Fragata*, Commander
e: *Capitán de Corbeta*, Lieutenant Commander   **f:** *Teniente de Navío*, Lieutenant   **g:** *Teniente de Fragata*, Sub Lieutenant   **h:** *Teniente de Corbeta*, Acting Sub Lieutenant   **i:** *Guardiamarinha*, Midshipman

Gold on navy blue.

Peru (Marina de Guerra)

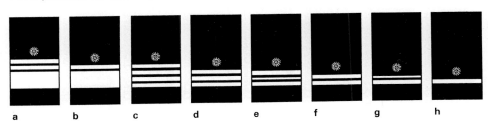

a: *Vicealmirante*, Vice Admiral   **b:** *Contraalmirante*, Rear Admiral   **c:** *Capitán de Navío*, Captain   **d:** *Capitán de Fragata*, Commander   **e:** *Capitán de Corbeta*, Lieutenant Commander   **f:** *Teniente Primero*, Lieutenant
g: *Teniente Segundo*, Sub Lieutenant   **h:** *Alférez de Fragata*, Acting Sub Lieutenant

Gold on navy blue.

Philippines

a: Commodore   b: Captain   c: Commander   d: Lieutenant Commander   e: Lieutenant
f: Lieutenant Junior Grade   g: Ensign

Gold on black. Commodore, dark blue edged, silver devices on gold.

Poland (Marynarita Wojenna)

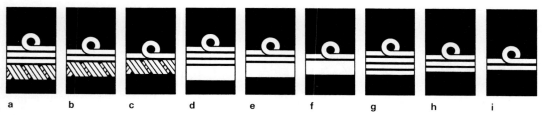

a: *Admiral*, Admiral   b: *Wice-Admiral*, Vice Admiral   c: *Kontradmiral*, Rear Admiral   d: *Komandor*, Captain   e: *Komandor Porucznik*, Commander   f: *Komandor Podporucznik*, Lieutenant Commander   g: *Kapitan Marynarki*, Lieutenant   h: *Porucznik Marynarki*, Sub Lieutenant   i: *Podporucznik Marynarki*, Acting Sub Lieutenant

Gold on dark blue.

Portugal (Marinha Portuguesa)

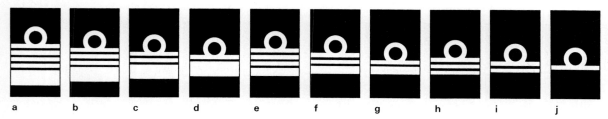

a: *Almirante da Armada*, Admiral of the Fleet   b: *Almirante*, Admiral   c: *Vice-Almirante*, Vice Admiral   d: *Contra-Almirante*, Rear Admiral
e: *Capitão-de-Mar-e-Guerra*, Captain   f: *Capitão-de-Fragata*, Commander   g: *Capitão-Tenente*, Lieutenant Commander   h: *Primeiro-Tenente*, Lieutenant   i: *Segundo-Tenente*, Sub Lieutenant   j: *Guarda-Marinha-ou-Subtenente*, Midshipman or Acting Sub Lieutenant

Gold on navy blue.

Romania (Marină Română)

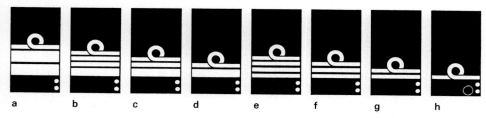

a: *Contra Amiral*, Rear Admiral   b: *Capitan de Rangel I*, Captain   c: *Capitan de Rangel II*, Commander   d: *Capitan de Rangel III*, Lieutenant Commander   e: *Capitan-Locotenent*, Senior Lieutenant   f: *Locotenent Major*, Lieutenant
g: *Locotenent*, Sub Lieutenant   h: *Sublocotenent*, Acting Sub Lieutenant

Gold on dark blue.

Russia (Rosiyskiy Voennomorskoy Flot)

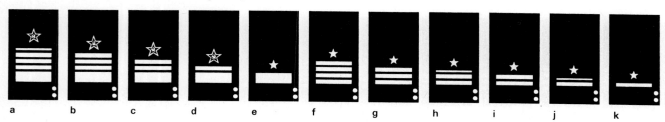

a: *Admiral Flota*, Admiral of the Fleet of the Russian Federation   b: *Admiral*, Admiral   c: *Vitse-Admiral*, Vice Admiral   d: *Kontr-Admiral*, Rear Admiral
e: *Kapitan Pervogo Ranga*, Captain   f: *Kapitan Vtorogo Ranga*, Commander   g: *Kapitan Tretyego Ranga*, Lieutenant Commander   h: *Kapitan-Leytenant*, Lieutenant   i: *Starshiy Leytenant*, Junior Lieutenant   j: *Leytenant*, Sub Lieutenant   k: *Mladshiy Leytenant*, Acting Sub Lieutenant

Ukraine Navy insignia currently as Russia but due to change in second half of 1994.

Gold on black.

Saudi Arabia (Royal Saudi Naval Forces)

a: *Lieutenant General (Navy)*, Vice Admiral   **b**: *Major General (Navy)*, Rear Admiral   **c**: *Brigadier General (Navy)*, Commodore
d: *Colonel (Navy)*, Captain   **e**: *Lieutenant Colonel (Navy)*, Commander   **f**: *Major (Navy)*, Lieutenant Commander   **g**: *Captain (Navy)*, Lieutenant   **h**: *Lieutenant (Navy)*, Sub Lieutenant   **i**: *Second Lieutenant (Navy)*, Acting Sub Lieutenant

Gold buttons, sabres and Arabic titles, light green stars and crowns on black.

Senegal (Marine Sénégalaise)

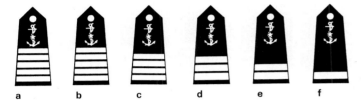

a: *Contre-Amiral*, Rear Admiral   **b**: *Capitaine de Vaisseau*, Captain   **c**: *Capitaine de Frégate*,
Commander   **d**: *Capitaine de Corvette*, Lieutenant Commander   **e**: *Lieutenant de Vaisseau*,
Lieutenant   **f**: *Enseigne de Vaisseau*, Sub Lieutenant

Gold on black. Captain, three gold and two silver stripes.

Singapore (Republic of Singapore Navy)

a: Vice Admiral   **b**: Rear Admiral   **c**: Commodore   **d**: Colonel   **e**: Lieutenant Colonel   **f**: Major   **g**: Captain   **h**: Lieutenant
i: Second Lieutenant

Gold on navy blue. Senior officers only have naval titles.

Slovenia (Naši Mornarji) (not to scale)

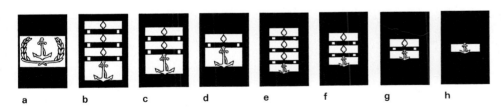

a: *Kapitan*, Commodore   **b**: *Kapitan Bojne Ladje*, Captain   **c**: *Kapitan Fregate*, Commander   **d**: *Kapitan Korvete*,
Lieutenant Commander   **e**: *Poročnik Bojne Ladje*, Senior Lieutenant   **f**: *Poročnik Fregate*, Lieutenant
g: *Poročnik Korvete*, Sub Lieutenant   **h**: *Podporočnik*, Acting Sub Lieutenant

Gold on navy blue. Currently gold badge worn on combat uniform.

South Africa

a: *Admiraal*, Admiral   **b**: *Vise-Admiraal*, Vice Admiral   **c**: *Skout-Admiraal*, Rear Admiral   **d**: *Kommodoor*, Commodore   **e**: *Kaptein*, Captain   **f**: *Kommandeur*,
Commander   **g**: *Luitenant-Kommandeur*, Lieutenant Commander   **h**: *Luitenant*, Lieutenant   **i**: *Onder Luitenant*, Sub Lieutenant   **j**: *Vaandrig*, Ensign

Gold on navy blue.

Spain (Armada Española)

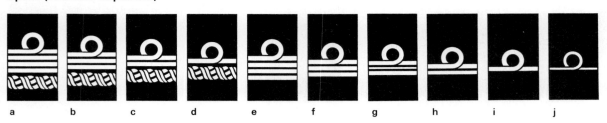

a: *Cap General de la Armada*, Admiral of the Fleet   b: *Almirante*, Admiral   c: *Vicealmirante*, Vice Admiral   d: *Contraalmirante*, Rear Admiral
e: *Capitán de Navío*, Captain   f: *Capitán de Fragata*, Commander   g: *Capitán de Corbeta*, Lieutenant Commander   h: *Teniente de Navío*,
Lieutenant   i: *Alférez de Navío*, Sub Lieutenant   j: *Alférez de Fragata*, Acting Sub Lieutenant

Gold on navy blue.

Sri Lanka

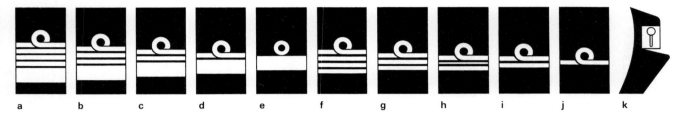

a: Admiral of the Fleet   b: Admiral   c: Vice Admiral   d: Rear Admiral   e: Commodore   f: Captain   g: Commander   h: Lieutenant Commander
i: Lieutenant   j: Sub Lieutenant   k: Midshipman

Gold on navy blue.

Sudan

a: *Fariq*, Vice Admiral   b: *Liwa'*, Rear Admiral   c: *'Awid*, Commodore   d: *'Aqid*, Captain   e: *Muqaddam*, Commander
f: *Ra'id*, Lieutenant Commander   g: *Naqib*, Lieutenant   h: *Mulazim Awwal*, Sub Lieutenant   i: *Mulazim Thani*, Acting Sub
Lieutenant

Gold on black.

Surinam

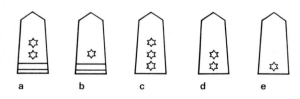

a: *Kapitein Ter Zee*, Commander   b: *Kapitein-Luitenant Ter Zee*, Lieutenant
Commander   c: *Luitenant Ter Zee Der 1e Klasse*, Lieutenant   d: *Luitenant
Ter Zee Der 2e Klasse Oudste Categorie*, Sub Lieutenant   e: *Luitenant Ter Zee
Der 3e Klasse*, Acting Sub Lieutenant

Gold on white.

Sweden (Marinen)

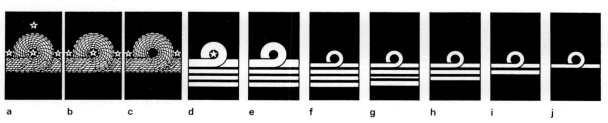

a: *Amiral*, Admiral   b: *Viceamiral*, Vice Admiral   c: *Konteramiral*, Rear Admiral   d: *Kommendör av 1. gr*, Commodore   e: *Kommendör*, Captain
f: *Kommendörkapten av 1. gr*, Commander   g: *Kommendörkapten av 2. gr*, Lieutenant Commander   h: *Kapten*, Lieutenant   i: *Löjtnant*, Sub Lieutenant
j: *Fänrik*, Acting Sub Lieutenant

Gold on dark blue.

Sweden Coast Guard (Kustbevakning)

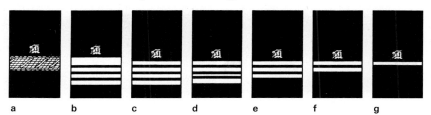

a b c d e f g

a: *Konteramiral*, Rear Admiral **b**: *Kommendör*, Captain **c**: *Kommendörkapten av 1. gr*, Commander
d: *Kommendörkapten av 2. gr*, Lieutenant Commander **e**: *Kapten*, Lieutenant **f**: *Löjtnant*, Sub
Lieutenant **g**: *Fänrik*, Acting Sub Lieutenant

Gold on dark blue.

Sweden Coastal Artillery (Kustarillereit)

a b c d e f g h i j

a: *General*, Admiral **b**: *Generallöjtnant*, Vice Admiral **c**: *Generalmajor*, Rear Admiral **d**: *Överste av 1 gr*, Commodore **e**: *Överste*,
Captain **f**: *Överstelöjtnant*, Commander **g**: *Major*, Lieutenant Commander **h**: *Kapten*, Lieutenant **i**: *Löjtnant*, Sub Lieutenant
j: *Fänrik*, Acting Sub Lieutenant

Admiral to Rear Admiral, silver on gold, remainder gold on mid grey.

Syria

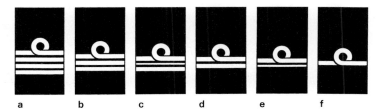

a b c d e f

a: *'Aqid*, Captain **b**: *Muqaddam*, Commander **c**: *Ra'id*, Lieutenant Commander
d: *Naqib*, Lieutenant **e**: *Mulazim Awwal*, Sub Lieutenant **f**: *Mulazim*, Acting Sub
Lieutenant

Gold on navy blue.

Taiwan (Republic of China)

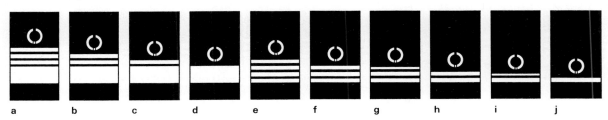

a b c d e f g h i j

a: Admiral **b**: Vice Admiral **c**: Rear Admiral **d**: Commodore **e**: Captain **f**: Commander **g**: Lieutenant Commander **h**: Lieutenant
i: Lieutenant JG (II) **j**: Sub Lieutenant

Gold on navy blue.

Thailand

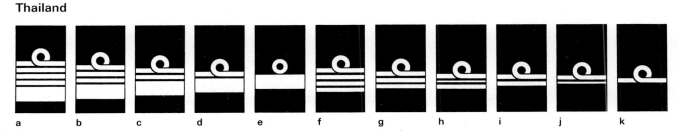

a b c d e f g h i j k

a: Admiral of the Fleet **b**: Admiral **c**: Vice Admiral **d**: Rear Admiral **e**: Commodore **f**: Captain **g**: Commander **h**: Lieutenant Commander
i: Lieutenant **j**: Sub Lieutenant **k**: Acting Sub Lieutenant

Gold on navy blue.

Togo

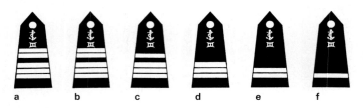

a b c d e f

a: *Capitaine de Vaisseau*, Captain   b: *Capitaine de Frégate*, Commander
c: *Capitaine de Corvette*, Lieutenant Commander   d: *Lieutenant de Vaisseau*,
Lieutenant   e: *Enseigne de Vaisseau 1re Classe*, Sub Lieutenant   f: *Enseigne de Vaisseau 2e classe*, Acting Sub Lieutenant

Gold on black. Commander, three gold two silver stripes.

Trinidad & Tobago Coast Guard

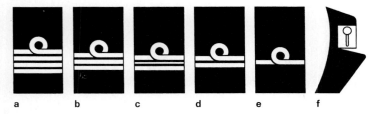

a b c d e f

a: Captain   b: Commander   c: Lieutenant Commander   d: Lieutenant   e: Sub Lieutenant
f: Midshipman

Gold on navy blue.

Tunisia

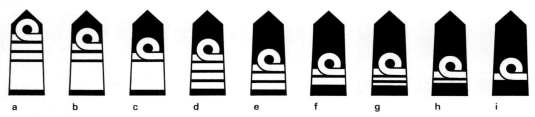

a b c d e f g h i

a: *Vice-Amiral d'Escadre*, Admiral   b: *Vice-Amiral*, Vice Admiral   c: *Contre-Amiral*, Rear Admiral   d: *Capitaine de Vaisseau*,
Captain   e: *Capitaine de Frégate*, Commander   f: *Capitaine de Corvette*, Lieutenant Commander   g: *Lieutenant de Vaisseau*,
Lieutenant   h: *Enseigne de Vaisseau 1re Classe*, Sub Lieutenant   i: *Enseigne de Vaisseau 2e Classe*, Acting Sub Lieutenant

Gold on black.

Turkey (Türk Deniz Kuvvetleri)

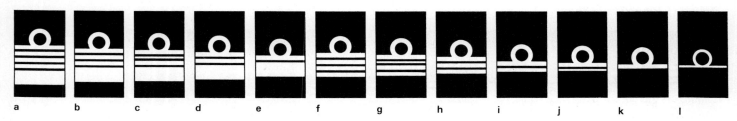

a b c d e f g h i j k l

a: *Büyükamiral*, Admiral of the Fleet   b: *Oramiral*, Admiral   c: *Koramiral*, Vice Admiral   d: *Tümamiral*, Rear Admiral   e: *Tugamiral*, Commodore   f: *Albay*, Captain
g: *Yarbay*, Commander   h: *Binbaşi*, Lieutenant Commander   i: *Yüzbaşi*, Lieutenant   j: *Üstegmen*, Sub Lieutenant   k: *Tegmen*, Acting Sub Lieutenant   l: *Astegmen*,
Warrant Officer

Gold on black.

United Arab Emirates

a b c d e f g h i

a: *Fariq*, Vice Admiral   b: *Liwa*, Rear Admiral   c: *'Amid*, Commodore   d: *'Aqid*, Captain   e: *Muqaddam*, Commander
f: *Ra'id*, Lieutenant Commander   g: *Rais*, Lieutenant   h: *Awwal*, Sub Lieutenant   i: *Mulazim*, Acting Sub Lieutenant

Gold on navy blue.

United Kingdom

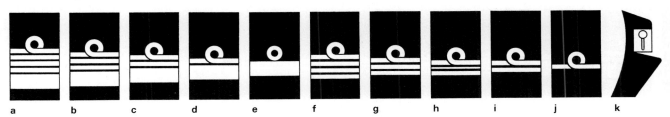

a: Admiral of the Fleet   b: Admiral   c: Vice Admiral   d: Rear Admiral   e: Commodore   f: Captain   g: Commander   h: Lieutenant Commander
i: Lieutenant   j: Sub Lieutenant   k: Midshipman

Gold on navy blue.

United Kingdom (Royal Fleet Auxiliary)

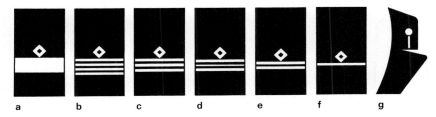

a: Commodore   b: Captain   c: Chief Officer   d: First Officer   e: 2nd Officer   f: 3rd Officer
g: Deck Cadet

Gold on navy blue.

United States

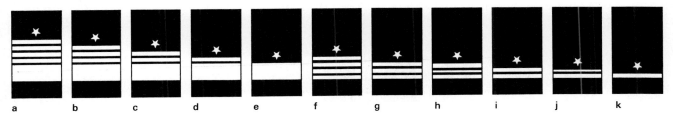

a: *Fleet Admiral*, Admiral of the Fleet   b: *Admiral*, Admiral   c: *Vice Admiral*, Vice Admiral   d: *Rear Admiral (Upper Half)*, Rear Admiral   e: *Rear Admiral (Lower Half)*,
Commodore   f: *Captain*, Captain   g: *Commander*, Commander   h: *Lieutenant Commander*, Lieutenant Commander   i: *Lieutenant*, Lieutenant   j: *Lieutenant Junior
Grade*, Sub Lieutenant   k: *Ensign*, Acting Sub Lieutenant

Gold on navy blue.

United States Coast Guard

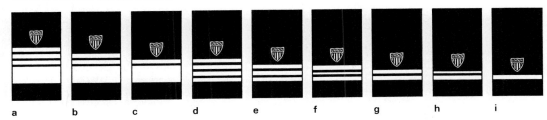

a: *Admiral*, Admiral   b: *Vice Admiral*, Vice Admiral   c: *Rear Admiral (Lower Half)*, Commodore   d: *Captain*, Captain
e: *Commander*, Commander   f: *Lieutenant Commander*, Lieutenant Commander   g: *Lieutenant*, Lieutenant   h: *Lieutenant Junior
Grade*, Sub Lieutenant   i: *Ensign*, Acting Sub Lieutenant

Gold on navy blue.

Uruguay (Armada Nacional)

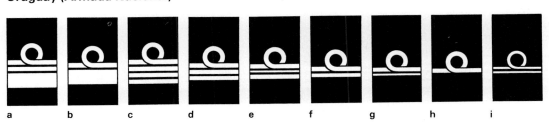

a: *Vicealmirante*, Vice Admiral   b: *Contraalmirante*, Rear Admiral   c: *Capitán de Navío*, Captain   d: *Capitán de Fragata*,
Commander   e: *Capitán de Corbeta*, Lieutenant Commander   f: *Teniente de Navío*, Lieutenant   g: *Alférez de Navío*, Sub Lieutenant
h: *Alférez de Fragata*, Acting Sub Lieutenant   i: *Guardiamarina*, Midshipman

Gold on navy blue.

Venezuela (Marina de Guerra de Venezuela)

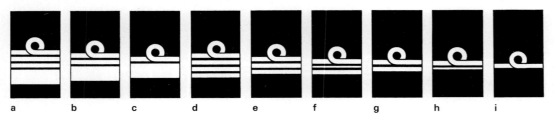

a: *Almirante*, Admiral   b: *Vicealmirante*, Vice Admiral   c: *Contraalmirante*, Rear Admiral   d: *Capitán de Navío*, Captain
e: *Capitán de Fragata*, Commander   f: *Capitán de Corbeta*, Lieutenant Commander   g: *Teniente de Navío*, Lieutenant
h: *Teniente de Fragata*, Sub Lieutenant   i: *Alférez de Navío*, Acting Sub Lieutenant

Gold on navy blue.

Vietnam

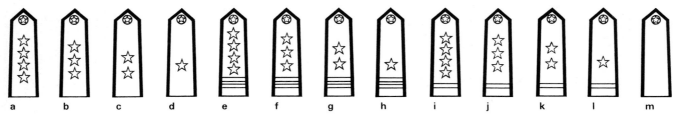

a: *Senior General*, Admiral of the Fleet   b: *Colonel General*, Admiral   c: *Lieutenant General*, Vice Admiral   d: *Major General*, Rear Admiral   e: *Senior Colonel*, Commodore   f: *Colonel*, Captain   g: *Lieutenant Colonel*, Commander   h: *Major*, Lieutenant Commander   i: *Senior Captain*, Senior Lieutenant
j: *Captain*, Lieutenant   k: *Senior Lieutenant*, Sub Lieutenant   l: *2d Lieutenant*, Acting Sub Lieutenant   m: *Student Officer*, Midshipman

Gold shoulder straps. Generals, edged red gold stars. Remainder, silver stars and lace.

Yemen

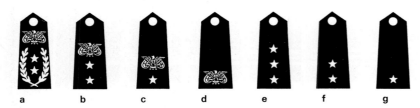

a: *'Amid*, Commodore   b: *'Aqid*, Captain   c: *Muqaddam*, Commander   d: *Ra'id*, Lieutenant
Commander   e: *Naqib*, Lieutenant   f: *Mulazim Awwal*, Sub Lieutenant   g: *Mulazim Thani*, Acting
Sub Lieutenant

Gold on black.

Yugoslavia (Jugoslovenska Ratna Mornarica)

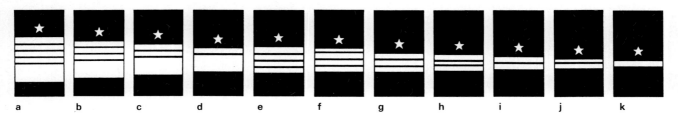

a: *Admiral Flote*, Admiral of the Fleet   b: *Admiral*, Admiral   c: *Viceadmiral*, Vice Admiral   d: *Kontraadmiral*, Rear Admiral   e: *Kapetan Bojnog Broda*, Captain
f: *Kapetan Fregate*, Commander   g: *Kapetan Korvete*, Lieutenant Commander   h: *Poručnik Bojnog Broda*, Lieutenant (Senior)   i: *Poručnik Fregate*, Lieutenant
j: *Poručnik Korvete*, Sub Lieutenant   k: *Potporučnik*, Acting Sub Lieutenant

Gold on dark blue.

Zaïre

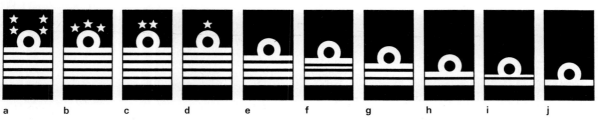

a: *Grand Amiral*, Admiral of the Fleet   b: *Amiral*, Admiral   c: *Vice-Amiral*, Vice Admiral   d: *Contre-Amiral*, Rear Admiral   e: *Capitaine de Vaisseau*,
Captain   f: *Capitaine de Frégate*, Commander   g: *Capitaine de Corvette*, Lieutenant Commander   h: *Lieutenant de Vaisseau*, Lieutenant   i: *Enseigne de Vaisseau 1re Classe*, Sub Lieutenant   j: *Enseigne de Vaisseau 2e Classe*, Acting Sub Lieutenant

Gold on black.

They take all the risks so we make sure they run none.

Supremacy at sea can only be achieved when sailors have total confidence in their weapon systems. Giving every crew the guarantee of technical superiority means providing total operational mastery in the neutralisation of opposing forces to facilitate penetration into enemy territory.

Listening to those who are operational at sea enables Matra Défense to supply naval forces with solutions to counter air, marine or submarine attacks.

Air to air - Magic - Mica.

Surface to surface - Otomat.

Surface to air - Simbad - Sadral.

Anti submarine - Milas.

Designing, developing and building reliable and effective systems is our constant concern.

Your confidence, our daily challenge.

Pennant list of major surface ships

Type abbreviations (for USA see page 764)

AD	Destroyer tender	BB	Battleship	FFLG	Guided missile light frigate or corvette
AEFS	Fleet replenishment ship	CA	Gun cruiser	HSS	Helicopter support ship
AFS	Combat stores ship	CG	Guided missile cruiser	LCC	Amphibious command ship
AG	Miscellaneous	CGH	Guided missile/helicopter cruiser	LHA	Amphibious assault ship (general purpose)
AG/FF	Frigate/FAC support ship	CGN	Guided missile cruiser (nuclear-powered)	LHD	Amphibious assault ship (multipurpose)
AGI	Research and Survey ship	CL	Light cruiser	LKA	Amphibious cargo ship
AGOR	Research ship	CLT	Light cruiser, training	LPD	Amphibious transport dock
AGS	Surveying ship	CV	Multipurpose aircraft carrier	LPH	Amphibious assault ship (helicopter)
AO	Oiler	CVA	Attack aircraft carrier	LSD	Dock landing ship
AOE	Fast combat support ship	CVH	Helicopter carrier	LSI	Landing ship, infantry
AOF(L)	Large fleet tanker	CVL	Light aircraft carrier	LSL	Landing ship, logistic
AOF(S)	Small fleet tanker	CVN	Multipurpose aircraft carrier (nuclear-powered)	LST	Tank landing ship
AOR	Replenishment oiler	CVS	ASW aircraft carrier	MH	Minehunter
AOS	Support tanker	DD	Destroyer	ML	Minelayer
AP	Transport	DDG	Guided missile destroyer (including surface-to-air missiles)	MSC	Coastal minesweeper
APA	Amphibious transport	FF	Frigate	MSO	Ocean minesweeper
AR	Repair ship	FFG	Guided missile frigate (including surface-to-air missiles)	PV	Patrol vessel
ARS	Salvage ship	FFL	Light frigate or corvette	TCD	Landing ship dock
AS	Submarine tender				
ATS	Training support ship				
AVT	Auxiliary aircraft landing training ship				

Pennant numbers of major surface ships in numerical order

Number	Ship's name	Type	Country
A 00	Britannia	AG	UK
01	Adelaide	FFG	Australia
01	Pohjanmaa	ML	Finland
A 01	Rio Panuco	LST	Mexico
A 01	Contramaestre Casado	AP	Spain
B 01	Durango	AP	Mexico
C 01	Capitán de Navio Sebastian Jose Holzinger	PV	Mexico
E 01	Cuitlahuac	DD	Mexico
FM 01	Presidente Eloy Alfaro	FFG	Ecuador
HQ 01	Pham Ngu Lao	FFG	Vietnam
S 01	Gladan	ATS	Sweden
1	Tachin	FF/ATS	Thailand
1	Khamronsin	FFL	Thailand
1	Rattanakosin	FFLG	Thailand
1	Thalang	MSC/AG	Thailand
1	Uruguay	FFG	Uruguay
1/508	Petya III class	FF	Syria
A 1	Comandante General Irigoyen	PV	Argentina
A 1	Al Mabrukah	PV/ATS	Oman
AOE 1	Sacramento	AOE	USA
ATS 1	Edenton	ATS	USA
D 1	Hercules	DDG	Argentina
L 1	Al Munassir	LSL	Oman
LHA 1	Tarawa	LHA	USA
LHD 1	Wasp	LHD	USA
LSV 1	General Frank S Besson Jr	LSV	USA
M 1	Neuquen	MSC	Argentina
MCM 1	Avenger	MSO	USA
MSF 1	Phosamton	ATS	Thailand
S 1	Shabab Oman	AG	Oman
02	Canberra	FFG	Australia
02	Hameenmaa	ML	Finland
A 02	Rio Papaloapan	LST	Mexico
C 02	Capitán De Navio Blas Godinez Brito	PV	Mexico
FM 02	Moran Valverde	FFG	Ecuador
M 02	Älvsborg	ML/AS	Sweden
P 02	Waspada	PV	Brunei
P 02	Nanawa	PV	Paraguay
S 02	Falken	ATS	Sweden
2	Thayanchon	FFL	Thailand
2	Prasae	FF/ATS	Thailand
2	Sukhothai	FFLG	Thailand
2	Bang Rachan	MH/MSC	Thailand
2	Chula	AOR	Thailand
2	General Artigas	FFG	Uruguay
2/508	Al Hirasa	FF	Syria
A 2	Teniente Olivieri	PV	Argentina
A 2	Al Sultana	AFS	Oman

Number	Ship's name	Type	Country
AOE 2	Camden	AOE	USA
ATS 2	Beaufort	ATS	USA
D 2	Santisima Trinidad	DDG	Argentina
L 2	Nasr Al Bahr	LSL	Oman
LHA 2	Saipan	LHA	USA
LHD 2	Essex	LHD	USA
LST 2	Chang	LST	Thailand
LSV 2	CW 3 Harold C Clinger	LSL	USA
M 2	Rio Negro	MSC	Argentina
MCM 2	Defender	MSO	USA
Q 2	Libertad	AG	Argentina
V 2	Veinticinco de Mayo	CV	Argentina
03	Sydney	FFG	Australia
03	Turunmaa	FFL	Finland
A 03	Rio Grijalva	AG	Mexico
C 03	Brigadier Jose Maria de la Vega Gonzalez	PV	Mexico
H 03	Alejandro de Humbolt	AGOR	Mexico
HQ 03	Dai Ky	FFG	Vietnam
M 03	Visborg	ML/AG	Sweden
P 03	Pejuang	PV	Brunei
P 03	Capitan Meza	PV	Paraguay
3	Pin Klao	FF	Thailand
3	Longlom	FFL	Thailand
3	Nongsarai	MH/MSC	Thailand
3	Maeklong	ATS	Thailand
3	Montevideo	FFG	Uruguay
A 3	Francisco de Gurruchaga	PV	Argentina
AFS 3	Niagara Falls	AFS	USA
AGF 3	La Salle	AG	USA
AOE 3	Seattle	AOE	USA
AOR 3	Kansas City	AOR	USA
ATS 3	Brunswick	ATS	USA
B 3	Canal Beagle	AP	Argentina
LHA 3	Belleau Wood	LHA	USA
LHD 3	Kearsage	LHD	USA
LST 3	Pangan	LST	Thailand
LSV 3	General Brehon B Somervell	LSL	USA
M 3	Chubut	MSC	Argentina
MCM 3	Sentry	MSO	USA
04	Darwin	FFG	Australia
04	Karjala	FFL	Finland
C 04	General Felipe B Berriozabal	PV	Mexico
H 04	Onjuku	AGS	Mexico
M 04	Carlskrona	ML/ATS	Sweden
N 04	Aktion	ML	Greece
P 04	Seteria	PV	Brunei
P 04	Teneinte Farina	PV	Paraguay
4	Sattahip	PV	Thailand
AFS 4	White Plains	AFS	USA

PENNANT LIST

Number	Ship's name	Type	Country	Number	Ship's name	Type	Country
AOE 4	Detroit	AOE	USA	L 10	Fearless	LPD	UK
AOR 4	Savannah	AOR	USA	LPD 10	Juneau	LPD	USA
B 4	Bahia San Blas	AP	Argentina	LPH 10	Tripoli	LPH	USA
LHA 4	Nassau	LHA	USA	MCM 10	Warrior	MSO	USA
LHD 4	Boxer	LHD	USA	P 10	Piratini	PV	Brazil
LPD 4	Austin	LPD	USA	11	Hawar	PV	Bahrain
LST 4	Lanta	LST	Thailand	11	Smeli	FFG	Bulgaria
LSV 4	Lt Gen William B Bunker	LSL	USA	11	Prat	DDG	Chile
M 4	Tierra del Fuego	MSC	Argentina	11	Kralj Petar Kresimir	FFLG	Croatia
MCM 4	Champion	MSO	USA	11	Mahamiru	MH	Malaysia
05	Melbourne	FFG	Australia	A 11	Minas Gerais	CVS	Brazil
05	Uusimaa	ML	Finland	A 11	Rio Coatzacoalcos	AG	Mexico
A 05	Tui	AGOR	New Zealand	A 11	Endeavour	AEFS	New Zealand
H 05	Altair	AGS	Mexico	A 11	Marqués de la Ensenada	AOF(L)	Spain
L 05	President El Hadj Omar Bongo	LCC	Gabon	AGF 11	Coronado	AG	USA
N 05	Amvrakia	ML	Greece	AGS 11	Chanthara	AGS	Thailand
R 05	Invincible	CVSG	UK	BE 11	Simon Bolivar	ATS	Venezuela
5	Tapi	FF	Thailand	BO 11	Punta Brava	AGS	Venezuela
5	Ladya	MSC	Thailand	C 11	Cadete Virgilio Uribe Robles	PV	Mexico
5	Klongyai	PV	Thailand	CM 11	Esmeraldas	FFLG	Ecuador
AOR 5	Wabash	AOR	USA	D 11	La Argentina	DDG	Argentina
B 5	Cabo de Hornos	AP	Argentina	E 11	Netzahualcoyotl	FFG	Mexico
LHA 5	Peleliu	LHA	USA	F 11	Grisha class	FFG	Lithuania
LHD 4	Bataan	LHD	USA	FFG 11	Clark	FFG	USA
LPD 5	Ogden	LPD	USA	HQ 11	Petya class	FF	Vietnam
LST 5	Prathong	LST	Thailand	K 11	Felinto Perry	ARS	Brazil
LSV 5	Major General Charles P Gross	LSL	USA	K 11	Stockholm	FFLG	Sweden
M 5	Chaco	MH	Argentina	L 11	Velasco	LST	Spain
MCM 5	Guardian	MSO	USA	L 11	Intrepid	LPD	UK
PC 5	Sukrip	PV	Thailand	LPH 11	New Orleans	LPH	USA
Q 5	Almirante Irizar	AG	Argentina	M 11	Galeb	ATS	Yugoslavia
06	Newcastle	FFG	Australia	MCM 11	Gladiator	MSO	USA
06	Condell	FFG	Chile	MUL 11	Kalvsund	ML	Sweden
A 06	Monowai	AGS	New Zealand	P 11	Pirajá	PV	Brazil
H 06	Antares	AGS	Mexico	PF 11	Rajah Humabon	FF	Philippines
R 06	Illustrious	CVSG	UK	R 11	Vikrant	CV	India
6	Khirirat	FF	Thailand	R 11	Principe de Asturias	CV	Spain
6	Bangkeo	MSC	Thailand	12	Druzki	FF	Bulgaria
6	Takbai	PV	Thailand	12	Cochrane	DDG	Chile
AOE 6	Supply	AOE	USA	12	Kralj class	FFLG	Croatia
AOR 6	Kalamazoo	AOR	USA	12	Tuisku	PV	Finland
LHD 6	Bonhomme Richard	LHD	USA	12	Jerai	MH	Malaysia
LPD 6	Duluth	LPD	USA	C 12	Teniente José Azueta Abad	PV	Mexico
LST 6	Sichang	LST	Thailand	CM 12	Manabi	FFLG	Ecuador
M 6	Formosa	MH	Argentina	D 12	Heroina	DDG	Argentina
MCM 6	Devastator	MSO	USA	F 12	Grisha class	FFG	Lithuania
07	Lynch	FFG	Chile	FFG 12	George Philip	FFG	USA
A 07	Cuauhtemoc	AG	Mexico	K12	Malmö	FFLG	Sweden
C 07	Guanajuata	PV	Mexico	L 12	Martin Alvarez	LST	Spain
HQ 07	Admirable class	FFL	Vietnam	LPD 12	Shreveport	LPD	USA
P 07	Général d'Armée Ba Oumar	PV	Gabon	LPH 12	Inchon	LPH	USA
R 07	Ark Royal	CVSG	UK	MCM 12	Ardent	MSO	USA
7	Makut Rajakumarn	FF	Thailand	MUL 12	Arkösund	ML	Sweden
7	Kantang	PV	Thailand	P 12	Pampeiro	PV	Brazil
AOE 7	Rainier	AOE	USA	13	Reshitelni	FFLG	Bulgaria
AOR 7	Roanoke	AOR	USA	13	Ledang	MH	Malaysia
E 7	Inkadh	FF	Tunisia	13	Vice Admiral Mihai Gavrilescu	FFL	Romania
FFG 7	Oliver Hazard Perry	FFG	USA	ASR 13	Kittiwake	ASR	USA
LPD 7	Cleveland	LPD	USA	C 13	Capitan de Fragata Pedro Sáinz de Baranda Borreyro	PV	Mexico
LPH 7	Guadalcanal	LPH	USA	CM 13	Los Rios	FFLG	Ecuador
LST 7	Surin	LST	Thailand	D 13	Sarandi	DDG	Argentina
MCM 7	Patriot	MSO	USA	FFG 13	Samuel Eliot Morison	FFG	USA
PC 7	Liulom	PV	Thailand	HQ 13	Petya class	FF	Vietnam
08	Ministro Zenteno	FFG	Chile	LPD 13	Nashville	LPD	USA
P 08	Colonel Djoue Dabany	PV	Gabon	MCM 13	Dextrous	MSO	USA
8	Donchedi	MSC	Thailand	MUL 13	Kalmarsund	ML	Sweden
8	Thepha	PV	Thailand	P 13	Parati	PV	Brazil
AOE 8	Arctic	AOE	USA	14	Bodri	FFLG	Bulgaria
ARS 8	Preserver	ARS	USA	14	Latorre	DDG	Chile
FFG 8	McInerney	FFG	USA	14	Tuuli	PV	Finland
LPD 8	Dubuque	LPD	USA	14	Kinabalu	MH	Malaysia
MCM 8	Scout	MSO	USA	14	Vice Admiral Ioan Balanescu	FFL	Romania
Q 8	Puerto Deseado	AGS	Argentina	A 14	Patiño	AOR/AEFS	Spain
09	General Baquedano	FFG	Chile	C 14	Comodoro Carlos Castillo Bretón Barrero	PV	Mexico
HQ 09	Petya class	FF	Vietnam	CM 14	El Oro	FFLG	Ecuador
9	Taimuang	PV	Thailand	FFG 14	John H Sides	FFG	USA
A 9	Alferez Sobral	PV	Argentina	J 14	Nirupak	AGS	India
FFG 9	Wadsworth	FFG	USA	L 14	Ghorpad	LSM	India
LPD 9	Denver	LPD	USA	LPD 14	Trenton	LPD	USA
LPH 9	Guam	LPH	USA	MCM 14	Chief	MSO	USA
MCM 9	Pioneer	MSO	USA	MUL 14	Alnósund	ML	Sweden
10	Al Riffa	PV	Bahrain	P 14	Penedo	PV	Brazil
A 10	Comodoro Somellera	PV	Argentina	15	Blanco Encalada	DDG	Chile
A 10	Rio Usumacinta	AG	Mexico	15	Vice Admiral Emil Gregescu	FFL	Romania
AOE 10	Bridge	AOE	USA	15	Tyrsky	PV	Finland
D 10	Almirante Brown	DDG	Argentina	A 15	Nireehshak	ARS	India
E 10	Ilhuicamina	DDG	Mexico				
FFG 10	Duncan	FFG	USA				

Number	Ship's name	Type	Country	Number	Ship's name	Type	Country
ASR 15	Sunbird	ASR	USA	V 21	Bahiana	PV	Brazil
C 15	Vicealmirante Othón Blanco Nunez de Caceres	PV	Mexico	22	Abdul Rahman Al Fadel	PV	Bahrain
CM 15	Los Galapagos	FFLG	Ecuador	22	Damour	PV	Lebanon
F 15	Abu Bakr	FF	Bangladesh	A 22	Rio Lerma	AP	Mexico
FFG 15	Estocin	FFG	USA	AE 22	Mauna Kea	AEFS	USA
HQ 15	Petya class	FF	Vietnam	ASR 22	Ortolan	ASR	USA
J 15	Investigator	AGS	India	E 22	Jose Maria Morelos Y Pavon	FF	Mexico
L 15	Kesari	LSM	India	F 22	Ganga	FFG	India
LPD 15	Ponce	LPD	USA	F 22	Almirante Brión	FFG	Venezuela
M 15	Aratú	MSC	Brazil	FFG 22	Fahrion	FFG	USA
MUL 15	Grundsund	ML	Sweden	G 22	Soares Dutra	AP	Brazil
P 15	Poti	PV	Brazil	H 22	Canopus	AGS	Brazil
V 15	Imperial Marinheiro	PV	Brazil	K 22	Gälve	FFLG	Sweden
16	Vice Admiral Ioan Georgescu	FFL	Romania	L 22	Kumbhir	LSM	India
C 16	Contraalmirante Angel Ortiz Monasterio	PV	Mexico	L 22	Aragón	AP	Spain
CM 16	Loja	FFLG	Ecuador	M 22	Ebro	MSC	Spain
DE 16	Boyaca	PV	Colombia	P 22	Aoife	PV	Ireland
F 16	Umar Farooq	FF	Bangladesh	P 22	Tagomago	PV	Spain
FFG 16	Clifton Sprague	FFG	USA	PS 22	Sultan Kudarat	FFL	Philippines
G 16	Barroso Pereira	AP	Brazil	R 22	Tridente	AG	Brazil
J 16	Jamuna	AGS	India	R 22	Viraat	CV	India
L 16	Shardul	LSM	India	V 22	Mearim	PV	Brazil
M 16	Anhatomirim	MSC	Brazil	23	Al Taweelah	PV	Bahrain
V 16	Iguatemi	PV	Brazil	AE 23	Nitro	AEFS	USA
F 17	Ali Haider	FF	Bangladesh	F 23	General Urdaneta	FFG	Venezuela
HQ 17	Petya class	FF	Vietnam	FFG 23	Lewis B Puller	FFG	USA
J 17	Sutlej	AGS	India	G 23	Almirante Gastão Motta	AOS	Brazil
L 17	Sharabh	LSM	India	K 23	Kalmar	FFLG	Sweden
M 17	Atalaia	MSC	Brazil	L 23	Gharial	LST	India
MUL 17	Skramsösund	AG	Sweden	LM 23	Guayaquil	PV	Ecuador
18	Almirante Riveros	DDG	Chile	M 23	Duero	MSC	Spain
F 18	Osman	FFG	Bangladesh	P 23	Aisling	PV	Ireland
J 18	Sandhayak	AGS	India	P 23	Marola	PV	Spain
L 18	Cheetah	LSM	India	PS 23	Datu Marikudo	FFL	Philippines
M 18	Araçatuba	MSC	Brazil	R 23	Triunfo	AG	Brazil
MUL 18	Öresund	ML	Sweden	V 23	Purus	PV	Brazil
P 18	Armatolos	PV	Greece	24	Rahmat	FF	Malaysia
V 18	Forte de Coimbra	PV	Brazil	24	Lieutenant Remus Lepri	MSC	Romania
19	Almirante Williams	DDG	Chile	F 24	General Soublette	FFG	Venezuela
CG 19	Dale	CG	USA	FFG 24	Jack Williams	FFG	USA
FFG 19	John A Moore	FFG	USA	G 24	Belmonte	AR	Brazil
J 19	Nirdeshak	AGS	India	K 24	Sundsvall	FFLG	Sweden
L 19	Mahish	LSM	India	LM 24	Cuenca	PV	Ecuador
LCC 19	Blue Ridge	LCC	USA	M 24	Tajo	MSC	Spain
M 19	Abrolhas	MSC	Brazil	P 24	Mouro	PV	Spain
MUL 19	Barösund	ML	Sweden	V 24	Solimões	PV	Brazil
P 19	Navmachos	PV	Greece	25	Kasturi	FFLG	Malaysia
PS 19	Miguel Malvar	FFL	Philippines	25	Lieutenant Lupu Dinescu	MSC	Romania
V 19	Caboclo	PV	Brazil	ARS 25	Chang Won	ARS	Korea, Republic
20	Ahmad El Fateh	PV	Bahrain	AT 25	Ang Pangulo	AP	Philippines
20	Capitan Miranda	ATS	Uruguay	CGN 25	Bainbridge	CGN	USA
ASL 20	Cormorant	AG	Canada	D 25	Marcilio Dias	DD	Brazil
CG 20	Richmond K Turner	CG	USA	F 25	General Salom	FFG	Venezuela
E 20	Miguel Hidalgo	FF	Mexico	FFG 25	Copeland	FFG	USA
F 20	Godavari	FFG	India	M 25	Genil	MSC	Spain
FFG 20	Antrim	FFG	USA	P 25	Grosa	PV	Spain
G 20	Custódio de Mello	AP	Brazil	26	Lekir	FFLG	Malaysia
L 20	Magar	LST	India	26	Vanguardia	ARS	Uruguay
LCC 20	Mount Whitney	LCC	USA	ARS 26	Gumi	ARS	Korea, Republic
M 20	Albardão	MSC	Brazil	CG 26	Belknap	CG	USA
MH 20	Henri Christophe	PV	Haiti	D 26	Mariz E Barros	DD	Brazil
MUL 20	Furusund	ML	Sweden	F 26	Almirante Garcia	FFG	Venezuela
P 20	Murature	PV	Argentina	FFG 26	Gallery	FFG	USA
P 20	Deirdre	PV	Ireland	G 26	Duque de Caxais	LST	Brazil
PS 20	Magat Salamat	FFL	Philippines	M 26	Odiel	MSC	Spain
U 20	Gastão Moutinho	AR	Brazil	P 26	Dzata	PV	Ghana
V 20	Angostura	PV	Brazil	P 26	Medas	PV	Spain
21	Al Jabiri	PV	Bahrain	AE 27	Butte	AEFS	USA
21	Sour	PV	Lebanon	D 27	Pará	FF	Brazil
AE 21	Suribachi	AEFS	USA	FFG 27	Mahlon S Tisdale	FFG	USA
CG 21	Gridley	CG	USA	G 27	Marajo	AOR	Brazil
E 21	Vincente Guerrero	FF	Mexico	M 27	Sil	MSC	Spain
F 21	Gomati	FFG	India	P 27	Sebo	PV	Ghana
F 21	Mariscal Sucre	FFG	Venezuela	P 27	Izaro	PV	Spain
FFG 21	Flatley	FFG	USA	U 27	Brasil	AG	Brazil
G 21	Ary Parreiras	AP	Brazil	AE 28	Santa Barbara	AEFS	USA
H 21	Sirius	AGS	Brazil	D 28	Paraíba	FF	Brazil
K 21	Göteborg	FFLG	Sweden	FFG 28	Boone	FFG	USA
L 21	Guldar	LSM	India	M 28	Miño	MSC	Spain
L 21	Castilla	AP	Spain	P 28	Achimota	PV	Ghana
LM 21	Quito	PV	Ecuador	P 28	Tabarca	PV	Spain
M 21	Júcar	MSC	Spain	PS 28	Cebu	FFL	Philippines
P 21	King	PV	Argentina	29	Uribe	AG	Chile
P 21	Emer	PV	Ireland	29	Lekiu	FFG	Malaysia
P 21	Anaga	PV	Spain	29	Lieutenant Dmitrie Nicolescu	MSC	Romania
R 21	Tritão	AG	Brazil	AE 29	Mount Hood	AEFS	USA
				CG 29	Jouett	CG	USA
				D 29	Paraná	FF	Brazil

Number	Ship's name	Type	Country	Number	Ship's name	Type	Country
FFG 29	Stephen W Groves	FFG	USA	37	Papudo	PV	Chile
M 29	Brecon	MH/MSC	UK	AD 37	Samuel Gompers	AD	USA
P 29	Yogaga	PVB	Ghana	AS 37	Dixon	AS	USA
P 29	Deva	PV	Spain	CGN 37	South Carolina	CGN	USA
PS 29	Negros Occidental	FFL	Philippines	D 37	Rio Grande do Norte	DD	Brazil
30	Jebat	FFG	Malaysia	FFG 37	Crommelin	FFG	USA
30	Sub Lieutenant Alexandru			LSD 37	Portland	LSD	USA
	Axente	MSC	Romania	M 37	Chiddingfold	MH/MSC	UK
D 30	Pernambuco	FF	Brazil	38	Perth	DDG	Australia
E 30	Comodoro Manuel Azueta			AD 38	Puget Sound	AD	USA
	Perillos	FF	Mexico	ARS 38	Bolster	ARS	USA
FFG 30	Reid	FFG	USA	CGN 38	Virginia	CGN	USA
G 30	Ceará	LSD	Brazil	D 38	Espirito Santo	DD	Brazil
M 30	Ledbury	MH/MSC	UK	FFG 38	Curts	FFG	USA
P 30	Kondori class	PV	Malta	LSD 38	Pensacola	LSD	USA
P 30	Bergantin	PV	Spain	M 38	Atherstone	MH/MSC	UK
V 30	Inhaúma	FFG	Brazil	39	Hobart	DDG	Australia
31	Drummond	FFG	Argentina	AS 39	Emory S Land	AS	USA
31	Iskar	MSC	Bulgaria	FFG 39	Doyle	FFG	USA
31	Contre Admiral Nicolae			LSD 39	Mount Vernon	LSD	USA
	Cristescu	FFL	Romania	M 39	Hurworth	MH/MSC	UK
31	Temerario	MSC	Uruguay	ARS 40	Hoist	ARS	USA
31	Split	FFG	Yugoslavia	AS 40	Frank Cable	AS	USA
A 31	Malaspina	AGOR	Spain	CGN 40	Mississippi	CGN	USA
AS 31	Hunley	AS	USA	E 40	Nicolas Bravo	FFG	Mexico
F 31	Descubierta	FFG	Spain	F 40	Niteroi	FFG	Brazil
FFG 31	Stark	FFG	USA	FFG 40	Halyburton	FFG	USA
G 31	Rio de Janeiro	LSD	Brazil	H 40	Antares	AGS	Brazil
M 31	Cattistock	MH/MSC	UK	K 40	Veer	FFLG	India
P 31	Eithne	FFL	Ireland	LSD 40	Fort Fisher	LSD	USA
P 31	Kondori class	PV	Malta	M 40	Berkeley	MH/MSC	UK
PS 31	Pangasinan	FFL	Philippines	P 40	Grajaú	PV	Brazil
Q 31	Piloto Alsina	AG	Argentina	41	Brisbane	DDG	Australia
V 31	Jaceguay	FFG	Brazil	41	Espora	FFG	Argentina
32	Guerrico	FFG	Argentina	41	Letyashti	FFL	Bulgaria
32	Zibar	MSC	Bulgaria	41	Yan Taing Aung	FFL	Burma
32	Contre Admiral Nicolae Negru	FFL	Romania	A 41	Dacca	AOR	Pakistan
32	Valiente	MSC	Uruguay	AD 41	Yellowstone	AD	USA
32	Kopar	FFG	Yugoslavia	ARS 41	Opportune	ARS	USA
A 32	Tofiño	AGOR	Spain	AS 41	McKee	AS	USA
AE 32	Flint	AEFS	USA	CGN 41	Arkansas	CGN	USA
AS 32	Holland	AS	USA	F 41	Defensora	FFG	Brazil
F 32	Diana	FFG	Spain	F 41	Taragiri	FFG	India
FFG 32	John L Hall	FFG	USA	FFG 41	McClusky	FFG	USA
M 32	Cottesmore	MH/MSC	UK	H 41	Almirante Câmara	AGS	Brazil
PS 32	Iloilo	FFL	Philippines	K 41	Nirbhik	FFLG	India
V 32	Julio de Noronha	FFG	Brazil	LSD 41	Whidbey Island	LSD	USA
33	Granville	FFG	Argentina	M 41	Guadalete	MSO	Spain
33	Dobrotich	MSC	Bulgaria	M 41	Quorn	MH/MSC	UK
33	Contre Admiral Irimescu	FFL	Romania	P 41	Guaiba	PV	Brazil
33	Fortuna	MSC	Uruguay	P 41	Orla	PV	Ireland
33	Kotor	FFG	Yugoslavia	42	Rosales	FFG	Argentina
A 33	Hespérides	AGOR	Spain	42	Bditelni	FFL	Bulgaria
AE 33	Shasta	AEFS	USA	42	Yan Gyi Aung	FFL	Burma
AS 33	Simon Lake	AS	USA	A 42	Portrero Del Llano	AOF(S)	Mexico
F 33	Nilgiri	FFG	India	AD 42	Acadia	AD	USA
F 33	Infanta Elena	FFG	Spain	ARS 42	Reclaimer	ARS	USA
FFG 33	Jarrett	FFG	USA	E 42	Hermenegildo Galeana	FFG	Mexico
M 33	Brocklesby	MH/MSC	UK	F 42	Constituição	FFG	Brazil
P 33	Abhay	FFLG	India	F 42	Vindhyagiri	FFG	India
PH 33	Andrija Mohorovičič	AGS	Croatia	FFG 42	Klakring	FFG	USA
V 33	Frontin	FFG	Brazil	H 42	Barao de Teffé	AGS	Brazil
34	Ekstati Vinarov	MSC	Bulgaria	K 42	Nipat	FFLG	India
34	Audaz	MSC	Uruguay	LSD 42	Germantown	LSD	USA
34	Pula	FFG	Yugoslavia	M 42	Guadalmedina	MSO	Spain
AE 34	Mount Baker	AEFS	USA	P 42	Graúna	PV	Brazil
AS 34	Canopus	AS	USA	P 42	Ciara	PV	Ireland
F 34	Himgiri	FFG	India	Q 42	Cabo San Antonio	LST	Argentina
F 34	Infanta Cristina	FFG	Spain	43	Spiro	FFG	Argentina
FFG 34	Aubrey Fitch	FFG	USA	43	Bezstrashni	FFL	Bulgaria
M 34	Middleton	MH/MSC	UK	43	Esmeralda	AG	Chile
P 34	Ajay	FFLG	India	A 43	Faja De Oro	AOF(S)	Mexico
AE 35	Kiska	AEFS	USA	AD 43	Cape Cod	AD	USA
CGN 35	Truxtun	CGN	USA	ARS 43	Recovery	ARS	USA
D 35	Sergipe	DD	Brazil	F 43	Liberal	FFG	Brazil
F 35	Udaygiri	FFG	India	FFG 43	Thach	FFG	USA
F 35	Cazadora	FFG	Spain	K 43	Nishank	FFLG	India
M 35	Dulverton	MH/MSC	UK	LSD 43	Fort McHenry	LSD	USA
P 35	Akshay	FFLG	India	M 43	Guadalquivir	MSO	Spain
AS 36	L Y Spear	AS	USA	N 43	Lindormen	ML	Denmark
CGN 36	California	CGN	USA	P 43	Goiana	PV	Brazil
D 36	Alagoas	DD	Brazil	44	Parker	FFG	Argentina
F 36	Dunagiri	FFG	India	44	Khrabri	FFL	Bulgaria
F 36	Vencedora	FFG	Spain	A 44	Tuxpan	AOF(S)	Mexico
FFG 36	Underwood	FFG	USA	AD 44	Shenandoah	AD	USA
LSD 36	Anchorage	LSD	USA	F 44	Independencia	FFG	Brazil
M 36	Bicester	MH/MSC	UK	K 44	Nirghat	FFLG	India
P 36	Agray	FFLG	India	LSD 44	Gunston Hall	LSD	USA

Number	Ship's name	Type	Country	Number	Ship's name	Type	Country
M 44	Guadiana	MSO	Spain	P 53	Savitri	PV	India
N 44	Lossen	ML	Denmark	A 54	Amba	AS	India
P 44	Guajará	PV	Brazil	C 54	Cadete Augustin Melgar	PV	Mexico
P 44	Kirpan	FFLG	India	CG 54	Antietam	CG	USA
T 44	Puerto Cabello	AFS	Venezuela	CM 54	Independiente	FFG	Colombia
45	Robinson	FFG	Argentina	D 54	Ranvir	DDG	India
45	Piloto Pardo	AG	Chile	DDG 54	Curtis Wilbur	DDG	USA
F 45	União	FFG	Brazil	FFG 54	Ford	FFG	USA
FFG 45	De Wert	FFG	USA	FM 54	Mariategui	FFG	Peru
K 45	Vibhuti	FFLG	India	MHC 54	Robin	MH	USA
LSD 45	Comstock	LSD	USA	P 54	Saryu	PV	India
P 45	Guaporé	PV	Brazil	55	Tonti class	AOS	RoK
46	Gomez Roca	FFG	Argentina	C 55	Teniente Juan De La Barrera	PV	Mexico
FFG 46	Rentz	FFG	USA	CG 55	Leyte Gulf	CG	USA
K 46	Vipul	FFLG	India	D 55	Ranvijay	DDG	India
LSD 46	Tortuga	LSD	USA	DDG 55	Stout	DDG	USA
P 46	Kuthar	FFLG	India	F 55	Waikato	FFG	New Zealand
A 47	Nasr	AOR	Pakistan	FFG 55	Elrod	FFG	USA
AP 47	Aquiles	AP	Chile	FV 55	Indaw	PV	Burma
CG 47	Ticonderoga	CG	USA	MHC 55	Oriole	MH	USA
FFG 47	Nicholas	FFG	USA	P 55	Sharada	PV	India
LSD 47	Rushmore	LSD	USA	56	Tonti class	AOS	RoK
M 47	Bedok	MH	Singapore	C 56	Cadete Juan Escutia	PV	Mexico
P 47	Khanjar	FFLG	India	CG 56	San Jacinto	CG	USA
CG 48	Yorktown	CG	USA	DDG 56	John S McCain	DDG	USA
FFG 48	Vandegrift	FFG	USA	FFG 56	Simpson	FFG	USA
LSD 48	Ashland	LSD	USA	FV 56	Inma	PV	Burma
M 48	Kallang	MH	Singapore	MHC 56	Kingfisher	MH	USA
49	Derwent	FF	Australia	P 56	Sujata	PV	India
CG 49	Vincennes	CG	USA	A 57	Shakti	AOR	India
FFG 49	Robert G Bradley	FFG	USA	AO 57	Chun Jee	AOE	Korea, Republic
LSD 49	Harpers Ferry	LSD	USA	C 57	Cadete Fernando Montes De Oca	PV	Mexico
M 49	Katong	MH	Singapore	CG 57	Lake Champlain	CG	USA
P 49	Khukri	FFLG	India	DDG 57	Mitscher	DDG	USA
50	Swan	FF	Australia	FFG 57	Reuben James	FFG	USA
50	Al Manama	FFLG	Bahrain	FV 57	Inya	PV	Burma
A 50	Alster	AGI	Germany	LT 57	Sierra Madre	LST	Philippines
A 50	Deepak	AOR	India	M 57	Arkö	MSC	Sweden
ARS 50	Safeguard	ARS	USA	MHC 57	Cormorant	MH	USA
C 50	General Miguel Negrete	PV	Mexico	C 58	General Pedro Maria Anaya	PV	Mexico
CG 50	Valley Forge	CG	USA	CG 58	Philippine Sea	CG	USA
FFG 50	Taylor	FFG	USA	DDG 58	Laboon	DDG	USA
L 50	Tobruk	LSH	Australia	FFG 58	Samuel B Roberts	FFG	USA
LSD 50	Carter Hall	LSD	USA	MHC 58	Black Hawk	MH	USA
M 50	Punggol	MH	Singapore	C 59	Cadete Francisco Marquez	PV	Mexico
P 50	Sukanya	PV	India	CG 59	Princeton	CG	USA
51	Al Muharraq	FFLG	Bahrain	DDG 59	Russell	DDG	USA
51	Damavand	DDG	Iran	FFG 59	Kauffman	FFG	USA
ARS 51	Grasp	ARS	USA	MHC 59	Falcon	MH	USA
C 51	General Juan M Mendez	PV	Mexico	60	Vidal Gormaz	AGOR	Chile
CG 51	Thomas S Gates	CG	USA	60	Helsinki	PV	Finland
CM 51	Almirante Padilla	FFG	Colombia	A 60	Gorch Fock	AG	Germany
D 51	Rajput	DDG	India	C 60	General Ignacio Zaragoza	PV	Mexico
DDG 51	Arleigh Burke	DDG	USA	CG 60	Normandy	CG	USA
FFG 51	Gary	FFG	USA	CV 60	Saratoga	CV	USA
FM 51	Meliton Carvajal	FFG	Peru	DDG 60	Paul Hamilton	DDG	USA
LSD 51	Oak Hill	LSD	USA	FFG 60	Rodney M Davis	FFG	USA
MHC 51	Osprey	MH	USA	MHC 60	Cardinal	MH	USA
P 51	Subhadra	PV	India	61	Briz	MSC	Bulgaria
52	Almirante Jorge Montt	AOF(L)	Chile	61	Turku	PV	Finland
A 52	Oste	AGI	Germany	61	Babr	DDG	Iran
ARS 52	Salvor	ARS	USA	A 61	Contramaestre Castelló	AG	Spain
C 52	General Manuel E Rincon	PV	Mexico	C 61	Cadete Vincente Suarez	PV	Mexico
CG 52	Bunker Hill	CG	USA	CG 61	Monterey	CG	USA
CM 52	Caldas	FFG	Colombia	DDG 61	Ramage	DDG	USA
D 52	Rana	DDG	India	FFG 61	Ingraham	FFG	USA
DDG 52	Barry	DDG	USA	M 61	Pondicherry	MSO	India
FFG 52	Carr	FFG	USA	MHC 61	Raven	MH	USA
FM 52	Manuel Villavicencio	FFG	Peru	P 61	Chilreu	PV	Spain
K 52	Vinash	FFLG	India	T 61	Capana	LST	Venezuela
LSD 52	Pearl Harbor	LSD	USA	TR 61	Hualcopo	LST	Ecuador
MHC 52	Heron	MH	USA	62	Shkval	MSC	Bulgaria
N 52	Vidar	ML	Norway	62	Oulu	PV	Finland
P 52	Suvarna	PV	India	62	Palang	DDG	Iran
53	Torrens	FF	Australia	CG 62	Chancellorsville	CG	USA
53	Araucano	AOF(L)	Chile	CV 62	Independence	CV	USA
A 53	Oker	AGI	Germany	DDG 62	Fitzgerald	DDG	USA
ARS 53	Grapple	ARS	USA	M 62	Porbandar	MSO	India
C 53	General Felipe Xicotencatl	PV	Mexico	MHC 62	Shrike	MH	USA
CG 53	Mobile Bay	CG	USA	P 62	Niki	FFL	Greece
CM 53	Antioquia	FFG	Colombia	T 62	Esequibo	LST	Venezuela
D 53	Ranjit	DDG	India	63	Ppiboy	MSC	Bulgaria
DDG 53	John Paul Jones	DDG	USA	63	Sargento Aldea	PV	Chile
FFG 53	Hawes	FFG	USA	63	Kotka	PV	Finland
FM 53	Montero	FFG	Peru	CG 63	Cowpens	CG	USA
K 53	Nashak	FFLG	India	CV 63	Kitty Hawk	CV	USA
MHC 53	Pelican	MH	USA	DDG 63	Stethem	DDG	USA
N 53	Vale	ML	Norway				

[95]

PENNANT LIST

Number	Ship's name	Type	Country
M 63	Bedi	MSO	India
P 63	Doxa	FFL	Greece
T 63	Goajira	LST	Venezuela
64	Shtorm	MSC	Bulgaria
64	Yelcho	AGS	Chile
CG 64	Gettysburg	CG	USA
CV 64	Constellation	CV	USA
DDG 64	Carney	DDG	USA
M 64	Bhavnagar	MSO	India
P 64	Eleftheria	FFL	Greece
T 64	Los Llanos	LST	Venezuela
CG 65	Chosin	CG	USA
CVN 65	Enterprise	CVN	USA
DDG 65	Benfold	DDG	USA
M 65	Alleppey	MSO	India
P 65	Carteria	FFL	Greece
CG 66	Hue City	CG	USA
CV 66	America	CV	USA
DDG 66	Gonzalez	DDG	USA
M 66	Ratnagiri	MSO	India
P 66	Agon	FFL	Greece
CG 67	Shiloh	CG	USA
CV 67	John F Kennedy	CV	USA
DDG 67	Cole	DDG	USA
M 67	Karwar	MSO	India
M 67	Nämdö	MSC	Sweden
ATF 68	Leucoton	AG	Chile
CG 68	Anzio	CG	USA
CVN 68	Nimitz	CVN	USA
DDG 68	The Sullivans	DDG	USA
M 68	Cannanore	MSO	India
M 68	Blidö	MSC	Sweden
P 68	Arnala	FF	India
A 69	Donau	AG	Germany
ATF 69	Colo Colo	AG	Chile
CG 69	Vicksburg	DDG	USA
CVN 69	Dwight D Eisenhower	CVN	USA
DDG 69	Milius	DDG	USA
F 69	Wellington	FFG	New Zealand
M 69	Cuddalore	MSO	India
P 69	Androth	FF	India
70	Rauma	PV	Finland
C 70	Leandro Valle	PV	Mexico
CG 70	Lake Erie	CG	USA
CVN 70	Carl Vinson	CVN	USA
DDG 70	Hopper	DDG	USA
M 70	Kakinada	MSO	India
71	Contramaestre Micalvi	PV	Chile
71	Raahe	PV	Finland
71	Alvand	FFG	Iran
A 71	Juan Sebastian de Elcano	ATS	Spain
C 71	Guillermo Prieto	PV	Mexico
CG 71	Cape St George	CG	USA
CVN 71	Theodore Roosevelt	CVN	USA
DDG 71	Ross	DDG	USA
F 71	Baleares	FFG	Spain
K 71	Vijay Durg	FFLG	India
M 71	Kozhikoda	MSO	India
M 71	Landsort	MH	Sweden
P 71	Serviola	PV	Spain
72	Contramaestre Ortiz	PV	Chile
72	Porvoo	PV	Finland
72	Alborz	FFG	Iran
A 72	Arosa	ATS	Spain
C 72	Mariano Escobedo	PV	Mexico
CG 72	Vella Gulf	CG	USA
CVN 72	Abraham Lincoln	CVN	USA
DDG 72	Mahan	DDG	USA
F 72	Andalucia	FFG	Spain
K 72	Sindhu Durg	FFLG	India
M 72	Konkan	MSO	India
M 72	Arholma	MH	Sweden
P 72	Centinela	PV	Spain
RM 72	Pedro de Heredia	PV	Colombia
73	Aspirante Isaza	PV	Chile
73	Naantali	PV	Finland
73	Sabalan	FFG	Iran
A 73	Moresby	AGS	Australia
C 73	Manuel Doblado	PV	Mexico
CG 73	Port Royal	CG	USA
CVN 73	George Washington	CVN	USA
DDG 73	Decatur	DDG	USA
F 73	Cataluña	FFG	Spain
K 73	Hos Durg	FFLG	India
M 73	Koster	MH	Sweden
P 73	Anjadip	FF	India
P 73	Vigia	PV	Spain
RM 73	Sebastion de Belal Calzar	PV	Colombia
74	Aspirante Morel	PV	Chile
A 74	Aris	AG	Greece
A 74	La Graciosa	ATS	Spain
C 74	Sebastian Lerdo de Tejada	PV	Mexico
CVN 74	John C Stennis	CVN	USA
DDG 74	McFaul	DDG	USA
DM 74	Ferré	DDG	Peru
F 74	Asturias	FFG	Spain
M 74	Kullen	MH	Sweden
P 74	Atalaya	PV	Spain
PS 74	Rizal	FFL	Philippines
RM 74	Rodrigo de Bastidas	PV	Colombia
C 75	Santos Degollado	PV	Mexico
CVN 75	United States	CVN	USA
DDG 75	Donald Cook	DDG	USA
F 75	Extremadura	FFG	Spain
M 75	Vinga	MH	Sweden
P 75	Amini	FF	India
76	Hang Tuah	FF	Malaysia
C 76	Ignacio de la Llave	PV	Mexico
DDG 76	Higgins	DDG	USA
M 76	Ven	MH	Sweden
C 77	Juan N Alvares	PV	Mexico
F 77	Anzac class	FFG	New Zealand
M 77	Ulvön	MH	Sweden
C 78	Manuel Gutierrez Zamora	PV	Mexico
P 78	Kadmath	FF	India
C 79	Valentin Gomez Farias	PV	Mexico
F 79	Lamine Sadji Kaba	PV	Guinea
80	Guacolda	PV	Chile
C 80	Ignacio Manuel Altamirano	PV	Mexico
M 80	Rushcutter	MH	Australia
N 80	Falster	ML	Denmark
81	Fresia	PV	Chile
81	Zhenghe	AT	China
81	Bayandor	FFL	Iran
A 81	Aka	ARS	Iraq
A 81	Brambleleaf	AOS	UK
C 81	Francisco Zarco	PV	Mexico
CH 81	Almirante Grau	CG	Peru
F 81	Santa María	FFG	Spain
M 81	Shoalwater	MH	Australia
N 81	Fyen	ML	Denmark
82	Quidora	PV	Chile
82	Naghdi	FFL	Iran
C 82	Ignacio L Vallarta	PV	Mexico
F 82	Victoria	FFG	Spain
N 82	Møen	ML	Denmark
83	Tegualda	PV	Chile
C 83	Jesus Gonzalez Ortega	PV	Mexico
F 83	Erinomi	FFLG	Nigeria
F 83	Numancia	FFG	Spain
N 83	Sjaelland	ML	Denmark
C 84	Melchor Ocampo	PV	Mexico
CH 84	Aguirre	CG	Peru
F 84	Enyimiri	FFLG	Nigeria
F 84	Reina Sofía	FFG	Spain
C 85	Juan Aldama	PV	Mexico
F 85	Navarra	FFG	Spain
F 85	Cumberland	FFG	UK
A 86	Tir	ATS	India
C 86	Mariano Matamoros	PV	Mexico
D 86	Birmingham	DDG	UK
F 86	Canarias	FFG	Spain
F 86	Campbeltown	FFG	UK
LT 86	Zamboanga del Sur	LST	Philippines
D 87	Newcastle	DDG	UK
F 87	Obuma	FF	Nigeria
F 87	Chatham	FFG	UK
D 88	Glasgow	DDG	UK
F 88	Broadsword	FFG	UK
P 88	Victory	FFLG	Singapore
D 89	Exeter	DDG	UK
F 89	Aradu	FFG	Nigeria
F 89	Battleaxe	FFG	UK
P 89	Valour	FFLG	Singapore
D 90	Southampton	DDG	UK
F 90	Brilliant	FFG	UK
P 90	Vigilance	FFLG	Singapore
BI 91	Orion	AGOR	Ecuador
D 91	Nottingham	DDG	UK
F 91	Brazen	FFG	UK
P 91	Valiant	FFLG	Singapore
R 91	Charles de Gaulle	CVN	France
D 92	Liverpool	DDG	UK
F 92	Boxer	FFG	UK
P 92	Vigour	FFLG	Singapore
F 93	Beaver	FFG	UK

Number	Ship's name	Type	Country	Number	Ship's name	Type	Country
P 93	Vengeance	FFLG	Singapore	132	Hefei	DDG	China
F 94	Brave	FFG	UK	132	Ibn Ouf	LST	Libya
D 95	Manchester	DDG	UK	A 132	Diligence	AR	UK
F 95	London	FFG	UK	DD 132	Asayuki	DDG	Japan
D 96	Gloucester	DDG	UK	133	Chongqing	DDG	China
F 96	Sheffield	FFG	UK	A 133	Hecla	AGS	UK
D 97	Edinburgh	DDG	UK	DD 133	Shimayuki	DDG	Japan
R 97	Jeanne d'Arc	CVH	France	134	Zunyi	DDG	China
D 98	York	DDG	UK	134	Ibn Harissa	LST	Libya
F 98	Coventry	FFG	UK	A 135	Argus	AVT	UK
R 98	Clemenceau	CV	France	A 138	Herald	AGS	UK
F 99	Cornwall	FFG	UK	139	Ropucha I class	LST	Yemen
R 99	Foch	CV	France	DD 141	Haruna	DDG	Japan
101	Mulniya	FFLG	Bulgaria	DT 141	Paita	LST	Peru
M 101	Sandown	MH	UK	DD 142	Hiei	DDG	Japan
A 102	Agnadeen	AOR	Iraq	DT 142	Pisco	LST	Peru
M 102	Inverness	MH	UK	DD 143	Shirane	DDG	Japan
M 103	Cromer	MH	UK	DT 143	Callao	LST	Peru
F 104	Southland	FFG	New Zealand	DD 144	Kurama	DDG	Japan
L 104	Inouse	LST	Greece	DT 144	Eten	LST	Peru
M 104	Walney	MH	UK	L 144	Siros	LST	Greece
N 104	Mersin	ML	Turkey	M 144	Iz	MSC	Croatia
P 104	Bakassi	PVG	Cameroon	150	Anzac	FFG	Australia
105	Jinan	DDG	China	ATP 150	Bayovar	AO	Peru
M 105	Bridport	MH	UK	151	Arunta	FFG	Australia
106	Xian	DDG	China	DD 151	Asagiri	DDG	Japan
107	Yinchuan	DDG	China	M 151	Vukov Klanac	MH	Croatia
108	Xining	DDG	China	152	Mutiara	AGS	Malaysia
D 108	Cardiff	DDG	UK	ATP 152	Talara	AOR	Peru
109	Kaifeng	DDG	China	DD 152	Yamagiri	DDG	Japan
A 109	Bayleaf	AOS	UK	M 152	Podgora	MH/MSC	Yugoslavia
110	Dalian	DDG	China	DD 153	Yuugiri	DDG	Japan
A 110	Orangeleaf	AOS	UK	L 153	Nafkratoussa	LSD	Greece
MSA 110	Anticosti	MSC	Canada	M 153	Blitvenica	MH/MSC	Yugoslavia
N 110	Nusret	ML	Turkey	DD 154	Amagiri	DDG	Japan
111	Al Tiyar	MSO	Libya	L 154	Ikaria	LST	Greece
111	Marasesti	DDG	Romania	155	Providencia	AGS	Colombia
A 111	Alerta	AGI	Spain	DD 155	Hamagiri	DDG	Japan
A 111	Oakleaf	AOS	UK	156	Malpelo	AGS	Colombia
F 111	Anzac class	FFG	New Zealand	DD 156	Setogiri	DDG	Japan
P 111	Sultanhisar	PV	Turkey	DD 157	Sawagiri	DDG	Japan
112	Haribing	DDG	China	L 157	Rodos	LST	Greece
MSA 112	Moresby	MSC	Canada	ATP 158	Zorritos	AOS	Peru
P 112	Demirhisar	PV	Turkey	DD 158	Umigiri	DDG	Japan
113	Luhu class	DDG	China	ATP 159	Lobitos	AOS	Peru
113	Al Isar	MSO	Libya	PBL 159	Fundy	PV	Canada
P 113	Yarhisar	PV	Turkey	160	Musytari	PV	Malaysia
P 114	Akhisar	PV	Turkey	D 160	Alamgir	DDG	Pakistan
115	Ras al Hamman	MSO	Libya	M 160	Mahmood	MSC	Pakistan
N 115	Mehmetcik	ML	Turkey	PBL 160	Chignecto	PV	Canada
P 115	Sivrihisar	PV	Turkey	161	Changsha	DDG	China
DD 116	Minegumo	DD	Japan	161	Marikh	PV	Malaysia
L 116	Kos	LST	Greece	PBL 161	Thunder	PV	Canada
P 116	Koçhisar	PV	Turkey	162	Nanning	DDG	China
117	Ras al Fulaijah	MSO	Libya	PBL 162	Cowichan	PV	Canada
DD 117	Natsugumo	DD	Japan	163	Nanchang	DDG	China
DD 118	Murakumo	DD	Japan	DD 163	Amatsukaze	DDG	Japan
119	Ras al Qula	MSO	Libya	PBL 163	Miramichi	PV	Canada
DD 119	Aokumo	DD	Japan	164	Guilin	DDG	China
DD 120	Akigumo	DD	Japan	DD 164	Takatsuki	DDG	Japan
NL 120	Bayraktar	LST	Turkey	M 164	Mujahid	MSC	Pakistan
121	Ras al Madwar	MSO	Libya	PBL 164	Chaleur	PV	Canada
AG 121	Riverton	AGOR	Canada	165	Zhanjiang	DDG	China
DD 121	Yugumo	DD	Japan	DD 165	Kikuzuki	DDG	Japan
J 121	Changxingdao	AS	China	166	Zhuhai	DDG	China
NL 121	Sancaktar	LST	Turkey	D 166	Taimur	DDG	Pakistan
A 122	Olwen	AOF (L)	UK	DD 166	Mochizuki	DDG	Japan
DD 122	Hatsuyuki	DDG	Japan	M 166	Munsif	MH	Pakistan
NL 122	Çakabey	LST	Turkey	D 167	Tughril	DDG	Pakistan
123	Ras al Massad	MSO	Libya	DD 167	Nagatsuki	DDG	Japan
A 123	Olna	AOF (L)	UK	M 167	Muhafiz	MH	Pakistan
DD 123	Shirayuki	DDG	Japan	D 168	Tachikaze	DDG	Japan
NL 123	Sarucabey	LST	Turkey	DD 169	Asakaze	DDG	Japan
A 124	Olmeda	AOF (L)	UK	DD 170	Sawakaze	DDG	Japan
DD 124	Mineyuki	DDG	Japan	A 171	Endurance	PV	UK
NL 124	Karamürselbey	LST	Turkey	AGOR 171	Endeavour	AGOR	Canada
125	Ras al Hani	MSO	Libya	DD 171	Hatakaze	DDG	Japan
DD 125	Sawayuki	DDG	Japan	L 171	Kriti	LST	Greece
NL 125	Osman Gazi	LST	Turkey	AGOR 172	Quest	AGOR	Canada
DD 126	Hamayuki	DDG	Japan	DD 172	Shimakaze	DDG	Japan
DD 127	Isoyuki	DDG	Japan	DD 173	Kongo	DDG	Japan
DD 128	Haruyuki	DDG	Japan	L 173	Samos	LST	Greece
DD 129	Yamayuki	DDG	Japan	DD 174	Kirishima	DDG	Japan
A 130	Roebuck	AGS	UK	L 174	Chios	LST	Greece
DD 130	Matsuyuki	DDG	Japan	L 175	Ikaria	LST	Greece
131	Nanjing	DDG	China	L 176	Lesbos	LST	Greece
ATC 131	Ilo	AP	Peru	AO 177	Cimarron	AO	USA
DD 131	Setoyuki	DDG	Japan	L 177	Rodos	LST	Greece

PENNANT LIST

Number	Ship's name	Type	Country	Number	Ship's name	Type	Country
AO 178	Monongahela	AO	USA	D 215	Tompazis	DDG	Greece
P 178	Ekpe	PV	Nigeria	DE 215	Chikugo	FF	Japan
AO 179	Merrimack	AO	USA	F 215	Brandenburg	FFG	Germany
P 179	Damisa	PV	Nigeria	216	Chung Kuang	LST	Taiwan
AO 180	Willamette	AO	USA	216	Gladstone	PV	Australia
P 180	Agu	PV	Nigeria	DE 216	Ayase	FF	Japan
F 181	Tariq	FFG	Pakistan	F 216	Schleswig-Holstein	FFG	Germany
P 181	Siri	PV	Nigeria	217	Chung Suo	LST	Taiwan
D 182	Schleswig-Holstein	DDG	Germany	217	Bunbury	PV	Australia
F 182	Babur	FFG	Pakistan	DE 217	Mikuma	FF	Japan
P 182	Ayam	PV	Nigeria	F 217	Bayern	FFG	Germany
F 183	Khaibar	FFG	Pakistan	D 218	Kimon	DDG	Greece
P 183	Ekun	PV	Nigeria	DE 218	Tokachi	FF	Japan
F 184	Badr	FFG	Pakistan	F 218	Mecklenburg-Vorpommern	FFG	Germany
A 185	Salmoor	ARS	UK	219	Kao Hsiung	AG	Taiwan
D 185	Lütjens	DDG	Germany	D 219	Nearchos	DDG	Greece
F 185	Shah Jahan	FFG	Pakistan	DE 219	Iwase	FF	Japan
A 186	Salmaster	ARS	UK	D 220	Formion	DDG	Greece
AO 186	Platte	AO	USA	DE 220	Chitose	FF	Japan
D 186	Mölders	DDG	Germany	221	Chung Chuan	LST	Taiwan
F 186	Tippu Sultan	FFG	Pakistan	D 221	Themistocles	DDG	Greece
A 187	Salmaid	ARS	UK	DE 221	Niyodo	FF	Japan
D 187	Rommel	DDG	Germany	P 221	Kaman	PV	Iran
188	Zborul	FFLG	Romania	222	Chung Sheng	LST	Taiwan
189	Lastunul	FFLG	Romania	DE 222	Teshio	FF	Japan
190	Pescarusul	FFLG	Romania	P 222	Zoubin	PV	Iran
191	Chung Cheng	LSD	Taiwan	223	Chung Fu	LST	Taiwan
192	Cheng Hai	LSD	Taiwan	DE 223	Yoshino	FF	Japan
O 195	Westralia	AOR	Australia	P 223	Khadang	PV	Iran
201	Chung Hai	LST	Taiwan	DE 224	Kumano	FF	Japan
201	Natya class	MSO	Yemen	DE 225	Noshiro	FF	Japan
A 201	Orion	AGI	Sweden	226	Chung Chih	LST	Taiwan
L 201	Endurance	LST	Singapore	DE 226	Ishikari	FFG	Japan
UAM 201	Creoula	ATS	Portugal	P 226	Falakhon	PV	Iran
202	Dimiter A Dimitrov	AOS	Bulgaria	227	Chung Ming	LST	Taiwan
L 202	Excellence	LST	Singapore	DE 227	Yubari	FFG	Japan
M 202	Atalanti	MSC	Greece	P 227	Shamshir	PV	Iran
203	Fremantle	PV	Australia	DE 228	Yubetsu	FFG	Japan
GT 203	Jervis Bay	AG	Australia	P 228	Gorz	PV	Iran
L 203	Intrepid	LST	Singapore	DE 229	Abukuma	FFG	Japan
204	Chung Hsing	LST	Taiwan	F 229	Lancaster	FFG	UK
204	Warrnambool	PV	Australia	P 229	Tolmi	PV	Greece
L 204	Resolution	LST	Singapore	P 229	Gardouneh	PV	Iran
P 204	Indépendencia	PV	Dominican Republic	230	Chung Pang	LST	Taiwan
205	Chung Chien	LST	Taiwan	DE 230	Jintsu	FFG	Japan
205	Townsville	PV	Australia	F 230	Norfolk	FFG	UK
L 205	Persistence	LST	Singapore	P 230	Ormi	PV	Greece
M 205	Antiopi	MSC	Greece	P 230	Khanjar	PV	Iran
P 205	Libertad	PV	Dominican Republic	231	Chung Yeh	LST	Taiwan
206	Kapitan Dmitry Dobrev	AG	Bulgaria	DE 231	Ohyodo	FFG	Japan
206	Wollongong	PV	Australia	F 231	Argyll	FFG	UK
M 206	Faedra	MSC	Greece	P 231	Neyzeh	PV	Iran
P 206	Restauracion	PV	Dominican Republic	DE 232	Sendai	FFG	Japan
207	Launceston	PV	Australia	P 232	Tabarzin	PV	Iran
F 207	Bremen	FFG	Germany	DE 233	Chikuma	FFG	Japan
P 207	Cambiaso	FFL	Dominican Republic	F 233	Marlborough	FFG	UK
208	Chung Shun	LST	Taiwan	DE 234	Tone	FFG	Japan
208	Whyalla	PV	Australia	F 234	Iron Duke	FFG	UK
F 208	Niedersachsen	FFG	Germany	F 235	Monmouth	FFG	UK
P 208	Separacion	FFL	Dominican Republic	236	Gatineau	FFG	Canada
209	Ipswich	PV	Australia	F 236	Montrose	FFG	UK
F 209	Rheinland-Pfalz	FFG	Germany	F 237	Westminster	FFG	UK
P 209	Calderas	FFL	Dominican Republic	F 238	Northumberland	FFG	UK
210	Chung Yung	LST	Taiwan	F 239	Richmond	FFG	UK
210	Cessnock	PV	Australia	P 239	Peacock	PV	UK
F 210	Emden	FFG	Germany	240	Kaszub	FFG	Poland
F 210	Mussa Ben Nussair	FFG	Iraq	F 240	Yavuz	FFG	Turkey
M 210	Thalia	MSC	Greece	F 240	Somerset	FFG	UK
211	Bendigo	PV	Australia	M 240	Pleias	MSC	Greece
F 211	Köln	FFG	Germany	P 240	Plover	PV	UK
F 211	Dat Assawari	FFG	Libya	DBM 241	Silba	LCT/ML	Yugoslavia
M 211	Alkyon	MSC	Greece	F 241	Turgutreis	FFG	Turkey
P 211	Meghna	PV	Bangladesh	F 241	Grafton	FFG	UK
212	Gawler	PV	Australia	M 241	Kichli	MSC	Greece
F 212	Karlsruhe	FFG	Germany	P 241	Starling	PV	UK
F 212	Tariq Ibn Ziad	FFG	Iraq	F 242	Fatih	FFG	Turkey
F 212	Al Hani	FFG	Libya	F 242	Sutherland	FFG	UK
P 212	Jamuna	PV	Bangladesh	M 242	Kissa	MSC	Greece
213	Geraldton	PV	Australia	F 243	Yildirim	FFG	Turkey
D 213	Kountouriotis	DDG	Greece	F 244	Barbaros	FFG	Turkey
F 213	Augsburg	FFG	Germany	F 245	Orucreis	FFG	Turkey
F 213	Al Qirdabiyah	FFG	Libya	M 246	Aigli	MSC	Greece
M 213	Klio	MSC	Greece	M 247	Dafni	MSC	Greece
214	Dubbo	PV	Australia	M 248	Aedon	MSC	Greece
A 214	Belos III	ARS	Sweden	F 250	Muavenet	FFG	Turkey
F 214	Lübeck	FFG	Germany	251	Wodnik	ATS	Poland
M 214	Avra	MSC	Greece	F 251	Adatepe	FFG	Turkey
215	Geelong	PV	Australia	252	Gryf	ATS	Poland

Number	Ship's name	Type	Country	Number	Ship's name	Type	Country
F 252	Kocatepe	FFG	Turkey	312	El Akid	PV	Morocco
F 253	Zafer	FFG	Turkey	313	Mifgav	PV	Israel
F 254	Trakya	FFG	Turkey	313	El Maher	PV	Morocco
M 254	Niovi	MSC	Greece	M 313	Tana	MH	Norway
F 255	Akdeniz	FFG	Turkey	314	El Majid	PV	Morocco
F 256	Ege	FFG	Turkey	M 314	Alta	MSC	Norway
F 257	Karadeniz	FFG	Turkey	315	El Bachir	PV	Morocco
258	Kootenay	FFG	Canada	316	El Hamiss	PV	Morocco
P 258	Leeds Castle	PV	UK	317	El Karib	PV	Morocco
259	Terra Nova	FFG	Canada	A 317	Bulldog	AGS	UK
P 259	Redpole	PV	UK	A 319	Beagle	AGS	UK
260	Admiral Petre Barbuneanu	FF	Romania	321	Pauk II class	FFLG	Cuba
P 260	Kingfisher	PV	UK	321	Eilath	PV	Israel
261	Kopernik	AGI	Poland	322	Haifa	PV	Israel
261	Vice Admiral Vasile Scodrea	FF	Romania	323	Akko	PV	Israel
A 261	Utö	AG	Sweden	A 324	Protea	AGS	South Africa
262	Navigator	AGI	Poland	330	Halifax	FFG	Canada
262	Vice Admiral Vasile Urseanu	FF	Romania	F 330	Vasco da Gama	FFG	Portugal
F 262	Zulfiquar	FFG	Pakistan	331	Vancouver	FFG	Canada
263	Hydrograf	AGI	Poland	331	Martha Kristina Tiyahahu	FFG	Indonesia
263	Vice Admiral Eugeniu Rosca	FF	Romania	F 331	Alvares Cabral	FFG	Portugal
F 263	Shamser	FFG	Pakistan	M 331	Tista	MSC	Norway
264	Contre Admiral Eustatiu Sebastian	FF	Romania	332	Ville de Québec	FFG	Canada
265	Annapolis	FF	Canada	332	W Zakarias Yohannes	FFG	Indonesia
265	Heweliusz	AGOR	Poland	F 332	Corte Real	FFG	Portugal
265	Improved Tetal class	FF	Romania	M 332	Kvina	MSC	Norway
P 265	Dumbarton Castle	PV	UK	333	Toronto	FFG	Canada
266	Nipigon	FF	Canada	333	Hasanuddin	FFG	Indonesia
266	Arctowski	AGOR	Poland	334	Regina	FFG	Canada
A 269	Grey Rover	AOF(S)	UK	M 334	Utla	MSC	Norway
271	Warszawa	DDG	Poland	335	Calgary	FFG	Canada
271	Vice Admiral Ioan Murgescu	ML/AR	Romania	336	Montreal	FFG	Canada
A 271	Gold Rover	AOF (S)	UK	337	Fredericton	FFG	Canada
A 273	Black Rover	AOF (S)	UK	338	Winnipeg	FFG	Canada
274	Vice Admiral Constantin Balescu	ML/AR	Romania	339	Charlottetown	FFG	Canada
P 277	Anglesey	PV	UK	P 339	Bora	PV	Turkey
P 278	Alderney	PV	UK	340	St John's	FFG	Canada
280	Iroquois	DDG	Canada	F 340	Beskytteren	FF	Denmark
281	Huron	DDG	Canada	M 340	Oksøy	MH	Norway
281	Piast	ARS	Poland	P 340	Dogan	PV	Turkey
281	Constanta	AFS	Romania	341	Ottawa	FFG	Canada
282	Athabaskan	DDG	Canada	341	Samadikun	FF	Indonesia
282	Lech	ARS	Poland	M 341	Karmøy	MH	Norway
283	Algonquin	DDG	Canada	P 341	Marti	PV	Turkey
283	Midia	AFS	Romania	342	Martadinata	FF	Indonesia
A 285	Auricula	AG	UK	M 342	Maløy	MH	Norway
P 297	Guernsey	PV	UK	P 342	Tayfun	PV	Turkey
P 298	Shetland	PV	UK	343	Monginsidi	FF	Indonesia
P 299	Orkney	PV	UK	M 343	Hinnøy	MH	Norway
P 300	Lindisfarne	PV	UK	P 343	Volkan	PV	Turkey
Y 300	Barsø	PV	Denmark	Y 343	Lunden	PV	Denmark
301	Shahrokh	MSC	Iran	344	Ngurah Rai	FF	Indonesia
A 301	Drakensberg	AOR	South Africa	P 344	Rüzgar	PV	Turkey
F 301	Bergen	FFG	Norway	D 345	Yücetepe	DDG	Turkey
MSO 301	Yaeyama	MSO/MH	Japan	P 345	Poyraz	PV	Turkey
P 301	Bizerte	PV	Tunisia	D 346	Alcitepe	DD	Turkey
Y 301	Drejø	PV	Denmark	P 346	Gurbet	PV	Turkey
302	Atiya	AOS	Bulgaria	D 347	Anittepe	DD	Turkey
302	Simorgh	MSC	Iran	P 347	Firtina	PV	Turkey
A 302	Outeniqua	AEFS	South Africa	D 348	Savaştepe	DDG	Turkey
F 302	Trondheim	FFG	Norway	P 348	Yildiz	PV	Turkey
J 302	Chongmingdao	AS	China	D 349	Kiliç Ali Paşa	DDG	Turkey
MSO 302	Tsushima	MSO/MH	Japan	P 349	Karayel	PV	Turkey
P 302	Horria	PV	Tunisia	350	Koni class	FFG	Cuba
Y 302	Romsø	PV	Denmark	D 350	Piyale Paşa	DDG	Turkey
303	Karkas	MSC	Iran	351	Djebel Chinoise	FFL	Algeria
F 303	Stavanger	FFG	Norway	351	Ahmed Yani	FFG	Indonesia
MSO 303	Hachijyo	MSO/MH	Japan	D 351	M Fevzi Çakmak	DDG	Turkey
Y 303	Samsø	PV	Denmark	352	Djebel Chinoise class	FFL	Algeria
304	El Khattabi	PV	Morocco	352	Slamet Riyadi	FFG	Indonesia
F 304	Narvik	FFG	Norway	D 352	Gayret	DDG	Turkey
OR 304	Success	AOR	Australia	353	Djebel Chinoise class	FFL	Algeria
P 304	Monastir	PV	Tunisia	353	Yos Sudarso	FFG	Indonesia
Y 304	Thurø	PV	Denmark	354	Oswald Siahann	FFG	Indonesia
305	Commandant Boutouba	PV	Morocco	F 354	Niels Juel	FFG	Denmark
Y 305	Vejrø	PV	Denmark	355	Abdul Halim Perdana Kusuma	FFG	Indonesia
306	Commandant El Harty	PV	Morocco	F 355	Olfert Fischer	FFG	Denmark
Y 306	Farø	PV	Denmark	356	Koni class	FFG	Cuba
307	Commandant Azougghar	PV	Morocco	356	Karel Satsuitubun	FFG	Indonesia
Y 307	Laesø	PV	Denmark	F 356	Peter Tordenskiold	FFG	Denmark
308	El Hahiq	PV	Morocco	357	Thetis	FF	Denmark
Y 308	Rømø	PV	Denmark	D 358	Berk	FF	Turkey
309	El Tawfiq	PV	Morocco	F 358	Triton	FF	Denmark
310	L V Rabhi	PV	Morocco	D 359	Peyk	FF	Turkey
311	Mivtach	PV	Israel	F 359	Vaedderen	FF	Denmark
311	Errachio	PV	Morocco	D 360	Gelibolu	FF	Turkey
312	Miznag	PV	Israel	F 360	Hvidbjørnen	FF	Denmark
				361	Fatahillah	FFG	Indonesia

PENNANT LIST

Number	Ship's name	Type	Country
D 361	Gemlik	FF	Turkey
362	Malahayati	FFG	Indonesia
363	Nala	FFG	Indonesia
364	Ki Hajar Dewantara	FFG	Indonesia
A 367	Newton	AG	UK
371	Kapitan Patimura	FFL	Indonesia
M 371	Ohue	MH/MSC	Nigeria
372	Untung Suropati	FFL	Indonesia
M 372	Marabai	MH/MSC	Nigeria
373	Nuku	FFL	Indonesia
A 373	Hermis	AGS	Greece
374	Lambung Mangkurat	FFL	Indonesia
375	Cut Nyak Dien	FFL	Indonesia
376	Sultan Thaha	FFL	Indonesia
377	Sutanto	FFL	Indonesia
A 377	Arethousa	AOS	Greece
378	Sutedi Senoputra	FFL	Indonesia
A 378	Kinterbury	AG	UK
379	Wiratno	FFL	Indonesia
380	Memet Sastrawiria	FFL	Indonesia
381	Tjiptadi	FFL	Indonesia
382	Hasan Basri	FFL	Indonesia
A 382	Arrochar	AG	UK
383	Koni class	FFG	Cuba
383	Iman Bonjol	FFL	Indonesia
384	Pati Unus	FFL	Indonesia
385	Teuku Umar	FFL	Indonesia
A 385	Fort Grange	AEFS	UK
386	Cut Meutia	FFL	Indonesia
A 386	Fort Austin	AEFS	UK
Y 386	Agdlek	PV	Denmark
A 387	Fort Victoria	AOR	UK
Y 387	Agpa	PV	Denmark
A 388	Fort George	AOR	UK
Y 388	Tulugaq	PV	Denmark
401	Admiral Branimir Ormanov	AGS	Bulgaria
L 401	Ertuğrul	LST	Turkey
P 401	Cassiopea	PV	Italy
402	Daoud Ben Aicha	LSL	Morocco
ASR 402	Fushimi	ARS	Japan
L 402	Serdar	LST	Turkey
P 402	Libra	PV	Italy
403	Ahmed Es Sakali	LSL	Morocco
P 403	Spica	PV	Italy
404	Abou Abdallah El Ayachi	LSL	Morocco
P 404	Vega	PV	Italy
405	Ad Dakhla	AFS	Morocco
AS 405	Chiyoda	AS	Japan
406	El Aigh	AFS	Morocco
407	Arrafiq	AP	Morocco
411	Kangan	AOS	Iran
412	Taheri	AOS	Iran
412	Assad Al Bihar	FFLG	Libya
MSC 412	Addriyah	MH/MSC	Saudi Arabia
413	Assad El Tougour	FFLG	Libya
414	Assad Al Khali	FFLG	Libya
A 414	Ariadni	AOS	Greece
MSC 414	Al Quysumah	MH/MSC	Saudi Arabia
415	Assad Al Hudud	FFLG	Libya
A 415	Evros	AG	Greece
416	Tariq Ibn Ziyad	FFLG	Libya
MSC 416	Al Wadeeah	MH/MSC	Saudi Arabia
417	Ean Al Gazala	FFLG	Libya
418	Ean Zara	FFLG	Libya
MSC 418	Safwa	MH/MSC	Saudi Arabia
420	Al Jawf	MSC	Saudi Arabia
421	N I Vaptsarov	FFL	Bulgaria
421	Bandar Abbas	AFS	Iran
421	Orkan	FFLG	Poland
AOE 421	Sagami	AOE	Japan
F 421	Canterbury	FFG	New Zealand
422	Boushehr	AFS	Iran
422	Piorun	FFLG	Poland
422	Shaqra	MSC	Saudi Arabia
AOE 422	Towada	AOE	Japan
423	Huragan	FFLG	Poland
423	Yung Chou	MSC	Taiwan
AOE 423	Tokiwa	AOE	Japan
424	Al Kharj	MSC	Saudi Arabia
AOE 424	Hamana	AOE	Japan
426	Al Zahraa	AP	Iraq
428	Khawla	AP	Iraq
429	Balqees	AP	Iraq
431	Kharg	AFS	Iran
434	Gornik	FFLG	Poland
435	Hutnik	FFLG	Poland
436	Metalowiec	FFLG	Poland
437	Rolnik	FFLG	Poland
441	Chah Bahar	AR	Iran
441	Yung Cheng	MSC	Taiwan
MSO 441	Exultant	MSO	USA
449	Yung An	MSC	Taiwan
F 450	Elli	FFG	Greece
F 451	Mella	FF	Dominican Republic
F 451	Limnos	FFG	Greece
F 452	Hydra	FFG	Greece
F 453	Spetsai	FFG	Greece
BM 454	Prestol	FFL	Dominican Republic
F 454	Psara	FFG	Greece
455	Chao Phraya	FFG	Thailand
BM 455	Tortuguero	FFL	Dominican Republic
F 455	Salamis	FFG	Greece
MSO 455	Implicit	MSO	USA
456	Bangpakong	FFG	Thailand
F 456	Epirus	FFG	Greece
457	Kraburi	FFG	Thailand
F 457	Thrace	FFG	Greece
458	Saiburi	FFG	Thailand
F 458	Makedonia	FFG	Greece
F 459	Adrias	FFG	Greece
F 460	Aegeon	FFG	Greece
461	Phutthayotfa Chulalok	FFG	Thailand
F 461	Navarino	FFG	Greece
462	Yung Sui	MSC	Taiwan
462	Phutthaloetla Naphalai	FFG	Thailand
MST 462	Hayase	AG	Japan
A 464	Axios	AFS	Greece
469	Yung Lo	MSC	Taiwan
F 471	Antonio Enes	FF	Portugal
472	Kalaat Beni Hammad	LSL	Algeria
473	Kalaat Beni Rached	LSL	Algeria
475	Pyhäranta	ML	Finland
F 475	João Coutinho	FF	Portugal
476	Yung Shan	MSC	Taiwan
F 476	Jacinto Candido	FF	Portugal
F 477	General Pereira d'Eça	FF	Portugal
A 478	Naftilos	AGS	Greece
479	Yung Nien	MSC	Taiwan
A 480	Resource	AEFS	UK
F 480	Comandante João Belo	FF	Portugal
F 481	Comandante Hermenegildo Capelo	FF	Portugal
ARC 482	Muroto	AG	Japan
F 482	Comandante Roberto Ivens	FF	Portugal
F 483	Comandante Sacadura Cabral	FF	Portugal
F 484	Augusto de Castilho	FF	Portugal
485	Yung Jen	MSC	Taiwan
F 485	Honorio Barreto	FF	Portugal
F 486	Baptista de Andrade	FF	Portugal
F 487	João Roby	FF	Portugal
488	Yung Hsin	MSC	Taiwan
F 488	Afonso Cerqueira	FF	Portugal
MSO 488	Conquest	MSO	USA
F 489	Oliveira E Carmo	FF	Portugal
P 495	Bambù	PV	Italy
P 496	Mango	PV	Italy
P 497	Mogano	PV	Italy
498	Lana	AGS	Nigeria
P 500	Palma	PV	Italy
501	Nawarat	FFL	Burma
501	Gharbiya	MSO	Egypt
501	Teluk Langsa	LST	Indonesia
501	Eilat	FFLG	Israel
501	Lieutenant Colonel Errhamani	FFG	Morocco
LT 501	Laguna	LST	Philippines
502	Nagakyay	FFL	Burma
502	Nanchong	FF	China
502	Teluk Bajur	LST	Indonesia
502	Lahav	FFLG	Israel
AOTL 502	Dundurn	AOF(S)	Canada
HQ 502	Qui Nonh	LST	Vietnam
503	Teluk Amboina	LST	Indonesia
503	Hanit	FFLG	Israel
HQ 503	Vung Tau	LST	Vietnam
504	Dongchuan	FF	China
504	Sharkia	MSO	Egypt
504	Teluk Kau	LST	Indonesia
504	Hittin	MSO	Syria
LT 504	Lanao del Norte	LST	Philippines
HQ 505	Da Nang	LST	Vietnam
506	Chengdu	FFG	China
J 506	Yongxingdao	AS	China
507	Pingxiang	FFG	China
507	Daqahliya	MSO	Egypt
507	Ibn Marjid	FF	Iraq
507	Hsin Lung	AOS	Taiwan

Number	Ship's name	Type	Country	Number	Ship's name	Type	Country
LT 507	Benguet	LST	Philippines	535	Teluk Peleng	LSL	Indonesia
M 507	Seymen	MSC	Turkey	536	Wu Hu	FFG	China
508	Teluk Tomini	LST	Indonesia	536	Qena	MSO	Egypt
AOR 508	Provider	AOR	Canada	536	Teluk Sibolga	LSL	Indonesia
M 508	Selçuk	MSC	Turkey	537	Zhoushan	FFG	China
509	Chang De	FFG	China	537	Teluk Manado	LSL	Indonesia
509	Teluk Ratai	LST	Indonesia	538	Teluk Hading	LSL:	Indonesia
AOR 509	Protecteur	AOR	Canada	539	Anqing	FFG	China
M 509	Seyhan	MSC	Turkey	539	Sohag	MSO	Egypt
510	Bahariya	MSO	Egypt	539	Teluk Parigi	LSL	Indonesia
510	Shaoxing	FFG	China	540	Huainan	FFG	China
510	Teluk Saleh	LST	Indonesia	540	Teluk Lampung	LSL	Indonesia
AOR 510	Preserver	AOR	Canada	A 540	Dannebrog	AG	Denmark
M 510	Samsun	MSC	Turkey	P 540	Bille	PV	Denmark
511	Nantong	FFG	China	541	Huaibei	FFG	China
511	Teluk Bone	LST	Indonesia	541	Teluk Jakarta	LSL	Indonesia
511	Hengam	LSL	Iran	P 541	Bredal	PV	Denmark
A 511	Shaheed Ruhul Amin	ATS	Bangladesh	542	Tongling	FFG	China
A 511	Elbe	AG	Germany	542	Teluk Sangkulirang	LSL	Indonesia
M 511	Sinop	MSC	Turkey	P 542	Hammer	PV	Denmark
512	Wuxi	FFG	China	543	Dandong	FFG	China
512	Teluk Semangka	LST	Indonesia	P 543	Huitfeld	PV	Denmark
512	Larak	LSL	Iran	544	Siping	FFG	China
A 512	Mosel	AG	Germany	P 544	Krieger	PV	Denmark
AOG 512	Wan Shou	AOS	Taiwan	545	Linfen	FFG	China
M 512	Surmene	MSC	Turkey	P 545	Norby	PV	Denmark
513	Huayin	FFG	China	P 546	Rodsteen	PV	Denmark
513	Sinai	MSO	Egypt	P 547	Sehested	PV	Denmark
513	Teluk Penju	LST	Indonesia	P 548	Suenson	PV	Denmark
513	Tonb	LSL	Iran	P 549	Willemoes	PV	Denmark
A 513	Shahjalal	PV	Bangladesh	C 550	Vittorio Veneto	CGH	Italy
A 513	Rhein	AG	Germany	D 550	Ardito	DDG	Italy
M 513	Seddülbahir	MSC	Turkey	F 550	Salvatore Todaro	FFL	Italy
514	Zhenjiang	FFG	China	LC 550	Bacolod City	LSL	Philippines
514	Lavan	LSL	Iran	P 550	Flyvefisken	PV/MH/ML	Denmark
514	Teluk Mandar	LST	Indonesia	551	Maoming	FFG	China
A 514	Werra	AG	Germany	C 551	Giuseppe Garibaldi	CVL	Italy
M 514	Silifke	MSC	Turkey	D 551	Audace	DDG	Italy
515	Xiamen	FFG	China	F 551	Minerva	FFLG	Italy
515	Teluk Sampit	LST	Indonesia	LC 551	Cagayan de Oro City	LSL	Philippines
515	Lung Chuan	AOS	Taiwan	MSC 551	Kum San	MSC	Korea, Republic
A 515	Khan Jahan Ali	AOS	Bangladesh	P 551	Hajen	PV	Denmark
A 515	Main	AG	Germany	552	Yibin	FFG	China
M 515	Saros	MSC	Turkey	F 552	Urania	FFLG	Italy
516	Jiujiang	FFG	China	MSC 552	Ko Hung	MSC	Korea, Republic
516	Assiout	MSO	Egypt	P 552	Havkatten	PV	Denmark
516	Teluk Banten	LST	Indonesia	553	Shaoguan	FFG	China
A 516	Donau	AG	Germany	F 553	Danaide	FFLG	Italy
LT 516	Kalinga Apayao	LST	Philippines	MSC 553	Kum Kok	MSC	Korea, Republic
M 516	Sigacik	MSC	Turkey	P 553	Laxen	PV	Denmark
517	Nanping	FFG	China	554	Anshun	FFG	China
517	Teluk Ende	LST	Indonesia	F 554	Sfinge	FFLG	Italy
M 517	Sapanca	MSC	Turkey	P 554	Makrelen	PV	Denmark
518	Jian	FFG	China	555	Zhaotong	FFG	China
518	Yun Tai	AP	Taiwan	F 555	Driade	FFLG	Italy
M 518	Sariyer	MSC	Turkey	MSC 555	Nam Yang	MSC	Korea, Republic
519	Changzhi	FFG	China	P 555	Støren	PV	Denmark
A 520	Sagres	ATS	Portugal	F 556	Chimera	FFLG	Italy
M 520	Karamürsel	MSC	Turkey	MSC 556	Ha Dong	MSC	Korea, Republic
521	Yu Tai	AR	Taiwan	P 556	Svaerdfisken	PV	Denmark
M 521	Kerempe	MSC	Turkey	557	Jishou	FFG	China
522	Tai Hu	AP	Taiwan	F 557	Fenice	FFLG	Italy
M 522	T 43 class	MSO	Algeria	MSC 557	Sam Kok	MSC	Korea, Republic
M 522	Kilimli	MSC	Turkey	P 557	Glenten	PV	Denmark
523	Yuen Feng	AP	Taiwan	558	Zigong	FFG	China
M 523	Kozlu	MSC	Turkey	F 558	Sibilla	FFLG	Italy
524	Ta Hu	AP	Taiwan	MSC 558	Yong Dong	MSC	Korea, Republic
M 524	Kuşadasi	MSC	Turkey	P 558	Gribben	PV	Denmark
525	Wu Kang	AP	Taiwan	559	Kangding	FFG	China
M 525	Kemer	MSC	Turkey	MSC 559	Ok Cheon	MSC	Korea, Republic
A 527	Almeida Carvalho	AGS	Portugal	P 559	Lommen	PV	Denmark
530	Giza	MSO	Egypt	560	Dongguan	FFG	China
530	Wu Yi	AFS	Taiwan	560	Sonya class	MSC/MH	Cuba
A 530	Horten	AG	Norway	D 560	Luigi Durand de La Penne	DDG	Italy
P 530	Trabzon	MSC/PV	Turkey	P 560	Ravnen	PV	Denmark
531	Yingtan	FFG	China	561	Shantou	FFG	China
531	Teluk Gilimanuk	LSL	Indonesia	561	Sonya class	MSC/MH	Cuba
P 531	Terme	MSC/PV	Turkey	561	Multatuli	AS	Indonesia
532	Teluk Celukan Bawang	LSL	Indonesia	561	Kang Kyeong	MH	Korea, Republic
532	Sonya class	MSO	Syria	D 561	Francesco Mimbelli	DDG	Italy
P 532	Tirebolu	MSC/PV	Turkey	P 561	Skaden	PV	Denmark
533	Ningpo	FFG	China	562	Kang Jin	MH	Korea, Republic
533	Aswan	MSO	Egypt	P 562	Viben	PV	Denmark
533	Teluk Cendrawasih	LSL	Indonesia	563	Ko Ryeong	MH	Korea, Republic
N 533	Norge	AG	Norway	P 563	Søløven	PV	Denmark
534	Jinhua	FFG	China	F 564	Lupo	FFG	Italy
534	Teluk Berau	LSL	Indonesia	565	Kim Po	MH	Korea, Republic
535	Huangshi	FFG	China	F 565	Sagittario	FFG	Italy

Number	Ship's name	Type	Country	Number	Ship's name	Type	Country
566	Ko Chang	MH	Korea, Republic	635	Mielno	MSC	Poland
F 566	Perseo	FFG	Italy	636	Wicko	MSC	Poland
567	Kum Wha	MH	Korea, Republic	637	Resko	MSC	Poland
F 567	Orsa	FFG	Italy	638	Sarbsko	MSC	Poland
A 568	Rimfaxe	AOS	Denmark	639	Necko	MSC	Poland
A 569	Skinfaxe	AOS	Denmark	640	Naklo	MSC	Poland
570	Sonya class	MSC/MH	Cuba	D 640	Georges Leygues	DDG	France
A 570	Taşkizak	AOS	Turkey	641	Druzno	MSC	Poland
F 570	Maestrale	FFG	Italy	D 641	Dupleix	DDG	France
A 571	Yüzbaşi Tolunay	AOS	Turkey	M 641	Éridan	MH	France
F 571	Grecale	FFG	Italy	642	Hancza	MSC	Poland
A 572	Albay Hakki Burak	AOS	Turkey	642	Natya class	PV	Syria
F 572	Libeccio	FFG	Italy	D 642	Montcalm	DDG	France
A 573	Binbaşi Saadettin Gürçan	AOS	Turkey	M 642	Cassiopée	MH	France
F 573	Scirocco	FFG	Italy	643	Mamry	MH	Poland
F 574	Aliseo	FFG	Italy	D 643	Jean de Vienne	DDG	France
M 574	Grønsund	MSC	Denmark	M 643	Andromède	MH	France
A 575	Inebolu	AOS	Turkey	644	Wigry	MH	Poland
F 575	Euro	FFG	Italy	A 644	Berry	AGOR	France
X 575	Taicang	AOR	China	D 644	Primauguet	DDG	France
F 576	Espero	FFG	Italy	M 644	Pégase	MH	France
A 577	Sokullu Mehmet Paşa	ATS	Turkey	645	Sniardwy	MH	Poland
F 577	Zeffiro	FFG	Italy	D 645	La Motte-Picquet	DDG	France
578	Sonya class	MSC/MH	Cuba	M 645	Orion	MH	France
M 578	Vilsund	MSC	Denmark	D 646	Latouche-Tréville	DDG	France
A 579	Cezayirli Gazi Hasan Pasa	ATS	Turkey	M 646	Croix du Sud	MH	France
A 580	Akar	AOR	Turkey	M 647	Aigle	MH	France
F 580	Alpino	FF	Italy	MSC 647	Hashira	MH/MSC	Japan
F 581	Carabiniere	FFG	Italy	M 648	Lyre	MH	France
F 582	Artigliere	FFG	Italy	MSC 648	Iwai	MH/MSC	Japan
F 583	Aviere	FFG	Italy	M 649	Persée	MH	France
A 584	Kurtaran	ARS	Turkey	MSC 649	Hatsushima	MH/MSC	Japan
F 584	Bersagliere	FFG	Italy	650	Sagittaire	MH	France
A 585	Akin	ARS	Turkey	MSC 650	Ninoshima	MH/MSC	Japan
F 585	Granatiere	FFG	Italy	651	Singa	PV	Indonesia
A 586	Ülkü	AS	Turkey	MSC 651	Miyajima	MH/MSC	Japan
A 588	Umur Bey	AS	Turkey	MSC 652	Enoshima	MH/MSC	Japan
A 589	Işin	ARS	Turkey	653	Ajak	PV	Indonesia
A 590	Yunus	AGS	Turkey	MSC 653	Ukishima	MH/MSC	Japan
A 601	Monge	AGOR	France	MSC 654	Ooshima	MH/MSC	Japan
A 601	Tekirdağ	MSC/AG	Turkey	MSC 655	Niijima	MH/MSC	Japan
P 601	Jayesagara	PV	Sri Lanka	MSC 656	Yakushima	MH/MSC	Japan
D 602	Suffren	DDG	France	MSC 657	Narushima	MH/MSC	Japan
P 602	Sagarawardene	PV	Sri Lanka	MSC 658	Chichijima	MH/MSC	Japan
D 603	Duquesne	DDG	France	MSC 659	Torishima	MH/MSC	Japan
A 607	Meuse	AOR	France	MSC 660	Hahajima	MH/MSC	Japan
A 608	Var	AOR	France	MSC 661	Takashima	MH/MSC	Japan
D 609	Aconit	DDG	France	MSC 662	Nuwajima	MH/MSC	Japan
A 610	Ile d'Oléron	AG	France	MSC 663	Etajima	MH/MSC	Japan
D 610	Tourville	DDG	France	MSC 664	Kamishima	MH/MSC	Japan
M 610	Ouistreham	MSO	France	MSC 665	Himeshima	MH/MSC	Japan
D 611	Duguay-Trouin	DDG	France	MSC 666	Ogishima	MH/MSC	Japan
612	Badr	FFLG	Saudi Arabia	MSC 667	Moroshima	MH/MSC	Japan
D 612	De Grasse	DDG	France	MSC 668	Yurishima	MH/MSC	Japan
614	Al Yarmook	FFLG	Saudi Arabia	MSC 669	Hikoshima	MH/MSC	Japan
D 614	Cassard	DDG	France	MSC 670	Awashima	MH/MSC	Japan
A 615	Loire	AG	France	LST 671	Un Bong	LST	Korea, Republic
D 615	Jean Bart	DDG	France	MSC 671	Sakushima	MH/MSC	Japan
X 615	Dongyun	AOR	China	MSC 672	Uwajima	MH/MSC	Japan
616	Hitteen	FFLG	Saudi Arabia	LST 673	Bi Bong	LST	Korea, Republic
616	Kormoran	MSO	Poland	MSC 673	Ieshima	MH/MSC	Japan
A 617	Garonne	AG	France	MSC 674	Tsukishima	MH/MSC	Japan
AP 617	Yakal	AR	Philippines	MSC 675	Maejima	MH/MSO	Japan
618	Albatros	MSO	Poland	LST 675	Kae Bong	LST	Korea, Republic
618	Tabuk	FFLG	Saudi Arabia	LST 676	Wee Bong	LST	Korea, Republic
A 618	Rance	AG	France	MSC 676	Kumejima	MH/MSC	Japan
620	Tukan	MSO	Poland	LST 677	Su Yong	LST	Korea, Republic
A 620	Jules Verne	AR	France	LST 678	Buk Han	LST	Korea, Republic
621	Mandau	PV	Indonesia	LST 679	Hwa San	LST	Korea, Republic
621	Flamingo	MSO	Poland	P 679	Grèbe	PV	France
621	Naresuan	FFG	Thailand	P 680	Sterne	PV	France
A 621	Rhin	AG	France	P 681	Albatros	PV	France
622	Rencong	PV	Indonesia	P 682	L'Audacieuse	PV	France
622	Rybitwa	MSO	Poland	P 683	La Boudeuse	PV	France
622	Taksin	FFG	Thailand	P 684	La Capricieuse	PV	France
A 622	Rhône	AG	France	P 685	La Fougueuse	PV	France
623	Badik	PV	Indonesia	P 686	La Glorieuse	PV	France
623	Mewa	MSO	Poland	P 687	La Gracieuse	PV	France
624	Keris	PV	Indonesia	P 688	La Moqueuse	PV	France
624	Czajka	MSO	Poland	P 689	La Railleuse	PV	France
A 629	Durance	AOR	France	P 690	La Rieuse	PV	France
630	Goplo	MSC	Poland	P 691	La Tapageuse	PV	France
A 630	Marne	AOR	France	701	Pulau Rani	PV/MSO	Indonesia
631	Gardno	MSC	Poland	702	Pulau Ratewo	PV/MSO	Indonesia
A 631	Somme	AOR	France	702	Madina	FFG	Saudi Arabia
632	Bukowo	MSC	Poland	704	Hofouf	FFG	Saudi Arabia
633	Dabie	MSC	Poland	706	Abha	FFG	Saudi Arabia
634	Jamno	MSC	Poland	708	Taif	FFG	Saudi Arabia

Number	Ship's name	Type	Country	Number	Ship's name	Type	Country
F 710	La Fayette	FFLG	France	A 793	Laplace	AGS	France
711	Pulau Rengat	MH/MSC	Indonesia	F 793	Commandant Blaison	FFLG	France
711	Zeltin	AR	Libya	F 794	Enseigne de Vaisseau Jacoubet	FFLG	France
F 711	Surcouf	FFLG	France	A 795	Arago	AGS	France
712	Pulau Rupat	MH/MSC	Indonesia	F 795	Commandant Ducuing	FFLG	France
F 712	Courbet	FFLG	France	F 796	Commandant Birot	FFLG	France
M 712	Cybèle	MH	France	F 797	Commandant Bouan	FFLG	France
F 713	Jaureguiberry	FFLG	France	L 800	Rotterdam	LPD	Netherlands
M 713	Calliope	MH	France	801	Rais Hamidou	FFLG	Algeria
F 714	Guepratte	FFLG	France	801	Yukan class	AFS	China
M 714	Clio	MH	France	801	Pandrong	PV	Indonesia
P 714	Abheetha	AG	Sri Lanka	A 801	Pelikaan	AP	Netherlands
F 715	Ronarc'h	FFLG	France	F 801	Tromp	FFG	Netherlands
M 715	Circé	MH	France	802	Salah Rais	FFLG	Algeria
P 715	Edithara	AG	Sri Lanka	802	Sura	PV	Indonesia
M 716	Cérès	MH	France	803	Rais Ali	FFLG	Algeria
P 716	Wickrama	AG	Sri Lanka	F 806	De Ruyter	FFG	Netherlands
721	Pulau Rote	MSC	Indonesia	F 807	Kortenaer	FFG	Netherlands
A 721	Khadem	AG	Bangladesh	811	Kakap	PV	Indonesia
722	Pulau Raas	MSC	Indonesia	811	Grunwald	LST	Poland
722	Al Munjed	ARS	Libya	F 811	Piet Heyn	FFG	Netherlands
723	Pulau Romang	MSC	Indonesia	812	Kerapu	PV	Indonesia
724	Pulau Rimau	MSC	Indonesia	F 812	Jacob van Heemskerck	FFG	Netherlands
725	Pulau Rondo	MSC	Indonesia	813	Tongkol	PV	Indonesia
725	Sariwon class	PV	Korea, Democratic People's Republic	F 813	Witte de With	FFG	Netherlands
				814	Bervang	PV	Indonesia
726	Pulau Ruso	MSC	Indonesia	F 816	Abraham Crijnssen	FFG	Netherlands
726	Sariwon class	PV	Korea, Democratic People's Republic	821	Lublin	LST/ML	Poland
				822	Gniezno	LST/ML	Poland
F 726	Commandant Bory	FFLG	France	823	Krakow	LST/ML	Poland
727	Pulau Rangsang	MSC	Indonesia	F 823	Philips van Almonde	FFG	Netherlands
727	Sariwon class	PV	Korea, Democratic People's Republic	824	Poznan	LST/ML	Poland
				F 824	Bloys van Treslong	FFG	Netherlands
728	Pulau Raibu	MSC	Indonesia	825	Torun	LST/ML	Poland
729	Pulau Rempang	MSC	Indonesia	F 825	Jan van Brakel	FFG	Netherlands
F 729	Balny	FFLG	France	F 826	Pieter Florisz	FFG	Netherlands
F 730	Floréal	FFLG	France	827	Tai Yuan	FF	Taiwan
F 731	Prairial	FFLG	France	F 827	Karel Doorman	FFG	Netherlands
F 732	Nivose	FFLG	France	F 828	Van Speijk	FFG	Netherlands
F 733	Ventose	FFLG	France	F 829	Willem van der Zaan	FFG	Netherlands
F 734	Vendémiaire	FFLG	France	F 830	Tjerk Hiddes	FFG	Netherlands
F 735	Germinal	FFLG	France	F 831	Van Amstel	FFG	Netherlands
751	Dong Hae	FFL	Korea, Republic	832	Yu Shan	FF	Taiwan
752	Su Won	FFL	Korea, Republic	A 832	Zuiderkruis	AOE	Netherlands
753	Kang Reung	FFL	Korea, Republic	F 832	Abraham van der Hulst	FFG	Netherlands
755	An Yang	FFL	Korea, Republic	F 833	Van Nes	FFG	Netherlands
756	Po Hang	FFLG	Korea, Republic	F 834	Van Galen	FFG	Netherlands
A 756	L'Espérance	AGS	France	835	Fu Shan	FF	Taiwan
757	Kun San	FFLG	Korea, Republic	A 835	Poolster	AOE	Netherlands
A 757	D'Entrecasteaux	AGS	France	836	Lu Shan	FF	Taiwan
758	Kyong Ju	FFLG	Korea, Republic	A 836	Amsterdam	AOE	Netherlands
759	Mok Po	FFLG	Korea, Republic	837	Shou Shan	FF	Taiwan
761	Kim Chon	FFLG	Korea, Republic	841	Dadie class	AGI	China
762	Chung Ju	FFLG	Korea, Republic	843	Chung Shan	FF	Taiwan
763	Jin Ju	FFLG	Korea, Republic	M 850	Alkmaar	MH	Netherlands
765	Yo Su	FFLG	Korea, Republic	HQ 851	Yurka class	MSO	Vietnam
766	An Dong	FFLG	Korea, Republic	M 851	Delfzyl	MH	Netherlands
767	Sun Chon	FFLG	Korea, Republic	HQ 852	Yurka class	MSO	Vietnam
768	Yee Ree	FFLG	Korea, Republic	M 852	Dordrecht	MH	Netherlands
769	Won Ju	FFLG	Korea, Republic	M 853	Haarlem	MH	Netherlands
771	Je Chon	FFLG	Korea, Republic	M 854	Harlingen	MH	Netherlands
772	Chon An	FFLG	Korea, Republic	M 855	Scheveningen	MH	Netherlands
773	Song Nam	FFLG	Korea, Republic	M 856	Maasluis	MH	Netherlands
775	Bu Chon	FFLG	Korea, Republic	V 856	Xing Fengshan	AGI	China
775	Kadisia	MSC	Syria	M 857	Makkum	MH	Netherlands
776	Dae Chon	FFLG	Korea, Republic	M 858	Middelburg	MH	Netherlands
776	Yarmuk	MSC	Syria	M 859	Hellevoetsluis	MH	Netherlands
777	Porkkala	ML	Finland	M 860	Schiedam	MH	Netherlands
777	Jin Hae	FFLG	Korea, Republic	M 861	Urk	MH	Netherlands
778	Sok Cho	FFLG	Korea, Republic	M 862	Zierikzee	MH	Netherlands
779	Yong Ju	FFLG	Korea, Republic	M 863	Vlaardingen	MH	Netherlands
781	Nam Won	FFLG	Korea, Republic	M 864	Willemstad	MH	Netherlands
F 781	D'Estienne d'Orves	FFLG	France	867	Ping Jin	FFL	Taiwan
782	Kwan Myong	FFLG	Korea, Republic	876	Pansio	ML	Finland
F 782	Amyot d'Inville	FFLG	France	U 891	Dagushan	AR	China
F 783	Drogou	FFLG	France	A 900	Mercuur	AS	Netherlands
F 784	Détroyat	FFLG	France	901	Mourad Rais	FFG	Algeria
F 785	Jean Moulin	FFLG	France	902	Rais Kellich	FFG	Algeria
F 786	Quartier Maître Anquetil	FFLG	France	902	Boraida	AOR	Saudi Arabia
F 787	Commandant De Pimodan	FFLG	France	M 902	J E Van Haverbeke	MSO	Belgium
F 788	Second Maître Le Bihan	FFLG	France	903	Rais Korfou	FFG	Algeria
F 789	Lieutenant de Vaisseau Le Hénaff	FFLG	France	903	Arun	AOF(S)	Indonesia
				903	Hua Yang	DDG	Taiwan
F 790	Lieutenant de Vaisseau Lavallée	FFLG	France	M 903	A F Dufour	MSO	Belgium
A 791	Lapérouse	AGS	France	904	Yunbou	AOR	Saudi Arabia
F 791	Commandant l'Herminier	FFLG	France	M 904	De Brouwer	MSO	Belgium
A 792	Borda	AGS	France	906	Huei Yang	DDG	Taiwan
F 792	Premier Maitre L'Her	FFLG	France	A 906	Tydeman	AGS	Netherlands

PENNANT LIST

Number	Ship's name	Type	Country	Number	Ship's name	Type	Country
M 906	Breydel	MSO	Belgium	DD 971	David R Ray	DDG	USA
907	Fu Yang	DDG	Taiwan	972	Tanjung Oisina	AP	Indonesia
908	Kwei Yang	DDG	Taiwan	DD 972	Oldendorf	DDG	USA
M 908	G Truffaut	MSO	Belgium	DD 973	John Young	DDG	USA
909	Chiang Yang	DDG	Taiwan	DD 974	Comte de Grasse	DDG	USA
M 909	F Bovesse	MSO	Belgium	DD 975	O'Brien	DDG	USA
F 910	Wielingen	FFG	Belgium	976	Taruntul class	FFLG	Yemen
911	Sorong	AOR	Indonesia	DD 976	Merrill	DDG	USA
911	Dang Yang	DDG	Taiwan	DD 977	Briscoe	DDG	USA
911	Chakri Naruebet	CVH	Thailand	DD 978	Stump	DDG	USA
F 911	Westdiep	FFG	Belgium	DD 979	Conolly	DDG	USA
912	Chien Yang	DDG	Taiwan	DD 980	Moosbrugger	DDG	USA
F 912	Wandelaar	FFG	Belgium	DD 981	John Hancock	DDG	USA
F 913	Westhinder	FFG	Belgium	DD 982	Nicholson	DDG	USA
914	Lo Yang	DDG	Taiwan	DD 983	John Rodgers	DDG	USA
915	Han Yang	DDG	Taiwan	DD 984	Leftwich	DDG	USA
DD 915	Chung Buk	DDG	Korea, Republic	DD 985	Cushing	DDG	USA
M 915	Aster	MH	Belgium	DD 986	Harry W Hill	DDG	USA
DD 916	Jeon Buk	DDG	Korea, Republic	DD 987	O'Bannon	DDG	USA
M 916	Bellis	MH	Belgium	DD 988	Thorn	DDG	USA
917	Nan Yang	DDG	Taiwan	DD 989	Deyo	DDG	USA
DD 917	Dae Gu	DD	Korea, Republic	DD 990	Ingersoll	DDG	USA
M 917	Crocus	MH	Belgium	DD 991	Fife	DDG	USA
918	An Yang	DDG	Taiwan	DD 992	Fletcher	DDG	USA
919	Kun Yang	DDG/ML	Taiwan	DDG 993	Kidd	DDG	USA
DD 919	Taejon	DDG	Korea, Republic	DDG 994	Callaghan	DDG	USA
920	Dazhi	AS	China	DDG 995	Scott	DDG	USA
920	Lai Yang	DDG	Taiwan	DDG 996	Chandler	DDG	USA
921	El Fateh	DD	Egypt	DD 997	Hayler	DDG	USA
921	Jaya Wijaya	AR	Indonesia	M 1060	Weiden	MH	Germany
921	Liao Yang	DDG	Taiwan	M 1061	Rottweil	MH	Germany
DD 921	Kwang Ju	DDG	Korea, Republic	M 1062	Sulzbach-Rosenberg	MH	Germany
M 921	Lobelia	MH	Belgium	M 1063	Bad Bevensen	MH	Germany
DD 922	Kang Won	DDG	Korea, Republic	M 1064	Grömitz	MH	Germany
M 922	Myosotis	MH	Belgium	M 1065	Dillingen	MH	Germany
923	Chen Yang	DDG	Taiwan	M 1066	Frankenthal	MH	Germany
DD 923	Kyong Ki	DDG	Korea, Republic	M 1067	Bad Rappenau	MH	Germany
M 923	Narcis	MH	Belgium	M 1068	Datteln	MH	Germany
924	Kai Yang	DDG	Taiwan	M 1069	Homburg	MH	Germany
M 924	Primula	MH	Belgium	M 1070	Göttingen	MH	Germany
925	Te Yang	DDG	Taiwan	M 1071	Koblenz	MH	Germany
DD 925	Jeon Ju	DDG	Korea, Republic	M 1072	Lindau	MH	Germany
926	Shao Yang	DDG	Taiwan	M 1073	Schleswig	MSC	Germany
927	Yukan class	LST	China	M 1074	Tübingen	MH	Germany
927	Yun Yang	DDG	Taiwan	M 1075	Wetzlar	MH	Germany
928	Yukan class	LST	China	M 1076	Paderborn	MSC	Germany
928	Cheng Yang	DDG	Taiwan	M 1077	Weilheim	MH	Germany
929	Yukan class	LST	China	M 1078	Cuxhaven	MH	Germany
929	Chao Yang	DDG	Taiwan	FF 1079	Bowen	FFG	USA
930	Lao Yang	DDG	Taiwan	M 1079	Düren	MSC	Germany
931	Tariq	FF	Egypt	M 1080	Marburg	MH	Germany
931	Burujulasad	AGOR	Indonesia	M 1081	Konstanz	MSC	Germany
932	Dewa Kembar	AGS	Indonesia	M 1082	Wolfsburg	MSC	Germany
932	Chin Yang	FFG	Taiwan	M 1083	Ulm	MSC	Germany
933	Jalanidhi	AGOR	Indonesia	FF 1084	McCandless	FFG	USA
933	Fong Yang	FFG	Taiwan	M 1085	Minden	MH	Germany
934	Feng Yang	FFG	Taiwan	M 1087	Volklingen	MH	Germany
F 941	El Suez	FFG	Egypt	FF 1090	Ainsworth	FFG	USA
F 946	Abu Qir	FFG	Egypt	M 1090	Pegnitz	MSC	Germany
951	Dayun class	AFS	China	M 1091	Kulmbach	MSC	Germany
951	Najim al Zaffer	FFG	Egypt	M 1092	Hameln	MSC	Germany
FF 951	Ulsan	FFG	Korea, Republic	M 1093	Auerbach	MSC	Germany
MMC 951	Souya	ML	Japan	M 1094	Ensdorf	MSC	Germany
952	Nan Yun	AFS	China	FF 1095	Truett	FFG	USA
FF 952	Seoul	FFG	Korea, Republic	M 1095	Überherrn	MSC	Germany
FF 953	Chung Nam	FFG	Korea, Republic	M 1096	Passau	MSC	Germany
FF 955	Masan	FFG	Korea, Republic	M 1097	Laboe	MSC	Germany
956	El Nasser	FFG	Egypt	M 1098	Siegburg	MSC	Germany
956	Teluk Mentawai	AP	Indonesia	M 1099	Herten	MSC	Germany
FF 956	Kyong Buk	FFG	Korea, Republic	1101	Cheng Kung	FFG	Taiwan
FF 957	Chon Nam	FFG	Korea, Republic	1103	Cheng Ho	FFG	Taiwan
FF 958	Che Ju	FFG	Korea, Republic	1105	Chi Kuang	FFG	Taiwan
FF 959	Busan	FFG	Korea, Republic	1106	Yueh Fei	FFG	Taiwan
960	Karimata	AP	Indonesia	1107	Tzu-I	FFG	Taiwan
A 960	Godetia	AG	Belgium	1108	Pan Chao	FFG	Taiwan
A 961	Zinnia	AG	Belgium	1109	Chang Chien	FFG	Taiwan
FF 961	Chung Ju	FFG	Korea, Republic	1110	Tien Tan	FFG	Taiwan
A 962	Belgica	AGOR	Belgium	M 1116	Wilton	ATS	UK
DD 963	Spruance	DDG	USA	LST 1184	Frederick	LST	USA
DD 964	Paul F Foster	DDG	USA	LST 1186	Cayuga	LST	USA
DD 965	Kinkaid	DDG	USA	LST 1189	San Bernardino	LST	USA
DD 966	Hewitt	DDG	USA	LST 1194	La Moure County	LST	USA
DD 967	Elliott	DDG	USA	LST 1196	Harlan County	LST	USA
DD 968	Arthur W Radford	DDG	USA	LST 1197	Barnstable County	LST	USA
DD 969	Peterson	DDG	USA	LST 1198	Bristol County	LST	USA
DD 970	Caron	DDG	USA	M 1210	Kimberley	MSC	South Africa
971	Tangung Pandan	AP	Indonesia	M 1214	Walvisbaai	MSC	South Africa
971	Tarantul class	FFLG	Yemen	M 1215	East London	MSC	South Africa

Number	Ship's name	Type	Country	Number	Ship's name	Type	Country
LST 1312	Ambe	LST	Nigeria	A 5327	Stromboli	AOR	Italy
LST 1313	Ofiom	LST	Nigeria	A 5329	Vesuvio	AOR	Italy
A 1407	Wittensee	AOS	Germany	A 5354	Piave	AG	Italy
A 1413	Freiburg	AG	Germany	A 5375	Simeto	AG	Italy
A 1414	Glücksburg	AG	Germany	A 5376	Ticino	AG	Italy
A 1416	Nienburg	AG	Germany	A 5377	Titso	AG	Italy
A 1418	Meersburg	AG	Germany	M 5504	Castagno	MH	Italy
A 1424	Walchensee	AOR	Germany	M 5505	Cedro	MH	Italy
A 1425	Ammersee	AOR	Germany	M 5509	Gelso	MH	Italy
A 1426	Tegernsee	AOR	Germany	M 5516	Platano	MH	Italy
A 1427	Westensee	AOR	Germany	M 5550	Lerici	MH/MSC	Italy
A 1435	Westerwald	AG	Germany	M 5551	Sapri	MH/MSC	Italy
A 1436	Odenwald	AG	Germany	M 5552	Milazzo	MH/MSC	Italy
A 1442	Spessart	AOR	Germany	M 5553	Vieste	MH/MSC	Italy
A 1443	Rhön	AOR	Germany	M 5554	Gaeta	MH/MSC	Italy
A 1450	Planet	AGOR	Germany	M 5555	Termoli	MH/MSC	Italy
A1456	Alliance	AGOR	NATO	M 5556	Alghero	MH/MSC	Italy
M 1498	Windhoek	MSC	South Africa	M 5557	Numana	MH/MSC	Italy
1501	Sri Banggi	LST	Malaysia	M 5558	Crotone	MH/MSC	Italy
1501	Jacmin	ARS	Korea, Republic	M 5559	Viareggio	MH/MSC	Italy
1502	Rajah Jarom	LST	Malaysia	M 5560	Chioggia	MH/MSC	Italy
1503	Sri Indera Sakti	AFS/ATS	Malaysia	M5561	Rimini	HH/MSC	Italy
1504	Mahawangsa	AFS/ATS	Malaysia	P 6111	Albatros	PV	Germany
P 1561	Jan Smuts	PV	South Africa	P 6112	Falke	PV	Germany
P 1562	P W Botha	PV	South Africa	P 6113	Geier	PV	Germany
P 1563	Frederic Creswell	PV	South Africa	P 6114	Bussard	PV	Germany
P 1564	Jim Fouché	PV	South Africa	P 6115	Sperber	PV	Germany
P 1565	Frans Erasmus	PV	South Africa	P 6116	Greif	PV	Germany
P 1566	Oswald Pirow	PV	South Africa	P 6117	Kondor	PV	Germany
P 1567	Hendrik Mentz	PV	South Africa	P 6118	Seeadler	PV	Germany
P 1568	Kobie Coetsee	PV	South Africa	P 6119	Habicht	PV	Germany
P 1569	Magnus Malan	PV	South Africa	P 6120	Kormoran	PV	Germany
F 1616	Petya II class	FF	Ethiopia	P 6121	Gepard	PV	Germany
F 1617	Petya II class	FF	Ethiopia	P 6122	Puma	PV	Germany
M 2008	Blackwater	MSC	UK	P 6123	Hermelin	PV	Germany
M 2009	Itchen	MSC	UK	P 6124	Nerz	PV	Germany
M 2011	Orwell	MSC	UK	P 6125	Zobel	PV	Germany
M 2013	Spey	MSC	UK	P 6126	Frettchen	PV	Germany
M 2014	Arun	MSC	UK	P 6127	Dachs	PV	Germany
3001	Tae Pung Yang	ARS	Korea, Republic	P 6128	Ozelot	PVB	Germany
L 3004	Sir Bedivere	LSL	UK	P 6129	Wiesel	PV	Germany
L 3005	Sir Galahad	LSL	UK	P 6130	Hyäne	PV	Germany
L 3027	Sir Geraint	LSL	UK	P 6141	Tiger	PV	Germany
L 3036	Sir Percivale	LSL	UK	P 6143	Luchs	PV	Germany
TV 3501	Katori	ATS	Japan	P 6144	Marder	PV	Germany
TV 3502	Kashima	ATS	Japan	P 6145	Leopard	PV	Germany
L 3505	Sir Tristram	LSL	UK	P 6146	Fuchs	PV	Germany
TV 3506	Yamagumo	ATS	Japan	P 6147	Jaguar	PV	Germany
TV 3507	Makigumo	ATS	Japan	P 6148	Löwe	PV	Germany
L 4001	Ardennes	LSL	UK	P 6149	Wolf	PV	Germany
L 4003	Arakan	LSL	UK	P 6150	Panther	PV	Germany
LST 4101	Atsumi	LST	Japan	P 6151	Häher	PV	Germany
LST 4102	Motobu	LST	Japan	P 6153	Pelikan	PV	Germany
LST 4103	Nemuro	LST	Japan	P 6154	Elster	PV	Germany
LST 4151	Miura	LST	Japan	P 6155	Alk	PV	Germany
LST 4152	Ojika	LST	Japan	P 6156	Dommel	PV	Germany
LST 4153	Satsuma	LST	Japan	P 6157	Weihe	PV	Germany
ATS 4201	Azuma	ATS	Japan	P 6158	Pinguin	PV	Germany
ATS 4202	Kurobe	ATS	Japan	P 6159	Reiher	PV	Germany
P 4401	Mubarraz	PV	UAE	P 6160	Kranich	PV	Germany
P 4402	Makasib	PV	UAE	P 6501	Muray Jip	FFLG	UAE
AGB 5002	Shirase	AG	Japan	P 6502	Das	FFLG	UAE
AGS 5101	Akashi	AGS	Japan	L 9011	Foudre	TCD	France
AGS 5102	Futami	AGS	Japan	L 9021	Ouragan	TCD	France
AGS 5103	Suma	AGS	Japan	L 9022	Orage	TCD	France
AGS 5104	Wakasa	AGS	Japan	L 9030	Champlain	LST	France
AOS 5201	Hibiki	AGS	Japan	L 9031	Francis Garnier	LST	France
AOS 5202	Harima	AGS	Japan	L 9032	Dumont d'Urville	LST	France
A 5210	Berrio	AOF(S)	Portugal	L 9033	Jacques Cartier	LST	France
A 5301	Pietro Cavezzale	AG	Italy	L 9034	La Grandière	LST	France
A 5303	Ammiraglio Magnaghi	AGS	Italy	L 9077	Bougainville	TCD	France
A 5309	Anteo	ARS	Italy	L 9892	San Giorgio	LPD	Italy
A 5310	Proteo	ARS	Italy	L 9893	San Marco	LPD/AG	Italy
A 5311	Palinuro	ATS	Italy	L 9894	San Giusto	LPD	Italy
A 5312	Amerigo Vespucci	ATS	Italy				

Ship Reference Section
(See also Glossary)

1. Details of major warships are grouped under six separate non-printable headings. These are:-

(a) **Number and Class Name**. Totals of vessels per class are listed as 'active + building (proposed)'.

(b) **Building Programme**. This includes builders' names and key dates. In general the 'laid down' column reflects keel laying but modern shipbuilding techniques are making it increasingly difficult to be specific about the start date of actual construction. In this edition any date after March 1994 is projected or estimated and therefore liable to change.

(c) **Hull**. This section tends to have only specification and performance parameters and contains little free text. Hull related details such as **Military lift** and **Cargo capacity** may be included when appropriate. **Displacement** and **Measurement** tonnages, **Dimensions**, **Horsepower** etc are defined in the Glossary. Throughout the life of a ship its displacement tends to creep upwards as additional equipment is added and redundant fixtures and fittings are left in place. For the same reasons, ships of the same class, active in different navies, frequently have different displacements and other dissimilar characteristics. Unless otherwise stated the lengths given are overall. Sustained maximum horsepower is given where the information is available and may not be the same for similar engines operating in different hulls under different conditions.

(d) **Weapon Systems**. This section contains operational details and some free text on weapons and sensors which are laid out in a consistent order using the same sub-headings throughout the book. The titles are:- **Missiles** (sub-divided into SLBM, SSM, SAM, A/S); **Guns** (numbers of barrels are given and the rate of fire is 'per barrel' unless stated otherwise); **Torpedoes**; **A/S mortars**; **Depth charges**; **Mines**; **Countermeasures**; **Combat data systems**; **Fire control**; **Radars**; **Sonars**. The Fire control heading is used for weapons' direction equipment. In most cases the performance specifications are those of the manufacturer and may therefore be considered to be at the top end of the spectrum of effective performance. So-called 'operational effectiveness' is difficult to define, depends upon many variables and in the context of range may be considerably less than the theoretical maximum. Numbers inserted in the text refer to similar numbers included on line drawings.

(e) **Aircraft**. Only the types and numbers are included here. Where appropriate each country has a separate section listing overall numbers and operational parameters of frontline shipborne and land-based maritime aircraft, normally included after the Frigate section. The main exception to this is that in the countries which only have Light Forces the aircraft details will be towards the end of the warship section.

(f) **General Comments**. A maximum of six sub-headings are used to sweep up the variety of additional information which is available but has no logical place in the other sections. These headings are: **Programmes**; **Modernisation**; **Structure**; **Operational**; **Sales** and **Opinion**. The last of these allows space for informed comment. Some ships remain theoretically in the order of battle in some navies even though they never go to sea and could be more accurately described as in reserve. Where this is known, comment is made under **Operational**.

2. Minor or less important ship entries follow the same format except that there is often much less detail in the first four headings and all additional remarks are put together under the single heading of **Comment**. The distinction between major and minor depends upon editorial judgement and is primarily a function of firepower. The age of the ship or class and its relative importance within the Navy concerned is also taken into account.

3. The space devoted to frontline maritime aircraft reflects the importance of air power as an addition to the naval weapon systems armoury, but the format used is necessarily brief and covers only numbers, roles and operational characteristics. Greater detail can be found in *Jane's All the World's Aircraft* and the appropriate volume of the *Jane's Weapon Systems* series.

4. Other than for coastal navies, tables are included at the front of each country section with such things as strength of the fleet, senior appointments, personnel numbers, bases etc. There is also a list of pennant numbers and a deletions column covering the previous three years. If you can't find your favourite ship, always look in the Deletions list first.

5. No addenda is included because modern typesetting technology allows changes to the main text to be made up to a few weeks before publication.

6. Shipbuilding companies and weapons manufacturers frequently change their names by merger or takeover. As far as possible the published name shows the title when the ship was completed or weapon system installed. It is therefore historically accurate.

7. Like many descriptive terms in international naval nomenclature, differences between Coast Guards, Armed Police craft, Customs and other paramilitary maritime forces are often indistinct and particular to an individual nation. Such vessels are usually included if they have a paramilitary function.

8. Where major defence industries build a speculative or demonstrator vessel, it is usually mentioned in a **Note**. Full details are only given if the ship is commissioned into the Navy.

9. When selecting photographs for inclusion, priority is given to those that have been taken most recently. A glossy picture five years old may look nice but often does not show the ship as it is now.

10. The Ship Reference section is geared to the professional user who needs to be able to make an assessment of the fighting characteristics of a Navy or class of ship without having to cross refer to other Navies and sections of the book. Much effort has also been made to prevent entries spilling across from one page to another.

11. A new innovation in 1994 is that regular updates are now sent to all who buy the book on subscription. Where appropriate new and revised entries should be pinned to the page indicated on the Information Update sheet.

ALBANIA

Headquarters' Appointments	Bases	Pennant Numbers	DELETIONS

Headquarters' Appointments

Commander of the Navy:
Commander Fitui Halil

Personnel

(a) 1994: 3000 including 350 coastal defence
(b) Ratings on three year military service

Bases

Durazzo (Durresi), Valona (Vlorë), Sazan Island
(Gulf of Vlorë), Sarande, Shingjin, Himara.

General

Operational effectiveness is very low due to a
lack of spares and the age of most of the ships.

Pennant Numbers

Pennant numbers are changed at intervals.

Mercantile Marine

Lloyd's Register of Shipping:
24 vessels of 59 060 tons gross

DELETIONS

1991   1 T 43
1993   5 Huchuan class

SUBMARINES

2 WHISKEY CLASS

Displacement, tons: 1080 surfaced; 1350 dived
Dimensions, feet (metres): 249.3 × 21.3 × 16.1 *(76 × 6.5 × 4.9)*
Main machinery: Diesel-electric; 2 Type 37-D diesels; 4000 hp(m) *(2.94 MW)*; 2 motors; 2700 hp(m) *(1.98 MW)*; 2 shafts
Speed, knots: 18 surfaced; 14 dived; 7 snorting
Range, miles: 8500 at 10 kts surfaced
Complement: 54

Torpedoes: 6—21 in *(533 mm)* tubes (4 bow, 2 stern). 12 obsolescent Soviet Type 53; dual purpose; active/passive homing up to 15 km *(8.1 nm)* at 40 kts; warhead 400 kg.
Mines: 24 instead of torpedoes.
Radars: Surface search: Snoop Plate; I band.
Sonars: Tamir; passive; high frequency.

Programmes: Two transferred from USSR in 1960 and two others acquired from the USSR in mid-1961.
Structure: Diving depth, 150 m *(500 ft)*.
Operational: A third submarine of the class is used as a harbour training boat and charging station. The fourth has been deleted. Based at Sazan and probably unfit to dive.

WHISKEY   *1989*

PATROL FORCES

Note: 12 P4 patrol craft still have limited operational status.

2 KRONSHTADT CLASS (LARGE PATROL CRAFT)

Displacement, tons: 303 standard; 335 full load
Dimensions, feet (metres): 170.9 × 21.3 × 6.9 *(52.1 × 6.5 × 2.1)*
Main machinery: 3 Kolomna Type 9-D-8 diesels; 3000 hp(m) *(2.2 MW)* sustained; 3 shafts
Speed, knots: 18. **Range, miles:** 1400 at 12 kts
Complement: 51 (4 officers)

Guns: 1—3.5 in *(85 mm)*/52; 85° elevation; 18 rounds/minute to 15.5 km *(8.5 nm)*; weight of shell 9.5 kg.
1—37 mm/63; 85° elevation; 160 rounds/minute to 4 km *(2.2 nm)*; weight of shell 0.7 kg.
6—12.7 mm (3 vertical twin) MGs.
A/S mortars: 2 RBU 1200 five-tubed rocket launchers; range 2 km; warhead 34 kg.
Depth charges: 2 projectors; 2 racks.
Mines: 2 rails; approx 8 mines.
Radars: Surface search: Ball Gun; E/F band; range 37 km *(20 nm)*.
Navigation: Neptun; I band.
IFF: High Pole.

Programmes: Four were transferred from the USSR in 1958. Albania sent two for A/S updating in 1960 and two others in 1961. Two subsequently deleted, but the two survivors were operational in 1993.

KRONSHTADT   *1989*

---

24 HUCHUAN CLASS (FAST ATTACK HYDROFOIL—TORPEDO)

Displacement, tons: 39 standard; 45 full load
Dimensions, feet (metres): 71.5 × 20.7 × 11.8 (hullborne) *(21.8 × 6.3 × 3.6)*
Main machinery: 3 Type M 50F diesels; 2200 hp(m) *(1.6 MW)* sustained; 2 shafts
Speed, knots: 50 foilborne. **Range, miles:** 500 at 30 kts
Complement: 11

Guns: 4—14.5 mm (2 twin) MGs.
Torpedoes: 2—21 in *(533 mm)* tubes. Obsolescent Soviet Type 53.
Radars: Surface search/fire control: Skin Head; I band; range 37 km *(20 nm)*.

Programmes: Built in Shanghai and transferred from China as follows; six in 1968, 15 in 1969, two in 1970, seven in 1971, two in June 1974. At least eight have been cannibalised for spares.
Structure: Have foils forward while the stern planes on the surface.
Operational: Not all are seaworthy. One escaped to Italy in May 1991 and was seized by the Italian authorities.

HUCHUAN 711   *2/1993*

HUCHUAN 712   *2/1993*

---

6 SHANGHAI II CLASS (FAST ATTACK CRAFT—GUN)

Displacement, tons: 113 standard; 131 full load
Dimensions, feet (metres): 127.3 × 17.7 × 5.6 *(38.8 × 5.4 × 1.7)*
Main machinery: 2 Type L-12V-180 diesels; 2400 hp(m) *(1.76 MW)* (forward)
2 Type 12-D-6 diesels; 1820 hp(m) *(1.34 MW)* (aft); 4 shafts
Speed, knots: 30. **Range, miles:** 700 at 16.5 kts
Complement: 34
Guns: 4 China 37 mm/63 (2 twin); 85° elevation; 180 rounds/minute to 8.5 km *(4.6 nm)*; weight of shell 1.42 kg.
4 USSR 25 mm/60 (2 twin); 85° elevation; 270 rounds/minute to 3 km *(1.6 nm)*; weight of shell 0.34 kg.
Depth charges: 2 projectors; 8 depth charges.
Mines: Rails can be fitted; probably only 10 mines.
Radars: Surface search/fire control: Skin Head; I band; range 37 km *(20 nm)*.
Sonars: Hull-mounted set probably fitted.

Comment: Four transferred from China in mid-1974 and two in 1975. Doubtful operational status.

SHANGHAI II (old number)   *1990*

3 PO 2 CLASS (COASTAL PATROL CRAFT)

Displacement, tons: 56 full load
Dimensions, feet (metres): 70.5 × 11.5 × 3.3 *(21.5 × 3.5 × 1)*
Main machinery: 1 Type 3-D-12 diesel; 300 hp(m) *(220 kW)* sustained; 1 shaft
Speed, knots: 12
Complement: 8
Guns: 2—12.7 mm MGs. At least one of the class has a twin 25 mm/60.

Comment: Three have survived from a total of 11 transferred from USSR 1957-60. Previous minesweeping gear has been removed and the craft are used for utility roles.

PO 2   *10/1990*

4 ARCOR 25 CLASS (HARBOUR PATROL CRAFT)

Displacement, tons: 2.1 full load
Dimensions, feet (metres): 25.3 × 9.8 × 2.6 *(7.7 × 3 × 0.8)*
Speed, knots: 35
Complement: 2
Guns: 1—7.62 mm MG.

Comment: Delivered in November 1990.

ARCOR 25   *1990, Arcor*

LAKE AND HARBOUR PATROL CRAFT

Comment: A number of patrol boats is stationed on the lakes bordering Greece and the former Yugoslavia.

NAVAL PATROL CRAFT   *5/1992*

MINE WARFARE FORCES

1 T 43 CLASS (MINESWEEPERS—OCEAN)

Displacement, tons: 500 standard; 580 full load
Dimensions, feet (metres): 190.2 × 27.6 × 6.9 *(58 × 8.4 × 2.1)*
Main machinery: 2 Kolomna Type 9-D-8 diesels; 2000 hp(m) *(1.47 MW)* sustained; 2 shafts
Speed, knots: 15. **Range, miles:** 3000 at 10 kts; 2000 at 14 kts
Complement: 65

Guns: 4—37 mm/63 (2 twin); 85° elevation; 160 rounds/minute to 9 km *(5 nm)*; weight of shell 0.7 kg.
    8—12.7 mm MGs.
Depth charges: 2 projectors.
Mines: 16.
Radars: Air/surface search: Ball End; E/F band.
Navigation: Neptun; I band.
Sonars: Stag Ear; hull-mounted set probably fitted.

Programmes: Two transferred from USSR in 1960. One deleted and the last survivor is probably non-operational.

T 43 (Egyptian colours)   *1988*

4 T 301 CLASS (MINESWEEPERS—INSHORE)

Displacement, tons: 146 standard; 170 full load
Dimensions, feet (metres): 124.6 × 18.7 × 5.2 *(38 × 5.7 × 1.6)*
Main machinery: 3—6-cyl diesels; 900 hp(m) *(661 kW)*; 3 shafts
Speed, knots: 14. **Range, miles:** 2200 at 9 kts
Complement: 25
Guns: 2—37 mm/63; 160 rounds/minute to 8.5 km *(5 nm)*; weight of shell 0.7 kg.
    4—14.5 mm (2 twin) MGs.
Mines: Mine rails fitted for 18.

Comment: Transferred from the USSR—two in 1957, two in 1959 and two in 1960. Two marginally operational since 1979; two in reserve; two deleted.

T 301 (old number)   *1991*

SURVEY SHIPS

Note: There are two survey vessels of 20 tons launched in 1956 and 1977 respectively. Pennant numbers in 1993 were 755 and 751.

AUXILIARIES

Note: There are reported to be twelve or so harbour and port tenders including a Duna class floating power barge, a water carrier and a barrack ship. The Atrek class submarine tender transferred from the USSR in 1961 as a depot ship was converted into a merchant ship.

2 SHALANDA I CLASS (SUPPORT SHIPS)

SERANDE   **SAZAN**

Comment: Civilian freighters transferred from USSR in early 1960s. One used as AKL and one as YF.

SHALANDA   *3/1991, Erik Laursen*

2 KHOBI CLASS (SUPPORT TANKERS)

PATOS   SEMANI

Displacement, tons: 700 light; 1500 full load
Measurement, tons: 1600 dwt
Dimensions, feet (metres): 206.6 × 33 × 14.8 *(63 × 10.1 × 4.5)*
Main machinery: 2 diesels; 1600 hp(m) *(1.18 MW)*; 2 shafts
Speed, knots: 13. **Range, miles:** 2500 at 12 kts
Complement: 35
Cargo capacity: 500 tons; oil fuel
Radars: Navigation: Neptun; I band.

Comment: Launched in 1956. Transferred from the USSR in September 1958 and February 1959.
Semani is civilian manned.

KHOBI   1989

1 TOPLIVO I CLASS (HARBOUR TANKER)

TOMB

Displacement, tons: 425 full load
Dimensions, feet (metres): 115 × 22 × 9.6 *(34.5 × 6.5 × 3)*
Main machinery: 1 diesel; 1 shaft
Speed, knots: 10. **Range, miles:** 400 at 7 kts
Complement: 16
Cargo capacity: 200 tons oil fuel

Comment: Transferred from the USSR in March 1960. Similar to Khobi class in appearance though
smaller.

TOPLIVO   4/1992, van Ginderen Collection

1 SEKSTAN CLASS (DEGAUSSING SHIP)

SHENJIN

Displacement, tons: 280 standard; 400 full load
Dimensions, feet (metres): 133.8 × 30.5 × 14.1 *(40.8 × 9.3 × 4.3)*
Main machinery: 1 diesel; 400 hp(m) *(294 kW)*; 1 shaft
Speed, knots: 11. **Range, miles:** 1000 at 11 kts
Complement: 24
Cargo capacity: 115 tons

Comment: Built in Finland in 1956. Transferred from the USSR in 1960.

SEKSTAN   1990, van Ginderen Collection

1 POLUCHAT I CLASS (TRV)

SKENDERBEU

Displacement, tons: 70 standard; 100 full load
Dimensions, feet (metres): 97.1 × 19 × 4.8 *(29.6 × 5.8 × 1.5)*
Main machinery: 2 Type M 50 diesels; 2200 hp(m) *(1.6 MW)* sustained; 2 shafts
Speed, knots: 20. **Range, miles:** 1500 at 10 kts
Complement: 15
Guns: 2—14.5 mm MGs.

Comment: Used for torpedo recovery. Transferred from USSR in 1958.

POLUCHAT   1989

1 NYRYAT 1 CLASS (DIVING TENDER)

SQIPETARI

Displacement, tons: 120 full load
Dimensions, feet (metres): 93 × 18 × 5.5 *(28.4 × 5.5 × 1.7)*
Main machinery: Diesel; 450 hp(m) *(330 kW)*; 1 shaft
Speed, knots: 12.5. **Range, miles:** 1600 at 10 kts
Complement: 15

Comment: Built about 1955 and transferred from USSR.

NYRYAT 1 (Russian colours)   4/1992, van Ginderen Collection

TUGS

Note: There are also two small harbour tugs; one is named *Bregdeti*.

2 TUGUR CLASS

MUJOULQINAKU   +1

Displacement, tons: 300 full load
Dimensions, feet (metres): 100.7 × 25.3 × 7.5 *(30.7 × 7.7 × 2.3)*
Main machinery: 2 boilers; 2 triple expansion steam reciprocating engines; 500 ihp(m) *(376 kW)*;
1 shaft
Speed, knots: 10

Comment: Built in Finland for the USSR in the 1950s.

TUGUR   7/1991, Erik Laursen

ALGERIA

Headquarters' Appointments

Commander of the Navy:
General Chabane Ghodbane
Inspector General of the Navy:
General Abdelmadjid Taright

Personnel

(a) 1994: 6800 (Navy); 500 (Coast Guard)
(b) Voluntary service

Bases

Algiers (1st Region), Mers-el-Kebir (2nd Region), Jijel (3rd Region), Annaba (CG HQ)

Mercantile Marine

Lloyd's Register of Shipping:
148 vessels of 921 258 tons gross

Strength of the Fleet

Type	Active	Building
Submarines	2	—
Frigates	3	—
Corvettes	5	1
Fast Attack Craft (Missile)	11	—
Fast Attack Craft (Gun)	12	4
Minesweepers—Ocean	1	(2)
LSLs	2	—
LCT	1	—
Survey Ships	3	—
Coast Guard	36	3

SUBMARINES

Note: The latest plan is to order two 1500 ton type when funds are available.

2 KILO CLASS (TYPE 877E)

Displacement, tons: 2325 surfaced; 3076 dived
Dimensions, feet (metres): 242.1 × 32.5 × 21.7 *(73.8 × 9.9 × 6.6)*
Main machinery: Diesel-electric; 2 diesels; 3650 hp(m) *(2.68 MW)*; 2 generators; 1 motor; 5500 hp(m) *(4.05 MW)*; 1 shaft
Speed, knots: 17 dived; 10 surfaced; 9 snorting
Range, miles: 6000 at 7 kts snorting; 400 at 3 kts dived
Complement: 52

Torpedoes: 6—21 in *(533 mm)* tubes. Combination of Russian TEST-71ME; anti-submarine active/passive homing to 15 km *(8.2 nm)* at 40 kts; warhead 205 kg and 53-65; anti-surface ship passive wake homing to 25 km *(13.5 nm)* at 50 kts; warhead 300 kg. Total of 18 weapons.
Mines: 24 in lieu of torpedoes.
Countermeasures: ESM: Brick Group; radar warning.
Radars: Surface search: Snoop Tray; I band.
Sonars: Sharks Teeth; hull-mounted; passive/active search and attack; medium frequency.
Mouse Roar; active attack; high frequency.

Programmes: New construction hulls; first one delivered from USSR in October 1987, second in January 1988 as replacements for the Romeo class. It is unlikely that more of this class will be acquired.

KILO   *6/1993*

Structure: Diving depth, 300 m *(985 ft)* maximum (240 m normal). 9700 kWh batteries.

Operational: One in refit at St Petersburg for nine months from June 1993. Reported in poor condition on arrival.

FRIGATES

Note: Planned to buy two light frigates from Bazán, Spain, derived from Descubierta class, when funds are available.

3 MOURAD RAIS (KONI) CLASS (TYPE II)

Name	No	Builders	Commissioned
MOURAD RAIS	901	Zelenodolsk Shipyard	Dec 1980
RAIS KELLICH	902	Zelenodolsk Shipyard	Apr 1982
RAIS KORFOU	903	Zelenodolsk Shipyard	Jan 1985

Displacement, tons: 1440 standard; 1900 full load
Dimensions, feet (metres): 316.3 × 41.3 × 11.5 *(96.4 × 12.6 × 3.5)*
Main machinery: CODAG; 1 SGW, Nikolayev, M8B gas-turbine (centre shaft); 18 000 hp(m) *(13.25 MW)* sustained; 2 Russki B-68 diesels; 15 820 hp(m) *(11.63 MW)* sustained; 3 shafts
Speed, knots: 27 gas; 22 diesel. **Range, miles:** 1800 at 14 kts
Complement: 130

Missiles: SAM: SA-N-4 Gecko twin launcher ❶; semi-active radar homing to 15 km *(8 nm)* at 2.5 Mach; height envelope 9-3048 m *(29.5-10 000 ft)*; warhead 50 kg; 20 missiles. Some anti-surface capability.
Guns: 4—3 in *(76 mm)*/60 (2 twin) ❷; 80° elevation; 90 rounds/minute to 15 km *(8 nm)*; weight of shell 6.8 kg.
4—30 mm/65 (2 twin) ❸; 85° elevation; 500 rounds/minute to 5 km *(2.7 nm)*; weight of shell 0.54 kg.
A/S mortars: 2—12-barrelled RBU 6000 ❹; range 6000 m; warhead 31 kg.
Depth charges: 2 racks.
Mines: Rails; capacity 22.
Countermeasures: Decoys: 2—16-barrelled chaff launchers.
ESM: Watch Dog. Cross Loop D/F.

MOURAD RAIS   *(Scale 1 : 900), Ian Sturton*

Radars: Air/surface search: Strut Curve ❺; F band; range 110 km *(60 nm)* for 2 m² target.
Navigation: Don 2; I band.
Fire Control: Hawk screech ❻; I band; range 27 km *(15 nm)* (for guns).
Drum tilt ❼; H/I band (for search and acquisition).
Pop Group ❽; F/H/I band (for missile control).
IFF: High Pole B. Two Square Head.
Sonars: Hull-mounted; active search and attack; medium frequency.

Programmes: New construction ships built in USSR with hull numbers 5, 7 and 10 in sequence. Others of the class built for Cuba, Yugoslavia, East Germany and Libya. Interest was shown in ex-GDR ships in 1991 but sale was rejected by the German Government.
Modernisation: New generators fitted 1992-94.
Structure: The deck house aft in Type II Konis houses air-conditioning machinery. No torpedo tubes.

MOURAD RAIS   *1992*

CORVETTES

3 NANUCHKA II CLASS (MISSILE CORVETTES)

RAIS HAMIDOU 801   **SALAH RAIS** 802   **RAIS ALI** 803

Displacement, tons: 850 full load
Dimensions, feet (metres): 194.5 × 38.7 × 8.5 *(59.3 × 11.8 × 2.6)*
Main machinery: 3 Type M 507 diesels; 21 600 hp(m) *(15.9 MW)* sustained; 3 shafts
Speed, knots: 36. **Range, miles:** 2500 at 12 kts; 900 at 31 kts
Complement: 70 (12 officers)

Missiles: SSM: 4 SS-N-2B; active radar or IR homing to 46 km *(25 nm)* at 0.9 Mach; warhead 513 kg. Preset altitude up to 300 m.
SAM: SA-N-4 Gecko twin launcher; semi-active radar homing to 15 km *(8 nm)* at 2.5 Mach; height envelope 9-3048 m *(29.5-10 000 ft)*; warhead 50 kg; 20 missiles. Some anti-surface capability.
Guns: 2—57 mm/80 (twin); 85° elevation; 120 rounds/minute to 6 km *(3.3 nm)*; weight of shell 2.8 kg.
Countermeasures: Decoys: 2—16-barrelled chaff launchers.
ESM: Bell Tap. Cross Loop; D/F.
Radars: Surface search: Square Tie (Radome); I band; range 73 km *(40 nm)* or limits of radar horizon.
Navigation: Don 2; I band.
Fire control: Pop Group; F/H/I band (SAN-4). Muff Cob; G/H band.
IFF: Square Head. High Pole.

Programmes: Delivered by USSR 4 July 1980, 9 February 1981, 8 May 1982 from Baltic. New construction.
Modernisation: Plans to re-engine with new diesels may start in 1994.

RAIS ALI   *1982, Ralf Bendfeldt*

2 + 1 DJEBEL CHINOISE CLASS

DJEBEL CHINOISE 351   **352**   **353**

Displacement, tons: 496 standard; 540 full load
Dimensions, feet (metres): 191.6 × 27.9 × 8.5 *(58.4 × 8.5 × 2.6)*
Main machinery: 3 MTU 20V 538 TB92 diesels; 12 800 hp(m) *(9.4 MW)*; 3 shafts
Speed, knots: 31
Complement: 52 (6 officers)

Guns: 1 OTO Melara 3 in *(76 mm)*/62 (not fitted).
2 Breda 40 mm/70 (twin); 85° elevation; 300 rounds/minute to 12.5 km *(6.8 nm)*; weight of shell 0.96 kg.
4 USSR 23 mm (2 twin).
Fire control: Optronic director for 76 mm.
Radars: Surface search: Racal Decca 1226; I band.

Programmes: Ordered July 1983. Project 802 is a class of corvette building at ECRN, Mers-el-Kebir with Bulgarian assistance. First one launched 3 February 1985 and completed trials in 1988. Second launched in early 1990. Work was suspended in 1992 due to shipyard debt problems but the third of class is expected to be laid down in 1994 when the second is completed.
Structure: Hull size suggests association with Bazán Cormoran class for Morocco. Main gun was still not fitted in *Djebel Chinoise* in late 1993.

DJEBEL CHINOISE (without 76 mm gun or optronic director)   *11/1988, French Navy*

PATROL FORCES

9 OSA II and 2 OSA I CLASSES (TYPE 205)
(FAST ATTACK CRAFT—MISSILE)

OSA II—644-652
OSA I—642-643

Displacement, tons: 171 standard; 210 full load (Osa I); 245 full load (Osa II)
Dimensions, feet (metres): 126.6 × 24.9 × 8.8 *(38.6 × 7.6 × 2.7)*
Main machinery: 3 Type M 504 diesels; 10 800 hp(m) *(7.94 MW)* sustained; 3 shafts (Osa II)
3 Type M 503A diesels; 8025 hp(m) *(5.9 MW)* sustained; 3 shafts (Osa I)
Speed, knots: 35 (Osa I); 37 (Osa II). **Range, miles:** 400 at 34 kts (Osa I); 500 at 35 kts (Osa II)
Complement: 30

Missiles: SSM: 4 SS-N-2A Styx (Osa I) or 2B (Osa II); active radar or IR homing to 46 km *(25 nm)* at 0.9 Mach; warhead 513 kg.
Guns: 4—30 mm/65 (2 twin); 85° elevation; 500 rounds/minute to 5 km *(2.7 nm)*; weight of shell 0.54 kg.
Radars: Surface search: Square Tie; I band.
Fire Control: Drum Tilt; H/I band.
IFF: Two Square Head. High Pole B.

Programmes: One Osa I was delivered by the USSR on 7 October 1967. Two others transferred later in same year. Osa II transferred 1976-77 (four), fifth in September 1978, sixth in December 1978, next pair in 1979 and one from the Black Sea on 7 December 1981. Osa I No 643 was rebuilt after an explosion in 1981.
Modernisation: Plans to re-engine were reported as starting in late 1992.

OSA 652   *1989*

12 + 4 KEBIR CLASS (FAST ATTACK CRAFT—GUN)

| EL YADEKH 341 | EL KECHEF 343 | EL RASSED 345 | 347-350 |
| EL MOURAKEB 342 | EL MOUTARID 344 | EL DJARI 346 | 360-365 |

Displacement, tons: 166 standard; 200 full load
Dimensions, feet (metres): 123 × 22.6 × 5.6 *(37.5 × 6.9 × 1.7)*
Main machinery: 2 MTU 12V 538 TB92 diesels; 5110 hp(m) *(3.8 MW)*; 2 shafts (see *Structure*)
Speed, knots: 27. **Range, miles:** 3300 at 12 kts; 2600 at 15 kts
Complement: 27 (3 officers)

Guns: 1 OTO Melara 3 in *(76 mm)*/62 compact (in first five); 85° elevation; 85 rounds/minute to 16 km *(9 nm)* anti-surface; 12 km *(6.5 nm)* anti-aircraft; weight of shell 6 kg.
4 USSR 25 mm/60 (2 twin) (remainder); 85° elevation; 270 rounds/minute to 3 km *(1.6 nm)*; weight of shell 0.34 kg.
2 USSR 14.5 mm (twin) (in first five).
Fire control: Lawrence Scott optronic director (in some).
Radars: Surface search: Racal Decca 1226; I band.

Programmes: Design and first pair ordered from Brooke Marine in June 1981. First left for Algeria without armament in September 1982, second arrived Algiers 12 June 1983. The remainder assembled or built at ECRN, Mers-el-Kebir with assistance from Vosper Thornycroft. 346 commissioned 10 November 1985. *347-349* ordered June 1986, and delivered in 1988-89; *350, 360-362* ordered in August 1989 and in service by the end of 1991. *363-365* were still under construction in 1993. *360-365* may be renumbered *354-359*.
Structure: Same hull as Barbados *Trident*. There are some variations in armament and *363-365* are reported as having lower powered engines.
Operational: Six of the class have been transferred temporarily to the Coast Guard.

EL MOURAKEB and EL YADEKH (with 76 mm gun)   *5/1990*

KEBIR 347 (with 25 mm guns)   *5/1993*

AMPHIBIOUS FORCES

2 LANDING SHIPS (LOGISTIC)

Name	No	Builders	Commissioned
KALAAT BENI HAMMAD	472	Brooke Marine, Lowestoft	Apr 1984
KALAAT BENI RACHED	473	Vosper Thornycroft Ltd	Oct 1984

Displacement, tons: 2450 full load
Dimensions, feet (metres): 305 × 50.9 × 8.1 *(93 × 15.5 × 2.5)*
Main machinery: 2 MTU 16V 1163 TB82 diesels; 8880 hp(m) *(6.5 MW)* sustained; 2 shafts
Speed, knots: 15. **Range, miles:** 3000 at 12 kts
Complement: 81
Military lift: 240 troops; 7 MBTs and 380 tons other cargo; 2 ton crane with athwartships travel

Guns: 2 Breda 40 mm/70 (twin); 85° elevation; 300 rounds/minute to 12.5 km *(6.8 nm)*; weight of shell 0.96 kg.
Countermeasures: Decoys: Wallop Barricade double layer chaff launchers.
Fire control: CSEE Naja optronic.
Radars: Navigation: Racal Decca TM 1226; I band.
Helicopters: Platform only.

Programmes: First ordered in June 1981, and launched 18 May 1983; second ordered 18 October 1982 and launched 15 May 1984. Similar hulls to Omani *Nasr El Bahr.*
Structure: These ships have a through tank deck closed by bow and stern ramps. The forward ramp is of two sections measuring length 18 m (when extended) × 5 m breadth, and the single section stern ramp measures 4.3 × 5 m with the addition of 1.1 m finger flaps. Both hatches can support a 60 ton tank, and are winch operated. In addition, side access doors are provided on each side forward. The tank deck side bulkheads extend 2.25 m above the upper deck between the forecastle and the forward end of the superstructure, and provide two hatch openings to the tank deck below.

KALAAT BENI RACHED   *7/1993, Diego Quevedo*

KALAAT BENI HAMMAD   *6/1993*

1 POLNOCHNY B CLASS (TYPE 771) (LCT)

471

Displacement, tons: 760 standard; 834 full load
Dimensions, feet (metres): 246.1 × 31.5 × 7.5 *(75 × 9.6 × 2.3)*
Main machinery: 2 Kolomna Type 40-D diesels; 4400 hp(m) *(3.2 MW)* sustained; 2 shafts
Speed, knots: 19. **Range, miles:** 1000 at 18 kts
Complement: 40
Military lift: 180 troops; 350 tons including up to 6 tanks
Guns: 2—30 mm/65 (twin); 85° elevation; 500 rounds/minute to 5 km *(2.7 nm)*; weight of shell 0.54 kg.
2—140 mm 18-tubed rocket launchers; shore bombardment; range 9 km *(5 nm)*.
Radars: Navigation: Don 2; I band.
Fire Control: Drum Tilt; H/I band.
IFF: Square Head. High Pole A.

Comment: Class built in Poland 1968-70. Transferred from USSR in August 1976.

POLNOCHNY 471   *1990, van Ginderen Collection*

MINE WARFARE FORCES

Note: Orders for two new vessels projected for the mid-1990s.

1 T 43 CLASS (MINESWEEPER—OCEAN)

M 522

Displacement, tons: 500 standard; 580 full load
Dimensions, feet (metres): 190.2 × 27.6 × 6.9 *(58 × 8.4 × 2.1)*
Main machinery: 2 Kolomna Type 9-D-8 diesels; 2000 hp(m) *(1.47 MW)* sustained; 2 shafts
Speed, knots: 15. **Range, miles:** 3000 at 10 kts
Complement: 65

Guns: 2—45 mm/85; 90° elevation; 75 rounds/minute to 9 km *(5 nm)*; weight of shell 2.2 kg.
A/S mortars: 2 projectors.
Mines: Can carry 16.
Radars: Navigation: Neptun; I band.
Sonars: Stag Ear; hull-mounted; active search; high frequency.

Programmes: Two transferred from USSR in 1968. One cannibalised for spares. Probably non-operational in 1994.

LAND-BASED MARITIME AIRCRAFT

Numbers/Type: 2 Beechcraft Super King Air 200T.
Operational speed: 282 kts *(523 km/h)*.
Service ceiling: 35 000 ft *(10 670 m)*.
Range: 2030 nm *(3756 km)*.
Role/Weapon systems: Operated by air force for close-range EEZ operations. Sensors: Weather radar only. Weapons: Unarmed.

Numbers/Type: 8 Fokker F27-400/600.
Operational speed: 250 kts *(463 km/h)*.
Service ceiling: 25 000 ft *(7620 m)*.
Range: 2700 nm *(5000 km)*.
Role/Weapon systems: Visual reconnaissance duties in support of EEZ, particularly offshore platforms. Sensors: Weather radar and visual means only. Weapons: Limited armament.

SURVEY SHIPS

EL IDRISSI A 673

Displacement, tons: 540 full load
Complement: 28 (6 officers)

Comment: Built by Matsukara, Japan and delivered 17 April 1980.

EL IDRISSI   *9/1990*

RAS TARSA   ALIDADE

Comment: Both are survey craft. *Ras Tarsa* is of 16 tons displacement, built in 1980 and has a crew of four. *Alidade* is of 20 tons, built in 1983 and has a crew of eight.

AUXILIARIES

1 POLUCHAT I CLASS (TRV)

A 641

Displacement, tons: 70 standard; 100 full load
Dimensions, feet (metres): 97.1 × 19 × 4.8 *(29.6 × 5.8 × 1.5)*
Main machinery: 2 Type M 50F diesels; 2200 hp(m) *(1.6 MW)* sustained; 2 shafts
Speed, knots: 20. **Range, miles:** 1500 at 10 kts
Complement: 15

1 NYRYAT 1 CLASS (DIVING TENDER)

YAVDEZAN VP 650

Displacement, tons: 120 full load
Dimensions, feet (metres): 93 × 18 × 5.5 *(28.4 × 5.5 × 1.7)*
Main machinery: Diesel; 450 hp(m) *(330 kW)*; 1 shaft
Speed, knots: 12.5. **Range, miles:** 1600 at 10 kts
Complement: 15

Comment: Delivered in 1965 from USSR.

1 HARBOUR TUG

KADER A 210

Displacement, tons: 265 full load
Dimensions, feet (metres): 85.3 × 21.7 × 9.2 *(26 × 6.6 × 2.8)*
Main machinery: 2 diesels; 1900 hp(m) *(1.4 MW)*; 2 shafts
Speed, knots: 11

Comment: Acquired in 1989.

KADER   *7/1989, van Ginderen Collection*

COAST GUARD

Note: Six Kebir class have been transferred temporarily from the Navy.

1 SUPPORT SHIP

GC 261

Displacement, tons: 600 full load
Dimensions, feet (metres): 193.6 × 27.6 × 6.9 *(59 × 8.4 × 2.1)*
Main machinery: 2 diesels; 2200 hp(m) *(1.6 MW)*; 2 shafts
Speed, knots: 14
Complement: 60

Comment: Delivered by transporter ship from China in April 1990. The design appears to be a derivative of the T43 minesweeper but with a stern gantry.

GC 261   *7/1991*

4 + 3 EL MOUDERRIB (CHUI-E) CLASS

EL MOUDERRIB I-VII GC 251-GC 257

Displacement, tons: 380 full load
Dimensions, feet (metres): 192.8 × 23.6 × 7.2 *(58.8 × 7.2 × 2.2)*
Main machinery: 2 PCR/Kolomna diesels; 2200 hp(m) *(1.6 MW)*; 2 shafts
Speed, knots: 24. **Range, miles:** 1400 at 15 kts
Complement: 42
Guns: 2 China 37 mm/63 (twin).

Comment: Two delivered by transporter ship from China in April 1990 and described as training vessels. Two more acquired in January 1991, and the last three are expected but delivery had not been confirmed by late 1993. Hainan class hull with modified propulsion and superstructure.

EL MOUDERRIB III   *1992*

6 MANGUSTA CLASS

OMBRINE GC 323	**REQUIN** GC 331	**MARSOUIN** GC 333
DORADE GC 324	**ESPADON** GC 332	**MURÈNE** GC 334

Displacement, tons: 91 full load
Dimensions, feet (metres): 98.4 × 19 × 7.2 *(30 × 5.8 × 2.2)*
Main machinery: 3 MTU diesels; 4000 hp(m) *(2.94 MW)*; 3 shafts
Speed, knots: 32.5. **Range, miles:** 800 at 24 kts
Complement: 14 (3 officers)
Guns: Can carry 1 Breda Bofors 40 mm/70 and 1 Oerlikon 20 mm.
Radars: Navigation: SMA 3 RM; I band; range 73 km *(40 nm)*.

Comment: First delivered early 1977 by Baglietto, Varazze, Italy. Some may have been scrapped.

10 BAGLIETTO TYPE 20 GC

GC 237   GC 321-329

Displacement, tons: 44 full load
Dimensions, feet (metres): 66.9 × 17.1 × 5.5 *(20.4 × 5.2 × 1.7)*
Main machinery: 2 CRM 18DS diesels; 2660 hp(m) *(2 MW)*; 2 shafts
Speed, knots: 36. **Range, miles:** 445 at 20 kts
Complement: 11 (3 officers)
Guns: 1 Oerlikon 20 mm.

Comment: The first pair delivered by Baglietto, Varazze in August 1976 and the remainder in pairs at two monthly intervals. Fitted with three radar sets and optical fire control. Appear to have been renumbered.

BAGLIETTO 20 GC CRAFT   *1978, Baglietto*

3 SAR CRAFT

GC 231-GC 233

Comment: 25 m SAR craft delivered by transporter ship from China which arrived in Algiers in April 1990. A fourth of class may be acquired. Unarmed.

GC 231-GC 233   *1991*

12 FISHERY PROTECTION CRAFT

JEBEL ANTAR	**JEBEL HANDA**	**+10**	GC 301-312

Displacement, tons: 18
Speed, knots: 15

Comment: Completed 1982/83 at Mers-el-Kebir.

CUSTOMS

3 P 1200 CLASS

BOUZAGZA   DJURDJURA   HODNA

Displacement, tons: 39 full load
Dimensions, feet (metres): 68.2 × 18.4 × 5.2 *(20.8 × 5.6 × 1.6)*
Main machinery: 2 MAN D2540 diesels; 1300 hp(m) *(955 kW)*; 2 shafts
Speed, knots: 33. **Range, miles:** 300 at 22 kts
Complement: 4
Guns: 2—7.62 mm MGs.

Comment: Ordered from Watercraft Ltd, Shoreham, England in late 1984. Completed 21 November 1985. GRP construction.

2 P 802 CLASS

AURES   HOGGAR

Comment: Ordered from Watercraft Ltd, Shoreham, England in late 1984. 8 m craft with two Volvo AQAD 40 inboard/outboard diesels for speed of 30+ kts. Completed 21 November 1985.

ANGOLA

Personnel

(a) 1994: 1200
(b) Voluntary service

Bases

Luanda, Lobito, Namibe. (There are other good harbours available on the 1000 mile coastline.) Naval HQ at Luanda on Ila de Luanda is fortified, as is Namibe.

Mercantile Marine

Lloyd's Register of Shipping:
   107 vessels of 88 320 tons gross

PATROL FORCES

Note: In the late 1970s and early 1980s six Osa II, four Shershen, one Zhuk and two Poluchat patrol vessels were acquired from the Soviet Union to join the four Portuguese Argos class commissioned in the mid-1960s. None of these vessels was seaworthy at the end of 1992 although most of them are still, in theory, in the Naval order of battle.

4 MANDUME (BAZÁN TYPE) CLASS (COASTAL PATROL CRAFT)

MANDUME P 101	POLAR P 102	ATLANTICO P 103	GOLFINHO P 104

Displacement, tons: 105 full load
Dimensions, feet (metres): 95.6 × 19.5 × 4.9 *(29.1 × 5.9 × 1.5)*
Main machinery: 2 Paxman Vega 16CM diesels; 3840 hp *(2.86 MW)* sustained; 2 shafts
Speed, knots: 27. **Range, miles:** 8000 at 15 kts
Complement: 11 (1 officer)
Guns: 1 Oerlikon 20 mm. 2—12.7 mm MG.
Radars: Surface search: Racal Decca; I band.

Comment: Ordered 27 March 1991. First two laid down November 1991 at Bazán Shipyard, San Fernando; launched 11 September 1992. First one handed over in January 1993, the others at three month intervals. Steel hulls, aluminium superstructure. These craft have a controlled clutch hydraulic drive system for slow speed operations.

POLAR   *3/1993, Bazán*

MINE WARFARE FORCES

2 YEVGENYA CLASS (MINEHUNTERS)

Displacement, tons: 77 standard; 90 full load
Dimensions, feet (metres): 80.4 × 18 × 4.6 *(24.5 × 5.5 × 1.4)*
Main machinery: 2 Type 3-D-12 diesels; 600 hp(m) *(440 kW)* sustained; 2 shafts
Speed, knots: 11. **Range, miles:** 300 at 10 kts
Complement: 10
Guns: 2 USSR 25 mm/80 (twin).
Radars: Navigation: Don 2; I band.
Sonars: VDS (lifted over stern on crane); minehunting; high frequency.

Comment: Both transferred from USSR in September 1987.

YEVGENYAs   *1988, P D Jones*

AMPHIBIOUS FORCES

Note: In addition to those below there are four derelict ex-Soviet T-4 class originally transferred in 1976. Also four out of nine ex-Portuguese LDM 400 class and three LDP 200 are in very poor condition.

3 POLNOCHNY B CLASS (TYPE 771) (LCT)

Displacement, tons: 760 standard; 834 full load
Dimensions, feet (metres): 246.1 × 31.5 × 7.5 *(75 × 9.6 × 2.3)*
Main machinery: 2 Kolomna Type 40-D diesels; 4400 hp(m) *(3.2 MW)* sustained; 2 shafts
Speed, knots: 19. **Range, miles:** 1000 at 18 kts
Complement: 40
Military lift: 180 troops; 350 tons including up to 6 tanks

Guns: 4—30 mm/65 (2 twin); 85° elevation; 500 rounds/minute to 5 km *(2.7 nm)*; weight of shell 0.54 kg.
   2—140 mm 18-tubed rocket launchers; shore bombardment; range 9 km *(5 nm)*.
Radars: Navigation: Don 2 or Spin Trough; I band.
Fire control: Drum Tilt; H/I band.
IFF: Square Head.

Programmes: First transferred from USSR in November 1977, the second 10 February 1979 and the third 11 December 1979.

POLNOCHNY class (Group B)

1 ALFANGE CLASS (LCT)

Name	No	Builders	Commissioned
Ex-**ALFANGE**	LDG 101	Estaleiros Navais do Mondego	11 Sep 1965

Displacement, tons: 480 full load
Dimensions, feet (metres): 185.4 × 38.7 × 4.3 *(56.5 × 11.8 × 1.3)*
Main machinery: 2 diesels; 1000 hp(m) *(735 kW)*; 2 shafts
Speed, knots: 11. **Range, miles:** 2860 at 9 kts
Complement: 20 (plus 35 troops)

Comment: Acquired from the Portuguese Navy and recommissioned 10 November 1975.

Ex-ALFANGE   *Portuguese Navy*

POLICE

Note: A total of 11 Bazán-built harbour patrol craft acquired in 1992/93. One of 16 m, ten of 11 m and two of 7.9 m.

LAND-BASED MARITIME AIRCRAFT

Numbers/Type: 2 Embraer EMB-111 Bandeirante.
Operational speed: 194 kts *(360 km/h)*.
Service ceiling: 25 500 ft *(7770 m)*.
Range: 1590 nm *(2945 km)*.
Role/Weapon systems: Armed MR and coastal patrol delivered in 1988. Sensors: APS-128 radar, limited EW. Weapons: ASV; 70 mm or 127 mm pods or rockets.

Numbers/Type: 1 Fokker F27-600.
Operational speed: 250 kts *(46.3 km/h)*.
Service ceiling: 25 000 ft *(7620 m)*.
Range: 2700 nm *(5000 km)*.
Role/Weapon systems: Visual/radar reconnaissance. Sensors: Litton 360° radar. Weapons: None.

Numbers/Type: 4 Aerospatiale SA 365F Dauphin.
Operational speed: 140 kts *(260 km/h).*
Service ceiling: 15 000 ft *(4575 m).*
Range: 410 nm *(758 km).*
Role/Weapon systems: ASV reconnaissance. Sensors: Possible radar fit.

Numbers/Type: 2 CASA C-212 Aviocar.
Operational speed: 190 kts *(353 km/h).*
Service ceiling: 24 000 ft *(7315 m).*
Range: 1650 nm *(3055 km).*
Role/Weapon systems: To be delivered in 1994.

DAUPHIN SA 365F   1988, Aerospatiale

ANGUILLA

Commissioner of Police

Elliot Mc N Richardson CPM, JP

Mercantile Marine

Lloyd's Register of Shipping:
   16 vessels of 4387 tons gross

DELETIONS

1991   *Mapleleaf,* 1 Interceptor class
1992   *Anguilletta*

PATROL FORCES

1 HALMATIC M160 CLASS (INSHORE PATROL CRAFT)

DOLPHIN

Displacement, tons: 18 light
Dimensions, feet (metres): 52.5 × 15.4 × 4.6 *(16 × 4.7 × 1.4)*
Main machinery: 2 Detroit 6V-92TA diesels; 520 hp *(390 kW)* sustained; 2 shafts
Speed, knots: 27. **Range, miles:** 500 at 17 kts
Complement: 8

Comment: Built by Halmatic and delivered 22 December 1989. Identical craft to Montserrat and Turks and Caicos Islands. GRP hulls. Rigid inflatable boat launched by gravity davit.

1 INSHORE PATROL CRAFT

LAPWING

Comment: 28 ft launch acquired in 1974 from Fairey Marine. Re-engined in 1992 with two Evinrude outboards; 450 hp *(330 kW).*

DOLPHIN   1989, Halmatic

ANTIGUA and BARBUDA

Headquarters' Appointment

Commanding Officer, Coastguard:
   Lieutenant Commander M J Wright

Base

St John's (capital).

Mercantile Marine

Lloyd's Register of Shipping:
   396 vessels of 1 063 444 tons gross

PATROL FORCES

Note: 40 ft SeaArk patrol craft are planned for 1994/95 depending upon US funding.

1 SWIFT 65 ft CLASS

Name	No	Builders	Commissioned
LIBERTA	P 01	Swiftships, Morgan City	30 Apr 1984

Displacement, tons: 31.7 full load
Dimensions, feet (metres): 65.5 × 18.4 × 5 *(20 × 5.6 × 1.5)*
Main machinery: 2 Detroit Diesel 12V-71TA diesels; 840 hp *(616 kW)* sustained; 2 shafts
Speed, knots: 22. **Range, miles:** 250 at 18 kts
Complement: 9
Guns: 1—12.7 mm MG. 2—7.62 mm MGs.
Radars: Surface search: Furuno; I band.

Comment: Ordered in November 1983. Aluminium construction.

LIBERTA   1991, Antigua Coastguard

ARGENTINA

Headquarters' Appointments

Chief of Naval General Staff:
    Admiral Emilio Molina Pico
Deputy Commander-in-Chief Navy:
    Vice Admiral Jorge Enrico
Naval Operations Commander:
    Rear Admiral Carlos Alberto Frasch

Senior Appointments

Commander Fleet:
    Rear Admiral Daniel Antonio Fusari
Naval Area South:
    Rear Admiral Carlos A Berisso
Naval Area Atlantic:
    Rear Admiral Eduardo Alfredo Rosenthal
Naval Area Fluvial:
    Captain Alfonso E Nicolas

Diplomatic Representation

Naval Attaché in Bolivia:
    Captain Carlos A Gaut
Naval Attaché in Brazil:
    Captain Ruben D Lopez
Naval Attaché in Chile:
    Captain Marcelo Llambi
Naval Attaché in France:
    Captain Luis C Testa
Naval Attaché in Germany and Holland:
    Captain Alberto V Pico
Naval Attaché in Italy:
    Captain Francisco Carbaza
Defence Attaché in London:
    Group Captain Anselmo Rojo-Arauz
Naval Attaché in Paraguay:
    Captain Marcelo R Boveda
Naval Attaché in Peru:
    Captain Carlos E Erenu
Naval Attaché in South Africa:
    Captain Juan I de Abelleyra
Naval Attaché in Spain:
    Captain Ricardo Corbeld
Naval Attaché in USA:
    Rear Admiral Joaquin E Stella
Naval Attaché in Uruguay:
    Captain Eduardo E Espina

Personnel

(a) 1994: 26 000 (3700 officers, 16 300 petty officers and
    ratings and 6000 conscripts)
    Marine Corps: 6000 officers and men
(b) Volunteers plus 12 months' national service (being phased
    out)

Organisation

Naval Area Atlantic (HQ Puerto Belgrano) covers area from River
Plate to Valdes Peninsula.
Naval Area South (HQ Ushuaia) covers coastal area from Valdes
Peninsula to Drake Passage.
Naval Area Fluvial (HQ Buenos Aires) covers coast of River Plate.
Naval Area Antarctica (HQ Buenos Aires) covers Antarctica.

Special Forces Command

Consists of frogmen who operate from submarines and other
naval units, and amphibious commanders who are trained in
parachuting and behind the lines operations. Total of about 400
officers and NCOs.

Bases

Buenos Aires (Dársena Norte): Some naval training
establishments.
Rio Santiago (La Plata): Schools, naval shipbuilding yard (AFNE),
1 slipway, 1 floating crane.
Mar del Plata: Submarine base with slipway.
Puerto Belgrano: Main naval base, schools, 2 dry docks, 1 float-
ing dock.
Ushuaia, Deseado, Dársena Sur: Small naval bases.

Naval Building Yards (being privatised)

(a) Astilleros y Fábricas Navales del Estado (AFNE), Rio
    Santiago.
(b) Tandanor, Dársena Norte (Planta 1) and Dársena Este
    (Planta 2); sold in 1991.
    Planta 1 has two dry docks and two floating docks. Planta 2
    has two floating docks (A and B) and a synchrolift of 185 ×
    32 m.
(c) Astillero Domecq Garcia, Buenos Aires. Submarine building
    yard.

Coast Guard (Prefectura Naval Argentina)

In January 1992 the Coast Guard was limited to operations
inside 12 mile territorial seas but this legislation was then cancelled in favour of the previous 200 mile operating zone.

Prefix to Ships' Names

ARA (Armada Republica Argentina)

Naval Aviation

Personnel: 2500
1st Naval Air Wing (Punta del Indio Naval Air Base): Naval
Aviation School with Beech T-34Cs, Beech King Airs and Turbo
Mentor T-34s.
2nd Naval Air Wing (Comandante Espora Naval Air Base): Anti-
Submarine Squadron with Grumman S-2E Trackers; 2nd Naval
Helicopter Squadron with Agusta/Sikorsky SH-3D and S-61D.
3rd Naval Air Wing (Comandante Espora Naval Air Base): 2nd
Naval Fighter/Attack Squadron with Super Etendards; 1st Naval
Helicopter Squadron with Alouette III.
4th Naval Air Wing (Punta Indio Naval Air Base): 1st Naval Attack
Squadron with Macchi MB 326B and Embraer EMB 326
Xavantes; Naval Aerophotographic Squadron with Beech Queen
Airs and Beech King Air 200s.
5th Naval Air Wing (Almirante Zar Naval Air Base): 1st Naval
Logistic Support Squadron with Lockheed Electra; 2nd Naval
Logistic Support Squadron with Fokker F28s.
6th Naval Air Wing (Almirante Zar Naval Air Base): Naval Recon-
naissance Squadron with Beech Queen Airs, Lockheed Electra
L-188E and Pilatus PC-6.
Approximately half the aircraft, including most of the Super Eten-
dards, are reported out of service due to shortage of spare parts.

Marine Corps

Organisation and Deployment

1st Marine Infantry Force (HQ Río Gallegos)
1st Marine Infantry Brigade (Baterías)
Amphibious Support Group (Puerto Belgrano)

1st Marine Infantry Battalion (HQ Baterías)
2nd Marine Infantry Battalion (Baterías)
3rd Marine Infantry Battalion (La Plata)
4th Marine Infantry Battalion (Río Gallegos)
5th Marine Infantry Battalion (Río Grande)

Marine Field Artillery Battalion (Puerto Belgrano)
Logistics Support Battalion (Baterías)
Amphibious Vehicles Battalion (Baterías)
Communications Battalion (Puerto Belgrano)
Marine A/A Battalion (Puerto Belgrano)
Scout Company (Baterías)
Marine A/T Company (Baterías)
Amphibious Engineers Company (Puerto Belgrano)
Amphibious Commandos Company (Baterías)
Navy Chief of Staff Security Battalion (Buenos Aires)
Puerto Belgrano Security Battalion (Puerto Belgrano)
There are Marine Security Companies in Buenos Aires, Rio San-
tiago, Punta Indio, Azul, Mar del Plata, Comandante Espora Naval
Air Base, Zárate, Ezeiza, Trelew, Ushuaia and Rio Grande.

Strength of the Fleet

Type	Active (Reserve)	Building (Planned)
Patrol Submarines	4	3
Aircraft Carriers	(1)	—
Destroyers	6	—
Frigates	7	2
Patrol Ships	8	—
Fast Attack Craft (Gun)	2	—
Coastal Patrol Craft	4	—
Minehunters/sweepers	6	—
Landing Ship (Tank)	1	—
Minor Landing Craft	20	—
Survey/Oceanographic Ships	3	—
Survey Launches	2	—
Transports	4	(1)
Training Ships	2	—
Tugs	13	—
Floating Docks	5	—
Sail Training Ships	4	—

Mercantile Marine

Lloyd's Register of Shipping:
    451 vessels of 772 928 tons gross

DELETION

1992 *Tequara* (for sale)

PENNANT LIST

Submarines

S 31	Salta
S 32	San Luis
S 41	Santa Cruz
S 42	San Juan
S 43	Santa Fé (bldg)
S 44	Santiago del Estero (bldg)

Aircraft Carrier

V 2	Veinticinco de Mayo

Destroyers

D 1	Hercules
D 2	Santisima Trinidad
D 10	Almirante Brown
D 11	La Argentina
D 12	Heroina
D 13	Sarandi

Frigates

31	Drummond
32	Guerrico
33	Granville
41	Espora
42	Rosales
43	Spiro
44	Parker
45	Robinson (bldg)
46	Gomez Roca (bldg)

Patrol Forces

A 1	Com G Irigoyen
A 2	Teniente Olivieri
A 3	Francisco de Gurruchaga
A 4	Suboficial Castillo
A 9	Alferez Sobral
A 10	Comodoro Somellera
P 20	Murature
P 21	King
P 61	Baradero
P 62	Barranqueras
P 63	Clorinda
P 64	Concepcion del Uruguay
P 85	Intrepida
P 86	Indomita

Amphibious Force

Q 42	Cabo San Antonio

Mine Warfare Forces

M 1	Neuquen
M 2	Rio Negro
M 3	Chubut
M 4	Tierra del Fuego
M 5	Chaco
M 6	Formosa

Miscellaneous

A 8	Sanaviron
B 3	Canal Beagle
B 4	Bahia San Blas
B 5	Cabo de Hornos
Q 2	Libertad
Q 5	Almirante Irizar
Q 8	Puerto Deseado
Q 11	Comodoro Rivadavia
15	Cormoran
16	Petrel
Q 25	Fortuna I
Q 26	Fortuna II
Q 31	Piloto Alsina
Q 73	Itati II
R 1	Huarpe
R 2	Querandi
R 3	Tehuelche
R 4	Mataco
R 5	Mocovi
R 6	Calchaqui
R 7	Ona
R 8	Toba
R 10	Chulupi
R 16	Capayan
R 18	Chiquillan
R 19	Morcoyan

SUBMARINES

2 + 3 SANTA CRUZ (TR 1700) CLASS

Name	No	Builders	Laid down	Launched	Commissioned
SANTA CRUZ	S 41	Thyssen Nordseewerke	6 Dec 1980	28 Sep 1982	18 Oct 1984
SAN JUAN	S 42	Thyssen Nordseewerke	18 Mar 1982	20 June 1983	19 Nov 1985
SANTA FÉ	S 43	Astilleros Domecq Garcia	4 Oct 1983	—	—
SANTIAGO DEL ESTERO	S 44	Astilleros Domecq Garcia	5 Aug 1985	—	—
—	S 45	Astilleros Domecq Garcia	June 1992	—	—

Displacement, tons: 2116 surfaced; 2264 dived
Dimensions, feet (metres): 216.5 × 23.9 × 21.3
(66 × 7.3 × 6.5)
Main machinery: Diesel-electric; 4 MTU 16V 652 MB81 diesels; 6720 hp(m) *(4.94 MW)* sustained; 4 alternators; 4.4 MW; 1 Siemens Type 1HR4525 + 1HR 4525 four circuit DC motor; 6.6 MW; 1 shaft
Speed, knots: 15 surfaced; 15 snorting; 25 dived
Range, miles: 12 000 at 8 kts surfaced; 20 at 25 kts; 460 at 6 kts dived
Complement: 26 plus 6 spare berths

Torpedoes: 6—21 in *(533 mm)* bow tubes. 22 AEG SST 4; wire-guided; active/passive homing to 12/28 km *(6.5/15 nm)* at

35/23 kts; warhead 260 kg; automatic reload in 50 seconds. Swim-out discharge. US Mk 37 are also carried.
Mines: Capable of carrying ground mines.
Countermeasures: ESM: Sea Sentry III; Radar warning.
Fire control: Signaal Sinbads; can handle 5 targets and 3 torpedoes simultaneously.
Radars: Navigation: Thomson-CSF Calypso IV; I band.
Sonars: Atlas Elektronik CSU 3/4; active/passive search and attack; medium frequency.
Thomson Sintra DUUX 5; passive ranging.

Programmes: Contract signed 30 November 1977 with Thyssen Nordseewerke for two submarines to be built at Emden with

parts and overseeing for four more boats to be built in Argentina by Astilleros Domecq Garcia, Buenos Aires. Little work was done in the shipyard in 1993 and S 43 is 70 per cent complete, S 44 50 per cent and S 45 has started construction. Other reports indicate either that completion depends on sales of Meko 140s, or that the unfinished hulls may be shipped back to Germany.
Structure: Diving depth, 270 m *(890 ft)*.
Operational: Maximum endurance is 70 days. The first two of the class remained operational in early 1994.
Sales: Taiwan has shown an interest.

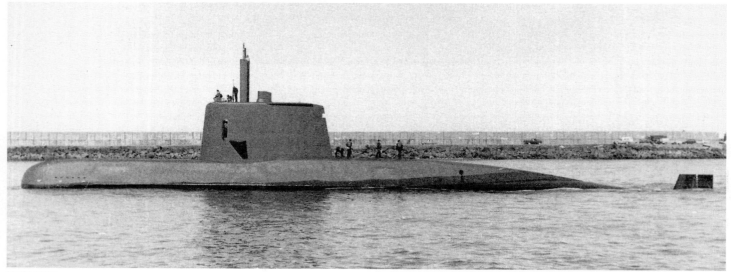

SANTA CRUZ   5/1987, van Ginderen Collection

2 SALTA (209—1200) CLASS

Name	No	Builders	Laid down	Launched	Commissioned
SALTA	S 31	Howaldtswerke, Kiel	30 Apr 1970	9 Nov 1972	7 Mar 1974
SAN LUIS	S 32	Howaldtswerke, Kiel	1 Oct 1970	3 Apr 1973	24 May 1974

Displacement, tons: 1248 surfaced; 1440 dived
Dimensions, feet (metres): 183.4 × 20.5 × 17.9
(55.9 × 6.3 × 5.5)
Main machinery: Diesel-electric; 4 MTU 12V 493 AZ80 diesels; 2400 hp(m) *(1.76 MW)* sustained; 4 alternators; 1.7 MW; 1 motor; 4600 hp(m) *(3.36 MW)*; 1 shaft
Speed, knots: 10 surfaced; 22 dived; 11 snorting
Range, miles: 6000 at 8 kts surfaced; 230 at 8 kts; 400 at 4 kts dived
Complement: 32

Torpedoes: 8—21 in *(533 mm)* bow tubes. 14 AEG SST 4; wire-guided; active/passive homing to 12/28 km *(6.5/15 nm)* at

35/23 kts; warhead 260 kg or US Mk 37; wire-guided; active/passive homing to 8 km *(4.4 nm)* at 24 kts; warhead 150 kg. Swim-out discharge.
Mines: Capable of carrying ground mines.
Countermeasures: ESM: DR 2000; radar warning.
Fire control: Signaal M8 digital; computer-based; up to 3 targets engaged simultaneously.
Radars: Navigation: Thomson-CSF Calypso II.
Sonars: Atlas Elektronik CSU 3 (AN 526/AN 5039/41); active/passive search and attack; medium frequency.
Thomson Sintra DUUX 2C and DUUG 1D; passive ranging.

Programmes: Ordered in 1968. Built in sections by Howaldts-

werke Deutsche Werft AG, Kiel from the IK 68 design of Ingenieurkontor, Lübeck. Sections were shipped to Argentina for assembly at Tandanor, Buenos Aires.
Modernisation: *Salta* is undergoing a mid-life modernisation at the Domecq Garcia Shipyard. New engines, weapons and electrical systems are being fitted and the last 15 m of the hull have been separated from the main hull to allow work in the main engineering section. Work was suspended in May 1990 for lack of funds. By October 1991 *San Luis* was also being refitted and work had restarted on *Salta*. Both were still in shipyard hands in early 1994 with little progress being made.
Structure: Diving depth, 250 m *(820 ft)*.

SALTA   1988

SALTA   1982, Argentine Navy

AIRCRAFT CARRIER

1 COLOSSUS CLASS

Name	No	Builders	Laid down	Launched	Commissioned
VEINTICINCO DE MAYO (ex-HrMs *Karel Doorman*, ex-HMS *Venerable*)	V 2	Cammell Laird & Co Ltd, Birkenhead	3 Dec 1942	30 Dec 1943	17 Jan 1945

Displacement, tons: 15 892 standard; 19 896 full load
Dimensions, feet (metres): 630 pp; 693.2 oa × 80 × 25 *(192; 211.3 × 24.4 × 7.6)*
Flight deck, feet (metres): 697.7 × 133.4 *(212.6 × 40.6)*
Main machinery: 2 shafts (see *Modernisation*)
Speed, knots: 24
Complement: 1000 plus up to 500 air crew

Guns: 9 Bofors 40 mm/70; 85° elevation; 300 rounds/minute to 12 km *(6.5 nm)* anti-surface; 4 km *(2.2 nm)* anti-aircraft; weight of shell 0.96 kg.
Combat data systems: Signaal SEWACO; Link 10.
Radars: Air search: Signaal LW 08; D band.
Surface/Air search: Signaal DA 08; F band.
Height finder: VI/SGR-109.
Navigation: Signaal ZW 01; I/J band.
Racal Decca 1226; I band.
CCA: Selenia MM/SPN 720; I band.
Tacan: URN 20.

Fixed-wing aircraft: 11 Super Etendards and 6 S-2E/G Trackers.
Helicopters: 4 SH-3D Sea King ASW and 1 A 103 Alouette III.

Programmes: Purchased from the UK on 1 April 1948 and commissioned in the Royal Netherlands Navy on 28 May 1948. Damaged by boiler fire on 29 April 1968. Sold to Argentina on 15 October 1968 and refitted at Rotterdam by N V Dok en Werf Mij Wilton-Fijenoord, being fitted with new turbines from HMS *Leviathan*. Commissioned in the Argentine Navy on 12 March 1969. Completed refit on 22 August 1969 and sailed for Argentina on 3 September 1969.
Modernisation: In 1980-81 her flight deck area was increased allowing for two extra aircraft in the deck-park and at the same time all necessary modifications, including lengthening and strengthening of catapult, were made to allow for operation of Super Etendards. In 1983 Plessey CAAIS was replaced by a SEWACO system compatible with the Meko 360 class. Major refit was planned to start in 1988 for modifications to main engines, flight deck, electrical systems, NBCD and the bridge. At that stage alternative main engine plans included COSAG

(new boilers plus GT boost) or CODOG (4 Sulzer diesels plus GT boost). In June 1990 Fincantieri won an initial contract to give technical assistance to AFNE, Santiago, to replace the Parsons turbines with GE/Fiat Aviazione LM 2500 gas-turbines, vp propellers, and a DMD power generation system. Also included was the repair of flight deck and lifts, modernisation of the C 41 system and a new steam plant for the catapults. By the end of 1992, old systems had been stripped out and work was ready to start if the funds could be found.
Structure: Hangar dimensions, feet (metres): 455 × 52 × 17.5 *(138.7 × 15.8 × 5.3)*. Modified bridge superstructure, tripod radar mast and tall raked funnel are distinctive changes from the original Colossus class.
Operational: The ship has not been fully operational since 1985 and was moored at the Puerto Belgrano Naval Base throughout 1993.
Opinion: This ship seems unlikely ever to complete a refit, but the recommissioning of the Brazilian carrier in late 1993 has given the Navy an added motivation to find the money.

VEINTICINCO DE MAYO (at Puerto Belgrano)   *8/1993*

DESTROYERS

4 ALMIRANTE BROWN (MEKO 360) CLASS

Name	No	Builders	Laid down	Launched	Commissioned
ALMIRANTE BROWN	D 10	Blohm & Voss, Hamburg	8 Sep 1980	28 Mar 1981	26 Jan 1983
LA ARGENTINA	D 11	Blohm & Voss, Hamburg	30 Mar 1981	25 Sep 1981	4 May 1983
HEROINA	D 12	Blohm & Voss, Hamburg	24 Aug 1981	17 Feb 1982	31 Oct 1983
SARANDI	D 13	Blohm & Voss, Hamburg	9 Mar 1982	31 Aug 1982	16 Apr 1984

Displacement, tons: 2900 standard; 3360 full load
Dimensions, feet (metres): 413.1 × 46 × 19 (screws) *(125.9 × 14 × 5.8)*
Main machinery: COGOG; 2 RR Olympus TM3B gas-turbines; 50 000 hp *(37.4 MW)* sustained; 2 RR Tyne RM1C gas-turbines; 9900 hp *(7.4 MW)* sustained; 2 shafts; cp props
Speed, knots: 30.5; 20.5 cruising. **Range, miles:** 4500 at 18 kts
Complement: 200 (26 officers)

Missiles: SSM: 8 Aerospatiale MM 40 Exocet (2 quad) launchers ❶; inertial cruise; active radar homing to 70 km *(40 nm)*; warhead 165 kg; sea-skimmer.
SAM: Selenia/Elsag Albatros octuple launcher ❷; 24 Aspide; semi-active homing to 13 km *(7 nm)* at 2.5 Mach; height envelope 15-5000 m *(49.2-16 405 ft)*; warhead 30 kg.
Guns: 1 OTO Melara 5 in *(127 mm)*/54 automatic ❸; 85° elevation; 45 rounds/minute to 16 km *(8.7 nm)* anti-surface; 7 km *(3.6 nm)* anti-aircraft; weight of shell 32 kg; ready ammunition 69 rounds using 3 loading drums; also fires chaff and illuminants.
8 Breda/Bofors 40 mm/70 (4 twin) ❹; 85° elevation; 300 rounds/minute to 12.6 km *(6.8 nm)* anti-surface; 4 km *(2.2 nm)* anti-aircraft; weight of shell 0.96 kg; ready ammunition 736 (or 444) using AP Tracer, impact or proximity fuzing.
Torpedoes: 6—324 mm ILAS 3 (2 triple) tubes ❺. Whitehead A 244; anti-submarine; active/passive homing to 7 km *(3.8 nm)* at 33 kts; warhead 34 kg (shaped charge); 18 reloads.
Countermeasures: Decoys: CSEE Dagaie double mounting; Graseby G1738 towed torpedo decoy system.
2 Breda 105 mm SCLAR chaff rocket launchers; 20 tubes per launcher; can be trained and elevated; chaff to 5 km *(2.7 nm)*; illuminants to 12 km *(6.6 nm)*.
ESM/ECM: Sphinx/Scimitar.
Combat data systems: Signaal SEWACO; Link 10/11. SATCOMs can be fitted.
Fire control: 2 Signaal LIROD radar/optronic systems ❻ each controlling 2 twin 40 mm mounts; Signaal WM 25 FCS ❼.
Radars: Air/surface search: Signaal DA 08A ❽; F band; range 204 km *(110 nm)* for 2 m² target.
Surface search: Signaal ZW 06 ❾; I band.
Navigation: Decca 1226; I band.
Fire control: Signaal STIR ❿; I/J/K band; range 140 km *(76 nm)* for 1 m² target.
Sonars: Atlas Elektronik 80; hull-mounted; active search and attack; medium frequency. DSQS 21BZ.

Helicopters: 2 SA 319B Alouette III ⓫.

ALMIRANTE BROWN   *(Scale 1 : 1200), Ian Sturton*

ALMIRANTE BROWN   *11/1990*

Programmes: Six were originally ordered in 1978, but later restricted to four when Meko 140 frigates were ordered in 1979.
Structure: Pennant numbers are displayed without the D prefix.
Operational: High operational availability was reflected in decision to send one of the class to take part in allied Gulf operations in late 1990.

Opinion: Currently deficient in ASW capability with obsolete helicopter equipment after order for Lynx cancelled in 1982. AB 212ASW was selected but acquisition not funded. Suitable helicopters are being sought in the United States which may provide Kaman SH-2 in due course.

2 HERCULES (TYPE 42) CLASS

Name	No
HERCULES	D 1 (ex-28)
SANTISIMA TRINIDAD	D 2

Builders	Laid down	Launched	Commissioned
Vickers, Barrow	16 June 1971	24 Oct 1972	12 July 1976
AFNE, Rio Santiago	11 Oct 1971	9 Nov 1974	July 1981

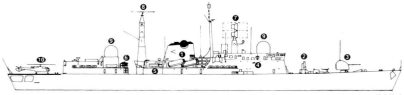

HERCULES
(Scale 1 : 1200), Ian Sturton

Displacement, tons: 3150 standard; 4100 full load
Dimensions, feet (metres): 412 × 47 × 19 (screws)
(125.6 × 14.3 × 5.8)
Main machinery: COGOG; 2 RR Olympus TM3B gas-turbines;
50 000 hp (37.3 MW) sustained
2 RR Tyne RM1A gas-turbines; 9900 hp (7.4 MW) sustained;
2 shafts; cp props
Speed, knots: 29; 18 (Tynes). **Range, miles:** 4000 at 18 kts
Complement: 300

Missiles: SSM: 4 Aerospatiale MM 38 Exocet ❶; inertial cruise;
active homing to 42 km (23 nm) at 0.9 Mach; warhead 165 kg;
sea-skimmer.
SAM: British Aerospace Sea Dart Mk 30 twin launcher ❷; semi-
active radar homing to 40 km (21.5 nm) at 2 Mach; height
envelope 100-18 300 m (328-60 042 ft); 22 missiles; limited
anti-ship capability.
Guns: 1 Vickers 4.5 in (115 mm)/55 Mk 8 automatic ❸; 25
rounds/minute to 22 km (12 nm); weight of shell 21 kg; also
fires chaff and illuminants.
2 Oerlikon 20 mm Mk 7 ❹.
Torpedoes: 6—324 mm ILAS 3 (2 triple) tubes ❺. Whitehead A
244/S; anti-submarine; active/passive homing to 7 km
(3.8 nm) at 33 kts; warhead 34 kg (shaped charge).
Countermeasures: Decoys; Graseby GI 738 towed torpedo
decoy. Knebworth Corvus 8-tubed trainable launchers for
chaff ❻.
ESM: Racal RDL 257; FH5 DF; radar intercept and DF.
ECM: Racal RCM 2 (Hercules only); jammer.
Combat data systems: Plessey-Ferranti ADAWS-4; Link 10.
Radars: Air search: Marconi Type 965P with double AKE2 array
and 1010/1011 IFF ❼; A band.
Surface search: Marconi Type 992Q ❽; E/F band.
Navigation, HDWS and helicopter control: Kelvin Hughes Type
1006; I band.
Fire control: Two Marconi Type 909 ❾; I/J band (for Sea Dart
missile control).
Sonars: Graseby Type 184M; hull-mounted; active search and
attack; medium frequency 6-9 kHz.
Kelvin Hughes Type 162M classification set; sideways looking;
active; high frequency.

Helicopters: 1 SA 319B Alouette III ❿.

Programmes: Contract signed 18 May 1970 between the Argentine Government and Vickers Ltd. This provided for the construction of these two ships, one built at Barrow-in-Furness and
the second at Rio Santiago with British assistance and overseeing. Santisima Trinidad was sabotaged on 22 August 1975

HERCULES
1982, Argentine Navy

whilst fitting-out and subsequently placed in floating-dock at
AFNE.
Modernisation: Combat Data Systems have been improved with
local modifications.

Operational: Although laid up for some time between 1983 and
1986, both ships were at sea for short periods in 1987 and
back with the Fleet from 1988. Santisima Trinidad is used as a
Flagship.

FRIGATES

3 DRUMMOND (TYPE A 69) CLASS

Name	No	Builders	Laid down	Launched	Completed
DRUMMOND (ex-Good Hope, ex-Lieutenant de Vaisseau le Hénaff F 789)	31	Lorient Naval Dockyard	12 Mar 1976	5 Mar 1977	Mar 1978
GUERRICO (ex-Transvaal, ex-Commandant l'Herminier F 791)	32	Lorient Naval Dockyard	1 Oct 1976	13 Sep 1977	Oct 1978
GRANVILLE	33	Lorient Naval Dockyard	1 Dec 1978	28 June 1980	22 June 1981

DRUMMOND
(Scale 1 : 900), Ian Sturton

Displacement, tons: 950 standard; 1170 full load
Dimensions, feet (metres): 262.5 × 33.8 × 9.8; 18 (sonar)
(80 × 10.3 × 3; 5.5)
Main machinery: 2 SEMT-Pielstick 12 PC2.2 V 400 diesels;
12 000 hp(m) (8.82 MW) sustained; 2 shafts; cp props
Speed, knots: 23. **Range, miles:** 4500 at 15 kts; 3000 at 18 kts
Complement: 93 (10 officers)

Missiles: SSM: 4 Aerospatiale MM 38 Exocet (2 twin) launchers
❶; inertial cruise; active radar homing to 42 km (23 nm);
warhead 165 kg; sea-skimmer.
Guns: 1 Creusot Loire 3.9 in (100 mm)/55 Mod 1953 ❷; 80°
elevation; 60 rounds/minute to 17 km (9 nm) anti-surface;
8 km (4.4 nm) anti-aircraft; weight of shell 13.5 kg.
2 Breda 40 mm/70 (twin) ❸; 300 rounds/minute to 12.5 km
(6.8 nm); weight of shell 0.96 kg; ready ammunition 736 (or
444) using AP tracer, impact or proximity fuzing.
2 Oerlikon 20 mm ❹; 1000 rounds/minute.
Torpedoes: 6—324 mm Mk 32 (2 triple) tubes ❺. Whitehead A
244; anti-submarine; active/passive homing to 7 km (3.8 nm)
at 33 kts; warhead 34 kg.
Countermeasures: Decoys: CSEE Dagaie double mounting; 10
or 6 replaceable containers; trainable; chaff to 12 km (6.5 nm);
illuminants to 4 km (2.2 nm); decoys in H-J bands.
ESM: DR 2000/DALIA 500; radar warning.
ECM: Thomson-CSF Alligator; jammer.
Fire control: Thomson-CSF Vega system. CSEE Naja optronics
director (Granville). CSEE Panda Mk 2 optical director ❻
(Drummond and Guerrico).
Radars: Air/surface search: Thomson-CSF DRBV 51A ❼ with
UPX12 IFF; G band.
Navigation: Decca 1226; I band.
Fire control: Thomson-CSF DRBC 32E ❽; I/J band (for 100 mm
gun).
Sonars: Thomson Sintra Diodon; hull-mounted; active search
and attack; selectable 11, 12 or 13 kHz.

Programmes: The first pair was originally built for the French
Navy and sold to the South African Navy in 1976 while under
construction. As a result of a UN embargo on arms sales to
South Africa this sale was cancelled. Purchased by Argentina
in Autumn 1978. Both arrived in Argentina 2 November 1978
(third ship being ordered some time later) and all have proved
very popular ships in the Argentine Navy.

GRANVILLE
11/1993 Maritime Photographic

Modernisation: Drummond has had her armament updated to
the same standard as the other two, replacing the Bofors
40/60.

Operational: Endurance, 15 days. Very economical in fuel
consumption.

4 + 2 ESPORA (MEKO 140) CLASS

Name	No	Builders	Laid down	Launched	Commissioned
ESPORA	41	AFNE, Rio Santiago	3 Oct 1980	23 Jan 1982	5 July 1985
ROSALES	42	AFNE, Rio Santiago	1 July 1981	4 Mar 1983	14 Nov 1986
SPIRO	43	AFNE, Rio Santiago	4 Jan 1982	24 June 1983	24 Nov 1987
PARKER	44	AFNE, Rio Santiago	2 Aug 1982	31 Mar 1984	17 Apr 1990
ROBINSON	45	AFNE, Rio Santiago	6 June 1983	15 Feb 1985	—
GOMEZ ROCA	46	AFNE, Rio Santiago	1 Dec 1983	14 Nov 1986	—

Displacement, tons: 1470 standard; 1790 full load
Dimensions, feet (metres): 299.1 × 36.4 × 11.2
(91.2 × 11.1 × 3.4)
Main machinery: 2 SEMT-Pielstick 16 PC2-5 V 400 diesels;
20 400 hp(m) *(15 MW)* sustained; 2 shafts
Speed, knots: 27. **Range, miles:** 4000 at 18 kts
Complement: 93 (11 officers)

Missiles: SSM: 4 Aerospatiale MM 38 Exocet ❶ or 8 MM 40;
inertial cruise; active radar homing to 42 km *(23 nm)* (MM 38);
70 km *(40 nm)* (MM 40); warhead 165 kg; sea-skimmer. Intention is to convert to 8 MM 40 and *Espora* was first to be fitted.
Guns: 1 OTO Melara 3 in *(76 mm)*/62 compact ❷; 85° elevation;
85 rounds/minute to 16 km *(8.7 nm)* anti-surface; 12 km
(6.5 nm) anti-aircraft; weight of shell 6 kg; also fires chaff and illuminants.
4 Breda 40 mm/70 (2 twin) ❸; 85° elevation; 300 rounds/minute to 12.5 km *(6.8 nm)*; weight of shell 0.96 kg; ready ammunition 736 (or 444) using AP tracer, impact or proximity fuzing.
2—12.7 mm MGs.
Torpedoes: 6—324 mm ILAS 3 (2 triple) tubes ❹. Whitehead A 244/S; anti-submarine; active/passive homing to 7 km
(3.8 nm) at 33 kts; warhead 34 kg (shaped charge).
Countermeasures: Decoys: CSEE Dagaie double mounting; 10 or 6 replaceable containers; trainable; chaff to 12 km *(6.5 nm)*;
illuminants to 4 km *(2.2 nm)*; decoys in H-J bands.
ESM: Racal RQN-3B; radar warning.
ECM: Racal TQN-2X; jammer.
Combat data systems: Signaal SEWACO.
Fire control: Signaal WM 22/41 integrated system; 1 LIROD 8 optronic director ❺ (plus 2 sights—one on each bridge wing).
Radars: Air/surface search: Signaal DA 05 ❻; E/F band; range 137 km *(75 nm)* for 2 m² target.
Navigation: Decca TM 1226; I band.
Fire Control: Signaal WM 28 ❼; I/J band; range 46 km *(25 nm)*.
IFF: Mk 10.
Sonars: Atlas Elektronik ASQ 4; hull-mounted; active search and attack; medium frequency.

Helicopters: 1 SA 319B Alouette III.

Programmes: A contract was signed with Blohm & Voss on 1 August 1979 for this group of ships which are scaled down Meko 360s. All six have been fabricated in AFNE, Rio Santiago.
Parker flooded while fitting out which delayed commissioning.
Completion of the last pair depends upon funds from foreign sales and no work was being done at the end of 1993.
Structure: *Parker* and later ships fitted with a telescopic hangar which will be retrofitted in first three. Fitted with stabilisers. At least two of the class have flight deck extensions for SH-2F or AS-555 helicopters in due course.
Operational: Mostly used for offshore patrol and fishery protection duties but *Spiro* and *Rosales* sent to the Gulf in 1990/91.
Sales: Taiwan has shown an interest.

ESPORA *(Scale 1 : 900), Ian Sturton*

SPIRO *12/1990*

ROBINSON *4/1992, Hartmut Ehlers*

SHIPBORNE AIRCRAFT

Notes: (1) New ASW helicopters are the highest procurement priority, 4 Fennec AS 550 Sea Squire reported ordered in late 1993.
(2) Fixed-wing aircraft fly once a year from USN aircraft carriers.

Numbers/Type: 4/4 Agusta-Sikorsky ASH-3H/AS-61D Sea King.
Operational speed: 120 kts *(222 km/h)*.
Service ceiling: 12 205 ft *(3720 m)*.
Range: 630 nm *(1165 km)*.
Role/Weapon systems: ASW Helicopter; carrier or land-based for ASW with limited surface search capability. Sensors: Search radar, Bendix sonar. Weapons: ASW; up to 4 × A 244 torpedoes or 4 × depth bombs.

Numbers/Type: 6 Aerospatiale SA 319B Alouette III.
Operational speed: 113 kts *(210 km/h)*.
Service ceiling: 10 500 ft *(3200 m)*.
Range: 290 nm *(540 km)*.
Role/Weapon systems: ASW Helicopter; used for liaison in peacetime; wartime role includes commando assault and ASW/ASVW. Sensors: Nose-mounted search radar. Weapons: ASW; 2 × Mk 44 torpedoes. ASV; 2 × AS12 missiles.

SEA KING *1990, Argentine Navy*

ALOUETTE III *1992*

Numbers/Type: 11 Dassault-Breguet Super Etendard.
Operational speed: Mach 1.
Service ceiling: 44 950 ft *(13 700 m).*
Range: 920 nm *(1700 km).*
Role/Weapon systems: Strike Fighter with anti-shipping ability proved in South Atlantic; carrier-borne strike, air defence and ASV roles, can also be land-based. Eight in service, three in reserve in 1992. Hi-lo-hi combat radius 460 nm *(850 km).* Sensors: Agave multi-mode radar, ECM. Weapons: Strike; 2.1 tons of 'iron' bombs. ASVW; 1 × Exocet or 1 × Martin Pescador missiles. Self-defence; 2 × Magic AAMs. Standard; 2 × 30 mm cannon.

SUPER ETENDARD   *1985, Argentine Navy*

Numbers/Type: 5/3 Grumman S-2E/G Tracker.
Operational speed: 130 kts *(241 km/h).*
Service ceiling: 25 000 ft *(7620 m).*
Range: 1350 nm *(2500 km).*
Role/Weapon systems: Carrier-borne medium-range ASW aircraft; also used for shore-based MR and EEZ patrol. One shipped to Israel in 1989 for Garrett turboprop installation. Prototype for fleet conversion in Argentina. Up to three turboprop aircraft to be acquired from the US in 1994. Sensors: Search radar up to 32 sonobuoys, echo-ranging depth charges. Weapons: ASW; torpedoes, bombs and depth charges.

TRACKER   *1985, Argentine Navy*

LAND-BASED MARITIME AIRCRAFT

Notes: (1) In addition there are three Fokker F28 for Logistic Support; One Pilatus PC-6 for reconnaissance and 10 T-34 Turbo Mentor training aircraft.
(2) Up to 20 A4M Skyhawk may be acquired by the Air Force from the USA in due course. There are also plans for six ex-USN P3 Orions.

Numbers/Type: 15 Aermacchi MB 326GB.
Operational speed: 468 kts *(867 km/h).*
Service ceiling: 47 000 ft *(14 325 m).*
Range: 1320 nm *(2446 km).*
Role/Weapon systems: Light Attack; supplements anti-shipping/strike; also has training role. Weapons: ASV; 1.8 tons of 'iron' bombs. Strike; 6 × rockets. Recce; underwing camera pod.

Numbers/Type: 3/1 Lockheed L-188/188E Electra.
Operational speed: 389 kts *(721 km/h).*
Service ceiling: 28 400 ft *(8655 m).*
Range: 3000 nm *(5570 km).*
Role/Weapon systems: At least one converted from transport aircraft for overwater Elint/EW role. Three more used for maritime reconnaissance. Sensors: Various EW systems including Elisra ESM. Weapons: Unarmed.

Numbers/Type: 7 Beechcraft Queen Air 200.
Operational speed: 260 kts *(482 km/h).*
Service ceiling: 31 000 ft *(9448 m).*
Range: 2000 nm *(3705 km).*
Role/Weapon systems: Multi-purpose including transport, and reconnaissance for protection of port installations; also has training role. Sensors: Bendix search radar. Weapons: Unarmed.

PATROL FORCES

2 KING CLASS (PATROL SHIPS)

Name	No	Builders	Commissioned
MURATURE	P 20	Base Nav Rio Santiago	12 Apr 1945
KING	P 21	Base Nav Rio Santiago	28 July 1946

Displacement, tons: 913 standard; 1000 normal; 1032 full load
Dimensions, feet (metres): 252.7 × 29.5 × 13.1 *(77 × 9 × 4)*
Main machinery: 2 Werkspoor diesels; 2500 hp(m) *(1.8 MW);* 2 shafts
Speed, knots: 18. **Range, miles:** 9000 at 12 kts
Complement: 130
Guns: 3 Vickers 4 in *(105 mm)/*45; 80° elevation; 16 rounds/minute to 19 km *(10 nm);* weight of shell 16 kg.
4 Bofors 40 mm/60 (1 twin, 2 single); 80° elevation; 120 rounds/minute/barrel to 10 km *(5.5 nm);* weight of shell 0.89 kg.
5—12.7 mm MGs.
Depth charges: 4 projectors.
Radars: Surface search: Racal Decca 1226; I band.

Comment: Named after Captain John King, an Irish follower of Admiral Brown, who distinguished himself in the war with Brazil, 1826-28; and Captain Jose Murature, who performed conspicuous service against the Paraguayans at the Battle of Cuevas in 1865. *King* laid down June 1938, launched 3 November 1943. *Murature* laid down March 1940, launched July 1943. Used for cadet training.

MURATURE (alongside *King*)   *4/1992, Hartmut Ehlers*

MURATURE and KING   *4/1992, Hartmut Ehlers*

3 CHEROKEE CLASS (PATROL SHIPS)

Name	No	Builders	Commissioned
COMANDANTE GENERAL IRIGOYEN	A 1	Charleston	10 Mar 1945
(ex-USS *Cahuilla*)		SB and DD Co	
FRANCISCO DE GURRUCHAGA	A 3	Charleston	16 June 1945
(ex-USS *Luiseno* ATF 156)		SB and DD Co	
— (ex-USS *Takelma* ATF 113)	—	United Engineering Co, Alameda	3 Aug 1944

Displacement, tons: 1235 standard; 1731 full load
Dimensions, feet (metres): 205 × 38.5 × 17 *(62.5 × 11.7 × 5.2)*
Main machinery: Diesel-electric; 4 GM 12-278 diesels; 4400 hp *(3.28 MW);* 4 generators; 1 motor; 3000 hp *(2.24 MW);* 1 shaft
Speed, knots: 16. **Range, miles:** 6500 at 15 kts; 15 000 at 8 kts
Complement: 85
Guns: 6 Bofors 40 mm/60 (2 twin; 2 single); 80° elevation; 120 rounds/minute to 10 km *(5.5 nm)* anti-surface; 3 km *(1.6 nm)* anti-aircraft; weight of shell 0.89 kg.
2 Oerlikon 20 mm (mounted only in *Comandante General Irigoyen*); 800 rounds/minute to 2 km.
Radars: Surface search: Racal Decca 626; I band.
Navigation: Racal Decca 1230; I band.

Comment: Fitted with powerful pumps and other salvage equipment. *Comandante General Irigoyen* transferred by the US at San Diego, California, on 9 July 1961. Classified as a tug until 1966 when she was re-rated as patrol ship. *Francisco De Gurruchaga* transferred on 1 July 1975 by sale. Ex-*Takelma* to be transferred in 1994.

GURRUCHAGA   *1989, Argentine Navy*

1 OLIVIERI CLASS (PATROL SHIP)

Name	No	Builders	Commissioned
TENIENTE OLIVIERI (ex-*Marsea 10*)	A 2	Quality SB, Louisiana	Dec 1987

Displacement, tons: 1640 full load
Dimensions, feet (metres): 184.8 × 40 × 14 *(56.3 × 12.2 × 4.3)*
Main machinery: 2 GM/EMD 16-645 E6; 3230 hp *(2.4 MW)* sustained; 2 shafts
Speed, knots: 16
Complement: 15 (4 officers)
Guns: 2—12.7 mm MGs.

Comment: Built by Quality Shipyards, New Orleans, as a large tug but rated as an Aviso. Acquired from US Maritime Administration in December 1987.

2 SOTOYOMO CLASS (PATROL SHIPS)

Name	No	Builders	Commissioned
ALFEREZ SOBRAL	A 9	Levingstone	9 Sep 1944
(ex-USS *Salish* ATA 187)		SB Co, Orange	
COMODORO SOMELLERA	A 10	Levingstone	7 Dec 1944
(ex-USS *Catawba* ATA 210)		SB Co, Orange	

Displacement, tons: 800 full load
Dimensions, feet (metres): 143 × 33.9 × 13 *(43.6 × 10.3 × 4)*
Main machinery: Diesel-electric; 2 GM 12-278A diesels; 2200 hp *(1.64 MW)*; 2 generators; 1 motor; 1500 hp *(1.12 MW)*; 1 shaft
Speed, knots: 12.5. **Range, miles:** 16 500 at 8 kts
Complement: 49

Comment: Former US ocean tugs transferred on 10 February 1972. *Sanaviron* (A 8) operates as a tug. *Alferez Sobral* was paid off in 1987 but is now back in service.

COMODORO SOMELLERA   *1986, Argentine Navy*

2 INTREPIDA CLASS (TYPE TNC 45) (FAST ATTACK CRAFT—GUN)

Name	No	Builders	Commissioned
INTREPIDA	P 85	Lürssen, Bremen	20 July 1974
INDOMITA	P 86	Lürssen, Bremen	12 Dec 1974

Displacement, tons: 268 full load
Dimensions, feet (metres): 147.3 × 24.3 × 7.9 *(44.9 × 7.4 × 2.4)*
Main machinery: 4 MTU MD 16V 538 TB90 diesels; 12 000 hp(m) *(8.82 MW)*; 4 shafts
Speed, knots: 38. **Range, miles:** 1450 at 20 kts
Complement: 39 (2 officers)
Guns: 1 OTO Melara 3 in *(76 mm)*/62 compact; 85 rounds/minute to 16 km *(9 nm)* anti-surface; 12 km *(6.5 nm)* anti-aircraft; weight of shell 6 kg.
2 Bofors 40 mm/70; 330 rounds/minute to 12 km *(6.5 nm)* anti-surface; 4 km *(2.2 nm)* anti-aircraft; weight of shell 0.89 kg.
2 Oerlikon 81 mm rocket launchers for illuminants.
Torpedoes: 2—21 in *(533 mm)* launchers. AEG SST-4; wire-guided; active/passive homing to 28 km *(15 nm)* at 23 kts.
Countermeasures: ESM: Racal RDL 1; radar warning.
Fire control: Signaal WM22 optronic for guns. Signaal M11 for torpedo guidance and control.
Radars: Surface search: Decca 626; I band.

Comment: These two vessels were ordered in 1970. *Intrepida* launched on 2 December 1973, *Indomita* on 8 April 1974.

INTREPIDA   *4/1993*

INTREPIDA and INDOMITA   *8/1993*

4 BARADERO (DABUR) CLASS (COASTAL PATROL CRAFT)

Name	No	Builders	Commissioned
BARADERO	P 61	Israel Aircraft Industries	1978
BARRANQUERAS	P 62	Israel Aircraft Industries	1978
CLORINDA	P 63	Israel Aircraft Industries	1978
CONCEPCIÓN DEL URUGUAY	P 64	Israel Aircraft Industries	1978

Displacement, tons: 33.7 standard; 39 full load
Dimensions, feet (metres): 64.9 × 18 × 5.8 *(19.8 × 5.5 × 1.8)*
Main machinery: 2 GM 12V-71TA diesels; 840 hp *(627 kW)* sustained; 2 shafts
Speed, knots: 19. **Range, miles:** 450 at 13 kts
Complement: 9
Guns: 2 Oerlikon 20 mm. 4—12.7 mm (2 twin) MGs.
Depth charges: 2 portable rails.
Radars: Navigation: Decca 101; I band.

Comment: Of all aluminium construction. Employed in 1991 and 1992 as part of the UN Central American peace-keeping force but now returned to normal duties.

BARADERO   *8/1993*

AMPHIBIOUS FORCES

1 LANDING SHIP (TANK)

Name	No	Builders	Commissioned
CABO SAN ANTONIO	Q 42	AFNE, Rio Santiago	1971

Displacement, tons: 4164 light; 8000 full load
Dimensions, feet (metres): 472.3 × 68.9 × 9.8 *(144 × 21 × 3)*
Main machinery: 6 diesels; 13 700 hp *(10.2 MW)*; 2 shafts
Speed, knots: 16
Complement: 124
Military lift: 700 troops; 23 medium tanks; 8 LCVPs each capable of carrying 36 troops or 3.5 tons
Guns: 12 Bofors 40/60 mm (3 quad); 120 rounds/minute to 10 km *(5.5 nm)* anti-surface; 3 km *(1.6 nm)* anti-aircraft; weight of shell 0.89 kg.
4 Oerlikon 20 mm (2 twin).
Fire control: 3 US Mk 5 Mod 2 optical GFCS.
Radars: Navigation: Plessey AWS-1; E/F band; has some air search capability.
Helicopters: Capable of operating up to CH-47 Chinook transport helicopter cross-deck.

Comment: Modified US De Soto County class—principal difference being the fitting of 60 tons Stülcken heavy-lift gear and different armament.

CABO SAN ANTONIO   *1978, Argentine Navy*

4 LCM 6 CLASS

EDM 1, 2, 3, 4

Displacement, tons: 56 full load
Dimensions, feet (metres): 56 × 14 × 3.9 *(17.1 × 4.3 × 1.2)*
Main machinery: 2 Gray 64 HN9 diesels; 330 hp *(246 kW)* sustained; 2 shafts
Speed, knots: 11. **Range, miles:** 130 at 10 kts
Military lift: 30 tons
Guns: 2—12.7 mm MGs.

Comment: Acquired from the US in June 1971.

8 LCVPs

EDVP 30-37

Displacement, tons: 13 full load
Dimensions, feet (metres): 35.8 × 10.5 × 3.6 *(10.9 × 3.2 × 1.1)*
Main machinery: 1 Gray 64 HN9 diesel; 165 hp *(123 kW)* sustained; 1 shaft
Speed, knots: 9. **Range, miles:** 110 at 9 kts
Military lift: 3.5 tons or 36 troops

Comment: Acquired from the US in May 1970.

8 LCVPs

Displacement, tons: 7.5
Dimensions, feet (metres): 35.8 × 10.5 × 1.6 *(10.9 × 3.2 × 0.5)*
Main machinery: Fiat diesel; 200 hp(m) *(147 kW)*; 1 shaft
Speed, knots: 9

Comment: Built by AFNE and El Tigre since 1971.

MINE WARFARE FORCES

6 NEUQUEN (TON) CLASS
(4 MINESWEEPERS—COASTAL and 2 MINEHUNTERS)

Name	No	Builders	Launched
NEUQUEN (ex-HMS *Hickleton*)	M 1	Thornycroft	26 Jan 1955
RIO NEGRO (ex-HMS *Tarlton*)	M 2	Doig	10 Nov 1954
CHUBUT (ex-HMS *Santon*)	M 3	Fleetlands	18 Aug 1955
TIERRA DEL FUEGO (ex-HMS *Bevington*)	M 4	Whites	17 Mar 1953
CHACO (ex-HMS *Rennington*)	M 5	Richards	27 Nov 1958
FORMOSA (ex-HMS *Ilmington*)	M 6	Camper & Nicholson	8 Mar 1954

Displacement, tons: 360 standard; 440 full load
Dimensions, feet (metres): 153 × 28.9 × 8.2 *(46.6 × 8.8 × 2.5)*
Main machinery: 2 Paxman Deltic/Mirrlees JVSS-12 diesels; 3000 hp *(2.24 MW)*; 2 shafts
Speed, knots: 15. **Range, miles:** 2500 at 12 kts
Complement: Minesweepers 27; Minehunters 36

Guns: 1 or 2 Bofors 40 mm/60 (in some); 80° elevation; 120 rounds/minute to 10 km *(5.5 nm)* anti-surface; 3 km *(1.6 nm)* anti-aircraft; weight of shell 0.89 kg.
Radars: Navigation: Decca 45; I band. Type 955 IFF transponder.
Sonars: Plessey Type 193 (in minehunters); active minehunting; 100/300 kHz.

Programmes: Former British coastal minesweepers of the Ton class. Purchased in 1967.
Modernisation: In 1968 *Chaco* and *Formosa* were converted into minehunters in HM Dockyard, Portsmouth, and the other four were refitted and modernised as minesweepers by the Vosper Thornycroft Group with Vosper activated-fin stabiliser equipment. Of composite wooden and non-magnetic metal construction.
Operational: All were active in 1992 and 1993 in spite of reports that they had been paid off.

NEUQUEN   *1988, Argentine Navy*

SURVEY AND RESEARCH SHIPS

Name	No	Builders	Commissioned
PUERTO DESEADO	Q 8	Astarsa, San Fernando	26 Feb 1979

Displacement, tons: 2133 standard; 2400 full load
Dimensions, feet (metres): 251.9 × 51.8 × 21.3 *(76.8 × 15.8 × 6.5)*
Main machinery: 2 Fiat-GMT diesels; 3600 hp(m) *(2.65 MW)*; 1 shaft
Speed, knots: 15. **Range, miles:** 12 000 at 12 kts
Complement: 61 (12 officers) plus 20 scientists
Radars: Navigation: I band.

Comment: Laid down on 17 March 1976 for Consejo Nacional de Investigaciones Tecnicas y Scientificas. Launched on 4 December 1976. For survey work fitted with: four Hewlett-Packard 2108-A, gravimeter, magnetometer, seismic systems, geological laboratory. Omega and NAVSAT equipped.

Name	No	Builders	Commissioned
COMODORO RIVADAVIA	Q 11	Mestrina, Tigre	6 Dec 1974

Displacement, tons: 609 standard; 700 full load
Dimensions, feet (metres): 171.2 × 28.9 × 8.5 *(52.2 × 8.8 × 2.6)*
Main machinery: 2 Stork Werkspoor RHO-218K diesels; 1160 hp(m) *(853 kW)*; 2 shafts
Speed, knots: 12. **Range, miles:** 6000 at 12 kts
Complement: 34 (8 officers)
Helicopters: Provision for SA 319B Alouette III helicopter.

Comment: Laid down on 17 July 1971 and launched on 2 December 1972. Used for research.

COMODORO RIVADAVIA   *8/1988, van Ginderen Collection*

Name	No	Builders	Commissioned
CORMORAN	15	AFNE, Rio Santiago	20 Feb 1964

Displacement, tons: 102 full load
Dimensions, feet (metres): 83 × 16.4 × 5.9 *(25.3 × 5 × 1.8)*
Main machinery: 2 diesels; 440 hp(m) *(323 kW)*; 2 shafts
Speed, knots: 11
Complement: 19 (3 officers)

Comment: Launched 10 August 1963. Classified as a coastal launch.

CORMORAN   *4/1992, Hartmut Ehlers*

Name	No	Builders	Commissioned
PETREL	16	Cadenazzi, Tigre	1965

Displacement, tons: 50 full load
Dimensions, feet (metres): 64.8 × 14.8 × 5.6 *(19.7 × 4.5 × 1.7)*
Main machinery: 2 diesels; 340 hp(m) *(250 kW)*; 2 shafts
Speed, knots: 9
Complement: 7 (1 officer)

Comment: Built using hull of EM 128 transferred from Prefectura Naval. Classified as a coastal launch.

PETREL   *4/1992, Hartmut Ehlers*

TRAINING SHIPS

Note: There are also three small yachts: *Itati II* (Q 73), *Fortuna I* (Q 25) and *Fortuna II* (Q 26) plus a 25 ton yawl *Tijuca* acquired in 1993.

Name	No	Builders	Commissioned
PILOTO ALSINA (ex-MV *Ciudad de Formosa*)	Q 31	UN Levante, Spain	1963

Displacement, tons: 2800 full load
Measurement, tons: 720 dwt; 3986 gross
Dimensions, feet (metres): 346 × 57.1 × 26.9 *(105.5 × 17.4 × 8.2)*
Main machinery: 3 Maquinista/B&W diesels; 4500 hp(m) *(3.3 MW)*; 1 shaft
Speed, knots: 14

Comment: Commissioned in Navy 17 March 1981. Former ferry.

PILOTO ALSINA   *4/1992, Hartmut Ehlers*

Name	No	Builders	Commissioned
LIBERTAD	Q 2	AFNE, Rio Santiago	28 May 1963

Displacement, tons: 3025 standard; 3765 full load
Dimensions, feet (metres): 262 wl; 301 oa × 45.3 × 21.8 *(79.9; 91.7 × 13.8 × 6.6)*
Main machinery: 2 Sulzer diesels; 2400 hp(m) *(1.76 MW)*; 2 shafts
Speed, knots: 13.5 under power. **Range, miles:** 12 000
Complement: 220 crew plus 150 cadets
Guns: 1—3 in *(76 mm)* and 4—40 mm (fitted for but not with). 4—47 mm saluting guns.
Radars: Navigation: Decca; I band.

Comment: Launched 30 May 1956. She set record for crossing the North Atlantic under sail in 1966, a record which still stands. Sail area, 27 265 sq m.

LIBERTAD   *11/1993, Robert Pabst*

AUXILIARIES

Note: There are plans for a large fleet replenishment ship to replace the *Punta Medanos* deleted in 1987. A lease from the USN seems the most likely way of meeting the requirement although the Navy would prefer a derivative of the Spanish *Mar del Norte*.

3 COSTA SUR CLASS (TRANSPORT)

Name	No	Builders	Commissioned
CANAL BEAGLE	B 3	Astillero Principe y Menghi SA	29 Apr 1978
BAHIA SAN BLAS	B 4	Astillero Principe y Menghi SA	27 Nov 1978
CABO DE HORNOS	B 5	Astillero Principe y Menghi SA	28 June 1979
(ex-*Bahia Camarones*)			

Measurement, tons: 5800 dwt; 4600 gross
Dimensions, feet (metres): 390.3 × 57.4 × 21 *(119 × 17.5 × 6.4)*
Main machinery: 2 AFNE-Sulzer diesels; 6400 hp(m) *(4.7 MW)*; 2 shafts
Speed, knots: 15

Comment: Ordered December 1975. Laid down 10 January 1977, 11 April 1977 and 29 April 1978. Launched 19 October 1977, 29 April 1978 and 4 November 1978. Used to supply off-shore research installations in Naval Area South. One operated in the Gulf in 1991.

CABO DE HORNOS   *10/1993, Diego Quevedo*

6 FLOATING DOCKS

Number	Dimensions, feet (metres)	Capacity, tons
Y 1 (ex-ARD 23)	492 × 88.6 × 56 *(150 × 27 × 17.1)*	3500
2	300.1 × 60 × 41 *(91.5 × 18.3 × 12.5)*	1500
—	215.8 × 46 × 45.5 *(65.8 × 14 × 13.7)*	750
A	565.8 × 85.3 *(172.5 × 26)*	12 000
B	360.8 × 59 *(110 × 18)*	2800
—	623.4 × 78.7 *(190 × 24)*	12 000

Comment: First one is at Mar del Plata naval base, the second at Dársena Norte, Buenos Aires, the third at Puerto Belgrano and last two at Dársena Este. No 2 was built in 1913, A in 1957-58 and B in 1956. Another 12 000 ton dock was built in 1987 at Rio Santiago Shipyard. A second ex-USN ARD was authorised for transfer in late 1993. There are also at least four floating cranes.

ARMY CRAFT

Comment: Several LCPs (BDPs) are operated by Batallón de Ingenieros Anfibios 601 at Santa Fé. Built by Ast Vicente Forte. Ferries for crossing Rio Paraña include two built in 1969. In addition there are over 1000 Ferramar 'Asalto' and 'Comando' inflatable craft.

FERRAMAR ASALTO   *1990, Ferramar*

ICEBREAKER

Name	No	Builders	Commissioned
ALMIRANTE IRIZAR	Q 5	Wärtsilä, Helsinki	15 Dec 1978

Displacement, tons: 14 900 full load
Dimensions, feet (metres): 392 × 82 × 31.2 *(119.3 × 25 × 9.5)*
Main machinery: Diesel-electric; 4 Wärtsilä-SEMT-Pielstick 8 PC2.5 L diesels; 18 720 hp(m) *(13.77 MW)* sustained; 4 generators; 2 motors; 16 200 hp(m) *(11.9 MW)*; 2 shafts
Speed, knots: 16.5
Complement: 133 ship's company plus 100 passengers
Guns: 2 Bofors 40 mm/70; 300 rounds/minute to 12 km *(6.5 nm)* anti-surface; 4 km *(2.2 nm)* anti-aircraft; weight of shell 0.96 kg.
Radars: Air/surface search: Plessey AWS 2; E/F band.
Navigation: Two Decca; I band.
Helicopters: 2 ASH-3H Sea King.

Comment: Fitted for landing craft with two 16 ton cranes, fin stabilisers, Wärtsilä bubbling system and a 60 ton towing winch. Red hull with white upperworks and red funnel. Designed for Antarctic support operations and able to remain in polar regions throughout the Winter with 210 people aboard. Used as a transport to South Georgia in December 1981 and as a hospital ship during the Falklands campaign April to June 1982. Currently used as the Patagonian supply ship.

ALMIRANTE IRIZAR   *7/1992, Miguel A Soto*

TUGS

Name	No	Builders	Commissioned
SANAVIRON	A 8	Levingstone SB Co, Orange	5 Aug 1947
(ex-US ATA 228)			

Comment: Details as for Sotoyomo class under *Patrol Ships*.

SANAVIRON   *8/1989, van Ginderen Collection*

Name	No	Builders	Commissioned
QUERANDI	R 2	Ast Vicente Forte, Buenos Aires	22 Aug 1978
TEHUELCHE	R 3	Ast Vicente Forte, Buenos Aires	2 Nov 1978

Displacement, tons: 270 full load
Dimensions, feet (metres): 110.2 × 27.6 × 9.8 *(33.6 × 8.4 × 3)*
Main machinery: 2 MAN diesels; 1320 hp(m) *(970 kW)*; 2 shafts
Speed, knots: 12. **Range, miles:** 1100 at 12 kts
Complement: 30
Radars: Navigation: Decca; I band.

Comment: Ordered 1973. Launched 20 December 1977.

Name	No	Name	No
HUARPE	R 1	ONA	R 7
MATACO	R 4	TOBA	R 8

Displacement, tons: 208 full load
Dimensions, feet (metres): 99.4 × 27.6 × 10.5 *(30.3 × 8.4 × 3.2)*
Main machinery: 2 MAN diesels; 830 hp(m) *(610 kW)*; 1 shaft
Speed, knots: 12
Complement: 10 (2 officers)

Comment: Transferred from the River Flotilla to the Navy in 1988.

Name	No	Name	No
MOCOVI	R 5 (ex-US YTL 441)	CAPAYAN	R 16 (ex-US YTL 443)
CALCHAQUI	R 6 (ex-US YTL 445)	CHIQUILLAN	R 18 (ex-US YTL 444)
CHULUPI	R 10 (ex-US YTL 426)	MORCOYAN	R 19 (ex-US YTL 448)

Displacement, tons: 70
Dimensions, feet (metres): 63 × 16.4 × 7.2 *(19.2 × 5 × 2.2)*
Main machinery: 1 Hoover-Owens-Rentscheer diesel; 310 hp(m) *(228 kW)*; 1 shaft
Speed, knots: 10
Complement: 5

Comment: YTL Type built in USA and transferred on lease in March 1965 (R 16, 18, 19), remainder in March 1969. All purchased on 16 June 1977.

PREFECTURA NAVAL ARGENTINA
(COAST GUARD)

Headquarters' Appointments

Commander:
Prefecto General Jorge H Maggi
Vice Commander:
Prefecto General Jorge A Gentiluomo

Senior Appointments

Director of Prefectura's Zones:
Prefecto General Juan M Redon
Director of Administration:
Prefecto General Ruben R Astiasaran
Director of Navigation, Police and Safety:
Prefecto General Pedro L Bustamante
Director of Materiel:
Prefecto General Andres R Lorenzo
Director of Personnel:
Prefecto General Fortunato C Benasulin
Director of Judicial Police:
Prefecto General Raul C Dimarco
Director of Intelligence:
Prefecto General Carlos J Leyes

Personnel

1994: 13 240 (1439 officers) including 621 civilians

Tasks

Under the General Organisation Act the PNA is charged with:
(a) Enforcement of Federal Laws on the high seas and waters subject to the Argentine Republic.
(b) Enforcement of environmental protection laws in Federal waters.
(c) Search and Rescue.
(d) Security of waterfront facilities and vessels in port.
(e) Operations of certain Navaids.
(f) Operation of some Pilot Services.
(g) Management and operation of Aviation Department, Coastguard Vessels, Salvage, Fire and Anti-Pollution Service, Yachtmaster School, National Diving School and several Fire Brigades.

Organisation

Formed in 10 districts; High Parana River, Upper Parana and Paraguay Rivers, Lower Parana River, Upper Uruguay River, Lower Uruguay River, Delta, River Plate, Northern Argentine Sea, Southern Argentine Sea, Lakes and Comahue.

History

The Spanish authorities in South America established similar organisations to those in Spain. In 1756 the Captainship of the Port came into being in Buenos Aires—in 1810 the Ship Registry office was added to this title. On 29 October 1896 the title of Capitania General de Puertos was established by Act of Congress, the beginning of the PNA. Today, as a security and safety force, it has responsibilities throughout the rivers of Argentina, the ports and harbours as well as within territorial waters out to the 200 mile EEZ. An attempt was made in January 1992 to restrict operations to a 12 mile limit but the legislation was cancelled.

Identity markings

Two unequal blue stripes with, superimposed, crossed white anchors followed by the title Prefectura Naval.

Strength of Prefectura

Patrol Ships	6
Large Patrol Craft	4
Coastal Patrol Craft	53
Training Ships	3
Pilot Stations	2
Pilot Craft	23

PENNANT LIST

Prefectura Naval Argentina					
GC 13	Delfin	GC 48-61	Patrol Craft	GC 75	Bahia Blanca
GC 21	Lynch	GC 64	Mar del Plata	GC 76	Ingeniero White
GC 22	Toll	GC 65	Martin Garcia	GC 77	Golfo San Matias
GC 24	Mantilla	GC 66	Rio Lujan	GC 78	Madryn
GC 25	Azopardo	GC 67	Rio Uruguay	GC 79	Rio Deseado
GC 26	Thompson	GC 68	Rio Paraguay	GC 80	Ushuaia
GC 27	Prefecto Fique	GC 69	Rio Parana	GC 81	Canal de Beagle
GC 28	Prefecto Derbes	GC 70	Rio de la Plata	GC 88-95	Patrol Craft
GC 43	Mandubi	GC 71	La Plata	GC 101	Dorado
GC 47	Tonina	GC 72	Buenos Aires	GC 102-114	Patrol Craft
		GC 73	Cabo Corrientes	GC 119	Lago Alumine
		GC 74	Rio Quequen		

PATROL FORCES

Notes: (1) In addition to the ships and craft listed below the PNA operates 450 craft, including floating cranes, runabouts and inflatables of all types including LS 11201-3, LS 11001-4, LS 9500-9, LS 6301-17, LS 6801-12, LS 5801-5865, SB9. A firefighting vessel *Cabo Riomayor* was acquired in August 1993.
(2) 25 harbour patrol craft with outboard engines are to be acquired in 1994.

5 HALCON (TYPE B 119) CLASS

Name	No	Builders	Commissioned
MANTILLA	GC 24	Bazán, El Ferrol	20 Dec 1982
AZOPARDO	GC 25	Bazán, El Ferrol	28 Apr 1983
THOMPSON	GC 26	Bazán, El Ferrol	20 June 1983
PREFECTO FIQUE	GC 27	Bazán, El Ferrol	29 July 1983
PREFECTO DERBES	GC 28	Bazán, El Ferrol	20 Nov 1983

Displacement, tons: 910 standard; 1084 full load
Dimensions, feet (metres): 219.9 × 34.4 × 13.8 *(67 × 10.5 × 4.2)*
Main machinery: 2 Bazán-MTU 16V 956 TB91 diesels; 7500 hp(m) *(5.52 MW)* sustained; 2 shafts
Speed, knots: 20. **Range, miles:** 5000 at 18 kts
Complement: 33 (10 officers)
Guns: 1 Breda 40 mm/70; 300 rounds/minute to 12.5 km *(7 nm)*; weight of shell 0.96 kg.
2—12.7 mm MGs.
Radars: Navigation: Decca 1226; I band.
Helicopters: Hangar and Platform for 1 light.

Comment: Ordered in 1979 from Bazán, El Ferrol, Spain. All have helicopter hangar and Magnavox MX 1102 SATNAV. Hospital with four beds. Carry one rigid rescue craft *(6.1 m)* with Perkins outboard and a capacity of 12 and two inflatable craft *(4.1 m)* with Evinrude outboard. Esquilo helicopters were to have replaced the Alouettes but as this acquisition was cancelled in 1992, helicopters are no longer carried.

MANTILLA   *4/1992, Hartmut Ehlers*

1 PATROL SHIP

Name	No	Builders	Completed
DELFIN	GC 13	Ijsselwerf, Netherlands	14 May 1957

Displacement, tons: 700 standard; 1000 full load
Dimensions, feet (metres): 193.5 × 29.8 × 13.8 *(59 × 9.1 × 4.2)*
Main machinery: 2 MAN diesels; 2300 hp(m) *(1.69 MW)*; 2 shafts
Speed, knots: 15. **Range, miles:** 6720 at 10 kts
Complement: 27
Guns: 1 Oerlikon 20 mm. 2—12.7 mm Browning MGs.
Radars: Navigation: Decca; I band.

Comment: Whaler acquired for PNA in 1969. Commissioned 23 January 1970.

PREFECTO FIQUE   *6/1992, Miguel A Soto*

DELFIN   *4/1992, Hartmut Ehlers*

2 LYNCH CLASS (LARGE PATROL CRAFT)

Name	No	Builders	Commissioned
LYNCH	GC 21	AFNE, Rio Santiago	20 May 1964
TOLL	GC 22	AFNE, Rio Santiago	7 July 1966

Displacement, tons: 100 standard; 117 full load
Dimensions, feet (metres): 98.4 × 21 × 5.6 (30 × 6.4 × 1.7)
Main machinery: 2 MTU Maybach diesels; 2700 hp(m) (1.98 MW); 2 shafts
Speed, knots: 22. **Range, miles:** 2000
Complement: 11
Guns: 1 Oerlikon 20 mm.

TOLL   1990, Prefectura Naval Argentina

1 LARGE PATROL CRAFT

Name	No	Builders	Commissioned
MANDUBI	GC 43	Base Naval Rio Santiago	1940

Displacement, tons: 270 full load
Dimensions, feet (metres): 108.9 × 20.7 × 6.2 (33.2 × 6.3 × 1.9)
Main machinery: 2 MAN G6V-23.5/33 diesels; 500 hp(m) (367 kW); 1 shaft
Speed, knots: 14. **Range, miles:** 800 at 14 kts; 3400 at 10 kts
Complement: 12
Guns: 2—12.7 mm Browning MGs.

Comment: Since 1986 has acted as training craft for PNA Cadets School carrying 20 cadets.

MANDUBI   1990, Prefectura Naval Argentina

1 RIVER PATROL SHIP

Name	No	Builders	Commissioned
TONINA	GC 47	SANYM SA San Fernando, Argentina	30 June 1978

Displacement, tons: 103 standard; 153 full load
Dimensions, feet (metres): 83.8 × 21.3 × 10.1 (25.5 × 6.5 × 3.3)
Main machinery: 2 GM 16V-71TA diesels; 1000 hp (746 kW) sustained; 2 shafts
Speed, knots: 10. **Range, miles:** 2800 at 10 kts
Complement: 11 (3 officers)
Guns: 1 Oerlikon 20 mm.
Radars: Navigation: Decca 1226; I band.

Comment: Served as training ship for PNA Cadets School until 1986. Now acts as salvage ship with salvage pumps and recompression chamber. Capable of operating divers and underwater swimmers.

TONINA   1/1993, Prefectura Naval Argentina

18 MAR DEL PLATA CLASS (COASTAL PATROL CRAFT)

MAR DEL PLATA GC 64	RIO DE LA PLATA GC 70	INGENIERO WHITE GC 76
MARTIN GARCIA GC 65	LA PLATA GC 71	GOLFO SAN MATIAS GC 77
RIO LUJAN GC 66	BUENOS AIRES GC 72	MADRYN GC 78
RIO URUGUAY GC 67	CABO CORRIENTES GC 73	RIO DESEADO GC 79
RIO PARAGUAY GC 68	RIO QUEQUEN GC 74	USHUAIA GC 80
RIO PARANA GC 69	BAHIA BLANCA GC 75	CANAL DE BEAGLE GC 81

Displacement, tons: 81 full load
Dimensions, feet (metres): 91.8 × 17.4 × 5.2 (28 × 5.3 × 1.6)
Main machinery: 2 MTU 8V 331 TC92 diesels; 1770 hp(m) (1.3 MW) sustained; 2 shafts
Speed, knots: 22. **Range, miles:** 1200 at 12 kts; 780 at 18 kts
Complement: 14 (3 officers)
Guns: 1 Oerlikon 20 mm. 2—12.7 mm Browning MGs.
Radars: Navigation: Decca 1226; I band.

Comment: Ordered 24 November 1978 from Blohm & Voss to a Z-28 design. First delivered mid-1979 and then at monthly intervals. Steel hulls. GC 82 and 83 were captured by the British Forces in 1982.

RIO LUJAN   4/1992, Hartmut Ehlers

1 COASTAL PATROL CRAFT

Name	No	Builders	Commissioned
DORADO	GC 101	Base Naval, Rio Santiago	17 Dec 1939

Displacement, tons: 43 full load
Dimensions, feet (metres): 69.5 × 14.1 × 4.9 (21.2 × 4.3 × 1.5)
Main machinery: 2 GM 6071-6A diesels; 360 hp (268 kW); 1 shaft
Speed, knots: 12. **Range, miles:** 1550
Complement: 7 (1 officer)

DORADO   4/1992, Tomas Lozada

34 SMALL PATROL CRAFT

GC 48-61	GC 88-95	GC 102-108	GC 110-114

Displacement, tons: 15 full load
Dimensions, feet (metres): 41 × 11.8 × 3.6 (12.5 × 3.6 × 1.1)
Main machinery: 2 GM diesels; 514 hp (383 kW); 2 shafts
Speed, knots: 20. **Range, miles:** 400 at 18 kts
Complement: 3
Guns: 12.7 mm Browning MG.

Comment: First delivered September 1978. First 14 built by Cadenazzi, Tigre 1977-79, remainder by Ast Belen de Escobar 1984-86. GC 102-114 are slightly smaller.

GC 61   7/1992, Julio Caufero

3 TRAINING SHIPS

ESPERANZA   ADHARA II   TALITA II

Displacement, tons: 33.5 standard
Dimensions, feet (metres): 62.3 × 14.1 × 8.9 *(19 × 4.3 × 2.7)*
Main machinery: 1 VM diesel; 90 hp(m) *(66 kW)*; 1 shaft
Speed, knots: 6; 15 sailing
Complement: 6 plus 6 cadets

Comment: Details given are for *Esperanza* built by Ast Central de la PNA. Launched and commissioned 20 December 1968 as a sail training ship. In addition there are two 30 ton training craft *Adhara II* and *Talita II* of similar dimensions.

TALITA II   *11/1988, Prefectura Naval Argentina*

6 HARBOUR TUGS

CANAL EMILIO MITRE SB 8   +SB 3, 4, 5, 9 and 10

Comment: *Canal Emilio Mitre* is of 53 tons full load and has a speed of 10 kts and was built by Damen Shipyard, Netherlands in 1982.

CANAL EMILIO MITRE   *1993, Prefectura Naval Argentina*

PILOT VESSELS

1 PILOT STATION

Name	No	Builders	Commissioned
LAGO LACAR	DF 14	Brodogradiliste, Split	1962

Displacement, tons: 10 900 full load
Dimensions, feet (metres): 515.1 × 65.6 × 25 *(157 × 20 × 7.6)*
Main machinery: 1 Fiat 759S diesel; 1 shaft
Speed, knots: 14
Complement: 28 (3 officers)

Comment: Commissioned as a Coast Guard ship 24 December 1986. Has a helicopter deck and a hospital with 40 beds.

LAGO LACAR   *6/1992, Miguel A Soto*

1 PILOT STATION

Name	No	Builders	Commissioned
RIO LIMAY	DF —	Astillero Astarsa	30 May 1972

Displacement, tons: 10 070 full load
Dimensions, feet (metres): 482.3 × 65.6 × 28 *(147 × 20 × 8.5)*
Speed, knots: 13
Complement: 28 (3 officers)

Comment: Commissioned as a Coast Guard ship 24 December 1991. Has a helicopter deck and a 20 bed hospital.

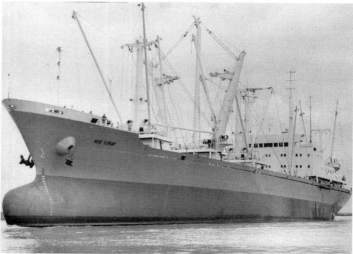

RIO LIMAY   *1990, Prefectura Naval Argentina*

23 PILOT CRAFT

ALUMINE GC 118 (ex-SP 14)	**SAN MARTIN** SP 21	**ROCA** SP 28
TRAFUL GC 119 (ex-SP 15)	**BUENOS AIRES** SP 22	**PUELO** SP 29
COLHUE SP 16	**FAGNANO** SP 23	**FUTALAUFQUEN** SP 30
MASCARDI GC 122 (ex-SP 17)	**LACAR** GC 120 (ex-SP 24)	**FALKNER** SP 31
MARIO L PENDO SP 18	**CARDIEL** SP 25	**FONTANA** GC 121 (ex-SP 32)
NAHUEL HUAPI SP 19	**MUSTERS** SP 26	**COLHUE HUAPI** SP 33
VIEDMA SP 20	**QUILLEN** SP 27	**HUECHULAFQUEN** SP 34
		YEHUIN SP 35

(All names preceded by **LAGO** except SP 18)

Comment: There are five different types of named pilot craft. SP 14-15 of 33.7 tons built in 1981; SP 16-18 of 47 tons built since 1981; SP 19-23 of 51 tons built since 1981; SP 24-27 of 20 tons built in 1981; SP 28-30 of 16.5 m built in 1983; SP 31-35 of 7 tons built in 1986-1991. Most built by Damen SY, Netherlands. The last three built by Astillero Mestrina, Tigre. No armament.

LAGO MUSTERS   *8/1992, Juan Sanchez*

LAND-BASED MARITIME AIRCRAFT

Notes: (1) 10 Helibras Esquilo or Bell shipborne helicopters will not now be acquired until funds are available. Until then no helicopters are embarked.
(2) In addition to the aircraft listed, there is a Piper Warrior II training aircraft.

Numbers/Type: 2 Aerospatiale SA 330 Super Puma.
Operational speed: 151 kts *(279 km/h)*.
Service ceiling: 15 090 ft *(4600 m)*.
Range: 335 nm *(620 km)*.
Role/Weapon systems: Support and SAR helicopter for patrol work. Sensors: Omera search radar. Weapons: Can carry pintle-mounted machine guns but are usually unarmed.

Numbers/Type: 5 CASA C-212 Aviocar.
Operational speed: 190 kts *(353 km/h)*.
Service ceiling: 24 000 ft *(7315 m)*.
Range: 1650 nm *(3055 km)*.
Role/Weapon systems: Two acquired in 1989, three more in 1990. Medium-range reconnaissance and coastal surveillance duties in EEZ. Sensors: Bendix RDS 32 surface search radar. Omega Global GNS-500. Weapons: ASW; can carry torpedoes, depth bombs or mines. ASV; 2 × rockets or machine gun pods not normally fitted.

AUSTRALIA

Headquarters' Appointments

Chief of Defence Force:
Vice Admiral A L Beaumont, AC
Chief of Naval Staff:
Vice Admiral R G Taylor, AO
Deputy Chief of Naval Staff:
Rear Admiral D J Campbell, AM
Assistant Chief of Naval Staff (Personnel):
Rear Admiral C J Oxenbould
Assistant Chief of Naval Staff (Materiel):
Rear Admiral N D H Hammond

Senior Appointments

Maritime Commander, Australia:
Rear Admiral D B Chalmers, AO
Flag Officer Naval Support Command:
Rear Admiral A L Hunt, AO
Commodore Flotillas:
Commodore J R Lord
Commodore Naval Training Command:
Rear Admiral P D Briggs, AM, CSC

Diplomatic Representation

Naval Attaché in Jakarta:
Captain K J Jordan
Defence Adviser in Seoul:
Captain R E Swinnerton
Defence Adviser in London:
Commodore G P Kable
Naval Adviser in London:
Captain P J Parkins
Defence Adviser in New Delhi:
Captain R G Dagworthy, AM
Defence Attaché in Manila:
Captain M C Webster, AM
Naval Attaché in Washington and Ottawa:
Commodore R J Letts, MVO, ADC
Defence Attaché in Paris:
Captain M J Carrel
Defence Attaché in Tokyo:
Captain J W Hewett
Naval Adviser in Honiara:
Commander K R Eglen
Naval Attaché in Suva:
Lieutenant Commander B F Vandepeer

Personnel

1994: 14 739 officers and sailors
4562 Reserves (active and inactive)

RAN Reserve

The Naval Reserve is integrated into the Permanent Force. Personnel are either Active Reservists with regular commitments or Inactive Reservists with periodic or contingent duty. The missions undertaken by the Reserve include Naval Control of Shipping, Aviation, MCM, Intelligence, Diving and patrol boat/landing craft operations. In addition, members of the Ready Reserve (a component of the Active Reserve) are shadow posted to selected major fleet units.

Shore Establishments

Sydney: Maritime Headquarters Australia, Fleet Base East (Garden Island), *Platypus* (Submarines), *Waterhen* (Mine warfare), *Watson* (Warfare Training), *Penguin* (Diving, NBCD, Hospital, Staff College), *Kuttabul* (Administration).
Jervis Bay Area: *Albatross* (Air Station), *Creswell* (Naval College and Fleet Support), Jervis Bay Range Facility.
Cockburn Sound (WA): Fleet Base West, *Stirling* (Administration and Maintenance Support), Submarine School.
Darwin: Minor warship base, *Coonawarra* (Communications Station).
Cairns: Headquarters Patrol Boat Force, *Cairns* (Minor warship base).
Canberra: Navy Office, *Harman* (Communications Station).
Westernport: *Cerberus* (Major training facility, minor warship base).
North West Cape: Harold E Holt Communications Station.
Note: *Moreton* (Brisbane), *Encounter* (Adelaide) and *Huon* (Hobart) closed in 1994.

Fleet Deployment 1994

Fleet Base East (and other Sydney bases): 3 SS, 3 DDG, 4 FFG, 1 AOR, 1 GT, 1 LSH, 1 ASR, 2 MHI, 4 MSA, 1 PTF, 2 LCH.
Fleet Base West: 1 SS, 2 FFG, 3 DE, 1 AO, 1 AGS, 2 PTF.
Darwin Naval Base: 6 PTF, 1 LCH.
Cairns: 5 PTF, 2 LCH, 5 AGS.
Westernport, Hobart, Adelaide: 1 PTF/PC each.
Brisbane: 1 LCH.

Fleet Air Arm (see *Shipborne Aircraft* section).

Squadron	Aircraft
HC-723 *	Squirrel AS 350B, utility, FFG embarked flights, SAR
	HS 748, Fixed wing, EW operations and training
	Bell 206B, survey support
HS-817	Sea King Mk 50, ASW
HS-816	Seahawk S-70B-2, ASW, ASST

Prefix to Ships' Names

HMAS. Her Majesty's Australian Ship

Strength of the Fleet

Type	Active	Building (Projected)
Patrol Submarines (SS)	4	6
Destroyers (DDG)	3	—
Frigates (FFG)	5	8
Escorts (DE)	3	—
Minehunters (Coastal)	—	(6)
Minehunters (Inshore)	2	—
Minesweepers (Auxiliary)	5	(1)
Offshore Patrol Vessels (OPV)	—	(12)
Large Patrol Craft (PTF)	15	—
Amphibious Heavy Lift Ship (LSH)	1	—
Landing Ships Tank (LST)	2	—
Heavy Landing Craft (LCH)	6	—
Light Landing Craft (LCVP)	4	—
Marine Science Ships (AGS)	6	(3)
Replenishment Ships (AO)	2	—
Training Ships	3	—
Trials and Safety Ship (ASR)	1	—
Tugs (AT)	5	—
Torpedo Recovery Vessels (TRV)	3	—

Mercantile Marine

Lloyd's Register of Shipping
633 vessels of 2 861 786 tons gross

DELETIONS

Submarines

1992 *Oxley*
1994 *Otway*

Frigates

1991 *Parramatta* (old), *Stuart* (old)

Patrol Forces

1992 *Adroit, Bass*
1993 *Ardent, Aware*

Minesweepers

1991 *Wave Rider* (returned to civilian use)
1992 *Salvatore V*
1994 *Carole S*

Miscellaneous

1991 TB 1536 (sold)
1992 *Gunundaal, AB 1052, AB 1054*
1993 *The Luke,* seven army work boats, all RAAF craft

PENNANT LIST

Submarines

60	Onslow
61	Orion
62	Otama
70	Ovens
71	Collins (trials)
72	Farncomb (bldg)
73	Waller (bldg)
74	Dechaineux (bldg)
75	Sheean (bldg)
76	Rankin (bldg)

Destroyers

38	Perth (old)
39	Hobart
41	Brisbane

Frigates

01	Adelaide
02	Canberra
03	Sydney
04	Darwin
05	Melbourne
06	Newcastle
49	Derwent
50	Swan
53	Torrens
150	Anzac (bldg)
151	Arunta (bldg)
152	Warumungu (bldg)
153	Stuart (bldg)
154	Parramatta (bldg)
155	Ballarat (bldg)
156	Toowoomba (bldg)
157	Perth (new) (bldg)

Mine Warfare Vessels

M 80	Rushcutter
M 81	Shoalwater
Y 298	Bandicoot
Y 299	Wallaroo
1102	Brolga
1185	Koraaga

Training Ships

GT 203	Jervis Bay
AG 244	Banks

Patrol Forces

203	Fremantle
204	Warrnambool
205	Townsville
206	Wollongong
207	Launceston
208	Whyalla
209	Ipswich
210	Cessnock
211	Bendigo
212	Gawler
213	Geraldton
214	Dubbo
215	Geelong
216	Gladstone
217	Bunbury

Replenishment Ships

O 195	Westralia
OR 304	Success

Amphibious Vessels

L 50	Tobruk
L 126	Balikpapan
L 127	Brunei
L 128	Labuan
L 129	Tarakan
L 130	Wewak
L 133	Betano

Survey Ships

A 73	Moresby
A 312	Flinders
A 01	Paluma
A 02	Mermaid
A 03	Shepparton
A 04	Benalla

Trials and Safety Ship

ASR 241	Protector

Torpedo Recovery Vessels

TRV 801	Tuna
TRV 802	Trevally
TRV 803	Tailor

SUBMARINES

0 + 6 COLLINS CLASS

Name	No	Builders	Laid down	Launched	Commissioned
COLLINS	71	Australia Submarine Corp, Adelaide	14 Feb 1990	28 Aug 1993	May 1995
FARNCOMB	72	Australia Submarine Corp, Adelaide	1 Mar 1991	Feb 1995	Feb 1996
WALLER	73	Australia Submarine Corp, Adelaide	19 Mar 1992	Aug 1995	Jan 1997
DECHAINEUX	74	Australia Submarine Corp, Adelaide	4 Mar 1993	Aug 1996	Dec 1997
SHEEAN	75	Australia Submarine Corp, Adelaide	17 Feb 1994	Aug 1997	Nov 1998
RANKIN	76	Australia Submarine Corp, Adelaide	Mar 1995	Aug 1998	Oct 1999

Displacement, tons: 3051 surfaced; 3353 dived
Dimensions, feet (metres): 254 × 25.6 × 23
(77.5 × 7.8 × 7)
Main machinery: Diesel-electric; 3 Hedemora/Garden Island
Type V18B/14Sub diesels; 6020 hp *(4.42 MW)*; 3 Jeumont
Schneider generators; 4.2 MW; 1 Jeumont Schneider motor;
7344 hp(m) *(5.4 MW)*; 1 shaft; 1 MacTaggart Scott DM
43006 hydraulic motor for emergency propulsion
Speed, knots: 10 surfaced; 10 snorting; 20 dived
Range, miles: 9000 at 10 kts (snorting); 11 500 at 10 kts
(surfaced)
Complement: 42 (6 officers)

Missiles: SSM: McDonnell Douglas Sub Harpoon; active radar
homing to 130 km *(70 nm)* at 0.9 Mach; warhead 227 kg.
Torpedoes: 6—21 in *(533 mm)* fwd tubes. Gould Mk 48 Mod 4;
dual purpose; wire-guided; active/passive homing to 38 km
(21 nm) at 55 kts or 50 km *(27 nm)* at 40 kts; warhead 267 kg.
Air turbine pump discharge. Total of 23 weapons including
Mk 48 and Sub Harpoon.
Mines: In lieu of torpedoes. The Swedish external attachment is
an option.
Countermeasures: Decoys: 2 SSDE.
ESM: Argo AR 740; radar warning.
Fire control: Librascope weapons control system.
Radars: Navigation: GEC Marconi Type 1007; I band.
Sonars: Thomson Sintra Scylla bow and flank arrays.
Kariwara or Thomson Sintra retractable passive towed array.

Programmes: Contract signed on 3 June 1987 for construction
of six Swedish-designed Kockums Type 471. Fabrication work
started in June 1989; bow and stern sections of the first submarines built in Sweden. The option on two additional boats,
recommended by the Navy, was not taken up.
Structure: Air independent propulsion (AIP) developments will
be monitored but acquisition is a low priority. Scylla is an
updated Eledone sonar suite. Diving depth, 250 m *(820 ft)*.
Anechoic tiles are to be fitted after first of class trials.

COLLINS   *8/1993, Ships of the World*

Operational: All based at Fleet Base West with one or two
deploying regularly to the east coast. A 'two crew' cycle was
considered and rejected. *Collins* started sea trials early in
1994.

COLLINS   *8/1993, John Mortimer*

---

4 OBERON CLASS

Name	No	Builders	Laid down	Launched	Commissioned
ONSLOW	60	Scotts' Shipbuilding & Eng Co Ltd, Greenock	4 Dec 1967	3 Dec 1968	22 Dec 1969
ORION	61	Scotts' Shipbuilding & Eng Co Ltd, Greenock	6 Oct 1972	16 Sep 1974	15 June 1977
OTAMA	62	Scotts' Shipbuilding & Eng Co Ltd, Greenock	25 May 1973	3 Dec 1975	27 Apr 1978
OVENS	70	Scotts' Shipbuilding & Eng Co Ltd, Greenock	17 June 1966	4 Dec 1967	18 Apr 1969

Displacement, tons: 1610 standard; 2030 surfaced; 2410
dived
Dimensions, feet (metres): 295.2 × 26.5 × 18 *(90 × 8.1 × 5.5)*
Main machinery: Diesel-electric; 2 ASR 16 VVS-ASR1 diesels;
3680 hp *(2.74 MW)*; 2 AEI motors; 6000 hp *(4.48 MW)*; 2
shafts
Speed, knots: 12 surfaced; 17 dived; 11 snorting
Range, miles: 9000 at 12 kts surfaced
Complement: 64 (8 officers)

Missiles: SSM: McDonnell Douglas Sub Harpoon; active radar
homing to 130 km *(70 nm)* at 0.9 Mach; warhead 227 kg.
Torpedoes: 6—21 in *(533 mm)* bow tubes (HP air discharge).
Gould Mk 48 Mod 4; dual purpose; wire-guided; active/passive
homing to 38 km *(21 nm)* at 55 kts; 50 km *(27 nm)* at 40 kts;
warhead 267 kg. Combined total of 20 SSM and torpedoes
carried.
Countermeasures: Decoys: 2 SSDE.
ESM: AWA Mavis ODU; radar warning.
Fire control: Singer Librascope SFCS Mk 1 data handling and
fire-control system.
Radars: Surface search: Kelvin Hughes Type 1006; I band.
Sonars: Atlas Elektronik Type CSU3-41; bow array; active/pass-
ive; medium frequency; has intercept and UWT capability.
BAC Type 2007; flank array; passive; long range; low
frequency.
Sperry BQQ 4 micropuffs; passive; range-finding.

Programmes: In 1963 an order was placed in the UK for four
submarines. Two more were ordered in October 1971. Scheduled deletion dates are *Ovens* 1995, *Orion* 1996, *Onslow*
1998, and *Otama* 1998.
Modernisation: Between October 1977 and October 1985 all
submarines of the class were given a mid-life modernisation at
Vickers, Cockatoo. Sub Harpoon fitted in 1985-86. The two
short stern tubes have been removed.
Operational: Submarine Squadron is based at *Platypus*, Neutral

ORION   *3/1993, Scott Connolly, RAN*

Bay, Sydney. *Orion* is based at *Stirling* in Western Australia. All
of the class have been used for trials of the Kariwara towed
array. AIP trials have been done ashore using a power source
of 200-600 kW. Stirling engines and solid fuel cell packs with
replaceable modules have also been investigated, but none
has been fitted in a submarine.

DESTROYERS

3 PERTH (MODIFIED CHARLES F ADAMS) CLASS (DDGs)

Name	No	Builders	Laid down	Launched	Commissioned
PERTH	38	Defoe Shipbuilding Co, Bay City, Michigan	21 Sep 1962	26 Sep 1963	17 July 1965
HOBART	39	Defoe Shipbuilding Co, Bay City, Michigan	26 Oct 1962	9 Jan 1964	18 Dec 1965
BRISBANE	41	Defoe Shipbuilding Co, Bay City, Michigan	15 Feb 1965	5 May 1966	16 Dec 1967

Displacement, tons: 3370 standard; 4618 full load
Dimensions, feet (metres): 440.8 × 47.1 × 20.1
(134.3 × 14.3 × 6.1)
Main machinery: 4 Foster-Wheeler boilers; 1200 psi
(84.37 kg/cm sq), 950°F (510°C); 2 GE turbines; 70 000 hp
(52 MW); 2 shafts
Speed, knots: 30+. **Range, miles:** 6000 at 15 kts; 2000 at
30 kts
Complement: 325 (25 officers)

Missiles: SSM: McDonnell Douglas Harpoon (fitted for but not
with).
SAM: 40 GDC Pomona Standard SM-1MR; Mk 13 Mod 6
launcher ❶; command guidance; semi-active radar homing to
46 km (25 nm) at 2 Mach; height 45.7-18 288 m (150-
60 000 ft). Dual capability launcher for SSM.
Guns: 2 FMC 5 in (127 mm)/54 Mk 42 Mod 10 automatic ❷; 85°
elevation; 40 rounds/minute to 24 km (13 nm) anti-surface;
14 km (8 nm) anti-aircraft; weight of shell 32 kg.
2 GE/GDC 20 mm Mk 15 Vulcan Phalanx ❸; 6 barrels per
mounting; 3000 rounds/minute combined to 1.5 km. Mountings rotated between ships.
Up to 6—12.7 mm MGs.
Torpedoes: 6—324 mm Mk 32 Mod 5 (2 triple) tubes ❹. Honeywell Mk 46 Mod 5; anti-submarine; active/passive homing to
11 km (5.9 nm) at 40 kts; warhead 44 kg. Some obsolete
Mk 44 torpedoes still in service.
Countermeasures: Decoys: 2 Loral Hycor SRBOC 6-barrelled
fixed Mk 36; chaff and IR flares to 1-4 km (0.6-2.2 nm). Nulka
quad expendable decoy launcher fitted in Brisbane for trials.
SLQ 25; towed torpedo decoy.
ESM/ECM: WLR-1H; intercept.
Combat data systems: NCDS with NTDS consoles and Univac
UYK-7 computers; Link 11. OE-2 SATCOM ❺.
Fire control: GFCS Mk 68. Missile control Mk 74 Mod 13. Electro-
optic sights may be fitted.
Radars: Air search: Hughes SPS 52C ❻; E/F band; range 439 km
(240 nm).
Lockheed SPS 40C ❼; E/F band; range 320 km (175 nm).
Surface search: Norden SPS 67V ❽; G band.
Fire control: Two Raytheon SPG 51C ❾; G/I band (for Standard
missile system).
Western Electric SPG 53F ❿; I/J band (for guns).
IFF: AIMS Mk 12.
Tacan: URN 20.
Sonars: Sangamo SQS 23KL; hull-mounted; active; medium fre-
quency; with limited bottom bounce capability.

Programmes: The USS Goldsborough which paid off in 1992 has
been acquired to provide spares and equipment for training.
Modernisation: Perth was first modernised in 1974 in the USA
with the installation of Standard missiles, replacement gun
mountings, new combat data system and modern radars.
Hobart and Brisbane were brought to the same standard in
1978 and 1979 at the Garden Island Dockyard in Sydney. A
second modernisation programme: Brisbane completed 1987;
Perth in 1989; Hobart in 1991. Major equipment upgraded:
search and fire-control radars, naval combat data system, gun
systems, the Mk 13 missile launcher (to take Harpoon). Missile

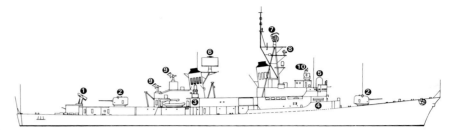

BRISBANE (Gulf fit)   (Scale 1 : 1200), Ian Sturton

BRISBANE   2/1993, John Mortimer

modernisation included decoy and improved ECM equipment;
three-dimensional radar SPS 52B upgraded to SPS 52C. In
1990/91 all ships were fitted for Phalanx CIWS, although the
mountings are rotated in a fleet pool system. To accommodate
Phalanx the ship's boats have been replaced by RIBs. Ikara
launchers and magazines have been removed. Nulka stand off
decoys installed in Brisbane for trials in 1992/93.
Structure: Generally similar to the US Charles F Adams class, but

they differ by the addition of a broad deckhouse between the
funnels which was the magazine for the now deleted Ikara system. The magazine complex has been converted for a variety of
uses, including accommodation and recreation spaces.
Operational: Operational deployments include communications
enhancements and portable RAM panels. All ships are capable
of fighter control.

PERTH (with Phalanx)   7/1993, John Mortimer

FRIGATES

6 ADELAIDE (OLIVER HAZARD PERRY) CLASS (FFGs)

Name	No	Builders	Laid down	Launched	Commissioned
ADELAIDE	01	Todd Pacific Shipyard Corporation, Seattle, USA	29 July 1977	21 June 1978	15 Nov 1980
CANBERRA	02	Todd Pacific Shipyard Corporation, Seattle, USA	1 Mar 1978	1 Dec 1978	21 Mar 1981
SYDNEY	03	Todd Pacific Shipyard Corporation, Seattle, USA	16 Jan 1980	26 Sep 1980	29 Jan 1983
DARWIN	04	Todd Pacific Shipyard Corporation, Seattle, USA	3 July 1981	26 Mar 1982	21 July 1984
MELBOURNE	05	Australian Marine Eng (Consolidated), Williamstown	12 July 1985	5 May 1989	15 Feb 1992
NEWCASTLE	06	Australian Marine Eng (Consolidated), Williamstown	21 July 1989	21 Feb 1992	11 Dec 1993

Displacement, tons: 4100 full load
Dimensions, feet (metres): 453 × 45 × 24.5 (sonar); 14.8 (keel) *(138.1 × 13.7 × 7.5; 4.5)*
Main machinery: 2 GE LM 2500 gas-turbines; 41 000 hp *(30.6 MW)* sustained; 1 shaft; cp prop; 2 auxiliary electric retractable propulsors fwd; 650 hp *(490 kW)*
Speed, knots: 29 (4 on propulsors). **Range, miles:** 4500 at 20 kts
Complement: 184 (15 officers) plus aircrew

Missiles: SSM: 8 McDonnell Douglas Harpoon; active radar homing to 130 km *(70 nm)* at 0.9 Mach; warhead 227 kg.
SAM: GDC Pomona Standard SM-1MR; Mk 13 Mod 4 launcher for both SAM and SSM systems ❶; command guidance; semi-active radar homing to 46 km *(25 nm)* at 2 Mach; height 45.7-18 288 m *(150-60 000 ft)*; 40 missiles (combined SSM and SAM).
Guns: 1 OTO Melara 3 in *(76 mm)*/62 US Mk 75 compact ❷; 85° elevation; 85 rounds/minute to 16 km *(9 nm)* anti-surface; 12 km *(6.5 nm)* anti-aircraft; weight of shell 6 kg. Guns for 05 and 06 manufactured in Australia.
1 General Electric/GDC 20 mm Mk 15 Vulcan Phalanx ❸; anti-missile system with 6 barrels; 4500 rounds/minute combined to 1.5 km. Retrofitted in 01 and 02 in 1985; 03-06 fitted on completion.
Up to 6—12.7 mm MGs.
Torpedoes: 6—324 mm Mk 32 (2 triple) tubes ❹. Honeywell Mk 46 Mod 5; anti-submarine; active/passive homing to 11 km *(5.9 nm)* at 40 kts; warhead 44 kg. Some Mk 44 torpedoes are still in service.
Countermeasures: Decoys: 2 Loral Hycor SRBOC Mk 36 chaff and IR decoy launchers; fixed 6-barrelled system; range 1-4 km. 4 Nulka quad expendable decoy launchers to be fitted. SLQ 25; towed torpedo decoy.
ESM/ECM: Raytheon SLQ-32C ❺; intercept and jammer.
Combat data systems: NCDS using NTDS consoles and Sperry Univac UYK 7 computers. OE-2 SATCOM; Link 11.
Fire control: Sperry Mk 92 Mod 2 gun and missile control (Signaal derivative). Electro-optic sights.
Radars: Air search: Raytheon SPS 49 ❻; C band; range 457 km *(250 nm)*.
Surface search/navigation: ISC Cardion SPS 55 ❼; I band.
Fire control: Lockheed SPG 60 ❽; I/J band; range 110 km *(60 nm)*; Doppler search and tracking.
Sperry Mk 92 (Signaal WM 28) ❾; I/J band; range 46 km *(25 nm)*.
IFF: AIMS Mk XII.
Tacan: URN-25.
Sonars: Raytheon SQS 56; hull-mounted; active; medium frequency. Commercial derivative of DE 1160 series. 05 and 06 will have EMI/Honeywell Mulloka system instead of SQS 56. Kariwara towed passive array in due course.

Helicopters: 2 Sikorsky S-70B-2 Seahawks ❿ or 1 Seahawk and 1 Squirrel.

Programmes: US numbers: *Adelaide* FFG 17; *Canberra* FFG 18; *Sydney* FFG 35; *Darwin* FFG 44.
Modernisation: *Adelaide* in November 1989, *Sydney* February 1989 and *Canberra* December 1991 completed a 12 month Helicopter Modification Programme to allow operation of Seahawk helicopters. The modification, fitted to *Darwin* during construction, involved angling the transom (increasing the ship's overall length by 8 ft) and fitting the RAST helo recovery system. *Melbourne* and *Newcastle* fitted during construction which also includes longitudinal strengthening and buoyancy upgrades. A number of options is being considered including SM2 missiles, a phased array radar, VLS launcher for Standard and Evolved Sea Sparrow, and towed arrays.
Operational: *Adelaide* based at Fleet Base West from October 1992, and joined by *Darwin* in 1993. The remainder are based at Fleet Base East. For operational tasks ships are fitted with enhanced communications, electro-optical sights, rigid inflatable boats and portable RAM panels. All ships are fighter control capable.

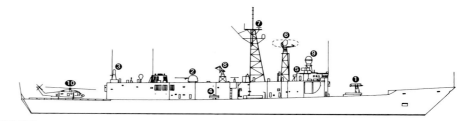

ADELAIDE

(Scale 1 : 1200), Ian Sturton

MELBOURNE

5/1993, John Mortimer

SYDNEY

10/1993, 92 Wing RAAF

ADELAIDE

10/1992, Scott Connolly, RAN

3 RIVER CLASS

Name	No	Builders	Laid down	Launched	Commissioned
DERWENT	49	HMA Naval Dockyard, Melbourne	16 June 1958	17 Apr 1961	30 Apr 1964
SWAN	50	HMA Naval Dockyard, Melbourne	18 Aug 1965	16 Dec 1967	20 Jan 1970
TORRENS	53	Cockatoo Island Dockyard, Sydney	18 Aug 1965	28 Sep 1968	19 Jan 1971

Displacement, tons: 2100 standard; 2700 full load
Dimensions, feet (metres): 360 wl; 370 oa × 41 × 17.3 (screws) *(109.8; 112.8 × 12.5 × 5.3)*
Main machinery: 2 B&W boilers; 550 psi *(38.7 kg/cm sq)*; 850°F *(450°C)*; 2 steam turbines; 30 000 hp *(22.4 MW)*; 2 shafts
Speed, knots: 30. **Range, miles:** 3400 at 12 kts
Complement: 234 (20 officers); 224 (21 officers) (in 49)

Guns: 2 Vickers 4.5 in *(114 mm)*/45 Mk 6 (twin) ❶; 80° elevation; 20 rounds/minute to 19 km *(10 nm)* anti-surface; 6 km *(3 nm)* anti-aircraft; weight of shell 25 kg.
4—12.7 mm MGs.
Torpedoes: 6—324 mm (2 triple) Mk 32 tubes ❷. Honeywell Mk 46; anti-submarine; active/passive homing to 11 km *(5.9 nm)* at 40 kts; warhead 44 kg. Some US Mk 44 torpedoes still in service.
Countermeasures: Decoys: SLQ 25 (50 and 53) and Type 182 (49) towed torpedo decoy.
ESM: ELT 901.
Radars: Air search: Signaal LW 02 ❸; D band; range 183 km *(100 nm)*.
Surface search: ISC Cardion SPS 55 (in 49) ❹; I/J band.
Atlas Elektronik 8600 ARPA (in 50 and 53); I band.
Fire control: Signaal M 22 ❺; I/J band; range 46 km *(25 nm)*.
IFF: AIMS Mk XII.
Sonars: EMI/Honeywell Mulloka; hull-mounted; active search and attack; medium frequency.
Kelvin Hughes Type 162 M; sideways looking classification; 50 kHz.

Modernisation: *Derwent* half-life modernisation completed December 1985. This programme included improved accommodation consequent on reduction in complement, installation of M22 system, the fitting of Australian Mulloka sonar, the conversion of the boilers to burn diesel fuel, installation of Mk 32 torpedo tubes in lieu of Mk 10 mortar and new navigation radar. *Swan* and *Torrens* had a half-life refit which completed in September 1985. This refit included installation of Mulloka sonar, Mk 32 torpedo tubes in lieu of Mk 10 mortar and a torpedo decoy. Seacat and Ikara deleted from operational service in 1991.
Structure: The design of *Derwent* is basically similar to that of British Type 12 (now deleted), the other pair to that of the Leander frigates. Note difference in silhouette between *Swan/Torrens* and *Derwent*, the former pair having a straight-run upper deck.
Operational: Classified as Destroyer Escorts. Based at Fleet Base West as part of the deployment of the fleet as a 'Two Ocean Navy'. An RBS 70 Mk 2 missile detachment can be embarked if required. *Derwent* to pay off in August 1994.

DERWENT   *(Scale 1 : 1200), Ian Sturton*

DERWENT   *2/1993, John Mortimer*

TORRENS   *(Scale 1 : 1200), Ian Sturton*

SWAN   *3/1993, Scott Connolly, RAN*

0 + 8 ANZAC (MEKO 200) CLASS

Name	No	Builders	Laid down	Launched	Commissioned
ANZAC	150	Transfield Amecon, Williamstown	5 Nov 1993	Nov 1994	Mar 1996
ARUNTA (ex-*Arrernte*)	151	Transfield Amecon, Williamstown	Oct 1995	July 1996	Nov 1997
WARUMUNGU	152	Transfield Amecon, Williamstown	July 1997	July 1998	Nov 1999
STUART	153	Transfield Amecon, Williamstown	July 1998	July 1999	Nov 2000
PARRAMATTA	154	Transfield Amecon, Williamstown	July 1999	July 2000	Nov 2001
BALLARAT	155	Transfield Amecon, Williamstown	July 2000	July 2001	Nov 2002
TOOWOOMBA	156	Transfield Amecon, Williamstown	July 2001	July 2002	Nov 2003
PERTH	157	Transfield Amecon, Williamstown	July 2002	July 2003	Nov 2004

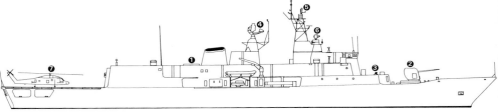

Displacement, tons: 3600 full load
Dimensions, feet (metres): 387.1 oa; 357.6 wl × 48.6 × 14.3 *(118; 109 × 14.8 × 4.35)*
Main machinery: CODOG: 1 GE LM 2500 gas-turbine; 30 172 hp *(22.5 MW)* sustained; 2 MTU 12V 1163 TB83 diesels; 8840 hp(m) *(6.5 MW)* sustained; 2 shafts; cp props
Speed, knots: 27. **Range, miles:** 6000 at 18 kts
Complement: 163 (22 officers)

Missiles: SAM: Raytheon Sea Sparrow RIM-7P; Martin Marietta Mk 41 Mod 5 octuple vertical launcher ❶; 8 missiles total. Quadpack Evolved Sea Sparrow (152-157).
Guns: 1 FMC 5 in (127 mm)/54 Mk 45 Mod 2 ❷. 2—12.7 mm MGs.
Torpedoes: 6—324 mm (2 triple) Mk 32 tubes; to be fitted after ship acceptance into the Navy.
Countermeasures: Decoys: G & D Aircraft GD 36 Mod 1 chaff launchers ❸ for SRBOC. 4 Nulka quad launchers.
SLQ-25 Nixie towed torpedo decoy (probably).
ESM: THORN EMI modified Sceptre A; radar intercept. Telefunken PST-1720 Telegon 10.
ECM: Jammer.
Combat data systems: CelsiusTech 9LV 453 Mk 3. Link 11. SHF SATCOM.
Fire control: CelsiusTech 9LV 453 optronic director with Raytheon CW Mk 73 (for SAM).
Radars: Air search: Raytheon SPS 49(V)8 ANZ ❹; C/D band.
Air/surface search: CelsiusTech 9LV 453 TIR (Ericsson Tx/Rx) ❺; G band.
Navigation: Atlas Elektronik 9600 ARPA; I band.
Fire control: CelsiusTech 9LV 453 ❻; J band.
IFF: Cossor AIMS Mk XII.
Sonars: Thomson Sintra Spherion B; hull-mounted; active search and attack; medium frequency. Provision for Kariwara towed array; passive search; very low frequency (may be fitted).

Helicopters: 1 S-70B Seahawk ❼ or equivalent size.

Programmes: Contract signed with Australian Marine Engineering Consolidated (now Transfield Amecon) on 10 November 1989 to build eight Blohm & Voss-designed MEKO 200 ANZ frigates for Australia and two for New Zealand, which has an option for two more. First ship started construction 27 March 1992. Modules are being constructed at Newcastle and shipped to Melbourne for assembly. The second and fourth ships are for New Zealand. The last six Australian ships will be 'Batch 2' fitted with Evolved Sea Sparrow. It is possible that a stretched version of this class may be ordered in due course as replacements for the DDGs.
Structure: 'Space and weight' reserved for a CIWS, Harpoon SSM, an additional octuple VLS, second channel of fire for VLS, towed array sonar, offboard active ECM, extended ESM frequency coverage, Helo data link and SATCOM. Stealth features are incorporated in the design. All steel construction. Fin stabilisers. Torpedo tubes will be taken from older classes and

ANZAC   (Scale 1 : 900), Ian Sturton

ANZACs (artist's impression)   1993, RAN

fitted after ship acceptance from the builders. Indal RAST helicopter recovery system. Sperry Mk 49 SINS.

Operational: The helicopter may be ASM missile fitted. Two RHIBs are to be carried.

SHIPBORNE AIRCRAFT

Note: Six maritime utility helicopters are to be ordered in the mid-1990s.

Numbers/Type: 6 Aerospatiale AS 350B Squirrel.
Operational speed: 125 kts *(232 km/h).*
Service ceiling: 10 000 ft *(3050 m).*
Range: 390 nm *(720 km).*
Role/Weapon systems: Support helicopter for operational training of naval personnel on new FFG-7 frigates during delivery of S-70B, then for utility tasks and training duties. Sensors: None. Weapons: ASV; two Mag 58 MGs.

SEAHAWK   1992, Scott Connolly, RAN

Numbers/Type: 7 Westland Sea King HAS 50/50A.
Operational speed: 125 kts *(230 km/h).*
Service ceiling: 10 500 ft *(3200 m).*
Range: 630 nm *(1165 km).*
Role/Weapon systems: Utility helicopter; embarked periodically for operations from Afloat Support Ships. Sensors: MEL 5955 radar. Weapons: Disarmed in 1992.

SQUIRREL   1992, A M Nixon, RAN

Numbers/Type: 16 Sikorsky S-70B-2 Seahawk.
Operational speed: 135 kts *(250 km/h).*
Service ceiling: 12 000 ft *(3810 m).*
Range: 600 nm *(1110 km).*
Role/Weapon systems: Seahawk derivative aircraft designed by Sikorsky to meet RAN specifications for ASW and ASST operations. Eight assembled by ASTA in Victoria. Helicopters embarked in FFG-7 and may be utilised in ANZAC frigates. Sensors: MEL Surface surveillance radar, CDC Sonobuoy Processor and Barra Side Processor, and CAE Magnetic Anomaly Detector Set controlled by a versatile Tactical Display/Management System, FLIR and ESM, possibly dipping sonar in due course. Weapons: ASW; two Mk 46 Mod 5 torpedoes. ASV; two Mag 58 MGs, possibly ASM in due course.

SEA KING   1992, RAN

LAND-BASED MARITIME AIRCRAFT

Numbers/Type: 2 British Aerospace HS 748.
Operational speed: 140 kts *(259 km/h).*
Service ceiling: 25 000 ft *(7620 m).*
Range: 2675 nm *(4950 km).*
Role/Weapon systems: EW training aircraft operated by Squadron RAN HC 723 specially equipped by Sanders Associates, USA. Sensors: Complete EW suite classified.

Numbers/Type: 36 General Dynamics F-111C.
Operational speed: 793 kts *(1469 km/h).*
Service ceiling: 60 000 ft *(18 290 m).*
Range: 2540 nm *(4700 km).*
Role/Weapon systems: Royal Australian Air Force operates the F-111 for anti-shipping strike and its small force of RF-111 for coastline surveillance duties using EW/ESM and photographic equipment underwing. 15 more F-111 acquired from US in 1993/94. Sensors: GE AN/APG-144, podded EW. Weapons: ASV; 4 × Harpoon missiles. Strike; 4 × Snakeye bombs. Self-defence; 2 × AIM-9P.

Numbers/Type: 19 Lockheed P-3C/Update II Orion.
Operational speed: 410 kts *(760 km/h).*
Service ceiling: 28 300 ft *(8625 m).*
Range: 4000 nm *(7410 km).*
Role/Weapon systems: Operated by air force for long-range ocean surveillance and ASW. Upgraded from 1992 with improvements to radar, acoustic processors, navigation and communications. Sensors: APS-115 radar, AQS-901 processor, AQS-81 MAD, ECM, Elta/IAI, ESM, 80 × BARRA sonobuoys. Weapons: ASW; 8 × Mk 44 or Mk 46 (Mod 5 after upgrade) torpedoes, Mk 25 mines, 8 × Mk 54 depth bombs. ASV; up to six Harpoon.

Numbers/Type: 72 McDonnell Douglas F-18 Hornet.
Operational speed: 1032 kts *(1910 km/h).*
Service ceiling: 50 000 ft *(15 240 m).*
Range: 1000 nm *(1829 km).*
Role/Weapon systems: Air defence and strike aircraft operated by RAAF but with fleet defence and anti-shipping secondary roles. Sensors: APG-65 attack radar, AAS-38 FLIR/ALR-67 radar warning receiver. Weapons: ASV; 4 × Harpoon missiles. Strike; 1 × 20 mm cannon, up to 7.7 tons of 'iron' bombs. Fleet defence; 4 × AIM-7 Sparrow and 4 × AIM-9L Sidewinder.

PATROL FORCES

Note: The plan is to build 12 Tier Two Offshore Patrol Vessels. The class will have better seakeeping, endurance, weapons and sensors than the Fremantle class. Provisional design includes 1200 tons, 80 m length, range 5500 nm, speed 26 kts in sea state 4, medium range gun, hard and soft kill defences and search radar. This could be a joint project with Malaysia, although the Malaysian Navy wants a helicopter capability which is not part of the Australian requirement.

15 FREMANTLE CLASS (LARGE PATROL CRAFT)

Name	No	Builders	Commissioned
FREMANTLE	203	Brooke Marine, Lowestoft	17 Mar 1980
WARRNAMBOOL	204	NQEA Australia, Cairns	14 Mar 1981
TOWNSVILLE	205	NQEA Australia, Cairns	18 July 1981
WOLLONGONG	206	NQEA Australia, Cairns	28 Nov 1981
LAUNCESTON	207	NQEA Australia, Cairns	1 Mar 1982
WHYALLA	208	NQEA Australia, Cairns	3 July 1982
IPSWICH	209	NQEA Australia, Cairns	13 Nov 1982
CESSNOCK	210	NQEA Australia, Cairns	5 Mar 1983
BENDIGO	211	NQEA Australia, Cairns	28 May 1983
GAWLER	212	NQEA Australia, Cairns	27 Aug 1983
GERALDTON	213	NQEA Australia, Cairns	10 Dec 1983
DUBBO	214	NQEA Australia, Cairns	10 Mar 1984
GEELONG	215	NQEA Australia, Cairns	2 June 1984
GLADSTONE	216	NQEA Australia, Cairns	8 Sep 1984
BUNBURY	217	NQEA Australia, Cairns	15 Dec 1984

Displacement, tons: 245 full load
Dimensions, feet (metres): 137.1 × 23.3 × 5.9 *(41.8 × 7.1 × 1.8)*
Main machinery: 2 MTU 16V 538 TB91 diesels; 6140 hp(m) *(4.5 MW)* sustained
1 centre line Dorman cruising diesel; 3 shafts
Speed, knots: 30; 8 on cruising diesel. **Range, miles:** 1450 at 30 kts; 4800 cruising
Complement: 24 (4 officers)

Guns: 1 Bofors AN 4—40 mm/60; 120 rounds/minute to 10 km *(5.5 nm).* The 40 mm mountings were designed by Australian Government Ordnance Factory and although the guns are of older manufacture, this mounting gives greater accuracy particularly in heavy weather.
1—81 mm mortar. 3—12.7 mm MGs.
Countermeasures: ESM: AWA Defence Industries Type 133 PRISM; radar warning.
Radars: Navigation: Kelvin Hughes Type 1006; I band.

Programmes: The decision to buy these PCF 420 class patrol craft was announced in September 1977. The design is by Brooke Marine Ltd, Lowestoft which built the lead ship.
Modernisation: A life extension programme, including sensor upgrade, was planned to keep these craft in service until OPV replacements are built. Whether it goes ahead depends on the timing of the programme for the new OPVs. ESM added from 1993.
Operational: Bases: Cairns—P 205, 208, 209, 211, 216. Darwin—P 206, 207, 210, 212, 214, 215. Sydney—P 203. Melbourne—P 204. Fremantle—P 213, 217.

DUBBO *8/1993, John Mortimer*

MINE WARFARE FORCES

Note: Of the four vessels involved in the early COOP programme, *Wave Rider* and *Salvatore V* were returned to their owners, and a replacement *Gunundaal* acquired in May 1992. This ship had hull problems and was in turn replaced by *Carole S* which was leased until 14 March 1994 (although this may be extended until 1995). Tenders out in early 1994 for a permanent replacement of at least 20 m length and with a non-magnetic hull. The full COOP programme involves having equipment available for large numbers of earmarked fishing vessels.

2 BAY CLASS (MINEHUNTERS—INSHORE)

Name	No	Builders	Commissioned
RUSHCUTTER	M 80	Carrington Slipways	1 Nov 1986
SHOALWATER	M 81	Carrington Slipways	10 Oct 1987

Displacement, tons: 170 approx
Dimensions, feet (metres): 101.7 × 29.5 × 6.6 *(30.9 × 9 × 2)*
Main machinery: 2 Poyaud 520-V8-S2 diesel generators; 650 hp(m) *(478 kW)*; 2 Schottel hydraulic transmission and steering systems (one to each hull)
Speed, knots: 10. **Range, miles:** 1200 at 10 kts
Complement: 14 (3 officers)

Guns: 2—12.7 mm MGs.
Countermeasures: MCM system is containerised allowing for rapid replacement or removal. As well as the hull sonar the MWS 80-5 has a TCD tactical system and NAV 1300/22 navigation and track control, and the active classification sonar. Three subsystems are located in the container—sonar, tactical data and mine disposal weapon control. The latter operates a remote-controlled ECA 38 system using two PAP 104 vehicles. The SYLEDIS precision navigation system is located on the bridge.
Radars: Navigation: Kelvin Hughes Type 1006; I band.
Sonars: Atlas Elektronik DSQS 11M; hull-mounted; minehunting; high frequency.

Programmes: Ordered January 1983. First launched 3 May 1986; second 20 June 1987.
Structure: The catamaran hull form was chosen as it provides stability, a large deck area, greater manoeuvrability than a mono-hull and reduction in signatures by placing heavy machinery high in the ship. Each hull is 3 m beam with 3 m space between. Foam sandwich construction was adopted and a policy of repair by replacement. *Shoalwater* fitted with two funnels in 1992 to assess impact on noise reduction; *Rushcutter* similarly modified in 1993.
Operational: Due to performance deficiencies of the MWS 80 minehunting weapon system, comparative trials were conducted in 1992 between the Atlas MWS 80-5 and the Thomson Sintra Ibis V Mk 2 systems. The Atlas system was selected. The two ships are based in Sydney and used for training and MCM operations in confined waters.

SHOALWATER (with twin funnels) *11/1993, John Mortimer*

1 MINESWEEPER AUXILIARY (SMALL) (MSA(S))

BROLGA (ex-*Lumen*) 1102

Displacement, tons: 268 full load
Dimensions, feet (metres): 93.2 × 26.6 × 11.5 *(28.4 × 8.1 × 3.5)*
Main machinery: 1 Mirrlees Blackstone diesel; 540 hp *(403 kW)*; 1 shaft; cp prop
Speed, knots: 10.5
Complement: 8 (1 officer)

Comment: Acquired from the Department of Transport on 10 February 1988 for the COOP programme. The COOP tow a magnetic body and acoustic noise makers for influence minesweeping, a mechanical sweep to counter moored mines and a Klein side scan sonar for route surveillance.

BROLGA *11/1993, John Mortimer*

0 + (6) MINEHUNTERS COASTAL (MHC)

M 82-M 87

Displacement, tons: 500 full load
Dimensions, feet (metres): 170.6 × 32.8 × 8.2 *(52 × 10 × 2.5)* approx
Main machinery: Diesels
Speed, knots: 14
Complement: 36
Guns: 30 mm (single or twin).
Countermeasures: ESM: Decoy launcher.
MCM: 2 ROVs; light mechanical sweep.
Radars: Navigation: I band.
Sonars: Plessey 2093 or Raytheon SQQ 32; VDS; active minehunting; high frequency.

Comment: The Force Structure Review of May 1991 recommended the acquisition, as a matter of priority, of Coastal Minehunters of proven design. These ships are required to operate in deeper and more exposed waters, to achieve lower transit times and remain on station longer than the two inshore minehunters currently in service. As a result, the Minehunter Coastal Project was established in June 1991 to manage the acquisition of up to six ships. A short-list of three contenders was announced 23 December 1992. These were: Transfield Shipbuilding/Vosper Thornycroft (Sandown class); Australian Submarine Corporation/Karlskronavarvet (MCMV 52 design based on the Landsort class) and Australian Defence Industries/Intermarine (modified Gaeta class). Tenders closed on 15 December 1993 and award of a contract to the successful tenderer is planned for 1994. Delivery of the first vessel is scheduled for December 1997 with the last one expected by 2002.

2 MINESWEEPERS AUXILIARY (TUGS) (MSA(T))

BANDICOOT (ex-*Grenville VII*) Y 298   **WALLAROO** (ex-*Grenville V*) Y 299

Displacement, tons: 412 full load
Dimensions, feet (metres): 95.8 × 28 × 11.3 *(29.6 × 8.5 × 3.4)*
Main machinery: 2 Stork Werkspoor diesels; 2400 hp(m) *(1.76 MW)*; 2 shafts
Speed, knots: 11. **Range, miles:** 6300 at 10 kts
Complement: 10
Radars: Navigation: Furuno 7040D; I band.

Comment: Built in Singapore 1982 and operated by Maritime (PTE) Ltd. Purchased by the RAN and refurbished prior to delivery 11 August 1990. Used for minesweeping trials towing large AMASS influence and mechanical sweeps. No side scan sonar. Also used as berthing tugs. Bollard pull, 30 tons.

WALLAROO   *11/1993, John Mortimer*

1 MINESWEEPER AUXILIARY (SMALL) (MSA(S))

KORAAGA (ex-*Grozdana 'A'*) 1185

Displacement, tons: 119 full load
Dimensions, feet (metres): 71.9 × 21 × 9.8 *(21.9 × 6.4 × 3)*
Main machinery: 1 Caterpillar D 346 diesel; 480 hp *(358 kW)* sustained; 1 shaft
Speed, knots: 11
Complement: 8 (1 officer)

Comment: Acquired 16 February 1989 for the COOP programme. Mast modified in 1993.

KORAAGA (with *Carole S* in background)   *11/1993, John Mortimer*

3 MINESWEEPING DRONES

MSD 01-03

Dimensions, feet (metres): 24 × 9.2 × 2 *(7.3 × 2.8 × 0.6)*
Main machinery: 2 Yamaha outboards; 300 hp(m) *(221 kW)*
Speed, knots: 45; 8 (sweeping)

Comment: Built by Hamil Haven in 1991/92. Remote-controlled drones. GRP hulls made by Hydrofield. Used for sweeping ahead of the MSA craft. Differential GPS navigation system with Syledis Vega backup.

MSD 03   *11/1992, John Mortimer*

AMPHIBIOUS FORCES

2 NEWPORT CLASS (LSTs)

Name	No	Builders	Laid down	Launched	Commissioned	Recommissioned
KANIMBLA (?) (ex-*Fairfax County*)	— (ex-1193)	National Steel & Shipbuilding	28 Mar 1970	19 Dec 1970	16 Oct 1971	Sep 1994
MANOORA (?) (ex-*Saginaw*)	— (ex-1188)	National Steel & Shipbuilding	24 May 1969	7 Feb 1970	23 Jan 1971	June 1994

Displacement, tons: 4975 light; 8450 full load
Dimensions, feet (metres): 522.3 (hull) × 69.5 × 17.5 (aft) *(159.2 × 21.2 × 5.3)*
Main machinery: 6 ARCO 16-251 diesels; 16 500 hp *(12.3 MW)* sustained; 2 shafts; cp props; bow thruster
Speed, knots: 20. **Range, miles:** 2500 at 14 kts
Complement: 160
Military lift: 400 troops (20 officers); 500 tons vehicles; 3 LCVPs and 1 LCPL on davits

Guns: 4 USN 3 in *(76 mm)*/50 (2 twin) Mk 33 (fitted for).
1 General Electric/General Dynamics 20 mm Vulcan Phalanx Mk 15.
Radars: Surface search: Raytheon SPS 67; G band.
Navigation: Raytheon CRP 3100 Pathfinder; I/J band.

Helicopters: 4 Army Black Hawks.

Programmes: Acquisition approved in December 1993 subject to US Congressional approval. These ships are to replace *Jervis Bay* and *Tobruk*. Names are uncertain.
Structure: The plan is to modify both ships by fitting a hangar to take four Black Hawk helicopters, to increase aviation fuel capacity and to dispense with the bow landing ramp. A stern gate to the tank deck would be retained. Mexeflotes are not

FAIRFAX COUNTY (US colours)   *1989, Giorgio Arra*

required. Details given show the ships in US service with the exception of the helicopters. Armament to be decided. Twin landing spots.

Operational: Operational range is to be increased. Complement to be reduced from the 250 in US service.

1 HEAVY LIFT SHIP (LSH)

Name	No	Builders	Laid down	Launched	Commissioned
TOBRUK	L 50	Carrington Slipways Pty Ltd	7 Feb 1978	1 Mar 1980	23 Apr 1981

Displacement, tons: 3300 standard; 5700 full load
Dimensions, feet (metres): 417 × 60 × 16
(127 × 18.3 × 4.9)
Main machinery: 2 Mirrlees Blackstone KDMR8 diesels;
9600 hp (7.2 MW); 2 shafts
Speed, knots: 18. **Range, miles:** 8000 at 15 kts
Complement: 144 (13 officers)
Military lift: 350-500 troops; 1300 tons cargo; 70 tons capacity
derrick; 2—4.25 ton cranes; 2 LCVP; 2 LCM

Guns: 2 Bofors 40 mm/60; dual purpose; 80° elevation; 120
rounds/minute to 10 km (5.5 nm) anti-surface.
2—12.7 mm MGs.
Radars: Surface search: Kelvin Hughes Type 1006; I band.
Navigation: Racal Decca RM 916; I band.

Helicopters: Platform only for up to 4 Sea King.

Structure: The design is an update of the British Sir Bedivere
class and provides facilities for the operation of helicopters,
landing craft, amphibians or side-carried pontoons for ship-to-
shore movement. A special feature is the ship's heavy lift derrick system for handling heavy loads. The LSH is able to
embark a squadron of Leopard tanks plus a number of wheeled
vehicles and artillery in addition to its troop lift. Bow and stern
ramps are fitted. Carries two 20 kt LCVPs at davits. Fitted for
side-carrying two NLE pontoons. Two LCM 8 carried on deck.
Helicopters can be operated from the well deck or the after
platform.
Operational: A comprehensive communication fit and minor
hospital facilities are provided. Can operate all in-service helicopters. Based at Sydney. To be withdrawn from service and
replaced by a Newport class LST.
Sales: Could be sold to New Zealand.

TOBRUK   3/1992, John Mortimer

6 LANDING CRAFT (HEAVY) (LCH)

Name	No	Builders	Commissioned
BALIKPAPAN	L 126	Walkers Ltd, Queensland	8 Dec 1971
BRUNEI	L 127	Walkers Ltd, Queensland	5 Jan 1973
LABUAN	L 128	Walkers Ltd, Queensland	9 Mar 1973
TARAKAN	L 129	Walkers Ltd, Queensland	15 June 1973
WEWAK	L 130	Walkers Ltd, Queensland	10 Aug 1973
BETANO	L 133	Walkers Ltd, Queensland	8 Feb 1974

Displacement, tons: 310 light; 503 full load
Dimensions, feet (metres): 146 × 33 × 6.5 (44.5 × 10.1 × 2)
Main machinery: 2 GM 6-71 diesels; 348 hp (260 kW) sustained; 2 shafts
Speed, knots: 10. **Range, miles:** 3000 at 10 kts
Complement: 13 (2 officers)
Military lift: 3 medium tanks or equivalent
Guns: 2—7.62 mm MGs.
Radars: Navigation: Racal Decca RM 916; I band.

Comment: Originally this class was ordered for the Army but only Balikpapan saw Army service
until being commissioned into the Navy on 27 September 1974. The remainder were built for the
Navy. Brunei and Betano act as diving tenders. Labuan at Cairns and Balikpapan at Darwin are
both operational. Wewak is laid up at Cairns. Tarakan operates from Cairns in a survey ship role
and for general duties. All are available for amphibious duties. Buna and Salamaua transferred to
Papua New Guinea Defence Force in November 1974.

TARAKAN   3/1992, John Mortimer

4 LANDING CRAFT (LIGHT) (LCVP)

T 4-T 7

Displacement, tons: 6.5 full load
Dimensions, feet (metres): 43.3 × 11.5 × 2.3 (13.2 × 3.5 × 0.7)
Main machinery: 2 Volvo Penta Sterndrives; 400 hp(m) (294 kW)
Speed, knots: 22; 15 (fully laden)
Complement: 3
Military lift: 4.5 tons cargo or 1 Land Rover or 36 troops

Comment: Prototype built by Geraldton, Western Australia. Trials conducted in late 1992. Three
more delivered in July 1993. Two for Tobruk, one for Success and one spare attached to Penguin.

LCVP   10/1992, RAN

SURVEY SHIPS (MARINE SCIENCE FORCE)

Notes: (1) In addition to the ships listed below there are four civilian survey vessels; Icebird, Franklin, Rig Seismic and Lady Franklin. Also an arctic supply ship Aurora Australis started operating in
the Antarctic in 1990; this vessel carries 70 scientists and has a helicopter hangar.
(2) Project Definition studies continue for two new hydrographic ships, pending a decision on com-
mercialisation of survey work. The plan for a third vessel for oceanography has been shelved.

Name	No	Builders	Commissioned
MORESBY	A 73	Dockyard, Newcastle	6 Mar 1964

Displacement, tons: 1714 standard; 2351 full load
Dimensions, feet (metres): 314 × 42 × 15 (95.7 × 12.8 × 4.6)
Main machinery: Diesel-electric; 3 diesel generators; 2 motors; 3990 hp (2.9 MW); 2 shafts
Speed, knots: 19
Complement: 138 (12 officers)
Guns: 2 Bofors 40 mm (removed).
Radars: Navigation: Racal Decca TM 916C; I band.
Sonars: Simrad SU2; high definition; retractable dome.
Helicopters: 1 Bell 206B.

Comment: The RAN's first specifically designed survey ship. Launched 7 September 1963. During
refit in 1973 Moresby's funnel was heightened, her 40 mm guns removed and an exhaust outlet
fitted on her forecastle. Three new survey launches with Qubit Hydlaps data logging and processing system were embarked in 1993. Based at Stirling (Cockburn Sound WA).

MORESBY   11/1993, Scott Connolly, RAN

Name	No	Builders	Commissioned
FLINDERS	A 312	HMA Dockyard, Williamstown	27 Apr 1973

Displacement, tons: 750
Dimensions, feet (metres): 161 × 33 × 12 *(49.1 × 10 × 3.7)*
Main machinery: 2 Paxman 8YJCM diesels; 2000 hp *(1.98 MW)* sustained; 2 shafts; cp props
Speed, knots: 13.5. **Range, miles:** 5000 at 9 kts
Complement: 43 (5 officers)
Radars: Navigation: Racal Decca TM 916C; I band.
Sonars: Simrad SU2; high definition; retractable dome.

Comment: Launched 29 July 1972. Similar in design to *Atyimba* built for the Philippines. A new survey launch with Qubit Hydlaps data logging and processing system was embarked in 1993. The ship is based at Cairns, with primary responsibility in the Barrier Reef area.

FLINDERS   *10/1986, John Mortimer*

Name	No	Builders	Commissioned
PALUMA	A 01	Eglo, Adelaide	27 Feb 1989
MERMAID	A 02	Eglo, Adelaide	4 Dec 1989
SHEPPARTON	A 03	Eglo, Adelaide	24 Jan 1990
BENALLA	A 04	Eglo, Adelaide	20 Mar 1990

Displacement, tons: 320 full load
Dimensions, feet (metres): 118.9 × 45.3 × 6.2 *(36.6 × 13.8 × 1.9)*
Main machinery: 2 Detroit 12V-92TA diesels; 1020 hp *(760 kW)* sustained; 2 shafts
Speed, knots: 12. **Range, miles:** 3500 at 11 kts
Complement: 12 (2 officers)
Radars: Navigation: JRC JMA-3710-6; I band.
Sonars: Skipper S113; hull-mounted; active; high frequency. ELAC LAZ 72; hull-mounted side scan; active; high frequency.

Comment: Catamaran design based on Prince class Ro-Ro passenger ferries. Steel hulls and aluminium superstructure. Contract signed in November 1987. Although she commissioned in February 1989, *Paluma* was not accepted into service until September 1989 because of noise problems. As a result other members of the class were about six months late completing. Qubit Hydlaps data logging and processing system fitted. All are based at Cairns and are fitted out for operations in shallow waters of Northern Australia. Normally operate in pairs.

SHEPPARTON   *7/1993, Ian Edwards*

7 SURVEY LAUNCHES

FANTOME	INVESTIGATOR	TOM THUMB	WYATT EARP
MEDA	DUYFKEN	JOHN GOWLLAND	

Dimensions, feet (metres): 35.1 × 9.5 × 5.6 *(10.7 × 2.9 × 1.7)*
Main machinery: 2 Volvo Penta diesel stern drives; 400 hp(m) *(294 kW)*; 2 props
Speed, knots: 29. **Range, miles:** 300 at 12 kts
Complement: 4 (1 officer)

Comment: Survey motor boats built by Pro Marine, Victoria between October 1992 and July 1993. Aluminium hulls. Equipment includes Hydlaps data logging and processing, a JRC radar and a side scan sonar towfish. *Fantome, Meda* and *Investigator* are embarked in *Moresby*, *Duyfken* has been allocated to *Flinders* and the last two to *Penguin*, the Hydrographic School. A seventh of the class *Wyatt Earp* is attached to the Antarctic Survey Unit (HODSU). Side numbers 1004-1010.

INVESTIGATOR   *4/1993, Scott Connolly, RAN*

TRAINING SHIPS

Note: In addition to *Young Endeavour* there are five Fleet class yachts. Of 36.1 ft *(11 m)*. GRP yachts named *Charlotte of Cerberus, Friendship of Leeuwin, Scarborough of Cerberus, Lady Penrhyn of Nirimba* and *Alexander of Creswell*. The names are a combination of Australia's first colonising fleet and the training base to which each yacht is allocated.

1 EXPLORER CLASS

Name	No	Builders	Commissioned
BANKS	AG 244	Walkers, Maryborough, Queensland	16 Feb 1960

Displacement, tons: 207 standard; 255 and 260 full load respectively
Dimensions, feet (metres): 90 pp; 101 oa × 22 × 8 *(27.5; 30.8 × 6.7 × 2.4)*
Main machinery: 2 diesels; 260 hp *(190 kW)*; 2 shafts
Speed, knots: 10
Complement: 12 (2 officers)
Radars: Navigation: Racal Decca 916; I band.

Comment: Explorer class; all steel construction. Fitted for fishery surveillance but is now used for navigation training based at *Waterhen*. The ship is unreliable and may be replaced by an ASI 315 class in due course.

BANKS   *5/1993, van Ginderen Collection*

1 SAIL TRAINING SHIP

YOUNG ENDEAVOUR

Displacement, tons: 239 full load
Dimensions, feet (metres): 144 × 26 × 13 *(44 × 7.8 × 4)*
Main machinery: 2 Perkins diesels; 334 hp *(294 kW)*; 2 shafts
Speed, knots: 14 sail; 10 diesel. **Range, miles:** 2500 at 7 kts
Complement: 33 (9 RAN, 24 youth)

Comment: Built to Lloyds 100 Al LMC yacht classification by Brooke Yachts, Lowestoft. Sail area 845.6 m². Presented to Australia by UK Government 25 January 1987 as a Bicentennial gift. Operated by RAN on behalf of the Young Endeavour Youth Scheme.

YOUNG ENDEAVOUR   *4/1992, Giorgio Ghiglione*

AUXILIARIES

Note: A Training and Helicopter Support ship of about 20 000 tons is required to replace *Jervis Bay* and complement the amphibious capability of *Tobruk*. Capabilities to include carrying a battalion of troops, up to 12 utility helicopters and 4 LCM, plus an 80 bed hospital. A project office was formed on 21 December 1992 to examine the concept but the project was cancelled in the August 1993 Defence budget, and the purchase of two Newport class LSTs is the most recent solution.

1 LEAF CLASS (UNDERWAY REPLENISHMENT TANKER)

Name	No	Builder	Laid down	Launched	Commissioned
WESTRALIA (ex-*Hudson Cavalier*, ex-*Appleleaf*)	O 195 (ex-A 79)	Cammell Laird, Birkenhead	1974	24 July 1975	Nov 1979

WESTRALIA   12/1993, Scott Connolly, RAN

Displacement, tons: 40 870 full load
Measurement, tons: 20 761 gross; 10 851 net; 33 595 dwt
Dimensions, feet (metres): 560 × 85 × 38.9
  (170.7 × 25.9 × 11.9)
Main machinery: 2 SEMT-Pielstick 14 PC2.2 V 400 diesels;
  14 000 hp(m) *(10.3 MW)* sustained; 1 shaft
Speed, knots: 16 (11 on one engine). **Range, miles:** 7260 at
  15 kts
Complement: 61 (8 officers) plus 9 spare berths
Cargo capacity: 20 000 tons dieso; 3000 tons aviation fuel;
  1500 tons water
Radars: Navigation: 2 Kelvin Hughes; 1007 ARPA (I band) and
  Radpak (E/F band).

Comment: Part of an order by the Hudson Fuel and Shipping Co
  which was subsequently cancelled. Leased by the RN from
  1979 until transferred on 9 October 1989 on a five year lease
  to the RAN, arriving in Fremantle 20 December 1989. Option
  to purchase in 1994. Has three 3 ton cranes and two 5 ton derricks. Hospital facilities. Two beam replenishment stations.
  Stern refuelling is to be restored in 1994/95. Based at *Stirling*.
  RBS 70 SAM systems (with Army detachment) and
  4—12.7 mm MGs may be embarked for operations. Also modified to provide a large Vertrep platform aft. Lifeboats have been
  replaced by liferafts.

1 DURANCE CLASS (UNDERWAY REPLENISHMENT TANKER)

Name	No	Builders	Laid down	Launched	Commissioned
SUCCESS	OR 304	Cockatoo Dockyard	9 Aug 1980	3 Mar 1984	19 Feb 1986

SUCCESS   7/1993, John Mortimer

Displacement, tons: 17 933 full load
Dimensions, feet (metres): 515.7 × 69.5 × 30.6
  (157.2 × 21.2 × 8.6)
Main machinery: 2 SEMT-Pielstick 16 PC2.5 V 400 diesels;
  20 800 hp(m) *(15.3 MW)* sustained; 2 shafts; cp props
Speed, knots: 20. **Range, miles:** 8616 at 15 kts
Complement: 212 (25 officers)
Cargo capacity: 10 200 tons: 8707 dieso; 975 Avcat; 116 dis-
  tilled water; 57 victuals; 250 munitions including SM1 missiles
  and Mk 46 torpedoes; 95 naval stores and spares

Guns: 3 Bofors 40 mm (2 fwd, 1 aft). 4—12.7 mm MGs.
Radars: Navigation. Two Kelvin Hughes Type 1006; I band.
Helicopters: 1 AS 350B Squirrel or Sea King or Sea Hawk.

Comment: Based on French Durance class design. Replenishment at sea from four beam positions (two having heavy transfer capability) and vertrep. Hangar modified to take Sea Kings.

1 HELICOPTER AND LOGISTIC SUPPORT SHIP

Name	No	Builders	Laid down	Launched	Commissioned
JERVIS BAY (ex-*Australian Trader*)	GT 203	State Dockyard, Newcastle, NSW	18 Aug 1967	17 Feb 1969	17 June 1969

Displacement, tons: 8770 full load
Dimensions, feet (metres): 445.1 × 70.6 × 20.1
  (135.7 × 21.5 × 6.1)
Main machinery: 2 SEMT Pielstick 16 PC2.2 V 400R diesels;
  13 180 hp(m) *(9.8 MW)* sustained; 2 shafts; bow thruster
Speed, knots: 19.5
Complement: 177 (14 officers) plus 76 trainees
Guns: 4—12.7 mm MGs.
Radars: Surface search: Kelvin Hughes Type 1006; I band.
Navigation: Atlas Elektronik 8600; I band.
  Racal Decca RM 916; I band.
Helicopters: Platform only for 1 Sea King or Sea Hawk.

Comment: Classified as a Helicopter, Logistic Support and Training Ship, the former roll-on roll-off vessel commissioned in the
  RAN on 25 August 1977. For the training role a navigation
  bridge was added in 1978. In 1987 the deckhouse was
  removed and the after deck strengthened for a Sea King sized
  helicopter. More ambitious plans to carry up to six aircraft were
  shelved but in August 1993 flight deck modifications were
  completed to allow the operation of Sea Hawks. Based at Sydney. The ship had severe engine problems during 1993 and is
  to be paid off in 1994. To be replaced by one of the Newport
  class LSTs.

JERVIS BAY   3/1992, John Mortimer

3 FISH CLASS (TORPEDO RECOVERY VESSELS)

TUNA TRV 801   **TREVALLY** TRV 802   **TAILOR** TRV 803

Displacement, tons: 91.6
Dimensions, feet (metres): 88.5 × 20.9 × 4.5 *(27 × 6.4 × 1.4)*
Main machinery: 3 GM diesels; 890 hp *(664 kW)*; 3 shafts
Speed, knots: 13
Complement: 9

Comment: All built at Williamstown completed between January 1970 and April 1971. Can transport eight torpedoes.

TREVALLY   *3/1993, van Ginderen Collection*

1 TRIALS AND SAFETY VESSEL

Name	No	Builders	Commissioned
PROTECTOR	ASR 241	Stirling Marine Services, WA	1984
(ex-*Blue Nabilla*)			

Displacement, tons: 670 full load
Dimensions, feet (metres): 140.1 × 31.2 × 9.8 *(42.7 × 9.5 × 3)*
Main machinery: 2 Detroit 12V-92TA diesels; 1020 hp *(760 kW)* sustained; 2 Heimdal cp props
Speed, knots: 11.5. **Range, miles:** 10 000 at 11 kts
Complement: 13
Radars: Navigation: JRC 310; I band. Decca RM 970BT; I band.
Sonars: Klein; side scan; high frequency.
Helicopters: Platform for one light.

Comment: A former National Safety Council of Australia vessel commissioned in November 1990 to be used to support contractor's sea trials of the Collins class submarines, and for mine warfare trials and diving operations. LIPS dynamic positioning, two ROVs and a recompression chamber. Helicopter deck and a submersible were removed in 1992. Based at *Stirling* from November 1993.

PROTECTOR   *11/1993, Scott Connolly, RAN*

3 DIVING TENDERS

SEAL 2001   **PORPOISE** 2002   **SHARK** 2004

Displacement, tons: 22 full load
Dimensions, feet (metres): 65.5 × 18.5 × 4.6 *(20 × 5.6 × 1.4)*
Speed, knots: 28. **Range, miles:** 350 at 18 kts
Complement: 6 plus 16 divers

Comment: Built by Geraldton Boat Builders, Western Australia and completed in August 1993. Carry 2 tons of diving equipment to support 24 hour diving operations in depths up to 54 m. *Shark* based at *Stirling*, the other pair in Sydney.

SHARK   *8/1993, Scott Connolly, RAN*

4 SELF-PROPELLED LIGHTERS

WARRIGAL WFL 8001   **WOMBAT** WFL 8003
WALLABY WFL 8002   **WYULDA** WFL 8004

Displacement, tons: 265 light; 1206 full load
Dimensions, feet (metres): 124.6 × 33.5 × 12.5 *(38 × 10.2 × 3.8)*
Main machinery: 2 Harbourmaster outdrives (1 fwd, 1 aft)

Comment: First three were laid down at Williamstown in 1978. The fourth, for HMAS *Stirling*, was ordered in 1981 from Williamstown Dockyard. Used for water/fuel transport. Steel hulls with twin, swivelling, outboard propellers. Based at Jervis Bay and Cockburn Sound (WFL 8001, 8004), other pair at Garden Island, Sydney.

WYULDA   *9/1991, van Ginderen Collection*

4 LIGHTERS—CATAMARAN

WATTLE CSL 01   **BORONIA** CSL 02   **TELOPEA** CSL 03   **AWL 304**

Comment: 175 ton self-propelled lighters used for general cargo duties.

WATTLE   *2/1993, van Ginderen Collection*

WORK BOATS

OTTER NWBD 1281	**DOLPHIN** NWBD 1286
WALRUS NWBD 1282	**DUGONG** NWBD 1287
BEAVER NWBD 1283	**TURTLE** NWBD 1292
GRAMPUS NWBD 1285	**AWB 400-445**

Comment: Of 12 tons and 39.3 ft *(12 m)* long. Built by North Queensland Engineers and Agents, Cairns of aluminium with varying superstructures. There are also four hydrofoil Cheetah remote-controlled surface targets capable of 35 kts.

WALRUS   *11/1991, John Mortimer*

TUGS

Note: In addition the two MSA(T) ships are used as tugs. Details under Mine Warfare Forces.

TAMMAR DT 2601

Displacement, tons: 265
Dimensions, feet (metres): 84.3 × 26.9 × 6.6 *(25.7 × 8.2 × 2)*
Main machinery: 2 diesels; 2800 hp *(2.09 MW)*; 2 shafts
Speed, knots: 11. **Range, miles:** 1450 at 11 kts
Complement: 6

Comment: Built by Australian Shipbuilding Industries, South Coogee, WA. Launched 10 March 1984 for service at *Stirling*, Cockburn Sound, completed 15 March 1984. Bollard pull 35 tons. Also used for torpedo recovery.

TAMMAR   *8/1992, Vic Jeffery, RAN*

QUOKKA DT 1801

Displacement, tons: 110
Dimensions, feet (metres): 59.4 × 19.4 × 7.9 *(18.1 × 5.9 × 2.4)*
Main machinery: 2 Detroit 6V-53 diesels; 300 hp *(224 kW)* sustained; 2 shafts
Speed, knots: 9
Complement: 4

Comment: Built by Shoreline Engineering Pty Ltd, Portland, Victoria. Launched October 1983 for service at *Stirling*, Cockburn Sound. Bollard pull 8 tons.

QUOKKA   *1992, A M Nixon, RAN*

BRONZEWING HTS 501	**MOLLYMAWK** HTS 504
CURRAWONG HTS 502	

Displacement, tons: 47.5
Dimensions, feet (metres): 50 × 15 × 6.2 *(15.2 × 4.6 × 1.9)*
Main machinery: 2 GM diesels; 340 hp *(250 kW)*; 2 shafts
Speed, knots: 8
Complement: 3

Comment: First pair with bipod mast funnel built by Stannard Bros, Sydney in 1969 and second pair (including 503) with conventional funnel by Perrin Engineering, Brisbane in 1972. Bollard pull 5 tons. 503 transferred to Papua New Guinea in 1974. *Mollymawk* has been modified with twin funnels following a berthing accident with *Tobruk*.

MOLLYMAWK   *3/1993, van Ginderen Collection*

NON-NAVAL PATROL CRAFT

Notes: (1) Various State and Federal agencies, including some fishery departments, have built off-shore patrol craft up to 25 m and 26 kts.
(2) Cocos Island patrol carried out by *Sir Zelman Cowan* of 47.9 × 14 ft *(14.6 × 4.3 m)* with two Cummins diesels; 20 kts, range 400 nm at 17 kts, complement 13 (3 officers). Operated by West Australian Department of Harbours and Lights.
(3) The Naval Police operate 4 Shark Cat class (0801-0804) which are similar to Army versions. These craft are based at Sydney and Rockingham.
(4) All previously listed RAAF craft have been sold for civilian use.

ARMY CRAFT

Notes: (1) Operated by Royal Australian Army Corps of Transport. Personnel: 300-400 as required.
(2) In addition to the craft listed below there are some 150 assault boats 16.4 ft *(5 m)* in length and capable of 30 kts. Can carry 12 troops or 1200 kg of equipment.

14 LCM(8) CLASS

AB 1050, 1051, 1053, 1056, 1058-1067

Displacement, tons: 116 full load
Dimensions, feet (metres): 73.5 × 21 × 5.2 *(22.4 × 6.4 × 1.6)*
Main machinery: 4 GM 6-71 diesels; 720 hp *(547 kW)*; 2 shafts
Speed, knots: 10. **Range, miles:** 520 at 10 kts
Complement: 4-5
Guns: 2—12.7 mm MGs.

Comment: Built by North Queensland Engineers, Cairns and Dillinghams, Fremantle to US design. Based at Sydney and Darwin. Can carry 54 tons of cargo. *AB 1057* transferred to Tonga 1982, *AB 1052* and *AB 1054* sold to civilian use in 1992.

AB 1056   *6/1993, Nikolaus Sifferlinger*

1 TUG

JOE MANN   AT 2700

Displacement, tons: 60
Dimensions, feet (metres): 60.5 × 17.3 × 5.5 *(18.4 × 5.3 × 1.7)*
Main machinery: 2 GM 6-71 diesels; 348 hp *(260 kW)* sustained; 1 shaft
Speed, knots: 10. **Range, miles:** 5060 at 10 kts
Complement: 6

Comment: Built in 1962. Fitted for firefighting and based at Sydney. Second of class sold in 1993.

JOE MANN   *1983, Graeme Andrews*

6 SHARK CAT CLASS

AM 215-220

Comment: Multi-hulled craft with twin Johnson engines from 175-200 hp. Length 27.2 ft *(8.3 m)*. Speed, 35 kts. Operated by Army Commando Units and Regional Force Surveillance Units.

AM 215   *11/1983, van Ginderen Collection*

AUSTRIA

Commanding Officer

Captain Manfred Zemsauer

Diplomatic Representation

Defence Attaché in London:
  Major General A Radauer

Personnel

(a) 1994: 34 (cadre personnel and national service), plus a
     small shipyard unit
(b) 6 months' national service plus 2 months a year for 12 years

Base

Marinekaserne Tegetthof, Wien-Kuchelau (under command of
Austrian School of Military Engineering)

Mercantile Marine

Lloyd's Register of Shipping:
  28 vessels of 159 937 tons gross

PATROL FORCES

1 RIVER PATROL CRAFT

Name	No	Builders	Commissioned
NIEDERÖSTERREICH	A 604	Korneuberg Werft AG	16 Apr 1970

Displacement, tons: 75 full load
Dimensions, feet (metres): 96.8 × 17.8 × 3.6 *(29.4 × 5.4 × 1.1)*
Main machinery: 2 MWM V16 diesels; 1640 hp(m) *(1.2 MW)*; 2 shafts
Speed, knots: 22
Complement: 9 (1 officer)
Guns: 1 Oerlikon 20 mm SPz Mk 66; 50° elevation; 800 rounds/minute to 2 km.
  1—12.7 mm MG. 1—7.62 mm MG. 1—84 mm PAR 66 'Carl Gustav' AT mortar.

Comment: Fully welded. Only one built of a projected class of 12. Re-engined in 1985.

NIEDERÖSTERREICH   *7/1991, Austrian Government*

1 RIVER PATROL CRAFT

Name	No	Builders	Commissioned
OBERST BRECHT	A 601	Korneuberg Werft AG	14 Jan 1958

Displacement, tons: 10 full load
Dimensions, feet (metres): 40.3 × 8.2 × 2.5 *(12.3 × 2.5 × 0.75)*
Main machinery: 2 MAN 6-cyl diesels; 290 hp(m) *(213 kW)*; 2 shafts
Speed, knots: 18
Complement: 5
Guns: 1—12.7 mm MG. 1—84 mm PAR 66 Carl Gustav AT mortar.

OBERST BRECHT   *7/1992, Austrian Government*

10 M-BOOT 80 CLASS

Displacement, tons: 4.7 full load
Dimensions, feet (metres): 24.6 × 8.2 × 2 *(7.5 × 2.5 × 0.6)*
Main machinery: 2 Klöckner-Humboldt-Deutz V diesel; 2 shafts
Speed, knots: 7

Comment: Built by Schottel-Werft, Spay, West Germany. Unarmed, they are general-purpose work boats.

M-BOOT 80   *5/1991, van Ginderen Collection*

AZERBAIJAN

General

Coast Guard formed in September 1992 with ships transferred
from the Russian Caspian Flotilla and Border Guard. In early 1994
the division between the Azerbaijan manned ships and the Russian flotilla remained in flux, Azerbaijan having rejoined the CIS in
1993. Details of all listed classes can be found in the Russia and
Associated States section.

Strength of the Fleet (1 January 1994)

Frigates: 2 Petya II (159A)
Patrol Forces: 10 Stenka (205P), 3 OSA II (205), 3 SO1, 1 Svet-
lyak (1140), 1 Zhuk (1400 M)
Mine Warfare Forces: 1 T43 (1785), 2 Yurka (266), 5 Sonya
(12650), 3 Vanya (257), 4 Yevgenya (1258)
Amphibious Forces: 3 Polnochny A (770), 1 Polnochny B (771)
Auxiliaries: 18 miscellaneous

Base

Baku

Mercantile Marine

Lloyd's Register of Shipping:
  270 vessels of 666 845 tons gross

BAHAMAS

Headquarters' Appointments	Personnel	Mercantile Marine
Commander Royal Bahamas Defence Force: Commodore L L Smith *Base Commander:* Commander A J Allens	1994: 850	*Lloyd's Register of Shipping:* 1121 vessels of 21 224 164 tons gross

Base	Prefix to Ships' Names	DELETIONS
HMBS *Coral Harbour*, New Providence Island	HMBS	1991 *P 106* (sunk)

PATROL FORCES

3 PROTECTOR CLASS

Name	No	Builders	Commissioned
YELLOW ELDER	P 03	Fairey Marine, Cowes	20 Nov 1986
PORT NELSON	P 04	Fairey Marine, Cowes	20 Nov 1986
SAMANA	P 05	Fairey Marine, Cowes	20 Nov 1986

Displacement, tons: 110 standard; 180 full load
Dimensions, feet (metres): 108.3 × 22 × 6.9 *(33 × 6.7 × 2.1)*
Main machinery: 3 Detroit 16V-149TI diesels; 3483 hp *(2.6 MW)* sustained; 3 shafts
Speed, knots: 30. **Range, miles:** 300 at 24 kts; 600 at 14 kts on 1 engine
Complement: 20 plus 5 spare berths
Guns: 1 Rheinmetall 20 mm. 3—7.62 mm MGs.

Comment: Ordered December 1984.

YELLOW ELDER   6/1992, RBDF

6 CAPE CLASS

Name	No	Name	No
FENRICK STURRUP (ex-*Shoalwater*)	P 06	EDWARD WILLIAMS (ex-*York*)	P 09
DAVID TUCKER (ex-*Upright*)	P 07	SAN SALVADOR II (ex-*Fox*)	P 10
AUSTIN SMITH (ex-*Current*)	P 08	FORT FINCASTLE (ex-*Morgan*)	P 11

Displacement, tons: 98 standard; 148 full load
Dimensions, feet (metres): 95 × 20.2 × 6.6 *(28.9 × 6.2 × 2)*
Main machinery: 2 Detroit 16V-149TI diesels; 2322 hp *(1.73 MW)* sustained; 2 shafts
Speed, knots: 20. **Range, miles:** 2500 at 10 kts
Complement: 18 (2 officers)
Guns: 2—12.7 mm MGs.
Radars: Navigation: Raytheon SPS 64; I band.

Comment: Built at the Coast Guard Yard, Maryland for the USCG between 1953 and 1959 and modernised 1977-81. Modernisation included new engines, electronics and improved habitability. P 06, 07, 09 and 10 commissioned into the Bahamian Navy in February 1989 and the remaining two in November 1989. Designed for port security and search and rescue, they are a formidable addition to the surveillance capabilities of the RBDF.

AUSTIN SMITH   12/1989, Giorgio Arra

1 MARLIN CLASS

Name	No	Builders	Commissioned
MARLIN	P 01	Vosper Thornycroft	23 May 1978

Displacement, tons: 96 standard; 109 full load
Dimensions, feet (metres): 103 × 19.8 × 5.5 *(31.4 × 6 × 1.7)*
Main machinery: 2 Paxman 12YJCM diesels; 3000 hp *(2.24 MW)* sustained; 2 shafts
Speed, knots: 25. **Range, miles:** 2000 at 13 kts
Complement: 19 (3 officers)
Guns: 1 Rheinmetall 20 mm. 2 MGs. 2 flare launchers.
Radars: Surface Search: Racal Decca; I band.

Comment: *Marlin* laid down 22 November 1976, launched 20 June 1977. Sister ship *Flamingo* sunk by Cuban aircraft on 10 May 1980.

MARLIN   1992, RBDF

5 ELEUTHERA (KEITH NELSON) CLASS

Name	No	Builders	Commissioned
ELEUTHERA	P 22	Vosper Thornycroft	5 Mar 1971
ANDROS	P 23	Vosper Thornycroft	5 Mar 1971
ABACO	P 25	Vosper Thornycroft	10 Dec 1977
EXUMA	P 26	Vosper Thornycroft	10 Dec 1977
INAGUA	P 27	Vosper Thornycroft	10 Dec 1977

Displacement, tons: 30 standard; 37 full load
Dimensions, feet (metres): 60 × 15.8 × 4.6 *(18.3 × 4.8 × 1.4)*
Main machinery: 2 Detroit 12V-71 diesels (P 22-23); 680 hp *(508 kW)*
2 Caterpillar 3408BTA diesels (P 25-27); 1070 hp *(800 kW)* sustained; 2 shafts
Speed, knots: 20. **Range, miles:** 650 at 16 kts
Complement: 11
Guns: 3—7.62 mm MGs.
Radars: Surface Search: Racal Decca; I band.

Comment: The first two were the original units of the Bahamas Police Marine Division. With air-conditioned living spaces, these craft are designed for patrol among the many islands of the Bahamas Group. Light machine guns mounted in sockets either side of the bridge. Main engines replaced in the first pair in 1990.

INAGUA   1992, RBDF

9 LAUNCHES

P 30-P 33   P 101-P 105

Displacement, tons: 8 standard *(P 30-33)*
Dimensions, feet (metres): 28.9 × 10 × 2.3 *(8.8 × 3 × 0.7) (P 30-33)*
Main machinery: 2 Volvo TAMD40A diesels; 220 hp(m) *(162 kW)* sustained; 2 shafts
Speed, knots: 24+. **Range, miles:** 350 at 21 kts
Complement: 4
Guns: 2—7.62 mm MGs.

Comment: *P 30-33* are GRP launches built by Phoenix Marine, Florida and commissioned in 1981-82. *P 101-105* are between 28 and 40 ft in length; *P 102* and *104* have Mercruises inboard engines, the remainder Mercury, Johnson or Yamaha twin outboards. *P 106* sank during an SAR mission in January 1991.

P 31   *4/1992, RBDF*

4 Ex-FISHING VESSELS

P 34 —(ex-*Lady Hero*)
P 35 —(ex-*Carey*)
P 36 —Hatteras 45 ft motor yacht
P 37 —(ex-*Maria Mercedes II*)

Comment: P 34, P 35 and P 37 have a single GM diesel; 12 kts. P 36 has twin diesels; 15 kts.

FORT CHARLOTTE A 02 (ex-YFU 97, ex-LCU 1611)

Displacement, tons: 339 full load
Dimensions, feet (metres): 134.9 × 29 × 6.1 *(41.1 × 8.8 × 1.9)*
Main machinery: 2 Detroit 12V-71 diesels; 680 hp *(508 kW)* sustained; 2 shafts
Speed, knots: 11. **Range, miles:** 1200 at 10 kts
Complement: 15 (2 officers)
Guns: 2—7.62 mm MGs.
Radars: Navigation: Raytheon AN/SPS-66; I band.

Comment: Constructed by the Christy Corporation, Sturgeon Bay, in 1958; later converted and assigned to AUTEC in 1978 as harbour utility craft. Commissioned in the RBDF on 19 June 1991. Large cargo capacity and main deck area. Used primarily as a supply ship and mobile support platform.

FORT CHARLOTTE   *6/1991, RBDF*

FORT MONTAGUE A 01

Displacement, tons: 90 full load
Dimensions, feet (metres): 94 × 23 × 6 *(28.6 × 7 × 1.8)*
Main machinery: 2 Detroit 12V-71 diesels; 680 hp *(508 kW)* sustained; 2 shafts
Speed, knots: 13. **Range, miles:** 3000 at 10 kts
Complement: 16
Guns: 2—7.62 mm MGs.
Radars: Navigation: Racal Decca; I band.

Comment: Acquired 6 August 1980. Used as a supply ship.

FORT MONTAGUE   *1984, RBDF*

BAHRAIN

Headquarters' Appointments

Chief of Staff:
   Major General Shaikh Abdullah Bin Salman Bin Khalid Al Khalifa
Commander of Navy:
   Major Yusuf Ahmad Malullah
Director of Coast Guard:
   Colonel Abdul-Aziz Attiyatullah Al Khalifa

Personnel

(a) 1994: 650 (Navy), 250 (Coast Guard—seagoing)
(b) Voluntary service

Bases

Mina Sulman (Navy), Al-Hadd (CG)

Coast Guard

This unit is under the direction of the Ministry of the Interior.

Mercantile Marine

Lloyd's Register of Shipping:
   91 vessels of 103 251tons gross

DELETIONS

Coast Guard
1992   *Al-Bayneh, Junnan, Quaimas*
1993   *Mashtan* (old), *Safra 1, Saham 1, 2* and *3, Noon, Askar, Suwad* (old)

PATROL FORCES

2 AL RIFFA (FPB 38) CLASS (FAST ATTACK CRAFT—GUN)

Name	No	Builders	Commissioned
AL RIFFA	10	Lürssen	3 Mar 1982
HAWAR	11	Lürssen	3 Mar 1982

Displacement, tons: 188 half load; 205 full load
Dimensions, feet (metres): 126.3 × 22.9 × 7.2 *(38.5 × 7 × 2.2)*
Main machinery: 2 MTU 16V 538 TB92 diesels; 6810 hp(m) *(5 MW)* sustained; 2 shafts
Speed, knots: 32. **Range, miles:** 1100 at 16 kts
Complement: 27 (3 officers)
Guns: 2 Breda 40 mm/70 (twin); dual purpose; 85° elevation; 300 rounds/minute to 12 km *(6.5 nm)* anti-surface; 4 km *(2.2 nm)*; weight of shell 0.96 kg.
   1—57 mm Starshell rocket launcher.
Mines: Mine rails fitted.
Fire control: CSEE Lynx optical director with Philips 9LV 100 optronic system.
Radars: Surface search: Philips 9GR 600; I band.
Navigation: Racal Decca 1226; I band.

Comment: Ordered in 1979. *Al Riffa* launched April 1981. *Hawar* launched July 1981.

HAWAR   *8/1990*

2 AL MANAMA (FPB 62) CLASS (FAST ATTACK CRAFT—MISSILE)

Name	No	Builders	Commissioned
AL MANAMA	50	Lürssen	14 Dec 1987
AL MUHARRAQ	51	Lürssen	3 Feb 1988

Displacement, tons: 632 full load
Dimensions, feet (metres): 206.7 × 30.5 × 9.5 *(63 × 9.3 × 2.9)*
Main machinery: 4 MTU 20V 538 TB92 diesels; 12 820 hp(m) *(9.42 MW)* sustained; 4 shafts
Speed, knots: 32. **Range, miles:** 4000 at 16 kts
Complement: 43 (7 officers)

Missiles: SSM: 4 Aerospatiale MM 38 Exocet launchers (2 twin); inertial cruise; active radar homing to 42 km *(23 nm)* at 0.9 Mach; warhead 165 kg; sea-skimmer.
Guns: 1 OTO Melara 3 in *(76 mm)*/62 compact; 85° elevation; 85 rounds/minute to 16 km *(8.7 nm)* anti-surface; 12 km *(6.5 nm)* anti-aircraft; weight of shell 6 kg.
2 Breda 40 mm/70 (twin); 85° elevation; 300 rounds/minute to 12.5 km *(6.8 nm)*; weight of shell 0.96 kg.
2 Oerlikon GAM-BO1 20 mm/93.
Countermeasures: Decoys: CSEE Dagaie; chaff and IR flares.
ESM/ECM: Racal Decca Cutlass/Cygnus; intercept and jammer.
Fire control: CSEE Panda Mk 2 optical director. Philips TV/IR optronic director.
Radars: Air/surface search: Philips Sea Giraffe 50 HC; G band.
Navigation: Racal Decca 1226; I band.
Fire control: Philips 9LV 331; J band.

Helicopters: 1 Dauphin 2 type (not carried).

Programmes: Ordered February 1984. Upgrade planned for mid-1990s.
Structure: Similar to Abu Dhabi and Singapore designs. Steel hull, aluminium superstructure. Fitted with a helicopter platform which incorporates a lift to lower the aircraft into the hangar. Eight ASM can be carried.
Operational: Planned SA 365F helicopters with anti-ship missiles are not embarked.

AL MUHARRAQ *4/1992*

4 AHMAD EL FATEH (FPB 45) CLASS
(FAST ATTACK CRAFT—MISSILE)

Name	No	Builders	Commissioned
AHMAD EL FATEH	20	Lürssen	5 Feb 1984
AL JABIRI	21	Lürssen	3 May 1984
ABDUL RAHMAN AL FADEL	22	Lürssen	10 Sep 1986
AL TAWEELAH	23	Lürssen	25 Mar 1989

Displacement, tons: 228 half load; 259 full load
Dimensions, feet (metres): 147.3 × 22.9 × 8.2 *(44.9 × 7 × 2.5)*
Main machinery: 4 MTU 16V 538 TB92 diesels; 13 640 hp(m) *(10 MW)* sustained; 4 shafts
Speed, knots: 40. **Range, miles:** 1600 at 16 kts
Complement: 36 (6 officers)

Missiles: SSM: 4 Aerospatiale MM 40 Exocet (2 twin); inertial cruise; active radar homing to 70 km *(40 nm)* at 0.9 Mach; warhead 165 kg; sea-skimmer.
Guns: 1 OTO Melara 3 in *(76 mm)*/62; dual purpose; 85° elevation; 85 rounds/minute to 16 km *(8.7 nm)* anti-surface; 12 km *(6.5 nm)* anti-aircraft; weight of shell 6 kg.
2 Breda 40 mm/70 (twin); 85° elevation; 300 rounds/minute to 12.5 km *(6.8 nm)*; weight of shell 0.96 kg.
3—7.62 mm MGs.
Countermeasures: Decoys: CSEE Dagaie launcher; trainable mounting; 10 containers firing chaff decoys and IR flares.
ESM: RDL 2 ABC; radar warning.
ECM: Racal Cygnus (not in 20 and 21); jammer.
Fire control: 1 Panda optical director for 40 mm guns.
Radars: Surface search/fire-control: Philips LV223; J band.
Navigation: Racal Decca 1226; I band.

Programmes: First pair ordered in 1979, second pair in 1985.

AHMAD EL FATEH *5/1993*

2 AL JARIM (FPB 20) CLASS (FAST ATTACK CRAFT—GUN)

Name	No	Builders	Commissioned
AL JARIM	30	Swiftships, Morgan City	9 Feb 1982
AL JASRAH	31	Swiftships, Morgan City	26 Feb 1982

Displacement, tons: 33 full load
Dimensions, feet (metres): 63 × 18.4 × 6.5 *(19.2 × 5.6 × 2)*
Main machinery: 2 Detroit 12V-71TA diesels; 840 hp(m) *(627 kW)* sustained; 2 shafts
Speed, knots: 30. **Range, miles:** 1200 at 18 kts
Guns: 1 Oerlikon 20 mm.
Radars: Navigation: Decca 110; I band.

Comment: Aluminium hulls.

AUXILIARIES

4 AJEERA CLASS (SUPPORT SHIPS)

AJEERA 41   **MASHTAN** 42   **RUBODH** 43   **SUWAD** 44

Displacement, tons: 420 full load
Dimensions, feet (metres): 129.9 × 36.1 × 5.9 *(39.6 × 11 × 1.8)*
Main machinery: 2 Detroit 16V-71 diesels; 811 hp *(605 kW)* sustained; 2 shafts
Speed, knots: 13. **Range, miles:** 1500 at 10 kts
Complement: 21
Guns: 2—12.7 mm MGs.

Comment: Built by Swiftships, Morgan City, USA. *Ajeera* commissioned in October 1982. Used as general-purpose cargo ships and can carry up to 200 tons of fuel and water. Built to an LCU design with a bow ramp and 15 ton crane.

AJEERA *9/1990*

COAST GUARD

Notes: (1) In addition to the craft listed below about ten small open fibreglass boats are used for patrol duties.
(2) Eight 13 ft Diver Support craft ordered in April 1992, from RTK Marine.

1 WASP 30 METRE CLASS

AL MUHARRAQ

Displacement, tons: 90 standard; 103 full load
Dimensions, feet (metres): 98.5 × 21 × 5.5 *(30 × 6.4 × 1.6)*
Main machinery: 2 Detroit 16V-149TI diesels; 2322 hp *(1.73 MW)* sustained; 2 shafts
Speed, knots: 25. **Range, miles:** 500 at 22 kts
Complement: 9
Guns: 1—30 mm. 2—7.62 mm MGs.

Comment: Ordered from Souters, Cowes, Isle of Wight in 1984. Laid down November 1984, launched August 1985, shipped 21 October 1985. GRP hull.

AL MUHARRAQ *12/1993, Bahrain Coast Guard*

4 HALMATIC 20 METRE CLASS

DERA'A 2, 6, 7 and **8**

Displacement, tons: 31.5 full load
Dimensions, feet (metres): 65.9 × 17.3 × 5.1 *(20.1 × 5.3 × 1.5)*
Main machinery: 2 Detroit 12V-71TA diesels; 840 hp *(626 kW)* sustained; 2 shafts
Speed, knots: 25. **Range, miles:** 500 at 20 kts
Complement: 7
Guns: 2—7.62 mm MG.

Comment: Three delivered in late 1991, the last in early 1992. GRP hulls.

DERA'A 6 *1991, Bahrain Coast Guard*

2 WASP 20 METRE

DERA'A 4 and 5

Displacement, tons: 36.3 full load
Dimensions, feet (metres): 65.6 × 16.4 × 4.9 (20 × 5 × 1.5)
Main machinery: 2 Detroit 12V-71TA diesels; 840 hp (626 kW) sustained; 2 shafts
Speed, knots: 24.5. **Range, miles:** 500 at 20 kts
Complement: 8
Guns: 2—7.62 mm MGs.

Comment: Built by Souters, Cowes, Isle of Wight. Delivered 1983. GRP hulls.

DERA'A 4 and 5   1983, Beken of Cowes Ltd

2 TRACKER CLASS

DERA'A 1 and 3

Displacement, tons: 31 full load
Dimensions, feet (metres): 64 × 16 × 5 (19.5 × 4.9 × 1.5)
Main machinery: 2 General Motors diesels; 1120 hp (823 kW); 2 shafts
Speed, knots: 29
Guns: 1 Oerlikon 20 mm.

Comment: All built by Fairey Marine Ltd. The first purchased in 1974, the other two in 1980. One deleted in 1990.

DERA'A 3   12/1993, Bahrain Coast Guard

6 HALMATIC 14 METRE CLASS

SAIF 5, 6, 7, 8, 9 and 10

Displacement, tons: 17 full load
Dimensions, feet (metres): 47.2 × 12.8 × 3.9 (14.4 × 3.9 × 1.2)
Main machinery: 2 Detroit 6V-92TA diesels; 520 hp (388 kW) sustained; 2 shafts
Speed, knots: 27. **Range, miles:** 500 at 22 kts
Complement: 4

Comment: Delivered in 1990/91. GRP hulls.

SAIF 9   1991, Bahrain Coast Guard

4 FAIREY SWORD CLASS

SAIF 1, 2, 3 and 4

Displacement, tons: 15
Dimensions, feet (metres): 44.9 × 13.4 × 4.3 (13.7 × 4.1 × 1.3)
Main machinery: 2 GM 8V-71 diesels; 590 hp (440 kW) sustained; 2 shafts
Speed, knots: 28
Complement: 6

Comment: Purchased in 1980. Built by Fairey Marine Ltd.

SAIF 1   1982, Bahrain Coast Guard

1 SUPPORT CRAFT

Name	No	Builders	Commissioned
SAFRA 3	—	Halmatic, Havant	1992

Displacement, tons: 165 full load
Dimensions, feet (metres): 85 × 25.9 × 5.2 (25.9 × 7.9 × 1.6)
Main machinery: 2 Detroit 16V-92TA diesels; 1380 hp (1.03 MW); 2 shafts
Speed, knots: 13. **Range, miles:** 700 at 12 kts
Complement: 6

Comment: Delivered in early 1992. General-purpose workboat equipped for towing and fire fighting. Can carry 15 tons.

SAFRA 3   1992, Halmatic

1 LANDING CRAFT

Name	No	Builders	Commissioned
SAFRA 2	40	Fairey Marine Ltd	1981

Displacement, tons: 150 full load
Measurement, tons: 90 dwt
Dimensions, feet (metres): 73.9 × 24.9 × 4 (22.5 × 7.5 × 1.2)
Main machinery: 2 Detroit 12V-71 diesels; 680 hp (508 kW) sustained; 2 shafts
Speed, knots: 8
Complement: 8

Comment: Based at Mina Sulman and may be on loan to the Navy.

SAFRA 2   12/1993, Bahrain Coast Guard

1 TIGER CLASS HOVERCRAFT

Displacement, tons: 4.5 full load
Dimensions, feet (metres): 26.2 × 12.5 × 7.5 (7.97 × 3.8 × 2.26)
Main machinery: 1 AMC 5900 cc petrol engine; 180 hp (134 kW)
Speed, knots: 35

Comment: Built by AVL Cowes.

BANGLADESH

Headquarters' Appointments

Chief of Naval Staff:
Rear Admiral Mohammad Mohaiminul Islam
Assistant Chief of Naval Staff (Personnel):
Commodore F Ahmed
Assistant Chief of Naval Staff (Logistics):
Commodore M G Rabbani
Assistant Chief of Naval Staff (Material):
Commodore A M A Alam
Assistant Chief of Naval Staff (Operations):
Commodore S I Mujtaba

Senior Appointments

Commodore Commanding BN Flotilla:
Commodore A K M Azad
Commodore Commanding Chittagong:
Commodore Z Ali
Commodore Commanding Khulna:
Commodore M N Islam

Bases

Chittagong (BNS *Issa Khan,* BN Dockyard Complex). Naval Academy (BNS *Patenga*). Dhaka (BNS *Haji Mohsin*). Khulna (BNS *Titumir* and *Mongla*). Kaptai (BNS *Shaheed Moazzam*)

Personnel

(a) 1994: 8000 (650 officers)
(b) Voluntary service

Prefix to Ships' Names

BNS

Mercantile Marine

Lloyd's Register of Shipping:
287 vessels of 388 244 tons gross

Strength of the Fleet

Type	Active
Frigates	4
Fast Attack Craft (Missile)	8
Fast Attack Craft (Torpedo)	8
Fast Attack Craft (Patrol)	2
Fast Attack Craft (Gun)	8
Large Patrol Craft	7
Coastal Patrol Craft	1
Riverine Patrol Craft	5
Training Ship	1
Repair Ship	1
Tanker	1
Coastal Survey Craft	2
Landing Craft	7

DELETIONS

1991   1 Huangfen class, 1 Hegu class
1993   *Shaheed Ruhul Amin* (old)

PENNANT LIST

Frigates

F 15	Abu Bakr
F 16	Umar Farooq
F 17	Ali Haider
F 18	Osman

Light Forces

P 111	Pabna
P 112	Noakhali
P 113	Patuakhali
P 114	Rangamati
P 115	Bogra
P 211	Meghna
P 212	Jamuna
P 311	Bishkhali

P 312	Padma
P 313	Surma
P 314	Karnaphuli (reserve)
P 315	Tista
P 411	Shaheed Daulat
P 412	Shaheed Farid
P 413	Shaheed Mohibullah
P 414	Shaheed Akhtaruddin
P 611	Tawheed
P 612	Tawfiq
P 613	Tawjeed
P 614	Tanveer
P 811	Durjoy
P 812	Nirbhoy
P 8111	Durbar
P 8112	Duranta
P 8113	Durvedya

P 8114	Durdam
P 8125	Durdharsha
P 8126	Durdanta
P 8127	Durnibar
P 8128	Dordanda
A 513	Shahjalal

Auxiliaries

A 511	Shaheed Ruhul Amin
A 512	Shahayak
A 515	Khan Jahan Ali
A 581	Darshak
A 582	Tallashi
A 721	Khadem
L 900	Shahamanat

FRIGATES

1 OSMAN (JIANGHU I) CLASS (TYPE 053 H1)

Name	No	Builders	Laid down	Launched	Commissioned
OSMAN (ex-*Xiangtan*)	F 18	Hutong SY, Shanghai	—	—	4 Nov 1989

Displacement, tons: 1425 standard; 1702 full load
Dimensions, feet (metres): 338.6 × 35.4 × 10.2 *(103.2 × 10.7 × 3.1)*
Main machinery: 2 Type 12 E 390V diesels; 14 400 hp(m) *(10.6 MW)* sustained; 2 shafts
Speed, knots: 26. **Range, miles:** 2700 at 18 kts
Complement: 300 (27 officers)

Missiles: SSM: 4 Hai Ying 2 (2 twin) launchers ❶; active radar or IR homing to 80 km *(43.2 nm)* at 0.9 Mach; warhead 513 kg.
Guns: 4 China 3.9 in *(100 mm)*/56 (2 twin) ❷; 85° elevation; 18 rounds/minute to 22 km *(12 nm)*; weight of shell 15.9 kg.
8 China 37 mm/76 (4 twin) ❸; 85° elevation; 180 rounds/minute to 8.5 km *(4.6 nm)* anti-aircraft; weight of shell 1.42 kg.
A/S mortars: 2 RBU 1200 5-tubed fixed launchers ❹; range 1200 m; warhead 34 kg.
Depth charges: 2 BMB-2 projectors; 2 racks.
Mines: Can carry up to 60.
Countermeasures: Decoys: 2 Loral Hycor SRBOC Mk 36 6-barrelled chaff launchers.
ESM: Watchdog; radar warning.
Radars: Air/surface search: MX 902 Eye Shield (922-1) ❺; possible E band.
Surface search/fire control: Square Tie (254) ❻; I band.

Navigation: Fin Curve (352); I band.
Fire control: Wok Won (752A) ❼.
IFF: High Pole A.
Sonars: Echo Type 5; hull-mounted; active search and attack; medium frequency.

Programmes: Transferred 26 September 1989 from China, arrived Bangladesh 8 October 1989. Second expected in 1991 but was either postponed or cancelled.

Structure: This is a Jianghu Type I (version 4) hull with twin 100 mm guns (vice the 57 mm in the ships sold to Egypt), Wok Won fire-control system, and a rounded funnel.
Operational: Damaged in collision with a merchant ship in August 1991. One 37 mm mounting uprooted and SSM and RBU mountings misaligned. Repaired in 1992/93.

OSMAN

(Scale 1 : 900), Ian Sturton

OSMAN

6/1990, G Jacobs

1 SALISBURY CLASS (TYPE 61)

Name	No	Builders	Laid down	Launched	Commissioned
UMAR FAROOQ (ex-*Llandaff*)	F 16	Hawthorn Leslie Ltd	27 Aug 1953	30 Nov 1955	11 Apr 1958

Displacement, tons: 2170 standard; 2408 full load
Dimensions, feet (metres): 339.8 × 40 × 15.5 (screws)
(103.6 × 12.2 × 4.7)
Main machinery: 8 VVS ASR 1 diesels; 12 380 hp *(9.2 MW)* sustained; 2 shafts
Speed, knots: 24. **Range, miles:** 2300 at full power; 7500 at 16 kts
Complement: 237 (14 officers)

Guns: 2 Vickers 4.5 in *(115 mm)*/45 (twin) Mk 6 ❶; dual purpose; 80° elevation; 20 rounds/minute to 19 km *(10 nm)* anti-surface; 6 km *(3.3 nm)* anti-aircraft; weight of shell 25 kg.
2 Bofors 40 mm/60 Mk 9 ❷; 80° elevation; 120 rounds/ minute to 3 km *(1.6 nm)* anti-aircraft; 10 km *(5.5 nm)* maximum.
A/S mortars: 1 triple-barrelled Squid Mk 4 ❸; fires pattern of 3 depth charges to 300 m ahead of ship.
Fire control: 1 Mk 6M gun director.
Radars: Air search: Marconi Type 965 with double AKE 2 array ❹;A band.
Air/surface search: Plessey Type 993 ❺; E/F band.

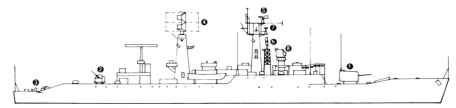

UMAR FAROOQ   *(Scale 1 : 900), Ian Sturton*

Height finder: Type 278M ❻; E band.
Surface search: Kelvin Hughes Type 1007 ❼; I/J band.
Navigation: Decca Type 978; I band.
Fire control: Type 275 ❽; F band.
Sonars: Type 174; hull-mounted; active search; medium frequency.
Graseby Type 170B; hull-mounted; active attack; 15 kHz.

Programmes: Transferred from UK at Royal Albert Dock, London 10 December 1976.
Operational: Suffered major machinery accident in 1985 but is now fully operational. The radar Type 982 aerial is still retained on the after mast but the set is non-operational. The ship is being refitted to remain in service until 2000.

UMAR FAROOQ   *5/1990, John Mortimer*

2 LEOPARD CLASS (TYPE 41)

Name	No	Builders	Laid down	Launched	Commissioned
ABU BAKR (ex-HMS *Lynx*)	F 15	John Brown & Co Ltd, Clydebank	13 Aug 1953	12 Jan 1955	14 Mar 1957
ALI HAIDER (ex-HMS *Jaguar*)	F 17	Wm Denny & Bros Ltd, Dumbarton	2 Nov 1953	30 July 1957	12 Dec 1959

Displacement, tons: 2300 standard; 2520 full load
Dimensions, feet (metres): 339.8 × 40 × 15.5 (screws)
(103.6 × 12.2 × 4.7)
Main machinery: 8 VVS ASR 1 diesels; 12 380 hp *(9.2 MW)* sustained; 2 shafts
Speed, knots: 24. **Range, miles:** 2300 at full power; 7500 at 16 kts
Complement: 235 (15 officers)

Guns: 4 Vickers 4.5 in *(115 mm)*/45 (2 twin) Mk 6 ❶; dual purpose; 80° elevation; 20 rounds/minute to 19 km *(10 nm)* anti-surface; 6 km *(3.3 nm)* anti-aircraft; weight of shell 25 kg.
1 Bofors 40 mm/60 Mk 9 ❷; 80° elevation; 120 rounds/ minute to 3 km *(1.6 nm)* anti-aircraft; 10 km *(5.5 nm)* maximum.
Countermeasures: ESM: Radar warning.
Fire control: Mk 6M gun director.
Radars: Air search: Marconi Type 965 with single AKE 1 array ❸; A band.
Air/surface search: Plessey Type 993 ❹; E/F band.
Navigation: Decca Type 978; Kelvin Hughes 1007; I band.
Fire control: Type 275 ❺; F band.

ABU BAKR   *(Scale 1 : 900), Ian Sturton*

Programmes: *Ali Haider* transferred from UK 16 July 1978 and *Abu Bakr* on 12 March 1982. *Ali Haider* refitted at Vosper Thornycroft August-October 1978. *Abu Bakr* extensively refitted in 1982. Could be replaced as frontline frigates by British Leanders if the funds can be found.

Structure: All welded. Fitted with stabilisers. Sonars removed while still in service with RN. Fuel tanks have a water compensation system to improve stability.
Operational: Designed as air-defence ships. May remain in service for several years as Training Ships.

ABU BAKR   *3/1993*

PATROL FORCES

4 DURDHARSHA (HUANGFEN) CLASS (TYPE 021)
(FAST ATTACK CRAFT—MISSILE)

DURDHARSHA P 8125	**DURNIBAR** P 8127
DURDANTA P 8126	**DORDANDA** P 8128

Displacement, tons: 171 standard; 205 full load
Dimensions, feet (metres): 110.2 × 24.9 × 8.9 *(33.6 × 7.6 × 2.7)*
Main machinery: 3 Type 42-160 diesels; 12 000 hp(m) *(8.8 MW)*; 3 shafts
Speed, knots: 35. **Range, miles:** 800 at 30 kts
Complement: 65 (5 officers)
Missiles: SSM: 4 Hai Ying 2; active radar or IR homing to 95 km *(51 nm)* at 0.9 Mach; warhead 513 kg.
Guns: 4 USSR 30 mm/69 (2 twin); 85° elevation; 1000 rounds/minute to 3 km *(1.6 nm)* anti-aircraft.
Radars: Surface search: Square Tie; I band.
IFF: High Pole A.

Comment: Built in China. Commissioned in Bangladesh Navy on 10 November 1988. Chinese equivalent of the Soviet Osa class which started building in 1985. All damaged in April 1991 typhoon and one sunk. A replacement was delivered in June 1992.

DURDHARSHA   *6/1990, G Jacobs*

4 DURBAR (HEGU) CLASS (TYPE 024)
(FAST ATTACK CRAFT—MISSILE)

DURBAR P 8111	**DURVEDYA** P 8113
DURANTA P 8112	**DURDAM** P 8114

Displacement, tons: 68 standard; 79.2 full load
Dimensions, feet (metres): 88.6 × 20.7 × 4.3 *(27 × 6.3 × 1.3)*
Main machinery: 4 Type L-12V-180 diesels; 4800 hp(m) *(3.53 MW)*; 4 shafts
Speed, knots: 37.5. **Range, miles:** 400 at 30 kts
Complement: 17 (4 officers)
Missiles: SSM: 2 SY-1; active radar or IR homing to 45 km *(24.3 nm)* at 0.9 Mach; warhead 513 kg.
Guns: 2—25 mm/80 (twin); dual purpose; 85° elevation; 270 rounds/minute to 3 km *(1.6 nm)*; weight of shell 0.34 kg.
Radars: Surface search: Square Tie; I band.

Comment: Built in China. First pair commissioned in Bangladesh Navy on 6 April 1983, second pair on 10 November 1983. Two badly damaged in April 1991 typhoon. One was scrapped and replaced in June 1992.

DURANTA   *6/1990, G Jacobs*

8 HUCHUAN CLASS (TYPE 026)
(FAST ATTACK CRAFT—TORPEDO)

TB 8235-TB 8238 + 4

Displacement, tons: 46 full load
Dimensions, feet (metres): 73.8 × 16.4 × 6.9 (foil) *(22.5 × 5 × 2.1)*
Main machinery: 3 Type L-12V-180 diesels; 3600 hp(m) *(2.64 MW)*; 3 shafts
Speed, knots: 50. **Range, miles:** 500 cruising
Complement: 23 (3 officers)
Guns: 4 China 14.5 mm (2 twin); 85° elevation; 600 rounds/minute to 7 km *(3.8 km)*.
Torpedoes: 2—21 in *(533 mm)*; anti-ship; active/passive homing; warhead 380 kg.
Radars: Surface search: Skin Head; I band.

Comment: This is the newer version of the Chinese Huchuan class with some minor differences. Two damaged in April 1991 typhoon, four more from Pakistan in 1993.

TB 8235   *4/1988, Bangladesh Navy*

TB 8237   *6/1990, G Jacobs*

2 DURJOY (HAINAN) CLASS (FAST ATTACK CRAFT—PATROL)

DURJOY P 811   **NIRBHOY** P 812

Displacement, tons: 375 standard; 392 full load
Dimensions, feet (metres): 192.8 × 23.6 × 7.2 *(58.8 × 7.2 × 2.2)*
Main machinery: 4 PCR/Kolomna Type 9-D-8 diesels; 4000 hp(m) *(2.94 MW)* sustained; 4 shafts
Speed, knots: 30.5. **Range, miles:** 1300 at 15 kts
Complement: 70
Guns: 4 China 57 mm/70 (2 twin); 85° elevation; 120 rounds/minute to 12 km *(6.5 nm)* anti-aircraft; weight of shell 6.31 kg.
4—25 mm (2 twin); 85° elevation; 270 rounds/minute to 3 km *(1.6 nm)* anti-aircraft.
A/S mortars: 4 RBU 1200 fixed 5-barrelled launchers; range 1200 m; warhead 34 kg.
Depth charges: 2 racks; 2 throwers. 18 DCs.
Mines: Fitted with rails for 12 mines.
Radars: Surface search: Pot Head (Skin Head in some); I band.
IFF: High Pole.
Sonars: Tamir II; hull-mounted; short range attack; high frequency.

Comment: First transferred from China and commissioned 10 September 1982 and the second 1 December 1985. Form part of Escort Squadron 81 at Chittagong. Some previous confusion over numbers of this class. Both damaged in April 1991 typhoon but have since been repaired.

NIRBHOY   *3/1993*

2 KARNAPHULI (KRALJEVICA) CLASS (LARGE PATROL CRAFT)

Name	*No*	*Builders*	*Commissioned*
KARNAPHULI (ex-*PBR 502*)	P 314	Yugoslavia	1956
TISTA (ex-*PBR 505*)	P 315	Yugoslavia	1956

Displacement, tons: 195 standard; 245 full load
Dimensions, feet (metres): 141.4 × 20.7 × 5.7 *(43.1 × 6.3 × 1.8)*
Main machinery: 2 MAN V8V 30/38 diesels; 3300 hp(m) *(2.42 MW)*; 2 shafts
Speed, knots: 19. **Range, miles:** 1500 at 12 kts
Complement: 44 (4 officers)
Guns: 2 Bofors 40 mm/70. 4 Oerlikon 20 mm. 2—128 mm rocket launchers (5 barrels per mounting).
Depth charges: 2 racks; 2 Mk 6 projectors.
Radars: Surface search: Decca 45; I band.
Sonars: QCU 2; hull-mounted; active; high frequency.

Comment: Transferred and commissioned 6 June 1975. *Karnaphuli* placed in Class III reserve in 1988.

KARNAPHULI   *1984, Bangladesh Navy*

8 SHAHEED (SHANGHAI II) CLASS (FAST ATTACK CRAFT—GUN)

SHAHEED DAULAT P 411	TAWHEED P 611
SHAHEED FARID P 412	TAWFIQ P 612
SHAHEED MOHIBULLAH P 413	TAWJEED P 613
SHAHEED AKHTARUDDIN P 414	TANVEER P 614

Displacement, tons: 113 standard; 131 full load
Dimensions, feet (metres): 127.3 × 17.7 × 5.6 *(38.8 × 5.4 × 1.7)*
Main machinery: 4 Type M 50 diesels; 4400 hp(m) *(3.2 MW)* sustained; 4 shafts
Speed, knots: 30. **Range, miles:** 800 at 16.5 kts
Complement: 36
Guns: 4—37 mm/63 (2 twin); 85° elevation; 180 rounds/minute to 8.5 km *(4.6 nm)*; weight of shell 1.4 kg.
4—25 mm/80 (2 twin); 85° elevation; 270 rounds/minute to 3 km *(1.6 nm)* anti-aircraft.
Depth charges: 2 throwers; 8 charges.
Mines: 10 can be carried.
Radars: Surface search: Skin Head/Pot Head; I band.
Sonars: Hull-mounted; active; short range; high frequency. Some reported to have VDS.

Comment: First four transferred from China March 1980, remainder in 1982. Different engine arrangement from Chinese craft. Four based at Chittagong form Patrol Squadron 41.

SHAHEED FARID   *1984, Bangladesh Navy*

TANVEER   *3/1993*

2 AKSHAY CLASS (LARGE PATROL CRAFT)

Name	No	Builders	Commissioned
PADMA (ex-INS *Akshay*)	P 312	Hooghly D & E Co, Calcutta	1962
SURMA (ex-INS *Ajay*)	P 313	Hooghly D & E Co, Calcutta	1962

Displacement, tons: 120 standard; 150 full load
Dimensions, feet (metres): 117.2 × 20 × 5.5 *(35.7 × 6.1 × 1.7)*
Main machinery: 2 Paxman YHAXM diesels; 1100 hp *(820 kW)*; 2 shafts
Speed, knots: 18
Complement: 35 (3 officers)
Guns: 8 Oerlikon 20 mm (2 quad).
Radars: Surface search: Racal Decca; I band.

Comment: Generally similar to the Royal Navy's former Ford class. Transferred from India and commissioned 12 April 1973 and 26 July 1974 respectively. *Surma* refitted in 1983.

PADMA   *1984, Bangladesh Navy*

2 MEGHNA CLASS (LARGE PATROL CRAFT)

MEGHNA P 211   JAMUNA P 212

Displacement, tons: 410 full load
Dimensions, feet (metres): 152.5 × 24.6 × 6.6 *(46.5 × 7.5 × 2)*
Main machinery: 2 Paxman Valenta 12CM diesels; 5000 hp *(3.73 MW)* sustained; 2 shafts
Speed, knots: 20. **Range, miles:** 2000 at 16 kts
Complement: 47 (3 officers)
Guns: 1 Bofors 57 mm/70 Mk 1; 75° elevation; 200 rounds/minute to 17 km *(9.3 nm)*; weight of shell 2.4 kg.
1 Bofors 40 mm/70; 90° elevation; 300 rounds/minute to 12 km *(6.5 nm)*; weight of shell 0.96 kg.
2—7.62 mm MGs; launchers for illuminants on the 57 mm gun.
Fire control: Selenia NA 18 B optronic system.
Radars: Surface search: Decca 1229; I band.

Comment: Built by Vosper Private Ltd, Singapore for EEZ work under the Ministry of Agriculture. *Meghna* launched 19 January 1984, *Jamuna* 19 March 1984. Both completed late 1984. Reported that MTU diesels may have been fitted giving a top speed of 24 kts. Both damaged in April 1991 typhoon.

MEGHNA   *6/1990, G Jacobs*

1 RIVER CLASS (LARGE PATROL CRAFT)

Name	No	Builders	Commissioned
BISHKHALI (ex-PNS *Jessore*)	P 311	Brooke Marine Ltd	20 May 1965

Displacement, tons: 115 standard; 143 full load
Dimensions, feet (metres): 107 × 20 × 6.9 *(32.6 × 6.1 × 2.1)*
Main machinery: 2 MTU 12V 538 TB90 diesels; 4500 hp(m) *(3.3 MW)* sustained; 2 shafts
Speed, knots: 24
Complement: 30
Guns: 2 Breda 40 mm/70; 85° elevation; 300 rounds/minute to 12.5 km *(6.8 nm)*; weight of shell 0.96 kg.
Radars: Surface search: Racal Decca; I band.

Comment: PNS *Jessore*, which was sunk during the 1971 war, was salvaged and extensively repaired at Khulna Shipyard and recommissioned as *Bishkhali* on 23 November 1978.

BISHKHALI   *1984, Bangladesh Navy*

5 PABNA CLASS (RIVERINE PATROL CRAFT)

Name	No	Builders	Commissioned
PABNA	P 111	DEW Narayangonj, Dhaka	12 June 1972
NOAKHALI	P 112	DEW Narayangonj, Dhaka	8 July 1972
PATUAKHALI	P 113	DEW Narayangonj, Dhaka	7 Nov 1974
RANGAMATI	P 114	DEW Narayangonj, Dhaka	11 Feb 1977
BOGRA	P 115	DEW Narayangonj, Dhaka	15 July 1977

Displacement, tons: 69.5
Dimensions, feet (metres): 75 × 20 × 3.5 *(22.9 × 6.1 × 1.1)*
Main machinery: 2 Cummins diesels; 2 shafts
Speed, knots: 10.8. **Range, miles:** 700 at 8 kts
Complement: 33 (3 officers)
Guns: 1 Bofors 40 mm/60; 80° elevation; 120 rounds/minute to 10 km *(5.5 nm)*; weight of shell 0.89 kg.

Comment: The first indigenous naval craft built in Bangladesh. Form River Patrol Squadron 11 at Mongla.

RANGAMATI   *1984, Bangladesh Navy*

1 COASTAL PATROL CRAFT

SHAHJALAL A 513

Displacement, tons: 600 full load
Dimensions, feet (metres): 131.8 × 29.7 × 12.6 *(40.2 × 9.1 × 3.8)*
Main machinery: 1 V-16 cyl Type diesel; 1 shaft
Speed, knots: 12. **Range, miles:** 7000 at 12 kts
Complement: 55 (3 officers)
Guns: 2 Oerlikon 20 mm.

Comment: Ex-Thai fishing vessel SMS *Gold 4*. Probably built in Tokyo. Commissioned on 15 January 1987 and used as a patrol craft in spite of its A pennant number.

SHAHJALAL   8/1987, Bangladesh Navy

TRAINING SHIP

1 ISLAND CLASS

Name	No	Builders	Commissioned
SHAHEED RUHUL AMIN (ex-*Jersey*)	A 511 (ex-P 295)	Hall Russell, Aberdeen	15 Oct 1976

Displacement, tons: 925 standard; 1260 full load
Dimensions, feet (metres): 176 wl; 195.3 oa × 36 × 15 *(53.7; 59.5 × 11 × 4.5)*
Main machinery: 2 Ruston 12RKC diesels; 5640 hp *(4.21 MW)* sustained; 1 shaft; cp prop
Speed, knots: 16.5. **Range, miles:** 7000 at 12 kts
Complement: 39
Guns: 1 Bofors 40 mm Mk 3. 2 FN 7.62 mm MGs.
Countermeasures: ESM: Orange Crop; intercept.
Combat data systems: Racal CANE DEA-1 action data automation.
Radars: Navigation: Kelvin Hughes Type 1006; I band.

Comment: Sale agreed with the UK in December 1993. Sailed for Bangladesh in February 1994 to replace the old training ship of the same name. This class has been fitted with enlarged keels, stabilisers and water ballast arrangements to damp down motion in a seaway.

ISLAND class (UK colours)   9/1993, van Ginderen Collection

AUXILIARIES

Notes: (1) Two LSLs built by Narayanganj Dockyard and launched in 1992 may be taken over by the Navy. Names are *Barkat* and *Bahasha Shaeed*.
(2) Six LCM 6 acquired from the US in 1992.

1 TANKER

KHAN JAHAN ALI A 515

Displacement, tons: 2900 full load
Measurement, tons: 1343 gross
Dimensions, feet (metres): 250.8 × 37.5 × 18.4 *(76.4 × 11.4 × 5.6)*
Main machinery: 1 diesel; 1350 hp(m) *(992 kW)*; 1 shaft
Speed, knots: 12
Complement: 26 (3 officers)
Cargo capacity: 1500 tons

Comment: Completed in Japan in 1983.

KHAN JAHAN ALI   6/1987, Gilbert Gyssels

1 REPAIR SHIP

SHAHAYAK A 512

Displacement, tons: 477 full load
Dimensions, feet (metres): 146.6 × 26.2 × 6.6 *(44.7 × 8 × 2)*
Main machinery: 1 Type 12 VTS 6 diesel; 1 shaft
Speed, knots: 11.5. **Range, miles:** 3800 at 11.5 kts
Complement: 45 (1 officer)
Guns: 1 Oerlikon 20 mm.

Comment: Re-engined and modernised at Khulna Shipyard and commissioned in 1978 to act as repair vessel.

SHAHAYAK   1984, Bangladesh Navy

1 OCEAN TUG

KHADEM A 721

Displacement, tons: 1472 full load
Dimensions, feet (metres): 197.5 × 38 × 16.1 *(60.2 × 11.6 × 4.9)*
Main machinery: 2 diesels; 2 shafts
Speed, knots: 14. **Range, miles:** 7200 at 14 kts
Complement: 56 (7 officers)
Guns: 2—12.7 mm MGs.

Comment: Commissioned 6 May 1984.

KHADEM   6/1990, G Jacobs

1 LANDING CRAFT LOGISTIC (LSL)

SHAHAMANAT L 900

Displacement, tons: 366 full load
Dimensions, feet (metres): 154.2 × 34.1 × 8 *(47 × 10.4 × 2.4)*
Main machinery: 2 Caterpillar D 343 diesels; 730 hp *(544 kW)* sustained; 2 shafts
Speed, knots: 9.5
Complement: 31 (3 officers)

Comment: One of two Danyard-built LSLs delivered in 1988 for civilian use and transferred to the Navy in 1990. The second may also be taken over by the Navy in due course.

SHAHAMANAT   *6/1990, Bangladesh Navy*

6 YUCH'IN CLASS (TYPE 068/069)

DARSHAK A 581   **TALLASHI** A 582
LCT 101-LCT 104 A 584-587

Displacement, tons: 85 full load
Dimensions, feet (metres): 81.2 × 17.1 × 4.3 *(24.8 × 5.2 × 1.3)*
Main machinery: 2 Type 12V 150 diesels; 600 hp(m) *(440 kW)*; 2 shafts
Speed, knots: 11.5. **Range, miles:** 450 at 11.5 kts
Complement: 23
Military lift: Up to 150 troops
Guns: 4 China 14.5 mm (2 twin) MGs.

Comment: Named craft transferred from China in 1983 and for a time were used as survey craft. Second pair transferred 4 May 1986; third pair 1 July 1986. Probably built in the late 1960s. Two badly damaged in April 1991 typhoon.

A 586   *6/1990, G Jacobs*

3 LCVP

LCVP 011, 012, 013

Displacement, tons: 83 full load
Dimensions, feet (metres): 69.9 × 17.1 × 4.9 *(21.3 × 5.2 × 1.5)*
Main machinery: 2 Cummins diesels; 365 hp *(272 kW)*; 2 shafts
Speed, knots: 12.
Complement: 10 (1 officer)

Comment: First two built at Khulna Shipyard and *013* at DEW Narayangong; all completed in 1984.

LCVP 012   *1984, Bangladesh Navy*

1 Ex-FISHING VESSEL

MFV 66

Displacement, tons: 96 full load
Dimensions, feet (metres): 91.9 × 19.7 × 5.9 *(28 × 6 × 1.8)*
Main machinery: 1 diesel; 1 shaft
Speed, knots: 8. **Range, miles:** 750 at 8 kts
Complement: 24 (1 officer)
Guns: 1 Oerlikon 20 mm.

Comment: Ex-Thai steel hulled fishing vessel. Confiscated and taken into naval service.

MFV 66   *1989, Bangladesh Navy*

SANKET

Displacement, tons: 80 full load
Dimensions, feet (metres): 96.5 × 20 × 5.9 *(29.4 × 6.1 × 1.8)*
Main machinery: 2 Deutz Sea diesels; 1215 hp(m) *(893 kW)*; 2 shafts
Speed, knots: 18. **Range, miles:** 1000 at 16 kts
Complement: 24 (1 officer)
Guns: 1 Oerlikon 20 mm.

Comment: Acquired in 1989. Used for general harbour duties.

1 FLOATING DOCK and 1 FLOATING CRANE

Comment: Floating Dock (*Sundarban*) acquired from Brodogradiliste Joso Lozovina-Mosor, Trogir, Yugoslavia in 1980; capacity 3500 tons. Floating crane (*Balaban*) is self-propelled at 9 kts and has a lift of 70 tons; built at Khulna Shipyard and commissioned 18 May 1988, she has a complement of 29 (2 officers).

SUNDARBAN   *1984, Bangladesh Navy*

BALABAN   *1990, Bangladesh Navy*

BARBADOS

Headquarters' Appointment

Chief of Staff, Barbados Defence Force:
Brigadier Rudyard E C Lewis

Commanding Officer Coast Guard Squadron

Lieutenant Commander D A Dowridge

Personnel

(a) 1994: 110 (12 officers)
(b) Voluntary service

Coast Guard

This was formed early in 1973. In 1979 it became the naval arm
of the Barbados Defence Force.

Base

Bridgetown (HMBS *Willoughby Fort*)

Headquarters

St Ann's Fort, Garrison, St Michael

Prefix to Ships' Names

HMBS

Mercantile Marine

Lloyd's Register of Shipping:
35 vessels of 49 224 tons gross

PATROL FORCES

1 KEBIR CLASS (LARGE PATROL CRAFT)

Name	No	Builders	Commissioned
TRIDENT	P 01	Brooke Marine Ltd	Nov 1981

Displacement, tons: 155.5 standard; 190 full load
Dimensions, feet (metres): 123 × 22.6 × 5.6 *(37.5 × 6.9 × 1.7)*
Main machinery: 2 Paxman Valenta 12CM diesels; 5000 hp
(3.73 MW) sustained; 2 shafts
Speed, knots: 29. **Range, miles:** 3000 at 12 kts
Complement: 28
Guns: 2—12.7 mm MGs.
Radars: Surface search: Racal Decca TM 1226C; I band.

Comment: Launched 14 April 1981. Similar to Algerian vessels.
Refitted by Bender Shipyard in 1990.

TRIDENT

11/1993, Maritime Photographic

3 GUARDIAN II CLASS (COASTAL PATROL CRAFT)

Name	No	Builders	Commissioned
T T LEWIS	P 04	Halmatic/Aquarius UK	Dec 1973
COMMANDER MARSHALL	P 05	Halmatic/Aquarius UK	Dec 1973
J T C RAMSEY	P 06	Halmatic/Aquarius UK	Nov 1974

Displacement, tons: 11
Dimensions, feet (metres): 41 × 12.1 × 3.3 *(12.5 × 3.7 × 1)*
Main machinery: 2 Caterpillar D 334TA diesels; 480 hp *(358 kW)*; 2 shafts
Speed, knots: 24
Complement: 4
Guns: 1—7.62 mm MG (fitted for but not with).

Comment: GRP hulls. Designed for coastal patrol/SAR duties by T T Boat Designs Ltd. Fitted out by
Aquarius Boat Co Ltd, Christchurch.

EXCELLENCE

11/1990, Bob Hanlon

COMMANDER MARSHALL

1988, BDF

3 INSHORE PATROL CRAFT

Comment: One Arctic 22 ft craft for SAR duties; speed 30 kts; commissioned November 1985.
Two 22 ft craft for law enforcement role; speed 40 kts; commissioned early 1989.

1 ENTERPRISE CLASS (OFFSHORE PATROL CRAFT)

Name	No	Builders	Commissioned
EXCELLENCE	P 03	Desco Marine	Dec 1981

Displacement, tons: 87 full load
Dimensions, feet (metres): 73.7 × 22 × 9 *(22.5 × 6.7 × 2.7)*
Main machinery: 1 Caterpillar diesel; 1 shaft
Speed, knots: 9.5
Complement: 9
Guns: 1—12.7 mm MG.
Radars: Surface search: Racal Decca TM 1229C; I band.

Comment: Shrimp boat converted for patrol duties by Swan Hunter (Trinidad) in 1980-81.

ARCTIC 22

1988, BDF

BELGIUM

Headquarters' Appointments

Chief of Naval Staff:
Vice Admiral W Herteleer
Deputy Chief of Naval Staff:
Captain D Deruytter

Diplomatic Representation

Naval, Military and Air Attaché in London:
Captain P A C Lavaert

Personnel

(a) 1994: 2893 (1536 national service). Numbers reducing to 2100 regulars by end 1997
(b) 10 months' national service (to end in 1994)

Strength of the Fleet

Type	Active	Building
Frigates	3	—
Minehunters (Ocean)	2	—
Minehunters (Coastal)	7	(4)
River Patrol Craft	1	(1)
Command and Support Ships	2	—
Training Ships	4	—
Research Ship	1	—
Auxiliaries and Tugs	8	—

Bases

Zeebrugge: Frigates, MCMV, Reserve Units.
Koksijde: Naval aviation.
Antwerp: *Liberation.*

Mercantile Marine

Lloyd's Register of Shipping:
199 vessels of 217 967 tons gross

DELETIONS

Frigates

1993 *Westhinder*

Mine Warfare Vessels

1991 *Andenne* (marine cadets), *Turnhout, Tongeren* (marine cadets), *Herstal, Vise* (marine cadets), *Nieuwport, Koksijde*
1992 *Merksem, Ougrée, Dinant, Heist, Rochefort*
1993 *Dianthus, Fuchsia, Iris* (all for sale) *Van Haverbeke* (divers boat), *De Brouwer, Breydel, Bovesse* (reserve)

Auxiliaries

1993 *Spa*

PENNANT LIST

Frigates

F 910	Wielingen
F 911	Westdiep
F 912	Wandelaar

Support Ships

A 960	Godetia
A 961	Zinnia

Mine Warfare Forces

M 903	Dufour
M 908	Truffaut
M 915	Aster
M 916	Bellis
M 917	Crocus
M 921	Lobelia
M 922	Myosotis
M 923	Narcis
M 924	Primula

River Patrol Craft

P 902	Liberation

Research Ship

A 962	Belgica

Training Ship

A 958	Zenobe Gramme

Auxiliaries and Tugs

A 950	Valcke
A 951	Hommel
A 953	Bij
A 954	Zeemeeuw
A 956	Krekel
A 981	Avila
A 997	Spin
A 998	Ekster

FRIGATES

3 WIELINGEN CLASS (E-71)

Name	No	Builders	Laid down	Launched	Commissioned
WIELINGEN	F 910	Boelwerf, Temse	5 Mar 1974	30 Mar 1976	20 Jan 1978
WESTDIEP	F 911	Cockerill, Hoboken	2 Sep 1974	8 Dec 1975	20 Jan 1978
WANDELAAR	F 912	Boelwerf, Temse	28 Mar 1975	21 June 1977	27 Oct 1978

Displacement, tons: 1940 light; 2430 full load
Dimensions, feet (metres): 349 × 40.3 × 18.4 *(106.4 × 12.3 × 5.6)*
Main machinery: CODOG; 1 RR Olympus TM3B gas-turbine; 25 440 hp *(19 MW)* sustained; 2 Cockerill 240 CO V 12 diesels; 6000 hp(m) *(4.4 MW)*; 2 shafts; cp props
Speed, knots: 26; 15 on 1 diesel; 20 on 2 diesels
Range, miles: 4500 at 18 kts; 6000 at 15 kts
Complement: 159 (13 officers)

Missiles: SSM: 4 Aerospatiale MM 38 Exocet (2 twin) launchers ❶; inertial cruise; active radar homing to 42 km *(23 nm)* at 0.9 Mach; warhead 165 kg; sea-skimmer.
SAM: Raytheon Sea Sparrow Mk 29 octuple launcher ❷; semi-active radar homing to 14.6 km *(8 nm)* at 2.5 Mach; warhead 39 kg.
Guns: 1 Creusot Loire 3.9 in *(100 mm)*/55 Mod 68 ❸; 80° elevation; 60-80 rounds/minute to 17 km *(9 nm)* anti-surface; 8 km *(4.4 nm)* anti-aircraft; weight of shell 13.5 kg.
Torpedoes: 2—21 in *(533 mm)* launchers. ECAN L5 Mod 4; anti-submarine; active/passive homing to 9.5 km *(5 nm)* at 35 kts; warhead 150 kg; depth to 550 m *(1800 ft)*.
A/S Mortars: 1 Creusot Loire 375 mm 6-barrelled trainable launcher ❹; Bofors rockets to 1600 m; warhead 107 kg.
Countermeasures: Decoys: 2 Tracor MBA SRBOC 6-barrelled Mk 36 launchers; chaff decoys and IR flares to 4 km *(2.2 nm)*. Nixie SLQ 25; towed anti-torpedo decoy.
ESM: Thomson-CSF DR 2000; radar warning.
Combat data systems: Signaal SEWACO IV action data automation; Link 11. SATCOM.

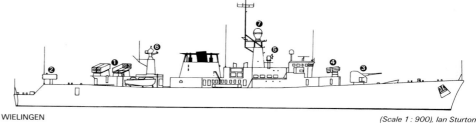

WIELINGEN

(Scale 1 : 900), Ian Sturton

Fire control: 2 CSEE DMAb optical directors ❺.
Radars: Air/surface search: Signaal DA 05 ❻; E/F band; range 137 km *(75 nm)* for 2 m² target.
Surface search/fire-control: Signaal WM 25 ❼; I/J band; range 46 km *(25 nm)*.
Navigation: Raytheon TM 1645/9X; I/J band.
IFF: Mk XII.
Sonars: Westinghouse SQS 505A; hull-mounted; active search and attack; medium frequency.

Programmes: This compact, well-armed class of frigate is the first class fully designed by the Belgian Navy and built in Belgian yards. The programme was approved on 23 June 1971 and design studies completed July 1973. An order was placed in October 1973 and F 910 and F 911 were first delivered in December 1976 and returned to the yard for engine overhaul which was completed a year later.
Modernisation: Plans to fit a CIWS were abandoned in 1993, but Sea Sparrow has been updated from 7M to 7P. In addition the existing search and fire-control radars are to be upgraded as well as the ESM. The fitting of an optronic scanner is also being considered. Sonar, IFF and communications updates are planned in due course.
Structure: Fully air-conditioned. Fin stabilisers fitted.
Operational: Based at Zeebrugge. Two of the three remaining ships of this class are to be kept in an operational status. The fourth of class was deleted after hitting rocks off the coast of Norway in mid-1993.

WANDELAAR

6/1993, van Ginderen Collection

MINE WARFARE FORCES

0 + 4 NEW MINESWEEPERS (COASTAL)

Displacement, tons: 620 full load
Dimensions, feet (metres): 171.9 oa; 157.5 wl × 34.1 × 10.2
(52.4; 48 × 10.4 × 3.1)
Speed, knots: 15; 10 (sweeping). **Range, miles:** 3000 at 12 kts
Complement: 25 plus 5 spare

Guns: 1 DCN 20 mm/20.
Radars: Navigation: I band.

Programmes: Memorandum of Understanding signed 6 April 1989 for a joint Belgium/Netherlands minesweeper project. Design contract awarded November 1990 to van der Giessen-de Noord Marinebouw in a joint venture with Beliard Polyship NV, completed in August 1992. Portugal joined the venture as an observer in 1991. In early 1993 the Netherlands pulled out due to budget restraints and Portugal has other priorities. Belgium therefore continues the project alone with four hulls authorised on 1 July 1993. The first is scheduled to complete in 1999.
Operational: The ship is to be equipped with a newly developed magnetic sweeping gear, 'Sterne M', by Thomson Sintra. This development, ordered by the joint navies, is based upon the concept of 'target simulation' and consists of six bodies, towed in array, each carrying two coils. By automatically computed coil settings a simulated ship's signature is generated without

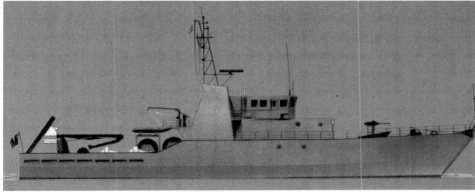

NEW MINESWEEPER (artist's impression)   1992, van der Giessen-de Noord

any assumption concerning the mine itself. In addition, proven acoustic and mechanic sweeping capabilities are installed. The requirement is to be able to sweep bottom mines which have sunk so far into soft sand that they are not detected by hunters.

7 FLOWER CLASS (TRIPARTITE) (MINEHUNTERS—COASTAL)

Name	No	Builders	Laid down	Launched	Commissioned
ASTER	M 915	Beliard SY, Ostend and Rupelmonde	26 Apr 1983	6 June 1985	17 Dec 1985
BELLIS	M 916	Beliard SY, Ostend and Rupelmonde	9 Feb 1984	14 Feb 1986	14 Aug 1986
CROCUS	M 917	Beliard SY, Ostend and Rupelmonde	9 Oct 1984	6 Aug 1986	5 Feb 1987
LOBELIA	M 921	Beliard SY, Ostend and Rupelmonde	4 Dec 1986	6 Jan 1988	9 May 1989
MYOSOTIS	M 922	Beliard SY, Ostend and Rupelmonde	6 July 1987	4 Aug 1988	14 Dec 1989
NARCIS	M 923	Beliard SY, Ostend and Rupelmonde	25 Feb 1988	30 Mar 1990	27 Sep 1990
PRIMULA	M 924	Beliard SY, Ostend and Rupelmonde	10 Nov 1988	17 Dec 1990	29 May 1991

Displacement, tons: 562 standard; 595 full load
Dimensions, feet (metres): 168.9 × 29.2 × 8.2
(51.5 × 8.9 × 2.5)
Main machinery: 1 Brons/Werkspoor A-RUB 215X-12 diesel; 1860 hp(m) *(1.37 MW)* sustained; 1 shaft; Lips cp prop; 2 motors; 240 hp(m) *(176 kW)*; 2 active rudders; 2 bow thrusters
Speed, knots: 15. **Range, miles:** 3000 at 12 kts
Complement: 46 (5 officers)

Guns: 1 DCN 20 mm/20; 60° elevation; 720 rounds/minute to 10 km *(5.5 nm)*. 1—12.7 mm MG.
Countermeasures: MCM: 2 PAP 104 remote-controlled mine locators; 39 charges.
Mechanical sweep gear (medium depth).
Radars: Navigation: Racal Decca 1229; I band.
Sonars: Thomson Sintra DUBM 21A; hull-mounted; active mine-hunting; 100 kHz ± 10 kHz.

Programmes: Developed in co-operation with France and the Netherlands. A 'ship factory' for the hulls was built at Ostend and the hulls were towed to Rupelmonde for fitting out. Each country built its own hulls but for all 35 ships France provided MCM gear and electronics, Belgium electrical installation and the Netherlands the engine room equipment.
Structure: GRP hull fitted with active tank stabilisation, full NBC protection and air-conditioning. Has automatic pilot and buoy tracking.
Operational: A 5 ton container can be carried, stored for varying tasks—HQ support, research, patrol, extended diving, drone control. The ship's company varies from 23-46 depending on the assigned task. Six divers are carried when minehunting. All of the class are based at Zeebrugge. *Crocus* has been modified as an ammunition transfer to relieve *Spa* which was deleted in July 1993.
Sales: Three of the class paid off for sale in July 1993.

PAP 104   3/1991, van Ginderen Collection

ASTER   2/1993, G Toremans

2 AGGRESSIVE CLASS (MINEHUNTERS/SWEEPERS — OCEAN)

Name	No	Builders	Laid down	Launched	Commissioned
A F DUFOUR (ex-*Lagen* M 950, ex-MSO 498, ex-AM 498)	M 903	Bellingham Shipyard Inc, Wash.	11 Feb 1954	13 Aug 1954	27 Sep 1955
G TRUFFAUT (ex-MSO 515, ex-AM 515)	M 908	Tampa Marine Co Inc, Tampa, Fla.	1 Feb 1955	1 Nov 1955	21 Sep 1956

Displacement, tons: 720 standard; 780 full load
Dimensions, feet (metres): 172.5 × 35.1 × 14.1
(52.6 × 10.7 × 4.3)
Main machinery: 4 GM 8-268A diesels; 1760 hp *(1.3 MW)*;
2 shafts; cp props
Speed, knots: 14. **Range, miles:** 2400 at 12 kts; 3000 at 10 kts
Complement: 40 (3 officers)

Guns: 2 Oerlikon 20 mm (twin). 2—12.7 mm MGs (M 908).
Radars: Navigation: Racal Decca 1229; I band.
Sonars: GE SQQ 14; VDS; minehunting; high frequency.

Programmes: Transfer dates from US; M 903 14 April 1966, M
908 12 October 1956. M 903 originally served in Royal
Norwegian Navy (1955-66).
Structure: Wooden hulls and non-magnetic structure. Capable of
sweeping mines of all types. Diesels of non-magnetic stainless
steel alloy. LIPS cp propellers.
Operational: Based at Zeebrugge. Remaining pair to be kept
operational. M 902 is used as a base ship for divers and M 909
is cocooned in reserve.

TRUFFAUT   *2/1993, G Toremans*

PATROL FORCES

Note: A new fast patrol craft is planned probably to be funded by the Ministry of Agriculture but
naval manned. Could be built in 1994 and in service in 1995.

1 RIVER PATROL CRAFT

Name	No	Builders	Commissioned
LIBERATION	P 902	Hitzler, Regensburg	4 Aug 1954

Displacement, tons: 275 full load
Dimensions, feet (metres): 85.5 × 13.1 × 3.2 *(26.1 × 4 × 1)*
Main machinery: 2 diesels; 440 hp(m) *(323 kW)*; 2 shafts
Speed, knots: 19
Complement: 7
Guns: 2—12.7 mm MGs.
Radars: Navigation: Racal Decca; I band.

Comment: Laid down 12 March 1954 and launched 29 July 1954. Paid off 12 June 1987 but put
back in active service 15 September 1989 after repairs. Last of a class of ten.

LIBERATION   *10/1993, van Ginderen Collection*

SHIPBORNE AIRCRAFT

Numbers/Type: 3 Aerospatiale SA 316B Alouette III.
Operational speed: 113 kts *(210 km/h)*.
Service ceiling: 10 500 ft *(3200 m)*.
Range: 290 nm *(540 km)*.
Role/Weapon systems: CG helicopter; used for close-range search and rescue and support for
commando forces. Sensors: Carries French-design search radar. Weapons: Unarmed. One SA
319B is used for transport on shore.

ALOUETTE III   *3/1991, van Ginderen Collection*

LAND-BASED MARITIME AIRCRAFT

Numbers/Type: 5 Westland Sea King Mk 48.
Operational speed: 140 kts *(260 km/h)*.
Service ceiling: 10 500 ft *(3200 m)*.
Range: 630 nm *(1165 km)*.
Role/Weapon systems: SAR helicopter; operated by air force; used for surface search and combat
rescue tasks. Sensors: MEL ARI 5955 search radar. Weapons: Unarmed.

SEA KING Mk 48   *1989, Paul Beaver*

AUXILIARIES

Note: There are four government patrol craft of 16.6 m completed by SKB Antwerp in 1992/93.
Names are *Nele 35, Tiji 36, Zannefin 37, Jan Bart 38*.

1 COMMAND AND SUPPORT SHIP

Name	No	Builders	Commissioned
ZINNIA	A 961	Cockerill, Hoboken	22 Sep 1967

Displacement, tons: 1705 light; 2620 full load
Dimensions, feet (metres): 324.7 × 45.9 × 11.8 *(99 × 14 × 3.6)*
Main machinery: 2 Cockerill Ougree 240 CO 12 TR diesels; 5000 hp(m) *(3.68 MW)*; 1 shaft; cp
prop
Speed, knots: 18. **Range, miles:** 14 000 at 12.5 kts
Complement: 125 (13 officers)
Guns: 3 Bofors 40 mm/60.
Radars: Surface search: Racal Decca 1229; I band.
Helicopters: 1 Alouette III.

Comment: Laid down 8 November 1966, launched on 6 May 1967. Design includes a telescopic
hangar. Rated as Command and Logistic Support Ship with an oil fuel capacity of 500 tons. Fitted with chaff launchers for prolonged operations. Based at Zeebrugge. Can also serve as a Royal
Yacht.

ZINNIA   *1/1992, van Ginderen Collection*

1 COMMAND AND SUPPORT SHIP

Name	No	Builders	Commissioned
GODETIA	A 960	Boelwerf, Temse	3 June 1966

Displacement, tons: 2000 standard; 2260 full load
Dimensions, feet (metres): 301 × 46 × 11.5 *(91.8 × 14 × 3.5)*
Main machinery: 4 ACEC-MAN diesels; 5400 hp(m) *(3.97 MW)*; 2 shafts; cp props
Speed, knots: 19. **Range, miles:** 8700 at 12.5 kts
Complement: 100 (10 officers) plus 35 spare billets
Guns: 1 Bofors 40 mm/60. 2 midships sponsons for 12.7 mm MGs.
Radars: Surface search: Racal Decca 1229; I band.

Comment: Laid down 15 February 1965 and launched 7 December 1965. Rated as Command and Logistic Support Ship. Refit (1979-80) and mid-life conversion (1981-82) included helicopter hangar and replacement cranes. Minesweeping cables fitted either side of helo deck. Refitted in early 1992. Can also serve as a Royal Yacht.

GODETIA
4/1993, van Ginderen Collection

SPIN A 997 **AVILA** A 981

Comment: *Spin* is a harbour launch of 32 tons built in Netherlands 1958. Based at Ostend.

AVILA
7/1991, Gilbert Gyssels

SURVEY AND RESEARCH SHIPS

Note: In addition to *Belgica* there are five small civilian manned survey craft: *Ter Streep, Scheldewacht II, De Parel II, Veremans* and *Prosper.*

Name	No	Builders	Commissioned
BELGICA	A 962	Boelwerf, Temse	5 July 1984

Displacement, tons: 1085
Dimensions, feet (metres): 167 × 32.8 × 14.4 *(50.9 × 10 × 4.4)*
Main machinery: 1 ABC 6M DZC diesel; 1600 hp(m) *(1.18 MW)* sustained; 1 Kort nozzle prop
Speed, knots: 13.5. **Range, miles:** 5000 at 12 kts
Complement: 26 (11 civilian)
Radars: Navigation: Racal Decca 1229; I band.

Comment: Ordered 1 December 1982. Laid down 17 October 1983, launched 6 January 1984. Used for hydrography, oceanography, meteorology and fishery control. Based at Zeebrugge. Painted white.

BELGICA
5/1992, van Ginderen Collection

TUGS

2 COASTAL TUGS

VALCKE (ex-*Steenbank*, ex-*Astroloog*) A 950
EKSTER (ex-*Schouwenbank*, ex-*Astronoom*) A 998

Displacement, tons: 183
Dimensions, feet (metres): 99.7 × 24.9 × 11.8 *(30.4 × 7.6 × 3.6)*
Main machinery: Diesel-electric; 2 Deutz diesel generators; 1240 hp(m) *(911 kW)*; 1 shaft
Speed, knots: 12
Complement: 12

Comment: Originally Netherlands civilian tugs built by H H Bodewes, Millingen in 1960. Bought by Belgian Navy in April 1980. Based at Zeebrugge.

VALCKE
7/1993, van Ginderen Collection

4 HARBOUR TUGS

BIJ A 953 **KREKEL** A 956 **HOMMEL** A 951 **ZEEMEEUW** A 954

Comment: *Bij* and *Krekel* are harbour tugs with firefighting facilities. Of 71 tons and twin shafts; 400 hp(m) *(294 kW)* with Voith-Schneider propellers; 10 kts. A 953 built at Akerboom, Lisse 1959 and based at Ostend, A 956 by Scheepswerf van Rupelmonde at Rupelmonde 1961 and based at Antwerp. *Hommel* is of 22 tons and was built in 1953 by Clausen. *Zeemeeuw* is of 220 tons and was built at Hemiksem in 1971 and acquired for the Navy on 8 December 1981. A 951 is based at Ostend and A 954 at Zeebrugge.

BIJ
6/1993, G Toremans

ZEEMEEUW
6/1993, G Toremans

TRAINING SHIPS

1 SAIL TRAINING VESSEL

Name	No	Builders	Commissioned
ZENOBE GRAMME	A 958	Boel and Zonen, Temse	27 Dec 1961

Displacement, tons: 149
Dimensions, feet (metres): 92 × 22.5 × 7 *(28 × 6.8 × 2.1)*
Main machinery: 1 MWM diesel; 200 hp(m) *(147 kW)*; 1 shaft
Speed, knots: 10
Complement: 14

Comment: Auxiliary sail ketch. Laid down 7 October 1960 and launched 23 October 1961. Designed for scientific research but now only used as a training ship.

3 MARINE CADET SHIPS

TONGEREN (ex-*M 475*)   **VISE** (ex-*M 482*)   **ANDENNE** (ex-*M 485*)

Displacement, tons: 190 full load
Dimensions, feet (metres): 111.5 × 19.7 × 6.9 *(34 × 6 × 2.1)*
Main machinery: 2 Fiat-Mercedes Benz diesels; 1260 hp(m) *(926 kW)*; 2 shafts
Speed, knots: 15. **Range, miles:** 2300 at 10 kts
Complement: 14 (2 officers)
Radars: Navigation: Racal Decca 1229; I band.

Comment: Herstal class ex-Inshore minesweepers built in 1957-59, paid off in 1991 and now used by marine cadets.

ZENOBE GRAMME   *4/1992, Giorgio Ghiglione*

MARINE CADET SHIP   *9/1992, G Toremans*

BELIZE

Headquarters' Appointment

Commanding Officer Defence Force Maritime Wing:
Captain Andrew C Lewis

Personnel

(a) 1994: 50 (8 officers)
(b) The Maritime Wing of the Belize Defence Force comprises volunteers from the Army.

Bases

Belize City, Punta Gorda

Mercantile Marine

Lloyd's Register of Shipping:
190 vessels of 147 649 tons gross

DELETIONS

1993   *Dangriga*

PATROL FORCES

0 + 2 (8) GUARDIAN CLASS

Dimensions, feet (metres): 26.6 × 10 × 1.7 *(8.1 × 3 × 0.5)*
Main machinery: 2 Johnson outboards; 400 hp *(294 kW)*
Speed, knots: 35. **Range, miles:** 250 at 30 kts
Complement: 3
Guns: 2—7.62 mm MGs.
Radars: Surface search: Furuno; I band.

Comment: First two ordered in late 1993. Boston Whaler 27 ft class. The plan is to order one more per year to a total of 10.

8 INSHORE PATROL CRAFT

Comment: The BDFMW has two Mexican Skiffs and two Avon type boats. The Police Maritime Wing has three armed Seacraft (P1-P3) with two outboard motors capable of 35 kts; one 12.7 mm MG. Also one Mexican Skiff.

GUARDIAN   *1993, Boston Whaler*

POLICE CRAFT   *7/1989, BDFMW*

1 WASP 20 METRE (COASTAL PATROL CRAFT)

Name	No	Builders	Commissioned
TOLEDO	PB 02	Souters, Cowes	19 Sep 1984

Displacement, tons: 36.3 full load
Dimensions, feet (metres): 65.6 × 16.4 × 4.9 (20 × 5 × 1.5)
Main machinery: 2 Detroit 16V-71 diesels; 812 hp (606 kW) sustained; 2 shafts
Speed, knots: 18
Complement: 10 (2 officers)
Guns: 1—12.7 mm MG. 2—7.62 mm MGs.

Comment: GRP hull. It is reported that this vessel has too great a draught for the shallow waters frequented by smugglers. Second of class paid off in 1993.

TOLEDO   6/1993, BDFMW

AUXILIARIES

3 AVON CLASS

EDEN   FORTH   MEDWAY

Displacement, tons: 100 full load
Dimensions, feet (metres): 72.2 × 20.5 × 5.5 (22 × 6.2 × 1.7)
Main machinery: 2 diesels; 870 hp (649 kW); 2 shafts
Speed, knots: 9
Complement: 6

Comment: Ramped powered lighters built in the mid-1960s. Used by the British Army in Belize and left behind in April 1994.

EDEN   3/1987, Michael Lennon

LAND-BASED MARITIME AIRCRAFT

Numbers/Type: 2 Pilatus Britten-Norman Defender.
Operational speed: 150 kts (280 km/h).
Service ceiling: 18 900 ft (5760 m).
Range: 1500 nm (2775 km).
Role/Weapon systems: Coastal patrol, EEZ protection and anti-drug operations. Sensors: Nose-mounted search radar, underwing searchlight. Weapons: Underwing rocket and gun pods possible.

BENIN

General

In 1978 a decision was taken to found a naval force. As the coastline of Benin is no more than 75 miles long the Patrol Craft can cover the whole coast in a little over two hours. Four Zhuk patrol craft still exist but are unlikely to go to sea again. There are also a Dornier Do 128 and a DHC-6 Twin Otter reconnaissance aircraft.

Personnel

1994: 150

Base

Cotonou

Mercantile Marine

Lloyd's Register of Shipping:
   7 vessels of 1022 tons gross

DELETIONS

1992   *Kondo* (civilian)

PATROL FORCES

1 PR 360T COASTAL PATROL CRAFT

PATRIOTE

Displacement, tons: 70 full load
Dimensions, feet (metres): 124.7 × 22.3 × 4.3 (38 × 6.8 × 1.3)
Main machinery: 3 Baudouin 12P15.2SR diesels; 3000 hp(m) (2.2 MW) sustained; 3 waterjets
Speed, knots: 35. **Range, miles:** 1500 at 16 kts
Complement: 23
Guns: 1 Oerlikon 20 mm. 2—12.7 mm MGs.
Radars: Surface search: Decca; I band.

Comment: Laid down by Société Bretonne de Construction Navale (Loctudy) in October 1986. Launched January 1988 and completed 15 May 1988. Has a wood/epoxy resin composite hull. Endurance 10 days. The craft was damaged shortly after delivery and was not operational again until early 1992.

PATRIOTE   1988, SBCN Loctudy

BERMUDA

General

A small group operated by the Bermuda Police under the charge of Inspector P J Every. There are also two tugs, *Powerful* and *Faithful*, operated by the Department of Port Services.

Base

Hamilton

Mercantile Marine

Lloyd's Register of Shipping:
96 vessels of 3 139 736 tons gross

POLICE

BLUE HERON

Comment: Delivered 22 May 1978 by Harris Boat, Newburyport, Massachusetts, USA. Of 7 tons, 36 ft *(10.9 m)* with two GM 8 2 Y diesels; 420 hp *(313 kW)*. Complement three.

HERON I   HERON II   HERON III

Comment: *Heron II* delivered in December 1988 and *Heron I* in August 1991. A new *Heron III* delivered in June 1992 to replace the craft of the same name. All are Boston Whaler type craft of 1.5 tons, 22 ft *(6.7 m)* and have twin Yamaha 115 hp(m) *(84.5 kW)* outboard engines.

HERON III   *7/1992, Bermuda Police*

RESCUE I   RESCUE II

Comment: First one delivered September 1986 and second May 1988 by Osborne Rescue Boats Ltd. An 'Arctic' rigid hull inflatable. Of 1.45 tons, 24 ft *(7.3 m)* with twin Yamaha 115 hp(m) *(84.5 kW)* outboard engines. Complement three.

BLUE HERON   *6/1993, Bermuda Police*

BOLIVIA

Headquarters' Appointments

Commander Armada Boliviana:
Vice Admiral Anibal Gutierrez Chavez
Chief of Staff:
Rear Admiral Rolando Herrera

General

A small navy, Armada Boliviana, used for patrolling Lake Titicaca and the Beni, Madre de Dios, Mamoré and Paraguay river systems was founded in 1963, receiving its present name in 1982. These rivers cover over 10 000 miles. Most of the advanced training of officers and senior ratings is carried out in friendly countries. The junior ratings are almost entirely converted soldiers. The vessels listed were those operational at the end of 1991, all the others have been deleted.

Personnel

(a) 1994: 5000 officers and men
(b) 12 months' selective military service

Organisation

The country is divided into five naval districts, each with one flotilla.

1st Naval District (HQ Riberalta). Patrol craft and two BTL logistic vessels on the Beni/Mamoré river system.
2nd Naval District (HQ Trinidad). Patrol craft and two BTL logistic vessels on the northern portion of Lake Titicaca.
3rd Naval District (HQ Puerto Guayaramerin). Four patrol craft and two BTL logistic vessels on the Madre de Dios river.
4th Naval District (HQ Tiquina). Patrol craft and the hospital ship on the southern portion of Lake Titicaca.
5th Naval District (HQ Puerto Quijarro). Three patrol craft and one BTL logistic vessel on the upper Paraguay river.

Marine Corps

Infanteria de Marina of 600 men based at Tiquina (Almirante Grau battalion)
Equipment: light infantry weapons and Unimog trucks

Prefix to Ships' Names

ARB

Mercantile Marine

Lloyd's Register of Shipping:
1 vessel of 9610 tons gross

PATROL FORCES

9 RIVER/LAKE PATROL CRAFT

Name	No	Tonnage
COMANDO	LP-01	10
TACTICA	LP-02	10
INTI	LP-04	10
MALLCU	LP-05	10
AUXILIAR	LP-08	10
SANTA CRUZ DE LA SIERRA	PR-51	50
TAMENGO	LP-502	10
SUAREZ ARANA	LP-510	10
MARISCAL SANTA CRUZ	LP-512	10

Comment: In addition to the above, four Boston Whalers were acquired from the US in late 1989 and 11 more in early 1991. A 55 ft craft *General Banzer* was launched in September 1990.

4 AUXILIARIES

Name	No	Tonnage
JULIAN APAZA	AH 01	150
GENERAL BELGRANO	LT 01	30
PIONERA	LH 01	30
CENTAURO	LH 03	30

Comment: AH 01 is a hospital ship given by the USA in 1972. LT 01 is a transport vessel and LH 01 and LH 03 are survey ships.

17 LOGISTIC SUPPORT and PATROL CRAFT

Name	No	Tonnage
GENERAL PANDO	BTL-01	40
NICOLAS SUAREZ	BTL-02	40
MARISCAL CRUZ	BTL-03	40
MAX PAREDES	BTL-04	40
V A H UGARTECHE	BTL-06	45
MANURIPI	BTL-07	40
ALMIRANTE GRAU	M-101	20
COMANDANTE ARANDIA	M-103	20
LIBERTADOR	M-223	20
TRINIDAD	M-224	20
LITORAL	M-18	20
J CHAVEZ SUAREZ	M-225	20
ING PALACIOS	M-315	20
ITENEZ	M-322	20
BRUNO RACUA	M-329	20
TF R RIOS V	M-331	20
ING GUMUCIO	M-341	70

Comment: The craft with BTL numbers have a liquid cargo capacity of 250 000 litres.

LAND-BASED MARITIME AIRCRAFT

Numbers/Type: 8 Helibras (Aerospatiale) SA 315B Gavião (Lama).
Operational speed: 124 kts *(230 km/h)*.
Service ceiling: 7710 ft *(2350 m)*.
Range: 390 nm *(720 km)*.
Role/Weapon systems: Support helicopter for SAR/commando forces. Sensors: Visual reconnaissance. Weapons: Unarmed.

Numbers/Type: 1 Cessna 402-C.
Operational speed: 210 kts *(389 km/h)*.
Service ceiling: 27 000 ft *(9000 m)*.
Range: 1080 nm *(2000 km)*.
Role/Weapon systems: Fixed-wing MR for short-range operations. Sensors: Visual reconnaissance. Weapons: Unarmed.

BRAZIL

Headquarters' Appointments

Chief of Naval Staff:
   Admiral Sergio Alves Lima
Chief of Naval Operations:
   Admiral Carlos Eduardo Cezar de Andrade
Chief of Naval Personnel:
   Admiral José Julio Pedrosa
Commandant General Brazilian Marines:
   Admiral Luiz Carlos da Silva Cantidio
General Secretary of Navy:
   Admiral Mauro Cesar Rodrigues Pereira
Vice Chief of Naval Staff:
   Vice Admiral Paulo Augusto Garcia Dumont

Senior Officers

Commander-in-Chief, Fleet:
   Vice Admiral Carlos Augusto Bastos de Oliveira
Commander, Fleet Marine Force:
   Vice Admiral (Marine Corps) Eugenio do Carmo Ribeiro
Commander, I Naval District:
   Vice Admiral Waldemar Nicolau Canellas Junior
Commander, II Naval District:
   Vice Admiral Carlos Edmundo de Lacerda Freire
Commander, III Naval District:
   Vice Admiral Luiz Eugenio de Albuquerque Lobo
Commander, IV Naval District:
   Vice Admiral José Luiz Feio Obino
Commander, V Naval District:
   Vice Admiral Luiz Philippe da Costa Fernandes
Commander, VI Naval District:
   Rear Admiral Oscar Moreira da Silva
Commander, Brasilia Naval Command:
   Rear Admiral José Alfredo Lourenço dos Santos

Diplomatic Representation

Naval Attaché in England, Sweden and Norway:
   Captain Otavio Sampaio de Almeida
Naval Attaché in Uruguay:
   Captain Daniel César Monteiro
Naval Attaché in France:
   Captain Luiz Alberto Marins Nascimento
Naval Attaché in Italy:
   Captain Rui da Fonseca Elia
Naval Attaché in Paraguay:
   Captain Edison da Silva Nunes Filho
Naval Attaché in Germany and Netherlands:
   Captain Aldo Raposo Neves
Naval Attaché in Argentina:
   Captain Carlos Farias de Pilla
Naval Attaché in Venezuela:
   Captain Adalberto de Souza Filho
Naval Attaché in Peru:
   Captain Carlos Alberto Pinto
Naval Attaché in Portugal:
   Captain Sergio Silvan Brasileiro da Silva
Naval Attaché in Chile:
   Captain Antonio Leonardo de Almeida Moura Costa
Naval Attaché in USA and Canada:
   Rear Admiral Roberto Costa Ferrenho
Head of Brazilian Naval Commission in Europe:
   Captain Flavio Lucio Cortez de Barros
Head of Brazilian Naval Commission in Washington:
   Captain José Raimundo Lopes de Almeida

Personnel

(a) 1994: 64 700 (5700 officers)
Figures include 14 600 marines and also auxiliary corps
(b) 1 year's national service

Bases

Arsenal de Marinha do Rio de Janeiro - Rio de Janeiro (Naval ship-yard with three dry docks and one floating dock with graving docks of up to 70 000 tons capacity)
Base Naval do Rio de Janeiro - Rio de Janeiro (Main Naval Base with two dry docks)
Base Almirante Castro e Silva - Rio de Janeiro (Naval Base for submarines)
Base Naval de Aratu - Bahia (Naval Base and repair yard with one dry dock and synchrolift)
Base Naval de Val-de-Cães - Pará (Naval River and repair yard with one dry dock)
Base Naval Almirante Ary Parreiras - Rio Grande do Norte (Small Naval Base and repair yard with one floating dock)
Base Fluvial de Ladário - Mato Grosso do Sul (Small Naval River Base and repair yard with one dry dock)
Base Aérea Naval de São Pedro d'Aldeia - Rio de Janeiro (Naval Air Station)
Estação Naval do Rio Negro - Amazonas (Small Naval River Station and repair yard with one floating dock)

Organisation

Naval Districts as follows:
I Naval District (HQ Rio de Janeiro)
II Naval District (HQ São Salvador)
III Naval District (HQ Natal)
IV Naval District (HQ Belém)
V Naval District (HQ Rio Grande)
VI Naval District (HQ Ladário)
VII Naval District (HQ Manaus)
Comando Naval de Brasilia (HQ Brasilia)

Naval Aviation

A Fleet Air Arm was formed on 26 January 1965. Squadrons: HA-1 Lynx; HS-1 Sea King; HI-1 Jet Ranger; HU-1 Ecureuil; HU-2 Super Puma.

Coast Guard

Plans to form a Coast Guard have been dropped.

Prefix to Ships' Names

These vary, indicating the type of ship for example, N Ae L = Aircraft Carrier; CT = Destroyer.

Pennant Numbers

As a result of cuts in Officer numbers, ships are formally decommissioned from the Navy and lose their pennant numbers. They are then retained in service as tenders to Naval establishments and are commanded by Warrant Officers.

Marines (Corpo de Fuzileiros Navais)

14 600 officers and men.

Headquarters at Fort São José, Rio de Janeiro
Divisão Anfibia: 1 Command Battalion, 3 Infantry Battalions (Riachuelo, Humaita and Paissandu), 1 Artillery group, 1 Service Battalion.
Comando de Reforço: 1 Special Forces Battalion (Tonelero), 1 Command Battalion, 1 Engineer Battalion, 1 Amphib Vehicles Battalion, 1 Maintenance and Supply Battalion.
Grupos Regionais: One security group in each naval district (Rio de Janeiro, Salvador, Natal, Belém, Rio Grande, Ladário, Manaus, Brasilia).

Strength of the Fleet

Type	Active	Building (Planned)
Submarines (Patrol)	4	3 (1)
Aircraft Carrier (light)	1	—
Destroyers	6	—
Frigates	14	1 (4)
Coastal Patrol Ships	9	—
River Monitor	1	—
River Patrol Ships	5	—
Large Patrol Craft	8	4 (2)
Coastal Patrol Craft	4	2
LSD/LST	3	—
Minesweepers (Coastal)	6	—
Survey and Research Ships	8	(1)
Survey Launches	6	—
Buoy Tenders	9	—
S/M Rescue Ship	1	—
Repair and Support Ships	2	—
Tankers	3	—
Hospital Ships	2	—
Training Ships	7	—
Transports	16	—
Tugs—Ocean	5	—

Mercantile Marine

Lloyd's Register of Shipping:
   573 vessels of 5 216 063 tons gross

DELETIONS

Submarines

1992   *Amazonas* (museum)
1993   *Bahia*

Auxiliaries and Survey Ships

1991   *Almirante Saldanha, Rio Doce*
1992   *Almirante Alvaro Alberto* (sunk)
1993   *Antonio Joao*

PENNANT LIST

Submarines

S 20	Humaitá
S 21	Tonelero
S 22	Riachuelo
S 30	Tupi
S 31	Tamoio (bldg)
S 32	Timbira (bldg)
S 33	Tapajos (bldg)
S 34	Toncantins (proj)

Aircraft Carrier

A 11	Minas Gerais

Destroyers

D 25	Marcílio Dias
D 26	Mariz E Barros
D 27	Pará
D 28	Paraiba
D 29	Paraná
D 30	Pernambuco
D 35	Sergipe
D 36	Alagoas
D 37	Rio Grande do Norte
D 38	Espírito Santo

Frigates

F 40	Niteroi
F 41	Defensora
F 42	Constituição
F 43	Liberal
F 44	Independência
F 45	União
V 30	Inhaúma
V 31	Jaceguay
V 32	Julio de Noronha
V 33	Frontin

Amphibious Forces

G 26	Duque de Caxias
G 30	Ceará
G 31	Rio de Janeiro
GED 10	Guarapari
GED 11	Tambaú
GED 12	Camboriú

Patrol Forces

V 15	Imperial Marinheiro
V 16	Iguatemi
V 18	Forte De Coimbra
V 19	Caboclo
V 20	Angostura
V 21	Bahiana
V 22	Mearim
V 23	Purus
V 24	Solimões
P 10	Piratini
P 11	Pirajá
P 12	Pampeiro
P 13	Parati
P 14	Penedo
P 15	Poti
P 20	Pedro Teixeira
P 21	Raposo Tavares
P 30	Roraima
P 31	Rondônia
P 32	Amapá
P 40	Grajaú
P 41	Guaíba
P 42	Graúna (bldg)
P 43	Goiana (bldg)
P 44	Guajará (bldg)
P 45	Guaporé (bldg)
P 46	Gurupá (proj)
P 47	Gurupi (proj)

Mine Warfare Forces

M 15	Aratú
M 16	Anhatomirim
M 17	Atalaia
M 18	Araçatuba
M 19	Abrolhos
M 20	Albardão

Survey Ships and Tenders

(ex-H 11)	Paraibano
(ex-H 12)	Rio Branco
H 13	Mestre João dos Santos
(ex-H 14)	Nogueira da Gama
(ex-H 15)	Itacurussá
(ex-H 16)	Camocim
(ex-H 17)	Caravelas
H 18	Comandante Varella
H 19	Tenente Castelo
H 20	Comandante Manhães
H 21	Sirius
H 22	Canopus
H 24	Castelhanos
H 25	Tenente Boanerges
H 26	Faroleiro Mário Seixas
H 27	Faroleiro Areas
H 30	Faroleiro Nascimento
H 31	Argus
H 32	Orion
H 33	Taurus
H 34	Almirante Graça Aranha
H 40	Antares
H 41	Almirante Câmara
H 42	Barão de Teffé

Auxiliaries

G 15	Paraguassú
G 16	Barroso Pereira
G 17	Potengi
G 20	Custódio de Mello
G 21	Ary Parreiras
G 22	Soares Dutra
G 23	Almirante Gastao Motta
G 24	Belmonte
G 27	Marajo
K 11	Felinto Perry
(ex-R 15)	Comandante Marroig
(ex-R 16)	Comandante Didier
(ex-R 17)	Tenente Magalhães
(ex-R 18)	Cabo Schramm
R 21	Tritão
R 22	Tridente
R 23	Triunfo
R 24	Almirante Guilhem
R 25	Almirante Guillobel
U 10	Aspirante Nascimento
U 11	Guarda Marinha Jensen
U 12	Guarda Marinha Brito
(ex-U 15)	Suboficial Oliveira
U 16	Trindade
U 17	Parnaiba
U 18	Oswaldo Cruz
U 19	Carlos Chagas
U 20	Gastão Moutinho
U 27	Brasil
U 29	Piraim
(ex-U 30)	Almirante Hess

SUBMARINES

Note: Plans for the construction of nuclear-powered submarines are advancing with a prototype nuclear reactor IPEN/MB-1 built at Aramar, Iperó, São Paulo. A uranium enrichment plant was inaugurated at Iperó in April 1988. The prototype SSN (S-NAC-2) to be about 2825 tons and have a power plant developing 50 MW for a speed of 25 kts. In spite of delays in the diesel submarine programme, the SSN has a very high priority.

0 + (1) IMPROVED TUPI (SNAC-1)

Name	No	Builders	Laid down	Launched	Commissioned
TONCANTINS	S 34	Arsenal de Marinha, Rio de Janeiro	1996	1998	2000

Displacement, tons: 1850 surfaced; 2425 dived
Dimensions, feet (metres): 219.7 × 26.2 × 18
  (67 × 8 × 5.5)
Main machinery: Diesel-electric; 4 MTU 12V 493 AZ80 GA31L diesels; 2400 hp(m) *(1.76 MW)*; 4 Siemens alternators; 1.8 MW; 1 Siemens motor; 4600 hp(m) *(3.38 MW)* sustained; 1 shaft
Speed, knots: 11 surfaced/snorting; 22 dived
Range, miles: 11 000 at 8 kts surfaced; 400 at 4 kts dived
Complement: 39 (8 officers)

Torpedoes: 8—21 in *(533 mm)* bow tubes. 16 Marconi Mk 24 Tigerfish Mod 1; wire-guided; active homing to 13 km *(7 nm)* at 35 kts; passive homing to 29 km *(15.7 nm)* at 24 kts; warhead 134 kg. Swim-out discharge. IPqM-designed A/S torpedoes may also be carried; 18 km *(9.7 nm)* at 45 kts.
Mines: 32 IPqM/Consub MCF-01/100 carried in lieu of torpedoes.
Countermeasures: ESM: Thomson-CSF DR-4000; radar warning.
Fire control: Ferranti KAFS-A10 action automation. 2 Kollmorgen Mod 76 periscopes.

Radars: Navigation: Thomson-CSF Calypso III; I band.
Sonars: Atlas Elektronik CSU-83/1; hull-mounted; passive/active search and attack; medium frequency.

Programmes: Planned intermediate stage between Tupi class and the first SSN. Designed by the Naval Engineering Directorate. The future of this project is uncertain.
Structure: Diving depth, 300 m *(985 ft)*. Very high capacity batteries with GRP lead-acid cells by Varta/Saturnia.
Operational: Endurance, 60 days.

1 + 3 TUPI CLASS (209 TYPE 1400)

Name	No	Builders	Laid down	Launched	Commissioned
TUPI	S 30	Howaldtswerke-Deutsche Werft, Kiel	8 Mar 1985	28 Apr 1987	6 May 1989
TAMOIO	S 31	Arsenal de Marinha, Rio de Janeiro	15 July 1986	18 Nov 1993	1994
TIMBIRA	S 32	Arsenal de Marinha, Rio de Janeiro	15 Sep 1987	1995	1996
TAPAJÓS	S 33	Arsenal de Marinha, Rio de Janeiro	1993	1997	1999

Displacement, tons: 1260 surfaced; 1440 dived
Dimensions, feet (metres): 200.1 × 20.3 × 18
  (61 × 6.2 × 5.5)
Main machinery: Diesel-electric; 4 MTU 12V 493 AZ80 GA31L diesels; 2400 hp(m) *(1.76 MW)*; 4 alternators; 1.7 MW; 1 Siemens motor; 4600 hp(m) *(3.36 MW)* sustained; 1 shaft
Speed, knots: 11 surfaced/snorting; 21.5 dived
Range, miles: 8200 at 8 kts surfaced; 400 at 4 kts dived
Complement: 30

Torpedoes: 8—21 in *(533 mm)* bow tubes. 16 Marconi Mk 24 Tigerfish Mod 1; wire-guided; active homing to 13 km *(7 nm)* at 35 kts; passive homing to 29 km *(15.7 nm)* at 24 kts; warhead 134 kg. IPqM anti-submarine torpedoes may also be carried; range 18 km *(9.7 nm)* at 45 kts. Swim-out discharge.
Countermeasures: ESM: Thomson-CSF DR-4000; radar warning.
Fire control: Ferranti KAFS-A10 action data automation. 2 Kollmorgen Mod 76 periscopes.
Radars: Navigation: Thomson-CSF Calypso III; I band.
Sonars: Atlas Elektronik CSU-83/1; hull-mounted; passive/active search and attack; medium frequency.

Programmes: Contract signed with Howaldtswerke in February 1984. Financial negotiations were completed with the West German Government in October 1984. Original plans included building four followed by two improved Tupis for a total of six by the end of the 1990s. However only three are now to be built by Arsenal de Marinha unless SNAC-1 is postponed.
Structure: Diving depth, 250 m *(820 ft)*.

TAMOIO   12/1993, Mário R V Carneiro

TUPI   5/1992, Miguel Soto

3 HUMAITÁ (OBERON) CLASS

Name	No	Builders	Laid down	Launched	Commissioned
HUMAITÁ	S 20	Vickers, Barrow	3 Nov 1970	5 Oct 1971	18 June 1973
TONELERO	S 21	Vickers, Barrow	18 Nov 1971	22 Nov 1972	10 Dec 1977
RIACHUELO	S 22	Vickers, Barrow	26 May 1973	6 Sep 1975	12 Mar 1977

Displacement, tons: 1610 standard; 2030 surfaced; 2410 dived
Dimensions, feet (metres): 295.2 × 26.5 × 18
  (90 × 8.1 × 5.5)
Main machinery: Diesel-electric; 2 ASR 16 VVS-ASR1 diesels; 3680 hp *(2.74 MW)*; 2 AEI motors; 6000 hp *(4.48 MW)*; 2 shafts
Speed, knots: 12 surfaced; 17 dived; 10 snorting
Range, miles: 9000 surfaced at 12 kts
Complement: 70 (6 officers)

Torpedoes: 8—21 in *(533 mm)* (6 bow, 2 stern) tubes. 20 Marconi Mk 24 Tigerfish Mod 1; wire-guided; active homing to 13 km *(7 nm)* at 35 kts; passive homing to 29 km *(15.7 nm)* at 24 kts; warhead 134 kg.
4 Honeywell Mk 37 Mod 2 (stern tubes); wire-guided; active/passive homing to 8 km *(4.4 nm)* at 24 kts; warhead 150 kg. Some Mk 8 Mod 4 anti-ship torpedoes (4.5 km at 45 kts) are still in service.
Countermeasures: ESM: Radar warning.
Fire control: Ferranti DCH tactical data system.
Radars: Navigation: Kelvin Hughes Type 1006; I band.
Sonars: Thorn-EMI Type 187; hull-mounted; search and attack; medium frequency.
  BAC Type 2007; flank array; passive search; low frequency.

Programmes: Two ordered from Vickers in 1969, the third in

TONELERO   6/1989, Mário R V Carneiro

1972. Completion of *Tonelero* was much delayed by a serious fire on board originating in the cabling. It was this fire which resulted in re-cabling of all Oberon class under construction.

Modernisation: The previously planned modernisation programme was finally cancelled in 1990.
Operational: Two short torpedo tubes aft are still in service.

AIRCRAFT CARRIER

1 COLOSSUS CLASS

Name	No	Builders	Laid down	Launched	Commissioned
MINAS GERAIS (ex-HMS Vengeance)	A 11	Swan Hunter & Wigham Richardson, Ltd, Wallsend on Tyne	16 Nov 1942	23 Feb 1944	15 Jan 1945

Displacement, tons: 15 890 standard; 17 500 normal; 19 890 full load (13 190 standard; 18 010 full load before reconstruction)
Dimensions, feet (metres): 695 × 80 × 24.5 (211.8 × 24.4 × 7.5)
Flight deck, feet (metres): 690 × 119.6 (210.3 × 36.4)
Main machinery: 4 Admiralty boilers; 400 psi (28.1 kg/cm sq), 700°F (371°C); 2 Parsons turbines; 40 000 hp (30 MW); 2 shafts
Speed, knots: 24. **Range, miles:** 12 000 at 14 kts; 6200 at 23 kts
Complement: 1300 (300 aircrew)

Guns: 10 Bofors 40 mm/56 (2 quad Mk 2, 1 twin Mk 1); 160 rounds/minute to 11 km (5.9 nm) anti-surface; 6 km (3.3 nm) anti-aircraft; weight of shell 0.89 kg. 2—47 mm saluting guns.
Countermeasures: Decoys: Plessey Shield chaff launcher. ESM: SLR-2; radar warning.
Combat data systems: Ferranti Link YB system compatible with CAAIS fitted ships. SATCOM.
Fire control: 2 Mk 63 GFCS. 1 Mk 51 Mod 2 GFCS.
Radars: Air search: Lockheed SPS 40B; E/F band; range 320 km (175 nm).
Air/surface search: Plessey AWS 4; E/F band.
Navigation: Signaal ZW 06; I band.
Fire control: Two SPG 34; I/J band.
CCA: Scanter Mil-Par; I band.

MINAS GERAIS

1992

Fixed wing aircraft: 6 Grumman S-2G Trackers.
Helicopters: 4-6 Agusta SH-3A/D Sea Kings; 2 Aerospatiale UH-13 Ecureuil II; 3 Aerospatiale UH-14 Super Puma.

Programmes: Served in the UK Navy from 1945 onwards. Fitted out 1948-49 for experimental cruise to the Arctic. Lent to the RAN early in August 1953, returned to the Royal Navy in 1955. Purchased by the Brazilian Government on 14 December 1956 and commissioned in the Brazilian Navy on 6 December 1960.
Modernisation: During reconstruction in 1957-60 at Rotterdam the steam capacity was increased when the boilers were retubed. New lifts were installed; also included were one Mac-Taggart-Scott single track steam catapult for launching, and arrester wires for recovering 30 000 lb aircraft at 60 kts. The conversion and overhaul also included the installation of the 8½ degrees angled deck, mirror-sight deck landing system, armament fire-control, a new island and radar equipment. Completed refit in 1981. Further modernisation was undertaken from July 1991 to October 1993. This included new CCA radars, electronics and communications, tactical control system (SICONTA) incorporating IPqM/Datanav TTI-2700 consoles, data link YB; retubing of boilers and other major engine overhauls.
Structure: Hangar dimensions: length, 135.6 m (445 ft); width, 15.8 m (52 ft); clear depth, 5.3 m (17.5 ft). Aircraft lifts: 13.7 × 10.4 m (45 × 34 ft). The ship's overall length quoted does not include the catapult spur.
Operational: Recommissioned after refit in October 1993.
Opinion: Plans delayed but still under consideration for a new 35 000-40 000 ton ship. It is reported that she will, if built, have a speed of 28 kts with two steam catapults, carry 30-40 aircraft and have modern anti-aircraft defences. The more likely alternative is a smaller 25 000 ton ship for use as a helicopter carrier.

MINAS GERAIS

10/1993, Brazilian Navy

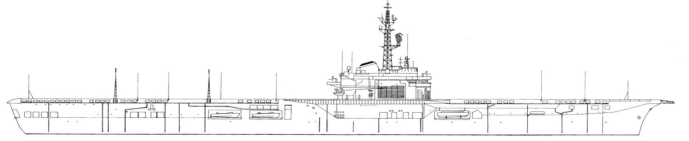

MINAS GERAIS

(Scale 1 : 1200), Ian Sturton

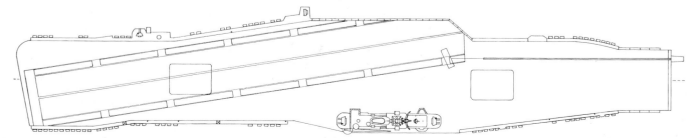

MINAS GERAIS

(Scale 1 : 1200), Ian Sturton

DESTROYERS

Note: Plans to acquire up to four ex-USN Charles F Adams class were cancelled in 1993.

2 GEARING (FRAM I) CLASS

Name	No	Builders	Laid down	Launched	Commissioned
MARCILIO DIAS (ex-USS *Henry W Tucker* DD 875)	D 25	Consolidated Steel	29 May 1944	8 Nov 1944	12 Mar 1945
MARIZ E BARROS (ex-USS *Brinkley Bass* DD 887)	D 26	Consolidated Steel	20 Dec 1944	26 May 1945	1 Oct 1945

Displacement, tons: 2425 standard; 3500 full load
Dimensions, feet (metres): 390.5 × 41.2 × 19
  (119 × 12.6 × 5.8)
Main machinery: 4 Babcock & Wilcox boilers; 600 psi
  (43.3 kg/cm sq); 850°F *(454°C)*; 2 GE turbines; 60 000 hp
  (45 MW); 2 shafts
Speed, knots: 32. **Range, miles:** 5800 at 15 kts
Complement: 274 (14 officers)

Missiles: A/S: Honeywell ASROC Mk 116 octuple launcher ❶.
  Not operational.
Guns: 4—5 in *(127 mm)*/38 (2 twin) Mk 38 ❷; 15 rounds/minute
  to 17 km *(9.2 nm)* anti-surface; 11 km *(5.9 nm)* anti-aircraft;
  weight of shell 25 kg.
Torpedoes: 6—324 mm Mk 32 (2 triple) tubes ❸. Honeywell Mk
  46 Mod 5; anti-submarine; active/passive homing to 11 km
  (5.9 nm) at 40 kts; warhead 44 kg.
Countermeasures: ESM: WLR 1C and WLR 3A; radar warning.
  ECM: ULQ 6B; jammer.
Fire control: Mk 37 GFCS.

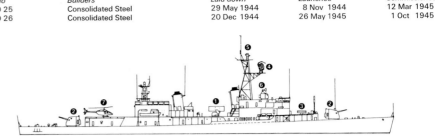

MARCILIO DIAS
(Scale 1 : 1200), Ian Sturton

Radars: Air search: Lockheed SPS 40 ❹; E/F band; range
  320 km *(175 nm)*.
  Surface search: Raytheon/Sylvania SPS 10 ❺; G band.
  Fire control: Western Electric Mk 25 Mod 3 ❻; I/J band.
Sonars: Sangamo SQS 23; hull-mounted; active search and
  attack; medium frequency; with bottom bounce.

Helicopters: 1 Bell JetRanger III ❼.

Programmes: Transferred from the US 8 December 1973.
Operational: Plans for new engines and re-arming have been
  dropped. JetRanger helicopter has replaced the deleted Wasp.
  ASROC is not operational.

MARCILIO DIAS
7/1990

4 ALLEN M SUMNER (FRAM II) CLASS

Name	No	Builders	Laid down	Launched	Commissioned
SERGIPE (ex-USS *James C Owens* DD 776)	D 35	Bethlehem Steel Co (San Pedro)	9 Apr 1944	1 Oct 1944	17 Feb 1945
ALAGOAS (ex-USS *Buck* DD 761)	D 36	Bethlehem Steel Co (San Francisco)	1 Feb 1944	11 Mar 1945	28 June 1946
RIO GRANDE DO NORTE (ex-USS *Strong* DD 758)	D 37	Bethlehem Steel Co (San Francisco)	25 July 1943	23 Apr 1944	8 Mar 1945
ESPIRITO SANTO (ex-USS *Lowry* DD 770)	D 38	Bethlehem Steel Co (San Pedro)	1 Aug 1943	6 Feb 1944	23 July 1944

Displacement, tons: 2200 standard; 3320 full load
Dimensions, feet (metres): 376.5 × 40.9 × 19
  (114.8 × 12.5 × 5.8)
Main machinery: 4 Babcock & Wilcox boilers; 600 psi
  (43.3 kg/cm sq); 850°F *(454°C)*; 2 GE turbines; 60 000 hp
  (45 MW); 2 shafts
Speed, knots: 34. **Range, miles:** 4600 at 15 kts; 1260 at 30 kts
Complement: 306 (18 officers)

ALAGOAS
(Scale 1 : 1200), Ian Sturton

Guns: 6—5 in *(127 mm)*/38 (3 twin) Mk 38 ❶; 15 rounds/minute
  to 17 km *(9.2 nm)* anti-surface; 11 km *(5.9 nm)* anti-aircraft;
  weight of shell 25 kg.
Torpedoes: 6—324 mm Mk 32 (2 triple) tubes ❷. Honeywell Mk
  46 Mod 5; anti-submarine; active/passive homing to 11 km
  (5.9 nm) at 40 kts; warhead 44 kg.
A/S mortars: 2 Hedgehogs Mk 10 ❸; 24 manually loaded rock-
  ets; range 250 m; warhead 13.6 kg.
Countermeasures: ESM: WLR 3; radar warning.
  ECM: ULQ-6 *(Espirito Santo)*; jammer.
Fire control: Mk 37 GFCS.
Radars: Air search: Westinghouse SPS 29 *(Espirito Santo)*; B/C
  band; range 457 km *(250 nm)*.
  Lockheed SPS 40 (others) ❹; E/F band; range 320 km
  (175 nm).
  Surface search: Raytheon/Sylvania SPS 10 ❺; G band.
  Fire control: Western Electric Mk 25 Mod 3 ❻; I/J band
Sonars: SQS 40; hull-mounted; active search and attack;
  medium frequency.

Helicopters: 1 Bell JetRanger ❼.

Programmes: Transferred from the US by sale as follows: *Sergipe* and *Alagoas* 16 July 1973, *Espirito Santo* 29 October
  1973 and *Rio Grande do Norte* 31 October 1973.
Operational: *Sergipe* VDS removed.

ESPIRITO SANTO
5/1990, Brazilian Navy

FRIGATES

Note: Four ex-US Knox class frigates are to be transferred in 1994/95 subject to approval by US Congress. The four ships are the *Hepburn* (FF 1055), *Patterson* (FF 1061), *Francis Hammond* (FF 1067) and *Downes* (FF 1070).

6 NITEROI CLASS

Name	No	Builders	Laid down	Launched	Commissioned
NITEROI	F 40	Vosper Thornycroft Ltd	8 June 1972	8 Feb 1974	20 Nov 1976
DEFENSORA	F 41	Vosper Thornycroft Ltd	14 Dec 1972	27 Mar 1975	5 Mar 1977
CONSTITUIÇÃO	F 42*	Vosper Thornycroft Ltd	13 Mar 1974	15 Apr 1976	31 Mar 1978
LIBERAL	F 43*	Vosper Thornycroft Ltd	2 May 1975	7 Feb 1977	18 Nov 1978
INDEPENDÊNCIA	F 44	Arsenal de Marinha, Rio de Janeiro	11 June 1972	2 Sep 1974	3 Sep 1979
UNIÃO	F 45	Arsenal de Marinha, Rio de Janeiro	11 June 1972	14 Mar 1975	12 Sep 1980

*GP design.

Displacement, tons: 3200 standard; 3707 full load
Dimensions, feet (metres): 424 × 44.2 × 18.2 (sonar)
 (129.2 × 13.5 × 5.5)
Main machinery: CODOG; 2 RR Olympus TM3B gas-turbines;
 50 880 hp *(37.9 MW)* sustained; 4 MTU 16V 956 TB91
 diesels; 15 000 hp(m) *(11 MW)* sustained; 2 shafts; cp props
Speed, knots: 30 gas; 22 diesels. **Range, miles:** 5300 at 17 kts
 on 2 diesels; 4200 at 19 kts on 4 diesels; 1300 at 28 kts on gas
Complement: 217 (22 officers)

Missiles: SSM: 4 Aerospatiale MM 40 Exocet (2 twin) launchers
 ❶; inertial cruise; active radar homing to 70 km *(40 nm)* at
 0.9 Mach; warhead 165 kg; sea-skimmer.
 SAM: 2 Short Bros Seacat triple launchers ❷; optical/radar guidance to 5 km *(2.7 nm)*; warhead 10 kg; 60 missiles. To be
 replaced.
 A/S: 1 Ikara launcher (Branik standard) (A/S version) ❸; command radio/radar guidance to 24 km *(13 nm)* at 0.8 Mach; 10
 missiles; payload Mk 46 torpedoes.
Guns: 2 Vickers 4.5 in *(115 mm)*/55 Mk 8 (GP version) ❹; 55°
 elevation; 25 rounds/minute to 22 km *(12 nm)* anti-surface;
 6 km *(3.2 nm)* anti-aircraft; weight of shell 21 kg. A/S version
 only has 1 mounting.
 2 Bofors 40 mm/70 ❺; 90° elevation; 300 rounds/minute to
 12 km *(6.5 nm)* anti-surface; 4 km *(2.2 nm)* anti-aircraft; weight
 of shell 0.96 kg.
Torpedoes: 6—324 mm Plessey STWS-1 (2 triple) tubes ❻.
 Honeywell Mk 46 Mod 5; anti-submarine; active/passive hom-
 ing to 11 km *(5.9 nm)* at 40 kts; warhead 44 kg.
A/S mortars: 1 Bofors 375 mm trainable rocket launcher (twin-
 tube) ❼; automatic loading; range 1600 m.
Depth charges: 1 rail; 5 charges (GP version).
Countermeasures: Decoys: 2 Plessey Shield chaff launchers.
 ESM: SDR-2 and SDR-7; radar warning. FH5 HF/DF.
Combat data systems: Ferranti CAAIS 400 with FM 1600B
 computers.
Fire control: Ikara tracker (A/S version).
Radars: Air/surface search: Plessey AWS 2 with Mk 10 IFF ❽;
 E/F band.
 Surface search: Signaal ZW 06 ❾; I band.
 Fire control: Two Selenia Orion RTN 10X ❿; I/J band.
Sonars: EDO 610E; hull-mounted; active search and attack;
 medium frequency.
 EDO 700E VDS (F 40 and 41); active search and attack;
 medium frequency.

Helicopters: 1 Westland Lynx SAH-11 ⓫.

Programmes: A contract announced on 29 September 1970
 was signed between the Brazilian Government and Vosper
 Thornycroft for the design and building of six Vosper Thornycroft Mark 10 frigates. Seventh ship with differing armament
 was ordered from Navyard, Rio de Janeiro in June 1981 and is
 used as a training ship.
Modernisation: The modernisation plan includes replacing Seacat by Matra Sadral, Plessey AWS 2 radar by AWS 5, ZW 06
 radar by Kelvin Hughes Type 1007, updating the Bofors gun
 and fitting the same Saab EOS 500 Optronic tracker, Plessey
 Shield countermeasures and Racal Cutlass ESM equipment as
 the Inhaúma class. ESM systems are being developed by the
 Instituto de Pesquisas da Marinas. All the ships of the class are
 to be updated with the emphasis on air defence but the programme is being delayed by lack of funds.

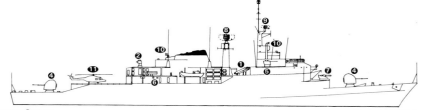

CONSTITUIÇÃO (GP)   *(Scale 1 : 1200), Ian Sturton*

NITEROI   6/1993

DEFENSORA   *(Scale 1 : 1200), Ian Sturton*

Structure: F 40, 41, 44 and 45 are of the A/S configuration. F 42
and 43 are General Purpose design. Materials, equipment and
lead-yard services supplied by Vosper Thornycroft at Navyard,
Rio de Janeiro. Fitted with retractable stabilisers.
Operational: At the time they were built these ships were economical in personnel, amounting to a 50 per cent reduction of
manpower in relation to previous warships of this size and
complexity. Endurance, 45 days' stores, 60 days' provisions.
Oil fuel, 530 tons. The helicopter has Sea Skua ASM.

DEFENSORA   6/1993, H M Steele

4 PARÁ (GARCIA) CLASS

Name	No	Builders	Laid down	Launched	Commissioned	Recommissioned
PARÁ (ex-*Albert David*)	D 27 (ex-FF 1050)	Lockheed SB & Construction Co	29 Apr 1964	19 Dec 1964	19 Oct 1968	18 Sep 1989
PARAÍBA (ex-*Davidson*)	D 28 (ex-FF 1045)	Avondale Shipyards	20 Sep 1963	2 Oct 1963	7 Dec 1965	25 July 1989
PARANÁ (ex-*Sample*)	D 29 (ex-FF 1048)	Lockheed SB & Construction Co	19 July 1963	28 Apr 1964	23 Mar 1968	24 Aug 1989
PERNAMBUCO (ex-*Bradley*)	D 30 (ex-FF 1041)	Bethlehem Steel, San Francisco	17 Jan 1963	26 Mar 1964	15 May 1965	25 Sep 1989

Displacement, tons: 2620 standard; 3403 full load
Dimensions, feet (metres): 414.5 × 44.2 × 24 sonar; 14.5 keel
(126.3 × 13.5 × 7.3; 4.4)
Main machinery: 2 Foster-Wheeler boilers; 1200 psi
(83.4 kg/cm sq); 950°F *(510°C)*; 1 Westinghouse or GE turbine; 35 000 hp *(26 MW)*; 1 shaft
Speed, knots: 27.5. **Range, miles:** 4000 at 20 kts
Complement: 286 (18 officers)

Missiles: A/S: Honeywell ASROC Mk 112 octuple launcher ❶;
inertial guidance to 1.6-10 km *(1-5.4 nm)*; payload Mk 46 torpedo. *Pará* and *Paraná* have automatic ASROC reload system.
Guns: 2 USN 5 in *(127 mm)*/38 Mk 30 ❷; 85° elevation; 15
rounds/minute to 17 km *(9.3 nm)*; weight of shell 25 kg.
Torpedoes: 6—324 mm Mk 32 (2 triple) tubes ❸. 14 Honeywell
Mk 46 Mod 5; anti-submarine; active/passive homing to 11 km
(5.9 nm) at 40 kts; warhead 44 kg.
Countermeasures: Decoys: 2 Loral Hycor Mk 33 RBOC 6 tubed
chaff launchers. T-Mk 6 Fanfare; torpedo decoy system.
Prairie/Masker; hull/blade rate noise suppression.
ESM: WLR-1; WLR-6; radar warning.
ECM: ULQ-6; jammer.
Fire control: Mk 56 GFCS. Mk 114 ASW FCS. SATCOM.
Radars: Air search: Lockheed SPS 40 ❹; E/F band; range
320 km *(175 nm)*.
Surface search: Raytheon SPS 10 ❺; G band.
Navigation: Marconi LN 66; I band.
Fire control: General Electric Mk 35 ❻; I/J band.
Tacan: SRN 15.
Sonars: EDO/General Electric SQS 26 AXR (D 29 and 30) or SQS
26B; bow-mounted; active search and attack; medium
frequency.

Helicopters: Westland Lynx SAH-11 ❼.

Programmes: First three transferred from US by lease 15 April
1989 and last one 1 October 1989. All arrived in Brazil on 13
December 1989. Classified as Destroyers in the Brazilian Navy.
It is intended to renew the lease in 1994.
Structure: All four have the enlarged hangar capable of taking a
Sea King size helicopter but in USN service *Pará* and *Paraná*
had the flight deck area converted to take SQR 15 towed array
which was removed on transfer.

PARAÍBA

(Scale 1 : 1200), Ian Sturton

PERNAMBUCO

5/1992, Hartmut Ehlers

4 + (1) INHAÚMA CLASS

Name	No	Builders	Laid down	Launched	Commissioned
INHAÚMA	V 30	Arsenal de Marinha do Rio de Janeiro	23 Sep 1983	13 Dec 1986	12 Dec 1989
JACEGUAY	V 31	Arsenal de Marinha do Rio de Janeiro	15 Oct 1984	8 June 1987	2 Apr 1991
JULIO DE NORONHA	V 32	Verolme, Angra dos Reis	8 Dec 1986	15 Dec 1989	27 Oct 1992
FRONTIN	V 33	Verolme, Angra dos Reis	14 May 1987	6 Feb 1992	Mar 1994

Displacement, tons: 1600 standard; 1970 full load
Dimensions, feet (metres): 314.2 × 37.4 × 12.1; 17.4 (sonar)
(95.8 × 11.4 × 3.7; 5.3)
Main machinery: CODOG; 1 GE LM2500 gas-turbine; 27 500 hp
(20.52 MW) sustained; 2 MTU 16V 396 TB94 diesels;
5800 hp(m) *(4.26 MW)* sustained; 2 shafts; cp props
Speed, knots: 27. **Range, miles:** 4000 at 15 kts
Complement: 122 (15 officers)

Missiles: SSM: 4 Aerospatiale MM 40 Exocet ❶; inertial cruise;
active radar homing to 70 km *(40 nm)* at 0.9 Mach; warhead
165 kg; sea-skimmer.
Guns: 1 Vickers 4.5 in *(115 mm)* Mk 8 ❷; 55° elevation; 25
rounds/minute to 22 km *(12 nm)* anti-surface; 6 km *(3.3 nm)*
anti-aircraft, weight of shell 21 kg.
2 Bofors 40 mm/70 ❸; 90° elevation; 300 rounds/minute to
12 km *(6.5 nm)* anti-surface; 4 km *(2.2 nm)* anti-aircraft; weight
of shell 0.96 kg.
Torpedoes: 6—324 mm Mk 32 (2 triple) tubes ❹. Honeywell
Mk 46 Mod 5; anti-submarine; active/passive homing to 11 km
(5.9 nm) at 40 kts; warhead 44 kg.
Countermeasures: Decoys: 2 Plessey Shield chaff launchers ❺;
fires chaff and IR flares in distraction, decoy or centroid
patterns.
ESM/ECM: IPqM SLQ 1 and Racal Cygnus B1 radar intercept ❻
and IPqM SDR-7 jammer ❼.
Combat data systems: Ferranti CAAIS 450/WSA 421.
Fire control: Saab EOS-400 missile and gun FCS with optronic ❽
director and two OFDLSE optical ❾ directors.
Radars: Surface search: Plessey AWS 4 ❿; E/F band; range
101 km *(55 nm)*.
Navigation: Kelvin Hughes Type 1007; I/J band.
Fire control: Selenia Orion RTN 10X ⓫; I/J band.
Sonars: Atlas Elektronik DSQS 21C; hull-mounted; active;
medium frequency.

Helicopters: 1 Westland Lynx ⓬.

Programmes: Designed by Brazilian Naval Design Office with
advice from West German private Marine Technik design company. Signature of final contract on 1 October 1981. First pair
ordered on 15 February 1982 and second pair 9 January 1986.
In mid-1986 the government approved, in principle, construction of a total of 16 ships but this has been reduced to four and
a stretched design has been authorised to start building in
1994. This ship is to have more powerful diesel engines and
Brazilian electronic equipment.
Structure: Plans to fit more Brazilian-made weapon systems
have been cancelled.

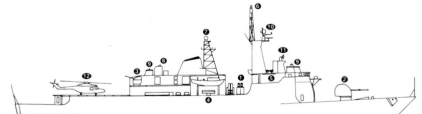
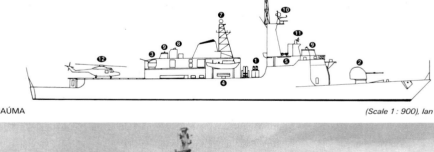

INHAÚMA

(Scale 1 : 900), Ian Sturton

JACEGUAY

10/1993, Brazilian Navy

SHIPBORNE AIRCRAFT (FRONT LINE)

Note: Nine Westland Super Lynx ordered in January 1994 for delivery in 1995/96.

Numbers/Type: 4/6 Agusta/Sikorsky SH 3A/SH 3D Sea King.
Operational speed: 100 kts *(182 km/h).*
Service ceiling: 12 200 ft *(3720 m).*
Range: 400 nm *(740 km).*
Role/Weapon systems: ASW helicopter; carrier-borne and shore-based for medium-range ASW, ASVW and SAR. Sensors: SMA APS-705(V)II search radar; Bendix AQS 13F dipping sonar. Weapons: ASW; up to 4 × Mk 44/46 torpedoes, or 4 × depth bombs. ASVW; 2 × AM 39 Exocet missiles.

SEA KING (with Exocet)   *8/1992, Mário R V Carneiro*

Numbers/Type: 5 Westland Lynx SAH-11 (HAS 21).
Operational speed: 125 kts *(232 km/h).*
Service ceiling: 12 000 ft *(3650 m).*
Range: 160 nm *(296 km).*
Role/Weapon systems: ASW helicopter; embarked in Niteroi, Inhaúma and Pará classes for ASW patrol and support; additional ASVW role from 1988. Being upgraded in 1994-96 to Super Lynx standard with Mk 3 radar and Racal Kestrel EW suite. Sensors: Sea Spray Mk 1 radar. Weapons: ASW; 2 × Mk 44 or Mk 46 torpedoes, or depth bombs. ASV; 4 × BAe Sea Skua missiles.

LYNX (with Sea Skua)   *8/1992, Mário R V Carneiro*

Numbers/Type: 5/7 Grumman S 2A/2E Tracker (Air Force).
Operational speed: 229 kts *(426 km/h).*
Service ceiling: 25 000 ft *(7620 m).*
Range: 799 nm *(1480 km).*
Role/Weapon systems: Air Force operated; carrier-borne surveillance and medium-range ASW aircraft re-engined with PT6A-67-CF turbos; supplemented by Sea King; land-based for coastal and EEZ surveillance. 1 P16H, 6 P16E and 2 P16A are the carrier-borne armed aircraft; 3 UP-16E are unarmed and used for training. Sensors: APS 138 search radar, ASQ 10 MAD 32 sonobuoys. Weapons: ASW; various internally stored bombs, mines or depth bombs, rockets on wings.

Numbers/Type: 5 Aerospatiale UH-14 (AS 332F1 Super Puma).
Operational speed: 100 kts *(182 km/h).*
Service ceiling: 20 000 ft *(6100 m).*
Range: 345 nm *(635 km).*
Role/Weapon systems: SAR, troop transport and ASVW. Sensors: Thomson-CSF Varan search radar. Weapons: None. Total of 15 planned.

SUPER PUMA   *1989, Brazilian Navy*

Numbers/Type: 12 Aerospatiale UH-12 (AS 350B and 350BA Ecureuil).
Operational speed: 120 kts *(222 km/h).*
Service ceiling: 10 000 ft *(3050 m).*
Range: 240 nm *(445 km).*
Role/Weapon systems: Support helicopters for Fleet liaison and Marine Corps transportation. Sensors: None. Weapons: 1 axial MG or 1 lateral MG or 2 rocket pods.

ECUREUIL   *1990, Brazilian Navy*

Numbers/Type: 9 Aerospatiale UH-13 (AS 355F2 Ecureuil 2).
Operational speed: 121 kts *(224 km/h).*
Service ceiling: 11 150 ft *(3400 m).*
Range: 240 nm *(445 km).*
Role/Weapon systems: SAR, liaison and utility in support of Marine Corps. Sensors: Search radar. Weapons: 2 axial MGs or 1 lateral MG or 2 rocket pods.

ECUREUIL 2   *1990, Brazilian Navy*

Numbers/Type: 19 UH-6B (Bell JetRanger III).
Operational speed: 115 kts *(213 km/h).*
Service ceiling: 20 000 ft *(6100 m).*
Range: 368 nm *(682 km).*
Role/Weapon systems: Utility and training helicopters. Sensors: None. Weapons: 2 MGs or 2 rocket pods.

JETRANGER   *8/1992, Mário R V Carneiro*

LAND-BASED MARITIME AIRCRAFT (FRONT LINE)

Numbers/Type: 10 Bandeirante P-95 (EMB-111(A)).
Operational speed: 194 kts *(360 km/h).*
Service ceiling: 25 500 ft *(7770 m).*
Range: 1590 nm *(2945 km).*
Role/Weapon systems: Air Force operated for coastal surveillance role by three squadrons in 7 Group. Sensors: AN/APS-128 search radar, ECM, searchlight pod on starboard wing. Weapons: 8 × 127 mm rockets or 28 × 70 mm rockets.

Numbers/Type: 10 Bandeirante P-95B (EMB-111(B)).
Operational speed: 194 kts *(360 km/h).*
Service ceiling: 25 500 ft *(7770 m).*
Range: 1590 nm *(2945 km).*
Role/Weapon systems: Air Force operated for coastal surveillance role by three squadrons in 7 Group. Sensors: MEL sea search radar, ECM, searchlight pod on starboard wing, EFIS-74 (electronic flight instrumentation) and Collins APS-65 (autopilot); ESM Thomson-CSF DR2000A/ Dalia 1000A Mk II, Marconi Canada CMA-771 Mk III (Omega navigation system). Weapons: 6 or 8 × 127 mm rockets, or up to 28 × 70 mm rockets.

Numbers/Type: 16 Xavante AT-26 (EMB-326GB).
Operational speed: 468 kts *(867 km/h).*
Service ceiling: 47 000 ft *(14 325 m).*
Range: 1320 nm *(2446 km).*
Role/Weapon systems: Air Force operated for light attack; supplements anti-shipping/strike; also has reconnaissance role by 3/10 Group. Sensors: None. Weapons: ASV; 1.8 tons of bombs. Strike; 28 × 70 mm rockets. Recce; underwing camera pod.

Numbers/Type: 8 Tucano AT-27 (EMB-312).
Operational speed: 270 kts *(500 km/h).*
Service ceiling: 30 000 ft *(9150 m).*
Range: 995 nm *(1844 km).*
Role/Weapon systems: Air Force operated for liaison and attack by 2 ELO. Sensors: None. Weapons: 6 or 8 × 127 mm rockets or bombs and 1 MG pod in each wing.

PATROL FORCES

Note: The *Porto Esperança* (P 8) River Patrol Craft project was postponed in 1990 but may be resurrected in due course.

9 IMPERIAL MARINHEIRO CLASS (COASTAL PATROL SHIPS)

Name	No	Builders	Commissioned	
IMPERIAL MARINHEIRO	V 15	Smit, Kinderdijk, Netherlands	8 June	1955
IGUATEMI	V 16	Smit, Kinderdijk, Netherlands	17 Sep	1955
FORTE DE COIMBRA	V 18	Smit, Kinderdijk, Netherlands	26 July	1955
CABOCLO	V 19	Smit, Kinderdijk, Netherlands	5 Apr	1955
ANGOSTURA	V 20	Smit, Kinderdijk, Netherlands	21 May	1955
BAHIANA	V 21	Smit, Kinderdijk, Netherlands	27 June	1955
MEARIM	V 22	Smit, Kinderdijk, Netherlands	3 Aug	1955
PURUS	V 23	Smit, Kinderdijk, Netherlands	17 Apr	1955
SOLIMÕES	V 24	Smit, Kinderdijk, Netherlands	3 Aug	1955

Displacement, tons: 911 standard; 960 full load
Dimensions, feet (metres): 184 × 30.5 × 11.7 *(56 × 9.3 × 3.6)*
Main machinery: 2 Sulzer diesels; 2160 hp(m) *(1.59 MW)*; 2 shafts
Speed, knots: 16
Complement: 60
Guns: 1—3 in *(76 mm)*/50 Mk 33; 85° elevation; 50 rounds/minute to 12.8 km *(6.9 nm)*; weight of shell 6 kg.
   2 or 4 Oerlikon 20 mm; 55° elevation.
Radars: Surface search: Racal Decca; I band.

Comment: Fleet tugs classed as corvettes. Equipped for firefighting. *Imperial Marinheiro* has acted as a submarine support ship but gave up the role in 1990.

IMPERIAL MARINHEIRO   *1989, Brazilian Navy*

2 PEDRO TEIXEIRA CLASS (RIVER PATROL SHIPS)

Name	No	Builders	Commissioned
PEDRO TEIXEIRA	P 20	Arsenal de Marinha, Rio de Janeiro	17 Dec 1973
RAPOSO TAVARES	P 21	Arsenal de Marinha, Rio de Janeiro	17 Dec 1973

Displacement, tons: 690 standard
Dimensions, feet (metres): 208.7 × 31.8 × 5.6 *(63.6 × 9.7 × 1.7)*
Main machinery: 2 MAN V6 V16/18 TL diesels; 1920 hp(m) *(1.41 MW)*; 2 shafts
Speed, knots: 16. **Range, miles:** 6800 at 13 kts
Complement: 60 (6 officers)
Guns: 1 Bofors 40 mm/60; 90° elevation; 300 rounds/minute to 12 km *(6.5 nm)* anti-surface; 4 km *(2.2 nm)* anti-aircraft; weight of shell 0.89 kg.
   6—12.7 mm MGs. 2—81 mm Mk 2 mortars.
Radars: Surface search: 2 Racal Decca; I band.
Helicopters: 1 Bell JetRanger.

Comment: *Pedro Teixeira* launched 14 October 1970, *Raposo Tavares* 11 June 1972. Belong to Amazon Flotilla. Can carry two armed LCVPs and 85 marines in deck accommodation.

RAPOSO TAVARES   *1988*

1 PARNAIBA CLASS (RIVER MONITOR)

Name	No	Builders	Commissioned
PARNAIBA	U 17 (ex-P 2)	Arsenal de Marinha, Rio de Janeiro	6 Nov 1938

Displacement, tons: 620 standard; 720 full load
Dimensions, feet (metres): 180.5 × 33.3 × 5.1 *(55 × 10.1 × 1.6)*
Main machinery: 2 Thornycroft triple expansion; 1300 ihp *(970 kW)*; 2 shafts
Speed, knots: 12. **Range, miles:** 1350 at 10 kts
Complement: 90
Guns: 1—3 in *(76 mm)*/50 Mk 33; 85° elevation; 50 rounds/minute to 12.8 km *(6.9 nm)*; weight of shell 6 kg.
   2 Bofors 40 mm/60 (twin). 6 Oerlikon 20 mm.
Radars: Surface search: Racal Decca; I band.
Navigation: Furuno 3600; I band.

Comment: Laid down 11 June 1936. Launched 2 September 1937. In Mato Grosso Flotilla. Re-armed with new guns in 1960. 3 in *(76 mm)* side armour and partial deck protection. Oil fuel, 70 tons. Was to have been replaced by *Porto Esperança* in 1991 but will now run on until at least 1994.

PARNAIBA   *1992, Brazilian Navy*

3 RORAIMA CLASS (RIVER PATROL SHIPS)

Name	No	Builders	Commissioned
RORAIMA	P 30	Maclaren, Niteroi	21 Feb 1975
RONDÔNIA	P 31	Maclaren, Niteroi	3 Dec 1975
AMAPÁ	P 32	Maclaren, Niteroi	12 Jan 1976

Displacement, tons: 340 standard; 365 full load
Dimensions, feet (metres): 151.9 × 27.9 × 4.6 *(46.3 × 8.5 × 1.4)*
Main machinery: 2 MAN V6 V16/18TL diesels; 1920 hp(m) *(1.41 MW)*; 2 shafts
Speed, knots: 14. **Range, miles:** 6000 at 12 kts
Complement: 40 (9 officers)
Guns: 1 Bofors 40 mm/60; 90° elevation; 300 rounds/minute to 12 km *(6.5 nm)* anti-surface; 4 km *(2.2 nm)* anti-aircraft; weight of shell 0.89 kg.
   2 Oerlikon 20 mm. 2—81 mm mortars. 6—12.7 mm MGs.
Radars: Surface search: 2 Racal Decca; I band.

Comment: *Roraima* launched 2 November 1972, *Rondônia* 10 January, *Amapá* 9 March 1973. Carry two armed LCVPs. Belong to Amazon Flotilla.

RONDÔNIA   *1989, Brazilian Navy*

2 + 4 (2) GRAJAÚ CLASS (LARGE PATROL CRAFT)

Name	No	Builders	Launched	Commissioned	
GRAJAÚ	P 40 (ex-P 42)	Arsenal de Marinha, Rio de Janeiro	21 May 1993	1 Dec	1993
GUAIBA	P 41 (ex-P 43)	Arsenal de Marinha, Rio de Janeiro	10 Dec 1993	June	1994
GRAÚNA	P 42 (ex-P 40)	Estaleiro Mauá, Niteroi	9 Dec 1988	1995	
GOIANA	P 43 (ex-P 41)	Estaleiro Mauá, Niteroi	9 Dec 1988	1995	
GUAJARÁ	P 44	Peenewerft, Germany	1995	1995	
GUAPORÉ	P 45	Peenewerft, Germany	1995	1995	
GURUPÁ	P 46	—	1996	1996	
GURUPI	P 47	—	1996	1996	

Displacement, tons: 410 full load
Dimensions, feet (metres): 152.6 × 24.6 × 7.5 *(46.5 × 7.5 × 2.3)*
Main machinery: 2 MTU 16V 396 TB94 diesels; 5800 hp(m) *(4.26 MW)* sustained; 2 shafts
Speed, knots: 22. **Range, miles:** 2000 at 12 kts
Complement: 31 (4 officers)
Guns: 1 Bofors 40 mm/70. 2 Oerlikon 20 mm.
Radars: Surface search: Racal Decca 1290A; I band.

Comment: Two ordered in late 1987 to a Vosper QAF design similar to Bangladesh Meghna class. Technology transfer in February 1988 and construction started in July 1988 for the first pair; second pair started construction in September 1990. Class name changed in 1993 when the first four were renumbered to reflect revised delivery dates. Building problems are also reflected in the replacing of the order for the third pair with Peenewerft in November 1993. The last two have still to be authorised. Used for patrol duties and diver support. Carry a RIB and telescopic launching crane.

GRAJAÚ   *10/1993, Brazilian Navy*

6 PIRATINI CLASS (LARGE PATROL CRAFT)

Name	No	Builders	Commissioned
PIRATINI (ex-PGM 109)	P 10	Arsenal de Marinha, Rio de Janeiro	Nov 1970
PIRAJÁ (ex-PGM 110)	P 11	Arsenal de Marinha, Rio de Janeiro	Mar 1971
PAMPEIRO (ex-PGM 118)	P 12	Arsenal de Marinha, Rio de Janeiro	May 1971
PARATI (ex-PGM 119)	P 13	Arsenal de Marinha, Rio de Janeiro	July 1971
PENEDO (ex-PGM 120)	P 14	Arsenal de Marinha, Rio de Janeiro	Sep 1971
POTI (ex-PGM 121)	P 15	Arsenal de Marinha, Rio de Janeiro	Oct 1971

Displacement, tons: 105 standard
Dimensions, feet (metres): 95 × 19 × 6.5 (29 × 5.8 × 2)
Main machinery: 4 Cummins VT-12M diesels; 1100 hp (820 kW); 2 shafts
Speed, knots: 17. **Range, miles:** 1700 at 12 kts
Complement: 15 (2 officers)
Guns: 1 Oerlikon 20 mm. 2—12.7 mm MGs.
Radars: Surface search: Racal Decca; I band.
Navigation: Furuno 3600; I band.

Comment: Built under offshore agreement with the USA. 81 mm mortar removed in 1988. Carries an inflatable launch. Based at Fluvial de Ladário.

PENEDO   1988, Brazilian Navy

4 + 2 TRACKER II CLASS (COASTAL PATROL CRAFT)

P 8002   P 8003   P 3004   P 3005

Displacement, tons: 37 full load
Dimensions, feet (metres): 68.6 × 17 × 4.8 (20.9 × 5.2 × 1.5)
Main machinery: 2 MTU 8V 396 TB83 diesels; 2100 hp(m) (1.54 MW) sustained; 2 shafts
Speed, knots: 27. **Range, miles:** 600 at 15 kts
Complement: 12 (4 officers)
Guns: 2—12.7 mm MGs.
Radars: Surface search: Racal Decca RM 1070A; I band.

Comment: First four ordered in February 1987 to a Fairey design and built at Estaleiro Shipyard, Porto Alegre. National input is 60 per cent. First of class completed building 22 February 1990. All entered service in May 1991. Plans for more were postponed in 1991 when the shipbuilder went bankrupt, but were resurrected in 1993 with AMRJ assistance. Designed for EEZ patrol.

P 8002   1991, Brazilian Navy

AMPHIBIOUS FORCES

2 CEARÁ (THOMASTON) CLASS (LSD)

Name	No	Builders	Laid Down	Launched	Commissioned	Recommissioned
CEARÁ (ex-Hermitage)	G 30 (ex-LSD 34)	Ingalls, Pascagoula	11 April 1955	12 June 1956	14 Dec 1956	28 Nov 1989
RIO DE JANEIRO (ex-Alamo)	G 31 (ex-LSD 33)	Ingalls, Pascagoula	11 Oct 1954	20 Jan 1956	24 Aug 1956	21 Nov 1990

Displacement, tons: 6880 light; 12 150 full load
Dimensions, feet (metres): 510 × 84 × 19 (155.5 × 25.6 × 5.8)
Main machinery: 2 Babcock & Wilcox boilers; 580 psi (40.8 kg/cm sq); 2 GE turbines; 24 000 hp (17.9 MW); 2 shafts
Speed, knots: 22.5. **Range, miles:** 10 000 at 18 kts
Complement: 345 (20 officers)
Military lift: 340 troops; 21 LCM 6s or 3 LCUs and 6 LCMs or 50 LVTs; 30 LVTs on upper deck
Guns: 6 USN 3 in (76 mm)/50 (3 twin) Mk 33; 85° elevation; 50 rounds/minute to 12.8 km (7 nm); weight of shell 6 kg.
Radars: Air search: Westinghouse SPS 6C; D band.
Surface search: Raytheon SPS 10; G band.
Navigation: Raytheon CRP 3100; I band.
Helicopters: Platform (over docking well).

Programmes: The original plan to build a 4500 ton LST was overtaken by the acquisition of these two LSDs from the US on a five year lease.
Structure: Have two 50 ton capacity cranes and a docking well of 391 × 48 ft (119.2 × 14.6 m). Phalanx guns and SRBOC chaff launchers removed before transfer. Rio de Janeiro has been fitted with a more modern air search radar.

RIO DE JANEIRO   5/1992, Hartmut Ehlers

3 LCU 1610 CLASS (EDCG)

Name	No	Builders	Commissioned
GUARAPARI	GED 10 (ex-L 10)	Arsenal de Marinha, Rio de Janeiro	27 Mar 1978
TAMBAÚ	GED 11 (ex-L 11)	Arsenal de Marinha, Rio de Janeiro	27 Mar 1978
CAMBORIÚ	GED 12 (ex-L 12)	Arsenal de Marinha, Rio de Janeiro	6 Jan 1981

Displacement, tons: 390 full load
Dimensions, feet (metres): 134.5 × 27.6 × 6.6 (41 × 8.4 × 2.0)
Main machinery: 2 GM 12V-71 diesels; 874 hp (650 kW) sustained; 2 shafts; cp props
Speed, knots: 11. **Range, miles:** 1200 at 8 kts
Military lift: 172 tons
Guns: 3—12.7 mm MGs.
Radars: Navigation: Racal Decca; I band.

Comment: Status changed in 1991 when all of the class were reclassified EDCG (landing craft) and lost their pennant numbers having been decommissioned from the Navy. They remain in service as support vessels to establishments.

CAMBORIÚ   1985, Ronaldo S Olive

6 EDVM CLASSES (LCM)

301-306

Displacement, tons: 55 full load
Dimensions, feet (metres): 55.8 × 14.4 × 3.9 (17 × 4.4 × 1.2)
Main machinery: 2 Saab Scania diesels; 470 hp(m) (345 kW); 2 shafts
Speed, knots: 9
Military lift: 80 troops plus 31 tons equipment

Comment: Three are EDVM 300 type and three are EDVM 17 of similar characteristics. LCM 6 type.

EDVM 301   1985, Ronaldo S Olive

1 DE SOTO COUNTY CLASS (LST)

Name	No	Builders	Commissioned
DUQUE DE CAXIAS	G 26	Avondale, New Orleans	8 Nov 1957
(ex-USS *Grant County* LST 1174)			

Displacement, tons: 4164 light; 7804 full load
Dimensions, feet (metres): 445 × 62 × 17.5 *(135.6 × 18.9 × 5.3)*
Main machinery: 4 Fairbanks-Morse 38D8-1/8-12 diesels; 8500 hp *(6.34 MW)* sustained; 2 shafts; cp props
Speed, knots: 16.5. **Range, miles:** 13 000 at 10 kts
Complement: 175 (11 officers)
Military lift: 575 troops
Guns: 6 FMC 3 in *(76 mm)*/50 (3 twin) Mk 33; 85° elevation; 50 rounds/minute to 12.8 km *(6.9 nm)*; weight of shell 6 kg.
Fire control: 1 Mk 51 Mod 5 GFCS.
Radars: Surface search: Raytheon SPS 21; G/H band.
Navigation: Racal Decca; I band.

Comment: Launched 12 October 1956 and transferred from the US 15 January 1973, purchased 11 February 1980. Has Stülcken 60 tons heavy-lift gear fitted. Four LCVPs carried on davits; helicopter platform.

DUQUE DE CAXIAS   *1/1994 van Ginderen Collection*

5 EDVM 25 CLASS (LCM)

Displacement, tons: 130 full load
Dimensions, feet (metres): 72.2 × 21.7 × 4.9 *(22 × 6.6 × 1.5)*
Speed, knots: 9
Military lift: 80 troops plus 70 tons equipment

Comment: Built in 1992/93 by AMRJ. LCM 8 type.

35 EDVP CLASSES 400 and 500 (LCP)

501-530   EDVP 2-6

Displacement, tons: 13 full load
Dimensions, feet (metres): 35.8 × 9.8 × 3 *(10.9 × 3 × 0.9)*
Main machinery: Saab Scania diesel; 235 hp(m) *(173 kW)*; 1 shaft
Speed, knots: 10
Military lift: 3.7 tons or 36 men

Comment: GRP hulls built in Brazil. Some in Mato Grosso Flotilla at Ladário, and some in Amazonas Flotilla at Manaus.

EDVP 512   *1985, Ronaldo S Olive*

MINE WARFARE FORCES

6 ARATÚ (SCHÜTZE) CLASS (MINESWEEPERS—COASTAL)

Name	No	Builders	Commissioned
ARATÚ	M 15	Abeking & Rasmussen	5 May 1971
ANHATOMIRIM	M 16	Abeking & Rasmussen	30 Nov 1971
ATALAIA	M 17	Abeking & Rasmussen	13 Dec 1972
ARAÇATUBA	M 18	Abeking & Rasmussen	13 Dec 1972
ABROLHOS	M 19	Abeking & Rasmussen	25 Feb 1976
ALBARDÃO	M 20	Abeking & Rasmussen	25 Feb 1976

Displacement, tons: 230 standard; 280 full load
Dimensions, feet (metres): 154.9 × 23.6 × 6.9 *(47.2 × 7.2 × 2.1)*
Main machinery: 4 MTU Maybach diesels; 4500 hp(m) *(3.3 MW)*; 2 shafts; 2 Escher-Weiss cp props
Speed, knots: 24. **Range, miles:** 710 at 20 kts
Complement: 39 (4 officers)
Guns: 1 Bofors 40 mm/70.
Radars: Surface search: Signaal ZW 06; I band.

Comment: Wooden hulled. First four ordered in April 1969 and last pair in November 1973. Same design as West German Schütze class. Can carry out wire, magnetic and acoustic sweeping. Modernisation expected in the mid-1990s.

ATALAIA   *1988, Brazilian Navy*

SURVEY AND RESEARCH SHIPS

Note: Survey ships are painted white except for those operating in the Antarctic which have red hulls.

0 + (1) ANTARCTIC SURVEY SHIP

Displacement, tons: 6000
Dimensions, feet (metres): 328 oa; 305 wl × 65.6 × 23 *(100; 93 × 20 × 7)*
Main machinery: Diesel-electric; 2 diesel generators; 10 000 hp(m) *(7.35 MW)*; 2 motors; 1300 kW; 2 pumpjets
Speed, knots: 17 (diesels); 3 (motors). **Range, miles:** 20 000 at 13 kts
Complement: 95 (22 officers) plus 40 scientists
Helicopters: 2 light.

Comment: Replacement for *Barão de Teffé* to be built by Caneco, Rio de Janeiro to a Cleaver and Walkinshaw (Vancouver) design. Six laboratories (seismic, meteorology, oceanography, geology, geophysical and marine biology) are planned. Cost (1987 prices) US $36 million for the ship and probably as much again for the equipment. Originally ordered in September 1987 but the project was suspended for lack of funds, and tenders were finally called for by January 1994.

1 POLAR RESEARCH SHIP

Name	No	Builders	Commissioned
BARÃO DE TEFFÉ (ex-*Thala Dan*)	H 42	Aalborg Vaerft	1957

Measurement, tons: 2183 gross
Dimensions, feet (metres): 246.6 × 45.2 × 20.8 *(75.2 × 14.2 × 6.3)*
Main machinery: 1 Burmeister & Wain diesel; 1970 hp(m) *(1.45 MW)*; 1 shaft; cp prop
Speed, knots: 12
Complement: 46 (11 officers)
Helicopters: 2 Aerospatiale UH-13 Ecureuil 2.

Comment: A Danish polar supply ship commissioned into the Navy on 28 September 1982. Planned to run on until 1999. Strengthened for ice. SATCOM fitted. This ship has a red hull, mast and funnel and a pale brown superstructure.

BARÃO DE TEFFÉ   *1992*

1 RESEARCH SHIP

Name	No	Builders	Commissioned
ANTARES (ex-M/V *Lady Harrison*)	H 40	Mjellem and Karlsen A/S, Bergen	1984

Displacement, tons: 1076 full load
Dimensions, feet (metres): 180.3 × 33.8 × 14.1 *(55 × 10.3 × 4.3)*
Main machinery: 1 Burmeister & Wain Alpha diesel; 1860 hp(m) *(1.37 MW)*; 1 shaft; bow thruster
Speed, knots: 13.5. **Range, miles:** 10 000 at 12 kts
Complement: 49 (9 officers)
Radars: Navigation: 2 Racal Decca; I band.

Comment: Research vessel acquired from Racal Energy Resources. Used for seismographic survey. Recommissioned 6 June 1988. Painted white with orange masts and funnels.

ANTARES   *1989, Brazilian Navy*

1 ROBERT D CONRAD CLASS (OCEANOGRAPHIC SHIP)

Name	No	Builders	Commissioned
ALMIRANTE CÂMARA	H 41	Marietta Co, Point Pleasant,	8 Feb 1965
(ex-USNS Sands T-AGOR 6)		West Va.	

Displacement, tons: 1200 standard; 1380 full load
Dimensions, feet (metres): 208.9 × 40 × 15.3 (63.7 × 12.2 × 4.7)
Main machinery: Diesel-electric; 2 Caterpillar diesel generators; 1 motor; 1000 hp (746 kW); 1 shaft; bow thruster
Speed, knots: 13.5. Range, miles: 12 000 at 12 kts
Complement: 36 (7 officers) plus 15 scientists
Radars: Navigation: RCA CRM-NIA-75; I/J band.

Comment: Built specifically for oceanographic research. Equipped for gravimetric, magnetic and geological research. 10 ton crane and 620 hp gas-turbine for providing 'quiet power'. Transferred from US 1 July 1974. Has a red hull and pale brown superstructure. SATCOM fitted.

ALMIRANTE CÂMARA   10/1990, Mário R V Carneiro

2 SIRIUS CLASS (SURVEY SHIPS)

Name	No	Builders	Commissioned
SIRIUS	H 21	Ishikawajima Co Ltd, Tokyo	1 Jan 1958
CANOPUS	H 22	Ishikawajima Co Ltd, Tokyo	15 Mar 1958

Displacement, tons: 1463 standard; 1800 full load
Dimensions, feet (metres): 255.7 × 39.3 × 12.2 (78 × 12.1 × 3.7)
Main machinery: 2 Sulzer 7T6-36 diesels; 2700 hp(m) (1.98 MW); 2 shafts; cp props
Speed, knots: 15.7. Range, miles: 12 000 at 11 kts
Complement: 116 (16 officers) plus 14 scientists
Radars: Navigation: Racal Decca TM 1226C; I band.
Helicopters: 1 Bell JetRanger.

Comment: Laid down 1955-56. Painted white with orange funnels and masts. Special surveying apparatus, echo sounders, Raydist equipment, sounding machines installed, and landing craft (LCVP), jeep, and survey launches carried. All living and working spaces are air-conditioned. SATCOM fitted.

CANOPUS   1987, Brazilian Navy

3 ARGUS CLASS (SURVEY SHIPS)

Name	No	Builders	Commissioned
ARGUS	H 31	Arsenal de Marinha, Rio de Janeiro	29 Jan 1959
ORION	H 32	Arsenal de Marinha, Rio de Janeiro	11 June 1959
TAURUS	H 33	Arsenal de Marinha, Rio de Janeiro	23 Apr 1959

Displacement, tons: 250 standard; 343 full load
Dimensions, feet (metres): 146.7 × 21.3 × 9.2 (44.7 × 6.5 × 2.8)
Main machinery: 2 Caterpillar D 379 diesels; 1098 hp (818 kW) sustained; 2 shafts
Speed, knots: 15. Range, miles: 3000 at 15 kts
Complement: 42 (6 officers)
Guns: 2 Oerlikon 20 mm (removed).
Radars: Navigation: 2 Racal Decca 1226C; I band.

Comment: All laid down in 1955 and launched between December 1957—February 1958. Orion re-engined in 1974. Replacement ships are needed. White hull and superstructure, orange funnel.

ORION   1985, Brazilian Navy

1 LIGHTHOUSE TENDER

Name	No	Builders	Commissioned
ALMIRANTE GRAÇA ARANHA	H 34	Ebin, Niteroi	9 Sep 1976

Displacement, tons: 2390 full load
Dimensions, feet (metres): 245.3 × 42.6 × 13.8 (74.8 × 13 × 4.2)
Main machinery: 1 diesel; 2440 hp(m) (1.8 MW); 1 shaft; bow thruster
Speed, knots: 14
Complement: 95 (13 officers)
Radars: Navigation: 2 Racal Decca; I band.
Helicopters: 1 Bell JetRanger.

Comment: Laid down in 1971 and launched 23 May 1974. Fitted with telescopic hangar, 10 ton crane, two landing craft, GP launch and two Land Rovers. Omega navigation system. White hull and superstructure, orange mast and funnel.

ALMIRANTE GRAÇA ARANHA   5/1990, Mário R V Carneiro

4 BUOY TENDERS

Name	No	Builders	Commissioned
COMANDANTE VARELLA	H 18	Arsenal de Marinha, Rio de Janeiro	20 May 1982
TENENTE CASTELO	H 19	Estanave, Manaus	15 Aug 1984
COMANDANTE MANHÃES	H 20	Estanave, Manaus	15 Dec 1983
TENENTE BOANERGES	H 25	Estanave, Manaus	29 Mar 1985

Displacement, tons: 440 full load
Dimensions, feet (metres): 123 × 28.2 × 8.5 (37.5 × 8.6 × 2.6)
Main machinery: 2—8-cyl diesels; 1300 hp(m) (955 kW); 2 shafts
Speed, knots: 12. Range, miles: 2880 at 10 kts
Complement: 28 (2 officers)
Radars: Navigation: Racal Decca; I band.

Comment: Dual purpose minelayers. Tenente Castelo is based at Santana, Tenente Boanerges at Sao Luiz. White hull and superstructure, orange mast and funnel.

COMANDANTE VARELLA   1987, Brazilian Navy

5 BUOY TENDERS

MESTRE JOÃO DOS SANTOS H 13   FAROLEIRO AREAS H 27
CASTELHANOS H 24   FAROLEIRO NASCIMENTO H 30
FAROLEIRO MÁRIO SEIXAS H 26
  (ex-Mestre Jerânimo)

Displacement, tons: 195 (H 13); 110 (H 24, 27 and 30); 242 (H 26)
Complement: 17 (1 or 2 officers)

Comment: Four taken over 1973—H 26 on 21 January 1984. H 13 launched in 1950 and H 26 in 1962; remainder 1954-57. All are white with orange masts and funnels.

6 SURVEY LAUNCHES

PARAIBANO (ex-H 11)   ITACURUSSÁ (ex-H 15)
RIO BRANCO (ex-H 12)   CAMOCIM (ex-H 16)
NOGUEIRA DA GAMA (ex-*Jaceguai*) (ex-H 14) CARAVELAS (ex-H 17)

Displacement, tons: 32 standard; 50 full load
Dimensions, feet (metres): 52.5 × 15.1 × 4.3 *(16 × 4.6 × 1.3)*
Main machinery: 2 GM diesels; 330 hp *(246 kW)*; 2 shafts
Speed, knots: 11. **Range, miles:** 600 at 11 kts
Complement: 10 (1 officer)

Comment: First pair commissioned 7 November 1969, second pair 8 March 1971 and last two 22
September 1972. Built by Bormann, Rio de Janeiro. Majority work in Amazon Flotilla. Wooden
hulls. All decommissioned in 1991 but retained in service as support to naval establishments and
reclassified AvHi (inshore survey craft). There are also four trawler types in service from October
1982; names are *Cabo Branco*, *Cabo Frio*, *Cabo Orange* and *Cabo Calcanhar*.

PARAIBANO   *1985, Brazilian Navy*

1 OCEAN SURVEY VESSEL

SUBOFICIAL OLIVEIRA (ex-U 15)

Displacement, tons: 170 full load
Dimensions, feet (metres): 116.4 × 22 × 15.7 *(35.5 × 6.7 × 4.8)*
Main machinery: 2 diesels; 740 hp(m) *(544 kW)*; 2 shafts
Speed, knots: 8. **Range, miles:** 1400 at 8 kts
Complement: 10 (2 officers)

Comment: Commissioned at Fortaleza for Naval Research Institute on 6 May 1981. Decommissioned in 1991 but retained in service as an AvPqOc (ocean survey craft).

SUBOFICIAL OLIVEIRA   *1990, Brazilian Navy*

TRAINING SHIPS

1 MODIFIED NITEROI CLASS

Name	No	Builders	Commissioned
BRASIL	U 27	Arsenal de Marinha, Rio de Janeiro	21 Aug 1986

Displacement, tons: 2380 light; 3400 full load
Dimensions, feet (metres): 430.7 × 44.3 × 13.8 *(131.3 × 13.5 × 4.2)*
Main machinery: 2 Pielstick/Ishikawajima (Brazil) 6 PC2.5 L 400 diesels; 7020 hp(m) *(5.17 MW)*
sustained; 2 shafts
Speed, knots: 18. **Range, miles:** 7000 at 15 kts
Complement: 221 (27 officers) plus 200 midshipmen
Guns: 2 Bofors 40 mm. 4 saluting guns.
Countermeasures: ESM: Racal RDL; radar intercept.
Fire control: Saab Scania TVT 300 optronic director.
Radars: Surface search: Racal Decca RMS 1230C; E/F band.
Navigation: Racal Decca TM 1226C; I band.
Helicopters: Platform for 2 Sea King.

Comment: A modification of the Vosper Thornycroft Mk 10 Frigate design ordered in June 1981.
Laid down 18 September 1981, launched 23 September 1983. Designed to carry midshipmen
and other trainees from the Naval and Merchant Marine Academies. Minimum electronics as
required for training. SATCOM fitted.

BRASIL   *7/1993, A Campanera i Rovira*

Name	No	Builders	Commissioned
ASPIRANTE NASCIMENTO	U 10	Ebrasa, Santa Catarina	13 Dec 1980
GUARDA MARINHA JENSEN	U 11	Ebrasa, Santa Catarina	22 July 1981
GUARDA MARINHA BRITO	U 12	Ebrasa, Santa Catarina	22 July 1981

Displacement, tons: 108.5 standard; 130 full load
Dimensions, feet (metres): 91.8 × 21.3 × 5.9 *(28 × 6.5 × 1.8)*
Main machinery: 2 MWM D232V12 diesels; 650 hp(m) *(478 kW)*; 2 shafts
Speed, knots: 10. **Range, miles:** 700 at 10 kts
Complement: 12
Guns: 1—12.7 mm MG.
Radars: Navigation: Racal Decca; I band.

Comment: Can carry 24 trainees overnight. All of the class are attached to the Naval Academy.

GUARDA MARINHA JENSEN   *10/1990, Mário R V Carneiro*

ROSCA FINA (ex-U 31)   VOGA PICADA (ex-U 32)   LEVA ARRIBA (ex-U 33)

Displacement, tons: 50
Dimensions, feet (metres): 61 × 15.4 × 3.9 *(18.6 × 4.7 × 1.2)*
Main machinery: 1 diesel; 650 hp(m) *(477 kW)*; 1 shaft
Speed, knots: 11. **Range, miles:** 200
Complement: 5 plus trainees
Radars: Navigation: Racal Decca; I band.

Comment: Built by Carbrasmar, Rio de Janeiro. All commissioned 21 February 1984 and attached
to the Naval College. Pennant numbers removed in 1989. In addition the former American fishing vessel *Night Hawk* is in use for training at Centro de Instrucao Almirante Braz de Aguiar.

VOGA PICADA   *1984, Brazilian Navy*

8 SAIL TRAINING VESSELS

SARGACO BL 177	**BREKELE** (ex-*Carro Chefe*) BL 898
SITIO FORTE BL 1130	**VENDAVAL**
ALBATROZ (ex-*Cisne Branco*)	**CISNE BRANCO** (ex-*Ondine*) BL 810
ITAPOA (ex-*Cri-Cri*)	**JACANA II**

Comment: Some are used for civilian training as well.

AUXILIARIES

Note: In addition to the vessels listed below there are (1) three 485 ton water tankers *Dr Gondim* (R 38), *Itapura* (R 42) and *Paulo Afonso* (R 43); (2) two general purpose auxiliaries *Guairia* (R 40) and *Iguacu* (R 41). There are also large numbers of small service craft.

1 SUBMARINE RESCUE SHIP

Name	No	Builders	Commissioned
FELINTO PERRY	K 11	Stord Verft, Norway	1979
(ex-*Holger Dane*, ex-*Wildrake*)			

Displacement, tons: 1380 full load
Dimensions, feet (metres): 256.6 × 57.4 × 15.1 *(78.2 × 17.5 × 4.6)*
Main machinery: Diesel-electric; 2 BMK KVG B12 and 2 KVG B16 diesels; 11 400 hp(m) *(8.4 MW)*; 2 motors; 7000 hp(m) *(5.15 MW)*; 2 shafts; cp props; 2 bow thrusters; 2 stern thrusters
Speed, knots: 14.5
Complement: 65 (9 officers)
Helicopters: Platform only.

Comment: Former oilfield support ship acquired 28 December 1988. Has an octagonal heliport (62.5 ft diameter) above the bridge. Has replaced *Gastão Moutinho* as the submarine rescue ship. Dynamic positioning system.

FELINTO PERRY   *11/1988, W Sartori*

1 PENGUIN CLASS (MCMV TENDER)

Name	No	Builders	Launched
GASTÃO MOUTINHO	U 20	Charleston SB & DD Co	19 Mar 1946
(ex-USS *Skylark* ASR 20)	(ex-K 10)		

Displacement, tons: 1653 standard; 2320 full load
Dimensions, feet (metres): 251.5 × 44 × 16 *(76.7 × 13.4 × 4.9)*
Main machinery: Diesel-electric; 4 GM 12-278A diesel generators; 4400 hp *(3.58 MW)*; 1 motor; 3000 hp *(2.2 MW)*; 1 shaft
Speed, knots: 15. **Range, miles:** 15 000 at 8 kts
Complement: 85
Guns: 2 Oerlikon 20 mm.
Radars: Surface search: Westinghouse SPS 5; G/H band.

Comment: Fitted with special pumps, compressors and submarine rescue chamber in 1947. Transferred 30 June 1973 and used as the submarine rescue ship until replaced by *Felinto Perry*. Now employed as a tender for the MCMV force at Aratu naval base.

GASTÃO MOUTINHO (old number)   *1988, Brazilian Navy*

1 ARISTAEUS CLASS (REPAIR SHIP)

Name	No	Builders	Commissioned
BELMONTE (ex-USS *Helios*	G 24	Maryland DD Co, Baltimore	26 Feb 1945
ARB 12, ex-LST 1127)			

Displacement, tons: 1625 light; 2030 standard; 4100 full load
Dimensions, feet (metres): 328 × 50 × 11 *(100 × 15.2 × 3.4)*
Main machinery: 2 GM 12-567A diesels; 1800 hp *(1.34 MW)*; 2 shafts
Speed, knots: 11.6. **Range, miles:** 6000 at 9 kts
Guns: 8 Bofors 40 mm/60 (2 quad); 90° elevation; 300 rounds/minute to 12 km *(6.5 nm)* anti-surface; 4 km *(2.2 nm)* anti-aircraft; weight of shell 0.89 kg.

Comment: Former US battle damage repair ship (ex-LST). Laid down 23 November 1944. Launched 14 February 1945. Transferred by lease to Brazil by USA 16 April 1963 under MAP and purchased 28 December 1977. Oil fuel, 1000 tons.

BELMONTE   *1985, Brazilian Navy*

4 BARROSO PEREIRA CLASS (TRANSPORTS)

Name	No	Builders	Commissioned
BARROSO PEREIRA	G 16	Ishikawajima Co Ltd, Tokyo	22 Mar 1955
CUSTÓDIO DE MELLO	G 20 (ex-U 26)	Ishikawajima Co Ltd, Tokyo	8 Feb 1955
ARY PARREIRAS	G 21	Ishikawajima Co Ltd, Tokyo	6 Mar 1957
SOARES DUTRA	G 22	Ishikawajima Co Ltd, Tokyo	27 May 1957

Displacement, tons: 4800 standard; 7300 full load
Measurement, tons: 4200 dwt; 4879 gross (Panama)
Dimensions, feet (metres): 362 pp; 391.8 oa × 52.5 × 20.5 *(110.4; 119.5 × 16 × 6.3)*
Main machinery: 2 Ishikawajima boilers and turbines; 4800 hp(m) *(3.53 MW)*; 2 shafts
Speed, knots: 15
Complement: 159 (15 officers)
Military lift: 1972 troops (overload); 497 troops (normal)
Cargo capacity: 425 m³ refrigerated cargo space; 4000 tons
Guns: 2—3 in *(76 mm)* Mk 33; 85° elevation; 50 rounds/minute to 12.8 km *(6.9 nm)* anti-aircraft; weight of shell 6 kg.
2 or 4 Oerlikon 20 mm; 55° elevation; 800 rounds/minute to 2 km.
Radars: Navigation: SPS 4 (*Custódio de Mello* only). Two Racal Decca (others); I band.

Comment: Transports and cargo vessels. Helicopter landing platform aft except in *Custódio de Mello* and *Barroso Pereira*. Medical, hospital and dental facilities. Working and living quarters are mechanically ventilated with partial air-conditioning. Refrigerated cargo space 15 500 cu ft. *Custódio de Mello* was classified as a training ship in July 1961, replaced by *Brasil* in 1987 and has now reverted to being a transport. All operate commercially from time to time.

SOARES DUTRA   *6/1993*

1 RIVER TRANSPORT

Name	No	Builders	Commissioned
PIRAIM	U 29	Estaleiro SNBP, Mato Grosso	10 Mar 1982

Displacement, tons: 91.5 full load
Dimensions, feet (metres): 82.0 × 18.0 × 3.2 *(25.0 × 5.5 × 0.97)*
Main machinery: 2 MWM diesels; 400 hp(m) *(294 kW)*; 2 shafts
Speed, knots: 7. **Range, miles:** 700 at 7 kts
Complement: 17 (2 officers)
Radars: Navigation: Furuno 3600; I band.

Comment: Used as a logistics support ship for the Mato Grosso Flotilla.

1 TRANSPORT SHIP

Name	No	Builders	Commissioned
PARAGUASSU	G 15	Amsterdam Drydock	1951
(ex-*Garapuava*)			

Displacement, tons: 285 full load
Dimensions, feet (metres): 131.2 × 23 × 6.6 *(40 × 7 × 2)*
Main machinery: 3 diesels; 2505 hp(m) *(1.84 MW)*; 1 shaft
Speed, knots: 13. **Range, miles:** 2500 at 10 kts
Complement: 43 (4 officers)
Military lift: 178 troops
Guns: 6—7.62 mm MGs.
Radars: Navigation: Furuno 3600; I band.

Comment: Passenger ship converted into a troop carrier in 1957 and acquired on 20 June 1972.

PARAGUASSU   1989, Brazilian Navy

2 HOSPITAL SHIPS

Name	No	Builders	Commissioned
OSWALDO CRUZ	U 18	Arsenal de Marinha, Rio de Janeiro	29 May 1984
CARLOS CHAGAS	U 19	Arsenal de Marinha, Rio de Janeiro	7 Dec 1984

Displacement, tons: 500 full load
Dimensions, feet (metres): 154.2 × 26.9 × 5.9 *(47.2 × 8.5 × 1.8)*
Main machinery: 2 diesels; 714 hp(m) *(525 kW)*; 2 shafts
Speed, knots: 9. **Range, miles:** 4000 at 9 kts
Complement: 46 (4 officers) plus 21 medical (6 doctors/dentists)
Radars: Navigation: Racal Decca; I band.
Helicopters: 1 Helibras HB-350B.

Comment: *Oswaldo Cruz* launched 11 July 1983, and *Carlos Chagas* 16 April 1984. Have two sick bays, dental surgery, a laboratory, two clinics and X-ray centre. The design is a development of the Roraima class with which they operate in the Amazon Flotilla. Since 1992 both ships painted grey with dark green crosses on the hull.

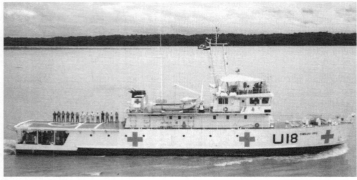
OSWALDO CRUZ   1992, Brazilian Navy

1 RIVER TANKER

Name	No	Builders	Commissioned
POTENGI	G 17	Papendrecht, Netherlands	28 June 1938

Displacement, tons: 600 full load
Dimensions, feet (metres): 178.8 × 24.5 × 6 *(54.5 × 7.5 × 1.8)*
Main machinery: 2 diesels; 550 hp(m) *(404 kW)*; 2 shafts
Speed, knots: 10. **Range, miles:** 600 at 8 kts
Complement: 19
Cargo capacity: 450 tons
Radars: Navigation: Furuno 3600; I band.

Comment: Launched 16 March 1938. Employed in the Mato Grosso Flotilla on river service.

POTENGI   1992, Brazilian Navy

1 REPLENISHMENT TANKER

Name	No	Builders	Commissioned
ALMIRANTE GASTÃO MOTTA	G 23	Ishibras, Rio de Janeiro	26 Nov 1991

Measurement, tons: 10 300 dwt
Dimensions, feet (metres): 442.9 × 62.3 × 24.6 *(135 × 19 × 7.5)*
Main machinery: Diesel-electric; 2 Wärtsilä 12V32 diesel generators; 11 700 hp(m) *(8.57 MW)* sustained; 1 motor; 1 shaft
Speed, knots: 20. **Range, miles:** 10 000 at 15 kts
Complement: 121 (13 officers)
Cargo capacity: 5000 tons liquid; 200 tons dry

Comment: Ordered March 1987. Laid down 11 December 1989 and launched 1 June 1990. Fitted for abeam and stern refuelling. Probably armed with light guns. SATCOM fitted.

ALMIRANTE GASTÃO MOTTA   6/1993

1 REPLENISHMENT TANKER

Name	No	Builders	Commissioned
MARAJO	G 27	Ishikawajima do Brasil	22 Oct 1968

Displacement, tons: 16 000 full load
Dimensions, feet (metres): 440.7 × 63.3 × 24 *(134.4 × 19.3 × 7.3)*
Main machinery: 1 Sulzer GRD 68 diesel; 8000 hp(m) *(5.88 MW)*; 1 shaft
Speed, knots: 13. **Range, miles:** 9200 at 13 kts
Complement: 121 (13 officers)
Cargo capacity: 6600 tons fuel

Comment: Launched 31 January 1968. Fitted for abeam replenishment. Was to have been replaced by *Gastão Motta* but has been retained in service until the end of the decade.

1 TARGET TOWING TUG

Name	No	Builders	Commissioned
TRINDADE (ex-*Nobistor*)	U 16	J G Hitzler, Lavenburg	1969

Displacement, tons: 590 light; 1308 full load
Dimensions, feet (metres): 176.1 × 20 × 6.9 *(53.7 × 6.1 × 2.1)*
Main machinery: 2 MWM diesels; 2740 hp(m) *(2 MW)* sustained; 2 shafts
Speed, knots: 12.7 kts
Complement: 22 (2 officers)
Radars: Navigation: Furuno 3600; I band.

Comment: Ex-Panamanian tug seized for smuggling in 1989 and commissioned in the Navy 31 January 1990. Used for target towing.

TRINDADE   1990, Mário R V Carneiro

9 RIO DOCE and RIO PARDO CLASSES

RIO DAS CONTAS (ex-U 21)
RIO FORMOSO (ex-U 22)
RIO REAL (ex-U 23)
RIO TURVO (ex-U 24)
RIO VERDE (ex-U 25)

RIO PARDO (ex-U 40)
RIO NEGRO (ex-U 41)
RIO CHUI (ex-U 42)
RIO OIAPOQUE (ex-U 43)

Displacement, tons: 150 full load
Dimensions, feet (metres): 120 × 21.3 × 6.2 *(36.6 × 6.5 × 1.9)*
Main machinery: 2 Sulzer 6TD24; 900 hp(m) *(661 kW)*; 2 shafts
Speed, knots: 14. **Range, miles:** 700 at 14 kts
Complement: 10

Comment: Can carry 600 passengers. The first five were built by Holland Nautic, commissioned in 1954 and the second group by Inconav de Niteroi in 1975/76. Pennant numbers removed in 1989. *Rio Doce* (ex-U 20) sold for civilian use in 1986.

1 TORPEDO RECOVERY VESSEL

ALMIRANTE HESS (ex-U 30)

Displacement, tons: 91 full load
Dimensions, feet (metres): 77.4 × 19.7 × 6.6 *(23.6 × 6 × 2)*
Speed, knots: 13

Comment: Built by Inace S/A, Fortaleza and commissioned 2 December 1983. Attached to Trem da Esquadra. Can transport up to four torpedoes. Decommissioned in 1991 but retained in service as an AvPpCo (coast support craft).

4 FLOATING DOCKS

CIDADE DE NATAL (ex-AFDL 39) G 27
AFONSO PENA (ex-*Ceara*, ex-ARD 14) G 25
ALMIRANTE SCHIECK

ALMIRANTE JERONIMO GONÇALVES
  (ex-*Goiaz* AFDL 4) G 26

Comment: The first three are floating docks loaned to Brazil by US Navy in the mid-1960s and purchased 11 February 1980. Ship lifts of 2800 tons, 1800 tons and 1000 tons respectively. *Almirante Schieck* of 3600 tons displacement was built by Arsenal de Marinha, Rio de Janeiro and commissioned 12 October 1989. There are also two Floating Cranes, *Campos Salles* and *Atlas* of 100 tons and 30 tons capacity respectively.

TUGS

Note: In addition to the vessels listed below there are two harbour tugs: *Wandenkolk* (R 20) and *Etchebarne* (R 28).

2 ALMIRANTE GUILHEM CLASS (FLEET OCEAN TUGS)

Name	No	Builders	Commissioned
ALMIRANTE GUILHEM	R 24	Sumitomo Heavy Industry, Japan	1976
(ex-*Superpesa 4*)			
ALMIRANTE GUILLOBEL	R 25	Sumitomo Heavy Industry, Japan	1976
(ex-*Superpesa 5*)			

Displacement, tons: 1200 dwt
Dimensions, feet (metres): 207 × 44 × 14.8 *(63.2 × 13.4 × 4.5)*
Main machinery: 2 GM EMD 20-645F7B diesels; 7120 hp *(5.31 MW)* sustained; 2 shafts; cp props; bow thruster
Speed, knots: 14
Complement: 40
Guns: 2 Oerlikon 20 mm (not always carried).

Comment: Originally built as civilian tugs. Bollard pull, 84 tons. Commissioned into the Navy 22 January 1981.

ALMIRANTE GUILLOBEL   *1985, Mário R V Carneiro*

4 COASTAL TUGS

INTREPIDO BNRJ 16
ARROJADO BNRJ 17

VALENTE BNRJ 18
IMPAVIDO BNRJ 19

Displacement, tons: 200 full load
Dimensions, feet (metres): 73.8 × 23 × 9.2 *(22.5 × 7 × 2.8)*
Main machinery: 2 Caterpillar 3508A DI-TA diesels; 1572 hp(m) *(1.16 MW)* sustained; 2 shafts
Speed, knots: 11.7
Complement: 6

Comment: Damen Shipyards Stan Tug 2207 type. First two delivered in May 1992, second pair in September 1992. Bollard pull 22.5 tons. The second pair have external firefighting equipment.

IMPAVIDO   *12/1993, Mário R V Carneiro*

3 TRITÃO CLASS (FLEET OCEAN TUGS)

Name	No	Builders	Commissioned
TRITÃO (ex-*Sarandi*)	R 21	Estanave, Manaus	19 Feb 1987
TRIDENTE (ex-*Sambaiba*)	R 22	Estanave, Manaus	8 Oct 1987
TRIUNFO (ex-*Sorocaba*)	R 23	Estanave, Manaus	5 July 1986

Displacement, tons: 1680 full load
Dimensions, feet (metres): 181.8 × 38.1 × 11.2 *(55.4 × 11.6 × 3.4)*
Main machinery: 2 diesels; 2480 hp(m) *(1.82 MW)*; 2 shafts
Speed, knots: 12
Complement: 49
Guns: 2 Oerlikon 20 mm.
Radars: Navigation: Racal Decca; I band.

Comment: Offshore supply vessels acquired from National Oil Company of Brazil and converted for naval use. Assumed names of previous three ships of Sotoyomo class. Fitted to act both as tugs and patrol vessels. Bollard pull, 23.5 tons. Firefighting capability. Endurance, 45 days.

TRIUNFO   *1987, Brazilian Navy*

4 COASTAL TUGS

COMANDANTE MARROIG (ex-R 15)
COMANDANTE DIDIER (ex-R 16)

TENENTE MAGALHÃES (ex-R 17)
CABO SCHRAMM (ex-R 18)

Displacement, tons: 115 standard
Dimensions, feet (metres): 65 × 23 × 6.5 *(19.8 × 7 × 2)*
Main machinery: 2 GM diesels; 900 hp(m) *(661 kW)*; 2 shafts
Complement: 6

Comment: Built by Turn-Ship Limited, USA. First pair commissioned 30 April 1981, second pair 14 September 1982. *Comandante Marroig* sank in 1990 in an incident with *Ceará* but was salvaged and active again in 1991. Decommissioned in 1991 but retained in service as support ships to naval establishments and designated Rb.

CABO SCHRAMM   *6/1989, Mário R V Carneiro*

2 COASTAL TUGS

LAHMEYER   DNOG

Comment: Built at Servimar, Rio de Janeiro. Both commissioned in 1972. Of 100 tons and 105 ft *(32 m)* long. Based at Aratu naval base.

BRUNEI

Headquarters' Appointment

Commander of the Navy:
Colonel P D P Hj Kefli

Personnel

(a)   1994: 700 (60 officers)
This total includes Special Combat Squadron
and River Division
(b)   Voluntary service

Base

Muara

Prefix to Ships' Names

KDB (Kapal Di-Raja Brunei)

General

Angkatan Tentera Laut Diraja Brunei (Royal Brunei Navy).

Mercantile Marine

Lloyd's Register of Shipping:
62 vessels of 365 056 tons gross

DELETIONS

1991	*Abadi, Penang*
1992	*Rotork S 25*
1993	*Norain*

CORVETTES

Note: Order placed in October 1989 for three Vosper Vigilance class was not confirmed. Tenders re-opened but further delays have been caused by priority being given to the purchase of Hawk aircraft. An order for three vessels of 1000 tons is expected in 1994. A 30 m Landing Craft may also be ordered.

PATROL FORCES

3 WASPADA CLASS (FAST ATTACK CRAFT—MISSILE)

Name	No	Builders	Commissioned
WASPADA	P 02	Vosper (Singapore)	2 Aug 1978
PEJUANG	P 03	Vosper (Singapore)	25 Mar 1979
SETERIA	P 04	Vosper (Singapore)	22 June 1979

Displacement, tons: 206 full load
Dimensions, feet (metres): 121 × 23.5 × 6 *(36.9 × 7.2 × 1.8)*
Main machinery: 2 MTU 20V 538 TB91 diesels; 7680 hp(m) *(5.63 MW)* sustained; 2 shafts
Speed, knots: 32. **Range, miles:** 1200 at 14 kts
Complement: 24 (4 officers)

Missiles: SSM: 2 Aerospatiale MM 38 Exocet; inertial cruise; active radar homing to 42 km *(23 nm)* at 0.9 Mach; warhead 165 kg.
Guns: 2 Oerlikon 30 mm GCM-B01 (twin); 85° elevation; 650 rounds/minute to 10 km *(5.5 nm)*; weight of shell 1 kg.
2—7.62 mm MGs. 2 MOD(N) 2 in launchers for illuminants.
Countermeasures: ESM: Decca RDL; radar warning.
Fire control: Sea Archer system with Sperry Co-ordinate Calculator and 1412A digital computer.
Radars: Surface search: Racal Decca TM 1629AC; I band.

Programmes: *Waspada* launched in August 1977, the remaining two in March and June 1978 respectively.
Modernisation: Started in 1988 and included improved gun fire-control and ESM equipment. MM 40 Exocet may be fitted in due course.
Structure: Welded steel hull with aluminium alloy superstructure. *Waspada* has an enclosed upper bridge for training purposes.

WASPADA   *5/1990, John Mortimer*

PEJUANG   *10/1993, 92 Wing RAAF*

3 PERWIRA CLASS (COASTAL PATROL CRAFT)

Name	No	Builders	Commissioned
PERWIRA	P 14	Vosper (Singapore)	9 Sep 1974
PEMBURU	P 15	Vosper (Singapore)	17 June 1975
PENYERANG	P 16	Vosper (Singapore)	24 June 1975

Displacement, tons: 38 full load
Dimensions, feet (metres): 71 × 20 × 5 *(21.7 × 6.1 × 1.2)*
Main machinery: 2 MTU MB 12V 331 TC81 diesels; 2450 hp(m) *(1.8 MW)* sustained; 2 shafts
Speed, knots: 32. **Range, miles:** 600 at 22 kts; 1000 at 16 kts
Complement: 14 (2 officers)
Guns: 2 Oerlikon/BMARC 20 mm GAM-B01; 800 rounds/minute to 2 km; weight of shell 0.24 kg.
2—7.62 mm MGs.
Radars: Surface search: Racal Decca RM 1290; I band.

Comment: *Perwira* launched May 1974, other two in January and March 1975 respectively. Of all wooden construction on laminated frames. Fitted with enclosed bridges—modified July 1976. At least one of this class was non-operational in early 1994.

PERWIRA   *10/1993, 92 Wing RAAF*

2 ROTORK TYPE (INSHORE PATROL CRAFT)

S 24   S 26

Displacement, tons: 8.8 full load
Dimensions, feet (metres): 41.5 × 10.5 × 4.8 *(12.7 × 3.2 × 1.5)*
Main machinery: 2 Ford Mermaid diesels; 430 hp *(320 kW)*; 2 Castoldi 06 waterjets
Speed, knots: 27 light; 12 heavy. **Range, miles:** 100 at 12 kts
Complement: 3
Guns: 3—7.62 mm MGs.
Radars: Navigation: Decca 60; I band.

Comment: Rotork Marine FPB 512 type for patrol and transport duties. *S 24* was delivered in November 1980, *S 26* in May 1981.

S 26   *1982, Royal Brunei Armed Forces*

24 FAST ASSAULT BOATS

Comment: Rigid Raider type with one 140 hp (103 kW) outboard mostly 16.4-19.7 ft (5-6 m) long. One 7.62 mm MG. Operated in rivers and estuaries by River Division for Infantry Battalions.

RIGID RAIDER (UK colours) 1992, H.M. Steele

LAND-BASED MARITIME AIRCRAFT

Numbers/Type: 3 CASA/IPTN CN-235.
Operational speed: 240 kts (445 km/h).
Service ceiling: 26 600 ft (8110 m).
Range: 669 nm (1240 km).
Role/Weapon systems: Long-range maritime patrol for surface surveillance and ASW. Sensors: Search radar: Litton AN/APS 504(V)5; MAD; acoustic processors; sonobuoys. Weapons; Mk 46 torpedoes.

CN-235 1989

AUXILIARIES

2 CHEVERTON LOADMASTERS

Name	No	Builders	Commissioned
DAMUAN	L 31	Cheverton Ltd, Isle of Wight	May 1976
PUNI	L 32	Cheverton Ltd, Isle of Wight	Feb 1977

Displacement, tons: 60; 64 (Puni)
Dimensions, feet (metres): 65 × 20 × 3.6 (19.8 × 6.1 × 1.1) (length 74.8 (22.8) Puni)
Main machinery: 2 Detroit 6-71 diesels; 442 hp (305 kW) sustained; 2 shafts
Speed, knots: 9. Range, miles: 1000 at 9 kts
Complement: 8
Military lift: 32 tons
Radars: Navigation: Racal Decca RM 1216; I band.

DAMUAN 1988, Royal Brunei Armed Forces

1 UTILITY CRAFT

BURONG NURI

Displacement, tons: 23 full load
Dimensions, feet (metres): 58.4 × 14.1 × 4.9 (17.8 × 4.3 × 1.5)
Main machinery: 2 diesels; 400 hp (298 kW); 2 shafts
Speed, knots: 12
Complement: 5

Comment: Built by Cheverton in 1982. Serves as tug, tender or anti-pollution vessel.

BURONG NURI 6/1990, James Goldrick

POLICE

Note: In addition to the vessels listed below there are two Rotork type Behagia 07 and Selamat 10 and four River Patrol Craft Aman 01, Damai 02, Sentosa 04 and Sejahtera 06.

5 COASTAL PATROL CRAFT

PDB 11-15

Displacement, tons: 20 full load
Dimensions, feet (metres): 47.7 × 13.9 × 3.9 (14.5 × 4.2 × 1.2)
Main machinery: 2 MAN D 2840 LE diesels; 1040 hp(m) (764 kW) sustained; 2 shafts
Speed, knots: 30. Range, miles: 310 at 22 kts
Complement: 7
Guns: 1—7.62 mm MG

Comment: Built by Singapore SBEC. First three handed over in October 1987, last pair in 1988. Aluminium hulls.

PDB 13 10/1987, Royal Brunei Police Force

3 COASTAL PATROL CRAFT

BENDEHARU P 21   MAHARAJALELA P 22   KEMAINDERA P 23

Displacement, tons: 68 full load
Dimensions, feet (metres): 91.8 × 17.7 × 5.9 (28.5 × 5.4 × 1.7)
Main machinery: 2 MTU diesels; 2260 hp(m) (1.6 MW); 2 shafts
Complement: 19
Guns: 1—12.7 mm MG.

Comment: Ordered for the Police from PT Pal Surabaya, Indonesia in 1989 and delivered in 1991. Similar to Indonesian craft. Reported as all being out of service in early 1994.

POLICE CRAFT (Indonesian colours) 1991

BULGARIA

Headquarters' Appointments

Commander-in-Chief:
Vice Admiral Ventseslav Velkov
Deputy Chief of General Staff (Navy):
Vice Admiral Dimiter Pavlov
Deputy Commander-in-Chief:
Rear Admiral Christo Kontrov
Chief of Staff:
Rear Admiral Iliya Popov

Diplomatic Representation

Defence Attaché, Brussels and NATO HQ:
Rear Admiral Peter Stranchevski
Naval Attaché, London:
Captain Ivan Yordanov
Defence Attaché, Washington:
Colonel Peter Petrov

General

The Navy is being restructured. The first stage (1992/93) saw the reduction of 22 per cent of the officers and 14 per cent of ratings, and the conscript ratio changed from 44 to 35 per cent. The second stage (1993-2000) involves a reduction to 52 ships paying off obsolete vessels and replacing others. By 2000 the Fleet is planned to be: 2 or 3 submarines, 10 patrol vessels, 8 FAC(M), 20 minehunters/sweepers, 12 minelayers and 12 helicopters.

Personnel

(a) 1994: 5400 (1560 afloat, 2640 ashore, 1000 training, 280 aviation)
(b) 18 months' national service, to reduce to 15 months

Bases

Varna; Naval HQ, Naval Base, Air Station
Burgas; Naval Base
Sozopol; Naval Base
Higher Naval School *(Nikola Yonkov Vaptsarov)* at Varna. Missile, gun, radar and signal stations on Black Sea coast under Navy command.

Strength of the Fleet

Type	Active
Patrol Submarines	2
Frigates	1
Corvettes	7
Fast Attack Craft (Missile)	6
Coastal Patrol Craft (Border Guard)	10
Minesweepers (Coastal)	8
Minesweepers (Inshore)	11
Landing Craft/Minelayers	21
Surveying Ships	3
Support Tankers	2
Training Ship	1

Mercantile Marine

Lloyd's Register of Shipping:
210 vessels of 1 313 917 tons gross

DELETIONS

Submarine

1993   *Poseda*

Frigate

1993   *Druzki*

Corvettes

1993   *Strogij, Naporisti*

Minesweepers

1991   1 T 43, 3 PO 2
1992   2 Vanya class, 8 PO 2
1993   2 PO 2

Patrol Forces

1992   4 Shershen class

Amphibious Forces

1991   4 MFP D-3 Type
1993   4 Vydra class (708-711)

Miscellaneous

1991   *Nikola Vaptzarov* (civilian), *Perun* (civilian)
1992   *Kiril Khalachev, Vladimir Zaimov*

SUBMARINES (PATROL)

2 ROMEO CLASS

NADEZHDA 83   **SLAVA** 84

Displacement, tons: 1475 surfaced; 1830 dived
Dimensions, feet (metres): 251.3 × 22 × 16.1
(76.6 × 6.7 × 4.9)
Main machinery: Diesel-electric; 2 Type 37-D diesels; 4 000 hp(m) *(2.94 MW)*; 2 motors; 2700 hp(m) *(1.98 MW)*; 2 creep motors; 2 shafts
Speed, knots: 16 surfaced; 13 dived. **Range, miles:** 9000 at 9 kts surfaced
Complement: 54

Torpedoes: 8—21 in *(533 mm)* tubes (6 bow, 2 stern). 14 SAET-60; passive homing to 15 km *(8.1 nm)* at 40 kts; warhead 400 kg.
Mines: Can carry up to 28 in lieu of torpedoes.
Radars: Surface search: Snoop Plate; I band.
Sonars: Hull-mounted; active/passive search and attack; high frequency.

ROMEO   *1992, S S Breyer*

Programmes: Built between 1958 and 1961. These were the last pair to transfer from the USSR in 1985 and 1986.

Operational: In 1993 these last two were operational but probably restricted to diving to about 50 m *(165 ft)*.

FRIGATE

1 KONI CLASS

SMELI (ex-*Delfin*) 11

Displacement, tons: 1440 standard; 1900 full load
Dimensions, feet (metres): 316.3 × 41.3 × 11.5
(96.4 × 12.6 × 3.5)
Main machinery: CODAG; 1 SGW, Nikolayev M8B gas-turbine (centre shaft); 18 000 hp(m) *(13.25 MW)* sustained; 2 Russki B-68 diesels; 15 820 hp(m) *(11.63 MW)* sustained; 3 shafts
Speed, knots: 27 gas; 22 diesel. **Range, miles:** 1800 at 14 kts
Complement: 110

Missiles: SAM: SA-N-4 Gecko twin launcher ❶; semi-active radar homing to 15 km *(8 nm)* at 2.5 Mach; warhead 50 kg; altitude 9.1-3048 m *(30-10 000 ft)*; 20 missiles.
Guns: 4—3 in *(76 mm)*/60 (2 twin) ❷; 80° elevation; 60 rounds/minute to 15 km *(8 nm)*; weight of shell 7 kg.
4—30 mm/65 (2 twin) ❸; 85° elevation; 500 rounds/minute to 5 km *(2.7 nm)*; weight of shell 0.54 kg.
A/S mortars: 2 RBU 6000 12-tubed trainable ❹; range 6000 m; warhead 31 kg.
Depth charges: 2 racks.
Mines: Capacity for 22.
Countermeasures: Decoys: 2—16-tubed chaff launchers.
ESM: 2 Watch Dog.
Radars: Air search: Strut Curve ❺; F band; range 110 km *(60 nm)* for 2 m² target.
Surface search: Don 2; I band.
Fire control: Hawk Screech ❻; I band (for 76 mm). Drum Tilt ❼; H/I band (for 30 mm). Pop Group ❽; F/H/I band (for SA-N-4).
IFF: High Pole B.
Sonars: Hull-mounted; active search and attack; medium frequency.

Programmes: First reported in the Black Sea in 1976. Type I retained by the USSR for training foreign crews but transferred in February 1990 when the Koni programme terminated. Others of the class acquired by the former East German Navy (now deleted), Yugoslavia, Algeria, Cuba and Libya.

SMELI   *(Scale 1 : 900), Ian Sturton*

SMELI   *7/1992*

LAND-BASED MARITIME AIRCRAFT (FRONT LINE)

Numbers/Type: 6 Mil Mi-14PL Haze A.
Operational speed: 120 kts *(222 km/h)*.
Service ceiling: 15 000 ft *(4570 m)*.
Range: 240 nm *(445 km)*.
Role/Weapon systems: Primary role as inshore/coastal ASW and Fleet support helicopter; one converted as transport. Coastal patrol and surface search. Sensors: Search radar, MAD, sonobuoys, dipping sonar. Weapons: ASW; up to 2 × torpedoes, or mines, or depth bombs.

HAZE   *1992, Bulgarian Navy*

CORVETTES

1 TARANTUL II CLASS

MULNIYA 101

Displacement, tons: 385 standard; 455 full load
Dimensions, feet (metres): 184.1 × 37.7 × 8.2 *(56.1 × 11.5 × 2.5)*
Main machinery: COGOG; 2 Nikolayev Type DR 77 gas-turbines; 16 016 hp(m) *(11.77 MW)* sustained; 2 Nikolayev Type DR 76 gas-turbines with reversible gearboxes; 4993 hp(m) *(3.67 MW)* sustained; 2 shafts
Speed, knots: 36 on 4 turbines. **Range, miles:** 400 at 36 kts; 2000 at 20 kts
Complement: 34 (5 officers)

Missiles: SSM: 4 SS-N-2C Styx (2 twin) launchers; active radar or IR homing to 83 km *(45 nm)* at 0.9 Mach; warhead 513 kg; sea-skimmer at end of run.
SAM: SA-N-5 Grail quad launcher; manual aiming; IR homing to 6 km *(3.2 nm)* at 1.5 Mach; altitude to 2500 m *(8000 ft)*; warhead 1.5 kg.
Guns: 1—3 in *(76 mm)*/60; 85° elevation; 120 rounds/minute to 7 km *(3.8 nm)*; weight of shell 7 kg.
2—30 mm/65; 6 barrels per mounting; 3000 rounds/minute to 2 km.
Countermeasures: Decoys: 2—16-barrelled chaff launchers.
ESM: 2 receivers.
Fire control: Hood Wink optronic director.
Radars: Air/surface search: Plank Shave (also for missile control); E band.
Navigation: Spin Trough; I band.
Fire control: Bass Tilt; H/I band.
IFF: Square Head. High Pole.

Programmes: Built at Volodarski, Rybinsk. Transferred from USSR in December 1989. Name means Thunderbolt.

MULNIYA   *4/1993, C D Yaylali*

4 POTI CLASS

LETYASHTI 41   **BDITELNI** 42   **BEZSTRASHNI** 43   **KHRABRI** 44

Displacement, tons: 545 full load
Dimensions, feet (metres): 196.8 × 26.2 × 6.6 *(60 × 8 × 2)*
Main machinery: CODAG; 2 gas-turbines; 30 000 hp(m) *(22.4 MW)*; 2 Type M 503A diesels; 5350 hp(m) *(3.91 MW)* sustained; 2 shafts
Speed, knots: 32. **Range, miles:** 3000 at 18 kts; 500 at 37 kts
Complement: 80

Guns: 2 USSR 57 mm/80 (twin); 85° elevation; 120 rounds/minute to 6 km *(3 nm)*; weight of shell 2.8 kg.
Torpedoes: 4—16 in *(406 mm)* tubes. Soviet Type 40; anti-submarine; active/passive homing up to 15 km *(8 nm)* at up to 40 kts; warhead 100-150 kg.
A/S mortars: 2 RBU 6000 12-tubed trainable launchers; automatic loading; range 6000 m; warhead 31 kg.
Countermeasures: ESM: Watch Dog; radar warning.
Radars: Air search: Strut Curve; F band; range 110 km *(60 nm)* for 2 m² target.
Surface search: Don; I band.
Fire control: Muff Cob; G/H band.
IFF: Square Head. High Pole.
Sonars: Hull-mounted; active search and attack; high frequency.

Programmes: Series built at Zelenodolsk between 1961 and 1968. Three transferred from USSR December 1975, the fourth at the end of 1986 and the last two in 1990. Two deleted in 1993. Names: 41 Flying, 42 Vigilant, 43 Fearless and 44 Gallant.

KHRABRI   *7/1992*

2 PAUK I CLASS

RESHITELNI 13   **BODRI** 14

Displacement, tons: 440 full load
Dimensions, feet (metres): 195.2 × 33.5 × 10.8 *(59.5 × 10.2 × 3.3)*
Main machinery: 2 Type M 507 diesels; 14 400 hp(m) *(10.6 MW)* sustained; 2 shafts
Speed, knots: 32. **Range, miles:** 2200 at 18 kts
Complement: 32

Missiles: SAM: SA-N-5 Grail quad launcher; manual aiming; IR homing to 6 km *(3.2 nm)* at 1.5 Mach; altitude to 2500 m *(8000 ft)*; warhead 1.5 kg; 8 missiles.
Guns: 1—3 in *(76 mm)*/60; 85° elevation; 120 rounds/minute to 7 km *(3.8 nm)*; weight of shell 7 kg.
1—30 mm/65; 6 barrels; 3000 rounds/minute combined to 2 km.
Torpedoes: 4—16 in *(406 mm)* tubes. Type 40; anti-submarine; active/passive homing up to 15 km *(8 nm)* at up to 40 kts; warhead 100-150 kg.
A/S mortars: 2 RBU 1200 5-tubed fixed; range 1200 m; warhead 34 kg.
Depth charges: 2 racks (12).
Countermeasures: Decoys: 2—16-barrelled chaff launchers.
ESM: Passive receivers.
Radars: Air/surface search: Peel Cone; E band.
Surface search: Spin Trough; I band.
Fire control: Bass Tilt; H/I band.
Sonars: Rat Tail VDS (mounted on transom); active attack; high frequency.

Programmes: *Reshitelni* transferred from USSR in September 1989, *Bodri* in December 1990.

BODRI   *1992, S S Breyer*

PATROL FORCES

Notes: (1) The Danube Flotilla was disbanded in 1992 but may be resurrected again in due course. (2) Customs craft operate on the Danube to enforce UN sanctions against Serbia. Vessels include three Boston Whalers donated by the US and RIBs given by the UK in 1992/93.

10 ZHUK (TYPE 1400M) CLASS (COASTAL PATROL CRAFT)

511-513   515   521-523   531-533

Displacement, tons: 39 full load
Dimensions, feet (metres): 78.7 × 16.4 × 3.9 *(24 × 5 × 1.2)*
Main machinery: 2 Type M 401B diesels; 2200 hp(m) *(1.6 MW)* sustained; 2 shafts
Speed, knots: 30. **Range, miles:** 1100 at 15 kts
Complement: 11 (3 officers)
Guns: 4 USSR 14.5 mm (2 twin) MGs.
Radars: Surface search: Spin Trough; I band.

Comment: Transferred from USSR 1980-81. Belong to the Border Police under the Minister of the Interior.

ZHUKs 522 and 523   *7/1992*

4 OSA II and 2 OSA I (TYPE 205) CLASSES
(FAST ATTACK CRAFT—MISSILE)

URAGON 102	**GRUM** 104	**TYPFOON** 112 (Osa I)
BURYA 103 (Osa I)	**SVETKAVITSA** 111	**SMERCH** 113

Displacement, tons: 245 full load; 210 (Osa I)
Dimensions, feet (metres): 126.6 × 24.9 × 8.8 *(38.6 × 7.6 × 2.7)*
Main machinery: 3 Type M 504 (M 503 (Osa I)) diesels; 10 800 hp(m) *(7.94 MW)* sustained; 3 shafts
Speed, knots: 37. **Range, miles:** 500 at 35 kts
Complement: 30
Missiles: SSM: 4 SS-N-2B Styx; active radar/IR homing to 46 km *(25 nm)* at 0.9 Mach; warhead 513 kg.
Guns: 4 USSR 30 mm/65 (2 twin); 85° elevation; 500 rounds/minute to 5 km *(2.7 nm)*; weight of shell 0.54 kg. SS-N-2A in Osa I.
Radars: Surface search/fire-control: Square Tie; I band.
Fire control: Drum Tilt; H/I band.
IFF: High Pole. Square Head.

Comment: Details given are for the Osa IIs built between 1965 and 1970, and transferred from USSR between 1977 and 1982. Both Osa Is transferred in 1971 and have survived longer than expected. Names: 102 Hurricane, 103 Storm, 104 Thunder, 111 Lightning, 112 Typhoon and 113 Tornado.

GRUM   *1993, Alexander Mladenov*

MINE WARFARE FORCES

Note: Six Vydra class (see *Amphibious Forces*) converted to minelayers in 1992/93.

4 SONYA (TYPE 12650) CLASS (MINESWEEPERS—COASTAL)

BRIZ 61   **SHKVAL** 62   **PPIBOY** 63   **SHTORM** 64

Displacement, tons: 450 full load
Dimensions, feet (metres): 157.4 × 28.9 × 6.6 *(48 × 8.8 × 2)*
Main machinery: 2 Kolomna Type 9-D-8 diesels; 2000 hp(m) *(1.47 MW)* sustained; 2 shafts
Speed, knots: 15. **Range, miles:** 1500 at 14 kts
Complement: 43
Guns: 2 USSR 30 mm/65 (twin); 85° elevation; 500 rounds/minute to 5 km *(2.7 nm)*; weight of shell 0.54 kg.
2 USSR 25 mm/60 (twin); 85° elevation; 270 rounds/minute to 3 km *(1.6 nm)* anti-aircraft; weight of shell 0.34 kg.
Mines: 5.
Radars: Surface search/navigation: Don 2; I band.
IFF: Two Square Head. High Pole B.

Comment: Wooden hulled ships transferred from USSR in 1981-84. Based at Atiya.

BRIZ   *1984*

4 VANYA (TYPE 257D) CLASS (MINESWEEPERS—COASTAL)

ISKAR 31   **ZIBAR** 32   **DOBROTICH** 33   **EVSTATI VINAROV** 34

Displacement, tons: 260 full load
Dimensions, feet (metres): 131.2 × 23.9 × 5.9 *(40 × 7.3 × 1.8)*
Main machinery: 2 Kolomna Type 9-D-8 diesels; 2000 hp(m) *(1.47 MW)* sustained; 2 shafts
Speed, knots: 16. **Range, miles:** 2400 at 10 kts
Complement: 30
Guns: 2 USSR 30 mm/65 (twin); 85° elevation; 500 rounds/minute to 5 km *(2.7 nm)*; weight of shell 0.54 kg.
Mines: Can carry 8.
Radars: Surface search: Don 2; I band.

Comment: Built 1961 to 1973. Transferred from the USSR—two in 1970, two in 1971 and two in 1985. Can act as minehunters. Two deleted in 1992.

VANYA class (old number)   *1991, S S Breyer*

4 YEVGENYA (TYPE 1258) CLASS (MINESWEEPERS—INSHORE)

65   66   67   68

Displacement, tons: 77 standard; 90 full load
Dimensions, feet (metres): 80.4 × 18 × 4.6 *(24.5 × 5.5 × 1.4)*
Main machinery: 2 Type 3-D-12 diesels; 600 hp(m) *(440 kW)* sustained; 2 shafts
Speed, knots: 11. **Range, miles:** 300 at 10 kts
Complement: 10
Guns: 2—14.5 mm MGs.
Radars: Navigation: Spin Trough; I band.
IFF: High Pole.

Comment: GRP hulls built at Kolpino. Transferred from USSR 1977.

YEVGENYA 65-68   *7/1992*

5 OLYA (TYPE 1259) CLASS (MINESWEEPERS—INSHORE)

51   52   53   54   55

Displacement, tons: 64 full load
Dimensions, feet (metres): 84.6 × 14.9 × 3.3 *(25.8 × 4.5 × 1)*
Main machinery: 2 Type 3D 6S11/235 diesels; 471 hp(m) *(346 kW)* sustained; 2 shafts
Speed, knots: 12. **Range (miles):** 300 at 10 kts
Complement: 15
Guns: 2—12.7 mm MGs (twin).
Radars: Navigation: Pechora; I band.

Comment: Built between 1988 and 1992 in Bulgaria to the Russian Olya design. Minesweeping equipment includes AT-6, SZMT-1 and 3 PKT-2 systems.

OLYA   *1992, Bulgarian Navy*

2 PO 2 (501) CLASS (MINESWEEPERS—INSHORE)

57   58

Displacement, tons: 56 full load
Dimensions, feet (metres): 70.5 × 11.5 × 3.3 *(21.5 × 3.5 × 1)*
Main machinery: 1 Type 3-D-12 diesel; 300 hp(m) *(220 kW)* sustained; 2 shafts
Speed, knots: 12
Complement: 8

Comment: Built in Bulgaria. First units completed in early 1950s and last in early 1960s. Originally a class of 24 and these two are the last to survive into 1994. Occasionally carry a 12.7 mm MG.

AMPHIBIOUS FORCES

2 POLNOCHNY A (TYPE 770) CLASS

SIRIUS (ex-*Ivan Zagubanski*) 701   **ANTARES** 702

Displacement, tons: 750 standard; 800 full load
Dimensions, feet (metres): 239.5 × 27.9 × 5.8 *(73 × 8.5 × 1.8)*
Main machinery: 2 Kolomna Type 40-D diesels; 4400 hp(m) *(3.2 MW)* sustained; 2 shafts
Speed, knots: 19. **Range, miles:** 1000 at 18 kts
Complement: 40
Military lift: 350 tons including 6 tanks; 180 troops
Guns: 2 USSR 30 mm (twin). 2—140 mm 18-barrelled rocket launchers.
Radars: Navigation: Spin Trough; I band.

Comment: Built 1963 to 1968. Transferred from USSR 1986/87. Not fitted either with the SA-N-5 Grail SAM system or with Drum Tilt fire-control radars. Plans to convert them to minelayers have been shelved and both are now used as transports.

SIRIUS   *9/1989, S S Breyer*

19 VYDRA (TYPE 106K) CLASS

601-613   703-707   712

Displacement, tons: 425 standard; 550 full load
Dimensions, feet (metres): 179.7 × 25.3 × 6.6 *(54.8 × 7.7 × 2)*
Main machinery: 2 Type 3-D-12 diesels; 600 hp(m) *(440 kW)* sustained; 2 shafts
Speed, knots: 12. **Range, miles:** 2500 at 10 kts
Complement: 20
Military lift: 200 tons or 100 troops or 3 MBTs
Radars: Navigation: Spin Trough; I band.
IFF: High Pole.

Comment: Built 1963 to 1969. Ten transferred from the USSR in 1970, the remainder built in Bulgaria between 1974 and 1978. In 1992/93 *703-707* and *712* converted to be used as mine-layers. Four deleted in 1993.

VYDRA 705   *11/1989, S S Breyer*

SURVEY SHIPS

1 MOMA (TYPE 861) CLASS (AGS)

ADMIRAL BRANIMIR ORMANOV 401

Displacement, tons: 1580 full load
Dimensions, feet (metres): 240.5 × 36.8 × 12.8 *(73.3 × 11.2 × 3.9)*
Main machinery: 2 Zgoda-Sulzer 6TD48 diesels; 3300 hp(m) *(2.43 MW)* sustained; 2 shafts
Speed, knots: 17. **Range, miles:** 9000 at 12 kts
Complement: 37 (5 officers)
Radars: Navigation: Two Don-2; I band.

Comment: Built at Northern Shipyard, Gdansk, Poland in 1977.

MOMA AGS (Russian number)   *1990, G Jacobs*

2 COASTAL SURVEY VESSELS

231   331

Displacement, tons: 114 full load
Dimensions, feet (metres): 87.6 × 19 × 4.9 *(26.7 × 5.8 × 1.5)*
Main machinery: 2 Type 3-D-12 diesels; 600 hp(m) *(440 kW)* sustained; 2 shafts
Speed, knots: 12. **Range, miles:** 600 at 10 kts
Complement: 9 (2 officers)

Comment: Built in Bulgaria in 1986 and 1988 respectively. Can carry 2 tons of equipment.

231   *1991, S S Breyer*

TRAINING SHIP

1 T 43 CLASS

N I VAPTSAROV 421

Displacement, tons: 500 standard; 580 full load
Dimensions, feet (metres): 190.2 × 27.6 × 6.9 *(58 × 8.4 × 2.1)*
Main machinery: 2 Kolomna Type 9-D-8 diesels; 2000 hp(m) *(1.47 MW)* sustained; 2 shafts
Speed, knots: 14. **Range, miles:** 3000 at 10 kts
Complement: 65
Guns: 2 USSR 37 mm/63 (twin); 80° elevation; 160 rounds/minute to 9 km *(5 nm)*; weight of shell 0.7 kg.
4—12.7 mm (2 twin) MGs.
Mines: Can carry 16.
Radars: Surface search: Ball End; E/F band.
Navigation: Neptun; I band.

Comment: Class built 1948 to 1957. The survivor of three transferred from the USSR in 1953, this is now the only short-hulled, low bridge, tripod mast T 43 in commission. Converted to a training ship in 1986.

N I VAPTSAROV   *1992, Bulgarian Navy*

AUXILIARIES

2 SUPPORT TANKERS (TYPE 102)

DIMITR A DIMITROV (ex-*Mesar*, ex-*Anlene*) 202   ATIYA 302

Displacement, tons: 3240 full load
Dimensions, feet (metres): 319.8 × 45.6 × 16.4 *(97.5 × 13.9 × 5)*
Main machinery: 2 diesels; 12 000 hp(m) *(8.82 MW)*; 2 shafts
Speed, knots: 18. **Range, miles:** 12 000 at 15 kts
Complement: 32
Cargo capacity: 1593 tons
Guns: 4 USSR 30 mm/65 (2 twin).

Comment: Both built in Bulgaria in 1979 and 1987 respectively. Abeam fuelling to port and astern fuelling. Mount 1.5 ton crane amidships. Also carry dry stores.

DIMITR A DIMITROV   *7/1992*

ATIYA   *7/1992*

1 DIVING TENDER (TYPE 245)

223

Displacement, tons: 112 full load
Dimensions, feet (metres): 91.5 × 17.1 × 7.2 (27.9 × 5.2 × 2.2)
Main machinery: Diesel-electric; 2 MCK 83-4 diesel generators; 1 motor; 300 hp(m) (220 kW); 1 shaft
Speed, knots: 10. **Range, miles:** 400 at 10 kts
Complement: 6 + 7 divers

Comment: Built in Bulgaria in mid-1980s. A twin 12.7 mm MG can be fitted. Capable of bell diving to 60 m.

DIVING TENDER (model)   *1992, Bulgarian Navy*

1 SALVAGE TUG

JUPITER 221

Displacement, tons: 792 full load
Dimensions, feet (metres): 146.6 × 35.1 × 12.7 (44.7 × 10.7 × 3.9)
Main machinery: 2—12 KVD 21 diesels; 1760 hp(m) (1.3 MW); 2 shafts
Speed, knots: 12.5. **Range, miles:** 3000 at 12 kts
Complement: 39 (6 officers)
Guns: 4—25 mm/70 (2 twin) automatic.

Comment: Bollard pull, 16 tons. Former DDR Type 700.

1 BEREZA (TYPE 130) CLASS

KAPITAN DIMITER DOBREV 206

Displacement, tons: 2051 full load
Dimensions, feet (metres): 228 × 45.3 × 13.1 (69.5 × 13.8 × 4)
Main machinery: 2 Zgoda-Sulzer 8 AL 25/30 diesels; 2925 hp(m) (2.16 MW) sustained; 2 shafts; cp props
Speed, knots: 13. **Range, miles:** 1000 at 13 kts
Complement: 48
Radars: Navigation: Kivach; I band.

Comment: New construction built in Poland and transferred July 1988. Used as a degaussing ship. Fitted with an NBC citadel and upper deck wash-down system. The ship has three laboratories.

KAPITAN DIMITER DOBREV   *4/1993, C D Yaylali*

5 AUXILIARIES

204   205   222   224   321

Comment: *204* is a water barge; *205* a torpedo recovery vessel; *222* a tug; *224* and *321* firefighting vessels.

BURMA

General

The title used by the current government is Myanmar. The unique characteristic of this Navy is that no ship ever seems to be scrapped. Although some of the hulls are very old, operating in predominantly fresh water has kept corrosion to within containable limits.

Headquarters' Appointment

Vice-Chief of Staff, Defence Services (Navy):
   Vice Admiral Than Nyunt
Chief of Naval Staff:
   Rear Admiral Tin Aye

Bases

Bassein, Mergui, Moulmein, Rangoon, Seikyi, Sittwe (Akyab), Sinmalaik, Hanggyi Island.

Personnel

(a) 1994: 12 600
(b) Voluntary service

Strength of the Fleet

Type	Active	Building
Corvettes	4	—
Offshore Patrol Vessels	3	—
Fast Attack Craft (Gun)	—	2
Coastal Patrol Craft	28	—
River Patrol Craft and Gunboats	64	—
Amphibious Vessels	15	—
Survey Vessels	3	—

Mercantile Marine

Lloyd's Register of Shipping:
   131 vessels of 710 679 tons gross

CORVETTES

Note: (1) All Corvettes come under the Major War Vessels Command.
(2) There are plans to augment the four corvettes by two ex-Chinese frigates possibly of the Jiangnan class.

1 PCE 827 CLASS

Name	No	Builders	Commissioned
YAN TAING AUNG	41	Willamette Iron & Steel Co,	10 Aug 1943
(ex-USS *Farmington* PCE 894)		Portland, Oregon	

Displacement, tons: 640 standard; 903 full load
Dimensions, feet (metres): 184 × 33 × 9.5 (56 × 10.1 × 2.9)
Main machinery: 2 GM 12-567A diesels; 1800 hp (1.34 MW); 2 shafts
Speed, knots: 15
Complement: 72

Guns: 1 US 3 in (76 mm)/50 Mk 26; 85° elevation; 20 rounds/minute to 12 km (6.6 nm); weight of shell 6 kg.
   2 Bofors 40 mm/60. 8 Oerlikon 20 mm (4 twin).
A/S mortars: 1 Hedgehog Mk 10; 24 rockets; manual loading; range 250 m; warhead 13.6 kg.
Depth charges: 2 racks. 2 Mk 6 projectors; range 160 m; warhead 150 kg.
Radars: Surface search: Raytheon SPS 5; G/H band; range 37 km (20 nm).
Sonars: RCA QCU-2; hull-mounted; active attack; high frequency.

Programmes: Laid down on 7 December 1942 and launched on 15 May 1943. Transferred from US on 18 June 1965.
Operational: In poor condition but still operational.

YAN TAING AUNG   *1987*

1 ADMIRABLE CLASS

Name	No	Builders	Commissioned
YAN GYI AUNG	42	Willamette Iron & Steel Co,	1944
(ex-USS *Creddock* MSF 356)		Portland, Oregon	

Displacement, tons: 650 standard; 945 full load
Dimensions, feet (metres): 184.5 × 33 × 9.8 *(56.2 × 10.1 × 3)*
Main machinery: 2 Busch-Sulzer BS-539 diesels; 1500 hp(m) *(1.1 MW)*; 2 shafts
Speed, knots: 14.8. **Range, miles:** 4300 at 10 kts
Complement: 73

Guns: 1 US 3 in *(76 mm)*/50 Mk 26; 85° elevation; 20 rounds/minute to 12 km *(6.6 nm)*; weight of shell 6 kg.
4 Bofors 40 mm/60 (2 twin). 4 Oerlikon 20 mm (2 twin).
A/S mortars: 1 Hedgehog Mk 10; 24 rockets; manual loading; range 250 m; warhead 13.6 kg.
Depth charges: 2 racks. 2 Mk 6 projectors; range 160 m; warhead 150 kg.
Radars: Surface search: Raytheon SPS 5; G/H band; range 37 km *(20 nm)*.
Sonars: RCA QCU-2; hull-mounted; active attack; high frequency.

Programmes: Laid down on 10 November 1943 and launched on 22 July 1944. Transferred from US at San Diego on 31 March 1967.
Operational: Minesweeping gear removed. Fully operational.

YAN GYI AUNG   *12/1991*

2 NAWARAT CLASS

Name	No	Builders	Commissioned
NAWARAT	501	Government Dockyard, Dawbon, Rangoon	26 Apr 1960
NAGAKYAY	502	Government Dockyard, Dawbon, Rangoon	3 Dec 1960

Displacement, tons: 400 standard; 450 full load
Dimensions, feet (metres): 163 × 26.8 × 5.8 *(49.7 × 8.2 × 1.8)*
Main machinery: 2 Paxman Ricardo diesels; 1160 hp(m) *(865 kW)*; 2 shafts
Speed, knots: 12
Complement: 43
Guns: 1—25 pdr (88 mm) QF. 1 Bofors 40 mm/60.

Comment: In spite of their size, these vessels are used mostly for river patrols and are in good condition. Armament reduced in 1989.

NAWARAT

PATROL FORCES

3 OSPREY CLASS (OFFSHORE PATROL VESSELS)

Name	No	Builders	Commissioned
INDAW	FV 55	Frederikshavn Dockyard	30 May 1980
INMA	FV 56	Frederikshavn Dockyard	25 Mar 1982
INYA	FV 57	Frederikshavn Dockyard	25 Mar 1982

Displacement, tons: 385 standard; 505 full load
Dimensions, feet (metres): 164 × 34.5 × 9 *(50 × 10.5 × 2.8)*
Main machinery: 2 Burmeister and Wain Alpha diesels; 4640 hp(m) *(3.4 MW)*; 2 shafts
Speed, knots: 20. **Range, miles:** 4500 at 16 kts
Complement: 20 (5 officers) (accommodation for 35)
Guns: 1 Bofors 40 mm/60. 2 Oerlikon 20 mm.

Comment: Operated by Burmese Navy for the People's Pearl and Fishery Department. Helicopter deck with hangar in *Indaw*. Carry David Still craft capable of 25 kts.

INYA   *1990*

0 + 2 FAST ATTACK CRAFT (GUN)

Displacement, tons: 213 full load
Dimensions, feet (metres): 147.3 × 23 × 8.2 *(45 × 7 × 2.5)*
Main machinery: 2 Mercedes Benz diesels; 2 shafts
Speed, knots: 30+
Complement: 34 (7 officers)
Guns: 2 Bofors 40 mm/60.
Radars: Surface search: I band.

Comment: Under construction at the Naval Engineering Depot, Rangoon in 1991 for completion in 1994.

FAC(G)   *(not to scale), Ian Sturton*

10 HAINAN (TYPE 037) CLASS (COASTAL PATROL CRAFT)

Name	No	Name	No	Name	No
YAN SIT AUNG	43	YAN KHWIN AUNG	46	YAN PAING AUNG	447
YAN MYAT AUNG	44	YAN MIN AUNG	47	YAN WIN AUNG	448
YAN NYEIN AUNG	45	YAN YE AUNG	48	YAN AYE AUNG	449
				YAN ZWE AUNG	450

Displacement, tons: 375 standard; 392 full load
Dimensions, feet (metres): 192.8 × 23.6 × 7.2 *(58.8 × 7.2 × 2.2)*
Main machinery: 4 PCR/Kolomna Type 9-D-8 diesels; 4000 hp(m) *(2.94 MW)* sustained; 4 shafts
Speed, knots: 30.5. **Range, miles:** 1300 at 15 kts
Complement: 69
Guns: 4 China 57 mm/70 (2 twin); dual purpose; 120 rounds/minute to 12 km *(6.5 nm)*; weight of shell 6.31 kg.
4 USSR 25 mm/60 (2 twin); 85° elevation; 270 rounds/minute to 3 km *(1.6 nm)* anti-aircraft; weight of shell 0.34 kg.
A/S mortars: 4 RBU 1200 5-tubed fixed launchers; range 1200 m; warhead 34 kg.
Depth charges: 2 BMB-2 projectors; 2 racks.
Mines: Rails fitted.
Radars: Surface search: Pot Head; I band.
Navigation: Raytheon Pathfinder; I band.
IFF: High Pole.
Sonars: Hull-mounted; active search and attack; high frequency.

Comment: First six delivered from China in January 1991, four more in mid-1993. Later variant of this class with tripod masts.

YAN SIT AUNG   *1991*

YAN WIN AUNG   *9/1993*

3 PB 90 CLASS (COASTAL PATROL CRAFT)

424   425   426

Displacement, tons: 80 standard
Dimensions, feet (metres): 89.9 × 21.5 × 7.2 *(27.4 × 6.6 × 2.2)*
Main machinery: 3 diesels; 4290 hp(m) *(3.15 MW)*; 3 shafts
Speed, knots: 32. **Range, miles:** 400 at 25 kts
Complement: 17
Guns: 8—20 mm M75 (two quad). 2—128 mm launchers for illuminants.
Radars: Navigation: I band.

Comment: Built by Brodotechnika, Yugoslavia for an African country and completed in 1986-87. Laid up when the sale did not go through and shipped to Burma arriving in October 1990. These vessels are proving to be unsatisfactory in service.

PB 90 (old number)   *1990, Yugoslav FDSP*

6 BURMA PGM TYPE (COASTAL PATROL CRAFT)

PGM 412-PGM 415   **THIHAYARZAR I and II**

Displacement, tons: 128 full load
Dimensions, feet (metres): 110 × 22 × 6.5 *(33.5 × 6.7 × 2)*
Main machinery: 2 Deutz SBA16MB816 LLKR diesels; 2720 hp(m) *(2 MW)*; 2 shafts
Speed, knots: 16. Range, miles: 1400 at 14 kts
Complement: 17
Guns: 2 Bofors 40 mm/60.

Comment: First two completed 1983. Two more built in Burma Naval Dockyard. Two more craft
with identical dimensions and named *Thihayarzar I* and *II* were delivered by Myanma Shipyard to
the Customs on 27 June 1993. Both craft are armed and may be taken over by the Navy.

PGM 415   *4/1993*

6 PGM TYPE (COASTAL PATROL CRAFT)

PGM 401-PGM 406

Displacement, tons: 141 full load
Dimensions, feet (metres): 101 × 21.1 × 7.5 *(30.8 × 6.4 × 2.3)*
Main machinery: 8 GM 6-71 diesels; 1392 hp *(1.04 MW)* sustained; 2 shafts
Speed, knots: 17. Range, miles: 1000 at 15 kts
Complement: 17
Guns: 1 Bofors 40 mm/60. 2 Oerlikon 20 mm (twin). 2—12.7 mm MGs.
Radars: Navigation: Raytheon 1500 (PGM 405-406).
    EDO 320 (PGM 401-404); I/J band.

Comment: Built by the Marinette Marine Corporation, USA in 1959-61. Ex-US PGM 43-46, 51 and
52 respectively.

PGM 406   *3/1992*

3 SWIFT TYPE PGM (COASTAL PATROL CRAFT)

421   422   423

Displacement, tons: 111 full load
Dimensions, feet (metres): 103.3 × 23.8 × 6.9 *(31.5 × 7.2 × 3.1)*
Main machinery: 2 MTU 12V 331 TC81 diesels; 2450 hp(m) *(1.8 MW)* sustained; 2 shafts
Speed, knots: 27. Range, miles: 1800 at 18 kts
Complement: 25
Guns: 2 Bofors 40 mm. 2 Oerlikon 20 mm. 2—12.7 mm MGs.

Comment: Swiftships construction completed in 1979. Acquired 1980 through Vosper,
Singapore.

PGM 421   *6/1991*

2 IMPROVED Y 301 CLASS (RIVER GUNBOATS)

Y 311   Y 312

Displacement, tons: 250 full load
Dimensions, feet (metres): 121.4 × 24 × 3.9 *(37 × 7.3 × 1.2)*
Main machinery: 2 MTU MB diesels; 1000 hp(m) *(735 kW)*; 2 shafts
Speed, knots: 12
Complement: 37
Guns: 2 Bofors 40 mm. 4 Oerlikon 20 mm.

Comment: Built at Simmilak in 1969 and based on similar Yugoslav craft.

Y 311   *6/1993*

10 Y 301 CLASS (RIVER GUNBOATS)

Y 301-Y 310

Displacement, tons: 120 full load
Dimensions, feet (metres): 104.8 × 24 × 3 *(32 × 7.3 × 0.9)*
Main machinery: 2 MTU MB diesels; 1000 hp(m) *(735 kW)*; 2 shafts
Speed, knots: 13
Complement: 29
Guns: 2 Bofors 40 mm/60 or 1 Bofors 40 mm/60 and 1—2 pdr.

Comment: All of these boats were completed in 1958 at the Uljanik Shipyard, Pula, Yugoslavia.

Y 304   *1991*

4 RIVER GUNBOATS (Ex-TRANSPORTS)

SAGU   SEINDA   SHWETHIDA   SINMIN

Displacement, tons: 98 full load
Dimensions, feet (metres): 94.5 × 22 × 4.5 *(28.8 × 6.7 × 1.4)*
Main machinery: 1 Crossley ERL 6 cyl diesel; 160 hp *(119 kW)*; 1 shaft
Speed, knots: 12
Complement: 32
Guns: 1—40 mm/60 *(Sagu)*. 1—20 mm (3 in *Sagu*).

Comment: Built in mid-1950s. *Sinmin, Seinda* and *Shwethida* have a roofed-in upper deck with a
20 mm gun forward of the funnel. *Sagu* has an open upper deck aft of the funnel but with a
40 mm gun forward and mountings for 20 mm aft on the upper deck and midships either side on
the lower deck. Four other ships of the same type are probably unarmed and are listed under
Miscellaneous.

SINMIN   *1989*

SAGU   *1990*

2 CGC TYPE (RIVER GUNBOATS)

MGB 102   MGB 110

Displacement, tons: 49 standard; 66 full load
Dimensions, feet (metres): 83 × 16 × 5.5 (25.3 × 4.9 × 1.7)
Main machinery: 4 GM diesels; 800 hp (596 kW); 2 shafts
Speed, knots: 11
Complement: 16
Guns: 1 Bofors 40 mm. 1 Oerlikon 20 mm.

Comment: Ex-USCG type cutters with new hulls built in Burma. Completed in 1960.

MGB 110

9 RIVER PATROL CRAFT

RPC 11   12   13   14   15   + 4

Displacement, tons: 37 full load
Dimensions, feet (metres): 50 × 14 × 3.5 (15.2 × 4.3 × 1.1)
Main machinery: 2 Thornycroft RZ 6 diesels; 250 hp (186 kW); 2 shafts
Speed, knots: 10. **Range, miles:** 400 at 8 kts
Complement: 8
Guns: 1 Oerlikon 20 mm or 2—12.7 mm MGs (twin). 1—12.7 mm MG.

Comment: Built by the Naval Engineering Depot, Rangoon. First five in mid-1980s; second batch of a modified design in 1990/91.

6 RIVER PATROL CRAFT

PBR 211-216

Displacement, tons: 9 full load
Dimensions, feet (metres): 32 × 11 × 2.6 (9.8 × 3.4 × 0.8)
Main machinery: 2 GM 6V-53 diesels; 348 hp (260 kW) sustained; 2 waterjets
Speed, knots: 25. **Range, miles:** 180 at 20 kts
Complement: 4 or 5
Guns: 2—12.7 mm (twin, fwd) MGs. 1—7.9 mm LMG (aft).

Comment: Acquired in 1978. Built by Uniflite, Washington.

PBR 211   1987

25 RIVER PATROL LAUNCHES

001-025

Comment: Small craft, 52 ft (15.8 m) long, acquired from Yugoslavia in 1965.

6 CARPENTARIA CLASS (RIVER PATROL CRAFT)

112-117

Displacement, tons: 26 full load
Dimensions, feet (metres): 51.5 × 15.7 × 4.3 (15.7 × 4.8 × 1.3)
Main machinery: 2 diesels; 1360 hp (1.01 MW); 2 shafts
Speed, knots: 29. **Range, miles:** 950 at 18 kts
Complement: 10
Guns: 1 Oerlikon 20 mm.

Comment: Built by De Havilland Marine, Sydney. First two delivered 1979, remainder in 1980. Similar to craft built for Indonesia and South Africa.

CARPENTARIA 113   1991

SHIPBORNE AIRCRAFT

Numbers/Type: 10 Aerospatiale SA 316B Alouette III.
Operational speed: 113 kts (210 km/h).
Service ceiling: 10 500 ft (3200 m).
Range: 290 nm (540 km).
Role/Weapon systems: Embarked in offshore patrol craft for support duties. Sensors: None. Weapons: 7.62 mm machine gun mountings.

LAND-BASED MARITIME AIRCRAFT

Numbers/Type: 10 Kawasaki-Bell 47G-3.
Operational speed: 74 kts (137 km/h).
Service ceiling: 13 200 ft (4023 m).
Range: 261 nm (483 km).
Role/Weapon systems: Light liaison and utility tasks. Sensors: None. Weapons: Unarmed, but a single 7.62 mm mounting has been supplied.

Numbers/Type: 3 Fokker F27M.
Operational speed: 250 kts (463 km/h).
Service ceiling: 25 000 ft (7620 m).
Range: 2700 nm (5000 km).
Role/Weapon systems: Long-range patrol of coastlines. Sensors: Bendix weather radar, wingtip searchlight. Weapons: Unarmed.

AMPHIBIOUS FORCES

Note: As well as the vessels listed below there are at least three Army Landing Craft (001-003) of about 75 tons.

LANDING CRAFT 001(2)   7/1992

4 LCUs

AIYAR MAI 604   **AIYAR MINTHAMEE** 606
AIYAR MAUNG 605   **AIYAR MINTHAR** 607

Displacement, tons: 250 full load
Dimensions, feet (metres): 125.6 × 29.8 × 4.6 (38.3 × 9.1 × 1.4)
Main machinery: 2 diesels; 600 hp(m) (441 kW); 2 shafts
Speed, knots: 10
Complement: 10
Military lift: 100 tons

Comment: All built at Yokohama in 1969.

AIYAR MAUNG   1991

1 LCU

AIYAR LULIN 603

Displacement, tons: 360 full load
Dimensions, feet (metres): 119 × 34 × 6 (36.3 × 10.4 × 1.8)
Main machinery: 2 diesels; 600 hp (448 kW); 2 shafts
Speed, knots: 10
Complement: 14
Military lift: 168 tons
Guns: 1—12.7 mm MG.

Comment: Built in Rangoon in 1966.

AIYAR LULIN   1990

10 LCM 3 TYPE

LCM 701-710

Displacement, tons: 52 full load
Dimensions, feet (metres): 50 × 14 × 4 *(15.2 × 4.3 × 1.2)*
Main machinery: 2 Gray Marine 64 HN9 diesels; 330 hp *(246 kW)*; 2 shafts
Speed, knots: 9

Comment: US-built LCM type landing craft. Used as local transports for stores and personnel. Cargo capacity, 30 tons. Guns have been removed.

LCM 710   *1991*

SURVEY SHIPS

Note: Thu Tay Thi means 'survey vessel'.

Name	No	Builders	Commissioned
—	801	Brodogradiliste Tito, Belgrade, Yugoslavia	1965

Displacement, tons: 1059 standard
Dimensions, feet (metres): 204 × 36 × 11.8 *(62.2 × 11 × 3.6)*
Main machinery: 2 MTU 12V 493 TY7 diesels; 2120 hp(m) *(1.62 MW)* sustained; 2 shafts
Speed, knots: 15
Complement: 99 (7 officers)
Guns: 2 Bofors 40 mm/60. 2 Oerlikon 20 mm (twin).

Comment: Has two surveying motor boats. The after gun can be removed to provide a helicopter platform. This ship is sometimes referred to as Thu Tay Thi which means 'survey vessel'.

801   *6/1993*

Name	No	Builders	Commissioned
— (ex-*Changi*)	802	Miho Shipyard, Shimizu	20 June 1973

Displacement, tons: 800 full load
Dimensions, feet (metres): 154.2 × 28.6 × 11.9 *(47 × 8.7 × 3.6)*
Main machinery: 1 Niigata diesel; 1 shaft
Speed, knots: 13
Complement: 45 (5 officers)
Guns: 2 Oerlikon 20 mm.

Comment: A fishery research ship of Singapore origin, arrested on 8 April 1974 and taken into service as a survey vessel in about 1981. Stern trawler type.

802   *3/1992*

807

Displacement, tons: 108 full load
Dimensions, feet (metres): 98.4 × 22.3 × 4.9 *(30 × 6.8 × 1.5)*
Main machinery: 2 diesels; 2 shafts
Speed, knots: 10.
Complement: 34 (2 officers)
Guns: 1—12.7 mm MG.

Comment: Used for river surveys.

807   *1990*

AUXILIARIES

Note: As well as the ships listed below there is a small coastal oil tanker, a harbour tug and several harbour launches and personnel carriers.

1 TRANSPORT VESSEL

Comment: Acquired in 1991. Of unknown origin. Looks like a mini liner, and may be used for survey work.

TRANSPORT VESSEL   *12/1991*

1 TANKER

INTERBUNKER

Displacement, tons: 4000 full load
Dimensions, feet (metres): 180.5 × 78.5 × 9.8 *(55 × 23.9 × 3)*
Main machinery: 2 diesels; 2 shafts
Speed, knots: 15
Complement: 15

Comment: Singapore registered tanker arrested in October 1991 and taken into the Navy.

INTERBUNKER   *12/1991*

1 DIVING SUPPORT VESSEL

YAN LON AUNG 200

Displacement, tons: 536 full load
Dimensions, feet (metres): 179 × 30 × 8 *(54.6 × 9.1 × 2.4)*
Speed, knots: 12
Complement: 88
Guns: 1 Bofors 40 mm/60. 2—12.7 mm MGs.

Comment: Light forces support diving ship acquired from Japan in 1967.

YAN LON AUNG   *7/1993*

4 TRANSPORT VESSELS

SABAN   SETHYA   SHWEPAZUN   SETYAHAT

Displacement, tons: 98 full load
Dimensions, feet (metres): 94.5 × 22 × 4.5 *(28.8 × 6.7 × 1.4)*
Main machinery: 1 Crossley ERL 6 cyl diesel; 160 hp *(119 kW)*; 1 shaft
Speed, knots: 12
Complement: 30

Comment: These are sister ships to the armed gunboats shown under *Patrol Forces.* It is possible that a 20 mm gun may be mounted on some occasions.

SHWEPAZUN   *1991*

1 BUOY TENDER

HSAD DAN

Displacement, tons: 706 full load
Dimensions, feet (metres): 130.6 × 37.1 × 8.9 *(39.8 × 11.3 × 2.7)*
Main machinery: 2 Deutz BA8M816 diesels; 1341 hp(m) *(986 kW)*; 2 shafts
Speed, knots: 10
Complement: 23

Comment: Built by Italthai in 1986. Operated by the Rangoon Port Authority.

HSAD DAN   *5/1992*

1 TRANSPORT VESSEL

PYI DAW AYE

Measurement, tons: 700 dwt
Dimensions, feet (metres): 160 × 27 × 11 *(48.8 × 8.2 × 3.4)*
Main machinery: 2 diesels; 600 hp *(447 kW)*; 2 shafts
Speed, knots: 11
Complement: 12

Comment: Completed in about 1975. Dimensions are approximate. Naval manned.

PYI DAW AYE   *1991*

8 MFVs

511   520-523   901   905   906

Comment: Armed vessels of approximately 200 tons *(901),* 80 tons *(905, 906)* and 50 tons (remainder) with a 12.7 mm MG mounted above the bridge in some.

MFV 906   *8/1993*

PRESIDENTIAL YACHT

YADANABON

Comment: Built in Burma and used for VIP cruises on the Irrawaddy river and in coastal waters. Armed with 2—7.62 mm MGs and manned by the Navy.

PRESIDENT'S YACHT   *1990*

BURUNDI

General	Base	Personnel
There is a paramilitary police force with a Maritime section for use on lakes and rivers.	Bujumbura	200

PATROL FORCES

Note: There are also up to four locally built patrol boats of 11 m with 1—12.7 mm MGs.

4 HUCHUAN CLASS (FAST ATTACK CRAFT)

Displacement, tons: 46 full load
Dimensions, feet (metres): 71.5 × 20.7 × 11.8 (hullborne) *(21.8 × 6.3 × 3.6)*
Main machinery: 3 Type M 50 diesels; 2200 hp(m) *(1.6 MW)* sustained; 2 shafts
Speed, knots: 50 (foilborne). **Range, miles:** 500 at 30 kts
Complement: 16
Guns: 4 China 14.5 mm (2 twin); 85° elevation; 600 rounds/minute to 7 km *(3.8 nm).*
Torpedoes: 2—21 in *(533 mm)* tubes.
Radars: Surface search: I band.

Comment: Transferred from China in 1991. These are probably the newer version with gun mountings forward and aft.

HUCHUAN (Chinese colours)   *2/1993*

CAMBODIA

General

The Marine Royale Khmer was established on 1 March 1954 and became Marine Nationale Khmer (MNK) on 9 October 1970. Originally Cambodia, became known as the Khmer Republic, then The People's Republic of Kampuchea and is now back to being Cambodia again. In 1992 all naval units were under UN command and painted white, but with the UN withdrawal in November 1993 all were repainted grey.

Personnel

1994: 2800 (781 officers) (including Marines)

Bases

Ream (coastal), Phnom Penh (river), Kompongson (civil)

Operational

Coastal Division has nine battalions and the River Division seven battalions.

Mercantile Marine

Lloyd's Register of Shipping:
4 vessels of 5772 tons gross

PATROL FORCES

2 TURYA CLASS (FAST ATTACK CRAFT—HYDROFOIL)

Displacement, tons: 190 standard; 250 full load
Dimensions, feet (metres): 129.9 × 24.9 (41 foils) × 5.9 (13.1 foils) *(39.6 × 7.6 (12.5) × 1.8 (4))*
Main machinery: 3 Type M 504 diesels; 10 800 hp(m) *(7.94 MW)* sustained; 3 shafts
Speed, knots: 14. **Range, miles:** 1450 at 14 kts hull
Complement: 30
Guns: 2—57 mm (twin). 2—25 mm (twin).
Radars: Surface search: Pot Drum; H/I band.
Fire control: Muff Cob; G/H band.
IFF: High Pole B. Square Head.

Comment: Transferred from USSR March 1984 and February 1985 without torpedo tubes and dipping sonars. Foils removed and now used mostly as Floating Barracks. In a poor state of repair but still available for river operations.

TURYAs   *8/1993*

4 MODIFIED STENKA CLASS (TYPE 205P)
(FAST ATTACK CRAFT—PATROL)

1131-1134 (ex-*51-54*)

Displacement, tons: 211 standard; 253 full load
Dimensions, feet (metres): 129.3 × 25.9 × 8.2 *(39.4 × 7.9 × 2.5)*
Main machinery: 3 Type M 517 diesels; 14 100 hp(m) *(10.36 MW)* sustained; 3 shafts
Speed, knots: 37. **Range, miles:** 800 at 24 kts; 500 at 35 kts
Complement: 25 (5 officers)
Guns: 4—30 mm/65 (2 twin) AK 230.
Radars: Surface search: Pot Drum (MR 104); H/I band.
Fire control: Muff Cob; G/H band.
Navigation: MR 220 or Furuno; I band.
IFF: High Pole. Two Square Head.

Comment: Transferred from USSR in November 1987. All are the export model without torpedo tubes and sonar. *1131* used for spares but the other three were operational in late 1993. Numbers were changed for UN operations but changed back again in November 1993.

STENKAs   *11/1993*

2 ZHUK CLASS (TYPE 1400M) (COASTAL PATROL CRAFT)

41   42

Displacement, tons: 39 full load
Dimensions, feet (metres): 78.7 × 16.4 × 3.9 *(24 × 5 × 1.2)*
Main machinery: 2 Type M 401 diesels; 2200 hp(m) *(1.6 MW)* sustained; 2 shafts
Speed, knots: 30. **Range, miles:** 1100 at 15 kts
Complement: 11 (3 officers)
Guns: 4—14.5 mm (2 twin) MGs.
Radars: Surface search: Spin Trough; I band.
Navigation: Furuno; I band.

Comment: Transferred from USSR via Vietnam between 1985 and 1987. Both operational in late 1993.

ZHUKs (in UN colours)   *6/1993*

4 SHMEL CLASS (TYPE 1204) (RIVER PATROL CRAFT)

31-34

Displacement, tons: 77 full load
Dimensions, feet (metres): 90.9 × 14.1 × 3.6 *(27.7 × 4.3 × 1.1)*
Main machinery: 2 Type M 50 diesels; 2200 hp(m) *(1.6 MW)* sustained; 2 shafts
Speed, knots: 25. **Range, miles:** 600 at 12 kts
Complement: 12 (4 officers)
Guns: 1—3 in *(76 mm)*. 2—25 mm (twin). 5—7.62 mm MGs. 1 BP6 rocket launcher.
Mines: 9.
Radars: Spin Trough; I band

Comment: Two transferred from USSR March 1984, two in January 1985. All in poor condition by late 1993.

SHMEL (alongside *Stenka*)   *1992, Ships of the World*

2 PCF CLASS

21   22

Displacement, tons: 30 full load
Dimensions, feet (metres): 47.6 × 14.8 × 4.9 *(14.5 × 4.5 × 1.5)*
Main machinery: 2 GM diesels; 900 hp *(664 kW)*; 2 shafts
Speed, knots: 9
Complement: 7 (2 officers)
Guns: 2 ZPU 1—14.5 mm (twin) MG. 1—75 mm mortar.
Radars: Surface search: Furuno; I band.

Comment: Transferred in 1974. Sole survivors of many and deleted in error some years ago.

11 KANO CLASS

1-11

Displacement, tons: 3.6 full load
Dimensions, feet (metres): 29.9 × 8.5 × 1.6 *(9.1 × 2.6 × 0.5)*
Main machinery: 1 Russian 3A-201C2 diesel; 1 shaft
Speed, knots: 20
Complement: 2
Guns: 1—7.62 mm MG.

Comment: Total of 17 acquired from the USSR. The remaining 11 were all operational in late 1993.

AUXILIARIES

Note: There are also two Ferries used by the River Flotilla.

5 RIVER LANDING CRAFT

63-65   68-69

Displacement, tons: 45 full load
Dimensions, feet (metres): 57.1 × 13.8 × 3.9 *(17.4 × 4.2 × 1.2)*
Main machinery: 2 GM diesels; 520 hp *(382 kW)*; 2 shafts
Speed, knots: 9
Complement: 5 (2 officers)

Comment: All operational in 1993.

3 T 4 CLASS (LCVPs)

60-62

Displacement, tons: 70 full load
Dimensions, feet (metres): 62.3 × 14 × 3.3 *(19 × 4.3 × 1)*
Main machinery: 2 diesels; 316 hp(m) *(232 kW)*; 2 shafts
Speed, knots: 10
Complement: 5 (2 officers)

Comment: Transferred from USSR January 1985. All operational in late 1993. About 15 tons cargo capacity.

T 4   *1992, Ships of the World*

CAMEROON

Headquarters' Appointment

Chief of Naval Staff:
  Commander Guillaume Ngouah Ngally

Personnel

1994: 1350

Bases

Douala, Limbe, Kribi

Mercantile Marine

Lloyd's Register of Shipping:
  50 vessels of 36 000 tons gross

DELETIONS

1992 *Indépendance,   Reunification,   Souellaba, Machtigal, Manoka*

PATROL FORCES

1 BAKASSI (TYPE P 48S) CLASS (MISSILE PATROL CRAFT)

Name	No	Builders	Commissioned
BAKASSI	P 104	SFCN, Villeneuve-La-Garenne	9 Jan 1984

Displacement, tons: 308 full load
Dimensions, feet (metres): 172.5 × 23.6 × 7.9 *(52.6 × 7.2 × 2.4)*
Main machinery: 2 SACM 195 V16 CZSHR diesels; 8000 hp(m) *(5.88 MW)* sustained; 2 shafts
Speed, knots: 25. **Range, miles:** 2000 at 16 kts
Complement: 39 (6 officers)

Missiles: SSM: 8 Aerospatiale MM 40 Exocet (2 quad) launchers; inertial cruise; active radar homing to 70 km *(40 nm)* at 0.9 Mach; warhead 165 kg; sea-skimmer.
Guns: 2 Bofors 40 mm/70; 85° elevation; 300 rounds/minute to 12.8 km *(7 nm)*; weight of shell 0.96 kg.
Fire control: Two Naja optronic systems. Racal Decca Cane 100 command system.
Radars: Navigation/surface search: Two Racal Decca 1226; I band.

Programmes: Ordered January 1981. Laid down 16 December 1981. Launched 22 October 1982.
Modernisation: Radars have been updated.

BAKASSI   *1984, SFCN*

1 L'AUDACIEUX (TYPE PR 48) CLASS (LARGE PATROL CRAFT)

Name	No	Builders	Commissioned
L'AUDACIEUX	P 103	SFCN, Villeneuve-La-Garenne	11 May 1976

Displacement, tons: 250 full load
Dimensions, feet (metres): 157.5 × 23.3 × 7.5 *(48 × 7.1 × 2.3)*
Main machinery: 2 SACM 195 V12 CZSHR diesels; 6000 hp(m) *(4.41 MW)* sustained; 2 shafts; cp props
Speed, knots: 23. **Range, miles:** 2000 at 16 kts
Complement: 25 (4 officers)
Missiles: SSM: Fitted for 8 Aerospatiale SS 12M; wire-guided to 5.5 km *(3 nm)* subsonic; warhead 30 kg.
Guns: 2 Bofors 40 mm/70; 85° elevation; 300 rounds/minute to 12.8 km *(7 nm)*; weight of shell 0.96 kg.

Comment: L'Audacieux ordered in September 1974. Laid down on 10 February 1975, launched on 31 October 1975. Similar to Bizerte class in Tunisia.

30 SWIFT PBR CLASS (RIVER PATROL CRAFT)

PR 01-30

Displacement, tons: 12 full load
Dimensions, feet (metres): 38 × 12.5 × 3.2 *(11.6 × 3.8 × 1)*
Main machinery: 2 Stewart and Stevenson 6V-92TA diesels; 520 hp *(388 kW)* sustained; 2 shafts
Speed, knots: 32. **Range, miles:** 210 at 20 kts
Complement: 4
Guns: 2—12.7 mm MGs. 2—7.62 mm MGs.

Comment: Built by Swiftships and supplied under the US Military Assistance Programme. First 10 delivered in March 1987, second 10 in September 1987 and the remainder by the end of 1987. Ten of the craft are used by the gendarmerie.

PR 01   *4/1992*

4 SIMONNEAU 30 CLASS (RIVER PATROL CRAFT)

Displacement, tons: 4 full load
Dimensions, feet (metres): 30.5 × 9.8 × 2.6 *(9.3 × 3 × 0.8)*
Main machinery: 2 Volvo TAMD41 diesels; 330 hp(m) *(243 kW)*; 2 shafts
Speed, knots: 27. **Range, miles:** 240 at 12 kts
Complement: 4
Guns: 1—7.62 mm MG.

Comment: Delivered in early 1991 for use by Customs.

SIMONNEAU 30   *1991, Simonneau Marine*

2 SIMONNEAU 36 CLASS (RIVER PATROL CRAFT)

Displacement, tons: 8 full load
Dimensions, feet (metres): 36.4 × 11.5 × 3.3 *(11.1 × 3.5 × 1)*
Main machinery: 2 Volvo TAMD61 diesels; 504 hp(m) *(368 kW)* ; 2 shafts
Speed, knots: 27. **Range, miles:** 230 at 18 kts
Complement: 6
Guns: 1—7.62 mm MG.

Comment: Delivered in early 1991 for use by Customs.

SIMONNEAU 36   *1991, Simonneau Marine*

3 RAIDER CRAFT

Comment: Supplied by Napco Int in 1987. 19.7 or 23 ft *(6 or 7 m)* in length Boston Whaler Type with twin 140 hp *(104 kW)* outboards giving a speed of 40 kts and a range in excess of 200 miles. Fitted for two 12.7 mm machine guns.

LAND-BASED MARITIME AIRCRAFT

Numbers/Type: 3 Dornier Do 128-6MPA.
Operational speed: 165 kts *(305 km/h)*.
Service ceiling: 32 600 ft *(9335 m)*.
Range: 790 nm *(1460 km)*.
Role/Weapon systems: Sole MR assets with short-range EEZ protection and coastal surveillance. Sensors: MEL Marec radar. Weapons: Unarmed.

AUXILIARIES

2 LCMs

BETIKA   BIBUNDI

Comment: *Betika* built by Carena, Abidjan, Ivory Coast and refitted in 1987. *Bibundi* built by Tanguy Marine, France in 1982/83. Both are 56 ft *(17.1 m)* in length and have a speed of 10 kts.

1 TUG

GRAND BATANGA

Comment: Completed by La Manche Dieppe 30 October 1985. Of 96.4 × 29.5 × 12.1 ft *(29.4 × 9 × 3.7 m)*. Fitted with 2 Sacha AGO diesels; 2000 hp(m) *(1.47 MW)*. Speed 12.8 kts.

8 AUXILIARIES

Comment: *Tornade* and *Ouragan*—built in 1966. *St Sylvestre*—built in 1967. *Mungo* operated by Transport Ministry. *Dr Jamot* operated by Health Ministry. *Sanaga* and *Bimbia* harbour launches. *Nyong* a 218 grt buoy tender was built by Cassens, Emden and delivered in December 1990.

CANADA

Headquarters' Appointments

Deputy Chief of Defence Staff:
  Vice Admiral L E Murray, OMM, CD
Director General Maritime Development
  Commodore J A King, CD

Flag Officers

Commander, Maritime Command:
  Vice Admiral P W Cairns, CMM, CD
Commander, Maritime Forces, Atlantic:
  Rear Admiral L G Mason, CMM, CD
Commander, Maritime Forces, Pacific:
  Rear Admiral R C Waller, OMM, CD

Diplomatic Representation

Military Representative, Brussels
  Vice Admiral R E George, CMM, CD
Commander, Canadian Defence Liaison Staff, Washington:
  Rear Admiral K J Summers, MSC, OMM, CD
Naval Adviser, London:
  Captain (N) E E Davie, CD
Naval Attaché, Moscow:
  Commander J J Olivier, CD
Naval Attaché, Washington:
  Commodore J D S Reilley, CD
Naval Attaché, Oslo
  Captain D E Pollard, CD
Naval Attaché, The Hague
  Captain J Nethercott, CD
Naval Attaché, Tokyo
  Captain G V Davidson
Naval Attaché, Paris
  Commander J C A Nadeau

Establishment

The Royal Canadian Navy (RCN) was officially established on 4 May 1910, when Royal Assent was given to the Naval Service Act. On 1 February 1968 the Canadian Forces Reorganisation Act unified the three branches of the Canadian Forces and the title 'Royal Canadian Navy' was dropped.

Personnel

1994:   (a) 11 800 (Navy)
(b) 7500 (Civilian)
(c) 4600 (Reserves)

Prefix to Ships' Names

HMCS

Bases

Halifax and Esquimalt

Maritime Air Group (MAG)

Commander MAG (Chief of Staff (Air) Marcom)—based in Halifax

Squadron/ Unit	Base	Aircraft	Function
MP 404	Greenwood, NS	Aurora/ Arcturus	LRMP/ Training
MP 405	Greenwood, NS	Aurora	LRMP
HT 406	Shearwater, NS	Sea King	Training
MP 407	Comox, BC	Aurora	LRMP
MP 415	Greenwood, NS	Aurora	LRMP
HS 423	Shearwater, NS	Sea King	ASW
HS 443	Victoria, BC	Sea King	ASW
HOTEF	Shearwater, NS	Sea King	Test
MPEU	Greenwood, NS	Aurora	Test

Notes

(a) Detachments from HS 423 and HS 443 meet ships' requirements in Atlantic and Pacific Fleets respectively.
(b) The Department of National Defence is currently in contract with European Helicopter Industries (Canada) for the replacement of the Sea King fleet with EH 101s.
(c) 413 Squadron based in Greenwood, NS, and 442 Squadron based in Comox, BC, are two maritime search and rescue squadrons under the command of Air Transport Group (ATG).
(d) 434 Combat Support (CS) Squadron along with 420 Air Reserve Squadron (ARS) located in Shearwater NS, and 414 CS along with 409 ARS located in Comox BC are Fighter Group Resources providing services to Maritime Command operations with CC/CE 144 Challengers and CT/CE-133 Silver Stars.

Strength of the Fleet

Type	Active	Building (Projected)
Submarines (Patrol)	3	(6)
Destroyers	4	—
Frigates	13	4
Corvettes	—	(6)
MCM Vessels	8	12
Patrol Vessels	7	—
Operational Support Ships	3	—
Auxiliaries	17	—
Tugs	12	—

Fleet Deployment

Atlantic:
Operations Group One (destroyers, frigates and AOR)
Operations Group Five (MSAs, YNGs, reserve training vessels, diving support vessel, Fleet diving unit and coastal defence districts)
Submarine Squadron One

Pacific:
Operations Group Two (destroyers, frigates and AOR)
Operations Group Four (PBLs, training vessels, Fleet diving unit and coastal defence districts)

Mercantile Marine

Lloyd's Register of Shipping:
  1049 vessels of 2 540 984 tons gross

DELETIONS

Frigates

1992 *Margaree, Ottawa, Qu'Appelle*
1993 *Mackenzie, Skeena, Yukon*
1994 *Saskatchewan, Fraser, Restigouche*

Tenders

1991 *Songhee, Nimpkish, Ehkoli,* YPT 4, *Cavalier, Burrard, Queensville, Plainsville, Youville, Loganville*
1992 *Nicholson, Caribou, Beamsville, Rally, Rapid*
1993 *St Charles*

PRESERVER

11/1993, Maritime Photographic

PENNANT LIST

Destroyers			Submarines			MCM Tenders			Tugs	
DDH 280	Iroquois		SS 72	Ojibwa		YDT	6, 8, 9, 10, 11, 12		ATA 531	Saint Anthony
DDH 281	Huron		SS 73	Onondaga					YTB 640	Glendyne
DDH 282	Athabaskan		SS 74	Okanagan		Gate Vessels			YTB 641	Glendale
DDH 283	Algonquin								YTB 642	Glenevis
			Operational Support Ships			YNG 180	Porte St Jean		YTB 643	Glenbrook
						YNG 183	Porte St Louis		YTB 644	Glenside
			AOR 508	Provider		YNG 184	Porte de la Reine		YTL 533	Wildwood
			AOR 509	Protecteur		YNG 185	Porte Quebec		YTL 590	Lawrenceville
			AOR 510	Preserver		YNG 186	Porte Dauphine		YTL 591	Parksville
									YTL 592	Listerville
Frigates			Support Ships			Sail Training Ship			YTL 593	Merrickville
									YTL 594	Marysville
DD 236	Gatineau		ASL 20	Cormorant		YAC 3	Oriole			
DD 258	Kootenay		AG 121	Riverton					TSRVs	
DD 259	Terra Nova					Survey and Research Vessels				
DDH 265	Annapolis		Patrol Vessels						YPT 610	Sechelt
DDH 266	Nipigon					AGOR 171	Endeavour		YPT 611	Sikanni
FFH 330	Halifax		PB 140	Fort Steele		AGOR 172	Quest		YPT 612	Sooke
FFH 331	Vancouver		PBL 159	Fundy					YPT 613	Stikine
FFH 332	Ville de Québec		PBL 160	Chignecto		Transport Oiler				
FFH 333	Toronto		PBL 161	Thunder					Naval Reserve Unit Tenders	
FFH 334	Regina		PBL 162	Cowichan		AOTL 502	Dundurn			
FFH 335	Calgary		PBL 163	Miramichi					PB 191	Adversus
FFH 336	Montreal		PBL 164	Chaleur					PB 193	Captor
FFH 337	Fredericton								PB 194	Acadian
FFH 338	Winnipeg (building)		Minesweepers			Tenders			PB 195	Sydney
FFH 339	Charlottetown (building)								PB 197	Crossbow
FFH 340	St John's (building)		MSA 110	Anticosti		YTR 561	Firebird		PB 198	Service
FFH 341	Ottawa (building)		MSA 112	Moresby		YTR 562	Firebrand		PB 199	Standoff
									YFL 104	Pogo

SUBMARINES

Notes: (1) The April 1992 Defence Policy Announcement stated that in a project continuing past the fifteen year planning period, the navy will replace its current submarine fleet with up to six modern conventional submarines in order to provide an under-water capability in both the Atlantic and the Pacific. A request for proposals is expected in 1994-1996 unless it is overtaken by an off-the-shelf purchase of British or Dutch submarines.

(2) Ex-British *Olympus* was purchased in August 1989 and is used for alongside training in Halifax. *Osiris* acquired in 1992 and cannibalised for spares.

3 OBERON CLASS (PATROL SUBMARINES)

Name	No	Builders	Laid down	Launched	Commissioned
OJIBWA (ex-*Onyx*)	72	HM Dockyard, Chatham	27 Sep 1962	29 Feb 1964	23 Sep 1965
ONONDAGA	73	HM Dockyard, Chatham	18 June 1964	25 Sep 1965	22 June 1967
OKANAGAN	74	HM Dockyard, Chatham	25 Mar 1965	17 Sep 1966	22 June 1968

Displacement, tons: 2030 surfaced; 2410 dived
Dimensions, feet (metres): 295.2 × 26.5 × 18 *(90 × 8.1 × 5.5)*
Main machinery: Diesel-electric; 2 ASR 16 VVS-ASR1 diesels; 3680 hp *(2.74 MW)*; 2 AEI motors; 6000 hp *(4.48 MW)*; 2 shafts
Speed, knots: 12 surfaced; 17 dived; 10 snorting
Range, miles: 9000 surfaced at 12 kts
Complement: 65 (7 officers)

Torpedoes: 6—21 in *(533 mm)* bow tubes. 20 Gould Mk 48 Mod 4; dual purpose; active/passive homing to 50 km *(27 nm)*/ 38 km *(21 nm)* at 40/55 kts; warhead 267 kg.
Countermeasures: ESM: Radar warning.
Fire control: Loral Librascope TFCS with Sperry UYK 20 computer.
Radars: Navigation: Kelvin Hughes Type 1006; I band.

Sonars: Plessey Triton Type 2051; hull-mounted; passive/active search and attack; medium frequency.
BAC Type 2007; flank array; passive search; long range; low frequency.
BQG 501 Sperry Micropuffs; passive ranging.
Hermes Electronics/MUSL towed arrays being fitted from 1993.

Programmes: In 1962 the Ministry of National Defence announced that Canada was to buy three Oberon class submarines in the UK. The first of these patrol submarines was obtained by the Canadian Government from the Royal Navy construction programme. She was laid down as *Onyx* but launched as *Ojibwa*. The other two were Canadian orders. There were some design changes to meet specific new needs including installation of RCN communications equipment and increase of air-conditioning capacity to meet the wide extremes of climate encountered in Canadian operating areas. All are to have their service lives extended until the end of the century.

Modernisation: All underwent SOUP (Submarine Operational Update Project) with more modern sonar and fire-control equipment fitted. *Ojibwa* 1980-82, *Onondaga* 1982-84 and *Okanagan* 1984-86. Starting in 1987 weapon launching and fire-control systems were upgraded to take the US Mk 48 torpedo which replaced the Mk 37. Plessey Triton Type 2051 sonar purchased in 1989. All three submarines are being fitted with towed array sonars starting with *Okanagan* in 1993. TFCS is being updated at the same time.
Structure: Diving depth, 200 m *(656 ft)*. Stern tubes have been blanked off.

ONONDAGA

1992, Canadian Maritime Command

DESTROYERS

4 IROQUOIS CLASS

Name	No
IROQUOIS	280
HURON	281
ATHABASKAN	282
ALGONQUIN	283

Builders	Laid down	Launched	Commissioned
Marine Industries Ltd, Sorel	15 Jan 1969	28 Nov 1970	29 July 1972
Marine Industries Ltd, Sorel	15 Jan 1969	3 Apr 1971	16 Dec 1972
Davie Shipbuilding, Lauzon	1 June 1969	27 Nov 1970	30 Sep 1972
Davie Shipbuilding, Lauzon	1 Sep 1969	23 Apr 1971	3 Nov 1973

Displacement, tons: 5100 full load

Dimensions, feet (metres): 398 wl; 426 oa × 50 × 15.5 keel/21.5 screws *(121.4; 129.8 × 15.2 × 4.7/6.6)*

Main machinery: COGOG; 2 Pratt & Whitney FT4A2 gas turbines; 50 000 hp *(37 MW)*; 2 GM Allison 570-KF gas-turbines; 12 700 hp *(9.5 MW)* sustained; 2 shafts; cp props

Speed, knots: 29+. **Range, miles:** 4500 at 20 kts

Complement: 255 (23 officers) plus aircrew 30 (11 officers)

Missiles: SAM: 1 Martin Marietta Mk 41 VLS ❶ for 29 GDC Standard SM-2MR; command/inertial guidance; semi active radar homing to 73 km *(40 nm)* at 2 Mach.

Guns: 1 OTO Melara 3 in *(76 mm)*/62 Super Rapid ❷; 85° elevation; 120 rounds/minute to 16 km *(8.7 nm)*; weight of shell 6 kg.

1 GE/GDC 20 mm/76 6-barrelled Vulcan Phalanx Mk 15 ❸; 3000 rounds/minute combined to 1.5 km.

Torpedoes: 6—324 mm Mk 32 (2 triple) tubes ❹. Honeywell Mk 46 Mod 5 (from 1993); anti-submarine; active/passive homing to 11 km *(5.9 nm)* at 40 kts; warhead 44 kg.

Countermeasures: Decoys: 2 Plessey Shield 6-tubed trainable launchers ❺.

SLQ 25 Nixie; torpedo decoy.

ESM: MEL SLQ 504 Canews ❻; radar warning.

ECM: ULQ-6; jammer.

Combat data systems: SHINPADS, automated data handling with UYQ-504 and UYK-507 processors. Links 11 and 14. WSC-IV and SSR-1 SATCOM.

Fire control: Signaal WM 25 including LIROD 8 ❼ optronic director. SAR-8 IRSTD will not now be fitted.

Radars: Air search: Signaal LW 08 ❽; D band.

Surface search/navigation: Signaal DA 08 ❾; E/F band.

Fire control: Two Signaal STIR 1.8 ❿; I/J band.

Tacan: URN 26.

Sonars: Westinghouse SQS 505 (being upgraded to 510); combined VDS and hull-mounted; active search and attack; 7 kHz.

Westinghouse SQS 501; hull-mounted; bottom target classification; high frequency.

C-Tech Spectra 3000; hull-mounted; active mine detection; high frequency.

Helicopters: 2 CH-124A Sea King ASW ⓫

Modernisation: A contract for the Tribal Class Update and Modernisation Project (TRUMP) was awarded to Litton Systems Canada Limited in June 1986. The new equipment reflects the changing role of the ship and replaces systems that did not meet the air defence requirement. *Algonquin* started modernisation in November 1987 at Mil Davie, Quebec, and completed October 1991, followed by *Iroquois*, started November 1988, and completed May 1992. *Athabaskan* entered the yard in September 1991 and is scheduled to complete in June 1994; *Huron* started in June 1992 and should complete in December 1994. SQS 505 sonar being upgraded to 510 from 1994.

Structure: These ships are also fitted with a landing deck equipped with double hauldown and Beartrap, pre-wetting system to counter NBC conditions, enclosed citadel, and bridge control of machinery. The flume type anti-roll tanks have been replaced during modernisation with a water displaced fuel system. Design weight limit has been reached.

Operational: Helicopters can carry 12.7 mm MGs and ESM/FLIR instead of ASW gear.

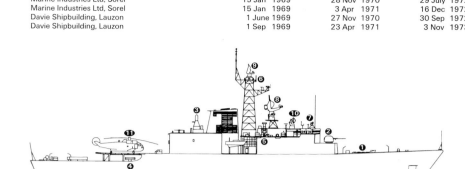

ALGONQUIN

(Scale 1 : 1200), Ian Sturton

ALGONQUIN

5/1993, Camil Busquets i Vilanova

ALGONQUIN

7/1991, Canadian Maritime Command

FRIGATES

Notes: (1) Up to six corvettes are to be acquired in due course. These ships are referred to as CASSEVs (Canadian Sovereignty Surveillance and Enforcement Vessels).
(2) *Yukon* (263) is used as an alongside training ship at Esquimalt, having replaced *Columbia* in 1994.

8 + 4 HALIFAX CLASS (FFH)

Name	No	Builders	Laid down	Launched	Completed	Commissioned
HALIFAX	330	St John SB Ltd, New Brunswick	19 Mar 1987	30 Apr 1988	28 June 1991	29 June 1992
VANCOUVER	331	St John SB Ltd, New Brunswick	19 May 1988	8 July 1989	11 Sep 1992	23 Aug 1993
VILLE DE QUÉBEC	332	Marine Industries Ltd, Sorel	16 Dec 1988	16 May 1991	23 Sep 1993	July 1994
TORONTO	333	St John SB Ltd, New Brunswick	24 Apr 1989	18 Dec 1990	23 Dec 1993	29 July 1993
REGINA	334	Marine Industries Ltd, Sorel	6 Oct 1989	25 Oct 1991	29 Mar 1994	1994
CALGARY	335	Marine Industries Ltd, Sorel	15 June 1991	28 Aug 1992	Sep 1994	1995
MONTREAL	336	St John SB Ltd, New Brunswick	29 Feb 1991	19 June 1992	27 July 1993	July 1994
FREDERICTON	337	St John SB Ltd, New Brunswick	25 Apr 1992	26 June 1993	27 Feb 1994	1994
WINNIPEG	338	St John SB Ltd, New Brunswick	21 Mar 1993	June 1994	Oct 1994	1995
CHARLOTTETOWN	339	St John SB Ltd, New Brunswick	18 Dec 1993	July 1994	May 1995	1995
ST JOHN'S	340	St John SB Ltd, New Brunswick	July 1994	Mar 1995	Dec 1995	1996
OTTAWA	341	St John SB Ltd, New Brunswick	Feb 1995	Aug 1995	June 1996	1997

Displacement, tons: 5235 full load
Dimensions, feet (metres): 441.9 oa; 408.5 pp × 53.8 × 16.1; 23.3 (screws) *(134.7; 124.5 × 16.4 × 4.9; 7.1)*
Main machinery: CODOG; 2 GE LM 2500 gas-turbines; 47 494 hp *(35.43 MW)* sustained 1 SEMT-Pielstick 20 PA6 V 280 diesel; 8800 hp(m) *(6.48 MW)* sustained; 2 shafts; cp props
Speed, knots: 28. **Range, miles:** 7100 at 15 kts (diesel); 4500 at 15 kts (gas)
Complement: 225 (23 officers)

Missiles: SSM: 8 McDonnell Douglas Harpoon Block 1C (2 quad) launchers ❶; active radar homing to 130 km *(70 nm)* at 0.9 Mach; warhead 227 kg.
SAM: 2 Raytheon Sea Sparrow Mk 48 octuple vertical launchers ❷; semi-active radar homing to 14.6 km *(8 nm)* at 2.5 Mach; warhead 39 kg; 28 missiles (16 normally carried).
Guns: 1 Bofors 57 mm/70 Mk 2 ❸; 77° elevation; 220 rounds/minute to 17 km *(9 nm)*; weight of shell 2.4 kg.
1 GE/GDC 20 mm Vulcan Phalanx Mk 15 Mod 1 ❹; anti-missile; 3000 rounds/minute (6 barrels combined) to 1.5 km.
8—12.7 mm MGs.
Torpedoes: 4—324 mm Mk 32 Mod 9 (2 twin) tubes ❺. 24 Honeywell Mk 46 Mod 5; anti-submarine; active/passive homing to 11 km *(5.9 nm)* at 40 kts; warhead 44 kg.
Countermeasures: Decoys: 4 Plessey Shield decoy launchers ❻; triple mountings; fires P8 chaff and P6 IR flares in distraction, decoy or centroid modes.
Nixie SLQ 25; towed acoustic decoy.
ESM: MEL/Lockheed Canews SLQ 504 ❼; radar intercept; (0.5-18 GHz). SRD 502.
ECM: MEL/Lockheed Ramses SLQ 503 ❽; jammer.
Combat data systems: UYC-501 SHINPADS action data automation with UYQ-504 and UYK-505 or 507 (336-341) processors. Links 11 and 14.
Fire control: SWG-1(V) for Harpoon. CDC UYS 503(V); sonobuoy processing system.
Radars: Air search: Raytheon SPS 49(V)5 ❾; C/D band; range 457 km *(250 nm)*.
Air/surface search: Ericsson Sea Giraffe HC 150 ❿; G/H band; range 100 km *(55 nm)* against missiles in clear conditions.
Fire control: Two Signaal VM 25 STIR ⓫; K/I band; range 140 km *(76 nm)* for 1 m² target.
Navigation: Sperry Mk 340; I band.
Tacan: URN 25. IFF Mk XII.
Sonars: Westinghouse SQS 505(V)6 (to be upgraded to SQS 510); hull-mounted; active search and attack; medium frequency.
CDC SQR 501 CANTASS towed array (uses part of Martin Marietta SQR 19 TACTASS).

Helicopters: 1 CH-124A ASW or 1 CH-124B Heltas Sea King ⓬.

Programmes: On 29 June 1983 St John Shipbuilding Ltd won

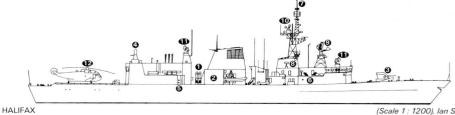

HALIFAX

(Scale 1 : 1200), Ian Sturton

VANCOUVER

8/1993, van Ginderen Collection

the competition for the first six of a new class of patrol frigates to be assisted by Paramax Electronics Inc of Montreal, a subsidiary of Unisys Co (formerly Sperry). Three were subcontracted to Marine Industries Ltd in Lauzon and Sorel. On 18 December 1987 six additional ships of the same design were ordered from St John SB Ltd with delivery by 1997. There have been problems keeping to the planned construction programme, but the dispute between SJSL and MIL was finally resolved in 1993.
Structure: Plans to lengthen some of the class to increase SAM

capacity and improve accommodation have been shelved which means there is limited reserve for mid-life modernisation. Much effort has gone into stealth technology. Gas turbine engines are raft mounted. It is claimed there is more equipment per cubic volume of space than in any other comparable NATO frigate.
Operational: Problems on first of class trials included higher than designed radiated noise levels which are reported as speed associated. These are being rectified.

TORONTO

7/1993, van Ginderen Collection

3 IMPROVED RESTIGOUCHE CLASS

Name	No	Builders	Laid down	Launched	Commissioned
GATINEAU	236	Davie Shipbuilding	30 Apr 1953	3 June 1957	17 Feb 1959
KOOTENAY	258	Burrard Dry Dock Co	21 Aug 1952	15 June 1954	7 Mar 1959
TERRA NOVA	259	Victoria Machinery Depot Co	14 Nov 1952	21 June 1955	6 June 1959

Displacement, tons: 2390 standard; 2900 full load
Dimensions, feet (metres): 371 × 42 × 14.1
 (113.1 × 12.8 × 4.3)
Main machinery: 2 Babcock & Wilcox boilers; 600 psi
 (43.3 kg/cm sq); 850°F (454°C); 2 English Electric turbines;
 30 000 hp (22.4 MW); 2 shafts
Speed, knots: 28. **Range, miles:** 4750 at 14 kts
Complement: 214 (13 officers)

Missiles: SSM: 8 McDonnell Douglas Harpoon 2 quad launchers
 ❶ (Gulf 1991/92); active radar homing to 130 km (70 nm) at
 0.9 Mach; warhead 227 kg.
 A/S: Honeywell ASROC Mk 112 octuple launcher ❷; 8 reloads;
 inertial guidance to 1.6-10 km (1-5.4 nm); payload Mk 46 torpedo. Replaced by 8 Harpoon during Gulf 1991/92.
Guns: 2 Vickers 3 in (76 mm)/70 (twin) Mk 6 ❸; dual purpose;
 90° elevation; 90 rounds/minute to 17 km (9 nm); weight of
 shell 7 kg.
 1 GE/GDC 20 mm/76 6-barrelled Vulcan Phalanx Mk 15
 (modified) ❹ (Gulf 1991/92); 3000 rounds/minute combined
 to 1.5 km.
 2 Bofors 40 mm/60 ❺ (Gulf 1991/92).
Torpedoes: 6—324 mm Mk 32 (2 triple) tubes ❻. Honeywell Mk
 46 Mod 5; anti-submarine; active/passive homing to 11 km
 (5.9 nm) at 40 kts; warhead 44 kg.
Countermeasures: Decoys: 4 Loral Hycor SRBOC Mk 36 ❼; 4
 launchers with 4 fixed barrels firing chaff decoys and IR flares
 to 4 km (2.2 nm). Plessey Shield chaff launchers (Gulf
 1991/92).
 ESM: Canews ❽; radar warning.
 ECM: ULQ-6; jammer.
Combat data systems: Litton ADLIPS; automated data handling;
 Links 11 and 14. SATCOM ❾.
Fire control: GFCS Mk 69.
Radars: Air search: Marconi SPS 503 (CMR 1820); E/F band; or
 Ericsson Sea Giraffe HC 150 ❿; G/H band.
 Surface search: Raytheon SPS 10 ⓫; G band.
 Navigation: Sperry 127E; I band.
 Fire control: Bell SPG 48 ⓬; I/J band.
 Tacan: URN 25.
Sonars: Westinghouse SQS 505 (510 in Terra Nova); combined
 VDS and hull-mounted; active search and attack; medium
 frequency.
 C-Tech Spectra 3000; hull-mounted; mine avoidance active;
 high frequency.
 SQS 501; hull-mounted; bottom target classification; high
 frequency.

Programmes: Officially classified as DD.
Modernisation: These ships were first refitted with ASROC aft
 and lattice foremast. Work included removing the after
 3 in/50 twin gun mounting and one Limbo A/S Mk 10 triple
 mortar, to make way for ASROC and variable depth sonar.
 Refits also included improvements to communications fit and
 completed 1968-73. Three other ships of the class were paid
 off without being refitted. All modernised again under Delex
 programme 1983-86 with new air search radar, GFCS, communications and EW equipment. The Bofors rocket launcher
 replaced by Super RBOC and Tacan fitted on a pole mast
 replacing the top section of the lattice mast. Triple Mark 32 torpedo tubes fitted.
Operational: For operational deployments to the Gulf in 1991
 and 1992 two ships had the ASROC launcher replaced by 8
 Harpoon SSM, the Limbo Mk 10 by Phalanx, and the ships
 boats by two single Bofors 40 mm/60. All reverted to standard
 fit by the end of 1992 except that the Limbo launchers have
 been removed and SATCOM fitted. SQS 510 sonar installed in
 Terra Nova in 1993. Kootenay based in the Pacific Fleet.
 Additional 12.7 mm MGs can be carried plus Blowpipe and
 Javelin shoulder-launched SAM.

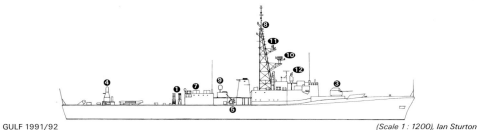

GULF 1991/92   (Scale 1 : 1200), Ian Sturton

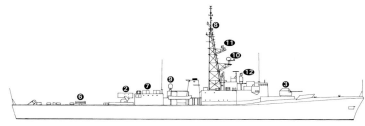

GATINEAU   (Scale 1 : 1200), Ian Sturton

GATINEAU   10/1992, C D Yaylali

GATINEAU   11/1993, Maritime Photographic

2 ANNAPOLIS CLASS

Name	No	Builders	Laid down	Launched	Commissioned
ANNAPOLIS	265	Halifax Shipyards Ltd, Halifax	July 1960	27 Apr 1963	19 Dec 1964
NIPIGON	266	Marine Industries Ltd, Sorel	Apr 1960	10 Dec 1961	30 May 1964

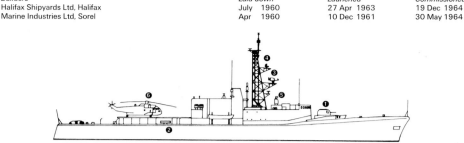

ANNAPOLIS   (Scale 1 : 1200), Ian Sturton

Displacement, tons: 2400 standard; 2930 full load
Dimensions, feet (metres): 371 × 42 × 14.4
(113.1 × 12.8 × 4.4)
Main machinery: 2 Babcock & Wilcox boilers; 600 psi
(43.3 kg/cm sq); 850°F (454°C); 2 English Electric turbines;
30 000 hp (22.4 MW); 2 shafts
Speed, knots: 28 (30 on trials). **Range, miles:** 4570 at 14 kts
Complement: 210 (11 officers)

Guns: 2 FMC 3 in (76 mm)/50 Mk 33 (twin) ❶; 85° elevation; 50
rounds/minute to 12.8 km (7 nm); weight of shell 6 kg.
Torpedoes: 6—324 mm Mk 32 (2 triple) tubes ❷. Honeywell Mk
46 Mod 5; anti-submarine; active/passive homing to 11 km
(5.9 nm) at 40 kts; warhead 44 kg.
Countermeasures: Decoys: 4 Loral Hycor SRBOC; chaff and IR
flares to 4 km (2.2 nm).
ESM: MEL Canews; radar warning; 0.5-18 GHz.
Combat data systems: Litton ADLIPS automated tactical data
handling; Links 11 and 14.
Fire control: GFCS Mk 60.
Radars: Air/surface search: Marconi SPS 503 (CMR 1820) ❸;
E/F band; range 128 km (70 nm).
Surface search: Raytheon/Sylvania SPS 10 ❹; G band.
Fire control: Bell SPG 48 ❺; I/J band.
Navigation: Sperry 127E; I band.
Tacan: URN 25.
Sonars: Westinghouse SQS 505 (Annapolis), SQS 510 (Nipigon);
hull-mounted; active search and attack.
SQS 501; hull-mounted; bottom target classification; high
frequency.
CDC SQR 501 CANTASS; trials towed array; passive; very low
frequency. Uses part of SQR-19.

Helicopters: 1 CH-124A Sea King ASW ❻.

Programmes: Officially classified as DDH. These two ships represented the logical development of the original St Laurent
class, through the Restigouche and Mackenzie designs.
Modernisation: A full Delex (Destroyer Life Extension Programme) took place in 1982-85 including new air radar, GFC,
communications, sonar and EW equipment. Extension until
1994-96. Both ships fitted with a trials CANTASS vice VDS in
1987/88.
Operational: Annapolis is based in the Pacific Fleet.

ANNAPOLIS   10/1993, Giorgio Arra

SHIPBORNE AIRCRAFT

Note: In 1992 the decision was taken to order 35 Petrel Anglo/Italian EH-101 naval helicopters, to
start replacing the Sea Kings in 1999. Number reduced to 28 in 1993, and then cancelled. Sea King
replacements are necessary.

Numbers/Type: 25/6 Sikorsky CH-124A ASW/CH-124B Heltas Sea King.
Operational speed: 110 kts (203 km/h).
Service ceiling: 17 000 ft (5150 m).
Range: 410 nm (760 km).
Role/Weapon systems: ASW, surface surveillance and support; Iroquois class carry two helicopters, AORs three. CH-124B Heltas Sea Kings dedicated to Annapolis and Halifax class ships. Sensors: CH-124A ASW - APS-503 radar, sonobuoys, ASQ-13 dipping sonar. Some modified for FLIR
and GPS. During Gulf operations, FLIR modified aircraft were also fitted with APR-39, ALE-37
chaff dispenser and ALQ-144 IR countermeasures. CH-124B Heltas - APS-503 radar, UYS-503
sonobuoy processor, GPS and ASQ-504 MAD. Weapons: Up to four Mk 46 torpedoes for both
aircraft types.

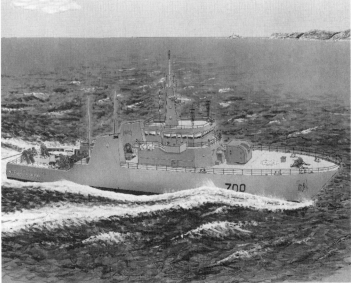

SEA KING   5/1993, Camil Busquets i Vilanova

LAND-BASED MARITIME AIRCRAFT (FRONT LINE)

Numbers/Type: 18/3 Lockheed CP-140 Aurora/CP-140A Arcturus.
Operational speed: 410 kts (760 km/h).
Service ceiling: 28 300 ft (8625 m).
Range: 4000 nm (7410 km).
Role/Weapon systems: Aurora operated for long-range maritime surveillance over Atlantic,
Pacific and Arctic Oceans; roles include ASW/ASV and SAR; Arcturus for unarmed Arctic patrol
and ASV and SAR training. Aurora sensors: APS-506 radar, IFF, ESM, ECM, FLIR OR 5008,
ASQ-502 MAD, OL 5004 acoustic processor. Weapons: 8 Mk 46 Mod 5 torpedoes. Arcturus
sensors: APS-507 radar, IFF.

MINE WARFARE FORCES

0 + 12 FRONTENAC CLASS (MCDV)

Name	No	Builders	Commissioned
FRONTENAC	700	Halifax-Dartmouth Industries	June 1995

Displacement, tons: 962 full load
Dimensions, feet (metres): 181.4 × 37.1 × 11.2 (55.3 × 11.3 × 3.4)
Main machinery: Diesel-electric; 4 Wärtsilä UD 23V12 diesels; 4 alternators; 7.2 MW; 2 motors;
3000 hp(m) (2.2 MW); 2 LIPS Z drive azimuth thrusters
Speed, knots: 15. **Range, miles:** 5000 at 8 kts
Complement: 37
Guns: 1 Bofors 40 mm/60 Mk 5C. 2—12.7 mm MGs.
Countermeasures: MCM: One of three modular payloads: (a) Deep mechanical minesweep sys-
tem (MMS); (b) Route survey system; (c) Mine inspection Sutec ROV.
Radars: Surface search: E/F band.
Navigation: I band.
Sonars: Towed sidescan; high frequency active; for route survey.

Comment: Tenders requested 31 August 1988. Contract awarded to Fenco Engineers on 2 October 1991. The design is by German Marine, Dartmouth and the ships are being built by Halifax-
Dartmouth Industries. Thomson-CSF is providing combat system support. Known as Maritime
Coastal Defence Vessels and combine MCM capabilities with general patrol duties and are to be
stationed on both coasts and in the St Lawrence. The programme provides for a limited number
of MCM modular payloads consisting of two MMS, four route survey and one ROV. The vessels
are manned by a mixed regular and reserve force crew. First of class to launch in July 1994. Pennant numbers 700-711.

FRONTENAC (artist's impression)   1991, Canadian Maritime Command

2 MINESWEEPERS AUXILIARY (MSA)

Name	No	Builders	Commissioned
ANTICOSTI (ex-Jean Tide)	MSA 110	Allied SB, Vancouver	7 May 1989
MORESBY (ex-Joyce Tide)	MSA 112	Allied SB, Vancouver	7 May 1989

Displacement, tons: 2205 full load
Dimensions, feet (metres): 191 × 43 × 17 *(58.2 × 13.1 × 5.2)*
Main machinery: 4 Nohab Polar SF 16RS diesels; 4600 hp(m) *(3.38 MW)*; 2 shafts; Gil Jet bow thruster; 575 hp *(429 kW)*
Speed, knots: 13.5. **Range, miles:** 12 000 at 13 kts
Complement: 18 (5 officers)
Guns: 2—7.62 mm MGs.
Countermeasures: MCM: BAJ Mk 9 mechanical sweep with WSMF (monitoring equipment).
Radars: Navigation: 2 Racal Decca; I band.
Sonars: Side scan towed VDS; high frequency.

Comment: Former offshore towing/supply vessels Ice class 3, suitable for navigation in light ice. Built in 1973 and purchased in March 1988. Mechanical sweeps, sonar, Hyperfix and PINS 9000 navigation system completed fitting in mid-1991. Mixed crews of Regulars and Reservists. Current plans include continued operational service after the MCDV vessels start to enter service in 1995.

MORESBY   8/1991, Canadian Maritime Command

6 MCM DIVING TENDERS

YDT 6, 8, 9, 10   YDT 11, 12

Displacement, tons: 70; 110 *(YDT 11-12)*
Dimensions, feet (metres): 78 × 18.5 × 8.5 *(22.9 × 5.6 × 2.6)* *(YDT 6-10)*
99 × 20 × 8.5 *(27.3 × 6.2 × 2.6)* *(YDT 11-12)*
Main machinery: 2 GM diesels; 165 hp *(123 kW)*; 228 hp *(170 kW)* *(YDT 11-12)*; 2 shafts
Speed, knots: 11
Complement: 9 (1 officer); 13 (2 officers) *(YDT 11-12)*

Comment: YDT 6-10 of wooden construction, 11-12 of steel. All have recompression chambers. 11-12 have a side scan sonar and are capable of deploying 100 m surface supplied diving systems. Divers carry hand-held sonars and use MCM diving sets for their primary role. These vessels are to be replaced in due course by a design based on *Sechelt*.

PATROL FORCES

1 FORT CLASS (PATROL VESSEL (PB))

Name	No	Builders	Commissioned
FORT STEELE	PB 140	Canadian SB and Eng Co	Nov 1955

Displacement, tons: 85
Dimensions, feet (metres): 118 × 21 × 7 *(36 × 6.4 × 2.1)*
Main machinery: 2 Paxman 12 YJCM diesels; 3000 hp *(2.24 MW)*; 2 shafts; KaMeWa cp props
Speed, knots: 18. **Range, miles:** 1200 at 16 kts
Complement: 16

Comment: Steel hull aluminium superstructure. Twin rudders. Acquired by DND in 1973 from RCMP—acts as Reserve Training ship based at Halifax.

FORT STEELE   11/1989, van Ginderen Collection

6 BAY CLASS (PBL)

Name	No	Builders	Commissioned
FUNDY	PBL 159	Davie Shipbuilding, Lauzon	27 Nov 1956
CHIGNECTO	PBL 160	Davie Shipbuilding, Lauzon	1 Aug 1957
THUNDER	PBL 161	Port Arthur SB Co	3 Oct 1957
COWICHAN	PBL 162	Yarrows Ltd, Esquimalt	19 Dec 1957
MIRAMICHI	PBL 163	Victoria Machinery Depot Co	28 Oct 1957
CHALEUR	PBL 164	Marine Industries Ltd, Sorel	12 Sep 1957

Displacement, tons: 370 standard; 470 full load
Dimensions, feet (metres): 164 × 30.2 × 9.2 *(50 × 9.2 × 2.8)*
Main machinery: 2 GM 12-278A diesels; 2200 hp *(1.64 MW)*; 2 shafts
Speed, knots: 15. **Range, miles:** 4500 at 11 kts
Complement: 35 (4 officers)
Guns: 1 Bofors 40 mm/60 (fitted for but not with).
Radars: Surface Search: Racal Decca; I band.

Comment: Wooden hulls with aluminium frames and decks. There were originally 20 vessels of this class of which six were transferred to France, four to Turkey and four sold commercially. Named after Canadian straits and bays. Designation changed from AMC to MCB in 1954. They were redesignated as Patrol Escorts (small) (PF) in 1972, being used as training ships and PB from 1979. *Fundy* and *Thunder* in reserve in 1992, but back in service in 1993.

MIRAMICHI   1993, Canadian Maritime Command

5 PORTE CLASS (GATE VESSELS)

Name	No	Builders	Commissioned
PORTE ST JEAN	YNG 180	Davie Shipbuilding, Lauzon	4 June 1952
PORTE ST LOUIS	YNG 183	Davie Shipbuilding, Lauzon	28 Aug 1952
PORTE DE LA REINE	YNG 184	Victoria Machinery Depot Co	7 Oct 1952
PORTE QUEBEC	YNG 185	Burrard Dry Dock Co	19 Sep 1952
PORTE DAUPHINE	YNG 186	Ferguson Ind.	10 Dec 1952

Displacement, tons: 429 full load
Dimensions, feet (metres): 125.5 × 26.3 × 13 *(38.3 × 8 × 4)*
Main machinery: Diesel-electric; 1 Fairbanks-Morse 38D8-1/8-6 diesel generator; 724 kW sustained; 1 shaft
Speed, knots: 11. **Range, miles:** 4000 at 10 kts
Complement: 23 (3 officers)
Radars: Navigation: Racal Decca; I band.

Comment: Of trawler design. Multipurpose vessels used for operating gates in A/S booms, fleet auxiliaries, anti-submarine netlayers for entrances to defended harbours. Can be fitted for minesweeping. First four used during Summer for training Reserves. *Porte Dauphine* was re-acquired from DOT in 1974 and employed on west coast with *Porte de la Reine* and *Porte Quebec*.

PORTE ST JEAN   1992, van Ginderen Collection

TRAINING SHIP

1 SAIL TRAINING SHIP

Name	No	Builders	Launched
ORIOLE	YAC 3	Owens	4 June 1921

Displacement, tons: 78.2 full load
Dimensions, feet (metres): 102 × 19 × 9 *(31.1 × 5.8 × 2.7)*
Main machinery: 1 Cummins diesel; 165 hp *(123 kW)*; 1 shaft
Speed, knots: 8
Complement: 24 (2 officers)

Comment: Commissioned in the Navy in 1948 and based at Esquimalt. Sail area (with spinnaker) 11 000 sq ft. Height of mainmast 94 ft *(28.7 m)*, mizzen 55.2 ft *(16.8 m)*. Usually cruises with 14 trainee officers at a time.

SURVEY AND RESEARCH SHIPS

Name	No	Builders	Commissioned
QUEST	AGOR 172	Burrard Dry Dock Co, Vancouver	21 Aug 1969

Displacement, tons: 2130
Dimensions, feet (metres): 235 × 42 × 15.5 *(71.6 × 12.8 × 4.6)*
Main machinery: Diesel-electric; 4 Fairbanks-Morse 38D8-1/8-9 diesel generators; 4.37 MW sustained; 2 shafts; cp props
Speed, knots: 16. **Range, miles:** 10 000 at 12 kts
Complement: 55
Helicopters: Platform only.

Comment: Built for the Naval Research Establishment of the Defence Research Board for acoustic, hydrographic and general oceanographic work. Capable of operating in heavy ice in the company of an icebreaker. Launched on 9 July 1968. Based at Halifax and does line array acoustic research in the straits of the northern archipelago.

Name	No	Builders	Commissioned
ENDEAVOUR	AGOR 171	Yarrows Ltd, Esquimalt	9 Mar 1965

Displacement, tons: 1560
Dimensions, feet (metres): 236 × 38.5 × 13 *(71.9 × 11.7 × 4)*
Main machinery: Diesel-electric; 4 Fairbanks-Morse 38D8-1/8-9 diesel generators; 4.36 MW; 2 shafts; cp props
Speed, knots: 16. **Range, miles:** 10 000 at 12 kts
Complement: 50 (10 officers, 13 scientists, 2 aircrew)
Helicopters: 1 light.

Comment: A naval research ship designed primarily for anti-submarine research. Flight deck 48 × 31 ft *(14.6 × 9.4 m)*. Stiffened for operating in ice-covered areas. Able to turn in 2.5 times her own length. Two 9 ton Austin-Weston telescopic cranes are fitted. There are two oceanographical winches each holding 5000 fathoms of wire, two bathythermograph winches and a deep-sea anchoring and coring winch. She has acoustic insulation in her machinery spaces.

QUEST

1986, Canadian Maritime Command

ENDEAVOUR

1990, Canadian Maritime Command

AUXILIARIES

2 IMPROVED PROVIDER CLASS (OPERATIONAL SUPPORT SHIPS)

Name	No	Builders	Laid down	Launched	Commissioned
PROTECTEUR	AOR 509	St John Dry Dock Co, NB	17 Oct 1967	18 July 1968	30 Aug 1969
PRESERVER	AOR 510	St John Dry Dock Co, NB	17 Oct 1967	29 May 1969	30 July 1970

Displacement, tons: 8380 light; 24 700 full load
Dimensions, feet (metres): 564 × 76 × 30 *(171.9 × 23.2 × 9.1)*
Main machinery: 2 boilers; 1 GE Canada turbine; 21 000 hp *(15.7 MW)*; 1 shaft; bow thruster
Speed, knots: 21. **Range, miles:** 4100 at 20 kts; 7500 at 11.5 kts
Complement: 290 (28 officers)
Cargo capacity: 13 700 tons fuel; 400 tons aviation fuel; 1048 tons dry cargo; 1250 tons ammunition; 2 cranes (15 ton lift)
Guns: 2 FMC 3 in *(76 mm)*/50 Mk 33 (twin). Mounted in the bow and under local control it was removed from both ships in 1983 but replaced in *Protecteur* in 1990 for Gulf deployment only.
2 GE/GDC 20 mm/76 6-barrelled Vulcan Phalanx Mk 15.
Countermeasures: Decoys: 4 Plessey Shield chaff launchers.
ESM: Racal Kestrel SLQ 504; radar warning.
Combat data systems: ADLIPS with Link 11; SATCOM WSC-3(V).
Radars: Surface search: SPS 502 with Mk XII IFF.
Navigation: Sperry Mk II. Racal Decca TM 969; I band.
Tacan: URN 20.
Sonars: Westinghouse SQS 505; hull-mounted; active search.
C-Tech mine avoidance for Gulf.
Helicopters: 3 CH-124A ASW or CH-124B Heltas Sea King.

Comment: An improved design based on the prototype *Provider*. Four replenishment positions. Both have been used as Flagships and troop carriers. They can carry anti-submarine helicopters, military vehicles and bulk equipment for sealift purposes; also four LCVPs. For the Gulf deployment in 1991, the 76 mm gun was remounted, two Vulcan Phalanx and two Bofors 40/60 guns were fitted, 4 Plessey Shield chaff launchers and ESM equipment were provided for *Protecteur*. Additionally, all helicopters carried 12.7 mm MGs and ESM/FLIR equipment instead of ASW gear. Bofors and 76 mm gun later removed from *Protecteur*. Remaining equipment retained and also installed in *Preserver* during her 1992 refit. Weapon system positions in *Protecteur* changed during her 1993/94 refit. *Protecteur* transferred to the Pacific Fleet November 1992.

PRESERVER

3/1993, Diego Quevedo

1 PROVIDER CLASS (OPERATIONAL SUPPORT SHIP)

Name	No	Builders	Laid down	Launched	Commissioned
PROVIDER	AOR 508	Davie Shipbuilding, Lauzon	1 May 1961	5 July 1962	28 Sep 1963

Displacement, tons: 7300 light; 22 000 full load
Dimensions, feet (metres): 555 × 76 × 32 *(169.2 × 23.2 × 9.8)*
Main machinery: 2 boilers; 1 GE Canada steam turbine; 21 000 hp *(15.7 MW)*; 1 shaft
Speed, knots: 21. **Range, miles:** 3600 at 20 kts
Complement: 225 (21 officers)
Cargo capacity: 12 000 tons fuel; 900 tons aviation fuel; 250 tons dry cargo
Countermeasures: ESM: Racal Kestrel SLQ 504; radar warning.
Combat data systems: ADLIPS with Link 11; SATCOM WSC-3(V).
Radars: Navigation: Racal Decca TM 969; I band.
Helicopters: 3 CH-124A Sea King ASW.

Comment: The flight deck can receive the largest and heaviest helicopters. A total of 20 electrohydraulic winches is fitted on deck for ship-to-ship movements of cargo and supplies, as well as shore-to-ship requirements when alongside. Based in the Pacific Fleet. Can be fitted with Bofors and Vulcan Phalanx guns, chaff and ESM if sent on operational deployments.

PROVIDER

10/1993, Giorgio Arra

1 DUN CLASS TANKER

DUNDURN AOTL 502 (ex-AOC 502)

Displacement, tons: 950 light; 1500 full load
Dimensions, feet (metres): 178.8 × 32.2 × 13
(54.5 × 9.8 × 3.9)
Main machinery: 1 Fairbanks-Morse 38D8-1/8-4 diesel; 708 hp (528 kW) sustained; 1 shaft
Speed, knots: 10
Complement: 24
Cargo capacity: 790 tons fuel; 25 tons dry cargo

Comment: Small tanker, classed as fleet auxiliary. Based on west coast.

DUNDURN   10/1992, Canadian Maritime Command

1 FLEET DIVING SUPPORT SHIP

Name	No	Builder	Re-commissioned
CORMORANT (ex-Aspa Quarto)	ASL 20	Marelli, Italy	10 Nov 1978 (CAF)

Displacement, tons: 2350 full load
Dimensions, feet (metres): 245 × 39 × 16.5 (74.7 × 11.9 × 5)
Main machinery: Diesel-electric; 3 Marelli-Deutz ACR 12456 EV diesels; 1800 hp(m) (1.32 MW); 1 shaft; cp prop
Speed, knots: 14. **Range, miles:** 13 000 at 12 kts
Complement: 74
Radars: Navigation: Two Decca 1229; I band.

Comment: Ex-Italian stern trawler bought in 1975 which underwent maintenance and design modification until 1977. She was then taken in hand for conversion by Davie Shipbuilding Ltd, Lauzon, returning to Halifax a year later to commission. She carries two submersibles, SDL-1 and PISCES IV, in a heated hangar, side scan sonar and a ROV. She is capable of conducting mixed gas diving operations to 330 ft (100 m). SDL-1 and PISCES IV are both untethered craft capable of operations to 2000 ft (610 m). SDL-1 has a lock-out compartment to support diving operations on air to 150 ft (45 m). Several high frequency sonic devices are fitted. In 1980, this was the first ship in the Canadian Navy to carry women crew members. To be replaced in the next five years.

CORMORANT   1990, van Ginderen Collection

1 OFFSHORE SUPPORT SHIP

Name	No	Builders	Commissioned
RIVERTON (ex-Smit-Lloyd 112)	AG 121	De Waal, Netherlands	1975

Displacement, tons: 2563 full load
Dimensions, feet (metres): 209 × 43.5 × 16.5 (63.9 × 13.3 × 5.1)
Main machinery: 2 6TM-410 Stork-Werkspoor diesels; 10 100 hp(m) (7.44 MW) sustained; 2 shafts; Kort nozzle bow thrusters
Speed, knots: 15.5. **Range, miles:** 13 000 at 12 kts
Complement: 23 (5 officers)

Comment: An offshore supply and support vessel acquired 3 March 1989 for conversion to a general purpose support ship. Replaced Bluethroat in mid-1990 and used for the CPF first of class trials.

RIVERTON   1991, Canadian Maritime Command

4 TORPEDO AND SHIP RANGING VESSELS (TSRV)

Name	No	Builders	Commissioned
SECHELT	YPT 610	West Coast Manly	10 Nov 1990
SIKANNI	YPT 611	West Coast Manly	10 Nov 1990
SOOKE	YPT 612	West Coast Manly	10 Nov 1990
STIKINE	YPT 613	West Coast Manly	10 Nov 1990

Displacement, tons: 290 full load
Dimensions, feet (metres): 108.5 × 27.8 × 7.8 (33.1 × 8.5 × 2.4)
Main machinery: 2 Caterpillar 3412T diesels; 1080 hp (806 kW) sustained; 2 shafts
Speed, knots: 12.5
Complement: 4

Comment: Based at the Nanoose Bay Maritime Experimental and Test Range. Replaced the 1940s vintage TRVs.

SECHELT   1993, Canadian Maritime Command

5 NAVAL RESERVE TENDERS

ADVERSUS	PB 191	SYDNEY	PB 195
CAPTOR	PB 193	STANDOFF	PB 199
ACADIAN	PB 194		

Displacement, tons: 48 full load (191-195); 85 (199)
Main machinery: 2 Paxman YJCM diesels; 2800 hp (2.1 MW); 2 shafts
Speed, knots: 16. **Range, miles:** 900 at 13 kts
Complement: 18

Comment: 191 to 195, completed by Smith and Rhulorel, Lunenburg, NS in 1968 transferred from RCMP in 1975. 199 transferred in 1980. Some deleted in 1992.

CAPTOR   1991, van Ginderen Collection

5 SERVICE CRAFT

CROSSBOW PB 197		FIREBIRD YTR 561
SERVICE PB 198		FIREBRAND YTR 562
POGO YFL 104		

Comment: The two YTRs are 130 ton firefighting craft. The other three craft are used as Naval Reserve Unit tenders.

TUGS

5 VILLE CLASS

Name	No	Builders	Commissioned
LAWRENCEVILLE	YTL 590	Vito Steel & Barge Co	17 Jan 1974
PARKSVILLE	YTL 591	Vito Steel & Barge Co	17 Jan 1974
LISTERVILLE	YTL 592	Georgetown SY, PEI	31 July 1974
MERRICKVILLE	YTL 593	Georgetown SY, PEI	11 Sep 1974
MARYSVILLE	YTL 594	Georgetown SY, PEI	11 Sep 1974

Displacement, tons: 70 full load
Dimensions, feet (metres): 64 × 15.5 × 9 (19.5 × 4.7 × 2.7)
Main machinery: 1 Diesel; 365 hp (272 kW); 1 shaft
Speed, knots: 9.8

Comment: Small harbour tugs employed at Esquimalt and Halifax.

1 SAINT CLASS

Name	No	Builders	Commissioned
SAINT ANTHONY	ATA 531	St John Dry Dock Co, NB	22 Feb 1957

Displacement, tons: 840 full load
Dimensions, feet (metres): 151.5 × 33 × 17 *(46.2 × 10 × 5.2)*
Main machinery: Diesel; 1920 hp *(1.43 MW)*; 1 shaft
Speed, knots: 14
Complement: 21

Comment: Ocean tug. Authorised under the 1951 Programme. Originally class of three. There are plans to replace this class with two 1500 ton support vessels.

SAINT ANTHONY   1983, Giorgio Arra

1 WOOD CLASS

Name	No	Builders	Commissioned
WILDWOOD	YTL 553	Falconer Marine	1944

Displacement, tons: 65 full load
Dimensions, feet (metres): 60 × 16 × 5 *(18.3 × 4.9 × 1.5)*
Main machinery: 1 diesel; 250 hp; 1 shaft
Speed, knots: 10
Complement: 3

Comment: Used as target towing vessel. Deleted in error in 1990.

5 GLEN CLASS (HARBOUR/COASTAL)

Name	No	Builders	Commissioned
GLENDYNE	YTB 640	Yarrows Ltd, Esquimalt	8 Aug 1975
GLENDALE	YTB 641	Yarrows Ltd, Esquimalt	16 Sep 1975
GLENEVIS	YTB 642	Georgetown SY, PEI	9 Aug 1976
GLENBROOK	YTB 643	Georgetown SY, PEI	16 Dec 1976
GLENSIDE	YTB 644	Georgetown SY, PEI	20 May 1977

Displacement, tons: 255
Dimensions, feet (metres): 92.5 × 28 × 14.5 *(28.2 × 8.5 × 4.4)*
Main machinery: 2 diesels; 1300 hp *(970 kW)*; 2 Voith-Schneider props
Speed, knots: 11.5
Complement: 6

Comment: Two of the class reported in error as sold to McKiel Workboats in late 1980s.

GLENEVIS   2/1993, van Ginderen Collection

COAST GUARD

Administration

Commissioner Canadian Coast Guard/Assistant Deputy Minister Marine:
   John F Thomas

Ships

The Canadian Coast Guard comprises 110 ships and craft of all types, operating in the Atlantic and Pacific coastal waters and from the head of the Great Lakes to the northernmost reaches of Canada's Arctic. The Fleet is composed of icebreakers of various sizes, buoy tenders and lighthouse resupply vessels, specialised vessels for tasks such as search and rescue, oil pollution clean-up, channel sounding and shallow-draught operations in areas such as the Mackenzie River system and Lake Winnipeg. In addition, the Fleet is supplemented by a wide variety of small craft such as shore-based workboats, landing craft and inflatable boats, used on all navigable waterways within Canadian waters.

Establishment

In January 1962 all ships owned and operated by the Federal Department of Transport, with the exception of pilotage and canal craft, were amalgamated into the Canadian Coast Guard Fleet. The Canadian Coast Guard is a civilian organisation and its members are public servants. Its Headquarters is in Ottawa while field operations are administered from five regional offices located in Vancouver, British Columbia; Toronto, Ontario; Quebec, Quebec; Dartmouth, Nova Scotia; and St John's, Newfoundland. The principal bases for the ships and aircraft are: St John's, Newfoundland; Dartmouth, NS; Saint John, NB; Charlottetown, PEI; Quebec and Sorel, Quebec; Prescott, Amherstburg and Parry Sound, Ontario; Victoria and Prince Rupert, BC; and Hay River, Northwest Territories.

Flag and Identity Markings

The Canadian Coast Guard has its own distinctive jack, a red maple leaf on a white ground at the hoist and two gold dolphins on a blue ground at the fly.
Canadian Coast Guard vessels have red hulls with white superstructures. The funnel is white with a red maple leaf on each side. A white diagonal stripe extends aft on the hull below the bridge on both sides. The words 'Coast Guard — Garde Côtière' appear aft of the stripe preceded by a stylised Canadian flag. The markings include the word 'Canada' on each side of the vessel near the stern. Search and Rescue vessels' superstructures are international yellow in colour.

Missions

The Canadian Coast Guard carries out the following missions:
(a) Icebreaking and Escort. Icebreaking and escort of commercial ships is carried out in waters off the Atlantic seaboard, in the Gulf of St Lawrence, St Lawrence River and the Great Lakes in Winter and in Arctic waters in Summer.
(b) Aids to Navigation. Installation, supply and maintenance of fixed and floating aids to navigation in Canadian waters.
(c) Organise and provide icebreaker escort to commercial shipping in support of the annual Northern Sealift which supplies bases and settlements in the Canadian Arctic, Hudson Bay and Foxe Basin.
(d) Provide and operate a wide range of marine search and rescue vessels.
(e) Provide and operate hydrographic survey and sounding vessels for the St Lawrence River Ship Channel.
(f) Operate a fleet of one fixed-wing aircraft and 31 helicopters primarily used for aids to navigation, ice reconnaissance when based in icebreakers, and pollution control work.

Strength of the Fleet

Type	Active
Heavy Icebreakers	7 + 1 (leased)
Navaids Tenders/Light Icebreaker	11
Navaids Tenders/Ice Strengthened	10
Small Navaids Tenders	6
Small River Navaids Tenders	5
Offshore SAR Cutters	3
Intermediate SAR Cutters	2
Small SAR Cutters	5
SAR Lifeboats	21
Small SAR Cutters/Ice Strengthened	2
Small SAR Utility Craft	9
Training Vessel	1
Survey and Sounding Vessel	1
Total	80 + 2

(plus approximately 29 Inshore Rescue Craft)

Note: This list does not include lifeboats, surfboats, self-propelled barges and other small craft which are carried on board the larger vessels. Also excluded are shore-based workboats, floating oil spill boats, oil slick-lickers or any of the small boats which are available for use at the various Canadian Coast Guard Bases and lighthouse stations.

DELETIONS

1991 *Thomas Carleton, George E Darby, Ready, Racer, John A MacDonald, Kenoki, Jackman*
1992 *Spindrift* (old), *Spray, CG 086*
1993 *Mikula, John Cabot*

HEAVY GULF ICEBREAKER

1 GULF CLASS (Type 1300)

Name	No	Builders	Commissioned
LOUIS S ST LAURENT	—	Canadian Vickers Ltd, Montreal	Oct 1969

Displacement, tons: 14 500 full load
Measurement, tons: 10 908 gross; 5370 net
Dimensions, feet (metres): 392.7 × 80.1 × 32.2 *(119.7 × 24.4 × 9.8)*
Main machinery: Diesel-electric; 5 Krupp MaK 16 M 453C diesels; 39 400 hp(m) *(28.96 MW)*; 5 Siemens alternators; 3 GE motors; 27 000 hp(m) *(19.85 MW)*; 3 shafts; bow thruster
Speed, knots: 18. **Range, miles:** 23 000 at 17 kts
Complement: 59
Helicopters: 2 light type, such as BO 105CBS.

Comment: Launched on 3 December 1966. Larger than any of the former Coast Guard icebreakers. Two 49.2 ft *(15 m)* landing craft embarked. Mid-life modernisation July 1988 to early 1993 included replacing main engines with a diesel-electric system, adding a more efficient *Henry Larsen* type ice breaking bow (adds 8 m to length) with an air bubbler system and improving helicopter facilities with a new fixed hangar. In addition the complement was reduced to 59. Based in the Maritimes at Dartmouth, NS.

LOUIS S ST LAURENT   8/1993, Canadian Coast Guard

MEDIUM GULF/RIVER ICEBREAKERS

3 R CLASS (Type 1200)

Name	No	Builders	Commissioned
PIERRE RADISSON	—	Burrard Dry Dock Co, Vancouver, BC	June 1978
SIR JOHN FRANKLIN	—	Burrard Dry Dock Co, Vancouver, BC	Mar 1979
DES GROSEILLIERS	—	Port Weller Dry Dock Co, Ontario	Aug 1983

Displacement, tons: 6400 standard; 8180 (7594, *Des Groseilliers*) full load
Measurement, tons: 5910 gross; 1678 net
Dimensions, feet (metres): 322 × 64 × 23.6 *(98.1 × 19.5 × 7.2)*
Main machinery: Diesel-electric; 6 Montreal Loco 251V-16F diesels; 17 580 hp *(13.1 MW)*; 6 GEC generators; 11.1 MW sustained; 2 motors; 13 600 hp *(10.14 MW)*; 2 shafts
Speed, knots: 16. **Range, miles:** 15 000 at 13.5 kts
Complement: 48
Helicopters: 1 Bell 212.

Comment: First two ordered on 1 May 1975. *Pierre Radisson* launched on 3 June 1977, *Franklin* on 10 March 1978 and *Des Groseilliers* on 20 February 1982. *Franklin* is based at Newfoundland, the other two in the Laurentides at Quebec.

PIERRE RADISSON   *1/1993, van Ginderen Collection*

1 MODIFIED R CLASS (Type 1200)

Name	No	Builders	Commissioned
HENRY LARSEN	—	Versatile Pacific SY, Vancouver, BC	29 June 1988

Displacement, tons: 5798 light; 8290 full load
Measurement, tons: 6172 gross; 1741 net
Dimensions, feet (metres): 327.3 × 64.6 × 24 *(99.8 × 19.7 × 7.3)*
Main machinery: Diesel-electric; 3 Wärtsilä Vasa 16V32 diesel generators; 17.13 MW/60 Hz sustained; 3 motors; 16 320 hp(m) *(12 MW)*; 3 shafts
Speed, knots: 16. **Range, miles:** 15 000 at 13.5 kts
Complement: 52 (15 officers) plus 20 spare berths
Helicopters: 1 Bell 212.

Comment: Contract date 25 May 1984, laid down 23 August 1985, launched 3 January 1987; she is officially designated as 'Medium Gulf/River Icebreaker'. Although similar in many ways to the R class she has a different hull form particularly at the bow and a very different propulsion system. Fitted with Wärtsilä air bubbling system which is also in the *Sir Humphrey Gilbert*. Based at Dartmouth for operations in the Maritimes.

HENRY LARSEN   *5/1992, van Ginderen Collection*

Name	No	Builders	Commissioned
NORMAN McLEOD ROGERS	—	Canadian Vickers Ltd, Montreal	Oct 1969

Displacement, tons: 6320 full load
Measurement, tons: 4179 gross; 1847 net
Dimensions, feet (metres): 294.9 × 62.5 × 20 *(89.9 × 19.1 × 6.1)*
Main machinery: 4 Fairbanks-Morse 38D8-1/8-12 diesels; 8496 hp *(6.34 MW)* sustained; 4 GE generators; 4.8 MW; 2 Ruston RK3CZ diesels; 7520 hp *(5.6 MW)* sustained; 2 GE generators; 2.76 MW; 2 GE motors; 12 000 hp *(8.95 MW)*; 2 shafts
Speed, knots: 15. **Range, miles:** 12 000 at 12 kts
Complement: 33
Helicopters: 1 light type, such as BO.105CBS.

Comment: Type 1200 based on the west coast at Victoria. Laid up in 1993.

NORMAN McLEOD ROGERS   *6/1992, van Ginderen Collection*

ICEBREAKER/SUPPLY TUGS

Name	No	Builders	Commissioned
TERRY FOX	—	Burrard Yarrow, Vancouver	1983

Measurement, tons: 4233 gross; 1955 net
Dimensions, feet (metres): 288.7 × 58.7 × 27.2 *(88 × 17.9 × 8.3)*
Main machinery: 4 Werkspoor 8-cyl 4SA diesels; 23 200 hp(m) *(17 MW)*; 2 shafts; cp props
Speed, knots: 15
Complement: 24

Comment: Initially leased for two years from Gulf Canada Resources during the completion of *Louis S St Laurent* conversion but may now be retained. Commissioned in Coast Guard colours 1 November 1991 and purchased 1 November 1993. Based in the Maritimes at Dartmouth.

TERRY FOX   *7/1992, D Maginley*

Name	No	Builders	Commissioned
ARCTIC IVIK	—	Alliance, Vancouver	1985

Measurement, tons: 1564 gross; 793 net
Dimensions, feet (metres): 224.3 × 47.5 × 16 *(68.4 × 14.5 × 4.9)*
Main machinery: 2 Alpha 4SA 12-cyl diesels; 2 shafts; cp props
Speed, knots: 15

Comment: Leased from Arctic Transportation for one year until July 1994, unless the lease is extended. Operates in the western Arctic.

ARCTIC IVIK   *1993, Canadian Coast Guard*

MAJOR NAVAIDS TENDERS/LIGHT ICEBREAKERS
(Type 1100)

Name	No	Builders	Commissioned
MARTHA L BLACK	—	Versatile Pacific, Vancouver, BC	30 Apr 1986
GEORGE R PEARKES	—	Versatile Pacific, Vancouver, BC	17 Apr 1986
EDWARD CORNWALLIS	—	Marine Industries Ltd, Tracy, Quebec	14 Aug 1986
SIR WILLIAM ALEXANDER	—	Marine Industries Ltd, Tracy, Quebec	13 Feb 1987
SIR WILFRID LAURIER	—	Canadian Shipbuilding Ltd, Collingwood, Ontario	15 Nov 1986
ANN HARVEY	—	Halifax Industries Ltd, Halifax, NS	29 June 1987

Displacement, tons: 4662
Measurement, tons: 3818 *(Martha L Black)*; 3809 *(George R Pearkes)*; 3812 *(Sir Wilfrid Laurier)*; 3727 *(Edward Cornwallis* and *Sir William Alexander)*; 3823 *(Ann Harvey)* gross
Dimensions, feet (metres): 272.2 × 53.1 × 18.9 *(83 × 16.2 × 5.8)*
Main machinery: Diesel-electric; 3 Bombadier/Alco 12V-251 diesels; 8019 hp *(6 MW)* sustained; 3 Canadian GE generators; 6 MW; 2 Canadian GE motors; 7040 hp *(5.25 MW)*; 2 shafts; bow thrusters
Speed, knots: 15.5. **Range, miles:** 6500 at 15 kts
Complement: 28
Helicopters: 1 light type, such as Bell 206L.

Comment: *Black, Laurier* and *Pearkes* based in the Laurentides at Quebec, *Cornwallis* and *Alexander* in the Maritimes at Dartmouth and *Ann Harvey* in Newfoundland.

SIR WILLIAM ALEXANDER   *1990, Canadian Coast Guard*

MARTHA L BLACK   *3/1993, van Ginderen Collection*

Name	No	Builders	Commissioned
GRIFFON	—	Davie Shipbuilding, Lauzon	Dec 1970

Displacement, tons: 3096
Measurement, tons: 2212 gross; 752 net
Dimensions, feet (metres): 233.9 × 49 × 15.5 *(71.3 × 14.9 × 4.7)*
Main machinery: Diesel-electric; 4 Fairbanks-Morse 38D8-1/8-12 diesel generators; 5.8 MW sustained; 2 motors; 5340 hp *(3.98 MW)*; 2 shafts
Speed, knots: 14. **Range, miles:** 5500 at 10 kts
Complement: 28
Helicopters: Platform for 1 light type, such as Bell 206L.

Comment: Based in the Central Region at Prescott, Ontario.

GRIFFON   *2/1993, van Ginderen Collection*

Name	No	Builders	Commissioned
J E BERNIER	—	Davie Shipbuilding, Lauzon	Aug 1967

Displacement, tons: 3096
Measurement, tons: 2457 gross; 705 net
Dimensions, feet (metres): 231 × 49 × 16 *(70.5 × 14.9 × 4.9)*
Main machinery: Diesel-electric; 4 Fairbanks-Morse 4SA 8-cyl diesels; 5600 hp *(4.12 MW)*; 4 generators; 3.46 MW; 2 motors; 4250 hp *(3.13 MW)*; 2 shafts
Speed, knots: 13.5. **Range, miles:** 8000 at 11 kts
Complement: 28
Helicopters: 1 Bell 206L/L-1.

Comment: Based in Newfoundland.

J E BERNIER   *12/1984, van Ginderen Collection*

Name	No	Builders	Commissioned
SIR HUMPHREY GILBERT	—	Davie Shipbuilding, Lauzon	June 1959

Displacement, tons: 3000 full load
Measurement, tons: 2152 gross; 728 net
Dimensions, feet (metres): 228 × 48 × 16.3 *(69.5 × 14.6 × 5)*
Main machinery: Diesel-electric; 4 Fairbanks-Morse 2SA 8-cyl diesels; 5120 hp *(3.77 MW)*; 4 generators; 3.46 MW; 2 motors; 4240 hp *(3.13 MW)*; 2 shafts
Speed, knots: 13. **Range, miles:** 10 000 at 11 kts
Complement: 41
Helicopters: 1 Bell 206L/L-1.

Comment: First Canadian Coast Guard vessel to be fitted with an air-bubbling system. In 1984-85 completed a major refit which included a diesel-electric a/c-a/c propulsion system, the fitting of a new bow and a new derrick. Based at Newfoundland.

SIR HUMPHREY GILBERT   *1989, B Briggs*

MEDIUM NAVAIDS TENDERS/LIGHT ICEBREAKERS
(Type 1050)

Name	No	Builders	Commissioned
SAMUEL RISLEY	—	Vito Construction Ltd, Delta, BC	4 July 1985
EARL GREY	—	Pictou Shipyards Ltd, Pictou, NS	30 May 1986

Displacement, tons: 2935 full load
Measurement, tons: 1988 gross *(Grey)*; 1967 gross *(Risley)*; 642 net *(Grey)*; 649.5 net *(Risley)*
Dimensions, feet (metres): 228.7 × 44.9 × 17.4 *(69.7 × 13.7 × 5.3)*
Main machinery: Diesel-electric; 4 Wärtsilä 4SA 12-cyl diesels; 8644 hp(m) *(6.4 MW) (Samuel Risley)*; 4 Deutz 4SA 9-cyl diesels; 8836 hp(m) *(6.5 MW) (Earl Grey)*; 2 shafts; cp props
Speed, knots: 13
Complement: 24

Comment: *Risley* based in the Central Region at Thunder Bay, Ontario, *Grey* in the Maritimes at Charlottetown, PEI.

SAMUEL RISLEY   *4/1993, Canadian Coast Guard*

MEDIUM NAVAIDS TENDERS/ICE STRENGTHENED
(Type 1000)

Name	No	Builders	Commissioned
TUPPER	—	Marine Industries Ltd, Sorel	Dec 1959
SIMON FRASER	—	Burrard Dry Dock Co, Vancouver	Feb 1960

Displacement, tons: 1375 full load
Measurement, tons: 1358 gross; 419 net
Dimensions, feet (metres): 204.5 × 42 × 15.1 (62.4 × 12.8 × 4.6)
Main machinery: Diesel-electric; 2 Fairbanks-Morse 2SA 8-cyl diesels (Tupper); 2 Alco 4SA 12-cyl diesels (Simon Fraser); 3330 hp (2.45 MW); 2 generators; 2.3 MW; 2 motors; 1900 hp (2.16 MW); 2 shafts
Speed, knots: 13. **Range, miles:** 5000 at 10 kts
Complement: 37; 25 (Simon Fraser)
Helicopters: Platform for 1 Bell 206L/L-1.

Comment: Both based in the Maritimes; Simon Fraser at Dartmouth and Tupper at Charlottetown, PEI.

TUPPER   1989, R Cotie

Name	No	Builders	Commissioned
NARWHAL	—	Canadian Vickers Ltd, Montreal	July 1963

Displacement, tons: 2220 full load
Measurement, tons: 2064 gross; 935 net
Dimensions, feet (metres): 259.8 × 42 × 12.5 (79.2 × 12.8 × 3.8)
Main machinery: 2 Cooper-Bessemer diesels; 3000 hp (2.9 MW); 2 shafts
Speed, knots: 12. **Range, miles:** 9500 at 10 kts
Complement: 38
Helicopters: 1 light type, such as BO 105CBS.

Comment: Re-engined in 1985. Helicopter deck and hangar added. Based on the west coast at Victoria.

NARWHAL   6/1992, van Ginderen Collection

Name	No	Builders	Commissioned
TRACY	—	Port Weller Drydocks, Ontario	1968

Displacement, tons: 1300
Measurement, tons: 963 gross; 290 net
Dimensions, feet (metres): 181.1 × 38 × 12.1 (55.2 × 11.6 × 3.7)
Main machinery: Diesel-electric; 2 Fairbanks-Morse 38D8-1/8-8 diesel generators; 1.94 MW sustained; 2 motors; 2000 hp (1.49 MW); 2 shafts
Speed, knots: 13. **Range, miles:** 5000 at 11 kts
Complement: 30

Comment: Based in Laurentides at Sorel.

TRACY   9/1993, van Ginderen Collection

Name	No	Builders	Commissioned
BARTLETT	—	Marine Industries, Sorel	1969
PROVO WALLIS	—	Marine Industries, Sorel	1969

Displacement, tons: 1620
Measurement, tons: 1317 gross; 491 net
Dimensions, feet (metres): 189.3; 209 (Provo Wallis) × 42.5 × 15.4 (57.7; 63.7 × 13 × 4.7)
Main machinery: 2 National Gas 6-cyl diesels; 2100 hp (1.55 MW); 2 shafts; cp props
Speed, knots: 12.5. **Range, miles:** 3300 at 11 kts
Complement: 29

Comment: Both Type 1000. Bartlett based in Western Region at Victoria, Wallis in the Maritimes at St Johns, New Brunswick. Bartlett was modernised in 1988 and Wallis completed one year modernisation at Marystown, Newfoundland at the end of 1990. Work included lengthening the hull by 6 m, installing new equipment and improving accommodation.

PROVO WALLIS   4/1991, Canadian Coast Guard

Name	No	Builders	Commissioned
SIMCOE	—	Canadian Vickers Ltd, Montreal	1962

Displacement, tons: 1300 full load
Measurement, tons: 961 gross; 361 net
Dimensions, feet (metres): 179.1 × 38 × 12.5 (54.6 × 11.6 × 3.8)
Main machinery: Diesel-electric; 2 Paxman 4SA 12-cyl diesels; 3000 hp (2.24 MW); 2 motors; 2000 hp (1.49 MW); 2 shafts
Speed, knots: 13. **Range, miles:** 5000 at 10 kts
Complement: 29

Comment: Based in Central Region at Prescott, Ontario.

SIMCOE   10/1989, van Ginderen Collection

SMALL NAVAIDS TENDERS/ICE STRENGTHENED
(Type 900)

Name	No	Builders	Commissioned
SIR JAMES DOUGLAS	—	Burrard Dry Dock Co	Nov 1956

Measurement, tons: 564 gross; 173 net
Dimensions, feet (metres): 149.6 × 30.8 × 10.5 (45.6 × 9.4 × 3.2)
Main machinery: 2 diesels; 850 hp (634 kW); 2 shafts
Speed, knots: 12
Complement: 31

Comment: Based in the Western Region at Victoria.

SIR JAMES DOUGLAS   6/1992, van Ginderen Collection

Name	No	Builders	Commissioned
MONTMAGNY	—	Russel Bros, Owen Sound, Ontario	May 1963

Displacement, tons: 565 full load
Measurement, tons: 497 gross; 195 net
Dimensions, feet (metres): 148 × 28.9 × 8.5 *(45.1 × 8.8 × 2.6)*
Main machinery: Diesel; 1000 hp *(746 kW)*; 2 shafts
Speed, knots: 12
Complement: 23

Comment: Based in Laurentides at Sorel. To be paid off in April 1994.

MONTMAGNY   *3/1993, van Ginderen Collection*

Name	No	Builders	Commissioned
NAMAO	—	Riverton Boat Works, Manitoba	1975

Displacement, tons: 380
Measurement, tons: 318 gross; 107 net
Dimensions, feet (metres): 110 × 28 × 7 *(33.5 × 8.5 × 2.1)*
Main machinery: 2 diesels; 1350 hp *(1 MW)*; 2 shafts
Speed, knots: 12
Complement: 11

Comment: Based in the Central Region on Lake Winnipeg at Selkirk.

SHIPBORNE AIRCRAFT

Numbers/Type: 2 Bell 206B JetRanger.
Operational speed: 115 kts *(213 km/h)*.
Service ceiling: 13 500 ft *(4115 m)*.
Range: 368 nm *(682 km)*.
Role/Weapon systems: Liaison and limited SAR helicopter. Sensors: None. Weapons: None.

Numbers/Type: 5/2 Bell 206L/206L-1 LongRanger.
Operational speed: 108 kts *(200 km/h)*.
Service ceiling: 19 000 ft *(5795 m)*.
Range: 304 nm *(563 km)*.
Role/Weapon systems: Liaison and limited SAR. Sensors: None. Weapons: None.

Numbers/Type: 5 Bell 212.
Operational speed: 100 kts *(185 km/h)*.
Service ceiling: 13 200 ft *(4023 m)*.
Range: 224 nm *(415 km)*.
Role/Weapon systems: Liaison and medium support helicopter. Sensors: None. Weapons: None.

Numbers/Type: 16 MBB BO 105CBS.
Operational speed: 110 kts *(204 km/h)*.
Service ceiling: 20 000 ft *(6090 m)*.
Range: 278 nm *(515 km)*.
Role/Weapon systems: Liaison, SAR and shipborne reconnaissance duties; replaces older single-engined types. Sensors: None. Weapons: None.

BO 105   *1991*

Numbers/Type: 1 Sikorsky S-61N.
Operational speed: 121 kts *(224 km/h)*.
Service ceiling: 12 500 ft *(3810 m)*.
Range: 440 nm *(815 km)*.
Role/Weapon systems: Based on west coast for long-range SAR and navigational aids. Sensors: Bendix search radar. Weapons: None.

SMALL NAVAIDS TENDERS (Type 800)

Name	No	Builders	Commissioned
PARTRIDGE ISLAND	—	Breton Industries, Port Hawkesbury, NS	31 Oct 1985
ILE DES BARQUES	—	Breton Industries, Port Hawkesbury, NS	26 Nov 1985
ILE SAINT-OURS	—	Breton Industries, Port Hawkesbury, NS	15 May 1986
CARIBOU ISLE	—	Breton Industries, Port Hawkesbury, NS	16 June 1986

Measurement, tons: 92 gross; 36 net
Dimensions, feet (metres): 75.5 × 19.7 × 4.4 *(23 × 6 × 1.4)*
Main machinery: 2 diesels; 475 hp *(354 kW)*; 2 shafts
Speed, knots: 11
Complement: 5

Comment: *Partridge Island* based in the Maritimes at St Johns, New Brunswick, *Caribou Isle* in the Central Region at Sault Ste Marie, Ontario, and the other two in the Laurentides at Sorel.

ILE SAINT-OURS   *4/1992, van Ginderen Collection*

Name	No	Builders	Commissioned
COVE ISLE	—	Canadian D and D, Kingston, Ontario	1980
GULL ISLE	—	Canadian D and D, Kingston, Ontario	1980

Measurement, tons: 80 gross; 33 net
Dimensions, feet (metres): 65.6 × 19.7 × 4.6 *(20 × 6 × 1.4)*
Main machinery: 2 diesels; 373 hp *(278 kW)*; 2 shafts
Speed, knots: 10
Complement: 5

Comment: Based in Central Region at Parry Sound, Ontario.

SPECIAL RIVER NAVAIDS TENDERS (Type 700)

Name	No	Builders	Commissioned
NAHIDIK	—	Allied Shipbuilders Ltd, N Vancouver	1974

Measurement, tons: 856 gross; 392 net
Dimensions, feet (metres): 175.2 × 49.9 × 6.6 *(53.4 × 15.2 × 2)*
Main machinery: 2 diesels; 4290 hp *(3.2 MW)*; 2 shafts
Speed, knots: 14
Complement: 15

Comment: Based at Hay River, North West Territories.

NAHIDIK   *1991, Canadian Coast Guard*

Name	No	Builders	Commissioned
DUMIT	—	Allied Shipbuilders Ltd, N Vancouver	1979

Measurement, tons: 569 gross; 176 net
Dimensions, feet (metres): 160.1 × 40 × 5.2 *(48.8 × 12.2 × 1.6)*
Main machinery: 2 diesels; 839 hp *(626 kW)*; 2 shafts
Speed, knots: 12
Complement: 10

Comment: Similar to *Eckaloo*. Based at Hay River, North West Territories.

Name	No	Builders	Commissioned
TEMBAH	—	Allied Shipbuilders Ltd, N Vancouver	1963

Measurement, tons: 189 gross; 58 net
Dimensions, feet (metres): 123 × 25.9 × 3 *(37.5 × 7.9 × 0.9)*
Main machinery: 2 diesels; 500 hp *(373 kW)*; 2 shafts
Speed, knots: 13
Complement: 9

Comment: Based at Hay River, North West Territories.

TEMBAH   *1978, Canadian Coast Guard*

Name	No	Builders	Commissioned
ECKALOO	—	Vancouver SY Ltd	July 1988

Displacement, tons: 534
Measurement, tons: 661 gross; 213 net
Dimensions, feet (metres): 160.8 × 44 × 4 *(49 × 13.4 × 1.2)*
Main machinery: 2 Caterpillar 3512TA; 2420 hp *(1.8 MW)* sustained; 2 shafts
Speed, knots: 13
Complement: 9
Helicopters: Platform for 1 Bell 206L/L-1.

Comment: Replaced vessel of the same name. Similar design to *Dumit*. Based at Hay River, North West Territories.

ECKALOO   *7/1988, Murray McLellan*

Name	No	Builders	Commissioned
MISKINAW	—	Allied Shipbuilders Ltd, N Vancouver	1958

Measurement, tons: 104 gross; 47 net
Dimensions, feet (metres): 64 × 19.7 × 3.9 *(19.5 × 6 × 1.2)*
Main machinery: 2 diesels; 358 hp *(267 kW)*; 2 shafts
Speed, knots: 10
Complement: 8

Comment: Based at Fort McMurray, Alta.

LARGE SEARCH AND RESCUE CUTTERS (Type 600)

Name	No	Builders	Commissioned
ALERT	—	Davie Shipbuilding, Lauzon	1969

Displacement, tons: 2025
Measurement, tons: 1752 gross; 495 net
Dimensions, feet (metres): 234.3 × 39.7 × 16.1 *(71.4 × 12.1 × 4.9)*
Main machinery: 4 Fairbanks-Morse 2SA 12-cyl diesels; 10 560 hp *(7.77 MW)*; 2 shafts
Speed, knots: 18.5
Complement: 25
Helicopters: 1 light type, such as BO 105CBS.

Comment: Based in the Maritimes at Dartmouth.

ALERT   *1983, Canadian Coast Guard*

Name	No	Builders	Commissioned
SIR WILFRED GRENFELL	—	Marystown SY, Newfoundland	1987

Displacement, tons: 3753
Measurement, tons: 2403 gross; 664.5 net
Dimensions, feet (metres): 224.7 × 49.2 × 16.4 *(68.5 × 15 × 5)*
Main machinery: 4 Deutz 4SA (2—16-cyl, 2—9-cyl) diesels; 12 862 hp(m) *(9.46 MW)*; 2 shafts; cp props
Speed, knots: 16
Complement: 20

Comment: Built on speculation in 1984/85. Modified to include an 85 tonne towing winch and additional SAR accommodation and equipment; replaced *Grenfell* in December 1987. Based at St John's, Newfoundland.

SIR WILFRED GRENFELL   *1989, Canadian Coast Guard*

Name	No	Builders	Commissioned
MARY HICHENS	—	Marystown SY, Newfoundland	1983

Displacement, tons: 3262
Measurement, tons: 1684 gross; 696 net
Dimensions, feet (metres): 210 × 45 × 19.7 *(64 × 13.8 × 6)*
Main machinery: 2 Burmeister & Wain Alpha 18 V 28/32-VO diesels; 10 800 hp(m) *(7.94 MW)* sustained; 2 shafts; 2 Kort nozzle cp props; bow thrusters
Speed, knots: 15
Complement: 18

Comment: Based in the Maritimes Region at Dartmouth.

MARY HICHENS   *7/1992, D Maginley*

INTERMEDIATE SAR CUTTERS (Type 500)

Name	No	Builders	Commissioned
GORDON REID	—	Versatile Pacific, Vancouver	Oct 1990
JOHN JACOBSON	—	Versatile Pacific, Vancouver	Nov 1990

Measurement, tons: 836 gross
Dimensions, feet (metres): 163.9 × 36.1 × 13.1 *(49.9 × 11 × 4)*
Main machinery: 4 Deutz SBV-6M-628 diesels; 2475 hp(m) *(1.82 MW)* sustained; 2 shafts; bow thruster; 400 hp *(294 kW)*
Speed, knots: 16. **Range, miles:** 2500 at 15 kts
Complement: 14 plus 8 spare

Comment: Type 500 Intermediate cutters. Designed for long-range patrols along the British Columbian coast out to 200 mile limit. They have a stern ramp for launching Zodiac Hurricane 733 rigid inflatables in up to Sea State 6. The Zodiac has a speed of 50 kts and is radar equipped. Both based in the Western Region at Victoria.

GORDON REID   *1992, Canadian Coast Guard*

SMALL SEARCH AND RESCUE CUTTERS (Type 400)

Name	No	Builders	Commissioned
SPUME	—	Crew Ltd, Prescott, Ontario	1963

Measurement, tons: 56 gross; 17 net
Dimensions, feet (metres): 69.9 × 16.7 × 4.6 *(21.3 × 5.1 × 1.4)*
Main machinery: 2 diesels; 1064 hp *(794 kW)*; 2 shafts
Speed, knots: 12.5
Complement: 4

Comment: Employed on Great Lakes patrol in the Central Region at Meaford. In reserve in 1994.

Name	No	Builders	Commissioned
POINT HENRY	—	Breton Industrial and Machinery	1980
ISLE ROUGE	—	Breton Industrial and Machinery	1980
POINT RACE	—	Pt Hawkesbury, NS	1982
CAPE HURD	—	Pt Hawkesbury, NS	1982

Displacement, tons: 49
Measurement, tons: 57 gross; 14 net
Dimensions, feet (metres): 70.8 × 18 × 5.6 *(21.6 × 5.5 × 1.7)*
Main machinery: 2 MTU 8V 396 TC82 diesels; 1740 hp(m) *(1.28 MW)* sustained; 2 shafts
Speed, knots: 20
Complement: 5

Comment: Aluminium alloy hulls. *Point Henry* based in Western Region, *Cape Hurd* in Central Region, and the other two in the Laurentides.

CAPE HURD   *1992, D N Glen*

SAR LIFEBOATS (Type 300)

Name	Builders	Commissioned
WESTPORT	Paspediac, Quebec	1969
BAMFIELD	McKay Cormack Ltd, Victoria, BC	1970
TOFINO	McKay Cormack Ltd, Victoria, BC	1970
PORT HARDY (ex-*Bull Harbour*)	McKay Cormack Ltd, Victoria, BC	1973
BURIN	Georgetown SY, PEI	1974
TOBERMORY	Georgetown SY, PEI	1974
WESTFORT (ex-*Thunder Bay*)	Georgetown SY, PEI	1974
BURGEO	Georgetown SY, PEI	1974
SHIPPEGAN	Eastern Equipment, Montreal, Quebec	1975
CLARK'S HARBOUR	Eastern Equipment, Montreal, Quebec	1975
SAMBRO	Eastern Equipment, Montreal, Quebec	1975
LOUISBOURG	Eastern Equipment, Montreal, Quebec	1975
PORT MOUTON	Georgetown SY, PEI	1982
CAP AUX MEULES	Georgetown SY, PEI	1982
SOURIS	Hike Metal Products Ltd, Wheatley, Ontario	1985
CAP GOÉLANDS	Hike Metal Products Ltd, Wheatley, Ontario	1985
CGR 100	Hurricane Rescue Craft, Richmond, BC	1986

Measurement, tons: 10 gross
Dimensions, feet (metres): 44.1 × 12.7 × 3.4 *(13.5 × 3.9 × 1)*
Main machinery: 2 diesels; 485 hp *(362 kW)*; 2 shafts
Speed, knots: 12.5; 26 *(CGR 100)*
Complement: 3 or 4

Comment: Seven based in the Maritimes, three Western, four Central, two Newfoundland and one in Laurentides. *CGR 100* is a self-righting Medina lifeboat (Type 300B) and has a speed of 26 kts.

TOFINO   *7/1988, Florian Jentsch*

Name	No	Builders	Commissioned
BICKERTON	—	Halmatic, Havant	Aug 1989
SPINDRIFT	—	Georgetown SY, PEI	Oct 1993
—	—	Industrie Raymond, Quebec	1994
—	—	Industrie Raymond, Quebec	1994

Measurement, tons: 34 gross
Dimensions, feet (metres): 52 × 17.5 × 4.6 *(15.9 × 5.3 × 1.5)*
Main machinery: 2 Caterpillar 3408BTA diesels; 1070 hp *(786 kW)* sustained; 2 shafts
Speed, knots: 16

Comment: Arun Type 300A high endurance lifeboats. First two based in the Maritimes. *Bickerton* has a GRP hull, remainder aluminium. More powerful engines may be fitted in due course.

BICKERTON   *7/1989, J Carter*

SMALL SAR CUTTERS/ICE STRENGTHENED
(Type 200)

Name	No	Builders	Commissioned
HARP	—	Georgetown SY, PEI	12 Dec 1986
HOOD	—	Georgetown SY, PEI	12 Dec 1986

Displacement, tons: 225
Measurement, tons: 179 gross; 69 net
Dimensions, feet (metres): 80.4 × 27.6 × 7.9 *(24.5 × 8.5 × 2.4)*
Main machinery: 2 diesels; 850 hp *(634 kW)*; 2 shafts
Speed, knots: 10. **Range, miles:** 500 at 10 kts
Complement: 7 plus 10 spare berths

Comment: Ordered 26 April 1985 and launched in September and November 1986. Based in Newfoundland.

HARP   *1992, Canadian Coast Guard*

SMALL SAR UTILITY CRAFT (Type 100)

Note: There are also 29 Inshore Rescue boats with CG numbers.

Name	Measurement, tons	Speed, knots	Built
BITTERN	20 gross	26	1982
SORA	20 gross	12	1968
SWIFT	5 gross	36	1981
CG 119	20 gross	18	1973
AVOCET (ex-*Sterne*)	20 gross	15	1973

Comment: All based in Central Region except *Swift* which is in reserve at Vancouver.

CG 119   *1990, van Ginderen Collection*

Name	Builders	Commissioned
MALLARD	Matsumoto Shipyard, Vancouver, B C	1985
SKUA	Matsumoto Shipyard, Vancouver, B C	1986
OSPREY	Matsumoto Shipyard, Vancouver, B C	1986
STERNE	Matsumoto Shipyard, Vancouver, B C	1987

Measurement, tons: 15 gross
Dimensions, feet (metres): 40.8 × 13.2 × 4.2 *(12.4 × 4.1 × 1.3)*
Main machinery: 2 diesels; 637 hp *(475 kW)*; 2 shafts
Speed, knots: 26
Complement: 3

Comment: *Sterne* based at Quebec, remainder in Western Region.

CCG COLLEGE CADET SEA TRAINING VESSELS

Note: In addition to *Robert Foulis* there are three 10.5 m craft, *Mink*, *Martin* and *Muskrat*.

Name	No	Builders	Commissioned
ROBERT FOULIS	—	St John Dry Dock Co, NB	1969

Displacement, tons: 260
Measurement, tons: 258 gross; 29 net
Dimensions, feet (metres): 104 × 25 × 7.9 *(31.7 × 7.6 × 2.4)*
Main machinery: 2 diesels; 960 hp *(716 kW)*; 2 shafts
Speed, knots: 12
Complement: 12

Comment: Used as CG College training ship and based at Sydney, Nova Scotia.

ROBERT FOULIS (at CG College)   6/1992, D Maginley

SURVEY AND SOUNDING VESSELS

Note: Two catamaran vessels are planned for 1994/95.

Name	No	Builders	Commissioned
NICOLET	—	Collingwood SY, Ontario	1966

Displacement, tons: 935 full load
Measurement, tons: 887 gross; 147 net
Dimensions, feet (metres): 169.6 × 36.4 × 10.2 *(51.7 × 11.1 × 3.1)*
Main machinery: 2 diesels; 1237 hp *(923 kW)*; 2 shafts; cp props
Speed, knots: 13
Complement: 27

Comment: Based in Laurentides. To be paid off in 1994.

NICOLET   9/1993, van Ginderen Collection

HOVERCRAFT

2 SRN 6 TYPE

CG 039   CG 045

Displacement, tons: 10.9 full load
Dimensions, feet (metres): 48.5 × 23 × 3.9 (skirt) *(14.8 × 7 × 1.2)*
Main machinery: 1 RR Gnome 1050 gas-turbine; 1050 hp *(783 kW)* sustained
Speed, knots: 60. **Range, miles:** 170 at 54 kts
Complement: 3

Comment: Built in 1968 and 1977. Based at Sea Island and Parksville, both in the Western Region. Can carry up to six tons of equipment. One of the class scrapped in 1992.

SRN 6 Type   1986, Canadian Coast Guard

1 + 1 AP. I-88/200/400 TYPES

Name	No	Builders	Commissioned
WABAN-AKI	—	Westland Aerospace	15 July 1987

Displacement, tons: 47.6 light
Dimensions, feet (metres): 80.4 × 36.7 × 19.6 *(24.5 × 11.2 × 6.6)* (height on cushion)
Main machinery: 4 diesels
Speed, knots: 50; 35 cruising
Complement: 3
Cargo capacity: 12 tons

Comment: *Waban-Aki* is based at Quebec and capable of year round operation as a Navaid Tender for flood control operations in the St Lawrence. Fitted with a hydraulic crane. The name means People of the Dawn. Second of class ordered in January 1993 (Type 400) with a crane for buoy tending operations. Planned to be in service in September 1994. More may be acquired in due course.

WABAN-AKI   5/1993, van Ginderen Collection

DEPARTMENT OF FISHERIES AND OCEANS

Senior Appointment

Director, Ship Branch:
Commodore D Wight

General

The department has two separate fleets. The hydrographic, oceanographic and fishery research vessels are painted white with buff masts and buff funnels with black tops. They are based on the East Coast at the Bedford Institute of Oceanography, Dartmouth NS and at St Johns, Newfoundland; on the West Coast at the Pacific Institute of Ocean Sciences, Sidney, BC; and in the Great Lakes at the Canada Centre for Inland Waters at Burlington, Ontario.

The fishery patrol vessels are painted grey with the departmental crest on the funnel. They are based in their respective patrol areas. These vessels can be armed with machine guns and carry armed boarding parties. In 1993 only Newfoundland based vessels were armed.

Apart from the major vessels whose details are given below there are over 300 medium and small patrol craft.

DELETIONS

FISHERY PATROL VESSELS

Name	Builders	Commissioned
LEONARD J COWLEY	Manly Shipyard, RivTow Ind, Vancouver BC	1985

Measurement, tons: 2244 grt
Dimensions, feet (metres): 236.2 × 45.9 × 16.1 *(72 × 14 × 4.9)*
Main machinery: 2 Nohab diesels; 2325 hp(m) *(1.71 MW)*; 1 shaft
Speed, knots: 14. **Range, miles:** 12 000 at 14 kts
Complement: 19
Guns: 2—12.7 mm MGs.
Helicopters: Capability for one light.

Comment: Based in Newfoundland.

LEONARD J COWLEY   6/1992, Harald Carstens

Name	Builders	Commissioned
CYGNUS	Marystown SY, Newfoundland	1981
CAPE ROGER	Ferguson Industries, Pictou NS	1977

Measurement, tons: 1255 grt
Dimensions, feet (metres): 205 × 40 × 13 *(62.5 × 12.2 × 4.1)*
Main machinery: 2 Nohab diesels, 2400 hp(m) *(1.76 MW)*; 1 shaft
Speed, knots: 16. **Range, miles:** 2450 at 10 kts
Complement: 19
Guns: 2—12.7 mm MGs.
Helicopters: Capability for one light.

Comment: *Cygnus* based in Nova Scotia, *Cape Roger* in Newfoundland. Two crews per ship work a 14 day patrol cycle.

CYGNUS   *1989, DFO*

Name	Builders	Commissioned
JAMES SINCLAIR	Manly Shipyard, RivTow Ind, Vancouver BC	1981

Measurement, tons: 323 grt
Dimensions, feet (metres): 124 × 27.5 × 12 *(37.8 × 8.4 × 3.7)*
Main machinery: 2 MTU diesels; 4600 hp(m) *(3.38 MW)*; 2 shafts
Speed, knots: 16.5
Complement: 14
Guns: 2—12.7 mm MGs.

Comment: Based in British Columbia.

JAMES SINCLAIR   *6/1992, Harald Carstens*

Name	Builders	Commissioned
TANU	Yarrows Ltd, Victoria BC	1968

Measurement, tons: 746 grt
Dimensions, feet (metres): 179.5 × 32.8 × 10.8 *(54.7 × 10 × 3.3)*
Main machinery: 1 diesel; 2624 hp *(1.96 MW)*; 1 shaft
Speed, knots: 12.
Complement: 18
Guns: 2—12.7 mm MGs.

Comment: Based in British Columbia.

TANU   *1990, van Ginderen Collection*

Name	Builders	Commissioned
CHEBUCTO	Ferguson Industries, Pictou NS	1966

Measurement, tons: 751 grt
Dimensions, feet (metres): 179 × 31 × 15 *(54.6 × 9.4 × 3.6)*
Main machinery: 2 Fairbanks-Morse diesels; 2560 hp *(1.91 MW)*; 2 shafts
Speed, knots: 14. **Range, miles:** 7320 at 10 kts
Complement: 21
Guns: 2—12.7 mm MGs.

Comment: Based in Nova Scotia. Mid-life refit in 1987. Operates a two crew system changing every 14 days.

CHEBUCTO   *1989, DFO*

SURVEY AND RESEARCH VESSELS

Name	Commissioned	Based	Displacement, tons	Complement
HUDSON	1963	East Coast	4800	71 (31 scientists)
MATTHEW	1990	East Coast	950	17 (5 scientists)
F C G SMITH	1986	East Coast	300	11 (4 scientists)
JOHN P TULLY	1985	West Coast	1800	33 (15 scientists)
PARIZEAU	1967	East Coast	1787	37 (13 scientists)
VECTOR	1967	West Coast	520	22 (8 scientists)
LOUIS M LAUZIER (ex-*Cape Harrison*)	1977	Great Lakes	267	20 (8 scientists)
LIMNOS	1968	Great Lakes	—	29 (14 scientists)
R B YOUNG	1990	West Coast	320	11 (5 scientists)
LOUISBOURG	1977	St Lawrence	295	20 (8 scientists)

JOHN P TULLY   *1993, DFO*

MATTHEW   *1991, Bedford Institute of Oceanography*

FISHERY RESEARCH VESSELS

Name	Commissioned	Based	Complement
ALFRED NEEDLER	1982	Nova Scotia	37 (15 scientists)
WILFRED TEMPLEMAN	1982	Nova Scotia	37 (15 scientists)
E E PRINCE	1966	Nova Scotia	20 (6 scientists)
W E RICKER	1978	West Coast	36 (12 scientists)
(ex-*Callistratus*)			

E E PRINCE   *1990, DFO*   ALFRED NEEDLER   *1989, DFO*

CAPE VERDE

Personnel

1994: 230

Bases

Praia, main naval base.
Porto Grande (Isle de Sao Vicente), naval repair yard.

Mercantile Marine

Lloyd's Register of Shipping:
   41 vessels of 22 728 tons gross

PATROL FORCES

3 ZHUK CLASS (TYPE 1400) (COASTAL PATROL CRAFT)

Displacement, tons: 39 full load
Dimensions, feet (metres): 78.7 × 16.4 × 3.9 *(24 × 5 × 1.2)*
Main machinery: 2 Type M 401B diesels; 2200 hp(m) *(1.6 MW)* sustained; 2 shafts
Speed, knots: 30. **Range, miles:** 1100 at 15 kts
Complement: 11 (3 officers)
Guns: 4—14.5 mm (2 twin) MGs.
Radars: Surface search: Spin Trough; I band.

Comment: Transferred from USSR in 1980. Only one was operational in 1993.

ZHUK   *1988, S S Breyer*

1 BIYA CLASS (TYPE 871) (SURVEY SHIP)

5th JULY A 450

Displacement, tons: 750 full load
Dimensions, feet (metres): 180.4 × 32.1 × 8.5 *(55 × 9.8 × 2.6)*
Main machinery: 2 diesels; 1200 hp(m) *(882 kW)*; 2 shafts; cp props
Speed, knots: 13. **Range, miles:** 4700 at 11 kts
Complement: 25

Comment: Transferred from USSR in 1979. Class built at Northern Shipyard Gdansk in Poland 1972-76. Probably non-operational.

BIYA (Libyan colours)   *10/1993, van Ginderen Collection*

2 SHERSHEN CLASS (FAST ATTACK CRAFT)

451   452

Displacement, tons: 145 standard; 170 full load
Dimensions, feet (metres): 113.8 × 22 × 4.9 *(34.7 × 6.7 × 1.5)*
Main machinery: 3 Type M 503A diesels; 8025 hp(m) *(5.9 MW)* sustained; 3 shafts
Speed, knots: 45. **Range, miles:** 460 at 42 kts; 850 at 30 kts
Complement: 23
Guns: 4 USSR 30 mm/65 (2 twin); 85° elevation; 500 rounds/minute to 5 km *(2.7 nm)*; weight of shell 0.54 kg.
Depth charges: 12.
Radars: Surface search: Pot Head; I band; range 37 km *(20 nm)*.
Fire control: Drum Tilt; H/I band.

Comment: Supplied without the usual four torpedo tubes. Delivered from USSR March and July 1979. Class built in period 1962-74.

SHERSHEN 451 and 452   *1991, van Ginderen Collection*

5 + (3) PETERSON Mk 4 TYPE (COASTAL PATROL CRAFT)

Displacement, tons: 22 full load
Dimensions, feet (metres): 51.3 × 14.8 × 4.3 *(15.6 × 4.5 × 1.3)*
Main machinery: 2 Detroit 6V-92TA diesels; 520 hp *(388 kW)* sustained; 2 shafts
Speed, knots: 24. **Range, miles:** 500 at 20 kts
Complement: 6
Guns: 2—12.7 mm MGs (twin). 2—7.62 mm MGs (twin).
Radars: Surface search: I band.

Comment: Ordered from Peterson Builders Inc (PBI), Sturgeon Bay, under FMS programme on 25 September 1992. First of five completed in December 1993. Option on three more. Aluminium hulls. The 12.7 mm mounting is aft with the smaller guns on the bridge roof.

Mk 4 CPC (US colours)   *11/1993, Peterson Builders*

CHILE

Headquarters' Appointments

Commander-in-Chief:
  Admiral Jorge Martinez
Chief of the Naval Staff:
  Vice Admiral Alfredo Gallegos
Flag Officer, Fleet:
  Vice Admiral Jorge Llorente
Flag Officer, Submarines:
  Rear Admiral Jorge Arancibia
Flag Officer, Naval Aviation:
  Rear Admiral Eduardo Schnaidt
Flag Officer, Marines:
  Rear Admiral Miguel Alvarez
Flag Officer, Maritime Territory:
  Vice Admiral Juan Mackay
Flag Officer, 1st Naval Zone:
  Vice Admiral Ariel Rosas
Flag Officer, 2nd Naval Zone:
  Rear Admiral Jorge Balaresque
Flag Officer, 3rd Naval Zone:
  Rear Admiral Arturo Oxley
Flag Officer, 4th Naval Zone:
  Rear Admiral Eduardo Berardi

Diplomatic Representation

Naval Attaché in London, The Hague and Stockholm:
  Rear Admiral Hugo Bruna
Naval Attaché in Washington:
  Rear Admiral Roman Fritis
Naval Attaché in Paris:
  Captain Enrique Leddihn
Naval Attaché in Buenos Aires:
  Captain Jorge Marchant
Naval Attaché in Brasilia:
  Captain Raul Silva
Naval Attaché in Quito:
  Captain Carlos Sanchez
Naval Attaché in Tel Aviv:
  Commander Juan Illanes
Naval Attaché in Lima:
  Captain Juan Pattillo
Naval Attaché in Madrid:
  Captain Pedro Frioli
Naval Attaché in Bogotá:
  Captain Ricardo Leon

Personnel

(a) 1994: 24 500 (excluding Marines) (2000 officers)
(b) 2 years' national service

Command Organisation

1st Naval Zone. HQ at Valparaiso. From 26°S to Topocalma Point (33°S).
2nd Naval Zone. HQ at Talcahuano. From Topocalma Point to 47°S.
3rd Naval Zone. HQ at Punta Arenas. From 47°S to South Pole including Beagle Naval District.
4th Naval Zone. HQ at Iquique. From Peruvian frontier to 26°S.

Naval Air Stations and Organisation

Having won the battle to own all military aircraft flying over the sea, a fixed-wing squadron of about 20 CASA/ENAER Halcón is envisaged when finances permit.
Viña del Mar (Valparaiso); *Almirante Von Schroeders* (Punta Arenas); *Guardiamarina Zañartu* (Puerto Williams).
Four Squadrons: VP1 (MP) Bandeirante; HS1 (Helicopters), Super Puma, Dauphin; VC1 (GP) Bandeirante, Aviocar, JetRangers; VT1 (Training) Pilatus PC-7.

Infanteria de Marina

Personnel: 5200.
Organisation: 4 detachments each comprising Amphibious Warfare, Coast Defence and Local Security. Also embarked are detachments of commandos, engineering units and a logistic battalion.
1st Marine Infantry Detachment 'Patricio Lynch'. At Iquique.
2nd Marine Infantry Detachment 'Miller'. At Viña del Mar.
3rd Marine Infantry Detachment 'Sargento Aldea'. At Talcahuano.
4th Marine Infantry Detachment 'Cochrane'. At Punta Arenas.
51 Commando Group. At Valparaiso.
Some embarked units, commando and engineering units and a logistics battalion.
Equipment: Infantry personnel and support weapons; LVTP 5 amphibious assault vehicles; MOWAG Roland APCs; light field artillery.

Bases

Valparaiso. Main naval base, schools, repair yard. HQ 1st Naval Zone. Air station.
Talcahuano. Naval base, schools, major repair yard (two dry docks, three floating docks), two floating cranes. HQ 2nd Naval Zone. Submarine base.
Punta Arenas. Naval base. Dockyard with slipway having building and repair facilities. HQ 3rd Naval Zone. Air station.
Iquique. Small naval base. HQ 4th Naval Zone.
Puerto Montt. Small naval base.
Puerto Williams (Beagle Channel). Small naval base. Air station.

Dawson Island (Magellan Straits). Small naval base.

Strength of the Fleet

Type	Active	Projected
Patrol Submarines	4	(4)
Destroyers	6	—
Frigates	4	—
Patrol Ships	2	(4)
Landing Ships (Tank)	3	—
Landing Craft	2	—
Fast Attack Craft (Missile)	4	—
Fast Attack Craft (Torpedo)	4	—
Large Patrol Craft	5	—
Coastal Patrol Craft	6	—
Survey Ships	2	—
Training Ships	3	—
Transports	3	—
Tankers	3	—
Tugs/Supply Ships	5	—
Coast Guard	37	2 (4)

Mercantile Marine

Lloyd's Register of Shipping:
  420 vessels of 624 398 tons gross

DELETIONS

Cruisers

1992   *O'Higgins*

Auxiliaries

1993   *Angamos, Aguila*

PENNANT LIST

Note: Chilean naval vessels do not carry visible pennant numbers.

Submarines		Patrol Forces						Training Ships	
20	Thomson	45	Piloto Pardo	1816	Grumete Salinas			29	Uribe
21	Simpson	63	Sargento Aldea	1817	Grumete Tellez			43	Esmeralda
22	O'Brien	30	Casma	1818	Grumete Bravo				
23	Hyatt	31	Chipana	1819	Grumete Campos			**Auxiliaries**	
		32	Iquique					AP 47	Aquiles
Destroyers/Frigates		33	Covadonga	**Survey Ships**				YFB 110	Meteoro
		37	Papudo	60	Vidal Gormaz			52	Almirante Jorge Montt
06	Condell	71	Contramaestre Micalvi	64	Yelcho			53	Araucano
07	Lynch	72	Contramaestre Ortiz					YOG 101	Guardian Brito
08	Ministro Zenteno	73	Aspirante Isaza						
09	General Baquedano	74	Aspirante Morel	**Amphibious Forces**				**Tugs/Supply Ships**	
11	Prat	80	Guacolda	90	Elicura			ATF 65	Janequeo
12	Cochrane	81	Fresia	91	Maipo			ATF 66	Galvarino
14	Latorre	82	Quidora	92	Rancagua			ATF 67	Lautaro
15	Blanco Encalada	83	Tegualda	93	Chacabuco			ATF 68	Leucoton
18	Almirante Riveros	1814	Grumete Diaz	94	Orompello			ATF 69	Colo Colo
19	Almirante Williams	1815	Grumete Bolados						

SUBMARINES

Notes: (1) Up to four new submarines are required. The equipment fit has been decided and an order for a new class of about 1400 tons is to be placed when funds are available. First to be built abroad, remainder by ASMAR.
(2) There are some Swimmer Delivery Vehicles Havas Mk 8 in service. This is the two-man version.

2 OBERON CLASS

Name	No	Builders	Laid down	Launched	Commissioned
O'BRIEN	22	Scott-Lithgow	17 Jan 1971	21 Dec 1972	15 Apr 1976
HYATT (ex-*Condell*)	23	Scott-Lithgow	10 Jan 1972	26 Sep 1973	27 Sep 1976

Displacement, tons: 1610 standard; 2030 surfaced; 2410 dived
Dimensions, feet (metres): 295.2 × 26.5 × 18.1
  (90 × 8.1 × 5.5)
Main machinery: Diesel-electric; 2 ASR 16 VVS-ASR1 diesels; 3680 hp *(2.74 MW)*; 2 AEI motors; 6000 hp *(4.48 MW)*; 2 shafts
Speed, knots: 12 surfaced; 17 dived; 10 snorting
Complement: 65 (7 officers)

Torpedoes: 8—21 in *(533 mm)* tubes (6 bow, 2 stern). 22 AEG SUT; wire-guided; active homing to 12 km *(6.5 nm)* at 35 kts; passive homing to 28 km *(15 nm)* at 23 kts; warhead 250 kg.
Fire control: Sisdef TFCS.
Radars: Navigation: Kelvin Hughes Type 1006; I band.
Sonars: BAC Type 2007; flank array; passive; long range; low frequency.
  EMI Type 187 or Atlas Elektronik CSU 90; bow-mounted; passive/active search and attack; medium frequency.

HYATT   *1992, Chilean Navy*

Programmes: Ordered from Scott's Shipbuilding & Engineering Co Ltd, Greenock, late 1969. Both suffered delays in fitting out due to re-cabling and a minor explosion in *Hyatt* in January 1976.

Modernisation: Sisdef fire-control system fitted in 1992. Atlas Elektronik CSU 90 to replace Type 187.
Operational: Stern tubes may no longer be used.

2 THOMSON (TYPE 209) CLASS (TYPE 1300)

Name	No	Builders	Laid down	Launched	Commissioned
THOMSON	20	Howaldtswerke	1 Nov 1980	28 Oct 1982	31 Aug 1984
SIMPSON	21	Howaldtswerke	15 Feb 1982	29 July 1983	18 Sep 1984

Displacement, tons: 1260 surfaced; 1390 dived
Dimensions, feet (metres): 195.2 × 20.3 × 18
  (59.5 × 6.2 × 5.5)
Main machinery: Diesel-electric; 4 MTU 12V 493 AZ80 GA31L
  diesels; 2400 hp(m) *(1.76 MW)* sustained; 4 Piller alternators;
  1.7 MW; 1 Siemens motor; 4600 hp(m) *(3.38 MW)* sustained;
  1 shaft
Speed, knots: 11 surfaced; 21.5 dived
Range, miles: 400 at 4 kts dived; 16 at 21.5 kts dived; 8200 at
  8 kts snorkel
Complement: 32 (5 officers)

Torpedoes: 8—21 in *(533 mm)* bow tubes. 14 AEG SUT; wire-
  guided; active homing to 12 km *(6.5 nm)* at 35 kts; passive
  homing to 28 km *(15 nm)* at 23 kts; warhead 250 kg.
Radars: Surface search: Thomson-CSF Calypso II; I band.
Sonars: Atlas Elektronik CSU 3; hull-mounted; active/passive
  search and attack; medium frequency.

Programmes: Ordered from Howaldtswerke, Kiel in 1980. Two
  more projected in 1988 Five Year Plan but this has been overtaken by the requirement for a new class of four of similar
  displacement.

SIMPSON
1992, Chilean Navy

Modernisation: *Thomson* refit completed at Talcahuano in late
1990, *Simpson* in 1991. Refit duration about 10 months each.

Structure: Fin and associated masts lengthened by 50 cm to
cope with wave size off Chilean coast.

DESTROYERS

2 ALMIRANTE CLASS

Name	No	Builders	Laid down	Launched	Commissioned
ALMIRANTE RIVEROS	18	Vickers-Armstrong Ltd, Barrow	12 Apr 1957	12 Dec 1958	31 Dec 1960
ALMIRANTE WILLIAMS	19	Vickers-Armstrong Ltd, Barrow	20 June 1956	5 May 1958	26 Mar 1960

Displacement, tons: 2730 standard; 3300 full load
Dimensions, feet (metres): 402 × 43 × 13.3
  (122.5 × 13.1 × 4)
Main machinery: 2 Babcock & Wilcox boilers; 600 psi
  (43.3 kg/cm sq); 850°F *(454°C)*; 2 Parsons Pametrada tur-
  bines; 54 000 hp *(40 MW)*; 2 shafts
Speed, knots: 34.5. **Range, miles:** 6000 at 16 kts
Complement: 266 (17 officers)

Missiles: SSM: 4 Aerospatiale MM 38 Exocet ❶; inertial cruise;
  active radar homing to 42 km *(23 nm)* at 0.9 Mach; warhead
  165 kg; sea-skimmer.
SAM: 2 Short Bros Seacat quad launchers ❷; optical/radar guidance to 5 km *(2.7 nm)*; warhead 10 kg; 16 reloads.
Guns: 3 or 4 Vickers 4 in *(102 mm)*/60 Mk(N)R ❸; 75° elevation;
  40 rounds/minute to 18 km *(10 nm)* anti-surface; 12 km
  (6.5 nm) anti-aircraft; weight of shell 16 kg.
  4 Bofors 40 mm/70 ❹; 90° elevation; 300 rounds/minute to
  12 km *(6.5 nm)* anti-surface; 4 km *(2.2 nm)* anti-aircraft; weight
  of shell 2.4 kg.
Torpedoes: 6—324 mm Mk 32 (2 triple) tubes ❺. Honeywell Mk
  44 Mod 1; active homing to 5.5 km *(3 nm)* at 30 kts; warhead
  34 kg.
A/S mortars: 2 Admiralty Squid DC mortars (3-barrelled) ❻;
  range 800 m; warhead 52 kg.

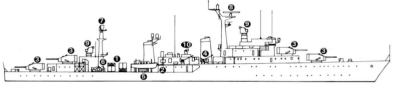

ALMIRANTE RIVEROS
(Scale 1 : 1200), Ian Sturton

Countermeasures: ESM: WLR-1; radar warning. Elta IR sensor.
Combat data systems: Ferranti action data with autonomous
  displays.
Fire control: 2 Signaal M-4 directors for Seacat SAMs
Radars: Air search: Plessey AWS 1 ❼; range 110 km *(60 nm)*.
Air/surface search: Marconi SNW 10 ❽; E/F band.
Navigation: Racal Decca 1629; I band.
Fire control: Two SGR 102 ❾; Signaal M4/3 ❿; I/J band.
Sonars: Graseby Type 184 B; hull-mounted; active search and
  attack; medium frequency (6/9 kHz).
  Type 170; hull mounted; active attack; high frequency
  (15 kHz).

Programmes: Ordered in May 1955.
Modernisation: Both modernised by Swan Hunter in co-operation with Plessey: *Almirante Williams* in 1971-74 and *Almirante Riveros* in 1973-75. In the late 1980s both were given a
  further extensive refit with the addition of modern electronic
  equipment including Netherlands M4 fire-control radars. Israeli
  Barak I may replace Seacat but these ships have a lower priority than the County and Leander classes. Additional ESM
  equipment fitted in 1990.
Operational: 4 in guns were removed one at a time for refurbishment in 1986-88 and ships operated minus one or two turrets each while the work was done.

ALMIRANTE WILLIAMS
3/1993, Chilean Navy

4 PRAT (COUNTY) CLASS

Name	No	Builders	Laid down	Launched	Commissioned
PRAT (ex-HMS Norfolk)	11	Swan Hunter, Wallsend	15 Mar 1966	16 Nov 1967	7 Mar 1970
COCHRANE (ex-HMS Antrim)	12	Fairfield SB & Eng Co Ltd, Govan	20 Jan 1966	19 Oct 1967	14 July 1970
LATORRE (ex-HMS Glamorgan)	14	Vickers (Shipbuilding) Ltd, Newcastle-upon-Tyne	13 Sep 1962	9 July 1964	11 Oct 1966
BLANCO ENCALADA (ex-HMS Fife)	15	Fairfield SB & Eng Co Ltd, Govan	1 June 1962	9 July 1964	21 June 1966

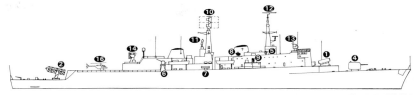

LATORRE (Scale 1 : 1500), Ian Sturton

Displacement, tons: 5440 standard; 6200 full load
Dimensions, feet (metres): 520.5 × 54 × 20.5
(158.7 × 16.5 × 6.3)
Main machinery: COSAG; 2 Babcock & Wilcox boilers; 700 psi
(49.2 kg/cm sq); 950°F (510°C); 2 AEI steam turbines;
30 000 hp (22.4 MW); 4 English Electric G6 gas-turbines;
30 000 hp (22.4 MW); 2 shafts
Speed, knots: 30. **Range, miles:** 3500 at 28 kts
Complement: 470 (36 officers)

Missiles: SSM: 4 Aerospatiale MM 38 Exocet ❶; inertial cruise;
active radar homing to 42 km (23 nm) at 0.9 Mach; warhead
165 kg; sea-skimmer.
SAM: Short Bros Seaslug Mk 2 (11 and 14 only) ❷; range 45 km
(25 nm) at 2 Mach; warhead HE; beam riding. Limited anti-
surface role.
2 Shorts Seacat quad launchers (not in 14 or 15); optical/radar
guidance to 5 km (2.7 nm); warhead 10 kg. Being replaced by
2 Israeli Barak I (15) ❸ command line-of-sight radar or optical
guidance to 10 km (5.5 nm) at 2 Mach; warhead 22 kg.
Guns: 2 Vickers 4.5 in (115 mm) Mk 6 semi-automatic (twin) ❹;
80° elevation; 20 rounds/minute to 19 km (10.3 nm) anti-surface; 6 km (3.2 nm) anti-aircraft; weight of shell 25 kg.
2 or 4 Oerlikon 20 mm Mk 9 ❺; 55° elevation; 800 rounds/
minute to 2 km.
2 Bofors 40 mm/60 (14 only) ❻; to be replaced by Barak I.
12.7 mm (single or twin) MGs.
Torpedoes: 6—324 mm Mk 32 (2 triple) tubes ❼; Honeywell Mk
44 Mod 1; active homing to 5.5 km (3 nm) at 30 kts; warhead
34 kg.
Countermeasures: Decoys: 2 Corvus 8-barrelled trainable chaff
launchers ❽; distraction or centroid patterns to 1 km.
2 Wallop Barricade double layer chaff launchers ❾; 6 sets triple-barrelled with four modes of fire.
ESM: UA 8/9; radar warning. Elta IR sensor.
ECM: Jammer.
Combat data systems: ADAWS-1 being replaced by Sisdef
Imagen SP 100 from 1993. SATCOM.
Fire control: Gunnery MRS 3 system. Seacat 2 GWS 22 systems
(not in 14 or 15 and being removed from the remainder).
Radars: Air search: Marconi Type 965 M or 966 (14 and 15) ❿;
A band.
Admiralty Type 277 M (11 and 14) ⓫; E band. For height
finding.
Surface search: Marconi Type 992 Q or R ⓬; E/F band; range
55 km (30 nm).
Navigation: Decca Type 978/1006; I band.
Fire control: Plessey Type 903 ⓭; I band (for Guns).
Marconi Type 901 (in 11 and 14) ⓮; G/H band (for Seaslug).
Two Elta EL/M-2221GM ⓯; I/J/K band (for Barak).
Two Plessey Type 904 (not in 14 or 15 and being removed
from remainder); I band (for Seacat).
Sonars: Kelvin Hughes Type 162 M; hull-mounted; sideways
looking classification; high-frequency.
Graseby Type 184 M or Type 184 S (15); hull-mounted; active
search and attack; medium range; 7-9 kHz.

Helicopters: 1 Bell 206B (11 and 14) ⓰. 2 NAS 332F Super
Puma (12 and 15) ⓱.

Programmes: Transferred from UK 6 April 1982 (Prat), 22 June
1984 (Cochrane), 3 October 1986 (Latorre) and 12 August
1987 (Blanco Encalada). Extensive refits carried out after transfer. Glamorgan renamed Latorre after the Swedish-built cruiser
which paid off in 1986. Although all are named after senior officers, the titles Almirante and Capitan are not used.

PRAT 1993, Chilean Navy

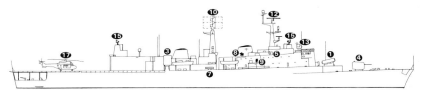

BLANCO ENCALADA (Scale 1 : 1500), Ian Sturton

Modernisation: Blanco Encalada converted at Talcahuano into
helicopter carrier for two Super Pumas completed May 1988;
Cochrane similar conversion completed in 1992. The remaining two serve as Flagships. All of the class are getting the Israeli
Barak I and new communications, optronic directors and ECM
equipment. VDS sonars and torpedo decoys are also a possibility. New combat data system fitted in 1993 to Blanco Encalada, remainder to follow. Latorre was transferred with 40 mm

guns in lieu of Seacats (damaged in the Falklands War). There
are no plans to remove Seaslug from the remaining two ships.
Structure: Blanco Encalada and Cochrane are markedly different
in appearance from their two half-sisters with a greatly
enlarged flight deck continued right aft to accommodate two
large helicopters simultaneously, making them effectively
flush-decked. The hangar has also been completely rebuilt and
the foremast extended.

BLANCO ENCALADA (with Barak) 8/1993, Chilean Navy

FRIGATES

4 + (2) LEANDER CLASS

Name	No	Builders	Laid down	Launched	Commissioned
CONDELL	06	Yarrow & Co, Scotstoun	5 June 1971	12 June 1972	21 Dec 1973
LYNCH	07	Yarrow & Co, Scotstoun	6 Dec 1971	6 Dec 1972	25 May 1974
MINISTRO ZENTENO (ex-*Achilles*)	08 (ex-F 12)	Yarrow & Co, Scotstoun	1 Dec 1967	21 Nov 1968	9 July 1970
GENERAL BAQUEDANO (ex-*Ariadne*)	09 (ex-F 72)	Yarrow & Co, Scotstoun	1 Nov 1969	10 Sep 1971	10 Feb 1973

Displacement, tons: 2500 standard; 2962 full load
Dimensions, feet (metres): 372 oa; 360 wl × 43 × 18 (screws) *(113.4; 109.7 × 13.1 × 5.5)*
Main machinery: 2 Babcock & Wilcox boilers; 550 psi *(38.7 kg/cm sq)*; 850°F *(450°C)*; 2 White/English Electric turbines; 30 000 hp *(22.4 MW)*; 2 shafts
Speed, knots: 29. **Range, miles:** 4500 at 12 kts
Complement: 263 (20 officers)

Missiles: SSM: 4 Aerospatiale MM 40 Exocet (06, 07) ❶; inertial cruise; active radar homing to 70 km *(40 nm)* at 0.9 Mach; warhead 165 kg; sea-skimmer.
SAM: Short Bros Seacat GWS 22 quad launcher ❷; optical/radar guidance to 5 km *(2.7 nm)*; warhead 10 kg; 16 reloads. To be replaced by Israeli Barak I vertical launch canisters.
Guns: 2 Vickers 4.5 in *(115 mm)*/45 Mk 6 (twin) semi-automatic ❸; 80° elevation; 20 rounds/minute to 19 km *(10 nm)* anti-surface; 6 km *(3.2 nm)* anti-aircraft; weight of shell 25 kg.
2 Oerlikon 20 mm Mk 9 ❹; 55° elevation; 800 rounds/minute to 2 km.
Torpedoes: 6—324 mm Mk 32 (2 triple) tubes ❺ (not in 09). Honeywell Mk 44 Mod 1; active homing to 5.5 km *(3 nm)* at 30 kts; warhead 34 kg. To be replaced by Murene in due course.
Countermeasures: Decoys: 2 Corvus 8-barrelled trainable chaff rocket launchers ❻; distraction or centroid patterns to 1 km. Wallop Barricade double layer chaff launchers.
ESM: UA 8/9; radar intercept. FH12 HF/DF. Elta IR sensor.
Combat data systems: Sisdef Imagen SP 100 (06); one more of the class to be fitted.
Fire control: MRS 3 system for gunnery. GWS 22 system for Seacat.
Radars: Air search: Marconi Type 965/966 ❼; A band.
Surface search: Marconi Type 992 Q ❽ (06 and 07); Plessey Type 994 ❾ (08 and 09); E/F band.
Navigation: Kelvin Hughes Type 1006; I band.
Fire control: Plessey Type 903 ❿; I band (for guns).
Plessey Type 904 ⓫; I band (for Seacat). Both radars may be replaced by IAI/Elta (for Barak) in due course.
Sonars: Graseby Type 184 P; hull-mounted; active search and attack; medium frequency (6/9 kHz).
Graseby Type 170 B; hull-mounted; active attack; high frequency (15 kHz).
Kelvin Hughes Type 162 M; hull-mounted; sideways looking classification; high frequency.

Helicopters: 1 Bell 206B ⓬ or Super Puma (06) ⓭.

Programmes: First two ordered from Yarrow & Co Ltd, Scotstoun in the late 1960s. Third ship purchased from UK in September 1990 and fourth in June 1992. Two more, *Andromeda* and *Scylla*, may be acquired in 1994.
Modernisation: In 1989 *Lynch* was considerably modified at Talcahuano Dockyard with two twin MM 40 Exocet launchers being mounted on each side of the hangar (instead of the MM 38 aft) and by moving the torpedo tubes down one deck. The enlarged flight deck can now take a Super Puma aircraft. Other planned modifications include Barak VLS canisters to replace Seacat in due course, improvements to the fire-control radars and Israeli EW systems. *Condell* completed a similar modernisation to *Lynch* in 1993 but with the addition of a larger hangar to take a Super Puma helicopter, and the fitting of a new combat data system. The increased hangar size has led to the flight deck being extended to the stern of the ship and the stern gear moved down a deck. The Seacat launcher is also further aft than in 07.
Structure: *Condell* and *Lynch* have slightly taller foremasts than ex-British Leander class.

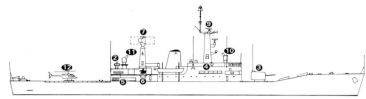

MINISTRO ZENTENO   *(Scale 1 : 1200), Ian Sturton*

CONDELL   *(Scale 1 : 1200), Ian Sturton*

LYNCH   *8/1993, Chilean Navy*

GENERAL BAQUEDANO   *6/1992, Maritime Photographic*

CONDELL (with Super Puma)   *8/1993, Chilean Navy*

SHIPBORNE AIRCRAFT

Numbers/Type: 4 Nurtanio (Aerospatiale) NAS 332SC Super Puma.
Operational speed: 151 kts *(279 km/h)*.
Service ceiling: 15 090 ft *(4600 m)*.
Range: 335 nm *(620 km)*.
Role/Weapon systems: ASV/ASW helicopters for DLG conversions; surface search and SAR secondary roles. Sensors: Thomson-CSF radar and Alcatel dipping sonar. Weapons: ASW; 2 × Mk 44 torpedoes (to be replaced by Murene) or depth bombs. ASV; 1 or 2 × AM 39 Exocet anti-ship missile.

SUPER PUMA   *8/1992, Chilean Navy*

Numbers/Type: 9 MBB BO 105C.
Operational speed: 113 kts *(210 km/h)*.
Service ceiling: 9845 ft *(3000 m)*.
Range: 407 nm *(754 km)*.
Role/Weapon systems: Coastal patrol helicopter for patrol, training and liaison duties; SAR as secondary role. Sensors: Bendix search radar. Weapons: Unarmed.

BO 105C   *6/1992, Chilean Navy*

Numbers/Type: 7 Bell 206B JetRanger.
Operational speed: 115 kts *(213 km/h)*.
Service ceiling: 13 500 ft *(4115 m)*.
Range: 368 nm *(682 km)*.
Role/Weapon systems: Some tasks and training carried out by torpedo-armed liaison helicopter; emergency war role for ASW. Weapons: ASW; 1 × Mk 44 torpedo.

JETRANGER   *6/1993, Chilean Navy*

LAND-BASED MARITIME AIRCRAFT (FRONT LINE)

Note: In addition there are EMB 110, Falcon 200 and Casa Aviocar 212 support aircraft. Two Gardian reconnaissance aircraft for sale in 1994.

Numbers/Type: 6 Embraer EMB-111 Bandeirante.
Operational speed: 194 kts *(360 km/h)*.
Service ceiling: 25 500 ft *(7770 m)*.
Range: 1590 nm *(2945 km)*.
Role/Weapon systems: Designated EMB-111N for peacetime EEZ and wartime MR. Sensors: Eaton-AIL AN/APS-128 search radar, ECM/ESM, searchlight. Weapons: Strike; 6 × 127 mm or 28 × 70 mm rockets.

Numbers/Type: 8 Pilatus PC-7 Turbo-Trainer.
Operational speed: 270 kts *(500 km/h)*.
Service ceiling: 32 000 ft *(9755 m)*.
Range: 1420 nm *(2630 km)*.
Role/Weapon systems: Training includes simulated attacks to exercise ships' AA defences; emergency war role for strike operations. Sensors: None. Weapons: 4 × 127 mm or similar rockets and machine gun pods.

Numbers/Type: 8 Lockheed P 3A Orion.
Operational speed: 410 kts *(760 km/h)*.
Service ceiling: 28 300 ft *(8625 m)*.
Range: 4000 nm *(7410 km)*.
Role/Weapon systems: Long range MR for surveillance and SAR. First one delivered from US in March 1993. Sensors: APS-115 radar. Weapons: Weapon systems removed but may be replaced in due course.

ORION   *8/1993, Chilean Navy*

PATROL FORCES

Note: Project Zonomac is the planned building of four offshore patrol vessels with a helo deck and light gun. Orders should have been placed in 1992 but have been delayed by lack of funds. Former ocean-going tugs are being purchased for both patrol and survey duties.

1 CHEROKEE CLASS (PATROL SHIP)

Name	No	Builders	Commissioned
SARGENTO ALDEA	63	Charleston S B. & D.D. Co	5 Jan 1944
(ex-USS *Arikara* ATF 98)			

Displacement, tons: 1235 standard; 1640 full load
Dimensions, feet (metres): 205 × 38.5 × 17 *(62.5 × 11.7 × 5.2)*
Main machinery: Diesel-electric; 4 Busch-Sulzer BS-539 diesels; 4 generators; 1 motor; 3000 hp *(2.24 MW)*; 1 shaft
Speed, knots: 16. **Range, miles:** 7000 at 15 kts; 15 000 at 8 kts
Complement: 85
Guns: 1 USN 3 in *(76 mm)*/50 Mk 26; 85° elevation; 20 rounds/minute to 12 km *(6.5 nm)* anti-surface; 9 km *(5 nm)* anti-aircraft; weight of shell 6 kg.
    2 Oerlikon 20 mm; 55° elevation; 800 rounds/minute to 2 km.
Radars: Surface search: Westinghouse SPS 5; G/H band; range 37 km *(20 nm)*.

Comment: Launched on 22 June 1943. Transferred by lease from US on 1 July 1971, and by grant aid on 30 September 1992.

SARGENTO ALDEA   *1991, Chilean Navy*

1 ANTARCTIC PATROL SHIP

Name	No	Builders	Commissioned
PILOTO PARDO	45	Haarlemsche Scheepsbouw, Netherlands	Aug 1958

Displacement, tons: 1250 light; 2930 full load
Dimensions, feet (metres): 269 × 39 × 15 *(82 × 11.9 × 4.6)*
Main machinery: Diesel-electric; 2000 hp(m) *(1.47 MW)*; 1 shaft
Speed, knots: 14. **Range, miles:** 6000 at 10 kts
Complement: 56 (8 officers)
Military lift: 24 troops
Guns: 1—3 in *(76 mm)* Mk 26 (not always embarked).
Helicopters: Platform for 2 MBB BO 105C.

Comment: Antarctic patrol ship, transport and research vessel with reinforced hull to navigate in ice. Launched on 11 June 1958. Also listed as a survey ship by the International Hydrographic Bureau. Possible replacement being sought together with an Icebreaker Tug.

PILOTO PARDO   5/1993, Chilean Navy

2 CASMA (SAAR 4) CLASS (FAST ATTACK CRAFT—MISSILE)

Name	No	Builders	Commissioned
CASMA (ex-*Romah*)	30	Haifa Shipyard	Mar 1974
CHIPANA (ex-*Keshet*)	31	Haifa Shipyard	Oct 1973

Displacement, tons: 415 standard; 450 full load
Dimensions, feet (metres): 190.6 × 25 × 8 *(58 × 7.8 × 2.4)*
Main machinery: 4 MTU 16V 538 TB82 diesels; 11 880 hp(m) *(8.74 MW)* sustained; 4 shafts
Speed, knots: 32. **Range, miles:** 1650 at 30 kts; 4000 at 17.5 kts
Complement: 45

Missiles: SSM: 4 IAI Gabriel I; radar or optical guidance; semi-active radar homing to 20 km *(10.8 nm)* at 0.7 Mach; warhead 75 kg HE.
Guns: 2 OTO Melara 3 in *(76 mm)*/62 compact; 85° elevation; 85 rounds/minute to 16 km *(8.7 nm)* anti-surface; 12 km *(6.5 nm)* anti-aircraft; weight of shell 6 kg.
2 Oerlikon 20 mm; 55° elevation; 800 rounds/minute to 2 km.
Countermeasures: Decoys: 4 Rafael LRCR chaff decoy launchers.
ESM: Elta Electronics MN-53; intercept.
ECM: Jammer.
Radars: Surface search: Thomson-CSF THD 1040 Neptune; E/F band; range 110 km *(60 nm)*.
Fire control: Elta Electronics M 2221; I/J band; range 40 km *(22 nm)*.

Programmes: One transferred from Israel late 1979 and second in February 1981 for refit and deployment to Beagle Channel.

CASMA   9/1993, Chilean Navy

2 IQUIQUE (SAAR 3) CLASS (FAST ATTACK CRAFT—MISSILE)

Name	No	Builders	Commissioned
IQUIQUE (ex-*Hamit*)	32	CMN Cherbourg	1969
COVADONGA (ex-*Hefz*)	33	CMN Cherbourg	1969

Displacement, tons: 220 standard; 250 full load
Dimensions, feet (metres): 147.6 × 23 × 8.2 *(45 × 7 × 2.5)*
Main machinery: 4 MTU MD 16V 537 TB80 diesels; 10 000 hp(m) *(7.35 MW)* sustained; 4 shafts
Speed, knots: 40+. **Range, miles:** 2500 at 15 kts; 1600 at 20 kts; 1000 at 30 kts
Complement: 35-40 (5 officers)

Missiles: SSM: 6 IAI Gabriel II; active radar or optical TV guidance; semi-active radar homing to 36 km *(20 nm)* at 0.7 Mach; warhead 75 kg.
Guns: 1 OTO Melara 3 in *(76 mm)*/62 DP; 85° elevation; 65 rounds/minute to 8 km *(4.4 nm)*; weight of shell 6 kg.
2—12.7 mm MGs.
Countermeasures: Decoys: 6—24 tube, 4 single tube chaff launchers.
ESM: Elta Electronics MN-53; intercept.
ECM: Jammer.
Radars: Air/surface search: Thomson-CSF TH-D 1040 Neptune; G band; range 33 km *(18 nm)* for 2 m² target.
Fire control: Selenia Orion RTN 10X; I/J band; range 40 km *(22 nm)*.

Programmes: Both acquired from Israel in December 1988 and commissioned into the Chilean Navy 3 May 1989. There are no plans to transfer any more of the class.

IQUIQUE   4/1993, Chilean Navy

4 GUACOLDA CLASS (FAST ATTACK CRAFT—TORPEDO)

Name	No	Builders	Commissioned
GUACOLDA	80	Bazán, San Fernando	30 July 1965
FRESIA	81	Bazán, San Fernando	9 Dec 1965
QUIDORA	82	Bazán, San Fernando	28 Mar 1966
TEGUALDA	83	Bazán, San Fernando	1 July 1966

Displacement, tons: 134 full load
Dimensions, feet (metres): 118.1 × 18.4 × 7.2 *(36 × 5.6 × 2.2)*
Main machinery: 2 MTU MB 16V 652 SB60 diesels; 3200 hp(m) *(2.35 MW)* sustained; 2 shafts
Speed, knots: 32. **Range, miles:** 1500 at 15 kts
Complement: 20
Guns: 2 Bofors 40 mm/70.
Torpedoes: 4—21 in *(533 mm)* tubes for heavyweight anti-ship torpedoes.
Radars: Navigation: Decca 505; I band.

Comment: Built to West German Lürssen design from 1963 to 1966. First launched 1964.

FRESIA   1989, Chilean Navy

4 MICALVI CLASS (LARGE PATROL CRAFT)

Name	No	Builders	Commissioned
CONTRAMAESTRE MICALVI	PSG 71	Asmar Talcahuano	30 Mar 1993
CONTRAMAESTRE ORTIZ	PSG 72	Asmar Talcahuano	15 Dec 1993
ASPIRANTE ISAZA	PSG 73	Asmar Talcahuano	30 Jan 1994
ASPIRANTE MOREL	PSG 74	Asmar Talcahuano	June 1994

Displacement, tons: 518 full load
Dimensions, feet (metres): 139.4 × 27.9 × 9.5 *(42.5 × 8.5 × 2.9)*
Main machinery: 2 Caterpillar 3512 TA diesels; 2560 hp(m) *(1.88 MW)*; 2 shafts
Speed, knots: 15. **Range, miles:** 4200 at 12 kts
Complement: 23 (5 officers)
Guns: 1 Bofors 40 mm/60. 2 Oerlikon 20 mm.
Radars: Surface search: I band.

Comment: Built under design project Taitao. First one launched 27 September 1992. Multi-purpose patrol vessels with a secondary mission of transport and servicing navigational aids. Provision for bow thruster, sonar and mine rails. Can carry 35 tons cargo in holds and 18 tons in containers. Crane lift of 2.5 tons.

CONTRAMAESTRE MICALVI   6/1993, Chilean Navy

1 PC-1638 CLASS (LARGE PATROL CRAFT)

Name	No	Builders	Commissioned
PAPUDO (ex-US *PC 1646*)	37	Asmar, Talcahuano	27 Nov 1971

Displacement, tons: 412 full load
Dimensions, feet (metres): 173.7 × 23 × 10.2 *(53 × 7 × 3.1)*
Main machinery: 2 GM-EMD 16—567 diesels; 2800 hp *(2.1 MW)*; 2 shafts
Speed, knots: 19. **Range, miles:** 5000 at 10 kts
Complement: 69 (4 officers)
Guns: 1 Bofors 40 mm/60; 90° elevation; 300 rounds/minute to 12 km *(6.5 nm)* anti-surface; 4 km *(2.2 nm)* anti-aircraft; weight of shell 0.89 kg.
4 Oerlikon 20 mm; 50° elevation; 800 rounds/minute to 2 km.
Depth charges: 2 K-type throwers; 4 racks.

Comment: Of similar design to the Turkish Hisar class built to the US PC plan. Hedgehog mortar has been removed.

PAPUDO ·   *6/1993, Chilean Navy*

6 GRUMETE DIAZ (DABUR) CLASS (COASTAL PATROL CRAFT)

GRUMETE DIAZ 1814		GRUMETE TELLEZ 1817	
GRUMETE BOLADOS 1815		GRUMETE BRAVO 1818	
GRUMETE SALINAS 1816		GRUMETE CAMPOS 1819	

Displacement, tons: 39 full load
Dimensions, feet (metres): 64.9 × 18 × 5.9 *(19.8 × 5.5 × 1.8)*
Main machinery: 2 Detroit 12V-71TA diesels; 840 hp *(627 kW)* sustained; 2 shafts
Speed, knots: 19. **Range, miles:** 450 at 13 kts
Complement: 8 (2 officers)
Guns: 1 Oerlikon 20 mm. 1—12.7 mm MG.
Radars: Surface search: Racal Decca Super 101 Mk 3; I band.

Comment: Transferred from Israel and commissioned 3 January 1991. A fast inflatable boat is carried on the stern. Deployed in the Fourth Naval Zone.

GRUMETE DIAZ   *8/1993, Chilean Navy*

AMPHIBIOUS FORCES

2 ELICURA CLASS (LSMs)

Name	No	Builders	Commissioned
ELICURA	90	Talcahuano	10 Dec 1968
OROMPELLO	94	Dade Dry Dock Co, Miami	15 Sep 1964

Displacement, tons: 290 light; 750 full load
Dimensions, feet (metres): 145 × 34 × 12.8 *(44.2 × 10.4 × 3.9)*
Main machinery: 2 Cummins VT-17-700M diesels; 900 hp *(660 kW)*; 2 shafts
Speed, knots: 10.5. **Range, miles:** 2900 at 9 kts
Complement: 20
Military lift: 350 tons
Guns: 3 Oerlikon 20 mm (can be carried).
Radars: Navigation: Raytheon 1500B; I/J band.

Comment: Two of similar class operated by Chilean Shipping Co. Oil fuel, 77 tons.

ELICURA   *1991, Chilean Navy*

3 MAIPO (BATRAL) CLASS (LSTs)

Name	No	Builders	Launched	Commissioned
MAIPO	91	Asmar, Talcahuano	26 Sep 1981	1 Jan 1982
RANCAGUA	92	Asmar, Talcahuano	6 Mar 1982	8 Aug 1983
CHACABUCO	93	Asmar, Talcahuano	16 July 1985	15 Apr 1986

Displacement, tons: 873 standard; 1409 full load
Dimensions, feet (metres): 260.4 × 42.7 × 8.2 *(79.4 × 13 × 2.5)*
Main machinery: 2 SEMT-Pielstick 12 PA4 V 185 VG; 4012 hp(m) *(2.95 MW)* sustained; 2 shafts; cp props
Speed, knots: 16. **Range, miles:** 3500 at 13 kts
Complement: 49
Military lift: 180 troops; 350 tons
Guns: 1 Bofors 40 mm/60. 1 Oerlikon 20 mm. 2—81 mm mortars.
Radars: Navigation: Decca; I/J band.
Helicopters: Platform for 1 Super Puma.

Comment: First pair laid down in 1980 to standard French design with French equipment.

MAIPO   *3/1993, Chilean Navy*

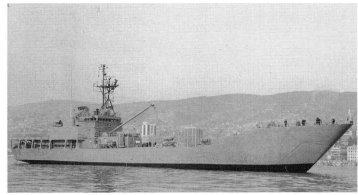

RANCAGUA   *1992, Chilean Navy*

SURVEY SHIPS

Note: *Piloto Pardo* also listed—see *Patrol Forces*. Plans to replace her have been postponed.

1 ROBERT D CONRAD CLASS

Name	No	Builders	Commissioned
VIDAL GORMAZ (ex-*Thomas Washington*)	60 (ex-AGOR 10)	Marinette Marine, WI	27 Sep 1965

Displacement, tons: 1370 full load
Dimensions, feet (metres): 208.9 × 40 × 15.3 *(63.7 × 12.2 × 4.7)*
Main machinery: Diesel-electric; 2 Cummins diesel generators; 1 motor; 1000 hp *(746 kW)*; 1 shaft
Speed, knots: 13.5. **Range, miles:** 12 000 at 12 kts
Complement: 41 (9 officers, 15 scientists)
Radars: Navigation: TM 1660/12S; I band.

Comment: Transferred from US on 28 September 1992. This is the first class of ships designed and built by the US Navy for oceanographic research. Fitted with instrumentation and laboratories to measure gravity and magnetism, water temperature, sound transmission in water, and the profile of the ocean floor. Special features include 10 ton capacity boom and winches for handling over-the-side equipment; 620 hp gas-turbine (housed in funnel structure) for providing 'quiet' power when conducting experiments; can propel the ship at 6.5 kts.
Ships of this class are in service with Brazil (*Sands*), Mexico (*James M Gilliss* and *S P Lee*), Tunisia (*De Stiguer*) and New Zealand (*Charles H Davies*).

VIDAL GORMAZ   *7/1993, Chilean Navy*

1 CHEROKEE CLASS

Name	No	Builders	Commissioned
YELCHO	64	Commercial Iron Works,	16 Aug 1943
(ex-USS *Tekesta* ATF 93)		Portland, OR	

Displacement, tons: 1235 standard; 1640 full load
Dimensions, feet (metres): 205 × 38.5 × 17 *(62.5 × 11.7 × 5.2)*
Main machinery: Diesel-electric; 4 GM 12-278A diesels; 4400 hp *(3.28 MW)*; 4 generators; 1 motor; 3000 hp *(2.24 MW)*; 1 shaft
Speed, knots: 16. **Range, miles:** 7000 at 15 kts; 15 000 at 8 kts
Complement: 72 (7 officers)
Guns: 1—3 in *(76 mm)* Mk 26; 85° elevation; 20 rounds/minute to 12 km *(6 nm)* anti-surface; 9 km *(5 nm)* anti-aircraft; weight of shell 6 kg.
2 Oerlikon 20 mm; 55° elevation; 800 rounds/minute to 2 km.

Comment: Was fitted with powerful pumps and other salvage equipment although these were removed on conversion for surveying. Laid down on 7 September 1942, launched on 20 March 1943 and loaned to Chile by the USA on 15 May 1960. Transferred by grant on 30 September 1992. Employed as Antarctic research ship and surveying vessel. Similar to *Sargento Aldea* listed under *Patrol Forces*.

YELCHO   *1987, Pedro del Fierro Carmona*

TRAINING SHIPS

Note: There is also a small training yacht *Blanca Estela* which can carry a crew of 14 cadets.

Name	No	Builders	Commissioned
URIBE (ex-USS *Daniel Griffin*, APD 38)	29	Bethlehem, Hingham	9 June 1943

Displacement, tons: 2130 full load
Dimensions, feet (metres): 306 × 37 × 12.6 *(93.3 × 11.3 × 3.8)*
Main machinery: Turbo-electric; 2 Foster-Wheeler boilers; 435 psi *(30.6 kg/cm sq)*; 750°F *(399°C)*; 2 GE turbo-generators; 12 000 hp *(9 MW)*; 2 motors; 2 shafts
Speed, knots: 22. **Range, miles:** 5000 at 15 kts
Complement: 209
Guns: 1—5 in *(127 mm)*/38 Mk 30. 6 Bofors 40 mm/60 (2 twin).
Radars: Surface search: SPS 4; E/F band.

Comment: Ex-US Charles Lawrence class converted transport transferred 1 December 1966. Paid off in 1984 but was back in commission again in 1988 as a training and general-purpose vessel based at Talcahuano.

URIBE   *1991, Chilean Navy*

Name	No	Builders	Commissioned
ESMERALDA (ex-*Don Juan de Austria*)	43	Bazán, Cadiz	15 June 1954

Displacement, tons: 3420 standard; 3754 full load
Dimensions, feet (metres): 269.2 pp; 360 oa × 44.6 × 23 *(82; 109.8 × 13.1 × 7)*
Main machinery: 1 Fiat diesel; 1400 hp(m) *(1.03 MW)*; 1 shaft
Speed, knots: 11. **Range, miles:** 8000 at 8 kts
Complement: 271 plus 80 cadets
Guns: 2—37 mm saluting guns.

Comment: Four-masted schooner originally intended for the Spanish Navy. Near sister ship of *Juan Sebastian de Elcano* in the Spanish Navy. Refitted Saldanha Bay, South Africa, 1977. Sail area, 26 910 sq ft.

ESMERALDA   *9/1993, John Mortimer*

AUXILIARIES

Note: A 4200 ton submarine support ship has been designed by ASMAR. An order is expected in 1994/95.

1 TRANSPORT SHIP

Name	No	Builders	Commissioned
AQUILES	AP 47	Asmar, Talcahuano	15 July 1988

Displacement, tons: 2767 light; 4550 full load
Dimensions, feet (metres): 337.8 × 55.8 × 18 *(103 × 17 × 5.5 (max))*
Main machinery: 2 Krupp MaK 8 M 453B diesels; 7080 hp(m) *(5.10 MW)* sustained; 1 shaft
Speed, knots: 18
Complement: 80
Military lift: 250 troops
Helicopters: Platform for up to Super Puma size.

Comment: Ordered 4 October 1985, launched 4 December 1987. Can be converted rapidly to act as hospital ship. Has replaced the old *Aquiles* (ex-*Tjaldur*).

AQUILES   *1992, Chilean Navy*

1 HARBOUR TRANSPORT

Name	No	Builders	Commissioned
METEORO	YFB 110	Asmar, Talcahuano	1967

Displacement, tons: 205 full load
Dimensions, feet (metres): 80 × 22 × 8.5 *(24.4 × 6.7 × 2.6)*
Main machinery: 1 diesel; 1 shaft
Speed, knots: 8
Military lift: 220 troops

Comment: Transferred to Seaman's School as harbour transport.

METEORO   *1990, Chilean Navy*

1 TIDE CLASS (REPLENISHMENT TANKER)

Name	No	Builders	Commissioned
ALMIRANTE JORGE MONTT	52	Hawthorn Leslie, Hebburn	28 June 1963
(ex-RFA Tidepool)			

Displacement, tons: 8531 light; 27 400 full load
Measurement, tons: 18 900 dwt; 14 130 gross
Dimensions, feet (metres): 583 × 71 × 32 *(177.6 × 21.6 × 9.8)*
Main machinery: 2 Babcock & Wilcox boilers; 850 psi *(60 kg/cm sq)*; 950°F *(510°C)*; Pametrada turbines; 15 000 hp *(11.2 MW)*; 1 shaft
Speed, knots: 18.3
Complement: 110
Cargo capacity: 18 000 tons liquids
Guns: 4 Oerlikon 20 mm Mk 9; 4 Browning 12.7 mm (2 twin) MGs.
Radars: Navigation: Kelvin Hughes 14/12; I band.
Helicopter Control: Kelvin Hughes 14/16; I band.
Helicopters: Platform for up to 3 Super Puma.

Comment: Eventually transferred August 1982, after being delayed by the British in April 1982 for use in the Falklands' campaign. Still in service in early 1994 but a replacement is needed.

ALMIRANTE JORGE MONTT   *11/1993, G Toremans*

1 REPLENISHMENT SHIP

Name	No	Builders	Commissioned
ARAUCANO	53	Burmeister & Wain, Copenhagen	10 Jan 1967

Displacement, tons: 17 300
Dimensions, feet (metres): 497.6 × 74.9 × 28.8 *(151.7 × 22.8 × 8.8)*
Main machinery: 1 Burmeister & Wain Type 62 VT 2BF140 diesel; 10 800 hp(m) *(7.94 MW)*; 1 shaft
Speed, knots: 17. **Range, miles:** 12 000 at 15.5 kts
Cargo capacity: 21 126 m³ liquid; 1444 m³ dry
Guns: 8 Bofors 40 mm/70 (4 twin); 80° elevation; 120 rounds/minute to 10 km *(5 nm)* anti-surface; 3 km *(1.6 nm)* anti-aircraft; weight of shell 0.89 kg.

Comment: Launched on 21 June 1966.

ARAUCANO   *1992, Chilean Navy*

1 COASTAL TANKER

Name	No	Builders	Commissioned
GUARDIAN BRITO	YOG 101	Marco Chilena Sa-Iquique	1966
(ex-MS Sylvia)			

Displacement, tons: 482 full load
Dimensions, feet (metres): 129.9 × 23.9 × 10.8 *(39.6 × 7.3 × 3.3)*
Main machinery: 1 MWM diesel; 400 hp(m) *(294 kW)*; 1 shaft
Speed, knots: 10. **Range, miles:** 3000 at 8 kts
Complement: (1 officer)

Comment: Small former commercial tanker. Enlarged for naval service at Asmar, Talcahuano after acquisition 13 January 1983.

GUARDIAN BRITO   *1990, Chilean Navy*

3 + 1 FLOATING DOCKS

Note: 1 Ex-USN dock to be transferred in 1994.

Name	No	Lift	Commissioned
INGENIERO MERY (ex-ARD 25)	131	3000 tons	1944 (1973)
MUTILLA (ex-ARD 32)	132	3000 tons	1944 (1960)
MARINERO GUTIERREZ	—	1200 tons	1991

TUGS

Note: Small harbour tugs *Caupolican, Reyes, Galvez* and *Cortés*, and the small personnel transport *Sobenes* are also in commission.

SOBENES   *1991, Chilean Navy*

3 VERITAS CLASS (TUG/SUPPLY VESSELS)

Name	No	Builders	Commissioned
JANEQUEO (ex-Maersk Transporter)	ATF 65	Salthammex Batbyggeri, Vestness	1974
GALVARINO (ex-Maersk Traveller)	ATF 66	Aukra Bruk, Aukra	1974
LAUTARO (ex-Maersk Tender)	ATF 67	Aukra Bruk, Aukra	1973

Displacement, tons: 941 light; 2380 full load
Dimensions, feet (metres): 191.3 × 41.4 × 12.8 *(58.3 × 12.6 × 3.9)*
Main machinery: 2 Krupp MaK 8 M 453AK diesels; 6400 hp(m) *(4.7 MW)*; 2 shafts; cp props; bow thruster
Speed, knots: 14
Complement: 11 plus 12 spare berths
Cargo capacity: 1400 tons
Radars: Navigation: Terma Pilot 7T-48; Furuno FR 240; I band.

Comment: First two delivered from Maersk and commissioned into Navy 26 January 1988. Third one delivered in 1991. Bollard pull, 70 metric tons; towing winch, 100 tons. Fully air-conditioned. Designed for towing large semi-submersible platform in extreme weather conditions. Ice strengthened.

GALVARINO   *4/1993, Chilean Navy*

2 SMIT LLOYD CLASS

Name	No	Builders	Commissioned
LEUCOTON (ex-Smit Lloyd 44)	ATF 68	de Waal, Zaltbommel	1972
COLO COLO (ex-Smit Lloyd —)	ATF 69	de Waal, Zaltbommel	1972

Displacement, tons: 1750 full load
Dimensions, feet (metres): 174.2 × 39.4 × 14.4 *(53.1 × 12 × 4.4)*
Main machinery: 2 Burmeister & Wain Alpha diesels; 4000 hp(m) *(2.94 MW)*; 2 shafts
Speed, knots: 13

Comment: Acquired in February 1991 and 1992 respectively. Modified at Punta Arenas and now used mainly as supply ships.

LEUCOTON   *4/1993, Chilean Navy*

COAST GUARD

2 BUOY TENDERS

Name	No	Builders	Commissioned
MARINERO FUENTEALBA	75	Asmar, Talcahuano	22 July 1966
CABO ODGER	76	Asmar, Talcahuano	21 Apr 1967

Displacement, tons: 215
Dimensions, feet (metres): 80 × 21 × 9 *(24.4 × 6.4 × 2.7)*
Main machinery: 1 Cummins diesel; 340 hp *(254 kW)*; 1 shaft
Speed, knots: 9. **Range, miles:** 2600 at 9 kts
Complement: 19
Guns: 1 Oerlikon 20 mm. 3 Browning 12.7 mm MGs.

MARINERO FUENTEALBA   *1991, Chilean Navy*

2 + 2 (4) PROTECTOR CLASS

ALACALUFE LEP 1603   **HALLEF** LEP 1604

Displacement, tons: 107 full load
Dimensions, feet (metres): 107.3 × 22 × 6.6 *(32.7 × 6.7 × 2)*
Main machinery: 2 MTU diesels; 5200 hp(m) *(3.82 MW)*; 2 shafts
Speed, knots: 20. **Range, miles:** 1000 at 15 kts
Complement: 16

Comment: Built under licence from FBM at Asmar, Talcahuano, in conjunction with FBM Marine. First commissioned 24 June 1989; options on six more and it is reported that two gun armed variants were building in 1992. Manned by the Navy for patrol and Pilot Service duties in the Magellan Straits.

HALLEF   *1991, Chilean Navy*

10 COASTAL PATROL CRAFT

PILLAN GC 1801	**LLAIMA** GC 1806
TRONADOR GC 1802	**ANTUCO** GC 1807
RANO KAU GC 1803	**OSORNO** GC 1808
VILLARRICA GC 1804	**CHOSHUENCO** GC 1809
CORCOVADO GC 1805	**COPAHUE** GC 1810

Displacement, tons: 43 full load
Dimensions, feet (metres): 61 × 17.3 × 5.6 *(18.6 × 5.3 × 1.7)*
Main machinery: 2 MTU 8V 331 TC82 diesels; 1740 hp(m) *(1.28 MW)* sustained; 2 shafts
Speed, knots: 30. **Range, miles:** 700 at 15 kts
Guns: 2 Oerlikon 20 mm; 85° elevation; 800 rounds/minute.
Depth charges: 2 racks.

Comment: Built by Maclaren, Niteroi, Brazil. Ordered 1977. GRP hulls. *Pillan* commissioned August 1979 (approx); *Tronador*, August 1980 (approx); *Rano Kau* and *Villarrica*, November 1980; *Corcovado*, 6 March 1981; *Llaima*, 10 April 1981; *Choshuenco* and *Copahue*, 16 April 1982.

CORCOVADO   *1991, Chilean Navy*

1 INSHORE PATROL CRAFT

BELLATRIX

Dimensions, feet (metres): 31.8 × 10.2 × 3 *(9.7 × 3.1 × 0.9)*
Main machinery: 2 Volvo diesels; 500 hp(m) *(367 kW)*; 1 shaft
Speed, knots: 24

Comment: Built in 1953.

1 PATROL VESSEL

CASTOR WPC 113

Displacement, tons: 149 full load
Dimensions, feet (metres): 70.8 × 20.7 × 10.5 *(21.6 × 6.3 × 3.2)*
Main machinery: 1 Cummins diesel; 365 hp *(272 kW)*; 1 shaft
Speed, knots: 8
Complement: 14
Guns: 2 Oerlikon 20 mm. 2 Browning 12.7 mm MGs.

Comment: Built in 1968 and commissioned into the Coast Guard in 1975.

2 COASTAL PATROL CRAFT

ONA LEP 1601   **YAGAN** LEP 1602

Displacement, tons: 79 full load
Dimensions, feet (metres): 80.7 × 17.4 × 9.5 *(24.6 × 5.3 × 2.9)*
Main machinery: 2 MTU 6V 331 TC82 diesels; 1300 hp(m) *(960 kW)* sustained; 2 shafts
Speed, knots: 22
Complement: 5
Guns: 2—12.7 mm MGs.

Comment: Built by Asenav and commissioned in 1980.

2 COASTAL PATROL CRAFT

KIMITAHI LPC 1701   **GUALE** LPC 1811

Comment: Details not known.

15 INSHORE PATROL CRAFT

MAULE LPM 1901	**LOA** LPM 1906	**RIO RINIHUE** LPM 1911
LAUCA LPM 1902	**MAULIN** LPM 1907	**CHADMO** LPM 1912
ACONCAGUA LPM 1903	**COPIAPO** LPM 1908	**CASPANA** LPM 1914
RAPEL LPM 1904	**CAU-CAU** LPM 1909	**PETROHUE** LPM 1916
ISLUGA LPM 1905	**PUDETO** LPM 1910	**RIO BUENO** LPM 1917

Displacement, tons: 14 full load
Dimensions, feet (metres): 43.3 × 11.5 × 3.5 *(13.2 × 3.5 × 1.1)*
Main machinery: 2 MTU 6V 331 TC82 diesels; 1300 hp(m) *(960 kW)* sustained; 2 shafts
Speed, knots: 18
Guns: 1 Browning 12.7 mm MG.

Comment: LPM 1901-1910 ordered in August 1981. Completed by Asenav 1982-83. Remainder built in the late 1980s.

COPIAPO   *1992, Chilean Navy*

1 HOSPITAL SHIP

Name	No	Builders	Commissioned
CIRUJANO VIDELA	GC 111	Asmar, Talcahuano	1964

Displacement, tons: 140 full load
Dimensions, feet (metres): 101.7 × 21.3 × 6.6 *(31 × 6.5 × 2)*
Main machinery: 2 Cummins VT-12-700M diesels; 1400 hp *(1.05 MW)*; 2 shafts
Speed, knots: 14

Comment: Hospital and dental facilities are fitted. A modified version of US PGM 59 design with larger superstructure and less power. Owned by Ministry of Health and operated by Coast Guard.

CIRUJANO VIDELA   *6/1993, Chilean Navy*

1 SAR CRAFT

Displacement, tons: 10 full load
Dimensions, feet (metres): 41.7 × 12.8 × 1.6 *(12.7 × 3.9 × 0.5)*
Main machinery: 2 Volvo Penta TAMD41A diesels; 400 hp(m) *(294 kW)* maximum; 2 waterjets
Speed, knots: 25
Complement: 4 + 32 survivors
Guns: 1—7.62 mm MG.

Comment: Built at Asmar, Talcahuano and completed 8 August 1991. GRP hull.

CHINA, People's Republic

Note: Chinese names are transliterated in Pin Yin.

Headquarters' Appointments

Commander-in-Chief of the Navy:
Vice Admiral Zhang Lianzhong
Political Commissar of the Navy:
Vice Admiral Zhou Kunren
Deputy Commanders-in-Chief of the Navy:
Vice Admiral Shi Yunsheng
Vice Admiral Chen Mingshan
Vice Admiral He Peng Fei

Fleet Commanders

North Sea Fleet:
Vice Admiral Wang Jiying
East Sea Fleet:
Vice Admiral Qu Zhenmou
South Sea Fleet:
Vice Admiral He Linzhong

Personnel

(a) 1994: 265 000 officers and men, including 25 000 naval air force, 5000 marines (28 000 in time of war) and 28 000 for coastal defence
(b) 4 years' national service for sailors afloat; 3 years for those in shore service. Some stay on for up to 15 years. 40 000 conscripts

General

The Soviet involvement with China after 1949 included plans to develop a Sino-Soviet naval presence in the Pacific. These fell apart in the early 1960s as the rift between the two countries deepened but, when Lin Biao was in charge of defence, there was a resurgence of naval programmes. With Lin's death in 1971 these again suffered an eclipse which was intensified in the later years of the Cultural Revolution. The results of this national disaster were the swingeing cuts made in scientific and industrial improvements which delayed any notable advance in naval architecture or weapons systems development. It was only by the mid-1980s that there were signs that this dead period had been put aside and the naval export market was probing beyond the transfer of current designs to Bangladesh, Egypt and Pakistan. New designs of submarines, frigates and patrol craft were advertised and assistance was actively sought from Western defence industries. Unfortunately the events of 1989 caused a check in co-operation with the West but an active market was maintained in Thailand, Bangladesh and North Africa. The three years to 1994 have seen the introduction into service of new classes of Destroyers and Frigates as well as further modifications to the older types. In addition there are new types of patrol, amphibious and support vessels. Much interest continues to be taken in aircraft carrier designs with unconfirmed rumours of new construction in China probably based on a merchant ship hull. Russian technology, now on the open market, is being taken up.

Operational Numbers

Because large numbers of vessels are kept in operational reserve, the Chinese version of the order of battle tends to show many fewer ships than are counted by Western observers.

Bases

North Sea Fleet. Major bases: Qingdao (HQ), Lushun, Xiaoping-dao. Minor bases: Weihai Wei, Qingshan, Luda, Huludao, Lien Yun, Ling Shan, Ta Ku Shan, Changshandao, Liuzhuang, Dayuanjiadun
East Sea Fleet. Major bases: Ningbo (HQ), Zhoushan, Shanghai, Fujan. Minor bases: Zhenjiangguan, Wusong, Xinxiang, Wenz-hou, Sanduao, Xiamen, Xingxiang, Quandou, Wen Zhou SE, Wuhan
South Sea Fleet. Major bases: Zhanjiang (HQ), Yulin, Guangzhou (Canton). Minor bases: Haikou, Huangfu, Shantou, Humen, Kuan-chuang, Tsun, Kuan Chung, Mawai, Beihai, Ping Tan, San Chou Shih, Tang-Chiah Huan, Longmen, Bailong, Dongcun, Baimajing, Xiachuandao

Strength of the Fleet (1 January 1994)

Type	Active (Reserve)	Building (Planned)
SSBN	1	(1)
SSB	(1)	—
Fleet Submarines (SSN)	5	(1)
Cruise Missile Submarine (SSG)	1	—
Patrol Submarines	38 (40)	1 (3)
Destroyers	18	2 (2)
Frigates	37	3 (1)
Offshore Patrol Vessels	—	3
Fast Attack Craft (Missile)	158 (60)	3
Fast Attack Craft (Gun)	110 (200)	8
Fast Attack Craft (Torpedo)	80 (20)	—
Fast Attack Craft (Patrol)	103	4
River Patrol Craft	12	4
Minesweepers (Ocean)	27 (60)	—
Minesweepers (Coastal)	36 (50)	2 (38)
Mine Warfare Drones	4 (56)	—
Minelayer	1	—
Hovercraft	1	—
Troop Transports	9	—
LSTs	16 (2)	2
LSMs	34	—
LCMs—LCUs	110 (200)	—
Submarine Support Ships	5	—
Salvage and Repair Ships	7	—
Survey and Research Ships	60	—
Supply Ships	26+	3
Tankers	33+	—
Boom Defence Vessels	5+	—
Icebreakers	4	—
Degaussing Ships	10	—
Miscellaneous	450+	—

Training

The main training centres are:

Dalian: First Surface Vessel Academy, Political School
Canton: Second Surface Vessel Academy
Qingdao: Submarine Academy, Aviation School
Wuhan: Engineering College
Nanjing: Naval Staff College, Medical School, Electronic Engineering College
Yan Tai: Aviation Engineering College

Naval Air Force

With 25 000 officers and men and over 700 aircraft, this is a considerable naval air force primarily land-based and with a defensive role. There is also some ASW capability.

Mercantile Marine

Lloyd's Register of Shipping:
  2510 vessels of 14 944 999 tons gross

DELETIONS

Submarines

1990-92   10 Romeo class

Destroyers

1992   *Anshan, Fushun, Changchun, Qingdao*

Frigates

1992-93   *Zhongdong, Xiaguan, Kaiyuan, Haikou, Kaifeng, Kunming, Xichang*

Patrol Forces

1989-92   12 Kronshtadt class, 50 Shantou class, 60 P 4 class, Yingkou class (militia), Beihai class, 20 Yulin class
1991-93   40 P 6 class, 45 Huangpu class

Minesweepers

1990-92   5 Fushun class

Amphibious Vessels

1990-93   20 Yuchai class, 14 Hua class, 7 ex-US LSIL

Auxiliaries

1990-92   3 Ding Hai class, *Haiyun* (merchant)

PENNANT LIST

Destroyers		166	Zhuhai	519	Changzhi	557	Jishou
		167	—	531	Yingtan	558	Zigong
105	Jinan			533	Ningpo	559	Kangding
106	Xian	**Frigates**		534	Jinhua	560	Dongguan
107	Yinchuan			535	Huangshi	561	Shantou
108	Xining	502	Nanchong	536	Wu Hu		
109	Kaifeng	504	Dongchuan	537	Zhoushan		
110	Dalian	506	Chengdu	539	Anqing		
112	Haribing	507	Pingxiang	540	Huainan	**Principal Auxiliaries**	
113	—	509	Chang De	541	Huaibei		
131	Nanjing	510	Shaoxing	542	Tongling	81	Zhenghe
132	Hefei	511	Nantong	543	Dandong	920	Dazhi
133	Chongqing	512	Wuxi	544	Siping	J 121	Changxingdao
134	Zunyi	513	Huayin	545	Linfen	J 302	Chongmingdao
161	Changsha	514	Zhenjiang	551	Maoming	J 506	Yongxingdao
162	Nanning	515	Xiamen	552	Yibin	U 891	Dagushan
163	Nanchang	516	Jiujiang	553	Shaoguan	X 575	Taicang
164	Guilin	517	Nanping	554	Anshun	X 615	Dongyun
165	Zhanjiang	518	Jian	555	Zhaotong	AK 952	Nan Yun

SUBMARINES
Strategic Missile Submarines

1 GOLF CLASS (SSB)

200

Displacement, tons: 2350 surfaced; 2950 dived
Dimensions, feet (metres): 321.5 × 28.2 × 21.7
  (98 × 8.6 × 6.6)
Main machinery: Diesel-electric; 3 Type 37-D diesels; 6000 hp(m) *(4.41 MW)*; 3 motors; 5500 hp(m) *(4 MW)*; 3 shafts
Speed, knots: 17 surfaced; 13 dived
Range, miles: 6000 surfaced at 15 kts
Complement: 86 (12 officers)

Missiles: SLBM: 2 CSS-N-3; two stage solid fuel; inertial guidance to 2700 km *(1460 nm)*; warhead nuclear 2 MT.
Torpedoes: 10—21 in *(533 mm)* tubes (6 bow, 4 stern). 12 Type SAET-60; passive homing to 15 km *(8.1 nm)* at 40 kts; warhead 400 kg.
Radars: Navigation: Snoop Plate; I band.

GOLF   1988

Programmes: Ballistic missile submarine similar but not identical to the USSR Golf class. Built at Dalian and launched in September 1966.
Structure: Two missile tubes only because the Chinese missile is reported as having a larger diameter than the Soviet SS-N-5.

Operational: This was the trials submarine for the CSS-N-3 ballistic missile which was successfully launched to 1800 km in October 1982. As the missile is now operational it is probable that the submarine is in reserve but still available if needed.

1 XIA CLASS (TYPE 092) (SSBN)

Name	No	Builders	Laid down	Launched	Commissioned
XIA	406	Huludao Shipyard	1978	30 Apr 1981	1987

Displacement, tons: 8000 dived
Dimensions, feet (metres): 393.6 × 33 × 26.2
  (120 × 10 × 8)
Main machinery: Nuclear; turbo-electric; 1 PWR; 90 MW; 1 shaft
Speed, knots: 22 dived
Complement: 104

Missiles: SLBM: 12 CSS-N-3; two stage solid fuel; inertial guidance to 2700 km *(1460 nm)*; warhead single nuclear 2 MT. An improved version called CSS-NX-4 is being developed.
Torpedoes: 6—21 in *(533 mm)* bow tubes.

Programmes: A second of class was reported launched in 1982 and an unconfirmed report suggests that one of the two was lost in an accident in 1985. A new design Type 094 is being developed with a longer range missile.
Modernisation: CSS-N-3 may be replaced by CSS-NX-4 possibly with MIRV but not until sometime in the mid-1990s.
Structure: Diving depth about 300 m *(985 ft)*.
Operational: First test launch of the two stage CSS-NX-3 missile took place on 30 April 1982 from a submerged pontoon near Huludao (Yellow Sea). Range 1800 km. Second launched on 12 October 1982, from a Golf class trials submarine. The first

firing from Xia was in 1985 and was unsuccessful (delaying final acceptance into service of the submarine) and it was not until 27 September 1988 that a satisfactory launch took place.
Opinion: To maintain one submarine on continuous patrol takes a minimum of three and, to be absolutely safe, an optimum number of five hulls. Because of this known requirement there has been a tendency in the West to exaggerate the Chinese SSBN programme both in terms of numbers and timescales.

XIA

1987, Xinhua

XIA

1987, Xinhua

XIA

1988, Chinese Gazette

Attack Submarines

Note: A new SSN design is being worked on probably in conjunction with Russian experts.

5 HAN CLASS (SSN)

401   402   403   404   405

Displacement, tons: 5000 dived
Dimensions, feet (metres): 330; 356 (403 onwards) × 36 ×
27.9 approx *(100; 108 × 11 × 8.5)*
Main machinery: Nuclear; turbo-electric; 1 PWR; 90 MW; 1 shaft
Speed, knots: 25 dived
Complement: 75

Missiles: SSM (403 onwards); Ying Ji (Eagle Strike) (C-801); inertial cruise; active radar homing to 40 km *(22 nm)* at 0.9 Mach;
warhead 165 kg; sea-skimmer.
Torpedoes: 6—21 in *(533 mm)* bow tubes.

Countermeasures: ESM: Radar warning.
Sonars: May include French DUUX-5, some having been
delivered in 1985.

Programmes: These are the first Chinese nuclear submarines.
With an Albacore hull the first of this class was laid down about
1968 in Huludao shipyard. Her construction may have been
delayed as problems were encountered with the power plant,
but she appears to have been launched in 1972 and ran trials
in 1974. Second Han class was launched in 1977, third in
1983, the fourth in 1987 and the fifth on 8 April 1990. A successor design is being worked on with Russian assistance but
no date has been given for construction work to start.

Modernisation: The basic Russian ESM equipment was probably
replaced by a French design. More recent reports indicate that
the SSM fitted hulls have been equipped with more modern
ESM, possibly for long-range targeting.
Structure: From 403 onwards the hull has been extended by
some 8 m and Ying Ji SSM tubes fitted aft of the fin.
Operational: In North Sea Fleet. The first pair were thought to be
non-operational for a time in the late 1980s but have been
extensively refitted and are now back in service. The submarine has to surface to fire missiles.
Opinion: Nuclear submarines remain a high priority but high
internal radiation levels and other problems have led to a cessation in the building of this class.

HAN 402   1990

Patrol Submarines

Note: There are five Whiskey class in service, with a further ten in reserve. All are used for training and are probably limited to periscope depth.

0 + (3) KILO (TYPE 636) CLASS

Displacement, tons: 2325 surfaced; 3076 dived
Dimensions, feet (metres): 242.1 × 32.5 × 21.7
(73.8 × 9.9 × 6.6)
Main machinery: Diesel-electric; 2 diesels; 3650 hp(m)
(2.68 MW); 2 generators; 1 motor; 5500 hp(m) *(4.05 MW)*; 1
shaft
Speed, knots: 17 dived; 10 surfaced
Complement: 52 (10 officers)

Torpedoes: 6—21 in *(533 mm)* tubes. 18 torpedoes.
Mines: 24 in lieu of torpedoes.
Radars: Surface search: Snoop Tray; I band.
Sonars: Shark Teeth; hull-mounted; passive/active search and
attack; medium frequency.
Mouse Roar; hull-mounted; active attack; high frequency.

Programmes: Reported, but not confirmed, that three of the
class were ordered in mid-1993. To be built at Komsomolsk
Shipyard on the river Amur for completion in 1996-97. Alterna-
tively they could be built in China under licence. There is also a
possibility that one ex-Russian boat may be acquired first.
Structure: The Type 636 is the latest export version of the elderly
Kilo design and has better weapon systems co-ordination and
improved accommodation than the earlier ships of the class.
Normal diving depth is 240 m.
Opinion: This is a logical step forward from the obsolescent
Romeo/Ming design and will be cheaper to build than the
French Agosta, which was previously projected as the next
class.

KILO (Russian colours)   1992

8 + 1 MING CLASS (TYPE 035)

232   233   342   352   353   354   356   357   358

Displacement, tons: 1584 surfaced; 2113 dived
Dimensions, feet (metres): 249.3 × 24.9 × 16.7
(76 × 7.6 × 5.1)
Main machinery: Diesel-electric; 2 diesels; 5200 hp(m)
(3.82 MW); 2 shafts
Speed, knots: 15 surfaced; 18 dived; 10 snorting
Range, miles: 8000 at 8 kts snorting; 330 at 4 kts dived
Complement: 57 (12 officers)

Torpedoes: 8—21 in *(533 mm)* (6 fwd, 2 aft) tubes. 16 Type
SAET-60; passive homing to 15 km *(8.1 nm)* at 40 kts; war-
head 400 kg.
Mines: 32 in lieu of torpedoes.
Radars: Surface search: Snoop Plate or Snoop Tray; I band.
Sonars: Hercules/Feniks; hull-mounted; active/passive search
and attack; high frequency.

Programmes: First three completed between 1971 and 1979
one of which was scrapped after a fire. These were Type
ES5C/D. Building resumed in 1987 at the rate of less than one

MING 353   1991

per year to a modified design ES5E. The programme was
thought to have terminated in 1992 but may slowly continue
until the new Russian design gets under way.

Structure: Diving depth, 300 m *(985 ft)*.
Operational: Active in the East Sea Fleet. Fitted with Magnavox
SATNAV.

1 MODIFIED ROMEO CLASS (SSG)

351

Displacement, tons: 1650 surfaced; 2100 dived
Dimensions, feet (metres): 251.3 × 22 × 17.1
(76.6 × 6.7 × 5.2)
Main machinery: Diesel-electric; 2 Type 37-D diesels; 4000
hp(m) *(2.94 MW)*; 2 motors; 2700 hp(m) *(1.98 MW)*; 2 creep
motors; 2 shafts
Speed, knots: 13 dived; 15 surfaced; 10 snorting
Complement: 54 (10 officers)

Missiles: SSM: 6 YJ-1 (Eagle Strike) (C-801); three launchers
either side of fin; inertial cruise; active radar homing to
40 km *(22 nm)* at 0.9 Mach; warhead 165 kg; sea-skimmer.
Torpedoes: 8—21 in *(533 mm)* (6 bow, 2 stern) tubes. 16 Type
SAET-60; passive homing to 15 km *(8.1 nm)* at 40 kts; war-
head 400 kg.
Mines: 20 in lieu of torpedoes.
Radars: Surface search: Snoop Plate and Snoop Tray; I band.
Sonars: Hercules or Tamir 5; hull-mounted; active/passive
search and attack; high frequency.

Programmes: This design, designated ES5G, is a modified
Romeo (Wuhan) rebuilt as a trials SSM platform. Others may
be converted in due course.
Structure: The six missile tubes are built into the casing abreast
the fin and elevate to fire much as in the Soviet Juliett class. To

MOD ROMEO 351 (firing YJ-1)   *1987, Xinhua*

provide target acquisition an additional radar mast (Snoop
Tray) is mounted between the two periscopes.
Operational: Has to surface to fire missiles.

30 (+ 40 RESERVE) ROMEO CLASS (TYPE 033)

Displacement, tons: 1475 surfaced; 1830 dived
Dimensions, feet (metres): 251.3 × 22 × 17.1
(76.6 × 6.7 × 5.2)
Main machinery: Diesel-electric; 2 Type 37-D diesels; 4000
hp(m) *(2.94 MW)*; 2 motors; 2700 hp(m) *(1.98 MW)*; 2 creep
motors; 2 shafts
Speed, knots: 15.2 surfaced; 13 dived; 10 snorting
Range, miles: 9000 at 9 kts surfaced
Complement: 54 (10 officers)

Torpedoes: 8—21 in *(533 mm)* (6 bow, 2 stern) tubes. 14 Type
SAET-60; passive homing to 15 km *(8.1 nm)* at 40 kts; war-
head 400 kg.
Mines: 28 in lieu of torpedoes.
Radars: Surface search: Snoop Plate or Snoop Tray; I band.
Sonars: Hercules or Tamir 5; hull-mounted; active/passive
search and attack; high frequency. Thomson Sintra DUUX 5 in
some of the class.

Programmes: The Chinese continued to construct their own submarines to the USSR Romeo design until the end of 1984. The
first boats of this class were built at Jiangnan SY, Shanghai in
mid-1962 with Wuzhang being used later. The basic Romeo
class design is at least 30 years old and has evolved from the
Type 031 (ES3B). Construction stopped around 1987 with the
resumption of the Ming Class programme.
Modernisation: Battery refits are being done and the more modern boats have French passive ranging sonar; Italian torpedoes
have also been reported but not confirmed.
Structure: Diving depth, 300 m *(984 ft)*. There are probably
some dimensional variations between newer and older ships
of the class.
Operational: Operational numbers are difficult to assess as no
submarine spends more than a few days at sea each year
because there are insufficient trained men. Of the original 84,
at least 40 are in various states of operational reserve and
some have been scrapped. ASW capability is virtually
non-existent.
Sales: Seven to North Korea in 1973-75. Two to Egypt February/
March 1982, two in 1984. All new construction.

ROMEO 346   *2/1993, Chien Chung*

ROMEO 250   *12/1989, G Jacobs*

DESTROYERS

1 + 1 (2) LUHU (TYPE 052) CLASS (DDG)

Name	No	Builders	Laid down	Launched	Commissioned
HARIBING	112	Jiangnan Shipyard	1988	June 1991	1994
—	113	Jiangnan Shipyard	1991	Oct 1993	1995

Displacement, tons: 4200 standard
Measurement, tons: 475.7 × 49.9 × 16.7
(145 × 15.2 × 5.1)
Main machinery: CODOG: 2 GE LM 2500 gas-turbines;
55 000 hp *(41 MW)* sustained; 2 MTU 12V 1163 TB83 die-
sels; 8840 hp(m) *(6.5 MW)* sustained; 2 shafts; cp props
Speed, knots: 30
Complement: 300

Missiles: SSM: 8 YJ-1 (Eagle Strike) (C-801) ❶; active radar homing to 40 km *(22 nm)* (possibly extended range version) at
0.9 Mach; warhead 165 kg; sea-skimmer.
SAM: 1 Thomson-CSF Crotale octuple launcher ❷; line-of-sight
guidance to 13 km *(7 nm)* at 2.4 Mach; warhead 14 kg.
Guns: 2—3.9 in *(100 mm)*/56 (twin) ❸; 85° elevation; 18
rounds/minute to 22 km *(12 nm)*; weight of shell 15 kg.
8—37 mm/63 (4 twin) ❹; 85° elevation; 180 rounds/minute
to 8.5 km *(4.6 nm)* anti-aircraft; weight of shell 1.42 kg.
Torpedoes: 6—324 mm Whitehead B515 (2 triple) tubes ❺.
Whitehead A 244S; anti-submarine.
A/S mortars: 2 FQF 2500 ❻ 12-tubed fixed launchers.
Countermeasures: Decoys: 2 SRBOC Mk 33; 6-barrelled chaff
launchers. 2 China 26-barrelled chaff launchers.
ESM/ECM: Intercept and jammer.
Combat data systems: Thomson-CSF TAVITAC; action data
automation.
Radars: Air search: Rice Screen ❼; 3D; G band.
Hai Ying ❽; G band.
Air/surface search: Thomson-CSF Sea Tiger ❾; E/F band.
Navigation: I band.
Fire control: Type 347G ❿; I band (for SSM and 100 mm).
Two Rice Lamp ⓫; I band.
Sonars: Hull-mounted; active search and attack; medium
frequency.
VDS; active attack; medium frequency.

Helicopters: 2 Harbin Z9A (Dauphin) ⓬.

HARIBING   5/1993

Programmes: First of a new class ordered in 1985 but delayed by
priority being given to export orders for Thailand. Now in series
production probably replacing the Luda class in due course.
The third of class may be delayed because of problems obtain-
ing more LM 2500 gas-turbines.

Structure: The most notable features are the new SAM launcher,
improved radar and fire-control systems and a modern
100 mm gun. The SSM is possibly an extended range version
of the C-801 but not yet the C-802, which is still to achieve production status.

Operational: Started trials in late 1992 and continued in 1993.
Opinion: By Chinese standards this is an impressive looking ship
and the assiduous wooing of Western manufacturers has
achieved a major step forward in operational capabilities.

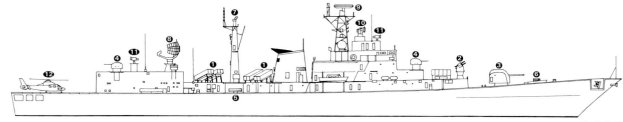

HARIBING   (Scale 1 : 900), Ian Sturton

HARIBING   9/1993, Hachiro Nakai

17 + 1 LUDA (TYPE 051) CLASS (DDG)

Name	No	Name	No	Name	No
JINAN	105 (Type II)	NANJING	131	CHANGSHA	161
XIAN	106	HEFEI	132	NANNING	162
YINCHUAN	107	CHONGQING	133	NANCHANG	163
XINING	108	ZUNYI	134	GUILIN	164
KAIFENG	109			ZHANJIANG	165
DALIAN	110			ZHUHAI	166 (Type III)
				—	167 (Type III)

Displacement, tons: 3250 standard; 3670 full load
Dimensions, feet (metres): 433.1 × 42 × 15.1
(132 × 12.8 × 4.6)
Main machinery: 2 boilers; 2 turbines; 72 000 hp(m) *(53 MW)*; 2 shafts
Speed, knots: 32. **Range, miles:** 2970 at 18 kts
Complement: 280 (45 officers)

Missiles: SSM: 6 HY-2 (C-201) (2 triple) launchers ❶; (Types I and II); active radar or IR homing to 95 km *(51 nm)* at 0.9 Mach; warhead 513 kg.
8 YJ-1 (Eagle Strike) (C-801) (4 twin) launchers (Type III) ❷; active radar homing to 40 km *(22 nm)* at 0.9 Mach; warhead 165 kg; sea-skimmer.
SAM: Thomson-CSF Crotale octuple launcher *(Kaifeng)* ❸; line-of-sight guidance to 13 km *(7 nm)* at 2.4 Mach; warhead 14 kg.
A/S: The after set of launchers in Type III may also be used for CY-1 anti-submarine missiles; range 8-15 km *(4.4-8.3 nm)*; payload anti-submarine torpedoes.
Guns: 4 (Type I) or 2 (Type II) USSR 5.1 in *(130 mm)*/58 (2 twin) (Type I) ❹; 85° elevation; 17 rounds/minute to 29 km *(16 nm)*; weight of shell 33.4 kg.
8 China 57 mm/70 (4 twin) ❺; 85° elevation; 120 rounds/minute to 12 km *(6.5 nm)*; weight of shell 6.31 kg. These guns are fitted in some of the class, the others have 37 mm.
8 China 37 mm/63 (4 twin) (some Type I and Type III) ❻; 85° elevation; 180 rounds/minute to 8.5 km *(4.6 nm)*; weight of shell 1.42 kg.
8 USSR 25 mm/60 (4 twin) ❼; 85° elevation; 270 rounds/minute to 3 km *(1.6 nm)* anti-aircraft; weight of shell 0.34 kg.
Torpedoes: 6—324 mm Whitehead B515 (2 triple tubes) ❽ (fitted in some Type I and Type III); Whitehead A 244S; anti-submarine.
A/S mortars: 2 FQF 2500 12-tubed fixed launchers ❾; 120 rockets; range 1200 m; warhead 34 kg. Similar in design to the Soviet RBU 1200.
Depth charges: 2 or 4 projectors; 2 or 4 racks.
Mines: 38.
Countermeasures: Decoys: chaff launchers (fitted to some).
ESM: Jug Pair (RW-23-1); 2-18 GHz; radar warning.
Combat data systems: Thomson-CSF TAVITAC with Vega FCS (in some).
Radars: Air search: Knife Rest or Cross Slot; A band or Bean Sticks or Pea Sticks ❿; E/F band.
Rice Screen ⓫ (on mainmast in some); 3D; G band. Similar to Hughes SPS-39A.
Surface search: Eye Shield ⓬; E band or Thomson-CSF Sea Tiger; E/F band.
Square Tie (not in all); I band.
Navigation: Fin Curve; I band.
Fire control: Wasp Head (also known as Wok Won) or Type 343 Sun Visor B (series 2) ⓭; G/H band.
2 Rice Lamp (series 2) ⓮; I band.
2 Type 347G ⓯; I band.
IFF: High Pole.
Sonars: Pegas 2M and Tamir 2; hull-mounted; active search and attack; high frequency.
VDS (Type III); active attack.
Helicopters: 2 Harbin Z-9A (Dauphin) ⓰ (Type II).

Programmes: The first Chinese-designed destroyers of such a capability to be built. First of class completed in 1971. 105-110 built at Luda; 131-134 at Shanghai and 161-167 at Guangzhou. Similar to the deleted USSR Kotlin class. The programme was much retarded after 1971 by drastic cuts in the defence budget. In early 1977 building of series two of this class was put in hand and includes those after 109, with the latest 164 in April 1987, 165 and 166 in 1992 and 167 in 1993. The order of completion was 105, 160 (scrapped), 106, 161, 107, 162, 131, 108, 132, 109, 163, 110, 133, 134, 164, 165, 166 and 167. More Type IIIs may be built or converted.
Modernisation: First of class 105 completed a major refit in 1987 as a Type II trials ship, with the after armament replaced by a twin helicopter hangar and deck. *Zhuhai* is the first Type III and shows many changes from the Type Is, including modified after SSM launchers which may fire the CY-1 anti-submarine missile.
Structure: Electronics vary in later ships. Some ships have 57 mm guns, others 37 mm. *Jinan* may have Alcatel 'Safecopter' landing aid. *Zhuhai* and 167 are Type III with Ying Ji launchers. Thomsea combat data system including Vega FCS has been installed in at least two of the class and Crotale SAM is fitted in *Kaifeng* in X gun position.
Operational: Capable of foreign deployment, although command and control is limited. Underway refuelling is practised.

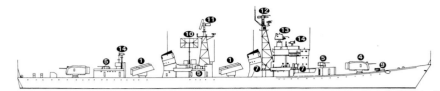
TYPE I (modified)   *(Scale 1 : 1200), Ian Sturton*

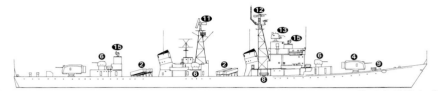
TYPE III   *(Scale 1 : 1200), Ian Sturton*

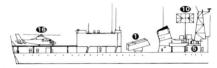
JINAN (with helo)

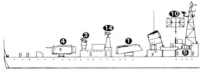
KAIFENG (with Crotale)   *(Scale 1 : 1200), Ian Sturton*

ZHUHAI (Type III)   *5/1992, Henry Dodds*

HEFEI   *9/1993, Hachiro Nakai*

Deployment; 105 series in North and East Sea Fleets; 131 series in East Sea Fleet; 161 series in South Sea Fleet. 160 was damaged by an explosion in 1978, and was scrapped.

Opinion: There have long been reports of a ballistic trajectory ASW weapon CY-1 and the different types of SSM launchers in Type III indicate that the weapon may now be operational.

KAIFENG (with Crotale)   *1992*

JINAN (Type II)   *1992*

NANJING   *5/1992*

HEFEI   *9/1993, Hachiro Nakai*

FRIGATES
25 + 2 JIANGHU I (TYPE 053) CLASS (FFG)

Name	No	Name	No	Name	No	Name	No
CHANG DE	509	JIUJIANG	516	DANDONG	543	ZHAOTONG	555
SHAOXING	510	NANPING	517	LINFEN	545	JISHOU	557
NANTONG	511	JIAN	518	MAOMING	551	ZIGONG	558
WUXI	512	CHANGZHI	519	YIBIN	552	KANGDING	559
HUAYIN	513	NINGPO	533	SHAOGUAN	553	DONGGUAN	560
ZHENJIANG	514	JINHUA	534	ANSHUN	554	SHANTOU	561
XIAMEN	515						

Displacement, tons: 1425 standard; 1702 full load
Dimensions, feet (metres): 338.5 × 35.4 × 10.2
  (103.2 × 10.8 × 3.1)
Main machinery: 2 Type 12E 390V diesels; 14 400 hp(m)
  (10.6 MW) sustained; 2 shafts
Speed, knots: 26. **Range, miles:** 4000 at 15 kts; 2700 at 18 kts
Complement: 200 (30 officers)

Missiles: SSM: 4 HY-2 (C-201) (2 twin) launchers ❶; active radar
  or IR homing to 80 km *(43.2 nm)* at 0.9 Mach; warhead
  513 kg.
Guns: 2 or 4 China 3.9 in *(100 mm)*/56 (2 single ❷ or 2 twin ❸);
  85° elevation; 18 rounds/minute to 22 km *(12 nm)*; weight of
  shell 15.9 kg.
  12 China 37 mm/63 (6 twin) ❹ (8 (4 twin), in some); 85° elevation; 180 rounds/minute to 8.5 km *(4.6 nm)* anti-aircraft;
  weight of shell 1.42 kg.
A/S mortars: 2 RBU 1200 5-tubed fixed launchers (4 in some) ❺;
  range 1200 m; warhead 34 kg.
Depth charges: 2 BMB-2 projectors; 2 racks.
Mines: Can carry up to 60.
Countermeasures: Decoys: 2 RBOC Mk 33 6-barrelled chaff
  launchers or 2 China 26-barrelled launchers.
ESM: Jug Pair or Watchdog; radar warning.
Fire control: Wok Won director (in some) ❻.
Radars: Air/surface search: MX 902 Eye Shield (Type 354) ❼;
  possible E band.
  Rice Screen (?) ❽ (560 and 561); G band.
  Surface search/fire control: Square Tie (Type 352) ❾; I band.
  Navigation: Don 2 or Fin Curve or Racal Decca; I band.
  Fire control: Rice Lamp (in some) ❿; I/J band.
  Sun Visor (in some) ⓫; I band.
IFF: High Pole A. Yard Rake or Square Head.
Sonars: Echo Type 5; hull-mounted; active search and attack;
  medium frequency.

Programmes: A modification of Jiangdong class with SSM in
  place of SAM. Pennant numbers changed in 1979. All built in
  Shanghai starting in the mid-1970s at the Hudong and Jiangnan shipyards and still continuing in 1994 as a cheaper alternative to the Jiangwei class. Ships were completed in the
  following order: 515, 516, 517, 511, 512, 513, 514, 518, 509,
  510, 519, 520, 551, 552, 533, 534, two for Egypt, 543, 553,
  554, 555, 545, 556 (to Bangladesh), 557, 544, 558, 559,
  560 and 561.
Modernisation: Fire-control and electronics equipment is being
  modernised. Sun Visor and Rice Lamp have been seen on
  newly refitted Type Is. Possible VDS or sonar towed array may
  be fitted in one of the class. The latest ships have gunhouses
  on the 37 mm guns and possibly a new air/surface search
  radar.
Structure: All of the class have the same hull dimensions. Previously reported Type numbers have been superseded by the
  following designations:
  Type I has at least five versions. Version 1 has an oval funnel
  and square bridge wings; version 2 a square funnel with bev-
  elled bridge face; version 3 an octagonal funnel; version 4
  reverts back to the oval funnel and version 5 has a distinctive
  fluting arrangement with cowls on the funnel, as well as gunhouses on the 37 mm guns. Some have bow bulwarks.
  Type II. See separate entry.
  Types III and IV. See separate entry.
Operational: *Kaifeng* 520 paid off in 1993.
Sales: Two have been transferred to Egypt, one in September
  1984, the other in March 1985, and one *(Xiangtan)* to Bangladesh in November 1989 (old number 556).

ZHENJIANG (single 100 mm gun)   *(Scale 1 : 900), Ian Sturton*

NINGPO (Rice Lamp FC radar)   *(Scale 1 : 900), Ian Sturton*

DONGGUAN (37 mm gunhouses)   *(Scale 1 : 900), Ian Sturton*

DONGGUAN   6/1993

JIANGHU 556 (old number)   6/1988

ZHENJIANG   *6/1993*

NINGPO   *6/1993*

1 JIANGHU II (TYPE 053) CLASS (FFGH)

SIPING 544

Displacement, tons: 1550 standard; 1820 full load
Dimensions, feet (metres): 338.5 × 35.4 × 10.2
  (103.2 × 10.8 × 3.1)
Main machinery: 2 Type 12E 390V diesels; 14 400 hp(m)
  (10.6 MW) sustained; 2 shafts
Speed, knots: 26. **Range, miles:** 4000 at 15 kts; 2700 at 18 kts
Complement: 200 (30 officers)

Missiles: SSM: 2 HY-2 (C-201) (twin) launchers ❶; active radar or
  IR homing to 80 km *(43.2 nm)* at 0.9 Mach; warhead 513 kg.
Guns: 1 Creusot Loire 3.9 in *(100 mm)*/55 ❷; 85° elevation;
  60-80 rounds/minute to 17 km *(9.3 nm)*; weight of shell
  13.5 kg.
  8 China 37 mm/63 (4 twin) ❸; 85° elevation; 180 rounds/
  minute to 8.5 km *(4.6 nm)* anti-aircraft; weight of shell 1.42 kg.
Torpedoes: 6–324 mm ILAS (2 triple) tubes ❹. Whitehead A
  244S; anti-submarine.
A/S mortars: 2 RBU 1200 5-tubed fixed launchers ❺; range
  1200 m; warhead 34 kg.
Depth charges: 2 BMB-2 projectors; 2 racks.
Countermeasures: Decoys: 2 SRBOC Mk 33 6-barrelled chaff
  launchers or 2 China 26-barrelled launchers.
ESM: Jug Pair or Watchdog; radar warning.
Fire control: CSEE Naja optronic director for 100 mm gun.
Radars: Air/surface search: MX 902 Eye Shield ❻; possible E
  band.
Surface search/fire control: Square Tie ❼; I band.
Navigation: Don 2 or Fin Curve; I band.
Fire control: Wok Won ❽; I/J band.
IFF: High Pole A. Yard Rake or Square Head.
Sonars: Echo Type 5; hull-mounted; active search and attack;
  medium frequency.

Helicopters: Harbin Z-9A (Dauphin) ❾.

Programmes: Built in 1984 as a standard Jianghu I and then converted, probably before being commissioned.
Structure: The after part of the ship has been rebuilt to take a
  hangar and flight deck for a single helicopter. Alcatel 'Safe-

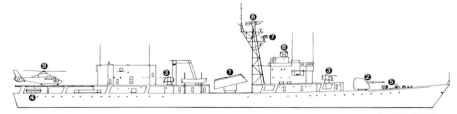

SIPING   *(Scale 1 : 900), Ian Sturton*

SIPING   *1990*

copter' landing aid. This ship also has a French 100 mm gun
and optronic director, and Italian triple torpedo tubes mounted
on the quarterdeck.

Opinion: More of the class were expected to be converted, but
this may have been a one-off helicopter trials ship for the Luhu
and Jiangwei designs. Other Jianghus may still be converted.

3 JIANGHU III and IV (TYPE 053 HT) CLASS (FFG)

HUANGSHI 535 (Type III)   **WU HU** 536 (Type III)   **ZHOUSHAN** 537 (Type IV)

Displacement, tons: 1924 full load
Dimensions, feet (metres): 338.5 × 35.4 × 10.2
(103.2 × 10.8 × 3.1)
Main machinery: 2 Type 12E 390V diesels; 14 400 hp(m)
(10.6 MW) sustained; 2 shafts
Speed, knots: 26. **Range, miles:** 4000 at 15 kts; 2700 at 18 kts
Complement: 200 (30 officers)

Missiles: SSM: 8 YJ-1 (Eagle Strike) (C-801) **❶**; active radar homing to 40 km *(22 nm)* at 0.9 Mach; warhead 165 kg. Type IV is
fitted for an improved version of this missile with an extended
range to 85 km *(45.9 nm).*
Guns: 4 China 3.9 in *(100 mm)*/56 (2 twin) **❷**; 85° elevation; 18
rounds/minute to 22 km *(12 nm)*; weight of shell 15.9 kg.
8 China 37 mm/63 (4 twin) **❸**; 85° elevation; 180 rounds/
minute to 8.5 km *(4.6 nm)* anti-aircraft; weight of shell 1.42 kg.
A/S mortars: 2 RBU 1200 5-tubed fixed launchers **❹**; range
1200 m; warhead 34 kg.
Depth charges: 2 BMB-2 projectors; 2 racks.
Mines: Can carry up to 60.
Countermeasures: Decoys: 2 China 26-barrelled chaff
launchers.
ESM: Elettronica Newton; radar warning.
ECM: Elettronica 929 (Type 981); jammer.
Radars: Air/surface search: MX 902 Eye Shield **❺**; possible E
band.
Surface search/fire control: Square Tie **❻**; I band.
Navigation: Fin Curve; I band.
Fire control: Rice Lamp **❼**; I/J band.
Sun Visor **❽**; I band.
IFF: High Pole A. Square Head.
Sonars: Echo Type 5; hull-mounted; active search and attack;
medium frequency.

Programmes: These ships are Jianghu hulls 27, 28 and 30 and
are referred to as New Missile Frigates. *Huangshi* commissioned 14 December 1986. *Zhoushan* completed in early
1993 and a fourth of the class may be building but this is not
confirmed.
Structure: The main deck is higher in the midships section and
the lower part of the mast is solid. Type IV has an improved
SSM missile which is probably a longer range version of C-801
rather than the turbojet C-802 which is not yet thought to be in
operational service. The arrangement of the launchers is side
by side, as opposed to the staggered pairings in Type III. These
are the first all-enclosed, air-conditioned ships built in China.
Sales: Four modified Type III to Thailand in 1991/92.

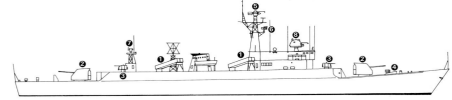

ZHOUSHAN   *(Scale 1 : 900), Ian Sturton*

HUANGSHI   *2/1993, Chien Chung*

WU HU   *5/1992*

ZHOUSHAN   *10/1992, Ships of the World*

4 + 1 (1) JIANGWEI CLASS (FFG)

Name	No
ANQING	539
HUAINAN	540
HUAIBEI	541
TONGLING	542
—	—

Builders	Laid down	Launched	Completed
Hudong Shipyard	1988	July 1991	Dec 1991
Hudong Shipyard	1989	Dec 1991	Dec 1992
Hudong Shipyard	1990	Mar 1993	Aug 1993
Hudong Shipyard	1991	Sep 1993	Mar 1994
Hudong Shipyard	1993	1995	1996

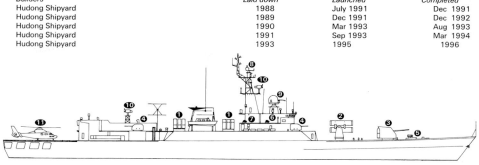

ANQING (Scale 1 : 900), Ian Sturton

Displacement, tons: 2180 standard
Dimensions, feet (metres): 367.5 × 40.7 × 14.1
(112 × 12.4 × 4.3)
Main machinery: 2 Type 12E 390 diesels (see *Structure*);
14 400 hp(m) *(10.6 MW)* sustained; 2 shafts
Speed, knots: 25. **Range, miles:** 4000 at 18 kts
Complement: 170

Missiles: SSM: 6 YJ-1 (Eagle Strike) (C-801) (2 triple) launchers
❶; active radar homing to 40 km *(22 nm)* at 0.9 Mach; warhead 165 kg; sea-skimmer. Extended range to 120 km *(66 nm)*
when C-802 is fitted.
SAM: 1 HQ-61 sextuple launcher ❷; PL-9; command guidance;
semi-active radar homing to 10 km *(5.5 nm)* at 3 Mach.
Guns: 2 China 3.9 in *(100 mm)/*56 (twin) ❸; 85° elevation; 18
rounds/minute to 22 km *(12 nm)*; weight of shell 15.9 kg.
8 China 37 mm/63 (4 twin) ❹; 85° elevation; 180 rounds/
minute to 8.5 km *(4.6 nm)* anti-aircraft; weight of shell 1.42 kg.
A/S mortars: 2 RBU 1200 ❺; 5-tubed fixed launchers; range
1200 m; warhead 34 kg.
Countermeasures: 2 SRBOC Mk 33 6-barrelled chaff launchers
❻. 2 China 26-barrelled chaff launchers ❼.
ESM: RWD8; intercept.
ECM: NJ81-3; jammer.
Fire control: Fog Lamp IR system (for SAM).
Radars: Air/surface search: Rice Screen ❽; G band.
Fire control: Sun Visor ❾; I band.
2 Rice Lamp ❿; I/J band.
Navigation: Fin Curve; I band.
Sonars: Echo Type 5; hull-mounted; active search and attack;
medium frequency.

Helicopters: 1 Harbin Z9A (Dauphin) ⓫.

Programmes: New programme started in 1988. First one conducted sea trials in late 1991. In series production with five
expected to be in service by 1996.
Structure: The sextuple launcher is a much needed multiple
launch SAM system using the PL-9 missile. Early reports indicated a possible ASW capability but this was not correct. There
is a possibility that CY-1 A/S missiles may also be launched
from the YJ-1 launchers as in Luda III. The export version of this
ship offers four main engines for a speed of 28 kts. It is therefore possible that four diesels are fitted in Jiangwei, with two to
each shaft.

HUAINAN 9/1993, Hachiro Nakai

HUAINAN 9/1993, Hachiro Nakai

1 JIANGDONG (TYPE 053K) CLASS (FFG)

YINGTAN 531

Displacement, tons: 1674 standard; 1924 full load
Dimensions, feet (metres): 338.5 × 35.1 × 10.2
(103.2 × 10.7 × 3.1)
Main machinery: 2 Type 12E 390V diesels; 14 400 hp(m)
(10.6 MW) sustained; 2 shafts
Speed, knots: 26. **Range, miles:** 4000 at 15 kts; 1800 at 25 kts
Complement: 198 (30 officers)

Missiles: SAM: 2 HQ-61 twin arm launchers ❶; PL-9; command
guidance; semi-active radar homing to 10 km *(5.5 nm)* at
3 Mach.
Guns: 4 China 3.9 in *(100 mm)/*56 (2 twin) ❷; 85° elevation; 18
rounds/minute to 22 km *(12 nm)*; weight of shell 15.9 kg.
8 China 37 mm/63 (4 twin) ❸; 85° elevation; 180 rounds/
minute to 8.5 km *(4.6 nm)* anti-aircraft; weight of shell 1.42 kg.
A/S mortars: 2 RBU 1200 5-tubed fixed launchers ❹; range
1200 m; warhead 34 kg.
Depth charges: 2 BMB-2 projectors; 2 racks.
Countermeasures: ESM: 2 Jug Pair.
Fire control: Fog Lamp ❺; IR system fitted in 531 in 1985.
Radars: Air search: Rice Screen ❻; 3D; G band.
Surface search: Square Tie ❼; I band.
Navigation: Fin Curve; I band.
Fire control: Sun Visor B ❽; G/H/I band (for 57 mm guns).
2 Rice Lamp ❾; I band.
IFF: Ski Pole. Yard Rake.
Sonars: Probably Pegas-2M and Tamir 2; hull-mounted; active
search and attack; medium/high frequency.

Programmes: *Yingtan* was laid down at Hudong, Shanghai in
1970 and commissioned in 1977. Second of class *Zhongdong*
built two years later at Jiuxin, but has now been scrapped.
Jiangdong class is called an 'Anti-Air Missile Frigate'.

YINGTAN (Scale 1 : 900), Ian Sturton

YINGTAN 1989, Chinese Gazette

Modernisation: May have started modernisation with some
Western weapon systems in 1992.

Structure: First SAM armed Chinese ship(s). Rice Screen is also
the first modern air search radar to be fitted.
Operational: The SAM system has a long history of problems.

2 JIANGNAN (TYPE 065) CLASS (FF)

NANCHONG 502   **DONGCHUAN** 504

Displacement, tons: 1350 standard; 1600 full load
Dimensions, feet (metres): 300.1 × 33.1 × 10.5
(91.5 × 10.1 × 3.2)
Main machinery: 2 Type 12E 390V diesels; 14 400 hp(m)
(10.6 MW) sustained; 2 shafts
Speed, knots: 28. **Range, miles:** 3000 at 10 kts; 900 at 26 kts
Complement: 180 (15 officers)

Guns: 3 China 3.9 in *(100 mm)*/56 (1 fwd, 2 aft) ❶; 85° elevation;
18 rounds/minute to 22 km *(12 nm)*; weight of shell 15.9 kg.
8 China 37 mm/63 (4 twin) ❷; 85° elevation; 180 rounds/
minute to 8.5 km *(4.6 nm)*; weight of shell 1.42 kg.
4 China 14.5 mm/93 (2 twin); 85° elevation; 600 rounds/
minute to 7 km *(3.8 nm)*.
A/S mortars: 2 RBU 1200 5-tubed fixed launchers ❸; range
1200 m; warhead 34 kg.
Depth charges: 4 BMB-2 projectors; 2 racks.
Mines: Can carry up to 60.
Radars: Surface search: Ball End ❹; E/F band; range 37 km
(20 nm).
Navigation: Neptun or Fin Curve; I band.
Fire control: Twin Eyes ❺.
Sonars: Pegas-2M and Tamir 2; hull-mounted; active search and
attack; medium/high frequency.

Programmes: The Chinese Navy embarked on a new building
programme in 1965 of which this class was the first. Five built
at Guangzhou and commissioned in 1967-68. Development of
Soviet Riga class. All had major refits since 1974.
Operational: The surviving pair serve with the South Sea Fleet.
The other three have been paid off in 1992/93.
Sales: Two of the class may have been offered to Burma in 1993,
but this is not confirmed.

JIANGNAN   *(Scale 1 : 900), Ian Sturton*

JIANGNAN (old number)   *1986*

2 CHENGDU (TYPE 01) CLASS (FFG)

Name	No	Builders	Laid down	Launched	Commissioned
CHENGDU	506	Guangzhou	1955	1957	1959
PINGXIANG	507	Hudong, Shanghai	1955	28 Apr 1956	1958

Displacement, tons: 1240 standard; 1460 full load
Dimensions, feet (metres): 300.1 × 33.1 × 10.5
(91.5 × 10.1 × 3.2)
Main machinery: 2 boilers; 2 turbines; 20 000 hp(m) *(14.7 MW)*;
2 shafts
Speed, knots: 28. **Range, miles:** 2000 at 10 kts
Complement: 170 (16 officers)

Missiles: SSM: 2 HY-2 (twin) launcher ❶; active radar or IR homing to 80 km *(43.2 nm)* at 0.9 Mach; warhead 513 kg.
Guns: 2 or 3 China 3.9 in *(100 mm)*/56 ❷; 85° elevation; 18
rounds/minute to 22 km *(12 nm)*; weight of shell 15.9 kg.
4 China 37 mm/63 (2 twin) ❸; 85° elevation; 180 rounds/
minute to 8.5 km *(4.6 nm)* anti-aircraft; weight of shell 1.42 kg.
4 China 14.5 mm/93 (2 twin) ❹; 85° elevation; 600 rounds/
minute to 7 km *(3.8 nm)*.
Depth charges: 4 BMB-2 projectors; 2 racks.
Mines: Can be carried.
Radars: Air/surface search: Slim Net ❺; E/F band.
Navigation: Neptun; I band.
Fire control: Sun Visor B ❻; G/H/I band (for guns).
Square Tie ❼; I or G/H band (for missiles).
IFF: High Pole A.
Sonars: Hull-mounted; active search and attack; medium/high
frequency.

Programmes: Similar to the Soviet Riga class and four of the
class assembled from Soviet components. Designated 'Old
Missile Frigates'.
Modernisation: Two started conversion in 1971 for the replacement of the torpedo tubes by a twin SS-N-2 launcher. All converted at Hudong SY. In 1978-79 additional 37 mm and
14.5 mm guns added.
Structure: All had light tripod mast and high superstructure, but
later converted with heavier mast and larger bridge. Two were
redesigned with modified superstructure and not all have the
after 100 mm gun.
Operational: Both survivors stationed in South Sea Fleet. *Kunming* 505 and *Xichang* 508 paid off in 1992/93.

CHENGDU   *(Scale 1 : 900), Ian Sturton*

CHENGDU (old number)   *1988*

SHIPBORNE AIRCRAFT

Note: Reported that two Kamov Ka-27 ASW helicopters are to be delivered in 1994 for evaluation.

Numbers/Type: 10/2 Aerospatiale SA 321G/Zhi-8 Super Frelon.
Operational speed: 134 kts *(248 km/h)*.
Service ceiling: 10 000 ft *(3100 m)*.
Range: 440 nm *(815 km)*.
Role/Weapon systems: ASW helicopter; SA 321G delivered from France but now being sup-
plemented by locally built Zhi-8, of which the first operational aircraft was delivered in late 1991.
Plans to fit Thomson Sintra HS-12 in three SA 321Gs completed for SSBN escort role. Sensors:
Early dipping sonar and processor, some have French-built search radar. Weapons: ASW; prob-
ably Whitehead A244 torpedo carried.

Numbers/Type: 50 Harbin Z-9A Haitun (Dauphin 2).
Operational speed: 140 kts *(260 km/h)*.
Service ceiling: 15 000 ft *(4575 m)*.
Range: 410 nm *(758 km)*.
Role/Weapon systems: New doctrine being developed for these licence-built helicopters, which
are embarked in latest Chinese escorts. China has an option to continue building after these first
50 have been produced. Not all are naval. Sensors: Thomson-CSF Agrion; HS-12 dipping sonar;
Crouzet MAD. Weapons: ASV; up to 4 × locally built radar-guided anti-ship missiles and White-
head A244 torpedoes or locally built Mk 46 Mod 2.

LAND-BASED MARITIME AIRCRAFT (FRONT LINE)

Numbers/Type: 26 Sukhoi Su-27 Flanker.
Operational speed: 1345 kts *(2500 km/h)*.
Service ceiling: 59 000 ft *(18 000 m)*.
Range: 2160 nm *(4000 km)*.
Role/Weapon systems: Air Force manned air defence fighter first acquired in 1991 for trials. 25
more purchased in 1992 and more are likely to be acquired in 1994. Sensors: Doppler radar.
Weapons: 1 × 30 mm cannon; 10 × AAMs.

Numbers/Type: 4 Beriev Be-6 (Madge).
Operational speed: 224 kts *(415 km/h)*.
Service ceiling: 20 000 ft *(6100 m)*.
Range: 2645 nm *(4900 km)*.
Role/Weapon systems: Flying-boat of obsolescent design now operated by one squadron only
and going out of service. Weapons: ASW/ASV; up to 4 tons of bombs and other weapons. Stan-
dard; 5 × 23 mm cannon.

Numbers/Type: 4 Harbin SH-5.
Operational speed: 243 kts *(450 km/h).*
Service ceiling: 23 000 ft *(7000 m).*
Range: 2563 nm *(4750 km).*
Role/Weapon systems: Multipurpose amphibian introduced into service in 1986. ASW and avionics upgrade planned. Sensors: Doppler radar; MAD; sonobuoys. Weapons: ASV; 4 C 101, two gun turret, bombs. ASW; Whitehead A 244 torpedoes, mines, depth bombs.

Numbers/Type: 3 Hanzhong Y-8MPA.
Operational speed: 351 kts *(650 km/h).*
Service ceiling: 34 120 ft *(10 400 m).*
Range: 3020 nm *(5600 km).*
Role/Weapon systems: Maritime patrol version of Y-8 (AN-12) transport; first flown 1985; now being evaluated to replace Be-6 for ASW and AEW roles. Sensors: Litton APSO-504(V)3 search radar in undernose radome. 2 Litton LTN 72R INS and Omega/Loran. Weapons: No weapons carried.

Numbers/Type: 80 Harbin H-5 (Il-28 Beagle).
Operational speed: 487 kts *(902 km/h).*
Service ceiling: 40 350 ft *(12 300 m).*
Range: 1175 nm *(2180 km).*
Role/Weapon systems: Overwater strike aircraft with ASW/ASVW roles. Being phased out and some moved into second line roles such as target towing and ECM training. Weapons: ASW; 2 × torpedoes or 4 × depth bombs. ASVW; 1 × torpedo + mines. Standard; 4 × 23 mm cannon.

Numbers/Type: 25 Harbin Z-5 (Mi-4 Hound).
Operational speed: 113 kts *(210 km/h).*
Service ceiling: 18 000 ft *(5500 m).*
Range: 217 nm *(400 km).*
Role/Weapon systems: ASW and SAR helicopter beginning to be retired; normally shore-based but some have been embarked for short periods, mainly for SAR. Sensors: Search radar only. Weapons: ASW; 1 × ASW torpedo.

Numbers/Type: 30 Shenyang J-8-I/II Finback.
Operational speed: 701 kts *(1300 km/h).*
Service ceiling: 65 620 ft *(20 000 m).*
Range: 1187 nm *(2200 km).*
Role/Weapon systems: Dual role, all weather fighter introduced into service in 1990 and production continues. There are at least 50 more in service with the Air Force. Weapons: 23 mm twin barrel cannon; AAM; 90 mm ASM.

Numbers/Type: 50 Nanchang Q-5 (Fantan).
Operational speed: 643 kts *(1190 km/h).*
Service ceiling: 52 500 ft *(16 000 m).*
Range: 650 nm *(1188 km).*
Role/Weapon systems: Strike aircraft developed from Shenyang J-6; operated by Chinese People's Naval Aviation Arm (CPNAA) in the beachhead and coastal shipping attack role. Q-5I version adapted to carry 2 torpedoes or C-801 ASM. Weapons: 2 × 23 mm cannon, 2 × cluster bombs, 1 or 2 × air-to-air missiles. Capable of carrying 1 ton warload.

Numbers/Type: 280 Shenyang J-6 (MiG-19 Farmer).
Operational speed: 831 kts *(1540 km/h).*
Service ceiling: 58 725 ft *(17 900 m).*
Range: 1187 nm *(2200 km).*
Role/Weapon systems: Strike fighter operated by CPNAA (supported by Air Force of PLA) for Fleet air defence and anti-shipping strike; is replacing the obsolete Shenyang J-5 Fresco although a few of these aircraft may still be in service. Weapons: Fleet air defence role; 4 × AA-1 ('Alkali') beam-riding missiles. Attack; some 1000 kg of underwing bombs or depth charges, PL-2 missile has anti-ship capability.

Numbers/Type: 30 Xian H-6 (Tu-16 Badger).
Operational speed: 535 kts *(992 km/h).*
Service ceiling: 40 350 ft *(12 300 m).*
Range: 2605 nm *(4800 km).*
Role/Weapon systems: Bomber and maritime reconnaissance aircraft. Sensors: Search/attack radar. Weapons: ASV; 2 × underwing anti-shipping missiles of local manufacture, including C-601. Self-protection; ECM, up to 5 × 23 mm cannon.

Numbers/Type: 70 Xian J-7 (MiG-21 Fishbed).
Operational speed: 1175 kts *(2175 km/h).*
Service ceiling: 61 680 ft *(18 800 m).*
Range: 804 nm *(1490 km).*
Role/Weapon systems: Land-based Fleet air defence fighter with limited strike role against enemy shipping or beachhead. Sensors: Search attack radar, some ECM. Weapons: Strike; 500 kg bombs or 36 × rockets. Standard; 2 × 30 mm cannon. AD; 2 × 'Atoll' AAMs.

PATROL FORCES

Notes: (1) A few obsolete Kronshtadt, Shantou, P 4 and P 6 class patrol craft may still be in reserve but none was operational in late 1993.
(2) A number of smaller patrol craft are operated by paramilitary forces such as the Maritime Militia, Customs etc.

0 + 3 TYPE 037/1A (OFFSHORE PATROL VESSELS)

Displacement, tons: 975 standard
Dimensions, feet (metres): 233.6 × 33.5 × 7.9 *(71.2 × 10.2 × 2.4)*
Main machinery: 2 MAN 66-28/32 diesels; 3200 hp(m) *(2.35 MW)*; 2 shafts
Speed, knots: 15
Complement: 60

Missiles: SSM: YJ-1 (Eagle Strike) (C-801) (2 triple); inertial cruise; active radar homing to 40 km *(22 nm)* at 0.9 Mach; warhead 165 kg.
Guns: 2—37 mm/63 (twin). 4—30 mm/65 (2 twin).

Programmes: Ordered from Wuchang Shipyard in December 1992.
Structure: This appears to be a larger and slower version of the Houjian class.
Operational: Designed as offshore patrol vessels with considerable endurance. May be for export.

1 HOUJIAN (OR HUANG) (TYPE 037/2) CLASS
(FAST ATTACK CRAFT—MISSILE)

Name	No	Builders	Commissioned
—	770	Huangpo Shipyard	July 1991

Displacement, tons: 520 standard
Dimensions, feet (metres): 214.6 × 27.6 × 7.9 *(65.4 × 8.4 × 2.4)*
Main machinery: 3 SEMT-Pielstick 12 PA6 280 diesels; 15 840 hp(m) *(11.7 MW)* sustained; 3 shafts
Speed, knots: 32. **Range, miles:** 1800 at 18 kts
Complement: 75

Missiles: SSM: 6 YJ-1 (Eagle Strike) (C-801) (2 triple); inertial cruise; active radar homing to 40 km *(22 nm)* at 0.9 Mach; warhead 165 kg.
Guns: 2—37 mm/63 (twin) Type 76A; 85° elevation; 180 rounds/minute to 8.5 km *(4.6 nm)* anti-aircraft; weight of shell 1.42 kg.
4—30 mm/65 (2 twin) Type 69; 500 rounds/minute to 5 km *(2.7 nm)*; weight of shell 0.54 kg.
Countermeasures: ESM/ECM: Intercept and jammer.
Fire control: China Type 88C WCS.
Radars: Surface search: Square Tie; I band.
Fire control: Rice Lamp; I band.

Programmes: Laid down in 1989 and built in a very short time probably with the export market in mind. Sometimes called the Huang class. No reports of more of the class by 1994.

8 + 3 HOUXIN CLASS (FAST ATTACK CRAFT—MISSILE)

751-758

Displacement, tons: 480 full load
Dimensions, feet (metres): 213.3 × 23.6 × 7.5 *(65 × 72 × 2.3)*
Main machinery: 4 diesels; 13 200 hp(m) *(9.7 MW)* 4 shafts
Speed, knots: 32. **Range, miles:** 750 at 18 kts
Complement: 60

Missiles: SSM: 4 YJ-1 (Eagle Strike) (C-801) (2 twin); active radar homing to 40 km *(22 nm)* at 0.9 Mach; warhead 165 kg; sea-skimmer. C-802 in due course.
Guns: 4—37 mm/63 (2 twin); 180 rounds/minute to 8.5 km *(4.6 nm)* anti-aircraft; weight of shell 1.42 kg
4—14.5 mm (2 twin); 600 rounds/minute to 7 km *(3.8 nm).*
Countermeasures: ESM/ECM: Intercept and jammer.
Radars: Surface search: Square Tie; I band.
Fire control: Rice Lamp; I band.

Programmes: First seen in 1991 and building at the rate of up to three per year at Qiuxin Shipyard to replace the Hegu/Hoku class.
Structure: This is a missile armed version of the prototype Haijui class. There are some variations in the bridge superstructure in later ships of the class.

HOUXIN *1991, CSSC*

HOUXIN 751 *1992*

HOUJIAN *5/1993*

79 (+ 35 RESERVE) HUANGFEN (TYPE 021) (OSA I TYPE) and 1 HOLA CLASS (FAST ATTACK CRAFT—MISSILE)

215, 218, 3103, 3113, 3114, 3115, 3128-3131, 5100, 7100 *et al*

Displacement, tons: 171 standard; 205 full load
Dimensions, feet (metres): 110.2 × 24.9 × 8.9 *(33.6 × 7.6 × 2.7)*
Main machinery: 3 Type M 503A diesels; 8025 hp(m) *(7.94 MW)* sustained; 3 shafts
Speed, knots: 35. **Range, miles:** 800 at 30 kts
Complement: 28

Missiles: SSM: 2 or 4 YJ-1 (Eagle Strike) (C-801); inertial cruise; active radar homing to 40 km *(22 nm)* at 0.9 Mach; warhead 165 kg; sea-skimmer. Some still have the older Hai Ying missiles. 4 HY-2 (2 twin) launchers (still fitted in some).
Guns: 4 USSR 25 mm/60 (2 twin); 85° elevation; 270 rounds/minute to 3 km *(1.6 nm)* anti-aircraft.
Being replaced in some by 4 USSR 30 mm/65 (2 twin); 85° elevation; 500 rounds/minute to 5 km *(2.7 nm)*; weight of shell 0.54 kg.
Radars: Surface search: Square Tie; I band; range 73 km *(40 nm)* or limits of radar horizon.
Fire control: Round Ball (in 30 mm boats) or Rice Lamp; H/I band.
IFF: 2 Square Head; High Pole A.

Programmes: Most of the original Osas transferred in the 1960s have been scrapped and replaced by a rolling programme of Huangfens, which was first reported in 1985.
Modernisation: The Ying Ji missile is slowly replacing the Hai Yings. Some of the class have Rice Lamp fire-control radars.
Structure: The only boat of the Hola class has a radome aft, four launchers, no guns, slightly larger dimensions (137.8 ft *(42 m)* long) and a folding mast. This radome is also fitted in others which carry 30 mm guns. Pennant numbers: Hola, 5100 and the remainder 100, 200, 1100 and 3100/7100 series.
Operational: China credits this class with a speed of 39 kts. At least 35 are in reserve, leaving an operational strength of 79 at the start of 1993.
Sales: Four to North Korea in 1980. Four to Pakistan in 1984. Four to Bangladesh in 1988 and one more in 1992 to replace one which sank.

HUANGFEN 3115 (with Round Ball)   *1990*

HUANGFEN 7127   *5/1993*

HUANGFEN (with YJ-1 and Rice Lamp)   *1993, CSSC*

70 (+ 25 RESERVE) HEGU or HOKU (TYPE 024) and 1 HEMA CLASS (FAST ATTACK CRAFT—MISSILE)

Displacement, tons: 68 standard; 79.2 full load
Dimensions, feet (metres): 88.6 × 20.7 × 4.3 *(27 × 6.3 × 1.3) (28.6 m*—Hema class)
Main machinery: 4 Type L-12V-180 diesels; 4800 hp(m) *(3.53 MW)*; 4 shafts
Speed, knots: 37.5. **Range, miles:** 400 at 30 kts
Complement: 17 (2 officers)

Missiles: SSM: 2 SY-1; inertial cruise; active radar homing to 45 km *(24.3 nm)* at 0.9 Mach; warhead 513 kg.
Guns: 2 USSR 25 mm/60 (twin) (4 (2 twin) in Hema class); 85° elevation; 270 rounds/minute to 3 km *(1.6 nm)* anti-aircraft; weight of shell 0.34 kg.
Radars: Surface search: Square Tie; I band; range 73 km *(40 nm)* or limits of radar horizon.
IFF: High pole A.

Programmes: The Komars delivered from the USSR in the 1960s have been deleted. They were followed by a building programme of ten a year (probably now stopped) of the Hegu class, a Chinese variant of the Komar with a steel hull instead of wooden. Pennant numbers: 1100 and 3100 series as some of the Huangfen class.
Modernisation: Plans to replace the missiles with C-801 have been shelved although a few may be fitted.
Structure: The chief external difference is the siting of the launchers clear of the bridge and further inboard, eliminating sponsons and use of pole instead of lattice mast. A hydrofoil variant, the Hema class, has a semi-submerged foil fwd. The extra 6 ft length allows for the mounting of a second twin 25 mm abaft the missile launchers.
Operational: 25 were in reserve in early 1993 leaving an operational strength of 70.
Sales: Four to Pakistan, 1981; four to Bangladesh, February 1983; six to Egypt, 1984; ten ordered for Iran in 1992.

HEGU   *4/1988, A Sheldon Duplaix*

4 HAIJUI CLASS (FAST ATTACK CRAFT—PATROL)

688   693   694   697

Displacement, tons: 430 standard
Dimensions, feet (metres): 203.4 × 23.6 × 7.2 *(62 × 7.2 × 2.2)*
Main machinery: 4 diesels; 8800 hp(m) *(6.47 MW)*; 4 shafts
Speed, knots: 28. **Range, miles:** 750 at 18 kts
Complement: 72
Guns: 4 China 57 mm/70 (2 twin); dual purpose; 85° elevation; 120 rounds/minute to 12 km *(6.5 nm)*; weight of shell 6.31 kg.
4 USSR 30 mm/65 (2 twin); 85° elevation; 500 rounds/minute to 5 km *(2.7 nm)* anti-aircraft; weight of shell 0.54 kg.
A/S mortars: 4 RBU 1200 5-tubed fixed launchers; range 1200 m; warhead 34 kg.
Depth charges: 2 rails.
Radars: Surface search: Pot Head; I band.
Fire control: I band.

Comment: A lengthened version of the Hainan class probably used as a prototype for the Houxin class now in series production. *688* seen in 1989 with a Thomson Sintra SS 12 VDS Sonar and again in 1990 with twin missile tubes replacing the forward 57 mm gun. At least one of the class has no funnel.

HAIJUI 693   *1986*

HAIJUI 688   *4/1990, John Mapletoft*

110 (+ 200 RESERVE) SHANGHAI CLASS (TYPE 062)
(FAST ATTACK CRAFT—GUN)

E 277, 301, 321   N 1121, 1127, 3140, 3141, 3215, 3313, 4301, 4324, 9342 *et al*

Displacement, tons: 113 standard; 134 full load
Dimensions, feet (metres): 127.3 × 17.7 × 5.6 *(38.8 × 5.4 × 1.7)*
Main machinery: 2 Type L-12V-180 diesels; 2400 hp(m) *(1.76 MW)* (forward); 2 Type 12-D-6 diesels; 1820 hp(m) *(1.34 MW)* (aft); 4 shafts
Speed, knots: 30. **Range, miles:** 700 at 16.5 kts on one engine
Complement: 38

Guns: 4 China 37 mm/63 (2 twin); 85° elevation; 180 rounds/minute to 8.5 km *(4.6 nm)*; weight of shell 1.42 kg.
4 USSR 25 mm/60 (2 twin); 85° elevation; 270 rounds/minute to 3 km *(1.6 nm)* anti-aircraft; weight of shell 0.34 kg.
Some are fitted with a twin 57 mm/70, some have a twin 75 mm Type 56 recoilless rifle mounted fwd and some have a twin 14.5 mm MG.
Depth charges: 2 projectors; 8 weapons.
Mines: Mine rails can be fitted for 10 mines.
Radars: Surface search: Skin Head or Pot Head; I band.
IFF: High Pole.
Sonars: It is reported that a hull-mounted set is fitted, with VDS in some.

Programmes: Construction began in 1961 and continued at Shanghai and other yards at rate of about ten a year for 30 years but is now beginning to tail off.
Structure: The five versions of this class vary slightly in the outline of their bridges. A few of the class have been reported as fitted with RBU 1200 anti-submarine mortars. Displacement and dimensions are for the Shanghai II class.
Sales: Eight to North Vietnam in May 1966, plus Romanian craft of indigenous construction. Seven to Tanzania in 1970-71, six to Guinea, twelve to North Korea, twelve to Pakistan, five to Sri Lanka in 1972, six to Albania, eight to Bangladesh in 1980-82, three to Congo, four to Egypt in 1984, three to Sri Lanka in 1991 and two to Tanzania in 1992. Many of these have since been deleted.

SHANGHAI II 3140 (with 57 mm gun)   1989

SHANGHAI II 3141 (with twin 14.5 mm MG)   1989

SHANGHAI II 4301   5/1993

95 + 3 HAINAN CLASS (TYPE 037)
(FAST ATTACK CRAFT—PATROL)

Nos 267-285, 290, 302, 305, 609, 610, 622, 628, 636-687, 689-692, 695, 696, 698, 699, 701, 707, 723-730

Displacement, tons: 375 standard; 392 full load
Dimensions, feet (metres): 192.8 × 23.6 × 7.2 *(58.8 × 7.2 × 2.2)*
Main machinery: 4 PCR/Kolomna Type 9-D-8 diesels; 4000 hp(m) *(2.94 MW)* sustained; 4 shafts
Speed, knots: 30.5. **Range, miles:** 1300 at 15 kts
Complement: 78

Missiles: Can be fitted with four YJ-1 launchers in lieu of the after 57 mm gun.
Guns: 4 China 57 mm/70 (2 twin); dual purpose; 120 rounds/minute to 12 km *(6.5 nm)*; weight of shell 6.31 kg.
4 USSR 25 mm/60 (2 twin); 85° elevation; 270 rounds/minute to 3 km *(1.6 nm)* anti-aircraft; weight of shell 0.34 kg.
A/S mortars: 4 RBU 1200 5-tubed fixed launchers; range 1200 m; warhead 34 kg.
Depth charges: 2 BMB-2 projectors; 2 racks. 18 DCs
Mines: Rails fitted for 12.
Radars: Surface search: Pot Head or Skin Head; I band.
IFF: High Pole.
Sonars: Stag Ear; hull-mounted; active search and attack; high frequency.
Thomson Sintra SS 12 (on at least two of the class); VDS.

Programmes: A larger Chinese-built version of Soviet SO 1. Low freeboard. Programme started 1963-64 and continues with new hulls replacing the first ships of the class.
Structure: Later ships have a tripod foremast in place of a pole and a short stub mainmast. Two trials SS 12 sonars fitted in 1987.
Sales: Two to Bangladesh, one in 1982 and one in 1985; eight to Egypt in 1983/84; six to North Korea 1975-78; four to Pakistan, two in 1976 and two in 1980; six to Burma in 1991.

HAINAN 707   5/1993

80 (+ 20 RESERVE) HUCHUAN CLASS (TYPE 025/026)
(FAST ATTACK CRAFT—TORPEDO)

205, 207-209, 248, 1247, 2201, 2203, 3206, 3214, 6218, 7230 *et al*

Displacement, tons: 39 standard; 45.8 full load
Dimensions, feet (metres): 71.5 × 20.7 oa × 11.8 (hullborne) *(21.8 × 6.3 × 3.6)*
Main machinery: 3 Type M 50 diesels; 3300 hp(m) *(2.42 MW)* sustained; 2 shafts
Speed, knots: 50 foilborne. **Range, miles:** 500 at 30 kts
Complement: 16

Guns: 4 China 14.5 mm (2 twin); 85° elevation; 600 rounds/minute to 7 km *(3.8 nm)*.
Torpedoes: 2—21 in *(533 mm)* tubes. Probably fires older Soviet Type 53.
Radars: Surface search: Skin Head (some variations); I band.

Programmes: Hydrofoils designed and built by China, in the Hudong yard, Shanghai. Construction started in 1966. Previously Hu Chwan class. Construction discontinued in 1988-89 and numbers are now declining. Another 18 are in reserve.
Structure: Of all-metal construction with a bridge well fwd and a low superstructure extending aft. Fwd pair of foils can be withdrawn into recesses in the hull. There are two variants. Older boats have a twin mounting amidships and one aft with the front of the bridge well fwd of the lips of the tubes. Newer versions have the front of the bridge in line with the lips of the tubes and the first mounting on the fo'c'sle and have differences in their electronics. Not all are hydrofoil fitted.
Sales: 32 to Albania, four to Pakistan, four to Tanzania, three to Romania plus additional craft of indigenous construction. Four to Bangladesh in 1989. Four to Burundi in 1991. Some have been deleted.

HUCHUAN 3214 (older version)   3/1988, DTM

HUCHUAN (newer version)   2/1993, Chien Chung

4 + 1 HULUDAO CLASS (TYPE 206)
(FAST ATTACK CRAFT—PATROL)

65   77   101   109

Displacement, tons: 180 full load
Dimensions, feet (metres): 147.6 × 21 × 5.6 *(45 × 6.4 × 1.7)*
Main machinery: 3 MWM TBD604BV12 diesels; 5204 hp(m) *(3.82 MW)* sustained; 3 shafts
Speed, knots: 29. **Range, miles:** 1000 at 15 kts
Complement: 24 (6 officers)
Guns: 4 China 14.5 mm Type 82 (2 twin); 85° elevation; 600 rounds/minute to 7 km *(3.8 nm)*; weight of shell 1.42 kg.

Comment: New class of EEZ patrol craft first seen at Wuxi Shipyard in 1988. Fourth and fifth of class reported ordered in May 1991. The craft looks like a scaled down version of the Pakistan Barkat class and has probably been built for export. First three were expected to go to Tunisia, but these may be Houxin or Shanghai II craft.

HULUDAO 109   *8/1992, Chien Chung*

12 + 4 HUXIN CLASS

Displacement, tons: 165 full load
Dimensions, feet (metres): 91.9 × 13.8 × 5.2 *(28 × 4.2 × 1.6)*
Main machinery: 2 diesels; 1000 hp(m) *(735 kW)*; 2 shafts
Speed, knots: 13. **Range, miles:** 400 at 10 kts
Complement: 26
Guns: 4 China 14.5 mm/93 (2 twin); 85° elevation; 600 rounds/minute to 7 km *(3.8 nm)*.
Radars: Surface search: Skin Head; I band.

Comment: This is a class of modified Huangpu design with a greater freeboard and a slightly larger displacement. First seen in 1989 and now in series production. All assigned to the Maritime Militia (MBDF).

HUXIN 62   *1989, P D Jones*

MINE WARFARE FORCES

Notes: (1) There are also some 60 auxiliary minesweepers of various types including trawlers and motor-driven junks.
(2) There are reported to be plans to build 38 Lerici type minehunters in the mid-1990s.

1 BELEIJAN CLASS (MINELAYER)

814

Comment: First of a new class probably built at Shanghai and completed successful sea trials in 1988. Displacement about 1000 tons, 93 × 14 m.

6 + 2 WOSAO CLASS (MINESWEEPER—COASTAL)

4422   + 5

Displacement, tons: 310 full load
Dimensions, feet (metres): 147 × 20.3 × 7.5 *(44.8 × 6.2 × 2.3)*
Main machinery: 2 diesels; 2000 hp(m) *(1.47 MW)*; 2 shafts
Speed, knots: 15.5. **Range, miles:** 500 at 15 kts
Complement: 21 (4 officers)
Guns: 4 China 25 mm/60 (2 twin); 85° elevation; 270 rounds/minute to 3 km *(1.6 nm)*.
Countermeasures: Acoustic, magnetic and mechanical sweeps.

Comment: Building programme started in 1986. First of class commissioned in 1988 and now building at about one per year. Steel hull with low magnetic properties.

WOSAO 4422   *1990, CSSC*

27 (+ 6 RESERVE) T 43 CLASS (TYPE 010)
(MINESWEEPERS—OCEAN)

124, 364-6, 377-9, 386-9, 396-9, 801-3, 807-9, 821-3, 829-832, 853-4, 863, 994-6 *et al*

Displacement, tons: 520 standard; 590 full load (Chinese-built)
Dimensions, feet (metres): 196.8 × 27.6 × 6.9 *(60 × 8.8 × 2.3)*
Main machinery: 2 PCR/Kolomna Type 9-D-8 diesels; 2000 hp(m) *(1.47 MW)*; 2 shafts
Speed, knots: 14. **Range, miles:** 3000 at 10 kts
Complement: 70 (10 officers)
Guns: 2 or 4 China 37 mm/63 (1 or 2 twin) (3 of the class have a 65 mm/52 forward instead of one twin 37 mm/63); dual purpose; 85° elevation; 180 rounds/minute to 8.5 km *(4.6 nm)*; weight of shell 1.42 kg.
4 USSR 25 mm/60 (2 twin); 85° elevation; 270 rounds/minute to 3 km *(1.6 nm)*.
4 China 14.5 mm/93 (2 twin); 85° elevation; 600 rounds/minute to 7 km *(3.8 nm)*.
Some ships also carry 1—85 mm/52 Mk 90K; 18 rounds/minute to 15 km *(8 nm)*; weight of shell 9.6 kg.
Depth charges: 2 BMB-2 projectors; 20 depth charges.
Mines: Can carry 12-16.
Countermeasures: MCMV; MPT-1 paravanes; MPT-3 mechanical sweep; acoustic and magnetic gear.
Radars: Surface search: Ball End; E/F band; range 37 km *(20 nm)*.
Navigation: Fin Curve or Neptun; I band.
IFF: High Pole or Yard Rake.
Sonars: Tamir II; hull-mounted; active search and attack; high frequency.

Programmes: Four were acquired from USSR in 1954-55, one being returned 1960; 26 more were built in Chinese shipyards, the first two in 1956. The construction of T 43 class fleet minesweepers started again in mid-1980s at Wuzhang and at Guangzhou.
Structure: Displacement figures are for Chinese-built ships. Three (Soviet ships) converted for surveying, three transferred as civilian research ships.
Operational: Seven in North Sea Fleet (364-6, 801-3, 807), nine in East Sea Fleet (821, 829, 830, 832, 853-4, 994-6) and eight in South Sea Fleet (386-9, 396-9). Remainder not known. Some are used as patrol ships with sweep gear removed. Three units reported as having a 65 mm/52 gun forward. Another six of the class were in reserve at the beginning of 1994.

T 43 831   *5/1992, Henry Dodds*

T 43 124   *12/1989, G Jacobs*

5 FUSHUN CLASS (MINESWEEPERS—COASTAL)

Displacement, tons: 275
Dimensions, feet (metres): 131.2 × 18 × 9.8 *(40 × 5.5 × 3)*
Main machinery: 2 Type M 50 diesels; 2200 hp(m) *(1.6 MW)* sustained; 2 Type 12-D-6 diesels; 1820 hp(m) *(1.34 MW)*; 4 shafts
Speed, knots: 18. **Range, miles:** 750 at 16 kts
Guns: 2 USSR 25 mm/60 (twin); forward.
  4 China 14.5 mm/93 (2 twin); midships.

Comment: A modification of the Shanghai II class fast attack craft fitted with minesweeping winch and two davits. Several have been deleted and these last five are expected to be scrapped in 1994.

FUSHUN class   *1986*

25 (+ 50 RESERVE) LIENYUN CLASS (MINESWEEPERS—COASTAL)

Displacement, tons: 400
Dimensions, feet (metres): 131.2 × 26.2 × 11.5 *(40 × 8 × 3.5)*
Main machinery: 1 diesel; 400 hp(m) *(294 kW)*; 1 shaft
Speed, knots: 8
Guns: 2—12.7 mm MGs.

Comment: Built to a converted trawler design with steel hulls. Have a minesweeping winch and davits aft. Approximately 50 more hulls were in reserve in early 1993.

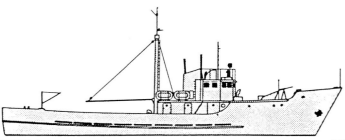

LIENYUN class   *1990*

4 (+ 56 RESERVE) FUTI CLASS (TYPE 312)
(DRONE MINESWEEPERS)

Displacement, tons: 47 standard
Dimensions, feet (metres): 68.6 × 12.8 × 6.9 *(20.9 × 3.9 × 2.1)*
Main machinery: Diesel-electric; 1 Type 12V 150C diesel generator; 300 hp(m) *(220 kW)*; 1 motor; cp prop
Speed, knots: 12. **Range, miles:** 144 at 12 kts
Complement: 3

Comment: A large number of these craft, similar to the German Troikas, has been built since the early 1970s. Fitted to carry out magnetic and acoustic sweeping under remote control up to 5 km *(2.7 nm)* from shore control station. Most were in reserve in early 1993.

DRONE Type 312   *1988, CSSC*

AMPHIBIOUS WARFARE FORCES

Notes: (1) In addition to the ships listed below there are up to 500 minor LCM/LCVP types used to transport stores and personnel. There is also a 67 ton DAGU class research hovercraft designed by Shanghai SB R&D Institute.
(2) A Ro-Ro conversion to an aviation support ship is being actively studied as one option to improve amphibious capability out of range of shore-based aircraft. If taken up the Navy may introduce STOVL aircraft to the Fleet. The Ministry of Communications ship *Huayuankou* has been mentioned as a possible candidate for conversion.
(3) All of the ex-US LSM Hua type, the Yuchai class LCMs and the ex-US LSILs have been scrapped.

4 YUDAO CLASS (LSM)

Displacement, tons: 1460 full load
Dimensions, feet (metres): 285.4 × 41.3 × 10.2 *(87 × 12.6 × 3.1)*
Guns: 8—25 mm/60 (2 quad); 85° elevation; 270 rounds/minute to 3 km *(1.6 nm)*.

Comment: First entered service in early 1980s. In South Fleet.

YUDAO   *12/1988, G Jacobs*

9 QIONSHA CLASS (7 AP + 2 AH)

Y 830   Y 831   Y 832   Y 833   + 5

Displacement, tons: 2150 full load
Dimensions, feet (metres): 282.1 × 44.3 × 13.1 *(86 × 13.5 × 4)*
Main machinery: 3 SKL 8 NVD 48 A-2U diesels; 3960 hp(m) *(2.91 MW)* sustained; 3 shafts
Speed, knots: 16
Complement: 59
Military lift: 400 troops; 350 tons cargo
Guns: 8 China 14.5mm/93 (4 twin); 85° elevation; 600 rounds/minute to 7 km *(3.8 nm)*.

Comment: Personnel attack transports begun about 1980 at Guangzhou. All South Sea Fleet. Have four sets of davits, light cargo booms serving fwd and aft. No helicopter pad. Twin funnels. Carry a number of LCAs. Two converted to Hospital Ships (AH) and painted white.

QIONSHA Y 832   *1985, G Jacobs*

QIONSHA Y 830   *2/1993, Chien Chung*

QIONSHA Y 833 (hospital ship)   *2/1993, Chien Chung*

1 + 2 YUTING CLASS (LST)

991

Displacement, tons: 3770 standard
Dimensions, feet (metres): 426.5 × 52.5 × 10.5 *(130 × 16 × 3.2)*
Main machinery: 2 diesels; 2 shafts
Speed, knots: 17. **Range, miles:** 3000 at 14 kts
Complement: 120
Guns: 6 China 37 mm/63 (3 twin); 85° elevation; 180 rounds/minute to 8.5 km *(4.6 nm)*; weight of shell 1.42 kg.
Radars: Navigation: 2 sets; I band.
Helicopters: 2 medium.

Comment: First of a new class seen fitting out in 1992 at Shanghai. In series production to augment amphibious lift capabilities and provide helicopter lift facilities. Bow and bridge structures are very similar to the Yukan class but the large helicopter deck is new. Gun armament may be augmented.

YUTING 991   *5/1992, Henry Dodds*

4 YUKAN CLASS (TYPE 072) (LST)

927   928   929   930

Displacement, tons: 3110 standard
Dimensions, feet (metres): 393.6 × 50 × 9.5 *(120 × 15.3 × 2.9)*
Main machinery: 2 Type 12E 390 diesels; 14 400 hp(m) *(10.6 MW)* sustained; 2 shafts
Speed, knots: 18. **Range, miles:** 3000 at 14 kts
Complement: 109
Military lift: 200 troops; 10 tanks; 2 LCVP
Guns: 8 China 57 mm/50 (4 twin) (some carry 4—57 mm (2 twin) and 4—37 mm (2 twin)); 85° elevation; 120 rounds/minute to 12 km *(6.5 nm)*; weight of shell 6.31 kg.
4—25 mm/60 (2 twin) (some also have 4—25 mm (2 twin) mountings amidships above the tank deck); 85° elevation; 270 rounds/minute to 3 km *(1.6 nm)*.
Radars: Navigation: 2 Neptun; I band.

Comment: First completed in 1980. Bow and stern ramps fitted. Carry two LCVPs. Some reports indicate up to 14 of this class may be completed with 10 earmarked for the South Fleet and four for the East Fleet. At least two of the class are active off the Spratley Islands. Bow ramp maximum load 50 tons, stern ramp 20 tons.

YUKAN 928   *5/1993*

YUKAN 927   *2/1993, Chien Chung*

11 (+ 2 RESERVE) 1-511 (SHAN) CLASS (LST)

351, 355, 902-3, 905-7, 921-6

Displacement, tons: 1653 standard; 4080 full load
Dimensions, feet (metres): 328 × 50 × 14 *(100 × 15.3 × 4.3)*
Main machinery: 2 GM 12-567A diesels; 1800 hp(m) *(1.32 MW)*; 2 shafts
Speed, knots: 11
Military lift: 165 troops; 2100 tons cargo; 2 LCVP
Guns: 2—76 mm/50; dual purpose; 85° elevation; 18 rounds/minute to 12.8 km *(7 nm)*; weight of shell 5.92 kg.
9 China 37 mm/63 (3 twin, 3 single); 180 rounds/minute to 8.5 km *(4.6 nm)*; weight of shell 1.42 kg.
Mines: All capable of minelaying.

Comment: Two transferred to North Vietnam as tankers. Some other ex-US LSTs are in the merchant service or used as tenders. Some armed with rocket launchers. All built between 1942 and 1945. Five (902-3, 905-7) in North Sea Fleet at Luda, six (921-6) in East Sea Fleet at Shanghai and two (351, 355) in South Sea Fleet at Guangzhou. Two are in reserve.

SHAN 926   *5/1993*

28 YULIANG CLASS (TYPE 079) and 1 YULING CLASS (LSM)

Displacement, tons: 800 standard; 1600 full load
Dimensions, feet (metres): 236.2 × 45.3 × 10.8 *(72 × 13.8 × 3.3)*
Main machinery: 2 diesels; 2 shafts
Military lift: 3 tanks
Guns: 4 China 37 mm/63 (2 twin) (Type I only); 85° elevation; 180 rounds/minute to 8.5 km *(4.6 nm)*; weight of shell 1.42 kg.
4—25 mm/60 (2 twin); 85° elevation; 270 rounds/minute to 3 km *(1.6 nm)*.
2 BM 21 MRL rocket launchers; range about 9 km *(5 nm)*.

Comment: Yuling started in China in 1971. Stationed at Qingdao. Yuliang class is a variation of what may have been a prototype. Data is similar but there are variations in the superstructure. Series production started in 1980 in three or four smaller shipyards (Shantou etc). Numbers have been overestimated in the past and production has stopped in favour of newer classes.

YULIANG 1122   *5/1992, Henry Dodds*

4 CHINESE TYPE (LSM)

972   990   + 2

Displacement, tons: 600 full load
Dimensions, feet (metres): 185.7 × 34.1 × 7.5 *(56.6 × 10.4 × 2.3)*
Main machinery: 2 diesels; 2 shafts
Speed, knots: 15. **Range, miles:** 1000 at 12 kts
Complement: 25
Military lift: 150 tons
Guns: 4—25 mm/60 (2 twin).

Comment: Details shown are for logistic supply LSM 972 first seen in 1991 on sea trials. Probably in series production and could be for export. At least three of the class completed by the end of 1992. LSM 990 was first seen in 1992 at Shanghai and is similar but not identical to 972.

LSM 972   *8/1992, Chien Chung*

110 (+ 200 RESERVE) YUNNAN CLASS (TYPE 067) (LCU)

Displacement, tons: 128 full load
Dimensions, feet (metres): 93.8 × 17.7 × 4.6 *(28.6 × 5.4 × 1.4)*
Main machinery: 2 diesels; 600 hp(m) *(441 kW)*; 2 shafts
Speed, knots: 12. **Range, miles:** 500 at 10 kts
Complement: 12
Military lift: 46 tons
Guns: 2—12.7 mm MGs.

Comment: Built in China 1968-72 although a continuing programme was reported in 1982. Pennant numbers in 3000 series (3313, 3321, 3344 seen). 5000 series (5526 seen) and 7000 series (7566 and 7568 seen). Numbers split evenly between the three fleets. One to Sri Lanka in 1991. Numbers have been overestimated in the past but another 200 are probably in reserve.

YUNNAN   *1992*

40-50 YUCH'IN (TYPE 068/069) CLASS (LCU/LCP)

Displacement, tons: 58 standard; 85 full load
Dimensions, feet (metres): 81.2 × 17.1 × 4.3 *(24.8 × 5.2 × 1.3)*
Main machinery: 2 Type 12V 150C diesels; 600 hp(m) *(441 kW)*; 2 shafts
Speed, knots: 11.5. **Range, miles:** 450 at 11.5 kts
Military lift: Up to 150 troops
Guns: 4—14.5 mm (2 twin) MGs.

Comment: Built in Shanghai 1962-72. Smaller version of Yunnan class with a shorter tank deck and longer poop deck. Primarily intended for personnel transport. Eight sold to Bangladesh.

YUCH'IN class   *1987*

1 JINGSAH II CLASS (HOVERCRAFT)

Displacement, tons: 70
Dimensions, feet (metres): 72.2 × 26.2 *(22 × 8)*
Main machinery: 2 propulsion motors; 2 lift motors
Speed, knots: 55
Military lift: 15 tons
Guns: 4—14.5 mm (2 twin) MGs.

Comment: The prototype was built at Dagu in 1979. This may now have been scrapped and this improved version could be in series production. Has a bow door for disembarkation.

JINGSAH II   *1993, Ships of the World*

TRAINING SHIP

1 DAXIN CLASS

ZHENGHE 81

Displacement, tons: 4500 standard
Dimensions, feet (metres): 390.4 × 51.8 × 15.7 *(119 × 15.8 × 4.8)*
Main machinery: 2 diesels; 7800 hp(m) *(5.73 MW)*; 2 shafts
Speed, knots: 15
Complement: 170 plus 30 instructors plus 200 Midshipmen
Guns: 4 China 57 mm/70 (2 twin). 4—37 mm/63 (2 twin). 4—12.7 mm MGs.
A/S mortars: 2 FQF 2500 12-tubed launchers.
Radars: Navigation: 2 Racal Decca; I band.
Helicopters: Platform only.

Comment: Built at Qiuxin SY, Shanghai. Launched 12 July 1986, commissioned 27 April 1987. Resembles a small cruise liner. Subordinate to the Naval Academy and replaced *Huian*.

ZHENGHE   *1992, Ships of the World*

AUXILIARIES

3 DAJIANG CLASS (SUBMARINE SUPPORT SHIPS)

CHANGXINGDAO J 121   CHONGMINGDAO J 302   YONGXINGDAO J 506

Displacement, tons: 10 975 full load
Dimensions, feet (metres): 511.7 × 67.2 × 22.3 *(156 × 20.5 × 6.8)*
Main machinery: 2 MAN K9Z60/105E diesels; 9000 hp(m) *(6.6 MW)*; 2 shafts
Speed, knots: 20
Guns: Light MGs. Can carry 6—37 mm (3 twin).
Radars: Surface search: Eye Shield; E band.
Navigation: Two Fin Curve; I band.
Helicopters: 2 Aerospatiale SA 321 G Super Frelon.

Comment: Submarine support and salvage ships built at Shanghai. First launched in mid-1973, operational in 1976. *Yongxingdao* has a smoke deflector on funnel and appears to have been fitted with a new foremast. Provision for DSRV on fwd well deck aft of launching crane. A fourth and fifth of the class are listed under *Research Ships*. New foremast on *Yongxingdao* suggests possible conversion to research ship role with long range communications similar to Russian *Fedor Vidyaev*.

CHANGXINGDAO   *1991*

CHONGMINGDAO   *9/1993, Hachiro Nakai*

1 DAZHI CLASS (SUBMARINE SUPPORT SHIP)

DAZHI 920

Displacement, tons: 5600 full load
Dimensions, feet (metres): 350 × 50 × 20 *(106.7 × 15.3 × 6.1)*
Main machinery: 2 diesels; 3500 hp(m) *(2.57 MW)*; 2 shafts
Speed, knots: 14. **Range, miles:** 6000 at 14 kts
Complement: 290
Cargo capacity: 500 tons dieso
Guns: 4 China 37 mm/63 (2 twin). 4—25 mm/60 (2 twin).
Radars: Navigation: Fin Curve; I band.

Comment: Built at Hudong, Shanghai 1963-65. Has four electrohydraulic cranes. Carries large stock of torpedoes and stores.

DAZHI   (not to scale)

1 DA DONG CLASS AND 1 DADAO CLASS (SALVAGE SHIPS)

J 304 + 1

Displacement, tons: 2500 approx
Dimensions, feet (metres): 269 × 36.1 × 8.9 *(82 × 11 × 2.7)*

Comment: J 304 reported to have been built at Hudong in late 1970s. Has a large and conspicuous crane aft. A second ship of approximately same dimensions and designed for the same duties was launched at Huludao shipyard and commissioned 12 January 1986 possibly with a civilian crew. Principal role is wreck location and salvage.

DADAO class   1989, Gilbert Gyssels

2 DALANG and 1 DONGXIU CLASS (SUBMARINE SUPPORT SHIPS)

J 503   J 504   U 911

Displacement, tons: 3700 standard; 4300 full load (est)
Dimensions, feet (metres): 367 × 47.9 × 14.1 *(111.9 × 14.6 × 4.3)*
Main machinery: 2 diesels; 4000 hp(m) *(2.94 MW)*; 2 shafts
Speed, knots: 16. **Range, miles:** 8000 at 14 kts
Guns: 8 China 37 mm/63 (4 twin). 4 or 8 China 14.5 mm (2 or 4 twin) MGs.
Radars: Navigation: Fin Curve; I band.

Comment: First two built at Guangzhou Shipyard. First one commissioned November 1975, second in 1986. The Dongxiu class ship (U 911) is slightly larger and was built at Wuhu Shipyard, commissioning in late 1986. Bulbous bow with notable rake to funnel amidships.

DALANG 504   12/1990, DTM

2 HUDUNG CLASS (SUBMARINE RESCUE SHIPS)

HAIJUI 512 (ex-J 301)   **HAIJUI** 403

Displacement, tons: 4500 standard (est); 4900+ full load (est)
Dimensions, feet (metres): 308.5 × 55.8 × 15.1 *(94 × 17 × 4.6)*
Main machinery: 2 diesels; 3600 hp(m) *(2.64 MW)*; 2 shafts
Speed, knots: 16. **Range, miles:** 5000 at 12 kts
Complement: 225 (est)
Guns: 6 China 37 mm/63 (3 twin).
Radars: Navigation: Fin Curve; I band.

Comment: Both built at Hudong Shipyard, Shanghai. Laid down 1965, launched 1967. Design revised before completion. 512 has two bow and two stern anchors. Two 5 ton booms and stern gantry for submarine rescue bell. 403 may be slightly smaller.

HAIJUI 512   1987

2 DSRV (SALVAGE SUBMARINES)

Dimensions, feet (metres): 48.9 × 13.1 × 8.5 *(15 × 4 × 2.6)*
Speed, knots: 4
Complement: 4

Comment: First tested in 1986 and can be carried on large salvage ships. Capable of 'wet' rescue at 200 m and of diving to 600 m. Capacity for six survivors. Underwater TV, high frequency active sonar and a manipulator arm are all fitted.

DSRV   1991, CSSC

4 YEN TING CLASS (SALVAGE SHIPS)

HAI LAO 456, 520, 523, 666

Displacement, tons: 260-275 standard
Dimensions, feet (metres): 103.3 × 23 × 8.2 *(31.5 × 7 × 2.5)*
Main machinery: 1 Type 3-D-12 diesel; 300 hp(m) *(220 kW)* sustained; 1 shaft
Speed, knots: 10
Complement: 18
Guns: 2 China 14.5 mm/93 (twin).

Comment: Trawler-type hull, similar to enlarged FT series. Built in 1972-74.

YEN TING 666   12/1989, G Jacobs

1 KANSHA CLASS (SALVAGE SHIP)

Displacement, tons: 1325
Dimensions, feet (metres): 229.3 × 34.4 × 11.8 *(69.9 × 10.5 × 3.6)*
Main machinery: 2 Type 8300 ZC diesels; 2200 hp(m) *(1.62 MW)*; 2 shafts
Speed, knots: 13.5. **Range, miles:** 2400 at 13 kts

Comment: Built at Chunghua SY, Shanghai in 1980-81. Trials July 1981. Designed by Chinese Marine Design and Research Institute. Carries one French SM-358-S DSRV (deep submergence recovery vehicle), 7 m long with a crew of five and an operating depth of 985 ft *(300 m)*. Ship has one 5 ton crane fwd and a 2 ton crane aft. Based in East China Sea.

1 ACHELOUS CLASS (REPAIR SHIP)

DAGUSHAN (ex-*Hsiang An*, ex-USS *Achilles* ARL 41, ex-LST 455) U 891

Displacement, tons: 1625 light; 4325 full load
Dimensions, feet (metres): 328 × 50 × 14 *(100 × 15.2 × 4.3)*
Main machinery: 2 GM 12-567A diesels; 1800 hp *(1.34 MW)*; 2 shafts
Speed, knots: 12
Complement: 270
Guns: 12 China 37 mm/63 (6 twin). 4 China 14.5 mm/93 (2 twin).
Radars: Navigation: Fin Curve; I band.

Comment: Launched on 17 October 1942. Transferred to Nationalist China from the US as *Hsiang An* in September 1947. Burned and grounded in 1949, salvaged and refitted. Has 60 ton A-frame and 25 ton crane. Mostly alongside in Shanghai.

DAGUSHAN   *7/1985, Fischer/Donko*

1 WULAI CLASS (CABLE SHIP)

230

Displacement, tons: 500 full load
Dimensions, feet (metres): 177.1 × 28.9 × 7.5 *(54 × 8.8 × 2.3)*
Complement: 50 approx
Guns: 4—25 mm/60 (2 twin).
Radars: Navigation: Skin Head; I band.

Comment: Built at Guangzhou in 1968-69 as coastal cable repair ship. Has noticeable davits aft. Fitted with bow sheaves. Also acts as salvage ship in South Sea Fleet. Several classes of cable layers are in service. These carry 'B' pennant numbers while similar ships with 'H' numbers act as buoy tenders and those with 'N' numbers are based at Nanjing. Examples are B 873, H 263 and N 2304, all of the same class.

5 AILANTHUS CLASS (BOOM DEFENCE SHIPS)

Displacement, tons: 560 standard; 805 full load
Dimensions, feet (metres): 194.5 × 34.5 × 14.8 *(59.3 × 10.5 × 4.5)*
Main machinery: Diesel-electric; 1200 hp(m) *(895 kW)*
Speed, knots: 14
Complement: 55
Guns: 1—14.5 mm MG.

Comment: Probably now used as service vessels. There are several classes of vessel including Yen Tai, Yen Bai, Yen Kuan, Hang Feng and some trawler conversions. Most are armed with at least 14.5 mm MGs.

2 GALATI CLASS (AK)

HAIYUN 318   HAIJIU 600

Displacement, tons: 5300
Dimensions, feet (metres): 328 × 45.6 × 21.6 *(100 × 13.9 × 6.6)*
Main machinery: 1 Sulzer 5TAD56 diesel; 2500 hp(m) *(1.84 MW)*; 1 shaft
Speed, knots: 12.5. **Range, miles:** 5000 at 12 kts
Complement: 50
Cargo capacity: 3750 tons; 20 ton; 3-5 ton cranes

Comment: Built at Santieral Shipyard, Galati, Romania in 1960s. Nine ships purchased of which these two were converted to AKs in early 1970s. Both reported operating in South Sea Fleet.

1 DAMEN CLASS (AK)

Y 529

Displacement, tons: 1050 standard; 1400 full load
Dimensions, feet (metres): 205.1 × 30.8 × 11.8 *(62.5 × 9.4 × 3.6)*
Complement: 30
Cargo capacity: 450 tons

Comment: Built at CSSC Shipyard, Xiamen in 1983.

2 DAYUN CLASS (AK)

951   952

Displacement, tons: 11 000 full load
Dimensions, feet (metres): 511.7 × 67.2 × 22.5 *(156 × 20.5 × 6.9)*
Main machinery: 2 diesels; 9000 hp(m) *(6.6 MW)*; 2 shafts
Speed, knots: 20
Guns: 4—37 mm/63 (2 twin).
Helicopters: 2 Super Frelon SA 321.

Comment: First of class completed in late 1991, second in 1992. Same hull as Dajiang class support ships and with a similar crane on the foredeck.

DAYUN 952   *7/1992, Ships of the World*

1 YUKAN CLASS (AK)

801

Displacement, tons: 3330 full load
Dimensions, feet (metres): 393.6 × 50 × 9.8 *(120 × 15.3 × 3)*
Main machinery: 2 diesels; 2 shafts
Speed, knots: 17
Complement: 100
Guns: 2 China 57 mm/50 (twin).

Comment: Either a new construction or a converted Yukan class hull. First seen in 1992.

YUKAN 801   *5/1992, Henry Dodds*

4 DANLIN CLASS (AK)

HAI LENG L 191, L 201   HAI YUN L 790, L 794

Displacement, tons: 900 standard; 1290 full load
Dimensions, feet (metres): 198.5 × 29.5 × 13.1 *(60.5 × 9 × 4)*
Main machinery: 1 Soviet/PRC Type 6DRN 30/50 diesel; 750 hp(m) *(551 kW)*; 1 shaft
Speed, knots: 15
Complement: 35
Cargo capacity: 750-800 tons
Guns: 4—25 mm/80 (2 twin).
Radars: Navigation: Fin Curve or Skin Head; I band.

Comment: Built in China in early 1960-62. Have a refrigerated stores capability. Two serve in each of South and East Sea Fleets. Two or more in civilian service.

DANLIN 794   *5/1992, Henry Dodds*

4 HONGQI CLASS (AK)

Y 443   Y 528   Y 755   Y 771

Displacement, tons: 1950 full load
Dimensions, feet (metres): 203.4 × 39.4 × 14.4 *(62 × 12 × 4.4)*
Main machinery: 1 diesel; 1 shaft
Speed, knots: 14. **Range, miles:** 2500 at 11 kts
Guns: 4 China 25/80 (2 twin).

Comment: Used to support offshore military garrisons. A further ship, L 202, appears to be similar but carries no armament.

HONGQI 755   *9/1993, Hachiro Nakai*

3 LEIZHOU CLASS (WTL)

HAI SHUI 412, 555, 558

Comment: Details under same class in *Tankers* section. Two in South Sea and one in East Sea Fleets.

9 FUZHOU CLASS (WTL)

HAI SHUI 416, HAI SHUI 419, HAI SHUI 556, HAI SHUI 557, HAI SHUI 608 *et al*

Displacement, tons: 1100 standard
Dimensions, feet (metres): 196.8 × 29.5 × 11.5 *(60 × 9 × 3.5)*
Main machinery: 1 diesel; 600 hp(m) *(441 kW)*; 1 shaft
Speed, knots: 12
Complement: 35
Guns: 4—25 mm (2 twin). 4—12.7 mm (2 twin) (not in all).

Comment: Built in Shanghai 1964-70. Large water carriers. Four in North Sea Fleet, two in East Sea Fleet, two in South Sea Fleet. Fourteen of same class in Tanker section.

FUZHOU 608   *7/1989*

2 FUQING CLASS (REPLENISHMENT SHIPS) (AOR)

TAICANG X 575   **DONGYUN** (ex-*Fenfcang*) X 615

Displacement, tons: 7500 standard; 21 750 full load
Dimensions, feet (metres): 552 × 71.5 × 30.8 *(168.2 × 21.8 × 9.4)*
Main machinery: 1 Sulzer 8RL B66 diesel; 15 000 hp(m) *(11 MW)* sustained; 1 shaft
Speed, knots: 18. **Range, miles:** 18 000 at 14 kts
Complement: 130 (24 officers)
Cargo capacity: 10 550 tons fuel; 1000 tons dieso; 200 tons feed water; 200 tons drinking water; 4 small cranes
Guns: 8—37 mm (4 twin) (fitted for but not with).
Radars: Navigation: Two Fin Curve; I band.

Comment: Operational in late 1979. This is the first class of ships built for underway replenishment in the Chinese Navy. Helicopter platform but no hangar. No armament. All built at Talien. Two liquid replenishment positions each side with one solid replenishment position each side by the funnel. X 615 has a rounded funnel vice the square shape of the X 575. A third of the class *Hongcang* (X 950) was converted to merchant use in 1989 and renamed *Hai Lang*, registered at Dalian. A fourth (X 350) was sold to Pakistan in 1987.

DONGYUN   *1992*

2 SHENGLI CLASS (AOT)

X 620   X 621

Displacement, tons: 3300 standard; 4950 full load
Dimensions, feet (metres): 331.4 × 45.3 × 18 *(101 × 13.8 × 5.5)*
Main machinery: 1 6 ESDZ 43/82B diesel; 2600 hp(m) *(1.91 MW)*; 1 shaft
Speed, knots: 14. **Range, miles:** 2400 at 11 kts
Cargo capacity: 3400 tons dieso
Guns: 2—57 mm (twin). 2—25 mm (twin).

Comment: Built at Hudong SY, Shanghai in late 1970s. Others of the class in commercial service.

SHENGLI 621   *5/1992, Henry Dodds*

3 JINYOU CLASS (AOT)

X 622   X 625   X 675

Displacement, tons: 2500 standard; 4800 full load
Dimensions, feet (metres): 324.8 × 45.3 × 18.7 *(99 × 31.8 × 5.7)*
Main machinery: 1 SEMT-Pielstick 8 PC2.2 L diesel; 4000 hp(m) *(2.94 MW)* sustained; 1 shaft
Speed, knots: 15. **Range, miles:** 4000 at 9 kts

Comment: Built at Kanashashi SY, Japan.

JINYOU 625   *9/1990, John Mapletoft*

7 FULIN CLASS (REPLENISHMENT SHIPS) (AOR)

X 583   X 606   X 607   X 609   X 628   X 629   X 633

Displacement, tons: 2300 standard
Dimensions, feet (metres): 216.5 × 42.6 × 13.1 *(66 × 13 × 4)*
Main machinery: 1 diesel; 600 hp(m) *(441 kW)*; 1 shaft
Speed, knots: 10. **Range, miles:** 1500 at 8 kts
Complement: 30
Guns: 4—25 mm/80 (2 twin).
Radars: Navigation: Fin Curve; I band.

Comment: A total of 20 of these ships built at Hudong, Shanghai, beginning 1972. Thirteen in civilian service. Naval ships painted dark grey. Some having single underway replenishment rig. One in South Sea Fleet.

FULIN 607   *5/1992, Henry Dodds*

14 FUZHOU CLASS (AOT)

X 573   X 580   X 606   X 629   *et al*

Cargo capacity: 600 tons fuel

Comment: Details under same class in Supply Ships. Built in Hudong SY, Shanghai 1964-70. Five in South Sea Fleet.

FUZHOU 606   *5/1992, Henry Dodds*

5 LEIZHOU CLASS (AOTL)

Displacement, tons: 900 standard
Dimensions, feet (metres): 173.9 × 32.2 × 10.5 *(53 × 9.8 × 3.2)*
Main machinery: 1 diesel; 500 hp(m) *(367 kW)*; 1 shaft
Speed, knots: 12. **Range, miles:** 1200 at 10 kts
Complement: 25-30
Cargo capacity: 450 tons
Guns: 4—37 mm (2 twin).
Radars: Navigation: Skin Head; I band.

Comment: Built in late 1960s probably at Qingdao or Wutong.

LEIZHOU 1104   *5/1992, Henry Dodds*

2 YEN PAI CLASS (ADG)

HAI DZU 746   DONG QIN 863

Displacement, tons: 746 standard
Dimensions, feet (metres): 213.3 × 29.5 × 8.5 *(65 × 9 × 2.6)*
Main machinery: Diesel-electric; 2 12VE 230ZC diesels; 2200 hp(m) *(1.62 MW)*; 2 ZDH-99/57 motors; 2 shafts
Speed, knots: 16. **Range, miles:** 800 at 15 kts
Complement: 55 (est)
Guns: 4—37 mm/63 (2 twin). 4—25 mm/80 (2 twin).

Comment: Enlarged version of T 43 MSF with larger bridge and funnel amidships. Reels on quarter-deck for degaussing function. Not all the guns are embarked.

HAI DZU   *1991, CSSC*

2 YENKA CLASS (ADG)

HAI DZU 745   +1

Displacement, tons: 395 full load
Dimensions, feet (metres): 154.2 × 24.6 × 7.2 *(47 × 7.5 × 2.2)*
Main machinery: 2 PRC/Kolomna 9-D-8 diesels; 2000 hp(m) *(1.47 MW)* sustained; 2 shafts
Speed, knots: 18. **Range, miles:** 3000 at 11 kts
Complement: 50
Guns: 2—37 mm/63 (twin). 2 or 4—14.5 mm/93 (1 or 2 twin) MGs.

Comment: Built at Chunghua Shipyard, Shanghai about 1966-68. Modified trawler hull. Prominent angled funnel and transom stern.

2 YEN FANG CLASS (ADG)

HAI DZU 950   HAI DZU 951

Displacement, tons: 110 standard; 125 full load
Dimensions, feet (metres): 101.7 × 20 × 5.9 *(31 × 6.1 × 1.8)*
Main machinery: 2 Soviet/PRC Type 3-D-6 diesels; 600 hp(m) *(440 kW)* sustained; 2 shafts
Speed, knots: 9
Complement: 14-16

Comment: Trawler hull conversion. Cable reels on stern. Converted mid-1960s.

SURVEY AND RESEARCH SHIPS

Notes: (1) In addition to naval ships listed the following ships work for the Hydrographic Bureau of the Ministry of Communications and therefore act as AGIs: *Sui Hang Biao No 1, Hu Hang Biao No 3* and *Jin Hang Biao No 1* (all of 1400 tons) and *Sui Hang CE Nos 318, 383, 343* and *344, Hu Hang CE Nos 5, 6, 11, 13, 14, 18* and *19*, and *Jin Hang CE No 3*. The most modern are *318, 383, 5, 6, 101* and *3*, all of which were launched in 1991/92.
(2) The following ships are declared as Survey Ships of the Hydrographic Guarantee Department: *Ocean 21* and *22* (of 3000 tons and 110 complement); *BH 2* and *3, DHC 12* and *13, NHC 7* (all of 100 tons and 24-30 complement); *BHC 5, DHC 14* and *NHC 8* (all of 1200 tons and 75 complement); and *NHC 6* (of 680 tons and 63 complement). The most modern are *Ocean 21* and *22* launched in 1982/83.

1 RESEARCH SHIP

JI DI HAO

Displacement, tons: 1050 full load
Dimensions, feet (metres): 164 × 34 × 16.4 *(50 × 10.4 × 5)*
Main machinery: 1 Burmeister and Wain Alpha 12V 23/30-V diesel; 2200 hp(m) *(1.62 MW)* sustained; 1 shaft
Speed, knots: 14. **Range, miles:** 12 000 at 11 kts
Complement: 26 plus 15 scientists

Comment: Ordered from Mjellem and Karlsen, Bergen, Norway in 1983. Laid down 15 November 1983. Similar to civilian research ships built for Mexico.

2 DAJIANG CLASS (RESEARCH SHIPS)

R 327   YUAN WANG 3

Displacement, tons: 10 975 full load
Dimensions, feet (metres): 511.7 × 67.2 × 37.7 *(156 × 20.5 × 11.5)*
Main machinery: 2 MAN K9Z60/105E diesels; 9000 hp(m) *(6.6 MW)*; 2 shafts
Speed, knots: 20
Helicopters: 2 Aerospatiale SA 321G Super Frelon (*R 237* only).

Comment: Built at Hudong, Shanghai. Completed 1981-82. Sisters of submarine support and salvage ships and operate for Academy of Sciences.

R 327   *1980, RNZAF*

YUAN WANG 3   *1984*

1 SHIH YEN CLASS (AGOR)

SHIH YEN (ex-*Kim Guam*)

Displacement, tons: 2500 full load
Dimensions, feet (metres): 213.3 × 38.1 × 16.4 *(65 × 11.6 × 5)*
Main machinery: 2 UK Polar diesels; 1200 hp *(895 kW)*; 2 shafts
Speed, knots: 11 (est)
Radars: Navigation: Fin Curve or Japan OKI NXE-12c; I band.

Comment: Former coastal steamer purchased by China from Quan Quan Shipping Ltd (Singapore) about 1973. Cargo holds forward and amidships. Believed rebuilt in late 1970s for oceanographic duties. Operated by one of China's research academies or China Institute of Oceanography. Painted white.

2 SPACE EVENT SHIPS

YUAN WANG 1 and **2**

Displacement, tons: 17 100 standard; 21 000 full load
Dimensions, feet (metres): 623.2 × 74.1 × 24.6 *(190 × 22.6 × 7.5)*
Main machinery: 1 diesel; 1 shaft
Speed, knots: 20

Comment: Built by Shanghai Jiangnan Yard. Probably commissioned in 1979. Have helicopter platform but no hangar. New communications, SATNAV and meteorological equipment fitted in Jiangnan SY in 1986-87. Both being refitted in 1991.

YUAN WANG 2   9/1988

2 SHIJIAN CLASS (AGOR)

SHIJIAN   **KEXUEYIHAO**

Displacement, tons: 3700 full load
Dimensions, feet (metres): 311.6 × 46 × 16.4 *(95 × 14 × 5)*
Main machinery: 2 Type 6 ESDZ 48/82 diesels; 4000 hp(m) *(2.94 MW)*; 2 shafts
Speed, knots: 15. **Range, miles:** 10 000 at 12 kts
Complement: 125 approx
Guns: 8 China 14.5 mm/93 (4 twin).
Radars: Navigation: Fin curve; I band.

Comment: *Shijian* built at Shanghai in 1965-68 as enlarged unit of Dong Fang Hong class AGOR. Electronics updated in 1991. Operates in East China Sea area under civil authority of the State Bureau of Oceanography and with scientists of the Chinese Academy of Sciences. Twelve labs on board. Painted white. *Kexueyihao* was first seen in late 1989 and is a slightly modified version.

SHIJIAN   5/1992, Henry Dodds

1 DADIE CLASS (AGI)

841

Displacement, tons: 2300 standard
Dimensions, feet (metres): 308.4 × 37.1 × 13.1 *(94 × 11.3 × 4)*
Main machinery: 2 diesels; 2 shafts
Speed, knots: 17
Complement: 170 (18 officers)
Guns: 4 China 37 mm/63 (2 twin).

Comment: Built at Wuhan shipyard, Wuchang and commissioned in 1986. North Sea Fleet and seen regularly in Sea of Japan and East China Sea.

841   1991, Ships of the World

2 HAI YING CLASS (AGOR)

KE XUE YIHAO 1   **KE XUE YIHAO 2**

Displacement, tons: 4500 standard
Dimensions, feet (metres): 412 × 51 × 24 *(125.6 × 15.5 × 7.3)*
Main machinery: 2 Type ESDZ diesels; 2 shafts
Speed, knots: 22
Complement: 148 (20 officers)
Radars: Navigation: 2 Fin Curve.

Comment: Successor design to Xiangyang Hong 9 series of civilian research ship. Believed to have been built in 1987-89. Fitted with deep sea cable reel on stern. Observed in East China Sea in March and September 1990 and Sea of Japan in 1991.

KE XUE YIHAO   12/1990, G Jacobs

1 KAN CLASS (AGOR)

KAN 102

Displacement, tons: 2300 standard
Dimensions, feet (metres): 225 × 22.5 × 9 *(68.6 × 6.9 × 2.7)*
Main machinery: 2 diesels; 2 shafts
Speed, knots: 18
Radars: Navigation: Fin Curve; I band.

Comment: Believed built in 1985-87, possibly at Shanghai. Large open stern area. Aft main deck area covered and may have cable reel system. Operated in East China Sea and Sea of Japan during 1991.

KAN 102   9/1990, G Jacobs

1 XING FENGSHAN CLASS (AGI)

XING FENGSHAN V 856

Displacement, tons: 5500

Comment: Launched in June 1987. Similar to Dalang class.

XING FENGSHAN   1987, Ships of the World

XIANGYANG HONG 01

Displacement, tons: 1100 standard; 1150 full load
Dimensions, feet (metres): 219.8 × 32.8 × 13.1 *(67 × 10 × 4)*
Main machinery: 2 diesels; 2 shafts
Guns: 2 China 37 mm/63 (twin). 8 China 14.5 mm/93 (2 quad).
Radars: Navigation: Fin Curve; I band.

Comment: The generic name Xiangyang Hong means 'The East is Red'. Initial vessel built either at Jiangnan or Tsingdao about 1970. Commissioned in 1971 and employed as research vessel but painted grey as if naval subordinated. Weapons not normally included on vessels subordinated to the Chinese Academy of Sciences.

XIANGYANG HONG 04, 06

Displacement, tons: 2000
Speed, knots: 15

Comment: Research ships built 1971-73.

XIANGYANG HONG 04   *1980, USN*

XIANGYANG HONG 02, 03, 08

Displacement, tons: 800 standard; 1000 full load
Dimensions, feet (metres): 236.2 × 26.2 × 8.2 *(72 × 8 × 2.5)*
Main machinery: 2 diesels; 2 shafts
Speed, knots: 14
Radars: Navigation: Fin Curve; I band.

Comment: Built in 1971-73 at Guangzhou. Operated by Chinese Academy of Sciences for coastal survey. Painted white.

XIANGYANG HONG 05

Displacement, tons: 14 500 full load
Dimensions, feet (metres): 500 × 64 × 28.9 *(152.5 × 19.5 × 8.8)*
Main machinery: 1 Cegielski Sulzer diesel; 6600 hp(m) *(4.85 MW)*; 1 shaft
Speed, knots: 16. **Range, miles:** 12-15 000
Radars: Navigation: Square Tie; I band.

Comment: Built as Polish B41 Type *(Francesco Nullo)* in 1967. Purchased by China and rebuilt 1970-72 in Guangzhou. Stationed at Guangzhou. Acts as environmental research ship. Four sister ships in Chinese mercantile fleet. Operated by Academy of Science. The goal post with a parabolic aerial has been removed from its position aft.

XIANGYANG HONG 05   *1980, RNZAF*

XIANGYANG HONG 09 (ex-*21*) V 350

Displacement, tons: 4435 standard
Dimensions, feet (metres): 400.3 × 49.9 × 23.6 *(122 × 15.2 × 7.2)*
Main machinery: 2 Type ESDZ 43/82B diesels; 8600 hp(m) *(6.32 MW)*; 2 shafts
Speed, knots: 22. **Range, miles:** 11 000 at 15 kts
Complement: 145 (20 officers)
Radars: Navigation: Type 756; I band.

Comment: Originally built as Xiang Yang Hong 21 (AGOR) at Hudong Shipyard, Shanghai, in 1978. Conversion to AGI completed about 1986 and has since been observed monitoring US-ROK 'Team Spirit' military exercises in Sea of Japan and Yellow Sea. Prominent 5 ton cargo boom aft and two forward kingposts with extensive electronics mounted. Painted dark grey. Operated in East China Sea in 1989.

XIANGYANG HONG 09   *6/1988, G Jacobs*

XIANGYANG HONG 10

Displacement, tons: 10 975
Dimensions, feet (metres): 512.3 × 67.6 × 22.3 *(156.2 × 20.6 × 6.8)*
Main machinery: 2 diesels; 2 shafts
Speed, knots: 20
Helicopters: 1 Aerospatiale SA 321G Super Frelon.

Comment: Built at Jiangnan Shipyard, Shanghai in 1979. Operates in conjunction with the Academy of Science.

XIANGYANG HONG 10   *3/1992*

XIANGYANG HONG 11-16

Measurement, tons: 2894 grt (14 and 16)
Dimensions, feet (metres): 364.2 × 49.9 × 23.3 *(111 × 15.2 × 7.1)*
Main machinery: 2 diesels; 2 shafts

Comment: A series of research ships of varying dimensions but similar appearance. 14 and 16 built in 1981.

XIANGYANG HONG 12   *7/1987*

1 YEN HSI CLASS (AGM)

HSUN 701

Displacement, tons: 930 standard; 1200 full load
Dimensions, feet (metres): 196.86 × 35.3 × 11.48 *(60 × 11 × 3.5)*
Main machinery: 2 diesels; 1800 hp(m) *(1.32 MW)*; 2 shafts
Speed, knots: 16 max; 11 cruise. **Range, miles:** 4500 at 11 kts
Complement: 110
Guns: 2 China 37 mm/63 (twin). 4 China 14.5 mm (2 twin) MGs.
Radars: Navigation: Fin Curve; I band.

Comment: Built in Shanghai in 1968-70. Has pronounced flare fwd and bow bulwark. Appearance is that of Hsiang Yang Hung 02-series of AGORs, though lighter in displacement and may have originally been planned as an AGOR/AGS unit.

3 GEOPHYSICAL RESEARCH SHIPS

NAN HAI 502   **BIN HAI** 511   **+ 1**

Measurement, tons: 697 dwt; 1257 gross
Dimensions, feet (metres): 215.5 × 36.9 × 13.5 *(65.7 × 11.2 × 4.1)*
Main machinery: 2 Yanmar CG-ST diesels; 2000 hp(m) *(1.47 MW)*; 1 shaft; cp prop
Speed, knots: 15
Complement: 50 (31 plus 19 scientists)

Comment: Built by Mitsubishi Heavy Industries in 1979. Designed for bathymetric and seismic research using satellite and terrestrial fixing. 511 modified in 1983 to include a helicopter deck. Arrays up to 3600 m can be towed.

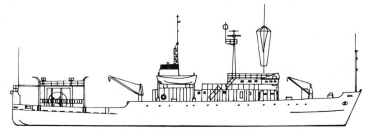

NAN HAI

1 YENLUN CLASS (AGS) + 2 Ex-US ARMY (AGS)

HAITSE 583   **HAITSE** 502   **HAITSE** 601

Displacement, tons: 1250 standard; 2000 full load (583)
Dimensions, feet (metres): 229.7 × 65.6 × 9.8 *(70 × 20 × 3)* (583)
Main machinery: 2 PRC/Kolomna Type 9-D-8 diesels; 2000 hp(m) *(1.47 MW)* sustained; 2 shafts
Speed, knots: 17
Guns: 4—25 mm/60 (2 twin).
Radars: Navigation: Fin Curve; I band.

Comment: 583 has prominent twin funnels amidships. First twin-hulled vessel built by PRC, with open well deck aft for supporting diving equipment and deep ocean survey work. Two small cranes aft. 502 and 601 are smaller ex-US Army craft of about 800 tons.

3 SHUGUANG CLASS (ex T-43) (AGOR/AGH)

SHUGUANG 1, 2 and 3

Displacement, tons: 500 standard; 570 full load
Dimensions, feet (metres): 190.3 × 28.9 × 11.5 *(58 × 8.8 × 3.5)*
Main machinery: 2 PRC/Kolomna Type 9-D-8 diesels; 2000 hp(m) *(1.47 MW)* sustained; 2 shafts
Speed, knots: 15. **Range, miles:** 5300 at 8 kts
Complement: 55-60

Comment: Converted from ex-Soviet T43 minesweepers in late 1960s. All painted white. One used for hydro-acoustic work in the East Sea Fleet has the number S994.

SHUGUANG 3   *1980*

5 SHUGUANG 04 CLASS (AGOR)

SHUGUANG 04, 05, 06, 07, 08

Displacement, tons: 1700 standard; 2400 full load
Dimensions, feet (metres): 214.9 × 32.8 × — *(65.5 × 10 × —)*
Main machinery: 2 diesels; 2 shafts
Speed, knots: 16
Guns: 2 China 37 mm/63 (twin). 4 China 25 mm/80 (2 twin).
Radars: Navigation: Fin Curve; I band.

Comment: Built at Guangzhou from 1970 to about 1975, based on modified design of *Hsiang Yan Hung 1* AGOR. Units differ slightly in superstructure appearance. At least three units subordinated to the Chinese Academy of Sciences and are without armament. Operated in East China and South China Seas.

SHUGUANG 04 class   *9/1990, John Mapletoft*

5 YENLAI CLASS (AGS)

K 200   226   426   427   943

Displacement, tons: 1100 full load
Dimensions, feet (metres): 229.6 × 32.1 × 9.7 *(70 × 9.8 × 3)*
Main machinery: 2 PRC/Kolomna Type 9-D-8 diesels; 2000 hp(m) *(1.47 MW)* sustained; 2 shafts
Speed, knots: 16. **Range, miles:** 4000 at 14 kts
Complement: 100
Guns: 4 China 37 mm/63 (2 twin). 4—25 mm/60 (2 twin).
Radars: Navigation: Fin Curve; I band.

Comment: Built at Zhonghua Shipyard, Shanghai in early 1970s. Carry four survey motor boats.

YENLAI 427   *1987, G Jacobs*

2 HAI YANG CLASS (AGOR)

HAI YANG 01   HAI YANG 02

Displacement, tons: 3300 standard; 4500 full load
Dimensions, feet (metres): 341.2 × 42.7 × 14.8 *(104 × 13 × 4.5)*
Main machinery: 2 diesels; 8000 hp(m) *(5.9 MW)*; 2 shafts
Speed, knots: 21. **Range, miles:** 10 000 at 18 kts
Complement: 150 including scientists
Guns: 4 China 37 mm/63 (2 twin).
Radars: Navigation: Fin Curve; I band.

Comment: Built at Shanghai during 1969-71. *Hai Yang 01* commissioned in 1972; *Hai Yang 02* in 1973 or 1974. Funnel amidships. Subordinated to Chinese Academy of Sciences. Painted white.

HAI YANG class   *7/1989, G Jacobs*

1 DONG FANG HONG CLASS (AGOR)

Displacement, tons: 3000 full load
Dimensions, feet (metres): 282.2 × 37.7 × 14.8 *(86 × 11.5 × 4.5)*
Main machinery: 2 diesels; 2 shafts
Speed, knots: 14
Radars: Navigation: Fin Curve; I band.

Comment: Built at Hudong, Shanghai 1964-66.

DONG FANG HONG   *1988*

1 HAI CLASS (AGOR)

HAI 521

Displacement, tons: 550 full load
Dimensions, feet (metres): 164 × 32.8 × 11.5 *(50 × 10 × 3.5)*
Main machinery: 2 Niigata Type 6M26KHHS diesels; 1600 hp(m) *(1.18 MW)*; 2 shafts; bow thruster
Speed, knots: 14. **Range, miles:** 5000 at 11 kts
Complement: 15 (7 officers) plus 25 scientists
Radars: Navigation: Japanese AR-M31; I band.

Comment: Built by Niigata Engineering Co., Niigata (Japan) in 1974-75. Launched 10 March 1975. Commissioned July 1975. First operated by the China National Machinery Export-Import Corp. on oceanographic duties. Operates on East and South China research projects but based in North China. For small vessel, has unique cruiser stern with raked bow, and small funnel well aft. Capability to operate single DSRV and the Chinese Navy has a number of Japanese-built KSWB-300 submersibles. Painted white.

1 GANZHU CLASS (AGS)

K 420

Displacement, tons: 850 standard; 1000 full load
Dimensions, feet (metres): 213.2 × 29.5 × 9.7 *(65 × 9 × 3)*
Main machinery: 4 diesels; 4400 hp(m) *(3.23 MW)*; 2 shafts
Speed, knots: 20
Complement: 125 (est)
Guns: 4—37 mm/63 (2 twin). 4—25 mm/60 (2 twin).

Comment: Built in Zhu Zhiang 1973-75. Frigate-type bridge. Prominent raked funnel.

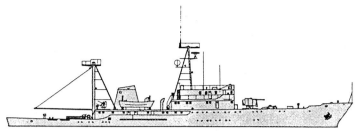

GANZHU   1990

1 YANXI CLASS (AGS)

V 201

Displacement, tons: 1150 standard
Dimensions, feet (metres): 213.9 × 34.4 × 10.8 *(65.2 × 10.5 × 3.3)*
Main machinery: 2 diesels; 4000 hp(m) *(2.9 MW)*; 2 shafts
Speed, knots: 16
Guns: 4 China 37 mm/63 Type 61/74 (2 twin); 4 China 25 mm/80 Type 61 (2 twin).

Comment: Built 1968-69; commissioned 1970. Outfitted initially to provide electronic monitoring support for China's SLBM missile tests.

2 YANNAN CLASS (AGS)

K 982   983

Displacement, tons: 1750 standard
Dimensions, feet (metres): 237.2 × 38.7 × 13.1 *(72.3 × 11.8 × 4)*
Main machinery: 1 diesel; 500 hp(m) *(367 kW)*; 1 shaft
Speed, knots: 12
Complement: 95
Guns: 4 China 37 mm/63 (2 twin).

Comment: Built 1978-79; commissioned 1980.

YANNAN 982   1992

2 DING HAI CLASS and 1 KAIBOBAN CLASS (AGS)

HAI SHENG 701, 702 and 623

Displacement, tons: 330 full load (701, 702)
Dimensions, feet (metres): 128 × 24.6 × 11.5 *(39 × 7.5 × 3.5)* (701, 702)
Main machinery: 2 PRC/Kolomna Type 3-D-12 diesels; 600 hp(m) *(440 kW)* sustained; 2 shafts
Speed, knots: 13
Guns: 4—14.5 mm/93 (2 twin).

Comment: Coastal trawler design. Naval subordinated. 701 and 702 are South Sea Fleet units. 623 is a larger craft of 67.5 m assigned to the North Sea Fleet.

ICEBREAKERS

2 HAIBING CLASS (AGB)

101 (ex-*C723*)   **102** (ex-*C721*)

Displacement, tons: 2900 standard; 3400 full load
Dimensions, feet (metres): 275 × 50 × 16.4 *(83.8 × 15.3 × 5)*
Main machinery: Diesel-electric; 2 diesel generators; 5250 hp(m) *(3.86 MW)*; 1 motor; 1 shaft
Speed, knots: 16
Complement: 90-95
Guns: 8—37 mm/63 (4 twin). 4 or 8—25 mm/80 (2 or 4 twin).
Radars: Navigation: Fin Curve; I band.

Comment: Built in 1969-73 at Chiu Hsin SY, Shanghai. Employed as icebreaking tugs in Bo Hai Gulf for port clearance. Sometimes deployed as AGIs.

102   1982, G Jacobs

1 MOD YANHA CLASS (AGB)

723

Displacement, tons: 4000 full load
Dimensions, feet (metres): 310 × 56 × 19.5 *(94.5 × 17.1 × 5.9)*
Main machinery: Diesel-electric; 2 diesel generators; 2 motors; 2 shafts
Speed, knots: 17.5
Complement: 95
Guns: 8—37 mm/63 Type 61/74 (4 twin).
Radars: Navigation: Fin Curve; I band.

Comment: Enlarged version of Yanha class icebreaker, with greater displacement, longer and wider hull, added deck level and curved upper funnel. In October 1990, painted white while operating in Sea of Japan.

723   1991, Ships of the World

1 YANHA CLASS (AGB)

519

Displacement, tons: 3400 full load
Dimensions, feet (metres): 290 × 53 × 17 *(88.4 × 16.2 × 5.2)*
Main machinery: Diesel-electric; 2 diesel generators; 1 motor; 1 shaft
Speed, knots: 17.5
Complement: 90
Guns: 8—37 mm/63 Type 61/74 (4 twin); 4—25 mm/80 Type 61.
Radars: Navigation: Fin Curve; I band.

Comment: Commissioned in 1989. Similar to Haibing class with minor differences. Painted in PLAN grey colour. Operated in East China Sea in late 1990.

519   10/1991, G Jacobs

TUGS

Notes: (1) The vessels below represent a small cross-section of the craft available.
(2) The latest to be built was seen fitting out in late 1993.

OCEAN TUG   9/1993, Hachiro Nakai

5 YUNG GANG CLASS (ATA)

Displacement, tons: 320
Dimensions, feet (metres): 87 × 31.4 × 10.8 *(26.5 × 9.6 × 3.3)*
Main machinery: 2 Daihatsu 6DLM-24 diesels; 3000 hp(m) *(2.2 MW)* sustained; 2 shafts
Speed, knots: 15

Comment: *Yung Gang 16* launched 29 July 1981 at Ishikawajima, built in Japan. It is not known whether these are for naval or civilian use.

1 YAN JIU CLASS (ATA)

YAN JIU 14

Comment: Probably one of a series with dual military civilian use.

YAN JIU 14   9/1991, G Jacobs

16 GROMOVOY CLASS (ATA)

HAITO 210, 221, 230, 231, 235, 319, **T** 147, **T** 716, **T** 802, **T** 814   +6

Displacement, tons: 795 standard; 890 full load
Dimensions, feet (metres): 149.9 × 31.2 × 15.1 *(45.7 × 9.5 × 4.6)*
Main machinery: 2 diesels; 1300 hp(m) *(956 kW)*; 2 shafts
Speed, knots: 11. **Range, miles:** 7000 at 7 kts
Complement: 25-30 (varies)
Guns: 4—14.5 mm (2 twin) or 12.7 mm (2 twin) MGs.
Radars: Navigation: Fin Curve or OKI X-NE-12 (Japanese); I band.

Comment: Built at Luda Shipyard and Shanghai International, 1958-62. Nine in North Sea Fleet and seven in East Sea Fleet. Oil fuel, 175 tons.

GROMOVOY 802   5/1992, Henry Dodds

4 HUJIU CLASS (ATA)

T 155   **T** 711   **T** 842   **T** 867

Displacement, tons: 750 full load
Dimensions, feet (metres): 160.8 × 31.2 × 12.1 *(49 × 9.5 × 3.7)*
Main machinery: 2 LVP 24 diesels; 1800 hp(m) *(1.32 MW)*; 2 shafts
Speed, knots: 13.5. **Range, miles:** 2200 at 13 kts

Comment: Built in 1980s.

HUJIU 155   1991

1 JIN JIAN XUN 05 CLASS (ARS)

Displacement, tons: 559 standard
Dimensions, feet (metres): 196.9 × 24.3 × 8.5 *(60 × 7.4 × 2.6)*
Main machinery: 2 Niigata 6M26BGT diesels; 1700 hp(m) *(1.25 MW)* sustained; 2 shafts
Speed, knots: 18.4

Comment: Built by Osaka Shipyard, Niigata, Japan in early 1986. Commissioned November 1986. Identified as a rescue ship and towing vessel.

4 ROSLAVL CLASS (ARS)

J 120, **HAITO** 302, 403   + 1

Displacement, tons: 670 full load
Dimensions, feet (metres): 149.9 × 31 × 15.1 *(45.7 × 9.5 × 4.6)*
Main machinery: Diesel-electric; 2 diesel generators; 1200 hp(m) *(882 kW)*; 1 motor; 1 shaft
Speed, knots: 12. **Range, miles:** 6000 at 11 kts
Complement: 28
Guns: 4—14.5 mm (2 twin) MGs.

Comment: First ship *(302)* transferred by the USSR late 1950s. Remainder built in China in mid-1960s. One carries diving bell and submarine rescue gear on stern. Fuel, 90 tons.

4 TUZHONG CLASS (ATR)

T 154   **T** 710   **T** 830   **T** 890

Displacement, tons: 3600 full load
Dimensions, feet (metres): 278.5 × 46 × 18 *(84.9 × 14 × 5.5)*
Main machinery: 2 10 ESDZ 43/82B diesels; 8600 hp(m) *(6.32 MW)*; 2 shafts
Speed, knots: 18.5
Radars: Navigation: Fin Curve; I band.

Comment: Built in late 1970s. Can be fitted with twin 37 mm AA armament and at least one of the class has been fitted with a Square Tie radar. 35 ton towing winch.

TUZHONG   1991

HARBOUR TUGS

HARBOUR TUG   1990

MARITIME MILITIA (MBDF)

Note: In the early 1950s certain ships of the deep-sea and coastal fishing fleets were formed into the Maritime Militia. These ships, under the control of the local branch of the party, act in support or as cover for naval forces. Their normal task is reconnaissance and surveillance but, on occasions, they have been armed with machine guns. About 100 ex-Soviet T 4 LCMs are used by the MBDF. Some Fuzhou class coastal tankers are operated by MBDF to support East Sea Fleet island garrisons. These ships have been reported as being responsible for acts of piracy in the China Seas.

MBDF 136   12/1991, 92 Wing RAAF

CUSTOMS

Note: There are large numbers of Customs craft in every major port.

CUSTOMS 801   1991, DTM

COLOMBIA

Headquarters' Appointments

Fleet Commander:
  Admiral Hernando Garcia Ramirez
Deputy Fleet Commander and Chief of Operations:
  Vice Admiral Holdan Delgado Villamil
Commander, Atlantic Force:
  Rear Admiral Hugo Sanchez Granados
Commander, Pacific Force:
  Rear Admiral Jose I Rozo Carvajal

Personnel

(a) 1994: 11 900 (including 9000 marines)
(b) 2 years' national service (few conscripts in the Navy)

Organisation

Atlantic Force Command: HQ at Cartagena.
Pacific Force Command: HQ at Bahia Malaga.
Naval Force South: HQ at Puerto Leguizamo.
River Forces Command: HQ at Bogotá.
Coast Guard: HQ at Bogotá.

Bases

Cartagena, ARC *Bolivar*: Main naval base (floating dock, 1 slip-way), schools.
ARC *Bahia Malaga*: Major Pacific base.
ARC *Barranquilla*: Naval Training base.
Puerto Leguizamo: Putumayo River base.
Leticia: Meta River base.
Puerto Carreño: River base.
San Andres, Providencia, Turbo, Bahia Solano, Buenaventura, Barrancabermeja: Minor bases.

Naval and Maritime Air

A Fleet Air Arm has been established with one fixed-wing squadron and one helicopter squadron.
The Colombian Air Force with 50 helicopters and a number of attack/reconnaissance aircraft provides support including Type A 37B.

Cuerpo de Infanteria de Marina

Organisation: Atlàntico Brigade: 1st Battalion (San Andrés).
3rd Battalion (Cartagena).
5th Battalion (Coveñas also has Amphibious Warfare School).
Paćifico Brigade: 2nd Battalion (Tumaco).
4th (Jungle) Battalion, subordinate to Western River Forces Command (Puerto Leguizamo).
6th Battalion (Buenaventura).
7th Battalion (Bogotá).

Prefix to Ships' Names

ARC (Armada Republica de Colombia)

Customs/Coast Guard

The Coast Guard was established in 1979 but then gave way to the Customs Service before being re-established in January 1992 under the control of the Navy.Ships have a red and yellow diagonal stripe on the hull.

Dimar

Maritime authority in charge of hydrography and navigational aids.

Strength of the Fleet

Type	Active
Patrol Submarines	2
Midget Submarines	2
Frigates	4
Patrol Ships	4
Fast Attack Craft (Gun)	2
Gunboats	3
Coastal/River Patrol Craft	40
Survey Vessels	4
Transports	14
Training Ship	1
Tugs	15

Mercantile Marine

Lloyd's Register of Shipping:
  109 vessels of 237 623 tons gross

DELETIONS

Patrol Forces

1993 *Espartana*

Auxiliaries

1992 *Turbo, Bahia Cupica*

PENNANT LIST

Submarines		
		111
		112
SS 20	Intrepido	
SS 21	Indomable	
SS 28	Pijao	
SS 29	Tayrona	

Frigates	
CM 51	Almirante Padilla
CM 52	Caldas
CM 53	Antioquia
CM 54	Independiente

Patrol Forces	
DE 16	Boyaca
RM 72	Pedro de Heredia
RM 73	Sebastion de Belal Calzar
RM 74	Rodrigo de Bastidas

CF 135	Riohacha
CF 136	Leticia
CF 137	Arauca
GC 101	Capitan R D Binney
GC 102	Rafael del Castillo y Rada
GC 103	Jose Maria Palas
GC 104	Medardo Monzon
GC 105	Jaime Gomez Castro
GC 106	Nepomuceno Peña
LR I	Rio Magdalena
LR II	Rio Cauca
LR III	Rio Sinu
LR IV	Rio Atrato
LR V	Rio San Jorge
LR 122	Juan Lucio
LR 123	Alfonso Vargas
LR 124	Fritz Hagale
LR 126	Humberto Cortes
LR 127	Calibio
LR 128	Carlos Galindo

Survey Vessels	
155	Providencia
156	Malpelo
BO 153	Quindio
BO 161	Gorgona

Auxiliaries	
BD 33	Socorro
BD 35	Hernando Gutierrez
RR 73	Teniente Sorzano
RM 76	Josué Alvarez
RR 81	Capitan Castro
RR 84	Capitan Alvaro Ruiz
RR 86	Capitan Rigoberto Giraldo
RR 87	Capitan Vladimir Valek
RR 88	Teniente Luis Bernal Baquero
RR 89	Teniente Miguel Silva
RR 90	Néstor Orpina
RM 93	Segeri
RR 96	Inirida
TM 44	Tolú
TM 45	Serranilla
TM 60	San Andres
LR 92	Igaraparana
LR 95	Manacasias
NF 141	Filogonio Hichamón
DF 141	Mayor Jaime Arias
TM 246	Morrosquillo
TN 247	Uraba
TM 248	Bahia Honda
TM 249	Bahia Portete
TM 251	Bahia Solano
TM 252	Bahia Cupica
TM 253	Bahia Utria
TM 254	Bahia Malaga

SUBMARINES

2 PIJAO (209 TYPE 1200) CLASS

Name	No	Builders	Laid down	Launched	Commissioned
PIJAO	SS 28	Howaldtswerke, Kiel	1 Apr 1972	10 Apr 1974	18 Apr 1975
TAYRONA	SS 29	Howaldtswerke, Kiel	1 May 1972	16 July 1974	16 July 1975

Displacement, tons: 1180 surfaced; 1285 dived
Dimensions, feet (metres): 183.4 × 20.5 × 17.9 *(55.9 × 6.3 × 5.4)*
Main machinery: Diesel-electric; 4 MTU 12V 493 AZ80 diesels; 2400 hp(m) *(1.76 MW)* sustained; 4 AEG alternators; 1.7 MW; 1 Siemens motor; 4600 hp(m) *(3.38 MW)* sustained; 1 shaft
Speed, knots: 22 dived; 11 surfaced
Range, miles: 8000 at 8 kts surfaced; 4000 at 4 kts dived
Complement: 34 (7 officers)

Torpedoes: 8—21 in *(533 mm)* bow tubes. 14 AEG SUT; dual purpose; wire-guided; active/passive homing to 12 km *(6.5 nm)* at 35 kts; 28 km *(15 nm)* at 23 kts; warhead 250 kg. Swim-out discharge.
Fire control: Signaal M8/24 action data automation.
Radars: Surface search: Thomson-CSF Calypso II; I band.
Sonars: Atlas Elektronik CSU 3-2; hull-mounted; active/passive search and attack; medium frequency.
  Atlas Elektronik PRS 3-4; passive ranging; integral with CSU 3.

Programmes: Ordered in 1971. Two more are required and an interest has been taken in Argentine sales but money is not available. Both refitted by HDW at Kiel; *Pijao* completed refit in July 1990 and *Tayrona* in September 1991. Main batteries were replaced.
Structure: Diving depth, 820 ft *(250 m)*.

TAYRONA   *8/1991, Foto Flite*

2 MIDGET SUBMARINES

INDOMABLE   *10/1990, Hartmut Ehlers*

INTREPIDO SS 20   **INDOMABLE** SS 21

Displacement, tons: 70 dived
Dimensions, feet (metres): 75.5 × 13.1 *(23 × 4)*
Speed, knots: 11 surfaced; 6 dived
Range, miles: 1200 surfaced; 60 dived
Complement: 4

Comment: They can carry eight swimmers with 2 tons of explosive as well as two swimmer delivery vehicles (SDVs). Built by
Cosmos, Livorno and commissioned in 1972 at 40 tons, but
subsequently enlarged in the early 1980s.

FRIGATES

4 ALMIRANTE PADILLA CLASS (TYPE FS 1500)

Name	No	Builders	Laid down	Launched	Commissioned
ALMIRANTE PADILLA	CM 51	Howaldtswerke, Kiel	17 Mar 1981	6 Jan 1982	31 Oct 1983
CALDAS	CM 52	Howaldtswerke, Kiel	14 June 1981	23 Apr 1982	14 Feb 1984
ANTIOQUIA	CM 53	Howaldtswerke, Kiel	22 June 1981	28 Aug 1982	30 Apr 1984
INDEPENDIENTE	CM 54	Howaldtswerke, Kiel	22 June 1981	21 Jan 1983	24 July 1984

Displacement, tons: 1500 standard; 2100 full load
Dimensions, feet (metres): 325.1 × 37.1 × 12.1
(99.1 × 11.3 × 3.7)
Main machinery: 4 MTU 20V 1163 TB92 diesels; 23 400 hp(m)
(17.2 MW) sustained; 2 shafts; cp props
Speed, knots: 27; 18 on 2 diesels. **Range, miles:** 7000 at 14 kts;
5000 at 18 kts
Complement: 94

Missiles: SSM: 8 Aerospatiale MM 40 Exocet ❶; inertial cruise;
active radar homing to 70 km *(40 nm)* at 0.9 Mach; warhead
165 kg; sea-skimmer.
SAM: ❷ To be fitted forward of the bridge when funds become
available.
Guns: 1 OTO Melara 3 in *(76 mm)*/62 compact ❸; 85° elevation;
85 rounds/minute to 16 km *(8.7 nm)*; weight of shell 6 kg.
2 Breda 40 mm/70 (twin) ❹; 85° elevation; 300 rounds/
minute to 12.5 km *(6.8 nm)* anti-surface; weight of shell
0.96 kg.
4 Oerlikon 30 mm/75 Mk 74 (2 twin); 85° elevation; 650
rounds/minute to 10 km *(5.5 nm)*; 950 ready use rounds.
Torpedoes: 6—324 mm Mk 32 (2 triple) tubes ❺;
anti-submarine.
Countermeasures: Decoys: 1 CSEE Dagaie double mounting; IR
flares and chaff decoys (H-J band).
ESM: AC672; radar warning.
ECM: Scimitar; jammer.
Combat data systems: Thomson-CSF TAVITAC action data auto-
mation. Possibly Link Y fitted.
Fire control: 2 Canopus optronic directors. Thomson-CSF Vega II
GFCS.
Radars: Combined search: Thomson-CSF Sea Tiger ❻; E/F band;
range 110 km *(60 nm)* for 2 m² target.
Fire control: Castor II B ❼; I/J band; range 15 km *(8 nm)* for 1 m²
target.
IFF: Mk 10.
Sonars: Atlas Elektronik ASO 4-2; hull-mounted; active attack;
medium frequency.

Helicopters: 1 MBB BO 105 CB, ASW ❽.

Programmes: Order for four Type FS 1500 placed late 1980.
Almirante Padilla started trials July 1982. Near sisters to Malaysian frigates.
Modernisation: No confirmation yet of SAM fit. Albatros/
Aspide, Crotale and Barak have all been mentioned. A modernisation programme remains the top priority when funds are
available.

ALMIRANTE PADILLA   *(Scale 1 : 900), Ian Sturton*

INDEPENDIENTE   *11/1990, Hartmut Ehlers*

ANTIOQUIA   *11/1990, Hartmut Ehlers*

SHIPBORNE AIRCRAFT

Note: Four more BO 105 are planned. 4 A37B Dragonfly aircraft acquired from the Air Force in 1991 and four Cessna A37Bs in 1993.

Numbers/Type: 2 MBB BO 105CB.
Operational speed: 113 kts *(210 km/h).*
Service ceiling: 9854 ft *(3000 m).*
Range: 407 nm *(754 km).*
Role/Weapon systems: Shipborne surface search and limited ASW helicopter. Sensors: Search/ weather radar. Weapons: ASW; provision to carry depth bombs. ASV; light attack role with machine gun pods.

BO 105   *1990, Colombian Navy*

PATROL FORCES

1 COURTNEY CLASS (PATROL SHIP)

Name	No	Builders	Commissioned
BOYACA (ex-USS *Hartley*)	DE 16	New York SB	26 Jan 1957

Displacement, tons: 1450 standard; 1914 full load
Dimensions, feet (metres): 314.5 × 36.8 × 13.6 *(95.9 × 11.2 × 4.1)*
Main machinery: 2 Foster-Wheeler boilers; 300 psi *(42 kg/cm sq)*; 950°F *(510°C)*; 1 De Laval turbine; 20 000 hp *(15 MW)*; 1 shaft
Speed, knots: 24. **Range, miles:** 4500 at 15 kts
Complement: 161 (11 officers)

Guns: 2 USN 3 in (76 mm)/50 Mk 33 (twin); 85° elevation; 50 rounds/minute to 12.8 km *(7 nm)*; weight of shell 6 kg.
Torpedoes: 6—324 mm Mk 32 (2 triple tubes); anti-submarine.
Depth charges: 1 rack.
Fire control: Mk 63 GFCS.
Radars: Surface search: Raytheon SPS 10; G band.
Fire control: Western Electric SPG 34; I/J band.
Sonars: Sangamo SQS 23; hull-mounted active search and attack; medium frequency.

Helicopters: Platform only.

Programmes: Transferred from the US 8 July 1972; paid off into reserve in 1983. Brought out of retirement in 1988 for use mostly as a Headquarters ship.

BOYACA   *11/1990, Hartmut Ehlers*

3 CHEROKEE CLASS (PATROL SHIPS)

Name	No	Builders	Commissioned
PEDRO DE HEREDIA (ex-*Choctaw*)	RM 72	Charleston SB & DD Co	21 Apr 1943
SEBASTION DE BELAL CALZAR (ex-*Carib*)	RM 73	Charleston SB & DD Co	24 July 1943
RODRIGO DE BASTIDAS (ex-*Hidatsa*)	RM 74	Charleston SB & DD Co	25 Apr 1944

Displacement, tons: 1235 standard; 1640 full load
Dimensions, feet (metres): 205 × 38.5 × 17 *(62.5 × 11.7 × 5.2)*
Main machinery: Diesel-electric; 4 GM 12-278 diesels; 4400 hp *(3.28 MW)*; 4 generators; 1 motor; 3000 hp *(2.24 MW)*; 1 shaft
Speed, knots: 15
Complement: 75
Guns: 1 USN 3 in *(76 mm)*/50 Mk 22.

Comment: Transferred from the US by sale on 15 March 1979 and paid off in 1987. Reactivated in 1990. Originally built as tugs but used as patrol ships.

CALZAR   *4/1993*

2 ASHEVILLE CLASS (FAST ATTACK CRAFT—GUN)

Name	No	Builders	Commissioned
ALBUQUERQUE (ex-USS *Welch*)	111	Peterson Builders	8 Sep 1969
QUITA SUENO (ex-USS *Tacoma*)	112	Tacoma Boat Building	14 July 1969

Displacement, tons: 225 standard; 245 full load
Dimensions, feet (metres): 164.5 × 23.8 × 9.5 *(50.1 × 7.3 × 2.9)*
Main machinery: CODOG; 2 Cummins VT12-875M diesels; 1450 hp *(1.08 MW)*; 1 GE LM-1500 gas-turbine; 13 300 hp *(9.92 MW)*; 2 shafts; cp props
Speed, knots: 40. **Range, miles:** 1700 at 16 kts on diesels; 325 at 37 kts
Complement: 24
Guns: 1 US 3 in *(76 mm)*/50 Mk 34; 85° elevation; 50 rounds/minute to 12.8 km *(7 nm)*; weight of shell 6 kg.
1 Bofors 40 mm/56; 45° elevation; 160 rounds/minute to 11 km *(5.9 nm)* anti-aircraft; weight of shell 0.96 kg.
2—12.7 mm (twin) MGs.
Radars: Surface search: Marconi LN 66/LP; I band.

Comment: Decommissioned in US Navy 30 September 1981. Transferred by lease 16 May 1983. Fire-control system removed. Unreliable propulsion system has prevented further transfers of this class.

QUITA SUENO   *11/1992, Paul Campbell*

3 ARAUCA CLASS (RIVER GUNBOATS)

Name	No	Builders	Commissioned
RIOHACHA	CF 135 (ex-35)	Union Industrial de Barranquilla	1956
LETICIA	CF 136 (ex-36)	Union Industrial de Barranquilla	1956
ARAUCA	CF 137 (ex-37)	Union Industrial de Barranquilla	1956

Displacement, tons: 184 full load
Dimensions, feet (metres): 163.5 × 23.5 × 2.8 *(49.9 × 7.2 × 0.9)*
Main machinery: 2 Caterpillar diesels; 916 hp *(683 kW)*; 2 shafts
Speed, knots: 14. **Range, miles:** 1890 at 14 kts
Complement: 43; 39 plus 6 orderlies (*Leticia*)
Guns: 2 USN 3 in *(76 mm)*/50. 4 Oerlikon 20 mm.

Comment: Launched in 1955. *Leticia* has been equipped as a hospital ship with six beds and reported as disarmed.

ARAUCA   *1991, Colombian Navy*

4 JOSE MARIA PALAS CLASS (LARGE PATROL CRAFT)

Name	No	Builders	Commissioned
JOSE MARIA PALAS	GC 103	Swiftships Inc, Berwick	Sep 1989
MEDARDO MONZON	GC 104	Swiftships Inc, Berwick	July 1990
JUAN NEPOMUCENO ESLAVA	113	Bender Marine, Mobile	1994
JOSE MARIA GARCIA DE TOLEDO	114	Bender Marine, Mobile	1994

Displacement, tons: 99 full load
Dimensions, feet (metres): 109.9 × 24.6 × 6.6 (33.5 × 7.5 × 2)
Main machinery: 2 MTU diesels; 2 shafts
Speed, knots: 25. **Range, miles:** 2250 at 15 kts
Complement: 19 (3 officers)
Guns: 1 Bofors 40 mm/60. 1—12.7 mm MG. 2—7.62 mm MGs.

Comment: Acquired under US FMS programme. Second pair ordered in 1992.

JOSE MARIA PALAS   1990, Colombian Navy

1 RAFAEL DEL CASTILLO Y RADA CLASS (LARGE PATROL CRAFT)

Name	No	Builders	Commissioned
RAFAEL DEL CASTILLO Y RADA	GC 102 (ex-AN 102)	Swiftships Inc, Berwick	Feb 1983

Displacement, tons: 103 full load
Dimensions, feet (metres): 105 × 22 × 7 (31.5 × 6.7 × 2.1)
Main machinery: 4 MTU 12V331 TC92 diesels; 5320 hp(m) (3.97 MW) sustained; 4 shafts
Speed, knots: 25. **Range, miles:** 1200 at 18 kts
Complement: 19 (3 officers)
Guns: 1 Bofors 40 mm/60. 2—12.7 mm MGs.

Comment: Second of two delivered in the early 1980s. The other craft was badly damaged in 1986 but is now back in service with the Customs. *Castillo y Rada* transferred to the Navy in 1989.

RAFAEL DEL CASTILLO Y RADA   1993, Colombian Navy

1 COASTAL PATROL CRAFT

Name	No	Builders	Commissioned
CAPITAN R D BINNEY	GC 101	Ast Naval, Cartagena	1947

Displacement, tons: 23 full load
Dimensions, feet (metres): 67 × 10.7 × 3.5 (20.4 × 3.3 × 1.1)
Main machinery: 2 Diesels; 115 hp(m) (85 kW); 2 shafts
Speed, knots: 13

Comment: Buoy and lighthouse inspection boat. Named after first head of Colombian Naval Academy, Lieutenant Commander Ralph Douglas Binney, RN. May finally be paid off in 1994.

CAPITAN R D BINNEY   1991, Colombian Navy

2 JAIME GOMEZ (Mk III PB) CLASS (COASTAL PATROL CRAFT)

Name	No	Builders	Commissioned
JAIME GOMEZ CASTRO	GC 105	Peterson Builders	1975
NEPOMUCENO PEÑA	GC 106	Peterson Builders	1977

Displacement, tons: 34 full load
Dimensions, feet (metres): 64.9 × 18 × 5.1 (19.8 × 5.5 × 1.6)
Main machinery: 3 Detroit 8V-71 diesels; 690 hp (515 kW) sustained; 3 shafts
Speed, knots: 28. **Range, miles:** 450 at 26 kts
Complement: 7 (1 officer)
Guns: 2—12.7 mm MGs. 2—7.62 mm MGs. 1 Mk 19 Grenade launcher.

Comment: Delivered from the US in 1990. Original 40 mm and 20 mm guns replaced by lighter armament. Both based in the Atlantic.

JAIME GOMEZ CASTRO   1990, Colombian Navy

6 RIVER PATROL CRAFT

Name	No	Builders	Commissioned
JUAN LUCIO	LR 122	Ast Naval, Cartagena	1953
ALFONSO VARGAS	LR 123	Ast Naval, Cartagena	1952
FRITZ HAGALE	LR 124	Ast Naval, Cartagena	1952
HUMBERTO CORTES	LR 126	Ast Naval, Cartagena	1953
CALIBIO	LR 127	Ast Naval, Cartagena	1953
CARLOS GALINDO	LR 128	Ast Naval, Cartagena	1954

Displacement, tons: 33 full load
Dimensions, feet (metres): 76 × 12 × 2.8 (23.2 × 3.7 × 0.8)
Main machinery: 2 GM diesels; 280 hp (209 kW); 2 shafts
Speed, knots: 13
Complement: 10
Guns: 2 Oerlikon 20 mm or 1 Oerlikon and 4 mortars.

Comment: Some may be unserviceable.

JUAN LUCIO   1991, Colombian Navy

9 TENERIFE CLASS (RIVER PATROL CRAFT)

TENERIFE 181	OROCUE 184	MONCLART 187
TARAPACA 182	CALAMAR 185	CAUCAYA 188
MOMPOX 183	MAGANGUE 186	MITU 189

Dimensions, feet (metres): 40.7 × 9.5 × 2 (12.4 × 2.9 × 0.6)
Main machinery: 2 Caterpillar 3208 TA diesels; 850 hp (634 kW) sustained; 2 shafts
Speed, knots: 29. **Range, miles:** 530 at 15 kts
Complement: 5 plus 12 troops
Guns: 3—12.7 mm MGs (1 twin, 1 single). 1 Mk 19 grenade launcher. 2—7.62mm MGs.

Comment: Built by Bender Marine, Mobile, Alabama. Acquired in October 1993 for anti-narcotics patrols.

TENERIFE   1993, Colombian Navy

2 OCTUBRE CLASS (RIVER PATROL CRAFT)

8 DE OCTUBRE   27 DE OCTUBRE

Displacement, tons: 18 full load
Dimensions, feet (metres): 45 × 15 × 1.8 *(13.7 × 4.6 × 0.5)*
Main machinery: 2 Detroit diesels; 2 waterjets
Speed, knots: 32. **Range, miles:** 600 at 22 kts
Complement: 4 plus 8 troops
Guns: 2—12.7 mm MGs. 2—7.62 mm MGs.

Comment: Built by Swiftships and delivered by the US Navy in September 1992 to assist in anti-narcotics patrols.

5 RIO CLASS (RIVER PATROL CRAFT)

RIO MAGDALENA 176	RIO ATRATO 179
RIO CAUCA 177	RIO SAN JORGE 180
RIO SINU 178	

Displacement, tons: 9 full load
Dimensions, feet (metres): 31 × 11.1 × 2 *(9.8 × 3.5 × 0.6)*
Main machinery: 2 Detroit 6V-53 diesels; 296 hp *(221 kW)* sustained; 2 waterjets
Speed, knots: 24. **Range, miles:** 150 at 22 kts
Complement: 4
Guns: 2—12.7 mm (twin) MGs. 1—7.62 mm MG. 1—60 mm mortar.
Radars: Surface search: Raytheon 1900; I band.

Comment: Acquired in November 1989. Ex-US PBR Mk II built by Uniflite in 1970. GRP hulls.

RIO SAN JORGE   11/1990, Hartmut Ehlers

2 ROTORK CRAFT

MANUELA SAENZ   JAMIE ROOK

Displacement, tons: 9 full load
Dimensions, feet (metres): 41.7 × 10.5 × 2.3 *(12.7 × 3.2 × 0.7)*
Main machinery: 2 Caterpillar diesels; 240 hp *(179 kW)*; 2 shafts
Speed, knots: 25
Complement: 4
Military lift: 4 tons
Guns: 1—12.7 mm MG. 2—7.62 mm MGs.

Comment: Acquired in 1989-90. Capable of transporting eight fully equipped marines.

JAMIE ROOK   1990, Colombian Navy

12 DELFIN CLASS

ESCORPION GC 27	ACQUARIO	TAURO	DENEB
LIBRA GC28	PISCIS	GEMINIS	BELLATRIX
CAPRICORNIO	ARIES	ALPHERAX	CANOPUS

Dimensions, feet (metres): 25.9 × 8.5 × 2 *(7.9 × 2.6 × 0.6)*
Main machinery: 2 Evinrude outboards; 700 hp *(522 kW)*
Speed, knots: 35
Complement: 6
Guns: 1—12.7 mm MG. 2—7.62 mm MGs.

Comment: GC 27 and 28 built by Mako Marine, Miami and delivered in December 1992. Six based in the Atlantic and six in the Pacific.

45 PIRANA CRAFT

Comment: These are 6.8 m river assault boats reported as being acquired from Boston Whaler for use by Marines. Armed with 1—12.7 mm and 2—7.62 mm MGs. The plan is to have 15 patrol units each operating with one Rio or Tenerife class and three Piranas. Capable of 25-30 kts depending on load. Not all of them in service by mid-1994.

PIRANA   1993

1 ADMIRAL'S YACHT

CONTRALMIRANTE BELL SALTER

Comment: Could be used as a patrol craft in an emergency.

CONTRALMIRANTE BELL SALTER   10/1990, Hartmut Ehlers

SURVEY SHIPS

Name	No	Builders	Commissioned
PROVIDENCIA	155	Martin Jansen SY, Leer	24 July 1981
MALPELO	156	Martin Jansen SY, Leer	24 July 1981

Displacement, tons: 1040 full load
Measurement, tons: 830 gross
Dimensions, feet (metres): 164.3 × 32.8 × 13.1 *(50.3 × 10 × 4)*
Main machinery: 1 MAN-Augsburg diesel; 1570 hp(m) *(1.15 MW)*; 1 shaft; bow thruster
Speed, knots: 13. **Range, miles:** 15 000 at 12 kts
Complement: 21 (5 officers) plus 6 scientists

Comment: Both launched in January 1981. *Malpelo* employed on fishery research and *Providencia* on geophysical research. Both are operated by DIMAR, the naval authority in charge of hydrographic, pilotage, navigational and ports services. Painted white.

PROVIDENCIA   1992, Colombian Navy

Name	No	Builders	Commissioned
GORGONA	154 (ex-BO 161, ex-FB 161)	Lidingoverken, Sweden	1955

Displacement, tons: 574 full load
Dimensions, feet (metres): 135 × 29.5 × 9.3 *(41.2 × 9 × 2.8)*
Main machinery: 2 diesels; 910 hp(m) *(669 kW)*; 2 shafts
Speed, knots: 13
Complement: 17 (2 officers)

Comment: Paid off in 1982 but after a complete overhaul at Cartagena naval base was back in service in late 1992.

GORGONA   1993, Colombian Navy

Name	No	Builders	Commissioned
QUINDIO (ex-US YFR 443)	153	Niagara SB Corporation	11 Nov 1943

Displacement, tons: 380 light; 600 full load
Dimensions, feet (metres): 131 × 29.8 × 9 *(40 × 9.1 × 2.7)*
Main machinery: 2 Union diesels; 300 hp *(224 kW)*; 2 shafts
Speed, knots: 10
Complement: 17 (2 officers)

Comment: Transferred by lease in July 1964 and by sale on 31 March 1979.

QUINDIO   11/1990, Hartmut Ehlers

AUXILIARIES

1 TRANSPORT

Name	No	Builders	Commissioned
SAN ANDRES (ex-*Philip P*)	TM 60 (ex-BO 154)	H Rancke, Hamburg	1956

Measurement, tons: 680 dwt
Dimensions, feet (metres): 170.3 × 27.6 × 11.5 *(51.9 × 8.4 × 3.5)*
Main machinery: 1 diesel; 300 hp(m) *(220 kW)*; 1 shaft
Speed, knots: 9

Comment: Former Honduran coaster confiscated for smuggling and commissioned in the Navy in 1986. Used as a transport ship.

SAN ANDRES   10/1990, Hartmut Ehlers

2 TRANSPORTS

Name	No	Builders	Commissioned
HERNANDO GUTIERREZ	BD 35 (ex-TF 52)	Ast Naval, Cartagena	1955
SOCORRO (ex-*Alberto Gomez*)	BD 33	Ast Naval, Cartagena	1956

Displacement, tons: 70
Dimensions, feet (metres): 82 × 18 × 2.8 *(25 × 5.5 × 0.9)*
Main machinery: 2 GM diesels; 260 hp *(194 kW)*; 2 shafts
Speed, knots: 9. **Range, miles:** 650 at 9 kts
Complement: 12 plus berths for 48 troops and medical staff
Guns: 2—12.7 mm MGs.

Comment: River transports. Named after Army officers. *Socorro* was converted in July 1967 into a floating surgery. *Hernando Gutierrez* was converted into a dispensary ship in 1970.

HERNANDO GUTIERREZ   10/1990, Hartmut Ehlers

3 TENDERS

3 TENDERS

TOLÚ TM 44   **FILOGONIO HICHAMÓN** NF 141
SERRANILLA TM 45

Comment: Captured drug running vessels of various characteristics and now 'poachers turned gamekeepers'. *Tolú* is used as a diving tender.

TOLÚ   10/1990, Hartmut Ehlers

8 MORROSQUILLO (LCU 1466A) CLASS (TRANSPORTS)

MORROSQUILLO	TM 246	BAHIA SOLANO	TM 251
URABA	TM 247	BAHIA CUPICA	TM 252
BAHIA HONDA	TM 248	BAHIA UTRIA	TM 253
BAHIA PORTETE	TM 249	BAHIA MALAGA	TM 254

Displacement, tons: 347 full load
Dimensions, feet (metres): 119 × 34 × 6 *(36.3 × 10.4 × 1.8)*
Main machinery: 3 Detroit 6-71 diesels; 522 hp *(389 kW)* sustained; 3 shafts
Speed, knots: 7. **Range, miles:** 700 at 7 kts
Complement: 14
Cargo capacity: 167 tons or 300 troops
Guns: 2—12.7 mm MGs.

Comment: Former US Army craft built in 1954 and transferred in 1991 and 1992 with new engines. Used as inshore transports. Speed quoted is fully laden.

MORROSQUILLO   1993

1 DEPOT SHIP

MAYOR JAIME ARIAS DF 141 (ex-170)

Displacement, tons: 700

Comment: Capacity of 165 tons, length 140 ft *(42.7 m)*. Used as a non self-propelled depot ship for the midget submarines.

MAYOR JAIME ARIAS (old number)   *10/1990, Hartmut Ehlers*

FLOATING DOCKS

Comment: The 6700 ton *Rodriguez Zamora* (ex-ARD 28), the small floating dock *Manuel Lara*, the floating workshop *Mantilla* (ex-YR 66) purchased April 1979 and the repair craft *Victor Cubillos* (ex-USS YFND 6) purchased on 31 March 1978, are in use by Compania Colombiana de Astilleros Limitada (CONASTIL), Cartagena which is the former dockyard owned by the Navy.

TUGS

CAPITAN CASTRO RR 81   **CAPITAN VLADIMIR VALEK** RR 87
CAPITAN ALVARO RUIZ RR 84   **TENIENTE LUIS BERNAL BAQUERO** RR 88
CAPITAN RIGOBERTO GIRALDO RR 86

Displacement, tons: 50
Dimensions, feet (metres): 63 × 14 × 2.5 *(19.2 × 4.3 × 0.8)*
Main machinery: 2 GM diesels; 260 hp *(194 kW)*; 2 shafts
Speed, knots: 9

TENIENTE SORZANO (ex-USS YTL 231) RR 73

Displacement, tons: 54
Dimensions, feet (metres): 65.7 × 17.5 × 9 *(20 × 5.3 × 2.7)*
Main machinery: 6-cyl diesel; 240 hp(m) *(176 kW)*; 1 shaft
Speed, knots: 9

Comment: Formerly on loan—purchased on 31 March 1978. Dockyard tug at CONASTIL, Cartagena.

IGARAPARANA LR 92   **MANACASIAS** LR 95

Displacement, tons: 104 full load
Dimensions, feet (metres): 102.4 × 23.6 × 2.8 *(31.2 × 7.2 × 0.9)*
Main machinery: 2 Detroit 4-71 diesels; 330 hp *(238 kW)* sustained; 2 shafts
Speed, knots: 7. **Range, miles:** 1600 at 7 kts
Complement: 7 (1 officer)

Comment: River tugs built by Servicio Naviero Armada R de Colombia at Puerto Leguizamo. Completed June 1985 (LR 92) and June 1986 (LR 95). Used to transport materials to places difficult to reach by road.

MANACASIAS   *1988, Juan Mazuero*

TENIENTE MIGUEL SILVA RR 89   **NÉSTOR ORPINA** RR 90

Dimensions, feet (metres): 73.3 × 17.5 × 3 *(22.4 × 5.3 × 0.9)*
Main machinery: 2 diesels; 260 hp *(194 kW)*; 2 shafts
Speed, knots: 9

Comment: River tugs built by Union Industrial (UNIMAL), Barranquilla.

SEGERI RM 93   **INIRIDA** RR 96   **JOSUÉ ALVAREZ** RM 76
MITU RR —   **CALIMA** RM —

Comment: Probably captured drug running vessels. Characteristics unknown.

CUSTOMS (ADUANAS)

Note: Pennant numbers are in the 200 series.

Name	No	Builders	Commissioned
OLAYA HERRERA	AN 201	Swiftships, Berwick	16 Oct 1981

Displacement, tons: 103 full load
Dimensions, feet (metres): 105 × 22 × 7 *(31.5 × 6.7 × 2.1)*
Main machinery: 4 MTU 12V 331 TC92 diesels; 5320 hp *(3.97 MW)*; 4 shafts
Speed, knots: 25. **Range, miles:** 1200 at 18 kts
Complement: 19
Guns: 1 Bofors 40 mm/60. 2—12.7 mm MGs.

Comment: Badly damaged in 1986 but repaired and brought back into service in 1991. Sister craft *Castillo y Rada* transferred to the Navy.

Name	No	Builders	Commissioned
CARLOS ALBAN	AN 208	Rauma Repola, Finland	1971

Displacement, tons: 130 full load
Dimensions, feet (metres): 108 × 18 × 5.9 *(33 × 5.5 × 1.8)*
Main machinery: 2 MTU diesels; 2500 hp(m) *(1.84 MW)*; 2 shafts; cp props
Speed, knots: 17
Complement: 20
Guns: 2 Oerlikon 20 mm.

Comment: Similar to Finnish Ruissalo class. Acquired in 1980. Second of class deleted in 1990.

TRAINING SHIP

Name	No	Builders	Commissioned
GLORIA	—	AT Celaya, Bilbao	May 1969

Displacement, tons: 1150 full load
Dimensions, feet (metres): 249.3 oa; 211.9 wl; × 34.8 × 21.7 *(76; 64.6 × 10.6 × 6.6)*
Main machinery: 1 auxiliary diesel; 530 hp(m) *(389 kW)*; 1 shaft
Speed, knots: 10.5
Complement: 51 (10 officers) plus 88 trainees

Comment: Sail training ship. Barque rigged. Hull is entirely welded. Sail area, 1675 sq yards *(1400 sq m)*. Endurance, 60 days.

GLORIA   *11/1990, Hartmut Ehlers*

COMORO ISLANDS

General	Base	Mercantile Marine
Three of the four main islands of this group joined in a unilateral Declaration of Independence in July 1975. This has been legitimised by France.	Moroni.	*Lloyd's Register of Shipping:* 5 vessels of 1897 tons gross

PATROL FORCES

2 YAMAYURI CLASS

Name	No	Builders	Commissioned
KARTHALA	—	Ishihara Dockyard Co Ltd	Oct 1981
NTRINGUI	—	Ishihara Dockyard Co Ltd	Oct 1981

Displacement, tons: 26.5 standard; 41 full load
Dimensions, feet (metres): 59 × 14.1 × 3.6 *(18 × 4.3 × 1.1)*
Main machinery: 2 Nissan RD10TA06 diesels; 900 hp(m) *(661 kW)* maximum; 2 shafts
Speed, knots: 20
Complement: 6
Guns: 2—12.7 mm (twin) MGs.

Comment: These two patrol vessels of the 18M type (steel-hulled) supplied under Japanese Government co-operation plan. Used for fishery protection services.

KARTHALA   *10/1981, Ishihara DY*

CONGO

Senior Officer

Head of the Navy:
Captain Jean-Felix Ongouya

General

The People's Republic of Congo became independent on 15 August 1960 and formed a naval service.

Personnel

(a) 1994: 300 officers and men
(b) Voluntary service

Base

Pointe-Noire.

Mercantile Marine

Lloyd's Register of Shipping:
25 vessels of 9533 tons gross

DELETIONS

1990-91   3 Shanghai II class

PATROL FORCES

3 ZHUK (TYPE 1400M) CLASS

301   302   303

Displacement, tons: 39 full load
Dimensions, feet (metres): 78.7 × 16.4 × 3.9 *(24 × 5 × 1.2)*
Main machinery: 2 M 401B diesels; 2200 hp(m) *(1.6 MW)* sustained; 2 shafts
Speed, knots: 30. **Range, miles:** 1100 at 15 kts
Complement: 11 (3 officers)
Guns: 4—14.5 mm (2 twin) MGs.
Radars: Surface search: Spin Trough; I band.

Comment: Transferred from USSR in 1982. Three more were expected in 1984 but did not materialise.

ZHUK   *1987*

4 ARCO RIVER PATROL CRAFT

Comment: Two of 42.6 ft *(13 m)* and two of 37.4 ft *(11.4 m)* with Volvo Penta diesels. Delivered 1982. Used for river patrols together with a number of small boats with outboard motors.

3 PIRAÑA CLASS (FAST ATTACK CRAFT—PATROL)

Name	No	Builders	Commissioned
MARIEN N'GOUABI (ex-*L'Intrepide*)	P 601	Bazán, Cadiz	16 Mar 1983
LES TROIS GLORIEUSES (ex-*Le Vaillant*)	P 602	Bazán, Cadiz	28 Mar 1983
LES MALOANGO (ex-*Le Terrible*)	P 603	Bazán, Cadiz	28 Mar 1983

Displacement, tons: 140 full load
Dimensions, feet (metres): 107.3 × 20.2 × 5.1 *(32.7 × 6.2 × 1.6)*
Main machinery: 2 MTU 12V 538 TB92 diesels; 5110 hp(m) *(3.76 MW)* sustained; 2 shafts
Speed, knots: 28. **Range, miles:** 700 at 17 kts
Complement: 19 (3 officers)
Guns: 1 Breda 40 mm/70; 85° elevation; 300 rounds/minute to 12.5 km *(6.8 nm)*; weight of shell 0.96 kg.
1 Oerlikon 20 mm. 2—12.7 mm MGs.
Fire control: CSEE Panda optronic director.
Radars: Navigation: Decca; I band.

Comment: Ordered in 1980. Steel hulls. Derivative of Barcelo class. All were officially commissioned on arrival at Pointe-Noire 3 April 1983. All probably unserviceable.

MARIEN N'GOUABI   *1983, Bazán*

TUG

HINDA

Displacement, tons: 200 full load
Dimensions, feet (metres): 96.8 × — × 12.5 *(29.5 × — × 3.8)*
Main machinery: 1 MGO diesel; 900 hp(m) *(661 kW)*; 1 shaft
Speed, knots: 11
Complement: 16

Comment: Ordered from La Manche, St Malo. Laid down 16 February 1981, launched 31 March 1981, completed 3 October 1981.

COOK ISLANDS

General

A group of islands which is self-governing in free association with New Zealand. Defence is the responsibility of New Zealand in consultation with the islands' government.

PATROL FORCES

1 PACIFIC FORUM TYPE
(LARGE PATROL CRAFT)

Name	Builders	Commissioned
TE KUKUPA	Australian Shipbuilding Industries	1 Sep 1989

Displacement, tons: 162 full load
Dimensions, feet (metres): 103.3 × 26.6 × 6.9 *(31.5 × 8.1 × 2.1)*
Main machinery: 2 Caterpillar 3516TA diesels; 2820 hp *(2.1 MW)* sustained; 2 shafts
Speed, knots: 20. **Range, miles:** 2500 at 12 kts
Complement: 17 (3 officers)
Radars: Surface search: Furuno 1011; I band.

Comment: Laid down 16 May 1988 and launched 27 January 1989. Cost, training and support provided by Australia under Defence Co-operation. Acceptance date was 9 March 1989 but the handover was deferred another six months because of the change in local government. Has Furuno D/F equipment, SATNAV and a seaboat with a 40 hp outboard engine.

TE KUKUPA   *10/1991, John Mortimer*

COSTA RICA

Personnel

(a) 1994: 160 officers and men
(b) Voluntary service

Bases

Golfito, Puntarenas, Puerto Limon

Mercantile Marine

Lloyd's Register of Shipping:
19 vessels of 7570 tons gross

PATROL FORCES

1 CAPE CLASS (LARGE PATROL CRAFT)

Name	No	Builders	Commissioned
ASTRONAUTA FRANKLIN CHANG	95-1	Coast Guard Yard, Curtis Bay	5 Dec 1958
(ex-*Cape Henlopen*)			

Displacement, tons: 98 standard; 148 full load
Dimensions, feet (metres): 94.8 × 20.3 × 6.6 *(28.9 × 6.2 × 2)*
Main machinery: 2 Detroit 16V-149TI diesels; 2070 hp *(1.54 MW)* sustained; 2 shafts
Speed, knots: 20. **Range, miles:** 2500 at 10 kts
Complement: 14 (1 officer)
Guns: 2—12.7 mm MGs.
Radars: Surface search: Raytheon SPS 64(V)1; I band.

Comment: Transferred from US Coast Guard 28 September 1989 after a refit by Bender SB and Repair Co. Painted white.

ASTRONAUTA FRANKLIN CHANG   *1989, Bender SB & R Co*

1 SWIFT 105 ft CLASS (FAST PATROL CRAFT)

ISLA DEL COCO 1055

Displacement, tons: 118 full load
Dimensions, feet (metres): 105 × 23.3 × 7.2 *(32 × 7.1 × 2.2)*
Main machinery: 3 MTU 12V 1163 TC92 diesels; 10 530 hp(m) *(7.74 MW)*; 3 shafts
Speed, knots: 33. **Range, miles:** 1200 at 18 kts; 2000 at 12 kts
Complement: 21 (3 officers)
Guns: 1—12.7 mm MG. 4—7.62 mm (2 twin) MGs. 1—60 mm mortar.
Radars: Navigation: Decca RM 916; I band.

Comment: Built by Swiftships, Morgan City in 1978. Refitted in 1985-86 under FMS funding. The twin MGs are fitted abaft the bridge and the mortar is on the stern.

ISLA DEL COCO   *2/1989*

1 POINT CLASS (COASTAL PATROL CRAFT)

— (ex-*Point Hope*)

Displacement, tons: 67 full load
Dimensions, feet (metres): 83 × 17.2 × 5.8 *(25.3 × 5.2 × 1.8)*
Main machinery: 2 Cummins diesels; 1600 hp *(1.19 MW)*; 2 shafts
Speed, knots: 23. **Range, miles:** 1500 at 8 kts
Complement: 10
Guns: 2—12.7 mm MGs.
Radars: Navigation: Raytheon SPS 64; I band.

Comment: Transferred from USCG 3 May 1991.

POINT class (US colours)   *10/1991, Giorgio Arra*

4 SWIFT 65 ft CLASS (COASTAL PATROL CRAFT)

CABO VELAS 656		CABO BLANCO 658	
ISLA UVITA 657		PUNTA BURICA 659	

Displacement, tons: 35 full load
Dimensions, feet (metres): 65.5 × 18.4 × 6.6 *(20 × 5.6 × 2)*
Main machinery: 2 MTU 8V 331 TC92 diesels; 1770 hp(m) *(1.3 MW)*; 2 shafts
Speed, knots: 23. **Range, miles:** 500 at 18 kts
Complement: 7 (2 officers)
Guns: 1—12.7 mm MG. 4—7.62 mm (2 twin) MGs. 1—60 mm mortar.
Radars: Navigation: Decca RM 916; I band.

Comment: Built by Swiftships, Morgan City in 1979. Refitted 1985-86 under FMS funding.

ISLA UVITA   *12/1987*

8 BOSTON WHALERS

181-188

Comment: The survivors of 13 delivered in 1983. Craft of 18 ft with 70 hp *(52 kW)* outboard engines.

BOSTON WHALER   *1988*

2 SWIFT 36 ft CLASS (INSHORE PATROL CRAFT)

TELAMANCA 361   **CARIARI** 362

Displacement, tons: 11 full load
Dimensions, feet (metres): 36 × 10 × 2.6 *(11 × 3.1 × 0.8)*
Main machinery: 2 Detroit diesels; 500 hp *(373 kW)*; 2 shafts
Speed, knots: 24. **Range, miles:** 250 at 18 kts
Complement: 4 (1 officer)
Guns: 1—12.7 mm MG. 1—60 mm mortar.

Comment: Built by Swiftships, Morgan City in 1986.

CARIARI   *1991*

1 SWIFT 42 ft CLASS (INSHORE PATROL CRAFT)

DONNA MARGARITA (ex-*Puntarena*) 421

Displacement, tons: 11 full load
Dimensions, feet (metres): 42 × 14.1 × 3 *(12.8 × 4.3 × 0.9)*
Main machinery: 2 Detroit 8V-92TA diesels; 700 hp *(522 kW)*; 2 shafts
Speed, knots: 33. **Range, miles:** 300 at 30 kts; 450 at 18 kts.
Complement: 4 (1 officer)

Comment: Built by Swiftships, Morgan City in 1986. The original name has been changed and she is now used as a hospital ship with armament removed.

DONNA MARGARITA   *1989*

CROATIA

Flag Officers

Commander-in-Chief:
Vice Admiral Sveto Letica
Deputy Commander and Chief of Staff:
Vice Admiral Carlo Grbac

General

The Navy was established on 11 September 1991. Ships captured from the Yugoslav federation form the bulk of the Fleet. The main task is the control and protection of territorial waters; border guard duties are left to police multipurpose craft.

Personnel

1994: 1080 (100 officers)

Bases and Organisation

Headquarters: Lora-Split.
Main bases: Sibenik, Split, Pula, Ploce.
There are three coastal command sectors: North Adriatic, North Dalmatia and South Dalmatia. Radar surveillance stations and coastal batteries are established on key islands and peninsulas. All the bases and naval installations of the former federal Navy have been taken over with the exception of those in the Bay of Cattaro.

Naval Infantry

Headquarters in Split. Companies deployed to Pula, Losinj, Zadar, Sibenik, Brac, Peljesac, Korcula, Dubrovnik and Jelsa (Hvar).

Mercantile Marine

Lloyd's Register of Shipping:
224 vessels of 192 682 tons gross

SUBMARINES

Note: Two Mala class Swimmer Delivery Vehicles were captured and are in use.

0 + 2 MIDGET SUBMARINES

Displacement, tons: 98 dived
Dimensions, feet (metres): 73.8 × 8.9 × 11.2 *(22.5 × 2.7 × 3.4)*
Speed, knots: 6
Complement: 7 (1 officer)

Comment: A new class reported building at Brodosplit in mid-1993. Exit/re-entry capability. Can carry two Mala class Swimmer Delivery Vehicles (SDV) or sea mines. Diving depth, 200 m *(656 ft)*. This appears to be a follow-on to the Una class with a longer hull possibly to take a diesel engine for recharging the batteries at sea.

1 UNA CLASS (MIDGET SUBMARINE)

SOCA (ex-914)

Displacement, tons: 76 surfaced; 88 dived
Dimensions, feet (metres): 61.7 × 9 × 8.2 *(18.8 × 2.7 × 2.5)*
Main machinery: 2 motors; 68 hp(m) *(50 kW)*; 1 shaft
Speed, knots: 6 surfaced; 8 dived. **Range, miles:** 200 at 4 kts
Complement: 6
Sonars: Atlas Elektronik; passive/active search; high frequency.

Comment: Building yard, Split. First of class commissioned May 1985. Exit/re-entry capability with mining capacity. Can carry six combat swimmers, plus four Swimmer Delivery Vehicles (SDV) and limpet mines. Diving depth, 105 m *(345 ft)*. Batteries can only be charged from shore or from a depot ship. The other five of the class are in the Yugoslav Navy.

CORVETTES

1 + 1 (2) KRALJ (TYPE 400) CLASS

Name	No	Builders	Commissioned
KRALJ PETAR KRESIMIR IV	11	Kraljevica Shipyard	1993
(ex-*Sergej Masera*)			
—	12	Kraljevica Shipyard	1994

Displacement, tons: 385 full load
Dimensions, feet (metres): 175.9 × 27.9 × 7.5 *(53.6 × 8.5 × 2.3)*
Main machinery: 3 M 504B-2 diesels; 12 500 hp(m) *(9.2 MW)* sustained; 3 shafts
Speed, knots: 36. **Range, miles:** 1500 at 20 kts
Complement: 33 (5 officers)

Missiles: SSM: 4 or 8 Saab RBS 15 (2 or 4 twin); active radar homing to 70 km *(37.8 nm)* at 0.8 Mach; warhead 150 kg. Mine rails removed if 8 are carried.
Guns: 1 Bofors 57 mm/70; 75° elevation; 200 rounds/minute to 17 km *(9.3 nm)*; weight of shell 2.4 kg. Launchers for illuminants on side of mounting.
1—30 mm/65 AK 630; 6 barrels; 85° elevation; 3000 rounds/minute combined to 2 km.
2 Oerlikon 20 mm or 2—12.7 mm MGs.
Mines: 4 AIM-70 magnetic or 6 SAG-1 acoustic.
Countermeasures: Decoys: Wallop Barricade chaff/IR launcher.
Fire control: BEAB 9LV 249 Mk 2 director.
Radars: Surface search: Racal BT 502; E/F band.
Fire control: BEAB 9LV 249 Mk 2; I/J band.
Navigation: Racal 1290A; I band.
Sonars: RIZ PP10M; hull-mounted; active search; high frequency.

KRALJ PETAR KRESIMIR IV   *5/1993, L Poggiali*

Programmes: The building of this class (formerly called Kobra) was officially announced as 'suspended' in 1989 but was restarted in 1991. First of class launched 21 March 1992. Projected numbers are uncertain after the first two. Designated as a missile Gunboat.
Structure: Derived from the Koncar class with a stretched hull and a new superstructure. Mine rails may be removed in favour of increasing SSM capability to eight missiles once the missiles have been acquired. There may also be a small mine detection high frequency active sonar.
Operational: *Kresimir IV* reported badly damaged in July 1993 when an SA-N-5 missile blew up during ammunition loading.

PATROL FORCES

Note: In addition to the listed vessels, there are large numbers of high-speed small craft and rubber boats, many civilian manned but naval controlled. Some have machine guns and rocket launchers.

1 KONČAR (TYPE 240) CLASS (FAST ATTACK CRAFT—MISSILE)

Name	No	Builders	Commissioned
SIBENIC (ex-*Vlado Cvetkovič*)	21 (ex-402)	Tito SY, Kraljevica	Mar 1978

Displacement, tons: 242 full load
Dimensions, feet (metres): 147.6 × 27.6 × 8.2 *(45 × 8.4 × 2.5)*
Main machinery: CODAG; 2 RR Proteus gas-turbines; 7200 hp *(5.37 MW)* sustained; 2 MTU 20V 538 TB92 diesels; 8530 hp(m) *(6.27 MW)* sustained; 4 shafts
Speed, knots: 39. **Range, miles:** 500 at 35 kts; 880 at 23 kts (diesels)
Complement: 30 (5 officers)

Missiles: SSM: 2 SS-N-2B Styx; active radar or IR homing to 46 km *(25 nm)* at 0.9 Mach; warhead 513 kg. May be replaced by RBS-15.
Guns: 1 Bofors 57 mm/70; 75° elevation; 200 rounds/minute to 17 km *(9.3 nm)*; weight of shell 2.4 kg. 128 mm rocket launcher for illuminants.
1—30 mm/65 AK 630; 6 barrels; 85° elevation; 3000 rounds/minute to 2 km.
Countermeasures: Decoys: Wallop Barricade double layer chaff launcher.
Fire control: PEAB 9LV 200 GFCS.
Radars: Surface search: Decca 1226; I band.
Fire control: Philips TAB; I/J band.

Programmes: Type name, Raketna Topovnjaca. A second of this class may have been captured, but this is not confirmed. Five others of the class serve with the Yugoslav Navy.
Structure: Aluminium superstructure. Designed by the Naval Shipping Institute in Zagreb based on Swedish Spica class with bridge amidships like Malaysian boats. The after 57 mm gun has been replaced by a 30 mm AK 630.

SIBENIC   *6/1993, L Poggiali*

2 OSA I (TYPE 205) CLASS (FAST ATTACK CRAFT—MISSILE)

DUBROVNIK (ex-*Mitar Acev*) 41 (ex-301)	VELIMIR ŠKORPIK 42 (ex-310)

Displacement, tons: 171 standard; 210 full load
Dimensions, feet (metres): 126.6 × 24.9 × 8.8 *(38.6 × 7.6 × 2.7)*
Main machinery: 3 Type M 503A diesels; 8025 hp(m) *(5.9 MW)* sustained; 3 shafts
Speed, knots: 35. **Range, miles:** 400 at 34 kts
Complement: 30 (4 officers)

Missiles: SSM: 4 SS-N-2A Styx; active radar or IR homing to 46 km *(25 nm)* at 0.9 Mach; warhead 513 kg.
Guns: 4 USSR 30 mm/65 (2 twin); 85° elevation; 500 rounds/minute to 5 km *(2.7 nm)*; weight of shell 0.54 kg.
Radars: Surface search: Square Tie; I band.
Fire control: Drum Tilt; H/I band.
IFF: High Pole. 2 Square Head.

Programmes: Type name, Raketni Čamac. Ex-USSR vessels captured from the Yugoslav Navy which still has several others.
Operational: *Dubrovnik* was badly damaged and nearly scrapped, but eventually repaired at Sibenik navy yard.

OSA 1 (Yugoslav colours)   *1982*

1 SHERSHEN (TYPE 201) CLASS
(FAST ATTACK CRAFT—TORPEDO)

VUKOVAR (ex-*Partizan III*) 51

Displacement, tons: 145 standard; 170 full load
Dimensions, feet (metres): 113.8 × 22.3 × 4.9 *(34.7 × 6.7 × 1.5)*
Main machinery: 3 M 503A diesels; 8025 hp(m) *(5.9 MW)* sustained; 3 shafts
Speed, knots: 45. **Range, miles:** 850 at 30 kts
Complement: 23
Guns: 4 USSR 30 mm/65 (2 twin); 85° elevation; 500 rounds/minute to 5 km *(2.7 nm)*; weight of shell 0.54 kg.
Torpedoes: 4—21 in *(533 mm)* tubes. Soviet Type 53.
Mines: 6.
Radars: Surface search: Pot Head; I band.
Fire control: Drum Tilt; H/I band.
IFF: High Pole. Square Head.

Comment: Built under licence by Tito Shipyard, Kraljevica. Type name, Torpedni Čamac. Four others still in service with Yugoslav Navy.

SHERSHEN (German colours)   *10/1989, Gilbert Gyssels*

3 MIRNA (TYPE 140) CLASS (FAST ATTACK CRAFT—PATROL)

SOLTA (ex-*Kozolo*) 62 (ex-181)	HRVATSKA KOSTAJNICA (ex-*Cer*) 63 (ex-180)
BIOKOVO 64 (ex-171)	

Displacement, tons: 120 full load
Dimensions, feet (metres): 104.9 × 22 × 7.5 *(32 × 6.7 × 2.3)*
Main machinery: 2 SEMT-Pielstick 12 PA4 200 VGDS diesels; 5292 hp(m) *(3.89 MW)* sustained; 2 shafts
Speed, knots: 30. **Range, miles:** 400 at 20 kts
Complement: 19 (3 officers)
Missiles: SAM: 1 SA-N-5 Grail quad mounting; manual aiming; IR homing to 6 km *(3.2 nm)* at 1.5 Mach; altitude to 2500 m *(8000 ft)*; warhead 1.5 kg.
Guns: 1 Bofors 40 mm/70. 1 Oerlikon 20 mm. 2—128 mm illuminant launchers.
Depth charges: 8 rails.
Sonars: Simrad SQS 3D/SF; active high frequency.

Comment: Builders, Kraljevica Yard. Commissioned 1981-85. A most unusual feature of this design is the fitting of an electric outboard motor giving a speed of up to 6 kts. Two were captured after sustaining heavy damage, one by a missile fired from Brac island and the other by a torpedo. Both fully repaired. *Biokovo* may have been renamed.

HRVATSKA KOSTAJNICA   *8/1992*

RIVER PATROL CRAFT (PB)

Comment: A number of naval tenders has been converted to serve as river patrol vessels, some of them heavily armed. The two shown below have a Bofors 40 mm/70 gun forward and a quadruple 12.7 mm MG aft.

PB 91   *1993, S S Breyer collection*

PB 92   *1993, S S Breyer collection*

2 GALEB CLASS (RIVER PATROL CRAFT)

CISTA VELIKA   **+ 1**

Displacement, tons: 19.5 full load
Dimensions, feet (metres): 55.4 × 12.8 × 2.3 *(16.9 × 3.9 × 0.7)*
Main machinery: 2 diesels; 330 hp(m) *(242 kW)*; 2 shafts
Speed, knots: 16. **Range, miles:** 160 at 12 kts
Complement: 6
Guns: 1 Oerlikon 20 mm; 2—7.62 mm MGs.
Radars: Surface search: Racal Decca 110; I band.

Comment: Commissioned in August 1992 for use in shallow water. Steel hulls with GRP
    superstructure.

MINE WARFARE FORCES

Note: The former federal Navy retained the whole inventory of mines.

1 SIRIUS CLASS (MINEHUNTER)

Name	No	Builders	Commissioned
VUKOV KLANAC (ex-*Hrabri*)	M 151 (ex-D 25)	A Normand, France	Sep 1957

Displacement, tons: 365 standard; 424 full load
Dimensions, feet (metres): 152 × 28 × 8.2 *(46.4 × 8.6 × 2.5)*
Main machinery: 2 SEMT-Pielstick PA1 175 diesels; 1620 hp(m) *(1.19 MW)*; 2 shafts
Speed, knots: 15. **Range, miles:** 3000 at 10 kts
Complement: 40
Guns: 2 Oerlikon 20 mm.
Countermeasures: MCMV: PAP 104; remote-controlled submersibles.
Radars: Navigation: Thomson-CSF DRBN 30; I band.
Sonars: Plessey Type 193M; hull-mounted; active minehunting; high frequency.

Comment: Built as a US 'off-shore' order and converted to a minehunter in 1981. Upper deck
    extensively damaged in November 1991, but has been repaired.

VUKOV KLANAC   *10/1990, Eric Grove*

1 HAM CLASS (MINESWEEPER—INSHORE)

IZ M 144

Displacement, tons: 120 standard; 159 full load
Dimensions, feet (metres): 106.5 × 21.3 × 5.5 *(32.5 × 6.5 × 1.7)*
Main machinery: 2 Paxman YHAXM diesels; 1100 hp *(821 kW)*; 2 shafts
Speed, knots: 14. **Range, miles:** 2000 at 9 kts
Complement: 22
Guns: 2 Oerlikon 20 mm (twin).

Comment: Built in Yugoslavia 1964-66 to a British design under the US Military Aid Programme.
    Wooden hull. Two others in service with the Yugoslav Navy.

AMPHIBIOUS FORCES

1 SILBA CLASS (LCT/MINELAYER)

Name	No	Builders	Launched	Commissioned
CETINA (ex-*Rab*)	81	Brodosplit, Split	18 July 1992	19 Feb 1993

Displacement, tons: 880 full load
Measurement, tons: 163.1 oa; 144 wl × 33.5 × 8.5 *(49.7; 43.9 × 10.2 × 2.6)*
Main machinery: 2 Alpha 10V23L-VO diesels; 3100 hp(m) *(2.28 MW)* sustained; 2 shafts; cp
    props
Speed, knots: 12. **Range, miles:** 1200 at 12 kts
Complement: 33 (3 officers)
Military lift: 460 tons or 6 medium tanks or 7 APCs or 4—130 mm guns plus towing vehicles or
    300 troops with equipment
Missiles: SAM: 1 SA-N-5 Grail quad mounting.
Guns: 4—30 mm/65 (2 twin) AK 230. 4—20 mm M75 (quad). 2—128 mm illuminant launchers.
Mines: 94 Type SAG-1.
Radars: Surface search: I band.

Comment: Ro-Ro design with bow and stern ramps. Can be used for minelaying, transporting
    weapons or equipment and personnel. This is the second of class, the first being commissioned
    in 1990 into the Yugoslav Navy.

SILBA (Yugoslav colours)   *1990*

3 MFPD-3 (DTM) TYPE + 1 DSM 501 TYPE (LCTs/MINELAYERS)

JASTREB   **DSM 501**   **+ 2**

Displacement, tons: 410 full load
Dimensions, feet (metres): 155.1 × 21 × 7.5 *(47.3 × 6.4 × 2.3)*
Main machinery: 3 Gray Marine 64 HN9 diesels; 495 hp *(369 kW)*; 3 shafts
Speed, knots: 9
Complement: 15
Military lift: 200 troops or 3 heavy tanks
Guns: 2—12.7 mm MGs.
Mines: Can carry 100.

Comment: Unlike other tank landing craft in that the centre part of the bow drops to form a ramp
    down which the tanks go ashore, the vertical section of the bow being articulated to form outer
    end of ramp. Built in Yugoslavia. Can also act as minelayers. DTM (Desantni Tenkonosac/
    Minopolagac) means landing ship tank/minelayer). Four of the class operate with the Yugoslav
    Navy.

JASTREB   *10/1990, Eric Grove*

3 TYPE 22 (LCUs)

Displacement, tons: 48 full load
Dimensions, feet (metres): 73.2 × 15.7 × 3.3 *(22.3 × 4.8 × 1)*
Main machinery: 2 MTU diesels; 1740 hp(m) *(1.28 MW)*; 2 waterjets
Speed, knots: 35. **Range, miles:** 320 at 22 kts
Complement: 8
Military lift: 40 troops or 15 tons cargo
Guns: 2—20 mm M71. 1—30 mm Grenade launcher.
Radars: Navigation: Decca 101; I band.

Comment: Built of polyester and glass fibre. Last one completed in 1987. A total of 12 built with
    numbers DJC 620-632.

TYPE 22   *1989*

4 TYPE 21 (LCUs)

Displacement, tons: 32 full load
Dimensions, feet (metres): 69.9 × 15.7 × 5.2 *(21.3 × 4.8 × 1.6)*
Main machinery: 1 diesel; 1450 hp(m) *(1.07 MW)*; 1 shaft
Speed, knots: 23. **Range, miles:** 320 at 22 kts
Complement: 6
Military lift: 6 tons
Guns: 1—20 mm M71. 2—30 mm Grenade launchers.

Comment: Built between 1976 and 1979. Two more were damaged and may be repaired. A total
    of 18 of the class were produced with numbers DJC 601-620. All captured in 1991.

TYPE 21   *5/1993, L Poggiali*

2 TYPE 11 (LCVP)

Displacement, tons: 10 full load
Dimensions, feet (metres): 37 × 10.2 × 1.6 *(11.3 × 3.1 × 0.5)*
Main machinery: 2 diesels; 2 waterjets
Speed, knots: 23. **Range, miles:** 100 at 15 kts
Complement: 2
Military lift: 4.8 tons of equipment or troops
Guns: 1—7.62 mm MG.

Comment: GRP construction built in late 1980s. Both captured in 1991.

SURVEY SHIP

1 MOMA (TYPE 861) CLASS (AGS)

Name	No	Builders	Commissioned
ANDRIJA MOHOROVIČIČ	PH 33	Northern Shipyard, Gdansk	1972

Displacement, tons: 1200 standard; 1475 full load
Dimensions, feet (metres): 240.5 × 33.5 × 12.8 *(73.3 × 10.2 × 3.9)*
Main machinery: 2 Zgoda-Sulzer 6TD48 diesels; 3300 hp(m) *(2.4 MW)* sustained; 2 shafts; cp props
Speed, knots: 15. **Range, miles:** 9000 at 12 kts
Complement: 37 (4 officers)
Radars: Navigation: Don 2; I band.

Comment: Built in 1971 for the Yugoslav Navy.

ANDRIJA MOHOROVIČIČ   *1982*

AUXILIARIES

Note: In addition there are two harbour tugs LR 71 and LR 73 captured from the Yugoslav Navy in 1991.

1 SPASILAC CLASS (ASR)

SPASILAC (ex-PS 12)

Displacement, tons: 1590 full load
Dimensions, feet (metres): 182 × 39.4 × 14.1 *(55.5 × 12 × 4.3)*
Main machinery: 2 diesels; 4340 hp(m) *(3.19 MW)*; 2 shafts; Kort nozzle props; bow thruster
Speed, knots: 13. **Range, miles:** 4000 at 12 kts
Complement: 53 plus 19 spare berths

Comment: Built at Tito SY, Belgrade. In service 10 September 1976. Fitted for firefighting and fully equipped for salvage work. Decompression chamber, and can support a manned rescue submersible. Can be fitted with two quadruple M 75 and two single M 71 20 mm guns. Sister ship in Libyan Navy.

SPASILAC   *1988*

1 PO TYPE (AET)

PO 51

Displacement, tons: 700
Main machinery: 2 Burmeister and Wain diesels; 600 hp(m) *(440 kW)*; 2 shafts
Speed, knots: 16
Complement: 43
Cargo capacity: 150 troops plus all types of ammunition

Comment: Built at Split in 1950s. Ammunition transport vessel.

1 HARBOUR TANKER

(ex-*PN 25*)

Displacement, tons: 430 full load
Dimensions, feet (metres): 151 × 23.6 × 10.2 *(46 × 7.2 × 3.1)*
Main machinery: 1 diesel; 300 hp(m) *(220 kW)*; 1 shaft
Speed, knots: 7

Comment: Built at Split in mid-1950s.

1 PT 71 TYPE (TRANSPORT)

MEDUZA (ex-PT 71)

Displacement, tons: 428 full load
Dimensions, feet (metres): 152.2 × 23.6 × 17.1 *(46.4 × 7.2 × 5.2)*
Main machinery: 1 Burmeister & Wain diesel; 300 hp(m) *(220 kW)*; 1 shaft
Speed, knots: 7

Comment: Built in 1953. Second of class in Yugoslav Navy.

CUBA

General

As a separate organisation the Navy was in disarray by early 1994. Most ships lack spares and fuel and seldom go to sea, and at least half are in a state where they are unlikely to become operational again.

Command Organisation

Territorial:
  Western Naval District (HQ Cabanas).
  Eastern Naval District (HQ Holguin).
Operational:
  Missile Boat Flotilla, Torpedo Boat Flotilla, ASW Flotilla, Mine Warfare Division. These are deployed in whole or part amongst the Territorial Flotillas. Submarine Flotilla is based at Cienfuegos. Guard Flotilla consists of 1000 marines.

Bases

Cabanas, Nicaro, Cienfuegos, Havana, Mariel, Punta Ballenatos, Varadero, Canasi.

Mercantile Marine

Lloyd's Register of Shipping:
  382 vessels of 625 962 tons gross

SUBMARINES

3 FOXTROT (TYPE 641) CLASS

725   727   729

Displacement, tons: 1950 surfaced; 2475 dived
Dimensions, feet (metres): 299.5 × 24.6 × 19.7 *(91.3 × 7.5 × 6)*
Main machinery: Diesel-electric; 3 Type 37-D diesels; 6000 hp(m) *(4.4 MW)*; 3 motors; (1 × 2700, 2 × 1350); 5400 hp(m) *(3.97 MW)*; 3 shafts; 1 auxiliary motor; 140 hp(m) *(103 kW)*
Speed, knots: 16 surfaced; 15 dived; 9 snorting
Range, miles: 20 000 at 8 kts surfaced; 380 at 2 kts dived
Complement: 75

Torpedoes: 10—21 in *(533 mm)* (6 bow, 4 stern) tubes. 22 Soviet Type 53; dual purpose; pattern active/passive homing up to 20 km *(10.8 nm)* at up to 45 kts; warhead 400 kg.
Mines: 44 in lieu of torpedoes.
Radars: Surface search: Snoop Tray; I band.
Sonars: Herkules/Feniks hull-mounted; active/passive search and attack; high frequency.

Programmes: First arrived from USSR 7 February 1979, second in January 1980 and third on 7 February 1984.
Structure: Diving depth, 250 m *(820 ft)* reducing with age.
Operational: *725* started a five year refit in Havana in March 1986 which completed in 1992. *727* started a similar refit in July 1989. None of these submarines was seen at sea in 1993 and all are probably non-operational.

FOXTROT 729   *1991*

FRIGATES

3 KONI CLASS

350   356   383 (ex-*353*)

Displacement, tons: 1440 standard; 1900 full load
Dimensions, feet (metres): 316.3 × 41.3 × 11.5
(96.4 × 12.6 × 3.5)
Main machinery: CODAG; 1 SGW, Nikolayev, M8B gas-turbine
(centre shaft); 18 000 hp(m) *(13.25 MW)* sustained; 2 Russki
B-68 diesels; 15 820 hp(m) *(11.63 MW)* sustained; 3 shafts
Speed, knots: 27 gas; 22 diesel. **Range, miles:** 1800 at 14 kts
Complement: 110

Missiles: SAM: SA-N-4 Gecko twin launcher ❶; semi-active
radar homing to 15 km *(8 nm)* at 2.5 Mach; height envelope
9-3048 m *(29.5-10 000 ft)*; warhead 50 kg; magazine silo
holds missiles. Some anti-surface capability.
Guns: 4 USSR 3 in *(76 mm)*/60 (2 twin) ❷; 80° elevation; 90
rounds/minute to 15 km *(8 nm)*; weight of shell 6.8 kg.
4 USSR 30 mm/65 (2 twin) (353 and 356) ❸; 85° elevation;
500 rounds/minute to 5 km *(2.7 nm)* anti-aircraft; weight of
shell 0.54 kg.
2—6-barrelled Gatlings (350 only); 3000 rounds/minute combined to 2 km anti-missile.
A/S mortars: 2 RBU 6000 12-tubed trainable launchers ❹; range
6000 m; warhead 31 kg.
Depth charges: 2 rails.
Mines: Can lay 22 mines.
Countermeasures: Decoys: 2—16-barrelled chaff launchers.
ESM: Watch Dog; radar warning.
Radars: Air search: Strut Curve ❺; F band; range 110 km *(60 nm)*
for 2 m² target.
Navigation: Don 2; I band.
Fire control: Hawk Screech ❻; I band; range 27 km *(15 nm)*.
Drum Tilt ❼; H/I band.
Pop Group ❽; F/H/I band (for SAM).
IFF: Two Square Head. High Pole A.
Sonars: Hull-mounted; active search and attack; medium
frequency.

Programmes: First transferred from USSR 24 September 1981;
second 8 February 1984; third 10 April 1988. These ships have
no names. Based at Cienfuegos. *353* was redesignated *383* in
October 1988.
Structure: Similar to the Algerian Konis.

KONI   *(Scale 1 : 900), Ian Sturton*

KONI 353 (old number)   *3/1988, van Boeijen*

CORVETTE

1 PAUK II CLASS

321

Displacement, tons: 520 full load
Dimensions, feet (metres): 195.2 × 33.5 × 11.2 *(59.5 × 10.2 × 3.4)*
Main machinery: 2 Type M 507 diesels; 14 400 hp(m) *(10.6 MW)* sustained; 2 shafts
Speed, knots: 32. **Range, miles:** 2200 at 18 kts
Complement: 32

Missiles: SAM: SA-N-5 quad launcher; manual aiming, IR homing to 10 km *(5.4 nm)* at 1.5 Mach;
warhead 1.1 kg.
Guns: 1 USSR 76 mm/60; 85° elevation; 120 rounds/minute to 7 km *(3.8 nm)*; weight of shell
16 kg.
1—30 mm/65; 6 barrels; 3000 rounds/minute combined to 2 km.
Torpedoes: 4—21 in *(533 mm)* (2 twin) tubes. Soviet type 53; active/passive homing up to 20 km
(11 nm) at up to 45 kts; warhead 400 kg.
A/S mortars: 2 RBU 1200 5-tubed fixed; range 1200 m; warhead 34 kg.
Countermeasures: 2—16-tubed chaff launchers.
Radars: Air/surface search: Positive E; E/F band.
Navigation: Pechora; I band.
Fire control: Bass Tilt; H/I band.
Sonars: Rat Tail; VDS (on transom); attack; high frequency.

Programmes: Built at Yaroslav Shipyard in the USSR and transferred in May 1990. Similar to the
ships built for India.
Structure: Has a longer superstructure than the Pauk I and new electronics with a radome similar
to the Parchim II class.

PAUK II (Russian number)   *1991, van Ginderen Collection*

PATROL FORCES

5 OSA I and 13 OSA II CLASS (TYPE 205)
(FAST ATTACK CRAFT—MISSILE)

251-255 (Osa I)
212, 225, 256-262, 267, 268, 271, 274 (Osa II)

Displacement, tons: 171 standard; 210 full load (Osa I); 245 full load (Osa II)
Dimensions, feet (metres): 126.6 × 24.9 × 8.8 *(38.6 × 7.6 × 2.7)*
Main machinery: 3 Type M 503A diesels; 8025 hp(m) *(5.9 MW)* sustained; 3 shafts (Osa I); 3 Type
M 504 diesels; 10 800 hp(m) *(7.94 MW)* sustained; 3 shafts (Osa II)
Speed, knots: 35 (Osa I); 37 (Osa II)
Range, miles: 400 at 34 kts (Osa I); 500 at 35 kts (Osa II)
Complement: 30
Missiles: SSM: 4 SS-N-2 Styx; active radar or IR homing to 46 km *(25 nm)* at 0.9 Mach; warhead
513 kg.
Guns: 4—30 mm/65 (2 twin); 80° elevation; 500 rounds/minute to 5 km *(2.7 nm)*; weight of shell
0.54 kg.
Radars: Surface search: Square Tie; I band.
Fire control: Drum Tilt; H/I band.
IFF: Square Head. High Pole A (Osa I). High Pole B (Osa II).

Comment: Two boats of Osa I class were transferred to Cuba from the USSR in January 1972 and
three in 1973. These were followed by one Osa I and one Osa II in mid-1976, one Osa II in January 1977 and one Osa II in March 1978. Further two Osa II delivered in December 1978, one in
April 1979, one in October 1979, two from Black Sea November 1981, four in February 1982.
One Osa I deleted in 1981. Most are non-operational.

OSA I 252   *1988*

9 TURYA CLASS (FAST ATTACK CRAFT—HYDROFOIL)

101   102   108   112   130   165   178   180   193

Displacement, tons: 190 standard; 250 full load
Dimensions, feet (metres): 129.9 × 24.9 (41 over foils) × 5.9 (13.1 over foils)
(39.6 × 7.6 (12.5) × 1.8 (4))
Main machinery: 3 Type M 504 diesels; 10 800 hp(m) *(7.94 MW)* sustained; 3 shafts
Speed, knots: 40 foilborne. **Range, miles:** 600 at 35 kts foilborne; 1450 at 14 kts
Complement: 30
Missiles: SAM: SA-N-5 Grail; IR homing to 6 km *(3.2 nm)* at 1.5 Mach; warhead 1.5 kg.
Guns: 2—57 mm/80 (twin, aft); 85° elevation; 120 rounds/minute to 6 km *(3.3 nm)*; weight of
shell 2.8 kg.
2—25 mm/80 (twin, fwd); 85° elevation; 270 rounds/minute to 3 km *(1.6 nm)*; weight of shell
0.34 kg.
Torpedoes: 4—21 in *(533 mm)* tubes (some). 4 Soviet Type 53; dual purpose; pattern active/
passive homing up to 20 km *(10.8 nm)* at up to 45 kts; warhead 400 kg.
Radars: Surface search: Pot Drum; H/I band.
Fire control: Muff Cob; G/H band.
IFF: High Pole. Square Head.
Sonars: May have helicopter type VDS.

Comment: Transferred from USSR February 1979 (first pair); February 1980 (second pair); from
the Pacific 17 February 1981 (third pair); 9 January 1983 (fourth pair); 13 November 1983 (single craft). All of the class in reserve in early 1994.

TURYA 102   *1988*

LAND-BASED MARITIME AIRCRAFT

Numbers/Type: 4 Kamov Ka-28 ('Helix A').
Operational speed: 135 kts *(250 km/h)*.
Service ceiling: 19 685 ft *(6000 m)*.
Range: 432 nm *(800 km)*.
Role/Weapon systems: Probably intended as replacements for the Haze. Delivered in 1988. Sen-
sors: Search radar, dipping sonar, sonobuoys, MAD, ECM. Weapons: 3 torpedoes, depth bombs,
mines.

Numbers/Type: 6 Mikoyan MiG-29 Fulcrum.
Operational speed: 1320 kts *(1520 mph)*.
Service ceiling: 56 000 ft *(17 000 m)*.
Range: 1130 nm *(2100 km)*.
Role/Weapon systems: Air force manned air defence or ground attack fighters acquired with two
training aircraft in 1989. Sensors: Pulse Doppler radar, IR scanner, laser rangefinder. Weapons:
1 × 30 mm cannon; 6 × AA-10 or AA-11.

MINE WARFARE FORCES

4 SONYA CLASS (MINESWEEPERS/HUNTERS)

560   561   570   578

Displacement, tons: 450 full load
Dimensions, feet (metres): 157.4 × 28.9 × 6.6 *(48 × 8.8 × 2)*
Main machinery: 2 Kolomna Type 9-D-8 diesels; 2000 hp(m) *(1.47 MW)* sustained; 2 shafts
Speed, knots: 15. **Range, miles:** 3000 at 10 kts
Complement: 43
Guns: 2—30 mm/65 (twin); 85° elevation; 500 rounds/minute to 5 km *(2.7 nm)*; weight of shell
0.54 kg.
2—25 mm/80 (twin); 85° elevation; 270 rounds/minute to 3 km *(1.6 nm)*.
Mines: Can carry 8.
Radars: Navigation: Don 2; I band.
IFF: Two Square Head. High Pole B.

Comment: Transferred from USSR August, December 1980, January and December 1985. First
two are probably non-operational.

SONYA (Russian number)   *5/1990*

12 YEVGENYA CLASS (MINEHUNTERS—INSHORE)

501, 502, 504, 507, 509, 510-514, 531, 538

Displacement, tons: 77 standard; 90 full load
Dimensions, feet (metres): 80.7 × 18 × 4.9 *(24.6 × 5.5 × 1.5)*
Main machinery: 2 Type 3-D-12 diesels; 600 hp(m) *(440 kW)* sustained; 2 shafts
Speed, knots: 11. **Range, miles:** 300 at 10 kts
Complement: 10
Guns: 2—14.5 mm (twin) MGs.
Countermeasures: Minehunting gear is lowered on a crane at the stern.
Radars: Navigation: Don 2; I band.

Comment: First pair transferred from USSR in November 1977, one in September 1978, two in
November 1979, two in December 1980, two from the Baltic on 10 December 1981, one in October 1982 and four on 1 September 1984. There are two squadrons, one central and one west. At
least six are non-operational having been cannibalised for spares.

YEVGENYA (Russian number)   *1990*

AMPHIBIOUS FORCES

2 POLNOCHNY B (TYPE 771) CLASS (LSM)

690   601

Displacement, tons: 760 standard; 834 full load
Dimensions, feet (metres): 246.1 × 31.5 × 7.5 *(75 × 9.6 × 2.3)*
Main machinery: 2 Kolomna Type 40-D diesels; 4400 hp(m) *(3.2 MW)* sustained; 2 shafts
Speed, knots: 19. **Range, miles:** 1000 at 18 kts
Complement: 40
Military lift: 350 tons including 6 tanks and 200 troops
Guns: 4—30 mm/65 (2 twin); 85° elevation; 500 rounds/minute to 5 km *(2.7 nm)*; weight of shell
0.54 kg.
2—140 mm rocket launchers; 18 tubes; range 9 km *(5 nm)*.
Radars: Navigation: Don 2 or Spin Trough; I band.
Fire control: Drum Tilt; H/I band.

Comment: Built at Northern Shipyard, Gdansk and transferred from USSR September/December
1982. *601* is providing spares for *690*.

SURVEY SHIPS

Note: In addition there are three other vessels: *Hatuey* H 107 of 430 tons, *Baconao* H 73 of
226 tons, and H 75 of 283 tons.

1 BIYA (TYPE 871) CLASS (AGS)

GUAMA H 103

Displacement, tons: 766 full load
Dimensions, feet (metres): 180.4 × 32.1 × 8.5 *(55 × 9.8 × 2.6)*
Main machinery: 2 diesels; 1200 hp(m) *(882 kW)*; 2 shafts; cp props
Speed, knots: 13. **Range, miles:** 4700+ at 11 kts
Complement: 29 (7 officers)
Radars: Navigation: Don 2; I band.

Comment: Has laboratory facilities, one survey launch and a five ton crane. Built in Poland and
acquired from USSR in 1970. Subordinate to Institute of Hydrography.

BIYA class   *1976*

SIBONEY H 101

Displacement, tons: 535 full load
Dimensions, feet (metres): 138.5 × 27.2 × 8.5 *(42.2 × 8.3 × 2.6)*
Main machinery: 2 diesels; 910 hp(m) *(669 kW)*; 2 shafts
Speed, knots: 11
Complement: 29 (7 officers)

Comment: An ex-fishing trawler/buoy tender also used for cadet training. Acquired from Spain in
1968.

TAINO H 102

Displacement, tons: 1123 full load
Dimensions, feet (metres): 173.9 × 34.1 × 11.5 *(53 × 10.4 × 3.5)*
Main machinery: 2 diesels; 1550 hp(m) *(1.14 MW)*; 2 shafts
Speed, knots: 12
Complement: 29 (7 officers)

Comment: Mostly used as a buoy tender. Acquired from Spain in 1979.

4 NYRYAT-1 CLASS

H 93-96

Displacement, tons: 125 full load
Dimensions, feet (metres): 93 × 18 × 5.5 *(28.4 × 5.5 × 1.7)*
Main machinery: 1 diesel; 450 hp(m) *(330 kW)*; 1 shaft
Speed, knots: 12.5
Complement: 15

Comment: Acquired from USSR in 1969. Mostly used for surveying. Two (*H 91-92*) deleted so far and the remainder are of doubtful operational status.

NYRYAT-1   1990

AUXILIARIES

Notes: (1) Tanker *Las Guasimas* of 8300 tons is capable of alongside refuelling. Civilian manned.
(2) Chemical tanker *Capitan Olo Pantoja* converted to carry oil fuel.

1 ARMINZA CLASS (AGI)

ISLA DE LA JUVENTUD

Measurement, tons: 1556 gross
Dimensions, feet (metres): 230 × 41.3 × 17.7 *(70 × 12.6 × 5.4)*
Main machinery: 1 diesel; 2200 hp(m) *(1.62 MW)*; 1 shaft
Speed, knots: 13

Comment: Ex-trawler used as an intelligence collection ship since 1982.

ISLA DE LA JUVENTUD   7/1984, US Navy

1 POLUCHAT 1 CLASS

RT 84

Displacement, tons: 100 full load
Dimensions, feet (metres): 97.1 × 19 × 4.8 *(29.6 × 5.8 × 1.5)*
Main machinery: 2 Type M 50 diesels; 2200 hp(m) *(1.6 MW)* sustained; 2 shafts
Speed, knots: 20. **Range, miles:** 1500 at 10 kts
Complement: 15
Guns: 4—14.7 mm (2 twin) MGs.

Comment: Used as a torpedo recovery vessel. Others of the class have been cannibalised for spares.

1 PELYM CLASS (DEGAUSSING SHIP)

ADG 40

Displacement, tons: 1300 full load
Dimensions, feet (metres): 214.8 × 38 × 11.2 *(65.5 × 11.6 × 3.4)*
Main machinery: 2 diesels; 2400 hp(m) *(1.76 MW)*; 2 shafts
Speed, knots: 14
Complement: 70

Comment: Built in USSR in mid-1970s. Transferred in 1982.

1 YELVA CLASS (DIVING TENDER)

B-015

Displacement, tons: 300 full load
Dimensions, feet (metres): 134.2 × 26.2 × 6.6 *(40.9 × 8 × 2)*
Main machinery: 2 Type 3-D-12 diesels; 600 hp(m) *(440 kW)* sustained; 2 shafts
Speed, knots: 12.5
Complement: 30
Radars: Navigation: Spin Trough; I band.

Comment: Built in early 1970s, transferred from USSR 1973. Two 1.5 ton cranes.

YELVA class   1973

4 OREL CLASS (SALVAGE TUGS)

R 21   R 23   R 27   R 29

Displacement, tons: 1750 full load
Dimensions, feet (metres): 201.2 × 39.2 × 14.8 *(61.4 × 12 × 4.5)*
Main machinery: 1 diesel; 1700 hp(m) *(1.25 MW)*; 1 shaft
Speed, knots: 15. **Range, miles:** 14 000 at 13.5 kts
Complement: 40

Comment: Built in Finland in the late 1950s. Probably acquired from Russian Ministry of Fisheries.

BORDER GUARD

Note: Operates under the Ministry of the Interior at a higher state of readiness than the Navy. Pennant numbers painted in red.

3 STENKA CLASS (FAST ATTACK CRAFT—PATROL)

Displacement, tons: 211 standard; 253 full load
Dimensions, feet (metres): 129.3 × 25.9 × 8.2 *(39.4 × 7.9 × 2.5)*
Main machinery: 3 Type M 517 diesels; 14 100 hp(m) *(10.4 MW)*; 3 shafts
Speed, knots: 37. **Range, miles:** 800 at 24 kts; 500 at 35 kts
Complement: 25 (5 officers)
Guns: 4—30 mm/65 (2 twin) AK 230; dual purpose; 85° elevation; 500 rounds/minute to 5 km *(2.7 nm)*; weight of shell 0.54 kg.
Radars: Surface search: Pot Drum; H/I band.
Fire control: Muff Cob; G/H band.
IFF: High Pole. Square Head.

Comment: Similar to class operated by Russian border guard with torpedo tubes and sonar removed. Transferred from USSR in February 1985 (two) and August 1985 (one).

STENKA   1990

27 ZHUK CLASS (FAST ATTACK CRAFT—PATROL)

Displacement, tons: 39 full load
Dimensions, feet (metres): 78.7 × 16.4 × 3.9 *(24 × 5 × 1.2)*
Main machinery: 2 Type M 401B diesels; 2200 hp(m) *(1.6 MW)* sustained; 2 shafts
Speed, knots: 30. **Range, miles:** 1100 at 15 kts
Complement: 11 (3 officers)
Guns: 4—14.5 mm (2 twin) MGs.
Radars: Surface search: Spin Trough; I band.

Comment: A total of 40 acquired since 1971. Last batch of two arrived December 1989. Some transferred to Nicaragua. The total has been reduced to allow for wastage. In some of the class the after gun has been removed.

ZHUK   1990

CYPRUS, Republic

Senior Officer

Chief of Navy:
Captain J Vragalis, HN

Personnel

1994: 320

General

In November 1983 Turkey set up an independent republic in the northern part of the island. Subsequently the UN declared this to be illegal. At least one unit of the Turkish Navy, *Caner Gönyeli* (P 145), is permanently based at Kyrenia (Girne) as are units of the Turkish Coast Guard flying the North Cyprus flag. For details of these vessels see Turkey section.

Base

Limassol

Mercantile Marine

Lloyd's Register of Shipping:
1416 vessels of 20 385 718 tons gross

PATROL FORCES

1 MODIFIED PATRA CLASS

Name	No	Builders	Commissioned
SALAMIS	P 01	Chantiers de l'Esterel	24 May 1983

Displacement, tons: 98 full load
Dimensions, feet (metres): 105.3 × 21.3 × 5.9 *(32.1 × 6.5 × 1.8)*
Main machinery: 2 SACM 195 CZSHRY12 diesels; 4680 hp(m) *(3.44 MW)* sustained; 2 shafts
Speed, knots: 30. **Range, miles:** 1200 at 15 kts
Complement: 22

Guns: 1 Breda 40 mm/70; 85° elevation; 300 rounds/minute to 12.5 km *(6.8 nm)* anti-surface; weight of shell 0.96 kg.
1 Rheinmetall Wegmann 20 mm. 2—12.7 mm MGs.
Radars: Surface search: I band.

Comment: Laid down in December 1981, completed in 1983 for Naval Command of National Guard.

SALAMIS

1992, Cyprus Navy

LAND-BASED MARITIME AIRCRAFT

Numbers/Type: 1 Pilatus Britten-Norman Maritime Defender.
Operational speed: 150 kts *(280 km/h)*.
Service ceiling: 18 900 ft *(5760 m)*.
Range: 1500 nm *(2775 km)*.
Role/Weapon systems: Operated around southern coastline of Cyprus to prevent smuggling and terrorist activity. Sensors: Search radar, searchlight mounted on wings. Weapons: ASV; various machine gun pods and rockets.

POLICE

2 POSEIDON CLASS

Name	No	Builders	Commissioned
POSEIDON	PV 20	Brodotehnika SY, Belgrade	21 Nov 1991
EVAGORAS	PV 21	Brodotehnika SY, Belgrade	21 Nov 1991

Displacement, tons: 57 full load
Dimensions, feet (metres): 80.7 × 18.7 × 3.9 *(24.6 × 5.7 × 1.2)*
Main machinery: 2 MTU 12V 396 TE94 diesels; 4270 hp(m) *(3.14 MW)*; 2 KaMeWa 56 waterjets
Speed, knots: 42. **Range, miles:** 600 at 20 kts
Complement: 9
Guns: 1 Breda KVA 25 mm; ISBRS rocket launcher. 2—12.7 mm MGs.
Radars: Surface search: I band.

Comment: Designated as FAC-23 Jets. Aluminium construction.

1 PLASCOA TYPE

Name	No	Builders	Commissioned
KINON	PL 2	C N de l'Esterel	1982

Displacement, tons: 28 full load
Dimensions, feet (metres): 62.3 × 17.1 × 4.3 *(19 × 5.2 × 1.3)*
Main machinery: 2 Poyaud V12 diesels; 2 shafts
Speed, knots: 26
Complement: 8
Guns: 1—12.7 mm MG.

Comment: GRP hull. Second of class deleted in 1991.

5 SAB 12 TYPE

ex-*G 50/GS 10*   ex-*G 52/GS 25*   ex-*G 54/GS 27*   ex-*G 55/GS 12*   ex-*G 57/GS 28*

Comment: Harbour patrol craft of the former GDR MAB 12 class transferred in December 1992.

POSEIDON

4/1993, Marine Police

SAB 12 (German colours)

10/1991, Hartmut Ehlers

DENMARK

Headquarters' Appointment

Flag Officer Denmark:
Rear Admiral K E J Borck
Inspector Naval Home Guard
Captain S V Andersen

Diplomatic Representation

Defence Attaché, Bonn and The Hague:
Colonel S S Jensen (Army)
Defence Attaché, London and Dublin:
Captain S Lund
Defence Attaché, Stockholm, Helsinki, Tallinn and Riga:
Commander N Friis
Defence Attaché, Warsaw and Vilnius:
Colonel C Barløse (Army)
Defence Attaché, Washington and Ottawa:
Brigadier E Lyngbye (Air Force)
Defence Attaché, Paris:
Colonel M Christensen (Air Force)
Defence Attaché, Moscow and Kiev:
Colonel S V Fandrup (Army)

Personnel

(a)   1994: 1006 officers, 2963 regular ratings,
800 national service ratings.
Reserves: 5500.
Naval Home Guard: 4030.
(b)   9 months' national service

Bases

Korsør (Corvettes, FACs, Stanflex), Frederikshavn (Submarines, MCMV, Fishery Protection Ships), Grønnedal (Greenland)

Naval Air Arm

Naval helicopters owned and operated by Navy in naval squadron based at Värlöse near Copenhagen. All servicing and maintenance by air force. LRMP are flown by the Air Force.

Naval Home Guard

Established in 1952. Duties include guarding naval installations, surveillance, harbour patrol and search and rescue operations.

Coast Defence

There are forts at Stevns and Langeland (on southern approaches to Sound and Great Belt) armed with 150 mm and 40 mm guns. Six radar stations and a number of coast watching stations in the area. There are also two mobile batteries planned to be operational in 1994. Linked by a Terma command and control system they will each consist of three trailers, one for command and two for carrying Harpoon missiles taken from deleted frigates.

Command and Control

It was originally the intention to have all government vessels under The Directorate of Waters (Farvandsdirektoratet). However the Ministry of Trade and Shipping now runs the icebreakers and some training ships (the icebreakers are maintained by the Navy and are based at Frederikshavn in the Summer) while the Ministry of the Environment (Miljøministeriet) controls two environmental protection divisions based at Copenhagen (being phased out) and Korsør (both manned and maintained by the Navy). Survey ships are run by the Farvandsdirektoratet Nautisk Afdeling (Administration of Navigation and Hydrography) under the Ministry of Defence and the Ministry of Fisheries has four rescue vessels and an Osprey class.

Appearance

Ships are painted in six different colours as follows:
Grey: Frigates, corvettes and patrol frigates.
Olive-green: FACs and tankers.
Black: Submarines.
Orange: Survey Vessels.
White: The Royal Yacht and the Sail Training Yawls.
Black/yellow: Service Vessels, tugs and ferryboats.

Prefix to Ships' Names

HDMS

Mercantile Marine

Lloyd's Register of Shipping:
1066 vessels of 5 292 732 tons gross

Strength of the Fleet

Type	Active	Building (Projected)
Submarines (Coastal)	5	—
Frigates	8	—
Fast Attack Craft (Missile)	10	—
Large Patrol Craft	23	3
Coastal Patrol Craft	3	—
Naval Home Guard	37	12 (6)
Minelayers	6	—
Minesweepers (Coastal)	2	—
Minehunters (Drones)	2	(10)
Transport Ship	1	—
Tankers (Small)	2	—
Icebreakers	4	—
Royal Yacht	1	—
Tugs	2	—
TRVs	3	—
Survey Craft	6	—
Training Ships	5	—

DELETIONS

Frigates

1991   *Fylla*
1992   *Ingolf, Vaedderen* (old), *Hvidbjørnen* (old)

Patrol Forces

1992   *Dryaden, Najaden, Nymfen, Maagen, Mallemukken*

Naval Home Guard

1992   *Aldebaran* (old), *Andromeda* (old)
1993   *Aries* (old), *Carina* (old)
1994   *Dubhe* (old), *Gemini* (old)

Minesweepers

1991   *Guldborgsund*

Auxiliaries

1992   *Havørnen* (civilian)
1993   *Havørnen* (Namibia)

PENNANT LIST

Submarines

S 320	Narhvalen
S 321	Nordkaperen
S 322	Tumleren
S 323	Saelen
S 324	Springeren

Frigates

F 340	Beskytteren
F 354	Niels Juel
F 355	Olfert Fischer
F 356	Peter Tordenskiold
F 357	Thetis
F 358	Triton
F 359	Vaedderen
F 360	Hvidbjørnen

Patrol Forces

P 540	Bille
P 541	Bredal
P 542	Hammer
P 543	Huitfeld
P 544	Krieger
P 545	Norby
P 546	Rodsteen
P 547	Sehested
P 548	Suenson
P 549	Willemoes
P 550	Flyvefisken
P 551	Hajen
P 552	Havkatten
P 553	Laxen
P 554	Makrelen
P 555	Støren
P 556	Svaerdfisken
P 557	Glenten
P 558	Gribben
P 559	Lommen

P 560	Ravnen
P 561	Skaden (building)
P 562	Viben (building)
P 563	Søløven (building)
Y 300	Barsø
Y 301	Drejø
Y 302	Romsø
Y 303	Samsø
Y 304	Thurø
Y 305	Vejrø
Y 306	Farø
Y 307	Laesø
Y 308	Rømø
Y 343	Lunden
Y 386	Agdlek
Y 387	Agpa
Y 388	Tulugaq

Mine Warfare Forces

N 43	Lindormen
N 44	Lossen

N 80	Falster
N 81	Fyen
N 82	Møen
N 83	Sjaelland
M 574	Grønsund
M 578	Vilsund

Auxiliaries

A 540	Dannebrog
A 559	Sleipner
A 568	Rimfaxe
A 569	Skinfaxe
TO 8	Hugin
TO 9	Munin
TO 10	Mimer
—	MSA 4
Y 101	Svanen
Y 102	Thyra

SUBMARINES

2 NARHVALEN CLASS

Name	No	Builders	Laid down	Launched	Commissioned
NARHVALEN	S 320	Royal Dockyard, Copenhagen	16 Feb 1965	10 Sep 1968	27 Feb 1970
NORDKAPEREN	S 321	Royal Dockyard, Copenhagen	4 Mar 1966	18 Dec 1969	22 Dec 1970

Displacement, tons: 420 surfaced; 450 dived
Dimensions, feet (metres): 145.3 × 15 × 13.8 *(44.3 × 4.6 × 4.2)*
Main machinery: Diesel-electric; 2 MTU 12V 493 TY7; 2250 hp(m) *(1.62 MW)*; 1 motor; 1200 hp(m) *(882 kW)*; 1 shaft
Speed, knots: 12 surfaced; 17 dived
Complement: 21 (4 officers)

Torpedoes: 8—21 in *(533 mm)* bow tubes. Combination of FFV Type 61; wire-guided; passive homing to 25 km *(13.7 nm)* anti-surface at 45 kts; warhead 240 kg and FFV Type 41; anti-submarine; passive homing to 20 km *(10.8 nm)* at 25 kts; warhead 45 kg; no reloads.
Fire control: Signaal M8.
Radars: Surface search: Thomson-CSF Calypso; I band.
Sonars: Atlas Elektronik CSU 3-2; hull-mounted; active/passive search and attack; medium frequency.
PRS 3-4; passive ranging; part of CSU 3.

Programmes: These coastal submarines are similar to the West German Improved Type 205 and were built under licence at the Royal Dockyard, Copenhagen with modifications for Danish needs.

NARHVALEN

10/1990, Maritime Photographic

Modernisation: A programme has been approved for an equipment update similar to the Tumleren class to enable both submarines to serve until the end of the decade. Work started on

Narhvalen in late 1993 and is planned for *Nordkaperen* in mid-1995 and includes new periscopes, a Sagem optronic mast, ESM, radar and sonar.

3 TUMLEREN (KOBBEN) (TYPE 207) CLASS

Name	No	Builders	Laid down	Launched	Commissioned	Recommissioned
TUMLEREN (ex-Utvaer)	S 322	Rheinstahl-Nordseewerke, Emden	24 Mar 1965	30 July 1965	1 Dec 1965	20 Oct 1989
SAELEN (ex-Uthaug)	S 323	Rheinstahl-Nordseewerke, Emden	31 May 1965	3 Oct 1965	16 Feb 1966	5 Oct 1990
SPRINGEREN (ex-Kya)	S 324	Rheinstahl-Nordseewerke, Emden	26 May 1963	20 Feb 1964	15 Jan 1964	10 Oct 1991

Displacement, tons: 459 surfaced; 524 dived
Dimensions, feet (metres): 155.5 × 15 × 14
(47.4 × 4.6 × 4.3)
Main machinery: Diesel-electric; 2 MTU 12V 493 AZ80 diesels;
1200 hp(m) *(880 kW)*; 1 motor; 1700 hp(m) *(1.25 MW)*; 1
shaft
Speed, knots: 12 surfaced; 18 dived
Range, miles: 5000 at 8 kts snorting
Complement: 18 (5 officers)

Torpedoes: 8—21 in *(533 mm)* bow tubes. FFV Type 61; anti-
surface; wire-guided; passive homing to 25 km *(13.7 nm)* at
45 kts; warhead 240 kg.
Countermeasures: ESM: Racal/Sea Lion; radar warning.
Fire control: Terma TFCS.
Radars: Surface search: Terma; I band.
Sonars: Atlas Elektronik PSU 83; passive search and attack;
medium frequency.

Programmes: First two acquired from Norway in 1986 for modernisation; the third in late 1989. Have replaced Delfinen class.
Modernisation: Work done at Urivale Shipyard, Bergen between
1987 and 1991 included lengthening by 5.2 ft *(1.6 m)* (which
has increased displacement) and new communications, ESM,
navigation and fire-control equipment. New sonar fitted in
1992/93.

SPRINGEREN
1993, Royal Danish Navy

Structure: Diving depth, 200 m *(650 ft)*.
Operational: *Saelen* sank in the Kattegat while unmanned and
under tow in late 1990. Salvaged and repaired using spares
taken from the ex-Norwegian *Kaura*, which was purchased for
cannibalisation. Back in service in August 1993.

FRIGATES

3 NIELS JUEL CLASS

Name	No	Builders	Laid down	Launched	Commissioned
NIELS JUEL	F 354	Aalborg Vaerft	20 Oct 1976	17 Feb 1978	26 Aug 1980
OLFERT FISCHER	F 355	Aalborg Vaerft	6 Dec 1978	10 May 1979	16 Oct 1981
PETER TORDENSKIOLD	F 356	Aalborg Vaerft	3 Dec 1979	30 Apr 1980	2 Apr 1982

Displacement, tons: 1320 full load
Dimensions, feet (metres): 275.5 × 33.8 × 10.2
(84 × 10.3 × 3.1)
Main machinery: CODOG; 1 GE LM 2500 gas-turbine;
24 600 hp *(18.35 MW)* sustained; 1 MTU 20 V 956 TB82 die-
sel; 5210 hp(m) *(3.83 MW)* sustained; 2 shafts
Speed, knots: 28 (gas); 20 (diesel). **Range, miles:** 2500 at 18 kts
Complement: 98 (18 officers)

Missiles: SSM: 8 McDonnell Douglas Harpoon (2 quad) launchers ❶; active radar homing to 130 km *(70 nm)* at 0.9 Mach;
warhead 227 kg.
SAM: Raytheon NATO Sea Sparrow Mk 29 octuple launcher ❷;
semi-active radar homing to 14.6 km *(8 nm)* at 2.5 Mach; warhead 39 kg; 8 missiles.
2 quad RAM launchers to be fitted in due course.
Guns: 1 OTO Melara 3 in *(76 mm)*/62 compact ❸; 85° elevation;
85 rounds/minute to 16 km *(8.7 nm)* anti-surface; 12 km
(6.6 nm) anti-aircraft; weight of shell 6 kg.
4 Oerlikon 20 mm (one each side of the funnel and two abaft
the mast) ❹.
Depth charges: 1 rack.
Countermeasures: Decoys: 2 THORN EMI Sea Gnat 6-barrelled
chaff launchers ❺.
ESM: Racal Cutlass; radar warning.
Combat data systems: Ericsson EPLO action data automation;
Link 11. SATCOMs ❻ (not always fitted).
Fire control: Philips 9LV 200 Mk 2 GFCS with TV tracker. Rayth-
eon Mk 91 Mod 1 MFCS with two directors. Harpoon to 1A(V)
standard.
Radars: Air search: Plessey AWS 5 ❼; 3D; E/F band; range
155 km *(85 nm)* for 4 m² target. To be replaced by TST TRS-3.
Surface search: Philips 9GR 600 ❽; I band.
Fire control: Two Mk 95 ❾; I/J band (for SAM).
Philips 9LV 200 ❿; J band (for guns and SSM).
Navigation: Burmeister & Wain Elektronik Scanter Mil 009;
E/I band.
Sonars: Plessey PMS 26; hull-mounted; active search and attack;
10 kHz.

Programmes: YARD Glasgow designed the class to Danish
order.

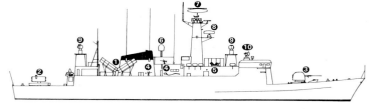

NIELS JUEL
(Scale 1 : 900), Ian Sturton

PETER TORDENSKIOLD
6/1993, Erik Laursen

Modernisation: A mid-life update is planned including 2 RAM
launchers, a 9LV Mk 3 combat data system and new communications. Air search radar is to be replaced by TST TRS-3D in
1994. The seaboat was replaced by a rigid inflatable type in
1989.

OLFERT FISCHER
5/1992, Gilbert Gyssels

4 THETIS CLASS

Name	No	Builders	Laid down	Launched	Commissioned
THETIS	F 357	Svenborg Vaerft	10 Oct 1988	14 July 1989	1 July 1991
TRITON	F 358	Svenborg Vaerft	27 June 1989	16 Mar 1990	2 Dec 1991
VAEDDEREN	F 359	Svenborg Vaerft	19 Mar 1990	21 Dec 1990	9 June 1992
HVIDBJØRNEN	F 360	Svenborg Vaerft	2 Jan 1991	11 Oct 1991	30 Nov 1992

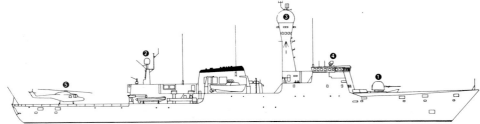

THETIS

(Scale 1 : 900), Ian Sturton

Displacement, tons: 2600 standard; 3500 full load
Dimensions, feet (metres): 369.1 oa; 327.4 wl × 47.2 × 19.7
(112.5; 99.8 × 14.4 × 6.0)
Main machinery: 3 MAN/Burmeister & Wain Alpha 12V 28/
32A diesels; 10 800 hp(m) *(7.94 MW)* sustained; 1 shaft; cp
prop; bow and azimuth thrusters; 880 hp(m) *(647 kW)*,
1100 hp(m) *(800 kW)*
Speed, knots: 20; 8 on thrusters. **Range, miles:** 8500 at 15.5 kts
Complement: 61 (11 officers) plus 12 spare berths

Guns: 1 OTO Melara 3 in *(76 mm)*/62; Super Rapid ❶; dual pur-
pose; 85° elevation; 120 rounds/minute to 16 km *(8.7 nm)*;
weight of shell 6 kg.
1 or 2 Oerlikon 20 mm.
Depth charges: 2 Rails (door in stern).
Countermeasures: ESM: Racal Cutlass; radar warning.
Combat data systems: Terma TDS; SATCOM ❷.
Fire control: Bofors 9LV 200 Mk 3 optronic director.
Radars: Air/surface search: Plessey AWS 6 ❸; G band; range
88 km *(48 nm)*.
Surface search: Terma Scanter Mil ❹; I band.
Navigation: Furuno FR1505DA; I band.
Fire control: Bofors Electronic 9LV 200; I/J band.
Sonars: Thomson Sintra TSM 2640 Salmon; hull-mounted and
VDS; active search and attack; medium frequency.

Helicopters: 1 Westland Lynx Mk 91 ❺.

Programmes: Preliminary study by YARD in 1986 led to Dwinger
Marine Consultants being awarded a contract for a detailed
design completed in mid-1987. All four ordered in October
1987.
Structure: The hull is some 30 m longer than the Hvidbjørnen
class to improve sea-keeping qualities and allow considerable
extra space for additional armament. The design allows the use
of containerised equipment to be shipped depending on role
and there is some commonality with the Flex 300 ships. Some
sensors have been transferred from the Hvidbjørnen class as
the latter paid off. The hull is ice strengthened to enable penetration of 1 m thick ice and efforts have been made to incorporate stealth technology, for instance by putting anchor
equipment, bollards and winches below the upper deck. There
is a double skin up to 2 m below the waterline. The flight deck
(28 × 14 m) is strengthened to take Sea King or Merlin helicopters. A rigid inflatable boarding craft plumbed by a hydraulic
crane is fitted alongside the fixed hangar. The bridge and ops
room are combined. *Thetis* has a modified stern for seismological equipment.
Operational: Primary role is fishery protection. *Thetis* is
employed for 3-4 months a year doing seismological surveys in

THETIS (modified stern)

7/1993, Hartmut Ehlers

the Greenland EEZ. A 4000 m towed array is used to receive
signals generated by pneumatic noise guns towed 800 m
astern.
Opinion: It seems likely that the built-in flexibility of the design
may allow the development of a fully armed frigate in due

course. The following systems have been considered: Harpoon, VLS Sea Sparrow, triple torpedo tubes, RAM PDMS,
SRBOC or Sea Gnat decoys, Nixie, fire-control radars and passive sonar towed array,

VAEDDEREN

12/1993, G Toremans

1 MODIFIED HVIDBJØRNEN CLASS

Name	No	Builders	Laid down	Launched	Commissioned
BESKYTTEREN	F 340	Aalborg Vaerft	11 Dec 1974	29 May 1975	27 Feb 1976

Displacement, tons: 1970 full load
Dimensions, feet (metres): 245 × 40 × 17.4
(74.7 × 12.2 × 5.3)
Main machinery: 3 MAN/Burmeister & Wain Alpha diesels;
7440 hp(m) *(5.47 MW)*; 1 shaft; cp prop
Speed, knots: 18. **Range, miles:** 4500 at 16 kts on 2 engines;
6000 at 13 kts on 1 engine
Complement: 67 (8 officers)

Guns: 1 USN 3 in *(76 mm)*/50; dual purpose.
Countermeasures: Decoys: THORN EMI Sea Gnat 6-barrelled
chaff launchers.
ESM: Racal Cutlass; radar warning.
Combat data systems: Terma TDS; SATCOM.
Radars: Air/surface search: Plessey AWS 6; G band.
Navigation: Burmeister & Wain Elektronik Scanter Mil 009; E/I
band.
Sonars: Plessey PMS 26; hull-mounted; active search and attack;
10 kHz.

Helicopters: 1 Westland Lynx Mk 91.

Modernisation: May be modernised in due course.
Structure: Strengthened for ice operations.
Operational: Used for fishery protection duties.

BESKYTTEREN

2/1991, Royal Danish Navy

PATROL FORCES

11 + 3 FLYVEFISKEN CLASS
(LARGE PATROL/ATTACK CRAFT AND MINEHUNTERS/LAYERS)

Name	No	Builders	Commissioned
FLYVEFISKEN	P 550	Danyard A/S, Aalborg	19 Dec 1989
HAJEN	P 551	Danyard A/S, Aalborg	19 July 1990
HAVKATTEN	P 552	Danyard A/S, Aalborg	1 Nov 1990
LAXEN	P 553	Danyard A/S, Aalborg	22 Mar 1991
MAKRELEN	P 554	Danyard A/S, Aalborg	1 Oct 1991
STØREN	P 555	Danyard A/S, Aalborg	24 Apr 1992
SVAERDFISKEN	P 556	Danyard A/S, Aalborg	1 Feb 1993
GLENTEN	P 557	Danyard A/S, Aalborg	29 Apr 1993
GRIBBEN	P 558	Danyard A/S, Aalborg	1 July 1993
LOMMEN	P 559	Danyard A/S, Aalborg	21 Jan 1994
RAVNEN	P 560	Danyard A/S, Aalborg	July 1994
SKADEN	P 561	Danyard A/S, Aalborg	Jan 1995
VIBEN	P 562	Danyard A/S, Aalborg	July 1995
SØLØVEN	P 563	Danyard A/S, Aalborg	Jan 1996

Displacement, tons: 450 full load
Dimensions, feet (metres): 177.2 × 29.5 × 8.2 *(54 × 9 × 2.5)*
Main machinery: CODAG; 1 GE LM 500 gas-turbine (centre shaft); 5450 hp *(4.1 MW)* sustained; 2 MTU 16V 396 TB94 diesels (outer shafts); 5800 hp(m) *(4.26 MW)* sustained; 3 shafts; cp props on outer shafts; bow thruster. Auxiliary propulsion by hydraulic motors on outer gearboxes; hydraulic pumps driven by 1 GM 12V-71 diesel; 500 hp *(375 kW)*
Speed, knots: 30; 20 on diesels; 10 on hydraulic propulsion. **Range, miles:** 2400 at 18 kts
Complement: 19-29 (depending on role)

Missiles: SSM: 8 McDonnell Douglas Harpoon; active radar homing to 130 km *(70 nm)* at 0.9 Mach; warhead 227 kg. Attack role only.
SAM: To be fitted for Attack, MCM and Minelaying roles.
Guns: 1 OTO Melara 3 in *(76 mm)*/62 Super Rapid; dual purpose; 85° elevation; 120 rounds/minute to 16 km *(8.7 nm)*; weight of shell 6 kg.
2—12.7 mm MGs.
Torpedoes: 2—21 in *(533 mm)* tubes; FFV Type 613; wire-guided passive homing to 15 km *(8.2 nm)* at 45 kts; warhead 240 kg. Attack role only.
Mines: 60. Minelaying role only.
Countermeasures: MCMV: Ibis 43 minehunting system with Thomson Sintra 2061 tactical system and 2054 sidescan sonar towed by SAV (see *Mine Warfare Forces* section). Bofors Double Eagle ROV. Minehunting role only.
Decoys: 2 Sea Gnat 6-barrelled launcher for chaff and IR flares.
ESM: Racal Sabre; radar warning.
Combat data systems: Terma/CelsiusTech.
Fire control: CelsiusTech 9LV Mk 3 optronic director. Harpoon to 1A(V) standard in attack role only.
Radars: Air/surface search: Plessey AWS 6; G band (P 550-P 556).
Telefunken SystemTechnik TRS-3D; G/H band (P 557-P 563).
Surface search: Terma Scanter Mil; I band.
Navigation: Furuno; I band.
Fire control: CelsiusTech 9LV 200; J band.
Sonars: CelsiusTech CTS-36; hull-mounted; active search; high frequency.
Thomson Sintra TSM 2640 Salmon; VDS; medium frequency. For ASW only.

Programmes: Standard Flex 300 which has replaced Daphne class (seaward defence craft) and Søløven class (fast attack craft torpedo), and will replace Sund (MCM) class. First batch of seven with option on a further nine contracted with Danyard on 27 July 1985. Second batch of six ordered 14 June 1990 and last one authorised in 1993. Building rate is two per year completing in 1996 with a total of 14 which is two less than originally planned.
Structure: GRP sandwich hulls. Four positions prepared to plug in armament and equipment containers in combinations meeting the requirements of the various roles. Torpedo tubes and mine-rails detachable. Combat data system modular with standard consoles of which three to six are embarked depending on the role. SAV control aerials are mounted on the bridge.
Operational: All vessels can be fitted out as patrol craft; the planned number of outfits for the other roles are: attack role 10; MCMV six; minelayer eight. In general outfits can be changed within a few hours. Outfits for non-military tasks such as pollution control and hydrographic survey have also been developed.

HAVKATTEN (Patrol)   *6/1992, Gunnar Olsen*

GLENTEN (with TRS-3D radar)   *6/1993, Royal Danish Navy*

MRD 2 (MCM DRONE)   *6/1993, Royal Danish Navy*

FLYVEFISKEN (MCM)   *8/1993, M Nitz*

HAJEN (Attack)   *1990, Royal Danish Navy*

10 WILLEMOES CLASS (FAST ATTACK CRAFT—MISSILE)

Name	No	Builders	Commissioned
BILLE	P 540	Frederikshavn V and F	1 Oct 1976
BREDAL	P 541	Frederikshavn V and F	21 Jan 1977
HAMMER	P 542	Frederikshavn V and F	1 Apr 1977
HUITFELD	P 543	Frederikshavn V and F	15 June 1977
KRIEGER	P 544	Frederikshavn V and F	22 Sep 1977
NORBY	P 545	Frederikshavn V and F	22 Nov 1977
RODSTEEN	P 546	Frederikshavn V and F	16 Feb 1978
SEHESTED	P 547	Frederikshavn V and F	19 May 1978
SUENSON	P 548	Frederikshavn V and F	10 Aug 1978
WILLEMOES	P 549	Frederikshavn V and F	21 June 1976

Displacement, tons: 260 full load
Dimensions, feet (metres): 151 × 24 × 8.2 *(46 × 7.4 × 2.5)*
Main machinery: CODOG; 3 RR 52M/544 gas-turbines; 12 750 hp *(9.51 MW)*; 2 GM 8V-71 diesels for cruising on wing shafts; 460 hp *(343 kW)* sustained; 3 shafts; cp props
Speed, knots: 38 (12 on diesels)
Complement: 25 (5 officers)

Missiles: SSM: 4 or 8 McDonnell Douglas Harpoon; active radar homing to 130 km *(70 nm)* at 0.9 Mach; warhead 227 kg.
Numbers carried depend on task and numbers of torpedoes.
Guns: 1 OTO Melara 3 in *(76 mm)*/62 compact; 85° elevation; 85 rounds/minute to 16 km *(8.7 nm)*; weight of shell 6 kg.
2 triple 103 mm illumination rocket launchers.
Torpedoes: 2 or 4—21 in *(533 mm)* tubes. FFV Type 61; wire-guided; passive homing to 25 km *(13.7 nm)* at 45 kts; warhead 240 kg.
Countermeasures: Decoys: Sea Gnat chaff dispensers.
ESM: Racal Cutlass; radar warning.
Combat data systems: EPLO action data automation. Being replaced by Terma.
Radars: Air/surface search: 9GA 208; E/F band.
Navigation: Terma Elektronik 20T 48 Super; E/I band.
Fire control: Philips 9LV 200; J band.

Programmes: Designed by Lürssen to Danish order. Very similar to Swedish Spica II class (also Lürssen). Original order to Frederikshavn for four boats, increased to eight and finally ten. *Willemoes* (prototype) laid down in July 1974.
Modernisation: *Norby* has conducted trials with a Simbad light SAM system fitted on the platform aft of the mast. It is reported that this may now be fitted in all of the class in due course probably starting in 1993. Sea Gnat decoy launchers were fitted in 1991/92, otherwise there are no further modernisation plans.
Operational: Patrols do not normally exceed 36 hours. The mix of weapons varies.

SEHESTED   5/1992, Antonio Moreno

RODSTEEN   8/1993, Erik Laursen

3 AGDLEK CLASS (LARGE PATROL CRAFT)

Name	No	Builders	Commissioned
AGDLEK	Y 386	Svendborg Vaerft	12 Mar 1974
AGPA	Y 387	Svendborg Vaerft	14 May 1974
TULUGAQ	Y 388	Svendborg Vaerft	26 June 1979

Displacement, tons: 300; 330 (Y 388) full load
Dimensions, feet (metres): 103 × 25.3 × 11.2 *(31.4 × 7.7 × 3.4)*
Main machinery: 1 Burmeister & Wain Alpha A08-26 VO diesel; 800 hp(m) *(588 kW)*; 1 shaft
Speed, knots: 12
Complement: 14
Guns: 2 Oerlikon 20 mm.
Radars: Surface search: Terma 20T 48 Super; E/I band.
Navigation: Skanter 009; I band.

Comment: Designed for service off Greenland. Ice strengthened. SATCOM fitted.

TULUGAQ   1990, Royal Danish Navy

9 Ø CLASS (LARGE PATROL CRAFT)

Name	No	Builders	Commissioned
BARSØ	Y 300	Svendborg Vaerft	13 June 1969
DREJØ	Y 301	Svendborg Vaerft	1 July 1969
ROMSØ	Y 302	Svendborg Vaerft	21 July 1969
SAMSØ	Y 303	Svendborg Vaerft	15 Aug 1969
THURØ	Y 304	Svendborg Vaerft	12 Sep 1969
VEJRØ	Y 305	Svendborg Vaerft	17 Oct 1969
FARØ	Y 306	Svendborg Vaerft	17 May 1973
LAESØ	Y 307	Svendborg Vaerft	23 July 1973
ROMØ	Y 308	Svendborg Vaerft	3 Sep 1973

Displacement, tons: 155 full load
Dimensions, feet (metres): 84 × 19.7 × 9.2 *(25.6 × 6 × 2.8)*
Main machinery: 1 diesel; 385 hp(m) *(283 kW)*; 1 shaft
Speed, knots: 11
Complement: 20
Guns: 2 Oerlikon 20 mm (not always fitted). 1—12.7 mm MG.
Radars: Navigation: Skanter 009; I band.

Comment: Rated as patrol cutters. *Laesø* acts as diver support ship with a recompression chamber. The last three have a wheelhouse which extends over the full beam.

DREJØ   9/1993, Erik Laursen

LAESØ (diver support)   1992, Royal Danish Navy

2 LARGE BOTVED TYPE (COASTAL PATROL CRAFT)

Y 375   Y 376

Displacement, tons: 12 (Y 376); 13.5 (Y 375) full load
Dimensions, feet (metres): 43.6 × 14.8 × 3.7 *(13.3 × 4.5 × 1.1)*
Main machinery: 2 diesels; 680 hp(m) *(500 kW)*; 2 shafts
Speed, knots: 26
Guns: 1—7.62 mm MG
Radars: Navigation: NWS 3; I band.

Comment: Built in 1974 by Botved Boats. Y 375 is 45.9 ft *(14 m)* in length overall having a stern ladder extension for divers.

Y 376   *1988, Royal Danish Navy*

1 Y TYPE (COASTAL PATROL CRAFT)

LUNDEN Y 343

Displacement, tons: 71.5 full load
Dimensions, feet (metres): 64.6 × 17.7 × 9.2 *(19.7 × 5.4 × 2.8)*
Speed, knots: 8
Guns: 1—7.62 mm MG.

Comment: Cutter of a similar type to trawlers MHV 51 and 76, built in 1941.

LUNDEN   *1988, Royal Danish Navy*

SHIPBORNE AIRCRAFT

Numbers/Type: 9 Westland Lynx Mk 91.
Operational speed: 125 kts *(232 km/h)*.
Service ceiling: 12 500 ft *(3810 m)*.
Range: 320 nm *(593 km)*.
Role/Weapon systems: Shipborne helicopter for EEZ and surface search tasks. Sensors: Bendix weather radar being replaced by Ferranti Seaspray; Kestrel ESM. Weapons: Unarmed.

LYNX   *1989, Royal Danish Navy*

LAND-BASED MARITIME AIRCRAFT

Numbers/Type: 3 Gulfstream Aerospace SMA-3 Gulfstream III.
Operational speed: 500 kts *(926 km/h)*.
Service ceiling: 45 000 ft *(13 720 m)*.
Range: 3940 nm *(7300 km)*.
Role/Weapon systems: MR and liaison aircraft; flown on EEZ patrol around Greenland coast and in Danish sea areas in Baltic; EW work undertaken. Sensors: APS-127 surveillance radar. Weapons: Unarmed.

Numbers/Type: 7 Sikorsky S-61A-1 Sea King.
Operational speed: 118 kts *(219 km/h)*.
Service ceiling: 14 700 ft *(4480 m)*.
Range: 542 nm *(1005 km)*.
Role/Weapon systems: Land-based SAR helicopter for peacetime search and rescue; wartime combat rescue and surface search. Sensors: Bendix weather radar; GEC Avionics FLIR to be fitted. Weapons: Unarmed.

NAVAL HOME GUARD

6 MHV 90 CLASS (COASTAL PATROL CRAFT)

BOPA MHV 90	**HOLGER DANSKE** MHV 92	**RINGEN** MHV 94
BRIGADEN MHV 91	**HVIDSTEN** MHV 93	**SPEDITØREN** MHV 95

Displacement, tons: 85 full load
Dimensions, feet (metres): 64.9 × 18.7 × 8.2 *(19.8 × 5.7 × 2.5)*
Main machinery: 1 Burmeister & Wain diesel; 400 hp(m) *(294 kW)*; 1 shaft
Speed, knots: 11
Guns: 2—7.62 mm MGs.
Radars: Navigation: RM 1290S; I band.

Comment: Built between 1973 and 1975.

HVIDSTEN   *7/1992, Gunnar Olsen*

9 KUTTER CLASS (COASTAL PATROL CRAFT)

ANTARES MHV 51	**CASSIOPEIA** MHV 63	**JUPITER** MHV 74
APOLLO MHV 56	**CRUX** MHV 64	**LUNA** MHV 75
BETELGEUSE MHV 61	**HERCULES** MHV 73	**LYRA** MHV 76 (ex-Y 339)

Displacement, tons: 35 full load
Dimensions, feet (metres): 60.4 × 17.1 × 7.5 *(18.4 × 5.2 × 2.3)*
Speed, knots: 9
Guns: 2—7.62 mm MGs.

Comment: Built between 1922 and 1941. All are similar in design. Apart from *Hercules* all are veterans of the Second World War. Being paid off as the 800 class come into service. Names are also being transferred to the 800 class.

LUNA   *7/1992, Gunnar Olsen*

6 + 12 (6) MHV 800 CLASS (COASTAL PATROL CRAFT)

Name	No	Builders	Commissioned
ALDEBARAN	MHV 801	Soby Shipyard	9 July 1992
CARINA	MHV 802	Soby Shipyard	30 Sep 1992
ARIES	MHV 803	Soby Shipyard	30 Mar 1993
ANDROMEDA	MHV 804	Soby Shipyard	30 Sep 1993
GEMINI	MHV 805	Soby Shipyard	28 Feb 1994
DUBHE	MHV 806	Soby Shipyard	June 1994
—	MHV 807	Soby Shipyard	Nov 1994
—	MHV 808	Soby Shipyard	May 1995
—	MHV 809	Soby Shipyard	Nov 1995
—	MHV 810	Soby Shipyard	May 1996
—	MHV 811	Soby Shipyard	Nov 1996
—	MHV 812	Soby Shipyard	May 1997

Displacement, tons: 83 full load
Dimensions, feet (metres): 77.8 × 18.4 × 6.6 *(23.7 × 5.6 × 2)*
Main machinery: 2 Saab Scania DSI-14 diesels; 900 hp(m) *(661 kW)*; 2 shafts
Speed, knots: 13. **Range, miles:** 990 at 11 kts
Complement: 8 + 4 spare
Guns: 2—7.62 mm MGs. 2—20 mm (can be fitted).
Radars: Navigation: Furuno 1505; I band.

Comment: A new class of Home Guard patrol craft. First six ordered in April 1991, second six in July 1992, six more in September 1993. Steel hulls with a moderate ice capability.

ALDEBARAN   5/1993, Erik Laursen

ALDEBARAN   7/1992, Royal Danish Navy

CARINA   7/1993, Hartmut Ehlers

7 MHV 80 CLASS (COASTAL PATROL CRAFT)

Name	No	Builders	Commissioned
FAENØ (ex-MHV 69, ex-MS 6)	MHV 80	Denmark	July 1941
ASKØ (ex-Y 386, ex-M 560, ex-MS 2)	MHV 81	Denmark	1 Aug 1941
ENØ (ex-Y 388, ex-M 562, ex-MS 5)	MHV 82	Denmark	18 Aug 1941
MANØ (ex-Y 391, ex-M 566, ex-MS 9)	MHV 83	Denmark	30 Oct 1941
BAAGØ (ex-Y 387, ex-M 561, ex-MS 3)	MHV 84	Denmark	9 Aug 1941
HJORTØ (ex-Y 389, ex-M 564, ex-MS 7)	MHV 85	Denmark	24 Sep 1941
LYØ (ex-Y 390, ex-M 565, ex-MS 8)	MHV 86	Denmark	22 Oct 1941

Displacement, tons: 80 full load
Dimensions, feet (metres): 80.1 × 15.1 × 5.2 *(24.4 × 4.6 × 1.6)*
Main machinery: 1 diesel; 350 hp(m) *(257 kW)*; 1 shaft
Speed, knots: 11
Guns: 2—7.62 mm MGs.
Radars: Navigation: RM 1290S; I band.

Comment: Of wooden construction. All launched in 1941. Former inshore minesweepers.

ENØ   6/1992, van Ginderen Collection

3 MHV 70 CLASS (COASTAL PATROL CRAFT)

SATURN MHV 70   **SCORPIUS** MHV 71   **SIRIUS** MHV 72

Displacement, tons: 76 full load
Dimensions, feet (metres): 64 × 16.7 × 8.2 *(19.5 × 5.1 × 2.5)*
Main machinery: 1 diesel; 200 hp(m) *(147 kW)*; 1 shaft
Speed, knots: 10
Guns: 2—7.62 mm MGs.
Radars: Navigation: RM 1290S; I band.

Comment: Patrol boats and training craft for the Naval Home Guard. Built in the Royal Dockyard, Copenhagen and commissioned in 1958. Formerly designated DMH, but allocated MHV numbers in 1969.

SCORPIUS   7/1992, Gunnar Olsen

6 MHV 20 CLASS (COASTAL PATROL CRAFT)

BAUNEN MHV 20   **KUREREN** MHV 22   **PATRIOTEN** MHV 24
BUDSTIKKEN MHV 21   **PARTISAN** MHV 23   **SABOTØREN** MHV 25

Displacement, tons: 60 full load
Dimensions, feet (metres): 54.1 × 13.8 × 4.9 *(16.5 × 4.2 × 1.5)*
Main machinery: 2 MTU diesels; 500 hp(m) *(367 kW)*; 2 shafts
Speed, knots: 15
Complement: 9
Guns: 2—7.62 mm MGs.
Radars: Navigation: Terma 9T48/9; I band.

Comment: Built of GRP by Ejvinds Plastikbodevaerft, Svendborg between 1978 and 1982. Used for patrols in The Sound.

SABOTØREN   8/1991, Gunnar Olsen

MINE WARFARE FORCES

Note: See also Flyvefisken class under *Patrol Forces*.

4 FALSTER CLASS (MINELAYERS)

Name	No	Builders	Commissioned
FALSTER	N 80	Nakskov Skibsvaerft	7 Nov 1963
FYEN	N 81	Frederikshavn Vaerft	18 Sep 1963
MØEN	N 82	Frederikshavn Vaerft	29 Apr 1964
SJAELLAND	N 83	Nakskov Skibsvaerft	7 July 1964

Displacement, tons: 1880 full load
Dimensions, feet (metres): 252.6 × 42 × 11.8 *(77 × 12.8 × 3.6)*
Main machinery: 2 GM/EMD 16-567D3 diesels; 4800 hp *(3.58 MW)* sustained; 2 shafts
Speed, knots: 17
Complement: 133 (10 officers)

Guns: 4 US 3 in *(76 mm)*/50 Mk 33 (2 twin); 85° elevation; 25 rounds/minute to 12.8 km *(7 nm)*; weight of shell 6 kg.
4 Oerlikon 20 mm. To be replaced by 2 twin Stinger SAM mountings.
Mines: 4 rails; 400.
Countermeasures: Decoys: 2—57 mm multiple chaff launchers.
Combat data systems: Terma TDS.
Fire control: Contraves.
Radars: Air/surface search: CWS 2; E/F band.
Fire control: CGS 1; I band.
Surface search: NWS 2; I band.
Navigation: Terma Pilot; E/I band.

Programmes: Ordered in 1960-61 and launched 1962-63. All are named after Danish islands. Similar to Turkish *Nusret*. *Sjaelland* converted in 1976 to act as depot ship for submarines and FAC but retains minelaying capability.
Modernisation: Refitted to allow them to serve until late 1990s; included Terma command and control system. Mine stocks updated in collaboration with Germany. Twin Stinger SAM mountings to be fitted in due course.
Structure: The steel hull is flush-decked with a raking stem, a full stern and a prominent knuckle fwd. The hull has been specially strengthened for ice navigation. In 1987 *Sjaelland* after mast was raised; *Falster* and *Fyen* similarly modified in 1989-91, *Møen* completed in 1993.
Operational: *Sjaelland* is used as a Command ship. *Møen* and sometimes *Fyen* employed on midshipmen's training.

FALSTER   *4/1993, Antonio Moreno*

SJAELLAND   *6/1993, H M Steele*

2 LINDORMEN CLASS (COASTAL MINELAYERS)

Name	No	Builders	Commissioned
LINDORMEN	N 43	Svendborg Vaerft	16 Feb 1978
LOSSEN	N 44	Svendborg Vaerft	14 June 1978

Displacement, tons: 570 full load
Dimensions, feet (metres): 146 × 29.5 × 8 *(44.5 × 9 × 2.6)*
Main machinery: 2 Frichs diesels; 1600 hp(m) *(1.2 MW)*; 2 shafts
Speed, knots: 14
Complement: 30
Guns: 3 Oerlikon 20 mm.
Mines: 50-60 (depending on type).
Radars: NWS 3; I band.

Comment: Controlled Minelayers. *Lindormen* laid down on 2 February 1977, launched on 7 June 1977 and *Lossen* laid down on 9 July 1977, launched on 11 October 1977.

LOSSEN   *1/1993, van Ginderen collection*

2 SUND (BLUEBIRD) CLASS (MINESWEEPERS—COASTAL)

Name	No	Builders	Commissioned
GRØNSUND (ex-*MSC 256*)	M 574	Stephen Bros Shipyard	21 Sep 1956
VILSUND (ex-*MSC 264*)	M 578	Harbor Boatyard	15 Nov 1956

Displacement, tons: 350 standard; 376 full load
Dimensions, feet (metres): 147.6 × 27.9 × 8.5 *(45 × 8.5 × 2.6)*
Main machinery: 2 GM 8-268A diesels; 880 hp *(656 kW)*; 2 shafts
Speed, knots: 13. **Range, miles:** 3000 at 10 kts
Complement: 35
Guns: 1 Bofors 40 mm/60.
Radars: Navigation: Terma Pilot; E/I band.

Comment: MSC (ex-AMS) 60 class NATO coastal minesweepers. *Grønsund* has been fitted with a charthouse between bridge and funnel, and has been employed on surveying duties. *Vilsund* has a deckhouse abaft the bridge after modernisation in 1985. Being replaced by Flyvefisken class.

GRØNSUND   *10/1993, G Toremans*

2 + (10) SAV CLASS (MINEHUNTER—DRONES)

MRD 1 (ex-*MRF 1*)   MRD 2 (ex-*MRF 2*)

Displacement, tons: 32 full load
Dimensions, feet (metres): 59.7 × 15.6 × 3.9 *(18.2 × 4.8 × 1.2)*
Main machinery: 1 Schottel pump jet propulsor
Speed, knots: 12
Complement: 4
Combat data systems: Terma link to Flyvefisken class (in MCMV configuration).
Radars: Navigation: Furuno; I band.
Sonars: Thomson Sintra TSM 2054 sidescan; active minehunting; high frequency.

Comment: Being built by Danyard with GRP hulls. First one completed in March 1991, second in December 1991. Trials continue into 1994. It is planned to order 10 more of the class. The vessels are robot drones (or Surface Auxiliary Vessels (SAV)) operated in pairs by the Flyvefisken class in MCMV configuration. Hull is based on the Hugin class TRVs with low noise propulsion. The towfish with sidescan sonar is lowered and raised from the stern-mounted gantry. The two craft have slightly different funnel designs (see Flyvefisken class).

MRD 1   *6/1993, Royal Danish Navy*

AUXILIARIES

Note: There is a road-borne support unit (MOBA) for the Fast Attack Craft with two sections. The first, of eight vehicles with radar, W/T and control offices is MOBA (Ops) and the second, of 25 vehicles for stores, fuel, provisions, torpedoes and workshops is MOBA (Log).

1 TRANSPORT SHIP

Name	No	Builders	Commissioned
SLEIPNER	A 559	Åbenrå Vaerft og A/S	18 July 1986

Displacement, tons: 150 full load
Dimensions, feet (metres): 119.6 × 24.9 × 8.8 *(36.5 × 7.6 × 2.7)*
Main machinery: 1 Callesen diesel; 1 shaft
Speed, knots: 11
Complement: 6
Cargo capacity: 150 tons

SLEIPNER   *1993, Royal Danish Navy*

2 YO 65 CLASS (TANKERS)

Name	No	Builders	Commissioned
RIMFAXE (ex-US YO 226)	A 568	Jefferson Bridge & Machine Co, USA	2 Nov 1945
SKINFAXE (ex-US YO 229)	A 569	Jefferson Bridge & Machine Co, USA	7 Dec 1945

Displacement, tons: 1400 full load
Dimensions, feet (metres): 174 × 32.9 × 13.3 *(53.1 × 10 × 4.1)*
Main machinery: 1 GM diesel; 560 hp *(418 kW)*; 1 shaft
Speed, knots: 10
Complement: 19
Cargo capacity: 900 tons fuel
Guns: 1 Oerlikon 20 mm.

Comment: Transferred from the USA on 2 August 1962. Act as tenders for the Willemoes class.

SKINFAXE   *4/1992, Erik Laursen*

1 ROYAL YACHT

Name	No	Builders	Commissioned
DANNEBROG	A 540	R Dockyard, Copenhagen	20 May 1932

Displacement, tons: 1130 full load
Dimensions, feet (metres): 246 × 34 × 12.1 *(75 × 10.4 × 3.7)*
Main machinery: 2 Burmeister & Wain Alpha T23L-KVO diesels; 1800 hp(m) *(1.32 MW)*; 2 shafts; cp props
Speed, knots: 14
Complement: 55
Guns: 2—37 mm saluting guns.

Comment: Laid down 2 January 1931, launched on 10 October 1931. Major refit 1980 included new engines and electrical gear. SATCOM fitted in 1992.

DANNEBROG   *7/1993, Marek Twardowski*

1 MINE TRANSPORT

Name	No	Builders	Commissioned
MSA 4	(ex-MK 5, ex-Y 383)	Holbaek Bädevaerft	1949

Displacement, tons: 34 full load
Dimensions, feet (metres): 62.3 × 13.8 × 4.9 *(19 × 4.2 × 1.5)*
Main machinery: 1 diesel; 1 shaft
Speed, knots: 8

MSA 4   *1992, Royal Danish Navy*

3 HUGIN CLASS (TORPEDO RECOVERY VESSELS)

HUGIN TO 8   **MUNIN** TO 9   **MIMER** TO 10

Displacement, tons: 23 full load
Dimensions, feet (metres): 53.1 × 13.8 × 3.9 *(16.2 × 4.2 × 1.2)*
Main machinery: 1 MWM diesel; 450 hp(m) *(330 kW)*; 1 shaft
Speed, knots: 15

Comment: Built by Ejvinds, Svenborg. The same hull, slightly lengthened, is the basis of the robot boats for MCM systems.

MUNIN   *1988, Royal Danish Navy*

4 RESCUE VESSELS

NORDJYLLAND   **NORDSØEN**   **VESTKYSTEN**   **JENS VAEVER**

Displacement, tons: 475; 657 *(Vestkysten)*; 141 *(Jens Vaever)*
Dimensions, feet (metres): 134.5 × 32.8 × 13 *(41 × 10 × 4)*
163.7 × 32.8 × 10.8 *(49.9 × 10 × 3.3) (Vestkysten)*
95.1 × 19.7 × 9.8 *(29 × 6 × 3) (Jens Vaever)*

Comment: Three for the North Sea, one for the Baltic. *Jens Vaever* commissioned 1960; *Nord-jylland* 1967 and *Nordsøen* 1968. *Vestkysten* commissioned in 1987 and replaced the old ship of the same name. Used for fishery protection.

NORDSØEN   *1/1992, Harald Carstens*

2 POLLUTION CONTROL CRAFT

MILJØ 101 and **102**

Displacement, tons: 16 full load
Dimensions, feet (metres): 53.8 × 14.4 × 7.1 *(16.2 × 4.2 × 2.2)*
Main machinery: 1 MWM TBD232V12 diesel; 454 hp(m) *(334 kW)* sustained; 1 shaft
Speed, knots: 15. **Range, miles:** 350 at 8 kts
Complement: 3

Comment: Built by Ejvinds Plastikbodevaerft, Svendborg. Carry derricks and booms for framing oil slicks and dispersant fluids. Naval manned. Delivered 1 November and 1 December 1977.

MILJØ 102   *1987, Royal Danish Navy*

2 SEA TRUCKS

METTE MILJØ   **MARIE MILJØ**

Displacement, tons: 157 full load
Dimensions, feet (metres): 97.7 × 26.2 × 5.2 *(29.8 × 8 × 1.6)*
Main machinery: 2 Grenaa diesels; 660 hp(m) *(485 kW)*; 2 shafts
Speed, knots: 10
Complement: 8

Comment: Built by Carl B Hoffmann A/S, Esbjerg and Søren Larsen & Sønners Skibsvaerft A/S, Nykøbing Mors. Delivered 22 February 1980. Have orange and yellow superstructure.

METTE MILJØ   *5/1991, Gunnar Olsen*

2 OIL POLLUTION CRAFT

GUNNAR THORSON   **GUNNAR SEIDENFADEN**

Displacement, tons: 750 full load
Dimensions, feet (metres): 183.7 × 40.3 × 12.8 *(56 × 12.3 × 3.9)*
Main machinery: 2 Burmeister and Wain Alpha diesels; 2320 hp(m) *(1.7 MW)*; 2 shafts
Speed, knots: 12.5
Complement: 17

Comment: Built by Ørnskov Stålskibsvaerft, Frederikshavn. Delivered May and July 1981 respectively. *G Thorson* at Copenhagen, *G Seidenfaden* at Korsør. Carry firefighting equipment. Large hydraulic crane fitted in 1988 for the secondary task of buoy tending. Orange painted hulls.

GUNNAR SEIDENFADEN   *1988, Royal Danish Navy*

ICEBREAKERS

Note: Icebreakers, once controlled by the Ministry of Trade and Shipping are being transferred to the Navy but will continue to have a combined naval and civilian crew. Maintenance is done at Frederikshavn in Summer. During Summer period one icebreaker may be employed on surveying duties in Danish waters for the Administration of Navigation and Hydrography.

Name	No	Builders	Commissioned
THORBJØRN	—	Svendborg Vaerft	1981

Displacement, tons: 2344 full load
Dimensions, feet (metres): 221.4 × 50.2 × 15.4 *(67.5 × 15.3 × 4.7)*
Main machinery: Diesel-electric; 4 Burmeister & Wain Alpha diesels; 6800 hp(m) *(5 MW)*; 2 motors; 2 shafts
Speed, knots: 16.5
Complement: 29 (8 officers)

Comment: No bow thruster. Side rolling tanks. Fitted for surveying duties in non-ice periods.

THORBJØRN   *7/1990, A Sheldon Duplaix*

Name	No	Builders	Commissioned
DANBJØRN	—	Lindø Vaerft, Odense	1965
ISBJØRN	—	Lindø Vaerft, Odense	1966

Displacement, tons: 3685
Dimensions, feet (metres): 252 × 56 × 20 *(76.8 × 17.1 × 6.1)*
Main machinery: Diesel-electric; 2 diesel generators; 10 500 hp(m) *(7.72 MW)*; 2 motors; 2 shafts
Speed, knots: 14
Complement: 34

ISBJØRN   *6/1990, van Ginderen Collection*

Name	No	Builders	Commissioned
ELBJØRN	—	Frederikshavn Vaerft	1966

Displacement, tons: 893 standard; 1400 full load
Dimensions, feet (metres): 156.5 × 40.3 × 14.5 *(47 × 12.1 × 4.4)*
Main machinery: Diesel-electric; 2 diesel generators; 3600 hp(m) *(2.64 MW)*; 2 motors; 2 shafts
Speed, knots: 12

ELBJØRN   *7/1990, A Sheldon Duplaix*

TRAINING SHIPS

Note: There are two small Sail Training Ships, *Svanen* Y 101 and *Thyra* Y 102.

3 TRAINING LAUNCHES

SKB 1   SKB 2   SKB 4

Displacement, tons: 27
Speed, knots: 9

Comment: Built 1958-68. Length 42.7 ft *(13 m)*.

SKB 1   *7/1991, Antonio Moreno*

SURVEY SHIPS

Note: *Thorbjorn* is also used as survey ship.

6 SURVEY LAUNCHES

SKA 11   12   13   14   15   16

Displacement, tons: 52
Dimensions, feet (metres): 65.6 × 17.1 × 6.9 *(20 × 5.2 × 2.1)*
Main machinery: 1 GM diesel; 540 hp *(403 kW)*; 1 shaft
Speed, knots: 12
Complement: 6 (1 officer)

Comment: GRP hulls. Built 1981-84. Have red hulls. Survey motor launches.

SKA 11   *1989, Royal Danish Navy*

TUGS

2 HARBOUR TUGS

BALDER   HERMOD

Dimensions, feet (metres): 39 × 13.1 × 3.9 *(11.9 × 4 × 1.2)*
Main machinery: 1 GM diesel; 300 hp *(224 kW)*; 1 shaft
Speed, knots: 8.5

Comment: Berthing tugs based at Korsør. Built in 1983 at Assens.

HERMOD   *8/1991, Gunnar Olsen*

DJIBOUTI

Headquarters' Appointment	Base	Mercantile Marine
Commander of the Navy: Colonel Ahmad Hossein	Djibouti	*Lloyd's Register of Shipping:* 10 vessels of 3758 tons gross
	French Navy	
Personnel	The permanent French naval contingent usually includes a command ship, four frigates, EDIC 9091, three small landing craft and two repair ships.	
1994: 90		

PATROL FORCES

2 PLASCOA CLASS (COASTAL PATROL CRAFT)

Name	No	Builders	Commissioned
MOUSSA ALI	P 10	Plascoa, Cannes	8 June 1985
MONT ARREH	P 11	Plascoa, Cannes	16 Feb 1986

Displacement, tons: 35 full load
Dimensions, feet (metres): 75.5 × 18 × 4.9 *(23 × 5.5 × 1.5)*
Main machinery: 2 SACM Poyaud V12-520 M25 diesels; 1700 hp(m) *(1.25 MW)*; 2 shafts
Speed, knots: 25. **Range, miles:** 750 at 12 kts
Complement: 15
Guns: 1 Giat 20 mm. 1—12.7 mm MG.
Radars: Navigation: Decca; I band.

Comment: Ordered in October 1984 and transferred as a gift from France. GRP hulls. Refitted in 1988.

3 SEA RIDERS and 2 ZODIACS

Comment: Rigid inflatable craft acquired from UK 25 October 1988.

1 TECIMAR CLASS (COASTAL PATROL CRAFT)

ZENA (ex-P 771)

Displacement, tons: 30 full load
Dimensions, feet (metres): 43.6 × 13.8 × 3.6 *(13.3 × 4.2 × 1.1)*
Main machinery: 2 GM 6V-71 diesels; 480 hp(m) *(350 kW)*; 2 shafts
Speed, knots: 25
Guns: 1—12.7 mm MG. 1—7.62 mm MG.

Comment: Built in 1974 and transferred by France after Declaration of Independence in 1977.

5 SAWARI CLASS (INSHORE PATROL CRAFT)

Displacement, tons: 7 full load
Dimensions, feet (metres): 36.1 × 8.2 × 2 *(11 × 2.5 × 0.6)*
Speed, knots: 22

Comment: Acquired from Iraq in 1989. Can be armed with MGs and rocket launchers. Outboard engines.

DOMINICA

Headquarters' Appointments

Commissioner of Police:
D Blanchard
Head of Coast Guard:
Sergeant Frederick

General

An independent island in the British Commonwealth situated north of Martinique.

Personnel

1994: 26

Base

Roseau

Mercantile Marine

Lloyd's Register of Shipping:
7 vessels of 1992 tons gross

PATROL FORCES

1 SWIFT 65 ft CLASS

MELVILLE   D 4

Displacement, tons: 33
Dimensions, feet (metres): 64.9 × 18.4 × 6.6 *(19.8 × 5.6 × 2)*
Main machinery: 2 Detroit 12V-71TA diesels; 650 hp *(478 kW)* sustained; 2 shafts
Speed, knots: 23. **Range, miles:** 500 at 18 kts
Complement: 10
Radars: Navigation: Furuno; I/J band.

Comment: Ordered from Swiftships, Morgan City in November 1983. Commissioned 1 May 1984. Similar craft supplied to Antigua and St Lucia.

2 PATROL CRAFT

VIGILANCE   OBSERVER

Displacement, tons: 2.4 full load
Dimensions, feet (metres): 27 × 8.4 × 1 *(8.2 × 2.6 × 0.3)*
Main machinery: 1 Johnson outboard motor; 225 hp *(168 kW)* sustained
Speed, knots: 28
Complement: 3

Comment: Boston Whalers acquired in 1988.

MELVILLE   *11/1993, Maritime Photographic*

OBSERVER   *11/1993*

DOMINICAN REPUBLIC

Headquarters' Appointments

Chief of Naval Staff:
Vice Admiral Ivan Vargas Cespedes
Vice Chief of Naval Staff:
Rear Admiral Victor F Garcia Alecont

Personnel

(a) 1994: 3900 officers and men (including naval infantry)
(b) Selective military service

Bases

27 de Febrero, Santo Domingo: HQ of CNS, Naval School. Supply base.
Las Calderas: Las Calderas, Bani: Naval dockyard, 700 ton synchrolift. Training centre. Supply base.
Haina: Dockyard facility. Supply base.
Puerto Plata. Small naval base.

General

Not all the ships listed are operational. Some of the older vessels are seaworthy but of questionable fighting capability.

Mercantile Marine

Lloyd's Register of Shipping:
28 vessels of 12 706 tons gross

DELETIONS

Patrol Forces

1992-93   *Indépendencia, Libertad, Restauracion*

FRIGATE

1 RIVER CLASS

Name	No	Builders	Laid down	Launched	Commissioned
MELLA (ex-*Presidente Trujillo*, ex-HMCS *Carlplace*)	F 451	Davie SB & Repairing Co, Lauzon, Canada	30 Nov 1943	6 July 1944	13 Dec 1944

Displacement, tons: 1445 standard; 2125 full load
Dimensions, feet (metres): 304 × 37.5 × 12.5 *(92.7 × 11.4 × 4.1)*
Main machinery: 2 boilers; 2 triple expansion reciprocating engines; 5500 ihp *(4.1 MW)*; 2 shafts
Speed, knots: 20. **Range, miles:** 7200 at 12 kts
Complement: 195 (15 officers, 50 midshipmen)
Guns: 1 Vickers 4 in *(102 mm)*/45 Mk 23; 80° elevation; 16 rounds/minute to 19 km *(10.4 nm)*; weight of shell 16 kg.
Fitted for 2—40 mm (twin) and 4—20 mm but these are not all always carried.
2—47 mm saluting guns.
Radars: Navigation: Raytheon SPS 64; I band.

Programmes: Transferred to the Dominican Navy by Canada in 1946. Pennant number as a frigate was F 101, but now carries pennant number 451 as flagship of Dominican naval forces. Renamed *Mella* in 1962.
Structure: Modified for use as Presidential yacht with extra accommodation and deckhouses built up aft in place of some armament.
Operational: Used by staff in naval operations and as a cadet training ship.

MELLA   *1/1993, A Sheldon Duplaix*

CORVETTES

3 COHOES CLASS

Name	No	Builders	Commissioned
CAMBIASO (ex-USS *Etlah* AN 79)	P 207	Marietta Manufacturing Co	16 Apr 1945
SEPARACION (ex-USS *Passaconaway* AN 86)	P 208	Marine SB Co	27 Apr 1945
CALDERAS (ex-USS *Passaic* AN 87)	P 209	Leatham D Smith SB Co	6 Mar 1945

Displacement, tons: 650 standard; 855 full load
Dimensions, feet (metres): 162.3 × 33.8 × 11.7 *(49.5 × 10.3 × 3.6)*
Main machinery: Diesel-electric; 2 Busch-Sulzer BS-539 diesels; 1500 hp(m) *(1.1 MW)*; 2 generators; 1 motor; 1 shaft
Speed, knots: 12
Complement: 64 (5 officers)
Guns: 2—3 in *(76 mm)*. 3 Oerlikon 20 mm.

Comment: Ex-netlayers in reserve in USA by 1963. Transferred by sale on 29 September 1976. Now used for patrol duties. P 207 and 208 modified in 1980 with the removal of the bow horns. P209 has only one 76 mm gun and is used as a survey ship.

SEPARACION　　　　　　　　　　　　1/1993, A Sheldon Duplaix

PATROL FORCES

2 ADMIRABLE CLASS (GUNSHIPS)

Name	No	Builders	Commissioned
PRESTOL (ex-*Separacion*, ex-USS *Skirmish* MSF 303)	BM 454	Associated SB	16 Aug 1943
TORTUGUERO (ex-USS *Signet* MSF 302)	BM 455	Associated SB	16 Aug 1943

Displacement, tons: 650 standard; 900 full load
Dimensions, feet (metres): 184.5 × 33 × 14.4 *(56.3 × 10.1 × 4.4)*
Main machinery: 2 Cooper-Bessemer GSB8 diesels; 1710 hp *(1.28 MW)*; 2 shafts
Speed, knots: 15. **Range, miles:** 4300 at 10 kts
Complement: 90 (8 officers)
Guns: 1—3 in *(76 mm)*/50. 2 Bofors 40 mm/60. 6 Oerlikon 20 mm.
Radars: Surface search: SPS 69; I band.

Comment: Former US fleet minesweepers. Purchased on 13 January 1965. BM 454 renamed early 1976. Sweep-gear removed. Classified as Cañoneros.

PRESTOL　　　　　　　　　　　　1/1993, A Sheldon Duplaix

1 LARGE PATROL CRAFT

Name	No	Builders	Commissioned
CAPITAN ALSINA (ex-*RL 101*)	GC 105	—	1944

Displacement, tons: 100 standard
Dimensions, feet (metres): 104.8 × 19.2 × 5.8 *(32 × 5.9 × 1.8)*
Main machinery: 2 GM diesels; 1000 hp *(746 kW)*; 2 shafts
Speed, knots: 17
Complement: 20
Guns: 2 Oerlikon 20 mm.

Comment: Former US SAR craft of wooden construction. Launched in 1944. Renamed in 1957. Rebuilt 1977 and used as an alongside training vessel.

CAPITAN ALSINA

2 CANOPUS (SWIFTSHIPS 110 ft) CLASS (LARGE PATROL CRAFT)

Name	No	Builders	Commissioned
CRISTOBAL COLON (ex-*Canopus*)	GC 107	Swiftships, Morgan City	June 1984
ORION	GC 109	Swiftships, Morgan City	Aug 1984

Displacement, tons: 93.5 full load
Dimensions, feet (metres): 109.9 × 23.9 × 5.9 *(33.5 × 7.3 × 1.8)*
Main machinery: 3 Detroit 12V-92TA diesels; 1020 hp *(760 kW)* sustained; 3 shafts
Speed, knots: 23. **Range, miles:** 1500 at 12 kts
Complement: 19 (3 officers)
Guns: 1 Bofors 40 mm/60. 2—12.7 mm MGs.

Comment: Built of aluminium.

ORION　　　　　　　　　　　　1/1993, A Sheldon Duplaix

4 BELLATRIX CLASS (COASTAL PATROL CRAFT)

Name	No	Builders	Commissioned
PROCION	GC 103	Sewart Seacraft Inc, Berwick, La.	1967
ALDEBARÁN	GC 104	Sewart Seacraft Inc, Berwick, La.	1972
BELLATRIX	GC 106	Sewart Seacraft Inc, Berwick, La.	1967
CAPELLA	GC 108	Sewart Seacraft Inc, Berwick, La.	1968

Displacement, tons: 60
Dimensions, feet (metres): 85 × 18 × 5 *(25.9 × 5.5 × 1.5)*
Main machinery: 2 GM 16V-71 diesels; 811 hp *(605 kW)* sustained; 2 shafts
Speed, knots: 18.7. **Range, miles:** 800 at 15 kts
Complement: 12
Guns: 3—12.7 mm MGs.

Comment: Transferred to the Dominican Navy by the USA. *Procion* and *Capella* are probably non-operational.

CAPELLA　　　　　　　　　　　　1/1994, A Sheldon Duplaix

1 PGM 71 CLASS (LARGE PATROL CRAFT)

Name	No	Builders	Commissioned
BETELGEUSE (ex-US *PGM 77*)	GC 102	Peterson, USA	1966

Displacement, tons: 130 standard; 145 full load
Dimensions, feet (metres): 101.5 × 21 × 5 *(30.9 × 6.4 × 1.5)*
Main machinery: 2 Caterpillar D 348 diesels; 1450 hp *(1.08 MW)* sustained; 2 shafts
Speed, knots: 21. **Range, miles:** 1500 at 10 kts
Complement: 20
Guns: 1 Oerlikon 20 mm. 2—12.7 mm MGs.

Comment: Built in the USA and transferred to the Dominican Republic under the Military Aid Programme on 14 January 1966. Re-engined in 1980.

1 COASTAL PATROL CRAFT

LUPERON GC 110

Comment: This is not a Swiftships 110 ft class as previously listed. Length about 60 ft *(18 m)*.

LAND-BASED MARITIME AIRCRAFT (FRONT LINE)

Numbers/Type: 2 Aerospatiale SA 316B Alouette III.
Operational speed: 113 kts *(210 km/h)*.
Service ceiling: 10 500 ft *(3200 m)*.
Range: 290 nm *(540 km)*.
Role/Weapon systems: Operated by air force liaison and SAR tasks. Sensors: None. Weapons: Possibly 7.62 mm machine gun.

Numbers/Type: 7 Cessna T-41D.
Operational speed: 102 kts *(188 km/h)*.
Service ceiling: 13 100 ft *(3995 m)*.
Range: 535 nm *(990 km)*.
Role/Weapon systems: Inshore/coastal reconnaissance reporting role; also used for training. Sensors: Hand-held cameras only. Weapons: Unarmed.

AUXILIARIES

1 LCU

Name	No	Builders	Commissioned
SAMANA (ex-*LA 2*)	LDM 302	Ast Navales Dominicanos	1958

Displacement, tons: 150 standard; 310 full load
Dimensions, feet (metres): 119.5 × 36 × 3 *(36.4 × 11 × 0.9)*
Main machinery: 3 GM 6X4NY diesels; 441 hp *(329 kW)*; 3 shafts
Speed, knots: 8
Complement: 17
Guns: 1—12.7 mm MG.

Comment: Similar characteristics to US LCT 5 type although slightly larger. Oil fuel, 80 tons.

SAMANA   *1972, Dominican Navy*

1 BUOY TENDER

Name	No	Builders	Commissioned
NEPTUNO (ex-*Toro*)	BA 10	John H Mathis, NJ	Feb 1954

Displacement, tons: 72 full load
Dimensions, feet (metres): 64 × 18.1 × 8 *(19.5 × 5.7 × 2.4)*
Main machinery: 1 GM 6-71 diesel; 174 hp *(130 kW)* sustained; 1 shaft
Speed, knots: 10
Complement: 7 (1 officer)

Comment: Also used as a survey craft.

NEPTUNO   *11/1990, Hartmut Ehlers*

1 HARBOUR TANKER

Name	No	Builders	Commissioned
CAPITAN BEOTEGUI (ex-US *YO 215*)	BT 5	Ira S Bushey, Brooklyn	17 Dec 1945

Displacement, tons: 422 light; 1400 full load
Dimensions, feet (metres): 174 × 32.9 × 13.3 *(53.1 × 10 × 4.1)*
Main machinery: 1 Union diesel; 525 hp *(392 kW)*; 1 shaft
Speed, knots: 8
Complement: 23
Cargo capacity: 6570 barrels
Guns: 2 Oerlikon 20 mm.

Comment: Former US self-propelled fuel oil barge. Lent by the USA in April 1964. Lease renewed 31 December 1980 and again 5 August 1992. Sister ship sank 21 February 1989.

CAPITAN BEOTEGUI   *1/1993, A Sheldon Duplaix*

TRAINING SHIPS

Note: In addition to those listed below there are various tenders mostly acquired 1986-88: *Cojinoa* BA 01, *Bonito* BA 02, *Beata* BA 14, *Albacora* BA 18, *Salinas* BA 19, *Carey* BA 20.

4 SAIL TRAINING SHIPS

Name	No	Builders	Commissioned
CARITE	BA 3	Ast Navales Dominicanos	1975
ATÚN	BA 6	Ast Navales Dominicanos	1975
PICÚA	BA 9	Ast Navales Dominicanos	1975
JUREL	BA 15	Ast Navales Dominicanos	1975

Displacement, tons: 24
Dimensions, feet (metres): 45 × 13 × 6.6 *(13.7 × 4 × 1.9)*
Main machinery: 1 GM diesel; 101 hp *(75 kW)*; 1 shaft
Speed, knots: 9
Complement: 4
Guns: 1—7.62 mm MG.

Comment: Auxiliary sailing craft with a sail area of 750 sq ft and a cargo capacity of 7 tons. There may be more of this class.

1 SAIL TRAINING SHIP

NUBE DEL MAR BA 7

Displacement, tons: 40
Dimensions, feet (metres): 42 × 12 × 1 *(12.8 × 3.6 × 0.3)*
Main machinery: 1 Volvo MD21A; 75 hp *(55 kW)* maximum; 1 shaft
Speed, knots: 10

Comment: Auxiliary yacht used for sail training at the Naval School. Completed 1979.

TUGS

1 CHEROKEE CLASS

Name	No	Builders	Commissioned
MACORIX (ex-USS *Kiowa* ATF 72)	RM 21	Charleston SB and DD Co	7 June 1943

Displacement, tons: 1235 standard; 1675 full load
Dimensions, feet (metres): 205 × 38.5 × 15.5 *(62.5 × 11.7 × 4.7)*
Main machinery: Diesel-electric; 4 GM 12-278 diesels; 4400 hp *(3.28 MW)*; 4 generators; 1 motor; 3000 hp *(2.24 MW)*; 1 shaft
Speed, knots: 16.5
Complement: 85
Guns: 1 US 3 in *(76 mm)*/50. 1 Oerlikon 20 mm.
Radars: Navigation: Raytheon SPS 5D; G/H band.

Comment: Carries additional salvage equipment. Transferred by US on 6 October 1972. Lease renewed 31 December 1980.

MACORIX   *1975, Dominican Navy*

2 SOTOYOMO CLASS

Name	No	Builders	Commissioned
CAONABO (ex-USS Sagamore ATA 208)	RM 18	Gulfport Boiler and Welding Works	19 Mar 1945
ENRIQUILLO (ex-USS Stallion ATA 193)	RM 22	Levington SB Co, Orange, TX	26 Feb 1945

Displacement, tons: 534 standard; 860 full load
Dimensions, feet (metres): 143 × 33.9 × 13 (43.6 × 10.3 × 4)
Main machinery: Diesel-electric; 2 GM 12-278A diesels; 2200 hp (1.64 MW); 2 generators; 1 motor; 1500 hp (1.12 MW); 1 shaft
Speed, knots: 13
Complement: 45
Guns: 1 US 3 in (76 mm). 2 Oerlikon 20 mm.
Radars: Surface search: Raytheon SPS 5D; G/H band.

Comment: RM 18 transferred on lease from US 1 February 1972. RM 22 leased from US 30 October 1980, renewed 15 June 1992. RM 18 is probably non-operational.

ENRIQUILLO   1/1993, A Sheldon Duplaix

2 HERCULES CLASS

Name	No	Builders	Commissioned
HERCULES (ex-R 2)	RP 12	Ast Navales Dominicanos	1960
GUACANAGARIX (ex-R 5)	RP 13	Ast Navales Dominicanos	1960

Displacement, tons: 200 approx
Dimensions, feet (metres): 70 × 15.6 × 9 (21.4 × 4.8 × 2.7)
Main machinery: 1 Caterpillar diesel; 500 hp (373 kW); 1 shaft
Complement: 8

1 LCU TUG

Name	No	Builders	Commissioned
OCOA	LDP 303	Ast Navales Dominicanos	1976

Displacement, tons: 50 full load
Dimensions, feet (metres): 56.2 × 14 × 3.9 (17.1 × 4.3 × 1.2)
Main machinery: 2 GM 6-71 diesels; 348 hp (260 kW) sustained; 2 shafts
Speed, knots: 9. **Range, miles:** 130 at 9 kts
Complement: 5
Cargo capacity: 30 tons

Comment: Converted for use as a tug, retaining bow ramp.

OCOA   1979, Dominican Navy

2 HARBOUR TUGS

BOHECHIO (ex-US YTL 600) RP 16   **CAYACCA** RP 19

Comment: Small tugs for harbour and coastal use. Not of uniform type and dimensions. RP 16 transferred January 1971. Lease extended 31 December 1980.

FLOATING DOCK

1 FLOATING DOCK

ENDEAVOR   DF 1 (ex-AFDL 1)

Comment: Lift, 1000 tons. Commissioned in 1943. Transferred on loan 8 March 1986.

ECUADOR

Headquarters' Appointments

Commander-in-Chief of the Navy:
   Vice Admiral Oswaldo Viteri Jerez
Chief of Naval Staff:
   Rear Admiral Jorge Donoso Moran
Chief of Naval Operations:
   Rear Admiral Hugo Cañarte Jalon
Chief of Naval Personnel:
   Rear Admiral Belisario Pinto Tapia
Chief of Naval Materiel:
   Captain Enrique Monteverde Nimbriotis

Diplomatic Representation

Naval Attaché in Rome and Bonn:
   Captain Marco Villegas Alarcon
Naval Attaché in London and Paris:
   Captain Mario Pinto Ricaurte
Naval Attaché in Washington:
   Captain Hernan Moreano Andrade

Personnel

(a) 1994: Total 8000 including 1900 marines
(b) 1 year's selective national service

Bases

Guayaquil (main naval base), Jaramijo, Salinas.
San Lorenzo and Galapagos Islands (small bases).

Establishments

The Naval Academy in Salinas; Naval War College and Merchant Navy Academy in Guayaquil.

Naval Aviation

Naval Aviation wing is based at Guayaquil Air Base. Annual budget comprises 5-7.5 per cent of naval budget. Personnel: 35 pilots, 75 aircrew, and 200 enlisted maintenance/other rating. Pilot training is conducted at foreign flight training facilities.

Naval Infantry

A force of naval infantry is based at Guayaquil, on the Galapagos Islands and at Oriente (Esmeraldas Manta).

Coast Guard

Small force formed in 1980.

Prefix to Ships' Names

BAE

Mercantile Marine

Lloyd's Register of Shipping:
   150 vessels of 286 305 tons gross

DELETIONS

Frigates

1991   *Presidente Eloy Alfaro* (old)

Coast Guard

1992   *9 de Octubre* (old)

PENNANT LIST

Submarines

S 101	Shyri
S 102	Huancavilca

Frigates

FM 01	Presidente Eloy Alfaro (new)
FM 02	Moran Valverde (new)

Corvettes

CM 11	Esmeraldas
CM 12	Manabi
CM 13	Los Rios
CM 14	El Oro
CM 15	Los Galapagos
CM 16	Loja

Patrol Forces

LM 21	Quito
LM 23	Guayaquil
LM 24	Cuenca
LM 25	Manta
LM 26	Tulcan
LM 27	Nuevo Rocafuerte

Amphibious Forces

TR 61	Hualcopo

Survey/Research Vessels

BI 91	Orion
LH 94	Rigel

Tugs

RA 70	Chimborazo
RA 71	Cayambe
RB 72	Sangay
RB 73	Cotopaxi
RB 74	Antizana
RB 75	Sirius
RB 76	Altar
RB 77	Tungurahua
RB 78	Quilotoa

Miscellaneous

TR 62	Calicuchima
TR 63	Atahualpa
TR 64	Quisquis
TR 65	Taurus
BE 51	Guayas
BT 84	Putumayo
DF 81	Amazonas
DF 82	Napo
UT 111	Isla de la Plata
UT 112	Isla Puná

Coast Guard

LGC 31	25 de Julio
LGC 32	24 de Mayo
LGC 33	10 de Agosto
LGC 34	3 de Noviembre
LGC 35	5 de Agosto
LGC 36	21 de Febrero
LGC 37	9 de Octubre
LGC 38	27 de Octubre
LGC 41	Rio Puyango
LGC 42	Rio Mataje
LGC 43	Rio Zarumilla
LGC 44	Rio Chone
LGC 45	Rio Daule
LGC 46	Rio Babahoyo

SUBMARINES

2 TYPE 209 CLASS (TYPE 1300)

Name	No	Builders	Laid down	Launched	Commissioned
SHYRI	S 101 (ex-S 11)	Howaldtswerke, Kiel	5 Aug 1974	6 Oct 1976	5 Nov 1977
HUANCAVILCA	S 102 (ex-S 12)	Howaldtswerke, Kiel	2 Jan 1975	15 Mar 1977	16 Mar 1978

Displacement, tons: 1285 surfaced; 1390 dived
Dimensions, feet (metres): 195.1 × 20.5 × 17.9 *(59.5 × 6.3 × 5.4)*
Main machinery: Diesel-electric; 4 MTU 12V 493 AZ80 GA31L diesels; 2400 hp(m) *(1.76 MW)* sustained; 4 Siemens alternators; 1.7 MW; 1 Siemens motor; 4600 hp(m) *(3.38 MW)* sustained; 1 shaft
Speed, knots: 11 surfaced/snorting; 21.5 dived
Complement: 33 (5 officers)

Torpedoes: 8—21 in *(533 mm)* bow tubes. 14 AEG SUT; dual purpose; wire-guided; active/passive homing to 28 km *(15 nm)* at 23 kts; 12 km *(6.5 nm)* at 35 kts; warhead 250 kg.
Fire control: Signaal M8 Mod 24.
Radars: Surface search: Thomson-CSF Calypso; I band.
Sonars: Atlas Elektronik CSU 3; hull-mounted; active/passive search and attack; medium frequency.
Thomson Sintra DUUX 2; passive ranging.

Programmes: Ordered in March 1974. *Shyri* underwent major refit in West Germany in 1983; *Huancavilca* in 1984. Second refits authorised in 1992 and being done with Chilean assistance in 1993/94.
Operational: Based at Guayaquil.

TYPE 209   *1988*

FRIGATES

2 LEANDER CLASS

Name	No	Builders	Laid down	Launched	Commissioned
PRESIDENTE ELOY ALFARO (ex-*Penelope*)	FM 01 (ex-F 127)	Vickers Armstrong, Newcastle	14 Mar 1961	17 Aug 1962	31 Oct 1963
MORAN VALVERDE (ex-*Danae*)	FM 02 (ex-F 47)	HM Dockyard, Devonport	16 Dec 1964	31 Oct 1965	7 Sep 1967

Displacement, tons: 2450 standard; 3200 full load
Dimensions, feet (metres): 360 wl; 372 oa × 41 × 14.8 (keel); 19 (screws) *(109.7; 113.4 × 12.5 × 4.5; 5.8)*
Main machinery: 2 Babcock & Wilcox boilers; 38.7 kg/cm sq; 850°F *(450°C)*; 2 English Electric/White turbines; 30 000 hp *(22.4 MW)*; 2 shafts
Speed, knots: 28. **Range, miles:** 4000 at 15 kts
Complement: 248 (20 officers)

Missiles: SSM: 4 Aerospatiale MM 38 Exocet ❶; inertial cruise; active radar homing to 42 km *(23 nm)* at 0.9 Mach; warhead 165 kg.
SAM: 3 Shorts Seacat GWS 22 quad launchers ❷; radar guidance to 5 km *(2.7 nm)*; warhead HE; sea-skimmer; anti-ship capability.
Guns: 2 Bofors 40 mm/60 Mk 9 ❸; 80° elevation; 120 rounds/minute to 10 km *(5.4 nm)* anti-surface; 3 km *(1.6 nm)* anti-aircraft; weight of shell 0.89 kg.
2 Oerlikon/BMARC 20 mm GAM-BO1 can be fitted midships or aft.
Countermeasures: Decoys: Graseby Type 182; towed torpedo decoy.
2 Vickers Corvus 8-barrelled trainable launchers ❹; chaff to 1 km.
ESM: UA-8/9; radar warning.
ECM: Type 667/668; jammer.
Combat data systems: CAAIS action data automation. Links 10 and 14 (receive).
Fire control: GWS 50.
Radars: Air search: Marconi Type 966 ❺; A band.
Surface search: Plessey Type 994 ❻; E/F band.
Navigation: Kelvin Hughes Type 1006; I band.
Fire control: Two Plessey Type 903/904 (for Seacat) ❼.
Sonars: Kelvin Hughes Type 162M; hull-mounted; bottom classification; 50 kHz.
Graseby Type 184P; hull-mounted; active search and attack; 7-9 kHz.

Helicopters: 1 Bell 206 B ❽.

Programmes: Both ships acquired from UK 25 April 1991 and sailed for Ecuador after working up in July and August respectively. Refits planned in 1995.
Structure: These are Batch 2 Exocet conversions completed in 1980 and 1982. Torpedo tubes were subsequently removed in 1988/89. The ships were transferred without Exocet or Seacat ammunition.

MORAN VALVERDE   *(Scale 1 : 1200), Ian Sturton*

MORAN VALVERDE   *6/1991, D & B Teague*

CORVETTES

6 ESMERALDAS CLASS

Name	No	Builders	Laid down	Launched	Commissioned
ESMERALDAS	CM 11	Fincantieri Muggiano	27 Sep 1979	1 Oct 1980	7 Aug 1982
MANABI	CM 12	Fincantieri Ancona	19 Feb 1980	9 Feb 1981	21 June 1983
LOS RIOS	CM 13	Fincantieri Muggiano	5 Dec 1979	27 Feb 1981	9 Oct 1983
EL ORO	CM 14	Fincantieri Ancona	20 Mar 1980	9 Feb 1981	11 Dec 1983
LOS GALAPAGOS	CM 15	Fincantieri Muggiano	4 Dec 1980	4 July 1981	26 May 1984
LOJA	CM 16	Fincantieri Ancona	25 Mar 1981	27 Feb 1982	26 May 1984

Displacement, tons: 685 full load
Dimensions, feet (metres): 204.4 × 30.5 × 8
(62.3 × 9.3 × 2.5)
Main machinery: 4 MTU 20V 956 TB92 diesels; 22 140 hp(m)
(16.27 MW) sustained; 4 shafts
Speed, knots: 37. **Range, miles:** 4400 at 14 kts
Complement: 51

Missiles: SSM: 6 Aerospatiale MM 40 Exocet (2 triple) launchers
❶; inertial cruise; active radar homing to 70 km (40 nm) at
0.9 Mach; warhead 165 kg; sea-skimmer.
SAM: Selenia Elsag Albatros quad launcher ❷; Aspide; semi-
active radar homing to 13 km (7 nm) at 2.5 Mach; height envelope 15-5000 m (49.2-16 405 ft); warhead 30 kg.
Guns: 1 OTO Melara 3 in (76 mm)/62 compact ❸; 85° elevation;
85 rounds/minute to 16 km (8.7 nm); weight of shell 6 kg.
2 Breda 40 mm/70 (twin) ❹; 85° elevation; 300 rounds/
minute to 12.5 km (6.8 nm) anti-surface; weight of shell
0.96 kg.
Torpedoes: 6—324 mm ILAS-3 (2 triple) tubes ❺; Whitehead
Motofides A244; anti-submarine; self adaptive patterns to
6 km (3.3 nm) at 30 kts; warhead 34 kg.
Countermeasures: Decoys: 1 Breda 105 mm SCLAR launcher;
chaff to 5 km (2.7 nm); illuminants to 12 km (6.6 nm).
ESM/ECM: Elettronika Gamma ED; radar intercept and jammer.
Combat data systems: Selenia IPN 10 action data automation.
Fire control: 2 Selenia NA21 with C03 directors.
Radars: Air/surface search: Selenia RAN 10S ❻; E/F band; range
155 km (85 nm).
Navigation: SMA 3 RM 20; I band; range 73 km (40 nm).
Fire control: 2 Selenia Orion 10X ❼; I/J band; range 40 km
(22 nm).
Sonars: Thomson Sintra Diodon; hull-mounted; active search
and attack; 11, 12 or 13 kHz.

Helicopters: 1 Bell 206B can be embarked (platform only).

Programmes: Ordered in 1979. El Oro out of commission for two
years from mid-1985 after a bad fire.
Modernisation: Contracts for updating command and weapons
control systems placed in 1993/94. The priority is for a Link
system compatible with the frigates.
Structure: Similar to Libyan and Iraqi corvettes, with a helicopter
deck and larger engines.

ESMERALDAS   (Scale 1 : 600), Ian Sturton

ESMERALDAS   1985

SHIPBORNE AIRCRAFT

Numbers/Type: 3 Bell 206B JetRanger.
Operational speed: 115 kts (213 km/h).
Service ceiling: 13 500 ft (4115 m).
Range: 368 nm (682 km).
Role/Weapon systems: Support helicopter for afloat reconnaissance and SAR. Sensors: None.
Weapons: None.

JETRANGER   1989, Textron

LAND-BASED MARITIME AIRCRAFT (FRONT LINE)

Numbers/Type: 3 Beech T-34C-1 Turbo-Mentor.
Operational speed: 250 kts (404 km/h).
Service ceiling: 30 000 ft (9145 m).
Range: 650 nm (1205 km).
Role/Weapon systems: Operated for training and surveillance tasks. Sensors: None. Weapons:
Underwing pylons for rockets, cannon and bombs.

Numbers/Type: 1 Beech Super King 200T.
Operational speed: 282 kts (523 km/h).
Service ceiling: 35 000 ft (10 670 m).
Range: 2030 nm (3756 km).
Role/Weapon systems: Maritime reconnaissance and drug interdiction. Sensors: Weather radar
only. Weapons: Unarmed.

PATROL FORCES

3 QUITO (LÜRSSEN 45) CLASS (FAST ATTACK CRAFT—MISSILE)

Name	No	Builders	Commissioned
QUITO	LM 21	Lürssen, Vegesack	13 July 1976
GUAYAQUIL	LM 23	Lürssen, Vegesack	22 Dec 1977
CUENCA	LM 24	Lürssen, Vegesack	17 July 1977

Displacement, tons: 255
Dimensions, feet (metres): 147.6 × 23 × 8.1 (45 × 7 × 2.5)
Main machinery: 4 MTU 16V 538 TB91 diesels; 12 240 hp(m) (9.11 MW) sustained; 4 shafts
Speed, knots: 40. **Range, miles:** 700 at 40 kts; 1800 at 16 kts
Complement: 35

Missiles: SSM: 4 Aerospatiale MM 38 Exocet; inertial cruise; active radar homing to 42 km (23 nm)
at 0.9 Mach; warhead 165 kg; sea-skimmer.
Guns: 1 OTO Melara 3 in (76 mm)/62 compact; 85° elevation; 85 rounds/minute to 16 km
(8.7 nm); weight of shell 6 kg.
2 Oerlikon 35 mm/90 (twin); 85° elevation; 550 rounds/minute to 6 km (3.3 nm); weight of
shell 1.55 kg.
Fire control: Thomson-CSF Vega system.
Radars: Air/surface search: Thomson-CSF Triton; G band; range 33 km (18 nm) for 2 m² target.
Fire control: Thomson-CSF Pollux; I/J band; range 31 km (17 nm) for 2 m² target.
Navigation: Racal Decca; I band.

Programmes: Launched—Quito on 20 November 1975; Guayaquil on 5 April 1976; Cuenca in
December 1976.

QUITO   9/1981, USN

3 MANTA CLASS (FAST ATTACK CRAFT—MISSILE)

Name	No	Builders	Commissioned
MANTA	LM 25	Lürssen, Vegesack	11 June 1971
TULCAN	LM 26	Lürssen, Vegesack	2 Apr 1971
NUEVO ROCAFUERTE	LM 27	Lürssen, Vegesack	23 June 1971

Displacement, tons: 119 standard; 134 full load
Dimensions, feet (metres): 119.4 × 19.1 × 6 *(36.4 × 5.8 × 1.8)*
Main machinery: 3 Mercedes-Benz diesels; 9000 hp(m) *(6.61 MW)*; 3 shafts
Speed, knots: 42. **Range, miles:** 700 at 30 kts; 1500 at 15 kts
Complement: 19

Missiles: SSM: 4 IAI Gabriel II; radar or optical guidance; semi-active radar homing to 36 km *(19.4 nm)* at 0.7 Mach; warhead 75 kg.
Guns: 2 Emerson Electric 30 mm (twin); 80° elevation; 1200 rounds/minute combined to 6 km *(3.3 nm)*; weight of shell 0.35 kg.
Fire control: Thomson-CSF Vega system.
Radars: Fire-control: Thomson-CSF Pollux; I/J band; range 31 km *(17 nm)* for 2 m² target.
Navigation: I band.

Modernisation: Rearmed in 1980 with new electronic fit and missiles. Torpedo tubes have been removed.
Structure: Similar design to the Chilean Guacolda class with an extra diesel, 3 kts faster.
Operational: Missiles are not carried when used on EEZ surveillance.

AMPHIBIOUS FORCES

1 512-1152 CLASS (LST)

Name	No	Builders	Commissioned
HUALCOPO	TR 61	Chicago Bridge and	9 June 1945
(ex-USS *Summit County* LST 1146)	(ex-T 61)	Iron Co	

Displacement, tons: 1653 standard; 4080 full load
Dimensions, feet (metres): 328 × 50 × 14 *(100 × 16.1 × 4.3)*
Main machinery: 2 GM 12-567A diesels; 1800 hp *(1.34 MW)*; 2 shafts
Speed, knots: 11.6. **Range, miles:** 7200 at 10 kts
Complement: 119
Military lift: 147 troops
Guns: 8 Bofors 40 mm. 2 Oerlikon 20 mm.

Comment: Purchased from US on 14 February 1977. Commissioned in November 1977 after extensive refit. May still have the ice strengthened bow fitted in the early 1950s. Plans for replacement not yet realised.

HUALCOPO (old number)   10/1984, R E Parkinson

6 ROTORK CRAFT (LCUs)

LF 91-96

Displacement, tons: 9 full load
Dimensions, feet (metres): 41.5 × 10.5 × 3 *(12.6 × 3.2 × 0.9)*
Main machinery: 2 Volvo AQD40A diesels; 182 hp(m) *(134 kW)* sustained; 2 shafts
Speed, knots: 26
Complement: 4
Military lift: 4 tons

Comment: Purchased 1979 from UK.

SURVEY AND RESEARCH SHIPS

Name	No	Builders	Commissioned
RIGEL	LH 94 (ex-LH 92)	Halter Marine	1975

Displacement, tons: 50
Dimensions, feet (metres): 64.5 × 17.1 × 3.6 *(19.7 × 5.2 × 1.1)*
Main machinery: 2 diesels; 2 shafts
Speed, knots: 10
Complement: 10 (2 officers)

Comment: Used for inshore oceanographic work.

Name	No	Builders	Commissioned
ORION (ex-*Dometer*)	BI 91 (ex-HI 91, ex-HI 92)	Ishikawajima, Tokyo	10 Nov 1982

Measurement, tons: 1105 gross
Dimensions, feet (metres): 210.6 pp × 35.1 × 11.8 *(64.2 × 10.7 × 3.6)*
Main machinery: Diesel-electric; 3 Detroit 16V-92TA diesel generators; 2070 hp *(1.54 MW)* sustained; 2 motors; 1900 hp *(1.42 MW)*; 1 shaft
Speed, knots: 12.6. **Range, miles:** 6000 at 12 kts
Complement: 45 (6 officers) plus 14 civilians
Radars: Navigation: Two Decca; I band.

Comment: Research vessel for oceanographic, hydrographic and meteorological work.

ORION (old number)   3/1990, T J Gander

TRAINING SHIP

1 SAIL TRAINING SHIP

Name	No	Builders	Commissioned
GUAYAS	BE 51 (ex-BE 01)	Ast Celaya, Spain	23 July 1977

Measurement, tons: 234 dwt; 934 gross
Dimensions, feet (metres): 264 × 33.5 × 13.4 *(80 × 10.2 × 4.2)*
Main machinery: 1 GM 12V-149T diesel; 875 hp *(652 kW)* sustained; 1 shaft
Speed, knots: 11.3

Comment: Three masted. Launched 23 September 1976. Has accommodation for 180.

GUAYAS   4/1992, Hartmut Ehlers

AUXILIARIES

1 YW CLASS (WATER TANKER)

Name	No	Builders	Commissioned
ATAHUALPA (ex-US *YW 131*)	TR 63 (ex-T 63, ex-T 62, ex-T 33, ex-T 41, ex-A 01)	Leatham D Smith SB Co	1945

Displacement, tons: 415 light; 1235 full load
Dimensions, feet (metres): 174 × 32 × 15 *(53.1 × 9.8 × 4.6)*
Main machinery: 2 GM 8-278A diesels; 1500 hp *(1.12 MW)*; 2 shafts
Speed, knots: 11.5

Comment: Acquired from the US on 2 May 1963. Purchased on 1 December 1977. Paid off in 1988 but back in service in 1990.

1 OIL TANKER

Name	No	Builders	Commissioned
TAURUS	TR 65 (ex-T 66)	Astinave, Guayaquil	1985

Measurement, tons: 1175 dwt; 1110 gross
Dimensions, feet (metres): 174.2 × 36 × 14.4 *(53.1 × 11 × 4.4)*
Main machinery: 1 GM diesel; 1050 hp *(783 kW)*; 1 shaft
Speed, knots: 11

Comment: Acquired for the Navy in 1987.

1 ARMAMENT STORES CARRIER (AKF)

Name	No	Builders	Commissioned
CALICUCHIMA (ex-Throsk)	TR 62 (ex-A 379)	Cleland SB Co, Wallsend	20 Sep 1977

Displacement, tons: 2207 full load
Dimensions, feet (metres): 231.2 × 39 × 15 *(70.5 × 11.9 × 4.6)*
Main machinery: 2 Mirrlees-Blackstone diesels; 3000 hp *(2.2 MW)*; 1 shaft
Speed, knots: 14.5. **Range, miles:** 4000 at 11 kts
Complement: 24 (8 officers)

Comment: Acquired from the UK in November 1991. Recommissioned 24 March 1992.

CALICUCHIMA (British colours)   *8/1982, Mike Lennon*

1 WATER CLASS (WATER TANKER)

Name	No	Builders	Commissioned
QUISQUIS (ex-Waterside)	TR 64 (ex-Y 20)	Drypool Engineering & Drydock Co, Hull	1968

Measurement, tons: 285 gross
Dimensions, feet (metres): 131.5 × 24.8 × 8 *(40.1 × 7.5 × 2.4)*
Main machinery: 1 Lister-Blackstone ERS-8-MCR diesel; 660 hp *(492 kW)*; 1 shaft
Speed, knots: 11
Complement: 8

Comment: Acquired from the UK in November 1991.

QUISQUIS (British colours)   *1989*

2 YP TYPE

ISLA DE LA PLATA UT 111   **ISLA PUNA** UT 112

Displacement, tons: 11
Dimensions, feet (metres): 42 × 11.5 × 3.9 *(12.8 × 3.5 × 1.2)*

Comment: Transferred 1962. Ex-US Coast Guard utility boats.

1 YR TYPE

Name	No	Builders	Commissioned
PUTUMAYO (ex-US YR 34)	BT 84 (ex-BT 123, ex-BT 62)	New York Navy Yard	—

Displacement, tons: 770 full load

Comment: Repair barge leased from US July 1962. Purchased on 1 December 1977. Used in conjunction with the Floating Docks.

2 ARD 12 CLASS (FLOATING DOCKS)

Name	No	Builders	Commissioned
AMAZONAS (ex-US ARD 17)	DF 81 (ex-DF 121)	USA	1944
NAPO (ex-US ARD 24)	DF 82	USA	1944

Dimensions, feet (metres): 492 × 81 × 17.7 *(150 × 24.7 × 5.4)*

Comment: *Amazonas* leased from US in 1961 and bought outright in 1982; *Napo* bought in 1988. Suitable for docking ships up to 3200 tons.

TUGS

2 CHEROKEE CLASS

Name	No	Builders	Commissioned
CAYAMBE (ex-USS Cusabo ATF 155)	RA 71 (ex-R 711, ex-R 101, ex-R 51)	Charleston SB & DD Co	28 Apr 1945
CHIMBORAZO (ex-USS Chowanoc ATF 100)	RA 70 (ex-R 710, ex-R 71, ex-R 105)	Charleston SB & DD Co	21 Feb 1945

Displacement, tons: 1235 standard; 1640 full load
Dimensions, feet (metres): 205 × 38.5 × 17 *(62.5 × 11.7 × 5.2)*
Main machinery: Diesel-electric; 4 GM 12-278 diesel generators; 4400 hp *(3.28 MW)*; 1 motor; 3000 hp *(2.24 MW)*; 1 shaft *(Cayambe)*
Diesel-electric; 4 Busch-Sulzer BS-539 diesels; 4 generators; 1 motor; 3000 hp *(2.24 MW)*; 1 shaft *(Chimborazo)*
Speed, knots: 16.5. **Range, miles:** 7000 at 15 kts
Complement: 85
Guns: 1—3 in *(76 mm)*. 2 Bofors 40 mm. 2 Oerlikon 20 mm (not all fitted).

Comment: *Cayambe* launched on 26 February 1945. Fitted with powerful pumps and other salvage equipment. Transferred from US by lease on 2 November 1960 and renamed *Los Rios*. Again renamed *Cayambe* in 1966 and purchased on 30 August 1978. *Chimborazo* transferred 1 October 1977.

CAYAMBE (old number)   *1970, Ecuadorean Navy*

Name	No	Builders	Commissioned
SANGAY (ex-Loja)	RB 72 (ex-R 720, ex-R 102, ex-R 53)	—	1952

Displacement, tons: 295 light; 390 full load
Dimensions, feet (metres): 107 × 26 × 14 *(32.6 × 7.9 × 4.3)*
Main machinery: 1 Fairbanks-Morse diesel; 1 shaft
Speed, knots: 12

Comment: Acquired in 1964. Renamed in 1966.

Name	No	Builders	Commissioned
COTOPAXI (ex-USS R T Ellis)	RB 73 (ex-R 721, ex-R 103, ex-R 52)	Equitable Building Corporation	1945

Displacement, tons: 150
Dimensions, feet (metres): 82 × 21 × 8 *(25 × 6.4 × 2.4)*
Main machinery: 1 Diesel; 650 hp *(478 kW)*; 1 shaft
Speed, knots: 9

Comment: Purchased from the USA in 1947.

ANTIZANA	RB 74 (ex-R 723)	**TUNGURAHUA**	RB 77 (ex-R 722)
SIRIUS	RB 75 (ex-R 724)	**QUILOTOA**	RB 78 (ex-R 726)
ALTAR	RB 76 (ex-R 725)		

Displacement, tons: 490
Dimensions, feet (metres): 100.4 × — × 8.2 *(30.6 × — × 2.5)*
Speed, knots: 8

COAST GUARD

2 PGM-71 CLASS (LARGE PATROL CRAFT)

Name	No	Builders	Commissioned
25 DE JULIO (ex-Quito)	LG 31 (ex-LGC 31, ex-LC 71)	Peterson, USA	30 Nov 1965
24 DE MAYO (ex-Guayaquil)	LG 32 (ex-LGC 32, ex-LC 72)	Peterson, USA	30 Nov 1965

Displacement, tons: 130 standard; 146 full load
Dimensions, feet (metres): 101.5 × 21 × 5 *(30.9 × 6.4 × 1.5)*
Main machinery: 4 diesels; 880 hp *(656 kW)*; 2 shafts
Speed, knots: 21. **Range, miles:** 1000 at 12 kts
Complement: 15
Guns: 1 Bofors 40 mm/60. 4 Oerlikon 20 mm (2 twin). 2—12.7 mm MGs.

Comment: Transferred from US to the Navy under MAP on 30 November 1965 and then to the Coast Guard in 1980. Paid off into reserve in 1983 and deleted from the order of battle. Refitted with new engines in 1988-89.

2 COASTAL PATROL CRAFT

Name	No	Builders	Commissioned
10 DE AGOSTO	LG 33	Schurenstedt, Bardenfleth	Aug 1954
3 DE NOVIEMBRE	LG 34	Schurenstedt, Bardenfleth	Aug 1954

Displacement, tons: 45 standard; 64 full load
Dimensions, feet (metres): 76.8 × 13.5 × 6.2 *(23.4 × 4.6 × 1.9)*
Main machinery: 2 Bohn & Kähler diesels; 1200 hp(m) *(882 kW)*; 2 shafts
Speed, knots: 22. **Range, miles:** 550 at 16 kts
Complement: 9
Guns: 1 or 2—7.62 mm MGs.

Comment: Ordered in 1954. One deleted in 1992.

2 ESPADA CLASS (LARGE PATROL CRAFT)

Name	No	Builders	Commissioned
5 DE AGOSTO	LG 35	Moss Point Marine, Escatawpa	May 1991
21 DE FEBRERO	LG 36	Moss Point Marine, Escatawpa	Nov 1991

Displacement, tons: 190 full load
Dimensions, feet (metres): 112 × 22.5 × 7 *(34.1 × 6.9 × 2.1)*
Main machinery: 2 Detroit 16V-149TI diesels; 2322 hp *(1.73 MW)* sustained; 1 Detroit 16V-92TA; 690 hp *(514 kW)* sustained; 3 shafts
Speed, knots: 27
Complement: 19 (5 officers)
Guns: 1 Bofors 40 mm/60. 2—12.7 mm MGs.
Radars: Surface search: Racal Decca; I band.

Comment: Steel hulls and aluminium superstructure. Accommodation is air-conditioned. Carry a 10 man RIB and launching crane on the stern.

5 DE AGOSTO (gun not fitted)   *1991, Trinity Marine*

2 SWIFTSHIPS CLASS (RIVERINE PATROL CRAFT)

Name	No	Builders	Commissioned
9 DE OCTUBRE	LG 37	Swiftships	1 Oct 1992
27 DE OCTUBRE	LG 38	Swiftships	1 Oct 1992

Displacement, tons: 17 full load
Dimensions, feet (metres): 45.5 × 11.8 × 1.8 *(13.9 × 3.6 × 0.6)*
Main machinery: 2 Detroit 6V-92TA diesels; 900 hp *(671 kW)*; 2 Hamilton waterjets
Speed, knots: 22. **Range, miles:** 600 at 22 kts
Complement: 4
Guns: 2 M2HB 12.7 mm MGs; 2 M60D 7.62 mm MGs.
Radars: Navigation: I band.

Comment: Transferred from US under MAP to the Navy and thence to the Coast Guard. Hard chine modified V hull form. Can carry up to eight troops.

9 DE OCTUBRE   *9/1992, Swiftships*

6 RIO PUYANGO CLASS (RIVERINE PATROL CRAFT)

Name	No	Builders	Commissioned
RIO PUYANGO	LG 41 (ex-LGC 40)	Halter Marine, New Orleans	15 June 1986
RIO MATAGE	LG 42 (ex-LGC 41)	Halter Marine, New Orleans	15 June 1986
RIO ZARUMILLA	LG 43 (ex-LGC 42)	Astinave, Guayaquil	11 Mar 1988
RIO CHONE	LG 44 (ex-LGC 43)	Astinave, Guayaquil	11 Mar 1988
RIO DAULE	LG 45 (ex-LGC 44)	Astinave, Guayaquil	17 June 1988
RIO BABAHOYO	LG 46 (ex-LGC 45)	Astinave, Guayaquil	17 June 1988

Displacement, tons: 17
Dimensions, feet (metres): 44 × 13.5 × 3.5 *(13.4 × 4.1 × 1.1)*
Main machinery: 2 Detroit 8V-71 diesels; 460 hp *(343 kW)* sustained; 2 shafts
Speed, knots: 26. **Range, miles:** 500 at 18 kts
Complement: 5 (1 officer)
Guns: 1—12.7 mm MG. 2—7.62 mm MGs.
Radars: Surface search: Furuno 2400; I band.

Comment: Two delivered by Halter Marine in June 1986. Four more ordered in February 1987; assembled under licence at Astinave shipyard, Guayaquil. Used mainly for drug interdiction.

RIO PUYANGO (old number)   *1/1988, Halter Marine*

14 BAYCRAFT CLASS (RIVER PATROL CRAFT)

Comment: Modified civilian sporting craft purchased in 1980 from the US. 40 ft launches.

EGYPT

Headquarters' Appointment

Commander of Naval Forces:
Vice Admiral Ahmed Ali Fadel

General

The cancellation of US debts on older contracts in 1991 released money to upgrade the Fleet. Operational availability has improved to the point where two-thirds of all units are active. Some vessels which had been laid up are returning to service and the intention is to upgrade many of the older ships.

Personnel

(a) 1994: 18 000 officers and men, including the Coast Guard (Reserves of about 14 000)
(b) 1-3 years' national service (depending on educational qualifications)

Bases

Alexandria, Port Said, Mersa Matru, Abu Qir, Suez. Safaqa and Hurghada on the Red Sea.
Naval Academy: Abu Qir.

Coastal Defences

The Samlet, Otomat and modified CSS-N-1 Styx missiles employed for Coastal Defence by the Border Guard are naval-manned. There are two Coastal Artillery Brigades.

Prefix to Ships' Name

ENS

Strength of the Fleet

Type	Active	Building (Projected)
Submarines (Patrol)	8	(2)
Destroyer	1	—
Frigates	7	—
Fast Attack Craft (Missile)	26	—
Fast Attack Craft (Torpedo)	2	—
Fast Attack Craft (Gun)	8	—
Fast Attack Craft (Patrol)	13	—
LSMs	3	—
LCUs	11	—
Minesweepers (Ocean)	10	—
Minehunters (Inshore)	—	3
Route Survey Vessels	4	(2)
Auxiliaries	17	—
Coast Guard	88	—

Maritime Air

Although the navy has no air arm the Air Force has a number of E2Cs, ASW Sea Kings and Gazelles with an ASM capability (see *Land-based Maritime Aircraft* section). The Sea Kings are controlled by the Anti-Submarine Brigade and have naval sensor operators. Seasprite helicopters may be obtained.

Mercantile Marine

Lloyd's Register of Shipping:
387 vessels of 1 149 046 tons gross

DELETIONS

Amphibious Forces

1991   3 Winchester Hovercraft

Miscellaneous

1991   1 Nyryat class

SUBMARINES

Notes: (1) After several attempts to buy second-hand had come to nothing, a request for quotation on two new construction submarines was made in September 1991. The German-built 209 or Dolphin class seem to be the most likely candidates when funds become available, which may not be for some years unless the US gives assistance. There are also rumours of a second-hand Kilo class acquisition. (2) Some two-man Swimmer Delivery Vehicles (SDVs) of Italian CF2 FX 100 design are in service.

8 ROMEO CLASS

831, 840, 843, 846—ex-USSR
849, 852, 855, 858—ex-Chinese

Displacement, tons: 1475 surfaced; 1830 dived
Dimensions, feet (metres): 251.3 × 22 × 16.1
(76.6 × 6.7 × 4.9)
Main machinery: Diesel-electric; 2 Type 37-D diesels; 4000 hp(m) *(2.94 MW)*; 2 motors; 2700 hp(m) *(1.98 MW)*; 2 creep motors; 2 shafts
Speed, knots: 16 surfaced; 13 dived
Range, miles: 9000 at 9 kts surfaced
Complement: 54

Missiles: SSM: McDonnell Douglas Harpoon; active radar homing to 130 km *(70 nm)* at 0.9 Mach; warhead 227 kg (after modernisation).
Torpedoes: 8—21 in *(533 mm)* tubes (6 bow, 2 stern). 14 SET 53; active/passive homing to 15 km *(8.1 nm)* at 45 kts; warhead 400 kg or Honeywell Mk 37F Mod 2; wire-guided; active/passive homing to 18 km *(9.7 nm)* at 32 kts; warhead 148 kg (after modernisation).
Mines: 28 in lieu of torpedoes.
Countermeasures: ESM: Racal; radar warning
Fire control: Singer Librascope Mk 2 (after modernisation).
Radars: Surface search: Snoop Plate; I band.

Sonars: Hercules or Atlas Elektronik; bow-mounted; active/passive; medium frequency.
Loral; hull-mounted; active attack; high frequency (after modernisation).

Programmes: One Romeo class was transferred to Egypt by the USSR in 1966. Two more replaced Whiskey class in May 1966 and another pair was delivered later that year. The sixth boat joined in 1969. Two transferred from China 22 March 1982. Second pair arrived from China 3 January 1984, commissioned 21 May 1984.
Modernisation: The ex-Soviet submarines have been refitted with limited up-date to bridge the gap until completion of a full modernisation programme of the four ex-Chinese vessels. In early 1988 a five year contract was signed with Tacoma, Washington to retrofit the ex-Chinese submarines with Harpoon, and convert them to fire Mk 37 wire-guided torpedoes; weapon systems improvements to include Loral active sonar, Atlas Elektronik passive sonar and fire-control system. The US Congress did not give approval to start work until July 1989 and a further series of delays in the Tacoma shipyard meant that work did not start until April 1992.
Operational: Two Soviet submarines deleted in 1989 and of the remaining four Soviet type, only two are operational. All based at Alexandria.

ROMEO 843   7/1993

DESTROYER

1 Z CLASS

Name	No	Builders	Laid down	Launched	Commissioned
EL FATEH (ex-*Zenith*, ex-*Wessex*)	921	Wm Denny & Bros, Dumbarton	19 May 1942	5 June 1944	22 Dec 1944

Displacement, tons: 1730 standard; 2575 full load
Dimensions, feet (metres): 362.8 × 35.7 × 16
(110.6 × 10.9 × 4.9)
Main machinery: 2 Admiralty boilers; 2 Parsons turbines; 40 000 hp *(30 MW)*; 2 shafts
Speed, knots: 24. **Range, miles:** 2800 at 20 kts
Complement: 186

Missiles: SAM: 2 SA-N-5 mountings.
Guns: 4 Vickers 4.5 in *(115 mm)*/45 hand-loaded Mk 5 mounting; 50° elevation; 14 rounds/minute to 17 km *(9.3 nm)*; weight of shell 25 kg.
6 China 37 mm/63 (3 twin); 180 rounds/minute to 8.5 km *(4.6 nm)*; weight of shell 1.42 kg.
Torpedoes: 4—21 in *(533 mm)* (quad) tubes. Type 53-56; anti-surface.
Depth charges: 4 projectors.
Fire control: Fly 4 director.
Radars: Air search: Marconi SNW 10; D band.
Surface search: Racal Decca 916; I band.
Fire control: Marconi Type 275; F band.

Programmes: Purchased from the UK in 1955. Before being taken over by Egypt, *El Fateh* was refitted by John I. Thornycroft & Co Ltd, Woolston, Southampton in July 1956, subsequently modernised by J S White & Co Ltd, Cowes, completed in July 1964.
Modernisation: Bofors replaced by Chinese 37 mm guns. Sonars removed. Boilers renewed in 1993 and SA-N-5 mountings fitted.
Operational: Used primarily for sea training, and the intention is to keep the ship in service until at least 2000.

EL FATEH   5/1985, van Ginderen Collection

FRIGATES

1 BLACK SWAN CLASS

Name	No	Builders	Laid down	Launched	Commissioned
TARIQ (ex-*Malek Farouk*, ex-*Whimbrel*)	931	Yarrows, Glasgow	31 Oct 1941	25 Aug 1942	13 Jan 1943

Displacement, tons: 1925 full load
Dimensions, feet (metres): 299 × 38.5 × 11.5 *(91.2 × 11.7 × 3.5)*
Main machinery: 2 Admiralty boilers; 2 Parsons geared turbines; 3600 hp *(2.69 MW)*; 2 shafts
Speed, knots: 18. **Range, miles:** 4500 at 12 kts
Complement: 180

Guns: 6 Vickers 4 in *(102 mm)*/45 (3 twin) Mk 19; 80° elevation; 16 rounds/minute to 19.5 km *(10.5 nm)*; weight of shell 15.9 kg.
4—37 mm (2 twin). 4—12.7 mm MGs.
Depth charges: 4 projectors; 2 racks.
Radars: Surface search: 2 Decca; I band.

Programmes: Transferred from UK in November 1949.
Structure: Still has the original class appearance with some minor modifications to the armament.
Operational: Relegated for a time in the mid-1980s to an accommodation ship and offered as part of a deal involving the acquisition of two Oberon class submarines in 1989. When this project was cancelled, the ship resumed service as a training platform and was described as "running like a train" in 1993.

TARIQ   10/1988, F Sadek

2 KNOX CLASS

Name	No	Builders	Laid down	Launched	Commissioned
DAMYAT (ex-Jesse L Brown)	961 (ex-FF 1089)	Avondale Shipyard	8 Apr 1971	18 Mar 1972	17 Feb 1973
RASHEED (ex-Moinester)	966 (ex-FF 1097)	Avondale Shipyard	25 Aug 1972	12 May 1973	2 Nov 1974

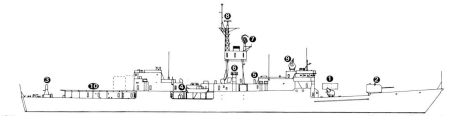

Displacement, tons: 3011 standard; 4260 full load
Dimensions, feet (metres): 439.6 × 46.8 × 15; 24.8 (sonar)
  (134 × 14.3 × 4.6; 7.8)
Main machinery: 2 Combustion Engineering/Babcock & Wilcox
  boilers; 1200 psi (84.4 kg/cm sq); 950°F (510°C); 1 turbine;
  35 000 hp (26 MW); 1 shaft
Speed, knots: 27. **Range, miles:** 4000 at 22 kts on 1 boiler
Complement: 288 (17 officers)

Missiles: SSM: 8 McDonnell Douglas Harpoon; active radar homing to 130 km (70 nm) at 0.9 Mach; warhead 227 kg.
  A/S: Honeywell ASROC Mk 16 octuple launcher with reload system (has 2 cells modified to fire Harpoon) ❶; inertial guidance
  to 1.6-10 km (1-5.4 nm); payload Mk 46.
Guns: 1 FMC 5 in (127 mm)/54 Mk 42 Mod 9 ❷; 85° elevation;
  20-40 rounds/minute to 24 km (13 nm) anti-surface; 14 km
  (7.7 nm) anti-aircraft; weight of shell 32 kg.
  1 General Electric/General Dynamics 20 mm/76 6-barrelled
  Mk 15 Vulcan Phalanx ❸; 3000 rounds/minute combined to
  1.5 km.
Torpedoes: 4—324 mm Mk 32 (2 twin) fixed tubes ❹. 22 Honeywell Mk 46; anti-submarine; active/passive homing to 11 km
  (5.9 nm) at 40 kts; warhead 44 kg.
Countermeasures: Decoys: 2 Loral Hycor SRBOC 6-barrelled
  fixed Mk 36 ❺; IR flares and chaff to 4 km (2.2 nm). T Mk-6
  Fanfare/SLQ-25 Nixie; torpedo decoy. Prairie Masker hull and
  blade rate noise suppression.
  ESM/ECM: SLQ 32(V)2 ❻; radar warning. Sidekick modification
  adds jammer and deception system.
Combat data systems: Link 14 receive only.
Fire control: SWG-1A Harpoon LCS. Mk 68 GFCS. Mk 114 ASW
  FCS. Mk 1 target designation system. MMS target acquisition
  sight (for mines, small craft and low flying aircraft).
Radars: Air search: Lockheed SPS 40B ❼; E/F band; range
  320 km (175 nm).
  Surface search: Raytheon SPS 10 or Norden SPS 67 ❽; G band.
  Navigation: Marconi LN 66; I band.
  Fire control: Western Electric SPG 53A/D/F ❾; I/J band.
  Tacan: SRN 15. IFF: UPX-12.
Sonars: EDO/General Electric SQS 26 CX; bow-mounted; active
  search and attack; medium frequency.
  EDO SQR 18A(V)1; passive towed array; very low frequency.

Helicopters: 1 medium ❿.

Programmes: Lease agreed from US in mid-1993. Both ships
  planned to arrive in Egypt in July 1994. Ships of this class have
  been transferred to Greece, Taiwan and Turkey and transfers
  are planned for Brazil, Morocco, Oman, Spain, Thailand and
  Venezuela in 1994/95.
Modernisation: Vulcan Phalanx replaced Sea Sparrow SAM in
  the mid-1980s. SQS 35 VDS sonar may be retrofitted.

KNOX   (Scale 1 : 1200), Ian Sturton

KNOX (US colours)   9/1993, Maritime Photographic

Structure: Four torpedo tubes are fixed in the midship superstructure, two to a side, angled out at 45°. A lightweight
anchor is fitted on the port side and an 8000 lb anchor fits in to
the after section of the sonar dome.

Operational: The ship carried a medium helicopter in USN service. SH-2G Seasprite are being acquired in due course.

2 JIANGHU I CLASS

Name	No	Builders	Commissioned
NAJIM AL ZAFFER	951	Hutong, Shanghai	27 Oct 1984
EL NASSER	956	Hutong, Shanghai	16 Apr 1985

Displacement, tons: 1425 standard; 1702 full load
Dimensions, feet (metres): 338.5 × 35.4 × 10.2
  (103.2 × 10.8 × 3.1)
Main machinery: 2 Type 12 E 390V diesels; 14 400 hp(m)
  (10.6 MW) sustained; 2 shafts
Speed, knots: 26. **Range, miles:** 4000 at 15 kts
Complement: 195

Missiles: SSM: 4 Hai Ying 2 (Flying Dragon) (2 twin) ❶; active
  radar or passive IR homing to 80 km (43.2 nm) at 0.9 Mach;
  warhead 513 kg.
Guns: 4 China 57 mm/70 (2 twin) ❷; 85° elevation;
  120 rounds/minute to 12 km (6.5 nm); weight of shell 6.31 kg.
  12 China 37 mm/63 (6 twin) ❸; 85° elevation; 180 rounds/
  minute to 8.5 km (4.6 nm); weight of shell 1.42 kg.
A/S mortars: 2 RBU 1200 5-tubed fixed launchers ❹; range
  1200 m; warhead 34 kg.
Depth charges: 2 projectors; 2 racks.
Mines: Up to 60.
Countermeasures: ESM: Elettronica SpA Beta; radar intercept.

NAJIM AL ZAFFER   (Scale 1 : 900), Ian Sturton

Radars: Air search: Type 765 ❺.
  Surface search: Eye Shield ❻; E band.
  Surface search/gun direction: Square Tie; I band; range 73 km
  (40 nm).
  Fire control: Fog Lamp.
  Navigation: Decca; I band.
Sonars: Hull-mounted; active search and attack; high frequency.

Programmes: Ordered from China in 1982. This is a Jianghu I
  class modified with 57 mm guns vice the standard 100 mm.
Modernisation: Combat data system to be fitted together with
  CSEE Naja optronic fire-control directors. There are also plans
  to remove the after superstructure and guns and build a flight
  deck for a LAMPS helicopter.
Structure: The funnel is the rounded version of the Jianghu class.

EL NASSER   5/1992, Hartmut Ehlers

2 DESCUBIERTA CLASS

Name	No	Builders	Laid down	Launched	Commissioned
ABU QIR (ex-Serviola)	F 946	Bazán	28 Feb 1979	20 Dec 1979	27 Oct 1984
EL SUEZ (ex-Centinela)	F 941	Bazán	31 Oct 1978	6 Oct 1979	21 May 1984

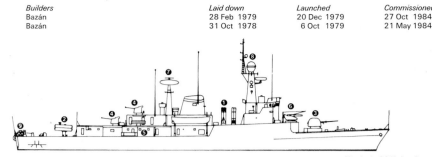

EL SUEZ
(Scale 1 : 900), Ian Sturton

Displacement, tons: 1233 standard; 1479 full load
Dimensions, feet (metres): 291.3 × 34 × 12.5
(88.8 × 10.4 × 3.8)
Main machinery: 4 MTU-Bazán 16V 956 TB91 diesels;
15 000 hp(m) *(11 MW)* sustained; 2 shafts; cp props
Speed, knots: 25.5; 28 trials. **Range, miles:** 4000 at 18 kts
Complement: 116

Missiles: SSM: 8 McDonnell Douglas Harpoon (2 quad) launchers ❶; active radar homing to 130 km *(70 nm)* at 0.9 Mach; warhead 227 kg.
SAM: Selenia Elsag Albatros octuple launcher ❷; 24 Aspide; semi-active radar homing to 13 km *(7 nm)* at 2.5 Mach; height envelope 15-5000 m *(49.2-16 405 ft)*; warhead 30 kg.
Guns: 1 OTO Melara 3 in *(76 mm)*/62 compact ❸; 85° elevation; 85 rounds/minute to 16 km *(8.7 nm)*; weight of shell 6 kg.
2 Bofors 40 mm/70 ❹; 85° elevation; 300 rounds/minute to 12.5 km *(6.8 nm)*; weight of shell 0.96 kg.
Torpedoes: 6—324 mm Mk 32 (2 triple) tubes ❺. MUSL Stingray; anti-submarine; active/passive homing to 11 km *(5.9 nm)* at 45 kts; warhead 35 kg (shaped charge); depth to 750 m *(2460 ft)*.
A/S mortars: 1 Bofors 375 mm twin-barrelled trainable launcher ❻; automatic loading; range 1600 m or 3600 m depending on type of rocket.
Countermeasures: ESM: Elettronica SpA Beta; radar intercept. Prairie Masker; acoustic signature suppression.
Combat data systems: Signaal SEWACO action data automation. Link Y.
Radars: Air/surface search: Signaal DA 05 ❼; E/F band; range 137 km *(75 nm)* for 2 m² target.
Navigation: Signaal ZW 06; I band.
Fire control: Signaal WM 25 ❽; I/J band; range 46 km *(25 nm)*.
Sonars: Raytheon 1160B; hull-mounted; active search and attack; medium frequency.
Raytheon 1167 ❾; VDS; active search; 12-7.5 kHz.

Programmes: Ordered September 1982 from Bazán, Spain. The two Spanish ships *Centinela* and *Serviola* were sold to Egypt prior to completion and transferred after completion at Ferrol and modification at Cartagena. *El Suez* completed 28 February 1984 and *Abu Qir* on 31 July 1984.
Operational: Stabilisers fitted. Modern noise insulation of main and auxiliary machinery.

ABU QIR
10/1991

EL SUEZ
10/1991

LAND-BASED MARITIME AIRCRAFT (FRONT LINE)

Notes: (1) There are plans to purchase SH-2G Seasprite helicopters.
(2) There are also 2/4 Westland Commando Mk 2B/2E helicopters.

Numbers/Type: 16 Aerospatiale SA 342L Gazelle.
Operational speed: 142 kts *(264 km/h)*.
Service ceiling: 14 105 ft *(4300 m)*.
Range: 407 nm *(755 km)*.
Role/Weapon systems: Land-based helicopter for coastal anti-shipping strike, particularly against FAC and insurgents. Sensors: SFIM sight. Weapons: ASV; 2 × AS-12 wire-guided missiles.

Numbers/Type: 4 Grumman E-2C Hawkeye.
Operational speed: 269 kts *(499 km/h)*.
Service ceiling: 30 800 ft *(9390 m)*.
Range: 1350 nm *(2500 km)*.
Role/Weapon systems: Airborne early warning and control tasks; capable of handling up to 30 tracks over water or land. Sensors: APS-125 search/warning radar, various ESM/ECM systems. Weapons: Unarmed.

Numbers/Type: 5 Westland Sea King Mk 47.
Operational speed: 112 kts *(208 km/h)*.
Service ceiling: 14 700 ft *(4480 m)*.
Range: 664 nm *(1230 km)*.
Role/Weapon systems: Shore-based helicopter for ASW and surface search; secondary role as SAR helicopter; may be embarked in due course. Airframe and engine refurbishment in 1990 for first five. A second five are in reserve and out of service. Sensors: MEL search radar. Weapons: ASW; 4 × Mk 46 or Stingray torpedoes or depth bombs. ASV: Otomat.

Numbers/Type: 2 Beechcraft 1900C.
Operational speed: 267 kts *(495 km/h)*.
Service ceiling: 25 000 ft *(7620 m)*.
Range: 1569 nm *(2907 km)*.
Role/Weapon systems: Two (of six) Air Force aircraft acquired in 1988 and used for maritime surveillance. Sensors: Litton search radar; Motorola multi-mode SLAMMR radar; Singer S-3075 ESM; Data Link Y. Weapons: Unarmed.

PATROL FORCES

6 RAMADAN CLASS (FAST ATTACK CRAFT—MISSILE)

Name	No	Builders	Laid down	Launched	Commissioned
RAMADAN	670	Vosper Thornycroft	22 Sep 1978	6 Sep 1979	20 July 1981
KHYBER	672	Vosper Thornycroft	23 Feb 1979	31 Jan 1980	15 Sep 1981
EL KADESSAYA	674	Vosper Thornycroft	24 Apr 1979	19 Feb 1980	6 Apr 1982
EL YARMOUK	676	Vosper Thornycroft	15 May 1979	12 June 1980	18 May 1982
BADR	678	Vosper Thornycroft	29 Sep 1979	17 June 1981	17 June 1982
HETTEIN	680	Vosper Thornycroft	29 Feb 1980	25 Nov 1980	28 Oct 1982

Displacement, tons: 307 full load
Dimensions, feet (metres): 170.6 × 25 × 7.5
(52 × 7.6 × 2.3)
Main machinery: 4 MTU 20V 538 TB91 diesels; 15 360 hp(m)
(11.29 MW) sustained; 4 shafts
Speed, knots: 40. **Range, miles:** 1600 at 18 kts
Complement: 30 (4 officers)

Missiles: SSM: 4 OTO Melara/Matra Otomat Mk 1; active radar
homing to 80 km *(43.2 nm)* at 0.9 Mach; warhead 210 kg.

Guns: 1 OTO Melara 3 in *(76 mm)* compact; 85° elevation; 85
rounds/minute to 16 km *(8.7 nm)*; weight of shell 6 kg.
2 Breda 40 mm/70 (twin); 85° elevation; 300 rounds/minute
to 12.5 km *(6.8 nm)* anti-surface; weight of shell 0.96 kg.
Countermeasures: Decoys: 4 Protean fixed launchers each with
4 magazines containing 36 chaff decoy and IR flare grenades.
ESM: Racal Cutlass; radar intercept.
ECM: Racal Cygnus; jammer.
Combat data systems: Ferranti CAAIS action data automation.
Fire control: Marconi Sapphire System with 2 radar/TV and 2
optical directors.

Radars: Air/surface search: Marconi S 820; E/F band; range
73 km *(40 nm)*.
Navigation: Marconi S 810; I band; range 48 km *(25 nm)*.
Fire control: Two Marconi ST 802; I band.

Programmes: The contract was carried out at the Porchester
yard of Vosper Thornycroft Ltd with some hulls built at Portsmouth Old Yard, being towed to Porchester for fitting out.
Modernisation: The intention is to double the SSM capability
with eight lightweight Otomat or Harpoon.
Operational: Portable SAM SA-N-5 sometimes carried.

RAMADAN   10/1991

6 OSA I (TYPE 205) CLASS (FAST ATTACK CRAFT—MISSILE)

631   633   637   639   641   643

Displacement, tons: 171 standard; 210 full load
Dimensions, feet (metres): 126.6 × 24.9 × 8.9
(38.6 × 7.6 × 2.7)
Main machinery: 3 MTU diesels; 12 000 hp(m) *(8.82 MW)*;
3 shafts
Speed, knots: 35. **Range, miles:** 400 at 34 kts
Complement: 30

Missiles: SSM: 4 SS-N-2A Styx; active radar or IR homing to
46 km *(25 nm)* at 0.9 Mach; altitude pre-set up to 300 m
(984.3 ft); warhead 513 kg.
SAM: SA-N-5 Grail; manual aiming; IR homing to 6 km *(3.2 nm)* at
1.5 Mach; altitude to 2500 m *(8000 ft)*; warhead 1.5 kg.
Guns: 4 USSR 30 mm/65 (2 twin); 85° elevation; 500 rounds/
minute to 5 km *(2.7 nm)* anti-aircraft; weight of shell 0.54 kg.
2—12.7 mm MGs.
Countermeasures: ESM: Thomson-CSF DR 875; radar warning.
ECM: Racal; jammer.
Radars: Air/surface search: Kelvin Hughes; I band.
Navigation: Racal Decca 916; I band.
Fire control: Drum Tilt; H/I band.
IFF: High Pole. Square Head.

Programmes: Thirteen reported to have been delivered to Egypt
by the Soviet Navy in 1966-68 but some were sunk in war with
Israel, October 1973. Four of the remaining seven were derelict in 1989 but one more was back in service in 1991 and two
more in 1993.
Modernisation: Refitted with MTU diesels and two machine
guns.

OSA 633   1986

6 OCTOBER CLASS (FAST ATTACK CRAFT—MISSILE)

781   783   785   787   789   791

Displacement, tons: 82 full load
Dimensions, feet (metres): 84 × 20 × 5 *(25.5 × 6.1 × 1.3)*
Main machinery: 4 CRM 12 D/SS diesels; 5000 hp(m) *(3.67 MW)* sustained; 4 shafts
Speed, knots: 40. **Range, miles:** 400 at 30 kts
Complement: 20

Missiles: SSM: 2 OTO Melara/Matra Otomat Mk 1; active radar homing to 80 km *(43.2 nm)* at
0.9 Mach; warhead 210 kg.
Guns: 4 BMARC/Oerlikon 30 mm/75 (2 twin); 85° elevation; 650 rounds/minute to 10 km
(5.5 nm) anti-surface; 3 km *(1.6 nm)* anti-aircraft; weight of shell 1 kg and 0.36 kg mixed.
Countermeasures: Decoys: 2 Protean fixed launchers each with 4 magazines containing 36 chaff
decoy and IR flare grenades.
ESM: Racal Cutlass; radar warning.
Fire control: Marconi Sapphire radar/TV system.
Radars: Air/surface search: Marconi S 810; range 48 km *(25 nm)*.
Fire control: Marconi/ST 802; I band.

Programmes: Built in Alexandria 1975-76. Hull of same design as USSR Komar class. Refitted by
Vosper Thornycroft, completed 1979-81. 791 was washed overboard on return trip, recovered
and returned to Portsmouth for refit. Left UK after repairs on 12 August 1982. Probably Link
fitted.

OCTOBER   7/1980, van Ginderen Collection

6 HEGU and 2 KOMAR CLASSES (FAST ATTACK CRAFT—MISSILE)

603 (Komar)   **607** (Komar)   **609**   **611**   **613**   **615**   **617**   **619**

Displacement, tons: 68 standard; 79.2 full load
Dimensions, feet (metres): 88.6 × 20.7 × 4.3 *(27 × 6.3 × 1.3)*
Main machinery: 4 Type L-12V-180 diesels; 4800 hp(m) *(3.53 MW)*; 4 shafts
Speed, knots: 37.5. **Range, miles:** 400 at 30 kts
Complement: 17 (2 officers)

Missiles: SSM: 2 SY-1 or SSN-2A Styx (Komar); active radar or passive IR homing to 40 km *(22 nm)* at 0.9 Mach; warhead 513 kg.
Guns: 2—23 mm (twin); locally constructed to fit 25 mm mounting.
Radars: Air/surface search: Square Tie; I band; range 73 km *(40 nm)*.
IFF: High Pole A.

Programmes: All Hegu class acquired from China and commissioned in Egypt on 27 October 1984. The two Komars were transferred from the USSR in the mid-1960s and paid off in 1986. They were reactivated in 1991. Two more may also be put back in service in due course. The Hegu is the Chinese version of the Komar.

HEGU 615   *4/1988, A Sheldon Duplaix*

6 SHERSHEN CLASS
(FAST ATTACK CRAFT—2 TORPEDO, 4 GUN)

751   **753**   **755**   **757**   **759**   **761**

Displacement, tons: 145 standard; 170 full load
Dimensions, feet (metres): 113.8 × 22 × 4.9 *(34.7 × 6.7 × 1.5)*
Main machinery: 3 Type M 503A diesels; 8025 hp(m) *(5.9 MW)* sustained; 3 shafts
Speed, knots: 45. **Range, miles:** 850 at 30 kts
Complement: 23

Missiles: SAM: SA-N-5 Grail *(755-761)*; manual aiming; IR homing to 6 km *(3.2 nm)* at 1.5 Mach; warhead 1.5 kg.
Guns: 4 USSR 30 mm/65 (2 twin); 85° elevation; 500 rounds/minute to 5 km *(2.7 nm)*; weight of shell 0.54 kg.
2 USSR 122 mm rocket launchers *(755-761* in lieu of torpedo tubes); 20 barrels per launcher; range 9 km *(5 nm)*.
Torpedoes: 4—21 in *(533 mm)* tubes *(751* and *753)*. Soviet Type 53; dual purpose; pattern active/passive homing up to 20 km *(10.8 nm)* at up to 45 kts; warhead 400 kg.
Depth charges: 12.
Countermeasures: ESM: Thomson-CSF DR 875; radar warning.
Radars: Surface search: Pot Drum; H/I band.
Fire control: Drum Tilt, H/I band.
IFF: High Pole.

Programmes: Five delivered from USSR in 1967 and two more in 1968. One deleted. 753 completed an extensive refit at Ismailia in 1987; 751 in 1988.
Structure: The last four have had their torpedo tubes removed to make way for multiple BM21 rocket-launchers and one SA-N-5 Grail.

SHERSHEN 757   *1990, US Navy*

4 SHANGHAI II CLASS
(FAST ATTACK CRAFT—GUN)

793   **795**   **797**   **799**

Displacement, tons: 113 standard; 131 full load
Dimensions, feet (metres): 127.3 × 17.7 × 5.6 *(38.8 × 5.4 × 1.7)*
Main machinery: 2 Type L12-180 diesels; 2400 hp(m) *(1.76 MW)* (forward); 2 Type L12-180Z diesels; 1820 hp(m) *(1.34 MW)* (aft); 4 shafts
Speed, knots: 30. **Range, miles:** 700 at 16.5 kts
Complement: 34

Guns: 4 China 37 mm/63 (2 twin); 85° elevation; 180 rounds/minute to 8.5 km *(4.6 nm)*; weight of shell 1.42 kg.
4—23 mm (2 twin); locally constructed to fit the 25 mm mountings.
Mines: Rails can be fitted for 10 mines.
Radars: Surface search: Pot Head; I band; range 37 km *(20 nm)*.
IFF: High Pole.

Programmes: Transferred from China in 1984.
Structure: Painted black.

SHANGHAI II 793   *3/1987*

8 HAINAN CLASS (FAST ATTACK CRAFT—PATROL)

AL NOUR 430	**AL HADY** 433	**AL HAKIM** 436	**AL WAKIL** 439
AL QATAR 442	**AL SADDAM** 445	**AL SALAM** 448	**AL RAFIA** 451

Displacement, tons: 375 standard; 392 full load
Dimensions, feet (metres): 192.8 × 23.6 × 7.2 *(58.8 × 7.2 × 2.2)*
Main machinery: 4 PRC/Kolomna Type 9-D-8 diesels; 4000 hp *(2.94 MW)* sustained; 4 shafts
Speed, knots: 30.5. **Range, miles:** 1300 at 15 kts
Complement: 69

Guns: 2 or 4 China 57 mm/70 (1 or 2 twin); 85° elevation; 120 rounds/minute to 12 km *(6.5 nm)*; weight of shell 6.31 kg.
4—23 mm (2 twin); locally constructed to fit the 25 mm mountings.
Torpedoes: 6—324 mm (2 triple) tubes (in two of the class). Mk 44 or MUSL Stingray.
A/S mortars: 4 RBU 1200 fixed 5-tubed launchers; range 1200 m; warhead 34 kg.
Depth charges: 2 projectors; 2 racks. 18 DCs.
Mines: Rails fitted. 12 mines.
Radars: Surface search: Pot Head or Skin Head; I band.
Navigation: Decca; I band.
IFF: High Pole.
Sonars: Stag Ear; hull-mounted; active search and attack; high frequency.

Programmes: First pair transferred from China in October 1983, next three in February 1984 (commissioned 21 May 1984) and last three late 1984.
Modernisation: Two fitted with torpedo tubes and with Singer Librascope fire-control. If successful the remainder of the class may follow.

HAINAN (Chinese colours)   *9/1991*

5 MODIFIED P 6 CLASS (FAST ATTACK CRAFT—PATROL)

701   **703**   **719**   **+2**

Displacement, tons: 73 full load
Dimensions, feet (metres): 85.3 × 20 × 4.9 *(26 × 6.1 × 1.5)*
Main machinery: 4 Type M 50 diesels; 4400 hp(m) *(3.2 MW)* sustained; 4 shafts
Speed, knots: 41. **Range, miles:** 450 at 30 kts
Complement: 15
Missiles: SAM: SA-N-5 Grail; IR homing to 6 km *(3.2 nm)* at 1.5 Mach; warhead 1.5 kg.
Guns: 2—25 mm/80 (twin); 85° elevation; 270 rounds/minute to 3 km *(1.6 nm)*.
1 BM 21 122 mm 8-barrelled rocket launcher; range 9 km *(5 nm)*.
Torpedoes: 2 or 4—21 in *(533 mm)* tubes (not in all).
Radars: Surface search: Racal Decca 1230; I band.

Comment: Paid off in the mid-1980s, these five were brought out of reserve in 1991. Originally acquired from the USSR 1960-62 and since modified with multi-barrelled rocket launchers.

P 6   *1991*

AMPHIBIOUS FORCES

Note: There are plans to build landing craft locally, probably to a Chinese design. There is also the possibility of leasing an LST/LSM from the US.

2 SMB 1 CLASS (LCUs)

374   **376**

Displacement, tons: 360 full load
Dimensions, feet (metres): 159.1 × 21.3 × 6.6 *(48.5 × 6.5 × 2)*
Main machinery: 2 diesels; 600 hp(m) *(441 kW)*; 2 shafts
Speed, knots: 10
Complement: 16
Military lift: 180 tons

Comment: Delivered from USSR in 1965. Deleted in error in 1991.

3 POLNOCHNY A (TYPE 770) CLASS (LSMs)

301	303	305

Displacement, tons: 800 full load
Dimensions, feet (metres): 239.5 × 27.9 × 5.8 *(73 × 8.5 × 1.8)*
Main machinery: 2 Kolomna Type 40-D diesels; 4400 hp(m) *(3.2 MW)* sustained; 2 shafts
Speed, knots: 19. **Range, miles:** 1000 at 18 kts
Complement: 40
Military lift: 6 tanks; 350 tons
Guns: 2 USSR 30 mm/65 (twin); 85° elevation; 500 rounds/minute to 5 km *(2.7 nm)*; weight of shell 0.54 kg.
2—140 mm rocket launchers; 18 barrels to 9 km *(4.9 nm)*.
Radars: Surface search: Spin Trough; I band.
Fire control: Drum Tilt; H/I band.

Comment: Built at Northern Shipyard, Gdansk and transferred from USSR 1973-74. All used for Gulf logistic support in 1990-91. SA-N-5 may be carried.

POLNOCHNY A   1987

9 VYDRA CLASS (LCUs)

330	332	334	336	338	340	342	344	346

Displacement, tons: 425 standard; 600 full load
Dimensions, feet (metres): 179.7 × 25.3 × 6.6 *(54.8 × 7.7 × 2)*
Main machinery: 2 Type 3-D-12 diesels; 600 hp(m) *(440 kW)* sustained; 2 shafts
Speed, knots: 11. **Range, miles:** 2500 at 10 kts
Complement: 20
Military lift: 200 troops; 250 tons
Guns: 2 or 4—37 mm/63 (1 or 2 twin) (may be fitted).

Comment: Built in late 1960s, transferred from USSR 1968-69. For a period after the Israeli war of October 1973 several were fitted with rocket launchers and two 37 or 40 mm guns, some of which have now been removed. At least two are in reserve.

VYDRA 332   10/1992, F Sadek

5 SEAFOX TYPE (SWIMMER DELIVERY CRAFT)

21	23	27	28	30

Displacement, tons: 11.3 full load
Dimensions, feet (metres): 36.1 × 9.8 × 2.6 *(11 × 3 × 0.8)*
Main machinery: 2 GM 6V-92TA diesels; 520 hp *(388 kW)* sustained; 2 shafts
Speed, knots: 30. **Range, miles:** 200 at 20 kts
Complement: 3
Guns: 2—12.7 mm MGs. 2—7.62 mm MGs.
Radars: Surface search: LN 66; I band.

Comment: Ordered from Uniflite, Washington in 1982. GRP construction painted black. There is a strong underwater team in the Egyptian Navy which is also known to use commercial two-man underwater chariots. Based at Abu Qir.

SEAFOX   1993

MINE WARFARE FORCES

6 T 43 CLASS (MINESWEEPERS—OCEAN)

GHARBIYA 501	DAQAHLIYA 507	SINAI 513
SHARKIYA 504	BAHARIYA 510	ASSIOUT 516

Displacement, tons: 580 full load
Dimensions, feet (metres): 190.2 × 27.6 × 6.9 *(58 × 8.4 × 2.1)*
Main machinery: 2 Kolomna Type 9-D-8 diesels; 2000 hp(m) *(1.47 MW)* sustained; 2 shafts
Speed, knots: 15. **Range, miles:** 3000 at 10 kts
Complement: 65
Guns: 4—37 mm/63 (2 twin); 85° elevation; 160 rounds/minute to 9 km *(5 nm)*; weight of shell 0.7 kg.
8—12.7 mm MGs.
Mines: Can carry 20.
Radars: Navigation: Don 2; I band.
Sonars: Stag Ear; hull-mounted; active search; high frequency.

Comment: Delivered in the early 1970s from the USSR. Others of the class have been sunk or used as targets or cannibalised for spares. The plan to fit them with VDS sonars and ROVs has been shelved in favour of new minehunters.

SINAI   7/1992, F Sadek

4 YURKA CLASS (MINESWEEPERS—OCEAN)

GIZA 530	ASWAN 533	QENA 536	SOHAG 539

Displacement, tons: 460 full load
Dimensions, feet (metres): 171.9 × 30.8 × 8.5 *(52.4 × 9.4 × 2.6)*
Main machinery: 2 Type M 503 diesels; 5350 hp(m) *(3.91 MW)* sustained; 2 shafts
Speed, knots: 17. **Range, miles:** 1500 at 12 kts
Complement: 60
Guns: 4 USSR 30 mm/65 (2 twin); 85° elevation; 500 rounds/minute to 5 km *(2.7 nm)*; weight of shell 0.54 kg.
Mines: Can lay 10.
Radars: Navigation: Don; I band.
Sonars: Stag Ear; hull-mounted; active search; high frequency.

Comment: Steel-hulled minesweepers transferred from the USSR in 1969. Built 1963-69. Egyptian Yurka class do not carry Drum Tilt radar and have a number of ship's-side scuttles. The plan to equip them with VDS sonar may have been shelved in favour of new minehunters. At least one operates an ROV.

GIZA   10/1986

0 + 3 SWIFTSHIPS TYPE (COASTAL MINEHUNTERS)

Displacement, tons: 175 full load
Dimensions, feet (metres): 110 × 27 × 8 *(33.5 × 8.2 × 2.4)*
Main machinery: 2 MTU 12V 183 TE61 diesels; 1068 hp(m) *(786 kW)*; 2 shafts
Speed, knots: 12.4. **Range, miles:** 2000 at 10 kts
Complement: 25 (5 officers)
Guns: 2—12.7 mm MGs.
Radars: Navigation: Sperry; I band.
Sonars: Thoray/Thomson Sintra TSM 2022; hull-mounted; active minehunting; high frequency.

Comment: MCM vessels with GRP hulls ordered from Swiftships in 1991 with FMS funding. First one to be delivered in September 1994. Fitted with a Paramax command data handling system. GPS and line-of-sight navigation system. The ROV is a Gayrobot Pluto.

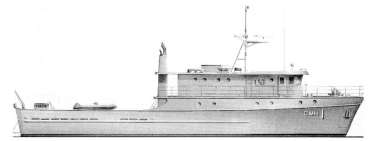

SWIFTSHIPS MCMV (artist's impression)   1991, Swiftships

2 K 8 CLASS (ROUTE SURVEY VESSELS)

SAFAGA 610   **ABU EL GHOSON** 613

Displacement, tons: 26 full load
Dimensions, feet (metres): 55.4 × 10.5 × 3.9 *(16.9 × 3.2 × 1.2)*
Main machinery: 2 Type 3-D-6 diesels; 300 hp(m) *(220 kW)* sustained; 2 shafts
Speed, knots: 18. **Range, miles:** 300 at 10 kts
Complement: 18 (4 officers)
Guns: 2—14.5 mm (twin) MGs.

Comment: Built in Poland and launched in 1968. Transferred from the USSR in 1969.

2 + (2) SWIFTSHIPS TYPE (ROUTE SURVEY VESSELS)

RSV 1   **RSV 2**

Displacement, tons: 165 full load
Dimensions, feet (metres): 90 × 24.8 × 8 *(27.4 × 7.6 × 2.4)*
Main machinery: 2 MTU 12V 183 TA 61 diesels; 928 hp(m) *(682 kW)*; 2 shafts; bow thruster; 60 hp(m) *(44 kW)*
Speed, knots: 12. **Range, miles:** 1500 at 10 kts
Complement: 16 (2 officers)
Guns: 1—12.7 mm MG.
Radars: Navigation: Furuno; I band.
Sonars: EG & G sidescan; active; high frequency.

Comment: Route survey vessels ordered from Swiftships in late 1990 and delivered in September 1993. Two more are to be built in Egyptian yards. Paramax command system. Provision for both shallow and deep towed bodies.

RSV 1   *9/1993, Swiftships*

AUXILIARIES

Note: There are also two survey launches *Misaha 1* and *2* with a crew of 14. Both were commissioned in 1991.

7 TOPLIVO 2 CLASS (TANKERS)

| AYEDA 4 210 | MARYUT ATBARAH 215 | AL NIL | AL BURULLUS |
| AKDU 214 | AYEDA 3 216 | AL FURAT | |

Displacement, tons: 1029 full load
Dimensions, feet (metres): 176.2 × 31.8 × 10.5 *(53.7 × 9.7 × 3.2)*
Main machinery: 1 6DR 30/50-5 diesel; 600 hp(m) *(441 kW)*; 1 shaft
Speed, knots: 10. **Range, miles:** 400 at 7 kts
Complement: 16
Cargo capacity: 500 tons diesel (some used for water)

Comment: Built in Egypt in 1972-77 to a USSR design.

TOPLIVO 2 (Russian colours)   *1990, van Ginderen Collection*

1 NYRYAT I CLASS

Displacement, tons: 120 full load
Dimensions, feet (metres): 93 × 18 × 5.5 *(28.4 × 5.5 × 1.7)*
Main machinery: 1 diesel; 450 hp(m) *(330 kW)*; 1 shaft
Speed, knots: 12
Complement: 15

Comment: Diving support ship transferred from USSR in 1964.

2 POLUCHAT I CLASS

Displacement, tons: 100 full load
Dimensions, feet (metres): 97.1 × 19 × 4.8 *(29.6 × 5.8 × 1.5)*
Main machinery: 2 Type M 50 diesels; 2200 hp(m) *(1.6 MW)* sustained; 2 shafts
Speed, knots: 20
Complement: 15

Comment: Torpedo recovery craft transferred from USSR.

POLUCHAT I   *11/1992*

TUGS

6 OKHTENSKY CLASS

| AL MEKS 103 | ANTAR 107 | AL ISKANDARANI 111 |
| AL AGAMI 105 | AL DIKHILA 109 | KALIR 113 |

Displacement, tons: 930 full load
Dimensions, feet (metres): 156.1 × 34 × 13.4 *(47.6 × 10.4 × 4.1)*
Main machinery: Diesel-electric; 2 BM diesel generators; 1 motor; 1500 hp(m) *(1.1 MW)*; 1 shaft
Speed, knots: 13. **Range, miles:** 6000 at 13 kts
Complement: 38

Comment: Two transferred from USSR in 1966, others assembled in Egypt.

AL AGAMI   *5/1991, F Sadek*

AMIRA RAMA

Comment: An ex-trawler used as a lighthouse tender and acquired by the Navy in 1987.

TRAINING SHIPS

5 TRAINING SHIPS

Comment: *Al Kousser* is a 1000 ton vessel belonging to the Naval Academy. *Intishat* is a 500 ton training ship. Pennant number 160 is a USSR Sekstan class used as a cadet training ship. Two YSB training craft acquired from the USA in 1989. A 3300 ton training ship *Aida IV* presented by Japan in 1988 for delivery in March 1992 belongs to the Arab Maritime Transport Academy.

PRESIDENTIAL YACHT

EL HORRIYA

Comment: Taken out of retirement in 1992 and prepared for the Columbus celebrations in Italy. In the end she did not go but is reported to be serviceable.

COAST GUARD

12 SPECTRE CLASS (COASTAL PATROL CRAFT)

Displacement, tons: 37 full load
Dimensions, feet (metres): 64.9 × 18 × 5.9 *(19.8 × 5.5 × 1.8)*
Main machinery: 3 GM 8V-71TI diesels; 1800 hp *(1.3 MW)*; 3 shafts
Speed, knots: 29. **Range, miles:** 450 at 25 kts
Complement: 9 (1 officer)
Guns: 2—12.7 mm MGs.

Comment: Built by Peterson, Sturgeon Bay and delivered in 1980/81. Mostly used for Customs duties.

13 TIMSAH CLASS (LARGE PATROL CRAFT)

01-13

Displacement, tons: 106 full load
Dimensions, feet (metres): 101.8 × 17 × 4.8 *(30.5 × 5.2 × 1.5)*
Main machinery: 2 MTU 8V 331 TC92 diesels; 1770 hp *(1.3 MW)* sustained; 2 shafts (first 6); 2 MTU 12V 331 TC92 diesels; 2660 hp(m) *(1.96 MW)* sustained; 2 shafts (second 6)
Speed, knots: 25
Complement: 13
Guns: 2 Oerlikon 30 mm (twin) or 2 Oerlikon 20 mm.

Comment: First three completed December 1981, second three December 1982 at Timsah SY, Ismailia. Further six ordered in January 1985 and completed in 1988-89 with a different type of engine and with waterline exhaust vice a funnel. Last of class in service in 1992 and more may be built in due course. One reported sunk in late 1993.

TIMSAH 2 (with funnel)   7/1992, F Sadek

11 SWIFTSHIPS 93 ft CLASS

322   332   335-342   346

Displacement, tons: 102 full load
Dimensions, feet (metres): 93.2 × 18.7 × 4.9 *(28.4 × 5.7 × 1.5)*
Main machinery: 2 MTU 12V 331 TC92 diesels; 2660 hp(m) *(1.96 MW)* sustained; 2 shafts
Speed, knots: 27. **Range, miles:** 900 at 12 kts
Complement: 14 (2 officers)
Guns: 2—23 mm (twin) (fwd); 1 Oerlikon 20 mm (aft).
Radars: Surface search: Furuno; I band.

Comment: Ordered November 1983. First three built in USA, remainder assembled by Osman Shipyard, Ismailia. First four commissioned 16 April 1985. Armament being upgraded with 23 mm guns fitted forward.

SWIFTSHIPS 336   1/1985

5 NISR CLASS (LARGE PATROL CRAFT)

NISR 713   THAR   NUR   NIMR   BAHR

Displacement, tons: 110 full load
Dimensions, feet (metres): 102 × 18 × 4.9 *(31 × 5.2 × 1.5)*
Main machinery: 2 Maybach diesels; 3000 hp(m) *(2.2 MW)*; 2 shafts
Speed, knots: 24
Guns: 1 Oerlikon 20 mm.
Radars: Surface search: Racal Decca 909; I band.

Comment: Built by Castro, Port Said. First three launched in May 1963. Two more completed 1983.

6 CRESTITALIA 70 ft CLASS (COASTAL PATROL CRAFT)

Displacement, tons: 36 full load
Dimensions, feet (metres): 68.9 × 17.4 × 3 *(21 × 5.3 × 0.9)*
Main machinery: 2 MTU 12V 331 TC92 diesels; 2660 hp(m) *(1.96 MW)* sustained; 2 shafts
Speed, knots: 35. **Range, miles:** 500 at 32 kts
Guns: 2 Oerlikon 30 mm A32 (twin). 1 Oerlikon 20 mm.

Comment: Ordered 1980—GRP hulls. Naval manned, employed on Coast Guard duties.

CRESTITALIA 70 ft   1980, Crestitalia

7 BERTRAM TYPE (COASTAL PATROL CRAFT)

702-708

Displacement, tons: 3 full load
Dimensions, feet (metres): 28 × 10.2 × 1.3 *(8.5 × 3.1 × 0.4)*
Main machinery: 2 Mercury diesels; 340 hp *(254 kW)*; 2 shafts
Speed, knots: 36
Guns: 2—7.62 mm MGs.

Comment: GRP hulls. Built in Miami, Florida in 1973. Armament changed on transfer. One of the original 20 craft is part of a permanent military Panorama Exhibition in Cairo.

BERTRAM Type   10/1974

30 DC 35 TYPE

Displacement, tons: 4 full load
Dimensions, feet (metres): 35.1 × 11.5 × 2.6 *(10.7 × 3.5 × 0.8)*
Main machinery: 2 diesels; 390 hp *(287 kW)*; 2 shafts
Speed, knots: 25
Complement: 4

Comment: Built by Dawncraft, Wroxham, UK, from 1977. Harbour launches.

4 DAMEN TYPE TUGS

KHOUFOU   KHAFRA   RAMSES   KREIR

Comment: Delivered by Damen, Netherlands in 1982.

EL SALVADOR

Senior Officer	Personnel	Bases	Mercantile Marine
Commander of the Navy: Captain Mario Argueta Franco	(a) 1994: 2200 (including a Naval Infantry Battalion and a Commando Company) (b) Voluntary service	Acajutla, La Libertad, El Triunfo y La Union	*Lloyd's Register of Shipping:* 13 vessels of 1634 tons gross

PATROL FORCES

3 CAMCRAFT TYPE (COASTAL PATROL CRAFT)

GC 6,   GC 7,   GC 8

Displacement, tons: 100 full load
Dimensions, feet (metres): 100 × 21 × 4.9 *(30.5 × 6.4 × 1.5)*
Main machinery: 3 Detroit 12V-71TA diesels; 1260 hp *(939 kW)* sustained; 3 shafts
Speed, knots: 25. **Range, miles:** 780 at 24 kts
Complement: 10
Guns: 1 Oerlikon 20 mm or 1–12.7 mm MG. 2–7.62 mm MGs. 1–81 mm mortar.
Radars: Surface search: Racal Decca; I band.

Comment: Delivered October, November, December 1975. Refitted in 1986. Sometimes carry a combined 12.7 mm MG/81 mm mortar mounting in the stern.

GC 8   *1993, Julio Montes*

1 SWIFTSHIPS 65 ft CLASS (COASTAL PATROL CRAFT)

GC 10

Displacement, tons: 36 full load
Dimensions, feet (metres): 65.6 × 18.3 × 5 *(20 × 6 × 1.5)*
Main machinery: 2 Detroit 12V-71TA diesels; 840 hp *(626 kW)* sustained; 2 shafts
Speed, knots: 23. **Range, miles:** 600 at 18 kts
Complement: 6
Guns: 1 Oerlikon 20 mm. 1 or 2–12.7 mm MGs. 1–81 mm mortar.
Radars: Surface search: Furuno; I band.

Comment: Aluminium hull. Delivered by Swiftships, Morgan City in June 1984. Was laid up for a time in 1989/90 but became operational again in 1991.

GC 10   *1993, Julio Montes*

1 SWIFTSHIPS 77 ft CLASS (COASTAL PATROL CRAFT)

GC 11

Displacement, tons: 48 full load
Dimensions, feet (metres): 77.1 × 20 × 4.9 *(23.5 × 6.1 × 1.5)*
Main machinery: 3 Detroit 12V-71TA diesels; 1260 hp *(939 kW)* sustained; 3 shafts
Speed, knots: 26
Guns: 2–12.7 mm MGs. Aft MG combined with 81 mm mortar.
Radars: Surface search: Furuno; I band.

Comment: Aluminium hull. Delivered by Swiftships, Morgan City in June 1985.

GC 11   *1993, Julio Montes*

6 PIRANHA CLASS (RIVER PATROL CRAFT)

LDF 021-026

Displacement, tons: 8.2 full load
Dimensions, feet (metres): 36 × 10.1 × 1.6 *(11 × 3.1 × 0.5)*
Main machinery: 2 Caterpillar 3208TA diesels; 680 hp *(507 kW)* sustained; 2 shafts
Speed, knots: 26
Complement: 5
Guns: 2–12.7 mm (twin) MGs. 2–7.62 mm (twin) MGs.
Radars: Surface search: Furuno 3600; I band.

Comment: Riverine craft with Kevlar hulls. Completed in March 1987 by Lantana Boatyard, Florida. Same type supplied to Honduras.

LDF 021   *1993, Julio Montes*

10 PROTECTOR CLASS (RIVER PATROL CRAFT)

LP 03 01-10

Displacement, tons: 9 full load
Dimensions, feet (metres): 40.4 × 13.4 × 1.4 *(12.3 × 4 × 0.4)*
Main machinery: 2 Caterpillar 3208TA diesels; 680 hp *(507 kW)* sustained; 2 shafts
Speed, knots: 28. **Range, miles:** 350 at 20 kts
Complement: 4
Guns: 2–12.7 mm MGs. 2–7.62 mm MGs.
Radars: Navigation: Furuno 3600; I band.

Comment: Ordered in December 1987 from SeaArk Marine (ex-MonArk). Five delivered in December 1988 and the remainder in February and March 1989.

LP 03 06   *1993, Julio Montes*

10 MERCOUGAR RIVERINE CRAFT

LP 04 1-5   LR 1-5

Comment: Five 40 ft monohulls *(LP 04)* and five 35 ft catamarans *(LR)* completed by Mercougar, Miami in 1988-89. Both types are powered by two Ford Merlin diesels, 600 hp *(448 kW)*, giving speeds up to 40 kts. The 40 ft craft have a range of 556 km *(300 nm)* which extends to 741 km *(400 nm)* in the 35 ft version. One 40 ft craft is equipped as a hospital vessel. There are also some Boston Whalers in service.

2 LCM 8

LD 2   **LD 3**

Displacement, tons: 113 full load
Dimensions, feet (metres): 72 × 20.5 × 4.8 *(22 × 6.3 × 1.4)*
Main machinery: 2 GM 6-71 diesels; 348 hp *(260 kW)* sustained; 2 shafts
Speed, knots: 9.5
Complement: 9
Guns: 1—12.7 mm (can be carried).

Comment: Transferred by the USA in January 1987. An older LCM 6 has been scrapped.

LD 03   *1992, Julio Montes*

EQUATORIAL GUINEA

Personnel

1994: 120 officers and men

Bases

Malabo (Fernando Po), Bata (Rio Muni)

Mercantile Marine

Lloyd's Register of Shipping:
  2 vessels of 3457 tons gross

PATROL FORCES

2 SHANTOU CLASS

Displacement, tons: 60 standard; 80 full load
Dimensions, feet (metres): 83.5 × 19 × 6.5 *(25.5 × 5.8 × 2)*
Main machinery: 2 Type 3-D-12 diesels; 600 hp(m) *(460 kW)* sustained; 2 Type M 50 diesels;
  2200 hp(m) *(1.6 MW)* sustained; 4 shafts
Speed, knots: 28. **Range, miles:** 500 at 28 kts
Complement: 17
Guns: 4—37 mm/63 (2 twin). 2—12.7 mm MGs.
Radars: Surface search: Skin Head; I band; range 37 km *(20 nm).*

Comment: Transferred by China in 1983. Doubtful operational status but seen alongside in 1993.

1 LANTANA TYPE

ISLA DE BIOKO

Displacement, tons: 33 full load
Dimensions, feet (metres): 68.8 × 18 × 4 *(21 × 5.5 × 1.5)*
Main machinery: 2 Detroit 8V-92TA diesels; 700 hp *(522 kW)* sustained; 2 shafts
Speed, knots: 24. **Range, miles:** 800 at 15 kts
Guns: 2—12.7 mm MGs. 2—7.62 mm MGs.
Radars: Surface search: Furuno; I band.

Comment: Completed in July 1988 by Lantana Boatyard, Florida, and paid for by USA.

1 VAN MILL TYPE

RIOWELE (ex-*P 220*)

Displacement, tons: 45 full load
Dimensions, feet (metres): 66.3 × 17.4 × 5.9 *(20.2 × 5.3 × 1.8)*
Main machinery: 2 MTU diesels; 2200 hp(m) *(1.62 MW)*; 2 shafts
Speed, knots: 35. **Range, miles:** 950 at 25 kts
Complement: 12 (2 officers)
Guns: 1 Rheinmetall 20 mm. 2—7.62 mm MGs.

Comment: Built by Van Mill, Netherlands in 1986 and transferred from Nigeria. This was one of the
  second group of three fitted with MTU diesels vice the GM type of the first batch.

ISLA DE BIOKO   *1987, Lantana Boatyard*

ESTONIA

General

Negotiations started in 1992 to form an independent Coast
Guard. Finland and Sweden have transferred patrol craft at no
cost.

Base

Tallinn

Mercantile Marine

Lloyd's Register of Shipping:
  262 vessels of 686 364 tons gross

PATROL FORCES

Note: Up to six Osa I class may be transferred from Germany in 1994. These are to be demilitarised
with missile and gun systems removed. The selected vessels are *Max Reichpietsch* (751), *Richard
Sorge* (713), *August Lüttgens* (732), *Karl Meseberg* (733), *Walter Kramer* (712) and *Paul Schulze*
(752).

0 + 2 KONDOR I CLASS

(ex-*Meteor*)   (ex-*Komet*)

Displacement, tons: 377 full load
Dimensions, feet (metres): 170.3 × 23.3 × 7.2 *(51.9 × 7.1 × 2.2)*
Main machinery: 2 Russki Kolomna diesels; 4408 hp(m) *(3.24 MW)* sustained; 2 shafts
Speed, knots: 20
Complement: 24
Radars: Navigation: TSR 333; I band.

Comment: Former GDR intelligence collection vessels. Built at Peenewerft, Wolgast and commissioned in 1972. Planned to be transferred in 1994 but this is still to be confirmed.

METEOR (German colours)   *3/1991, Hartmut Ehlers*

3 KOSKELO CLASS (COASTAL PATROL CRAFT)

101 (ex-*Kuikka*)   **102** (ex-*Tavi*)   **103** (ex-*Kurki*)

Displacement, tons: 95 full load
Dimensions, feet (metres): 95.1 × 16.4 × 4.9 *(29 × 5 × 1.5)*
Main machinery: 2 MTU MB diesels; 2700 hp(m) *(1.98 MW)*; 2 shafts
Speed, knots: 23
Complement: 11
Guns: 1 Oerlikon 20 mm.

Comment: Acquired from the Finnish Coast Guard in November 1992 and transferred on 15 September 1993. Steel hulled craft built between 1955 and 1960 and modernised in 1973.

KOSKELO   *1991, Finnish Frontier Guard*

2 ZHUK CLASS (COASTAL PATROL CRAFT)

Displacement, tons: 50 full load
Dimensions, feet (metres): 75.4 × 17 × 6.2 *(23 × 5.2 × 1.9)*
Main machinery: 2 Type M 50 diesels; 2200 hp(m) *(1.6 MW)* sustained; 2 shafts
Speed, knots: 30. **Range, miles:** 1100 at 15 kts
Complement: 17
Guns: 2—14.5 mm (twin) MGs.
Radars: Surface search: Spin Trough; I band.

Comment: Acquired from Russia in late 1992. In poor condition and may be scrapped.

ZHUK   1990

1 LARGE PATROL CRAFT

ex-Kemio

Displacement, tons: 340 full load
Dimensions, feet (metres): 118.1 × 29.5 × 9.8 *(36 × 9 × 3)*
Main machinery: 1 diesel; 670 hp(m) *(492 kW)*; 1 shaft
Speed, knots: 11
Complement: 10
Guns: 2—23 mm/60 (twin).

Comment: Built in 1958 as a buoy tender and converted to a command ship in 1983. Transferred in December 1992 having paid off from the Finnish Navy. Armament changed in 1988.

Ex-KEMIO (old number and old gun)   *1987, Finnish Navy*

3 INSHORE PATROL CRAFT

001 (ex-*KBV 257*)   **002** (ex-*KBV 259*)   **003** (ex-*KBV 246*)

Displacement, tons: 17 full load
Dimensions, feet (metres): 63 × 13.1 × 4.3 *(19.2 × 4 × 1.3)*
Main machinery: 2 Volvo Penta TAMD120A diesels; 700 hp(m) *(515 kW)*; 2 shafts
Speed, knots: 22
Complement: 5

Comment: Transferred on 4 April 1992, 20 October 1993 and 6 December 1993. Former Swedish Coast Guard vessel built in 1970. Similar craft to Latvia and Lithuania, and more may be acquired.

001   *8/1993*

AUXILIARIES

1 MAYAK CLASS (TRANSPORT)

TORI 003

Displacement, tons: 920 full load
Dimensions, feet (metres): 178.1 × 30.5 × 11.8 *(54.3 × 9.3 × 3.6)*
Main machinery: 1 diesel; 1000 hp(m) *(735 kW)*; 1 shaft
Speed, knots: 12. **Range, miles:** 11 000 at 11 kts
Cargo capacity: 240 tons
Radars: Navigation: Spin Trough; I band.

Comment: Converted trawler transferred from Russia in 1992.

TORI   *1992*

RESEARCH SHIP

1 AKEDEMIK SHULEYKIN CLASS

ARNOLD VEIMER

Displacement, tons: 2000 full load
Dimensions, feet (metres): 236.2 × 42.6 × 15.4 *(72 × 13 × 4.7)*
Main machinery: 2 Gorkiy G-74 diesels; 3060 hp(m) *(2.25 MW)*; 2 shafts
Speed, knots: 14
Complement: 70

Comment: Built by Laivateollisuus, Finland in 1983. Ice strengthened. Works for Estonia Academy and is painted dark blue.

ARNOLD VEIMER   *3/1989, van Ginderen Collection*

ETHIOPIA AND ERITREA

General

In 1993 it seemed likely that Eritrea would form a separate Navy based at Massawa and Dahlak, while the remains of the Ethiopian fleet either used Aseb or retreated to Djibouti. Of the 10 ships which sought sanctuary in Yemen in May 1991, some were scuttled, but those that went to Saudi Arabian ports have returned. One or two of the patrol craft listed under *Deletions* in 1992 may now be back in service but the whole Navy was dormant throughout 1993 so it is difficult to be certain. In early 1994 discussions were still continuing about the division of the Navy, and there has been agreement for Ethiopia to use the port of Aseb.

Bases

Massawa, Aseb, Dahlak, Djibouti

Mercantile Marine

Lloyd's Register of Shipping:
    28 vessels of 69 585 tons gross

DELETIONS

Frigates

1991-92   *Ethiopia* (Hulk in Yemen port)

Patrol Forces

1990-92   3 Osa II class, 2 Turya class, 1 Mol class, 1 Swiftships 105 ft class, 2 Zhuk class, 4 Boghammar, 4 Sewart class

Amphibious Forces

1990-92   2 Chamo class (civilian), 4 T 4 class, 1 Edic class

---

FRIGATES

2 PETYA II CLASS

F 1616   F 1617

Displacement, tons: 950 standard; 1180 full load
Dimensions, feet (metres): 268.3 × 29.9 × 9.5 *(81.8 × 9.1 × 2.9)*
Main machinery: CODAG; 1 Type 61V-3 diesel on centre shaft; 5400 hp(m) *(3.97 MW)* sustained; 2 gas-turbines on outer shafts; 30 000 hp(m) *(22 MW)*; 3 shafts; cp prop on centre shaft
Speed, knots: 32. **Range, miles:** 4870 at 10 kts; 450 at 29 kts
Complement: 98 (8 officers)

Guns: 4 USSR 3 in *(76 mm)*/60 (2 twin) ❶; 80° elevation; 90 rounds/minute to 15 km *(8 nm)*; weight of shell 6.8 kg.
    1 Multi Barrelled Rocket Launcher (MBRL) is mounted on the stern ❷.
    1—12.7 mm MG.
Torpedoes: 5—16 in *(406 mm)* (1 quin) tubes ❸. SAET-40; dual purpose; active/passive homing to 10 km *(5.4 nm)* at 30 kts; warhead 100 kg.
A/S mortars: 2 RBU 6000 12-tubed trainable mountings ❹; range 6000 m; warhead 31 kg.
Depth charges: 2 racks.
Mines: 22.
Countermeasures: ESM: Watch Dog; radar warning.
Radars: Air search: Strut Curve ❺; F band.
Navigation: Don 2; I band.
Fire control: Hawk Screech ❻; I band.
IFF: High Pole B.
Sonars: Hull-mounted; active search and attack; medium frequency.

Programmes: First transferred from USSR 21 July 1983; second 19 March 1984. Both were towed to Massawa by USSR warships. F 1616 was named *Zerai Deres* but this had been expunged by 1990.
Structure: This is the standard armament except that one MBRL replaces the after quintuple torpedo tubes.
Operational: In early 1993 F 1616 was at Dahlak. F 1617 was at Djibouti throughout 1993.

F 1616   *(Scale 1 : 900), Ian Sturton*

F 1616   *1990, Ethiopian Navy*

PATROL FORCES

1 OSA II CLASS (FAST ATTACK CRAFT—MISSILE)

FMB 163

Displacement, tons: 245 full load
Dimensions, feet (metres): 126.6 × 24.9 × 8.8 *(38.6 × 7.6 × 2.7)*
Main machinery: 3 Type M 504 diesels; 10 800 hp(m) *(7.94 MW)* sustained; 3 shafts
Speed, knots: 37. **Range, miles:** 800 at 30 kts
Complement: 30

Missiles: SSM: 4 SS-N-2A Styx; active radar or IR homing to 46 km *(25 nm)* at 0.9 Mach; warhead 513 kg.
Guns: 4—30 mm/65 (2 twin); 85° elevation; 500 rounds/minute to 5 km *(2.7 nm)* anti-aircraft; weight of shell 0.54 kg.
Radars: Surface search: Square Tie; I band.
Fire control: Drum Tilt; H/I band.
IFF: Square Head. High Pole B.

Programmes: Acquired from USSR on 13 January 1981. Based at Djibouti. The rest of the class has been sunk or scuttled except one which may be repairable.

1 MOL CLASS (FAST ATTACK CRAFT—TORPEDO)

FTB 111

Displacement, tons: 160 standard; 200 full load
Dimensions, feet (metres): 127.9 × 26.6 × 5.9 *(39 × 8.1 × 1.8)*
Main machinery: 3 Type M 504 diesels; 10 800 hp(m) *(7.94 MW)* sustained; 3 shafts
Speed, knots: 36. **Range, miles:** 1250 at 14 kts
Complement: 25 (3 officers)
Guns: 4—30 mm/65 (2 twin); 85° elevation; 500 rounds/minute to 5 km *(2.7 nm)*; weight of shell 0.54 kg.
Torpedoes: 4—21 in *(533 mm)* tubes. SAET-60; passive homing to 15 km *(8.1 nm)* at 40 kts; warhead 400 kg.
Depth charges: 12.
Radars: Surface search: H/I band.
Fire control: Drum Tilt; H/I band.
IFF: Square Head. High Pole B.

Comment: Transferred from USSR January 1978. Seen in Djibouti in 1993. One other may be repairable.

FMB 163   *1991*

FTB 111   *1989*

6 SUPER DVORA CLASS (FAST ATTACK CRAFT—GUN)

Displacement, tons: 54 full load
Dimensions, feet (metres): 71 × 18 × 5.9 (screws) *(21.6 × 5.5 × 1.8)*
Main machinery: 3 Detroit 16V-92TA diesels; 2070 hp *(1.54 MW)* sustained; 3 shafts
Speed, knots: 46. **Range, miles:** 1200 at 17 kts
Complement: 9
Guns: 2—23 mm (twin).
Depth charges: 1 rail.
Radars: Surface search: Raytheon; I band.

Comment: Built by Israeli Aircraft Industries and delivered from July 1993 to the Eritreans at Massawa. The details given are for the three engine version of the craft. If there are only two engines the top speed is 36 kts.

SUPER DVORA   *1993, IAI*

2 SWIFTSHIPS 105 ft CLASS (LARGE PATROL CRAFT)

P 203   P 204

Displacement, tons: 118 full load
Dimensions, feet (metres): 105 × 23.6 × 6.5 *(32 × 7.2 × 2)*
Main machinery: 2 MTU MD 16V 538 TB90 diesels; 6000 hp(m) *(4.41 MW)* sustained; 2 shafts
Speed, knots: 30. **Range, miles:** 1200 at 18 kts
Complement: 21
Guns: 4 Emerlec 30 mm (2 twin); 80° elevation; 600 rounds/minute to 6 km *(3.3 nm)*; weight of shell 0.35 kg.
2—23 mm (twin) (201). 2—12.7 mm (twin) (203, 204).
Radars: Surface search: Decca RM 916; I band.

Comment: Six ordered in 1976 of which four were delivered in April 1977 before the cessation of US arms sales to Ethiopia. Built by Swiftships, Louisiana. One deserted to Somalia and served in that Navy for a time. These two are based at Djibouti. One more may be repairable.

P 203   1989

1 PGM 53 CLASS (LARGE PATROL CRAFT)

P 15

Displacement, tons: 146 full load
Dimensions, feet (metres): 95 × 19 × 5.2 *(29 × 5.8 × 1.6)*
Main machinery: 4 diesels; 2200 hp *(1.64 MW)*; 2 shafts
Speed, knots: 21. **Range, miles:** 1500 at 18 kts
Complement: 20
Guns: 1 Bofors 40 mm/60. 1—12.7 mm MG.

Comment: Built by Peterson for the US Navy and commissioned in 1962. Transferred and then paid off in 1986. Seen again at sea in 1992.

PGM 53   1980

2 ZHUK CLASS (COASTAL PATROL CRAFT)

P 206 (ex-*PC 17*)   P 207

Displacement, tons: 39 full load
Dimensions, feet (metres): 78.7 × 16.4 × 3.9 *(24 × 5 × 1.2)*
Main machinery: 2 Type M 401B diesels; 2200 hp(m) *(1.6 MW)* sustained; 2 shafts
Speed, knots: 30. **Range, miles:** 1100 at 15 kts
Complement: 12 (3 officers)
Guns: 2—14.5 mm (twin) MGs.
Radars: Surface search: Spin Trough; I band.

Comment: First two delivered from USSR 9 October 1982 in Fizik Korchatov. Second pair arrived in Assad on 9 June 1990. Two destroyed in 1991.

P 206 (old number)   *1985*

AMPHIBIOUS FORCES

2 POLNOCHNY B (TYPE 771) CLASS

LTC 1037   LTC 1038

Displacement, tons: 760 standard; 834 full load
Dimensions, feet (metres): 246.1 × 31.5 × 7.5 *(75 × 9.6 × 2.3)*
Main machinery: 2 Kolomna Type 40-D diesels; 4400 hp(m) *(3.2 MW)* sustained; 2 shafts
Speed, knots: 19. **Range, miles:** 1000 at 18 kts
Complement: 40
Military lift: 350 tons including 6 tanks; 180 troops
Guns: 4—30 mm (2 twin). 2—140 mm rocket launchers; range 9 km *(4.9 nm)*.
Radars: Surface search: Don 2; I band.
Fire control: Drum Tilt; H/I band.

Comment: Built at Northern Shipyard, Gdansk. First transferred under tow from USSR 9 November 1981, second 8 January 1983. Both still operational.

POLNOCHNY 1038   *1990, Ethiopian Navy*

1 EDIC CLASS

LTC 1036

Displacement, tons: 250 standard; 670 full load
Dimensions, feet (metres): 193.5 × 39.2 × 4.2 *(59 × 12 × 1.3)*
Main machinery: 2 SACM MGO 175 V12 diesels; 1200 hp(m) *(882 kW)* sustained; 2 shafts
Speed, knots: 12. **Range, miles:** 1800 at 8 kts
Complement: 16 (1 officer)
Military lift: 5 heavy vehicles or 11 personnel carriers
Guns: 4 DCN 20 mm (2 twin).

Comment: Two of the class completed by SFCN, Villeneuve la Garenne, France in May 1977. Cargo deck space 28.5 × 5 m *(93.5 × 16.4 ft)*. One deleted in 1990. This one was non-operational in 1992/93 but may be repairable. Based at Massawa.

LTC 1036   *1990, Ethiopian Navy*

1 NATYA CLASS (MINESWEEPER—OCEAN)

634

Displacement, tons: 770 full load
Dimensions, feet (metres): 200.1 × 31.8 × 8.9 *(61 × 9.7 × 2.7)*
Main machinery: 2 Type M 504 diesels; 7200 hp(m) *(5.3 MW)* sustained; 2 shafts
Speed, knots: 19. **Range, miles:** 4000 at 10 kts
Complement: 65
Guns: 4—30 mm/65 (2 twin); 85° elevation; 500 rounds/minute to 5 km *(2.7 nm)*; weight of shell
    0.54 kg.
    4—25 mm/80 (2 twin); 270 rounds/minute to 3 km *(1.6 nm)*; weight of shell 0.34 kg.
A/S mortars: 2 RBU 1200 five-tubed fixed launchers; range 1200 m; warhead 34 kg.
Mines: 10.
Radars: Surface search: Don 2; I band.
Sonars: Hull-mounted; active minehunting; high frequency.

Comment: Acquired from Russia in October 1991 but then took shelter in Aden until returning to
    Massawa in July 1992. In consequence, for a period, was mistaken for a Yemeni naval vessel.

SONYA (Russian colours)   *1991, Ships of the World*

NATYA 634   *10/1991, Foto Flite*

1 SONYA CLASS (MINESWEEPER—COASTAL)

441

Displacement, tons: 400 full load
Dimensions, feet (metres): 157.4 × 28.9 × 6.6 *(48 × 8.8 × 2)*
Main machinery: 2 Kolomna 9-D-8 diesels; 2000 hp(m) *(1.47 MW)* sustained; 2 shafts
Speed, knots: 15. **Range, miles:** 3000 at 10 kts
Complement: 43
Guns: 2—30 mm/65 (twin); 85° elevation; 500 rounds/minute to 5 km *(2.7 nm)*; weight of shell
    0.54 kg.
    2—25 mm/80 (twin); 85° elevation; 270 rounds/minute to 3 km *(1.6 nm)*.
Mines: 8.
Radars: Surface search: Don 2; I band.

Comment: Acquired from Russia in January 1991 but sheltered in Aden from 1991 to mid-1992
    and like Natya 634 was mistaken for a Yemeni vessel. Based at Djibouti.

AUXILIARY

1 TOPLIVO 2 CLASS (TANKER)

A 502

Displacement, tons: 1029 full load
Dimensions, feet (metres): 176.2 × 31.8 × 10.5 *(53.7 × 9.7 × 3.2)*
Main machinery: 1 6DR 30/50-5 diesel; 600 hp(m) *(441 kW)*; 1 shaft
Speed, knots: 10.5. **Range, miles:** 400 at 7 kts
Complement: 23
Cargo capacity: 500 tons fuel
Guns: 2—12.7 mm MGs.
Radars: Navigation: Don; I band.

Comment: Acquired from USSR in 1989-90. Not reported in 1993 and may have been sunk.

A 502   *1990, Ethiopian Navy*

FAEROES

COAST GUARD

1 PATROL CRAFT

TJALDRID

Displacement, tons: 650 full load
Dimensions, feet (metres): 146 × 33.1 × 10.5 *(44.5 × 10.1 × 3.2)*
Main machinery: 2 MWM diesels; 2400 hp(m) *(1.76 MW)*; 2 shafts
Speed, knots: 14.5
Complement: 18
Guns: 1 Oerlikon 20 mm can be carried.

Comment: Originally a commercial tug built in 1976 by Svolvaer, Verksted and acquired by the
    local government in 1987. Although Denmark retains control of defence, the Coast Guard and
    Fisheries come under the Landsstyri which is the islands' local government. The ship is based at
    Tórshavn on the island of Streymoy. The old 57 mm gun has been replaced.

1 PATROL SHIP

ÓLAVUR HALGI

Measurement, tons: 748 grt
Dimensions, feet (metres): 200.1 × 31.2 × 10 *(61 × 9.5 × 3.1)*
Main machinery: 1 MAN diesel; 1470 hp(m) *(1.08 MW)*; 1 shaft; bow thruster
Speed, knots: 15. **Range, miles:** 8000 at 11 kts
Complement: 20 plus 4 divers
Guns: 1 Oerlikon 20 mm.
Radars: Surface search: 2 Raytheon TM/TCPA; I band.
    Navigation: Furuno; I band.

Comment: A former trawler built in Portugal but converted at Svendborg Shipyard in 1978 for
    duties with the Faeroes Government. Refitted in 1991/92 and back in service. Carries towing,
    pumping, salvage and fire-fighting equipment. The ship is based at Torshavn where the crew
    changes every two weeks or so. Also used as a training ship and has comprehensive navigation
    equipment.

TJALDRID   *1993, Royal Danish Navy*

ÓLAVUR HALGI   *1993, Royal Danish Navy*

FALKLAND ISLANDS

General

A dependent territory of the United Kingdom. The capital and principle town is at Stanley. In 1987 Britain declared a fishing zone off the Falklands within which only licensed ships may work. On 26 December 1990 a further outer zone was declared, extending the original zones. No fishing is allowed in this outer area. Both zones were patrolled by two vessels throughout the year but in 1993 it was decided to reduce this to two ships in high season (first half of the year) and one for the remainder. Ships have red hulls and white superstructures.

Aircraft

There are also two Pilatus Britten-Norman Defender unarmed maritime surveillance aircraft.

Mercantile Marine

Lloyd's Register of Shipping:
  6 vessels of 15 260 tons gross

DELETIONS

Patrol Forces

1991   *Falkland Sound* (civilian), *Mount Kent* (civilian)
1993   *Falkland Protector, Falkland Desire*

PATROL FORCES

CORDELLA

Measurement, tons: 1535 grt
Dimensions, feet (metres): 226 × 41.7 × 20 *(68.9 × 12.7 × 6.1)*
Main machinery: 1 Mirrlees diesel; 3246 hp(m) *(2.39 MW)*; 1 shaft; cp prop
Speed, knots: 16
Complement: 25

Comment: Built in 1974. Fishery patrol vessel chartered from Marr, Hull in January 1993. Ice class III hull. Carries two RIBs capable of 30 kts. Sister ship to *Northella* on charter to the British Navy.

RESOLUTION

Measurement, tons: 800 grt
Dimensions, feet (metres): 173.2 × 31.3 × 18 *(52.8 × 9.5 × 5.5)*
Main machinery: 2 Klockner Humboldt Deutz SBV M536 diesels; 1800 hp(m) *(1.32 MW)*; 2 shafts; cp props; bow thruster; 258 hp(m) *(190 kW)*
Speed, knots: 13.5
Complement: 12 + 16 spare

Comment: An oceanographic vessel chartered from Gardline Surveys to act as the second, or back up, ship to *Cordella* in 1994. Carries an Avon Searider RIB.

CORDELLA   *1993, Falkland Islands*

RESOLUTION   *1993, Gardline Surveys*

FIJI

Headquarters' Appointments

Commander, Military Forces:
  Brigadier E G Ganilau MC, MSD
Commander, Navy:
  Commander J V Bainimarama

Personnel

1994: 276

Base

FNS *Viti,* at Togalevu (Training).
Operation base at Walu Bay, Suva.

General

On 12 June 1975 the then Royal Fiji Military Forces were authorised to raise a Naval Division to carry out Fishery Protection, Surveillance, Hydrographic Surveying and Coast Guard duties. On 14 May 1987 a military coup overthrew the government and Fiji became a Republic on 10 October 1987. The Fiji Navy comes under the authority of the Minister of Home Affairs, and has been accountable to the CinC Military Forces since June 1989.

Prefix to Ships' Names

FNS

Mercantile Marine

Lloyd's Register of Shipping:
  60 vessels of 38 653 tons gross

DELETIONS

1991   *Kikau* (old)
1993   *Tovuto* (civilian)

PATROL FORCES

1 REDWING CLASS (TRAINING SHIP)

Name	No	Builders	Commissioned
KIRO (ex-USS *Warbler*, MSC 206)	206	Bellingham SY, USA	23 July 1955

Displacement, tons: 370 full load
Dimensions, feet (metres): 144 × 28 × 8.5 *(43.9 × 8.5 × 2.5)*
Main machinery: 2 GM 8-268A diesels; 880 hp *(656 kW)*; 2 shafts
Speed, knots: 12. **Range, miles:** 3300 at 8 kts
Complement: 28
Guns: 1 Oerlikon 20 mm. 2—12.7 mm MGs.
Radars: Navigation: SPS 5C; I band.
Sonars: UQS-1B; hull-mounted; high frequency active.

Comment: Transferred from US in June 1976. Formerly a minesweeper but retained in 1991 as a training ship. *Kula* (deleted in 1990) was the only one of the class to have a helicopter platform.

KIRO   *1989, Ships of the World*

1 + 2 PACIFIC FORUM CLASS (LARGE PATROL CRAFT)

Name	No	Builders	Commissioned
KULA	—	Transfield Shipbuilding	28 May 1994
KIKAU	—	Transfield Shipbuilding	May 1995
RUVE	—	Transfield Shipbuilding	Oct 1995

Displacement, tons: 162 full load
Dimensions, feet (metres): 103.3 × 26.6 × 6.9 *(31.5 × 8.1 × 2.1)*
Main machinery: 2 Caterpillar 3516TA diesels; 2820 hp *(2.09 MW)* sustained; 2 shafts
Speed, knots: 20. **Range, miles:** 2500 at 12 kts
Complement: 17
Guns: 1—12.7 mm MG.

Comment: Ordered in December 1992. These are hulls 17, 19 and 20 of the class offered by the Australian Government under UD Defence Co-operation. Transfield is the former ASI.

PACIFIC FORUM   *1991, G Toremans*

1 COASTAL PATROL/TRAINING CRAFT

CAGIDONU

Displacement, tons: 304 full load
Dimensions, feet (metres): 113.2 × 24.3 × 13.5 *(34.5 × 7.4 × 4.1)*
Main machinery: 1 GM 12V-71 diesel; 1 shaft
Speed, knots: 9
Complement: 16

Comment: Built by Fiji Marine Shipyard, Suva in 1978 as a Presidential Motor Yacht. Transferred to the Navy in 1992.

2 COASTAL PATROL CRAFT

LEVUKA 101   **LAUTOKA** 102

Displacement, tons: 97 full load
Dimensions, feet (metres): 110 × 24 × 5 *(33.8 × 7.4 × 1.5)*
Main machinery: 4 GM 12V-71TA diesels; 1680 hp *(1.25 MW)* sustained; 4 shafts
Speed, knots: 12
Guns: 1—12.7 mm MG.

Comment: Built in 1979-80 by Beaux's Bay Craft Inc, Louisiana as oil rig support craft. Purchased in September 1987 and commissioned on 22 and 28 October 1987 respectively. All aluminium construction.

LAUTOKA   *1992, Fiji Navy*

4 VAI (DABUR) CLASS (COASTAL PATROL CRAFT)

VAI 301		**SAKU** 303
OGO 302		**SAQA** 304

Displacement, tons: 39 full load
Dimensions, feet (metres): 64.9 × 18 × 5.8 *(19.8 × 5.5 × 1.8)*
Main machinery: 4 GM 12V-71TA diesels; 1680 hp *(1.25 MW)* sustained; 4 shafts
Speed, knots: 19. **Range, miles:** 450 at 13 kts
Complement: 9
Guns: 1 Oerlikon 20 mm. 1—12.7 mm MG.
Radars: Surface search: Racal Decca Super 101 Mk 3; I band.

Comment: Built in mid-1970s by Israeli Aircraft Industries and transferred from Israel 22 November 1991. Torpedo tubes are not fitted.

SAQA   *1993, Fiji Navy*

FINLAND

Headquarters' Appointments

Commander-in-Chief Defence Forces:
  Admiral Jan Klenberg
Commander-in-Chief Finnish Navy:
  Rear Admiral Sakari Visa
Chief Engineer Defence Forces:
  Rear Admiral (E) Auvo Vappula
Chief of Staff FNHQ:
  Captain Seppo Lintula

Diplomatic Representation

Defence Attaché in London:
  Colonel Risto Noopila
Defence Attaché in Moscow:
  Colonel Lauri Kiianlinna
Defence Attaché in Paris:
  Lieutenant Colonel Jukka Roiha
Defence Attaché in Washington:
  Colonel Pertti Suominen
Defence Attaché in Bonn:
  Commander Matti Mäkinen
Defence Attaché in Brussels:
  Captain Juhani Kaskeala

Treaty Limitations

The Treaty of Paris (1947) limited the Navy to 10 000 tons of ships and 4500 personnel with submarines and torpedo boats prohibited. In September 1990 the government announced that these limitations were no longer valid.

Personnel

(a) 1994: 1800 (200 officers, 500 POs and 1100 conscripts)
(b) 11 months' national service
(c) 600 Frontier Guards

Fleet Organisation

Organisation changed on 1 January 1993.
Gulf of Finland Naval Command; main base Uppinniemi, Helsinki.
Archipelago Sea Naval Command; main base Turku.
Not all ships are fully manned all the time but all are rotated on a regular basis.

Coastal Artillery

The following vessels are used by the Coastal Artillery: *Vahakari, Vaarlahti, Vänö, Kampela 1* and *2, Pyhäranta,* two Lohi class, six Hauki class, *Askeri, Parainen, Träskö, Torsö.* There are also numerous smaller vessels.

Strength of the Fleet

Type	Active	Building (Planned)
Corvettes	2	—
Fast Attack Craft (Missile)	11	—
Fast Attack Craft (Gun)	5	—
Large Patrol Craft	5	—
Coastal Patrol Craft	1	—
Minelayers	7	—
Minesweepers, Inshore	13	—
Tugs	2	—
Command Craft	8	—
Transports (Landing Craft)	46	—
Cable Ship	1	—
Icebreakers	10	—
Support and Transport Ships	14	—

Frontier Guard

All Frontier Guard vessels come under the Ministry of the Interior.

Type	Active	Building
Large Patrol Craft	8	1 (2)

Hydrographic Department

This office and the survey ships come under the Ministry of Trade and Industry.

Icebreakers

All these ships work for the Board of Navigation.

Mercantile Marine

Lloyd's Register of Shipping:
  274 vessels of 1 354 332 tons gross

DELETIONS

Minelayers

1992 *Keihässalmi*

Patrol Forces

1992 *Kuikka, Tavi, Kurki, Telkkä* (three to Estonia, November 1992), *Nuoli 5*

Auxiliaries

1991 *Pansio* (old), *Porkkala* (old)
1992 *Kemiö* (to Estonia), *Kala 2, Kala 5, Vihuri*
1993 *Kala 3*

PENNANT LIST

Corvettes		61	Turku	Auxiliaries		420	Parainen
		62	Oulu			431	Hakuni
03	Turunmaa	63	Kotka	91	Viiri	436	Houtskar
04	Karjala	70	Rauma	92	Putsaari	452	Lohm
		71	Raahe	97	Valas	511	Jymy
Patrol Forces		72	Porvoo	98	Mursu	521	Raju
		73	Naantali	99	Kustaanmiekka	531	Syöksy
12	Tuisku			121	Vahakari	541	Vinha
14	Tuuli			133	Havouri	731	Haukipää
15	Tyrsky	Mine Warfare Forces		171	Kala 1	776	Kala 6
30	Hurja			222	Vaarlahti	799	Hylje
38	Nuoli 8	01	Pohjanmaa	232	Hauki	831	Kallanpää
40	Nuoli 10	02	Hämeenmaa	235	Hirsala	874	Kala 4
41	Nuoli 11	05	Uusimaa	237	Hila	877	Kampela 3
42	Nuoli 12	11	Tuima	238	Harun	899	Halli
43	Nuoli 13	21-26	Kuha 21-26	241	Askeri	992	Träskö
51	Rihtniemi	475	Pyhäranta	251	Lohi	993	Torsö
52	Rymättylä	521-		272	Kampela 2		
53	Ruissalo	527	Kiiski 1-7	323	Vänö		
54	Raisio	777	Porkkala	334	Hankoniemi		
55	Röytta	826	Isku	339	Hästö		
60	Helsinki	876	Pansio	371	Kampela 1		

CORVETTES

2 TURUNMAA CLASS

Name	No	Builders	Laid down	Launched	Commissioned
TURUNMAA	03	Wärtsilä, Helsinki	Mar 1967	11 July 1967	29 Aug 1968
KARJALA	04	Wärtsilä, Helsinki	Mar 1967	16 Aug 1967	21 Oct 1968

Displacement, tons: 660 standard; 770 full load
Dimensions, feet (metres): 243.1 × 25.6 × 7.9
(74.1 × 7.8 × 2.4)
Main machinery: CODOG; 1 RR Olympus TM1A gas-turbine;
15 000 hp *(11.2 MW)* sustained; 3 MTU MB diesels; 3000
hp(m) *(2.2 MW)*; 3 shafts; cp props
Speed, knots: 35; 17 diesel. **Range, miles:** 2500 at 14 kts
Complement: 70

Guns: 1 Bofors 4.7 in *(120 mm)*/46 ❶; 80° elevation; 80
rounds/minute to 18.5 km *(10 nm)*; weight of shell 21 kg.
6—103 mm rails for illuminants are fitted on the side of the
mounting.
2 Bofors 40 mm/70 ❷; 90° elevation; 300 rounds/minute to
12 km (6.6 nm); weight of shell 0.96 kg.
4 USSR 23 mm/87 (2 twin) ❸.
A/S mortars: 2 RBU 1200 5-tubed fixed launchers ❹ (mounted
inside main deck superstructure abaft the pennant number);
range 1200 m; warhead 34 kg.
Depth charges: 2 racks.
Countermeasures: Decoys: Wallop Barricade double chaff
launcher.
ESM: Argo ❺; radar intercept.

Fire control: SAAB EOS-400 optronic director ❻.
Radars: Surface search: Terma 20T 48 Super ❼; E/F band.
Fire control: Signaal WM 22 ❽; I/J band; range 46 km *(25 nm)*.
Navigation: Raytheon ARPA; I band.
Sonars: Hull-mounted; active search and attack; high frequency.
Optimised for operations in archipelago waters.

Programmes: Ordered on 18 February 1965.

Modernisation: Both completed refit at the Wärtsilä Shipyard,
Turku in 1986. New equipment included radar, EW and sonar.
Structure: Flush decked. Fitted with Vosper Thornycroft fin
stabiliser equipment. The exhaust system is trunked on either
side of the quarter-deck, the two plumes coalescing some 50 ft
abaft the stern.

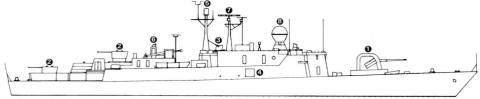

TURUNMAA   *(Scale 1 : 600), Ian Sturton*

KARJALA   *10/1993, Finnish Navy*

PATROL FORCES

3 TUIMA CLASS (FAST ATTACK CRAFT—MISSILE)

TUISKU 12   **TUULI** 14   **TYRSKY** 15

Displacement, tons: 210 standard; 245 full load
Dimensions, feet (metres): 110.2 × 24.9 × 8.8 *(33.6 × 7.6 × 2.7)*
Main machinery: 3 Type M 504 diesels; 10 800 hp(m) *(7.94 MW)* sustained; 3 shafts
Speed, knots: 37. **Range, miles:** 500 at 35 kts
Complement: 30

Missiles: SSM: 4 SS-N-2B Styx; active radar or IR homing to 46 km *(25 nm)* at 0.9 Mach; warhead
513 kg.
Guns: 4 USSR 30 mm/65 (2 twin); 85° elevation; 500 rounds/minute to 5 km *(2.7 nm)*; weight of
shell 0.54 kg.
Radars: Surface search: Square Tie; I band.
Fire control: Drum Tilt; H/I band.
Navigation: Racal Decca; I band.

Programmes: Ex-USSR Osa II class purchased from 1974-75.
Modernisation: New construction but with Finnish electronics and Western navigational radar.
Tuima of the same class converted in 1993 to a minelayer and is listed under *Mine Warfare
Forces*. The others may also be converted in due course.

TYRSKY   *6/1993, van Ginderen Collection*

4 HELSINKI CLASS (FAST ATTACK CRAFT—MISSILE)

Name	No	Builders	Commissioned
HELSINKI	60	Wärtsilä, Helsinki	1 Sep 1981
TURKU	61	Wärtsilä, Helsinki	3 June 1985
OULU	62	Wärtsilä, Helsinki	1 Oct 1985
KOTKA	63	Wärtsilä, Helsinki	16 June 1986

Displacement, tons: 280 standard; 300 full load
Dimensions, feet (metres): 147.6 × 29.2 × 9.9 *(45 × 8.9 × 3)*
Main machinery: 3 MTU 16V 538 TB92 diesels; 10 230 hp(m) *(7.52 MW)* sustained; 3 shafts
Speed, knots: 30
Complement: 30

Missiles: SSM: 8 Saab RBS 15; inertial guidance; active radar homing to 70 km *(37.8 nm)* at 0.8 Mach; warhead 150 kg; sea-skimmer.
Guns: 1 Bofors 57 mm/70; 75° elevation; 200 rounds/minute to 17 km *(9.3 nm)*; weight of shell 2.4 kg. 6—103 mm rails for rocket illuminants.
4 USSR 23 mm/87 (2 twin); can be replaced by Sadral SAM launcher.
Depth charges: 2 rails.
Countermeasures: Decoys: Philax chaff and IR flare launcher.
ESM: Argo; radar intercept.
Fire control: Saab EOS 400 optronic.
Radars: Surface search: 9GA 208; I band.
Fire control: Philips 9LV 225; J band.
Sonars: Simrad Marine SS 304; high resolution active scanning.

Programmes: *Helsinki* was launched 5 November 1980. Next three ordered to a revised design on 13 January 1983.
Modernisation: *Helsinki's* bridge and armament have been modified and are now the same as the other three of the class. A *Kotka* type barbet can take either twin 23 mm guns or a Sadral SAM launcher.
Structure: The light armament can be altered to suit the planned role. Hull and superstructure of light alloy.

KOTKA   *10/1990, Antonio Moreno*

KOTKA (left) and HELSINKI   *6/1991, Harald Carstens*

OULU   *10/1993, Finnish Navy*

4 RAUMA CLASS (FAST ATTACK CRAFT—MISSILE)

Name	No	Builders	Commissioned
RAUMA	70	Hollming, Rauma	18 Oct 1990
RAAHE	71	Hollming, Rauma	20 Aug 1991
PORVOO	72	Finnyards, Rauma	27 Apr 1992
NAANTALI	73	Finnyards, Rauma	23 June 1992

Displacement, tons: 215 standard; 248 full load
Dimensions, feet (metres): 157.5 × 26.2 × 4.5 *(48 × 8 × 1.5)*
Main machinery: 2 MTU 16V 538 TB93 diesels; 7510 hp(m) *(5.52 MW)* sustained; 2 Riva Calzoni waterjets
Speed, knots: 30
Complement:19 (5 officers)

Missiles: SSM: 6 Saab RBS 15SF (could embark 8); active radar homing to 150 km *(80 nm)* at 0.8 Mach; warhead 200 kg.
SAM: Matra Sadral sextuple launcher; Mistral; IR homing to 4 km *(2.2 nm)*; warhead 3 kg.
Guns: Bofors 40 mm/70; 90° elevation; 300 rounds/minute to 12 km *(6.6 nm)*; weight of shell 96 kg.
6—103 mm rails for rocket illuminants. 2—12.7 mm MGs.
2 USSR 23 mm/87 (twin); can be fitted instead of Sadral.
A/S mortars: 4 Saab Elma LLS-920 9-tubed launchers; range 300 m; warhead 4.2 kg shaped charge.
Depth charges:1 rail.
Countermeasures: Decoys: Philax chaff and IR flares.
ESM: MEL Matilda; radar intercept.
Fire control: Bofors Electronic 9LV200 Mk 3 optronic director with TV camera; infra-red and laser telemetry.
Radars: Surface search: 9GA 208; I band.
Fire control: Bofors Electronic 9LV 225; J band.
Navigation: Raytheon ARPA; I band.
Sonars: Simrad Subsea toadfish sonar; search and attack; active high frequency.

Programmes: Four ordered 27 August 1987. Another eight of these craft are planned for the future, but further orders are uncertain.
Structure: Developed from Helsinki class. Hull and superstructure of light alloy. SAM and 23 mm guns are interchangeable within the same barbet.
Operational: Primary function is the anti-ship role but there is some ASW capability and mention is also made of a secondary role in mine warfare, as it is in all Finnish war vessels. Towed array cable is 78 m with 24 hydrophones and can be used at speeds between 3 and 12 kts.

RAUMA (with SAM)   *6/1992, Marko Enqvist*

RAAHE (with 23 mm gun)   *1992, Finnish Navy*

NAANTALI   *5/1993, Finnish Navy*

5 NUOLI CLASS (FAST ATTACK CRAFT—GUN)

Name	No	Builders	Commissioned
NUOLI 8, 10—13	38, 40—43	Laivateollisuus, Turku	1961-66

Displacement, tons: 40 standard
Dimensions, feet (metres): 72.2 × 21.7 × 5 *(22 × 6.6 × 1.5)*
Main machinery: 3 Type M 50 diesels; 3300 hp(m) *(2.4 MW)* sustained; 3 shafts
Speed, knots: 40
Complement: 15
Guns: 1 Bofors 40 mm/70 or 2 USSR 23 mm/87 (twin, aft). 1 Oerlikon 20 mm or 12.7 mm (fwd) MG.
Depth charges: 4
Radars: Surface search: Decca; I band.

Comment: Delivery dates: 22 August 1962, 5 May 1964, 5 May 1964, 30 November 1964, 12 October 1966. This class is split into two: *Nuoli 1* (8) and *Nuoli 2* (10-13). The main difference is a lower superstructure in *Nuoli 2*. These five were modernised under the 1979 estimates.

NUOLI 13 (with 40 mm gun)   *1991, Finnish Navy*

3 RUISSALO CLASS (LARGE PATROL CRAFT)

Name	No	Builders	Commissioned
RUISSALO	53	Laivateollisuus, Turku	11 Aug 1959
RAISIO	54	Laivateollisuus, Turku	12 Sep 1959
RÖYTTA	55	Laivateollisuus, Turku	14 Oct 1959

Displacement, tons: 110 standard; 130 full load
Dimensions, feet (metres): 108.9 × 18.5 × 5.9 *(33 × 5.6 × 1.8)*
Main machinery: 2 MTU MB diesels; 2500 hp(m) *(1.84 MW)*; 2 shafts
Speed, knots: 17
Complement: 20
Guns: 2 or 4 USSR 23 mm/87 (1 or 2 twin).
A/S mortars: 2 RBU 1200 fixed 5-tubed launchers; range 1200 m; warhead 34 kg.
Mines: Can lay mines.
Radars: Navigation: Decca; I band.
Sonars: Hull-mounted; active search and attack; high frequency.
  Finnyards Sonac/PTA towed array; passive search; low frequency.

Comment: Ordered in January 1958. Launched on 16 June, 2 July and 2 June 1959. *Ruissalo* was modernised in 1976, other pair in 1980. In 1991 *Ruissalo* was fitted with a lightweight towed sonar array replacing the after gun mounting. The other two have also been fitted with towed arrays but have retained the after gun.

RAISIO (with towed array)   *8/1993, Finnish Navy*

2 RIHTNIEMI CLASS (LARGE PATROL CRAFT)

Name	No	Builders	Commissioned
RIHTNIEMI	51	Rauma-Repola, Rauma	21 Feb 1957
RYMÄTTYLÄ	52	Rauma-Repola, Rauma	20 May 1957

Displacement, tons: 90 standard; 110 full load
Dimensions, feet (metres): 101.7 × 18.7 × 5.9 *(31 × 5.6 × 1.8)*
Main machinery: 2 MTU MB diesels; 2500 hp(m) *(1.84 MW)*; 2 shafts; cp props
Speed, knots: 18
Complement: 20
Guns: 4 USSR 23 mm/87 (2 twin).
A/S mortars: 2 RBU 1200 fixed 5-tubed launchers; range 1200 m; warhead 34 kg.
Mines: Can lay mines.
Radars: Navigation: Decca; I band.
Sonars: Hull-mounted; active search and attack; high frequency.

Comment: Ordered in June 1955, launched in 1956. Both modernised for A/S work—further modernisation completed 1981.

RIHTNIEMI   *1990, van Ginderen Collection*

1 EXPERIMENTAL COASTAL PATROL CRAFT

HURJA 30

Displacement, tons: 30
Dimensions, feet (metres): 72.2 × 16.4 × 6.6 *(22 × 5 × 2)*
Main machinery: 3 diesels; 3800 hp(m) *(2.2 MW)*; 3 waterjets
Speed, knots: 30
Complement: 10

Comment: Built by Fiskars, Turun, Turku. Completed 1981. GRP hull. Probably did not come up to expectations and is now used as trials craft.

HURJA   *1991, Finnish Navy*

MINE WARFARE FORCES

1 MINELAYER

Name	No	Builders	Laid down	Launched	Commissioned
POHJANMAA	01	Wärtsilä, Helsinki	4 May 1978	28 Aug 1978	8 June 1979

Displacement, tons: 1000 standard; 1100 full load
Dimensions, feet (metres): 255.8 × 37.7 × 9.8 *(78.2 × 11.6 × 3)*
Main machinery: 2 Wärtsilä Vasa 16V22 diesels; 6300 hp(m) *(4.64 MW)* sustained; 2 shafts; cp props; bow thruster
Speed, knots: 19. **Range, miles:** 3500 at 15 kts
Complement: 90

Guns: 1 Bofors 4.7 in *(120 mm)*/46; 80° elevation; 80 rounds/minute to 18.5 km *(10 nm)*; weight of shell 21 kg. 6—103 mm launchers for illuminants fitted to the mounting.
  2 Bofors 40 mm/70; 90° elevation; 300 rounds/minute to 12 km *(6.6 nm)*; weight of shell 0.96 kg.
  4 USSR 23 mm/87 (2 twin). 2—12.7 mm MGs.
A/S mortars: 2 RBU 1200 fixed 5-tubed launchers; range 1200 m; warhead 34 kg.
Depth charges: 2 rails.
Mines: 120 including UK Stonefish.
Countermeasures: Decoys: Philax chaff and IR flare launcher.
ESM: Argo; radar intercept.
Radars: Air search: Signaal DA 05; E/F band; range 137 km *(75 nm)* for 2 m² target.
Fire control: Phillips 9LV 200; J band.
Navigation: I band.
Sonars: Hull-mounted; active search and attack; high frequency.
  Bottom classification; search; high frequency.

POHJANMAA   *8/1993, Finnish Navy*

Programmes: Design completed 1976. Ordered late 1977.
Modernisation: In 1992 the forward 23 mm guns were replaced by 12.7 mm MGs.

Operational: Also serves as training ship. Carries 70 trainees accommodated in Portakabins on the mine deck. Helicopter area on quarter-deck but no hangar.

2 HÄMEENMAA CLASS (MINELAYERS)

Name	No	Builders	Laid down	Launched	Commissioned
HÄMEENMAA	02	Finnyards, Rauma	2 Apr 1991	11 Nov 1991	15 Apr 1992
UUSIMAA	05	Finnyards, Rauma	12 Nov 1991	June 1992	2 Dec 1992

Displacement, tons: 1330 full load
Dimensions, feet (metres): 252.6 oa; 228.3 wl × 38.1 × 9.8
(77; 69.6 × 11.6 × 3)
Main machinery: 2 Wärtsilä 16V22 diesels; 6300 hp(m)
(4.64 MW) sustained; 2 KaMeWa cp props; bow thruster; 247
hp(m) *(184 kW)*
Speed, knots: 19
Complement: 70

Missiles: SAM: Matra Sadral sextuple launcher; Mistral; IR hom-
ing to 4 km *(2.2 nm)*; warhead 3 kg.
Guns: 2 Bofors 40 mm/70. 4 or 6 Sako 23 mm/87 (2 or 3 twin)
(the third mounting is interchangeable with Sadral launcher).
A/S mortars: 2 RBU 1200 fixed 5-tubed launchers; range
1200 m; warhead 34 kg.
Depth charges: 2 launchers.
Mines: 4 rails for 100-150.
Countermeasures: Decoys: 2 ML/Wallop Superbarricade multi-
chaff and IR launchers.
ESM: Radar warning.
Fire control: Radamec System 2400 optronic director; 2 Galileo
optical directors.
Radars: Surface search and Navigation: Three Selesmar ARPA; I
band.
Sonars: Simrad; hull-mounted; active mine detection; high
frequency.

Programmes: First one ordered 29 December 1989 after the
original order in July from Wärtsilä had been cancelled. Second ordered 13 February 1991. Dual role as a transport and
support ship.
Structure: Steel hull and alloy superstructure. Ice-strengthened
(Ice class 1A) and capable of breaking up to 40 mm ice. Ramps
in bow and stern. The Sadral launcher is mounted at the stern.
The after 40 mm gun is on the after end of the superstructure.
SAM system can be replaced by a third twin 23 mm mounting
within the same barbet.

HÄMEENMAA   *3/1993, Finnish Navy*

HÄMEENMAA   *8/1992, Finnish Navy*

3 PANSIO CLASS (MINELAYERS—LCU TYPE)

Name	No	Builders	Commissioned
PANSIO	876	Olkiluoto Shipyard	25 Sep 1991
PYHÄRANTA	475	Olkiluoto Shipyard	26 May 1992
PORKKALA	777	Olkiluoto Shipyard	29 Oct 1992

Displacement, tons: 450 standard
Dimensions, feet (metres): 144.3 oa; 128.6 wl × 32.8 × 6.6 *(44; 39.2 × 10 × 2)*
Main machinery: 2 MTU 12V 183 TE62 diesels; 1500 hp(m) *(1.1 MW)*; 2 shafts; bow thruster
Speed, knots: 10
Complement: 12
Guns: 2 USSR 23 mm/87 (twin). 1—12.7 mm MG.
Mines: 50.
Radars: Navigation: Raytheon ARPA; I band.

Comment: Ordered in May 1990. Used for inshore minelaying and transport with a capacity of 100
tons. Ice-strengthened with ramps in bow and stern. Has a 15 ton crane fitted aft.

1 TUIMA CLASS (MINELAYER)

TUIMA 11

Displacement, tons: 245 full load
Dimensions, feet (metres): 110.2 × 24.9 × 8.8 *(33.6 × 7.6 × 2.7)*
Main machinery: 3 Type M 504 diesels; 10 800 hp(m) *(7.94 MW)* sustained; 3 shafts
Speed, knots: 37. Range, miles: 500 at 35 kts
Complement: 28
Guns: 2 USSR 30 mm/65 (twin).
Mines: Converted to Minelayer.
Radars: Surface search: Racal Decca; I band.

Comment: Ex-USSR Osa II purchased in 1974. Converted in 1993 to a minelayer with missile systems and after gun mounting removed. Others of the class (see *Patrol Forces*) may follow.

PANSIO   *8/1993, Finnish Navy*

TUIMA   *11/1993, Finnish Navy*

2 MINELAYING BARGES

721   821

Displacement, tons: 130 full load
Dimensions, feet (metres): 49.2 × 23 × 4.9 *(15 × 7 × 1.5)*

Comment: Built by Lehtinen, Rauma in 1987. Dumb barges used to transport and lay mines in port approaches.

1 TRIALS SHIP

Name	No	Builders	Commissioned
ISKU	826 (ex-16)	Reposaaron Konepaja	1970

Displacement, tons: 180 standard
Dimensions, feet (metres): 108.5 × 28.5 × 5.9 *(33 × 8.7 × 1.8)*
Main machinery: 4 Type M 50 diesels; 4400 hp(m) *(3.3 MW)* sustained; 4 shafts
Speed, knots: 18
Complement: 25
Radars: Navigation: Raytheon ARPA; I band

Comment: Formerly a missile experimental craft, now used for various equipment trials. Modernised in 1989-90 by Uusikaupunki Shipyard and lengthened by 7 metres. Can quickly be converted to a minelayer.

ISKU   1990, Finnish Navy

6 KUHA CLASS (MINESWEEPERS—INSHORE)

Name	No	Builders	Commissioned
KUHA 21—26	21—26	Laivateollisuus, Turku	1974-75

Displacement, tons: 90 full load
Dimensions, feet (metres): 87.2 × 22.7 × 6.6 *(26.6 × 6.9 × 2)*
Main machinery: 2 Cummins MT-380M diesels; 600 hp(m) *(448 kW)*; 1 shaft; cp prop; active rudder
Speed, knots: 12
Complement: 15
Guns: 2 USSR 23 mm/60 (twin). 1—12.7 mm MG.
Radars: Navigation: Decca; I band.

Comment: All ordered 1972. *Kuha 21* completed 28 June 1974, *Kuha 26* in late 1975. Fitted for magnetic, acoustic and pressure-mine clearance. Hulls are of GRP. May carry a Pluto ROV.

KUHA 25   10/1993, Finnish Navy

7 KIISKI CLASS (MINESWEEPERS—INSHORE)

Name	No	Builders	Commissioned
KIISKI 1-7	521-527	Fiskars, Turku	1983-84

Displacement, tons: 20
Dimensions, feet (metres): 49.9 × 13.4 × 3.3 *(15.2 × 4.1 × 1.2)*
Main machinery: 2 Valmet 611 CSMP diesels; 340 hp(m) *(250 kW)*; 2 waterjets
Speed, knots: 11
Complement: 4

Comment: Ordered January 1983. All completed by 24 May 1984. GRP hull. Built to be used with Kuha class for unmanned teleguided sweeping, but this was not successful and they are now used for manned sweeping operations with crew of four.

KIISKI 4   .1992, Finnish Navy

ICEBREAKERS

Note: Controlled by Board of Navigation which also operates 14 transport ships and 9 oil recovery vessels. There is also the German-owned, Finnish-manned, icebreaker *Hansa,* of the Karhu class, completed on 25 November 1966, which operates off Germany in Winter and off Finland at other times.

2 KARHU 2 CLASS

OTSO   KONTIO

Measurement, tons: 9200 dwt
Dimensions, feet (metres): 324.7 × 79.4 × 26.2 *(99 × 24.2 × 8)*
Main machinery: Diesel-electric; 4 Wärtsilä Vasa 16V32 diesel generators; 22.84 MW 60 Hz sustained; 2 motors; 17 700 hp(m) *(13 MW)*; 2 shafts
Speed, knots: 18.5
Complement: 28
Helicopters: 1 light.

Comment: First ordered from Wärtsilä 29 March 1984, completed 30 January 1986. Second ordered 29 November 1985, delivered 29 January 1987.

KONTIO   1/1987, Wärtsilä

2 URHO CLASS

URHO   SISU

Displacement, tons: 7800 *Urho* (7900, *Sisu*) standard; 9500 full load
Dimensions, feet (metres): 343.1 × 78.1 × 27.2 *(104.6 × 23.8 × 8.3)*
Main machinery: Diesel-electric; 5 Wärtsilä-SEMT-Pielstick diesel generators; 25 000 hp(m) *(18.37 MW)*; 4 motors; 22 000 hp(m) *(16.2 MW)*; 4 shafts (2 fwd, 2 aft)
Speed, knots: 18
Complement: 47
Helicopters: 1 light.

Comment: Built by Wärtsilä and commissioned on 5 March 1975 and 28 January 1976 respectively. Fitted with two screws aft, taking 60 per cent of available power and two fwd, taking the remainder. Sisters to Swedish Atle class.

URHO and SISU   5/1993, A Sheldon Duplaix

3 TARMO CLASS

TARMO   VARMA   APU

Displacement, tons: 4890 full load
Dimensions, feet (metres): 281 × 71 × 23.9 *(85.7 × 21.7 × 7.3)*
Main machinery: Diesel-electric; 4 Wärtsilä-Sulzer diesel generators; 12 000 hp(m) *(8.82 MW)*; 4 shafts (2 screws fwd, 2 aft)
Speed, knots: 17
Complement: 45-55
Helicopters: 1 light.

Comment: Built by Wärtsilä and commissioned in 1963, 1968 and 1970 respectively.

APU   5/1993, A Sheldon Duplaix

2 FENNICA CLASS

FENNICA   NORDICA

Measurement, tons: 1650 (Winter); 3900 (Arctic); 4800 (Summer) dwt
Dimensions, feet (metres): 380.5 × 85.3 × 27.6 *(116 × 26 × 8.4)*
Main machinery: Diesel-electric; 2 Wärtsilä Vasa 16V32D/ABB Strömberg diesel generators;
   12 MW; 2 Wärtsilä Vasa 12V32D/ABB Strömberg diesel generators; 9 MW; 2 ABB Strömberg
   motors; 2 Aquamaster US ARC 1 nozzles; 20 400 hp(m) *(15 MW)*; 3 Brunvoll bow thrusters;
   6120 hp(m) *(4.5 MW)*
Speed, knots: 16
Complement: 16 + 80 passengers
Helicopters: 1 light.

Comment: First of class ordered in October 1991, second in May 1992, from Finnyards, Rauma.
Fennica launched 10 September 1992 and completed 15 March 1993. *Nordica* launched July
1993 and completed January 1994. Bollard pull 230 tons. Capable of 8 kts at 0.8 m level ice and
continuous slow speed at 1.8 m arctic level ice. 120 ton A frame and two deck cranes of 15 and 5
tons each. Combination of azimuth propulsion units and bow thrusters gives full dynamic positioning capability.

FENNICA   *3/1993, Finnyards*

1 VOIMA CLASS

VOIMA

Displacement, tons: 4415 full load
Dimensions, feet (metres): 274 × 63.7 × 23 *(83.6 × 19.4 × 7)*
Main machinery: Diesel-electric; 6 Wärtsilä Vasa 16V22 diesel generators; 16.8 MW sustained;
   4 motors; 13 600 hp(m) *(10 MW)*; 4 shafts (2 fwd, 2 aft)
Speed, knots: 16.5
Complement: 45

Comment: Launched in 1953. Modernised in 1978-79 with new main machinery and a remodelled
superstructure and living quarters by Wärtsilä. This has given her a life expectancy until 1994.
Voima when built was sister to the Soviet Kapitan Belousov class and the Swedish *Oden* (since
deleted).

VOIMA   *1991, van Ginderen Collection*

AUXILIARIES

1 COMMAND SHIP

KUSTAANMIEKKA (ex-*Valvoja III*) 99

Displacement, tons: 340 full load
Dimensions, feet (metres): 118.1 × 29.5 × 9.8 *(36 × 9 × 3)*
Main machinery: 1 diesel; 670 hp(m) *(492 kW)*; 1 shaft
Speed, knots: 11
Complement: 10
Guns: 2—12.7 mm MGs (not always carried).

Comment: Completed in 1963. Former buoy tender transferred from Board of Navigation and converted by Hollming, Rauma in 1989. Bofors 40 mm gun replaced in 1988.

5 VALAS CLASS (GP TRANSPORTS)

VALAS 97   **MURSU** 98   **VAHAKARI** 121   **VAARLAHTI** 222   **VANO** 323

Displacement, tons: 300 full load
Dimensions, feet (metres): 100.4 × 26.5 × 10.4 *(30.6 × 8.1 × 3.2)*
Main machinery: 1 Wärtsilä Vasa 8V22 diesel; 1576 hp(m) *(1.16 MW)* sustained; 1 shaft
Speed, knots: 12
Complement: 11
Military lift: 35 tons
Guns: 2—23 mm/60 (twin). 1—12.7 mm MG.
Mines: 28 can be carried.

Comment: Completed 1979-80. *Mursu* acts as a diving tender; *Vahakari*, *Vaarlahti* and *Vano* are
used by the Coastal Artillery. Funnel is offset to starboard. Can be used as minelayers or trans-
port/cargo carriers and are capable of breaking thin ice.

VALAS   *5/1993, van Ginderen Collection*

3 KAMPELA CLASS (LCU TRANSPORTS)

Name	No	Builders	Commissioned
KAMPELA 1	371	Enso Gutzeit	29 July 1976
KAMPELA 2	272	Enso Gutzeit	21 Oct 1976
KAMPELA 3	877	Finnmekano	23 Oct 1979

Displacement, tons: 90 light; 260 full load
Dimensions, feet (metres): 106.6 × 26.2 × 4.9 *(32.5 × 8 × 1.5)*
Main machinery: 2 Scania diesels; 460 hp(m) *(338 kW)*; 2 shafts
Speed, knots: 9
Complement: 10
Guns: 2 or 4 USSR 23 mm/60 (1 or 2 twin).
Mines: About 20 can be carried.

Comment: Can be used as amphibious craft, transports, minelayers or for shore support. Armament can be changed to suit role. *Kampela 1* and *2* are used by the Coastal Artillery.

KAMPELA 2   *1988, Finnish Navy*

3 KALA CLASS (LCU TRANSPORTS)

KALA 1 171   **KALA 4** 874   **KALA 6** 776

Displacement, tons: 60 light; 200 full load
Dimensions, feet (metres): 88.6 × 26.2 × 6 *(27 × 8 × 1.8)*
Main machinery: 2 Valmet diesels; 360 hp(m) *(265 kW)*; 2 shafts
Speed, knots: 9
Complement: 10
Guns: 1 Oerlikon 20 mm (not in all).
Mines: 34.

Comment: Completed between 20 June 1956 *(Kala 1)* and 4 December 1959 *(Kala 6)*. Can be used
as transports, amphibious craft, minelayers or for shore support. Armament can be changed to
suit role. Pennant numbers changed in 1990. Two deleted in 1992, one in 1993.

KALA 6   *1991, Finnish Navy*

6 HAUKI CLASS (TRANSPORTS)

| HAVOURI 133 | HIRSALA 235 | HAKUNI 431 |
| HAUKI 232 | HANKONIEMI 334 | HOUTSKÄR 436 |

Displacement, tons: 45 full load
Dimensions, feet (metres): 47.6 × 15.1 × 7.2 *(14.5 × 4.6 × 2.2)*
Main machinery: 2 Valmet 611 CSM diesels; 586 hp(m) *(431 kW)*; 1 shaft
Speed, knots: 12
Complement: 4
Cargo capacity: 6 tons or 40 passengers

Comment: Completed 1979. Ice-strengthened; two serve isolated island defences. Four converted in 1988 as tenders to the Marine War College, but from 1990 back in service as light transports. All used by the Coastal Artillery.

HIRSALA   *1991, Finnish Navy*

4 HILA CLASS (TRANSPORTS)

| HILA 237 | HARUN 238 | HÄSTÖ 339 | + 1 |

Displacement, tons: 50 full load
Dimensions, feet (metres): 49.2 × 13.1 × 5.9 *(15 × 4 × 1.8)*
Main machinery: 2 diesels; 416 hp(m) *(306 kW)*; 2 shafts
Speed, knots: 12
Complement: 4

Comment: Ordered from Kotkan Telakka in August 1990. Second pair to complete in 1994. Ice-strengthened. All for use by Coastal Artillery.

HILA   *10/1991, Finnish Navy*

2 LOHI CLASS (LCU TRANSPORTS)

| LOHI 251 | LOHM 452 |

Displacement, tons: 38 full load
Dimensions, feet (metres): 65.6 × 19.7 × 3 *(20 × 6 × 0.9)*
Main machinery: 2 WMB diesels; 1200 hp(m) *(882 kW)*; 2 waterjets
Speed, knots: 20. **Range, miles:** 240 at 20 kts
Complement: 4
Guns: 2 USSR 23 mm/60 (twin). 1—14.5 mm MG.

Comment: Commissioned September 1984. Used as troop carriers and for light cargo by the Coastal Artillery. Guns not always carried.

LOHI   *1992, Finnish Navy*

2 TRANSPORT and COMMAND LAUNCHES

| ASKERI   241 | VIIRI   91 |

Displacement, tons: 25 full load
Dimensions, feet (metres): 52.6 × 14.5 × 4.5 *(16 × 4.4 × 1.4)*
Main machinery: 2 diesels; 1100 hp(m) *(808 kW)*; 2 shafts
Speed, knots: 22
Complement: 6
Radars: Surface search: I band.
Navigation: Raytheon; I band.

Comment: Closely resemble Spanish PVC II class. *Askeri* is used by the Coastal Artillery.

VIIRI   *8/1993, Finnish Navy*

6 VIHURI CLASS (COMMAND LAUNCHES)

| JYMY 511 | SYÖKSY 531 | TRÄSKÖ 992 |
| RAJU 521 | VINHA 541 | TORSÖ 993 |

Displacement, tons: 13 full load
Dimensions, feet (metres): 42.7 × 13.1 × 3 *(13 × 4 × 0.9)*
Main machinery: 2 diesels; 772 hp(m) *(567 kW)*; 2 waterjets
Speed, knots: 30
Complement: 6
Radars: Surface search: I band.

Comment: First of class *Vihuri* delivered in 1988, the next five in 1991 and the last in 1993. *Träskö, Torsö* and *Jymy* act as fast transports for Coastal Artillery. *Vinha, Raju* and *Syöksy* are command launches for Navy squadrons. *Vihuri* was destroyed by fire in late 1991.

SYÖKSY   *8/1993, Finnish Navy*

1 SUPPORT SHIP

PARAINEN (ex-*Pellinki*, ex-*Meteor*) 420 (ex-210)

Displacement, tons: 404
Dimensions, feet (metres): 126.3 × 29.5 × 14.8 *(38.5 × 9 × 4.5)*
Main machinery: 1 diesel; 1800 hp(m) *(1.32 MW)*; 1 shaft
Speed, knots: 13
Complement: 17
Guns: 1 Madsen 20 mm.

Comment: Built as a tug in 1960. Acquired late 1980 from Oy Neptun Ab and modernised in 1987 by Teijon Telakka. Used by the Coastal Artillery.

PARAINEN   *4/1993, van Ginderen Collection*

38 MERIUISKO CLASS (LCAs)

U 201-U 238

Displacement, tons: 9.8 full load
Dimensions, feet (metres): 36 × 11.5 × 2.9 *(11 × 3.5 × 0.9)*
Main machinery: 2 Volvo TAMD70E diesels; 418 hp(m) *(307 kW)* sustained; 2 waterjets
Speed, knots: 36; 30 full load
Military lift: 48 troops

Comment: First batch of eleven completed by Alumina Varvet from 1983 to 1986. Last four ordered in 1989. Constructed of light alloy. Two of the class equipped with cable handling system for boom defence work. Batch one has smaller cabins.

U 207 (small cabin)   *1991, Finnish Navy*

U 214 (large cabin)   *1991, Finnish Navy*

1 CABLE SHIP

PUTSAARI 92

Displacement, tons: 45
Dimensions, feet (metres): 149.5 × 28.6 × 8.2 *(45.6 × 8.7 × 2.5)*
Main machinery: 1 Wärtsilä diesel; 510 hp(m) *(375 kW)*; 1 shaft; active rudder; bow thruster
Speed, knots: 10
Complement: 20

Comment: Built by Rauma-Repola, Rauma and commissioned in 1966. Modernised by Wärtsilä in 1987. Fitted with two 10 ton cable winches. Strengthened for ice operations.

PUTSAARI   *1992, Finnish Navy*

2 POLLUTION CONTROL VESSELS

HYLJE 799   **HALLI** 899

Displacement, tons: 1500
Dimensions, feet (metres): 164 × 41 × 9.8 *(50 × 12.5 × 3)*
Main machinery: 2 Saab diesels; 680 hp(m) *(500 kW)*; 2 shafts; active rudders; bow thruster
Speed, knots: 7

Comment: Painted grey. Strengthened for ice. Owned by Board of Navigation, civilian-manned but operated by Navy from Turku. *Hylje* commissioned 3 June 1981, *Halli* in January 1987. Capacity is about 1400 cu m of contaminated seawater. The ships have slightly different superstructure lines aft.

HYLJE   *1992, Finnish Navy*

HALLI   *5/1993, van Ginderen Collection*

TUGS

2 HARBOUR TUGS

HAUKIPÄÄ 731   **KALLANPÄÄ** 831

Displacement, tons: 38
Dimensions, feet (metres): 45.9 × 16.4 × 7.5 *(14 × 5 × 2.3)*
Main machinery: 2 diesels; 360 hp(m) *(265 kW)*; 2 shafts
Speed, knots: 9
Complement: 2

Comment: Delivered by Teijon Telakka Oy in December 1985. Similar to Hauki class.

KALLANPÄÄ   *5/1993, van Ginderen Collection*

SURVEY AND RESEARCH SHIPS

Note: Controlled by Ministry of Trade and Industry.

9 SURVEY SHIPS

Name	Displacement	Launched	Complement
PRISMA	1080 tons	1978	50 (12)
KALLA	920 tons	1963	50 (12)
SAARISTO	537 tons	1965	32 (7)
LINSSI	444 tons	1979	29 (6)
AIRISTO	350 tons	1972	13 (6)
TAUVO	187 tons	1963	13 (4)
SESTA	119 tons	1979	11 (2)
SEXTANT	1081 tons	1970	30 (6)
TUTKA	535 tons	1960	17 (4)

Plus 36 surveying launches.

1 RESEARCH SHIP

ARANDA

Displacement, tons: 1800 full load
Dimensions, feet (metres): 193.6 × 44.6 × 15.7 *(59 × 13.6 × 4.8)*
Main machinery: 1 Wärtsilä diesel; 2720 hp(m) *(2 MW)*; 1 shaft; bow and stern thrusters
Speed, knots: 12
Complement: 12 plus 12-25 research staff
Helicopters: Platform only.

Comment: Ordered from Laivateollisuus, Turku, to a Wärtsilä design in February 1988 and
delivered in Spring 1989. Has 270 square metres of laboratory space. Replacement for old
Aranda whose conversion in 1985 was not satisfactory.

ARANDA   *1991, van Ginderen Collection*

FRONTIER GUARD

Note: Controlled by Ministry of the Interior.

0 + 1 IMPROVED TURSAS CLASS (OFFSHORE PATROL VESSEL)

Displacement, tons: 1100 full load
Dimensions, feet (metres): 189.6 × 36.1 × 15.1 *(57.8 × 11 × 4.6)*
Main machinery: 2 diesels; 3808 hp(m) *(2.8 MW)* sustained; 2 shafts; cp props
Speed, knots: 15
Guns: 2–23 mm/87 (twin).
Radars: Surface search. Navigation.

Comment: Ordered 17 June 1993 from Finnyards, for delivery in October 1994. Capable of 5 kts in
50 cm of ice. To be used as an all weather patrol ship in the Baltic, capable of Command, SAR,
tug work and environmental pollution cleaning up.

IMPROVED TURSAS (artist's impression)   *1993, Finnyards*

2 TURSAS CLASS (OFFSHORE PATROL VESSELS)

TURSAS   UISKO

Displacement, tons: 700 full load
Dimensions, feet (metres): 149 × 34.1 × 13.1 *(45.4 × 10.4 × 4)*
Main machinery: 2 Wärtsilä Vasa 8R22 diesels; 3152 hp(m) *(2.32 MW)* sustained; 2 shafts
Speed, knots: 16
Guns: 2 USSR 23 mm/60 (twin).
Sonars: Simrad SS105; active scanning; 14 kHz.

Comment: First ordered from Rauma-Repola on 21 December 1984. Launched 31 January 1986.
Delivered June 1986. Second ordered 20 March 1986. Delivered 27 January 1987. Operate as
offshore patrol craft and can act as salvage tugs. Ice-strengthened.

UISKO   *4/1993, van Ginderen Collection*

1 IMPROVED VALPAS CLASS (LARGE PATROL CRAFT)

TURVA

Displacement, tons: 550
Dimensions, feet (metres): 159.1 × 28 × 12.8 *(48.5 × 8.6 × 3.9)*
Main machinery: 2 Wärtsilä diesels; 2000 hp(m) *(1.47 MW)*; 1 shaft
Speed, knots: 15
Guns: 1 Oerlikon 20 mm.
Sonars: Simrad SS105; active scanning; 14 kHz.

Comment: Built by Laivateollisuus, Turku and commissioned 15 December 1977.

TURVA   *8/1992, Finnish Navy*

1 VALPAS CLASS (LARGE PATROL CRAFT)

VALPAS

Displacement, tons: 545
Dimensions, feet (metres): 159.1 × 27.9 × 12.5 *(48.5 × 8.5 × 3.8)*
Main machinery: 1 Werkspoor diesel; 2000 hp(m) *(1.47 MW)*; 1 shaft
Speed, knots: 15
Complement: 22
Guns: 1 Oerlikon 20 mm.
Sonars: Simrad SS105; active scanning; 14 kHz.

Comment: An improvement on the *Silmä* design. Built by Laivateollisuus, Turku, and commissioned 21 July 1971. Ice-strengthened.

VALPAS   *1/1990, van Ginderen Collection*

1 SILMÄ CLASS (LARGE PATROL CRAFT)

SILMÄ

Displacement, tons: 530
Dimensions, feet (metres): 158.5 × 27.2 × 14.1 *(48.3 × 8.3 × 4.3)*
Main machinery: 1 Werkspoor diesel; 1800 hp(m) *(1.32 MW)*; 1 shaft
Speed, knots: 15
Complement: 22
Guns: 1 Oerlikon 20 mm.
Sonars: Simrad SS105; active scanning; 14 kHz.

Comment: Built by Laivateollisuus, Turku and commissioned 19 August 1963.

SILMÄ   *4/1990, van Ginderen Collection*

2 + (2) KIISLA CLASS (LARGE PATROL CRAFT)

KIISLA   KURKI

Displacement, tons: 270 full load
Dimensions, feet (metres): 158.5 × 28.9 × 7.2 *(48.3 × 8.8 × 2.2)*
Main machinery: 2 MTU 16V 538 TB93 diesels; 7510 hp(m) *(6.9 MW)* sustained; 2 KaMeWa waterjets
Speed, knots: 25
Complement: 22
Guns: 2 USSR 23 mm/60 (twin) or 1 Madsen 20 mm.
Sonars: Simrad SS304 hull-mounted and VDS; active search; high frequency.

Comment: First ordered from Hollming on 23 November 1984 and commissioned 25 May 1987 after lengthy trials. Three more of an improved type ordered 22 November 1988, the first of which was laid down 3 August 1989 and commissioned in late 1990. Work on the last pair has been postponed. Have replaced the Koskelo class. The design allows for rapid conversion to attack craft, ASW craft, minelayer, minesweeper or minehunter. A central telescopic crane over the engine room casing is used to launch a 5.7 m rigid inflatable sea boat. A fire monitor is mounted in the bows. The KaMeWa steerable waterjets extend the overall hull length by 2 m.

KIISLA   *1992, Finnish Navy*

1 LARGE PATROL CRAFT

VIIMA

Displacement, tons: 135
Dimensions, feet (metres): 118.1 × 21.7 × 7.5 *(36 × 6.6 × 2.3)*
Main machinery: 3 MTU MB diesels; 4050 hp(m) *(2.98 MW)*; 3 shafts; cp props
Speed, knots: 25
Complement: 13
Guns: 1 Oerlikon 20 mm.

Comment: Built by Laivateollisuus, Turku and commissioned in 1964.

VIIMA   *1991, Gilbert Gyssels*

4 LOKKI CLASS (COASTAL PATROL CRAFT)

LOKKI   TIIRA   KAJAVA   KIHU

Displacement, tons: 59 *(Lokki)*; 64 (remainder)
Dimensions, feet (metres): 87.9 × 18 × 6.2 *(26.8 × 5.5 × 1.9)*
  87.9 × 17.1 × 8.5 *(26.8 × 5.2 × 2.1)* (*Lokki*)
Main machinery: 2 MTU 8V 396 TB82 diesels; 1740 hp(m) *(1.28 MW)* sustained (*Lokki*)
  2 MTU 8V 396 TB84 diesels; 2100 hp(m) *(1.54 MW)* sustained (remainder); 2 shafts
Speed, knots: 25
Complement: 8

Comment: Under a contract signed on 12 May 1980 Valmet/Laivateollisuus Oy (Turku) built the prototype craft *Lokki* which completed in Autumn 1981. *Tiira* completed 1 November 1985, *Kajava* 28 August 1986 and *Kihu* in December 1986. Built in light metal alloy. *Lokki* has a V-shaped hull.

LOKKI   *1991, Finnish Navy*

55 INSHORE PATROL CRAFT AND TENDERS

Class	Total	Tonnage	Speed	Commissioned
RV 1 (ex-RV 41)	1	17	10	1965
RV 8	1	10	10	1958
RV 9	9	12	10	1959-60
RV 10	11	18	10	1961-63
RV 30	7	19	10	1973-74
TENDERS	2	6	13	1986
RV 153	10	25	12	1992-96
PV 11	14	10	28	1984-90

PV 120   *1992, Finnish Navy*

LAND-BASED MARITIME AIRCRAFT

Note: Both Mi-8s transferred to the Air Force in 1990.

Numbers/Type: 2 Agusta AB 412 Griffon.
Operational speed: 122 kts *(226 km/h)*.
Service ceiling: 14 200 ft *(4330 m)*.
Range: 227 nm *(420 km)*.
Role/Weapon systems: Operated by Coast Guard/Frontier force for patrol and SAR. Sensors: Possible radar. Weapons: Unarmed at present but possible mountings for machine guns.

GRIFFON   *5/1993, A Sheldon Duplaix*

Numbers/Type: 2 Aerospatiale AS 332B Super Puma.
Operational speed: 151 kts *(279 km/h)*.
Service ceiling: 15 090 ft *(4600 m)*.
Range: 335 nm *(620 km)*.
Role/Weapon systems: Coastal patrol, surveillance and SAR helicopters. Sensors: Surveillance radar, tactical navigation systems and SAR equipment. Weapons: Unarmed.

SUPER PUMA   *9/1993, M Enqvist*

Numbers/Type: 3 Agusta AB 206B JetRanger.
Operational speed: 116 kts *(215 km/h)*.
Service ceiling: 13 500 ft *(4120 m)*.
Range: 311 nm *(576 km)*.
Role/Weapon systems: Coastal patrol and inshore surveillance helicopters. Sensors: Visual means only. Weapons: Unarmed.

Numbers/Type: 2 Piper PA-31 Navajo.
Operational speed: 220 kts *(410 km/h)*.
Service ceiling: 27 200 ft *(8290 m)*.
Range: 755 nm *(1400 km)*.
Role/Weapon systems: Medium range maritime patrol aircraft. Sensors: Weather/search radar. Weapons: Unarmed.

FRANCE

Headquarters' Appointments

Chief of the Naval Staff:
Amiral Coatanea
Inspector General of the Navy:
Amiral Turcat
Director of Personnel:
Vice-Amiral d'escadre Bonnot
Major General of the Navy:
Vice-Amiral d'escadre Moysan
Controller of the Navy:
Vice Amiral d'escadre Canonne

Senior Appointments

C-in-C Atlantic Theatre (CECLANT):
Vice-Amiral d'escadre Deramond
C-in-C Mediterranean Theatre (CECMED):
Vice-Amiral d'escadre Gazzano
Flag Officer ASW Action Group (GASM):
Contre-Amiral Girard
Flag Officer Naval Action Force (FAN):
Vice-Amiral Lefebvre
Flag Officer, Cherbourg:
Contre-Amiral Mallard
Flag Officer French Forces Polynesia:
Vice-Amiral Euverte
Flag Officer Indian Ocean:
Contre-Amiral Delaunay
Flag Officer (Submarines):
Vice-Amiral Guilhem-Ducléon
Flag Officer (Naval Air):
Vice-Amiral Wild
Flag Officer (Embarked Aviation):
Contre-Amiral Godard
Flag Officer (Maritime Patrol Aviation):
Contre-Amiral Bernaudin
Flag Officer Mine Warfare Force (FGM):
Contre-Amiral Delbrel
Commandant Marines:
Capitaine de Vaisseau Lorin

Diplomatic Representation

Naval Attaché in London:
Vice-Amiral Garibal
Naval Attaché in Washington:
Capitaine de Vaisseau Viriot
Military Attaché in Saudi Arabia:
Contre-Amiral La Tourette
Military Attaché to SACLANT:
Contre-Amiral Lapoyade-Deschamps
Military Attaché to CINC South:
Contre-Amiral Raguet

Bases

Cherbourg: Channel Command base (Flomanche)
Brest: Main Atlantic base. SSBN base
Lorient: Atlantic submarine base (until 1995)
Toulon: Mediterranean Command base (Flomed)
Papeete (Tahiti): Refitting base with 3800 ton capacity floating docks, 23 ton floating crane and earth stations for Syracuse communications
Fort-de-France (Martinique): Small base; Syracuse communications
Nouméa (New Caledonia): Small base
Degrad des Cannes (French Guiana): Small base
Saint Denis (La Réunion): Small base; Syracuse communications

Personnel

(a) 1994: 64 200 (4600 officers)
(b) 10 months' national service (18 500) (15 months for seagoers)

Shipyards (Naval)

Cherbourg: Submarines and Fast Attack Craft (private shipyard)
Brest: Major warships and refitting
Lorient: Destroyers and Frigates, MCMVs, Patrol Craft
Toulon: Major refits.

Dates

Armement pour essais: After launching when the ship is sufficiently advanced to allow a crew to live on board, and the commanding officer has joined. From this date the ship hoists the French flag and is ready to undertake her first harbour trials.
Armement définitif: On this date the ship has received her full complement and is able to undergo sea trials.
Clôture d'armement: Trials are completed and the ship is now able to undertake her first endurance cruise.
Croisière de longue durée or traversée de longue durée: The endurance cruise follows the clôture d'armement and lasts until the ship is accepted with all systems fully operational.
Admission au service actif: Commissioning date.

Reserve

A ship in 'Reserve Normale' has no complement but is available at short notice. 'Reserve Speciale' means that a refit will be required before the ship can go to sea again. 'Condamnation' is the state before being broken up or sold; at this stage a Q number is allocated.

Prefix

FS is used in NATO communications but is not official.

Strength of the Fleet

Type	Active (Reserve)	Building (Projected)
Submarines (Ballistic Missile)	5	3 (1)
Submarines (Attack)	6	—
Submarines (Patrol)	7	—
Aircraft Carriers	2	1 (1)
Helicopter Carrier	1	—
Destroyers	15	(4)
Frigates	24	6
Public Service Force	3	3
Fast Attack Craft (Patrol)	10	—
LSDs	4	1
LCTs	11	—
LCMs	26	—
Minesweepers/Route Survey	2	2
Minehunters	14	1
Diving Tenders	4	—
Surveying Ships	6	—
Tankers (URs)	5	—
Maintenance Ship	1	(1)
Depot Ships	5	—
Trials Ships	6	1 (1)
Boom Defence Vessels	7	—
Supply Tenders	8	—
Transports	15	—
Tenders	18	—
Training Ships	16	—

Mercantile Marine

Lloyd's Register of Shipping:
863 vessels of 4 331 940 tons gross

Fleet Air Arm Bases

Base/Squadron No	Aircraft	Task
Embarked Squadrons (68 fixed-wing aircraft; 40 helicopters)		
Lann Bihoué/4F	Alizé (modernised)	Surveillance
Nîmes Garons/6F	Alizé (modernised)	Surveillance
Landivisiau/11F	Super Étendard	Assault
Landivisiau/12F	F-8E(FN) Crusader	Fighters
Landivisiau/17F	Super Étendard (modernised)	Assault
Landivisiau/16F	Étendard IVP	Reconnaissance
St Mandrier/31F	Lynx	ASW
Lanvéoc-Poulmic/32F	Super Frelon	Support
St Mandrier/33F	Super Frelon	Support
Lanvéoc-Poulmic/34F	Lynx	ASW
Lanvéoc-Poulmic/35F	Alouette III/ Panther	Surveillance/ Support

Base/Squadron No	Aircraft	Task
Support Squadrons		
Lann Bihoué/2S	Xingu/Nord 262 A/E	Support Atlantic Region
Hyères/3S	Falcon 10 MER/ Nord 262 A/E/	Support Mediterranean Region
Hyères/10S	Alouette II/III Super Frelon	Trials CEPA
Dugny-Le-Bourget/11S	Nord 262A/Xingu	Support
Lanvéoc-Poulmic/22S	Alouette III	Support Atlantic Region, SAR
St Mandrier/23S	Alouette II/III Dauphin	Support Mediterranean Region, SAR
Landivisiau/57S	Falcon 10 MER/Paris	Support

Base/Squadron No	Aircraft	Task
Maritime Patrol Squadrons		
Nîmes-Garons/21F	Atlantique Mk 2	MP
Nîmes-Garons/22F	Atlantic Mk 1	MP
Lann Bihoué/23F	Atlantique Mk 2	MP
Lann Bihoué/24F	Atlantique Mk 2	MP

Base/Squadron No	Aircraft	Task
Training Squadrons		
Lann Bihoué/52S	Xingu	Flying School
Nimes Garons/56S	Nord 262E	Flying School
Hyères/59S	Super Étendard/ Zéphyr	Fighter School
Lanvéoc-Poulmic/50S	MS 880 Rallye	Naval School Recreational
Dax/SME Dax	Alouette II	Helicopter School
Rochefort/51S	CAP 10/MS 880 Rallye	Initial Flying School

Base/Squadron No	Aircraft	Task
Overseas Detachments		
Tontouta/9S	Gardian	MP
Faaa (Papeete)/12S	Gardian	MP
	Alouette III	Support

In addition, Atlantic Mk 1 aircraft are permanently deployed to Dakar, Fort-de-France and Djibouti.

Approximate Fleet Dispositions mid-1994

	FAN	GASM	FOST	FGM	Mediterranean	Atlantic	Channel	Indian Ocean	Pacific	Antilles
Carriers	2	—	—	—	—	1 (hel)	—	—	—	—
SSBN	—	—	5	—	—	—	—	—	—	—
SSN	—	—	6	—	—	—	—	—	—	—
SS	—	—	6	—	—	—	—	—	—	—
DDG/DD	9	6	—	—	—	—	—	—	—	—
FF	—	10	—	—	7	1	—	4/3	3/4	1
MCMV (incl tenders)	—	—	—	20	4	—	—	—	—	—
Light Forces	—	—	—	—	2	16	2	3	4	4
LPD/LCD	5	—	—	—	—	—	—	—	—	—
AOR	2	1	—	—	2	—	—	1	—	—

FAN = Force d'Action Navale (based at Toulon). All foreign operational deployments
GASM = Groupe d'Action Sous-Marine (based at Brest)
FOST = Force Océanique Stratégique (HQ at Houilles, near Paris). SSBNs based at l'Ile Longue near Brest. All SSNs and two SSs based at Toulon. Four SSs based at Lorient (Brest by 1995)
FGM = Force de Guerre des Mines (HQ and main base at Brest). One diving tender based at Cherbourg. Three MHCs and one diving tender at Toulon. Remainder plus one tender and one trials ship at Brest

Notes: (1) CEP Nuclear Test Range Pacific: *Bougainville*; EDICs, L 9051; L 9072; L 9074; Supply Tenders, *Taape, Chamois, Rari, Revi*; Tugs, *Maroa, Maito, Manini*.
(2) Craft counted in the Light Forces total are:
(a) All patrol craft manned by the Navy
(b) Training ships which have a secondary EEZ patrol role: eight Leopard class vessels and two Glycine class trawlers

(c) Major patrol craft manned by the Gendarmerie Maritime: four Patras and two 24 m patrol craft (P 775-776)
(d) Excluded are *Tourmaline* (firing range surveillance craft, manned by civilians) and smaller patrol craft from the Gendarmerie Maritime

DELETIONS

Submarines

1991   Le Redoutable, Galatée
1992   Dauphin
1994   Doris

Cruisers

1991   Colbert

Destroyers

1991   Du Chayla
1992   Duperré

Frigates

1991   Doudart de Lagrée
1992   Protet
1994   Balny, Enseigne de Vaisseau Henry

Patrol Forces

1991   Mercure
1992   Iris (civilian)

Mine Warfare Forces

1992   Phénix, Sagittaire (old) (sold to Pakistan)
1993   Baccarat, Alençon

Amphibious Forces

1991   L 9094
1993   L 9072

Survey and Research Ships

1991   L'Estafette
1992   Henri Poincaré, Agnes 200, Commandant Rivière

Auxiliaries

1991   Engageante, Vigilante
1993   Papenoo, Tapatai (civilian), Triton

Tugs

1991   Hercule, Balsa, Geyser
1992   Robuste
1993   Acajou, Charme, Latanier, Pin, Alouette, Vanneau, Sarcelle, Oued, Valeureux, Chene, Cygne, Cigogne

PENNANT LIST

Submarines

S 601	Rubis
S 602	Saphir
S 603	Casabianca
S 604	Emeraude
S 605	Amethyste
S 606	Perle
S 610	Le Foudroyant
S 612	Le Terrible
S 613	L'Indomptable
S 614	Le Tonnant
S 615	L'Inflexible
S 616	Le Triomphant
S 617	Le Téméraire (bldg)
S 618	Le Vigilante (bldg)
S 620	Agosta
S 621	Bévéziers
S 622	La Praya
S 623	Ouessant
S 643	Doris
S 648	Junon
S 650	Psyché
S 651	Sirène

Aircraft and Helicopter Carriers

R 91	Charles de Gaulle (bldg)
R 97	Jeanne d'Arc
R 98	Clemenceau
R 99	Foch

Destroyers

D 602	Suffren
D 603	Duquesne
D 609	Aconit
D 610	Tourville
D 611	Duguay-Trouin
D 612	De Grasse
D 614	Cassard
D 615	Jean Bart
D 640	Georges Leygues
D 641	Dupleix
D 642	Montcalm
D 643	Jean de Vienne
D 644	Primauguet
D 645	La Motte-Picquet
D 646	Latouche-Tréville

Frigates

F 710	La Fayette (bldg)
F 711	Surcouf (bldg)
F 712	Courbet (bldg)
F 713	Jaureguiberry (bldg)
F 714	Guepratte (bldg)
F 715	Ronarc'h (bldg)
F 726	Commandant Bory
F 730	Floréal
F 731	Prairial
F 732	Nivôse
F 733	Ventôse
F 734	Vendémiaire
F 735	Germinal
F 781	D'Estienne d'Orves
F 782	Amyot d'Inville
F 783	Drogou
F 784	Détroyat
F 785	Jean Moulin
F 786	Quartier Maître Anquetil
F 787	Commandant de Pimodan
F 788	Second Maître Le Bihan
F 789	Lieutenant de Vaisseau le Hénaff
F 790	Lieutenant de Vaisseau Lavallée
F 791	Commandant l'Herminier
F 792	Premier Maître l'Her
F 793	Commandant Blaison
F 794	Enseigne de Vaisseau Jacoubet
F 795	Commandant Ducuing
F 796	Commandant Birot
F 797	Commandant Bouan

Mine Warfare Forces

M 610	Ouistreham
M 611	Vulcain
M 614	Styx
M 622	Pluton
M 641	Éridan
M 642	Cassiopée
M 643	Andromède
M 644	Pégase
M 645	Orion
M 646	Croix du Sud
M 647	Aigle
M 648	Lyre
M 649	Persée
M 650	Sagittaire (bldg)
M 660	Narvik (bldg) (trials)
M 712	Cybèle
M 713	Calliope
M 714	Clio
M 715	Circé
M 716	Cérès
M 770	Antares
M 771	Altair
M 772	Aldebaran

Light Forces

P 670	Trident GM
P 671	Glaive GM
P 672	Épée GM
P 673	Pertuisane GM
P 679	Grèbe
P 680	Sterne
P 681	Albatros
P 682	L'Audacieuse
P 683	La Boudeuse
P 684	La Capricieuse
P 685	La Fougueuse
P 686	La Glorieuse
P 687	La Gracieuse
P 688	La Moqueuse
P 689	La Railleuse
P 690	La Rieuse
P 691	La Tapageuse
P 730	La Combattante (GM)
P 760	Pétulante (GM)
P 761	Mimosa (GM)
P 772	Oeillet (GM)
P 774	Camélia (GM)
P 775	Stellis (GM)
P 776	Stenia (GM)
P 778	Réséda
P 779	Mascareigne (GM)
P 780	Karukéra (GM)
P 789	Mellia (GM)
P 790	Vétiver (GM)
P 791	Hortensia (GM)
P 792	— (GM)

Amphibious Forces

L 9011	Foudre
L 9012	—
L 9021	Ouragan
L 9022	Orage
L 9030	Champlain
L 9031	Francis Garnier
L 9032	Dumont D'Urville
L 9033	Jacques Cartier
L 9034	La Grandière
L 9051	EDIC
L 9052	EDIC
L 9061	CDIC
L 9062	CDIC
L 9070	EDIC
L 9074	EDIC
L 9077	Bougainville
L 9090	Gapeau

Auxiliaries Survey and Support Ships

A 601	Monge
A 607	Meuse
A 608	Var
A 610	Ile d'Oléron
A 613	Achéron
A 615	Loire
A 617	Garonne
A 618	Rance
A 620	Jules Verne
A 621	Rhin
A 622	Rhône
A 629	Durance
A 630	Marne
A 631	Somme
A 632	Punaruu
A 633	Taape
A 634	Rari
A 635	Revi
A 636	Maroa
A 637	Maito
A 638	Manini
A 644	Berry
A 649	L'Étoile
A 650	La Belle Poule
A 652	Mutin
A 653	La Grande Hermine
A 664	Malabar
A 669	Tenace
A 671	Le Fort
A 672	Utile
A 673	Lutteur
A 674	Centaure
A 675	Fréhel
A 676	Saire
A 677	Armen
A 678	La Houssaye
A 679	Kereon
A 680	Lardier
A 686	Actif
A 687	Laborieux
A 688	Valeureux
A 692	Travailleur
A 693	Acharné
A 694	Efficace
A 695	Bélier
A 696	Buffle
A 697	Bison
A 702	Girelle
A 712	Athos
A 713	Aramis
A 714	Tourmaline
A 722	Poséidon
A 731	Tianée
A 743	Denti
A 748	Léopard
A 749	Panthère
A 750	Jaguar
A 751	Lynx
A 752	Guépard
A 753	Chacal
A 754	Tigre
A 755	Lion
A 756	L'Espérance
A 757	D'Entrecasteaux
A 767	Chamois
A 768	Élan
A 770	Glycine
A 771	Eglantine
A 774	Chevreuil
A 775	Gazelle
A 776	Isard
A 785	Thétis
A 789	L'Archéonaute
A 790	Coralline
A 791	Lapérouse
A 792	Borda
A 793	Laplace
A 795	Arago

Auxiliaries

GFA 1-6	Floating Cranes
Y 604	Ariel
Y 611	Bengali
Y 613	Faune
Y 617	Mouette
Y 618	Cascade
Y 620	Chataigner
Y 621	Mésange
Y 628	Colibri
Y 629	Cormier
Y 630	Bonite
Y 634	Rouget
Y 636	Martinet
Y 637	Fauvette
Y 644	Frêne
Y 645	Gave
Y 648	Goéland
Y 654	Hêtre
Y 655	Hévéa
Y 656	Phaeton
Y 657	Machaon
Y 661	Korrigan
Y 662	Dryade
Y 666	Manguier
Y 667	Tupa
Y 668	Méléze
Y 669	Merisier
Y 670	Merle
Y 671	Morgane
Y 673	Moineau
Y 675	Martin Pêcheur
Y 686	Palétuvier
Y 687	Passereau
Y 688	Peuplier
Y 691	Pinson
Y 692	Telenn Mor
Y 694	Pivert
Y 695	Platane
Y 696	Alphée
Y 698	Calmar
Y 700	Nereide
Y 701	Ondine
Y 702	Naiade
Y 706	Chimère
Y 708	Saule
Y 709	Sycomore
Y 710	Sylphe
Y 711	Farfadet
Y 717	Ébène
Y 718	Érable
Y 719	Olivier
Y 720	Santal
Y 723	Engoulevent
Y 725	Marabout
Y 726	Toucan
Y 727	Macreuse
Y 728	Grand Duc
Y 729	Eider
Y 730	Ara
Y 732	DGV—S de D No 3
Y 735	Merlin
Y 736	Mélusine
Y 738	Maronnier
Y 739	Noyer
Y 740	Papayer
Y 741	Elfe
Y 745	Aiguière
Y 746	Embrun
Y 747	Loriot
Y 748	Gélinotte
Y 749	La Prudente
Y 750	La Persévérante
Y 751	La Fidèle
Y 790-799	Tenders

GM = Gendarmerie Maritime

SUBMARINES

Strategic Missile Submarines (Sous-Marins Nucléaires Lanceurs d'Engins (SNLE))

0 + 3 (1) LE TRIOMPHANT CLASS (SNLE-NG)

Name	No	Builders	Laid down	Launched	Operational
LE TRIOMPHANT	S 616	Cherbourg Naval Dockyard	9 June 1989	13 July 1993	Mar 1996
LE TÉMÉRAIRE	S 617	Cherbourg Naval Dockyard	1994	1996	July 1998
LE VIGILANT	S 618	Cherbourg Naval Dockyard	1995	1998	July 2001

Displacement, tons: 12 640 surfaced; 14 335 dived
Dimensions, feet (metres): 453 × 41; 55.8 (aft planes) × 41
(138 × 12.5; 17 × 12.5)
Main machinery: Nuclear; turbo-electric; 1 PWR Type K15
(enlarged CAS 48); 150 MW; 2 turbo-alternators; 1 motor;
41 500 hp(m) *(30.5 MW)*; diesel-electric auxiliary propulsion;
2 SEMT-Pielstick 8 PA4 V 200 SM diesels; 900 kW; 1 emergency motor; 1 shaft; pump jet propulsor
Speed, knots: 25 dived
Complement: 111 (15 officers) (2 crews)

Missiles: SLBM: 16 Aerospatiale M45/TN 71; three stage solid
fuel rockets; inertial guidance to 5300 km *(2860 nm)*; thermonuclear warhead with 6 MRV each of 150 kT. (To be replaced
by M5/TN 75 which has a planned range of 11 000 km
(6000 nm) and 10-12 MRVs).
SSM: Aerospatiale SM 39 Exocet; launched from 21 in *(533 mm)*
torpedo tubes; inertial cruise; active radar homing to 50 km
(27 nm) at 0.9 Mach; warhead 165 kg.
Torpedoes: 4—21 in *(533 mm)* tubes. ECAN L5 Mod 3; dual purpose; active/passive homing to 9.5 km *(5.1 nm)* at 35 kts; warhead 150 kg; depth to 550 m *(1800 ft)*; total of 18 torpedoes
and SSM carried in a mixed load.
Countermeasures: ESM: Thomson-CSF ARUR 13/DR 3000U;
intercept.
Fire control: SAD (Système d'Armes de Dissuasion) data system
(for SLBMs); SAT (Système d'Armes Tactique) and DLA 4A
weapon control system (for SSM and torpedoes).
Radars: Search: Dassault; I band.
Sonars: Thomson Sintra DMUX 80 'multi-function' passive bow
and flank arrays.
DUUX 5; passive ranging and intercept; low frequency.
DSUV 61; towed array.

Programmes: First of class ordered 10 March 1986 with building decision taken 18 June 1987. Second of class ordered 18
October 1989; third delayed until 27 May 1993 and fourth
into 1996. Class of six originally planned but this is now
reduced to a total of four. Will replace the Redoutable class.
SNLE-NG (Sous-Marins Nucléaires Lanceurs Engins-Nouvelle
Génération).
Modernisation: The M5 missile development was first funded in
the 1988 budget and the programme has been brought forward to start in 1993, which is earlier than planned. *Le Vigilant*
will be the first to commission with M5, the others being back
fitted in due course. Four sets of missiles were to have been
ordered but this number may now be reduced.
Structure: Later versions may be longer, up to 170 m. Built of
HLES 100 steel capable of withstanding pressures of more
than 100 kg/mm². Diving depth 500 m *(1640 ft)*. Height from
keel to top of fin is 21.3 m *(69.9 ft)*.
Operational: Sea trials of *Le Triomphant* started in early 1994.

LE TRIOMPHANT   *7/1993, DCN*

5 L'INFLEXIBLE CLASS (SNLE)

Name	No	Builders	Laid down	Launched	Operational
LE FOUDROYANT	S 610	Cherbourg Naval Dockyard	12 Dec 1969	4 Dec 1971	6 June 1974
LE TERRIBLE	S 612	Cherbourg Naval Dockyard	24 June 1967	12 Dec 1969	1 Jan 1973
L'INDOMPTABLE	S 613	Cherbourg Naval Dockyard	4 Dec 1971	17 Sep 1974	23 Dec 1976
LE TONNANT	S 614	Cherbourg Naval Dockyard	19 Oct 1974	17 Sep 1977	3 May 1980
L'INFLEXIBLE	S 615	Cherbourg Naval Dockyard	21 Mar 1980	23 June 1982	1 Apr 1985

Displacement, tons: 8080 surfaced; 8920 dived
Dimensions, feet (metres): 422.1 × 34.8 × 32.8
(128.7 × 10.6 × 10)
Main machinery: Nuclear; turbo-electric; 1 PWR; 2 turbo-
alternators; 1 Jeumont Schneider motor; 16 000 hp(m)
(11.76 MW); twin SEMT-Pielstick/Jeumont Schneider 8 PA4 V
185 SM diesel-electric auxiliary propulsion; 1.5 MW; 1 emergency motor; 1 shaft
Speed, knots: 25 dived; 20 surfaced
Range, miles: 5000 at 4 kts on auxiliary propulsion only
Complement: 114 (14 officers) (2 crews)

Missiles: SLBM: 16 Aerospatiale M4; three stage solid fuel rockets; inertial guidance to 5300 km *(2860 nm)*; thermonuclear
warhead with 6 MRV each of 150 kT.
SSM: Aerospatiale SM 39 Exocet; launched from 21 in *(533 mm)*
torpedo tubes; inertial cruise; active radar homing to 50 km
(27 nm) at 0.9 Mach; warhead 165 kg (to be carried in all in
due course).
Torpedoes: 4—21 in *(533 mm)* tubes. ECAN L5 Mod 3; dual purpose; active/passive homing to 9.5 km *(5.1 nm)* at 35 kts; warhead 150 kg; depth to 550 m *(1800 ft)*; and ECAN F17 Mod 2;
wire-guided; active/passive homing to 20 km *(10.8 nm)* at
40 kts; warhead 250 kg; depth 600 m *(1970 ft)*; total of 18 torpedoes and SSM carried in a mixed load.
Countermeasures: ESM: Thomson-CSF ARUR 13/DR 3000U;
intercept.

Fire control: SAD (Système d'Armes de Dissuasion) data system
(for SLBMs); SAT (Système d'Armes Tactique) and DLA 1A
weapon control system (for SSM and torpedoes).
Radars: Navigation: Thomson-CSF DRUA 33; I band.
Sonars: Thomson Sintra DSUX 21 'multi-function' passive bow
and flank arrays.
DUUX 5; passive ranging and intercept; low frequency.
DSUV 61; towed array.

Programmes: With the paying off of *Le Redoutable* in December
1991, the remaining submarines of the class are now known
as L'Inflexible class SNLE M4.
Modernisation: All are fitted with M4 missiles. *Le Tonnant*
recommissioned 15 October 1987; *L'Indomptable* 15 June
1989; *Le Terrible* 7 June 1990; *Le Foudroyant* 15 February
1993. As well as replacing the missile system, work included
an improved reactor core, noise reduction efforts, updating
sonar and other equipment to the same standard as *L'Inflexible*
on build.
Structure: Diving depth, 250 m *(820 ft)* approx. Improved
streamlining of M4 conversion submarines changes the silhouette so that they resemble *L'Inflexible*.
Operational: First operational launch of M4 by *Le Tonnant* on 15
September 1987 in the Atlantic.

L'INFLEXIBLE   *8/1993, van Ginderen Collection*   LE TERRIBLE   *1992, DCN*

Attack Submarines (Sous-Marins Nucléaires d'Attaque (SNA))

6 RUBIS CLASS (SNA 72)

Name	No	Builders	Laid down	Launched	Operational
RUBIS	S 601	Cherbourg Naval Dockyard	11 Dec 1976	7 July 1979	23 Feb 1983
SAPHIR	S 602	Cherbourg Naval Dockyard	1 Sep 1979	1 Sep 1981	6 July 1984
CASABIANCA	S 603	Cherbourg Naval Dockyard	19 Sep 1979	22 Dec 1984	21 Apr 1987
EMERAUDE	S 604	Cherbourg Naval Dockyard	1 Mar 1983	12 Apr 1986	16 Sep 1988
AMETHYSTE	S 605	Cherbourg Naval Dockyard	11 Oct 1984	14 May 1988	20 Mar 1992
PERLE	S 606	Cherbourg Naval Dockyard	27 Mar 1987	22 Sep 1990	7 July 1993

Displacement, tons: 2385 (2410, S 605 onwards) surfaced; 2670 dived

Dimensions, feet (metres): 236.5 (241.5, S 605 onwards) × 24.9 × 21 *(72.1 (73.6) × 7.6 × 6.4)*

Main machinery: Nuclear; turbo-electric; 1 PWR CAS 48; 48 MW; 2 turbo-alternators; 1 motor; 9500 hp(m) *(7 MW)*; SEMT-Pielstick/Jeumont Schneider 8 PA4 V 185 SM diesel-electric auxiliary propulsion; 450 kW; 1 emergency motor; 1 shaft

Speed, knots: 25

Complement: 2 alternating crews each of 70 (8 officers)

Missiles: SSM: Aerospatiale SM 39 Exocet; launched from 21 in *(533 mm)* torpedo tubes; inertial cruise; active radar homing to 50 km *(27 nm)* at 0.9 Mach; warhead 165 kg.

Torpedoes: 4—21 in *(533 mm)* tubes. ECAN L5 Mod 3; dual purpose; active/passive homing to 9.5 km *(5.1 nm)* at 35 kts; warhead 150 kg; depth to 550 m *(1800 ft)*; and ECAN F17 Mod 2; wire-guided; active/passive homing to 20 km *(10.8 nm)* at 40 kts; warhead 250 kg; depth 600 m *(1970 ft)*. Total of 18 torpedoes and missiles carried in a mixed load.

Mines: Up to 32 FG 29 in lieu of torpedoes.

Countermeasures: ESM: Thomson-CSF ARUR 13/DR 3000U; intercept.

Fire control: SAT (Système d'Armes Tactique) and DLA 2B or 3 weapon control system. OPSMER command support system; Syracuse 2 SATCOM.

Radars: Search: Thomson-CSF DRUA 33; I band.

Sonars: Thomson Sintra DMUX 20 multi-function; passive search; low frequency.
DUUA 2B; active; medium frequency; 8 kHz.
DUUX 5; passive ranging and intercept.
DSUV 62C; towed passive array; very low frequency.

Programmes: The programme has been slowed down by defence economies with the seventh of class *Turquoise* (may be completed for export with diesel propulsion) and eighth of class *Diamant* being cancelled. SNA No 7 (displacement: 4000 tons) will be of a new and improved class with VLS SSM and may be funded under the 1995-97 Loi de Programmation.

Modernisation: Between 1989 and 1995 the first four boats of this class are being converted under operation Améthyste (AMÉlioration Tactique HYdrodynamique Silence Transmission Ecoute) to bring them to the same standard of ASW

AMETHYSTE   *1991, DCN*

(includes new sonars) efficiency as the later boats rather than that required for the original anti-surface ship role. Two F17 torpedoes can be guided simultaneously against separate targets. *Saphir* recommissioned 1 July 1991, *Rubis* in February 1993; *Casabianca* scheduled to return to service in 1994 and *Emeraude* in 1995.

Structure: Diving depth, greater than 300 m *(984 ft)*. As this is the smallest class of SSNs ever designed except for the 400 ton NR-1 of the US Navy there has clearly been a marked reduction in the size of the reactor compared with the Le Redoutable class. S 605 and onwards have had their length

increased to 241.5 ft (73.6 m) and were built to a modified design. This included a new bow form, Syracuse 2 SATCOM System, a new design sonar DMUX 20 in place of DSUV 22, a DSUV 62C towed array sonar, a major silencing programme, a streamlining of the superstructure as well as new tactical and attack systems and improved electronics.

Operational: All operational SSNs are based at Toulon but frequently deploy to the Atlantic. Endurance rated at 45 days, limited by amount of food carried. *Rubis* collided with a tanker on 17 July 1993 and has undergone extensive repairs.

EMERAUDE   *4/1992, W Sartori*

AMETHYSTE   *5/1993, Maritime Photographic*

Patrol Submarines (Sous-Marins d'Attaque)

4 AGOSTA CLASS

Name	No	Builders	Laid down	Launched	Commissioned
AGOSTA	S 620	Cherbourg Naval Dockyard	1 Nov 1972	19 Oct 1974	28 July 1977
BÉVÉZIERS	S 621	Cherbourg Naval Dockyard	17 May 1973	14 June 1975	27 Sep 1977
LA PRAYA	S 622	Cherbourg Naval Dockyard	1974	15 May 1976	9 Mar 1978
OUESSANT	S 623	Cherbourg Naval Dockyard	1974	23 Oct 1976	27 July 1978

AGOSTA   10/1992

Displacement, tons: 1230 standard; 1510 surfaced; 1760 dived

Dimensions, feet (metres): 221.7 × 22.3 × 17.7 *(67.6 × 6.8 × 5.4)*

Main machinery: Diesel-electric; 2 SEMT-Pielstick 16 PA4 V 185 VG diesels; 3600 hp(m) *(2.65 MW)*; 2 alternators; 1.7 MW; 1 motor; 4600 hp(m) *(3.4 MW)*; 1 cruising motor; 31 hp(m) *(23 kW)*; 1 shaft

Speed, knots: 12 surfaced; 20 dived

Range, miles: 8500 at 9 kts snorting; 350 at 3.5 kts dived

Complement: 58 (7 officers)

Missiles: SSM: Aerospatiale SM 39 Exocet; launched from 21 in *(533 mm)* tubes; inertial cruise; active radar homing to 50 km *(27 nm)* at 0.9 Mach; warhead 165 kg.

Torpedoes: 4—21 in *(533 mm)* bow tubes. ECAN L5 Mod 3; dual purpose; active/passive homing to 9.5 km *(5.1 nm)* at 35 kts; warhead 150 kg; depth to 550 m *(1800 ft)* and ECAN F17 Mod 2; wire-guided; active/passive homing to 20 km *(10.8 nm)* at 40 kts; warhead 250 kg; depth 600 m *(1970 ft)*. Total of 20 torpedoes and missiles carried in a mixed load.

Mines: Up to 36 in lieu of torpedoes.

Countermeasures: ESM: ARUR, ARUD; intercept and warning.

Fire control: DLA 2A weapon control system.

Radars: Search: Thomson-CSF DRUA 33; I band.

Sonars: Thomson Sintra DSUV 22; passive search; medium frequency.
DUUA 2D; active search and attack; 8 kHz.
DUUA 1D; active search. DUUX 2; passive ranging.
DSUV 62A; passive towed array; very low frequency.

Programmes: Building of this class was announced in 1970 under the third five-year new construction plan 1971-75. Considerable efforts have been made to improve noise reduction, including a clean casing and the damping of internal noise. Service lives: *Ouessant* 2003, remainder 2002 but these dates may be extended.

Modernisation: Included fitting of SM 39 Exocet and better torpedo discharge and reloading. Completed in 1987.

Structure: First diesel submarines in the French Navy to be fitted with 21 in *(533 mm)* tubes. Diving depth, 320 m *(1050 ft)*. Has twice the battery capacity of the Daphne class.

Operational: All based at Lorient but will move to Brest by 1 July 1995. Endurance, 45 days. Torpedoes can be fired at all speeds and down to full diving depth. Rapid reloading gear fitted.

Sales: Four built at Cartagena for Spanish Navy and two for Pakistan by Dubigeon (with a possible three more to follow in due course).

OUESSANT   5/1993, van Ginderen Collection

3 DAPHNÉ CLASS

Name	No	Builders	Laid down	Launched	Commissioned
JUNON	S 648	Cherbourg Naval Dockyard	July 1961	11 May 1964	25 Feb 1966
PSYCHÉ	S 650	Brest Naval Dockyard	May 1965	28 June 1967	1 July 1969
SIRÈNE	S 651	Brest Naval Dockyard	May 1965	28 June 1967	1 Mar 1970

Displacement, tons: 860 surfaced; 1038 dived

Dimensions, feet (metres): 189.6 × 22.3 × 15.1 *(57.8 × 6.8 × 4.6)*

Main machinery: Diesel-electric; 2 SEMT-Pielstick 12 PA1 diesels (S 643 and 648); 2 SEMT-Pielstick 12 PA4 V 185 diesels (S 650 and 651); 2 Jeumont Schneider alternators; 900 kW; 2 motors; 2600 hp(m) *(1.9 MW)*; 2 shafts

Speed, knots: 13.5 surfaced; 16 dived

Range, miles: 2700 at 12.5 kts; 10 000 at 7 kts surfaced; 4500 at 5 kts; 3000 at 7 kts snorting

Complement: 53 (7 officers)

Torpedoes: 12—21.7 in *(550 mm)* (8 bow, 4 stern) tubes. 12 ECAN E15; dual purpose; passive homing to 12 km *(6.6 nm)* at 25 kts; warhead 300 kg. Larger version of shorter range E14. Submarine target must be cavitating; no reloads.

Fire control: DLT D3 torpedo control.

Radars: Search: Thomson-CSF Calypso; I/J band.

Sonars: Thomson Sintra DSUV 2; passive search; medium frequency.
DUUA 2; active search and attack.
DUUX 2; passive ranging.

Programmes: Service lives have been extended as SSN completion rate is slower than planned. *Flore* paid off in 1989 and is used as a training submarine.

Modernisation: Carried out between 1971 and 1981.

Structure: Diving depth, 300 m *(984 ft)*; crushing at 575 m *(1886 ft)*.

Operational: *Junon* based at Toulon, *Psyché* and *Sirène* at Lorient. Two of the class to have major refits in 1995/96 at Lorient and then all will be based at Toulon.

Sales: South Africa (1967) (three), Pakistan (1966) (three), (one from Portugal later), Portugal (1964) (four), Spain (built in Spain) (1965) (four).

PSYCHÉ   7/1992, van Ginderen Collection

AIRCRAFT CARRIERS (Porte-Avions)

0 + 1 (1) CHARLES DE GAULLE CLASS (Porte-Avions Nucléaires PAN) (CVN)

Name	No	Builders	Laid down	Launched	Commissioned
CHARLES DE GAULLE	R 91	Brest Naval Dockyard	14 Apr 1989	7 May 1994	July 1999

Displacement, tons: 35 500 standard; 39 680 full load
Dimensions, feet (metres): 857.7 oa; 780.8 wl × 211.3 oa; 103.3 wl × 27.8 *(261.5; 238 × 64.4; 31.5 × 8.5)*
Flight deck, feet (metres): 857.7 × 211.3 *(261.5 × 64.4)*
Main machinery: Nuclear; 2 PWR Type K15; 300 MW; 2 GEC Alsthom turbines; 83 000 hp(m) *(61 MW)*; 2 shafts
Speed, knots: 27
Complement: 1150 ship's company plus 550 aircrew plus 50 Flag Staff; (accommodation for 1950) (plus temporary 800 marines)

Missiles: SAM: 4 Thomson-CSF SAAM VLS octuple launchers ❶; Aerospatiale ASTER 15; anti-missile system with inertial guidance and mid-course update; active radar homing to 15 km *(8.1 nm)*; warhead 13 kg.
2 Matra Sadral PDMS sextuple launchers ❷; Mistral; IR homing to 4 km *(2.2 nm)*; warhead 3 kg; anti-sea-skimmer; able to engage targets down to 10 ft above sea level.
Guns: 8 Giat 20F2 20 mm; 60° elevation; 720 rounds/minute to 8 km *(4.3 nm)*; weight of shell: 0.25 kg.
Countermeasures: Decoys: 4 CSEE Sagaie 10-barrelled trainable launchers ❸; medium range; chaff to 8 km *(4.3 nm)*; IR flares to 3 km *(1.6 nm)*.
ESM: ARBR 17; radar warning. DIBV 1A Vampir ❹; IR detector.
ECM: 2 ARBB 33 ❺; jammers.
Combat data systems: SENIT; Links 11, 14 and 16. Syracuse 2 SATCOM ❻. AIDCOMER command support system.
Fire control: 2 Sagem VIGY-105 optronic systems.
Radars: Air search: Thomson-CSF DRBJ 11D/E ❼; 3D; E/F band; range 366 km *(200 nm)*.
Thomson-CSF DRBV 26D ❽; D band; range 183 km *(100 nm)* for 2 m² target.
Air/surface search: Thomson-CSF DRBV 15C ❾; E/F band; range 50 km *(27 nm)*.
Navigation: Two Racal 1229; I band.
Fire control: Arabel ❿; I/J band (for SAAM); range 30 km *(16.2 nm)* for 2 m² target.
Tacan: NRBP 20A ⓫.
Sonars: To include SLAT torpedo attack warning.

Fixed wing aircraft: 35-40 including Rafale M (SU 0), Super Étendards (to be replaced by Rafale SU 2), AEW aircraft (possibly E-2C Hawkeye).

Programmes: On 23 September 1980 the Defence Council decided to build two nuclear-propelled carriers to replace *Clemenceau* in 1996 and *Foch* some years later. First of class ordered 4 February 1986, first metal cut 24 November 1987. Hull floated for technical trials on 19 December 1992, and back in dock on 8 January 1993. Second ship, if built, will probably be called *Richelieu* or *Clemenceau* and was to have been ordered in 1992 but this has been postponed to 1997 for an in-service date of 2004. Funds for preliminary work at Brest provided in 1984 estimates and for the construction and trials of the nuclear-power plant at Cadarache in the 1982-83 estimates. A 19.8 m *(65 ft)* long one-twelfth scale model has been built. Constructed of light alloy, and with a crew of three, it is used for hydrodynamic trials. Building programme delayed two and a half years due to defence budget cuts but sea trials are planned to start in 1997.
Structure: Two lifts 62.3 × 41 ft *(19 × 12.5 m)* of 36 tons capacity. Hangar for 20-25 aircraft; dimensions 454.4 × 96.5 × 20 ft *(138.5 × 29.4 × 6.1 m)*. Angled deck 8.5°. Catapults: 2 USN Type C13; length 75 m *(246 ft)* for Super Étendards and up to 22 tonne aircraft. Enhanced weight capability of flight deck to allow operation of AEW aircraft. Island placed well fwd so that both lifts can be abaft it and thus protected from the weather. CSEE Dallas (Deck Approach and Landing Laser System) fitted, later to be replaced by MLS system.
Operational: Five years continuous steaming at 25 kts available before refuelling (same reactors as *Le Triomphant*).

CHARLES DE GAULLE (model)   *1990, DCN*

CHARLES DE GAULLE (artist's impression)   *1993, Aerospatiale*

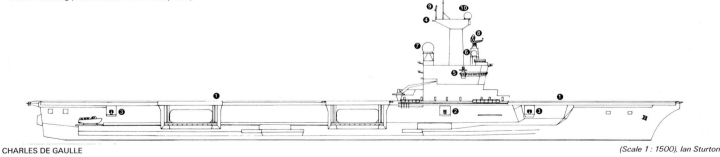

CHARLES DE GAULLE   *(Scale 1 : 1500), Ian Sturton*

CHARLES DE GAULLE   *(Scale 1 : 1500), Ian Sturton*

2 CLEMENCEAU CLASS (CV)

Name	No	Builders	Laid down	Launched	Commissioned
CLEMENCEAU	R 98	Brest Naval Dockyard	Sep 1955	21 Dec 1957	22 Nov 1961
FOCH	R 99	Chantiers de l'Atlantique, St. Nazaire	Feb 1957	28 July 1960	15 July 1963

Displacement, tons: 27 307 standard; 32 780 full load
Dimensions, feet (metres): 869.4 × 104.1 hull (168 oa) × 28.2 *(265 × 31.7 (51.2) × 8.6)*
Flight deck, feet (metres): 543 × 96.8 *(165.5 × 29.5)*
Main machinery: 6 boilers; 640 psi *(45 kg/cm sq)*; 840°F *(450°C)*; 2 Parsons (R 98) or GEC Alsthom (R 99) turbines; 126 000 hp(m) *(93 MW)*; 2 shafts
Speed, knots: 32. **Range, miles:** 7500 at 18 kts; 4800 at 24 kts; 3500 at full power
Complement: 1017 (47 officers) plus 672 aircrew

Missiles: SAM: 2 Thomson-CSF Crotale EDIR octuple launchers ❶; 18 missiles per magazine; radar and IR line-of-sight guidance to 13 km *(7 nm)* at 2.4 Mach; warhead 14 kg. Replaced 4 of the 100 mm guns. 2 Sadral SAM to be fitted to R 99 in due course.
Guns: 4 DCN 3.9 in *(100 mm)*/55 Mod 1953 automatic ❷; 80° elevation; 60 rounds/minute to 17 km *(9 nm)* anti-surface; 8 km *(4.4 nm)* anti-aircraft; weight of shell 13.5 kg. Several M2 12.7 mm MGs.
Countermeasures: Decoys: 2 CSEE Sagaie 10-barrelled trainable launchers ❸; medium range decoy rockets; chaff to 8 km *(4.3 nm)*; IR flares to 3 km *(1.6 nm)*.
ESM: ARBR 17; radar warning.
ECM: ARBB 33; jammer.
Combat data systems: SENIT 2 tactical data automation system; Links 11 and 14 (later 16); Syracuse 1 SATCOM; Inmarsat; FLEETSATCOM; AIDCOMER command support system.
Fire control: Two C T Analogiques; two Sagem DMAa optical sights.
Radars: Air search: Thomson-CSF DRBV 23B ❹; D band; range 201 km *(110 nm)*.
Air/surface search: Two DRBI 10 ❺; E/F band; range 256 km *(140 nm)*.
DRBV 15 ❻; E/F band.
Navigation: Racal Decca 1226; I band.
Fire control: Two Thomson-CSF DRBC 32B ❼ (for guns); I band; two Crotale ❶ (for SAM); I band.
Tacan: SRN-6.
Landing approach control: NRBA 51 ❽; I band.
Sonars: Westinghouse SQS 505; hull-mounted; active search; medium frequency; 7 kHz.

Fixed wing aircraft: 18 Super Étendard; 4 Étendard IVP; 8 Crusaders; 7 Alizé.
Helicopters: 2 SA 365F Dauphin 2.

Programmes: First aircraft carriers designed as such and built from the keel to be completed in France. Authorised in 1953 and 1955 respectively. Under current plans *Clemenceau* is due to pay off (when *Charles de Gaulle* commissions) in 1999 and *Foch* in 2004.
Modernisation: *Clemenceau* refitted in 1978 to accommodate Super Étendard aircraft and tactical nuclear weapons. *Foch* had a similar refit to *Clemenceau*'s in 1980-81. *Clemenceau* started a refit 1 September 1985, ended October 1986. This included the replacement of four of the 100 mm guns by two Crotale EDIR, retubing of boilers and other major engine overhauls, fitting of stronger aircraft lifts and catapults, modernisation of communications (including Syracuse 1 SATCOM) and electronics, fitting of Sagaie, new long-range air warning radar and passive radar detection system, and modernised combat data system. *Foch* similarly modified in her 1987-88 refit, which also included a trial CSEE Dallas (Deck Approach and Landing Laser System), and a capability to accommodate ASMP nuclear missiles for Super Étendard. *Foch* was fitted in 1992/93 with a removable 1.5° mini ski-jump (10 × 4.2 × 0.2 m) on the forward catapult as well as a nose gear launch device. The landing mirror has been moved forward, and the combat system of the ship has been slightly modified. *Clemenceau* has received similar modifications (but to a lesser extent).

FOCH

1/1993, Ships of the World

CLEMENCEAU

10/1993, J Y Robert

In 1995/96, more work will be done on *Foch* to enable the carrier to operate Rafale M aircraft permanently. A foldable mini ski-jump (wider) will be fitted to both catapults. The jet deflectors will be enlarged (this implies reducing the area of the forward lift). *Foch* is planned to get two Sadral SAM systems in 1996.
Structure: Flight deck, island superstructure and bridges, hull (over machinery spaces and magazines) are all armour plated. There are 3 bridges: Flag, Command and Aviation.
2 Mitchell-Brown steam catapults; Mk BS 5; able to launch 20 ton aircraft at 110 kts. The flight deck is angled at 8 degrees. Two lifts 52.5 × 36 ft *(16 × 10.97 m)* one of which is on the

starboard deck edge. Dimensions of the hangar are 590.6 × 78.7 × 23 ft *(180 × 24 × 7 m)*. *Clemenceau* mainmast shortened in 1990.
Operational: Oil fuel capacity is 3720 tons. Flight deck letters: F = *Foch*, U = *Clemenceau*. The aircraft complement for the helicopter carrier role includes between 30 and 40 with a mixture of Super Frelon, Lynx, Super Puma, Puma and Gazelle (the last three types being army-owned). Crusaders refitted to be able to fly until 1995. Deck trials of Rafale M aircraft were carried out in *Foch* in April/May 1993, and further trials are scheduled for 1994.

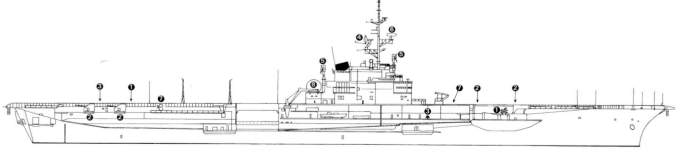

CLEMENCEAU

(Scale 1 : 1500), Ian Sturton

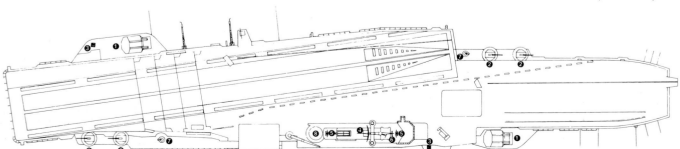

CLEMENCEAU

(Scale 1 : 1500), Ian Sturton

HELICOPTER CARRIER (Porte-Hélicoptères) (CVH)

Name	No	Builders	Laid down	Launched	Commissioned
JEANNE D'ARC (ex-*La Résolue*)	R 97	Brest Naval Dockyard	7 July 1960	30 Sep 1961	16 July 1964

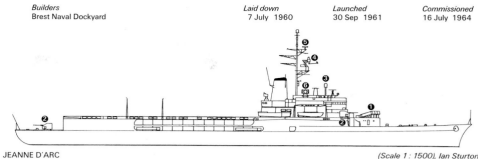

JEANNE D'ARC
(Scale 1 : 1500), Ian Sturton

Displacement, tons: 10 000 standard; 13 270 full load
Dimensions, feet (metres): 597.1 × 78.7 hull × 24
  (182 × 24 × 7.3)
Flight deck, feet (metres): 203.4 × 68.9 *(62 × 21)*
Main machinery: 4 boilers; 640 psi *(45 kg/cm sq)*; 840°F
  (450°C); 2 Rateau-Bretagne turbines; 40 000 hp(m)
  (29.4 MW); 2 shafts
Speed, knots: 26.5. **Range, miles:** 6000 at 15 kts
Complement: 626 (30 officers) plus 140 cadets

Missiles: SSM: 6 Aerospatiale MM 38 Exocet (2 triple) ❶; inertial
  cruise; active radar homing to 42 km *(23 nm)* at 0.9 Mach;
  warhead 165 kg; sea-skimmer.
Guns: 4 DCN 3.9 in *(100 mm)*/55 Mod 1964 CADAM automatic
  ❷; 80° elevation; 80 rounds/minute to 17 km *(9 nm)* anti-
  surface; 8 km *(4.4 nm)* anti-aircraft; weight of shell 13.5 kg.
  4—12.7 mm MGs.
Countermeasures: Decoys: 2 CSEE/VSEL Syllex 8-barrelled
  trainable launchers for chaff (may not be fitted).
  ESM: Thomson-CSF ARBR 16/ARBX 10; intercept.
Fire control: Three C T Analogiques; two Sagem DMAa optical
  sights. SATCOM ❸.
Radars: Air search: Thomson-CSF DRBV 22D ❹; D band; range
  366 km *(200 nm)*.
  Air/surface search: DRBV 50 (51 in due course) ❺; G band.
  Navigation: 2 DRBN 34A (Racal-Decca); I band.
  Fire control: Three Thomson-CSF DRBC 32A ❻; I band.
  Tacan: SRN-6.
Sonars: Thomson Sintra DUBV 24C; hull-mounted; active search;
  medium frequency; 5 kHz.

Helicopters: 4 Alouette III (to be replaced by Dauphin). War
  inventory includes 8 Super Puma and Lynx.

Programmes: Due to pay off after 2005.
Modernisation: Long refits in the Summers of 1989 and 1990
  have allowed equipment to be updated to enable the ship to
  continue well into the next century. SENIT 2 combat data system was to have been fitted but this was cancelled as a cost
  saving measure. DRBV 51 radar is to be fitted in due course.
Structure: Flight deck lift has a capacity of 12 tons. Some of the
  hangar space is used to accommodate officers under training.
  The ship is almost entirely air-conditioned. Carries two LCVPs.
Operational: Used for training officer cadets in peacetime. In
  wartime, after rapid modification, she would be used as a commando ship, helicopter carrier or troop transport with commando equipment and a battalion of 700 men. Flagship of the
  Training Squadron for an Autumn/Spring cruise with Summer
  refit. Army helicopters Super Puma/Cougar and Gazelle are
  embarked during training cruises.

JEANNE D'ARC
5/1993, French Navy

DESTROYERS (Frégates)

1 TYPE F 65 (ASW)

Name	No	Builders	Laid down	Launched	Commissioned
ACONIT	D 609 (ex-*F 703*)	Lorient Naval Dockyard	Jan 1966	7 Mar 1970	30 Mar 1973

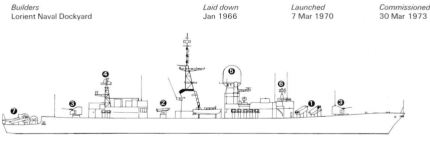

ACONIT
(Scale 1 : 1200), Ian Sturton

Displacement, tons: 3500 standard; 3900 full load
Dimensions, feet (metres): 416.7 × 44 × 18.9
  (127 × 13.4 × 5.8)
Main machinery: 2 boilers; 640 psi *(45 kg/cm sq)*; 842°F
  (450°C); 1 Rateau turbine; 28 650 hp(m) *(21 MW)*; 1 shaft
Speed, knots: 27. **Range, miles:** 5000 at 18 kts
Complement: 228 (15 officers)

Missiles: SSM: 8 Aerospatiale MM 40 Exocet ❶; inertial cruise;
  active radar homing to 70 km *(40 nm)* at 0.9 Mach; warhead
  165 kg; sea-skimmer.
  SAM: 2 Matra Simbad twin launchers for Mistral (can be fitted on
  20 mm gun pedestals).
  A/S: Latecoere Malafon ❷; range 13 km *(7 nm)* at 450 kts; payload L4 acoustic homing torpedo; warhead 100 kg; 13
  missiles.
Guns: 2 DCN 3.9 in *(100 mm)*/55 Mod 68 CADAM automatic ❸;
  80° elevation; 80 rounds/minute to 17 km *(9 nm)* anti-surface;
  8 km *(4.4 nm)* anti-aircraft; weight of shell 13.5 kg.
  2 Oerlikon 20 mm; 2—12.7 mm MGs.
Torpedoes: 2 launchers. 10 ECAN L5; anti-submarine; active/
  passive homing to 9.5 km *(5.1 nm)* at 35 kts; warhead 150 kg;
  depth to 550 m *(1800 ft)*.
Countermeasures: Decoys: 2 CSEE/VSEL Syllex 8-barrelled
  trainable launchers; chaff to 1 km in distraction and centroid
  patterns. Nixie; towed torpedo decoy.
  ESM: ARBR 16; radar warning.
  ECM: ARBB 32; jammer.
Combat data systems: SENIT 3 action data automation; Links 11
  and 14. Syracuse SATCOM. OPSMER command support
  system.
Fire control: SENIT 3 radar/TV tracker (possibly SAT Murène in
  due course). Two Sagem DMAa optical directors.
Radars: Air search: DRBV 22A ❹; D band.
  Air/surface search: Thomson-CSF DRBV 15A ❺; E/F band.
  Navigation: DRBN 32 (Decca 1226); I band.
  Fire control: DRBC 32D ❻; I band (for guns).
Sonars: Thomson Sintra DUBV 23; bow-mounted; active search
  and attack; 5 kHz.
  DUBV 43C ❼; VDS; medium frequency 5 kHz; tows at up to
  24 kts at 200 m.
  DSBV 62C; passive linear towed array; very low frequency.

Programmes: Forerunner of the F 67 Type. A one-off class
  ordered under 1965 programme. Due to pay off in 2004.
Modernisation: Two quadruple Exocet launchers fitted in
  1984/85. Mid-life refit from June 1991 to April 1992 included
  DSBV 62 passive sonar towed array, a lightweight DRBC 32D
  fire-control radar and SATCOM.
Operational: Assigned to GASM.

ACONIT
6/1993, H M Steele

7 GEORGES LEYGUES CLASS (TYPE F 70 (ASW))

Name	No	Builders	Laid down	Launched	Commissioned
GEORGES LEYGUES	D 640	Brest Naval Dockyard	16 Sep 1974	17 Dec 1976	10 Dec 1979
DUPLEIX	D 641	Brest Naval Dockyard	17 Oct 1975	2 Dec 1978	13 June 1981
MONTCALM	D 642	Brest Naval Dockyard	5 Dec 1975	31 May 1980	28 May 1982
JEAN DE VIENNE	D 643	Brest Naval Dockyard	26 Oct 1979	17 Nov 1981	25 May 1984
PRIMAUGUET	D 644	Brest Naval Dockyard	17 Nov 1981	17 Mar 1984	5 Nov 1986
LA MOTTE-PICQUET	D 645	Brest Naval Dockyard/Lorient	12 Feb 1982	6 Feb 1985	18 Feb 1988
LATOUCHE-TRÉVILLE	D 646	Brest Naval Dockyard/Lorient	15 Feb 1984	19 Mar 1988	16 July 1990

Displacement, tons: 3830 standard; 4300 (D 640-643); 4490 (D 644-646) full load

Dimensions, feet (metres): 455.9 × 45.9 × 18.7 *(139 × 14 × 5.7)*

Main machinery: CODOG; 2 RR Olympus TM3B gas-turbines; 46 200 hp *(34.5 MW)* sustained; 2 SEMT-Pielstick 16 PA6 V280 diesels; 12 800 hp(m) *(9.41 MW)* sustained; 2 shafts; cp props

Speed, knots: 30; 21 on diesels. **Range, miles:** 8500 at 18 kts on diesels; 2500 at 28 kts

Complement: 218 (16 officers) plus 16 spare billets

Missiles: SSM: 4 Aerospatiale MM 38 Exocet (MM 40 in D 642-646) ❶; inertial cruise; active radar homing to 42 km *(23 nm)* at 0.9 Mach (MM 38); active radar homing to 70 km *(40 nm)* at 0.9 Mach (MM 40); warhead 165 kg; sea-skimmer. 4 additional Exocet missiles can be carried as a warload (D 644-646).
SAM: Thomson-CSF Crotale Naval EDIR octuple launcher ❷; command line-of-sight guidance; radar/IR homing to 13 km *(7 nm)* at 2.4 Mach; warhead 14 kg; 26 missiles.
2 Matra Simbad twin launchers ❸ may be mounted in lieu of 20 mm guns; Mistral; IR homing to 4 km *(2.2 nm)*; warhead 3 kg.
Guns: 1—3.9 in *(100 mm)*/55 Mod 68 CADAM automatic ❹; dual purpose; 80° elevation; 78 rounds/minute to 17 km *(9 nm)* anti-surface; 8 km *(4.4 nm)* anti-aircraft; weight of shell 13.5 kg.
2 Oerlikon 20 mm ❺; 720 rounds/minute to 10 km *(5.5 nm)*.
4 M2HB 12.7 mm MGs.
Torpedoes: 2 fixed launchers. 10 ECAN L5; anti-submarine; active/passive homing to 9.5 km *(5.1 nm)* at 35 kts; warhead 150 kg; depth to 550 m *(1800 ft)*. 12 Honeywell Mk 46 for helicopters.
Countermeasures: Decoys: 2 CSEE Dagaie 10-barrelled double trainable launcher (replacing Syllex) ❻; chaff and IR flares; H-J band.
ESM: ARBR 17 ❼; radar warning. DIBV 1A Vampir; IR detector (D 644-646).
ECM: ARBB 32 B; jammer.
Combat data systems: SENIT 4 action data automation; Links 11 and 14. SLASM integrated ASW (to be fitted in due course). Syracuse 1 SATCOM ❽. OPSMER command support system.
Fire control: Thomson-CSF Vega (D 640-643) and DCN CTMS (D 644-646) optronic/radar systems. SAT Murène IR tracker to be added to CTMS and possibly Vega systems. CSEE Panda optical director. 2 Sagem VIGY-105 optronic systems to be fitted 1995-97. DLT L4 (D 640-643) and DLT L5 (D 644-646) torpedo control system.
Radars: Air search: DRBV 26 (not in D 644-646) ❾; D band; range 182 km *(100 nm)* for 2 m² target.
Air/surface search: Thomson-CSF DRBV 51C ❿ (DRBV 15A ⓫ in D 644-646); G band; range 120 km *(65 nm)* for 2 m² target.
Navigation: Two Decca 1226; I band (one for close-range helicopter control).
Fire control: Thomson-CSF Vega with DRBC 32E (D 640-643) ⓬; I band; DRBC 33A (D 644-646) ⓭; I band.
Crotale ⓮; I band (for SAM).
Sonars: Thomson Sintra DUBV 23D (DUBV 24C in D 644-646); bow-mounted; active search and attack; 5 kHz.
DUBV 43B (43C in D 643-646) ⓯; VDS; search; medium frequency; paired with DUBV 23D/24; tows at 24 kts down to 200 m *(650 ft)*, (700 m *(3000 ft)* for 43C). Length of tow 600 m *(2000 ft)*; being upgraded to 43C.
DSBV 61B (in D 644 onward); passive linear towed array; very low frequency; 365 m *(1200 ft)*. DSBV 62C may be fitted in first four during mid-life refits in 1990s.

Helicopters: 2 Lynx Mk 4 ⓰.

Programmes: First three were in the 1971-76 new construction programme, fourth in 1978 estimates, fifth in 1980 estimates, sixth in 1981 estimates, seventh in 1983 estimates. D 645 and 646 were towed from Brest to Lorient for completion. Service lives: *Georges Leygues*, 2004; *Dupleix* and *Montcalm*, 2006; *Jean de Vienne*, 2008; *Primauguet*, 2011; *La Motte-Picquet*, 2012; *Latouche-Tréville*, 2014. Re-rated F 70 'frégates anti-sous-marines (FASM)' (ex-C 70) on 6 June 1988.

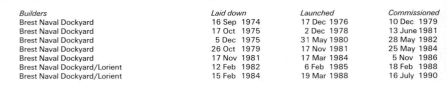

PRIMAUGUET (with 20 mm guns)   *(Scale 1 : 1200), Ian Sturton*

PRIMAUGUET   *5/1993, Wright & Logan*

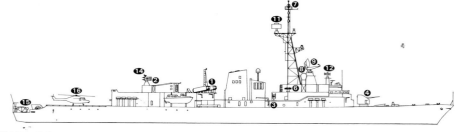

GEORGES LEYGUES (with Simbad SAM)   *(Scale 1 : 1200), Ian Sturton*

Modernisation: The class is to receive the new OTO Melara/Matra ASW missile Milas. The projected SLASM update from 1997 includes a new bow sonar and a VLF towed active sonar with separate passive array. The first four may be back-fitted with towed arrays in mid-life refits in 1990s. Simbad twin SAM launchers are interchangeable with 20 mm guns.

Structure: Bridge raised one deck in the last three of the class.
Operational: The ships' helicopters are dual roled, either carrying sonar or sonobuoy dispenser and ASW weapons or AS 12 anti-ship missiles. *Primauguet* and *Latouche-Tréville* allocated to GASM, remainder to FAN. Simbad may be fitted.

LATOUCHE-TRÉVILLE   *11/1993, Harald Carstens*

LATOUCHE-TRÉVILLE (with VDS and towed array)   *6/1992, G Toremaus*

2 CASSARD CLASS (TYPE F 70 (A/A))

Name	No	Builders	Laid down	Launched	Commissioned
CASSARD	D 614	Lorient Naval Dockyard	3 Sep 1982	6 Feb 1985	28 July 1988
JEAN BART	D 615	Lorient Naval Dockyard	12 Mar 1986	19 Mar 1988	21 Sep 1991

Displacement, tons: 4230 standard; 4700 full load
Dimensions, feet (metres): 455.9 × 45.9 × 21.3 (sonar)
(139 × 14 × 6.5)
Main machinery: 4 SEMT-Pielstick 18 PA6 V 280 BTC diesels;
43 200 hp(m) *(31.75 MW)* sustained; 2 shafts
Speed, knots: 29.5. **Range, miles:** 8200 at 17 kts; 4800 at
24 kts
Complement: 244 (22 officers) accommodation for 251

Missiles: SSM: 8 Aerospatiale MM 40 Exocet ❶; inertial cruise;
active radar homing to 70 km *(40 nm)* at 0.9 Mach; warhead
165 kg; sea-skimmer.
SAM: 40 GDC Pomona Standard SM-1MR; Mk 13 Mod 5
launcher ❷; semi-active radar homing to 46 km *(25 nm)* at
2 Mach; height envelope 45-18 288 m *(150-60 000 ft)*.
Launchers taken from T 47 (DDG) ships.
2 Matra Sadral PDMS sextuple launchers ❸; Mistral; IR homing
to 4 km *(2.2 nm)*; warhead 3 kg; anti-sea-skimmer; able to
engage targets down to 10 ft above sea level.
Guns: 1 DCN 3.9 in *(100 mm)*/55 Mod 68 CADAM automatic ❹;
80° elevation; 80 rounds/minute to 17 km *(9 nm)* anti-surface;
8 km *(4.4 nm)* anti-aircraft; weight of shell 13.5 kg.
2 Oerlikon 20 mm ❺; 720 rounds/minute to 10 km *(5.5 nm)*.
4—12.7 mm MGs.
Torpedoes: 2 fixed launchers model KD 59E ❻. 10 ECAN L5 Mod
4; anti-submarine; active/passive homing to 9.5 km *(5.1 nm)* at
35 kts; warhead 150 kg; depth to 550 m *(1800 ft)*. Honeywell
Mk 46 torpedoes for the helicopter.
Countermeasures: Decoys: 2 CSEE Dagaie ❼ and 2 Sagaie 10-
barrelled trainable launchers ❽; fires a combination of chaff
and IR flares. Nixie; towed torpedo decoy.
ESM: ARBR 17B ❾; radar warning. DIBV 1A Vampir ❿; IR detector (integrated with search radar for active/passive tracking in
all weathers). Saigon radio intercept at masthead.
ECM: ARBB 33; jammer; H, I and J bands.
Combat data systems: SENIT 6 action data automation; Links 11
and 14 (later 16). Syracuse 1 SATCOM ⓫. OPSMER command
support system.
Fire control: DCN CTMS optronic/radar system with DIBC 1A Pi-
ranha II IR/TV tracker; CSEE Najir optronic secondary director.
Radars: Air search: Thomson-CSF DRBJ 11B ⓬; 3D; range
366 km *(200 nm)*.
Air/surface search: DRBV 26C ⓭; D band; range 182 km
(100 nm).
Navigation: Two Racal DRBN 34A; I band (one for close-range
helicopter control ⓮).
Fire control: Thomson-CSF DRBC 33A ⓯; I band (for guns).
Two Raytheon SPG 51C ⓰; G/I band (for missiles).
Sonars: Thomson Sintra DUBA 25A (D 614) or DUBV 24C
(D 615); hull-mounted; active search and attack; medium
frequency. May be fitted later with DSBV 62C passive towed
array; very low frequency.

Helicopters: 1 Lynx Mk 4 ⓱.

Programmes: On the same hull as the F 70 (A/S) a very different
armament and propulsion system has been introduced. Funds
for the first ship allotted in 1978 estimates, for the second in
1979 estimates (ordered 27 September 1979), and for the
third and fourth ships ordered 27 February 1984, but then cancelled. The building
programme was considerably slowed down by finance prob-
lems and doubts about the increasingly obsolescent Standard
SM 1 missile system, and the SM 2 is reported as being too
expensive. Service lives: First, 2013; second, 2015. Re-rated
F 70 (ex-C 70) on 6 June 1988, officially 'frégates anti-
aériennes (FAA)'.
Structure: Samahe 210 helicopter handling system. It is reported
that both ships are to be fitted with Aster SAM during their first
refits. *Cassard* fitted with DRBJ 11B radar (replacing DRBV 15)
in 1992. Displacement is creeping up to over 4700 tons.
Operational: Helicopter used for third party targeting for the
SSM. Both ships are assigned to FAN.

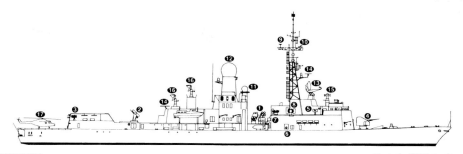

JEAN BART   *(Scale 1 : 1200), Ian Sturton*

JEAN BART   *4/1993, van Ginderen Collection*

CASSARD   *7/1993, van Ginderen Collection*

0 + (4) COMMON NEW GENERATION TYPE

Displacement, tons: 6500 full load
Dimensions, feet (metres): 486.9 × 65.3 × 15.7
(148.4 × 19.9 × 4.8)
Main machinery: CODLAG; 2 gas-turbines; 4 diesels; 2 motors;
2 shafts
Speed, knots: 30. **Range, miles:** 7000 at 18 kts
Complement: 200 plus 35 spare

Missiles: SSM: 8 (2 quad) ❶ or VLS.
SAM: Aster VLS ❷ PAAMS (principal air defence missile system).
Guns: 1—100/114 mm ❸; anti-surface.
2—30 mm ❹. 2 ILMS (inner layer missile system) ❺.
Torpedoes: 4 (2 twin) fixed launchers ❻.
Countermeasures: Decoys: Chaff and IR flare launchers. Tor-
pedo defence system.
ESM/ECM ❼.
Combat data systems: Link 16 included. SATCOM ❽.
Radars: Air/surface search ❾.
Surveillance/fire-control ❿; MESAR or EMPAR;
multi-function.
Sonars: Hull-mounted; active search and attack; medium
frequency.

Helicopters: 1 Marine Nationale NH 90 ⓫.

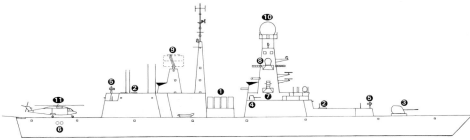

CNG   *(Scale 1 : 1200), Ian Sturton*

Programmes: Trinational project for a new AAW ship with the
UK and Italy. Warship design contract expected in late 1994
for first order in 1997 and an in-service date of 2004. A Joint
Project Office was established in London in 1993.
Structure: Details given are speculative and the drawing rep-
resents the state of the design in early 1994.

Opinion: Collaborative projects for complex multipurpose warships have an unhappy history. The amount of time already lost
is not encouraging and in early 1994 there are fundamental
disagreements over such key equipments as the target indication and fire-control radar.

2 SUFFREN CLASS

Name	No
SUFFREN	D 602
DUQUESNE	D 603

Builders	Laid down	Launched	Commissioned
Lorient Naval Dockyard	21 Dec 1962	15 May 1965	20 July 1967
Brest Naval Dockyard	1 Feb 1965	12 Feb 1966	1 Apr 1970

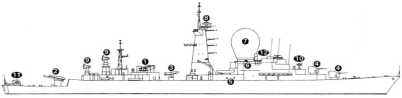

SUFFREN   (Scale 1 : 1500), Ian Sturton

SUFFREN   10/1993, C D Yaylali

Displacement, tons, VDS: 5090 standard; 6910 full load
Dimensions, feet (metres): 517.1 × 50.9 × 20
(157.6 × 15.5 × 6.1)
Main machinery: 4 boilers; 640 psi (45 kg/cm sq); 842°F
(450°C); 2 Rateau turbines; 72 500 hp(m) (53 MW); 2 shafts
Speed, knots: 34. **Range, miles:** 5100 at 18 kts; 2400 at 29 kts
Complement: 355 (23 officers)

Missiles: SSM: 4 Aerospatiale MM 38 Exocet ❶; inertial cruise;
active radar homing to 42 km (23 nm) at 0.9 Mach; warhead
165 kg; sea-skimmer.
SAM: ECAN Ruelle Masurca twin launcher ❷; Mk 2 Mod 3 semi-
active radar homers; range 55 km (30 nm); warhead 98 kg; 48
missiles.
A/S: Latecoere Malafon ❸; range 13 km (7 nm) at 450 kts; payload L4 acoustic homing torpedo; warhead 100 kg; 13
missiles.
Guns: 2 DCN 3.9 in (100 mm)/55 Mod 1964 CADAM automatic
❹; 80° elevation; 80 rounds/minute to 17 km (9 nm) anti-surface; 8 km (4.4 nm) anti-aircraft; weight of shell 13.5 kg.
4 or 6 Oerlikon 20 mm; 720 rounds/minute to 10 km (5.5 nm).
Torpedoes: 4 launchers (2 each side) ❺. 10 ECAN L5; anti-submarine; active/passive homing to 9.5 km (5.1 nm) at 35 kts;
warhead 150 kg; depth to 550 m (1800 ft).
Countermeasures: Decoys: 2 CSEE Sagaie 10-barrelled trainable launchers; chaff to 8 km (4.4 nm) and IR flares to 3 km
(1.6 nm). 2 Dagaie launchers ❻.
ESM: ARBR 17; intercept.
ECM: ARBB 33; jammer.
Combat data systems: SENIT 2 action data automation; Links 11
and 14. Syracuse 1 SATCOM ⓬. OPSMER command support
system.
Fire control: DCN CTMS radar/optronic control system with SAT
DIBC 1A Piranha IR and TV tracker. 2 Sagem DMA optical
directors.
Radars: Air search (radome): DRBI 23 ❼; D band.
Air/surface search: DRBV 15A ❽; E/F band.
Navigation: Racal Decca 1226; I band.
Fire control: Two Thomson-CSF DRBR 51 ❾; G/I band (for
Masurca).
Thomson-CSF DRBC 33A ❿; I band (for guns).
Tacan: URN 20.
Sonars: Thomson Sintra DUBV 23; hull-mounted; active search
and attack; 5 kHz.
DUBV 43 ⓫; VDS; medium frequency 5 kHz; tows at up to
24 kts at 200 m (656 ft).

Programmes: Ordered under the 1960 programme. Service
lives: Both extended to over 2000.
Modernisation: MM 38 Exocet fitted in 1977 (Duquesne) and
1979 (Suffren); Masurca modernised in 1984-85 (Duquesne)
and 1988-89 (Suffren), with new computers. DRBV 15A radars
replaced DRBV 50. Suffren had a major refit from May 1988 to
September 1989 and Duquesne from June 1990 to March
1991: modernisation of the DRBI-23 radar; new computers for
the SENIT combat data system; new CTMS fire-control system
for 100 mm guns fitted (with DRBC-33A radar, TV camera and
DIBC-1A Piranha IR tracker). New ESM/ECM suite: ARBR 17
radar interceptor, ARBB 33 jammer and Sagaie decoy launchers. Two 20 mm guns fitted either side of DRBC 33A.
Structure: Equipped with gyro-controlled stabilisers operating
three pairs of non-retractable fins. NBC citadel fitted during
modernisation. Air-conditioning of accommodation and operational areas. Excellent sea boats and weapon platforms.
Operational: Both ships operate in the Mediterranean under
FAN. Officially frégates lance-missiles (FLM).

3 TOURVILLE CLASS (TYPE F 67)

Name	No
TOURVILLE	D 610
DUGUAY-TROUIN	D 611
DE GRASSE	D 612

Builders	Laid down	Launched	Commissioned
Lorient Naval Dockyard	16 Mar 1970	13 May 1972	21 June 1974
Lorient Naval Dockyard	25 Feb 1971	1 June 1973	17 Sep 1975
Lorient Naval Dockyard	14 June 1972	30 Nov 1974	1 Oct 1977

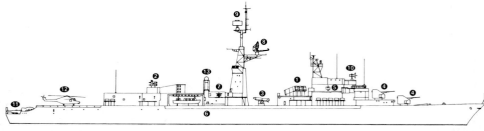

TOURVILLE   (Scale 1 : 1200), Ian Sturton

TOURVILLE   11/1993, Harald Carstens

Displacement, tons: 4580 standard; 5950 full load
Dimensions, feet (metres): 501.6 × 52.4 × 18.7
(152.8 × 16 × 5.7)
Main machinery: 4 boilers; 640 psi (45 kg/cm sq); 840°F
(450°C); 2 Rateau turbines; 58 000 hp(m) (43 MW); 2 shafts
Speed, knots: 32. **Range, miles:** 5000 at 18 kts
Complement: 301 (21 officers)

Missiles: SSM: 6 Aerospatiale MM 38 Exocet ❶; inertial cruise;
active radar homing to 42 km (23 nm) at 0.9 Mach; warhead
165 kg; sea-skimmer.
SAM: Thomson-CSF Crotale Naval EDIR octuple launcher ❷;
command line-of-sight guidance; radar/IR homing to 13 km
(7 nm) at 2.4 Mach; warhead 14 kg.
A/S: Latecoere Malafon (to be replaced by Milas from 1997) ❸;
range 13 km (7 nm) at 450 kts; payload L4 acoustic homing
torpedo; warhead 100 kg; 13 missiles. Removed from D 611 in
1993 and D 610 in 1994.
Guns: 2 DCN 3.9 in (100 mm)/55 Mod 68 CADAM automatic ❹;
dual purpose; 80° elevation; 80 rounds/minute to 17 km
(9 nm) anti-surface; 8 km (4.4 nm) anti-aircraft; weight of shell
13.5 kg.
2 Oerlikon 20 mm ❺; 720 rounds/minute to 10 km (5.5 nm).
Torpedoes: 2 launchers ❻. 10 ECAN L5; anti-submarine; active/
passive homing to 9.5 km (5.1 nm) at 35 kts; warhead 150 kg;
depth to 550 m (1800 ft). Honeywell Mk 46 torpedoes for
helicopters.
Countermeasures: Decoys: 2 CSEE/VSEL Syllex 8-barrelled
trainable launcher (to be replaced by 2 Dagaie systems) ❼;
chaff to 1 km in centroid and distraction patterns.
ESM: ARBR 16; radar warning.
ECM: ARBB 32; jammer.
Combat data systems: SENIT 3 action data automation; Links 11
and 14. Syracuse 1 or 2 SATCOM ⓭. OPSMER command support system.
Fire control: SENIT 3 radar/TV tracker (possibly SAT Murène in
due course). Two Sagem DMAa optical directors.
Radars: Air search: DRBV 26 ❽; D band; range 182 km (100 nm)
for 2 m² target.
Air/surface search: Thomson-CSF DRBV 51B ❾; G band; range
29 km (16 nm).
Navigation: Two Racal Decca Type 1226; I band (one for helicop-
ter control).
Fire control: Thomson-CSF DRBC 32D ❿; I band.
Crotale ❷; J band (for SAM).
Sonars: Thomson Sintra DUBV 23; bow-mounted; active search
and attack; 5 kHz.
DUBV 43C ⓫; VDS; medium frequency 5 kHz; tows at up to
24 kts at 200 m.
DSBV 62C; passive linear towed array; very low frequency.

Helicopters: 2 Lynx Mk 4 ⓬.

Programmes: Developed from the Aconit design. Originally rated
as corvettes but reclassified as 'frégates anti-sous-marins
(FASM)' on 8 July 1971 and given D pennant numbers like
destroyers. De Grasse completed major refit September 1981,
Duguay-Trouin in 1984-85.
Service lives: Tourville, 2000; Duguay-Trouin, 2001; De Grasse,
2003. These will probably be extended.
Modernisation: Duguay-Trouin modernised as a Flagship from
February 1993 to January 1994, to include female accommodation for 30. Major communications and combat data systems updates. The SLASM ASW combat suite is to be installed
in the other two ships. The plan is to start Tourville March
1994, De Grasse October 1995. This includes new bow sonar
plus VLF towed active sonar with separate towed passive
array, Murene torpedoes launched from (a) helicopter (b) ships'
tubes and (c) using OTO Melara/Matra Milas vice Malafon as
stand-off delivery vehicle. Passive towed arrays fitted to all
three ships in 1990. Malafon removed from Duguay-Trouin in
1993 and Tourville in 1994.
Operational: All assigned to GASM. Helicopters are dual roled
either with sonar or sonobuoy dispenser and ASW weapons, or
AS 12 anti-ship missiles.

FRIGATES (Frégates, Avisos-escorteurs, Avisos)

0 + 6 LA FAYETTE CLASS (LIGHT FRIGATES)

Name	No
LA FAYETTE	F 710
SURCOUF	F 711
COURBET	F 712
JAUREGUIBERRY	F 713
GUEPRATTE	F 714
RONARC'H	F 715

Builders	Laid down	Launched	Commissioned
Lorient Naval Dockyard	15 Dec 1990	13 June 1992	Dec 1994
Lorient Naval Dockyard	6 July 1992	3 July 1993	May 1996
Lorient Naval Dockyard	15 Sep 1993	Aug 1994	Jan 1998
Lorient Naval Dockyard	1994	1995	1998
Lorient Naval Dockyard	1995	1996	1999
Lorient Naval Dockyard	1996	1997	2000

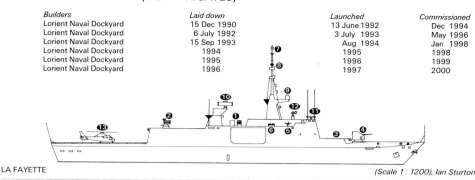

LA FAYETTE *(Scale 1 : 1200), Ian Sturton*

Displacement, tons: 3500 full load
Dimensions, feet (metres): 410.1 oa; 377.3 pp × 50.5 × 13.1 *(125; 115 × 15.4 × 4)*
Main machinery: CODAD; 4 SEMT-Pielstick 12 PA6 V 280 STC diesels; 21 107 hp(m) *(15.52 MW)* sustained; 2 shafts
Speed, knots: 25. **Range, miles:** 7000 at 15 kts; 9000 at 12 kts
Complement: 139 (15 officers) plus 25 spare

Missiles: SSM: 8 Aerospatiale MM 40 Exocet ❶; inertial cruise; active radar homing to 70 km *(40 nm)* at 0.9 Mach; warhead 165 kg; sea-skimmer.
SAM: Thomson-CSF Crotale Naval CN 2 (variant of NG) octuple launcher ❷; command line-of-sight guidance; radar/IR homing to 13 km *(7 nm)* at 3.5 Mach; warhead 14 kg. To be replaced by SAAM VLS ❸ with 16 Aster 15 missiles in second three.
Guns: 1 DCN 3.9 in *(100 mm)*/55 Mod 68 CADAM ❹; 80° elevation; 80 rounds/minute to 17 km *(9 nm)*; weight of shell 13.5 kg.
2 Giat 20F2 20 mm ❺; 720 rounds/minute to 10 km *(5.5 nm)*.
2—12.7 mm MGs.
Countermeasures: Decoys: 2 CSEE Dagaie ❻ 10-barrelled trainable launchers; chaff and IR flares. SLAT anti-wake homing torpedoes system (when available).
ESM: Thomson-CSF ARBR 21 (DR 3000-S) ❼; radar intercept. DIBV 10 Vampir ❽; IR detector.
ECM: Dassault ARBB 33; jammer.
Combat data systems: Thomson-CSF TAVITAC 2000. Syracuse 2 SATCOM ❾. OPSMER combat support system.
Fire control: Thomson-CSF CTM radar/IR system.
Radars: Air/surface search: Thomson-CSF Sea Tiger (DRBV 15C) ❿; E/F band.
Navigation: Racal Decca 1226 ⓫; I band. A second set fitted for helicopter control.
Fire control: Thomson-CSF Castor II ⓬; J band; range 15 km *(8 nm)* for 1 m² target.
Crotale ❷; J band (for SAM).
Arabel for SAAM (for second three).

Helicopters: 1 Aerospatiale AS 565 MA Panther ⓭.

Programmes: Originally described as 'Frégates Légères' but this was changed in 1992 to 'Frégates type La Fayette'. First three ordered 25 July 1988; three more 24 September 1992. Planned total of up to 10 but may stop at 6. The programme was delayed by up to one year by the 1989 defence budget. First steel cut for each hull about 14 months before the keel is laid.

Structure: Space left for a SAAM launcher forward of the bridge which will replace Crotale in the second three of the class on build and the first three at refit. This might mean putting the Arabel fire-control radar on top of a more solid looking foremast once Crotale is removed. Superstructure inclines at 10° to the vertical to reduce radar echoing area. The radar echoing area is claimed to be 60 per cent less than for a traditional design. External equipment such as capstans, bollards etc either 'hidden' or installed as low as possible. Radar absorbent paint is used extensively. Sensitive areas are armour-plated. SLAT anti-torpedo system may be fitted when available. Magazine for AM 39 Exocet and AS 15 for the NFH-90 helicopter.

Plans to fit sonar have been dropped but in the future an ASW version of the ship could be built with hull and towed array sonars, lightweight torpedo launchers, and an ASW configured helicopter.

Operational: La Fayette started full sea trials 27 September 1993. Surcouf planned for May 1994 and Courbet in 1996. These frigates are designed for out of area operations on overseas stations and the first three are assigned to the Indian Ocean.

Sales: Three of an improved design to Saudi Arabia if the order is confirmed and the first six of a possible 16 are being prefabricated for shipping to Taiwan for completion.

6 FLORÉAL CLASS (PATROL FRIGATES)

Name	No
FLORÉAL	F 730
PRAIRIAL	F 731
NIVÔSE	F 732
VENTÔSE	F 733
VENDÉMIAIRE	F 734
GERMINAL	F 735

Builders	Laid down	Launched	Commissioned
Chantiers de L'Atlantique, St Nazaire	2 Apr 1990	6 Oct 1990	27 May 1992
Chantiers de L'Atlantique, St Nazaire	11 Sep 1990	23 Mar 1991	20 May 1992
Chantiers de L'Atlantique, St Nazaire	16 Jan 1991	10 Aug 1991	16 Oct 1992
Chantiers de L'Atlantique, St Nazaire	28 June 1991	14 Mar 1992	5 May 1993
Chantiers de L'Atlantique, St Nazaire	17 Jan 1992	29 Aug 1992	20 Oct 1993
Chantiers de L'Atlantique, St Nazaire	17 Aug 1992	13 Mar 1993	Apr 1994

Displacement, tons: 2600 standard; 2950 full load
Dimensions, feet (metres): 306.8 × 45.9 × 14.1 *(93.5 × 14 × 4.3)*
Main machinery: CODAD; 4 SEMT-Pielstick 6 PA6 L 280 diesels; 8820 hp(m) *(6.5 MW)* sustained; 2 shafts; cp props; bow thruster; 340 hp(m) *(250 kW)*
Speed, knots: 20. **Range, miles:** 10 000 at 15 kts
Complement: 86 (10 officers) (including air crew) plus 24 Marines + 13 spare

Missiles: SSM: 2 Aerospatiale MM 38 Exocet ❶; inertial cruise; active radar homing to 42 km *(23 nm)* at 0.9 Mach; warhead 165 kg; sea-skimmer.
SAM: 2 Matra Simbad twin launchers to replace 20 mm guns in due course.
Guns: 1 DCN 3.9 in *(100 mm)*/55 Mod 68 CADAM ❷; 80° elevation; 80 rounds/minute to 17 km *(9 nm)*; weight of shell 13.5 kg.
2 Giat 20 F2 20 mm ❸; 720 rounds/minute to 10 km *(5.5 nm)*.
Countermeasures: Decoys: 2 CSEE Dagaie II; 10-barrelled trainable launchers ❹; chaff and IR flares.
ESM: Thomson-CSF ARBR 17 ❺; radar intercept.
Fire control: CSEE Najir optronic director ❻. Syracuse 2 SATCOM ❼.
Radars: Air/surface search: Thomson-CSF Mars DRBV 21A ❽; D band.
Navigation: Two Racal Decca DRBN 34A (1226); I band (one for helicopter control ❾).

Helicopters: 1 Dauphin II/Panther or 1 Alouette III or 1 AS 332F Super Puma ❿.

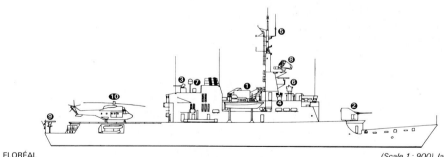

FLORÉAL *(Scale 1 : 900), Ian Sturton*

Programmes: Officially described as 'Frégates de Surveillance' or 'Ocean capable patrol vessel' and designed to operate in the offshore zone in low intensity operations. First two ordered 20 January 1989; built at Chantiers de L'Atlantique, St Nazaire, with weapon systems fitted by DCAN Lorient. Second pair ordered 9 January 1990; third pair in January 1991. Named after the months of the Revolutionary calendar.
Structure: Built to merchant passenger marine standards with stabilisers and air-conditioning. New funnel design improves airflow over the flight deck. Has one freight bunker aft for about 100 tons cargo. Second-hand Exocet MM 38 has been fitted instead of planned MM 40.

NIVÔSE *12/1993, G Toremans*

Operational: Endurance, 50 days. Range proved to be better than expected during sea trials. Able to operate a helicopter up to seastate 5. Stations as follows: Floreal in South Indian Ocean, Ventose in Antilles, Germinal tender to Jeanne d'Arc, Prairial and Vendémiaire in Tahiti, Nivôse in Noumea.

1 COMMANDANT RIVIÈRE CLASS (Avisos Escorteurs)

Name	No	Builders	Laid down	Launched	Commissioned
COMMANDANT BORY	F 726	Lorient Naval Dockyard	14 Mar 1958	11 Oct 1958	5 Mar 1964

COMMANDANT BORY

(Scale 1 : 1200), Ian Sturton

Displacement, tons: 1750 standard; 2250 full load
Dimensions, feet (metres): 336.9 × 38.4 × 14.1
(102.7 × 11.7 × 4.3)
Main machinery: 2 SEMT-Pielstick 12 PA6 V280 BTC diesels;
13 200 hp(m) (9.7 MW); 2 shafts; cp props
Speed, knots: 25. **Range, miles:** 7500 at 15 kts
Complement: 159 (9 officers)

Missiles: SSM: 4 Aerospatiale MM 38 Exocet ❶; active radar
homing to 42 km (23 nm) at 0.9 Mach; warhead 165 kg;
sea-skimmer.
Guns: 2 DCN 3.9 in (100 mm)/55 Mod 1953 automatic ❷; dual
purpose; 80° elevation; 60 rounds/minute to 17 km (9 nm)
anti-surface; 8 km (4.4 nm) anti-aircraft; weight of shell
13.5 kg.
2 Bofors 40/60 ❸. 2—12.7 mm MGs.
Countermeasures: Decoys: 2 CSEE Dagaie 10-barrelled trainable launchers ❹; chaff and IR flares; H-J band.
ESM: ARBR 16; radar warning.
Fire control: C T Analogique; Sagem DMAa optical secondary
director.
Radars: Air/surface search: Thomson-CSF DRBV 22A ❺; D band.
Surface search: Racal Decca 1226 ❻; I band.
Fire control: Thomson-CSF DRBC 32C ❼; I band.
Sonars: EDO SQS 17; hull-mounted; active search; medium
frequency.
Thomson Sintra DUBA 3; active attack; high frequency.

Programmes: The last survivor of the class. Remainder replaced
by Floréal class.
Structure: A/S mortar and torpedo tubes removed in 1993.
Operational: Can carry a senior officer and staff. If necessary a
force of 80 soldiers can be embarked as well as two 30 ft (9 m)
LCPs with a capacity of 25 men at 11 kts. Planned to pay off in
1995.
Sales: Victor Schoelcher sold to Uruguay 30 September 1988,
Commandant Bourdais and Amiral Charner, 14 March 1990.

COMMANDANT BORY

10/1993, V Jeffery, RAN

17 D'ESTIENNE D'ORVES (TYPE A 69) CLASS

Name	No	Builders	Laid down	Launched	Commissioned
D'ESTIENNE D'ORVES	F 781	Lorient Naval Dockyard	1 Sep 1972	1 June 1973	10 Sep 1976
AMYOT D'INVILLE	F 782	Lorient Naval Dockyard	2 July 1973	30 Nov 1974	13 Oct 1976
DROGOU	F 783	Lorient Naval Dockyard	16 Oct 1973	30 Nov 1974	1 Oct 1976
DÉTROYAT	F 784	Lorient Naval Dockyard	15 Dec 1974	31 Jan 1976	4 May 1977
JEAN MOULIN	F 785	Lorient Naval Dockyard	15 Jan 1975	31 Jan 1976	11 May 1977
QUARTIER MAÎTRE ANQUETIL	F 786	Lorient Naval Dockyard	1 Aug 1975	7 Aug 1976	4 Feb 1978
COMMANDANT DE PIMODAN	F 787	Lorient Naval Dockyard	15 July 1975	7 Aug 1976	20 May 1978
SECOND MAÎTRE LE BIHAN	F 788	Lorient Naval Dockyard	1 Nov 1976	13 Aug 1977	7 July 1979
LIEUTENANT DE VAISSEAU LE HÉNAFF	F 789	Lorient Naval Dockyard	21 Mar 1977	16 Sep 1978	13 Feb 1980
LIEUTENANT DE VAISSEAU LAVALLÉE	F 790	Lorient Naval Dockyard	30 Nov 1977	11 May 1979	8 Oct 1980
COMMANDANT L'HERMINIER	F 791	Lorient Naval Dockyard	29 May 1979	7 Mar 1981	19 Jan 1986
PREMIER MAÎTRE L'HER	F 792	Lorient Naval Dockyard	24 July 1979	28 June 1980	5 Dec 1981
COMMANDANT BLAISON	F 793	Lorient Naval Dockyard	15 Nov 1979	7 Mar 1981	26 Apr 1982
ENSEIGNE DE VAISSEAU JACOUBET	F 794	Lorient Naval Dockyard	June 1980	28 Sep 1981	23 Oct 1982
COMMANDANT DUCUING	F 795	Lorient Naval Dockyard	1 Oct 1980	28 Sep 1981	17 Mar 1983
COMMANDANT BIROT	F 796	Lorient Naval Dockyard	23 Mar 1981	22 May 1982	14 Mar 1984
COMMANDANT BOUAN	F 797	Lorient Naval Dockyard	12 Oct 1981	23 Apr 1983	1 Nov 1984

Displacement, tons: 1175 standard; 1250 (1330, later ships) full
load
Dimensions, feet (metres): 262.5 × 33.8 × 18 (sonar)
(80 × 10.3 × 5.5)
Main machinery: 2 SEMT-Pielstick 12 PC2 V 400 diesels;
12 000 hp(m) (8.82 MW); 2 shafts; cp props
2 SEMT-Pielstick 12 PA6 V 280 BTC diesels; 14 400 hp(m)
(10.6 MW) sustained; 2 shafts; cp props (Commandant
L'Herminier)
Speed, knots: 23. **Range, miles:** 4500 at 15 kts
Complement: 90 (7 officers) plus 9 marines (in some)

Missiles: SSM: 4 Aerospatiale MM 40 (or 2 MM 38) Exocet ❶;
inertial cruise; active radar homing to 70 km (40 nm) (or 42 km
(23 nm)) at 0.9 Mach; warhead 165 kg; sea-skimmer. Most will
get dual fit capability ITL in due course (see Modernisation) but
a few only have MM 38 capability (ITS) and some none at all.
Guns: 1 DCN 3.9 in (100 mm)/55 Mod 68 CADAM automatic ❷;
80° elevation; 80 rounds/minute to 17 km (9 nm) anti-surface;
8 km (4.4 nm) anti-aircraft; weight of shell 13.5 kg.
2 Oerlikon 20 mm ❸; 720 rounds/minute to 10 km (5.5 nm).
Torpedoes: 4 fixed tubes ❹. ECAN L5; dual purpose; active/
passive homing to 9.5 km (5.1 nm) at 35 kts; warhead 150 kg;
depth to 550 m (1800 ft).
A/S mortars: 1 Creusot Loire 375 mm Mk 54 6-tubed trainable
launcher ❺; range 1600 m; warhead 107 kg. Removed from
F 793, F 794 and others in due course.
Countermeasures: Decoys: 2 CSEE Dagaie 10-barrelled train-
able launchers (fitted from F 792 onwards; remainder being fit-
ted at refit) ❻; chaff and IR flares; H-J band.
Nixie torpedo decoy.
ESM: ARBR 16; radar warning.
Combat data systems: Syracuse II SATCOM (Commandant Blai-
son and Jacoubet).
Fire control: Thomson-CSF Vega system; CSEE Panda optical
secondary director.
Radars: Air/surface search: Thomson-CSF DRBV 51A ❼; G band.
Navigation: Racal Decca 1226; I band.
Fire control: Thomson-CSF DRBC 32E ❽; I band.
Sonars: Thomson Sintra DUBA 25; hull-mounted; search and
attack; medium frequency.

Programmes: Classified as 'Avisos'. Service lives: Extended to
2000 and beyond.
Modernisation: In 1985 Commandant L'Herminier, F 791, fitted
with 12PA6 BTC Diesels Rapides as trial for Type F 70. Most
have dual MM 38/MM 40 ITL (Installation de Tir Légère) capability. Weapon fit depends on deployment and operational
requirement. Those without ITL are being retrofitted with ITS
(Installation de Tir Standard). Syracuse II SATCOM fitted in
Commandant Blaison and Enseigne de Vaisseau Jacoubet in
1993 vice the A/S mortar, and accommodation provided for

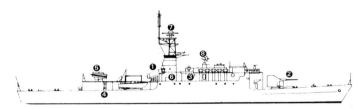

D'ESTIENNE D'ORVES

(Scale 1 : 900), Ian Sturton

SECOND MAÎTRE LE BIHAN

7/1993, Erik Laursen

nine Commandoes. Others of the class may be similarly modified in due course.
Operational: Endurance, 30 days and primarily intended for
coastal A/S operations. Also available for overseas patrols. Ten
assigned to GASM; remainder to Commander Mediterranean
Flotilla or abroad.

Sales: The original Lieutenant de Vaisseau Le Hénaff and Commandant l'Herminier sold to South Africa in 1976 while under
construction. As a result of the UN embargo on arms sales to
South Africa, they were sold to Argentina in September 1978
followed by a third, specially built.

SHIPBORNE AIRCRAFT

Note: Four Grumman E-2C Hawkeye AEW aircraft to be acquired for *Charles de Gaulle*. APS-145 radar and Link 16.

Numbers/Type: 2 Dassault Aviation ACM Rafale M.
Operational speed: Mach 2.
Service ceiling: 50 000 ft *(15 240 m).*
Range: 1800 nm *(3335 km).*
Role/Weapon systems: Fighter (SU 0) and strike/recce (SU 2) variants. Deck trials in *Foch* in April/May 1993. 86 aircraft required; five production aircraft funded by 1994, first one for delivery in 1997. Sensors: Thomson-CSF/Dassault RBE2 radar, Spectra EW suite. Weapons: Strike; Exocet AM 39, Aerospatiale AS 30L stand-off ASM (SU 2), Apache weapon dispenser, 30 mm cannon (SU 0), ASMP nuclear bomb. Air defence; 8 Matra MICA AAMs (SU 0), 8 tons of weapons total limited to 6 tons for carrier operations.

RAFALE M   *1992, Dassault Aviation*

Numbers/Type: 59 Dassault-Bréguet Super Étendard.
Operational speed: Approx Mach 1.
Service ceiling: 45 000 ft *(13 700 m).*
Range: 920 nm *(1682 km).*
Role/Weapon systems: Carrier-borne strike fighter with limited air defence role with nuclear strike. 51-55 are being modernised, of which 20 are to carry ASMP missiles. 18 completed by mid-1994. Unmodernised aircraft: Sensors: Thomson-CSF Agave radar, ECM/ESM. Weapons: Strike; 1 × Aerospatiale ASMP stand-off weapon; range 300 km; nuclear warhead, 2.1 tons of underwing stores including AM 39 Exocet. Defence; 2 × Magic AAM and drop tanks. Self protection; 2 × 30 mm DEFA cannon. Modernised aircraft: Sensors: radar (Dassault Electronique Anémone); computer (SAGEM UAT 90); Thomson-CSF Sherloc ESM, Barracuda jammer ECM, Alkan flare dispenser. Weapons: AS 30L (laser) missile.

SUPER ÉTENDARD   *5/1992, F Gámez*

Numbers/Type: 11 Dassault Étendard IV-P.
Operational speed: Mach 1.02.
Service ceiling: 49 000 ft *(15 000 m).*
Range: 1520 nm *(2817 km).*
Role/Weapon systems: Primary role is photo-reconnaissance and overwater surveillance; carrier-borne and land-based depending on needs and updated in 1991/92. Sensors: Up to 5 × Omera cameras, ESM pods. Weapons: 2 × Magic 1 or 2 AAMs.

ÉTENDARD IV-P   *1988, French Navy*

Numbers/Type: 19 LTV F-8E(FN) Crusader.
Operational speed: 868 kts *(1610 km/h).*
Service ceiling: 50 000 ft *(15 240 m).*
Range: 740 nm *(1370 km).*
Role/Weapon systems: Carrier-borne air defence fighter modified for French needs. 17 being refurbished (9 completed by mid-1994) to last until replaced by Rafale. Sensors: Search/attack radar, ESM/ECM. Weapons: AD; 2 × Magic 1 or 2 AAM or 2 × R530 AAM. Self protection; 4 × 20 mm cannon.

CRUSADER   *1993, French Navy*

Numbers/Type: 26 Bréguet Br 1050 Alizé (modernised).
Operational speed: 254 kts *(470 km/h).*
Service ceiling: 26 250 ft *(8000 m).*
Range: 1350 nm *(2500 km).*
Role/Weapon systems: ASW and strike aircraft embarked in CVLs for surface search, ASV and ASW roles; updated 1985-86 and again in 1992-93. Sensors: Thomson-CSF Iguane surveillance radar, Chlio FLIR (in 15 aircraft), sonobuoys, ECM/ESM. Weapons: ASW; 1 × torpedo or 3 × 160 kg depth bombs or 1 × nuclear depth bomb. ASV; 2 × AS12 missiles and 6 × rockets.

ALIZÉ   *1987, Breguet*

Numbers/Type: 17 Aerospatiale SA 321G Super Frelon.
Operational speed: 148 kts *(275 km/h).*
Service ceiling: 10 170 ft *(3100 m).*
Range: 442 nm *(820 km).*
Role/Weapon systems: Formerly ASW helicopter; now used for assault and support tasks embarked on carriers and LSDs; possible update for ASV not proceeded with but radar updated; provision for 27 passengers. Sensors: Omera ORB search radar. Weapons: Provision for 20 mm gun.

SUPER FRELON   *10/1992, Peter Felstead*

Numbers/Type: 34 Westland Lynx Mk 4 (FN).
Operational speed: 125 kts *(232 km/h).*
Service ceiling: 12 500 ft *(3810 m).*
Range: 320 nm *(593 km).*
Role/Weapon systems: Sole French ASW helicopter, all now of the Mk 4 variant; embarked in destroyers and deployed on training tasks. Sensors: Omera 31 search radar, Alcatel (HS-12 in Mk 2, DUAV 4 in Mk 4) dipping sonar, sonobuoys. Weapons: ASV; 4 × AS12 missiles/SFIM M335 sight. ASW; 2 × Mk 46 Mod 1 (or MU 90 in due course) torpedoes, or depth charges.

LYNX   *10/1992, Peter Felstead*

Numbers/Type: 6/15 Aerospatiale SA 365F/AS 565MA Dauphin 2/Panther.
Operational speed: 140 kts *(260 km/h).*
Service ceiling: 15 000 ft *(4575 m).*
Range: 410 nm *(758 km).*
Role/Weapon systems: SA 365F replace Alouette III for carrier-borne SAR. Three more used for SAR from Channel ports and one from Toulon. These four aircraft being taken over by the Navy from civilian companies. 15 AS 565 ordered in several batches for light and patrol frigates, five delivered by late 1994. Sensors: Agrion search radar. Weapons: Unarmed (SA 365F); ASV Aerospatiale AS 15TT ASM (AS 565).

DAUPHIN 2   *5/1992, Camil Busquets i Vilanova*

Numbers/Type: 32 Aerospatiale SA 319B Alouette III.
Operational speed: 113 kts *(210 km/h)*.
Service ceiling: 10 500 ft *(3200 m)*.
Range: 290 nm *(540 km)*.
Role/Weapon systems: General-purpose helicopter; replaced by Lynx for ASW; now used for trials, surveillance and training tasks. Sensors: Some radar. Weapons: Unarmed.

ALOUETTE III   *1988, French Navy*

LAND-BASED MARITIME AIRCRAFT (FRONT LINE)

Note: Three Dassault Gardian or Cessna Caravan II may be ordered to replace the deployed Atlantic Mk 1s.

Numbers/Type: 15 Bréguet Atlantic (NATO) Mk 1.
Operational speed: 355 kts *(658 km/h)*.
Service ceiling: 32 800 ft *(10 000 m)*.
Range: 4855 nm *(8995 km)*.
Role/Weapon systems: Maritime reconnaissance carried out in Atlantic and Mediterranean; regularly deployed overseas. Primarily ASW but useful ASV role; being replaced by Atlantique 2 and numbers are scheduled to reduce to 10 in 1996, none by 1997. Sensors: Thomson-CSF radar, ECM/ESM, MAD, sonobuoys. Weapons: ASW; 9 × torpedoes (including Mk 46) or depth bombs and mines. ASV; 3/4 Martel ARM.

ATLANTIC   *1992, van Ginderen Collection*

Numbers/Type: 22 Dassault Aviation Atlantique Mk 2.
Operational speed: 355 kts *(658 km/h)*.
Service ceiling: 32 800 ft *(10 000 m)*.
Range: 8 hours patrol at 1000 nm from base; 4 hours patrol at 1500 nm from base.
Role/Weapon systems: Maritime reconnaissance. ASW, ASV, COMINT/ELINT roles. 28 ordered with 22 delivered by late 1994. Last one to be delivered in 1997. Sensors: Thomson-CSF Iguane radar, ARAR 13 ESM, ECM, FLIR, MAD, sonobuoys (with DSAX-1 Thomson-CSF Sadang processing equipment). Link 11 (in due course). COMINT/ELINT equipment optional. Integrated sensor/weapon system built around a CIMSA 15/125X computer. Weapons: 2 × AM 39 Exocet ASMs in ventral bay, or up to eight lightweight torpedoes (Mk 46 and later MU 90), or depth charges, mines or bombs.

Numbers/Type: 4 Boeing E-3F Sentry AWAC.
Operational speed: 460 kts *(853 km/h)*.
Service ceiling: 30 000 ft *(9145 m)*.
Range: 870 nm *(1610 km)*.
Role/Weapon systems: Air defence early warning aircraft with secondary role to provide coastal AEW for the Fleet; six hours endurance at the range given above. Sensors: Westinghouse APY-2 surveillance radar, Bendix weather radar, Mk XII IFF, Yellow Gate, ESM, ECM. Weapons: Unarmed. Operated by the Air Force.

Numbers/Type: 6 Dassault-Bréguet Falcon 10MER.
Operational speed: 492 kts *(912 km/h)*.
Service ceiling: 35 500 ft *(10 670 m)*.
Range: 1920 nm *(3560 km)*.
Role/Weapon systems: Primary aircrew/ECM training role in peacetime but also has overwater surveillance role in wartime; France sole user. Sensors: Search radar. Weapons: Unarmed.

Numbers/Type: 5 Dassault-Bréguet Gardian.
Operational speed: 470 kts *(870 km/h)*.
Service ceiling: 45 000 ft *(13 715 m)*.
Range: 2425 nm *(4490 km)*.
Role/Weapon systems: Maritime reconnaissance role in French Pacific area. Sensors: Thomson-CSF Varan radar, Omega navigation, ECM/ESM pods. Weapons: Unarmed.

Numbers/Type: 15 Aerospatiale N262E.
Operational speed: 226 kts *(420 km/h)*.
Service ceiling: 26 900 ft *(8200 m)*.
Role/Weapon systems: Crew training and EEZ surveillance role. Used by Escadrille 56S in training role and by Escadrilles 2S and 3S in EEZ surveillance role. Modified N262A aircraft. Other N262As in the liaison/transport role. Sensors: Omera ORB 32 radar; photo pod. Weapons: Unarmed. Target towing capability.

Numbers/Type: 4 Aerospatiale/MBB Transall C-160H Astarté.
Operational speed: 278 kts *(515 km/h)*.
Service ceiling: 26 200 ft *(8000 m)*.
Range: 3212 nm *(5950 km)*.
Role/Weapon systems: TACAMO role; support SSBN force; comprehensive communication equipment. Operated by the Air Force with mixed Air Force/Navy crews.

AMPHIBIOUS FORCES

5 BATRAL TYPE (LIGHT TRANSPORTS and LANDING SHIPS)

Name	No	Builders	Commissioned
CHAMPLAIN	L 9030	Brest Naval Dockyard	5 Oct 1974
FRANCIS GARNIER	L 9031	Brest Naval Dockyard	27 Oct 1974
DUMONT D'URVILLE	L 9032	CMN, Cherbourg	5 Feb 1983
JACQUES CARTIER	L 9033	CMN, Cherbourg	29 Sep 1983
LA GRANDIÈRE	L 9034	CMN, Cherbourg	20 Jan 1987

Displacement, tons: 750 standard; 1330 (1400, second pair) full load
Dimensions, feet (metres): 262.4 × 42.6 × 7.9 *(80 × 13 × 2.4)*
Main machinery: 2 SACM AGO 195 V12 diesels; 3600 hp(m) *(2.65 MW)* sustained; 2 shafts; cp props
Speed, knots: 16. **Range, miles:** 4500 at 13 kts
Complement: 50 (5 officers)
Military lift: 138 troops (180 in second pair); 12 vehicles; 350 tons load; 10 ton crane

Missiles: SAM: 2 Matra Simbad twin launchers (may be fitted).
Guns: 2 Bofors 40 mm/60 (L 9030, L 9031). 2 Giat 20F2 20 mm (L 9032, L 9033). 1—81 mm mortar. 2—12.7 mm MGs.
Radars: Navigation: DRBN 32; I band.
Sonars: Two; hull-mounted.

Helicopters: 1 SA 319B Alouette III.

Programmes: Classified as Batral 3F. Bâtiments d'Assaut et de TRAnsport Légers (BATRAL). First two launched 17 November 1973. *Dumont D'Urville* floated out 27 November 1981. *Jacques Cartier* launched 28 April 1982 and *La Grandière* 15 December 1985.
Structure: 40 ton bow ramp; stowage for vehicles above and below decks. One LCVP and one LCPS carried. Helicopter landing platform. Last three of class have bridge one deck higher.
Operational: Deployment: *La Grandière*, Toulon (FAN); *F Garnier*, Antilles/French Guiana; *D D'Urville*, Papeete; *J Cartier*, New Caledonia; *Champlain*, Indian Ocean.
Sales: Ships of this class built for Chile, Gabon, Ivory Coast and Morocco. *La Grandière* was also built for Gabon under Clause 29 arrangements but funds were not available.

CHAMPLAIN   *11/1992, van Ginderen Collection*

FRANCIS GARNIER   *11/1993, Maritime Photographic*

2 EDIC CLASS (LCT)

L 9070 (29 Mar 1967)   L 9074 (7 Feb 1970)

Displacement, tons: 635 (L 9070)
Dimensions, feet (metres): 193.5 × 39.2 × 4.5 *(59 × 12 × 1.3)*
Main machinery: 2 SACM MGO 175 V12 diesels; 1000 hp(m) *(753 kW)* sustained; 2 shafts
Speed, knots: 8. **Range, miles:** 1800 at 8 kts
Complement: 17
Military lift: 5 LVTs or 11 lorries
Guns: 2 Oerlikon 20 mm.

Comment: L 9095 to Senegal 1 July 1974 as *La Falence*. L 9082 transferred to Madagascar in 1985 and renamed *Aina Vao Vao*. L 9070 is at Lorient and L 9074 at Toulon. L 9096 was paid off in 1990 but is now employed as special harbour craft at Brest.

L 9074   *8/1990, J Y Robert*

1 + 1 (2) FOUDRE CLASS (LANDING SHIPS (DOCK)) (TYPE TCD 90)

Name	No	Builders	Laid down	Launched	Commissioned
FOUDRE	L 9011	Brest Naval Dockyard	26 Mar 1986	19 Nov 1988	8 Dec 1990
—	L 9012	Brest Naval Dockyard	1994	1997	1999

Displacement, tons: 8190 light; 11 900 full load; 17 200 flooded

Dimensions, feet (metres): 551 × 77.1 × 17 (30.2 flooded) *(168 × 23.5 × 5.2 (9.2))*

Main machinery: 2 SEMT-Pielstick 16 PC2.5 V 400 diesels; 15 600 hp(m) *(11.48 MW)* sustained; 2 shafts; cp props; bow thruster; 1000 hp(m) *(735 kW)*

Speed, knots: 21. **Range, miles:** 11 000 at 15 kts

Complement: 210 (13 officers)

Military lift: 470 troops plus 1810 tons load; 2 CDIC or 10 CTM or 1 P 400 patrol craft

Missiles: SAM: 2 Matra Simbad twin launchers ❶; Mistral; IR homing to 4 km *(2.2 nm)*; warhead 3 kg.

Guns: 1 Bofors 40 mm/60 ❷. 2 Giat 20F2 20 mm guns ❸. 2—12.7 mm MGs.

Combat data systems: Syracuse SATCOM ❹. OPSMER command support system.

Fire control: Sagem VIGY-105 optronic system (in 1996/97).

Radars: Air/surface search: Thomson-CSF DRBV 21A Mars ❺; D band.

Surface search: Racal Decca 2459 ❻; I band.

Navigation: 2 Racal Decca RM 1229; I band (1 for helo control ❼).

Helicopters: 4 AS 332F Super Puma ❽ or 2 Super Frelon.

Programmes: First ordered 5 November 1984, second in November 1993. Third and fourth in due course although there may be some design changes. Transportes de Chalands de Débarquement (TCD).

Modernisation: Sadral SAM replaced by two lightweight Simbad SAMs either side of bridge. New air search radar. Sagem optronic fire-control to be fitted in 1996/97.

Structure: Designed to take a mechanised regiment of the Rapid Action Force and act as a logistic support ship. Extensive command and hospital facilities include two operating theatres and 47 beds. Hangar capacity: two Super Frelons or four Super Pumas. Two landing spots. Well dock 122 × 14.2 × 7.7 m. Lift of 52 tons capacity. Flight deck 1450 m² with Samahe haul down system. Flume stabilisation fitted in 1993.

Operational: Two landing spots on flight deck plus one on deck well rolling cover. Can operate up to seven Super Puma helicopters. Could carry up to 1600 troops in emergency. Endurance, 30 days (with 700 persons aboard). A 400 ton ship can be docked. Assigned to FAN. Typical loads: one CDIC, four CTM, 10 AMX 10RC armoured cars and 50 vehicles or total of 180-200 vehicles (without landing craft).

FOUDRE

(Scale 1 : 1500), Ian Sturton

FOUDRE

1993, Ships of the World

2 OURAGAN CLASS (LANDING SHIPS (DOCK) (TCDs))

Name	No	Builders	Laid down	Launched	Commissioned
OURAGAN	L 9021	Brest Naval Dockyard	June 1962	9 Nov 1963	1 June 1965
ORAGE	L 9022	Brest Naval Dockyard	June 1966	22 Apr 1967	1 Apr 1968

Displacement, tons: 5800 light; 8500 full load; 15 000 when fully docked down

Dimensions, feet (metres): 488.9 × 75.4 × 17.7 (28.5 flooded) *(149 × 23 × 5.4 (8.7))*

Main machinery: 2 SEMT-Pielstick diesels; 8600 hp(m) *(6.32 MW)*; 2 shafts; cp props

Speed, knots: 17. **Range, miles:** 9000 at 15 kts

Complement: 213 (10 officers)

Military lift: 343 troops (plus 129 short haul only); 2 LCTs (EDIC) with 11 light tanks each or 8 loaded CTMs; logistic load 1500 tons; 2 cranes (35 tons each)

Missiles: SAM: 2 Matra Simbad twin launchers; Mistral; IR homing to 4 km *(2.2 nm)*; warhead 3 kg; anti-sea-skimmer.

Guns: 2—4.7 in *(120 mm)* mortars; 42 rounds/minute to 20 km *(10.8 nm)*; weight of shell 24 kg.

4 Bofors 40 mm; 300 rounds/minute to 12 km *(6.5 nm)*.

Fire control: Sagem VIGY-105 optronic system (in 1996/97).

Radars: Air/surface search: Thomson-CSF DRBV 51A; G band.

Navigation: 2 Racal Decca 1226; I band.

Sonars: EDO SQS-17 *(Ouragan)*; search; medium frequency.

Helicopters: 4 SA 321G Super Frelon or Super Pumas or 10 SA 319B Alouette III.

Programmes: Service lives extended until L 9012 and L 9013 are commissioned.

Modernisation: Simbad SAM and new search radars fitted in 1993. Sagem VIGY-105 optronic fire-control system to be fitted in 1996/97.

Structure: Normal helicopter platform for operating three Super Frelon or 10 Alouette III plus a portable platform for a further one Super Frelon or three Alouette III. Bridge is on the starboard side. Three LCVPs can also be carried. Extensive workshops.

Operational: Typical loads—18 Super Frelon or 80 Alouette III helicopters or 120 AMX 13 tanks or 84 DUKWs or 340 Jeeps or 12—50 ton barges. A 400 ton ship can be docked. Command facilities for directing amphibious and helicopter operations. Both ships assigned to FAN and transferred to Toulon.

Typical loads: one CDIC, four CTM, 10 AMX 10RC armoured cars and 21 vehicles or total of 150-170 vehicles (without landing craft).

OURAGAN

10/1993, J Y Robert

1 BOUGAINVILLE CLASS (BTS)

Name	No	Builders	Laid down	Launched	Commissioned
BOUGAINVILLE	L 9077	Chantier Dubigeon, Nantes	28 Jan 1986	3 Oct 1986	June 1988

Displacement, tons: 4876 standard; 5100 full load
Dimensions, feet (metres): 372.3; 344.4 wl × 55.8 × 14.1
  (113.5; 105 × 17 × 4.3)
Flight deck, feet (metres): 85.3 × 55.8 *(26 × 17)*
Main machinery: 2 SACM AGO 195 V12 RVR diesels; 4410
  hp(m) *(3.24 MW)* sustained; 2 shafts; cp props; bow thruster;
  400 hp(m) *(294 kW)*
Speed, knots: 15. **Range, miles:** 6000 at 12 kts
Complement: 53 (5 officers) plus 10 staff
Military lift: 500 troops for 8 days; 1180 tons cargo; 2 LCU in
  support or 10 LCP plus 2 LCM for amphibious role

Missiles: SAM: 2 Matra Simbad twin launchers (may be fitted).
Guns: 2—12.7 mm MGs.
Radars: Navigation: Two Decca 1226; I band.

Helicopters: Platform for 2 AS 332B Super Puma.

Programmes: Ordered November 1984 for the Direction du Centre d'Experimentations Nucléaires (DIRCEN). As Chantier Dubigeon closed down after her launch she was completed by Chantier de l'Atlantique of the Alsthom group. Bâtiment de Transport et de Soutien (BTS).

Structure: Well size is 78 × 10.2 m *(256 × 33.5 ft)*. It can receive tugs and one BSR or two CTMs, a supply tender of the Chamois class, containers, mixed bulk cargo. Has extensive repair workshops and repair facilities for helicopters. Can act as mobile crew accommodation and has medical facilities. Storerooms for spare parts, victuals and ammunition. Hull to civilian standards. Carries a 37 ton crane.
Operational: Completed sea trials 25 February 1988. Based in the Pacific Squadron for use at the nuclear test base. Can dock a 400 ton ship.

BOUGAINVILLE   *1988, Alsthom*

2 EDIC 700 CLASS (LCT)

L 9051   L 9052

Displacement, tons: 736 full load
Dimensions, feet (metres): 193.6 × 38.1 × 5.8 *(59 × 11.6 × 1.7)*
Main machinery: 2 SACM Uni Diesel UD 30 V12 M1 diesels; 1200 hp(m) *(882 kW)* sustained;
  2 shafts
Speed, knots: 12. **Range, miles:** 1800 at 12 kts
Complement: 17
Military lift: 350 tons
Guns: 2 Giat 20F2 20 mm. 2—12.7 mm MGs.

Comment: Ordered 10 March 1986 from SFCN, Villeneuve la Garenne. Commissioned on 13 June 1987 and 19 December 1987 respectively. Rated as Engins de Débarquement d'Infanterie et Chars (EDIC III). Based at the Pacific Test Centre (*L 9051*) and Djibouti (*L 9052*).

L 9061   *10/1992*

24 CTMs (LCMs)

CTM 2, 3, 5, 9, 10, 12, 14-31

Displacement, tons: 56 standard; 150 full load
Dimensions, feet (metres): 78 × 21 × 4.2 *(23.8 × 6.4 × 1.3)*
Main machinery: 2 Poyaud 520 V8 diesels; 225 hp(m) *(165 kW)*; 2 shafts
Speed, knots: 9.5. **Range, miles:** 350 at 8 kts
Complement: 6
Military lift: 90 tons (maximum); 48 tons (normal)

Comment: First series of 16 built 1966-70 and so far seven have been deleted. Second series built at CMN, Cherbourg 1982-92. All have a bow ramp but the second series has a different shaped pilot house. Chalands de Transport de Matériel (CTM). Ten are assigned to FAN. Others based at naval bases as service craft or deployed overseas as amphibious/service craft. Others of the class operated by the French Army Transport Corps.

L 9052   *4/1991, Guy Toremans*

2 CDIC CLASS (LCT)

L 9061   L 9062

Displacement, tons: 380 light; 710 full load
Dimensions, feet (metres): 194.9 × 39 × 5.9 *(59.4 × 11.9 × 1.8)*
Main machinery: 2 SACM Uni Diesel UD 30 V12 M1 diesels; 1200 hp(m) *(882 kW)* sustained;
  2 shafts
Speed, knots: 10.5. **Range, miles:** 1000 at 10 kts
Complement: 12 (1 officer)
Military lift: 336 tons
Guns: 2 Giat 20F2 20 mm. 2—12.7 mm MGs.

Comment: First laid down September 1987 at SFCN, Villeneuve la Garenne. Commissioned 19 October 1988 and 2 March 1989 respectively. CDIC (Chaland de Débarquement d'Infanterie et de Chars) designed to replace the EDICs and specially built to work with Foudre class. The wheelhouse can be lowered to facilitate docking manoeuvres in the LPDs. Assigned to l'FAN.

CTM 12   *8/1990, J Y Robert*

2 LCM 6s

1057   1058

Comment: Of 52 tons full load and 8 kts. Built in Réunion for service at Mayotte Naval Base. Completed March 1983. Some others operated by French Army overseas.

PATROL FORCES

Note: The Thomson-CSF demonstrator *Iris* P 696 was returned by the Navy in 1992.

10 P 400 CLASS (FAST ATTACK CRAFT—PATROL)

Name	No	Builders	Commissioned
L'AUDACIEUSE	P 682	CMN, Cherbourg	18 Sep 1986
LA BOUDEUSE	P 683	CMN, Cherbourg	15 Jan 1987
LA CAPRICIEUSE	P 684	CMN, Cherbourg	13 Mar 1987
LA FOUGUEUSE	P 685	CMN, Cherbourg	13 Mar 1987
LA GLORIEUSE	P 686	CMN, Cherbourg	18 Apr 1987
LA GRACIEUSE	P 687	CMN, Cherbourg	17 July 1987
LA MOQUEUSE	P 688	CMN, Cherbourg	18 Apr 1987
LA RAILLEUSE	P 689	CMN, Cherbourg	16 May 1987
LA RIEUSE	P 690	CMN, Cherbourg	13 June 1987
LA TAPAGEUSE	P 691	CMN, Cherbourg	11 Feb 1988

Displacement, tons: 406 standard; 454 full load
Dimensions, feet (metres): 178.6 × 26.2 × 8.5 *(54.5 × 8 × 2.5)*
Main machinery: 2 SEMT-Pielstick 16 PA4 200 VGDS diesels; 8000 hp(m) *(5.88 MW)* sustained; 2 shafts; cp props
Speed, knots: 24.5. **Range, miles:** 4200 at 15 kts
Complement: 26 (3 officers) plus 20 passengers

Guns: 1 Bofors 40 mm/60; 1 Giat 20F2 20 mm; 2—12.7 mm MGs.
Radars: Surface search: Racal Decca 1226; I band.

Programmes: First six ordered in May 1982, with further four in March 1984. The original engines of this class were unsatisfactory. Replacements were ordered and construction was slowed. Those completed were laid up at Lorient until new engines became available. This class relieved the Patra fast patrol craft which have all transferred to the Gendarmerie.
Structure: Steel hull and superstructure protected by an upper deck bulwark. Design modified from original missile craft configuration. Now capable of transporting personnel with appropriate store-rooms. Of more robust construction than previously planned—to be used as overseas transports. Can be converted for missile armament (MM 38) with dockyard assistance and Sadral PDMS has been considered. *L'Audacieuse* has done trials with a VDS-12 sonar. Twin funnels replaced the unsatisfactory submerged diesel exhausts in 1990/91.
Operational: Deployments: Antilles/French Guiana; P 684, 685. Noumea; P 686, 688. Mayotte (Indian Ocean); P 683. Djibouti; 690. Tahiti; P 687, 689, 691. Cherbourg; P 682. Endurance, 15 days with 45 people aboard.

L'AUDACIEUSE   *8/1992, Guy Toremans*

FORCE DE SURFACE A MISSIONS CIVILES—FSMC

Note: This designation is applied to a programme of ships and craft designed for offshore and coastal patrol, fishery protection, maritime traffic surveillance, anti-pollution duties and search and rescue, all being manned by the Navy.

Name	No	Builders	Commissioned
ALBATROS (ex-*Névé*)	P 681	Ch de la Seine Maritime	1967

Displacement, tons: 2800 full load
Dimensions, feet (metres): 278.1 × 44.3 × 18.4 *(84.8 × 13.5 × 5.6)*
Main machinery: Diesel-electric; 2 Uni Diesel UD 33 V12 M6 diesel generators; 4410 hp(m) *(3.24 MW)* sustained; 2 motors; 3046 hp(m) *(2.24 MW)*; 1 shaft
Speed, knots: 15
Complement: 46 (5 officers) plus 16 passengers
Guns: 1 Bofors 40 mm/60. 2—12.7 mm MGs.
Helicopters: Platform for Alouette III.

Comment: Former trawler bought in April 1983 from Compagnie Nav. Caennaise for conversion into a patrol ship. Commissioned 19 May 1984. Conducts patrols from Réunion to Kerguelen, Crozet, St Paul and Amsterdam Islands with occasional deployments to South Pacific. Can carry 200 tons cargo, has extensive sick berth arrangements and VIP accommodation. Major refit in Lorient from June 1990 to March 1991 which included new diesel-electric propulsion. Service life: 2015.

ALBATROS   *1986, French Navy*

Name	No	Builders	Commissioned
STERNE	P 680	La Perrière, Lorient	20 Oct 1980

Displacement, tons: 380 full load
Dimensions, feet (metres): 160.7 × 24.6 × 9.2 *(49 × 7.5 × 2.8)*
Main machinery: 2 SACM 195 V12 CZSHR diesels; 4340 hp(m) *(3.19 MW)* sustained; electro-hydraulic auxiliary propulsion on starboard shaft; 150 hp(m) *(110 kW)*; 2 shafts
Speed, knots: 20; 6 on auxiliary propulsion. **Range, miles:** 4900 at 12 kts; 1500 at 20 kts
Complement: 18 (3 officers); 2 crews
Guns: 2—12.7 mm MGs.
Radars: Navigation: Racal Decca; I band.

Comment: *Sterne* was the first ship for the FSMC. Has active tank stabilisation. Completed 18 July 1980 for the 'Affaires Maritimes' but then transferred and is now manned and operated by the Navy from Brest.

STERNE   *5/1992, French Navy*

1 GRÈBE CLASS

Name	No	Builders	Commissioned
GRÈBE	P 679	SFCN, Villeneuve La Garenne	6 Apr 1991

Displacement, tons: 410 full load
Dimensions, feet (metres): 170.6 × 32.2 × 9 *(52 × 9.8 × 2.8)*
Main machinery: 2 Uni Diesel UD 33 V12 M6 diesels; 4410 hp(m) *(3.24 MW)*; diesel-electric auxiliary propulsion; 2 shafts; cp props
Speed, knots: 23; 7.5 on auxiliary propulsion. **Range, miles:** 4500 at 12 kts
Complement: 19 (4 officers); accommodation for 24; 2 crews
Guns: 2—12.7 mm MGs.
Radars: Navigation: Racal Decca; I band.

Comment: Type Espadon 50 ordered 17 July 1988 and launched 16 November 1989. 'Deep V' hull; stern ramp for craft handling. Large deck area (8 × 8 m) for Vertrep operations. Pollution control equipment and remotely operated waterjet gun for firefighting. Based at Brest.

GRÈBE   *10/1992*

0 + 3 MODIFIED GRÈBE (OPV 54) CLASS

Name	No	Builders	Commissioned
FLAMANT	P 680 (new)	CMN, Cherbourg	1995
CORMORAN	P 681 (new)	CMN, Cherbourg	1995
PLUVIER	—	Leroux & Lotz, Lorient	1996

Displacement, tons: 374 full load
Dimensions, feet (metres): 177.2 × 32.8 × 7.2 *(54 × 10 × 2.2)*
Main machinery: 2 diesels; 4410 hp(m) *(3.24 MW)*; 2 shafts
Speed, knots: 22
Range, miles: 4500 at 12 knots
Complement: 19
Guns: 2—12.7 mm MGs.

Comment: The Grèbe design was acquired by Leroux & Lotz from the defunct SFCN. These three were authorised in July 1992. The prototype is being built for Mauritania by Leroux & Lotz.

MINE WARFARE FORCES

Note: Narvik class project cancelled in 1992. For details see *Trials/Research Ships* section.

9 + 1 ÉRIDAN (TRIPARTITE) CLASS (MINEHUNTERS)

Name	No	Laid down	Launched	Commissioned
ÉRIDAN	M 641	20 Dec 1977	2 Feb 1979	16 Apr 1984
CASSIOPÉE	M 642	26 Mar 1979	26 Sep 1981	5 May 1984
ANDROMÈDE	M 643	6 Mar 1980	22 May 1982	18 Oct 1984
PÉGASE	M 644	22 Dec 1980	23 Apr 1983	30 May 1985
ORION	M 645	17 Aug 1981	6 Feb 1985	14 Jan 1986
CROIX DU SUD	M 646	22 Apr 1982	6 Feb 1985	14 Nov 1986
AIGLE	M 647	2 Dec 1982	8 Mar 1986	1 July 1987
LYRE	M 648	13 Oct 1983	14 Nov 1986	16 Dec 1987
PERSÉE	M 649	30 Oct 1984	19 Apr 1988	4 Nov 1988
SAGITTAIRE	M 650	31 July 1993	Aug 1995	July 1995

Displacement, tons: 562 standard; 595 full load
Dimensions, feet (metres): 168.9 × 29.2 × 8.2 *(51.5 × 8.9 × 2.5)*
Main machinery: 1 Brons Werkspoor A-RUB 215X-12 diesel; 1860 hp(m) *(1.37 MW)* sustained; 1 shaft; Lips cp prop
Auxiliary propulsion; 2 motors; 240 hp(m) *(179 kW)*; 2 active rudders; 2 bow thrusters
Speed, knots: 15; 7 on auxiliary propulsion. **Range, miles:** 3000 at 12 kts
Complement: 46 (5 officers)

Guns: 1 Giat 20F2 20 mm; 1–12.7 mm MG.
Countermeasures: MCM: 2 PAP 104 systems; mechanical sweep gear. AP-4 acoustic sweep.
Radars: Navigation: Racal Decca 1229; I band.
Sonars: Thomson Sintra DUBM 21B; hull-mounted; active; high frequency; 100 kHz (±10 kHz).

Programmes: All built in Lorient. Belgium, France and the Netherlands each agreed to build 15 (10 in Belgium with option on five more). Subsequently the French programme was cut to 10. Each country provided people to man a joint bureau de programme in Paris and built its own GRP hulls to a central design. Belgium provided all the electrical installations, France all the minehunting gear and some electronics and the Netherlands the propulsion systems. Replacement for the last of class (sold to Pakistan) was ordered in January 1992.
Structure: GRP hull. Equipment includes: autopilot and hovering; automatic radar navigation; navigation aids by Loran and Syledis; Evec data system; Decca Hifix.
Operational: Minehunting, minesweeping, patrol, training, directing ship for unmanned minesweeping, HQ ship for diving operations and pollution control. Pre-packed 5 ton modules of equipment to be embarked for separate tasks. M 641-646 based at Brest, remainder at Toulon. Chasseurs de Mines Tripartites (CMT).
Sales: The original tenth ship of the class, completed in 1989, was transferred to Pakistan 24 September 1992 as part of an order for three; the second is being built in Lorient, the third in Karachi.

ORION   *7/1993, van Ginderen Collection*

1 AGGRESSIVE CLASS (MINESWEEPER)

OUISTREHAM (ex-MSO 513) M 610

Displacement, tons: 700 standard; 780 full load
Dimensions, feet (metres): 172 × 36 × 13.6 *(52.4 × 11 × 4.1)*
Main machinery: 4 GM 8-268A diesels; 1760 hp *(1.31 MW)*; 2 shafts; cp props
Speed, knots: 13.5. **Range, miles:** 3000 at 10 kts
Complement: 58 (5 officers)

Guns: 1 Bofors 40 mm/60; 2–12.7 mm MGs.
Countermeasures: MCM: Mechanical minesweeping capabilities; AP 4 acoustic sweep.
Radars: Navigation: Racal Decca 1229; I band.
Sonars: DUBM 41B; towed; side scanning; active search; high frequency.

Programmes: The USA transferred MSOs to France in three batches during 1953. Being replaced by Antares class. This last survivor of the class is planned to pay off in December 1994.
Modernisation: Modernised with improved DUBM 41 and AP 4 acoustic sweep.

OUISTREHAM   *2/1991, van Ginderen Collection*

5 CIRCÉ CLASS (MINEHUNTERS)

Name	No	Builders	Commissioned
CYBÈLE	M 712	CMN, Cherbourg	28 Sep 1972
CALLIOPE	M 713	CMN, Cherbourg	28 Sep 1972
CLIO	M 714	CMN, Cherbourg	18 May 1972
CIRCÉ	M 715	CMN, Cherbourg	18 May 1972
CÉRÈS	M 716	CMN, Cherbourg	7 Mar 1973

Displacement, tons: 460 standard; 495 normal; 510 full load
Dimensions, feet (metres): 167 × 29.2 × 11.2 *(50.9 × 8.9 × 3.4)*
Main machinery: 1 MTU diesel; 1800 hp(m) *(1.32 MW)*; 2 active rudders; 1 shaft
Speed, knots: 15. **Range, miles:** 3000 at 12 kts
Complement: 48 (5 officers)

Guns: 1 Oerlikon 20 mm.
Countermeasures: MCM: The 9 ft *(2.74 m)* long PAP is propelled by two electric motors at 6 kts and is wire-guided to a maximum range of 500 m. Fitted with a television camera, this machine detects the mine and lays its 100 kg charge nearby. This is then detonated by an ultrasonic signal. These ships carry no normal minesweeping equipment.
Radars: Navigation: Racal Decca 1229; I band.
Sonars: Thomson Sintra DUBM 20B; hull-mounted; active search; high frequency.

Programmes: Ordered in 1968. Due for deletion 1991-93 but will be retained until BAMOs come into service.
Modernisation: Programmes completed 1989 included computer-aided sonar classification.
Operational: All based at Brest.

CYBÈLE   *7/1993, Wright & Logan*

CYBÈLE   *5/1993, Harald Carstens*

1 + 2 ANTARES (BINRS) CLASS (ROUTE SURVEY VESSELS)

Name	No	Builders	Commissioned
ANTARES	M 770	Socarenam, Boulogne	15 Dec 1993
ALTAIR	M 771	Socarenam, Boulogne	July 1994
ALDEBARAN	M 772	Socarenam, Boulogne	March 1995

Displacement, tons: 340 full load
Dimensions, feet (metres): 92.8 × 25.3 × 12.5 *(28.3 × 7.7 × 3.8)*
Main machinery: 1 Baudouin diesel; 800 hp(m) *(590 kW)*; 1 shaft; bow thruster
Speed, knots: 10. **Range, miles:** 3600 at 10 kts
Complement: 25 (1 officer)
Radars: Navigation: Two Racal-Decca; I band.
Sonars: Thomson Sintra DUBM 41B; towed side scan; active search; high frequency.

Comment: To replace the Aggressive class for Navigation training and route survey at Brest. BINRS—Bâtiments d'Instruction à la Navigation Remorqueurs de Sonars. Trawler type similar to Glycine class (see *Training Ships* section). *Antares* launched 30 May 1993. The DUBM 41B towed bodies have been taken from the older MSOs. A mechanical sweep is also carried.

ANTARES   *1993, Ships of the World*

4 MCM DIVING TENDERS

Name	No	Builders	Commissioned
VULCAIN	M 611	La Perrière, Lorient	11 Oct 1986
PLUTON	M 622	La Perrière, Lorient	10 Dec 1986
ACHÉRON	A 613	CMN, Cherbourg	21 Apr 1987
STYX	M 614	CMN, Cherbourg	22 July 1987

Displacement, tons: 375 standard; 505 full load
Dimensions, feet (metres): 136.5 × 24.6 × 12.5 *(41.6 × 7.5 × 3.8)*
Main machinery: 2 SACM MGO 175 V16 ASHR diesels; 2200 hp(m) *(1.62 MW)*; 2 shafts; bow thruster; 70 hp(m) *(51 kW)*
Speed, knots: 13.7. **Range, miles:** 2800 at 13 kts; 7400 at 9 kts
Complement: 14 (1 officer) plus 12 divers
Guns: 1—12.7 mm MG.
Radars: Navigation: Decca 1226; I band.

Comment: First pair ordered in December 1984. Second pair ordered July 1985. Designed to act as support ships for clearance divers. (Bâtiments Bases pour Plongeurs Démineurs - BBPD). *Vulcain* launched 17 January 1986, based at Cherbourg. *Pluton* launched 13 May 1986, based at Toulon. *Achéron* launched 9 November 1986, based at Toulon as a diving school tender and *Styx* launched 3 March 1987, based at Brest. Modified Chamois (BSR) class design. 5 ton hydraulic crane.

PLUTON   *11/1993, Giorgio Ghiglione*

SURVEY AND RESEARCH SHIPS

Notes: (1) These ships are painted white.
(2) A total of about 100 officers and technicians with oceanographic and hydrographic training is employed in addition to the ships' companies listed here. They occupy the extra billets marked as 'scientists'.
(3) In addition to the ships listed below there is a civilian-manned 25 m trawler *L'Aventurière II* (launched July 1986) operated by GESMA, Brest for underwater research which comes under DCN.
(4) A new *Berry* is to be ordered as soon as possible as a purpose-built electronics intelligence gathering ship to complete in 1997.
(5) *Agnes 200* A 786 returned to owners 13 March 1992 and may now be used for commercial service.
(6) *L'Archéonaute* A 789, a small underwater research vessel, paid off in 1991 but back in service in 1993.

4 LAPÉROUSE (BH2) CLASS

Name	No	Builders	Commissioned
LAPÉROUSE	A 791	Lorient Naval Dockyard	20 Apr 1988
BORDA	A 792	Lorient Naval Dockyard	18 June 1988
LAPLACE	A 793	Lorient Naval Dockyard	5 Oct 1989
ARAGO	A 795	Lorient Naval Dockyard	9 July 1991

Displacement, tons: 970 standard; 1100 full load
Dimensions, feet (metres): 193.5 × 35.8 × 11.9 *(59 × 10.9 × 3.6)*
Main machinery: 2 SACM MGO 175 V12 RVR diesels; 2500 hp(m) *(1.84 MW)*; 2 cp props; bow thruster
Speed, knots: 15. **Range, miles:** 6000 at 12 kts
Complement: 27 (2 officers) plus 11 scientists plus 7 spare berths
Radars: Navigation: Decca 1226; I band.
Sonars: Thomson-Sintra DUBM 42 or DUBM 21C (A 791); active search; high frequency.

Comment: Have replaced L'Espérance and L'Astrolabe classes. Ordered under 1982 and 1986 estimates, first pair on 24 July 1984, third 22 January 1986 and fourth 12 April 1988. BH2 (Bâtiments Hydrographiques de 2e classe).
Two variants: BH2A (A 791)—Carry Thomson Sintra DUBM 21C sonar for detection of underwater obstacles. Based at Brest; BH2C (remainder)—Carry two VH8 survey launches for hydrographic work. A 793 sailed for the Pacific 9 October 1989, joined by A 795 on 1 October 1991. A 792 based at Brest. *Borda* has the TSM 5260 Lennermor multi-path echo sounder.

LAPÉROUSE   *3/1992, H M Steele*

Name	No	Builders	Commissioned
D'ENTRECASTEAUX	A 757	Brest Naval Dockyard	8 Oct 1971

Displacement, tons: 2400 full load
Dimensions, feet (metres): 292 × 42.7 × 14.4 *(89 × 13 × 4.4)*
Main machinery: Diesel-electric; 2 diesel generators; 2720 hp(m) *(2 MW)*; 2 motors; 2 shafts; cp props
Auxiliary propulsion; 2 Schottel trainable and retractable props
Speed, knots: 15. **Range, miles:** 10 000 at 12 kts
Complement: 76 (8 officers) plus 36 scientific staff
Radars: Navigation: Two Racal Decca 1226; I band.
Helicopters: 1 SA 319B Alouette III.

Comment: This ship was specially designed for oceanographic surveys capable of working to 6000 m *(19 686 ft)*. Bâtiment Océanographique (BO). Carries one LCP and three survey launches. Telescopic hangar. Serves in the Mediterranean but is to be based at Brest from September 1995. Replacement planned.

D'ENTRECASTEAUX   *2/1993, J Y Robert*

Name	No	Builders	Commissioned
L'ESPÉRANCE (ex-*Jacques Coeur*)	A 756	Gdynia	25 June 1969

Displacement, tons: 956 standard; 1360 full load
Dimensions, feet (metres): 208.3 × 32.1 × 19.4 *(63.5 × 9.8 × 5.9)*
Main machinery: 2 MAN diesels; 1850 hp(m) *(1.36 MW)*; 2 shafts
Speed, knots: 15. **Range, miles:** 7500 at 13 kts
Complement: 32 (3 officers) plus 14 scientists

Comment: Former trawler first commissioned in 1962 at Gdynia and purchased by the Navy in 1968. Adapted as survey ship. Based in Atlantic. Has a Simrad EM 12D multi-path echo sounder. To be deleted in 1998.

L'ESPÉRANCE   *1/1989, van Ginderen Collection*

Name	No	Builders	Commissioned
MONGE	A 601	Chantiers de l'Atlantique, St Nazaire	5 Dec 1992

Displacement, tons: 21 040 full load
Dimensions, feet (metres): 740.2 × 81.4 × 25.3 *(225.6 × 24.8 × 7.7)*
Main machinery: 2 SEMT-Pielstick 8 PC2.5 L 400 diesels; 10 400 hp(m) *(7.65 MW)* sustained; 1 shaft; bow thruster
Speed, knots: 16. **Range, miles:** 15 000 at 15 kts
Complement: 110 plus 100 military and 98 civilian technicians
Guns: 2 Giat F2 20 mm.
Combat data systems: Tavitac 2000 for trials.
Radars: Air search: Thomson-CSF DRBV 15C; E/F band.
Missile tracking: L band (new model); Gascogne; two Armor; Savoie; two Antares.
Navigation: Two Racal Decca (one for helo control); I band.
Helicopters: 2 Super Frelon.

Comment: Ordered 25 November 1988. Rated as a BEM (Bâtiment d'Essais et de Mesures). Laid down 26 March 1990, and launched 6 October 1990. She has 14 telemetry antennas; optronic tracking unit; LIDAR; Syracuse SATCOM. Flume tank stabilisation restricts the ship to a maximum of 9° roll at slow speed in Sea State 6. Flagship of the Trials Squadron.

MONGE   *8/1993, van Ginderen Collection*

Name	No	Builders	Commissioned
ILE D'OLÉRON (ex-*München*, ex-*Mür*)	A 610	Weser, Bremen	Apr 1939

Displacement, tons: 5500 standard; 6500 full load
Dimensions, feet (metres): 378 × 50 × 21.3 *(115.2 × 15.2 × 6.5)*
Main machinery: 2 MAN 6-cyl diesels; 3500 hp(m) *(2.57 MW)*; 1 shaft
Speed, knots: 14.5. **Range, miles:** 7200 at 12 kts
Complement: 195 (12 officers)
Radars: Various, according to experiments (DRBV 22C, DRBV 50).
Navigation: Racal Decca 1226; I band.
Helicopters: Platform only for Alouette III.

Comment: Taken as a war prize. Commissioned in French Navy 29 August 1945. Formerly rated as a transport. Converted to experimental guided missile ship in 1957-58 by Chantiers de Provence and l'Arsenal de Toulon. Commissioned early in 1959. Fitted with one launcher for target planes. Has been fitted with various equipment and weapon systems for trials: Masurca, Crotale, Otomat, MM 40 Exocet, Sadral, 100 mm gun with CTMS fire-control system, Crotale Modulaire, Sagaie, Simbad. Fitted for sea trials of Milas in 1992 (ASW torpedo delivery missile with a range of 50 km). Also trials continue on prototype Sylver launchers for VLS Aster 15 PDMS and Aster 30 Area SAM. Arabel radar fitted in 1994. Based at Toulon.

ILE D'OLÉRON   10/1993, J Y Robert

Name	No	Builders	Commissioned
BERRY (ex-M/S *Médoc*)	A 644	Roland Werft, Bremen	26 Nov 1964

Displacement, tons: 1148 standard; 2700 full load
Dimensions, feet (metres): 284.5 × 38 × 15 *(86.7 × 11.6 × 4.6)*
Main machinery: 2 MWM diesels; 2400 hp(m) *(1.76 MW)*; 1 shaft
Speed, knots: 13. **Range, miles:** 7000 at 15 kts
Guns: 2—12.7 mm MGs.
Radars: Navigation: Racal Decca 1226; I band.

Comment: Launched on 10 May 1958. In 1976-77 converted at Toulon from victualling stores ship to Mediterranean electronic trials ship. Recommissioned February 1977. Deleted in error in 1991. It is planned to replace her by 1997, her performance as an AGI having been inadequate in the Gulf in 1991.

BERRY   2/1993, J Y Robert

Name	No	Builders	Commissioned
THÉTIS (ex-*Nereide*)	A 785	Lorient Naval Dockyard	9 Nov 1988

Displacement, tons: 720 standard; 1000 full load
Dimensions, feet (metres): 185.4 × 35.8 × 11.8 *(56.5 × 10.9 × 3.6)*
Main machinery: 2 Uni Diesel UD 30 V16 M4 diesels; 2710 hp(m) *(1.99 MW)* sustained; 1 shaft; cp prop
Speed, knots: 15. **Range, miles:** 6000
Complement: 36 (2 officers) plus 7 passengers
Guns: 2—12.7 mm MGs.
Radars: Navigation: Racal Decca 1226; I band.
Sonars: VDS; Thomson Sintra DUBM 42 and DUBM 60A; active search; high frequency.

Comment: Same hull as Lapérouse class. Classified as Bâtiment Expérimental Guerre de Mines (BEGM). Operated by the Centre d'Études, d'Instruction et d'Entraînement de la Guerre des Mines (CETIEGM) in Brest. Launched 19 March 1988. Renamed to avoid confusion with Y 700. Equipped to conduct trials on all underwater weapons and sensors for mine warfare. Can lay mines. Can support six divers. Fitted with the Thomson Sintra mine warfare combat system designed for the cancelled Narvik class.

THÉTIS   11/1992, van Ginderen Collection

Name	No	Builders	Commissioned
DENTI	A 743	DCAN Toulon	15 July 1976

Displacement, tons: 170 full load
Dimensions, feet (metres): 113.8 × 21.6 × 7.5 *(34.7 × 6.6 × 2.3)*
Main machinery: 2 Baudouin DP8 diesels; 960 hp(m) *(706 kW)*; 2 shafts; cp props
Speed, knots: 12. **Range, miles:** 800 at 12 kts
Complement: 6 (2 officers)

Comment: Launched 7 October 1975. Employed on ammunition trials off Toulon.

DENTI   6/1991, van Ginderen Collection

Name	No	Builders	Launched
NARVIK	M 660	Lorient Naval Dockyard	22 Mar 1991

Displacement, tons: 905 full load
Dimensions, feet (metres): 170.6 oa; 152.9 wl × 48.6 × 11.8 *(52; 46.6 × 14.8 × 3.6)*
Main machinery: 2 diesels; 2700 hp(m) *(1.98 MW)*; 2 shafts; cp props; auxiliary propulsion: diesel-electric; 500 kW; bow thruster; 204 hp(m) *(150 kW)*
Speed, knots: 15. **Range, miles:** 5000 at 10 kts
Complement: 46
Guns: 1 Giat 20 mm F2. 2—12.7 mm MGs.
Countermeasures: MCM: One or two remote-controlled minehunting PAP Mk 5 with DUBM 60 sonar and television. Mechanical, magnetic and acoustic (DCN AP4) sweeps.
Sonars: Thomson Sintra DUBM 42; towed; active; high frequency; can be towed at 10 kts down to 300 m *(984 ft)*.

Comment: Designed by DCN. BAMO (Bâtiment Anti-Mines Océanique). Programme of six cancelled in 1992 leaving an unfinished *Narvik* at Lorient. May be used as a trials ship. GRP hull with a catamaran design. This type of hull offers a larger working area than a monohull of equivalent displacement. Other claimed advantages include seakeeping, stability and manoeuvrability.

NARVIK   8/1992, J Y Robert

AUXILIARIES

Notes: (1) The commercial tankers *Penhors* and *Mascarin* (included in 1988-89 edition) are fitted for replenishment at sea and are available for loan to the Navy.
(2) *Punaruu* A 632 had her service life extended into 1994. She is an ex-Norwegian tanker with a capacity of 2500 m³.

1 MAINTENANCE and REPAIR SHIP

Name	No	Builders	Commissioned
JULES VERNE (ex-*Achéron*)	A 620	Brest Naval Dockyard	1 June 1976

Displacement, tons: 6485 standard; 10 250 full load
Dimensions, feet (metres): 482.2 × 70.5 × 21.3 *(147 × 21.5 × 6.5)*
Main machinery: 2 SEMT-Pielstick 18 PC2.2 V 400 diesels; 18 000 hp(m) *(13.2 MW)* sustained; 2 shafts
Speed, knots: 18. **Range, miles:** 9500 at 18 kts
Complement: 294 (15 officers)
Guns: 2 Bofors 40 mm/60. Several 12.7 mm MGs.
Helicopters: 2 SA 319B Alouette III.

Comment: Ordered in 1961 budget, originally as an Armament Supply Ship. Role and design changed whilst building—now rated as Engineering and Electrical Maintenance Ship. Launched 30 May 1970. Serves in Indian Ocean, providing general support for all ships. Carries stocks of torpedoes and ammunition. Refit in France November 1988-June 1989.

JULES VERNE   9/1989, Photo Sami

5 DURANCE CLASS (UNDERWAY REPLENISHMENT TANKERS)

Name	No	Builders	Laid down		Launched		Commissioned
MEUSE	A 607	Brest Naval Dockyard	2 June 1977		2 Dec 1978		21 Nov 1980
VAR	A 608	Brest Naval Dockyard	8 May 1979		1 June 1981		29 Jan 1983
DURANCE	A 629	Brest Naval Dockyard	12 Dec 1973		6 Sep 1975		1 Dec 1976
MARNE	A 630	Brest Naval Dockyard	4 Aug 1982		2 Feb 1985		16 Jan 1987
SOMME	A 631	Normed, la Seyne	3 May 1985		3 Oct 1987		7 Mar 1990

Displacement, tons: 17 900 full load
Dimensions, feet (metres): 515.9 × 69.5 × 38.5
 (157.3 × 21.2 × 10.8)
Main machinery: 2 SEMT-Pielstick 16 PC2.5 V 400 diesels;
 20 800 hp(m) *(15.3 MW)* sustained; 2 shafts; cp props
Speed, knots: 19. **Range, miles:** 9000 at 15 kts
Complement: 164 (18 officers)
Cargo capacity: 7500 tons FFO; 1500 diesel; 500 TR5 Avcat;
 140 distilled water; 170 victuals; 150 munitions; 50 naval
 stores *(Durance)*. 5000 tons FFO; 3200 diesel; 1800 TR5
 Avcat; 130 distilled water; 170 victuals; 150 munitions; 50
 naval stores *(Meuse)*. 5090 tons FFO; 3310 diesel; 1090 TR5
 Avcat; 260 distilled water; 180 munitions; 15 stores *(Var and
 Marne)*

Guns: 2 Bofors 40 mm/60 *(Durance)*. 1 Bofors 40 mm/60. 2
 Oerlikon 20 mm (remainder). 4—12.7 mm MGs.
Combat data systems: Syracuse SATCOM. OPSMER command
 support system (fitted for BCR ships).
Radars: Navigation: 2 Racal Decca 1226; I band.

Helicopters: 1 Lynx Mk 2/4.

Programmes: Two classed as Pétroliers Ravitailleurs d'Escadres
 (PRE). Three classed as Bâtiments de Commandement et de
 Ravitaillement (BCR; Command and Replenishment Ships).
Structure: Four beam transfer positions and two astern, two of
 the beam positions having heavy transfer capability. *Var,
 Marne* and *Somme* differ from the others in several respects.

The bridge extends further aft, boats are located either side of
the funnel and a crane is located between the gantries. Also fitted with Syracuse SATCOM.
Operational: *Var, Marne* and *Somme* are designed to carry a
 Maritime Zone staff or Commander of a Logistic Formation and
 a commando unit of up to 45 men. Capable of accommodating
 250 men. *Durance* assigned to GASM, others to FAN with one
 of the three BCR ships deployed to the Indian Ocean as a
 Flagship.
Sales: One to Australia built locally; two of similar but smaller
 design to Saudi Arabia.

VAR   10/1993, Vic Jeffery, RAN

SOMME   11/1993, Harald Carstens

2 RR 4000 TYPE (SUPPLY TENDERS)

Name	No	Builders	Commissioned
RARI	A 634	Breheret	21 Feb 1985
REVI	A 635	Breheret	9 Mar 1985

Displacement, tons: 900 light; 1450 full load
Dimensions, feet (metres): 167.3 × 41.3 × 13.1 *(51 × 12.6 × 4)*
Main machinery: 2 SACM AGO 195 V12 diesels; 4410 hp(m) *(3.24 MW)*; 2 shafts; cp props; bow
 thruster
Speed, knots: 14.5. **Range, miles:** 6000 at 12 kts
Complement: 22 plus 18 passengers

Comment: Two 'remorqueurs ravitailleurs' for le Centre d'Expérimentation du Pacifique. Can carry
 400 tons of cargo on deck.

1 TRANSPORT LANDING SHIP

Name	No	Builders	Commissioned
GAPEAU	L 9090	Chantier Serra, la Seyne	2 Oct 1987

Displacement, tons: 509 standard; 1058 full load
Dimensions, feet (metres): 216.5 × 40 × 11.2 *(66 × 12.2 × 3.4)*
Main machinery: 2 diesels; 2 shafts
Speed, knots: 10
Complement: 6 + 30 scientists
Cargo capacity: 460 tons

Comment: Supply ship with bow doors. Operates for Centre d'Essais de la Mediterranée, Levant
 Island (missile range).

RARI   8/1985, J Y Robert

GAPEAU   5/1991, Giorgio Ghiglione

5 RHIN CLASS (DEPOT and SUPPORT SHIPS)

Name	No	Builders	Commissioned
LOIRE	A 615	Lorient Naval Dockyard	10 Oct 1967
GARONNE	A 617	Lorient Naval Dockyard	1 Sep 1965
RANCE	A 618	Lorient Naval Dockyard	5 Feb 1966
RHIN	A 621	Lorient Naval Dockyard	1 Apr 1964
RHÔNE	A 622	Lorient Naval Dockyard	1 Dec 1964

Displacement, tons: 2075 (2320, *Garonne* and *Loire*) standard; 2445 full load
Dimensions, feet (metres): 331.5 × 43 × 12.1 *(101.1 × 13.1 × 3.7)*
Main machinery: 2 SEMT-Pielstick 16 PA2 V 400 diesels (*Rhin* and *Rhône*); 3300 hp(m) *(2.43 MW)*; 1 shaft
2 SEMT-Pielstick 12 PA4 V 400 diesels (*Rance*, *Loire* and *Garonne*); 4000 hp(m) *(2.94 MW)*; 1 shaft
Speed, knots: 16.5; 13 *(Rance)*. **Range, miles:** 13 000 at 13 kts
Complement: 165 (11 officers) (*Rhin* and *Rhône*); 120 (7 officers) and about 118 passengers *(Rance)*; 167 (19 officers) *(Garonne)*; 156 (12 officers) *(Loire)*
Guns: 3 Bofors 40 mm/60 (*Loire*, *Rhin* and *Rhône*). 1 Bofors 40 mm/60. 2 Oerlikon 20 mm *(Garonne)*. None in *Rance*. 3—12.7 mm MGs.
Radars: Air search: DRBV 23C (in *Rance* in addition).
Air/surface search: Thomson-CSF DRBV 50; D band.
Helicopters: 1-3 SA 310B Alouette III (except *Garonne*). Platform only *(Rhône)*.

Comment: Designed for supporting various classes of ships. Have a 5 ton crane, carry two LCPs and have a helicopter platform (except *Garonne*). *Rhin* has a hangar and carries two helicopters; *Rance* has two platforms and carries three in her hangar; *Loire* has a hangar for one. *Garonne* is designed as a Repair Workshop, *Loire* for minesweeper support, *Rhin* for electronic maintenance and *Rhône* for submarines. *Rance* has been converted as a command and medical support ship for La Force d'Assistance Rapide with several modifications, and is also used as flagship of the Fleet Training Centre (Mediterranean). *Rhône* operates in the Atlantic, *Garonne* in the Indian Ocean/Pacific, *Loire* at Brest and *Rhin* in the Mediterranean until late 1994 when she returns to the Indian Ocean. Another ship (Bâtiment de Soutien Logistique—BSL) was to have been ordered in 1992 but this has been postponed and the service lives of all these ships have been extended.

LOIRE   *9/1993, van Ginderen Collection*

RANCE   *7/1993, van Ginderen Collection*

RHÔNE (*Agosta* alongside)   *5/1993, van Ginderen Collection*

6 CHAMOIS CLASS (SUPPLY TENDERS)

Name	No	Builders	Commissioned
TAAPE	A 633	La Perrière, Lorient	2 Nov 1983
CHAMOIS	A 767	La Perrière, Lorient	24 Sep 1976
ÉLAN	A 768	La Perrière, Lorient	7 Apr 1978
CHEVREUIL	A 774	La Perrière, Lorient	7 Oct 1977
GAZELLE	A 775	La Perrière, Lorient	13 Jan 1978
ISARD	A 776	La Perrière, Lorient	15 Dec 1978

Displacement, tons: 495 (500, *Taape*) full load
Dimensions, feet (metres): 136.1 × 24.6 × 10.5 *(41.5 × 7.5 × 3.2)*
Main machinery: 2 SACM AGO 175 V16 diesels; 2700 hp(m) *(1.98 MW)*; 2 shafts; cp props; bow thruster
Speed, knots: 14.2. **Range, miles:** 6000 at 12 kts
Complement: 13 plus 7 spare berths
Radars: Navigation: Racal Decca 1226; I band.

Comment: Similar to the standard fish oil rig support ships. Can act as tugs, oil pollution vessels, salvage craft (two 30 ton and two 5 ton winches), coastal and harbour controlled minelaying, torpedo recovery, diving tenders and a variety of other tasks. Bollard pull 25 tons. Can carry 100 tons of stores on deck or 125 tons of fuel and 40 tons of water or 65 tons of fuel and 120 tons of water. *Taape* ordered in March 1982 from La Perrière—of improved design but basically similar with bridge one deck higher. *Taape* and *Chamois* based at Centre d'Expérimentation du Pacifique. Remainder based in France. *Isard* serves as a special diving support ship with an extra deckhouse. Seventh of class *Tapatai* returned to owners in 1992.

ISARD   *6/1991, van Ginderen Collection*

GAZELLE   *5/1991, J Y Robert*

TAAPE (high bridge)   *1990, van Ginderen Collection*

3 NETLAYERS

Name	No	Builders	Commissioned
LA PRUDENTE	Y 749	AC Manche	27 July 1969
LA PERSÉVÉRANTE	Y 750	AC La Rochelle	3 Mar 1969
LA FIDÈLE	Y 751	AC Manche	10 June 1969

Displacement, tons: 626 full load
Dimensions, feet (metres): 142.8 × 32.8 × 9.2 *(43.5 × 10 × 2.8)*
Main machinery: Diesel-electric; 2 Baudouin diesels; 620 hp(m) *(441 kW)*; 1 shaft
Speed, knots: 10. **Range, miles:** 4000 at 10 kts
Complement: 30 (1 officer)

Comment: Net layers and tenders. Launched on 13 May 1968 *(La Prudente)*, 14 May 1968 *(La Persévérante)* and 26 August 1968 *(La Fidèle)*. Have a 25 ton lift. Based at Brest, Toulon and Cherbourg respectively.

LA FIDÈLE *9/1992, Guy Toremans*

1 BOOM DEFENCE SHIP

Name	No	Builders	Commissioned
TIANÉE	A 731	Arsenal de Brest	8 July 1975

Displacement, tons: 842 standard; 905 full load
Dimensions, feet (metres): 178.1 × 34.8 × 11.2 *(54.3 × 10.6 × 3.4)*
Main machinery: Diesel-electric; 2 diesel generators; 1300 hp(m) *(960 kW)*; 1 motor; 1200 hp(m) *(880 kW)*; 1 shaft
Speed, knots: 12. **Range, miles:** 5200 at 12 kts
Complement: 37 (1 officer)

Comment: Launched 17 November 1973. Fitted with lateral screws in bow tunnel. Refitted early 1985, based at Toulon.

TIANÉE *10/1991, Aldo Fraccaroli*

3 MOORING VESSELS

TUPA Y 667   **TELENN MOR** Y 692

Comment: 292 tons with 210 hp(m) *(154 kW)* diesel. *Tupa* commissioned 16 March 1974, *Telenn Mor* on 16 January 1986. *Tupa* based at Papeete.

TELENN MOR *8/1988, J Y Robert*

CALMAR Y 698

Comment: A 270 ton harbour tug converted for raising moorings. One diesel engine. Commissioned 12 August 1970. Based at Lorient.

CALMAR *8/1990, J Y Robert*

9 AERIEL CLASS (TRANSPORTS)

ARIEL Y 604	**DRYADE** Y 662	**ONDINE** Y 701
FAUNE Y 613	**ALPHÉE** Y 696	**NAIADE** Y 702
KORRIGAN Y 661	**NEREIDE** Y 700	**ELFE** Y 741

Displacement, tons: 195 standard; 225 full load
Dimensions, feet (metres): 132.8 × 24.5 × 10.8 *(40.5 × 7.5 × 3.3)*
Main machinery: 2 SACM MGO or Poyaud diesels; 1640 hp(m) *(1.21 MW)* or 1730 hp(m) *(1.27 MW)*; 2 shafts
Speed, knots: 15.3. **Range, miles:** 940 at 14 kts
Complement: 9

Comment: All built by Société Française de Construction Naval (ex-Franco-Belge) except for *Nereide, Ondine* and *Naiade* by DCAN Brest. *Ariel* in service 1964, *Elfe* in 1980; the remainder at approximately two year intervals. Can carry 400 passengers (250 seated). *Naiade* based with CEM Toulon.

NAIADE *8/1993, van Ginderen Collection*

1 TRANSPORT VESSEL

SYLPHE Y 710

Displacement, tons: 171 standard; 189 full load
Dimensions, feet (metres): 126.5 × 22.7 × 8.2 *(38.5 × 6.9 × 2.5)*
Main machinery: 1 SACM MGO diesel; 833 hp(m) *(612 kW)*; 1 shaft
Speed, knots: 12
Complement: 9

Comment: Small transport for passengers, built by Chantiers Franco-Belges in 1959-60. Based at Brest since 1981.

SYLPHE *8/1992, J Y Robert*

1 TRANSPORT VESSEL

TREBERON

Comment: Commissioned at Brest 26 November 1979.

TREBERON *8/1988, J Y Robert*

3 FERRIES

MORGANE Y 671   **MERLIN** Y 735   **MÉLUSINE** Y 736

Displacement, tons: 170 full load
Dimensions, feet (metres): 103.3 × 23.2 × 7.9 *(31.5 × 7.1 × 2.4)*
Main machinery: 2 SACM MGO diesels; 940 hp(m) *(691 kW)*; 2 shafts
Speed, knots: 11

Comment: Small ferries for 400 passengers built by Chantiers Navals Franco-Belges at Châlons-sur-Saône *(Mélusine* and *Merlin)* and Toulon Dockyard *(Morgane).* First one commissioned in June 1968. Based at Toulon.

MORGANE   *7/1993, van Ginderen Collection*

5 TENDERS

POSÉIDON A 722

Displacement, tons: 220 full load
Dimensions, feet (metres): 132.9 × 23.6 × 7.3 *(40.5 × 7.2 × 2.2)*
Main machinery: 1 diesel; 600 hp(m) *(441 kW)*; 1 shaft
Speed, knots: 13
Complement: 42

Comment: Base ship for assault swimmers. Completed 6 August 1975.

POSÉIDON   *6/1991, van Ginderen Collection*

TOURMALINE A 714

Displacement, tons: 45
Dimensions, feet (metres): 88 × 16.8 × 4.8 *(26.8 × 5.1 × 1.5)*
Main machinery: 2 diesels; 1120 hp(m) *(823 kW)*; 2 shafts
Speed, knots: 27

Comment: Commissioned 14 February 1974. Built by Chantiers Navals de L'Esterel. Attached to Mediterranean Test Range. Civilian-manned. Based at Port Pothau near Toulon.

TOURMALINE   *6/1985, Giorgio Arra*

ATHOS A 712   **ARAMIS** A 713

Displacement, tons: 100 full load
Dimensions, feet (metres): 105.3 × 21.3 × 6.2 *(32.1 × 6.5 × 1.9)*
Main machinery: 2 SACM diesels; 4400 hp(m) *(3.23 MW)*; 2 shafts
Speed, knots: 32. **Range, miles:** 1500 at 15 kts
Complement: 12 plus 6 passengers
Guns: 1 Oerlikon 20 mm. 2—12.7 mm MGs.
Radars: Navigation: Racal Decca 1226; I band.

Comment: Built by Chantiers Navals de l'Esterel for Missile Trials Centre of Les Landes (CEL). Based at Bayonne, forming Groupe des Vedettes de l'Adour. Commissioned 1980.

ATHOS   *9/1983, van Ginderen Collection*

Y 732

Comment: Built in Lorient. Commissioned 3 March 1979. Based at Brest. Designated 'Station de Démagnétisation No 3'.

Y 732   *8/1992, J Y Robert*

10 DIVING TENDERS

CORALLINE A 790   **Y 790-798**

Displacement, tons: 44 full load
Dimensions, feet (metres): 68.9 × 14.8 × 3.6 *(21 × 4.5 × 1.1)*
Main machinery: 2 diesels; 264 hp(m) *(194 kW)*; 2 shafts
Speed, knots: 13
Complement: 4 plus 14 divers

Comment: Diving tenders building at Lorient. First one delivered in February 1990. *Coralline* is used for radioactive monitoring in Cherbourg. *Y 790-791* are divers training craft (VIP) at Toulon. *Y 792-793* are clearance diver support craft (VIPD) based at Toulon. Others are based at Cherbourg and Brest.

Y 792   *7/1993, van Ginderen Collection*

2 PHAETON CLASS (TOWED ARRAY TENDERS)

PHAETON Y 656   **MACHAON** Y 657

Comment: 18.6 m catamarans built in 1993. Waterjet propulsion, speed 8 kts. Hydraulic crane and winch to handle submarine towed arrays. Based at Toulon.

19 HARBOUR CRAFT

| Y 753-755 | Y 776-777 | Y 783-785 |
| Y 762-765 | Y 779-781 | Y 786-789 |

Displacement, tons: 18-21 full load
Dimensions, feet (metres): 47.9 × 15.1 × 3.3 *(14.6 × 4.6 × 1)*
Main machinery: 2 Baudouin diesels; 900 or 500 hp(m) *(661 kW or 368 kW)*; 2 shafts
Speed, knots: 20 or 13. **Range, miles:** 400 at 11 kts
Complement: 4

Comment: All except *Y 783-785* built by DCN Lorient between 1988 and 1992. *Y 762-765* are patrol craft and can carry one 12.7 mm MG; *Y 779-781* are pilot craft; *Y 753-755* and *Y 786-789* are transport craft based in the Pacific; *Y 783-785* were completed in 1993/94 by Alan Sibiril Shipyard, Carentec and are for fire-fighting; *Y 776-777* are radiological monitoring craft and have smaller engines.

Y 765   *8/1992, J Y Robert*

25 HARBOUR SUPPORT CRAFT

Comment: There are 11 harbour oil barges (CIC), five water barges (CIE), six oily bilge barges (CIEM) and three anti-pollution barges (CIEP/BAPM). Most have a capability of 400 cu m and CIC and CIE craft are self-propelled.

CIE 23   8/1992, J Y Robert

1 FLOATING DOCK

Comment: Of 3800 tons capacity, built at Brest in 1975. Based at Papeete for use by Centre Expérimentation du Pacifique. 150 × 33 m.

6 FLOATING CRANES

GFA 1-6

Comment: With lifts of 7.5-15 tons. One in Cherbourg, three in Brest, two in Toulon. Self-propelled. Grue Flottante Automotrice (GFA).

20 HARBOUR SUPPORT CRAFT

CHA 8   14   17   19   23-38

Comment: Of 20 tons based at Cherbourg, Brest, Lorient, Toulon, Rochefort. Used as harbour craft. *CHA 27-34* in service 1988, *35-38* in service 1989.

CHA 32   8/1992, J Y Robert

TRAINING SHIPS

2 GLYCINE CLASS

Name	No	Builders	Commissioned
GLYCINE	A 770	Socarenam, Boulogne	11 Apr 1992
EGLANTINE	A 771	Socarenam, Boulogne	9 Sep 1992

Displacement, tons: 295 full load
Dimensions, feet (metres): 92.8 × 25.3 × 12.5 *(28.3 × 7.7 × 3.8)*
Main machinery: 1 Baudouin diesel; 800 hp(m) *(588 kW)*; 1 shaft
Speed, knots: 10. **Range, miles:** 3600 at 10 kts
Complement: 10 + 16 trainees
Radars: Navigation: 2 Furuno; I band.

Comment: Trawler type. Three more building as route survey craft (included under *Mine Warfare Forces* section).

EGLANTINE   5/1993, G Toremans

8 LÉOPARD CLASS

Name	No	Builders	Commissioned
LÉOPARD	A 748	ACM, St Malo	4 Dec 1982
PANTHÈRE	A 749	ACM, St Malo	4 Dec 1982
JAGUAR	A 750	ACM, St Malo	18 Dec 1982
LYNX	A 751	La Perrière, Lorient	18 Dec 1982
GUÉPARD	A 752	ACM, St Malo	1 July 1983
CHACAL	A 753	ACM, St Malo	10 Sep 1983
TIGRE	A 754	La Perrière, Lorient	1 July 1983
LION	A 755	La Perrière, Lorient	10 Sep 1983

Displacement, tons: 463 full load
Dimensions, feet (metres): 141 × 27.1 × 10.5 *(43 × 8.3 × 3.2)*
Main machinery: 2 SACM MGO 175 V16 ASHR diesels; 2200 hp(m) *(1.62 MW)*; 2 shafts
Speed, knots: 15. **Range, miles:** 4100 at 12 kts
Complement: 14 plus 21 trainees
Guns: 2 Oerlikon 20 mm.
Radars: Navigation: Racal Decca 1226; I band.

Comment: First four ordered May 1980. Further four ordered April 1981. Form 20ème Divec (Training division) for shiphandling training and occasional EEZ patrols.

JAGUAR   12/1993, van Ginderen Collection

CHIMÈRE Y 706   **FARFADET** Y 711

Displacement, tons: 100
Main machinery: 1 diesel; 200 hp(m) *(147 kW)*; 1 shaft
Speed, knots: 11

Comment: Built at Bayonne in 1971. Tenders to the Naval School. Re-engined in 1991/92.

LA GRANDE HERMINE (ex-*La Route Est Belle*, ex-*Ménestrel*) A 653

Comment: Ex-sailing fishing boat built in 1932 by Chantiers Fidèle, Marseilles. Purchased in 1964 as the Navigation School (EOR) training ship. Length 46 ft *(14.02 m)*.

L'ÉTOILE A 649   **LA BELLE POULE** A 650

Displacement, tons: 227
Dimensions, feet (metres): 105.9 × 22.9 × 10.5 *(32.3 × 7 × 3.2)*
Main machinery: Sulzer diesel; 125 hp(m) *(92 kW)*; 1 shaft
Speed, knots: 6

Comment: Auxiliary sail vessels. Built by Chantiers de Normandie (Fécamp) in 1932. Accommodation for three officers, 30 cadets, five petty officers, 12 men. Attached to Naval School.

LA BELLE POULE   7/1992, van Ginderen Collection

Name	No	Builders	Launched
MUTIN	A 652	Chaffeteau, Les Sables d'Olonne	18 May 1927

Displacement, tons: 57 full load
Dimensions, feet (metres): 108.3 × 21 × 11.2 *(33 × 6.4 × 3.4)*
Main machinery: 1 diesel; 112 hp(m) *(82 kW)*; 1 auxiliary prop
Speed, knots: 6 (diesel). **Range, miles:** 860 at 6 kts
Complement: 12 + 6 trainees

Comment: Attached to the Navigation School. Has a sail area of 240 m². This is the oldest ship in the French Navy.

MUTIN   *7/1993, Hartmut Ehlers*

TUGS

3 OCEAN TUGS (Remorqueurs de Haute Mer RHM)

MALABAR A 664   **TENACE** A 669   **CENTAURE** A 674

Displacement, tons: 1080 light; 1454 full load
Dimensions, feet (metres): 167.3 × 37.8 × 18.6 *(51 × 11.5 × 5.7)*
Main machinery: 2 Krupp MaK 9 M US2 AK diesels; 4600 hp(m) *(3.38 MW)*; 1 shaft; Kort nozzles
Speed, knots: 15. **Range, miles:** 9500 at 15 kts
Complement: 42

Comment: *Malabar* and *Tenace* built by J. Oelkers, Hamburg, *Centaure* built at La Pallice. *Tenace* commissioned 15 November 1973, *Centaure* on 15 November 1974 and *Malabar* on 7 October 1975. All based at Brest with one operating as Fishery Protection ship off US coast. Carry fire-fighting equipment. Bollard pull, 60 tons.

TENACE   *8/1993, van Ginderen Collection*

23 COASTAL TUGS (Remorqueurs Côtiers RC)

BÉLIER A 695   **BUFFLE** A 696   **BISON** A 697

Displacement, tons: 500 standard; 800 full load
Dimensions, feet (metres): 104.9 × 28.9 × 10.5 *(32 × 8.8 × 3.2)*
Main machinery: 2 SACM AGO 195 V8 CSHR diesels; 2600 hp(m) *(1.91 MW)*; 2 Voith-Schneider props
Speed, knots: 11
Complement: 12

Comment: Built at Cherbourg. *Bélier* commissioned 10 July 1980, *Buffle* on 19 July 1980, *Bison* on 16 April 1981. All based at Toulon. Bollard pull, 25 tons.

BISON   *10/1993, J Y Robert*

MAROA A 636   **MAITO** A 637   **MANINI** A 638

Displacement, tons: 245 full load
Dimensions, feet (metres): 90.5 × 27.2 × 11.5 *(27.6 × 8.9 × 3.5)*
Main machinery: 2 SACM diesels; 1280 hp(m) *(941 kW)*; 2 Voith-Schneider props
Speed, knots: 11. **Range, miles:** 1200 at 10 kts
Complement: 10

Comment: Built by SFCN and Villeneuve La Garonne (A 638) for CEP Nuclear Test Range. *Maito* commissioned 25 July 1984, *Maroa* 28 July 1984, *Manini* 12 September 1985. Bollard pull, 12 tons.

LE FORT A 671 (12 July 1971)	**LABORIEUX** A 687 (14 Aug 1963)
UTILE A 672 (8 Apr 1971)	**TRAVAILLEUR** A 692 (11 July 1963)
LUTTEUR A 673 (19 July 1963)	**ACHARNÉ** A 693 (5 July 1974)
ACTIF A 686 (11 July 1963)	**EFFICACE** A 694 (17 Oct 1974)

Displacement, tons: 230 full load
Dimensions, feet (metres): 92 × 26 × 13 *(28.1 × 7.9 × 4)*
Main machinery: 1 SACM MGO diesel; 1050 hp(m) *(773 kW)* or 1450 hp(m) *(1.07 MW)* (later ships); 1 shaft
Speed, knots: 11. **Range, miles:** 2400 at 10 kts
Complement: 15

Comment: Commissioning dates in brackets. Bollard pull, 13 tons.

ACHARNÉ   *6/1990, Gilbert Gyssels*

FRÉHEL A 675	**LA HOUSSAYE** A 678	**GIENS** —
SAIRE A 676	**KEREON** (ex-*Sicie*) A 679	**OROHENA** —
ARMEN A 677	**LARDIER** A 680	**SICIÉ** —

Displacement, tons: 259 full load
Dimensions, feet (metres): 82 × 27.6 × 11.2 *(25 × 8.4 × 3.4)*
Main machinery: 2 diesels; 1280 hp(m) *(941 kW)* (1320 hp(m) *(970 kW)* in later vessels); 2 Voith-Schneider props
Speed, knots: 10. **Range, miles:** 800 at 10 kts
Complement: 8 (coastal); 5 (harbour)

Comment: Building at Lorient Naval et Industries shipyard (formerly Chantiers et Ateliers de la Perrière, now part of Leroux et Lotz). *Fréhel* in service 23 May 1989, based at Cherbourg, *Saire* 16 October 1989 at Cherbourg, *Armen* 6 December 1991 at Brest, *La Houssaye* 30 October 1992 at Lorient and *Kereon* 5 December 1992 at Brest, *Lardier* commissioned in 1993 and based at Toulon. When completed, *Giens* at Toulon, *Orohena* at Mururoa and *Sicié* at Toulon. It is planned to build craft on this pattern until 2005. Bollard pull 12 tons.

ARMEN   *8/1992, J Y Robert*

73 HARBOUR TUGS (Remorqueurs de port)

CHATAIGNER Y 620	**MANGUIER** Y 666	**PLATANE** Y 695	**OLIVIER** Y 719
CORMIER Y 629	**MÉLÈZE** Y 668	**SAULE** Y 708	**SANTAL** Y 720
FRÊNE Y 644	**MERISIER** Y 669	**SYCOMORE** Y 709	**MARONNIER** Y 738
HÊTRE Y 654	**PALETUVIER** Y 686	**ÉBÈNE** Y 717	**NOYER** Y 739
HEVEA Y 655	**PEUPLIER** Y 688	**ÉRABLE** Y 718	**PAPAYER** Y 740

Comment: Of 105 tons, 10 ton bollard pull with 700 hp(m) *(514 kW)* diesel and maximum speed of 11 kts. Being deleted. Known as Type 700 CH.

ÉBÈNE   *8/1992, J Y Robert*

BONITE Y 630   **ROUGET** Y 634

Comment: Of 93 tons, 7 ton bollard pull with 380 hp(m) *(279 kW)* and maximum speed of 10 kts. Based at Brest. In service in 1974/75.

ROUGET and BONITE   *8/1990, J Y Robert*

BENGALI Y 611	**GOÉLAND** Y 648	**PIVERT** Y 694	**GRAND DUC** Y 728
MOUETTE Y 617	**MERLE** Y 670	**ENGOULEVENT** Y 723	**EIDER** Y 729
MÉSANGE Y 621	**MOINEAU** Y 673	**MARABOUT** Y 725	**ARA** Y 730
COLIBRI Y 628	**MARTIN PÊCHEUR** Y 675	**TOUCAN** Y 726	**LORIOT** Y 747
MARTINET Y 636	**PASSEREAU** Y 687	**MACREUSE** Y 727	**GÉLINOTTE** Y 748
FAUVETTE Y 637	**PINSON** Y 691		

Comment: Of 65 tons, 3.5 ton bollard pull with 250 hp(m) *(184 kW)* diesel and maximum speed of 9 kts. *Ibis* Y 658 loaned to Senegal. Built 1960-73. Known as Type 250 CH.

65 TON TYPE   *8/1990, J Y Robert*

P 1-23   **101-102**   **1-4**

Displacement, tons: 24
Dimensions, feet (metres): 37.7 × 14.1 × 4.6 *(11.5 × 4.3 × 1.4)*
Main machinery: 2 SACM Poyaud 520 V8M diesels; 440 hp(m) *(323 kW)*; 2 shafts
Speed, knots: 9.2

Comment: *P 1-23* are pusher-tugs built by Ch et A de La Perrière. First of the second series *(P 13)* delivered 23 December 1980. Bollard push, 4 tons. *101-102* in service at Brest for *Le Triomphant* in 1993; bollard push, 10 tons. *1-4* are for SSBNs at Brest and displace 44 tons and have a bollard push of 4 tons.

P 16   *5/1991, J Y Robert*

CASCADE Y 618   **GAVE** Y 645   **AIGUIÈRE** Y 745   **EMBRUN** Y 746

Displacement, tons: 85 full load
Dimensions, feet (metres): 78.1 × 17.4 × 5.6 *(23.8 × 5.3 × 1.7)*
Main machinery: 2 SACM Poyaud diesels; 410 hp(m) *(301 kW)*; 2 shafts
Speed, knots: 11.3

Comment: Fire-fighting tugs with red hulls and white superstructure. Beginning to be paid off.

GAVE   *8/1992, J Y Robert*

FLOTTE AUXILIAIRE OCCASIONNELLE (FAO)

Note: There are some 120 vessels on the FAO list. These are civilian-manned and 'taken up' as required for transport and other duties.

ABEILLE FLANDRE (ex-*Neptun Suecia*)   **ABEILLE LANGUEDOC** (ex-*Neptun Gothia*)

Displacement, tons: 1577
Dimensions, feet (metres): 208 × 48.2 × 2.9 *(63.4 × 14.7 × 0.9)*
Main machinery: 4 Atlas diesels; 23 000 hp(m) *(16.9 MW)*; 2 shafts
Speed, knots: 17

Comment: *Abeille Flandre* based at Brest, *Abeille Languedoc* at Cherbourg. Used as salvage tugs.

ABEILLE FLANDRE   *7/1990, M Voss*

ALBACORE (ex-*Beryl Fish*)   **MÉROU** (ex-*King Fish*)
GIRELLE (ex-*Moon Fish*) A 702

Comment: All of about 55 m in length and capable of 12 kts. *Mérou* and *Girelle* built in the Netherlands in 1981-82 and based in Toulon. *Albacore* on loan from Feronica International and also based in the Mediterranean. Used as supply ships.

GIRELLE   *7/1993, van Ginderen Collection*

GOVERNMENT MARITIME FORCES

POLICE (GENDARMERIE MARITIME AND GENDARMERIE DÉPARTE-MENTALE)

Notes: (1) These ships are operated and maintained by the Navy but are manned by Gendarmes. Gendarmerie Maritime has a personnel strength of 1250 (27 officers), and 22 patrol craft increasing to 31 by 1995. Tasked to protect naval bases and establishments ashore.
(2) The Gendarmerie Départementale operates minor craft in territorial waters and overseas, but is being taken over by the Gendarmerie Maritime.

1 LA COMBATTANTE I CLASS

Name	No	Builders	Commissioned
LA COMBATTANTE	P 730	CMN, Cherbourg	1 Mar 1964

Displacement, tons: 202 full load
Dimensions, feet (metres): 147.8 × 24.2 × 6.5 *(45 × 7.4 × 2.5)*
Main machinery: 2 SEMT-Pielstick 8 PA4 V200; 3840 hp(m) *(2.8 MW)*; 2 shafts; cp props
Speed, knots: 28. **Range, miles:** 2000 at 12 kts
Complement: 25 (3 officers)
Guns: 1 Bofors 40 mm/60. 2—12.7 mm MGs.
Radars: Surface search: Racal Decca 1226; I band.

Comment: Former naval craft withdrawn in 1991 but now returned to service at Cherbourg.

4 PATRA CLASS (FAST PATROL CRAFT)

Name	No	Builders	Commissioned
TRIDENT	P 670	Auroux, Arcachon	17 Dec 1976
GLAIVE	P 671	Auroux, Arcachon	2 Apr 1977
ÉPÉE	P 672	CMN, Cherbourg	9 Oct 1976
PERTUISANE	P 673	CMN, Cherbourg	20 Jan 1977

Displacement, tons: 115 standard; 147.5 full load
Dimensions, feet (metres): 132.5 × 19.4 × 5.2 *(40.4 × 5.9 × 1.6)*
Main machinery: 2 SACM AGO 195 V12 diesels; 4410 hp(m) *(3.24 MW)*; 2 shafts; cp props
Speed, knots: 26. **Range, miles:** 1750 at 10 kts; 750 at 20 kts
Complement: 18 (1 officer)
Guns: 1 Bofors 40 mm/60. 1 or 2—12.7 mm MGs.
Radars: Surface search: Racal Decca 1226; I band.

Comment: P 672 transferred to Gendarmerie in February 1986, P 670 in June 1987, P 671 in September 1987 and P 673 in November 1987. The class proved to be too small for their intended naval role. SS-12 SSM removed. P 670 and 672 based at Lorient, P 671 at Cherbourg and P 673 at Toulon.

PERTUISANE   *11/1993, Giorgio Ghiglione*

2 STELLIS CLASS

Name	No	Builders	Commissioned
STELLIS	P 775	DCN, Lorient	5 Sep 1992
STENIA	P 776	DCN, Lorient	1 Mar 1993

Displacement, tons: 52 full load
Dimensions, feet (metres): 81.7 × 20 × 5.6 *(24.9 × 6.1 × 1.7)*
Main machinery: 3 diesels; 2500 hp(m) *(1.8 MW)*; 2 shafts; 1 waterjet
Speed, knots: 28; 10 (waterjet only). **Range, miles:** 700 at 22 kts
Complement: 8
Guns: 1—12.7 mm MG. 2—7.62 mm MGs.

Comment: *Stellis* based at Cayenne, *Stenna* at Kourou. GRP hulls. An improved version of 32 m is to be built.

2 OLD TYPE

MASCAREIGNE P 779   KARUKÉRA P 780

Displacement, tons: 30 full load
Dimensions, feet (metres): 81.7 × 17.4 × 5.2 *(24.9 × 5.3 × 1.6)*
Main machinery: 2 Detroit 8V-71 diesels; 460 hp *(343 kW)* sustained; 2 shafts
Speed, knots: 24
Complement: 4
Guns: 1—12.7 mm MG.

Comment: Built in 1973/74. *Karukéra* in Antilles/French Guiana; *Mascareigne* at Papeete.

7 VEDETTE DE SURVEILLANCE

PÉTULANTE P 760   MELLIA P 789   HORTENSIA P 791
MIMOSA P 761   VÉTIVER P 790   — P 792
RÉSÉDA P 778

Displacement, tons: 18 full load
Dimensions, feet (metres): 47.9 × 15.1 × 3.3 *(14.6 × 4.6 × 1)*
Main machinery: 2 Baudouin 12 F11 SM diesels; 800 hp(m) *(588 kW)*; 2 shafts
Speed, knots: 20. **Range, miles:** 360 at 18 kts
Guns: 2—12.7 mm MGs.

Comment: Type V14 SC. Built 1985-1993. Similar to naval tenders with Y pennant numbers. Based at Noumea, Ajaccio, Bayonne, Toulon, Port-des-Galets and Brest.

HORTENSIA   *8/1992, J Y Robert*

2 TECIMAR CLASS

OEILLET P 772   CAMÉLIA P 774

Displacement, tons: 14 full load
Dimensions, feet (metres): 43.6 × 13.5 × 3.6 *(13.3 × 4.1 × 1.1)*
Main machinery: 2 diesels; 440 hp(m) *(323 kW)*; 2 shafts
Speed, knots: 25
Guns: 1—12.7 mm MG. 2—7.62 mm MGs.

Comment: Tecimar Volte 43 class. Commissioned in 1975 and based at Toulon and Brest respectively.

OEILLET (with *Hortensia*)   *8/1990, J Y Robert*

6 ARCOR 34 CLASS

LILAS P 703	PIVOINE P 705	MDLC ROBET P 707
BÉGONIA P 704	NYMPHÉA P 706	GENDARME PEREZ P 708

Comment: 10 m craft built 1985-1992. Based at Dunkirk, Rochefort, Saint-Raphaël, Boulogne, Saint-Malo and Sète.

CUSTOMS (DOUANES FRANÇAISES)

Note: The French customs service has a number of tasks not normally associated with such an organisation. In addition to the usual duties of dealing with ships entering either its coastal area or ports it also has certain responsibilities for rescue at sea, control of navigation, fishery protection and pollution protection. For these purposes 650 officers and men operate a number of craft of various dimensions: Class I of 30 m, 24 kts and a range of 1200 miles; Class II of 27 m, 24 kts and with a range of 900 miles; Class III of 17-20 m, 24 kts and a range of 400 miles; Class IV of 12-17 m, 24 kts and a range of 400 miles. All vessels have DF numbers painted on the bow. There are also five Cessna 404 Titan, and nine Reims-Cessna F406 Caravan II maritime patrol aircraft.

DF 47   *7/1993, van Ginderen Collection*

AFFAIRES MARITIMES

Note: A force of some 30 patrol ships and craft of varying sizes. The vessels are unarmed and manned by civilians on behalf of the Préfectures Maritimes. Their duties mainly involve navigation and pilotage supervision as well as search and rescue. All have PM numbers painted on the bow and Affaires Maritime written on the superstructure in the vicinity of the bridge.

PM 31   *2/1993, van Ginderen Collection*

GABON

Headquarters' Appointment

Commanding Officer of the Navy:
  Captain Major Jean-Léonard Mbini

Bases

Port Gentil, Mayumba

Personnel

(a) 1994: 510 (56 officers)

Coast Guard

Has a number of small inshore patrol launches. Three named *N'Djolé, N'Gombé* and *Omboué* are of doubtful operational status but eleven smaller 'vedettes' are in regular service.

Mercantile Marine

Lloyd's Register of Shipping:
  29 vessels of 36 176 tons gross

PATROL FORCES

2 P 400 CLASS (FAST ATTACK CRAFT—PATROL)

Name	No	Builders	Commissioned
GÉNÉRAL d'ARMÉE BA-OUMAR	P 07	CMN, Cherbourg	27 June 1988
COLONEL DJOUE-DABANY	P 08	CMN, Cherbourg	14 Sep 1990

Displacement, tons: 446 full load
Dimensions, feet (metres): 179 × 26.2 × 8.5 *(54.6 × 8 × 2.5)*
Main machinery: 2 SACM UD 33 V16 M7 diesels; 8000 hp(m) *(5.88 MW)* sustained; 2 shafts; cp props
Speed, knots: 24. **Range, miles:** 4200 at 15 kts
Complement: 32 (4 officers)
Military lift: 20 troops

Guns: 1 Bofors 57 mm/70 SAK 57 Mk 2 (P 07); 75° elevation; 220 rounds/minute to 17 km *(9 nm)*; weight of shell 2.4 kg. Not in P 08 which has a second Oerlikon 20 mm.
  2 Giat F2 20 mm (twin) (P 08).
Fire control: CSEE Naja optronic director (P 07).
Radars: Navigation: Racal Decca 1226C; I band.

Programmes: Contract signed May 1985 with CMN Cherbourg. First laid down 2 July 1986, launched 18 December 1987 and arrived in Gabon 6 August 1988 for a local christening ceremony. Second ordered in February 1989 and launched 29 March 1990.
Structure: There is space on the quarter-deck for two MM 40 Exocet surface-to-surface missiles. These craft are similar to the French vessels but with different engines. *Ba-Oumar* had twin funnels fitted in 1992, similar to French P 400 class conversions.

GÉNÉRAL d'ARMÉE BA-OUMAR   *1988, CMN Cherbourg*

1 FAST ATTACK CRAFT (MISSILE)

Name	No	Builders	Commissioned
GÉNÉRAL NAZAIRE BOULINGUI	P 10	Chantiers Navals de l'Estérel	7 Aug 1978
(ex-*President Omar Bongo*)			

Displacement, tons: 160 full load
Dimensions, feet (metres): 138 × 25.3 × 6.5 *(42 × 7.7 × 1.9)*
Main machinery: 3 SACM 195 V12 CSHR diesels; 5400 hp(m) *(3.97 MW)*; 3 shafts
Speed, knots: 32. **Range, miles:** 1500 at 15 kts
Complement: 20 (3 officers)

Missiles: SSM: 4 Aerospatiale SS 12M; wire-guided to 5.5 km *(3 nm)* subsonic; warhead 30 kg.
Guns: 1 Bofors 40 mm/60; 90° elevation; 300 rounds/minute to 12 km *(6.5 nm)* anti-surface; 4 km *(2.2 nm)* anti-aircraft; weight of shell 0.89 kg.
  1 DCN 20 mm; 50° elevation; 800 rounds/minute to 2 km; weight of shell 0.24 kg.
Radars: Navigation: Racal Decca RM1226; I band.

Programmes: Launched 12 January 1978. Engines changed in 1985 when the MTU diesels were replaced and top speed was reduced from 38 kts.
Structure: Triple skinned mahogany hull.

GÉNÉRAL NAZAIRE BOULINGUI   *1978, Chantiers Navals de l'Estérel*

AMPHIBIOUS FORCES

1 BATRAL TYPE

Name	No	Builders	Launched	Commissioned
PRESIDENT EL HADJ OMAR BONGO	L 05	CMN, Cherbourg	16 Apr 1984	26 Nov 1984

Displacement, tons: 770 standard; 1336 full load
Dimensions, feet (metres): 262.4 × 42.6 × 7.9 *(80 × 13 × 2.4)*
Main machinery: 2 SACM Type 195 V12 CSHR diesels; 3600 hp(m) *(2.65 MW)*; 2 shafts; cp props
Speed, knots: 16. **Range, miles:** 4500 at 13 kts
Complement: 39
Military lift: 188 troops; 12 vehicles; 350 tons cargo
Guns: 1 Bofors 40 mm/60; 90° elevation; 300 rounds/minute to 12 km *(6.5 nm)* anti-surface; 4 km *(2.2 nm)* anti-aircraft; weight of shell 0.89 kg.
  2—81 mm mortars. 2 Browning 12.7 mm MGs. 1—7.62 mm MG.
Radars: Navigation: Racal Decca 1226; I band.
Helicopters: Capable of operating up to SA 330 Puma size.

Comment: Sister to French *La Grandière*. Carries one LCVP and one LCP.

PRESIDENT EL HADJ OMAR BONGO   *1993, Gabon Navy*

1 LCM

Name	No	Builders	Commissioned
MANGA	—	DCAN, Dakar	11 May 1976

Displacement, tons: 152 full load
Dimensions, feet (metres): 78.8 × 21 × 4.2 *(24 × 6.4 × 1.3)*
Main machinery: 2 Poyaud V8-250 diesels; 480 hp(m) *(353 kW)*; 2 shafts
Speed, knots: 8. **Range, miles:** 600 at 5 kts
Complement: 10
Guns: 2—12.7 mm MGs.
Radars: Navigation: Racal Decca 110; I band.

Comment: Fitted with bow doors.

2 SEA TRUCKS

Comment: Built by Tanguy Marine, Le Havre in 1985. One of 12.2 m with two 165 hp(m) *(121 kW)* engines and one of 10.2 m with one engine.

LAND-BASED MARITIME AIRCRAFT

Note: In addition there are also two EMB 110s.

Numbers/Type: 1 Embraer EMB-111 Bandeirante.
Operational speed: 194 kts *(360 km/h)*.
Service ceiling: 25 500 ft *(7770 m)*.
Range: 1590 nm *(2945 km)*.
Role/Weapon systems: Coastal surveillance and EEZ protection tasks are primary roles. Sensors: APS-128 search radar, limited ECM, searchlight. Weapons: ASV; 8 × 127 mm rockets or 28 × 70 mm rockets.

POLICE

Note: The Police have a number of 6.8 m LCVPs and Simmoneau 11 m patrol craft delivered in 1989.

SIMMONEAU SM 360   *1989, Simmoneau Marine*

GAMBIA

Headquarters' Appointment

Commander, Marine Unit:
Major A M M Saho

Personnel

(a) 1994: 60 officers and men
(b) Voluntary service

General

On 1 February 1982 the two countries of Senegal and Gambia united to form the confederation of Senegambia, which included merging the armed forces. Confederation was cancelled on 30 September 1989 and the forces again became national and independent of each other. The patrol craft come under 3 Marine Company of the National Army. A Nigerian liaison officer replaced the British in 1992.

Base

Banjul

Mercantile Marine

Lloyd's Register of Shipping:
8 vessels of 2013 tons gross

PATROL FORCES

2 SHANGHAI II CLASS (FAST ATTACK CRAFT—GUN)

GUNJUR 101   **BRUFUT** 102

Displacement, tons: 113 standard; 131 full load
Dimensions, feet (metres): 127.3 × 17.4 × 5.2 *(38.8 × 5.3 × 1.6)*
Main machinery: 2 L12-180 diesels (fwd); 2400 hp(m) *(1.76 MW)*; 2 L12-180Z diesels (aft); 1820 hp(m) *(1.34 MW)*; 4 shafts
Speed, knots: 26. **Range, miles:** 700 at 16 kts (on 2 diesels)
Complement: 34
Guns: 6—25 mm/80 (3 twin).
Radars: Surface search: Furuno 1505; I band.

Comment: Built in May 1979. Delivered as a gift from China on 2 February 1989 and commissioned in May 1989. Refitted in China in mid-1988, and refitted again in 1993 with Chinese assistance. The 37 mm gun normally mounted aft in this class has been replaced by a boat davit.

JATO   *8/1993*

1 FAIREY MARINE LANCE CLASS (COASTAL PATROL CRAFT)

Name	*No*	*Builders*	*Commissioned*
SEA DOG	P 11	Fairey Marine, UK	28 Oct 1976

Displacement, tons: 17 full load
Dimensions, feet (metres): 48.7 × 15.3 × 4.3 *(14.8 × 4.7 × 1.3)*
Main machinery: 2 GM 8V-71TA diesels; 650 hp *(485 kW)* sustained; 2 shafts
Speed, knots: 24. **Range, miles:** 500 at 16 kts
Complement: 9
Guns: 2—7.62 mm MGs (not carried).
Radars: Surface search: Racal Decca 110; I band.

Comment: Delivered 28 October 1976. Unarmed and used for training. Operational status doubtful.

BRUFUT   *1/1993*

1 FAIREY MARINE TRACKER 2 CLASS (COASTAL PATROL CRAFT)

Name	*No*	*Builders*	*Commissioned*
JATO	P 12	Fairey Marine, UK	1978

Displacement, tons: 31.5 full load
Dimensions, feet (metres): 65.7 × 17 × 4.8 *(20 × 5.2 × 1.5)*
Main machinery: 2 GM 12V-71TA diesels; 840 hp *(617 kW)* sustained; 2 shafts
Speed, knots: 29. **Range, miles:** 650 at 20 kts
Complement: 11
Guns: 1 Oerlikon 20 mm. 2—7.62 mm MGs.
Radars: Surface search: Racal Decca; I band.

Comment: Hull and superstructure of GRP. Air-conditioned accommodation. Re-engined in 1991. Used for fishery patrol. The other two of the class returned to Senegal in 1989.

SEA DOG   *1/1990, E Grove*

2 COASTAL PATROL CRAFT

BOLONG   **KANTAA**

Comment: 51 ft craft delivered from the US in January 1994.

GEORGIA

Headquarters' Appointment

Commander of the Navy:
Captain B Dzavachishvili

General

Georgia intends to control its own Coast Guard in due course but the civil war has delayed implementation. Some of the patrol craft based at Poti in early 1993 had fled to Russian ports by the end of the year.

Base

Poti

Patrol Ships Based at Poti in 1993

1 Grisha I, 1 Grisha V, 1 Turya, 9 Stenka, 3 Muravey. There is also a support ship. Details in Russia section.

GRISHA V (Russian colours)   *1992*

STENKA (Russian colours)   *4/1993, van Ginderen Collection*

GERMANY

Headquarters' Appointments

Chief of Naval Staff:
Vice Admiral Hein-Peter Weyher
Chief of Staff:
Rear Admiral Dirk Horten

Commander-in-Chief

Commander-in-Chief, Fleet:
Vice Admiral Hans Rudolf Boehmer
Deputy Commander-in-Chief, Fleet:
Rear Admiral Hans Lüsson

Diplomatic Representation

Defence and Naval Attaché in London:
Rear Admiral Karlheinz Reichert
Naval Assistant in London:
Commander U P Stickdorn
Naval Attaché in Washington:
Captain Rudolf Lange
Naval Attaché in Rome:
Commander P Schreck

Personnel

(a) 1994: 26 700 (4415 officers) (including naval air arm)
(b) 12 months' national service (6115)

Squadron Allocations

Lütjens class, 1st DS; Hamburg class, 2nd DS; 4 Bremen class, 2nd FS; 4 Bremen class, 4th FS.

Naval Air Arm

MFG (Marine Flieger Geschwader)
MFG 2   (Fighter Bomber and Reconnaissance Wing at Eggebek)
PA 200 Tornado
MFG 3   'Graf Zeppelin' (LRMP Wing at Nordholz). To take over the assets of MFG 5
Breguet Atlantic of which 5 converted for Sigint, Sea Lynx (landbase for embarkation and maintenance)
MFG 5   (SAR and Liaison Wing at Kiel). To be evacuated and returned to civil use in due course
Sea King Mk 41, Do 28D-2 Skyservant of which 2 converted for pollution control plus 1 Dornier Do 228
MFHubschraubergruppe (SAR and Liaison Wing at Parow/Stralsund)
Mi-8 Hip

Prefix to Ships' Names

Prefix FGS is used in communications.

Bases

C-in-C Fleet: Glücksburg. Flag Officer Naval Command: Rostock.
Baltic: Kiel, Olpenitz (all mine warfare forces in due course), Flensburg*, Neustadt*, Warnemunde (all patrol craft in due course). Eckernförde may become a submarine base.
North Sea: Wilhelmshaven, Borkum*, Emden*.
Naval Arsenal: Wilhelmshaven (all frigates in due course), Kiel (all destroyers and submarines in due course).
Training (other than in Bases above): Bremerhaven, Brake*, Glückstaat, List/Sylt, Plön, Grossenbrode*, Parow.

The administration of the bases is vested in the Naval Support Command at Wilhelmshaven. Those marked with an asterisk are to close by 2005 although Flensburg and Neustadt may retain some minor support facilities.

Strength of the Fleet (1 June 1994)

Type	Active	Building (Projected)
Submarines—Patrol	20	(4)
Destroyers	4	—
Frigates	8	4 (4)
Fast Attack Craft—Missile	38	—
LCUs	5	—
LCMs	11	—
Minehunters	15	5
Minesweepers—Coastal	16	—
Minesweepers—Inshore	10	—
Minesweepers—Drones	18	—
Tenders	5	2
Support Ships	4	—
Replenishment Tankers	6	—
Support Tankers	2	—
Accommodation Ships	5	—
Ammunition Transports	2	—
Water Boats	1	—
Tugs—Salvage	5	—
Tugs—Icebreaking	2	—
Tugs—Coastal/Harbour	13	6
AGIs	3	—
Sail Training Ships	2	—
TRVs	3	—
Trials Ships	16	—
Non-naval Vessels		
Coast Guard Patrol Craft	27	—
Police Patrol Craft	18+	—
Fishery Protection Ships	8	1
Research and Survey Ships	14	—
Army craft	43	—

Volksmarine

The former GDR Navy ceased to exist after reunification on 3 October 1990. Most of the warships organised into a Coastal Guard Squadron subordinate to the District Command at Rostock were paid off in 1991 and have either been sold or scrapped. A few auxiliaries have been retained.

Future Projects

Building:
4 + (8) submarines to replace the Type 205 and unmodernised Type 206 in late 1990s (early 2000s). Type 212
4 Type 124 frigates to replace the Type 103 destroyers from 2004 onwards
4 Type 702 combat store ships in early 2000s
1 floating dock to replace *Schwimmdock B*
Note: Projects Type 748, 751 and 752 have all been deferred

Weapons:
New SSMs 'Anti-Navire Supersonique' (ANS) for Type 143B, 143A and 123 in late 1990s
262 ASMs 'Kormoran 2' for PA 200 Tornado in early 1990s
58 RAM launchers with 1923 SAMs in 1992-96
4432 SAMs 'Fliegerfaust 2' in 1989-98
New torpedoes for modernised submarines
New influence mines 'SGM 80' in 1990-96

Modernisation
10 FAC Type 143 in mid-1990s including new SSMs
RAM-ASDM launchers for Types 103(2), 122(2), 123(2), 143(1) 1992-96
Light SAMs 'Fliegerfaust 2' (similar to USSR SA-N-5, with Stinger-SAM) for support ships and minor combatants

Hydrographic Service

This service, under the direction of the Ministry of Transport, is civilian-manned with HQ at Hamburg. Survey ships are listed at the end of the section.

Mercantile Marine

Lloyd's Register of Shipping:
1234 vessels of 4 978 566 tons gross

DELETIONS

Submarines

1991   *U 1* (TNSW trials)
1992   *U 2*
1993   *U 9, U 10*

Destroyers

1993   *Bayern*
1994   *Hamburg*

Frigates

1991   *Rostock* (ex-GDR), *Halle* (ex-GDR)

Corvettes

1991   16 Parchim I class (ex-GDR) (to Indonesia in 1992)*Thetis, Najade* (both to Greece)
1992   *Hermes, Triton* (to Greece)
1993   *Theseus* (to Greece)

Patrol Forces

1992   *Iltis, Storch* (both to Greece)
1993   3 Osa I (to Latvia) (ex-GDR)
1994   3 Osa I (to Lithuania) (ex-GDR), 6 Osa I (to Estonia) (ex-GDR)

Mine Warfare Vessels

1991   *Castor, Flensburg, Tangerhütte, Bitterfeld, Eisleben, Bernau, Eilenburg* (last three ex-GDR, last three to Uruguay)
1992   *Spica, Schütze, Waage, Freya, Hertha, Nymphe, Nixe, Pollux, Mars, Fulda, Ariadne, Vineta, Amazone, Gazelle, Hansa, Sömmerda* (last 12 to Indonesia)
1993   *Steigerwald*, 2 Kondor II (to Latvia)

Amphibious Forces

1991   *LCM 1-11, Barbe, Delphin, Dorsch, Felchen, Forelle, Makrele* (all to Greece)
1992   *Rochen, Muräne* (both to Greece), *Butt, Karpfen, Stör, Tümmler, Wels, Inger, Brasse*
1993   *Sprotte, Sardine, Saibling, Stint, Aesche*

Auxiliaries

1991   *Saar, Lahn, Werra, Sachsenwald, Odin, Wotan, Wittow, Mönchgut, Darss, Kühlung, Werdau* (last five ex-GDR), *Coburg* (to Greece), EF 3, *FW 4* (to Turkey), *FW 6* (to Greece), *Kollicker Ort* (ex-GDR), KW 3, *Otto Von Guericke, Zingst* (last two to Uruguay)
1992   *Eifel, Harz, Rhein* (old), *Elbe* (old) (to Turkey), *Havelland* (ex-GDR), *Kölpinsee* (ex-GDR), *Förde, Jade, Jasmund* (ex-GDR) (to Spain), *H 13, TF 2, Ummanz, Havel, Oder, Saale* (last four ex-GDR)
1993   *Offenburg, Main* (old), FW 1, *Heinz Roggenkamp*, VB 2, AK 5, KW 15, KW 16, KW 18, H 11, *A 42* (ex-GDR), A 43 (ex-GDR), *Amrum*
1994   *Lüneburg, Saarburg* (to Greece), KW 17, KW 20, TF 3, *Ellerbek, Holnis*

Coast Guard

1992   6 Kondor I class (ex-GDR) (four to Tunisia, two to Malta), 9 Bremse class (ex-GDR) (five to Tunisia, two to Malta, two to Jordan)

PENNANT LIST

Submarines

S 170	U 21
S 171	U 22
S 172	U 23
S 173	U 24
S 174	U 25
S 175	U 26
S 176	U 27
S 177	U 28
S 178	U 29
S 179	U 30
S 190	U 11
S 191	U 12
S 192	U 13
S 193	U 14
S 194	U 15
S 195	U 16
S 196	U 17
S 197	U 18
S 198	U 19
S 199	U 20

Destroyers

D 182	Schleswig-Holstein (old)
D 185	Lütjens
D 186	Mölders
D 187	Rommel

Frigates

F 207	Bremen
F 208	Niedersachsen
F 209	Rheinland-Pfalz
F 210	Emden
F 211	Köln
F 212	Karlsruhe
F 213	Augsburg
F 214	Lübeck
F 215	Brandenburg
F 216	Schleswig-Holstein (new) (bldg)
F 217	Bayern (new) (bldg)
F 218	Mecklenburg-Vorpommern (bldg)

Patrol Forces

P 6111	S 61 Albatros
P 6112	S 62 Falke
P 6113	S 63 Geier
P 6114	S 64 Bussard
P 6115	S 65 Sperber
P 6116	S 66 Greif
P 6117	S 67 Kondor
P 6118	S 68 Seeadler
P 6119	S 69 Habicht
P 6120	S 70 Kormoran
P 6121	S 71 Gepard
P 6122	S 72 Puma
P 6123	S 73 Hermelin
P 6124	S 74 Nerz
P 6125	S 75 Zobel
P 6126	S 76 Frettchen
P 6127	S 77 Dachs
P 6128	S 78 Ozelot
P 6129	S 79 Wiesel
P 6130	S 80 Hyäne
P 6141	S 41 Tiger
P 6143	S 43 Luchs
P 6144	S 44 Marder
P 6145	S 45 Leopard
P 6146	S 46 Fuchs
P 6147	S 47 Jaguar
P 6148	S 48 Löwe
P 6149	S 49 Wolf
P 6150	S 50 Panther
P 6151	S 51 Häher
P 6153	S 53 Pelikan
P 6154	S 54 Elster
P 6155	S 55 Alk
P 6156	S 56 Dommel
P 6157	S 57 Weihe
P 6158	S 58 Pinguin
P 6159	S 59 Reiher
P 6160	S 60 Kranich

Mine Warfare Forces

M 1053	Stier
M 1060	Weiden
M 1061	Rottweil
M 1062	Sulzbach-Rosenberg (bldg) (new)
M 1063	Bad Bevensen
M 1064	Grömitz (bldg)
M 1065	Dillingen (bldg)
M 1066	Frankenthal
M 1067	Bad Rappenau
M 1068	Datteln (bldg)
M 1069	Homburg (bldg)
M 1070	Göttingen
M 1071	Koblenz
M 1072	Lindau
M 1073	Schleswig
M 1074	Tübingen
M 1075	Wetzlar
M 1076	Paderborn
M 1077	Weilheim
M 1078	Cuxhaven
M 1079	Düren
M 1080	Marburg
M 1081	Konstanz
M 1082	Wolfsburg
M 1083	Ulm
M 1085	Minden
M 1087	Völklingen
M 1090	Pegnitz
M 1091	Kulmbach
M 1092	Hameln
M 1093	Auerbach
M 1094	Ensdorf
M 1095	Überherrn
M 1096	Passau
M 1097	Laboe
M 1098	Siegburg
M 1099	Herten
M 2658	Frauenlob
M 2659	Nautilus
M 2660	Gefion
M 2661	Medusa
M 2662	Undine
M 2663	Minerva
M 2664	Diana
M 2665	Loreley
M 2666	Atlantis
M 2667	Acheron

Amphibious Forces

L 760	Flunder
L 762	Lachs
L 763	Plötze
L 765	Schlei
L 769	Zander
LCM 14	Sardelle
LCM 15	Hering
LCM 16	Orfe
LCM 21	Hummer
LCM 22	Krill
LCM 23	Krabbe
LCM 24	Auster
LCM 25	Muschel
LCM 26	Koralle
L 786	LCM 27 Garnele
L 787	LCM 28 Languste

Support Ships and Auxiliaries

A 50	Alster
A 52	Oste
A 53	Oker
A 60	Gorch Fock
A 69	Donau (old)
A 511	Elbe
A 512	Mosel
A 513	Rhein
A 514	Werra
A 515	Main (bldg)
A 516	Donau (new) (bldg)
A 1401	Eisvogel
A 1402	Eisbär
A 1405	FW 5
A 1407	Wittensee
A 1408	SP 1
A 1409	Wilhelm Pullwer
A 1410	Walther von Ledebur
A 1413	Freiburg
A 1414	Glücksburg
A 1416	Nienburg
A 1418	Meersburg
A 1424	Walchensee
A 1425	Ammersee
A 1426	Tegernsee
A 1427	Westensee
A 1435	Westerwald
A 1436	Odenwald
A 1439	Baltrum
A 1440	Juist
A 1441	Langeoog
A 1442	Spessart
A 1443	Rhön
A 1450	Planet
A 1451	Wangerooge
A 1452	Spiekeroog
A 1455	Norderney
A 1457	Helgoland
A 1458	Fehmarn
Y 811	Knurrhahn
Y 812	Lütje Hörn
Y 814	Knechtsand
Y 815	Scharhorn
Y 816	Vogelsand
Y 817	Nordstrand
Y 819	Langeness
Y 820	Sylt
Y 821	Föhr
Y 823	Neuwerk
Y 834	Nordwind
Y 835	Todendorf
Y 836	Putlos
Y 837	Baumholder
Y 838	Bergen
Y 839	Munster
Y 842	Schwimmdock A
Y 844	Barbara
Y 851	TF 1
Y 855	TF 5
Y 856	TF 6
Y 860	Schwedeneck
Y 861	Kronsort
Y 862	Helmsand
Y 863	Stollergrund
Y 864	Mittelgrund
Y 865	Kalkgrund
Y 866	Breitgrund
Y 867	Bant
Y 875	Hiev
Y 876	Griep
Y 879	Schwimmdock B
Y 890	Vogtland
Y 891	Altmark
Y 893	Uckermark
Y 894	Borde
Y 895	Wische
Y 1643	Bottsand
Y 1644	Eversand
Y 1651	Koos
Y 1656	Wustrow
Y 1657	Fleesensee
Y 1658	Dranske
Y 1670	MT 1
Y 1671	AK 1
Y 1672	AK 3
Y 1674	AM 6
Y 1675	AM 8
Y 1676	MA 2
Y 1677	MA 3
Y 1678	MA 1
Y 1679	AM 7
Y 1680	Neuende
Y 1681	Heppens
Y 1683	AK 6
Y 1684	Peter Bachmann
Y 1685	Aschau
Y 1686	AK 2
Y 1687	Borby
Y 1689	Bums
Y 1690	LP 3

SUBMARINES

Note: Ex-*U 1* is used as an AIP trials ship. Civilian manned. Painted green with an orange top to the fin.

2 TYPE 205

Name	No	Builders	Laid down	Launched	Commissioned
U 11	S 190	Howaldtswerke, Kiel	1 Apr 1966	9 Feb 1968	21 June 1968
U 12	S 191	Howaldtswerke, Kiel	1 Sep 1966	10 Sep 1968	14 Jan 1969

Displacement, tons: 419 surfaced; 450 dived
Dimensions, feet (metres): 144 × 15.1 × 14.1
(43.9 × 4.6 × 4.3)
Main machinery: Diesel-electric; 2 MTU 12V 493 AZ80 GA 31L diesels; 1200 hp(m) *(882 kW)* sustained; 2 alternators; 810 kW; 1 Siemens motor; 1800 hp(m) *(1.32 MW)* sustained; 1 shaft
Speed, knots: 10 surfaced; 17 dived
Complement: 22 (4 officers)

Torpedoes: 8—21 in *(533 mm)* tubes. AEG Seeal; wire-guided; active homing to 13 km *(7 nm)* at 35 kts; passive homing to 28 km *(15 nm)* at 23 kts; warhead 260 kg; no reloads.
Mines: 16 in place of torpedoes.
Countermeasures: ESM: Radar warning.
Fire control: Signaal Mk 8.
Radars: Surface search: Thompson-CSF Calypso II; I band.
Sonars: Atlas Elektronik SRS M1H; passive/active search and attack; high frequency.

Programmes: Built in floating docks. First submarines designed and built by West Germany after the Second World War.
Structure: Diving depth, 159 m *(490 ft)*. Hulls of steel alloys with non-magnetic properties. *U 11* (Type 205A) converted as a padded target in 1988; *U 12* (Type 205B) acts as a sonar trials platform.

U 12

6/1992, Stefan Terzibaschitsch

Operational: The boats are trimmed by the stern to load through the bow caps.

Sales: *U 1* decommissioned 29 November 1991 and is on loan to TNSW for trials of a 250 kW closed cycle diesel developed by Cosworth Deep Sea Systems and TNSW.

U 11

2/1992, Horst Dehnst

0 + (4) TYPE 212

Displacement, tons: 1320 surfaced; 1800 dived
Dimensions, feet (metres): 174.5 × 22.3 × 19
(53.2 × 6.8 × 5.8)
Main machinery: Diesel-electric; 1 MTU 16V 396 diesel;
1440 hp(m) *(1.06 MW)*; 1 Siemens Permasyn motor; 2400 hp
(m) *(1.76 MW)*; 1 shaft; HDW fuel cell (AIP); sodium sulphide
high energy batteries
Speed, knots: 20 dived; 12 surfaced
Complement: 23 + 5 training

Torpedoes: 6—21 in *(533 mm)* bow tubes; water ram discharge;
DMT (formerly AEG) Seeal 3 or Seehecht.
Countermeasures: ESM: TST FL 1800U; radar warning.
Fire control: NFT (formerly Kongsberg) MFI-90U weapons con-
trol system.
Radars: Navigation: Kelvin Hughes 1007; I band.
Sonars: Atlas Elektronik DBQS-21DG; passive ranging and
intercept.
Atlas Elektronik DBQS-90FTC; FAS-3 flank and TAS-3 clip-on
passive towed array.
Ferranti FMS 52; high frequency; active.

Programmes: Design phase completed in 1992 by IKL in conjunction with HDW and TNSW. The HDW/TNSW consortium
expected to contract the building of the first batch of four in
1995, but this has been delayed to 1997. First of class to enter
service in 2003.
Structure: Primarily equipped for Baltic and North Sea operations with a hybrid fuel cell/battery propulsion based on the
HDW prototype successfully evaluated in *U1* in 1988-89. This
prototype had 16 fuel cells each generating 25 kW of power.
An increase of power will be achieved by replacing the liquid
electrolyte with solid polymer technology. The submarine is
designed with a partial double hull which has a larger diameter
forward. This is joined to the after end by a short conical section which houses the fuel cell plant. Two LOX tanks and hydro-
gen stored in metal cylinders are carried around the
circumference of the smaller hull section.

TYPE 212 (artist's impression)   *1990, HDW*

6 TYPE 206 and 12 TYPE 206A

Name	No	Builders	Laid down	Launched	Commissioned
U 13	S 192	Howaldtswerke, Kiel	15 Nov 1969	28 Sep 1971	19 Apr 1973
U 14	S 193	Rheinstahl Nordseewerke, Emden	1 Mar 1970	1 Feb 1972	19 Apr 1973
U 15*	S 194	Howaldtswerke, Kiel	1 June 1970	15 June 1972	17 July 1974
U 16*	S 195	Rheinstahl Nordseewerke, Emden	1 Nov 1970	29 Aug 1972	9 Nov 1973
U 17*	S 196	Howaldtswerke, Kiel	1 Oct 1970	10 Oct 1972	28 Nov 1973
U 18*	S 197	Rheinstahl Nordseewerke, Emden	1 Apr 1971	31 Oct 1972	19 Dec 1973
U 19	S 198	Howaldtswerke, Kiel	5 Jan 1971	15 Dec 1972	9 Nov 1973
U 20	S 199	Rheinstahl Nordseewerke, Emden	3 Sep 1971	16 Jan 1973	24 May 1974
U 21	S 170	Howaldtswerke, Kiel	15 Apr 1971	9 Mar 1973	16 Aug 1974
U 22*	S 171	Rheinstahl Nordseewerke, Emden	18 Nov 1971	27 Mar 1973	26 July 1974
U 23*	S 172	Rheinstahl Nordseewerke, Emden	5 Mar 1973	25 May 1974	2 May 1975
U 24*	S 173	Rheinstahl Nordseewerke, Emden	20 Mar 1972	26 June 1973	16 Oct 1974
U 25*	S 174	Howaldtswerke, Kiel	1 July 1971	23 May 1973	14 June 1974
U 26*	S 175	Rheinstahl Nordseewerke, Emden	14 July 1972	20 Nov 1973	13 Mar 1975
U 27	S 176	Howaldtswerke, Kiel	1 Oct 1971	21 Aug 1973	16 Oct 1974
U 28*	S 177	Rheinstahl Nordseewerke, Emden	4 Oct 1972	22 Jan 1974	18 Dec 1974
U 29*	S 178	Howaldtswerke, Kiel	10 Jan 1972	5 Nov 1973	27 Nov 1974
U 30*	S 179	Rheinstahl Nordseewerke, Emden	5 Dec 1972	26 Mar 1974	13 Mar 1975

* Type 206A (see *Modernisation*)

Displacement, tons: 450 surfaced; 498 dived
Dimensions, feet (metres): 159.4 × 15.1 × 14.8
(48.6 × 4.6 × 4.5)
Main machinery: Diesel-electric; 2 MTU 12V 493 AZ80 GA
31L diesels; 1200 hp(m) *(882 kW)* sustained; 2 alternators;
810 kW; 1 Siemens motor; 1800 hp(m) *(1.32 MW)* sustained;
1 shaft
Speed, knots: 10 surfaced; 17 dived
Range, miles: 4500 at 5 kts surfaced
Complement: 22 (4 officers)

Torpedoes: 8—21 in *(533 mm)* bow tubes. AEG Seeschlange
(Type 206); wire-guided; active homing to 6 km *(3.3 nm)* at
35 kts; passive homing to 14 km *(7.6 nm)* at 23 kts; warhead
100 kg.
DMT (ex-AEG) Seeal 3 (Type 206A); wire-guided; active homing to 13 km *(7 nm)* at 35 kts; passive homing to 28 km
(15 nm) at 23 kts; warhead 260 kg.
Mines: GRP container secured outside hull each side. Each container holds 12 mines, carried in addition to the normal torpedo or mine armament (16 in place of torpedoes).
Countermeasures: ESM: Thomson-CSF DR 2000U with THORN
EMI Sarie 2 (in 206A); intercept.
Fire control: Signaal Mk 8 (Type 206). CSU 83 (Type 206A).

Radars: Surface search: Thomson-CSF Calypso II; I band; range
31 km *(17 nm)* for 10 m² target.
Sonars: Thomson Sintra DUUX 2; passive ranging.
Atlas Elektronik 410 A4 (Type 206); Atlas Elektronik
DBQS-21D (Type 206A); passive/active search and attack;
medium frequency.

Programmes: Authorised on 7 June 1969 from Howaldtswerke
Deutsche Werft (8) and Rheinstahl Nordseewerke, Emden
(10).
Modernisation: Mid-life conversion of 12 of the class (Type
206A) was a very extensive one, including the installation of
new sensors (sonar DBQS-21D with training simulator STU-5),
periscopes, weapon control system (LEWA), ESM, weapons
(torpedo Seeal), GPS navigation, and a comprehensive refitting
of the propulsion system, as well as habitability improvements.
Conversion work was shared between Thyssen Nordseewerke
(*U 23, 30, 22, 27, 15, 26*) at Emden and HDW (*U 29, 16, 25,
28, 17, 18*) at Kiel. The work started in mid-1987 and completed in February 1992.
Structure: Type 206 hulls are built of high-tensile non-magnetic
steel. In this the West German submarines are unique. Modernised Type 206A submarines have a slight difference in superstructure shape.

Operational: First squadron *(Meersburg)*: four Type 205; six
unmodernised Type 206; based at Kiel.
Third squadron: 12 Type 206A; based at Eckernförde.

U 23   *5/1993, Harald Carstens*   U 30 (with mine containers)   *5/1992, Horst Dehnst*

DESTROYERS

3 LÜTJENS (MODIFIED CHARLES F ADAMS) CLASS (TYPE 103B) (DDGs)

Name	No	Builders	Laid down	Launched	Commissioned
LÜTJENS (ex-US DDG 28)	D 185	Bath Iron Works Corporation	1 Mar 1966	11 Aug 1967	22 Mar 1969
MÖLDERS (ex-US DDG 29)	D 186	Bath Iron Works Corporation	12 Apr 1966	13 Apr 1968	20 Sep 1969
ROMMEL (ex-US DDG 30)	D 187	Bath Iron Works Corporation	22 Aug 1967	1 Feb 1969	2 May 1970

Displacement, tons: 3370 standard; 4500 full load
Dimensions, feet (metres): 437 × 47 × 20
(133.2 × 14.3 × 6.1)
Main machinery: 4 Combustion Engineering boilers; 1200 psi
(84.4 kg/cm sq); 950°F *(510°C)*; 2 turbines; 70 000 hp
(52.2 MW); 2 shafts
Speed, knots: 32. **Range, miles:** 4500 at 20 kts
Complement: 337 (19 officers)

Missiles: SSM: McDonnell Douglas Harpoon; active radar homing to 130 km *(70 nm)* at 0.9 Mach; warhead 227 kg. Combined Mk 13 single-arm launcher with SAM system ❶.
SAM: GDC Pomona Standard SM-1MR; Mk 13 Mod 0 launcher;
command guidance; semi-active radar homing to 46 km
(25 nm) at 2 Mach; 40 missiles—combined SSM and SAM.
2 RAM 21 cell Mk 49 launchers ❷; passive IR/anti-radiation
homing to 9.6 km *(5.2 nm)* at 2 Mach; warhead 9.1 kg.
A/S: Honeywell ASROC Mk 112 octuple launcher ❸; inertial guidance to 1.6-10 km *(1-5.4 nm)*; payload Mk 46 torpedo.
Guns: 2 FMC 5 in *(127 mm)*/54 Mk 42 Mod 10 automatic ❹; 65°
elevation; 20 rounds/minute to 23 km *(12.4 nm)* anti-surface;
15 km *(8 nm)* anti-aircraft; weight of shell 32 kg.
Torpedoes: 6—324 mm US Mk 32 (2 triple) tubes ❺. Honeywell
Mk 46; anti-submarine; active/passive homing to 11 km
(5.9 nm) at 40 kts; warhead 44 kg.
Depth charges: 1 projector ❻.
Countermeasures: Decoys: Loral Hycor Mk 36 SRBOC 6-bar-
relled chaff launcher; range 1-4 km *(0.6-2.2 nm)*.
ESM/ECM: AEG FL-1800S; radar intercept and jammer. To be
replaced by Stage II in 1995.
Combat data systems: SATIR 1 action data automation; Link 11.
SATCOM.

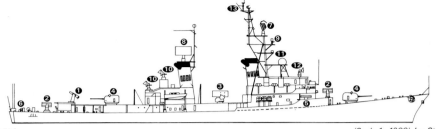

MÖLDERS   *(Scale 1 : 1200), Ian Sturton*

Fire control: Mk 86 GFCS. Mk 74 MFCS.
Radars: Air search: Lockheed SPS 40 ❼; E/F band; range
320 km *(175 nm)*.
Hughes SPS 52 ❽; 3D; E/F band; range 439 km *(240 nm)*.
Surface search: Raytheon/Sylvania SPS 10 ❾; G band.
Fire control: Two Raytheon SPG 51 ❿; G/I band (for missiles).
Lockheed SPQ 9 ⓫; I/J band; range 37 km *(20 nm)*.
Lockheed SPG 60 ⓬; I/J band; range 110 km *(60 nm)*.
Tacan: URN 20 ⓭.
Sonars: Atlas Elektronik DSQS 21B; hull-mounted; active search
and attack; medium frequency.

Programmes: Modified to suit West German requirements and
practice. 1965 contract.
Modernisation: The Type 103B modernisation and other modifi-

cations included: installation of one single-arm Mk 13 launcher
for Standard SAM and Harpoon SSM; improved fire-control
with digital in place of analogue computers; higher superstructure abaft bridge with SPG 60 and SPQ 9 on a mast platform.
Carried out by Naval Arsenal, Kiel and Howaldtswerke, Kiel;
Mölders completed 29 March 1984, *Rommel* 26 July 1985,
Lütjens 16 December 1986. RAM launchers are being fitted in
front of the bridge and aft of the Mk 13 launcher. First in *Mölders* in 1993, then *Rommel* by mid-1994 and *Lütjens* in 1995.
EW update in 1995/96.
Structure: Some differences from Charles F Adams in W/T
aerials and general outline, particularly the funnels.
Operational: These ships are planned to have a life of at least 30
years.

MÖLDERS (with RAM)   *11/1993, van Ginderen Collection*

1 HAMBURG CLASS (TYPE 101A)

Name	No	Builders	Laid down	Launched	Commissioned
SCHLESWIG-HOLSTEIN	D 182	HC Stülcken Sohn, Hamburg	20 Aug 1959	20 Aug 1960	12 Oct 1964

Displacement, tons: 3340 standard; 4680 full load
Dimensions, feet (metres): 438.5 × 44 × 20.3
(133.7 × 13.4 × 6.2)
Main machinery: 4 Wahodag boilers; 910 psi *(64 kg/cm sq)*;
860°F *(460°C)*; 2 Wahodag turbines; 68 000 hp *(51 MW)*;
2 shafts
Speed, knots: 34. **Range, miles:** 6000 at 13 kts; 920 at 34 kts
Complement: 268 (19 officers)

Missiles: SSM: 4 Aerospatiale MM 38 Exocet (2 twin) launchers
❶; inertial cruise; active radar homing to 42 km *(23 nm)* at
0.9 Mach; warhead 165 kg; sea-skimmer.
Guns: 3 DCN 3.9 in *(100 mm)*/55 Mod 1954 ❷; 80° elevation;
60-80 rounds/minute to 17 km *(9 nm)* anti-surface; 8 km
(4.4 nm) anti-aircraft; weight of shell 13.5 kg.
8 Breda 40 mm/70 (4 twin) ❸; 85° elevation; 300 rounds/
minute to 12.5 km *(6.8 nm)*; weight of shell 0.96 kg.
Torpedoes: 4—21 in *(533 mm)* single tubes ❹.
A/S mortars: 2 Bofors 375 mm 4-barrelled trainable mortars ❺;
automatic loading; range 1600 m.
Depth charges: 2 projectors ❻; DC rails.
Mines: Can lay mines.
Countermeasures: Decoys: 2 Breda 105 mm SCLAR; 20 barrels
per launcher; chaff to 5 km *(2.7 nm)*; illuminants to 12 km
(6.6 nm).
ESM: WLR-6; radar warning.
Fire control: Signaal M 45 series.
Radars: Air search: Signaal LW 04 ❼; D band; range 219 km
(120 nm) for 2 m² target.
Air/surface search: Signaal DA 08 ❽; F band; range 204 km
(110 nm) for 2 m² target.
Surface search: Signaal ZW 01 ❾; I/J band.
Navigation: Kelvin Hughes 14/9; I band.
Fire control: Three Signaal M 45 ❿; I/J band; short range.
Sonars: Atlas Elektronik ELAC 1BV; hull-mounted; active search
and attack; medium frequency.

Operational: There are no plans to fit RAM and further limited
modernisation has been shelved. Being replaced by the Type
123 class. Scheduled to pay off in December 1994.

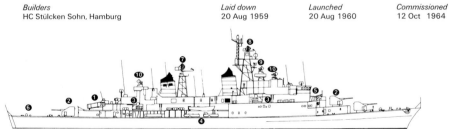

SCHLESWIG-HOLSTEIN   *(Scale 1 : 1200), Ian Sturton*

SCHLESWIG-HOLSTEIN   *11/1993, Harald Carstens*

FRIGATES

Note: Four Type 124 air defence ships will be needed from 2004 onwards to replace the Lütjens class. A collaborative design with the Netherlands and Spain is evolving with a common AAW system based on the Evolved Seasparrow missile. A Memorandum of Understanding (MoU) was signed in October 1993 between Blohm & Voss, Royal Schelde and Bazán shipyards. The aim is a hull comparable in size to the Type 123.

0 + 4 BRANDENBURG CLASS (TYPE 123)

Name	No	Builders	Laid down	Launched	Commissioned
BRANDENBURG	F 215	Blohm & Voss, Hamburg	11 Feb 1992	28 Aug 1992	Oct 1994
SCHLESWIG-HOLSTEIN	F 216	Howaldtswerke, Kiel	1 July 1993	June 1994	Dec 1995
BAYERN	F 217	Thyssen Nordseewerke, Emden	15 Dec 1993	July 1994	May 1996
MECKLENBURG-VORPOMMERN	F 218	Bremer Vulkan	23 Nov 1993	Feb 1995	Nov 1996

Displacement, tons: 4700 full load
Dimensions, feet (metres): 455.7 oa; 416.3 wl × 54.8 × 14.4 *(138.9; 126.9 × 16.7 × 4.4)*
Main machinery: CODOG; 2 GE 7LM2500SA-ML gas-turbines; 51 000 hp *(38 MW)* sustained; 2 MTU 20V 956 TB92 diesels; 11 070 hp(m) *(8.14 MW)* sustained; 2 shafts; cp props
Speed, knots: 29; 18 on diesels. **Range, miles:** 4000 at 18 kts
Complement: 199 plus 19 aircrew

Missiles: SSM: 4 Aerospatiale MM 38 Exocet (2 twin) ❶ (from Type 101A); inertial cruise; active radar homing to 42 km *(23 nm)* at 0.9 Mach; warhead 165 kg; sea-skimmer.
SAM: Martin Marietta VLS Mk 41 Mod 3 ❷ for 16 NATO Sea Sparrow; semi-active radar homing to 14.6 km *(8 nm)* at 2.5 Mach; warhead 39 kg.
2 RAM 21 cell Mk 49 launchers ❸; passive IR/anti-radiation homing to 9.6 km *(5.2 nm)* at 2 Mach; warhead 9.1 kg; 32 missiles.
Guns: 1 OTO Melara 76 mm/62 ❹; 3 in *(76 mm)*/62 Mk 75 ❹; 85° elevation; 85 rounds/minute to 16 km *(8.6 nm)* anti-surface; 12 km *(6.5 nm)* anti-aircraft; weight of shell 6 kg.
Torpedoes: 4—324 mm Mk 32 Mod 9 (2 twin) tubes ❺; anti-submarine. Honeywell Mk 46; anti-submarine; active/passive homing to 11 km *(5.9 nm)* at 40 kts; warhead 44 kg.
Countermeasures: Decoys: 2 Breda SCLAR ❻.
ESM/ECM: TST FL 1800S Stage II; intercept and jammers.
Combat data systems: Atlas Elektronik/Paramax SATIR action data automation with Unisys UYK 43 computer; Link 11. SATCOM ❼.
Fire control: Signaal MWCS.
Radars: Air search: Signaal LW 08 ❽; D band.
Air/Surface search ❾: Signaal SMART; 3D; F band.
Fire control: Two Signaal STIR 180 trackers ❿.
Navigation: Two Raypath; I band.
Sonars: Atlas Elektronik DSQS 23BZ; hull-mounted; medium frequency.
Towed array (provision only).

Helicopters: 2 Sea Lynx Mk 88 ⓫.

Programmes: Formerly Deutschland class. Four ordered 28 June 1989. Developed by Blohm & Voss whose design was selected in October 1988. Replacing Hamburg class. First metal cut 5 February 1991.
Structure: The design is a mixture of MEKO and improved serviceability Type 122 having the same propulsion as the Type 122. Contemporary stealth features. All steel. Fin stabilisers.
Operational: Initial sea trials in December 1993 for first of class. Weapon systems trials started in May 1994.

BRANDENBURG
(Scale 1 : 1200), Ian Sturton

BRANDENBURG
12/1993, Michael Nitz

BRANDENBURG
12/1993, Harald Carstens

BRANDENBURG
12/1993, Blohm & Voss

8 BREMEN CLASS (TYPE 122)

Name	No	Builders	Laid down	Launched	Commissioned
BREMEN	F 207	Bremer Vulkan	9 July 1979	27 Sep 1979	7 May 1982
NIEDERSACHSEN	F 208	AG Weser/Bremer Vulkan	9 Nov 1979	9 June 1980	15 Oct 1982
RHEINLAND-PFALZ	F 209	Blohm & Voss/Bremer Vulkan	29 Sep 1979	3 Sep 1980	9 May 1983
EMDEN	F 210	Thyssen Nordseewerke, Emden/Bremer Vulkan	23 June 1980	17 Dec 1980	7 Oct 1983
KÖLN	F 211	Blohm & Voss/Bremer Vulkan	16 June 1980	29 May 1981	19 Oct 1984
KARLSRUHE	F 212	Howaldtswerke, Kiel/Bremer Vulkan	10 Mar 1981	8 Jan 1982	19 Apr 1984
AUGSBURG	F 213	Bremer Vulkan	4 Apr 1987	17 Sep 1987	3 Oct 1989
LÜBECK	F 214	Thyssen Nordseewerke, Emden/Bremer Vulkan	1 June 1987	15 Oct 1987	19 Mar 1990

Displacement, tons: 3600 full load
Dimensions, feet (metres): 426.4 × 47.6 × 21.3
(130 × 14.5 × 6.5)
Main machinery: CODOG; 2 GE LM 2500 gas-turbines;
51 000 hp *(38 MW)* sustained; 2 MTU 20V 956 TB92 diesels;
11 070 hp(m) *(8.14 MW)* sustained; 2 shafts; cp props
Speed, knots: 30; 20 on diesels. **Range, miles:** 4000 at 18 kts
Complement: 207 (aircrew 18)

Missiles: SSM: 8 McDonnell Douglas Harpoon (2 quad) launchers **❶**; active radar homing to 130 km *(70 nm)* at 0.9 Mach;
warhead 227 kg.
SAM: 16 Raytheon NATO Sea Sparrow; Mk 29 octuple launcher
❷; semi-active radar homing to 14.6 km *(8 nm)* at 2.5 Mach;
warhead 39 kg.
2 GDC RAM 21 cell point-defence systems **❸**; passive IR/anti-
radiation homing to 9.6 km *(5.2 nm)* at 2 Mach; warhead
9.1 kg. Goalkeeper fitted as a contingency in three of the class
in 1991.
Guns: 1 OTO Melara 3 in *(76 mm)*/62 Mk 75 **❹**; 85° elevation;
85 rounds/minute to 16 km *(8.6 nm)* anti-surface; 12 km
(6.5 nm) anti-aircraft; weight of shell 6 kg.
Torpedoes: 4—324 mm Mk 32 (2 twin) tubes **❺**. 8 Honeywell
Mk 46 Mod 1; anti-submarine; active/passive homing to 11 km
(5.9 nm) at 40 kts; warhead 44 kg.
Countermeasures: Decoys: 4 Loral Hycor SRBOC **❻** 6-barrelled
fixed Mk 36; chaff and IR flares to 4 km *(2.2 nm)*.
SLQ 25 Nixie; towed torpedo decoy. Prairie bubble noise
reduction.
ESM/ECM: AEG FL 1800 **❼**; radar warning and jammers. To be
replaced by TST 1800S by 1994.

Combat data systems: SATIR action data automation; Link 11;
SCOT 1A SATCOM **❽** (in some).
Fire control: Signaal WM 25/STIR.
Radars: Air/surface search: Signaal DA 08 **❾**; F band; range
204 km *(110 nm)* for 2 m² target.
Navigation: SMA 3 RM 20; I band; range 73 km *(40 nm)*.
Fire control: Signaal WM 25 **❿**; I/J band; range 46 km *(25 nm)*.
Signaal STIR **⓫**; I/J/K band; range 140 km *(76 nm)* for 1 m²
target.
Sonars: Atlas Elektronik DSQS 21 BZ (BO); hull-mounted; active
search and attack; medium frequency.

Helicopters: 2 Westland Sea Lynx Mk 88 **⓬**.

Programmes: Approval given in early 1976 for first six of this
class, a modification of the Netherlands Kortenaer class.

NIEDERSACHSEN

(Scale 1 : 1200), Ian Sturton

Replaced the deleted Fletcher and Köln classes. Equipment
ordered February 1986 after order placed 6 December 1985
for last pair. Hulls and some engines are provided in the five
building yards. Ships are then towed to the prime contractor
Bremer Vulkan where weapon systems and electronics are fitted and trials conducted. The three names for F210-212 were
changed from the names of Länder to take the well known
town names of the Köln class as they were paid off.
Modernisation: RAM being fitted from 1993: F 208, F 214 and
F 209 in 1993, F 207, F 210 in 1994, remainder in 1995.
Updated EW fit from 1994.
Operational: Form 2nd and 4th Frigate Squadrons. Three containerised SCOT 1A terminals acquired in 1988 and when fitted are mounted on the hangar roof. Dutch Goalkeeper CIWS
was installed on the port side of the hangar roof in F 207, 208
and 212 as a short-term contingency in 1991.

NIEDERSACHSEN (with RAM)

7/1993, M Nitz

LÜBECK

3/1993, Giorgio Arra

KARLSRUHE (with Goalkeeper)

1/1994, van Ginderen Collection

BREMEN

11/1993, Harald Carstens

SHIPBORNE AIRCRAFT

Numbers/Type: 18 Westland Sea Lynx Mk 88.
Operational speed: 125 kts *(232 km/h)*.
Service ceiling: 12 500 ft *(3010 m)*.
Range: 320 nm *(593 km)*.
Role/Weapon systems: Shipborne ASW/ASV role in support of coastal defence roles and North/Baltic Seas anti-submarine warfare. Sensors: Ferranti Sea Spray Mk 1 radar, ECM and Bendix AQS-18 dipping sonar. Weapons: ASW; up to 2 × Mk 46 torpedoes or depth charges. ASV; possible update.

SEA LYNX   *7/1993, M Nitz*

LAND-BASED MARITIME AIRCRAFT (FRONT LINE)

Note: 7 Mi-8 Hip retained for SAR and liaison duties until due next major inspection (latest 1994). Mi-14 Haze taken out of service in 1992.

HIP   *6/1992, Hartmut Ehlers*

Numbers/Type: 22 Westland Sea King Mk 41 KWS.
Operational speed: 140 kts *(260 km/h)*.
Service ceiling: 10 500 ft *(3200 m)*.
Range: 630 nm *(1165 km)*.
Role/Weapon systems: Role change from primary combat rescue helicopter to ASV started in 1988 with new camouflage appearance and an update programme by MBB with BAe/Ferranti support which completed in 1994. Sensors: Ferranti Sea Spray Mk 3 radar, Link 11, ECM. Weapons: ASV; 4 × Sea Skua missiles.

SEA KING   *11/1989, Ralf Bendfeldt*

Numbers/Type: 19 Breguet Atlantic 1.
Operational speed: 355 kts *(658 km/h)*.
Service ceiling: 32 800 ft *(10 000 m)*.
Range: 4850 nm *(8990 km)*.
Role/Weapon systems: Long-range/endurance MR tasks carried out in North and Baltic Seas, also Atlantic Ocean; five aircraft allocated to Elint/SIGINT tasks in Baltic Sea area. Sensors: APS 184 radar, Loral ESM/ECM, MAD, sonobuoys. Weapons: ASW; 8 × torpedoes (including Mk 46) or mines or depth bombs.

Numbers/Type: 3/2 Dornier Do 28D-2/Do 228-212.
Operational speed: 156 kts *(290 km/h)*.
Service ceiling: 20 700 ft *(6300 m)*.
Range: 667 nm *(1235 km)*.
Role/Weapon systems: Short-range surveillance tasks flown; SAR and EEZ protection. Two converted for pollution control. Sensors: Weather radar; converted aircraft also have SLAR, IR/UR scanner, microwave radiometer, LLL TV camera and data downlink. Weapons: Unarmed.

Numbers/Type: 64 Panavia Tornado IDS.
Operational speed: Mach 2.2.
Service ceiling: 80 000 ft *(24 385 m)*.
Range: 1500 nm *(2780 km)*.
Role/Weapon systems: Swing-wing strike and recce; shore-based for fleet air defence and ASV strike primary roles; two wings have been equipped for North and Baltic Sea defence; update with Kormoran 2 and Texas Instruments HARM; 40 transferred to the Air Force on 1 January 1994. Sensors: Texas Instruments nav/attack system. Weapons: ASV; 4 × Kormoran missiles. Fleet AD; 2 × 27 mm cannon, 4 × AIM-9L Sidewinder.

PATROL FORCES

Note: Vessels in this section have an 'S' number as part of their name as well as a 'P' pennant number. The 'S' number is shown in the Pennant List at the front of this country.

10 GEPARD CLASS (TYPE 143 A) (FAST ATTACK CRAFT—MISSILE)

Name	No	Builders	Commissioned
GEPARD	P 6121	AEG/Lürssen	13 Dec 1982
PUMA	P 6122	AEG/Lürssen	24 Feb 1983
HERMELIN	P 6123	AEG/Kröger	5 May 1983
NERZ	P 6124	AEG/Lürssen	14 July 1983
ZOBEL	P 6125	AEG/Kröger	25 Sep 1983
FRETTCHEN	P 6126	AEG/Lürssen	15 Dec 1983
DACHS	P 6127	AEG/Kröger	22 Mar 1984
OZELOT	P 6128	AEG/Lürssen	3 May 1984
WIESEL	P 6129	AEG/Lürssen	12 July 1984
HYÄNE	P 6130	AEG/Lürssen	13 Nov 1984

Displacement, tons: 391 full load
Dimensions, feet (metres): 190 × 25.6 × 8.5 *(57.6 × 7.8 × 2.6)*
Main machinery: 4 MTU MA 16V 956 SB80 diesels; 13 200 hp(m) *(9.7 MW)* sustained; 4 shafts
Speed, knots: 40. **Range, miles:** 2600 at 16 kts; 600 at 33 kts
Complement: 34 (4 officers)

Missiles: SSM: 4 Aerospatiale MM 38 Exocet; inertial cruise; active radar homing to 42 km *(23 nm)* at 0.9 Mach; warhead 165 kg; sea-skimmer. Possibly to be replaced by ANS in due course.
SAM: GDC RAM 21 cell point defence system (being fitted behind Exocet 1992-95); passive IR/anti-radiation homing to 9.6 km *(5.2 nm)* at 2 Mach; warhead 9.1 kg.
Guns: 1 OTO Melara 3 in *(76 mm)*/62 compact; 85° elevation; 85 rounds/minute to 16 km *(8.6 nm)* anti-surface; 12 km *(6.5 nm)* anti-aircraft; weight of shell 6 kg.
Mines: Can lay mines.
Countermeasures: Decoys: Buck-Wegmann Hot Dog/Silver Dog; IR/chaff dispenser.
ESM/ECM: AEG FL 1800s; radar intercept and jammer. FL 1800 Mk 2 to be fitted in 1994.
Combat data systems: AEG AGIS action data automation; Link 11.
Radars: Surface search/fire-control: Signaal WM 27; I/J band; range 46 km *(25 nm)*.
Navigation: SMA 3 RM 20; I band; range 73 km *(40 nm)*.

Programmes: Ordered mid-1978 from AEG-Telefunken with subcontracting to Lürssen (P 6121, 6122, 6124-6128) and Kröger (P 6123, 6129, 6130). First of class laid down 11 July 1979.
Modernisation: Includes plans for new SSM in mid-1990s and an updated EW fit in 1994. RAM fitted in *Puma* in 1992, *Nerz* in 1993 and *Wiesel*, *Hyäne* and *Gepard* in 1994. All to be RAM equipped in due course.
Structure: Wooden hulls on aluminium frames.
Operational: Form 7th Squadron based at Kiel.

OZELOT   *9/1993, Stefan Terzibaschitsch*

PUMA (with RAM)   *1/1993 German Navy*

10 ALBATROS CLASS (TYPE 143B)
(FAST ATTACK-CRAFT—MISSILE)

Name	No	Builders	Commissioned
ALBATROS	P 6111	Lürssen, Vegesack	1 Nov 1976
FALKE	P 6112	Lürssen, Vegesack	13 Apr 1976
GEIER	P 6113	Lürssen, Vegesack	2 June 1976
BUSSARD	P 6114	Lürssen, Vegesack	14 Aug 1976
SPERBER	P 6115	Kröger, Rendsburg	27 Sep 1976
GREIF	P 6116	Lürssen, Vegesack	25 Nov 1976
KONDOR	P 6117	Kröger, Rendsburg	17 Dec 1976
SEEADLER	P 6118	Lürssen, Vegesack	28 Mar 1977
HABICHT	P 6119	Kröger, Rendsburg	23 Dec 1977
KORMORAN	P 6120	Lürssen, Vegesack	29 July 1977

Displacement, tons: 398 full load
Dimensions, feet (metres): 189 × 25.6 × 8.5 *(57.6 × 7.8 × 2.6)*
Main machinery: 4 MTU 16V 956 TB91 diesels; 17 700 hp(m) *(13 MW)* sustained; 4 shafts
Speed, knots: 40. **Range, miles:** 1300 at 30 kts
Complement: 40 (4 officers)

Missiles: SSM: 4 Aerospatiale MM 38 Exocet (2 twin) launchers; inertial cruise; active radar homing to 42 km *(23 nm)* at 0.9 Mach; warhead 165 kg; sea-skimmer.
Guns: 2 OTO Melara 3 in *(76 mm)*/62 compact; 85° elevation; 85 rounds/minute to 16 km *(8.6 nm)* anti-surface; 12 km *(6.5 nm)* anti-aircraft; weight of shell 6 kg.
Torpedoes: 2—21 in *(533 mm)* aft tubes. AEG Seeal; wire-guided; active homing to 13 km *(7 nm)* at 35 kts; passive homing to 28 km *(15 nm)* at 23 kts; warhead 260 kg.
Countermeasures: Decoys: Buck-Wegmann Hot Dog/Silver Dog; IR/chaff dispenser.
ESM/ECM: Racal Octopus (Cutlass intercept, Scorpion jammer).
Combat data systems: Fully automatic data processing command and fire-control system; Link 11.
Fire control: ORG7/3 optronics GFCS.
Radars: Surface search/fire-control: Signaal WM 27; I/J band; range 46 km *(25 nm)*.
Navigation: SMA 3 RM 20; I band; range 73 km *(40 nm)*.

Programmes: AEG-Telefunken main contractor with construction by subcontractors. Ordered in 1972.
Modernisation: *Habicht* started trials with RAM-ASDM mounting in 1983. Plans for major modernisation have been reduced to fitting a new EW system, Racal Octopus, which completed in 1994 changing the classification to Type 143B.
Structure: Wooden hulled craft.
Operational: Form 2nd Squadron at Olpenitz. Tender *Donau.*

BUSSARD   *1993, German Navy*

SPERBER   *6/1992, Horst Dehnst*

18 TIGER CLASS (TYPE 148) (FAST ATTACK CRAFT—MISSILE)

Name	No	Builders	Commissioned
TIGER	P 6141	CMN, Cherbourg	30 Oct 1972
LUCHS	P 6143	CMN, Cherbourg	9 Apr 1973
MARDER	P 6144	CMN, Cherbourg	14 June 1973
LEOPARD	P 6145	CMN, Cherbourg	21 Aug 1973
FUCHS	P 6146	CMN, Cherbourg	17 Oct 1973
JAGUAR	P 6147	CMN, Cherbourg	13 Nov 1973
LÖWE	P 6148	CMN, Cherbourg	9 Jan 1974
WOLF	P 6149	CMN, Cherbourg	26 Feb 1974
PANTHER	P 6150	CMN, Cherbourg	27 Mar 1974
HÄHER	P 6151	CMN, Cherbourg	12 June 1974
PELIKAN	P 6153	CMN, Cherbourg	24 Sep 1974
ELSTER	P 6154	CMN, Cherbourg	14 Nov 1974
ALK	P 6155	CMN, Cherbourg	7 Jan 1975
DOMMEL	P 6156	CMN, Cherbourg	12 Feb 1975
WEIHE	P 6157	CMN, Cherbourg	3 Apr 1975
PINGUIN	P 6158	CMN, Cherbourg	22 May 1975
REIHER	P 6159	CMN, Cherbourg	24 June 1975
KRANICH	P 6160	CMN, Cherbourg	6 Aug 1975

Displacement, tons: 234 standard; 265 full load
Dimensions, feet (metres): 154.2 × 23 × 8.9 *(47 × 7 × 2.7)*
Main machinery: 4 MTU MD 16V 538 TB90 diesels; 12 000 hp(m) *(8.82 MW)* sustained; 4 shafts
Speed, knots: 36. **Range, miles:** 570 at 30 kts; 1600 at 15 kts
Complement: 30 (4 officers)

Missiles: SSM: 4 Aerospatiale MM 38 Exocet (2 twin) launchers; inertial cruise; active radar homing to 42 km *(23 nm)* at 0.9 Mach; warhead 165 kg; sea-skimmer.
Guns: 1 OTO Melara 3 in *(76 mm)*/62 compact; 85° elevation; 85 rounds/minute to 16 km *(8.6 nm)* anti-surface; 12 km *(6.5 nm)* anti-aircraft; weight of shell 6 kg.
1 Bofors 40 mm/70; 80° elevation; 330 rounds/minute to 12 km *(6.5 nm)* anti-surface; 4 km *(2.2 nm)* anti-aircraft; weight of shell 0.96 kg; fitted with GRP dome (1984) (see *Modernisation*).
Mines: Laying capability.
Countermeasures: Decoys: Wolke chaff launcher.
ESM/ECM: Racal Octopus (Cutlass B1 radar intercept and Scorpion jammer).
Combat data systems: PALIS and Link 11.
Fire control: CSEE Panda optical director. Thomson-CSF Vega PCET system, controlling missiles and guns.
Radars: Air/surface search: Thomson-CSF Triton; G band; range 33 km *(18 nm)* for 2 m² target.
Navigation: SMA 3 RM 20; I band; range 73 km *(40 nm)*.
Fire control: Thomson-CSF Castor; I/J band.

Programmes: Ordered in December 1970 from DTCN as main contractors. Some hulls contracted to Lürssen (P 6146, 6148, 6150, 6154, 6156, 6158, 6160) but all fitted out in France.
Modernisation: New Triton search and Castor fire-control radars fitted to the whole class; also Racal EW systems as part of a mid-life update. *Dommel* had the 40 mm/70 gun replaced by a Mauser Vierling Taifun CIWS for trials in September 1991. The gun has four 27 mm barrels and a combined rate of fire of 6800 rounds/minute.
Structure: Steel-hulled craft. Similar to Combattante II craft.
Operational: 3rd Sqn: P 6141-6150 based at Flensburg.
5th Sqn: P 6151-6160 based at Olpenitz. Two paid off in 1992 and transferred to Greece in 1993.

JAGUAR   *8/1993, Harald Carstens*

PANTHER   *6/1992, Horst Dehnst*

AMPHIBIOUS FORCES

Note: As with Light Forces, the LCMs have an LCM number as part of their name. These numbers are in the Pennant List. Only two have retained hull pennant numbers.

11 TYPE 521 (LCMs)

SARDELLE LCM 14	KRILL LCM 22	KORALLE LCM 26
HERING LCM 15	KRABBE LCM 23	GARNELE L 786
ORFE LCM 16	AUSTER LCM 24	LANGUSTE L 787
HUMMER LCM 21	MUSCHEL LCM 25	

Displacement, tons: 168 full load
Dimensions, feet (metres): 77.4 × 20.9 × 4.9 *(23.6 × 6.4 × 1.5)*
Main machinery: 2 MWM 8-cyl diesels; 685 hp(m) *(503 kW)*; 2 shafts
Speed, knots: 10.5
Complement: 7
Military lift: 60 tons or 50 troops

Comment: Built by Rheinwerft, Walsam. Completed in 1964-67 and later placed in reserve. LCM 21-28 recommissioned 4 September 1980 as L 780-787 but all except the last two were decommissioned again on 31 December 1992 and placed in reserve. LCM 14-26 are rated as 'floating equipment' without permanent crews. The design is similar to US LCM 8—LCM 14-16 have a derrick and can be used for carrying 18 torpedoes. LCM 1-11 sold to Greece in April 1991. Bases: Kiel; LCM 16, LCM 21. Flensburg; LCM 23. Wilhelmshaven; LCM 14, LCM 22. Borkum; LCM 15. Olpenitz; LCM 24. Neustadt; LCM 26. Eckernförde; LCM 25. Warnemunde; L 786-L 787.

LANGUSTE   *7/1993, Hartmut Ehlers*

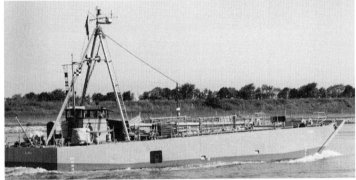

SARDELLE   *9/1992, van Ginderen Collection*

5 TYPE 520 (LCUs)

FLUNDER L 760	LACHS L 762	PLOTZE L 763	SCHLEI L 765	ZANDER L 769

Displacement, tons: 430 full load
Dimensions, feet (metres): 131.2 × 28.9 × 7.2 *(40 × 8.8 × 2.2)*
Main machinery: 2 MWM 12-cyl diesels; 1020 hp(m) *(750 kW)*; 2 shafts
Speed, knots: 11
Complement: 17
Military lift: 150 tons
Guns: 2 Oerlikon 20 mm; 55° elevation; 800 rounds/minute to 2 km; weight of shell 0.24 kg.

Comment: Similar to the US LCU (Landing Craft Utility) type. Provided with bow and stern ramp. Built by Howaldtswerke, Hamburg, 1965-66. Two sold to Greece in November 1989 and six more in 1992. Based at Olpenitz from 1 April 1993. Probably to be sold in 1994.

SCHLEI   *8/1993, Hartmut Ehlers*

MINE WARFARE FORCES

Note: Squadrons

Minesweeper Squadron 1 (Olpenitz)	10 Frankenthal class
Minesweeper Squadron 4 (Wilhelmshaven)	10 Lindau class
Minesweeper Squadron 5 (Olpenitz)	10 Hameln class
Minesweeper Squadron 6 (Wilhelmshaven)	6 Lindau class
	18 Seehund class
Minesweeper Squadron 7 (Neustadt)	10 Frauenlob class
Clearance Diver Company (Eckernförde)	*Stier* (diver support ship)

16 LINDAU CLASS
(TYPE 331, MINEHUNTERS (10); TYPE 351, TROIKA (6))
(MINESWEEPERS—COASTAL and MINEHUNTERS)

Name	No	Builders	Commissioned
GÖTTINGEN	M 1070	Burmester, Bremen	31 May 1958
KOBLENZ	M 1071	Burmester, Bremen	8 July 1958
LINDAU	M 1072	Burmester, Bremen	24 Apr 1958
SCHLESWIG*	M 1073	Burmester, Bremen	30 Oct 1958
TÜBINGEN	M 1074	Burmester, Bremen	25 Sep 1958
WETZLAR	M 1075	Burmester, Bremen	20 Aug 1958
PADERBORN*	M 1076	Burmester, Bremen	16 Dec 1958
WEILHEIM	M 1077	Burmester, Bremen	28 Jan 1959
CUXHAVEN	M 1078	Burmester, Bremen	11 Mar 1959
DÜREN*	M 1079	Burmester, Bremen	22 Apr 1959
MARBURG	M 1080	Burmester, Bremen	11 June 1959
KONSTANZ*	M 1081	Burmester, Bremen	23 July 1959
WOLFSBURG*	M 1082	Burmester, Bremen	8 Oct 1959
ULM*	M 1083	Burmester, Bremen	7 Nov 1959
MINDEN	M 1085	Burmester, Bremen	22 Jan 1960
VOLKLINGEN	M 1087	Burmester, Bremen	21 May 1960

* Troika control ships

Displacement, tons: 463 full load (Hunters); 465 full load (Troika)
Dimensions, feet (metres): 154.5 × 27.2 × 9.8 (9.2 Troika) *(47.1 × 8.3 × 3) (2.8)*
Main machinery: 2 MTU MD diesels; 4000 hp(m) *(2.94 MW)*; 2 shafts (Hunters)
2 MTU MD 16V 538 TB90 diesels; 5000 hp(m) *(3.68 MW)*; 2 shafts
Speed, knots: 16.5. **Range, miles:** 850 at 16.5 kts
Complement: 43 (5 officers) (Hunters); 44 (4 officers) (Troika)

Guns: 1 Bofors 40 mm/70; 90° elevation; 330 rounds/minute to 12 km *(6.5 nm)* anti-surface; 4 km *(2.2 nm)* anti-aircraft; weight of shell 0.96 kg.
Radars: Navigation: Kelvin Hughes 14/9; I band or Atlas Elektronik TRS N. Being replaced by Raytheon.
Sonars: Atlas Elektronik DSQS 11; minehunting; high frequency or Plessey 193 m; minehunting; high frequency (100/300 kHz).

Programmes: *Lindau,* first West German-built vessel for the Navy since the Second World War, launched on 16 February 1957. *Volklingen* was to have been scrapped in 1992 but was reprieved.
Modernisation: Minehunter conversions (Type 331) were completed in 1978/79.
This conversion involved the fitting of Plessey 193M sonar and ECA/PAP 105 disposal vehicles. Prime contractor was VFW-Fokker.
Troika conversions: (Type 351) The six ships *(Düren, Konstanz, Paderborn, Ulm, Schleswig* and *Wolfsburg)* not being converted to minehunters but converted as guidance ships for Troika between 1981 and 1983. Each guide three of these unmanned minesweeping vehicles as well as maintaining their moored minesweeping capabilities. *Göttingen, Koblenz, Lindau, Schleswig, Tübingen* and *Wetzlar* were modified with lower bridges in 1958-59. All were lengthened by 6.8 ft *(2.07 m)* in 1960-64. New gun mountings fitted in some in 1992.
Structure: The hull is of wooden construction, laminated with plastic glue. The engines are of non-magnetic materials.

GÖTTINGEN (hunter)   *3/1993, J L M van der Burg*

PADERBORN (Troika)   *7/1993, van Ginderen Collection*

10 FRAUENLOB CLASS (TYPE 394)
(MINESWEEPERS—INSHORE)

Name	No	Builders	Commissioned
FRAUENLOB	M 2658	Krögerwerft, Rendsburg	27 Sep 1966
NAUTILUS	M 2659	Krögerwerft, Rendsburg	26 Oct 1966
GEFION	M 2660	Krögerwerft, Rendsberg	17 Feb 1967
MEDUSA	M 2661	Krögerwerft, Rendsburg	17 Feb 1967
UNDINE	M 2662	Krögerwerft, Rendsburg	20 Mar 1967
MINERVA	M 2663	Krögerwerft, Rendsburg	16 June1967
DIANA	M 2664	Krögerwerft, Rendsburg	21 Sep 1967
LORELEY	M 2665	Krögerwerft, Rendsburg	29 Mar 1968
ATLANTIS	M 2666	Krögerwerft, Rendsburg	29 Mar 1968
ACHERON	M 2667	Krögerwerft, Rendsburg	10 Feb 1969

Displacement, tons: 246 full load
Dimensions, feet (metres): 124.6 × 26.9 × 6.6 *(38 × 8.2 × 2)*
Main machinery: 2 MTU MB 12V 493 TY70 diesels; 2200 hp(m) *(1.62 MW)* sustained; 2 shafts
Speed, knots: 12+. **Range, miles:** 700 at 14 kts
Complement: 25 (2 officers)

Guns: 1 Bofors 40 mm/70; 90° elevation; 330 rounds/minute to 12 km *(6.5 nm)* anti-surface; 4 km *(2.2 nm)* anti-aircraft; weight of shell 0.96 kg.
Mines: Laying capability.
Radars: Navigation: I band.

Programmes: Launched in 1965-67. Originally designed coast guard boats with W numbers. Rated as inshore minesweepers in 1968 with the M numbers. All subsequently allocated Y numbers and later reallocated M numbers. Scheduled for deletion in 1994/95.

UNDINE   *1993, German Navy*

5 + 5 FRANKENTHAL CLASS (TYPE 332)
(MINEHUNTERS—COASTAL)

Name	No	Builders	Launched	Commissioned
FRANKENTHAL	M 1066	Lürssenwerft	6 Feb 1992	16 Dec 1992
WEIDEN	M 1060	Abeking & Rasmussen	14 May 1992	30 Mar 1993
ROTTWEIL	M 1061	Krögerwerft	12 Mar 1992	7 July 1993
BAD BEVENSEN	M 1063	Lürssenwerft	21 Jan 1993	9 Dec 1993
BAD RAPPENAU	M 1067	Abeking & Rasmussen	3 June 1993	Apr 1994
GRÖMITZ	M 1064	Krögerwerft	29 Apr 1993	Aug 1994
DATTELN	M 1068	Lürssenwerft	2 Feb 1994	Dec 1994
DILLINGEN	M 1065	Abeking & Rasmussen	June 1994	Apr 1995
HOMBURG	M 1069	Krögerwerft	Apr 1994	Aug 1995
SULZBACH-ROSENBERG	M 1062	Lürssenwerft	Feb 1995	Dec 1995

Displacement, tons: 650 full load
Dimensions, feet (metres): 178.8 × 30.2 × 8.5 *(54.5 × 9.2 × 2.6)*
Main machinery: 2 MTU 16V 396 TB84 diesels; 5550 hp(m) *(4.08 MW)* sustained; 2 shafts; cp props. 1 motor (minehunting)
Speed, knots: 18
Complement: 37 (5 officers)

Missiles: SAM: 2 Stinger quad launchers.
Guns: 1 Bofors 40 mm/70; 90° elevation; 330 rounds/minute to 12 km *(6.5 nm)* anti-surface; 4 km *(2.2 nm)* anti-aircraft; weight of shell 0.96 kg.
Radars: Navigation: Raytheon; I band.
Sonars: Atlas Elektronik DSQS-11M; hull-mounted; high frequency.

Programmes: Ordered in September 1988 with STN Systemtechnik Nord as main contractor. M 1066 laid down at Lürssen 6 December 1989.
Structure: Same hull, similar superstructure and high standardisation as Type 343. Built of amagnetic steel. Two STN Systemtechnik Nord Pinguin-B3 drones with sonar, TV cameras and two countermining charges, but not Troika control and minelaying capabilities. Fitted with Atlas Elektronik MWS 80-4 minehunting control system.

FRANKENTHAL   *1993, STN Systemtechnik Nord*

BAD BEVENSEN   *6/1993, Hartmut Ehlers*

10 HAMELN CLASS (TYPE 343) (MINESWEEPERS—COASTAL)

Name	No	Builders	Launched	Commissioned
HAMELN	M 1092	Lürssenwerft	15 Mar 1988	29 June 1989
ÜBERHERRN	M 1095	Abeking & Rasmussen	30 Aug 1988	19 Sep 1989
LABOE	M 1097	Krögerwerft	13 Sep 1988	7 Dec 1989
PEGNITZ	M 1090	Lürssenwerft	13 Mar 1989	9 Mar 1990
KULMBACH	M 1091	Abeking & Rasmussen	15 June 1989	24 Apr 1990
SIEGBURG	M 1098	Krögerwerft	14 Apr 1989	17 July 1990
ENSDORF	M 1094	Lürssenwerft	8 Dec 1989	25 Sep 1990
PASSAU	M 1096	Abeking & Rasmussen	1 Mar 1990	18 Dec 1990
HERTEN	M 1099	Krögerwerft	22 Dec 1989	26 Feb 1991
AUERBACH	M 1093	Lürssenwerft	18 June 1990	7 May 1991

Displacement, tons: 635 full load
Dimensions, feet (metres): 178.5 × 30.2 × 8.2 *(54.4 × 9.2 × 2.5)*
Main machinery: 2 MTU 16V 538 TB91 diesels; 6140 hp(m) *(4.5 MW)* sustained; 2 shafts; cp props
Speed, knots: 18
Complement: 37 (4 officers)

Missiles: SAM: 2 Stinger quad launchers.
Guns: 2 Bofors 40 mm/70; 90° elevation; 330 rounds/minute to 12 km *(6.5 nm)* anti-surface; 4 km *(2.2 nm)* anti-aircraft; weight of shell 0.96 kg.
Mines: 60.
Countermeasures: Decoys: 2 Silver Dog chaff rocket launchers.
ESM: Thomson-CSF DR 2000; radar warning.
Radars: Surface Search/fire-control: Signaal WM 20/2; I/J band; range 46 km *(25 nm)*.
Navigation: Raytheon SPS 64; I band.
Sonars: Atlas Elektronik DSQS-11M; hull-mounted; high frequency.

Programmes: On 3 January 1985 an STN Systemtechnik Nord-headed consortium was awarded the order. The German designation of 'Schnelles Minenkampfboot' was changed in 1989 to 'Schnelles Minensuchboot'.
Structure: Ships built of amagnetic steel adapted from submarine construction. Signaal M 20 System removed from the deleted Zobel class fast attack craft. PALIS active link. Sonar fitted from 1991.
Operational: Primary task is minesweeping. Plans to fit Troika control from 1998.

PASSAU   *1993, German Navy*

18 TROIKA (MINESWEEPERS—DRONES)

SEEHUND 1-18

Displacement, tons: 99
Dimensions, feet (metres): 88.5 × 15 × 4.5 *(26.9 × 4.6 × 1.4)*
Main machinery: 1 Deutz MWM D602 diesel; 446 hp(m) *(328 kW)*; 1 shaft
Speed, knots: 10. **Range, miles:** 520 at 9 kts
Complement: 3 (passage crew)

Comment: Built by MaK, Kiel and Blohm & Voss, Hamburg between August 1980 and May 1982. Commissioned in groups of three with the converted parent vessels. Remote-control using magnetic and acoustic sweeping gear.

SEEHUND 6   *6/1993, van Ginderen Collection*

1 SCHÜTZE CLASS (TYPE 732) (DIVER—SUPPORT SHIP)

Name	No	Builders	Commissioned
STIER	M 1053 (ex-Y 849)	Abeking & Rasmussen	1961

Displacement, tons: 305 full load
Dimensions, feet (metres): 155.5 × 22.9 × 7.2 *(47.4 × 7 × 2.2)*
Main machinery: 2 Maybach diesels; 4500 hp(m) *(3.31 MW)*; 2 shafts
Speed, knots: 24. **Range, miles:** 2000 at 13 kts
Complement: 36 (4 officers)
Guns: Bofors 40 mm/70.
Radars: Navigation: Atlas Elektronik TRS N; I band.

Comment: Deckhouse and recompression chamber added. Original pennant number M 1061. Operates clearance divers.

STIER   *6/1993, Hartmut Ehlers*

AUXILIARIES

Note: Three EGV combat support ships (Type 702) are projected for completion not before 2003. Of 18 000 tons for underway replenishment of fuel, ammunition and solids. Will carry helicopters for VERTREP.

4 + 2 ELBE CLASS (TYPE 404) (TENDERS)

Name	No	Builders	Launched	Commissioned
ELBE	A 511	Bremer Vulkan	24 June 1992	28 Jan 1993
MOSEL	A 512	Bremer Vulkan	22 Apr 1993	22 July 1993
RHEIN	A 513	Flensburger Schiffbau	11 Mar 1993	22 Sep 1993
WERRA	A 514	Flensburger Schiffbau	17 June 1993	9 Dec 1993
MAIN	A 515	Lürssen/Krögerwerft	15 June 1993	July 1994
DONAU	A 516	Lürssen/Krögerwerft	5 May 1994	Nov 1994

Displacement, tons: 3586 full load
Dimensions, feet (metres): 329.7 oa; 285.4 wl × 49.2 × 13.5 *(100.5; 87 × 15 × 4.1)*
Main machinery: 1 Deutz MWM 8V 12M 628 diesel; 3335 hp(m) *(2.45 MW)*; 1 shaft; bow thruster
Speed, knots: 15. **Range, miles:** 2000 at 15 kts
Complement: 40 (4 officers) plus 12 squadron staff plus 50 maintainers
Cargo capacity: 450 tons dieso; 150 tons water; 11 tons luboil; 130 tons ammunition
Missiles: SAM: 2 Stinger (Fliegerfaust 2) quad launchers.
Guns: 4 Mauser 27 mm (quad) may be fitted.
Helicopters: Platform for 1 medium.

Comment: Funds released in November 1990 for the construction of six ships to replace the Rhein class. Containers for maintenance and repairs, spare parts and supplies for fast attack craft and minesweepers. Waste disposal capacity: 270 cu m liquids, 60 cu m solids. The use of the Darss class (all sold in 1991) was investigated as an alternative but rejected on the grounds of higher long-term costs because of the age of the ships. Allocated as follows: *Elbe* to 7th Squadron FPBs, *Mosel* to 5th Squadron MSC, *Rhein* to 3rd Squadron MSC, *Werra* to 1st Squadron MSC, *Main* to 5th Squadron FPBs, *Donau* to 2nd Squadron FPBs.

MOSEL   *10/1993, Bremer Vulkan*

1 TYPE 763 (SUPPORT TANKER)

Name	No	Builders	Commissioned
WITTENSEE (ex-*Sioux*)	A 1407	Lindenau, Kiel	26 Mar 1959

Displacement, tons: 1854 full load
Dimensions, feet (metres): 221.4 × 32 × 14.1 *(67.5 × 9.8 × 4.3)*
Main machinery: 1 MaK diesel; 1050 hp(m) *(772 kW)*; 1 shaft
Speed, knots: 12
Complement: 21

Comment: Civilian manned. *Bodensee* sold to Turkey in 1977. Planned to pay off in late 1996.

WITTENSEE   *6/1990, Stefan Terzibaschitsch*

1 RHEIN CLASS (TYPE 401) (TENDER)

Name	No	Builders	Commissioned
DONAU	A 69	Schlichting, Travemünde	23 May 1964

Displacement, tons: 2940 full load
Dimensions, feet (metres): 322.1 × 38.8 × 14.4/19.7 *(98.2 × 11.8 × 4.4/6)*
Main machinery: 6 Maybach diesels; 14 400 hp(m) *(10.58 MW)*; 2 shafts
Speed, knots: 20.5. **Range, miles:** 1625 at 15 kts
Complement: 153; 163 *(Elbe)*

Guns: 2 DCN 3.9 in *(100 mm)*; 80° elevation; 60-80 rounds/minute to 17 km *(9.2 nm)* anti-surface; 8 km *(4.4 nm)* anti-aircraft; weight of shell 13.5 kg.
2 or 4 Bofors 40 mm/70 (2 singles or 2 twin); 90° elevation; 300 rounds/minute to 12 km *(6.5 nm)* anti-surface; 4 km *(2.2 nm)* anti-aircraft; weight of shell 0.96 kg.
Fire control: 2 Signaal M 45 GFCS for gunnery.
Radars: Surface search: Signaal ZW 01; I/J band.
Signaal DA 02; E/F band; range 73 km *(40 nm)*.
Navigation: Kelvin Hughes 14/9; I band.
Fire control: Two Signaal M 45; I/J band; short range for gunnery.
Sonars: Atlas Elektronik; hull-mounted; active search; medium frequency.

Programmes: Originally a class of 13.
Operational: *Donau*, 2nd FPB Squadron; to pay off in December 1994.
Sales: *Weser* to Greece 1975. *Ruhr* to Turkey 1976. *Isar* to Turkey October 1982. *Elbe* to Turkey March 1993. *Main* may transfer to Turkey in 1994.

DONAU   *8/1993, Hartmut Ehlers*

2 REPLENISHMENT TANKERS (TYPE 704)

Name	No	Builders	Commissioned
SPESSART (ex-*Okapi*)	A 1442	Kröger, Rendsburg	1974
RHÖN (ex-*Okene*)	A 1443	Kröger, Rendsburg	1974

Displacement, tons: 14 169 full load
Measurement, tons: 6103 grt; 10 800 dwt
Dimensions, feet (metres): 427.1 × 63.3 × 26.9 *(130.2 × 19.3 × 8.2)*
Main machinery: 1 MaK 12-cyl diesel; 8000 hp(m) *(5.88 MW)*; 1 shaft
Speed, knots: 16. **Range, miles:** 7400 at 16 kts
Complement: 42
Cargo capacity: 11 000 cu m fuel; 400 cu m water

Comment: Completed for Terkol Group as tankers. Acquired in 1976 for conversion *(Spessart* at Bremerhaven, *Rhön* at Kröger)*. The former commissioned for naval service on 5 September 1977 and the latter on 23 September 1977. Unarmed and civilian manned.

RHÖN   *8/1993, H M Steele*

4 WALCHENSEE CLASS (TYPE 703)
(REPLENISHMENT TANKERS)

Name	No	Builders	Commissioned
WALCHENSEE	A 1424	Lindenau, Kiel	29 June 1966
AMMERSEE	A 1425	Lindenau, Kiel	2 Mar 1967
TEGERNSEE	A 1426	Lindenau, Kiel	23 Mar 1967
WESTENSEE	A 1427	Lindenau, Kiel	6 Oct 1967

Displacement, tons: 2191
Dimensions, feet (metres): 235.8 × 36.7 × 13.5 *(71.9 × 11.2 × 4.1)*
Main machinery: 2 MWM 12-cyl diesels; 1370 hp(m) *(1 MW)*; 2 shafts
Speed, knots: 12.6. **Range, miles:** 3250 at 12 kts
Complement: 21

Comment: Civilian manned.

WESTENSEE   *8/1993, H M Steele*

1 GUSTAV KÖNIGS CLASS (TYPE 670) (HARBOUR TANKER)

FLEESENSEE Y 1657 (ex-C 40)

Displacement, tons: 1010 full load
Dimensions, feet (metres): 219.8 × 26.9 × 7.2 *(67 × 8.2 × 2.2)*
Main machinery: 1 R8DV 148 diesel; 420 hp(m) *(308 kW)*; 1 shaft
Speed, knots: 8

Comment: Ex-GDR built by VEB/Rosslau-Elbe. Based at Warnemünde. Able to pass under river
bridges. Sister ship *Kölpinsee* was sold for civilian use in September 1992.

FLEESENSEE   *7/1993, Hartmut Ehlers*

4 LÜNEBURG CLASS (TYPE 701) (SUPPORT SHIPS)

Name	No	Builders	Commissioned
FREIBURG*	A 1413	Blohm & Voss	27 May 1968
GLÜCKSBURG*	A 1414	Bremer Vulkan/Flensburger Schiffbau	9 July 1968
NIENBURG	A 1416	Bremer Vulkan/Flensburger Schiffbau	1 Aug 1968
MEERSBURG*	A 1418	Bremer Vulkan/Flensburger Schiffbau	25 June 1968

*conversions

Displacement, tons: 3483; 3709 (conversions); 3900 *Freiburg*
Dimensions, feet (metres): 341.2 × 43.3 × 13.8 *(104 × 13.2 × 4.2)*
  (374.9 ft *(114.3 m)* for conversions; 388.1 ft *(118.3 m)* for *Freiburg*)
Main machinery: 2 MTU MD 16V 538 TB90 diesels; 6000 hp(m) *(4.1 MW)* sustained; 2 shafts; cp
  props; bow thruster
Speed, knots: 17. **Range, miles:** 3200 at 14 kts
Complement: 71
Cargo capacity: 1100 tons
Guns: 4 Bofors 40 mm/70 (2 twin) (not carried in all).

Comment: Four of this class were lengthened in 1975-76 by 33.7 ft *(10.3 m)* and modernised to
serve the missile installations of the new classes of fast attack craft and converted destroyers,
including MM 38 Exocet maintenance. *Freiburg* was lengthened in 1984 by 46.9 ft *(14.3 m)*, has
a helicopter deck, portside larger crane and acts as support ship for Bremen class carrying nine
spare Harpoons. The others serve as support ships for fast attack craft or MCM squadrons.
Meersburg replaced *Lahn* as depot ship for 1st Submarine Squadron and *Nienburg* replaced
Werra in 1991. *Coburg* transferred to Greece 25 September 1991. One was paid off in April 1993
and two more in June 1994.

FREIBURG   *8/1993, H M Steele*

NIENBURG (with helo deck)   *7/1993, A Sheldon Duplaix*

5 OHRE CLASS (ACCOMMODATION SHIPS)

VOGTLAND Y 890 (ex-H 71)   **BÖRDE** Y 894 (ex-H 72)
ALTMARK Y 891 (ex-H 11)   **WISCHE** (ex-*Harz*) Y 895 (ex-H 31)
UCKERMARK Y 893 (ex-H 91)

Displacement, tons: 1320 full load
Dimensions, feet (metres): 231 × 39.4 × 5 *(70.4 × 12 × 1.6)*
Main machinery: 2 SKL VEB 6V D18/15 AL-1 diesels; 944 hp(m) *(694 kW)* sustained; 2 shafts;
  bow thruster

Comment: Ex-GDR built by Peenewerft, Wolgast. One hydraulic 8 ton crane fitted. First commissioned 1985. Classified as 'Schwimmende Stuetzpunkte'. Propulsion and armament is being
removed and vessels are used as non self-propelled accommodation ships for crews of vessels in
refit. Civilian manned. *Vogtland* and *Börde* based at Warnemünde and the other three at Wilhelmshaven. Most do not display pennant numbers.

BÖRDE   *7/1993, Hartmut Ehlers*

2 WESTERWALD CLASS (TYPE 760)
(AMMUNITION TRANSPORTS)

Name	No	Builders	Commissioned
WESTERWALD	A 1435	Orenstein and Koppel, Lübeck	11 Feb 1967
ODENWALD	A 1436	Orenstein and Koppel, Lübeck	23 Mar 1967

Displacement, tons: 3460 standard; 4042 full load
Dimensions, feet (metres): 344.4 × 46 × 12.2 *(105 × 14 × 3.7)*
Main machinery: 2 MTU MD 16V 538 TB90 diesels; 6000 hp(m) *(4.1 MW)* sustained; 2 shafts; cp
  props; bow thruster
Speed, knots: 17. **Range, miles:** 3500 at 17 kts
Complement: 47 *(Westerwald)*; 31 *(Odenwald)* (civilian manned)
Cargo capacity: 1080 tons ammunition
Guns: 4 Bofors 40 mm/70 (2 twin) (cocooned in *Odenwald*).

Comment: Both based at Wilhelmshaven.

WESTERWALD   *8/1993, H M Steele*

1 TYPE 705 (WATER BOAT)

FW 5 A 1405 (ex-Y 868)

Displacement, tons: 626 full load
Dimensions, feet (metres): 144.4 × 25.6 × 8.2 *(44.1 × 7.8 × 2.5)*
Main machinery: 1 MWM diesel; 230 hp(m) *(169 kW)*; 1 shaft
Speed, knots: 9.5
Complement: 6
Cargo capacity: 340 tons

Comment: Originally class of six built in pairs by Schiffbarges, Unterweser, Bremerhaven;
H. Rancke, Hamburg and Jadewerft, Wilhelmshaven, in 1963-64. *FW 2* (3 December 1975) and
FW 4 (12 April 1991) to Turkey; *FW 3* (22 April 1976) and *FW 6* (5 March 1991) to Greece. *FW 1*
may transfer to Turkey in 1994.

FW 5   *6/1993, Stefan Terzibaschitsch*

1 KNURRHAHN CLASS (TYPE 730) (ACCOMMODATION SHIP)

Name	No	Builders	Commissioned
KNURRHAHN	Y 811	Sietas, Hamburg	Nov 1989

Displacement, tons: 1424 full load
Dimensions, feet (metres): 157.5 × 45.9 × 5.9 *(48 × 14 × 1.8)*

Comment: Based at Bremerhaven. Accommodation for 230 people.

KNURRHAHN   *6/1993, Erik Laursen*

3 BATTERY CHARGING CRAFT (TYPE 718)

Name	No	Builders	Commissioned
LP 1	—	Jadewerft, Wilhelmshaven	18 Feb 1964
LP 2	—	Oelkers, Hamburg	17 Apr 1964
LP 3	Y 1690	Jadewerft, Wilhelmshaven	12 Sep 1974

Displacement, tons: 234 (267 *LP 3*) full load
Dimensions, feet (metres): 90.6 × 23 × 5.2 *(27.6 × 7.0 × 1.6)*
Main machinery: 1 MTU MB diesel; 250 hp(m) *(184 kW)*; 1 shaft
Speed, knots: 9
Complement: 6

Comment: Have diesel charging generators for submarine batteries. *LP 3* is 1.6 ft *(0.5 m)* more in beam than the first two.

LP 2 6/1993, Hartmut Ehlers

5 TOWING LAUNCHES (TYPE 946)

AK 1 Y 1671   AK 3 Y 1672   MA 2 Y 1676   MA 3 Y 1677   BORBY Y 1687

Dimensions, feet (metres): 39.4 × 12.8 × 6.2 *(12.0 × 3.9 × 1.9)*
Main machinery: 1 MAN D2540MTE diesel; 366 hp(m) *(269 kW)*; 1 shaft

Comment: Built by Hans Boost, Trier. All completed in 1985.

AK 3 1/1993, van Ginderen Collection

2 UTILITY LAUNCHES (TYPE 945)

MA 1 Y 1678   ASCHAU Y 1685

Dimensions, feet (metres): 53.1 × 14.8 × 6.6 *(16.2 × 4.5 × 2)*
Main machinery: 1 MAN D2866TE diesel; 300 hp(m) *(221 kW)*; 1 shaft

Comment: Built by Hans Boost, Trier and commissioned 30 August 1992.

MA 1 8/1993, M Nitz

5 RANGE SAFETY CRAFT (TYPE 905)

TODENDORF Y 835   BERGEN Y 838
PUTLOS Y 836   MUNSTER Y 839
BAUMHOLDER Y 837

Displacement, tons: 78 full load
Dimensions, feet (metres): 91.2 × 19.7 × 4.6 *(27.8 × 6 × 1.4)*
Main machinery: 2 KHD TBD 234 diesels; 2054 hp(m) *(1.51 MW)*; 2 shafts
Speed, knots: 18
Complement: 15

Comment: Built by Lürssen, Vegesack and completed in 1993/94 replacing previous Types 369 and 909 craft.

7 GENERAL SERVICE LAUNCHES (TYPES 740, 743, 744, 744A)

MT 1 (ex-*MT-Boot*) Y 1670   AM 7 Y 1679
AM 6 Y 1674   AK 6 Y 1683
AM 8 Y 1675   PETER BACHMANN Y 1684
   AK 2 Y 1686

Dimensions, feet (metres): 52.5 × 13.1 × 3.9 *(16 × 4 × 1.2)* approx
Main machinery: 1 or 2 diesels

Comment: For personnel transport and trials work. Types 744 and 744A *(AK 2)* are radio calibration craft.

AK 2 6/1993, Stefan Terzibaschitsch

2 TWIN HULL OIL RECOVERY SHIPS (TYPE 738)

Name	No	Builders	Commissioned
BOTTSAND	Y 1643	Lühring, Brake	24 Jan 1985
EVERSAND	Y 1644	Lühring, Brake	11 June 1988

Measurement, tons: 500 gross; 650 dwt
Dimensions, feet (metres): 151.9 × 39.4 (137.8, bow opened) × 10.2 *(46.3 × 12 (42) × 3.1)*
Main machinery: 1 Deutz BA12M816 diesel; 1000 hp(m) *(759 kW)* sustained; 2 shafts
Speed, knots: 10
Complement: 6

Comment: Built with two hulls which are connected with a hinge in the stern. During pollution clearance the bow will be opened. Ordered by Ministry of Transport but taken over by West German Navy. Normally used as tank cleaning vessels. Civilian manned. *Bottsand* based at Olpenik, *Eversand* at Wilhelmshaven. A third of class *Thor* belongs to the Ministry of Transport.

BOTTSAND 8/1992, Hartmut Ehlers

EVERSAND (hulls open) 8/1993, Hartmut Ehlers

27 PERSONNEL TENDERS (TYPES 934 and GDR 407)

V 2-V 21   B 03   B 11   B 30   B 33   B 83   B 86   B 88

Comment: V 2-V 21 built in 1987/88 by Hatecke. The B series are ex-GDR craft built by Yachtwerft, Berlin.

B 86   7/1993, Hartmut Ehlers

3 TORPEDO RECOVERY VESSELS (TYPE 430A)

TF 1 Y 851   TF 5 Y 855   TF 6 Y 856

Comment: All built in 1966 of approximately 56 tons. Provided with stern ramp for torpedo recovery. One sold to the Turkish Navy, two to Greece in 1989 and two more in 1991.

TF 6   6/1992, Stefan Terzibaschitsch

12 OIL BARGES (TYPE 737)

Comment: Numbered Ölschute 1-12 and completed in 1986-87. 65.6 ft (20 m) dumb barges with 150 tons capacity.

5 FLOATING DOCKS (TYPES 712-715) and 2 CRANES (TYPE 711)

SCHWIMMDOCKS A Y 842   HIEV   Y 875
SCHWIMMDOCKS B Y 879   GRIEP Y 876
C, 2 and 3

Comment: Dock lift capacity: 3 (8000 tons); B (4500 tons); A and 2 (1000 tons). C is used for submarine pressure tests; Cranes (100 tons).

Y 879   6/1991, Stefan Terzibaschitsch

INTELLIGENCE VESSELS (AGIs)

3 OSTE CLASS (TYPE 423) (AGI)

Name	No	Builders	Commissioned
ALSTER	A 50	Schiffsbaugesellschaft, Flensburg	5 Oct 1989
OSTE	A 52	Schiffsbaugesellschaft, Flensburg	30 June 1988
OKER	A 53	Schiffsbaugesellschaft, Flensburg	10 Nov 1988

Displacement, tons: 3200 full load
Dimensions, feet (metres): 273.9 × 47.9 × 13.8 (83.5 × 14.6 × 4.2)
Main machinery: 2 Deutz-MWM BV16M728 diesels; 8980 hp(m) (6.6 MW) sustained; 1 shaft; 1 motor (for slow speed)
Speed, knots: 19
Complement: 40 plus 40 specialists (2 crews)

Comment: Ordered in March 1985 and December 1986 and have replaced the Radar Trials Ships of the same name (old Oker and Alster transferred to Greece and Turkey respectively). Oste launched 15 May 1987, Oker 24 September 1987, Alster 4 November 1988. Carry Atlas Elektronik passive sonar and optical ELAM and electronic surveillance equipment. Particular attention has been given to accommodation standards.

ALSTER   6/1993, van Ginderen Collection

SURVEY AND RESEARCH SHIPS

Note: Type 749 project to build new torpedo and sonar trials vessels has been deferred until 2005.

1 TRIALS SHIP (TYPE 742)

Name	No	Builders	Commissioned
WALTHER VON LEDEBUR	A 1410 (ex-Y 841)	Burmester, Bremen	21 Dec 1967

Displacement, tons: 775 standard; 825 full load
Dimensions, feet (metres): 206.6 × 34.8 × 8.9 (63 × 10.6 × 2.7)
Main machinery: 2 Maybach MTU 16-cyl diesels; 5200 hp(m) (3.82 MW); 2 shafts
Speed, knots: 19
Complement: 11 plus 10 trials party

Comment: Wooden hulled vessel. Launched on 30 June 1966 as a prototype minesweeper but completed as a trials ship. To be replaced in 1995 by fourth Type 748. Scheduled to pay off in April 1994.

WALTHER VON LEDEBUR   5/1993, A Sheldon Duplaix

3 SCHWEDENECK CLASS (TYPE 748) (MULTIPURPOSE)

Name	No	Builders	Commissioned
SCHWEDENECK	Y 860	Krögerwerft, Rendsburg	20 Oct 1987
KRONSORT	Y 861	Elsflether Werft	2 Dec 1987
HELMSAND	Y 862	Krögerwerft, Rendsburg	4 Mar 1988

Displacement, tons: 1018 full load
Dimensions, feet (metres): 185.3 × 35.4 × 17 (56.5 × 10.8 × 5.2)
Main machinery: Diesel-electric; 3 MTU 6V 396 TB53 diesel generators; 1485 kW 60 Hz sustained; 1 motor; 1 shaft
Speed, knots: 13. Range, miles: 2400 at 13 kts
Complement: 13 plus 10 trials parties
Radars: Navigation: Two Raytheon; I band.

Comment: Order for first three placed in mid-1985. One more planned after 1995 to replace Walther von Ledebur but may not now be funded.

KRONSORT   6/1993, Stefan Terzibaschitsch

5 STOLLERGRUND CLASS (TYPE 745)
(MULTIPURPOSE)

Name	No	Builders	Commissioned
STOLLERGRUND	Y 863	Krögerwerft	31 May 1989
MITTELGRUND	Y 864	Elsflether Werft	23 Aug 1989
KALKGRUND	Y 865	Krögerwerft	23 Nov 1989
BREITGRUND	Y 866	Elsflether Werft	19 Dec 1989
BANT	Y 867	Krögerwerft	28 May 1990

Displacement, tons: 450 full load
Dimensions, feet (metres): 126.6 × 30.2 × 10.5 *(38.6 × 9.2 × 3.2)*
Main machinery: 1 Deutz-MWM BV6M628 diesel; 1690 hp(m) *(1.24 MW)* sustained; 1 shaft
Speed, knots: 12. **Range, miles:** 1000 at 12 kts.
Complement: 7 plus 6 trials personnel

Comment: Five ordered from Lürssen in November 1987; two subcontracted to Elsflether. Equipment includes two I band radars and an intercept sonar. The first four are based at the Armed Forces Technical Centre; *Bant* at Wilhelmshaven. Two more planned for the mid-1990s may be cancelled.

BANT   *11/1992, G Koop*

1 RESEARCH SHIP (TYPE 750)

Name	No	Builders	Commissioned
PLANET	A 1450	Norderwerft, Hamburg	15 Apr 1967

Displacement, tons: 1943 full load
Dimensions, feet (metres): 263.8 × 41.3 × 13.1 *(80.4 × 12.6 × 4)*
Main machinery: Diesel-electric; 4 MWM diesel generators; 1 motor; 1390 hp(m) *(1.02 MW)*; 1 shaft; bow thruster
Speed, knots: 13. **Range, miles:** 9400 at 13 kts
Complement: 39 plus 22 scientists
Radars: Navigation: Two Raytheon; I band.
Sonars: Hull-mounted; high frequency search.
Helicopters: 1 Bell 206B or MBB BO105CB can be embarked.

Comment: Weapons research ship launched 23 September 1965. Planned to be replaced by SWATH type ship (Type 751).

PLANET   *9/1992, Horst Dehnst*

2 TRIALS SHIPS (TYPE 741)

Name	No	Builders	Commissioned
SP 1	A 1408 (ex-A 837)	Schürenstadt, Bardenfleth	29 June 1967
WILHELM PULLWER	A 1409 (ex-Y 838)	Schürenstadt, Bardenfleth	22 Dec 1967

Displacement, tons: 160 full load
Dimensions, feet (metres): 103.3 × 24.6 × 7.2 *(31.5 × 7.5 × 2.2)*
Main machinery: 2 MTU MB diesels; 700 hp(m) *(514 kW)*; 2 Voith-Schneider props
Speed, knots: 12.5
Complement: 17

Comment: Wooden hulled trials ships for barrage systems. *SP 1* works for the Naval Service Test Command.

SP 1   *6/1992, Stefan Terzibaschitsch*

1 TRIAL BOAT (TYPE 740)

Name	No	Builders	Commissioned
BUMS	Y 1689	Howaldtswerke, Kiel	—

Dimensions, feet (metres): 86.6 × 22.3 × 4.9 *(26.4 × 6.8 × 1.5)*

Comment: Single diesel engine. Has a 3 ton crane.

BUMS   *1983, Ralf Bendfeldt*

0 + (1) SES TRIALS CRAFT (TYPE 751)

Displacement, tons: 720 full load
Dimensions, feet (metres): 219.8 × 52.8 × 9.4 (hullborne) *(67.0 × 16.1 × 2.8)*
Main machinery: 4 Allison 571-KF gas-turbines, 30 776 hp(m) *(23 MW)* sustained; 2 KaMeWa waterjets
Speed, knots: 50+

Comment: MTG Marinetechnik Hamburg has been contracted to design a craft characterised by a top speed of 50 knots for construction in the 1990s.
Prior to construction of the full scale SES a manned and self-propelled model in scale 1:6.3 has been built at Lürssen and completed on 21 Aug 1990. Named *Moses* this craft has two Tohatsu outboard engines giving a speed of 25 kts.

1 MEKAT PROJECT TRIALS CRAFT

CORSAIR

Displacement, tons: 160 full load
Dimensions, feet (metres): 120.7 × 42.7 × 5.9 *(36.8 × 13 × 1.8)*
Main machinery: 2 MTU diesels; 4280 hp(m) *(3.15 MW)*; 2 shafts; cp props
Speed, knots: 47

Comment: A Blohm & Voss catamaran hull launched in February 1989. Has done trials with a 57 mm gun and Signaal weapon control systems. Several variants of the craft are projected.

CORSAIR   *1993, Blohm & Voss*

1 TRIALS PLATFORM

BARBARA Y 844

Comment: Artillery testing ship of 3500 tons and 170.9 ft *(52.1 m)*. Commissioned in June 1964. No propulsion. Named after the patron saint of artillery.

BARBARA   *1990, van Ginderen Collection*

TRAINING SHIPS

Note: In addition to the two listed below there are 54 other sail training vessels (Types 910-915).

Name	No	Builders	Commissioned
GORCH FOCK	A 60	Blohm & Voss, Hamburg	17 Dec 1958

Displacement, tons: 1760 standard; 1870 full load
Dimensions, feet (metres): 293 × 39.2 × 16.1 *(89.3 × 12 × 4.9)*
Main machinery: Auxiliary 1 Deutz MWM BV6M628 diesel; 1690 hp(m) *(1.24 MW)* sustained; 1 shaft; KaMeWa cp prop
Speed, knots: 11 power; 15 sail. **Range, miles:** 1990 at 10 kts
Complement: 206 (10 officers, 140 cadets)

Comment: Sail training ship of the improved Horst Wessel type. Barque rig. Launched on 23 August 1958. Sail area, 21 141 sq ft. Major modernisation in 1985 at Howaldtswerke. Second major refit in 1991 at Motorenwerke, Bremerhaven included a new propulsion engine and three diesel generators.

GORCH FOCK   6/1993, Harald Carstens

Name	No	Builders	Commissioned
NORDWIND	Y 834	—	1944

Displacement, tons: 110
Dimensions, feet (metres): 78.8 × 21 × 8.2 *(24 × 6.4 × 2.5)*
Main machinery: 1 Demag diesel; 150 hp(m) *(110 kW)*; 1 shaft
Speed, knots: 8. **Range, miles:** 1200 at 7 kts
Complement: 10

Comment: Ketch rigged. Sail area, 2037.5 sq ft. Ex-Second World War patrol craft. Taken over from Border Guard in 1956.

NORDWIND   6/1993, Stefan Terzibaschitsch

TUGS

2 HELGOLAND CLASS (TYPE 720) (SALVAGE TUGS)

Name	No	Builders	Commissioned
HELGOLAND	A 1457	Unterweser, Bremerhaven	8 Mar 1966
FEHMARN	A 1458	Unterweser, Bremerhaven	1 Feb 1967

Displacement, tons: 1310 standard; 1643 full load
Dimensions, feet (metres): 223.1 × 41.7 × 14.4 *(68 × 12.7 × 4.4)*
Main machinery: Diesel-electric; 4 MWM 12-cyl diesel generators; 2 motors; 3300 hp(m) *(2.43 MW)*; 2 shafts
Speed, knots: 17. **Range, miles:** 6400 at 16 kts
Complement: 34
Guns: 2 Bofors 40 mm/70 (twin) (cocooned or removed)
Mines: Laying capacity.
Radars: Navigation: Raytheon; I band.
Sonars: High definition, hull-mounted for wreck search.

Comment: Launched on 25 November 1965 and 9 April 1965. Carry fire-fighting equipment and have an ice-strengthened hull. *Fehmarn* (Type 720B) modernised and employed as safety ship for the submarine training group.

HELGOLAND   8/1993, H M Steele

6 WANGEROOGE CLASS (3 TYPE 722 and 3 TYPE 754)

Name	No	Builders	Commissioned
WANGEROOGE	A 1451	Schichau, Bremerhaven	9 Apr 1968
SPIEKEROOG	A 1452	Schichau, Bremerhaven	14 Aug 1968
NORDERNEY	A 1455	Schichau, Bremerhaven	15 Oct 1970
BALTRUM	A 1439	Schichau, Bremerhaven	8 Oct 1968
JUIST	A 1440	Schichau, Bremerhaven	1 Oct 1971
LANGEOOG	A 1441	Schichau, Bremerhaven	14 Aug 1968

Displacement, tons: 854 standard; 1024 full load
Dimensions, feet (metres): 170.6 × 39.4 × 12.8 *(52 × 12.1 × 3.9)*
Main machinery: Diesel-electric; 4 MWM 16-cyl diesel generators; 2 motors; 2400 hp(m) *(1.76 MW)*; 2 shafts
Speed, knots: 14. **Range, miles:** 5000 at 10 kts
Complement: 24 plus 33 trainees (A 1439-1441)
Guns: 1 Bofors 40 mm/70 (cocooned in some, not fitted in all).

Comment: First three are salvage tugs with fire-fighting equipment and ice-strengthened hulls. *Wangerooge* sometimes used for pilot training and *Spiekeroog* and *Norderney* as submarine safety ships. The second three were converted 1974-78 to training ships with *Baltrum* and *Juist* being used as diving training vessels with recompression chambers and civilian crews.

SPIEKEROOG   6/1993, Antonio Moreno

3 HARBOUR TUGS (TYPE 724)

Name	No	Builders	Commissioned
SYLT	Y 820	Schichau, Bremerhaven	1962
FÖHR	Y 821	Schichau, Bremerhaven	1962
NEUWERK	Y 823	Schichau, Bremerhaven	1963

Displacement, tons: 244 standard; 266 full load
Dimensions, feet (metres): 100.7 × 24.6 × 13.1 *(30.6 × 7.5 × 4)*
Main machinery: 1 Deutz MaK 8-cyl diesel; 1000 hp(m) *(735 kW)*; 1 shaft
Speed, knots: 12
Complement: 10

Comment: Launched in 1961. Civilian manned. Carry fire-fighting equipment.

FÖHR   8/1993, Hartmut Ehlers

2 HARBOUR TUGS (TYPE 724)

Name	No	Builders	Commissioned
NEUENDE	Y 1680	Schichau, Bremerhaven	27 Oct 1971
HEPPENS	Y 1681	Schichau, Bremerhaven	17 Dec 1971

Displacement, tons: 232
Dimensions, feet (metres): 87.2 × 24.3 × 8.5 *(26.6 × 7.4 × 2.6)*
Main machinery: 1 MWM 8-cyl diesel; 800 hp(m) *(588 kW)*; 1 shaft
Speed, knots: 12
Complement: 6

TYPE 724 (old number)   *6/1993, Harald Carstens*

6 + 6 HARBOUR TUGS (TYPE 725)

Name	No	Builders	Commissioned
VOGELSAND	Y 816	Orenstein und Koppel, Lübeck	14 Apr 1987
NORDSTRAND	Y 817	Orenstein und Koppel, Lübeck	20 Jan 1987
LANGENESS	Y 819	Orenstein und Koppel, Lübeck	5 Mar 1987
LÜTJE HORN	Y 812	Husumer Schiffswerft	31 May 1990
KNECHTSAND	Y 814	Husumer Schiffswerft	16 Nov 1990
SCHARHÖRN	Y 815	Husumer Schiffswerft	1 Oct 1990

Displacement, tons: 445
Dimensions, feet (metres): 99.3 × 29.8 × 8.5 *(30.3 × 9.1 × 2.6)*
Main machinery: 2 Deutz MWM BV6M628 diesels; 3360 hp(m) *(2.47 MW)* sustained; 2 Voith-Schneider props
Speed, knots: 12
Complement: 10

Comment: Bollard pull, 23 tons. Six more to complete 1994-97, to replace Type 724.

VOGELSAND   *7/1993, A Sheldon Duplaix*

3 HARBOUR TUGS (TYPE 414)

KOOS (ex-*Delphin*) Y 1651 (ex-A 08)   DRANKSE (ex-*Kormoran*) Y 1658 (ex-A 68)
WUSTROW (ex-*Zander*) Y 1656 (ex-A 45)

Displacement, tons: 320 full load
Dimensions, feet (metres): 96.1 × 27.2 × 12.1 *(29.3 × 8.3 × 3.7)*
Main machinery: 2 diesels; 1200 hp(m) *(882 kW)*; 2 shafts
Speed, knots: 11. **Range, miles:** 1800 at 11 kts
Complement: 3

Comment: Ex-GDR vessels being retained in service until 1998.

WUSTROW   *7/1993, Hartmut Ehlers*

3 WARNOW CLASS HARBOUR TUGS

A 15   A 16   A 41

Comment: Ex-GDR Type 1344 berthing tugs built by Yachtwerft Berlin. Retained in service at Peenemünde and Warnemünde.

A 41   *7/1993, Hartmut Ehlers*

ICEBREAKERS

Name	No	Builders	Commissioned
EISVOGEL	A 1401	J G Hitzler, Lauenburg	11 Mar 1961
EISBÄR	A 1402	J G Hitzler, Lauenburg	1 Nov 1961

Displacement, tons: 560 standard
Dimensions, feet (metres): 125.3 × 31.2 × 15.1 *(38.2 × 9.5 × 4.6)*
Main machinery: 2 Maybach 12-cyl diesels; 2400 hp(m) *(1.76 MW)*; 2 shafts
Speed, knots: 13
Complement: 16

Comment: Launched on 28 April and 9 June 1960 respectively. Icebreaking tugs of limited capability. Civilian manned. Fitted for but not with one Bofors 40 mm/70.

EISVOGEL   *8/1993, Horst Dehnst*

ARMY

Note: Four companies of River Engineers are located along the River Rhine at Krefeld, Koblenz, Neuwied and Wiesbaden. Each company is provided with Landing Craft (Mannheim 59 or Bodan class), River Patrol Craft and one River Tug and each has its own numbered series: 80101-31, 80111-31, 85011-31, 85111-31.

14 MANNHEIM 59 CLASS (RIVER LANDING CRAFT) (LCMs)

Displacement, tons: 89 standard
Dimensions, feet (metres): 89.9 × 23.6 × 3.9 *(27.4 × 7.2 × 1.2)*
Main machinery: 2 MWM RHS518A diesels; 440 hp(m) *(323 kW)*; 2 shafts
Speed, knots: 9
Complement: 9
Guns: 4—7.62 mm MGs.

Comment: Ordered in April 1959 and built by Schiffs und Motorenwerke AG, Mannheim. Normal load 70 tons but can carry 90 tons. One transferred to Tonga in 1989. Eight paid off for sale in August 1991.

LCM 85131   *9/1991, van Ginderen Collection*

13 BODAN CLASS (RIVER LANDING CRAFT) (LCMs)

Dimensions, feet (metres): 98.4 × 19 *(30 × 5.8)* (loading area)
Main machinery: 4 diesels; 596 hp(m) *(438 kW)*; 4 Schottel props
Guns: 1 Oerlikon 20 mm.

Comment: Built of 12 pontoons, provided with bow and stern ramp. Can carry 90 tons.

BODAN 85031   *6/1992, Horst Dehnst*

12 RIVER PATROL CRAFT

Dimensions, feet (metres): 82 × 12.5 × 3.3 *(25 × 3.8 × 1)*
Main machinery: 2 MWM RHS518A diesels; 440 hp(m) *(323 kW)*; 2 shafts
Speed, knots: 20.5
Complement: 7
Guns: 4—12.7 mm Browning MGs.

Comment: Resemble the Belgian river patrol craft *Liberation*.

S 80102   *1991, van Ginderen Collection*

4 RIVER TUGS

T 80001   T 80101   T 85001   T 85101

Dimensions, feet (metres): 91.8 × 19.4 × 3.9 *(28 × 5.9 × 1.2)*
Main machinery: 2 KHD SBF 12M716 diesels; 760 hp(m) *(559 kW)*; 2 shafts
Speed, knots: 11
Complement: 7
Guns: 2—7.62 mm MGs.

T 80101   *8/1984, Gunnar Olsen*

COAST GUARD

(Bundesgrenzschutz—See)

Notes: (1) This police force consists of about 600 men. Headquarters is at Neustadt and bases at Warnemünde, Sassnitz, Karnin, Stralsund and Frankfurt/Oder.
(2) A maritime section of the anti-terrorist force GSG 9 is attached to the Bundesgrenzschutz.
(3) Craft have blue hulls and white superstructures.

3 KONDOR I CLASS (COASTAL PATROL CRAFT)

BOLTENHAGEN BG 31 (ex-GS 09, ex-G 443)   **AHRENSHOOP** BG 33 (ex-GS 08, ex-G 415)
KÜHLUNGSBORN BG 32 (ex-GS 07, ex-G 445)

Displacement, tons: 327 standard; 377 full load
Dimensions, feet (metres): 170.3 × 23.3 × 7.2 *(51.9 × 7.1 × 2.2)*
Main machinery: 2 Russki Kolomna Type 40-D diesels; 4408 hp(m) *(3.24 MW)* sustained; 2 shafts
Speed, knots: 20
Complement: 24
Guns: 2—25 mm (twin) automatic (can be carried).
Radars: Navigation; Racal Decca 360; I band.

Comment: Built by Peenewerft, Wolgast in 1969-71. Ex-GDR Grenzebrigade Küste (GBK) former minesweepers originally taken over from the Navy. All mining and sonar gear removed. Form 3rd Flotilla based at Warnemünde. Four of the class sold to Tunisia in May 1992 and two to Malta in July 1992.

BOLTENHAGEN   *7/1993, Hartmut Ehlers*

1 BREDSTEDT CLASS (LARGE PATROL CRAFT)

Name	No	Builders	Commissioned
BREDSTEDT	BG 21	Elsflether Werft	24 May 1989

Displacement, tons: 673 full load
Dimensions, feet (metres): 214.6 × 30.2 × 10.5 *(65.4 × 9.2 × 3.2)*
Main machinery: 1 MTU 20V 1163 TB93 diesel; 8325 hp(m) *(6.12 MW)* sustained; 1 shaft; bow thruster; 1 auxiliary diesel generator; 1 motor
Speed, knots: 25 (12 on motor). **Range, miles:** 2000 at 25 kts; 7000 at 10 kts
Complement: 18 plus 4 spare
Guns: 1 Bofors 40 mm/70; 90° elevation; 300 rounds/minute to 12 km *(6.5 nm)*; weight of shell 0.96 kg.
Radars: Surface search: Racal AC 2690 BT; I band.
Navigation: Racal ARPA; I band.
Helicopters: Platform for 1 light.

Comment: Ordered 27 November 1987, laid down 3 March 1988 and launched 18 December 1988. An Avon Searider rigid inflatable craft can be lowered by a stern ramp. A second RIB on the port side is launched by crane. Based in the German Bight.

BREDSTEDT   *6/1991, Harald Carstens*

3 SASSNITZ CLASS (TYPE 153) (LARGE PATROL CRAFT)

Name	No	Builders	Commissioned
NEUSTRELITZ	BG 22	Peenewerft, Wolgast	31 July 1990
(ex-*Sassnitz*)	(ex-P 6165, ex-591)		
SELLIN	BG 23 (ex-592)	Peenewerft, Wolgast	2 Oct 1990
BINZ	BG 24 (ex-593)	Peenewerft, Wolgast	23 Dec 1990

Displacement, tons: 369 full load
Dimensions, feet (metres): 160.4 oa; 147.6 wl × 28.5 × 7.2 *(48.9; 45 × 8.7 × 2.2)*
Main machinery: 2 MTU 12V 595 TE90 diesels; 8800 hp(m) *(6.48 MW)* sustained; 2 shafts
Speed, knots: 25. **Range, miles:** 2400 at 20 kts
Complement: 33 (7 officers)
Guns: 1 Bofors 40 mm/70; 90° elevation; 300 rounds/minute to 12 km *(6.5 nm)*; weight of shell 0.96 kg.
Radars: Surface search: Racal AC 2690 BT; I band.
Navigation: Racal ARPA; I band.

Comment: Ex-GDR designated Balcom 10 and seen for the first time in the Baltic in August 1988. The original intention was to build up to 50 for the USSR, Poland and the GDR. In 1991 the first three were transferred to the Border Guard, based at Neustadt. *Neustrelitz* fitted with German engines and electronics in 1992/93. The original design had the SS-N-25 SSM and three engines. Three hulls transferred to Poland for completion at Gdynia. *Sellin* on loan to WTD 71 (weapons trials) in 1993.

NEUSTRELITZ   *1993 German Navy*

7 NEUSTADT CLASS (LARGE PATROL CRAFT)

Name	No		Name	No
NEUSTADT	BG 11		ALSFELD	BG 16
BAD BRAMSTEDT	BG 12		BAYREUTH	BG 17
DUDERSTADT	BG 14		ROSENHEIM	BG 18
ESCHWEGE	BG 15			

Displacement, tons: 218 full load
Dimensions, feet (metres): 127.1 × 23 × 5 *(38.5 × 7 × 2.2)*
Main machinery: 2 MTU MD diesels; 6000 hp(m) *(4.41 MW)*; 1 MWM diesel; 685 hp(m) *(500 kW)*; 3 shafts
Speed, knots: 30. **Range, miles:** 450 at 27 kts
Complement: 24
Guns: 1 Bofors 40 mm/70; 90° elevation; 300 rounds/minute to 12 km *(6.5 nm)*; weight of shell 0.96 kg.
Radars: Surface search: Selenia ARP 1645; I band.
Navigation: Kelvin Hughes KH 17/9; I band.

Comment: All built between 1969 and late 1970 by Lürssen, Vegesack. Form two flotillas: BG 11-14 the first and BG 15-18 the second. BG 13 was sold to Mauritania in February 1990. The after gun mounting has been removed from all.

BAD BRAMSTEDT   *6/1993, Stefan Terzibaschitsch*

2 RIVER PATROL CRAFT

BG 6 (ex-*AM 1* (Y 1671))   **BG 7** (ex-*ST 2* (Y 1670))

Comment: Former river engineers craft acquired in May 1978. Length 15 m and capable of about 6 kts.

BG 6   *10/1993, Hartmut Ehlers*

4 BREMSE CLASS (TYPE GB 23) (INSHORE PATROL CRAFT)

Name	No		Name	No
PRIGNITZ	BG 61 (ex-G 20, ex-GS 31)		ALTMARK	BG 63 (ex-G 21, ex-GS 21)
UCKERMARK	BG 62 (ex-G 34, ex-GS 23)		BÖRDE	BG 64 (ex-G 35, ex-GS 50)

Displacement, tons: 42 full load
Dimensions, feet (metres): 74.1 × 15.4 × 3.6 *(22.6 × 4.7 × 1.1)*
Main machinery: 2 DM 6VD 18/5 AL-1 diesels; 1020 hp(m) *(750 kW)*; 2 shafts
Speed, knots: 14
Complement: 6
Guns: 2—14.5 mm (twin) MGs can be carried.
Radars: Navigation: TSR 333; I band.

Comment: Built in 1971-72 for the ex-GDR GBK. BG 61 and 62 based at Warnemünde, BG 63 and 64 at Sassnitz. Five of the class sold to Tunisia, two to Malta and two to Jordan, all in 1992.

UCKERMARK   *6/1993, van Ginderen Collection*

4 TYPE SAB 12 (HARBOUR PATROL CRAFT)

Name	No		Name	No
VOGTLAND	BG 51 (ex-G 56, ex-GS 17)		SPREEWALD	BG 53 (ex-G 51, ex-GS 16)
RHON	BG 52 (ex-G 53, ex-GS 26)		ODERBRUCH	BG 54

Comment: Ex-GDR MAB 12 craft based at Karnin, Stralsund and Frankfurt/Oder. Five sold to Cyprus in 1992.

VOGTLAND   *5/1993, Hartmut Ehlers*

1 ICEBREAKING TUG (TYPE 724)

Name	No	Builders	Commissioned
RETTIN	BG 5	Mützelfeldwerft	3 Dec 1976

Measurement, tons: 120 grt
Dimensions, feet (metres): 73.8 × 21.7 × 9.5 *(22.5 × 6.6 × 2.9)*
Main machinery: 2 MWM diesels; 590 hp(m) *(434 kW)*; 2 Voith-Schneider props
Speed, knots: 9
Complement: 4
Radars: Navigation: Racal Decca MA 180; I band.

Comment: Launched 29 October 1976. Bollard pull, 7.5 tons. Carries firefighting equipment.

RETTIN   *7/1992, German Coast Guard*

FISHERY PROTECTION AND RESEARCH SHIPS

(Operated by Ministry of Agriculture and Fisheries)

WARNEMUNDE of 399 tons and 18 kts. Ex-*Kondor I* class completed 1969
FRITHJOF of 2150 tons and 16 kts. Completed September 1968
MEERKATZE of 2250 tons and 15 kts. Completed December 1977
SEEFALKE of 1820 tons gross and 20 kts. Completed August 1981
SOLEA of 340 tons and 12 kts. Completed May 1974
UTHÖRN of 200 tons and 10 kts. Completed June 1982
WALTHER HERWIG of 2500 tons and 15 kts. Completed October 1972
HEINCKE of 1322 tons gross and 13 kts. Completed in June 1990

Comment: First four are Fishery Protection ships serving the fleet in the North Atlantic. *Seefalcke* has a helicopter platform. The remainder are research ships carrying scientists. A new ship ordered in 1991 from Peenewerft should complete in 1994.

MEERKATZE   *11/1992, van Ginderen Collection*

CIVILIAN SURVEY AND RESEARCH SHIPS

Note: The following ships operate for the Bundesamt für Seeschiff-fahrt und Hydrographie (BSH), either under the Ministry of Transport or the Ministry of Research and Technology (*Polarstern, Meteor, Poseidon, Sonne* and *Alkor*).

ATAIR (survey), **ALKOR** (research), **WEGA** (survey) 1050 tons, diesel-electric, 11.5 kts. Complement 16 plus 6 scientists. Built by Krögerwerft, completed 3 August 1987, 2 May 1990 and 26 October 1990 respectively
METEOR (research) 97.5 × 16.5 × 4.8 m, diesel-electric, 14 kts, range 10 000 nm. Complement 33 plus 29 research staff. Completed by Schlichting, Travemünde 15 March 1986
KOMET (survey and research) 1535 grt, speed 15 kts. Complement 42 plus 4 scientists. Completed 26 August 1969 by Jadewerft
GAUSS (survey and research) 1813 grt, completed 6 May 1980 by Schlichting, speed 13.5 kts, complement 19 + 12 scientists. Modernised 1985
CARL FR GAUSS (survey) 490 tons; speed 19 kts. Kondor II hull built at Peenewerft in 1976
DENEB (ex-*Wega*) (survey) 157 grt; speed 10 kts. Complement 12. Completed 4 May 1962 by Schlichting
POLARSTERN (polar research) 10 878 grt; completed 1982
POSEIDON (research) 1049 grt; completed 1976
SONNE (research) 1200 grt; completed 1990

METEOR   *1991, Harald Carstens*

POLARSTERN   *12/1993, Robert Pabst*

GAUSS   *4/1993, van Ginderen Collection*

CUSTOMS

Notes: (1) Operated by Ministry of Finance with a total of over 100 craft. Green hulls with grey superstructure and sometimes carry machine guns.
(2) Seaward patrol craft include *Hamburg, Bremerhaven, Schleswig-Holstein, Emden, Kniepsand, Alte Liebe, Priwall, Glückstadt, Helgoland, Oldenburg, Laboe, Ner Darchau* and *Hohwacht.*

PRIWALL   *8/1992, Maritime Photographic*

POLICE

Notes: (1) Under the control of regional governments. Blue hulls with white superstructure.
(2) There are 11 seaward patrol craft: *Wasserschutzpolizei 5, WSP 1* and *4, Bremen 2, 3* and *9, Helgoland, Sylt, Fehmarn, Birknack* and *Falshöft.*
(3) Harbour craft include *Dithmarchen, Probstei, Schwansen, Vossbrook, Angela, Brunswick, Habicht.*

WSP 4   *11/1991, Antonio Moreno*

WATER AND NAVIGATION BOARD

Notes: (1) Comes under the Ministry of Transport. Most ships have black hulls with black/red/yellow stripes.
(2) Four icebreakers: *Polarstern, Hanse, Max Waldeck* and *Stephan Jantzen* (ex-GDR).
(3) Eight buoy tenders: *Walter Körte, Kurt Burkowitz, Otto Treplin, Gustav Meyer, Bruno Illing, Konrad Meisel, Barsemeister Brehme, J G Repsold.*
(4) Five oil recovery ships: *Scharhörn, Oland, Nordsee, Mellum, Kiel.*
(5) Several SKB 64 types (ex-GDR).

STEPHAN JANTZEN   *8/1993, Hartmut Ehlers*

GHANA

Headquarters' Appointment	Personnel	Bases	Mercantile Marine
Commander, Navy: Rear Admiral Tom Kwesi Annan	(a) 1994: 973 (b) Voluntary service	Sekondi (Western Naval Command) Tema (near Accra) (Eastern Naval Command)	*Lloyd's Register of Shipping:* 164 vessels of 118 388 tons gross

PATROL FORCES

2 LÜRSSEN PB 57 CLASS (FAST ATTACK CRAFT—GUN)

Name	*No*	*Builders*	*Commissioned*
ACHIMOTA	P 28	Lürssen, Vegesack	27 Mar 1981
YOGAGA	P 29	Lürssen, Vegesack	27 Mar 1981

Displacement, tons: 389 full load
Dimensions, feet (metres): 190.6 × 25 × 9.2 *(58.1 × 7.6 × 2.8)*
Main machinery: 3 MTU 16V 538 TB91 diesels; 9210 hp(m) *(6.78 MW)* sustained; 3 shafts
Speed, knots: 30
Complement: 55 (5 officers)
Guns: 1 OTO Melara 3 in *(76 mm)* compact; 85° elevation; 85 rounds/minute to 16 km *(8.6 nm)* anti-surface; 12 km *(6.5 nm)* anti-air; weight of shell 6 kg; 250 rounds.
1 Breda 40 mm/70; 85° elevation; 300 rounds/minute to 12.5 km *(6.8 nm)* anti-surface; weight of shell 0.96 kg; 750 rounds.
Fire control: LIOD optronic director.
Radars: Surface search/fire control: Thomson-CSF Canopus A; I/J band.
Navigation: Decca TM 1226C; I band.

Comment: Ordered in 1977. *Yogaga* completed a major overhaul at Swan Hunter's Wallsend, Tyneside yard 8 May 1989. *Achimota* started a similar refit at CMN Cherbourg in May 1991 and was joined by *Yogaga* for repairs in late 1991. Both completed by August 1992. Employed on Fishery Protection duties.

2 LÜRSSEN FPB 45 CLASS (FAST ATTACK CRAFT—GUN)

Name	*No*	*Builders*	*Commissioned*
DZATA	P 26	Lürssen, Vegesack	4 Dec 1979
SEBO	P 27	Lürssen, Vegesack	2 May 1980

Displacement, tons: 269 full load
Dimensions, feet (metres): 147.3 × 23 × 8.9 *(44.9 × 7 × 2.7)*
Main machinery: 2 MTU 16V 538 TB91 diesels; 6140 hp(m) *(4.5 MW)* sustained; 2 shafts
Speed, knots: 27. Range, miles: 1800 at 16 kts; 700 at 25 kts
Complement: 45 (5 officers)
Guns: 2 Bofors 40 mm/70; 80° elevation; 300 rounds/minute to 12.5 km *(6.8 nm)*; weight of shell 0.96 kg.
Radars: Surface search: Decca TM 1226C; I band.

Comment: Ordered in 1976. *Dzata* completed a major overhaul at Swan Hunter's Wallsend, Tyneside yard on 8 May 1989. *Sebo* started a similar refit at CMN Cherbourg in May 1991 which completed in August 1992. Employed in Fishery Protection role.

SEBO   *11/1993, G Toremans*

LAND-BASED MARITIME AIRCRAFT

Note: In addition four Skyvan and four Defender aircraft are available for maritime reconnaissance.

Numbers/Type: 2 Fokker F27 400M.
Operational speed: 250 kts *(463 km/h)*.
Service ceiling: 25 000 ft *(7 620 m)*.
Range: 2700 nm *(5000 km)*.
Role/Weapon systems: Operated for coastal surveillance, SAR and shipping control tasks. Sensors: Weather radar. Weapons: Unarmed.

ACHIMOTA   *2/1993, Ghana Navy*

GREECE

Headquarters' Appointments

Chief of National Defence Staff:
Admiral C Limberis
Chief of the Hellenic Navy:
Vice Admiral G Stagas
Deputy Chief of the Hellenic Navy:
Rear Admiral D Paleogiorgos
Commander, Navy Training Command:
Rear Admiral S Kehris
Commander, Navy Logistics Command:
Rear Admiral A Nomikos

Fleet Command

Commander of the Fleet:
Vice Admiral N Themelides
Chief of Staff, Fleet HQ:
Rear Admiral C Torvas

Diplomatic Representation

Naval Attaché in Ankara:
Commander N Kostakis
Naval Attaché in Algiers:
Commander P Stratigis
Naval Attaché in Bonn:
Captain G Voulgarakis
Naval Attaché in Cairo:
Captain G Antonopoulos
Naval Attaché in London:
Captain I Theophanides
Naval Attaché in Paris:
Captain D Hatzidakis
Naval Attaché in Tunis:
Commander I Rakkas
Naval Attaché in Washington:
Captain D Rapantzikos

Personnel

(a) 1994: 19 500 (2900 officers)
(b) Between 19 and 23 months' national service depending on location

Bases

Salamis and Suda Bay

Naval Commands

Commander of the Fleet has under his flag all combatant ships. Navy Logistic Command is responsible for the bases at Salamis and Suda Bay, the Supply Centre and all auxiliary ships. Navy Training Command is in charge of the Naval Officers' Academy, Petty Officers' School, three training centres and a training ship.

Naval Aviation

Alouette III helicopters (No 1 Squadron).
AB 212ASW helicopters (No 2 and 3 Squadrons).
HU-16B Albatros are operated under naval command by mixed Air Force and Navy crews.

Strength of the Fleet

Type	Active	Building (Planned)
Patrol Submarines	8	—
Destroyers	6	—
Frigates	8	3 + 1
Corvettes	5	—
Fast Attack Craft—Missile	16	—
Fast Attack Craft—Torpedo	10	—
Fast Attack Craft—Patrol	5	1
Large Patrol Craft	2	—
Coastal Patrol Craft	3	—
LST/LSD/LSM	10	4
LCUs	6	—
LCTs	2	—
Minor Landing Craft	77	—
Minelayers—Coastal	2	—
Minesweepers—Coastal	14	(3)
Survey and Research Ships	7	—
Support Ship	1	(1)
Training Ships	4	—
Tankers	13	—
Lighthouse Tenders	2	—
Tugs	21	—
Netlayer	1	—
Auxiliary Transports	2	—
Ammunition Ship	1	—

Mercantile Marine

Lloyd's Register of Shipping:
1929 vessels of 29 134 435 tons gross

Naval Districts

Aegean, Ionian and Northern Greece

Prefix to Ships' Names

HS (Hellenic Ship)

DELETIONS

Note: Some of the deleted ships are in unmaintained reserve in anchorages.

Submarines

1993 *Katsonis, Papanikolis*

Destroyers

1991 *Aspis, Velos, Lonchi, Sfendoni*
1992 *Miaoulis, Themistocles* (old)
1993 *Sachtouris, Apostolis, Kriezis* (reserve)
1994 *Kanaris* (reserve)

Frigates

1991 *Aetos*
1992 *Panthir, Ierax, Leon*

Patrol Forces

1991 *E Panagopoulos 1*
1992 *Adamidis*
1993 *E Panagopoulos 2 and 3*

Amphibious Forces

1991 *Lesbos* (old), *Kassos, Karpathos*
1992 *Kimolos, Sifnos, Skiathos, Kithnos*
1993 *Grigoropoulos, Daniolos*

Auxiliaries

1991 *Argo* (sold), *Aegeon, Arhikelefstis Stassis*
1992 *Kastoria*

PENNANT LIST

Submarines

S 110	Glavkos
S 111	Nereus
S 112	Triton
S 113	Proteus
S 116	Posydon
S 117	Amphitrite
S 118	Okeanos
S 119	Pontos

Destroyers

D 213	Kountouriotis
D 215	Tompazis
D 218	Kimon
D 219	Nearchos
D 220	Formion
D 221	Themistocles

Frigates

F 450	Elli
F 451	Limnos
F 452	Hydra
F 453	Spetsai (bldg)
F 454	Psara (bldg)
F 455	Salamis (bldg)
F 456	Epirus
F 457	Thrace
F 458	Makedonia
F 459	Adrias
F 460	Aegeon
F 461	Navarino

Corvettes

P 62	Niki
P 63	Doxa
P 64	Eleftheria
P 65	Carteria
P 66	Agon

Patrol Forces

P 14	Anthipoploiarhos Anninos
P 15	Ipoploiarhos Arliotis
P 16	Ipoploiarhos Konidis
P 17	Ipoploiarhos Batsis
P 18	Armatolos
P 19	Navmachos
P 20	Antiploiarhos Laskos
P 21	Plotarhis Blessas
P 22	Ipoploiarhos Mikonios
P 23	Ipoploiarhos Troupakis
P 24	Simeoforos Kavaloudis
P 25	Anthipoploiarhos Kostakos
P 26	Ipoploiarhos Deyiannis
P 27	Simeoforos Xenos
P 28	Simeoforos Simitzopoulos
P 29	Simeoforos Starakis
P 30	Antipliarhos Pezopoulos
P 50	Hesperos
P 51	Ipopliarhos Votsis
P 52	Kentauros
P 53	Kyklon
P 54	Lelaps
P 55	Skorpios
P 56	Tyfon
P 57	Pirpolitis
P 61	Polemistis
P 196	Andromeda
P 198	Kyknos
P 199	Pigasos
P 228	Toxotis
P 229	Tolmi
P 230	Ormi
P 267	Dilos
P 268	Knossos
P 269	Lindos
P 286	Diopos Antoniou
P 287	Kelefstis Stamou

Amphibious Forces

L 104	Inouse
L 116	Kos
L 144	Siros
L 153	Nafkratoussa
L 154	Ikaria (old)
L 157	Rodos (old)

L 164	I Roussen
L 165	I Krystalidis
L 167	Ios
L 168	Sikinos
L 169	Irakleia
L 170	Folegandros
L 171	Kriti
L 173	Samos
L 174	Chios (bldg)
L 175	Ikaria (bldg)
L 176	Lesbos (bldg)
L 177	Rodos (bldg)
L 178	Naxos
L 179	Paros
L 185	Kithera
L 189	Milos

Minelayers

N 04	Aktion
N 05	Amvrakia

Minesweepers

M 202	Atalanti
M 205	Antiopi
M 206	Faedra
M 210	Thalia
M 211	Alkyon
M 213	Klio
M 214	Avra
M 240	Pleias
M 241	Kichli
M 242	Kissa
M 246	Aigli
M 247	Dafni
M 248	Aedon
M 254	Niovi

Auxiliaries, Training and Survey Ships

A 74	Aris
A 233	Maistros
A 234	Sorokos
A 307	Thetis
A 359	Ostria

A 373	Hermis
A 375	Zeus
A 376	Orion
A 377	Arethousa
A 407	Antaios
A 408	Atlas
A 409	Acchileus
A 410	Atromitos
A 411	Adamastos
A 412	Aias
A 413	Pilefs
A 414	Ariadni
A 415	Evros
A 416	Ouranos
A 417	Hyperion
A 419	Pandora
A 420	Pandrosos
A 422	Nestor
A 423	Heraklis
A 424	Iason
A 425	Odisseus
A 426	Kiklops
A 427	Danaos
A 428	Kadmos
A 430	Pelops
A 431	Titan
A 432	Gigas
A 433	Kerkini
A 434	Prespa
A 435	Kekrops
A 436	Minos
A 437	Pelias
A 438	Aegeus
A 460	Evrotas
A 461	Arachthos
A 462	Strymon
A 463	Nestos
A 464	Axios
A 465	Yliki
A 466	Trichonis
A 467	Doirani
A 468	Kalliroe
A 469	Stimfalia
A 474	Pytheas
A 475	Doris
A 476	Strabon
A 478	Naftilos
A 479	I Karavoyiannos Theophilopoulos
A 481	St Likoudis

SUBMARINES

8 GLAVKOS CLASS (209 TYPES 1100 and 1200)

Name	No	Builders	Laid down	Launched	Commissioned
GLAVKOS	S 110	Howaldtswerke, Kiel	1 Sep 1968	15 Sep 1970	6 Sep 1971
NEREUS	S 111	Howaldtswerke, Kiel	15 Jan 1969	7 June 1971	10 Feb 1972
TRITON	S 112	Howaldtswerke, Kiel	1 June 1969	14 Oct 1971	8 Aug 1972
PROTEUS	S 113	Howaldtswerke, Kiel	1 Oct 1969	1 Feb 1972	8 Aug 1972
POSYDON	S 116	Howaldtswerke, Kiel	15 Jan 1976	21 Mar 1978	22 Mar 1979
AMPHITRITE	S 117	Howaldtswerke, Kiel	26 Apr 1976	14 June 1978	14 Sep 1979
OKEANOS	S 118	Howaldtswerke, Kiel	1 Oct 1976	16 Nov 1978	15 Nov 1979
PONTOS	S 119	Howaldtswerke, Kiel	25 Jan 1977	21 Mar 1979	29 Apr 1980

Displacement, tons: 1100 surfaced; 1210 (1285, S 112 and 116-119) dived

Dimensions, feet (metres): 178.4; 183.4 (112, 116-119) × 20.3 × 17.9 *(54.4; 55.9 × 6.2 × 5.5)*

Main machinery: Diesel-electric; 4 MTU 12V 493 AZ80 diesels; 2400 hp(m) *(1.76 MW)* sustained; 4 Siemens alternators; 1.7 MW; 1 Siemens motor; 4600 hp(m) *(3.38 MW)* sustained; 1 shaft

Speed, knots: 11 surfaced; 21.5 dived

Complement: 31 (6 officers)

Missiles: McDonnell Douglas Sub Harpoon (after modernisation); active radar homing to 130 km *(70 nm)* at 0.9 Mach; warhead 258 kg. Can be discharged from 4 tubes only.

Torpedoes: 8—21 in *(533 mm)* bow tubes. 14 probably AEG SST 4; wire-guided; active homing to 13 km *(7 nm)* at 35 kts; passive homing to 28 km *(15 nm)* at 23 kts; warhead 260 kg. Swim-out discharge. Probably to be replaced by AEG SEEAL 3.

Countermeasures: ESM: Argo AR-700-S5 (after modernisation). Thomson-CSF DR 2000U (unmodernised); radar warning.

Fire control: Signaal (S 116-S 119). Unisys/Kanaris with UYK-44 computers (after modernisation). Kanaris (unmodernised).

Radars: Surface search: Thomson-CSF Calypso II; I band.

Sonars: Atlas Elektronik CSU 3-2 (unmodernised); hull-mounted; active/passive search and attack; medium frequency.
Atlas Elektronik PRS-3-4; passive ranging.
Atlas Elektronik CSU 83-90 (DBQS-21) (after modernisation); flank array; passive search; low frequency.
Atlas Elektronik CSU-3-4 (S 112, 116-119); hull-mounted; active/passive search and attack; medium frequency.
Thomson Sintra DUUX 2; passive ranging.

Programmes: Designed by Ingenieurkontor, Lübeck for construction by Howaldtswerke, Kiel and sale by Ferrostaal, Essen all acting as a consortium.

Modernisation: Contract signed 5 May 1989 with HDW and Ferrostaal to implement a Neptune update programme to bring first four up to the same standard as the others and along the same lines as the German S 206A class. Includes Sub Harpoon, flank array sonar, Unisys FCS, Sperry Mk 29 Mod 3 inertial navigation system, Magnavox GPS, Omega and SATNAV, and Argo ESM. *Triton* completed refit at Kiel in May 1993, remainder starting with *Proteus* are being done at Salamis between 1993 and 1996 in a Synchrolift purchased by the Navy. A quarter of the cost is covered by German Military Aid.

TRITON (after modernisation)   *9/1993, Hellenic Navy*

Structure: A single-hull design with two ballast tanks and fwd and after trim tanks. Fitted with snort and remote machinery control. The single screw is slow revving. Very high capacity batteries with GRP lead-acid cells and battery cooling—by Wilh Hagen and VARTA. Diving depth, 250 m *(820 ft)*. Fitted with two periscopes.

Operational: Endurance, 50 days.

DESTROYERS

4 KIMON (CHARLES F ADAMS) CLASS

Name	No	Builders	Laid down	Launched	Commissioned	Recommissioned
KIMON (ex-*Semmes*)	D 218 (ex-DDG 18)	Avondale Marine Ways	18 Aug 1960	20 May 1961	10 Dec 1962	12 Sep 1992
NEARCHOS (ex-*Waddell*)	D 219 (ex-DDG 24)	Todd Shipyards	6 Feb 1962	26 Feb 1963	28 Aug 1964	1 Oct 1992
FORMION (ex-*Miltiadis*, ex-*Strauss*)	D 220 (ex-DDG 16)	New York Shipbuilding	27 Dec 1960	9 Dec 1961	20 Apr 1963	1 Oct 1992
THEMISTOCLES (ex-*Konon*, ex-*Berkeley*)	D 221 (ex-DDG 15)	New York Shipbuilding	1 June 1960	29 July 1961	15 Dec 1962	1 Oct 1992

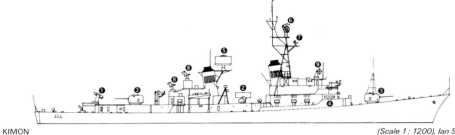

Displacement, tons: 3370 standard; 4825 full load
Dimensions, feet (metres): 437 × 47 × 15.6; 21 (sonar)
(133.2 × 14.3 × 4.8; 6.4)
Main machinery: 4 boilers (Foster-Wheeler in D 219, 221, Combustion Engineering in D 218, 220); 2 turbines (General Electric in D 218, 220, Westinghouse in D 219, 221); 70 000 hp *(52.2 MW)*; 2 shafts
Speed, knots: 30. **Range, miles:** 6000 at 15 kts; 1600 at 30 kts
Complement: 340 (22 officers)

Missiles: SSM: 6 McDonnell Douglas Harpoon; active radar homing to 130 km *(70 nm)* at 0.9 Mach; warhead 227 kg.
SAM: 34 GDC Standard SM-1MR; command guidance; semi-active radar homing to 46 km *(25 nm)* at 2 Mach; height 150-60 000 ft *(45.7-18 288 m)*.
1 single Mk 13 launcher ❶; can load, direct, and fire about 6 missiles per minute. There are 40 missiles carried. 6 Harpoons are stored in the magazines as part of the load.
A/S: Honeywell ASROC Mk 16 octuple launcher ❷; inertial guidance to 1.6-10 km *(1-5.4 nm)*; payload Mk 46.
Guns: 2 FMC 5 in *(127 nm)*/54 Mk 42 ❸; 85° elevation; 20-40 rounds/minute to 24 km *(13 nm)*; weight of shell 32 kg.
4—12.7 mm MGs.
Torpedoes: 6—324 mm Mk 32 (2 triple) tubes ❹. Honeywell Mk 46; anti-submarine; active/passive homing to 11 km *(5.9 nm)* at 40 kts; warhead 44 kg.
Countermeasures: Decoys: 4 Loral Hycor SRBOC 6-barrelled fixed Mk 36; IR flares and chaff to 4 km *(2.2 nm)*.
T—Mk-6 Fanfare; torpedo decoy.
ESM/ECM: SLQ 32V(2); radar warning.
Combat data systems: Links 11 and 14 receive only. SATCOM. NTDS being replaced by Signaal STACOS.
Fire control: Mk 68 GFCS. Mk 4 WDS. Mk 70 MFCS. Mk 114 FCS ASW. SYS-1 IADT.
Radars: Air search: Hughes SPS 52B/C ❺; 3D; E/F band; range 439 km *(240 nm)*.
Lockheed SPS 40B/D ❻; E/F band; range 320 km *(175 nm)*.
Surface search: Raytheon SPS 10D/F ❼; G band.
Navigation: Marconi LN 66; I band.
Fire control: Two Raytheon SPG 51D ❽; G/I band.
Lockheed SPG 53A ❾; K band.
Tacan: URN 25/SRN 6. IFF Mk XII.
Sonars: Sangamo SQS 23D; hull-mounted (bow-mounted SQQ 23 Pair in D 219); active search and attack; medium frequency. Being replaced by DE 1191.

Programmes: Leased as part of the Defence Co-operation Agreement signed with the USA on 8 July 1990. *Kimon* recommissioned at Salamis, the remainder in San Diego prior to sailing for Greece in late 1992. A fifth of class *Richard E Byrd* (DDG 23) was towed to Salamis on 12 October 1993 where she is used for spares.

KIMON   *(Scale 1 : 1200), Ian Sturton*

NEARCHOS   *6/1993, H M Steele*

Modernisation: DE 1191 sonars being fitted. A Signaal STACOS command system is to replace NTDS.

Structure: *Nearchos* has a stern anchor because of the sonar Pair arrangement.

NEARCHOS   *5/1993, Maritime Photographic*

KIMON   *6/1993, Hellenic Navy*

2 GEARING (FRAM I) CLASS

Name	No	Builders	Laid down	Launched	Commissioned
KOUNTOURIOTIS (ex-USS *Rupertus* DD 851)	D 213	Bethlehem (Quincy)	2 May 1945	21 Sep 1945	8 Mar 1946
TOMPAZIS (ex-USS *Gurke* DD 783)	D 215	Todd Pacific Shipyards	Oct 1944	15 Feb 1945	12 May 1945

Displacement, tons: 2425 standard; 3500 full load
Dimensions, feet (metres): 390.5 × 41.2 × 19
(119 × 12.6 × 5.8)
Main machinery: 4 Babcock & Wilcox boilers; 600 psi
(43.3 kg/cm sq); 850°F *(454°C)*; 2 Westinghouse turbines;
60 000 hp *(45 MW)*; 2 shafts
Speed, knots: 32.5. **Range, miles:** 4800 at 15 kts
Complement: 269 (16 officers)

Missiles: SSM: 4 McDonnell Douglas Harpoon (not in D 216-
217) ❶; active radar homing to 130 km *(70 nm)* at 0.9 Mach;
warhead 227 kg.
SAM: Portable Redeye; shoulder-launched; short range.
A/S: Honeywell ASROC Mk 112 octuple launcher ❷; inertial guidance to 10 km *(5.4 nm)*. Mk 46 torpedo; active/passive homing to 11 km *(5.9 nm)* at 40 kts; warhead 45 kg.
Guns: 4 USN 5 in *(127 mm)*/38 (2 twin) Mk 38 ❸; 85° elevation;
15 rounds/minute to 17 km *(9 nm)* anti-surface; 11 km
(5.9 nm) anti-aircraft; weight of shell 25 kg.
1 OTO Melara 3 in *(76 mm)*/62 compact aft ❹; 85° elevation;
85 rounds/minute to 16 km *(8.6 nm)* anti-surface; 12 km
(6.5 nm) anti-aircraft; weight of shell 6 kg.
1 Bofors 40 mm/70 (D 216-217); 90° elevation; 300 rounds/
minute to 12 km *(6.5 nm)*; weight of shell 2.4 kg.
2—12.7 mm MGs.
Torpedoes: 6—324 mm Mk 32 (2 triple) tubes ❺. Honeywell
Mk 46; anti-submarine; active/passive homing to 11 km
(5.9 nm) at 40 kts; warhead 44 kg.
Depth charges: 2 racks.
Countermeasures: Decoys: 2 Loral Hycor SRBOC fixed triple
6-barrelled chaff launchers; range 1-4 km *(0.6-2.2 nm)*.
ESM: WLR-1; radar warning.
ECM: ULQ-6; jammer.
Fire control: Mk 37 GFCS. Elsag NA 21/30.
Radars: Air search: Westinghouse SPS 37 (D 215) ❻; B/C band;
range 556 km *(300 nm)*.
Lockheed SPS 40 (D 213); E/F band; range 320 km *(175 nm)*.
Surface search: Raytheon/Sylvania SPS 10 ❼; G band.
Navigation: Decca; I band.
Fire control: Western Electric Mk 25 ❽; I/J band.
Selenia RTN 10X ❾; I/J band; range 40 km *(22 nm)*.
Sonars: Sangamo SQS 23; hull-mounted; active search and
attack; medium frequency.

KOUNTOURIOTIS
(Scale 1 : 1200), Ian Sturton

KOUNTOURIOTIS
9/1992, Gilbert Gyssels

Programmes: From USA: D 213, 10 July 1973 (sold 11 July
1978); D 215, by sale 17 Mar 1977.
Modernisation: Major modernisation programme in 1987-88.
Included Harpoon, OTO Melara 76 mm/62 gun placed aft and
a new FCS (NA-30 or NA-21). Harpoon is not always carried.

SQS 23 was to have been replaced by DE 1191 but the new
sonars are now being fitted in the Kimon class.
Operational: To be paid off by the end of 1994. Two others (D
212 and D 217) are in reserve.

FRIGATES

1 + 3 HYDRA CLASS (MEKO 200HN)

Name	No	Builders	Laid down	Launched	Commissioned
HYDRA	F 452	Blohm & Voss, Hamburg	17 Dec 1990	25 June 1991	12 Nov 1992
SPETSAI	F 453	Blohm & Voss/Hellenic Shipyards, Skaramanga	11 Aug 1992	9 Dec 1993	June 1995
PSARA	F 454	Hellenic Shipyards, Skaramanga	12 Dec 1993	Sep 1994	July 1996
SALAMIS	F 455	Hellenic Shipyards, Skaramanga	Sep 1994	Aug 1995	Aug 1997

Displacement, tons: 2710 light; 3200 full load
Dimensions, feet (metres): 383.9; 357.6 (wl) × 48.6 × 13.5
(117; 109 × 14.8 × 4.1)
Main machinery: CODOG; 2 GE LM 2500 gas turbines;
60 000 hp *(44.76 MW)* sustained; 2 MTU 20V 956 TB82 die-
sels; 10 420 hp(m) *(7.66 MW)* sustained; 2 shafts; cp props
Speed, knots: 31 gas; 20 diesel. **Range, miles:** 4100 at 16 kts
Complement: 173 (22 officers) plus 16 flag staff

Missiles: SSM: 8 McDonnell Douglas Harpoon Block 1C; 2 quad
launchers ❶; active radar homing to 130 km *(70 nm)* at
0.9 Mach; warhead 227 kg.
SAM: Raytheon NATO Sea Sparrow Mk 48 Mod 2A vertical
launcher ❷; 16 missiles; semi-active radar homing to 14.6 km
(8 nm) at 2.5 Mach; warhead 39 kg.
Guns: 1 FMC Mk 45 Mod 2A 5 in *(127 mm)*/54 ❸; dual purpose.
2 GD/GE Vulcan Phalanx 20 mm Mk 15 Mod 12 ❹; 6 barrels
per mounting; 3000 rounds/minute combined to 1.5 km.
Torpedoes: 6—324 mm Mk 32 Mod 5 (2 triple) tubes ❺. Honey-
well Mk 46; anti-submarine; active/passive homing to 11 km
(5.9 nm) at 40 kts; warhead 44 kg.
Countermeasures: Decoys: 4 Mk 36 Mod 2 SRBOC chaff
launchers ❻.
SLQ-25 Nixie; torpedo decoy.
ESM: Argo AR 700; Telegon 10; intercept.
ECM: Argo APECS II; jammer.
Combat data systems: Signaal STACOS Mod 2; Links 11 and 14.
Fire control: Two Signaal Mk 73 Mod 1 (for SAM). Vesta Helo
transponder with data link for OTHT. SAR-8 IR search. SWG 1
A(V) Harpoon LCS.
Radars: Air search: Signaal MW 08 ❼; 3D; F/G band.
Air Surface search: Signaal/Magnavox; DA 08 ❽, F band.
Navigation: Racal Decca 2690 BT; ARPA; I band.
Fire Control: 2 Signaal STIR ❾; I/J/K band.
IFF: Mk XII Mod 4.
Sonars: Raytheon SQS-56/DE 1160; hull-mounted and VDS.

Helicopters: 1 Sikorsky S-70B6 Seahawk ❿ (from 1995).

Programmes: Decision to buy four Meko 200 Mod 3HN
announced on 18 April 1988. West German Government 'offset' of tanks and aircraft went with the sale, and the electronics
and some of the weapon systems are being secured through
US FMS credits. The first ship ordered 10 February 1989 built
by Blohm & Voss, Hamburg and the remainder ordered 10 May
1989 at Hellenic Shipyards, Skaramanga, with German technical assistance. Programme has been delayed by financial problems at Hellenic Shipyards in 1992 and some of the
prefabrication of *Spetsai* has been done in Hamburg.
Structure: The design follows the Portuguese Vasco da Gama
class. All steel fin stabilisers.

HYDRA
(Scale 1 : 1200), Ian Sturton

HYDRA
6/1992, Hartmut Ehlers

HYDRA
11/1992, Harald Carstens

4 + 1 ELLI (KORTENAER) CLASS

Name	No
ELLI (ex-*Pieter Florisz* F 812)	F 450
LIMNOS (ex-*Witte de With* F 813)	F 451
AEGEON (ex-*Banckert* F 810)	F 460
ADRIAS (ex-*Callenburgh* F 808)	F 459
NAVARINO (ex-*Van Kinsbergen* F 809)	F 461

Builders	Laid down	Launched	Commissioned
Koninklijke Maatschappij de Schelde, Flushing	1 July 1977	15 Dec 1979	10 Oct 1981
Koninklijke Maatschappij de Schelde, Flushing	13 June 1978	27 Oct 1979	18 Sep 1982
Koninklijke Maatschappij de Schelde, Flushing	25 Feb 1976	13 July 1978	29 Oct 1980
Koninklijke Maatschappij de Schelde, Flushing	30 June 1975	12 Mar 1977	26 July 1979
Koninklijke Maatschappij de Schelde, Flushing	2 Sep 1975	16 Apr 1977	24 Apr 1980

Displacement, tons: 3050 standard; 3630 full load
Dimensions, feet (metres): 428 × 47.9 × 20.3 (screws)
  (130.5 × 14.6 × 6.2)
Main machinery: COGOG; 2 RR Olympus TM3B gas turbines;
  50 880 hp *(39.7 MW)* sustained; 2 RR Tyne RM1C gas tur-
  bines; 9900 hp *(7.4 MW)* sustained; 2 shafts; cp props
Speed, knots: 30. **Range, miles:** 4700 at 16 kts
Complement: 176 (17 officers)

Missiles: SSM: 8 McDonnell Douglas Harpoon (2 quad) launchers ❶; active radar homing to 130 km *(70 nm)* at 0.9 Mach;
  warhead 227 kg; 16 missiles.
SAM: Raytheon NATO Sea Sparrow ❷; 24 missiles; semi-active
  radar homing to 14.6 km *(8 nm)* at 2.5 Mach; warhead 39 kg.
  Portable Redeye; shoulder-launched; short range.
Guns: 2 OTO Melara 3 in *(76 mm)/*62 compact ❸; 85° elevation;
  85 rounds/minute to 16 km *(8.6 nm)* anti-surface; 12 km
  (6.5 nm) anti-aircraft; weight of shell 6 kg.
  2 GE/GD Vulcan Phalanx 20 mm Mk 15 6-barreled ❹; 90°
  elevation; 3000 rounds/minute combined to 1.5 km.
Torpedoes: 4—324 mm Mk 32 (2 twin) tubes ❺. 16 Honeywell
  Mk 46 Mod 1/2; anti-submarine; active/passive homing to
  11 km *(5.9 nm)* at 40 kts; warhead 44 kg.
Countermeasures: Decoys: 2 Loral Hycor Mk 36 SRBOC chaff
  launchers.
  ESM: Elettronika Sphinx; radar warning.
  ECM: Jammer.
Combat data systems: Signaal SEWACO II action data auto-
  mation; Links 10 and 11.
Radars: Air search: Signaal LW 08 ❻; D band; range 264 km
  (145 nm) for 2 m² target.
  Surface search: Signaal ZW 06 ❼; I band; range 26 km *(14 nm)*.
  Fire control: Signaal WM 25 ❽; I/J band; range 46 km *(25 nm)*.
  Signaal STIR ❾; I/J/K band; range 140 km *(76 nm)* for 1 m²
  target.
Sonars: Canadian Westinghouse SQS 505; hull-mounted; active
  search and attack; 7 kHz.

Helicopters: 2 AB 212ASW ❿.

Programmes: A contract was signed with the Netherlands on 15
  September 1980 for the purchase of one of the Kortenaer class

building for the Netherlands' Navy, and an option on a second
of class, which was taken up 7 June 1981. A second contract,
signed on 9 November 1992, transferred three more of the
class. Recommissioning dates for the second batch are
Aegeon 14 May 1993, *Adrias* 30 March 1994 and *Navarino* 1
February 1995.
Modernisation: The original plan was to fit one Phalanx CIWS in
place of the after 76 mm gun but for Gulf deployments in

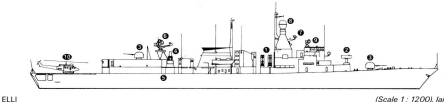

ELLI   *(Scale 1 : 1200), Ian Sturton*

LIMNOS   *10/1992, D Dervissis*

1990-91 the gun was retained and two Phalanx fitted on the
deck above the torpedo tubes. Corvus chaff launchers replaced
by SRBOC (fitted either side of the bridge). The three ex-Nether-
lands ships are being modified to the same standard with a
second 76 mm gun, 2 Phalanx (vice Goalkeeper) and a larger
hangar.
Structure: Hangar is 2 m longer than in Netherlands' ships to
accommodate AB 212ASW helicopters.

3 EPIRUS (KNOX) CLASS

Name	No
EPIRUS (ex-*Connole*)	F 456 (ex-FF 1056)
THRACE (ex-*Trippe*)	F 457 (ex-FF 1075)
MAKEDONIA (ex-*Vreeland*)	F 458 (ex-FF 1068)

Builders	Laid down	Launched	Commissioned	Recommissioned
Avondale Shipyards	23 Mar 1967	20 July 1968	30 Aug 1969	30 Aug 1992
Avondale Shipyards	29 July 1968	1 Nov 1969	19 Sep 1970	30 July 1992
Avondale Shipyards	20 Mar 1968	14 June 1969	13 June 1970	25 July 1992

Displacement, tons: 3011 standard; 3877 full load
Dimensions, feet (metres): 439.6 × 46.8 × 15; 24.8 (sonar)
  (134 × 14.3 × 4.6; 7.8)
Main machinery: 2 Combustion Engineering/Babcock & Wilcox
  boilers; 1200 psi *(84.4 kg/cm sq)*; 950°F *(510°C)*; 1 turbine;
  35 000 hp *(26 MW)*; 1 shaft
Speed, knots: 27. **Range, miles:** 4000 at 22 kts on 1 boiler
Complement: 288 (17 officers)

Missiles: SSM: 8 McDonnell Douglas Harpoon; active radar homing to 130 km *(70 nm)* at 0.9 Mach; warhead 227 kg.
SAM: 4 Stinger or Redeye posts fitted.
A/S: Honeywell ASROC Mk 16 octuple launcher with reload system (has 2 cells modified to fire Harpoon) ❶; inertial guidance
  to 1.6-10 km *(1-5.4 nm)*; payload Mk 46.
Guns: 1 FMC 5 in *(127 mm)/*54 Mk 42 Mod 9 ❷; 85° elevation;
  20-40 rounds/minute to 24 km *(13 nm)* anti-surface; 14 km
  (7.7 nm) anti-aircraft; weight of shell 32 kg.
  1 General Electric/General Dynamics 20 mm/76 6-barrelled
  Mk 15 Vulcan Phalanx ❸; 3000 rounds/minute combined to
  1.5 km. 4—12.7 mm MGs.
Torpedoes: 4—324 mm Mk 32 (2 twin) fixed tubes ❹. 22 Honeywell Mk 46; anti-submarine; active/passive homing to 11 km
  (5.9 nm) at 40 kts; warhead 44 kg.
Countermeasures: Decoys: 2 Loral Hycor SRBOC 6-barrelled
  fixed Mk 36 ❺; IR flares and chaff to 4 km *(2.2 nm)*. T Mk-6
  Fanfare/SLQ-25 Nixie; torpedo decoy. Prairie Masker hull and
  blade rate noise suppression.
ESM/ECM: SLQ 32(V)2 ❻; radar warning. Sidekick modification
  adds jammer and deception system.
Combat data systems: Link 14 receive only.
Fire control: SWG-1A Harpoon LCS. Mk 68 GFCS. Mk 114 ASW
  FCS. Mk 1 target designation system. MMS target acquisition
  sight (for mines, small craft and low flying aircraft).
Radars: Air search: Lockheed SPS 40B ❼; E/F band; range
  320 km *(175 nm)*.
  Surface search: Raytheon SPS 10 or Norden SPS 67 ❽; G band.
  Navigation: Marconi LN 66; I band.
  Fire control: Western Electric SPG 53 ❾; I/J band.
  Tacan: SRN 15. **IFF:** UPX-12.
Sonars: EDO/General Electric SQS 26 CX; bow-mounted; active
  search and attack; medium frequency.
  EDO SQS 35; independent VDS.

Helicopters: 1 AB 212ASW ❿.

Programmes: Officially announced on 11 February 1992 that
  three Knox class would be leased from the US and then transferred to the Hellenic Navy. *Makedonia* arrived at Salamis 25
  August 1992, *Thrace* 15 September 1992 and *Epirus* 12 February 1993.
Modernisation: From 1972 to 1976 they were modified to
  accommodate the Light Airborne Multi-Purpose System
  (LAMPS) and the SH-2F Seasprite anti-submarine helicopter;
  hangar and flight deck are enlarged. In 1979 a programme was
  initiated to fit 3.5 ft bow bulwarks and spray strakes adding 9.1
  tons to the displacement. Sea Sparrow SAM replaced by Phal-

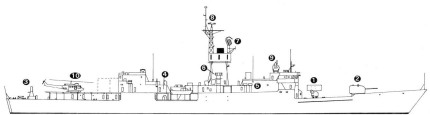
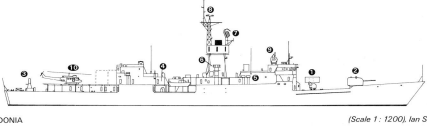

MAKEDONIA   *(Scale 1 : 1200), Ian Sturton*

MAKEDONIA   *4/1993*

anx 1982-88. There are plans to improve air defence
capabilities.
Structure: Improved ASROC-torpedo reloading capability (note
slanting face of bridge structure immediately behind ASROC).
Four Mk 32 torpedo tubes are fixed in the midships superstruc-

ture, two to a side, angled out at 45 degrees. The arrangement
provides improved loading capability over exposed triple Mk
32 torpedo tubes. A 4000 lb lightweight anchor is fitted on the
port side and an 8000 lb anchor fits into the after section of the
sonar dome. 4 SAM launchers for Stinger.

SHIPBORNE AIRCRAFT

Numbers/Type: 5 Sikorsky S-70B6 Seahawk.
Operational speed: 135 kts *(250 km/h).*
Service ceiling: 10 000 ft *(3050 m).*
Range: 600 nm *(1110 km).*
Role/Weapon systems: Ordered 25 July 1991 with an option for three more. First one to be delivered in 1994. To be used on the Hydra class. Sensors: Telephonica APS 143(V)3 search radar, Bendix AQS 18(V)3 dipping sonar, Litton ALR 606(V)2 ESM, ASN 150(V) tactical data system with CD22 or Link 11. Weapons: ASV; Penguin Mk 2 Mod 7 (from 1994). ASW; 2 × Mk 46 torpedoes.

SEAHAWK   *1990, Sikorsky*

Numbers/Type: 4 Aerospatiale SA 319B Alouette III.
Operational speed: 113 kts *(210 km/h).*
Service ceiling: 10 500 ft *(3200 m).*
Range: 290 nm *(540 km).*
Role/Weapon systems: Shipborne ASW/SAR role on older escorts and for training; limited to daylight operations only. Sensors: None. Weapons: ASW; 1 or 2 × Mk 44/46 torpedoes.

Numbers/Type: 9 Agusta AB 212ASW.
Operational speed: 106 kts *(196 km/h).*
Service ceiling: 14 200 ft *(4330 m).*
Range: 230 nm *(425 km).*
Role/Weapon systems: Shipborne ASW (7) and Elint (2) and surface search role from new escorts. Sensors: Selenia APS-705 radar, ESM/ECM (Elint version), AQS-18 dipping sonar (ASW version). Weapons: ASW; 2 × Mk 46 or 2 × A244/S homing torpedoes.

AB 212ASW   *1987, Hellenic Navy*

LAND-BASED MARITIME AIRCRAFT

Numbers/Type: 4/6 Lockheed P-3B/C Orion.
Operational speed: 410 kts *(760 km/h).*
Service ceiling: 28 300 ft *(8625 m).*
Range: 4000 nm *(7410 km).*
Role/Weapon systems: Four maritime reconnaissance aircraft transferred from the USN in 1992/93 as part of the Defence Co-operation Agreement signed in July 1990; six P-3C may be acquired in 1995. Sensors: APS 115 radar; sonobuoys; ESM. Weapons: ASW; Mk 44/46 torpedoes, depth bombs and mines.

CORVETTES

5 NIKI (THETIS) (TYPE 420) CLASS (GUNBOATS)

Name	No	Commissioned	Recommissioned
NIKI (ex-*Thetis*)	P 62 (ex-P 6052)	1 July 1961	6 Sep 1991
DOXA (ex-*Najade*)	P 63 (ex-P 6054)	12 May 1962	6 Sep 1991
ELEFTHERIA (ex-*Triton*)	P 64 (ex-P 6055)	10 Nov 1962	7 Sep 1992
CARTERIA (ex-*Hermes*)	P 65 (ex-P 6053)	16 Dec 1961	7 Sep 1992
AGON (ex-*Andreia*, ex-*Theseus*)	P 66 (ex-P 6056)	15 Aug 1963	8 Nov 1993

Displacement, tons: 575 standard; 732 full load
Dimensions, feet (metres): 229.7 × 26.9 × 8.6 *(70 × 8.2 × 2.7)*
Main machinery: 2 MAN V84V diesels; 6800 hp(m) *(5 MW)*; 2 shafts
Speed, knots: 19.5. **Range, miles:** 2760 at 15 kts
Complement: 64 (4 officers)

Guns: 2 Breda 40 mm/70 (twin); 85° elevation; 300 rounds/minute to 12.5 km *(6.7 nm)*; weight of shell 0.96 kg. 2—12.7 mm MGs.
Torpedoes: 4—324 mm single tubes. 4 Honeywell Mk 46; active/passive homing to 11 km *(5.9 nm)* at 40 kts; warhead 44 kg.
A/S mortars: 1 Bofors 375 mm 4-barrelled trainable launcher; automatic loading; range 1600 m; 20 rockets.
Depth charges: 2 rails.
Fire control: Signaal Mk 9 TFCS.
Radars: Surface search: Thomson-CSF TRS 3001; E/F band.
Navigation: Kelvin Hughes 14/9; I band.
Sonars: Atlas Elektronik ELAC 1 BV; hull-mounted; active search and attack; high frequency.

Programmes: All built by Rolandwerft, Bremen, and transferred from Germany. The last one was delayed by engine repairs.
Structure: *Doxa* has a deckhouse before bridge for sick bay. Torpedo tubes have liners effectively reducing their diameter to 324 mm.

NIKI   *8/1993, Hellenic Navy*

PATROL FORCES

2 OSPREY 55 CLASS (FAST ATTACK CRAFT—PATROL)

Name	No	Builders	Commissioned
ARMATOLOS	P 18	Hellenic Shipyards, Skaramanga	27 Mar 1990
NAVMACHOS	P 19	Hellenic Shipyards, Skaramanga	15 July 1990

Displacement, tons: 555 full load
Dimensions, feet (metres): 179.8; 166.7 (wl) × 34.4 × 8.5 *(54.8; 50.8 × 10.5 × 2.6)*
Main machinery: 2 MTU 16V 1163 TB63 diesels; 10 000 hp(m) *(7.3 MW)* sustained; 2 shafts; cp props
Speed, knots: 25. **Range, miles:** 500 at 25 kts, 2800 at 12 kts
Complement: 36 plus 25 troops
Missiles: SSM: 2 McDonnell Douglas Harpoon (to be fitted in 1993).
Guns: 1 OTO Melara 3 in *(76 mm)*/62 compact; 85° elevation; 85 rounds/minute to 16 km *(8.6 nm)* anti-surface; 12 km *(6.6 nm)* anti-aircraft; weight of shell 6 kg (to be fitted).
2 Bofors 40 mm/70 (twin) (to be replaced by OTO Melara 76 mm in due course).
2 Rheinmetall 20 mm.
Mines: Rails.
Countermeasures: Decoys: 2 chaff launchers.
Fire control: Selenia Elsag NA 21.
Radars: Surface search: Thomson-CSF Triton; G band.
Fire control: Selenia RTNX; I/J band.

Comment: Built in co-operation with Danyard A/S. Ordered in March 1988. First one laid down 8 May 1989 and launched 19 December 1989. Second laid down 9 November 1989 and launched 16 May 1990. Armament is of modular design and therefore can be changed. Harpoon and 76 mm guns are to be fitted after being taken from decommissioned Gearing class destroyers. Options on more of the class were shelved in favour of the Hellenic 56 design.

ARMATOLOS   *8/1993, Hellenic Navy*

1 + 1 HELLENIC 56 CLASS (FAST ATTACK CRAFT—PATROL)

Name	No	Builders	Commissioned
PIRPOLITIS	P 57	Hellenic Shipyard, Skaramanga	4 May 1993
POLEMISTIS	P 61	Hellenic Shipyard, Skaramanga	1994

Displacement, tons: 550 full load
Dimensions, feet (metres): 185.4 × 32.8 × 8.9 *(56.5 × 10 × 2.7)*
Main machinery: 2 Wärtsilä Nohab 16V25 diesels; 9200 hp(m) *(6.76 MW)* sustained; 2 shafts
Speed, knots: 24. **Range, miles:** 2200 at 15 kts; 800 at 24 kts
Complement: 36 plus 23 spare
Guns: 1 OTO Melara 3 in *(76 mm)*/62 compact; 85° elevation; 85 rounds/minute to 16 km
(8.6 nm) anti-surface; 12 km *(6.6 nm)* anti-aircraft; weight of shell 6 kg.
1 Bofors 40 mm/70. 2 Rheinmetall 20 mm.
Mines: 2 rails.
Fire control: Selenia Elsag NA 21.
Radars: Surface search: Thomson-CSF Triton; I band.

Comment: Ordered 20 February 1990. This is a design by the Hellenic Navy which uses the modular concept so that weapons and sensors can be changed as required. Appearance is similar to Osprey 55 class. *Pirpolitis* launched 16 September 1992, *Polemistis* 21 June 1993. Completion delayed by the shipyard's financial problems. Alternative guns and two Harpoon SSM can be fitted. 25 fully equipped troops can be carried.

10 LA COMBATTANTE III CLASS (FAST ATTACK CRAFT—MISSILE)

Name	No	Builders	Commissioned
ANTIPLOIARHOS LASKOS	P 20	CMN Cherbourg	20 Apr 1977
PLOTARHIS BLESSAS	P 21	CMN Cherbourg	7 July 1977
IPOPLOIARHOS MIKONIOS	P 22	CMN Cherbourg	10 Feb 1978
IPOPLOIARHOS TROUPAKIS	P 23	CMN Cherbourg	8 Nov 1977
SIMEOFOROS KAVALOUDIS	P 24	Hellenic Shipyards, Skaramanga	14 July 1980
ANTHIPOPLOIARHOS KOSTAKOS	P 25	Hellenic Shipyards, Skaramanga	9 Sep 1980
IPOPLOIARHOS DEYIANNIS	P 26	Hellenic Shipyards, Skaramanga	Dec 1980
SIMEOFOROS XENOS	P 27	Hellenic Shipyards, Skaramanga	31 Mar 1981
SIMEOFOROS SIMITZOPOULOS	P 28	Hellenic Shipyards, Skaramanga	June 1981
SIMEOFOROS STARAKIS	P 29	Hellenic Shipyards, Skaramanga	12 Oct 1981

Displacement, tons: 359 standard; 425 full load (P 20-23)
329 standard; 429 full load (P 24-29)
Dimensions, feet (metres): 184 × 26.2 × 7 *(56.2 × 8 × 2.1)*
Main machinery: 4 MTU 20V 538 TB92 diesels; 17 060 hp(m) *(12.54 MW)* sustained; 4 shafts
(P 20-23)
4 MTU 20V 538 TB91 diesels; 15 360 hp(m) *(11.29 MW)* sustained; 4 shafts (P 24-29)
Speed, knots: 36 (P 20-23); 32.5 (P 24-29). **Range, miles:** 700 at 32 kts; 2700 at 15 kts
Complement: 42 (5 officers)

Missiles: SSM: 4 Aerospatiale MM 38 Exocet (P 20-P 23); inertial cruise; active radar homing to
42 km *(23 nm)* at 0.9 Mach; warhead 165 kg.
6 Kongsberg Penguin Mk 2 (P 24-P 29); inertial/IR homing to 27 km *(15 nm)* at 0.8 Mach; warhead 120 kg.
Guns: 2 OTO Melara 3 in *(76 mm)*/62 compact; 85° elevation; 85 rounds/minute to 16 km
(8.6 nm) anti-surface; 12 km *(6.5 nm)* anti-aircraft; weight of shell 6 kg.
4 Emerson Electric 30 mm (2 twin); multi-purpose; 80° elevation; 1200 rounds/minute combined to 6 km *(3.2 nm)*; weight of shell 0.35 kg.
Torpedoes: 2—21 in *(533 mm)* aft tubes. AEG SST-4; wire-guided; active homing to
12 km *(6.5 nm)* at 35 kts; passive homing to 28 km *(15 nm)* at 23 kts; warhead 250 kg.
Countermeasures: Decoys: Wegmann chaff launchers.
Fire control: 2 CSEE Panda optical directors for 30 mm guns. Thomson-CSF Vega I or II system.
Radars: Surface search: Thomson-CSF Triton; G band; range 33 km *(18 nm)* for 2 m² target.
Navigation: Decca 1226C; I band.
Fire control: Thomson-CSF Castor II; I/J band; range 31 km *(17 nm)* for 2 m² target.
Thomson-CSF Pollux; I/J band; range 31 km *(17 nm)* for 2 m² target.

Programmes: First four ordered in September 1974. Second group of six ordered 1978.
Structure: First four fitted with SSM Exocet; remainder have Penguin.

PLOTARHIS BLESSAS (with Exocet)   *1988, Hellenic Navy*

IPOPLOIARHOS DEYIANNIS (with Penguin)   *1988, Hellenic Navy*

2 LA COMBATTANTE IIA (TYPE 148) CLASS
(FAST ATTACK CRAFT—MISSILE)

Name	No	Builders	Commissioned
IPOPLIARHOS VOTSIS (ex-*Iltis*)	P 51	CMN, Cherbourg	8 Jan 1973
ANTIPLIARHOS PEZOPOULOS (ex-*Storch*)	P 30	CMN, Cherbourg	17 July 1974

Displacement, tons: 265 full load
Dimensions, feet (metres): 154.2 × 23 × 8.9 *(47 × 7 × 2.7)*
Main machinery: 4 MTU MD 16V 538 TB90 diesels; 12 000 hp(m) *(8.82 MW)* sustained; 4 shafts
Speed, knots: 36. **Range, miles:** 570 at 30 kts; 1600 at 15 kts
Complement: 30 (4 officers)

Missiles: SSM: 4 Aerospatiale MM 38 Exocet (2 twin) launchers; inertial cruise; active radar homing to 42 km *(23 nm)* at 0.9 Mach; warhead 165 kg; sea-skimmer.
Guns: 1 OTO Melara 3 in *(76 mm)*/62 compact; 85° elevation; 85 rounds/minute to 16 km
(8.6 nm) anti-surface; 12 km *(6.5 nm)* anti-aircraft; weight of shell 6 kg.
1 Bofors 40 mm/70; 80° elevation; 330 rounds/minute to 12 km *(6.5 nm)* anti-surface; 4 km
(2.2 nm) anti-aircraft; weight of shell 0.96 kg; fitted with GRP dome (1984).
Mines: Laying capability.
Countermeasures: Decoys: Wolke chaff launcher.
ESM/ECM: Racal Octopus (Cutlass B1 radar intercept and Scorpion jammer).
Combat data systems: PALIS and Link 11.
Fire control: CSEE Panda optical director. Thomson-CSF Vega PCET system, controlling missiles and guns.
Radars: Air/surface search: Thomson-CSF Triton; G band; range 33 km *(18 nm)* for 2 m² target.
Navigation: SMA 3 RM 20; I band; range 73 km *(40 nm)*.
Fire control: Thomson-CSF Castor; I/J band.

Programmes: Transferred from Germany in September 1993.
Modernisation: Mid-life updates in 1980s.
Structure: Steel hulls. Similar to Combattante II class.

COMBATTANTE IIA (German colours)   *4/1993, Antonio Moreno*

4 LA COMBATTANTE II CLASS (FAST ATTACK CRAFT—MISSILE)

Name	No	Builders	Commissioned
ANTHIPOPLOIARHOS ANNINOS (ex-*Navsithoi*)	P 14	CMN Cherbourg	June 1972
IPOPLOIARHOS ARLIOTIS (ex-*Evniki*)	P 15	CMN Cherbourg	Apr 1972
IPOPLOIARHOS KONIDIS (ex-*Kymothoi*)	P 16	CMN Cherbourg	July 1972
IPOPLOIARHOS BATSIS (ex-*Calypso*)	P 17	CMN Cherbourg	Dec 1971

Displacement, tons: 234 standard; 255 full load
Dimensions, feet (metres): 154.2 × 23.3 × 8.2 *(47 × 7.1 × 2.5)*
Main machinery: 4 MTU MD 16V 538 TB90 diesels; 12 000 hp(m) *(8.82 MW)* sustained; 4 shafts
Speed, knots: 36.5. **Range, miles:** 850 at 25 kts
Complement: 40 (4 officers)

Missiles: SSM: 4 Aerospatiale MM 38 Exocet; inertial cruise; active radar homing to 42 km *(23 nm)*
at 0.9 Mach; warhead 165 kg; sea-skimmer.
Guns: 4 Oerlikon 35 mm/90 (2 twin); 85° elevation; 550 rounds/minute to 6 km *(3.2 nm)* anti-surface; 5 km *(2.7 nm)* anti-aircraft; weight of shell 1.55 kg.
Torpedoes: 2—21 in *(533 mm)* tubes. AEG SST-4; wire-guided; active homing to 12 km *(6.5 nm)* at
35 kts; passive homing to 28 km *(15 nm)* at 23 kts; warhead 250 kg.
Fire control: Thomson-CSF Vega system.
Radars: Surface search: Thomson-CSF Triton; G band; range 33 km *(18 nm)* for 2 m² target.
Navigation: Decca 1226C; I band.
Fire Control: Thomson-CSF Pollux; I/J band; range 31 km *(17 nm)* for 2 m² target.
IFF: Plessey Mk 10.

Programmes: Ordered in 1969. P 15 launched 8 September 1971; P 14 on 20 December 1971;
P 17 on 27 April 1971; P 16 on 26 January 1972.
Modernisation: Plans to modernise include updating the fire control system but work has been delayed.

IPOPLOIARHOS BATSIS   *1989, Hellenic Navy*

6 JAGUAR CLASS (FAST ATTACK CRAFT—TORPEDO)

Name	No	Builders	Commissioned
HESPEROS (ex-*Seeadler* P 6068)	P 50	Lürssen, Vegesack	29 Aug 1958
KENTAUROS (ex-*Habicht* P 6075)	P 52	Krogerwerft, Rendsburg	15 Nov 1958
KYKLON (ex-*Greif* P 6071)	P 53	Lürssen, Vegesack	3 Mar 1959
LELAPS (ex-*Kondor* P 6070)	P 54	Lürssen, Vegesack	24 Feb 1959
SKORPIOS (ex-*Kormoran* P 6077)	P 55	Krogerwerft, Rendsburg	9 Nov 1959
TYFON (ex-*Geier* P 6073)	P 56	Lürssen, Vegesack	3 June 1959

Displacement, tons: 160 standard; 190 full load
Dimensions, feet (metres): 139.4 × 23.6 × 7.9 *(42.5 × 7.2 × 2.4)*
Main machinery: 4 MTU MD 16V 538 TB90 diesels; 12 000 hp(m) *(8.82 MW)* sustained; 4 shafts
Speed, knots: 42. **Range, miles:** 500 at 40 kts; 1000 at 32 kts
Complement: 39
Guns: 2 Bofors 40 mm/70; 90° elevation; 300 rounds/minute to 12 km *(6.5 nm)* anti-surface; 4 km *(2.2 nm)* anti-aircraft; weight of shell 2.4 kg.
Torpedoes: 4—21 in *(533 mm)* tubes. Probably AEG SST-4; anti-surface; wire-guided; passive homing to 28 km *(15.3 nm)* at 23 kts; active homing to 12 km *(6.6 nm)* at 35 kts; warhead 260 kg.
Mines: 2 in lieu of each torpedo.

Comment: Transferred from Germany 1976-77. P 53 and P 56 commissioned in Hellenic Navy 12 December 1976. P 50 and P 54 on 24 March 1977, P 52 and P 55 on 22 May 1977. Three others (ex-*Albatros*, ex-*Bussard*, and ex-*Sperber*) transferred at same time for spares.

KENTAUROS   8/1993, D A Cromby

4 NASTY CLASS (FAST ATTACK CRAFT—TORPEDO)

Name	No	Builders	Commissioned
ANDROMEDA	P 196	Mandal, Norway	Nov 1966
KYKNOS	P 198	Mandal, Norway	Feb 1967
PIGASOS	P 199	Mandal, Norway	Apr 1967
TOXOTIS	P 228	Mandal, Norway	May 1967

Displacement, tons: 72 full load
Dimensions, feet (metres): 80.4 × 24.6 × 6.9 *(24.5 × 7.5 × 2.1)*
Main machinery: 2 MTU 12V 331 TC92 diesels; 2660 hp(m) *(1.96 MW)* sustained; 2 shafts
Speed, knots: 40. **Range, miles:** 676 at 17 kts
Complement: 20
Guns: 1 Bofors 40 mm/70. 1 Rheinmetall 20 mm.
Torpedoes: 4—21 in *(533 mm)* tubes.
Radars: Navigation: I band.

Comment: Six of the class acquired from Norway in 1967 and paid off into reserve in the early 1980s. Four re-engined and brought back into service in 1988.

KYKNOS   1988, Hellenic Navy

2 ASHEVILLE CLASS (LARGE PATROL CRAFT)

Name	No	Builders	Commissioned
TOLMI (ex-*Green Bay*)	P 229	Peterson, Wisconsin	5 Dec 1969
ORMI (ex-*Beacon*)	P 230	Peterson, Wisconsin	21 Nov 1969

Displacement, tons: 225 standard; 245 full load
Dimensions, feet (metres): 164.5 × 23.8 × 9.5 *(50.1 × 7.3 × 2.9)*
Main machinery: 2 Cummins VT12-875 diesels; 1450 hp *(1.07 MW)*; 2 shafts
Speed, knots: 16. **Range, miles:** 1700 at 16 kts
Complement: 24 (3 officers)
Missiles: SSM: 4 Aerospatiale SS 12M; wire-guided to 5.5 km *(3 nm)* subsonic; warhead 30 kg.
Guns: 1 USN 3 in *(76 mm)*/50 Mk 34; 85° elevation; 50 rounds/minute to 12.8 km *(7 nm)*; weight of shell 6 kg.
1 Bofors 40 mm/56 Mk 10. 4—12.7 mm (2 twin) MGs.
Fire control: Mk 63 GFCS.
Radars: Surface search: Sperry SPS 53; I/J band.
Fire control: Western Electric SPG 50; I/J band.

Comment: Transferred from the US in mid-1990 after a refit and recommissioned 18 June 1991. Both were in reserve from April 1977 having originally been built for the Cuban crisis. Similar craft in Turkish, Colombian and South Korean navies. Gas turbine propulsion engine removed prior to transfer.

TOLMI   1990, Hellenic Navy

2 FAST ATTACK CRAFT (PATROL)

Name	No	Builders	Commissioned
DIOPOS ANTONIOU	P 286	Ch N de l'Esterel	4 Dec 1975
KELEFSTIS STAMOU	P 287	Ch N de l'Esterel	28 July 1975

Displacement, tons: 115 full load
Dimensions, feet (metres): 105 × 19 × 5.3 *(32 × 5.8 × 1.6)*
Main machinery: 2 MTU 12V 331 TC81 diesels; 2610 hp(m) *(1.92 MW)* sustained; 2 shafts
Speed, knots: 30. **Range, miles:** 1500 at 15 kts
Complement: 17
Missiles: SSM: 4 Aerospatiale SS 12M; wire-guided to 5.5 km *(3 nm)* subsonic; warhead 30 kg.
Guns: 1 Rheinmetall 20 mm. 1—12.7 mm MG.

Comment: Originally ordered for Cyprus, later transferred to Greece. Wooden hulls.

DIOPOS ANTONIOU   1990, Hellenic Navy

3 DILOS CLASS (COASTAL PATROL CRAFT)

DILOS P 267   **KNOSSOS** P 268   **LINDOS** P 269

Displacement, tons: 74.5 standard; 86 full load
Dimensions, feet (metres): 95.1 × 16.2 × 5.6 *(29 × 5 × 1.7)*
Main machinery: 2 MTU 12V 331 TC92 diesels; 2660 hp(m) *(1.96 MW)* sustained; 2 shafts
Speed, knots: 27. **Range, miles:** 1600 at 24 kts
Complement: 15
Guns: 2 Rheinmetall 20 mm.
Radars: Surface search: Racal Decca 1226C; I band.

Comment: Ordered from Hellenic Shipyards, Skaramanga in May 1976 to a design by Abeking & Rasmussen. The Navy uses these craft for air-sea rescue duties. Based at the National SAR centre. Four more of this class serve in Coast Guard and three in Customs service.

KNOSSOS   7/1989, D Dervissis

AMPHIBIOUS FORCES

Note: There is a number of paid off LSTs and LSMs in unmaintained reserve at Salamis.

1 CABILDO CLASS (LSD)

Name	No	Builders	Commissioned
NAFKRATOUSSA (ex-USS *Fort Mandan* LSD 21)	L 153	Boston Navy Yard	31 Oct 1945

Displacement, tons: 4790 light; 9357 full load
Dimensions, feet (metres): 457.8 × 72.2 × 18 *(139.6 × 22 × 5.5)*
Main machinery: 2 boilers; 435 psi *(30.6 kg/cm sq)*; 750°F *(393°C)*; 2 turbines; 7000 hp *(5.22 MW)*; 2 shafts
Speed, knots: 15.4. **Range, miles:** 8000 at 12 kts
Complement: 250
Military lift: 18 LCMs; 2—35 ton cranes
Guns: 12 Bofors 40 mm/60 (2 quad and 2 twin); 90° elevation; 300 rounds/minute to 12 km *(6.5 nm)* anti-surface; 4 km *(2.2 nm)* anti-aircraft; weight of shell 0.89 kg.
Radars: Air search: Bendix SPS 6; D band; range 146 km *(80 nm)*.
Surface search: Westinghouse SPS 5; G/H band; range 37 km *(20 nm)*.
Helicopters: Platform for 1 light.

Comment: Laid down on 2 January 1945. Launched on 22 May 1945. Taken over on lease from USA in 1971, acquired by sale 5 February 1980. Headquarters ship for Captain Landing Forces.

NAFKRATOUSSA   7/1988, D Dervissis

1 + 4 JASON CLASS (LST)

Name	No	Builders	Commissioned
SAMOS	L 173	Eleusis Shipyard	Mar 1994
CHIOS	L 174	Eleusis Shipyard	Dec 1994
LESBOS	L 176	Eleusis Shipyard	Apr 1995
IKARIA	L 175	Eleusis Shipyard	Aug 1995
RODOS	L 177	Eleusis Shipyard	Oct 1995

Displacement, tons: 4400 full load
Dimensions, feet (metres): 380.5 × 50.2 × 11.3 *(116 × 15.3 × 3.4)*
Main machinery: 2 Wärtsilä Nohab 16V25 diesels; 9200 hp(m) *(6.76 MW)* sustained; 2 shafts
Speed, knots: 16
Military lift: 300 troops plus vehicles; 4 LCVPs
Guns: 1 OTO Melara 76 mm/62 Mod 9 compact; 85° elevation; 100 rounds/minute to 16 km *(8.6 nm)* anti-surface; 12 km *(6.5 nm)* anti-aircraft; weight of shell 6 kg.
  4 Breda 40 mm/70 (2 twin) compact; 85° elevation; 900 rounds/minute to 12 km *(6.5 nm)*; weight of shell 2.4 kg.
  4 Rheinmetall 20 mm (2 twin).
Fire control: 1 CSEE Panda optical director. Thomson-CSF Canopus GFCS.
Radars: Thomson-CSF Triton; G band.
Fire control: Thomson-CSF Pollux; I/J band.
Navigation: Kelvin Hughes Type 1007; I band.
Helicopters: Platform for one.

Comment: Contract for construction of five LSTs by Eleusis Shipyard signed 15 May 1986. Bow and stern ramps, drive through design. First laid down 18 April 1987, second in September 1987, third in May 1988, fourth April 1989 and fifth November 1989. First launched 16 December 1988, second 6 April 1989, third 5 July 1990. Completion of all five severely delayed by shipyard financial problems. Combat data system is a refurbished German system.

CHIOS (model) *1989, Eleusis Shipyard*

2 TERREBONNE PARISH CLASS (LSTs)

Name	No	Builders	Commissioned
INOUSE (ex-USS *Terrell County* LST 1157)	L 104	Bath Iron Works Corporation	19 Mar 1953
KOS (ex-USS *Whitfield County* LST 1169)	L 116	Christy Corporation	14 Sep 1954

Displacement, tons: 2590 light; 5800 full load
Dimensions, feet (metres): 384 × 55 × 17 *(117.1 × 16.8 × 5.2)*
Main machinery: 4 GM 16-278A diesels; 6000 hp *(4.48 MW)*; 2 shafts; cp props
Speed, knots: 15
Complement: 115
Military lift: 400 troops; 4 LCVPs
Guns: 6 USN 3 in *(76 mm)*/50 Mk 21 (3 twin); 85° elevation; 20 rounds/minute to 12 km *(6.5 nm)* anti-surface; 9 km *(4.9 nm)* anti-aircraft; weight of shell 6 kg.
  3 Rheinmetall 20 mm S 20.
Fire control: 2 Mk 63 GFCS.
Radars: Surface search: Raytheon/Sylvania SPS 10; G band.
Fire control: Two Western Electric Mk 34; I/J band.

Comment: Part of class of 16 of which these two were transferred from US 17 March 1977 by sale.

INOUSE *1992, Ships of the World*

11 TYPE 521 LCMs

Displacement, tons: 168 full load
Dimensions, feet (metres): 77.4 × 20.9 × 4.9 *(23.6 × 6.4 × 1.5)*
Main machinery: 1 MWM 8-cyl diesel; 685 hp(m) *(503 kW)*; 2 shafts
Speed, knots: 10.5
Complement: 7
Military lift: 60 tons or 50 troops

Comment: Built in 1964-67 but spent much of their time in reserve. Transferred from Germany in April 1991 and numbered ABM 20-30.

LCM Type 521 (German number) *7/1991, Hartmut Ehlers*

4 511—1152 and 1—510 CLASSES (LSTs)

Name	No	Builders	Commissioned
IKARIA (ex-USS *Potter County* LST 1086)	L 154	AM Bridge Co	14 Mar 1945
KRITI (ex-USS *Page County* LST 1076)	L 171	Bethlehem Steel Co, Hingham	1 May 1945
SIROS (ex-USS LST 325)	L 144	Philadelphia Navy Yard	1 Feb 1943
RODOS (ex-USS *Bowman County* LST 391)	L 157	Newport News	3 Dec 1942

Displacement, tons: 1653 standard; 2366 beaching; 4080 full load
Dimensions, feet (metres): 328 × 50 × 14 *(100 × 15.3 × 4.3)*
Main machinery: 2 GM 12-567A diesels; 1800 hp *(1.34 MW)*; 2 shafts
Speed, knots: 11.6. **Range, miles:** 9500 at 9 kts
Complement: 93 (8 officers)
Military lift: 2100 tons; 4 LCVPs
Guns: 8 Bofors 40 mm/60 (2 twin, 4 single) (10 in L 157).
  4 Oerlikon 20 mm/2 Rheinmetall 20 mm S 20.
Radars: Navigation: I band.

Comment: Former US tank landing ships. L 154 and 171 are 511—1152 class and L 144 and 157 are 1—510 class. L 157 and 154 were transferred to the Hellenic Navy in May 1960 and August 1960 respectively. L 144 was transferred on 29 May 1964, L 171 in March 1971. To be replaced by the Jason class.

LST 1-510 class (old number) *5/1990, Gilbert Gyssels*

2 LSM 1 CLASS

Name	No	Builders	Commissioned
IPOPLOIARHOS ROUSSEN (ex-USS *LSM 399*)	L 164	Charleston Navy Yard	13 Aug 1945
IPOPLOIARHOS KRYSTALIDIS (ex-USS *LSM 541*)	L 165	Brown SB Co, Houston	7 Dec 1945

Displacement, tons: 743 beaching; 1095 full load
Dimensions, feet (metres): 203.5 × 34.2 × 8.3 *(62.1 × 10.4 × 2.5)*
Main machinery: 2 Fairbanks-Morse 38D8-1/8-10 diesels; 3540 hp *(2.64 MW)* sustained; 2 shafts (L 161, 163 and 165); 4 GM 16-278A diesels; 3000 hp *(2.24 MW)*; 2 shafts (L 164)
Speed, knots: 13. **Range, miles:** 4900 at 12 kts
Complement: 60
Guns: 2 Bofors 40 mm/60 (twin). 8 Oerlikon 20 mm.

Comment: *LSM 541* was handed over by US at Salamis on 30 October 1958 and *LSM 399* at Portsmouth, Virginia on 3 November 1958. Both were renamed after naval heroes killed during the Second World War. Two deleted in 1993.

LSM 1 class (old number) *5/1990, Erik Laursen*

2 LCTs

Name	No	Builders	Commissioned
KITHERA (ex-*LCT 1198*)	L 185	UK	1945
MILOS (ex-*LCT 1300*)	L 189	UK	1945

Displacement, tons: 400 full load
Dimensions, feet (metres): 187.2 × 38.7 × 4.3 *(57 × 11.8 × 1.3)*
Main machinery: 2 Paxman diesels; 1000 hp *(746 kW)*; 2 shafts
Speed, knots: 7. **Range, miles:** 3000 at 7 kts
Complement: 12
Military lift: 350 tons
Guns: 2 Oerlikon 20 mm.

Comment: The survivors of a class of 12 acquired in 1946 from the UK.

KITHERA *6/1993, Hellenic Navy*

6 TYPE 520 LCUs

NAXOS (ex-*Renke*) L 178   **IOS** (ex-*Barbe*) L 167   **IRAKLEIA** (ex-*Forelle*) L 169
PAROS (ex-*Salm*) L 179   **SIKINOS** (ex-*Dorsch*) L 168   **FOLEGANDROS** (ex-*Delphin*) L 170

Displacement, tons: 430 full load
Dimensions, feet (metres): 131.2 × 28.9 × 7.2 *(40 × 8.8 × 2.2)*
Main machinery: 2 MWM 12-cyl diesels; 1020 hp(m) *(750 kW)*; 2 shafts
Speed, knots: 11
Complement: 17
Military lift: 150 tons
Guns: 2 Oerlikon 20 mm.

Comment: First two transferred from Germany 16 November 1989, remainder in 1992. Built by HDW, Hamburg in 1966. Bow and stern ramps similar to US Type. Two others (ex-*Rochan* and *Murane*) used for spares.

LCU TYPE 520 (German number)   *8/1992, Hartmut Ehlers*

11 LCMs

Displacement, tons: 56 full load
Dimensions, feet (metres): 56 × 14.4 × 3.9 *(17 × 4.4 × 1.2)*
Main machinery: 2 Gray Marine 64 HN9 diesels; 330 hp *(264 kW)*; 2 shafts
Speed, knots: 10. **Range, miles:** 130 at 10 kts
Military lift: 30 tons

Comment: Transferred from the USA in 1956-58.

34 LCVPs + 14 LCPs + 7 LCAs

Displacement, tons: 13 full load
Speed, knots: 6-9
Military lift: 36 troops or 3 tons equipment

Comment: LCVPs transferred from the USA between 1956-71, LCPs built in Greece in 1977 and LCAs in 1981.

L 70   *9/1993, Harald Carstens*

MINE WARFARE FORCES

Note: Three Tripartite minehunters may be acquired from Belgium in 1994.

2 COASTAL MINELAYERS

Name	No	Builders	Commissioned
AKTION (ex-*LSM 301*, ex-*MMC 6*)	N 04	Charleston Naval Shipyard	1 Jan 1945
AMVRAKIA (ex-*LSM 303*, ex-*MMC 7*)	N 05	Charleston Naval Shipyard	6 Jan 1945

Displacement, tons: 720 standard; 1100 full load
Dimensions, feet (metres): 203.5 × 34.5 × 8.3 *(62.1 × 10.5 × 2.5)*
Main machinery: 2 GM 16-278A diesels; 3000 hp *(2.24 MW)*; 2 shafts
Speed, knots: 12.5. **Range, miles:** 3000 at 12 kts
Complement: 65
Guns: 8 Bofors 40 mm/60 (4 twin). 6 Oerlikon 20 mm.
Mines: Capacity 100-130; 2 rails.
Fire control: 4 Mk 51 optical directors for 40 mm guns.
Radars: Navigation: I band.

Comment: Former US LSM 1 class. N 04 was launched on 1 January 1945 and N 05 on 14 November 1944. Converted in the USA into minelayers for the Hellenic Navy. Underwent extensive rebuilding from the deck up. Twin rudders. Transferred on 1 December 1953.

AKTION   *7/1993, van Ginderen Collection*

9 MSC 294 CLASS (MINESWEEPERS—COASTAL)

Name	No	Builders	Commissioned
ALKYON (ex-*MSC 319*)	M 211	Peterson Builders	3 Dec 1968
KLIO (ex-*Argo*, ex-*MSC 317*)	M 213	Peterson Builders	7 Aug 1968
AVRA (ex-*MSC 318*)	M 214	Peterson Builders	3 Oct 1968
PLEIAS (ex-*MSC 314*)	M 240	Peterson Builders	22 June 1967
KICHLI (ex-*MSC 308*)	M 241	Peterson Builders	14 July 1964
KISSA (ex-*MSC 309*)	M 242	Peterson Builders	1 Sep 1964
AIGLI (ex-*MSC 299*)	M 246	Tacoma, California	4 Jan 1965
DAFNI (ex-*MSC 307*)	M 247	Peterson Builders	23 Sep 1964
AEDON (ex-*MSC 310*)	M 248	Peterson Builders	13 Oct 1964

Displacement, tons: 320 standard; 370 full load
Dimensions, feet (metres): 144 × 28 × 8.2 *(43.3 × 8.5 × 2.5)*
Main machinery: 2 Waukesha L-1616 diesels; 1200 hp *(882 kW)*; or 2 GM-268A diesels (all by early 1995); 1760 hp *(1.3 MW)*; 2 shafts
Speed, knots: 13. **Range, miles:** 2500 at 10 kts
Complement: 39 (4 officers)
Guns: 2 Oerlikon 20 mm (twin).
Radars: Navigation: I band.
Sonars: UQS 1D; active; high frequency.

Comment: Built in the USA for Greece, wooden hulls. *Doris* acts as survey ship. Modernisation programme started in 1990 with replacement main engines and navigation radar. All to complete by early 1995. New sonar under consideration.

DAFNI   *8/1993, D A Cromby*

5 ADJUTANT CLASS (MINESWEEPERS—COASTAL)

Name	No
ATALANTI (ex-Belgian *St Truiden* M 919, ex-USS *MSC 169*)	M 202
ANTIOPI (ex-Belgian *Herve* M 921, ex-USS *MSC 153*)	M 205
FAEDRA (ex-Belgian *Malmedy* M 922, ex-USS *MSC 154*)	M 206
THALIA (ex-Belgian *Blankenberge* M 923, ex-USS *MSC 170*)	M 210
NIOVI (ex-Belgian *Laroche* M 924, ex-USS *MSC 171*)	M 254

Displacement, tons: 330 standard; 402 full load
Dimensions, feet (metres): 145 × 27.9 × 8 *(44.2 × 8.5 × 2.4)*
Main machinery: 2 GM 8-268A diesels; 880 hp *(656 kW)*; 2 shafts
Speed, knots: 14. **Range, miles:** 2500 at 10 kts
Complement: 38 (4 officers)
Guns: 1 Oerlikon 20 mm.

Comment: Originally supplied by the US to Belgium under MDAP. All built in 1954 in the USA—M 202, M 210 and M 254 by Consolidated SB Corp, Morris Heights and the other pair by Hodgson Bros, Goudy and Stevens, East Booth Bay. Subsequently returned to the USA and simultaneously transferred to Greece as follows: 29 July 1969 (*Herve* and *St Truiden*) and 26 September 1969 (*Laroche*, *Malmedy* and *Blankenberge*).

ATALANTI   *8/1993, D A Cromby*

4 MINESWEEPING LAUNCHES

Displacement, tons: 21 full load
Dimensions, feet (metres): 49.9 × 13.1 × 4.3 *(15.2 × 4 × 1.3)*
Main machinery: 1 diesel; 60 hp(m) *(44 kW)*; 1 shaft
Speed, knots: 8
Complement: 6

Comment: Transferred from USA in 1971 on loan and bought in 1981.

SURVEY AND RESEARCH SHIPS

Name	No	Builders	Commissioned
NAFTILOS	A 478	Annastadiades Tsortanides (Perama)	3 Apr 1976

Displacement, tons: 1400 full load
Dimensions, feet (metres): 207 × 38 × 13.8 *(63.1 × 11.6 × 4.2)*
Main machinery: 2 Burmeister & Wain SS28LM diesels; 2640 hp(m) *(1.94 MW)*; 2 shafts
Speed, knots: 15
Complement: 74 (8 officers)

Comment: Launched 19 November 1975. Of similar design to the two lighthouse tenders.

NAFTILOS *1989, Hellenic Navy*

Name	No	Builders	Commissioned
HERMIS (ex-*Oker*, ex-*Hoheweg*)	A 373	Unterweser, Bremen	19 Oct 1960

Displacement, tons: 1497 full load
Dimensions, feet (metres): 237.8 × 34.4 × 16.1 *(72.5 × 10.5 × 4.9)*
Main machinery: Diesel-electric: 1 KHD diesel; 1800 hp(m) *(1.32 MW)*
1 KHD auxiliary diesel; 400 hp(m) *(294 kW)*; 1 shaft
Speed, knots: 15
Complement: 30

Comment: First converted in 1972 to serve as an AGI in the West German Navy. Transferred 12 February 1988 and now based at Suda Bay. Serves as an AGI.

HERMIS *9/1989, Hellenic Navy*

Name	No	Builders	Commissioned
PYTHEAS	A 474	Annastadiades Tsortanides (Perama)	Dec 1983

Displacement, tons: 670 standard; 840 full load
Dimensions, feet (metres): 164.7 × 31.5 × 21.6 *(50.2 × 9.6 × 6.6)*
Main machinery: 2 Detroit 12V-92TA diesels; 1020 hp *(760 kW)* sustained; 2 shafts
Speed, knots: 14
Complement: 58 (8 officers)

Comment: *Pytheas* ordered in May 1982. Launched 19 September 1983. A similar ship, *Aigeo*, was constructed to Navy specification in 1985 but belongs to the National Maritime Research Centre.

PYTHEAS *10/1987, D Dervissis*

Name	No	Builders	Commissioned
STRABON	A 476	Emanuil-Maliris, Perama	27 Feb 1989

Displacement, tons: 252 full load
Dimensions, feet (metres): 107.3 × 20 × 8.2 *(32.7 × 6.1 × 2.5)*
Main machinery: 1 MAN D2842LE; 571 hp(m) *(420 kW)* sustained; 1 shaft
Speed, knots: 12.5
Complement: 20 (2 officers)

Comment: Ordered in 1987, launched September 1988.

STRABON (*Pytheas* behind) *1991, Hellenic Navy*

Name	No	Builders	Commissioned
AEGEON	—	Chalkis Shipyards	8 Nov 1984

Comment: Survey ship acquired in 1993. Belongs to the Maritime Research Institute.

AEGEON *6/1993, Paul Beaver*

Name	No	Builders	Commissioned
DORIS (ex-*MSC 298*)	A 475 (ex-M 245)	Tacoma, California	9 Nov 1964

Comment: Of same details as MSC 294 class in *Mine Warfare* section except that her displacement is now 383 tons full load and complement 35 (3 officers).

OLYMPIAS

Dimensions, feet (metres): 121.4 × 17.1 × 4.9 *(37 × 5.2 × 1.5)*
Main machinery: 170 oars (85 each side in three rows)
Speed, knots: 8
Complement: 180

Comment: Construction started in 1985 and completed in 1987. Made of Oregon pine. Built for historic research and as a reminder of the naval hegemony of ancient Greeks. Part of the Hellenic Navy. Refit in 1992/93.

OLYMPIAS *6/1993*

TRAINING SHIPS

1 TRAINING SHIP

Name	No	Builders	Commissioned
ARIS	A 74	Salamis	Jan 1980

Displacement, tons: 2400 standard; 2630 full load
Dimensions, feet (metres): 328 × 48.2 × 14.8 *(100 × 14.7 × 4.5)*
Main machinery: 2 MAK diesels; 10 000 hp(m) *(7.35 MW)*; 2 shafts
Speed, knots: 18
Complement: 500 (21 officers, up to 370 cadets)
Guns: 2 US 3 in *(76 mm)* Mk 26; 85° elevation; 50 rounds/minute to 12 km *(6.5 nm)*; weight of shell 6 kg.
2 Bofors 40 mm/70 (twin); 90° elevation; 300 rounds/minute to 12 km *(6.5 nm)* anti-surface; 4 km *(2.2 nm)* anti-aircraft; weight of shell 0.96 kg.
4 Rheinmetall 20 mm.
Radars: Surface search: Two Racal Decca 1226C; I band.
Helicopters: 1 Aerospatiale SA 319B Alouette III.

Comment: Laid down October 1976 at Salamis. Launched 4 October 1978. Hangar reactivated in 1986. The 76 mm guns are mounted on sponsons forward of the funnel. Can be used as transport or hospital ship. SATCOM fitted.

ARIS   7/1991, W Sartori

3 SAIL TRAINING CRAFT

MAISTROS A 233   **SOROKOS** A 234   **OSTRIA** A 359

Displacement, tons: 12 full load (A 233 and 234)
Dimensions, feet (metres): 48.6 × 12.8 × 6.9 *(14.8 × 3.9 × 2.1)*

Comment: Sail training ships acquired in 1983/84 (A 233-234) and 1989 (A 359). A 359 is slightly smaller at 12.1 × 3.6 m.

SOROKOS   6/1993, Hellenic Navy

AUXILIARIES

Note: Tenders requested by September 1992 for a hospital ship, which is to be operated by the Health Ministry, not the Navy.

1 + 1 LÜNEBURG (TYPE 701) CLASS (SUPPORT SHIPS)

Name	No	Builders	Commissioned	Recommissioned
AXIOS	A 464	Bremer Vulcan	9 July 1968	30 Sep 1991
(ex-*Coburg*)	(ex-A 1412)			
— (ex-*Saarburg*)	— (ex-A 1415)	Blohm & Voss	30 July 1968	1994

Displacement, tons: 3709 full load
Dimensions, feet (metres): 374.9 × 43.3 × 13.8 *(114.3 × 13.2 × 4.2)*
Main machinery: 2 MTU MD 16V 538 TB90 diesels; 6000 hp(m) *(4.41 MW)* sustained; 2 shafts; cp props; bow thruster
Speed, knots: 17. **Range, miles:** 3200 at 14 kts
Complement: 71
Cargo capacity: 1100 tons
Guns: 4 Bofors 40 mm/70 (2 twin); 90° elevation; 300 rounds/minute to 12 km *(6.5 nm)*; weight of shell 0.96 kg.

Comment: Lengthened by 33.7 ft *(10.3 m)* and modified in 1975. First one transferred from Germany in 1991, second planned for mid-1994. *Axios* serves as a depot ship for fast attack craft and is capable of servicing all weapons including missiles.

AXIOS   1993, Hellenic Navy

2 PATAPSCO CLASS (SUPPORT TANKERS)

Name	No	Builders	Commissioned
ARETHOUSA	A 377	Cargill Inc, Savage, Minn	11 June 1945
(ex-USS *Natchaug* AOG 54)			
ARIADNI	A 414	Cargill Inc, Savage, Minn	12 July 1944
(ex-USS *Tombigbee* AOG 11)			

Displacement, tons: 1850 light; 4335 full load
Measurement, tons: 2575 dwt
Dimensions, feet (metres): 292 wl; 310.8 oa × 48.5 × 15.7 *(89.1; 94.8 × 14.8 × 4.8)*
Main machinery: 2 GM 16-278A diesels; 3000 hp *(2.24 MW)*; 2 shafts
Speed, knots: 14
Complement: 43 (6 officers)
Cargo capacity: 2040 tons
Guns: 1 USN 3 in *(76 mm)*/50; 85° elevation; 20 rounds/minute to 12 km *(6.6 nm)*; weight of shell 6 kg.
2 Oerlikon 20 mm/85; 55° elevation; 800 rounds/minute to 2 km.
Fire control: 1 Mk 26 system for guns.
Radars: Surface search: Westinghouse SPS 5; G/H band; range 37 km *(20 nm)*.
Navigation: Decca; I band.

Comment: Former US petrol carriers. A 377 laid down on 15 August 1944. Launched on 16 December 1944. Transferred from the USA under the Mutual Defense Assistance Program in July 1959 and A 414 transferred 7 July 1972 (sold 11 July 1978), both at Pearl Harbour.

ARETHOUSA   1988, Hellenic Navy

4 TANKERS

Name	No	Builders	Commissioned
OURANOS	A 416	Kinosoura Shipyard	27 Jan 1977
HYPERION	A 417	Kinosoura Shipyard	27 Apr 1977
ZEUS	A 375 (ex-A 490)	Hellenic Shipyards	21 Feb 1989
ORION	A 376	Hellenic Shipyards	5 May 1989

Displacement, tons: 1900 full load
Dimensions, feet (metres): 219.8; 198.2 (wl) × 32.8 × 13.8 *(67; 60.4 × 10 × 4.2)*
Main machinery: 1 MAN-Burmeister & Wain 12V 20/27 diesel; 1632 hp(m) *(1.2 MW)* sustained; 1 shaft
Speed, knots: 12
Complement: 28
Cargo capacity: 1323 cu m
Guns: 2 Rheinmetall 20 mm.

Comment: First two are oil tankers. The others were ordered from Hellenic Shipyards, Skaramanga in December 1986 and are used as petrol tankers. There are some minor superstructure differences between the first two and the last two which have a forward crane.

ORION   8/1993, D A Cromby

7 WATER TANKERS

KERKINI (ex-German *FW 3*) A 433   **TRICHONIS** (ex-German *FW 6*) A 466   **KALLIROE** A 468
PRESPA A 434   **DOIRANI** A 467   **STIMFALIA** A 469
YLIKI A 465

Comment: All built between 1964 and 1990. Capacity, 600 tons except A 433 and A 466 which can carry 300 tons and A 469 which can carry 1000 tons. Three in reserve. *Stimfalia* is similar to *Ouranos*.

STIMFALIA   7/1993, van Ginderen Collection

1 AMMUNITION SHIP

Name	No	Builders	Commissioned
EVROS (ex-FDR *Schwarzwald* A 1400, ex-*Amalthee*)	A 415	Ch Dubigeon Nantes	1957

Displacement, tons: 2400
Measurement, tons: 1667 gross
Dimensions, feet (metres): 263.1 × 39 × 15.1 *(80.2 × 11.9 × 4.6)*
Main machinery: 1 Sulzer 6SD60 diesel; 3000 hp(m) *(2.2 MW)*; 1 shaft
Speed, knots: 15
Guns: 4 Bofors 40 mm/60.

Comment: Bought by FDR from Société Navale Caënnaise in February 1960. Transferred to Greece 6 June 1976.

EVROS   *1987, Hellenic Navy*

1 NETLAYER

Name	No	Builders	Commissioned
THETIS (ex-USS *AN 103*)	A 307	Kröger, Rendsburg	Apr 1960

Displacement, tons: 680 standard; 805 full load
Dimensions, feet (metres): 169.5 × 33.5 × 11.8 *(51.7 × 10.2 × 3.6)*
Main machinery: Diesel-electric; 1 MAN GTV-40/60 diesel generator; 1 motor; 1470 hp(m) *(1.08 MW)*; 1 shaft
Speed, knots: 12. **Range, miles:** 6500 at 10 kts
Complement: 48 (5 officers)
Guns: 1 Bofors 40 mm/60. 3 Rheinmetall 20 mm.

Comment: US offshore order. Launched in 1959. Some guns not always embarked.

THETIS   *1988, Hellenic Navy*

2 AUXILIARY TRANSPORTS

Name	No	Builders	Commissioned
PANDORA	A 419	Perama Shipyard	26 Oct 1973
PANDROSOS	A 420	Perama Shipyard	1 Dec 1973

Displacement, tons: 390 full load
Dimensions, feet (metres): 153.5 × 27.2 × 6.2 *(46.8 × 8.3 × 1.9)*
Main machinery: 2 diesels; 2 shafts
Speed, knots: 12
Military lift: 500 troops

Comment: Launched 1972 and 1973.

PANDROSOS   *7/1993, van Ginderen Collection*

4 TYPE 430A (TORPEDO RECOVERY VESSELS)

EVROTAS (ex-*TF 106*) A 460 (ex-Y 872)   **STRYMON** (ex-*TF 107*) A 462 (ex-Y 873)
ARACHTHOS (ex-*TF 108*) A 461 (ex-Y 874)   **NESTOS** (ex-*TF 4*) A 463 (ex-Y 854)

Comment: First two acquired from Germany on 16 November 1989, second pair on 5 March 1991. Of about 56 tons with stern ramps for torpedo recovery. Built in 1966.

EVROTAS (German colours)   *5/1989, Ralf Bendfeldt*

2 LIGHTHOUSE TENDERS

Name	No	Builders	Commissioned
I KARAVOYIANNOS THEOPHILOPOULOS	A 479	Perama Shipyard	17 Mar 1976
ST LIKOUDIS	A 481	Perama Shipyard	2 Jan 1976

Displacement, tons: 1450 full load
Dimensions, feet (metres): 207.3 × 38 × 13.1 *(63.2 × 11.6 × 4)*
Main machinery: 1 Deutz MWM TBD5008UD diesel; 2400 hp(m) *(1.76 MW)*; 1 shaft
Speed, knots: 15
Complement: 40
Radars: Navigation: Racal Decca; I band.
Helicopters: Platform for 1 light.

ST LIKOUDIS   *7/1993, van Ginderen Collection*

1 FLOATING DOCK and 5 FLOATING CRANES

Comment: The floating dock is 45 m *(147.6 ft)* in length and has a 6000 ton lift. Built at Eleusis with Swedish assistance and launched 5 May 1988; delivered 1989. The cranes were all built in Greece.

TUGS

3 COASTAL TUGS

HERAKLIS A 423   **IASON** A 424   **ODISSEUS** A 425

Displacement, tons: 345 full load
Dimensions, feet (metres): 98.5 × 26 × 11.3 *(30 × 7.9 × 3.4)*
Main machinery: 1 Deutz MWM diesel; 1200 hp(m) *(882 kW)*; 1 shaft
Speed, knots: 12

Comment: Laid down 1977 at Perama Shipyard. Commissioned 6 April, 6 March and 28 June 1978 respectively.

HERAKLIS   *8/1993, van Ginderen Collection*

18 HARBOUR TUGS

Name	No	Commissioned
ANTAIOS (ex-USS *Busy* YTM 2012)	A 407	1947
ATLAS (ex-HMS *Mediator*)	A 408	1944
ACCHILEUS (ex-USS *Confident*)	A 409	1947
ATROMITOS	A 410	1968
ADAMASTOS	A 411	1968
AIAS (ex-USS *Ankachak* YTM 767)	A 412	1972
PILEFS (ex-German)	A 413	1991
NESTOR (ex-US)	A 422	1989
KIKLOPS	A 426	1947
DANAOS (ex-US)	A 427	1989
KADMOS (ex-US)	A 428	1989
PELOPS	A 430	1989
TITAN	A 431	1962
GIGAS	A 432	1961
KEKROPS	A 435	1989
MINOS (ex-German)	A 436	1991
PELIAS (ex-German)	A 437	1991
AEGEUS (ex-German)	A 438	1991

ACCHILEUS   1982

COAST GUARD (Limenikon Soma)

Senior Officers

Commander-in-Chief:
Vice Admiral E Peloponnisios
Deputy Commander-in-Chief:
Rear Admiral M Plakiotis

Bases

HQ: Piraeus
Main bases: Piraeus, Eleusis, Thessalonika, Volos, Patra, Corfu, Rhodes, Mytilene, Heraklion (Crete), Chios, Kavala, Chalcis
Minor bases: Every port and island of Greece

Ships and Craft

In general very similar in appearance to naval ships, being painted grey. Since 1990 pennant numbers have been painted white and on both sides of the hull they carry a blue and white band with two crossed anchors.

Personnel

1994: 4557 (863 officers). Includes about 235 women.

General

This force consists of some 142 patrol craft and anti-pollution vessels including 24 inflatables for the 48 man Underwater Missions Squad and 12 anti-pollution vessels. Administration in peacetime is by the Ministry of Merchant Marine. In wartime it would be transferred to naval command. Officers are trained at the Naval Academy and ratings at two special schools.
The pennant numbers are all preceded as in the accompanying photographs by Greek 'Lambda Sigma' for Limenikon Soma.

Duties

The policing of all Greek harbours, coasts and territorial waters, navigational safety, SAR operations, anti-pollution surveillance and operations, supervision of port authorities, merchant navy training, inspection of Greek merchant ships world-wide.

Coast Guard Air Service

In October 1981 the Coast Guard acquired two Cessna Cutlass 172 RG aircraft and in July 1988 two Socata TB 20s. Maintenance and training by the Air Force. Based at Dekelia air base. New plans include larger aircraft.

---

4 DILOS CLASS

010-040 (ex-*80-83*)

Displacement, tons: 86 full load
Dimensions, feet (metres): 95.1 × 16.2 × 5.6 *(29 × 5 × 1.7)*
Main machinery: 2 MTU 12V 331 TC92 diesels; 2660 hp(m) *(1.96 MW)* sustained; 2 shafts
Speed, knots: 27. **Range, miles:** 1600 at 24 kts
Complement: 18
Guns: 2 Rheinmetall 20 mm.
Radars: Surface search: Racal Decca 1226C; I band.

Comment: Same design as naval craft and built at Hellenic Shipyards in the early 1980s.

LS 010   7/1993, van Ginderen Collection

4 + 8 (32) COLVIC CRAFT

Displacement, tons: 23.5 full load
Dimensions, feet (metres): 53.5 × 15.4 × 4.6 *(16.3 × 4.7 × 1.4)*
Main machinery: 2 MAN D2840-LXE diesels; 1644 hp(m) *(1.21 MW)* sustained; 2 shafts
Speed, knots: 34. **Range, miles:** 500 at 25 kts
Complement: 5 (1 officer)
Guns: 1—12.7 mm MG. 1—7.62 mm MG.

Comment: Ordered from Colvic Craft, Colchester in 1993. Shipped to Motomarine, Glifada for engine and electronics installation. GRP hulls with a stern platform for recovery of divers.

COLVIC   12/1993, Colvic Craft

13 OL 44 CLASS

Displacement, tons: 14 full load
Dimensions, feet (metres): 44.9 × 14.4 × 2 *(13.7 × 4.4 × 0.6)*
Main machinery: 2 diesels; 630 hp(m) *(463 kW)*; 2 shafts
Speed, knots: 23
Complement: 4
Guns: 1—7.62 mm MG.

Comment: Built by Olympic Marine. GRP hulls.

LS 101   9/1993, Harald Carstens

16 LS 51 CLASS

Displacement, tons: 13 full load
Dimensions, feet (metres): 44 × 11.5 × 3.3 *(13.4 × 3.5 × 1)*
Main machinery: 2 diesels; 630 hp(m) *(463 kW)*; 2 shafts
Speed, knots: 25. **Range, miles:** 400 at 18 kts
Complement: 4
Guns: 1—7.62 mm MG.

Comment: Built by Olympic Marine. GRP hulls.

LS 156   7/1993, van Ginderen Collection

61 COASTAL CRAFT and 23 CRISS CRAFT

Comment: There are 18 of 8.2 m, 17 of 7.9 m, 26 of 5.8 m and 23 ex-US Criss craft. In addition the Coast Guard operates 24 Inflatable craft.

CUSTOMS

Note: The Customs service also operates large numbers of coastal and inshore patrol craft including 3 Dilos class with the same characteristics as the Coast Guard. The craft have a distinctive Alpha Lambda (A/Λ) on the hull and are sometimes armed with 7.62 mm MGs.

LS 231   *7/1993, van Ginderen Collection*

AL 10   *9/1993, Harald Carstens*

GRENADA

Headquarters' Appointments

Commissioner of Police:
  Lieutenant Colonel Nestor Ogilvie
Coast Guard Commander:
  Superintendent Charles

Personnel

1994: 44

Bases

Prickly Bay (main), St George, Grenville, Hillsborough

General

Grenada was granted self-government, in association with the UK (which was responsible for its defence) on 3 March 1967. Independence was achieved in February 1974. Coast Guard craft are operated under the direction of the Commissioner of Police.

Mercantile Marine

Lloyd's Register of Shipping:
  4 vessels of 1031 tons gross

PATROL FORCES

1 GUARDIAN CLASS (COASTAL PATROL CRAFT)

Name	*No*	*Builders*	*Commissioned*
TYRREL BAY	PB 01	Lantana, Florida	21 Nov 1984

Displacement, tons: 90 full load
Dimensions, feet (metres): 105 × 20.6 × 7 *(32 × 6.3 × 2.1)*
Main machinery: 3 Detroit 12V-71TA diesels; 1260 hp *(939 kW)* sustained; 3 shafts
Speed, knots: 24. **Range, miles:** 1500 at 18 kts
Complement: 15 (2 officers)
Guns: 3—12.7 mm MGs. 2—7.62 mm MGs.
Radars: Surface search: Furuno 1411 Mk II; I band.

Comment: Similar to Jamaican and Honduras vessels.

2 BOSTON WHALERS

Displacement, tons: 1.3 full load
Dimensions, feet (metres): 22.3 × 7.4 × 1.2 *(6.7 × 2.3 × 0.4)*
Main machinery: 2 outboards; 240 hp *(179 kW)*
Speed, knots: 40+
Complement: 4
Guns: 1—12.7 mm MG.

Comment: Acquired in 1988-89.

TYRREL BAY   *11/1990, Bob Hanlon*

BOSTON WHALER   *11/1990, Bob Hanlon*

GUATEMALA

Senior Appointments

Commander Atlantic Naval Base:
  Captain Jose Maria Valladares Lanuza
Commander Pacific Naval Base:
  Captain Miguel Posadas Perez

Personnel

(a) 1994: 1245 (130 officers) including 700 Marines (2 battalions) (mostly volunteers)
(b) 2¼ years' national service
Note: With army logistic support the total employed on naval work is about 1500 (including 900 conscripts).

Bases

Santo Tomás de Castillas (Atlantic); Sipacate and Puerto Quetzal (Pacific)

Mercantile Marine

Lloyd's Register of Shipping:
  7 vessels of 1374 tons gross

PATROL FORCES

Notes: (1) There is also a naval manned Ferry *15 de Enero* (T 691).
(2) Three 32 m patrol boats reportedly ordered from CMN Cherbourg in February 1990 were cancelled.

1 BROADSWORD CLASS (COASTAL PATROL CRAFT)

Name	No	Builder	Commissioned
KUKULKÁN	GC 1051 (ex-P 1051)	Halter Marine	4 Aug 1976

Displacement, tons: 90.5 standard; 110 full load
Dimensions, feet (metres): 105 × 20.4 × 6.3 *(32 × 6.2 × 1.9)*
Main machinery: 2 GM 16V-149TI diesels; 3483 hp *(2.6 MW)* sustained; 2 shafts
Speed, knots: 32. **Range, miles:** 1150 at 20 kts
Complement: 20 (5 officers)
Guns: 1—75 mm recoilless. 2 Oerlikon GAM/204 GK 20 mm. 2—7.62 mm MGs.
Radars: Surface search: Furuno; I band.

Comment: As the flagship she used to rotate between Pacific and Atlantic bases every two years but has remained in the Pacific since 1989. Rearmed with 20 mm guns in 1989. These were replaced by GAM guns in 1990/91 when the ship received a new radar.

KUKULKÁN (old number) *5/1985*

2 SEWART CLASS (COASTAL PATROL CRAFT)

Name	No	Builders	Commissioned
UTATLAN	GC 851 (ex-P 851)	Sewart, Louisiana	May 1967
SUBTENIENTE OSORIO SARAVIA	GC 852 (ex-P 852)	Sewart, Louisiana	Nov 1972

Displacement, tons: 43 standard; 54 full load
Dimensions, feet (metres): 85 × 18.7 × 7.2 *(25.9 × 5.7 × 2.2)*
Main machinery: 2 GM 16V-71TI diesels; 2000 hp *(1.49 MW)* sustained; 2 shafts
Speed, knots: 23. **Range, miles:** 400 at 12 kts
Complement: 17 (4 officers)
Guns: 2—75 mm recoilless. 2 Oerlikon GAM/204 GK 20 mm. 2—7.62 mm MGs.
Radars: Surface search: Furuno; I band.

Comment: Aluminium superstructure. P 851 rearmed with 20 mm guns in 1990 and is based in the Atlantic; P 852 in the Pacific.

SUBTENIENTE OSORIO SARAVIA *1992, Julio Montes*

6 CUTLASS CLASS (5 COASTAL PATROL CRAFT AND 1 SURVEY CRAFT)

Name	No	Builders	Commissioned
TECUN UMAN	GC 651 (ex-P 651)	Halter Marine	26 Nov 1971
KAIBIL BALAM	GC 652 (ex-P 652)	Halter Marine	8 Feb 1972
AZUMANCHE	GC 653 (ex-P 653)	Halter Marine	8 Feb 1972
TZACOL	GC 654 (ex-P 654)	Halter Marine	10 Mar 1976
BITOL	GC 655 (ex-P 655)	Halter Marine	4 Aug 1976
GUCUMAZ	BH 656	Halter Marine	15 May 1981

Displacement, tons: 45 full load
Dimensions, feet (metres): 64.5 × 17 × 3 *(19.7 × 5.2 × 0.9)*
Main machinery: 2 GM 12V-71 diesels; 680 hp *(507 kW)* sustained; 2 shafts
Speed, knots: 25. **Range, miles:** 400 at 15 kts
Complement: 10 (2 officers)
Guns: 2 Oerlikon GAM/204 GK 20 mm. 2—7.62 mm MGs.
Radars: Surface search: Furuno; I band.

Comment: First five rearmed with 20 mm guns in 1991. P 651, 654 and 655 are in the Atlantic, remainder in the Pacific. *Gucumaz* is used as a survey craft. She is unarmed and has a single thick red and two thin blue diagonal stripes on the hull.

AZUMANCHE *1992, Julio Montes*

2 MACHETE CLASS (TROOP CARRIERS)

Name	No	Builders	Commissioned
PICUDA	D 361	Halter Marine	4 Aug 1976
BARRACUDA	D 362	Halter Marine	4 Aug 1976

Displacement, tons: 8.3 full load
Dimensions, feet (metres): 36 × 12.5 × 2 *(11 × 3.8 × 0.6)*
Main machinery: 2 GM 6V-53; 296 hp *(221 kW)* sustained; 2 waterjets
Speed, knots: 36
Complement: 2
Military lift: 20 troops

Comment: Armoured, open deck, aluminium craft. Both based in the Pacific.

BARRACUDA *1986*

8 VIGILANTE CLASS

Displacement, tons: 2 full load
Dimensions, feet (metres): 26.6 × 10 × 1.8 *(8.1 × 3 × 0.5)*
Main machinery: 2 Johnson outboards; 600 hp *(448 kW)*
Speed, knots: 40+
Complement: 4
Guns: 1—7.62 mm MG.
Radars: Surface search: Furuno; I band.

Comment: Ordered in 1993 from Boston Whaler. To be divided four to each coast.

VIGILANTE *1993, Boston Whaler*

18 RIVER PATROL CRAFT

Group A	Group B	Group C	Group D
DENEB	LAGO DE ATITLAN	KOCHAB	MERO
SIRIUS	MAZATENANGO	ALIOTH	SARDINA
PROCYON	RETALHULEU	MIRFA	PAMPANA
VEGA	ESCUINTLA	SCHEDAR	
POLUX			
SPICA			
STELLA MARIS			

Comment: Group A are wooden hull craft with a speed of 19 kts. Group B have aluminium hulls and a speed of 28 kts. Group C are probably of Israeli design and Group D are commerical craft caught smuggling and confiscated. All can be armed with 7.62 mm MGs and are used by Naval Infantry battalions.

GUINEA

Senior Appointment	**Personnel**	**Mercantile Marine**
Commander of the Navy: Commander Amara Bangoura	(a) 1994: 400 officers and men (b) 2 years' conscript service	*Lloyd's Register of Shipping:* 24 vessels of 5591 tons gross

General

Some of the craft listed below are probably non-operational. Little time is spent at sea.

Bases

Conakry, Kakanda

DELETION

1993   *Lamine Sadji Kaba* (derelict)

PATROL FORCES

3 BOGOMOL CLASS (FAST ATTACK CRAFT—GUN)

Displacement, tons: 245 full load
Dimensions, feet (metres): 127.9 × 25.6 × 5.9 *(39 × 7.8 × 1.8)*
Main machinery: 3 Type M 504 diesels; 10 800 hp(m) *(7.94 MW)* sustained; 3 shafts
Speed, knots: 37. **Range, miles:** 500 at 35 kts
Complement: 30
Guns: 1 USSR 3 in *(76 mm)*/66; 85°elevation; 120 rounds/minute to 15 km *(8 nm)*; weight of shell 7 kg.
2 USSR 30 mm/65 (twin); 85° elevation; 500 rounds/minute to 5 km *(2.7 nm)*; weight of shell 0.54 kg.
Radars: Surface search: Pot Head; H/I band.
Fire control: Bass Tilt; H/I band.

Comment: Built by Isora (Kolpino) in the Pacific and completed in April 1989. A USSR export model with an Osa hull and machinery.

BOGOMOL (in transporter)   *1989, G Jacobs*

1 SWIFTSHIPS 77 ft CLASS (COASTAL PATROL CRAFT)

Name	No	Builders	Commissioned
INTREPIDE	P 328	Swiftships, Morgan City	Feb 1987

Displacement, tons: 47.5 full load
Dimensions, feet (metres): 77.1 × 20 × 4.9 *(23.5 × 6.1 × 1.5)*
Main machinery: 3 Detroit 12V-71TA diesels; 1260 hp *(993 kW)* sustained; 3 shafts
Speed, knots: 26. **Range, miles:** 600 at 18 kts
Complement: 10
Guns: 2 Browning 12.7 mm MGs. 2—7.62 mm MGs.

Comment: Ordered in July 1985 and completed 18 December 1986. Aluminium hull.

INTREPIDE   *1987, Swiftships*

1 COASTAL PATROL CRAFT

Name	No	Builder	Commissioned
ALMAMY BOCAR BIRO BARRY	P 400	Chantiers Navals d l'Esterel	Aug 1979

Displacement, tons: 56 full load
Dimensions, feet (metres): 91.8 × 17.1 × 5.2 *(28 × 5.2 × 1.6)*
Main machinery: 2 MTU 12V 331 TC82 diesels; 2605 hp(m) *(1.91 MW)* sustained; 2 shafts
Speed, knots: 35. **Range, miles:** 750 at 15 kts
Complement: 13
Guns: 1—12.7 mm MG.

Comment: Two more of the class were expected in 1987 but the order was cancelled.

1 SWIFTSHIPS 65 ft CLASS (COASTAL PATROL CRAFT)

Name	No	Builders	Commissioned
VIGILANTE	P 300	Swiftships, Morgan City	6 Jan 1986

Displacement, tons: 36.5
Dimensions, feet (metres): 64.9 × 18.4 × 5.2 *(19.8 × 5.6 × 1.6)*
Main machinery: 2 Detroit 12V-71TA diesels; 840 hp *(627 kW)* sustained; 2 shafts
Speed, knots: 24. **Range, miles:** 500 at 18 kts
Complement: 10
Guns: 2 Browning 12.7 mm MGs. 2—7.62 mm MGs.

Comment: Ordered in October 1984. Aluminium hull.

VIGILANTE   *1985, Swiftships*

2 ZHUK CLASS (COASTAL PATROL CRAFT)

Displacement, tons: 39 full load
Dimensions, feet (metres): 78.7 × 16.4 × 3.9 *(24 × 5 × 1.2)*
Main machinery: 2 Type M 401 B diesels; 2200 hp(m) *(1.6 MW)* sustained; 2 shafts
Speed, knots: 30. **Range, miles:** 1100 at 15 kts
Complement: 11 (3 officers)
Guns: 2—14.5 mm (twin) MGs. 1—12.7 mm MG.
Radars: Surface search: Spin Trough; I band.

Comment: Transferred from USSR July 1987 after refurbishment.

ZHUK   *1990*

2 STINGER CLASS

P 30   P 35

Displacement, tons: 2.9 full load
Dimensions, feet (metres): 26.3 × 11.1 × 1.5 *(8 × 3.4 × 0.5)*
Main machinery: 2 MC outboards; 310 hp *(231 kW)*
Speed, knots: 35
Complement: 4
Guns: 2—12.7 mm MGs.
Radars: Navigation: Raytheon 1200; I band.

Comment: Coastal/river patrol craft delivered in 1986 by SeaArk Marine (ex-MonArk).

STINGER   *1987, MonArk Boats*

GUINEA-BISSAU

Headquarters' Appointments

Commanding Officer:
   Commander Feiciano Gomes

Personnel

(a)   1994: 350 officers and men
(b)   Voluntary service

Base

Bissau

General

A Cessna 337 patrol aircraft is used for offshore surveillance, although it was out of service in early 1994. Several small craft including some ex-USSR and Chinese LCU types may still be in use.

Mercantile Marine

Lloyd's Register of Shipping:
   17 vessels of 4091 tons gross

DELETIONS

1991   4 Bazán Type
1993   3 Bazán Type, 1 Bogomol

PATROL FORCES

1 KONDOR I CLASS (COASTAL PATROL CRAFT)

Name	No	Builders	Commissioned
(ex-*Greifswald*, ex-*G 413*)	V 814 (ex-V 87)	Peenewerft	29 May 1969

Displacement, tons: 377 full load
Dimensions, feet (metres): 170.3 × 23.3 × 7.2 *(51.9 × 7.1 × 2.2)*
Main machinery: 2 Russki Kolomna Type 40DM diesels; 4408 hp(m) *(3.24 MW)* sustained; 2 shafts
Speed, knots: 20
Complement: 24
Guns: 1—12.7 mm MG or Oerlikon 20 mm.
Radars: Navigation: TSR 333; I band.

Comment: Transferred from Germany in September 1990 having been 'demilitarised'. Former East German first series production *Kondor I* which has a slightly different funnel shape from others of the class. Probably non-operational by 1994.

V 814   9/1990, Hartmut Ehlers

2 BOGOMOL CLASS (FAST ATTACK CRAFT—GUN)

Displacement, tons: 245 full load
Dimensions, feet (metres): 127.9 × 25.6 × 5.9 *(39 × 7.8 × 1.8)*
Main machinery: 3 Type M 504 diesels; 10 800 hp(m) *(7.94 MW)* sustained; 3 shafts
Speed, knots: 37. **Range, miles:** 500 at 35 kts
Complement: 30
Guns: 1 USSR 3 in *(76 mm)*/60; 85° elevation; 120 rounds/minute to 15 km *(8 nm)*; weight of shell 7 kg.
   2 USSR 30 mm/65 (twin); 85° elevation; 500 rounds/minute to 5 km *(2.7 nm)*; weight of shell 0.54 kg.
Radars: Surface search: Pot Head; H/I band.
   Fire control: Bass Tilt; H/I band.

Comment: Built in the Pacific by Isora (Kolpino), USSR export model with an Osa hull and machinery. First one delivered in early 1988, second in June 1990 from Vladivostock. By 1994 both were non-operational, waiting for spares.

BOGOMOL (in transporter)   1989, G Jacobs

2 SHANTOU CLASS

Displacement, tons: 80 full load
Dimensions, feet (metres): 83.3 × 19 × 6.5 *(25.5 × 5.8 × 2)*
Main machinery: 2 Type 3-D-12 diesels; 600 hp(m) *(440 kW)* sustained; 2 Type M 50 diesels; 2200 hp(m) *(1.6 MW)* sustained; 4 shafts
Speed, knots: 28. **Range, miles:** 500 at 28 kts
Complement: 36
Guns: 4—37 mm/63 (2 twin); 85° elevation; 160 rounds/minute to 8.5 km *(4.6 nm)*; weight of shell 1.46 kg.
   2—12.7 mm MGs.
Depth charges: 8.
Radars: Surface search: Skin Head; I band; range 37 km *(20 nm)*.

Comment: Two delivered from China in 1983, two more in March 1986. First two used to provide spares for the others.

2 ALFEITE TYPE (COASTAL PATROL CRAFT)

Displacement, tons: 55 full load
Dimensions, feet (metres): 64.6 × 19 × 10.6 *(19.7 × 5.8 × 3.2)*
Main machinery: 3 MTU 12V 183 TE92 diesels; 3000 hp(m) *(2.2 MW)* maximum; 3 Hamilton MH 521 waterjets
Speed, knots: 28
Complement: 9 (1 officer)
Radars: Navigation: Furuno FR 2010

Comment: Ordered from Arsenal do Alfeite in 1991. First one delivered in January 1994, second in April 1994. Used for fishery protection patrols.

ALFEITE Type   (not to scale), Ian Sturton

1 LDM 100 CLASS (LCM)

LDM 119

Displacement, tons: 50 full load
Dimensions, feet (metres): 50 × 14.4 × 3.6 *(15.3 × 4.4 × 1.1)*
Main machinery: 2 GM diesels; 450 hp *(336 kW)*; 2 shafts
Speed, knots: 9

Comment: Built at the Estaleiros Navais do Mondego in 1965. Transferred from Portuguese Navy in early 1994.

GUYANA

Headquarters' Appointment

Commanding Officer Coast Guard:
   Captain Harry B Hinds

General

In early 1994 all craft were derelict, either flooded or pulled up on shore, except one 17 ft Boston Whaler donated by the US in April 1993. If funds become available one or two of the converted trawlers may be salvaged.

Bases

Georgetown, New Amsterdam

Prefix to Ships' Names

GDFS

Mercantile Marine

Lloyd's Register of Shipping:
   78 vessels of 16 831 tons gross

DELETIONS

1991   *Kimbia*
1992   *Peccari, Ekereku*
1993   *Houri, Seafood, Waitipu, Maipuri*

HAITI

Bases

Main: Port Au Prince
Secondary: Les Cayes, Port de Paix

Mercantile Marine

Lloyd's Register of Shipping:
4 vessels of 868 tons gross

PATROL FORCES

Note: 2 Swift class patrol craft were also reported in 1993. These may have been the 21 m Sewart type MH 22 and 23, laid up in 1990.

5—3812-VCF CLASS (COASTAL PATROL CRAFT)

CHAVANNES MH 13
CAPOIS MH 14
CHARLEMAGNE PERRAULT MH 17

SONTHONAX MH 18
BOIS ROND TONNERRE MH 19

Displacement, tons: 15 full load
Dimensions, feet (metres): 40.8 × 13.3 × 1.4 *(12.4 × 4.1 × 0.4)*
Main machinery: 2 Detroit 6-71 diesels; 348 hp *(260 kW)* sustained; 2 shafts
Speed, knots: 25. **Range, miles:** 350 at 20 kts
Complement: 4
Guns: 1 Browning 12.7 mm MG. 2 FN Herstal 7.62 mm (twin) MGs.

Comment: Built by MonArk, Monticello, Arkansas in 1981. By the end of 1993 five were operational, four others had been cannibalised for spares.

SONTHONAX   *1988, van Ginderen Collection*

HONDURAS

Headquarters' Appointments

Chief of the Armed Forces:
Brigadier Luis Discua Elvir
Commander of Honduran Navy:
Colonel Reynaldo Andino Flores

Personnel

(a)   1994: 900 (95 officers)
(b)   24 months' conscript service

Bases

Puerto Cortés, Amapala, Puerto Castilla, La Ceiba, Puerto Trujillo

General

Two ex-Polish Polnochny class LCTs were seen flying the Honduran flag at Kiel in April 1990. These ships had been bought commercially for scrapping in a Spanish shipyard, and not to be transferred to the Honduran Navy.

Mercantile Marine

Lloyd's Register of Shipping:
1203 vessels of 1 116 137 tons gross

PATROL FORCES

3 SWIFT 105 ft CLASS (FAST ATTACK CRAFT—GUN)

GUAYMURAS FNH 101   **HONDURAS** FNH 102   **HIBUERAS** FNH 103

Displacement, tons: 103 full load
Dimensions, feet (metres): 105 × 20.6 × 7 *(32 × 6.3 × 2.1)*
Main machinery: 2 MTU 16V 538 TB90 diesels; 6000 hp(m) *(4.4 MW)* sustained; 2 shafts
Speed, knots: 30. **Range, miles:** 1200 at 18 kts
Complement: 17 (3 officers)
Guns: 1 General Electric Sea Vulcan 20 mm Gatling (FNH 101-102). 2—12.7 mm MGs.
6 Hispano-Suiza 20 mm (2 triple) (FNH 103).

Comment: First delivered by Swiftships, Morgan City in April 1977 and last two in March 1980. Gatling guns acquired in 1987 with HSV-20NCS fire control system.

COPAN   *7/1986, Giorgio Arra*

1 COASTAL PATROL CRAFT

CHAMELECON FN 8501

Displacement, tons: 50 full load
Dimensions, feet (metres): 85.3 × 19 × 3.3 *(26 × 5.8 × 1)*
Main machinery: 2 GM 12V-71TA diesels; 840 hp *(627 kW)* sustained; 2 shafts
Speed, knots: 23. **Range, miles:** 780 at 18 kts
Complement: 10 (2 officers)
Guns: 1 Oerlikon 20 mm. 2—12.7 mm MGs.

Comment: Built by Swiftships, Morgan City in 1967. Ex-*Rio Kuringuras* defected from Nicaragua in 1979.

HONDURAS   *4/1991*

2 GUARDIAN CLASS (COASTAL PATROL CRAFT)

COPAN FNH 106   **TEGUCIGALPA** FNH 107

Displacement, tons: 94 full load
Dimensions, feet (metres): 106 × 20.6 × 7 *(32.3 × 6.3 × 2.1)*
Main machinery: 3 Detroit 16V-92TA diesels; 2070 hp *(1.54 MW)* sustained; 3 shafts
Speed, knots: 30. **Range, miles:** 1500 at 18 kts
Complement: 17 (3 officers)
Guns: 1 General Electric Sea Vulcan 20 mm Gatling.
3 Hispano Suiza 20 mm (1 triple). 2—12.7 mm MGs.
Radars: Navigation: Furuno; I band.

Comment: Delivered by Lantana Boatyard, Florida in January 1983 and August 1986. A third of the class, completed in May 1984, became the Jamaican *Paul Bogle*.

CHAMELECON and GOASCORAN   *1988*

5 SWIFT 65 ft CLASS (COASTAL PATROL CRAFT)

NACAOME (ex-*Aguan*, ex-*Gral*) FNH 651   **ULUA** FNH 654
GOASCORAN (ex-*General J T Cabanas*) FNH 652   **CHOLUTECA** FNH 655
PETULA FNH 653

Displacement, tons: 33 full load
Dimensions, feet (metres): 69.9 × 17.1 × 5.2 *(21.3 × 5.2 × 1.6)*
Main machinery: 2 GM 12V-71TA diesels; 840 hp *(627 kW)* sustained; 2 shafts (FNH 651-2)
  2 MTU 8V 396 TB93 diesels; 2180 hp(m) *(1.6 MW)* sustained; 2 shafts (FNH 653-5)
Speed, knots: 25 (FNH 651-2); 36 (FNH 653-5). **Range, miles:** 2000 at 22 kts (FNH 651-2)
Complement: 9 (2 officers)
Guns: 1 Oerlikon 20 mm. 2—12.7 mm (twin) MGs. 2—7.62 MGs.

Comment: First pair built by Swiftships, Morgan City originally for Haiti. Contract cancelled and Honduras bought the two which had been completed in 1973-74. Delivered in 1977. Last three ordered in 1979 and delivered 1980.

PETULA   5/1993

10 PIRANHA CLASS (RIVER PATROL CRAFT)

Displacement, tons: 8.2
Dimensions, feet (metres): 36 × 10 × 1.6 *(11 × 3.1 × 0.5)*
Main machinery: 2 Caterpillar diesels; 630 hp *(470 kW)*; 2 shafts
Speed, knots: 26
Complement: 5
Guns: 2—12.7 mm MGs. 2—7.62 mm MGs.

Comment: Eight built by Lantana Boatyard, Florida, and delivered on 3 February 1986. Three more in 1991. Also supplied to El Salvador. One reported sunk in September 1988 in a clash with Nicaraguan craft.

PIRANHA   1988, Honduras Navy

12 OUTRAGE CLASS (RIVER PATROL CRAFT)

Displacement, tons: 2.2
Dimensions, feet (metres): 24.9 × 7.9 × 1.3 *(7.6 × 2.4 × 0.4)*
Main machinery: 2 Evinrude outboards; 300 hp *(224 kW)*
Speed, knots: 30. **Range:** 200 at 30 kts
Complement: 4
Guns: 1—12.7 mm MG. 2—7.62 mm MGs.

Comment: Built by Boston Whaler in 1982.

OUTRAGE   4/1991

AUXILIARIES

1 HOLLYHOCK CLASS (BUOY TENDER)

YOJOA (ex-USS *Walnut*) FNH 252

Displacement, tons: 989 full load
Dimensions, feet (metres): 175.2 × 34.1 × 12.1 *(53.4 × 10.4 × 3.7)*
Main machinery: 2 diesels; 1350 hp *(1 MW)*; 2 shafts
Speed, knots: 12
Complement: 40 (4 officers)

Comment: Transferred from US in July 1982. Built by Moore Drydock Co in 1939.

YOJOA   8/1989

1 LANDING CRAFT (LCU)

PUNTA CAXINAS FNH 1491

Displacement, tons: 625 full load
Dimensions, feet (metres): 149 × 33 × 6.5 *(45.4 × 10 × 2)*
Main machinery: 3 Caterpillar 3412 diesels; 1821 hp *(1.4 MW)*; 3 shafts
Speed, knots: 14. **Range:** 3500 at 12 kts
Complement: 18 (3 officers)
Military lift: 100 tons equipment or 50 000 gallons dieso plus 4 standard containers

Comment: Ordered in 1986 from Lantana, Florida, and commissioned 12 January 1988.

PUNTA CAXINAS   1988, Honduras Navy

10 TRANSPORT CRAFT

Comment: In addition to the above, three old ex-US LCM 8 (*Warunta* FNH 7401, *Tansin* FNH 7402, *Caratasca* FNH 7403) transferred in 1987, and six ex-Fishing Boats (*Juliana* FNH 7501, *San Rafael* FNH 7502, *Carmen* FNH 7503, *Mairy* FNH 7504, *Yosuro* FNH 7505, *Gregori* FNH 7506) are used as transport vessels. There is also a 75 m cargo ship *Tatubla II* built in 1959 in Germany and taken over in the late 1980s.

TATUBLA II (YOJOA alongside)   5/1993

HONG KONG

General

All the listed craft are operated by the Marine Region of the Royal Hong Kong Police Force (RHKP). This is a Coast Guard Force responsible for the territorial waters of Hong Kong including the colony's 244 islands. The four main tasks are the prevention of illegal immigration from China, the detention of Vietnamese boat people, the prevention of smuggling by water between Hong Kong and mainland China and SAR operations.

Organisation

Marine Police Regional HQ, Tsim Sha Tsui, Kowloon
Bases at Ma Liu Shui, Tui Min Hoi, Tai Lam Chung, Aberdeen, Sai Wan Ho

Senior Officers

Regional Commander:
 Lim Sak-Yeung
Deputy Regional Commander:
 Foo Tsun-Kong

Personnel

(a) 1994: 2700
(b) Voluntary service

Mercantile Marine

Lloyd's Register of Shipping:
 418 vessels of 7 664 300 tons gross

DELETIONS

1992 *Sea Cat, Sea Puma, Sea Leopard, Sea Eagle, Sea Hawk, Sea Lynx, Sea Falcon, PL 37-45*
1993 *Sea Lion, Sea Tiger, PL 86*

POLICE

2 COMMAND VESSELS

SEA PANTHER PL 3   **SEA HORSE** PL 4

Displacement, tons: 420
Dimensions, feet (metres): 131.2 × 28.2 × 10.5 *(40 × 8.6 × 3.2)*
Main machinery: 2 Caterpillar 3512TA diesels; 2420 hp *(1.81 MW)* sustained; 2 shafts
Speed, knots: 14. Range, miles: 1500 at 14 kts
Complement: 33
Guns: 2—12.7 mm MGs.
Radars: Surface search: Two Racal Decca; I band.

Comment: Built by Hong Kong SY, PL 3 completed 27 July 1987, PL 4 on 29 September 1987. Both commissioned 1 February 1988. Steel hulls. Both have a Racal Cane command system.

SEA PANTHER   *9/1993, RHKP*

6 PROTECTOR (ASI 315) CLASS (COMMAND/PATROL CRAFT)

PROTECTOR PL 51   **DEFENDER** PL 53   **RESCUER** PL 55
GUARDIAN PL 52   **PRESERVER** PL 54   **DETECTOR** PL 56

Displacement, tons: 170 full load
Dimensions, feet (metres): 107 × 26.9 × 5.2 *(32.6 × 8.2 × 1.6)*
Main machinery: 2 Caterpillar 3516TA diesels; 4400 hp *(3.28 MW)* sustained; 2 shafts; 1 Caterpillar 3412TA; 1860 hp *(1.24 MW)* sustained; Hamilton jet (centre line); 764 hp *(570 kW)*
Speed, knots: 24. Range, miles: 600 at 18 kts
Complement: 18
Guns: 1 Browning 12.7 mm MG.
Fire control: GEC V3901 optronic director.
Radars: Surface search: Racal Decca; I band.

Comment: Ordered from Australian Shipbuilding Industries in August 1991. First one in service 23 November 1992, last one in July 1993. As well as patrol work, the craft provide command platforms for Divisional commanders.

GUARDIAN   *9/1993, RHKP*

15 KING LAI (DAMEN Mk III) (PATROL CRAFT)

KING LAI PL 70	**KING DAI** PL 74	**KING CHI** PL 78	**KING YAN** PL 82
KING YEE PL 71	**KING CHUNG** PL 75	**KING TAI** PL 79	**KING YUNG** PL 83
KING LIM PL 72	**KING SHUN** PL 76	**KING KWAN** PL 80	**KING KAN** PL 84
KING HAU PL 73	**KING TAK** PL 77	**KING MEI** PL 81	

Displacement, tons: 95
Dimensions, feet (metres): 87 × 19 × 6 *(26.5 × 5.8 × 1.8)*
Main machinery: 2 MTU 12V 396 TC82 diesels; 2610 hp(m) *(1.92 MW)* sustained; 2 shafts
 1 Mercedes-Benz OM 424A 12V diesel; 341 hp(m) *(251 kW)* sustained; 1 KaMeWa waterjet
Speed, knots: 26 on 3 diesels; 8 on waterjet and cruising diesel. Range, miles: 600 at 14 kts
Complement: 17
Guns: 1 Browning 12.7 mm MG.
Radars: Surface search: Racal Decca.

Comment: Steel-hulled craft constructed by Chung Wah SB & Eng Co Ltd 1984/85.

KING LAI   *9/1993, RHKP*

9 DAMEN CLASS (PATROL CRAFT)

PL 60-68

Displacement, tons: 86
Dimensions, feet (metres): 85.9 × 19.4 × 5.9 *(26.2 × 5.9 × 1.8)*
Main machinery: 2 MTU 12V 396 TC82 diesels; 2610 hp(m) *(1.92 MW)* sustained; 2 shafts
 1 MAN D2566 diesel; 195 hp(m) *(143 kW)*; Schottel prop (centre line)
Speed, knots: 23 MTU; 6 MAN. Range, miles: 600 at 14 kts
Complement: 14
Guns: 1 Browning 12.7 mm MG.
Radars: Surface search: Racal Decca; I band.

Comment: Designed by Damen SY, Netherlands. Steel-hulled craft built by Chung Wah SB & Eng Co Ltd. Delivered February 1980 to January 1981.

PL 67   *9/1993, RHKP*

7 PETREL CLASS (HARBOUR PATROL CRAFT)

PETREL PL 11   **TERN** PL 14   **PUFFIN** PL 16
AUK PL 12   **SKUA** PL 15   **GANNET** PL 17
GULL PL 13

Displacement, tons: 36
Dimensions, feet (metres): 52.5 × 15.1 × 4.9 *(16 × 4.6 × 1.5)*
Main machinery: 2 Cummins NTA-855-M diesels; 700 hp *(522 kW)* sustained; 2 waterjets
Speed, knots: 12
Complement: 7

Comment: Built by Chung Wah SB & Eng Co Ltd in 1986-87. Replaced old patrol craft some of
which had the same names.

PUFFIN   9/1993, RHKP

3 JET CLASS (SHALLOW WATER PATROL CRAFT)

JETSTREAM PL 6   **SWIFTSTREAM** PL 7   **TIDESTREAM** PL 8

Displacement, tons: 24
Dimensions, feet (metres): 53.8 × 14.8 × 2.8 *(16.4 × 4.5 × 0.8)*
Main machinery: 2 Daimler-Benz OM 422A 8V diesels; 490 hp(m) *(434 kW)* sustained; 2 Hamilton
421 waterjets
Speed, knots: 18. **Range, miles:** 300 at 15 kts
Complement: 8

Comment: Fibreglass hull built by Choy Lee Shipyards Limited. Completed April 1986 *(Jetstream)*,
May 1986 *(Swiftstream)*, and June 1986 *(Tidestream)*.

SWIFTSTREAM   9/1993, RHKP

3 MERCURY CLASS (LOGISTIC CRAFT)

MERCURY PL 57   **VULCAN** PL 58   **CERES** PL 59

Displacement, tons: 86
Dimensions, feet (metres): 85.9 × 19.4 × 5.9 *(26.2 × 5.9 × 1.8)*
Main machinery: 2 MTU 12V 396 TC82 diesels; 2610 hp(m) *(1.92 MW)* sustained; 2 shafts
1 Daimler-Benz OM 422 8V diesel; 245 hp(m) *(217 kW)* sustained; 1 Hamilton 421 waterjet
Speed, knots: 23+ MTU; 7 waterjet and cruising diesels. **Range, miles:** 600 at 14 kts
Complement: 5 (10 for patrol work)
Military lift: 2 platoons of troops
Guns: 1—12.7 mm MG.
Radars: Navigation: Decca 150; I band.

Comment: Modified PL 60 design by Damen SY, Netherlands. Built by Chung Wah SB & Eng Co Ltd.
Completed 26 January 1982 *(Mercury)*, 22 March 1982 *(Vulcan)*, 29 March 1982 *(Ceres)*. To be con-
verted to patrol craft in 1993, with improved communications and accommodation, the addition of an
RIB and launching davit and an MG mounting.

CERES   9/1993, RHKP

4 SEASPRAY CLASS (LOGISTIC CRAFT)

PL 46-49

Dimensions, feet (metres): 37.4 × 13.8 × 4.3 *(11.4 × 4.2 × 1.3)*
Main machinery: 2 Caterpillar 3208TA diesels; 550 hp *(410 kW)* sustained; 2 shafts
Speed, knots: 30
Complement: 4 + 16 fully equipped men
Radars: Navigation: Koden; I band.

Comment: Built by Seaspray Boats, Fremantle. First one in service in June 1992, remainder by the
end of the year. Catamaran hulls capable of carrying 6 people in VIP conditions or 16 for operational purposes.

PL 48   9/1993, RHKP

11 SEASPRAY CLASS (INSHORE PATROL CRAFT)

PL 22-32

Dimensions, feet (metres): 32.5 × 13.8 × 4.3 *(9.9 × 4.2 × 1.3)*
Main machinery: 2 Caterpillar 3208TA diesels; 680 hp *(508 kW)*; 2 shafts
Speed, knots: 35
Complement: 4
Radars: Surface search: Koden; I band.

Comment: Built by Seaspray Boats, Fremantle. First three delivered in mid-1992, remainder in
early 1993.

PL 29   9/1993, RHKP

2 SHARK CAT INTERCEPTORS

PL 20-21

Displacement, tons: 4.5
Dimensions, feet (metres): 27 × 9.2 × 1.6 *(8.3 × 2.8 × 0.5)*
Main machinery: 2 outboards; 540 hp *(403 kW)*
Speed, knots: 40+
Complement: 4
Radars: Surface search: Koden; I band.

Comment: Catamaran construction. Commissioned in October 1988.

PL 20   *9/1993, RHKP*

6 WIN CLASS (MOTOR BOATS)

PL 35   PL 36   PL 85   PL 87-89

Comment: Built by Choy Lee SY in 1970. Of 4.8 tons and 20 kts with a range of 160 miles at full speed. Being deleted.

WIN class (old number)   *1987, RHKP*

11 HIGH SPEED INTERCEPTORS

PV 10-12   PV 30-37

Comment: *PV 10-12* are 9.5 m and *PV 30-37* are 7.5 m Typhoon RHIBs. Operated by the Small Boat Unit. Others of this type (fluctuating numbers) are operated as tenders to larger patrol craft.

PV 11   *9/1993, RHKP*

LAND-BASED MARITIME AIRCRAFT

Numbers/Type: 6/2 Sikorsky S-76 A/C.
Operational speed: 145 kts *(269 km/h)*.
Service ceiling: 10 800 ft *(3565 m)*.
Range: 430 nm *(798 km)*.
Role/Weapon systems: Coastal surveillance/SAR and transport helicopters acquired in 1993-95. Sensors: FLIR. Weapons: Unarmed.

Numbers/Type: 1 Cessna 404 Titan.
Operational speed: 258 kts *(478 km/h)*.
Service ceiling: 30 200 ft *(9200 m)*.
Range: 1485 nm *(2748 km)*.
Role/Weapon systems: Coastal surveillance for smugglers and 'boat people'. Sensors: Weather radar and cameras. Weapons: Unarmed.

Numbers/Type: 1 Pilatus Britten-Norman Islander.
Operational speed: 150 kts *(280 km/h)*.
Service ceiling: 18 900 ft *(5760 m)*.
Range: 1500 nm *(2775 km)*.
Role/Weapon systems: Supports RHKP in inter-island surveillance and against smugglers. Sensors: Weather radar and cameras. Weapons: Unarmed.

CUSTOMS

Note: Among other craft three Damen 26 m Sector command launches were completed in 1986 by Chung Wah SB & Eng Co Ltd, Kowloon. In all essentials these craft are sisters of the 15 operated by the Royal Hong Kong Police with the exception of the latter's slow speed waterjet. Names: *Sea Glory* (Customs 6), *Sea Guardian* (Customs 5), *Sea Leader* (Customs 2).

HUNGARY

Headquarters' Appointment

Chief of General Staff:
    Lieutenant General Janos Deak
Head of Maritime Wing:
    Lieutenant Colonel István Horváth

Diplomatic Representation

Defence Attaché in London:
    Colonel Peter Szücs

Personnel

(a)   1994: 400 officers and men
(b)   12 months' national service

General

The Navy was dissolved by 1968 but a maritime wing of the Army is active on the Danube in the form of an independent maritime brigade. Based in Budapest to patrol 420 km of the Danube. Live ordnance is still a hazard in the river.

Mercantile Marine

Lloyd's Register of Shipping:
    9 vessels of 45 105 tons gross

DELETIONS

1991   1 Transport Barge 511-001
1993   AM 14, AM 24

MINE WARFARE FORCES

6 NESTIN CLASS (RIVER MINESWEEPERS)

ÚJPEST AM 11   **SZÁZHALOMBATTA** AM 21   **DUNAÚJVÁROS** AM 31
BAJA AM 12   **ÓBUDA** AM 22   **DUNAFOLDVAR** AM 32

Displacement, tons: 72 full load
Dimensions, feet (metres): 88.6 × 20.7 × 5.2 *(27 × 6.3 × 1.6)*
Main machinery: 2 Torpedo 12-cyl diesels; 520 hp(m) *(382 kW)*; 2 shafts
Speed, knots: 15. **Range, miles:** 860 at 11 kts
Complement: 17 (1 officer)
Guns: 5 Hispano 20 mm (1 triple fwd, 2 single aft).
Mines: 24 ground mines.
Radars: Navigation: Decca; I band.

Comment: Built by Brodotehnika, Belgrade in 1979-80. Full magnetic/acoustic and wire sweeping capabilities. Kram minesweeping system employs a towed sweep at 200 m.

SZÁZHALOMBATTA   *2/1992, Eric Grove*

45 AN-2 CLASS MINE WARFARE/PATROL CRAFT

542-001 to 542-053

Displacement, tons: 11.5
Dimensions, feet (metres): 44 × 12.5 × 2 *(13.4 × 3.8 × 0.6)*
Main machinery: 2 diesels; 220 hp(m) *(162 kW)*; 2 shafts
Speed, knots: 9
Complement: 6
Guns: 2—12.7 mm (twin) MGs.
Mines: Can lay ground mines.

Comment: Aluminium hulls built between 1955 and 1965. Act as MCMV/patrol craft using mechanical sweeps and countermining. About 40 are active each Summer, being laid up in the Winter. Can be taken by road transport to the Tisza river. One of the craft, *542-004*, acts as a diving tender.

542-051   *9/1990, Per Kornefeldt*

AUXILIARIES

One transport barge (CSSZ-001 ex-511-002) can double as landing craft (one tank) or bridging elements. New engines fitted in 1990. Of 170 tons and 50 × 6 m.
One fireboat 531-001.
Two Volvo motor boats 583-001/002.
Two dumb diving pontoons and one tug.
Additional craft are taken up from civilian trade when required.

ICELAND

Senior Officer

Director of Coast Guard:
Hafsteinn Hafsteinsson

Duties

The Coast Guard Service deals with fishery protection, salvage, rescue, hydrographic research, surveying and lighthouse duties. All ships have at least double the number of berths required for the complement.

Personnel

1994: 126 officers and men

Colours

In 1990 all vessels were marked with red, white and blue diagonal stripes on the ships' side and the Coast Guard name (Landhelgisgaeslan).

Base

Reykjavik

Research Ships

A number of government Research Ships bearing RE pennant numbers operate off Iceland.

Aircraft

Maritime aircraft include a Fokker Friendship plus Dauphin 2 and Ecureuil helicopters

Mercantile Marine

Lloyd's Register of Shipping:
381 vessels of 173 506 tons gross

COAST GUARD

Name	No	Builders	Commissioned
AEGIR	—	Aalborg Vaerft, Denmark	1968
TYR	—	Dannebrog Vaerft, Denmark	15 Mar 1975

Displacement, tons: 1200 (1300 *Tyr*) standard; 1500 full load
Dimensions, feet (metres): 229.6 × 33 × 14.8 *(70 × 10 × 4.6)*
Main machinery: 2 MAN/Burmeister & Wain 8L 40/54 diesels; 13 200 hp(m) *(9.68 MW)* sustained; 2 shafts
Speed, knots: 19 *(Aegir)*; 20 *(Tyr)*
Complement: 19
Guns: 1 Bofors 40 mm/60.
Radars: Surface search: Sperry; E/F band.
Navigation: Furuno; I band.
Sonars: Hull-mounted; active search; high frequency *(Tyr)*.
Helicopters: Platform for 1 light.

Comment: Similar ships but *Tyr* has a slightly improved design and *Aegir* has no sonar. The hangar is between the funnels. The 57 mm gun has been replaced.

AEGIR   *1993, Iceland Coast Guard*

TYR   *6/1993, H M Steele*

Name	No	Builders	Commissioned
ODINN	—	Aalborg Vaerft, Denmark	Jan 1960

Displacement, tons: 1200 full load
Dimensions, feet (metres): 210 × 33 × 13 *(64 × 10 × 4)*
Main machinery: 2 MAN/Burmeister & Wain diesels; 5700 hp(m) *(4.19 MW)*; 2 shafts
Speed, knots: 18
Complement: 19
Guns: 1 Bofors 40 mm/60.
Radars: Surface search: Sperry; E/F band.
Navigation: Furuno; I band.
Helicopters: Platform for 1 light.

Comment: Refitted in Denmark by Aarhus Flydedock AS late 1975. Has twin funnels and helicopter hangar. A large crane was fitted in 1989 on the starboard side at the forward end of the flight deck. The original 57 mm gun has been replaced.

ODINN   *1993, Iceland Coast Guard*

Name	No	Builders	Commissioned
BALDUR	—	Vélsmiöja Seyöisfjaröar	8 May 1991

Displacement, tons: 54 full load
Dimensions, feet (metres): 65.6 × 17.1 × 5.6 *(20 × 5.2 × 1.7)*
Main machinery: 2 Caterpillar 3406TA diesels; 640 hp *(480 kW)*; 2 shafts
Speed, knots: 12
Complement: 5
Radars: Navigation: Furuno; I band.

Comment: Built in an Icelandic Shipyard. Used for survey work.

BALDUR   *1993, Iceland Coast Guard*

INDIA

Headquarters' Appointments

Chief of Naval Staff:
Admiral V S Shekhawat, PVSM, AVSM, VrC, ADC
Vice Chief of Naval Staff:
Vice Admiral S K Chand, PVSM, AVSM, ADC
Deputy Chief of Naval Staff:
Vice Admiral Vishnu Bhagwat, AVSM
Controller of Warship Production and Acquisition:
Vice Admiral A R Tandon, AVSM
Chief of Personnel:
Vice Admiral R B Suri, AVSM, VSM
Chief of Logistics Support:
Vice Admiral V Koithara

Senior Appointments

Flag Officer C-in-C Western Naval Command:
Vice Admiral K A S Z Raju, PVSM, AVSM, NM
Flag Officer C-in-C Eastern Naval Command:
Vice Admiral B Guha, AVSM
Flag Officer C-in-C Southern Naval Command:
Vice Admiral Inderjit Bedi, AVSM
Flag Officer Commanding Western Fleet:
Rear Admiral R Ganesh
Flag Officer Commanding Eastern Fleet:
Rear Admiral Harinder Singh
Fortress Commander, Andaman and Nicobar Islands:
Vice Admiral P S Das, UYSM, VSM
Flag Officer, Naval Aviation and Goa Area (at Goa):
Rear Admiral V Pasricha
Flag Officer, Submarines (Vishakapatnam):
Rear Admiral S C Anand

Naval Air Arm

Squadron	Aircraft	Role
300 (Goa)	Sea Harrier FRS Mk 51	Fighter/Strike
	Sea Harrier T Mk 60	Trainer
312 (Madras)	Tu-142M 'Bear F'	LRMP/ASW
315 (Goa)	Il-38 May	LRMP/ASW
318 (Goa)	PBN Defender	Utility
321 (Goa)	HAL Chetak	Utility/SAR (Flight)
330 (Cochin)	Sea King Mk 42/42A	ASW
331 (Cochin)	HAL Chetak	Utility/SAR
333 (ships) (Goa)	Kamov Ka-25 'Hormone'	ASW
	Kamov Ka-28 'Helix'	ASW
336 (Cochin)	Sea King Mk 42/42A	ASW
339 (Bombay)	Sea King 42B	ASW/ASVW
550 (Vishwanath)	Tu-142M 'Bear F'	LRMP/ASW (Flight)
551 (Goa)	HAL HJT-16 Kiran	Training (OCU)
561 (Cochin)	HAL Chetak	Training
562 (Cochin)	Hughes 300, Chetak	Training
	HAL Jaguar	Strike

Air Stations

Name	Location	Role
INS *Garuda*	Willingdon Island, Cochin	Helicopters
INS *Hansa*	Goa	HQ Flag Officer Naval Air Stations, LRMP, Strike/Fighter
INS *Sea Bird*	Karwar	Fleet Support (late 1990s)
INS *Utkrosh*	Port Blair, Andaman Isles	Maritime Patrol
	Uchipuli, Tamil Nadu	Maritime Patrol
	Ramanathuram	Maritime Patrol
	Vishakapatnam	Fleet support and maritime patrol building
	Tiruchirapalli	
INS *Rajali*	Arakonam	LRMP, Helo Training
	Bangalore	LRMP building Naval Air Technical School

Personnel

(a) 1994: 55 000 officers and ratings (including 5000 Naval Air Arm)
(b) Voluntary service
(c) A Marine Commando Force was formed in 1986.

Bases and Establishments

New Delhi, HQ (INS *India*)
Bombay, C-in-C **Western Command**, barracks and main Dockyard; with one 'Carrier' dock. New submarine pens being built. Supply school (INS *Hamla*). The region includes Mazagon and Goa shipyards.
Vishakapatnam, C-in-C **Eastern Command**, submarine base (INS *Virbahu*), submarine school (INS *Satyavahana*) and major dockyard built with Soviet support and being extended. Naval Air Station (INS *Dega*). New entry training (INS *Chilka*). At Vijayaraghavapuram is the submarine VLF W/T station completed in September 1986. Facilities at Madras and Calcutta. The region includes Hindustan and Garden Reach shipyards.
Cochin, C-in-C **Southern Command**, Naval Air Station, and professional schools (INS *Venduruthy*) (all naval Training now comes under Southern Command). Ship repair yard. Trials establishment (INS *Dronacharya*).
Goa is HQ Flag Officer Naval Air Stations.
Karwar (near Goa) has been selected as the site for a new naval base; first phase due for completion after 1994 but may be delayed at least two years. Alongside berthing for Aircraft Carriers and a naval air station are planned. At Lakshadweep in the Laccadive Islands there is a patrol craft base. There are also limited support facilities including a floating dock at Andaman and Nicobar bases.
Naval Academy at Goa to move to Ezhimala, new base called INS *Jawarhalal Nehru*. A college of naval warfare has been established at Karanja.
Shipbuilding: Bombay (submarines, destroyers, frigates, corvettes); Calcutta (frigates, corvettes, LSTs, auxiliaries); Goa (patrol craft, LCU, MCMV facility planned).

Prefix to Ships' Names

INS

Weapons and Sensors

Indian developments include:
SSM: Prithvi test fired in 1987; range 240 km; warhead 1000 kg.
SAM: Agni, Akash and Trishul; all being developed, at least one for the Navy. Trishul has a reported range of 10 km and is to be in service in 1994/95.
Medium range chaff decoy rocket. Sonar towed arrays. Remote piloted vehicle (RPV).

Strength of the Fleet

Type	Active (Reserve)	Building (Projected)
Patrol Submarines	14 (3)	3
Attack Carriers (Medium)	2	(2)
Destroyers	5	3 (1)
Frigates	14	3
Corvettes	18 (1)	7 (11)
Patrol Ships	7	3
Fast Attack Craft—Missile	4 (4)	—
Fast Attack Craft—Patrol/Torpedo	12	1
Landing Ships	10	1
LCUs	7	—
Minesweepers—Ocean	12	—
Minesweepers—Inshore	6 (4)	—
Minehunters	—	(6)
Survey Ships	10	—
Training Ships	1	(1)
Submarine Tender	1	—
Diving Support/Rescue Ships	1	2
Replenishment Tankers	2	1
Support Tankers	4	—
Water Carriers	3	—
Tugs	15	—
Coast Guard	43	10 (3)

Mercantile Marine

Lloyd's Register of Shipping:
886 vessels of 6 574 733 tons gross

DELETIONS

Submarines

1991 *Chakra, Kanderi*
1992 *Kalvari*

Frigates

1991 *Kamorta, Betwa*
1992 *Beas*
1993 *Trishul*

PENNANT LIST

Submarines

S 20	Kursura
S 21	Karanj
S 40	Vela
S 41	Vagir
S 42	Vagli
S 43	Vagsheer
S 44	Shishumar
S 45	Shankush
S 46	Shalki
S 47	Shankul
S 55	Sindhughosh
S 56	Sindhudhvaj
S 57	Sindhuraj
S 58	Sindhuvir
S 59	Sindhuratna
S 60	Sindhukesari
S 61	Sindhukiri
S 62	Sindhuvijay

Aircraft Carriers

R 11	Vikrant
R 22	Viraat

Destroyers

—	Delhi (bldg)
—	Mysore (bldg)
D 51	Rajput
D 52	Rana
D 53	Ranjit
D 54	Ranvir
D 55	Ranvijay

Frigates

F 20	Godavari
F 21	Gomati
F 22	Ganga
F 33	Nilgiri
F 34	Himgiri
F 35	Udaygiri
F 36	Dunagiri
F 41	Taragiri
F 42	Vindhyagiri
P 68	Arnala
P 69	Androth
P 73	Anjadip
P 75	Amini
P 78	Kadmath

Corvettes

P 33	Abhay
P 34	Ajay
P 35	Akshay
P 36	Agray
P 44	Kirpan
P 46	Kuthar
P 47	Khanjar
P 49	Khukri
—	Kora (bldg)
—	Kirch (bldg)
K 40	Veer
K 41	Nirbhik
K 42	Nipat
K 43	Nishank
K 44	Nirghat
K 45	Vibhuti
K 46	Vipul
K 52	Vinash
K 53	Nashak
K 71	Vijay Durg
K 72	Sindhu Durg
K 73	Hos Durg

Patrol Forces

P 50	Sukanya
P 51	Subhadra
P 52	Saryu
P 53	Savitri
P 54	Saryu
P 55	Sharada
P 56	Sujata
K 90	Prachand
K 91	Pralaya
K 92	Pratap
K 93	Prabal
K 94	Chapal
K 95	Chamak
K 96	Chatak
K 97	Charag

Mine Warfare Forces

M 61	Pondicherry
M 62	Porbandar
M 63	Bedi
M 64	Bhavnagar
M 65	Alleppey
M 66	Ratnagiri
M 67	Karwar
M 68	Cannanore
M 69	Cuddalore
M 70	Kakinada
M 71	Kozhikoda
M 72	Konkan
M 83	Mahé
M 84	Malvan
M 85	Mangalore
M 86	Malpe
M 87	Mulki
M 88	Magdala
M 89	Bulsar
M 90	Bhatkal
M 2705	Bimlipitan
M 2707	Bassein

Amphibious Forces

L 14	Ghorpad
L 15	Kesari
L 16	Shardul
L 17	Sharabh
L 18	Cheetah
L 19	Mahish
L 20	Magar
L 21	Guldar
L 22	Kumbhir
L 23	Gharial
L 24	— (bldg)
L 34	Vasco da Gama
L 38	Midhur
L 39	Mangala

Auxiliaries

A —	Aditya
A 15	Nireekshak
A 50	Deepak
A 51	Gaj
A 54	Amba
A 57	Shakti
A 86	Tir
J 14	Nirupak
J 15	Investigator
J 16	Jamuna
J 17	Sutlej
J 18	Sandhayak
J 19	Nirdeshak
J 33	Makar
J 34	Mithun
J 35	Meen
J 36	Mesh

SUBMARINES

Notes: (1) The ex-Soviet Charlie class nuclear-powered submarine *Chakra* was leased for three years from January 1988. The lease was not extended and she returned to Vladivostock in January 1991. Although interest is still being taken in buying a modern SSN, the likely plan now is to build a nuclear propelled submarine in India. For this purpose there is an R&D project called the Advanced Technology Vessel which is reasonably well funded and has facilities in Delhi, Hyderabad, Vishakapatnam and Kalpakkam. A Navy-Defence Research and Development Organisation (DRDO) runs the project and since the mid-1980s has had a Vice Admiral in charge. The submarine will be a development of a Russian design with an Indian PWR. The nuclear reactor facility has been tested. This project has priority over the new aircraft carrier and is running to time. A 2000 ton submarine is planned to be laid down in 1997.

(2) In spite of many negotiations, India has not acquired midget submarines. In 1991 up to 12 Cosmos CE2F/FX100 swimmer delivery vessels were delivered. These are two-man underwater chariots for commando operations.

4 + 2 SHISHUMAR (209) CLASS (TYPE 1500)

Name	No	Builders	Laid down	Launched	Commissioned
SHISHUMAR	S 44	Howaldtswerke, Kiel	1 May 1982	13 Dec 1984	22 Sep 1986
SHANKUSH	S 45	Howaldtswerke, Kiel	1 Sep 1982	11 May 1984	20 Nov 1986
SHALKI	S 46	Mazagon Dock Ltd, Bombay	5 June 1984	30 Sep 1989	7 Feb 1992
SHANKUL	S 47	Mazagon Dock Ltd, Bombay	3 Sep 1989	21 Mar 1992	1994
—	S 48	Mazagon Dock Ltd, Bombay	July 1994	1997	1997
—	S 49	Mazagon Dock Ltd, Bombay	June 1995	1998	1998

Displacement, tons: 1450 standard; 1660 surfaced; 1850 dived

Dimensions, feet (metres): 211.2 × 21.3 × 19.7 *(64.4 × 6.5 × 6)*

Main machinery: Diesel-electric; 4 MTU 12V 493 AZ80 GA31L diesels; 2400 hp(m) *(1.76 MW)* sustained; 4 alternators; 1.8 MW; 1 Siemens motor; 4600 hp(m) *(3.38 MW)* sustained; 1 shaft

Speed, knots: 11 surfaced; 22 dived

Range, miles: 8000 snorting at 8 kts; 13 000 surfaced at 10 kts

Complement: 40 (8 officers)

Torpedoes: 8—21 in *(533 mm)* tubes. 14 AEG SUT; wire-guided; active/passive homing to 28 km *(15.3 nm)* at 23 kts; 12 km *(6.6 nm)* at 35 kts; warhead 250 kg.

Mines: External 'strap-on' type.

Countermeasures: ESM: Phoenix II; radar warning.

Fire control: Singer Librascope Mk 1.

Radars: Surface search: Thomson-CSF Calypso; I band.

Sonars: Atlas Elektronik CSU 83; active/passive search and attack; medium frequency.
Thomson Sintra DUUX-5 (S 46 and 47); passive ranging and intercept.

Programmes: After several years of discussion Howaldtswerke concluded an agreement with the Indian Navy on 11 December 1981. This was in four basic parts: the building in West Germany of two Type 1500 submarines; the supply of 'packages'

SHALKI   6/1992, G Toremans

for the building of two more boats at Mazagon, Bombay; training of various groups of specialists for the design and construction of the Mazagon pair; logistic services during the trials and early part of the commissions as well as consultation services in Bombay.

The first two sailed for India February 1987. The second two delayed by assembly problems caused by faulty welding.

In 1984 it was announced that a further two submarines would be built at Mazagon for a total of six but this was overtaken by events in 1987-88 and the agreement with HDW terminated at four. This was reconsidered in 1992 and two more are

now to be built. The medium term plan is for an indigenous design of 2000 tons to be built at Bombay after the 209 class programme is completed and Western designs have been evaluated.

Structure: The Type 1500 has a central bulkhead and an IKL designed integrated escape sphere which can carry the full crew of up to 40 men, has an oxygen supply for eight hours, and can withstand pressures at least as great as those that can be withstood by the submarine's pressure hull. Diving depth 260 m *(853 ft)*. DUUX-5 sonar will be back-fitted to the first pair in the mid-1990s.

8 KILO (TYPE 877EM) CLASS

Name	No	Builders	Commissioned
SINDHUGHOSH	S 55	Sudomekh, Leningrad	30 Apr 1986
SINDHUDHVAJ	S 56	Sudomekh, Leningrad	12 June 1987
SINDHURAJ	S 57	Sudomekh, Leningrad	20 Oct 1987
SINDHUVIR	S 58	Sudomekh, Leningrad	26 Aug 1988
SINDHURATNA	S 59	Sudomekh, Leningrad	16 Feb 1989
SINDHUKESARI	S 60	Sudomekh, Leningrad	10 Mar 1989
SINDHUKIRI	S 61	Sudomekh, Leningrad	4 Mar 1990
SINDHUVIJAY	S 62	Sudomekh, Leningrad	8 Mar 1991

Displacement, tons: 2325 surfaced; 3076 dived

Dimensions, feet (metres): 242.1 × 32.5 × 21.7 *(73.8 × 9.9 × 6.6)*

Main machinery: Diesel-electric; 2 diesels; 3650 hp(m) *(2.68 MW)*; 2 generators; 1 motor; 5500 hp(m) *(4.05 MW)*; 1 shaft

Speed, knots: 10 surfaced; 17 dived

Range, miles: 6000 at 7 kts snorting; 400 at 3 kts dived

Complement: 52

Missiles: SAM: SA-N-8/14 (S 58 onwards, but not confirmed).

Torpedoes: 6—21 in *(533 mm)* tubes. Combination of Type 53-65; passive wake homing to 25 km *(13.5 nm)* at 50 kts; warhead 300 kg and TEST 71/96; anti-submarine; active/passive homing to 15 km *(8.1 nm)* at 40 kts; warhead 205 kg. Total of 18 weapons.

Mines: 24 in lieu of torpedoes.

Countermeasures: ESM: Stop Light; radar warning. Quad Loop D/F.

Radars: Navigation: Snoop Tray; I band.

Sonars: Shark Teeth; hull-mounted; active/passive search and attack; medium frequency.
Whale series; passive search; low frequency.
Mouse Roar; hull-mounted; active search; high frequency.

Programmes: The Kilo class was launched in the Soviet Navy in 1979 and although India was the first country to acquire one they have since been transferred to Algeria, Poland and Romania. Because of the slowness of the S 209 programme and its early termination, the original order in 1983 for six Kilo class expanded to ten but was then cut back again to eight. Plans to manufacture the class under licence in India have been shelved for the time being but design drawings are held should this project be resurrected.

Structure: Diving depth, 350 m *(1150 ft)*. Reported that from *Sindhuvir* onwards these submarines have an SA-N-8/14 SAM capability. Two torpedo tubes can fire wire-guided torpedoes.

Operational: Based at Vishakapatnam and Bombay.

SINDHUVIJAY   2/1992

6 FOXTROT (TYPE 641) CLASS

KURSURA S 20	**KARANJ** S 21	**VELA** S 40	**VAGIR** S 41	**VAGLI** S 42	**VAGSHEER** S 43

Displacement, tons: 1952 surfaced; 2475 dived

Dimensions, feet (metres): 299.5 × 24.6 × 19.7 *(91.3 × 7.5 × 6)*

Main machinery: Diesel-electric; 3 Type 37-D diesels; 6000 hp(m) *(4.4 MW)*; 3 motors (1 × 2700 and 2 × 1350); 5400 hp(m) *(3.97 MW)*; 3 shafts; 1 auxiliary motor; 140 hp(m) *(103 kW)*

Speed, knots: 16 surfaced; 15 dived

Range, miles: 20 000 at 8 kts surfaced; 380 at 2 kts dived

Complement: 75 (8 officers)

Torpedoes: 10—21 in *(533 mm)* (6 fwd, 4 aft) tubes. 22 SET-65E/SAET-60; active/passive homing to 15 km *(8.1 nm)* at 40 kts; warhead 205/400 kg.

Mines: 44 in lieu of torpedoes.

Countermeasures: ESM: Stop Light; radar warning.

Radars: Surface search: Snoop Tray; I band.

Sonars: Herkules/Fenik; bow-mounted; passive search and attack; medium frequency.

Programmes: Built at Sudomekh Yard, Leningrad. *Karanj* arrived in India in October 1970, *Kursura* in December 1970, *Vela*

VAGLI   11/1987, G Jacobs

November 1973, *Vagir* December 1973, *Vagli* September 1974, *Vagsheer* December 1975. All new construction. At least two have been refitted in the USSR.

Structure: Diving depth 250 m *(820 ft)*, reducing with age.

Operational: First one paid off in 1990 and has been cannibalised for spares, second in 1992 and of the remaining six, up to three are operational at any one time and are used mostly for training. One is being upgraded in 1994 but the rest may be withdrawn from service by 1996.

AIRCRAFT CARRIERS

Note: The plan announced in 1989 was to build two new aircraft carriers, the first to replace *Vikrant* in 1997. A design study contract was signed with DCN (France) for a ship of about 28 000 tons and with a speed in excess of 30 kts. Size restricted by available construction dock capacity. Options included Ski Jump and CTOL. The Indian Naval Design Organisation was to translate the design study into the production model with construction to start at Cochin in 1993. However in mid-1991 the Committee on Defence Expenditure told the Navy to abandon plans for large carriers, and design effort should be shifted to Italian *Garibaldi* type. In October 1993 the retiring Commander-in-Chief of the Navy restarted the commitment to a large carrier "to be ready for trials by the turn of the century" but it is unlikely that funds are available. The alternative of a helicopter support ship (LPH) has also been rumoured. The whole project takes second priority to the nuclear submarine effort.

1 HERMES CLASS

Name	No	Builders	Laid down	Launched	Commissioned
VIRAAT (ex-HMS *Hermes*)	R 22	Vickers Shipbuilding Ltd, Barrow-in-Furness	21 June 1944	16 Feb 1953	18 Nov 1959

Displacement, tons: 23 900 standard; 28 700 full load
Dimensions, feet (metres): 685 wl; 744.3 oa × 90; 160 oa × 28.5 *(208.8; 226.9 × 27.4; 48.8 × 8.7)*
Main machinery: 4 Admiralty boilers; 400 psi *(28 kg/cm sq)*; 700°F *(370°C)*; 2 Parsons geared turbines; 76 000 hp *(57 MW)*; 2 shafts
Speed, knots: 28
Complement: 1350 (143 officers)

Missiles: SAM: 2 Shorts Seacat quad launchers; radar guidance to 5 km *(3.3 nm)*.
Guns: Some 30 mm/65 6-barrelled ADGs may be fitted.
Countermeasures: Decoys: 2 Knebworth Corvus chaff launchers.
ESM: Radar intercept and jamming.
Combat data systems: CAAIS action data automation; Link 10. SATCOM.

Fire control: GWS 22 for SAM.
Radars: Air search: Marconi Type 966; A band with IFF 1010.
Air/surface search: Plessey Type 994; E/F band.
Navigation: Two Racal Decca 1006; I band.
Fire control: Two Plessey Type 904; I/J band.
Tacan: FT 13-S/M.
Sonars: Graseby Type 184M; hull-mounted; active search and attack; 6-9 kHz.

Fixed wing aircraft: 12 Sea Harriers FRS Mk 51 (capacity for 30).
Helicopters: 7 Sea King Mk 42B/C ASW/ASV/Vertrep and Ka-27 Helix.

Programmes: Purchased in May 1986 from the UK, thence to an extensive refit in Devonport Dockyard. Life extension of at least 10 years. Commissioned in Indian Navy 20 May 1987.

Modernisation: Devonport refit included new fire control equipment, navigation radars, and deck landing aids. Boilers were converted to take distillate fuel and the ship was given improved NBC protection. Seacat launchers removed but subsequently replaced.
Structure: Fitted with 12° ski jump. Reinforced flight deck (0.75 in); 1-2 inches of armour over magazines and machinery spaces. Four LCVP on after davits. Magazine capacity includes 80 lightweight torpedoes.
Operational: The Sea Harrier complement will normally be no more than 12 or 18 aircraft leaving room for a greater mix of Sea King and Hormone helicopters (see *Shipborne Aircraft* section). The engine room was flooded in September 1993, taking the ship out of service for several months.

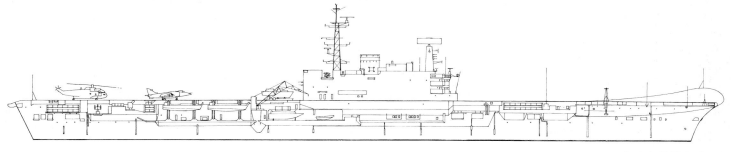

VIRAAT
(Scale 1 : 1200), Ian Sturton

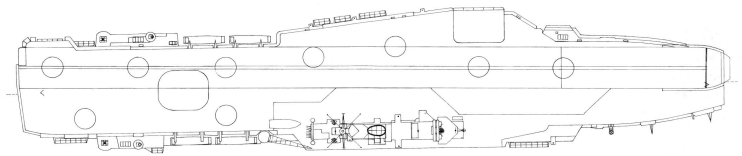

VIRAAT
(Scale 1 : 1200), Ian Sturton

VIRAAT
6/1993, 92 Wing RAAF

1 MAJESTIC CLASS

Name	No	Builders	Laid down	Launched	Commissioned
VIKRANT (ex-HMS *Hercules*)	R 11	Vickers-Armstrong Ltd, Tyne	14 Oct 1943	22 Sep 1945	4 Mar 1961

Displacement, tons: 16 000 standard; 19 500 full load
Dimensions, feet (metres): 700 × 80; 128 oa × 24
(*213.4 × 24.4; 39 oa × 7.3*)
Flight deck, feet (metres): 690 × 112 *(210 × 34)*
Main machinery: 4 Admiralty boilers; 400 psi *(28 kg/cm sq)*;
700°F *(370°C)*; 2 Parsons turbines; 40 000 hp *(30 MW)*; 2
shafts
Speed, knots: 24.5
Range, miles: 12 000 at 14 kts; 6200 at 23 kts
Complement: 1075 peace; 1345 war

Guns: 7 Bofors 40 mm/70; 90° elevation; 300 rounds/minute to
12 km *(6.6 nm)* anti-aircraft; weight of shell 2.4 kg. Some may
have been replaced by 30 mm/65 6-barrelled ADGs.
Combat data systems: Selenia IPN-10 action data automation.
Radars: Air search: Signaal LW 08; D band; range 264 km
(145 nm) for 2 m² target.
Air/surface search: Signaal DA 05; E/F band; range 137 km
(75 nm) for 2 m² target.
Navigation: Signaal ZW 06; I band.
Sonars: Graseby 750; hull-mounted; active search and attack;
medium frequency.

Fixed wing aircraft: 6 Sea Harriers FRS Mk 51.
Helicopters: 9 Sea Kings Mk 42 ASW/ASV. 1 Chetak SAR.

Programmes: Acquired from the UK in January 1957 after having been suspended in May 1946 when structurally almost
complete and 75% fitted out. Taken in hand by Harland & Wolff
Ltd, Belfast, in April 1957 for completion in 1961. Commissioned on 4 March 1961 and renamed *Vikrant*.
Modernisation: Major two-year refit began in January 1979. Re-
entered service 3 January 1982. Second major refit in 1983.
Third refit in 1987-89 (recommissioned 12 February 1989) to
increase life expectancy to 1997 at least; ski jump fitted and
possible improvements made to CIWS.
Structure: Flight deck: Two electrically operated lifts. 9.75° ski-
ramp to take '150 ton lift' installed during 1987-89 modernisation; steam catapults removed. The original ski jump structure
was not strong enough for a fully loaded Sea Harrier and further modifications were made in 1990/91.
Operational: Total capacity for 22 aircraft.

VIKRANT (modified ski jump)   *1992*

VIKRANT   *1992*

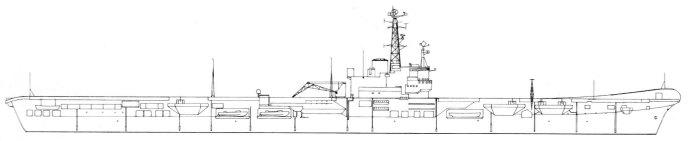

VIKRANT   *(Scale 1 : 1200), Ian Sturton*

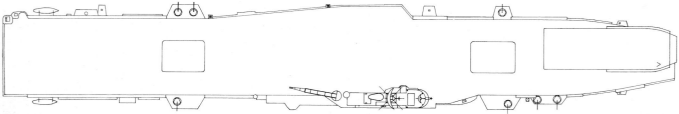

VIKRANT   *(Scale 1 : 1200), Ian Sturton*

VIKRANT   *1992*

DESTROYERS

5 RAJPUT (KASHIN II) CLASS (TYPE 61MP)

Name	No	Builders	Commissioned
RAJPUT	D 51	Kommuna, Nikolayev	30 Sep 1980
RANA	D 52	Kommuna, Nikolayev	28 June 1982
RANJIT	D 53	Kommuna, Nikolayev	24 Nov 1983
RANVIR	D 54	Kommuna, Nikolayev	28 Aug 1986
RANVIJAY	D 55	Kommuna, Nikolayev	15 Jan 1988

Displacement, tons: 3950 standard; 4974 full load
Dimensions, feet (metres): 480.5 × 51.8 × 15.7
(146.5 × 15.8 × 4.8)
Main machinery: COGAG; 4 gas turbines; 72 000 hp(m)
(53 MW); 2 shafts
Speed, knots: 35. **Range, miles:** 4500 at 18 kts; 2600 at 30 kts
Complement: 320 (35 officers)

Missiles: SSM: 4 SS-N-2D Styx ❶; IR homing to 83 km *(45 nm)* at
0.9 Mach; warhead 513 kg; sea-skimmer at end of run.
SAM: 2 SA-N-1 Goa twin launchers ❷; command guidance to
31.5 km *(17 nm)* at 2 Mach; height 91-22 860 m *(300-
75 000 ft)*; warhead 60 kg; 44 missiles. Some SSM capability.
Guns: 2—3 in *(76 mm)*/60 (twin, fwd) ❸; 80° elevation; 90
rounds/minute to 15 km *(8 nm)*; weight of shell 6.8 kg.
8—30 mm/65 (4 twin) *(Rajput, Rana and Ranjit)* ❹; 85° elevation; 500 rounds/minute to 5 km *(2.7 nm)*; weight of shell
0.54 kg.
4—30 mm/65 ADG 630 (6 barrels per mounting) *(Ranvir and
Ranvijay)*; 85° elevation; 3000 rounds/minute combined to
2 km.
Torpedoes: 5—21 in *(533 mm)* (quin) tubes ❺. Combination of
SET-65E; anti-submarine; active/passive homing to 15 km
(8.1 nm) at 40 kts; warhead 205 kg and Type 53-65; passive
wake homing to 25 km *(13.5 nm)* at 50 kts; warhead 300 kg.
A/S mortars: 2 RBU 6000 12-tubed trainable ❻; range 6000 m;
warhead 31 kg.
Countermeasures: 4—16-barrelled chaff launchers for radar
decoy and distraction.

RANA   *(Scale 1 : 1200), Ian Sturton*

ESM: Two Watch Dog. Two Top Hat A and B; radar warning.
Radars: Air search: Big Net A ❼; C band; range 183 km *(100 nm)*
for 2 m² target.
Air/surface search: Head Net C ❽; 3D; E band; range 128 km
(70 nm).
Navigation: Two Don Kay; I band.
Fire control: Two Peel Group ❾; H/I band; range 73 km *(40 nm)*
for 2 m² target.
Owl Screech ❿; G band.
Two Drum Tilt ⓫ or Two Bass Tilt *(Ranvir and Ranvijay)*; H/I
band.
IFF: Two High Pole B.
Sonars: Hull-mounted and VDS; active search and attack;
medium frequency.

Helicopters: 1 Ka-28 Helix ⓬.

Programmes: First batch of three ordered in the mid-1970s. *Ranvir* was the first of the second batch ordered on 20 December
1982.
Structure: All built as new construction for India at Nikolayev
with considerable modifications to the Kashin design. Helicopter hangar, which is reached by a lift from the flight deck,
replaces after 76 mm twin mount and the SS-N-2D launchers
are sited forward of the bridge. *Ranvir* and *Ranvijay* differ from
previous ships in class by being fitted with ADGM-630 30 mm
guns and two Bass Tilt fire control radars. It is possible that an
Italian combat data system compatible with Selenia IPN-10 is
installed. Inmarsat fitted.

RANVIJAY   *6/1992*

RANVIR   *6/1993, 92 Wing RAAF*

Name	No
DELHI	—
MYSORE	—
—	—

Displacement, tons: 6200 full load
Dimensions, feet (metres): 524.9 × 55.8 × 21.3 *(160 × 17 × 6.5)*
Main machinery: CODAG; 2 AM-50 Soviet gas turbines (GE/HAL LM 2500 in later ships); 54 000 hp(m) *(49 MW)*; 2 Bergen/Garden Reach KVM-18 diesels; 9920 hp(m) *(7.73 MW)* sustained; 2 shafts
Speed, knots: 28

Missiles: SSM: 4 SS-N-22 Sunburn.
SAM: SA-N-7 twin launcher (aft of the 76 mm gun) and/or 2 Trishul.
Guns: 1 USSR 3 in *(76 mm)*/60 or OTO Melara 76 mm/62 (on the forecastle).
4 USSR 30 mm/65; 6 barrels per mounting (2 each side).
Torpedoes: 6 Whitehead 324 mm (2 triple tubes)
Depth charges: 2 rails.
Countermeasures: ESM/ECM DRDO/Selenia EW equipment
Combat data systems: IPN type.
Radars: Air search: Bharat/Signaal RALW (LW 08); D band.
Surface search: Indra; E band.
Fire control: Bass Tilt; H/I/J band.
Sonars: Thomson Sintra TSM 2633 Spherion; hull-mounted; active search; medium frequency.
Indal/Garden Reach Model 15-750 VDS.

0 + 3 (1) DELHI CLASS (DDG)

Builders	Laid down	Launched	Commissioned
Mazagon Dock Ltd, Bombay	14 Nov 1987	1 Feb 1991	1995
Mazagon Dock Ltd, Bombay	2 Feb 1991	4 June 1993	1997
Mazagon Dock Ltd, Bombay	Dec 1992	1996	1999

DELHI   *2/1991*

Helicopters: 2 Westland Sea Kings Mk 42B or 2 Hindustan Aeronautics ALH.

Programmes: Being built with Russian assistance. *Delhi* ordered in March 1986. *Mysore* ordered in 1990 and laid down as soon as *Delhi* was launched. Third of class laid down in late 1992. Programme is called Project 15. Much delay has been caused by the breakdown in the central control of Russian export equipment.

Structure: The design is described as a 'stretched *Rajput*' with some *Godavari* features. Russian gas turbines have been fitted in *Delhi* (and may be in *Mysore*), later ships will have LM 2500 built in India by HAL under licence. A combination of Russian and Indian weapon systems is being fitted but delays in supplying Russian equipment may mean bringing forward plans to fit later vessels with Western technology.

FRIGATES

3 + 3 GODAVARI CLASS

Name	No
GODAVARI	F 20
GOMATI	F 21
GANGA	F 22
—	F 23
—	F 24
—	F 25

Builders	Laid down	Launched	Commissioned
Mazagon Dock Ltd, Bombay	2 June 1978	15 May 1980	10 Dec 1983
Mazagon Dock Ltd, Bombay	1981	19 Mar 1984	16 Apr 1988
Mazagon Dock Ltd, Bombay	1980	21 Oct 1981	30 Dec 1985
Garden Reach SY, Calcutta	1989	1994	1996
Garden Reach SY, Calcutta	1994	1996	1999
Garden Reach SY, Calcutta	1996	1998	2001

Displacement, tons: 3600; 4500 (F 23-F 25) standard; 3850 full load
Dimensions, feet (metres): 414.9 × 47.6 × 14.8 (29.5 sonar) (F 20-F 22) *(126.5 × 14.5 × 4.5 (9))*
Main machinery: 2 Babcock & Wilcox boilers; 550 psi *(38.7 kg/cm sq)*; 850°F *(450°C)*; 2 turbines; 30 000 hp *(22.4 MW)*; 2 shafts
Speed, knots: 27. **Range, miles:** 4500 at 12 kts
Complement: 313 (40 officers including 13 aircrew)

Missiles: SSM: 4 SS-N-2D Styx ❶; IR homing to 83 km *(45 nm)* at 0.9 Mach; warhead 513 kg; sea-skimmer at end of run. Indian designation P 20 or P 21 (which may have radar homing).
SAM: SA-N-4 Gecko twin launcher ❷; semi-active radar homing to 15 km *(8 nm)* at 2.5 Mach; height 9.1-3048 m *(130-10 000 ft)*; warhead 50 kg; limited surface-to-surface capability; 20 missiles. System called 'Osa-M'.
Trishul may be fitted in F 23-F 25.
Guns: 2—57 mm/70 (twin) ❸; 90° elevation; 120 rounds/minute to 8 km *(4.4 nm)*; weight of shell 2.8 kg.
8—30 mm/65 (4 twin) AK 230 ❹ (F 20-F 22); 85° elevation; 500 rounds/minute to 5 km *(2.7 nm)*; weight of shell 0.54 kg.
4—30 mm/65 AK 630 (F 23-F 25); 6 barrels per mounting; 3000 rounds/minute combined to 2 km.
Torpedoes: 6—324 mm ILAS 3 (2 triple) tubes ❺. Whitehead A244S; anti-submarine; active/passive homing to 7 km *(3.8 nm)* at 33 kts; warhead 34 kg (shaped charge). *Godavari* has tube modifications for the Indian NST 58 version of A244S.
Countermeasures: Decoys: 2 chaff launchers (Super Barricade in due course). Graseby G738 towed torpedo decoy.
ESM/ECM: Selenia INS-3; intercept and jammer.
Combat data systems: Selenia IPN-10 action data automation. Inmarsat communications (JRC) ❻.
Fire control: MR 301 MFCS. MR 103 GFCS.
Radars: Air search: Signaal LW 08 ❼; D band; range 264 km *(145 nm)* for 2 m² target.
Air/surface search: Head Net C ❽; 3D; E band; range 128 km *(70 nm)*.
Navigation/helo control: 2 Signaal ZW 06 ❾; or Don Kay; I band.
Fire control: Two Drum Tilt (F 20-F 22) ❿; H/I band (for 30 mm).
Contraves Seaguard (F 23-F 25); I band (for 30 mm).
Pop Group ⓫; F/H/I band (for SA-N-4).
Muff Cob ⓬; G/H band (for 57 mm).
Sonars: Graseby 750 *(Godavari)*; Bharat APSOH *(Ganga and Gomati)*; hull-mounted; active panoramic search and attack; medium frequency.
Fathoms Oceanic VDS (not in *Godavari*).
Type 162M; bottom classification; high frequency.

Helicopters: 2 Sea King or 1 Sea King and 1 Chetak ⓭.

Programmes: The second batch of three ordered from Garden Reach SY, Calcutta. This is Project 16A, indicating an improved Godavari design but probably with the same hull. Work is proceeding very slowly and hull number 5 is unlikely to be laid down until 1994.
Structure: The first three were a further modification of the original Leander design with an indigenous content of 72% and a larger hull. Poor welding is noticeable in *Godavari*. *Gomati* is the first Indian ship to have digital electronics in her combat data system. The second three have structural modifications based on lessons learned from the first three. The size is increased by some 1000 tons to improve stability; length increased by about 4 m and width by 1.5 m. Trishul SAM may be fitted (perhaps not in F 23) and the AK 230 guns are replaced by AK 630 gatlings. The steam plant is retained with Bhopal turbines.

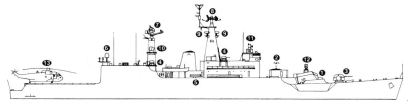

GODAVARI   *(Scale 1 : 1200), Ian Sturton*

GANGA   *5/1990, John Mortimer*

GOMATI   *8/1992, 92 Wing RAAF*

Operational: French helicopter handling equipment is fitted. Usually only one helo is carried with more than one crew. The first three have a unique mixture of Soviet, Western and Indian weapon systems which has inevitably led to some equipment compatibility problems. The first ship of the second batch is scheduled for sea trials in 1995 and has been delayed by Russian equipment supply problems.

6 NILGIRI (LEANDER) CLASS

Name	No	Builders	Laid down	Launched	Commissioned
NILGIRI	F 33	Mazagon Dock Ltd, Bombay	Oct 1966	23 Oct 1968	3 June 1972
HIMGIRI	F 34	Mazagon Dock Ltd, Bombay	1967	6 May 1970	23 Nov 1974
UDAYGIRI	F 35	Mazagon Dock Ltd, Bombay	Jan 1973	9 Mar 1974	5 May 1977
DUNAGIRI	F 36	Mazagon Dock Ltd, Bombay	14 Sep 1970	24 Oct 1972	18 Feb 1976
TARAGIRI	F 41	Mazagon Dock Ltd, Bombay	1974	25 Oct 1976	16 May 1980
VINDHYAGIRI	F 42	Mazagon Dock Ltd, Bombay	1975	12 Nov 1977	8 July 1981

Displacement, tons: 2682 standard; 2962 full load
Dimensions, feet (metres): 372 × 43 × 18
(113.4 × 13.1 × 5.5)
Main machinery: 2 Babcock & Wilcox boilers; 550 psi
(38.7 kg/cm sq); 850°F *(450°C)*; 2 turbines; 30 000 hp
(22.4 MW); 2 shafts
Speed, knots: 27; 28 *(Taragiri and Vindhyagiri).*
Range, miles: 4500 at 12 kts
Complement: 267 (17 officers)

Missiles: SAM: 1 or 2 Short Bros Seacat quad launchers **❶**;
optical radar guidance to 5 km *(2.7 nm)*; warhead 10 kg; 32
missiles. *Nilgiri* and *Himgiri* have 1 Seacat with GWS22 control.
Remainder have 2 Seacat with 2 Dutch M44 directors.
Guns: 2 Vickers 4.5 in *(114 mm)*/45 (twin) Mk 6 **❷**; 80° elevation; 20 rounds/minute to 19 km *(10.4 nm)* anti-surface; 6 km
(3.3 nm) anti-aircraft; weight of shell 25 kg.
2 Oerlikon 20 mm/70 **❸**; 800 rounds/minute to 2 km.
Torpedoes: 6—324 mm ILAS 3 (2 triple) tubes *(Taragiri and Vindhyagiri)* **❹**. Whitehead A244S or Indian NST 58 version; anti-
submarine; active/passive homing to 7 km *(3.8 nm)* at 33 kts;
warhead 34 kg (shaped charge).
A/S mortars: 1 Bofors 375 mm twin-tubed launcher *(Taragiri*
and *Vindhyagiri)* **❺**; range 1600 m.
1 Limbo Mk 10 triple-tubed launcher (remainder) **❻**; range
1000 m; warhead 92 kg.
Countermeasures: Decoys: Graseby G 738; towed torpedo
decoy; effective against both active and passive torpedoes.
ESM: Bharat; intercept. FH5 Telegon D/F (in some).
ECM: Type 667; jammer.
Fire control: 2 M44 MFCS. 1 GWS 22 *(Nilgiri)*. MRS 3 GFCS
(Nilgiri).
Radars: Air search: Signaal LW 08 **❼**; D band; range 265 km
(145 nm) for 2 m² target.
Marconi Type 965M *(Nilgiri)* **❽**; A band.
Surface search: Signaal ZW 06 **❾**; I band; range 26 km *(14 nm)*.
RN Type 993 *(Nilgiri)* **❿**; E/F band.
Navigation: Decca 1226; I band.
Fire control: Two Signaal M44 (not in *Nilgiri* and *Himgiri*) **⓫**; I/J
band (for Seacat).
Plessey Type 904 *(Nilgiri* and *Himgiri)* **⓬**; I band (for Seacat).
Signaal M 45 **⓭**; I/J band.
Plessey Type 903 **⓮** *(Nilgiri* and *Himgiri)*; I band.
IFF: Type 944; 954M.
Sonars: Graseby 750 (APSOH fitted in *Himgiri* as trials ship); hull-
mounted; active search and attack; medium frequency. Type
170; active attack; high frequency.
EMI Type 199 or Westinghouse VDS (first four only); active;
medium frequency. Thomson Sintra VDS in *Taragiri* and *Vind-
hyagiri*. Type 162M; bottom classification; high frequency.

Helicopters: 1 Chetak (in first 4) **⓯**.
1 Sea King Mk 42 (in *Taragiri* and *Vindhyagiri*) **⓰**.

Programmes: The first major warships built in Indian yards to a
UK design with a 60% indigenous component.
Modernisation: At future refits earlier ships are to have their
armament brought into line with later ships. Westinghouse has
supplied the Indian Navy with ASW sonar systems, two hull-
mounted arrays and three variable depth sonar (VDS) arrays.
The VDS arrays are installed inside towed bodies built by
Fathom Oceanology Ltd of Canada. The transducer elements
in both cases are identical.

NILGIRI *(Scale 1 : 1200), Ian Sturton*

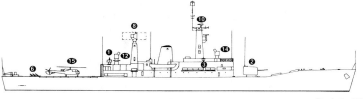

TARAGIRI *(Scale 1 : 1200), Ian Sturton*

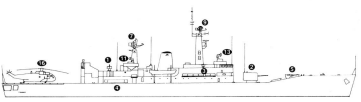

UDAYGIRI 6/1992

Structure: Of similar design to the Broad-beam Leanders but
with several differences. In the first four the hangar was provided with telescopic extension to take the Alouette III helicopter while in the last pair, a much-changed design, the Mk 10
Mortar has been removed as well as VDS and the aircraft space
increased to make way for a Sea King helicopter with a telescopic hangar and Canadian Beartrap haul-down gear. In these
two an open deck has been left below the flight deck for handling mooring gear and there is a cut-down to the stern.
Operational: It is reported that *Vindhyagiri* and *Taragiri* have
more powerful engines than the remainder. Form 14th Frigate
Squadron. Oil fuel, 382 tons plus 10 tons avgas.

TARAGIRI 1993, Indian Navy

5 PETYA II CLASS

ARNALA P 68   **ANDROTH** P 69   **ANJADIP** P 73   **AMINI** P 75   **KADMATH** P 78

Displacement, tons: 950 standard; 1100 full load
Dimensions, feet (metres): 270 × 29.9 × 10.5
(82.3 × 9.1 × 3.2)
Main machinery: CODOG; 2 gas turbines; 30 000 hp(m)
(22 MW); 1 Type 6I-V3 diesel (centre shaft); 5400 hp(m)
(3.97 MW) sustained; 3 shafts
Speed, knots: 32. **Range, miles:** 4000 at 20 kts
Complement: 98

Guns: 4 USSR 3 in *(76 mm)*/60 (2 twin) ❶; 80° elevation; 90
rounds/minute to 15 km *(8 nm)*; weight of shell 6.8 kg.
Torpedoes: 3—21 in *(533 mm)* (triple) tubes ❷. Probably Soviet
Type 53; pattern active/passive homing up to 20 km *(10.8 nm)*
at up to 45 kts; warhead 400 kg.
A/S mortars: 4 RBU 2500 16-tubed trainable launchers ❸; range
2500 m; warhead 21 kg.
Depth charges: 2 racks.
Mines: 2 rails.
Radars: Surface search: Slim Net ❹; E/F band.
Navigation: Don 2; I band.
Fire control: Hawk Screech ❺; I band; range 27 km *(15 nm)*.
IFF: High Pole B.
Sonars: Hercules; hull-mounted; active search and attack;
medium/high frequency.

Programmes: A USSR export version of Petya II class with simpli-
fied communications.
Transfers: *Kadmath* (originally built for Egypt) February 1969;
Arnala and *Androth* August 1972; *Anjadip* (built at Khabarovsk)
February 1973; *Amini* (built at Khabarovsk) March 1974.
Operational: Form 31st and 32nd Frigate Squadrons. *Andaman*
(P 74) sank in heavy weather in the Bay of Bengal 22 August
1990. Fourteen of the crew were lost. Four deleted so far, last
one in October 1991. The remainder are of doubtful oper-
ational capability.

PETYA II class   *(Scale 1 : 900), Ian Sturton*

PETYA II class (old number)   *7/1987, G Jacobs*

SHIPBORNE AIRCRAFT

Note: Naval versions of the Advanced Light Aircraft are being developed.

Numbers/Type: 21/3 British Aerospace Sea Harrier FRS Mk 51/Mk 60 (trainers).
Operational speed: 640 kts *(1186 km/h)*.
Service ceiling: 51 200 ft *(15 600 m)*.
Range: 800 nm *(1480 km)*.
Role/Weapon systems: Fleet air defence, strike and reconnaissance STOVL fighter with future
ASV role with Sea Eagle missiles; mid-life update planned after 1995; seven on order. Sensors:
Ferranti Blue Fox air interception radar, limited ECM/RWR. Weapons: Air defence; 2 × Magic
AAMs, 2 × 30 mm Aden cannon. Strike; 2 × Sea Eagle missiles or 3.6 tons of 'iron' bombs.

SEA HARRIER   *1991, Indian Navy*

Numbers/Type: 7 Westland Sea King Mks 42/42A.
Operational speed: 112 kts *(208 km/h)*.
Service ceiling: 11 500 ft *(3500 m)*.
Range: 664 nm *(1230 km)*.
Role/Weapon systems: Primary ASW helicopter for large escorts and CVL; some are shore-based
for training and surface search. Sensors: MEL search radar, Alcatel dipping sonar. Weapons:
ASW; 4 × Whitehead A244S torpedoes, BAe Mk 11 depth bombs or mines.

SEA KING 42B   *5/1993*

Numbers/Type: HAL Advanced Light Helicopter (ALH).
Operational speed: 156 kts *(290 km/h)*.
Service ceiling: 9850 ft *(3000 m)*.
Range: 216 nm *(400 km)*.
Role/Weapon systems: Full production expected from 1994/95 to replace Chetak.

Numbers/Type: 18 Kamov Ka-27 (Helix A).
Operational speed: 110 kts *(204 km/h)*.
Service ceiling: 12 000 ft *(3660 m)*.
Range: 270 nm *(500 km)*.
Role/Weapon systems: ASW helicopter embarked in large escorts. Has replaced Ka-25. Sensors:
Search radar, dipping sonar, sonobuoys. Weapons: ASW; 2 × Whitehead A244S torpedoes or 4
× depth bombs.

HELIX   *5/1993*

Numbers/Type: 19/5 Westland Sea King Mks 42B/42C.
Operational speed: 112 kts *(208 km/h)*.
Service ceiling: 11 500 ft *(3500 m)*.
Range: 664 nm *(1230 km)*.
Role/Weapon systems: Advanced shipborne helicopter for embarked and shore-based role; Mk
42B has primary ASV capability; Mk 42C for commando assault/vertrep; Mk 42D for AEW were
not acquired and an Indian AEW radar is being developed. Intention is to buy up to nine more.
Sensors: MEL Super Searcher radar, Thomson Sintra H/S-12 dipping sonar, AQS 902B acoustic
processor; Marconi Hermes ESM (Mk 42B); Bendix weather radar (Mk 42C). Weapons: ASW; 2
Whitehead A244S torpedoes; Mk 11 depth bombs, mines (Mk 42B only). ASV; 2 × Sea Eagle
(Mk 42B only). Unarmed (Mk 42C).

Numbers/Type: 9 Aerospatiale (HAL) SA 319B Chetak (Alouette III).
Operational speed: 113 kts *(210 km/h)*.
Service ceiling: 10 500 ft *(3200 m)*.
Range: 290 nm *(540 km)*.
Role/Weapon systems: Several helicopter roles still performed including embarked ASW and car-
rier-based SAR, utility and support to commando forces. Sensors: Some helicopters have search
radar. Weapons: ASW; 2 × Whitehead A244S torpedoes.

CHETAK   *5/1993*

LAND-BASED MARITIME AIRCRAFT (FRONT LINE)

Numbers/Type: 36 Dornier 228.
Operational speed: 200 kts *(370 km/h).*
Service ceiling: 28 000 ft *(8535 m).*
Range: 940 nm *(1740 km).*
Role/Weapon systems: Coastal surveillance and EEZ protection duties for Navy and Coast Guard. Sensors: MEL Marec 2 search radar, cameras and searchlight. Weapons: Unarmed, but will carry anti-ship missiles eventually, type unknown.

Numbers/Type: 5 Ilyushin Il-38 (May).
Operational speed: 347 kts *(645 km/h).*
Service ceiling: 32 800 ft *(10 000 m).*
Range: 3887 nm *(7200 km).*
Role/Weapon systems: Shore-based long-range ASW reconnaissance into Indian Ocean. Sensors: Search radar, MAD, sonobuoys, ESM. Weapons: ASW; various torpedoes, mines and depth bombs.

Numbers/Type: 18 Pilatus Britten-Norman Maritime Defender.
Operational speed: 150 kts *(280 km/h).*
Service ceiling: 18 900 ft *(5760 m).*
Range: 1500 nm *(2775 km).*
Role/Weapon systems: Coastal and short-range reconnaissance tasks undertaken in support of Navy (5) and Coast Guard. Sensors: Search radar, camera. Weapons: Unarmed.

Numbers/Type: 8 Tupolev Tu-142M (Bear F).
Operational speed: 500 kts *(925 km/h).*
Service ceiling: 45 000 ft *(13 720 m).*
Range: 6775 nm *(12 550 km).*
Role/Weapon systems: First entered service in April 1988 for long-range surface surveillance and ASW. Air Force manned. Sensors: Search and attack radars, MAD, cameras. Active and passive sonobuoys. Weapons: ASW; 12 × torpedoes, depth bombs. ASV: 2 × 23 mm cannon (no AS-4 ASM).

Numbers/Type: 2 Fokker F-27 Friendship.
Operational speed: 250 kts *(463 km/h).*
Service ceiling: 29 500 ft *(8990 m).*
Range: 2700 nm *(5000 km).*
Role/Weapon systems: Operated by Coast Guard for long-range patrol. Sensors: Search radar only. Weapons: Unarmed.

Numbers/Type: 12 SEPECAT/HAL Jaguar International.
Operational speed: 917 kts *(1699 km/h)* (max).
Service ceiling: 36 000 ft *(11 000 m).*
Range: 760 nm *(1408 km).*
Role/Weapon systems: A maritime strike squadron. Sensors: Thomson-CSF Agave radar. Weapons: ASV; 2 BAe Sea Eagle anti-ship missiles underwing; 2 DEFA 30 mm cannon or up to 8—1000 lb bombs. Can carry two air-to-air missiles overwing.

CORVETTES

4 + 4 (4) KHUKRI CLASS (PROJECTS 25 and 25A)

Name	No	Builders	Laid down	Launched	Commissioned
KHUKRI	P 49	Mazagon Dock Ltd, Bombay	27 Sep 1985	3 Dec 1986	23 Aug 1989
KUTHAR	P 46	Mazagon Dock Ltd, Bombay	13 Sep 1986	15 Apr 1989	7 June 1990
KIRPAN	P 44	Garden Reach SY, Calcutta	15 Nov 1985	16 Aug 1988	12 Jan 1991
KHANJAR	P 47	Garden Reach SY, Calcutta	15 Nov 1985	16 Aug 1988	22 Oct 1991
KORA	—	Garden Reach SY, Calcutta	10 Jan 1990	10 Oct 1992	1994
KIRCH	—	Garden Reach SY, Calcutta	31 Jan 1992	1995	1997
—	—	Garden Reach SY, Calcutta	1994	1996	1998
—	—	Garden Reach SY, Calcutta	1995	1997	1999

Displacement, tons: 1350 full load
Dimensions, feet (metres): 298.6 × 34.4 × 8.2 *(91 × 10.5 × 2.5)*
Main machinery: 2 SEMT-Pielstick/Kirloskar 18 PA6 V 280 diesels; 14 400 hp(m) *(10.58 MW)* sustained; 2 shafts; cp props
Speed, knots: 25. **Range, miles:** 4000 at 16 kts
Complement: 79 (10 officers)

Missiles: SSM: 2 or 4 SS-N-2D Styx (1 or 2 twin) launchers **❶**; IR homing to 83 km *(45 nm)* at 0.9 Mach; warhead 513 kg; seaskimmer at end of run.
SAM: SA-N-5 Grail **❷**; manual aiming; IR homing to 6 km *(3.2 nm)* at 1.5 Mach; altitude to 2500 m *(8000 ft)*; warhead 1.5 kg.
Guns: 1 USSR AK 176 3 in *(76 mm)*/60 **❸**; 85° elevation; 120 rounds/minute to 15 km *(8 nm)*; weight of shell 7 kg.
2—30 mm/65 AK 630 **❹**; 6 barrels per mounting; 85° elevation; 3000 rounds/minute to 2 km.
Countermeasures: Decoys: 2—16-barrelled chaff launchers **❺**. NPOL (Cochin); towed torpedo decoy.
ESM: Bharat Ajanta P; radar warning.
Combat data systems: Selenia system *(Khukri)*; Bharat Vympal system (remainder).
Radars: Air search: Positive E/Cross Dome **❻**; E/F band; range 130 km *(70 nm).*
Air/surface search: Plank Shave **❼**; I band.

KHUKRI

(Scale 1 : 900), Ian Sturton

Fire control: Bass Tilt **❽**; H/I band.
Navigation: Bharat 1245; I band.

Helicopters: Platform only **❾** for Chetak (to be replaced by Hindustan Aeronautics ALH in due course).

Programmes: First two ordered December 1983; two more ordered in 1985 and the next batch of four from Garden Reach/Mazagon in April 1990. Total of 12 planned. The diesels are assembled in India under licence by Kirloskar. Indigenous content of the whole ship is about 65 per cent. This class is replacing the Petyas. The follow-on class is an upgraded version which has been slowed down by delays in the supply of Russian equipment.

Structure: SA-N-4 may be fitted in the second batch of four. The reported plan was to make the first four ASW ships, and the remainder anti-aircraft or general purpose. However Khukri has neither torpedo tubes nor a sonar (apart from an Atlas Elektronik echo sounder), so if the plan is correct these ships will rely on an ALH helicopter which will have dunking sonar and ASW torpedoes and depth charges. All have fin stabilisers and full air-conditioning.
Operational: Based in Bombay. The advanced light helicopter (ALH) to have Sea Eagle SSM, torpedoes and dipping sonar.

KIRPAN

6/1993, 92 Wing RAAF

4 ABHAY (PAUK II) CLASS

Name	No	Builders	Commissioned
ABHAY	P 33	Volodarski, Rybinsk	Mar 1989
AJAY	P 34	Volodarski, Rybinsk	24 Jan 1990
AKSHAY	P 35	Volodarski, Rybinsk	Dec 1990
AGRAY	P 36	Volodarski, Rybinsk	Feb 1991

AGRAY   1/1991, Photo Sami

Displacement, tons: 520 full load
Dimensions, feet (metres): 195.2 × 33.5 × 10.8
(59.5 × 10.2 × 3.3)
Main machinery: 2 Type M 507T diesels; 11 520 hp(m)
(8.47 MW) sustained; 2 shafts
Speed, knots: 32. **Range, miles:** 2400 at 14 kts
Complement: 32

Missiles: SAM: SA-N-5 Grail quad launcher; manual aiming, IR
homing to 6 km *(3.2 nm)* at 1.5 Mach; warhead 1.5 kg.
Guns: 1 USSR 3 in *(76 mm)*/60; 85° elevation; 120 rounds/
minute to 15 km *(8 nm)*; weight of shell 7 kg.
1—30 mm/65 AK 630; 6 barrels; 3000 rounds/minute com-
bined to 2 km.
Torpedoes: 4—21 in *(533 mm)* (2 twin) tubes. SET-65E; active/
passive homing to 15 km *(8.1 nm)* at 40 kts; warhead 205 kg.
A/S mortars: 2 RBU 1200 5-tubed fixed; range 1200 m; war-
head 34 kg.
Countermeasures: 2—16-tubed chaff launchers.
Radars: Air/Surface search: Positive E/Cross Dome; E/F band.
Navigation: Pechora; I band.
Fire Control: Bass Tilt; H/I band.
Sonars: Rat Tail VDS (on transom); attack; high frequency.

Programmes: Modified Pauk II class built in the USSR for export.
Original order in late 1983 but completion of the first delayed
by lack of funds and the order for the others was not reinstated
until 1987. A fifth of class has probably been cancelled. Names
associated with former coastal patrol craft. One of the same
class has been acquired by Cuba.
Structure: Has a longer superstructure than the Pauk I, larger torpedo tubes and new electronics.

9 + 3 (7) VEER (TARANTUL I) CLASS (TYPE 1241)

Name	No	Builders	Laid down	Launched	Commissioned
VEER	K 40	Volodarski, Rybinsk	—	—	May 1987
NIRBHIK	K 41	Volodarski, Rybinsk	—	—	Jan 1988
NIPAT	K 42	Volodarski, Rybinsk	—	—	Jan 1989
NISHANK	K 43	Volodarski, Rybinsk	—	—	Sep 1989
NIRGHAT	K 44	Volodarski, Rybinsk	—	—	Feb 1990
VIBHUTI	K 45	Mazagon Dock, Bombay	Mar 1988	26 Apr 1990	3 June 1991
VIPUL	K 46	Mazagon Dock, Bombay	July 1988	3 Jan 1991	16 Mar 1992
VINASH	K 52	Mazagon Dock, Goa	June 1990	24 Jan 1992	20 Nov 1993
NASHAK	K 53	Mazagon Dock, Goa	Aug 1992	12 Nov 1993	1995
—	K 48-50	Mazagon Dock, Bombay	—	—	—
—	K 54-59	Mazagon Dock, Goa	—	—	—

NIRGHAT   1991

Displacement, tons: 385 standard; 450 full load
Dimensions, feet (metres): 184.1 × 37.7 × 8.2
(56.1 × 11.5 × 2.5)
Main machinery: COGOG; 2 Nikolayev Type DR 77 gas turbines;
16 016 hp(m) *(11.77 MW)* sustained; 2 Nikolayev Type DR 76
gas turbines with reversible gearboxes; 4993 hp(m)
(3.67 MW) sustained; 2 shafts (K 40-44)
CODOG; 1 GE LM 2500 gas turbine; 23 300 hp *(17.38 MW)* sustained; 2 MTU 12V 538 TB92 diesels; 5110 hp(m) *(3.76 MW)*
sustained; 2 shafts (K 45 onwards)
Speed, knots: 36. **Range, miles:** 2000 at 20 kts; 400 at 36 kts
Complement: 41 (5 officers)

Missiles: SSM: 4 SS-N-2D Styx; IR homing to 83 km *(45 nm)* at
0.9 Mach; warhead 513 kg; sea-skimmer at end of run.
SAM: SA-N-5 Grail quad launcher; manual aiming; IR homing to
6 km *(3.2 nm)* at 1.5 Mach; warhead 1.5 kg.
Guns: 1 USSR 3 in *(76 mm)*/60; 85° elevation; 120 rounds/
minute to 15 km *(8 nm)*; weight of shell 7 kg.
2—30 mm/65 AK 630; 6 barrels per mounting; 85° elevation;
3000 rounds/minute combined to 2 km.
Fire control: Hood Wink optronic director.
Radars: Air/surface search: Plank Shave; E band.
Navigation: Pechora; I Band.
Fire Control: Bass tilt; H/I band.
IFF: Salt Pot, Square Head A.

Programmes: First five are USSR Tarantul I class built for export.
Remainder of this type are building in India. Because of supply
problems from Russia, numbers to be built are uncertain but
are likely to be revised downwards and the programme may
even be suspended.

Structure: Variations in the Indian-built ships include CODOG
propulsion (with one gas turbine and two diesels) and
improved countermeasures equipment. It is possible that the
early Indian-built ships also have Russian gas turbines.

VIBHUTI   1991

3 DURG (NANUCHKA II) CLASS

Name	No	Commissioned
VIJAY DURG	K 71	Apr 1976
SINDHU DURG	K 72	Sep 1977
HOS DURG	K 73	Apr 1978

Displacement, tons: 850 full load
Dimensions, feet (metres): 194.5 × 38.7 × 8.5
 (59.3 × 11.8 × 2.6)
Main machinery: 3 Type M 507 diesels; 21 600 hp(m)
 (15.9 MW) sustained; 3 shafts
Speed, knots: 34. **Range, miles:** 2500 at 12 kts; 900 at 31 kts
Complement: 60

Missiles: SSM: 4 SS-N-2C Styx; active radar or IR homing to
 46 km *(25 nm)* at 0.9 Mach; warhead 513 kg.
 SAM: SA-N-4 Gecko twin launcher; semi-active radar homing to
 15 km *(8 nm)* at 2.5 Mach; height envelope 9-3048 m *(29.5-
 10 000 ft)*; warhead 50 kg; 20 missiles.
Guns: 2 USSR 57 mm/80 (twin); 90° elevation; 120 rounds/
 minute to 8 km *(4.4 nm)*; weight of shell 2.8 kg.
Countermeasures: 2—16-barrelled chaff launchers.
ESM: Radar warning.
Radars: Air/surface search: Square Tie; I band; range 73 km
 (40 nm) (mounted in radome).
 Fire control: Pop Group; F/H/I band (for SAN-4).
 Muff Cob; G/H band.
 Navigation: Don 2; I band.
 IFF: High Pole. Two Square Head.

Programmes: Transferred from the USSR in the late 1970s.
Structure: The radome is mounted lower than in Russian ships of
 this class due to the absence of Fish Bowl because of the use of
 SS-N-2 missiles in place of SS-N-9.
Operational: At least one is non-operational, supplying spares for
 the others.

VIJAY DURG   1990

PATROL FORCES

7 + 3 SUKANYA CLASS (OFFSHORE PATROL SHIPS)

Name	No	Builders	Launched	Commissioned
SUKANYA	P 50	Korea Tacoma, Masan	1989	31 Aug 1989
SUBHADRA	P 51	Korea Tacoma, Masan	1989	25 Jan 1990
SUVARNA	P 52	Korea Tacoma, Masan	22 Aug 1990	4 Apr 1991
SAVITRI	P 53	Hindustan SY, Vishakapatnam	23 May 1989	27 Nov 1990
SARYU	P 54	Hindustan SY, Vishakapatnam	16 Oct 1989	8 Oct 1991
SHARADA	P 55	Hindustan SY, Vishakapatnam	22 Aug 1990	27 Oct 1991
SUJATA	P 56	Hindustan SY, Vishakapatnam	25 Aug 1991	3 Nov 1993
—	P 57	Mazagon Dock Ltd, Goa	26 Aug 1992	1994
—	P 58-59	Mazagon Dock Ltd, Goa	—	—

Displacement, tons: 1890 full load
Dimensions, feet (metres): 334.6 oa; 315 wl × 37.7 × 11.2 *(102;
 96 × 11.5 × 3.4)*
Main machinery: 2 SEMT-Pielstick 16 PA6 V 280 diesels;
 12 800 hp(m) *(9.41 MW)* sustained; 2 shafts
Speed, knots: 21. **Range, miles:** 7000 at 15 kts
Complement: 145 (12 officers)
Guns: 1 Oerlikon 20 mm.
Radars: Surface search: Selenia; I band.
 Navigation: Racal Decca; I band.
Helicopters: 1 Chetak.

Comment: First three ordered in March 1987 from Korea
Tacoma to an Ulsan class design. Second four ordered in
August 1987. The Korean-built ships commissioned at Masan
and then sailed for India where the armament was fitted. Three
more reported ordered from Goa in April 1990. Lightly armed
and able to 'stage' helicopters, they are fitted out for offshore
patrol work only but have the capacity to be much more heavily
armed. Fin stabilisers fitted. Firefighting pump on hangar roof

SUBHADRA   4/1992

aft. These are naval ships (not Coast Guard) used for harbour
defence, protection of offshore installations and patrol of the
EEZ. Potential for role change is considerable. Inmarsat can be
fitted on the hangar roof.

---

8 OSA II CLASS (FAST ATTACK CRAFT—MISSILE)

PRACHAND K 90		CHAPAL K 94	
PRALAYA K 91		CHAMAK K 95	
PRATAP K 92		CHATAK K 96	
PRABAL K 93		CHARAG K 97	

Displacement, tons: 245 full load
Dimensions, feet (metres): 126.6 × 24.9 × 8.6 *(38.6 × 7.6 × 2.7)*
Main machinery: 3 Type M 504 diesels; 10 800 hp(m) *(7.94 MW)* sustained; 3 shafts
Speed, knots: 37. **Range, miles:** 800 at 25 kts
Complement: 30

Missiles: SSM: 4 SS-N-2A or B Styx; active radar or IR homing to 46 km *(25 nm)* at 0.9 Mach; war-
 head 513 kg.
Guns: 4 USSR 30 mm/65 (2 twin); 85° elevation; 500 rounds/minute to 5 km *(2.7 nm)*; weight of
 shell 0.54 kg.
Radars: Surface search: Square Tie; I band.
 Fire control: Drum Tilt; H/I band.
 IFF: High Pole. Square Head.

Programmes: Eight Osa II class delivered from USSR January 1976-September 1977. Being
 replaced by Tarantul class and beginning to be paid off. Most are in reserve.

CHAPAL   2/1989, G Jacobs

---

7 SDB Mk 3 CLASS (FAST ATTACK CRAFT—PATROL)

Displacement, tons: 210 full load
Dimensions, feet (metres): 124 × 24.6 × 6.2 *(37.8 × 7.5 × 1.9)*
Main machinery: 2 MTU 16V 538 TB92 diesels; 6820 hp(m) *(5 MW)* sustained; 2 shafts
Speed, knots: 30
Complement: 32
Guns: 2 Bofors 40 mm/60; 80° elevation; 120 rounds/minute to 10 km *(5.5 nm)*; weight of shell
 0.89 kg.

Comment: First pair and Nos 4 and 5 ordered from Garden Reach SY, Calcutta, remainder from
 Mazagon Dock Ltd, Goa. First three completed in 1984, remainder in 1985-86.

SDB Mk 3   1989, G Jacobs

5 SDB Mk 2 CLASS (FAST ATTACK CRAFT—PATROL)

Displacement, tons: 203 full load
Dimensions, feet (metres): 123 × 24.6 × 5.9 *(37.5 × 7.5 × 1.8)*
Main machinery: 2 Paxman Deltic 18-42K diesels; 6240 hp *(4.66 MW)*; 2 shafts. Auxiliary propulsion; 1 Kirloskar-Cummins diesel; 165 hp *(123 kW)*
Speed, knots: 29; 4 on auxiliary diesel
Range, miles: 1400 at 14 kts
Complement: 28 (4 officers)
Guns: 1 Bofors 40 mm/60; 80° elevation; 120 rounds/minute to 10 km *(5.5 nm)*; weight of shell 0.89 kg.
1—7.62 mm MG.
Depth charges: 18 Mk 7; 10 Mk 12.
Sonars: Hull-mounted; active attack; high frequency.

Comment: First three commissioned in 1977-78; last two in 1984. All built by Garden Reach SY, Calcutta. Reported that problems delayed launchings of the first group. This might be due to use of GRP hulls. All with Eastern Naval Command. Same class built for Coast Guard.

0 + 1 FAST ATTACK CRAFT (TORPEDO)

Displacement, tons: 90 full load
Dimensions, feet (metres): 84.6 × 22.6 × 3.9 *(25.8 × 6.9 × 1.2)*
Main machinery: 2 diesels; 5000 hp *(3.73 MW)*; 2 shafts
Speed, knots: 30. **Range, miles:** 400 at 20 kts
Complement: 7 (3 officers)
Guns: 2—12.7 mm MGs.
Torpedoes: 2—21 in *(533 mm)* tubes; anti-surface.
Radars: Surface search: I band.

Comment: A Mazagon Dock design reported building for the Indian Navy. Numbers not known.

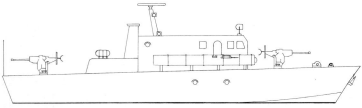

FAST ATTACK CRAFT *(not to scale), Ian Sturton*

AMPHIBIOUS FORCES

Note: An agreement has been reached for the production of US LCAs in India. Project definition started 1 April 1990 and full production is expected by 1995.

2 + 1 MAGAR CLASS (LST)

Name	No	Builders	Commissioned
MAGAR	L 20	Garden Reach, Calcutta	15 July 1987
GHARIAL	L 23	Hindustan/Garden Reach	1994
—	L 24	Hindustan/Garden Reach	1995

Displacement, tons: 5655 full load
Dimensions, feet (metres): 409.4 oa; 393.7 wl × 57.4 × 13.1 *(124.8; 120 × 17.5 × 4)*
Main machinery: 2 SEMT-Pielstick 12 PA6 V280 diesels; 8560 hp(m) *(6.29 MW)* sustained; 2 shafts
Speed, knots: 15. **Range, miles:** 3000 at 14 kts
Complement: 136 (16 officers)
Guns: 4 Bofors 40 mm/60. 2 multi-barrel rocket launchers in the bow.
Helicopters: 1 Sea King 42C; platform for 2.

Comment: A new *Magar*, maintaining the name of the deleted ex-British LST 3 and based on the *Sir Lancelot* design, was launched on 7 November 1984. *Gharial* ordered in 1985, launched 1 April 1991 at Hindustan Shipyard but is fitting out at Garden Reach. A third of class was laid down in 1992 and is scheduled to be launched in 1994. Carries four LCVPs on davits. Bow door. Can beach on gradients 1 in 40 or more. Original plan was for eight of the class and the priority being given to the third ship, suggests this may still be the intention.

MAGAR *10/1990, 92 Wing RAAF*

8 POLNOCHNY C (TYPE 773) and D CLASS (LSMs)

GHORPAD L 14	**SHARABH** L 17	**GULDAR** L 21
KESARI L 15	**CHEETAH** L 18	**KUMBHIR** L 22
SHARDUL L 16	**MAHISH** L 19	

Displacement, tons: 1120 standard; 1305 (D class); 1150 full load
Dimensions, feet (metres): 266.7; 275.3 (D class) × 31.8 × 7.9 *(81.3; 83.9 × 9.7 × 2.4)*
Main machinery: 2 Kolomna Type 40-D diesels; 4400 hp(m) *(3.2 MW)* sustained; 2 shafts
Speed, knots: 15. **Range, miles:** 2000 at 12 kts
Complement: 45
Military lift: 350 tons; 160 troops
Guns: 4—30 mm (2 twin). 2—140 mm 18-tubed rocket launchers.
Radars: Navigation: Don 2 or Krivach (SRN 745); I band.
Fire control: Drum Tilt; H/I band (in D class).
Helicopters: Platform only (in D class).

Comment: All new construction direct from Naval Shipyard, Gdynia. *Ghorpad* and *Kesari* transferred in March 1975, *Shardul* and *Sharabh* in February 1976, *Cheetah* in February 1985, *Mahish* in July 1985, *Guldar* in March 1986 and *Kumbhir* in November 1986. The last four are Polnochny Ds with the flight deck forward of the bridge and different radars. At least two are in reserve.

CHEETAH *12/1992 92 Wing RAAF*

7 Mk 3 LANDING CRAFT (LCU)

VASCO DA GAMA L 34	**MANGALA** L 39
MIDHUR L 38	**L 35-37, L 40**

Displacement, tons: 500 full load
Dimensions, feet (metres): 188.6 oa; 174.5 pp × 26.9 × 5.2 *(57.5; 53.2 × 8.2 × 1.6)*
Main machinery: 3 Kirloskar-MAN V8V 17.5/22 AMAL diesels; 1686 hp(m) *(1.24 MW)*; 3 shafts
Speed, knots: 11. **Range, miles:** 1000 at 8 kts
Complement: 287 including troops
Military lift: 250 tons; 2 PT 76 or 2 APC
Guns: 2 Bofors 40 mm/60 (aft).
Mines: Can be embarked.

Comment: First two built by Hooghly D and E Co and remainder at Goa SY (subsidiary of Mazagon Dock Ltd). First craft *(Vasco da Gama)* launched 29 November 1978 and the last one commissioned 25 March 1987.

MANGALA *1987, Mazagon Dock Ltd*

MINE WARFARE FORCES

Note: A need for at least 10 minehunters has been accepted with the lead vessels to be built overseas and the remainder at Goa. An alternative is to build all 10 to a Soviet design. Hulls to be of GRP. In 1990 it was reported that six (M 89-M 94) of 800 tons and 50 m in length were to be ordered from Goa Shipyard which is installing GRP facilities. Progress is slow.

6 MAHÉ (YEVGENYA) CLASS (MINESWEEPERS—INSHORE)

MAHÉ M 83	**MANGALORE** M 85	**MULKI** M 87
MALVAN M 84	**MALPE** M 86	**MAGDALA** M 88

Displacement, tons: 77 standard; 90 full load
Dimensions, feet (metres): 80.7 × 18 × 4.9 *(24.6 × 5.5 × 1.5)*
Main machinery: 2 Type 3-D-12 diesels; 600 hp(m) *(440 kW)* sustained; 2 shafts
Speed, knots: 11. **Range, miles:** 300 at 10 kts
Complement: 10
Guns: 2 USSR 25 mm/80 (twin).
Radars: Navigation: Don 2; I band.
Sonars: A small transducer streamed over the stern on a crane.

Comment: First three delivered from USSR 16 May 1983 and second three on 3 February 1984. A mid-1960s design with GRP hulls built at Kolpino. All based at Cochin.

MAHÉ *2/1992*

12 PONDICHERRY (NATYA I) CLASS (MINESWEEPERS—OCEAN)

PONDICHERRY M 61	**ALLEPPEY** M 65	**CUDDALORE** M 69
PORBANDAR M 62	**RATNAGIRI** M 66	**KAKINADA** M 70
BEDI M 63	**KARWAR** M 67	**KOZHIKODA** M 71
BHAVNAGAR M 64	**CANNANORE** M 68	**KONKAN** M 72

Displacement, tons: 770 full load
Dimensions, feet (metres): 200.1 × 31.8 × 8.9 *(61 × 9.7 × 2.7)*
Main machinery: 2 Type 504 diesels; 7200 hp(m) *(5.29 MW)* sustained; 2 shafts
Speed, knots: 19. **Range, miles:** 4000 at 10 kts
Complement: 58

Guns: 4—30 mm/65 (2 twin); 85° elevation; 500 rounds/minute to 5 km *(2.7 nm)*; weight of shell 0.54 kg.
4—25 mm/70 (2 twin); 85° elevation; 270 rounds/minute to 3 km *(1.6 nm)*.
A/S mortars: 2 RBU 1200 5-tubed fixed; range 1200 m; warhead 34 kg.
Mines: Can carry 10.
Radars: Navigation: Don 2; I band.
Fire control: Drum Tilt; H/I band.
IFF: Two Square Head. High Pole B.
Sonars: Hull-mounted; active mine detection; high frequency.

Programmes: Built for export at Isora Yard, Leningrad. First pair transferred from USSR April 1978, second pair July 1979, third pair August 1980, one in October 1986, one in June 1987, one in December 1987, one in May 1988, one in November 1988 and the last in early 1989. Last six have been delivered out of pennant number order.
Structure: Steel hulls but do not have stern ramp as in Soviet class.
Operational: Some are fitted with two quad SA-N-5 systems. All are capable of magnetic, acoustic and mechanical sweeping. *Pondicherry* was painted white and used as the Presidential yacht for the Indian Fleet Review by President R Venkataramen on 15 February 1989; she reverted to her normal role and colour on completion. One serves as an AGI.

CANNANORE   *1989, van Ginderen Collection*

4 HAM CLASS (MINESWEEPERS—INSHORE)

Name	No	Builders	Commissioned
BULSAR	M 89	Mazagon Dock Ltd, Bombay	1970
BHATKAL	M 90	Mazagon Dock Ltd, Bombay	1968
BIMLIPITAN	M 2705	Vosper, Portsmouth	1954
(ex-HMS *Hildersham*)			
BASSEIN	M 2707	Brooke Marine, Lowestoft	1954
(ex-HMS *Littleham*)			

Displacement, tons: 120 standard; 159 full load
Dimensions, feet (metres): 107.5 × 22 × 5.8 *(32.8 × 6.7 × 1.8)*
Main machinery: 2 Paxman YHAZM diesels; 1100 hp *(821 kW)*; 2 shafts
Speed, knots: 14; 9 sweeping
Complement: 15 (2 officers)
Guns: 1 Oerlikon 20 mm.
Radars: Decca 978; I band.

Comment: Of wooden construction; two were built for the UK but transferred to the Indian Navy in 1955. *Bassein* was launched on 4 May 1954, *Bimlipitan* on 5 February 1954, *Bhatkal* in April 1967, and *Bulsar* on 17 May 1969. Seldom seen and may be in reserve.

SURVEY SHIPS

Note: The National Institute of Oceanography operates several research and survey ships including *Sagar Kanya, Samudra Manthan, Sagar Sampada, Samudra Sarvekshak, Samudra Nidhi* and *Samudra Sandhari*. A new acoustic research ship *Mars* was launched in May 1991 at Garden Reach SY, Calcutta.

4 MAKAR CLASS (SURVEY CRAFT)

MAKAR J 33	**MEEN** J 35
MITHUN J 34	**MESH** J 36

Displacement, tons: 210 full load
Dimensions, feet (metres): 123 × 24.6 × 6.2 *(37.5 × 7.5 × 1.9)*
Main machinery: 2 diesels; 1124 hp(m) *(826 kW)*; 2 shafts
Speed, knots: 12. **Range, miles:** 1500 at 12 kts
Complement: 36 (4 officers)
Guns: 1 Bofors 40 mm/60.

Comment: Launched at Goa in 1981-82. Similar hulls to SDB Mk 2 class but with much smaller engines. Only *Makar* and *Meen* were active in 1993.

MAKAR   *4/1992*

6 SANDHAYAK CLASS (SURVEY SHIPS)

Name	No	Builders	Commissioned
SANDHAYAK	J 18	Garden Reach, Calcutta	1 Mar 1981
NIRDESHAK	J 19	Garden Reach, Calcutta	4 Oct 1982
NIRUPAK	J 14	Garden Reach, Calcutta	14 Aug 1985
INVESTIGATOR	J 15	Garden Reach, Calcutta	11 Jan 1990
JAMUNA	J 16	Garden Reach, Calcutta	31 Aug 1991
SUTLEJ	J 17	Garden Reach, Calcutta	19 Feb 1993

Displacement, tons: 1929 full load
Dimensions, feet (metres): 281.3 × 42 × 11 *(85.8 × 12.8 × 3.3)*
Main machinery: 2 GRSE MAN G8V 30/45 ATL diesels; 3860 hp(m) *(2.84 MW)*; 2 shafts; active rudder
Speed, knots: 16. **Range, miles:** 6000 at 14 kts; 14 000 at 10 kts
Complement: 189 (14 officers) plus 30 scientists
Guns: 1 Bofors 40 mm/60.
Countermeasures: ESM: Telegon IV HF D/F.
Radars: Navigation: Racal Decca 1629; I band.
Helicopters: 1 Alouette III.

Comment: *Investigator* launched 8 August 1987 and *Jamuna* in September 1989. Total of seven planned but programme may terminate at six. Telescopic hangar. Fitted with three echo sounders, extensively equipped laboratories, and carries four GRP survey launches on davits amidships. Painted white with yellow funnels. An active rudder with a DC motor gives speeds of up to 5 kts.

NIRUPAK   *1987, Gilbert Gyssels*

TRAINING SHIPS

1 TIR CLASS (TRAINING SHIP)

Name	No	Builders	Commissioned
TIR	A 86	Mazagon Dock Ltd, Bombay	21 Feb 1986

Displacement, tons: 2400 full load
Dimensions, feet (metres): 347.4 × 43.3 × 15.7 *(105.9 × 13.2 × 4.8)*
Main machinery: 2 Crossley-Pielstick 8 PC2 V Mk 2 diesels; 8000 hp(m) *(5.88 MW)* sustained; 2 shafts
Speed, knots: 18. **Range, miles:** 6000 at 12 kts
Complement: 239 (35 officers) plus 120 cadets
Guns: 2 Bofors 40 mm/60 (twin) with launchers for illuminants.
4 saluting guns.
Countermeasures: ESM: Telegon IV D/F.
Radars: Navigation: Two Indian design.
Helicopters: Platform for Alouette III.

Comment: First launched 15 April 1983. Second reported ordered May 1986 but may have been cancelled. Built to commercial standards, Decca collision avoidance plot and SATNAV. Can carry up to 120 cadets and 20 instructors.

TIR   *5/1991, 92 Wing RAAF*

1 SAIL TRAINING SHIP

VARUNA

Displacement, tons: 105

Comment: Completed in April 1981 by Alcock-Ashdown, Bhavnagar. Can carry 26 cadets.

VARUNA   *1/1988, van Ginderen Collection*

AUXILIARIES

1 UGRA CLASS (SUBMARINE TENDER)

AMBA A 54

Displacement, tons: 6750 standard; 9650 full load
Dimensions, feet (metres): 462.6 × 57.7 × 23 *(141 × 17.6 × 7)*
Main machinery: Diesel-electric; 4 Kolomna Type 2-D-42 diesel generators; 2 motors; 8000 hp(m) *(5.88 MW)*; 2 shafts
Speed, knots: 17. **Range, miles:** 21 000 at 10 kts
Complement: 400
Guns: 4 USSR 3 in *(76 mm)*/60 (2 twin); 80° elevation; 90 rounds/minute to 15 km *(8 nm)*; weight of shell 6.8 kg.
Radars: Air/surface search: Slim Net; E/F band.
Fire control: Two Hawk Screech; I band.
Navigation: Don 2; I band.
IFF: Two Square Head. High Pole A.

Comment: Acquired from the USSR in 1968. Provision for helicopter. Can accommodate 750. Two cranes, one of 6 tons and one of 10 tons. Differs from others of the class by having 76 mm guns.

AMBA   *4/1992*

0 + 1 MODIFIED DEEPAK CLASS
(REPLENISHMENT AND REPAIR SHIP)

Name	No	Builders	Launched	Commissioned
ADITYA (ex-*Rajaba Gan Palan*)	—	Garden Reach, Calcutta	15 Nov 1993	1995

Displacement, tons: 22 000 full load
Dimensions, feet (metres): 564.3 × 75.5 × 29.9 *(172 × 23 × 9.1)*
Main machinery: 2 diesels; 24 000 hp(m) *(17.6 MW)*; 1 shaft
Speed, knots: 20. **Range, miles:** 10 000 at 16 kts
Complement: 191 plus 6 spare berths
Cargo capacity: 14 200 cu m diesel and avcat; 2250 cu m water; 2170 cu m ammunition and stores
Guns: 3 Bofors 40 mm/60.
Helicopters: 1 Chetak.

Comment: Ordered in July 1987 to a Bremer-Vulkan design. Lengthened version of Deepak class but with a multi-purpose workshop. The bridge and accommodation superstructure are towards the stern, with the helicopter platform right aft. Fully air-conditioned. A second one may follow in due course.

1 DIVING SUPPORT SHIP

Name	No	Builders	Commissioned
NIREEKSHAK	A 15	Mazagon Dock Ltd, Bombay	8 June 1989

Displacement, tons: 3600 full load
Dimensions, feet (metres): 231.3 × 57.4 × 16.4 *(70.5 × 17.5 × 5)*
Main machinery: 2 Bergen KRM-8 diesels; 4410 hp(m) *(3.24 MW)* sustained; 2 shafts; cp props; 2 bow thrusters; 2 stern thrusters; 990 hp(m) *(727 kW)*
Speed, knots: 12
Complement: 63 (15 officers)

Comment: Laid down in August 1982 and launched January 1984. Acquired on lease with an option for purchase. The vessel was built for offshore support operations but has been modified for naval requirements. Two DSRV, capable of taking 12 men to 300 m, are carried together with two six-man recompression chambers and one three-man bell. Kongsberg ADP-503 Mk II. Dynamic positioning system. The ship is used for submarine SAR until the purpose-built ships are completed.

NIREEKSHAK   *1991*

0 + 2 SUPPORT AND RESCUE SHIPS

Displacement, tons: 7000 full load
Dimensions, feet (metres): 334 × 298.6 × 28.5 *(101.8 × 91 × 8.7)*
Main machinery: Diesel-electric; 5 diesel generators; 11.6 MW; 2 motors; 1 shaft; cp prop; 2 bow thrusters; 4020 hp(m) *(2.95 MW)*; 2 stern thrusters; 4830 hp(m) *(3.5 MW)*
Speed, knots: 13. **Range, miles:** 19 500 at 12 kts
Complement: 84 (28 officers) plus 26 spare berths

Comment: Reported authorised in mid-1990 to a Rauma Repola design for delivery of the first in the mid-1990s. Kongsberg ADP 503 Mk II dynamic positioning system. One 120 ton crane. Two DSRVs for 12 men to 300 m. Helicopter platform forward. Two hospitals. One might be used by the Coast Guard as an SAR and pollution control ship.

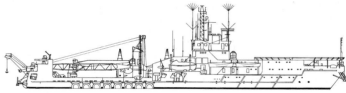

SUPPORT SHIP   *(not to scale), Ian Sturton*

2 DEEPAK CLASS (REPLENISHMENT TANKERS)

Name	No	Builders	Commissioned
DEEPAK	A 50	Bremer-Vulkan	20 Nov 1967
SHAKTI	A 57	Bremer-Vulkan	31 Dec 1975

Displacement, tons: 6785 light; 15 828 full load
Measurement, tons: 12 013 gross
Dimensions, feet (metres): 552.4 × 75.5 × 30 *(168.4 × 23 × 9.2)*
Main machinery: 2 Babcock & Wilcox boilers; 1 BV/BBC steam turbine; 16 500 hp(m) *(12.13 MW)*; 1 shaft
Speed, knots: 18.5. **Range, miles:** 5500 at 16 kts
Complement: 169
Cargo capacity: 1280 tons diesel; 12 624 tons FFO; 1495 tons avcat; 812 tons FW
Guns: 4 Bofors 40 mm/60. 2 Oerlikon 20 mm.
Countermeasures: ESM: Telegon IV HF D/F.
Radars: Navigation: Decca Type 1006; I band.
Helicopters: 1 Chetak.

Comment: *Deepak* on charter to Indian Navy from Mogul Lines which paid for the construction when the Navy could not afford the expense. Automatic tensioning fitted to replenishment gear. Heavy and light jackstays. Stern fuelling as well as alongside. DG fitted.

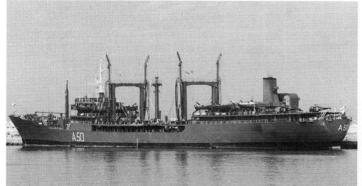

DEEPAK   *5/1993*

3 POSHAK CLASS (SUPPORT TANKERS)

POSHAK   PURAN   PUSHPA

Displacement, tons: 650 full load
Dimensions, feet (metres): 197.2 × 32.2 × 9.8 *(60.1 × 9.8 × 3)*
Main machinery: 2 diesels; 1540 hp(m) *(1.13 MW)* sustained; 2 shafts
Speed, knots: 12
Complement: 22
Cargo capacity: 200 tons

Comment: Built at Mazagon Dock Ltd, Bombay. *Poshak* completed April 1982, and *Puran* in November 1988.

PUSHPA   *1990, Mazagon Dock*

2 PRADHAYAK CLASS (SUPPORT TANKERS)

PRADHAYAK   PURAK

Displacement, tons: 960 full load
Dimensions, feet (metres): 163 × 26.2 × 9.8 *(49.7 × 8 × 3)*
Main machinery: 1 diesel; 560 hp(m) *(412 kW)*; 1 shaft
Speed, knots: 9
Cargo capacity: 376 tons

Comment: Built at Rajabagan Yard, Calcutta. *Pradhayak* completed February 1978, *Purak* June 1977.

3 WATER CARRIERS

AMBUDA   COCHIN   +1

Displacement, tons: 200
Dimensions, feet (metres): 108.3 × — × 8 *(32 × — × 2.4)*
Speed, knots: 9

Comment: First laid down Rajabagan Yard 18 January 1977. Second and third built at Mazagon Dock Ltd, Bombay.

AMBUDA   *4/1992*

3 TORPEDO RECOVERY VESSELS

A 71   A 72   ASTRAVAHINI

Displacement, tons: 110
Dimensions, feet (metres): 93.5 × 20 × 4.6 *(28.5 × 6.1 × 1.4)*
Main machinery: 2 Kirloskar V12 diesels; 720 hp(m) *(529 kW)*; 2 shafts
Speed, knots: 11
Complement: 13

Comment: Details above apply only to *A 71* and *A 72*. First completed early 1980, second 1981 at Goa Shipyard. *Astravahini* completed in 1984 at Vishakapatnam.

TRV A 72   *2/1989, G Jacobs*

1 HOSPITAL SHIP

LAKSHADWEEP

Dimensions, feet (metres): 171 × 29.5 × 10.5 *(52 × 9 × 3.2)*
Main machinery: 2 diesels; 900 hp(m) *(661 kW)*; 2 shafts
Speed, knots: 12
Complement: 35 (including 16 medical)

Comment: Ordered from Hindok, Calcutta in 1980. Launched 28 August 1981. Has accommodation for 90 patients.

3 DIVING TENDERS

Displacement, tons: 36
Dimensions, feet (metres): 48.9 × 14.4 × 3.9 *(14.9 × 4.4 × 1.2)*
Main machinery: 2 diesels; 130 hp(m) *(96 kW)*; 2 shafts
Speed, knots: 12

Comment: Built at Cleback Yard. First completed 1979; second and third in 1984.

TUGS

2 TUGS (OCEAN)

GAJ A 51   **MATANGA**

Displacement, tons: 1465 *(Gaj)*; 1600 *(Matanga)* full load
Dimensions, feet (metres): 216.5 × 37.7 × 13.1 *(66 × 11.5 × 4) (Gaj)*
Main machinery: 2 GRSE/MAN G7V diesels; 3920 hp(m) *(2.88 MW)*; 2 shafts
Speed, knots: 15. **Range, miles:** 8000 at 12 kts.
Guns: 1 Bofors 40 mm/60.

Comment: Built by Garden Reach SY. *Gaj* completed September 1973, *Matanga* launched 29 October 1977. Bollard pull of 40 tons and capable of towing a 20 000 ton ship at 8 kts. *Matanga* is 3 m longer and 1 m broader.

GAJ   *4/1992*

1 TUG (COASTAL)

RAJAJI

Displacement, tons: 428
Dimensions, feet (metres): 100 × 31.3 × 12.5 *(30.5 × 9.5 × 3.8)*
Main machinery: 2 GRSE-MAN diesels; 2120 hp(m) *(1.56 MW)*; 2 shafts; Kort nozzles
Speed, knots: 12.5

Comment: Built by Garden Reach SY. Completed July 1982.

12 HARBOUR TUGS

AGARAL   ARJUN   BALSHIL   BALRAM   BAJRANG   ANAND   + 6
Measurement, tons: 216 grt
Dimensions, feet (metres): 96.1 × 27.9 × 8.5 *(29.3 × 8.5 × 2.6)*
Main machinery: 2 SEMT-Pielstick 8 PA4 V 200 diesels; 3200 hp(m) *(2.35 MW)*; 2 shafts
Speed, knots: 11
Complement: 12

Comment: First three built by Mazagon Dock Ltd, Bombay in 1973-74. Five more delivered in 1988-89, and four more in 1991 from Mazagon Dock Ltd, Goa. Details given are for *Balram* and *Bajrang*; the others are smaller and of varying types.

HARBOUR TUG   *4/1992*

COAST GUARD

Administration

Director General:
Vice Admiral K K Kohli, AVSM
Deputy Director General:
Inspector General A K Sharma, NM, PTM

Future plans

Future plans include the following total strength by 2000: 24 OPVs, six for each region and six for offshore oil platform protection; 36 IPVs for regional work; six Deep Sea Patrol Vessels for deep water surveillance; four specialised pollution control vessels; six medium range surveillance aircraft; 36 light surveillance aircraft; six twin-engined helicopters for SAR and 30 light helicopters for shipborne operations.

General

An Interim Coast Guard Force started operations as a part of the Indian Navy on 1 February 1977. It was constituted as an independent paramilitary service on 19 August 1978 with the passing of the Coast Guard Act, 1978 by the Indian Parliament. It functions under the Ministry of Defence but with the budget met by the Department of Revenue.

Its responsibilities include:
(a) Ensuring the safety and protection of artificial islands, offshore terminals and other installations in the Maritime Zones.
(b) Measures for the safety of life and property at sea including assistance to mariners in distress.
(c) Measures to preserve and protect the marine environment and control marine pollution.
(d) Assisting the Customs and other authorities in anti-smuggling operations.
(e) Enforcing the provisions of enactments in force in the Maritime Zones.

Bases

The Headquarters of the Coast Guard is located in Delhi with Regional Headquarters in Bombay, Madras and Port Blair. District Headquarters established at Bombay, Haldia, New Mangalore, Paradip, Porbandar, Cochin, Vishakhapatnam, Campbell Bay and Diglipur. Stations at Vadinar, Mandapam, Okha and Tuticorin. Air Squadrons at Daman CGAS 750 (5 Dorniers 228), Madras CGAS 744 and CGAS 800 (6 Dorniers 228 and 2 Chetaks), Calcutta CGAS 700 (2 F 27), Goa CGAS 800 (3 Chetaks) and Bombay CGAS 841 (2 Chetaks).

Personnel

1994:   5300 (660 officers)

PATROL FORCES

0 + 3 (3) SAMAR CLASS (OFFSHORE PATROL VESSELS)

Name	No	Builders	Commissioned
SAMAR	42	Goa Shipyard	1994
SANGRAM	43	Goa Shipyard	1995
SARANG	44	Goa Shipyard	1996

Displacement, tons: 1950 full load
Dimensions, feet (metres): 334.6 oa; 315 wl × 37.7 × 11.5 *(102; 96 × 11.5 × 3.5)*
Main machinery: 2 SEMT-Pielstick 16 PA6 V 280 diesels; 12 800 hp(m) *(9.41 MW)* sustained; 2 shafts
Speed, knots: 21. **Range, miles:** 7000 at 15 kts
Complement: 45 (2 officers)
Guns: 2—30 mm (twin). 2—7.62 mm MGs.
Radars: Surface search: F/I band.

Comment: First three ordered in 1991. Second three reported to be building at Hindustan Shipyard. These are the largest Coast Guard vessels built so far. Almost identical to the Navy's Sukanya class but more heavily armed.

9 VIKRAM CLASS (OFFSHORE PATROL VESSELS TYPE P 957)

Name	No	Builders	Commissioned
VIKRAM	33	Mazagon Dock, Bombay	20 Dec 1983
VIJAYA	34	Mazagon Dock, Bombay	12 Apr 1985
VEERA	35	Mazagon Dock, Bombay	3 May 1986
VARUNA	36	Mazagon Dock, Bombay	27 Feb 1988
VAJRA	37	Mazagon Dock, Bombay	22 Dec 1988
VIVEK	38	Mazagon Dock, Bombay	19 Aug 1989
VIGRAHA	39	Mazagon Dock, Bombay	12 Apr 1990
VARAD	40	Goa Shipyard	19 July 1990
VARAHA	41	Goa Shipyard	11 Mar 1992

Displacement, tons: 1224 full load
Dimensions, feet (metres): 243.1 × 37.4 × 10.5 *(74.1 × 11.4 × 3.2)*
Main machinery: 2 SEMT-Pielstick 16 PA6 V 280 diesels; 12 800 hp(m) *(9.41 MW)* sustained; 2 shafts; cp props
Speed, knots: 22. **Range, miles:** 4000 at 16 kts
Complement: 96 (11 officers)
Guns: 1 or 2 Bofors 40 mm/60. 2—7.62 mm MGs.
Fire control: Lynx optical sights.
Radars: Navigation: Two Decca 1226; I band.
Helicopters: 1 HAL (Aerospatiale) Chetak or 1 Sea King.

Comment: Owes something to a NEVESBU (Netherlands) design, being a stretched version of its 750 ton offshore patrol vessels. Ordered in 1979. Fin stabilisers. Diving equipment. 4.5 ton deck crane. External firefighting pumps. Has one GRP boat and two inflatable craft. This class is considered too small for its required task and hence the need for the larger Samar class.

VAJRA   *12/1988, Indian Coast Guard*

7 JIJA BAI CLASS (TYPE 956) (INSHORE PATROL CRAFT)

JIJA BAI 64	RANI JINDAN 67	RAMADEVI 69
CHAND BIBI 65	HABBAKHATUN 68	AVVAYAR 70
KITTUR CHINNAMA 66		

Displacement, tons: 181 full load
Dimensions, feet (metres): 144.3 × 24.3 × 7.5 *(44 × 7.4 × 2.3)*
Main machinery: 2 MTU 12V 538 TB82 diesels; 5940 hp(m) *(4.37 MW)* sustained; 2 shafts
Speed, knots: 25. **Range, miles:** 2375 at 14 kts
Complement: 34 (7 officers)
Guns: 1 Bofors 40 mm/60. 2—7.62 mm MGs.
Radars: Surface search: Racal Decca 1226; I band.

Comment: The first three were completed by Sumidagawa and subsequent four craft built at Garden Reach, Calcutta. First of class commissioned 20 June 1983 and the last on 19 October 1985.

AVVAYAR   *1985, Indian Coast Guard*

5 SDB Mk 2 RAJ CLASS (INSHORE PATROL CRAFT)

RAJHANS 56	RAJKIRAN 59	RAJKAMAL 61
RAJTARANG 57	RAJSHREE 60	

Displacement, tons: 203 full load
Dimensions, feet (metres): 123 × 24.6 × 5.9 *(37.5 × 7.5 × 1.8)*
Main machinery: 2 Paxman Deltic 18-42K diesels; 6240 hp *(4.66 MW)*; 2 shafts. Auxiliary propulsion; 1 Kirloska-Cummins diesel; 165 hp *(123 kW)*
Speed, knots: 29; 4 auxiliary. **Range, miles:** 1400 at 14 kts
Complement: 28
Guns: 2 Bofors 40 mm/60.

Comment: Built by Garden Reach SY, Calcutta. Commissioned—*Rajhans*, 23 December 1980; *Rajtarang*, 25 November 1981; *Rajkiran* March 1984; *Rajshree* September 1984 and *Rajkamal* September 1986. All other previously reported vessels of this class belong to the Navy.

RAJKAMAL   *1989, Indian Coast Guard*

8 INSHORE PATROL CRAFT

C 01-08

Displacement, tons: 32 full load
Dimensions, feet (metres): 65.6 × 15.4 × 5 *(20 × 4.7 × 1.5)*
Main machinery: 2 Detroit 12V-71TA diesels; 840 hp *(627 kW)* sustained; 2 shafts
Speed, knots: 20. **Range, miles:** 400 at 20 kts
Complement: 8
Guns: 1—7.62 mm MG.
Radars: Navigation: I band.

Comment: Built by Swallow Craft Co, Pusan, South Korea. Six commissioned 24 September 1980, and two on 22 May 1982 having been taken over from India Oil Corporation.

C 03 (old number)   *1982, Swallow Craft*

11 JIJA BAI MOD I CLASS (INSHORE PATROL CRAFT)

TARA BAI 71	**NAIKI DEVI** 75	**ANNIE BESANT** 223
AHALYA BAI 72	**GANGA DEVI** 76	**KAMLA DEVI** 224
LAKSHMI BAI 73	**PRIYADARSHINI** 221	**AMRIT KAUR** 225
AKKA DEVI 74	**RAZIA SULTANA** 222	

Displacement, tons: 306 full load
Dimensions, feet (metres): 147.3 × 24.6 × 8.5 *(44.9 × 7.5 × 2.6)*
Main machinery: 2 MTU 12V 538 TB82 diesels; 5940 hp(m) *(4.37 MW)* sustained; 2 shafts
Speed, knots: 23. **Range, miles:** 2400 at 12 kts
Complement: 33 (5 officers)
Guns: 1 Bofors 40 mm/60. 2—7.62 mm MGs.
Radars: Surface search: Racal Decca 1226 or BEL 1245/6X (221-225); I band.

Comment: Two ordered in June 1986 from Singapore Shipbuilding and Engineering Ltd and built at Singapore to a Lürssen 45 design; completed May and July 1987. Four more laid down in 1987 at Garden Reach, Calcutta, first completed in April 1989, *Akka Devi* in September 1989, and the last two December 1989 and April 1990 respectively. A further batch of five followed with *Priyadarshini* commissioning 25 May 1992, *Razia Sultana* in December 1992, *Annie Besant* 7 December 1991, *Kamla Devi* 20 May 1992 and *Amrit Kaur* in December 1992. This is a 'follow-on' class to the Type 956 and is known as the Jija Bai Mod I class.

3 + 7 INSHORE PATROL CRAFT

C 32	**C 33**	**C 34** + 7

Displacement, tons: 49 full load
Dimensions, feet (metres): 68.2 × 19 × 5.9 *(20.8 × 5.8 × 1.8)*
Main machinery: 2 Deutz MWM TBD234V12 diesels; 1360 hp(m) *(1.00 MW)*; 1 Deutz MWM TBD234V8 diesel; 550 hp(m) *(404 kW)*; 3 Hamilton 402 waterjets
Speed, knots: 40. **Range, miles:** 600 at 15 kts
Complement: 10 (4 officers)
Guns: 1 Oerlikon 20 mm. 1—7.62 mm MG.
Radars: Navigation: I band.

Comment: Ordered from Anderson Marine, Goa in September 1990 to a P-2000 design by Amgram, similar to British Archer class. GRP hull. Official description is 'Interceptor Boats'. Five building at Goa and five at Cochin. First one launched June 1993 and completed late 1993.

AHALYA BAI   *5/1993, van Ginderen Collection*

RAZIA SULTANA   *12/1992, Garden Reach*

C 32   *1/1994, Anderson Marine*

INDONESIA

Headquarters' Appointments

Chief of the Naval Staff:
  Admiral Tanto Kuswanto
Deputy Chief of the Naval Staff (Operations):
  Rear Admiral Fx Murdjijo
Deputy Chief of the Naval Staff (Logistics):
  Rear Admiral Nyoman Suharta
Deputy Chief of the Naval Staff (Personnel):
  Rear Admiral Tonny Soekaton
Inspector General of the Navy:
  Major General Mar Hartarto Raden

Fleet Command

Commander-in-Chief Western Fleet (Barat):
  Rear Admiral Soeratmin
Commander-in-Chief Eastern Fleet (Timur):
  Rear Admiral Mochamad Sochid
Commandant of Navy Marine Corps:
  Major General Mar Gafur Chalik
Commander Military Sealift Command:
  Rear Admiral Haryono

Personnel

(a) 1994: 41 000 including 12 000 Marine Commando Corps and 1000 Naval Air Arm
(b) Selective national service

Prefix to Ships' Names

KRI (Kapal di Republik Indonesia)

Bases

Tanjung Priok (Jakarta), Ujung (Surabaya), Sabang, Medan (Sumatra), Makasar (Celebes), Balikpapan (East Borneo), Biak (New Guinea), Tanjung Pinang, Manado (Celebes), Teluk Ratai (South Sumatra). Naval Air Arm at Ujung, Biak and Pekan Baru. Ujung (Surabaya) is concerned with building, particularly naval patrol craft, and is the main naval dockyard as well as housing Eastern Command. New base to be built at Teluk Ratai in Lampung.

Strength of the Fleet

Type	Active (Reserve)	Building (Projected)
Patrol Submarines	2	(2)
Frigates	13 (4)	—
Corvettes	16	—
Fast Attack Craft—Missile	4	—
Large Patrol Craft	16	4
Coastal Patrol Craft	18	—
Hydrofoils	5	—
LSTs/LSM	26	—
LCM/LCU	44+	—
MCMV	13	—
Survey Ships	6	—
Submarine Tender	1	—
Repair Ship	1	—
Replenishment Tankers	2	—
Coastal Tankers	2	—
Support Ships	5	—
Transports	2	—
Cable Ship	1	—
Tugs	4	—
Sail Training Ship	1	—

Command Structure

Eastern Command (Surabaya)
Western Command (Teluk Ratai)
Training Command
Military Sea Communications Command (Maritime Security Agency)
Military Sealift Command (Logistic Support)

Mercantile Marine

Lloyd's Register of Shipping:
  2041 vessels of 2 440 471 tons gross

DELETIONS

Patrol Forces

1992 *Lajang*
1993 *Dorang, Todak*

Amphibious Forces

1992 *Amurang*

Auxiliaries

1991 *Talaud*
1992 *Natuna*
1993 *Nusa Telu, Karimundsa*

PENNANT LIST

Submarines

401 Cakra
402 Nanggala

Frigates

331 Martha Kristina Tiyahahu
332 W Zakarias Yohannes
333 Hasanuddin
341 Samadikun
342 Martadinata
343 Monginsidi
344 Ngurah Rai
351 Ahmed Yani
352 Slamet Riyadi
353 Yos Sudarso
354 Oswald Siahann
355 Abdul Halim Perdana Kusuma
356 Karel Satsiutubun
361 Fatahillah
362 Malahayati
363 Nala
364 Ki Hajar Dewantara

Corvettes

371 Kapitan Patimura
372 Untung Suropati
373 Nuku
374 Lambung Mangkurat
375 Cut Nyak Dien
376 Sultan Thaha Syaifuddin
377 Sutanto
378 Sutedi Senoputra
379 Wiratno
380 Memet Sastrawiria

381 Tjiptadi
382 Hasan Basri
383 Iman Bonjol
384 Pati Unus
385 Teuku Umar
386 Cut Meutia

Patrol Forces

621 Mandau
622 Rencong
623 Badik
624 Keris
651 Singa
653 Ajak
801 Pandrong
802 Sura
811 Kakap
812 Kerapu
813 Tongkol
814 Bervang
829 Tohok
830 Sembilang
847 Sibarau
848 Siliman
851 Samadar
852 Sasila
853 Sabola
854 Sawangi
855 Sadarin
856 Salmaneti
857 Sigalu
858 Silea
859 Siribua
862 Siada
863 Sikuda
864 Sigurot

Amphibious Forces

501 Teluk Langsa
502 Teluk Bajur
503 Teluk Amboina
504 Teluk Kau
508 Teluk Tomini
509 Teluk Ratai
510 Teluk Saleh
511 Teluk Bone
512 Teluk Semangka
513 Teluk Penju
514 Teluk Mandar
515 Teluk Sampit
516 Teluk Banten
517 Teluk Ende
531 Teluk Gilimanuk
532 Teluk Celukan Bawang
533 Teluk Cendrawasih
534 Teluk Berau
535 Teluk Peleng
536 Teluk Sibolga
537 Teluk Manado
538 Teluk Hading
539 Teluk Parigi
540 Teluk Lampung
541 Teluk Jakarta
542 Teluk Sangkulirang
580 Dore
582 Kupang
583 Dili
584 Nusantara

Survey Ships

931 Burujulasad
932 Dewa Kembar
933 Jalanidhi

Mine Warfare Forces

701 Pulau Rani
702 Pulau Retewo
711 Pulau Rengat
712 Pulau Rupat
721 Pulau Rote
722 Pulau Raas
723 Pulau Romang
724 Pulau Rimau
725 Pulau Rondo
726 Pulau Ruso
727 Pulau Rangsang
728 Pulau Raibu
729 Pulau Rempang

Auxiliaries

543 Teluk Cirebon
544 Teluk Sabang
561 Multatuli
901 Balikpapan
903 Arun
909 Pakan Baru
911 Sorong
921 Jaya Wijaya
922 Rakata
934 Lampo Batang
935 Tambora
936 Bromo
956 Teluk Mentawai
960 Karimata
971 Tangung Pandan
972 Tangung Oisina

SUBMARINES

2 + (2) CAKRA (209) CLASS (1300 TYPE)

Name	No	Builders	Laid down	Launched	Commissioned
CAKRA	401	Howaldtswerke, Kiel	25 Nov 1977	10 Sep 1980	19 Mar 1981
NANGGALA	402	Howaldtswerke, Kiel	14 Mar 1978	10 Sep 1980	6 July 1981

Displacement, tons: 1285 surfaced; 1390 dived
Dimensions, feet (metres): 195.2 × 20.3 × 17.9
(59.5 × 6.2 × 5.4)
Main machinery: Diesel-electric; 4 MTU 12V 493 AZ80 GA31L
  diesels; 2400 hp(m) *(1.76 MW)* sustained; 4 Siemens alter-
  nators; 1.7 MW; 1 Siemens motor; 4600 hp(m) *(3.38 MW)*
  sustained; 1 shaft
Speed, knots: 11 surfaced; 21.5 dived
Range, miles: 8200 at 8 kts
Complement: 34 (6 officers)

Torpedoes: 8—21 in *(533 mm)* bow tubes. 14 AEG SUT; dual

purpose; wire-guided; active/passive homing to 12 km
(6.5 nm) at 35 kts; 28 km *(15 nm)* at 23 kts; warhead 250 kg.
Fire control: Signaal Sinbad system.
Radars: Surface search: Thomson-CSF Calypso; I band.
Sonars: Atlas Elektronik CSU 3-2; active/passive search and
  attack; medium frequency.
  PRS-3/4; (integral with CSU) passive ranging.

Programmes: First pair ordered on 2 April 1977. Designed by
Ingenieurkontor, Lübeck for construction by Howaldtswerke,
Kiel and sale by Ferrostaal, Essen—all acting as a consortium.
Orders for two 1400 Type planned and funds were authorised

in December 1992. In spite of this, negotiations continued
with Australia/Sweden and France in 1993. The German
option remains the most likely with some construction being
done in Surabaya.
Modernisation: Major refits at HDW spanning three years from
1986 to 1989. These refits were expensive, and lengthy, and
may have discouraged further orders at that time.
Structure: Have high capacity batteries with GRP lead-acid cells
and battery cooling supplied by Wilhelm Hagen AG. Diving
depth, 240 m *(790 ft)*.
Operational: Endurance, 50 days. *Cakra* started 18 month refit
at Surabaya in June 1993.

NANGGALA

FRIGATES

Notes: (1) Ambitious plans for 23 new frigates have probably been indefinitely postponed in favour of German corvettes, although it was reported in 1993 that MEKO 200 and Dutch M class had been shortlisted.
(2) Interest is being shown in buying the two Dutch Tromp class, when they become available.

6 VAN SPEIJK CLASS

Name	No	Builders	Laid down	Launched	Commissioned
AHMAD YANI (ex-*Tjerk Hiddes*)	351	Nederlandse Dok en Scheepsbouw Mij, Amsterdam	1 June 1964	17 Dec 1965	16 Aug 1967
SLAMET RIYADI (ex-*Van Speijk*)	352	Nederlandse Dok en Scheepsbouw Mij, Amsterdam	1 Oct 1963	5 Mar 1965	14 Feb 1967
YOS SUDARSO (ex-*Van Galen*)	353	Koninklijke Maatschappij de Schelde, Flushing	25 July 1963	19 June 1965	1 Mar 1967
OSWALD SIAHAAN (ex-*Van Nes*)	354	Koninklijke Maatschappij de Schelde, Flushing	25 July 1963	26 Mar 1966	9 Aug 1967
ABDUL HALIM PERDANA KUSUMA (ex-*Evertsen*)	355	Koninklijke Maatschappij de Schelde, Flushing	6 July 1965	18 June 1966	21 Dec 1967
KAREL SATSUITUBUN (ex-*Isaac Sweers*)	356	Nederlandse Dok en Scheepsbouw Mij, Amsterdam	5 May 1965	10 Mar 1967	15 May 1968

Displacement, tons: 2225 standard; 2835 full load
Dimensions, feet (metres): 372 × 41 × 13.8
(113.4 × 12.5 × 4.2)
Main machinery: 2 Babcock & Wilcox boilers; 550 psi
(38.7 kg/cm sq); 850°F *(450°C)*; 2 Werkspoor/English Electric
turbines; 30 000 hp *(22.4 MW)*; 2 shafts
Speed, knots: 28.5. **Range, miles:** 4500 at 12 kts
Complement: 180

Missiles: SSM: 8 McDonnell Douglas Harpoon ❶; active radar
homing to 130 km *(70 nm)* at 0.9 Mach; warhead 227 kg.
SAM: 2 Short Bros Seacat quad launchers ❷; optical/radar guidance to 5 km *(2.7 nm)*; warhead 10 kg.
Guns: 1 OTO Melara 3 in *(76 mm)*/62 compact ❸; 85° elevation;
85 rounds/minute to 16 km *(8.7 nm)* anti-surface; 12 km
(6.6 nm) anti-aircraft; weight of shell 6 kg.
Torpedoes: 6—324 mm Mk 32 (2 triple) tubes ❹. Honeywell
Mk 46; anti-submarine; active/passive homing to 11 km
(5.9 nm) at 40 kts; warhead 44 kg.
Countermeasures: Decoys: 2 Knebworth Corvus 8-tubed train-
able; radar distraction or centroid chaff to 1 km.
ESM: UA 8/9; UA 13 (355 and 356); radar warning. FH5 D/F.
Combat data systems: SEWACO V action data automation and
Daisy data processing.
Fire control: Signaal LIROD optronic director.
Radars: Air search: Signaal LW 03 ❺; D band; range 219 km
(120 nm) for 2 m² target.
Air/surface search: Signaal DA 05 ❻; E/F band; range 137 km
(75 nm) for 2 m² target.
Navigation: Racal Decca 1229; I band.
Fire control: Signaal M 45 ❼; I/J band (for 76 mm gun).
2 Signaal M 44 ❽; I/J band (for Seacat).
Sonars: Signaal CWE 610; hull-mounted; active search and
attack; medium frequency. VDS; medium frequency.

Helicopters: 1 Westland Wasp ❾.

Programmes: On 11 February 1986 agreement signed with the
Netherlands for transfer of two of this class with an option on
two more. Transfer dates:—*Tjerk Hiddes*, 31 October 1986;
Van Speijk, 1 November 1986; *Van Galen*, 2 November 1987;
Van Nes, 31 October 1988. Contract of sale for the last two of
the class signed 13 May 1989. *Evertsen* transferred 1 November 1989 and *Isaac Sweers* 1 November 1990. Ships provided
with all spare parts but not towed arrays or helicopters.
Modernisation: This class underwent mid-life modernisation at
Rykswerf Den Helder from 1976. This included replacement of
4.5 in turret by 76 mm, A/S mortar by torpedo tubes, new electronics and electrics, updating combat data system, improved
communications, extensive automation with reduction in
complement, enlarged hangar for Lynx and improved habitability. Update on transfer included LIROD optronic director. Harpoon for first two only initially because there was no FMS
funding for the others. However the USN then provided sufficient SWG 1A panels for all of the class to be retrofitted with
Harpoon missiles.

AHMAD YANI (Scale 1 : 1200), Ian Sturton

OSWALD SIAHAAN 3/1992

AHMAD YANI 8/1991, L P Duane, RAN

3 FATAHILLAH CLASS

Name	No	Builders	Laid down	Launched	Commissioned
FATAHILLAH	361	Wilton Fijenoord, Schiedam	31 Jan 1977	22 Dec 1977	16 July 1979
MALAHAYATI	362	Wilton Fijenoord, Schiedam	28 July 1977	19 June 1978	21 Mar 1980
NALA	363	Wilton Fijenoord, Schiedam	27 Jan 1978	11 Jan 1979	4 Aug 1980

Displacement, tons: 1200 standard; 1450 full load
Dimensions, feet (metres): 276 × 36.4 × 10.7
(84 × 11.1 × 3.3)
Main machinery: CODOG; 1 RR Olympus TM3B gas turbine;
25 440 hp (19 MW) sustained; 2 MTU 20V 956 TB92 diesels;
11 070 hp(m) (8.14 MW) sustained; 2 shafts; LIPS cp props
Speed, knots: 30. **Range, miles:** 4250 at 16 kts
Complement: 89 (11 officers)

Missiles: SSM: 4 Aerospatiale MM 38 Exocet ❶; inertial cruise;
active radar homing to 42 km (23 nm) at 0.9 Mach; warhead
165 kg; sea-skimmer.
Guns: 1 Bofors 4.7 in (120 mm)/46 ❷; 80° elevation; 80 rounds/
minute to 18.5 km (10 nm); weight of shell 21 kg.
1 or 2 Bofors 40 mm/70 (2 in Nala) ❸; 90° elevation; 300
rounds/minute to 12 km (6.6 nm); weight of shell 0.96 kg.
2 Rheinmetall 20 mm; 55° elevation; 1000 rounds/minute to
2 km anti-aircraft; weight of shell 0.24 kg.
Torpedoes: 6—324 mm Mk 32 or ILAS 3 (2 triple) tubes (none in
Nala) ❹. 12 Mk 46 (or A244S); anti-submarine; active/passive
homing to 11 km (5.9 nm) at 40 kts; warhead 44 kg.
A/S mortars: 1 Bofors 375 mm twin-barrelled trainable ❺; 54
Erika; range 1600 m and Nelli; range 3600 m.

NALA   FATAHILLAH   (Scale 1 : 1200), Ian Sturton

Countermeasures: Decoys: 2 Knebworth Corvus 8-tubed train-
able chaff launchers ❻; radar distraction or centroid modes to
1 km. 1 T-Mk 6; torpedo decoy.
ESM: MEL Susie 1; radar intercept.
Combat data systems: Signaal SEWACO-RI action data
automation.
Fire control: GFCS has Signaal LIROD laser/TV directors.
Radars: Air/surface search: Signaal DA 05 ❼; E/F band; range
137 km (75 nm) for 2 m² target.
Surface search: Racal Decca AC 1229 ❽; I band.

Fire control: Signaal WM 28 ❾; I/J band; range 46 km (25 nm).
Sonars: Signaal PHS 32; hull-mounted; active search and attack;
medium frequency.

Helicopters: 1 Westland Wasp (Nala only) ❿.

Programmes: Ordered August 1975. Officially rated as
Corvettes.
Structure: NEVESBU design. Nala is fitted with a folding hangar/
landing deck.

MALAHAYATI   10/1993, John Mortimer

NALA (with helo deck)   7/1993, G Toremans

1 KI HAJAR DEWANTARA CLASS

Name	No
KI HAJAR DEWANTARA	364

Builders	Laid down	Launched	Commissioned
Split SY, Yugoslavia	11 May 1979	11 Oct 1980	31 Oct 1981

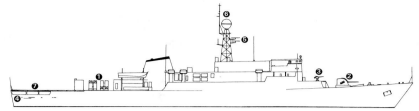

KI HAJAR DEWANTARA

(Scale 1 : 900), Ian Sturton

Displacement, tons: 2050 full load
Dimensions, feet (metres): 317.3 × 36.7 × 15.7
  (96.7 × 11.2 × 4.8)
Main machinery: CODOG; 1 RR Olympus TM3B gas turbine;
  24 525 hp *(18.3 MW)* sustained; 2 MTU 16V 956 TB92 diesels; 11 070 hp(m) *(8.14 MW)* sustained; 2 shafts; cp props
Speed, knots: 26 gas; 20 diesels. **Range, miles:** 4000 at 18 kts;
  1150 at 25 kts
Complement: 76 (11 officers) plus 14 instructors and 100 cadets

Missiles: SSM: 4 Aerospatiale MM 38 Exocet ❶; inertial cruise;
  active radar homing to 42 km *(23 nm)* at 0.9 Mach; warhead
  165 kg; sea-skimmer.
Guns: 1 Bofors 57 mm/70 ❷; 75° elevation; 200 rounds/minute
  to 17 km *(9.3 nm)*; weight of shell 2.4 kg.
  2 Rheinmetall 20 mm ❸.
Torpedoes: 2—21 in *(533 mm)* tubes ❹. AEG SUT; dual purpose;
  wire-guided; active/passive homing to 28 km *(15 nm)* at
  23 kts; 12 km *(6.5 nm)* at 35 kts; warhead 250 kg.
Depth charges: 1 projector/mortar.
Countermeasures: Decoys: 2—128 mm twin-tubed flare
  launchers.
ESM: Susie; radar intercept.
Fire control: Signaal SEWACO-RI action data automation.
Radars: Surface search: Racal Decca 1229 ❺; I band.
  Fire control: Signaal WM 28 ❻; I/J band; range 46 km *(25 nm)*.
Sonars: Signaal PHS 32; hull-mounted; active search and attack;
  medium frequency.

Helicopters: Platform ❼ for 1 NBO 105 helicopter.

Programmes: First ordered 14 March 1978 from Split SY, Yugoslavia where the hull was built and engines fitted. Armament
  and electronics fitted in the Netherlands and Indonesia. Near
  sister to Iraqi *Ibn Khaldoum*.
Structure: Two LCVPs on davits either side of the funnel. For the
  training role there is a classroom and additional wheelhouse,
  navigation and radio rooms. Torpedo tubes are fixed in the
  stern transom.
Operational: Used for training and troop transport. War roles
  include escort, ASW and troop transport. This ship is rarely
  seen outside the Indonesian archipelago.

KI HAJAR DEWANTARA

10/1993, John Mortimer

3 TRIBAL CLASS

Name	No	Builders	Laid down	Launched	Commissioned
MARTHA KRISTINA TIYAHAHU (ex-HMS *Zulu*)	331	Alex Stephen & Sons Ltd, Govan	13 Dec 1960	3 July 1962	17 Apr 1964
WILHELMUS ZAKARIAS YOHANNES (ex-HMS *Gurkha*)	332	J I Thornycroft Ltd, Woolston	3 Nov 1958	11 July 1960	13 Feb 1963
HASANUDDIN (ex-HMS *Tartar*)	333	HM Dockyard, Devonport	22 Oct 1959	19 Sep 1960	26 Feb 1962

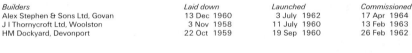

HASANUDDIN

(Scale 1 : 1200), Ian Sturton

Displacement, tons: 2300 standard; 2700 full load
Dimensions, feet (metres): 350 wl; 360 oa × 42.5 × 18
  (screws), 12.5 (keel) *(106.7; 109.7 × 13 × 5.5, 3.8)*
Main machinery: COSAG; 1 Babcock & Wilcox boiler; 550 psi
  (38.7 kg/cm sq); 850°F *(450°C)*; 1 Parsons Metrovick turbine;
  12 500 hp *(9.3 MW)*; 2 Yarrow/AEI G-6 gas turbines; 7500 hp
  (5.6 MW); 1 shaft; cp prop
Speed, knots: 25; 17 gas turbines. **Range, miles:** 5400 at 12 kts
Complement: 250 (19 officers)

Missiles: SAM: 2 Short Bros Seacat quad launchers ❶; optical/
  radar guidance to 5 km *(2.7 nm)*; warhead 10 kg.
Guns: 2 Vickers 4.5 in *(114 mm)* ❷; 50° elevation; 14 rounds/
  minute to 17 km *(9.3 nm)*; weight of shell 25 kg.
  2 Oerlikon 20 mm ❸; 55° elevation; 800 rounds/minute to
  2 km anti-aircraft.
  2—12.7 mm MGs.
A/S mortars: 1 Limbo 3-tubed Mk 10 ❹; range 1000 m; warhead
  92 kg.
Countermeasures: Decoys: 2 Knebworth Corvus 8-tubed chaff
  launchers; distraction or centroid modes to 1 km.
ESM: Radar warning.
Fire control: MRS 3 (for guns). 2 GWS 21 ❺ optical directors (for
  SAM).
Radars: Air search: Marconi Type 965 ❺; A band.
  Surface search: Type 993 ❻; E/F band.
  Navigation: Decca 978; I band.
  Fire control: Plessey Type 903 ❼; I band (for guns).
Sonars: Graseby Type 177; hull-mounted; active search; 7-9 kHz.
  Graseby Type 170 B; hull-mounted; active attack; 15 kHz.
  Kelvin Hughes Type 162; classification; 50 kHz.

Helicopters: 1 Westland Wasp ❾.

Programmes: Refitted by Vosper Thornycroft before transfer
  from UK. 331 commissioned in Indonesian Navy on 2 May
  1985, 332 on 16 October 1985 and 333 on 3 April 1986.
Structure: Helicopter descends by flight deck lift and is covered
  by portable panels. MGs fitted just aft of the GWS 21 directors.

WILHELMUS ZAKARIAS YOHANNES

7/1991, 92 Wing RAAF

4 CLAUD JONES CLASS

Name	No	Builders	Laid down	Launched	Commissioned
SAMADIKUN (ex-USS *John R Perry* DE 1034)	341	Avondale Marine Ways	1 Oct 1957	29 July 1958	5 May 1959
MARTADINATA (ex-USS *Charles Berry* DE 1035)	342	American SB Co, Toledo, Ohio	29 Oct 1958	17 Mar 1959	25 Nov 1959
MONGINSIDI (ex-USS *Claud Jones* DE 1033)	343	Avondale Marine Ways	1 June 1957	27 May 1958	10 Feb 1959
NGURAH RAI (ex-USS *McMorris* DE 1036)	344	American SB Co, Toledo, Ohio	5 Nov 1958	26 May 1959	4 Mar 1960

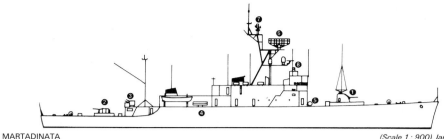

Displacement, tons: 1720 standard; 1968 full load
Dimensions, feet (metres): 310 × 38.7 × 18
(95 × 11.8 × 5.5)
Main machinery: 2 Fairbanks-Morse 38TD 8-1/8-12 diesels (not in 343); 7000 hp *(5.2 MW)* sustained; 1 shaft
Speed, knots: 22. **Range, miles:** 3000 at 18 kts
Complement: 171 (12 officers)

Guns: 1 US 3 in *(76 mm)*/50 Mk 34 ❶; 85° elevation; 50 rounds/minute to 12.8 km *(7 nm)*; weight of shell 6 kg.
2 USSR 37 mm/63 (twin) ❷; 80° elevation; 160 rounds/minute to 9 km *(5 nm)*; weight of shell 0.7 kg.
2 USSR 25 mm/80 (twin) ❸; 85° elevation; 270 rounds/minute to 3 km *(1.6 nm)*; weight of shell 0.34 kg.
Torpedoes: 6—324 mm Mk 32 (2 triple) tubes ❹. Probably fires Honeywell Mk 46; anti-submarine; active/passive homing to 11 km *(5.9 nm)* at 40 kts; warhead 44 kg.
A/S mortars: 2 Hedgehog 24-tubed launchers ❺; range 250 m; warhead 13.6 kg.
Countermeasures: ESM: WLR-1C (except *Samadikun*); radar warning.
Fire control: Mk 70 Mod 2 for guns. Mk 105 for A/S weapons.
Radars: Air search: Westinghouse SPS 6E ❻; D band; range 146 km *(80 nm)* (for fighter).
Surface search: Raytheon SPS 5D ❼; G/H band; range 37 km *(20 nm)*.
Raytheon SPS 4 *(Ngurah Rai)*; G/H band.
Navigation: Racal Decca 1226; I band.
Fire control: Lockheed SPG 52 ❽; K band.
Sonars: EDO *(Samadikun)*; SQS 45V *(Martadinata)*; SQS 39V *(Monginsidi)*; SQS 42V *(Ngurah Rai)*; hull-mounted; active search and attack; medium/high frequency.

Programmes: *Samadikun* transferred from US 20 February 1973; *Martadinata,* 31 January 1974; *Monginsidi* and *Ngurah Rai,* 16 December 1974. All refitted at Subic Bay 1979-82.
Operational: Replaced by Van Speijk class and all are reported to be in reserve.

MARTADINATA   *(Scale 1 : 900), Ian Sturton*

MARTADINATA   *6/1989, 92 Wing RAAF*

SHIPBORNE AIRCRAFT

Numbers/Type: 4 Bell 47J.
Operational speed: 74 kts *(137 km/h)*.
Service ceiling: 13 200 ft *(4025 m)*.
Range: 261 nm *(483 km)*.
Role/Weapon systems: Embarked for survey ship liaison duties. Sensors: None. Weapons: Unarmed.

Numbers/Type: 27 Nurtanio (Aerospatiale) NAS-332 Super Puma.
Operational speed: 151 kts *(279 km/h)*.
Service ceiling: 15 090 ft *(4600 m)*.
Range: 335 nm *(620 km)*.
Role/Weapon systems: ASW and assault operations with secondary role in utility and SAR; ASVW development possible with Exocet or similar. Sensors: Thomson-CSF Omera radar and Alcatel dipping sonar in some. Weapons: ASW; 2 × Mk 46 torpedoes or depth bombs. ASV; planned for future.

Numbers/Type: 8 Nurtanio (MBB) NBO 105C.
Operational speed: 113 kts *(210 km/h)*.
Service ceiling: 9845 ft *(3000 m)*.
Range: 407 nm *(754 km)*.
Role/Weapon systems: Embarked for liaison and support duties. Numbers are increasing slowly. Sensors: None. Weapons: Unarmed.

NBO 105C   *11/1990*

Numbers/Type: 9 Westland Wasp (HAS Mk 1).
Operational speed: 96 kts *(177 km/h)*.
Service ceiling: 12 200 ft *(3720 m)*.
Range: 263 nm *(488 km)*.
Role/Weapon systems: Shipborne ASW helicopter weapons carrier and reconnaissance; SAR and utility as secondary roles. Preferred replacement is Westland Navy Lynx. Sensors: None. Weapons: ASW; 2 × Mk 44 or 1 × Mk 46 torpedoes, depth bombs or mines.

LAND-BASED MARITIME AIRCRAFT (FRONT LINE)

Numbers/Type: 5 Boeing 737-200 Surveiller.
Operational speed: 462 kts *(856 km/h)*.
Service ceiling: 50 000 ft *(15 240 m)*.
Range: 2530 nm *(4688 km)*.
Role/Weapon systems: Land-based for long-range maritime surveillance roles. Two more acquired in 1994. Sensors upgraded in 1991 to include IFF. Sensors: 2 × Motorola APS-135(v) SLAM MR radars, various specialist radars. Weapons: Unarmed.

Numbers/Type: 10/6 GAF Searchmaster B/L.
Operational speed: 168 kts *(311 km/h)*.
Service ceiling: 21 000 ft *(6400 m)*.
Range: 730 nm *(1352 km)*.
Role/Weapon systems: Short-range maritime patrol, EEZ protection and anti-smuggler duties. Nomad type built in Australia. Sensors: Nose-mounted search radar. Weapons: Unarmed.

Numbers/Type: 4 Grumman HU-16B Albatross.
Operational speed: 205 kts *(379 km/h)*.
Service ceiling: 21 000 ft *(6400 m)*.
Range: 2850 nm *(3280 km)*.
Role/Weapon systems: Peacetime role as SAR amphibian; in wartime could operate for ASW, surface search and combat rescue tasks. Sensors: Search radar. Weapons: Generally unarmed but can carry depth bombs or 'iron' bombs.

Numbers/Type: 3 Lockheed C-130H-MP Hercules.
Operational speed: 325 kts *(602 km/h)*.
Service ceiling: 33 000 ft *(10 060 m)*.
Range: 4250 nm *(7876 km)*.
Role/Weapon systems: Long-range maritime reconnaissance role. Sensors: Search/weather radar. Weapons: Unarmed.

Numbers/Type: 15 Northrop F-5E Tiger II.
Operational speed: 940 kts *(1740 km/h)*.
Service ceiling: 51 800 ft *(15 790 m)*.
Range: 300 nm *(556 km)*.
Role/Weapon systems: Fleet air defence and strike fighter, formed 'naval co-operation unit'. Sensors: AI radar. Weapons: AD; 2 × AIM-9 Sidewinder, 2 × 20 mm cannon. Strike; 3175 tons of underwater stores.

Numbers/Type: 5 CASA/Nurtanio CN-235 MPA
Operational speed: 240 kts *(445 km/h)*.
Service ceiling: 26 600 ft *(8110 m)*.
Range: 669 nm *(1240 km)*.
Role/Weapon systems: Medium-range maritime reconnaissance role; 12 transport variants also in service. Sensors: Search/weather radar. Weapons: ASV; may have ASMs.

CORVETTES

16 KAPITAN PATIMURA (PARCHIM I) CLASS (TYPE 133)

Name	No	Builders	Commissioned	Recommissioned
KAPITAN PATIMURA (ex-*Prenzlau*)	371 (ex-231)	Peenewerft, Wolgast	11 May 1983	23 Sep 1993
UNTUNG SUROPATI (ex-*Ribnitz*)	372 (ex-233)	Peenewerft, Wolgast	29 Oct 1983	23 Sep 1993
NUKU (ex-*Waren*)	373 (ex-224)	Peenewerft, Wolgast	23 Nov 1982	15 Dec 1993
LAMBUNG MANGKURAT (ex-*Angermünde*)	374 (ex-214)	Peenewerft, Wolgast	26 July 1985	1994
CUT NYAK DIEN (ex-*Lübz*)	375 (ex-P 6169, ex-221)	Peenewerft, Wolgast	12 Feb 1982	25 Feb 1994
SULTAN THAHA SYAIFUDDIN (ex-*Bad Doberan*)	376 (ex-222)	Peenewerft, Wolgast	30 June 1982	25 Feb 1994
SUTANTO (ex-*Wismar*)	377 (ex-P 6170, ex-241)	Peenewerft, Wolgast	9 July 1981	1994
SUTEDI SENOPUTRA (ex-*Parchim*)	378 (ex-242)	Peenewerft, Wolgast	9 Apr 1981	1994
WIRATNO (ex-*Perleberg*)	379 (ex-243)	Peenewerft, Wolgast	19 Sep 1981	1994
MEMET SASTRAWIRIA (ex-*Bützow*)	380 (ex-244)	Peenewerft, Wolgast	30 Dec 1981	1994
TJIPTADI (ex-*Bergen*)	381 (ex-213)	Peenewerft, Wolgast	1 Feb 1985	1994
HASAN BASRI (ex-*Güstrow*)	382 (ex-223)	Peenewerft, Wolgast	10 Nov 1982	1994
IMAN BONJOL (ex-*Teterow*)	383 (ex-P 6168, ex-234)	Peenewerft, Wolgast	27 Jan 1984	1994
PATI UNUS (ex-*Ludwiglust*)	384 (ex-232)	Peenewerft, Wolgast	4 July 1983	1994
TEUKU UMAR (ex-*Grevesmühlen*)	385 (ex-212)	Peenewerft, Wolgast	21 Sep 1984	1994
CUT MEUTIA (ex-*Gadebusch*)	386 (ex-P 6167, ex-211)	Peenewerft, Wolgast	31 Aug 1984	1994

Displacement, tons: 769 standard
Dimensions, feet (metres): 246.7 × 32.2 × 11.5
(75.2 × 9.8 × 3.5)
Main machinery: 3 Type M 504A diesels; 10 812 hp(m)
(7.95 MW) sustained; 3 shafts
Speed, knots: 28
Complement: 60

Guns: 2 USSR 57 mm/80 (twin) ❶ automatic; 85° elevation;
120 rounds/minute to 6 km *(3.2 nm)*; weight of shell 2.8 kg.
2—30 mm (twin) ❷; 85° elevation; 500 rounds/minute to
5 km *(2.7 nm)* anti-aircraft; weight of shell 0.54 kg.
Torpedoes: 4—400 mm tubes ❸.
A/S mortars: 2 RBU 6000 12-barrelled trainable launchers ❹;
automatic loading; range 6000 m; warhead 31 kg.
Depth charges: 2 racks.
Mines: Mine rails fitted.
Countermeasures: Decoys: 2—16-tubed chaff rocket launchers.
ESM: 2 Watch Dog; radar warning.
Radars: Air/surface search: Strut Curve ❺; F band; range 110 km
(60 nm) for 2 m² target.
Navigation: TSR 333; I band.
Fire control: Muff Cob ❻; G/H band.
IFF: High Pole B.
Sonars: Hull-mounted; active search and attack; high frequency.
VDS system on starboard side (in some hulls).

Programmes: Ex-GDR ships mostly paid off in 1991. Formally
transferred on 4 January 1993 and became Indonesian ships
on 25 August 1993. First three arrived Indonesia in November
1993. All to have transferred by late 1994.
Modernisation: All refitted prior to sailing for Indonesia. Range
increased and air-conditioning added to accommodation.
Structure: Basically very similar to Soviet Grisha class but with a
higher freeboard and different armament.
Operational: Crews were still being trained into 1994 and the
same teams were being used for more than one transit.

KAPITAN PATIMURA (Scale 1 : 600), Ian Sturton

KAPITAN PATIMURA 10/1993, van Ginderen Collection

PATROL FORCES

Note: It is reported that two ex-Soviet Kronstadt class patrol craft (*Tohok* 829 and *Sembilang* 830) were resurrected in 1988.

4 DAGGER CLASS
(FAST ATTACK CRAFT—MISSILE)

Name	No	Builders	Commissioned
MANDAU	621	Korea Tacoma, Masan	20 July 1979
RENCONG	622	Korea Tacoma, Masan	20 July 1979
BADIK	623	Korea Tacoma, Masan	Feb 1980
KERIS	624	Korea Tacoma, Masan	Feb 1980

Displacement, tons: 270 full load
Dimensions, feet (metres): 164.7 × 23.9 × 7.5
(50.2 × 7.3 × 2.3)
Main machinery: CODOG; 1 GE LM 2500 gas turbine;
23 000 hp *(17.16 MW)* sustained; 2 MTU 12V 331 TC81 die-
sels; 2240 hp(m) *(1.65 MW)* sustained; 2 shafts; cp props
Speed, knots: 41 gas; 17 diesel. **Range, miles:** 2000 at 17 kts
Complement: 43 (7 officers)

Missiles: SSM: 4 Aerospatiale MM 38 Exocet; inertial cruise;
active radar homing to 42 km *(23 nm)* at 0.9 Mach; warhead
165 kg; sea-skimmer.
Guns: 1 Bofors 57 mm/70 Mk 1; 75° elevation; 200 rounds/
minute to 17 km *(9.3 nm)*; weight of shell 0.96 kg. Launchers
for illuminants on each side.
1 Bofors 40 mm/70; 90° elevation; 300 rounds/minute to
12 km *(6.6 nm)*; weight of shell 2.4 kg.
2 Rheinmetall 20 mm.
Countermeasures: ESM (in 623 and 624).
Fire Control: Selenia NA-18 optronic director.
Radars: Surface search: Racal Decca 1226; I band.
Fire control: Signaal WM 28; I/J band; range 46 km *(25 nm)*.

Programmes: PSMM Mk 5 type craft ordered in 1975.
Structure: Shorter in length and smaller displacement than
South Korean units. *Mandau* has a different shaped mast with
a tripod base.

BADIK 7/1993, John Mortimer

4 + 4 SINGA (PB 57) CLASS (NAV I and II) (LARGE PATROL CRAFT)

Name	No	Builders	Commissioned
SINGA	651	Lürssen/PT Pal Surabaya	Apr 1988
AJAK	653	Lürssen/PT Pal Surabaya	5 Apr 1989
PANDRONG	801	PT Pal Surabaya	1990
SURA	802	PT Pal Surabaya	1991

Displacement, tons: 447 full load (NAV I); 428 full load (NAV II)
Dimensions, feet (metres): 190.6 × 25 × 9.2 *(58.1 × 7.6 × 2.8)*
Main machinery: 2 MTU 16V 956 TB92 diesels; 8850 hp(m) *(6.5 MW)* sustained; 2 shafts
Speed, knots: 27. **Range, miles:** 6100 at 15 kts; 2200 at 27 kts
Complement: 42 (6 officers)
Guns: 1 Bofors SAK 57 mm/70 Mk 2; 75° elevation; 220 rounds/minute to 14 km *(7.6 nm)*; weight of shell 2.4 kg.
  1 Bofors SAK 40 mm/70; 90° elevation; 300 rounds/minute to 12 km *(6.6 nm)*; weight of shell 0.96 kg.
  2 Rheinmetall 20 mm (NAV II).
Torpedoes: 2—21 in *(533 mm)* Toro tubes (NAV I). AEG SUT; anti-submarine; wire-guided; active/passive homing to 12 km *(6.6 nm)* at 35 kts; 28 km *(15 nm)* at 23 kts; warhead 250 kg.
Countermeasures: Decoys: CSEE Dagaie single trainable launcher; automatic dispenser for IR flares and chaff; H/J band.
ESM: DR 2000 S3 with Dalia analyser; radar intercept. Telegon VIII D/F.
Fire control: Signaal LIOD 73 Ri optronic director. Signaal WM 22 72 Ri WCS.
Radars: Surface search: Racal Decca 2459; I band.
Fire control: Signaal WM 22; I/J band.
Sonars: Signaal PMS 32 (NAV I); active search and attack; medium frequency.

Comment: Class ordered from Lürssen in 1982. First launched and shipped incomplete to P T Pal Surabaya for fitting out in January 1984. Second shipped July 1984. The first two are NAV I ASW versions with torpedo tubes and sonars. The second pair are NAV II AAW versions with an augmented gun armament but without torpedo tubes and sonars. Four more reported ordered in 1993 to a NAV V design which sounds similar to NAV II but with an updated combat data system.

AJAK   5/1990, 92 Wing RAAF

PANDRONG   8/1993, John Mortimer

4 KAKAP (PB 57) CLASS (NAV III and IV) (LARGE PATROL CRAFT)

Name	No	Builders	Commissioned
KAKAP	811	Lürssen/PT Pal Surabaya	29 June 1988
KERAPU	812	Lürssen/PT Pal Surabaya	5 Apr 1989
TONGKOL	813	PT Pal Surabaya	1991
BERVANG	814	PT Pal Surabaya	1992

Displacement, tons: 423 full load
Dimensions, feet (metres): 190.6 × 25 × 9.2 *(58.1 × 7.6 × 2.8)*
Main machinery: 2 MTU 16V 956 TB92 diesels; 8850 hp(m) *(6.5 MW)* sustained; 2 shafts
Speed, knots: 27. **Range, miles:** 6100 at 15 kts; 2200 at 27 kts
Complement: 40 plus 17 spare berths
Guns: 1 Bofors 40 mm/60. 90° elevation; 240 rounds/minute to 12.6 km *(6.8 nm)*; weight of shell 0.96 kg. 2—12.7 mm MGs.
Radars: Surface search: Racal Decca 2459; I band.
Navigation: KH 1007; I band.
Helicopters: Platform for 1 NBO 105 or Wasp.

Comment: Ordered in 1982. First pair shipped from West Germany and completed at P T Pal Surabaya. Second pair assembled at Surabaya. The first pair are NAV III SAR versions and by comparison with NAV I are very lightly armed and have a 13 × 7.1 m helicopter deck in place of the after guns and torpedo tubes. The ship can be used for Patrol purposes as well as SAR, and can transport two rifle platoons. There is also a fast seaboat with launching crane at the stern and two water guns for firefighting. The NAV IV version has some minor variations. These are naval craft, not Maritime Security Agency as previously indicated.

KAKAP   5/1990, John Mortimer

8 SIBARAU (ATTACK) CLASS (LARGE PATROL CRAFT)

Name	No	Builders	Commissioned
SIBARAU (ex-HMAS *Bandolier*)	847	Walkers, Australia	14 Dec 1968
SILIMAN (ex-HMAS *Archer*)	848	Walkers, Australia	15 May 1968
SIGALU (ex-HMAS *Barricade*)	857	Walkers, Australia	26 Oct 1968
SILEA (ex-HMAS *Acute*)	858	Evans Deakin	24 Apr 1968
SIRIBUA (ex-HMAS *Bombard*)	859	Walkers, Australia	5 Nov 1968
SIADA (ex-HMAS *Barbette*)	862	Walkers, Australia	16 Aug 1968
SIKUDA (ex-HMAS *Attack*)	863	Evans Deakin	17 Nov 1967
SIGUROT (ex-HMAS *Assail*)	864	Evans Deakin	12 July 1968

Displacement, tons: 146 full load
Dimensions, feet (metres): 107.5 × 20 × 7.3 *(32.8 × 6.1 × 2.2)*
Main machinery: 2 Paxman 16YJCM diesels; 4000 hp *(2.98 MW)* sustained; 2 shafts
Speed, knots: 21. **Range, miles:** 1220 at 13 kts
Complement: 19 (3 officers)
Guns: 1 Bofors 40 mm/60. 1—12.5 mm MG.
Radars: Surface search: Decca 916; I band; range 88 km *(48 nm)*.

Comment: Transferred from Australia after refit—*Bandolier* 16 November 1973, *Archer* in 1974, *Barricade* March 1982, *Acute* 6 May 1983, *Bombard* September 1983, *Attack* 22 February 1985 (recommissioned 24 May 1985), *Barbette* February 1985, *Assail* February 1986. All carry rocket/flare launchers. Two similar craft with pennant numbers 860 and 861 have been reported. These are probably locally built ships of the same class.

SIGUROT   10/1992, van Ginderen Collection

18 KAL KANGEAN CLASS (COASTAL PATROL CRAFT)

Displacement, tons: 44.7 full load
Dimensions, feet (metres): 80.4 × 14.1 × 3.3 *(24.5 × 4.3 × 1)*
Main machinery: 2 diesels; 2 shafts
Speed, knots: 18
Guns: 2 USSR 25 mm/80 (twin). 2 USSR 14.5 mm (twin) MGs.

Comment: Ordered from PT Kabrick Kapal in about 1984 and completed between 1987 and 1990.

KAL KANGEAN 1112   10/1988, Trevor Brown

5 BOEING JETFOILS

BIMA SAMUDERA 1-5

Displacement, tons: 117 full load
Dimensions, feet (metres): 102 × 30 × 17.5/7.8 *(31 × 9.1 × 5.3/2.4)*
Main machinery: 2 Allison 501-K20A gas turbines; 7560 hp *(5.64 MW)*; 2 shafts; 2 Detroit 8V-92TA diesels; 700 hp *(522 kW)* sustained; 2 waterjets
Speed, knots: 48. **Range, miles:** 900 at 40 kts; 1500 at 15 kts
Complement: 12
Military lift: 100 troops
Guns: Combinations of 1 Bofors 40 mm/60. 1 Rheinmetall 20 mm. 2—12.7 mm MGs.
Radars: Navigation: Decca; I band.

Comment: First ordered for evaluation in sundry naval and civilian roles including gunboat and troop transporter. Launched 22 October 1981, arrived Indonesia January 1982 for start of trials in March. In 1983 further four ordered from Boeing for delivery incomplete in 1984, 1985 and 1986. Plans to increase the total to 47 have been abandoned, but attempts have been made in 1992/93 to finish the fitting out of the second batch of four. Operational status is doubtful.

BOEING JETFOIL   *1987*

AMPHIBIOUS FORCES

Note: This section includes some vessels of the Military Sealift Command—Kolinlamil.

7 LST 1-511 and 512-1152 CLASSES

Name	No	Builders	Commissioned
TELUK LANGSA (ex-USS *LST 1128*)	501	Chicago Bridge and Iron Works	9 Mar 1945
TELUK BAJUR (ex-USS *LST 616*)	502	Chicago Bridge and Iron Works	29 May 1944
TELUK KAU (ex-USS *LST 652*)	504	Chicago Bridge and Iron Works	1 Jan 1945
TELUK TOMINI (ex-MV *Inagua Crest*, ex-MV *Brunei*, ex-USS *Bledsoe County, LST 356*)	508	Charleston NY	22 Dec 1942
TELUK RATAI (ex-Liberian *Inagua Shipper*, ex-USS *Presque Isle*, APB 44, ex-*LST 678*, ex-*Teluk Sindoro*)	509	American Bridge Co, Pennsylvania	30 June 1944
TELUK SALEH (ex-USS *Clark County, LST 601*)	510	Chicago Bridge and Iron Works	25 Mar 1944
TELUK BONE (ex-USS *Iredell County, LST 839*)	511	American Bridge Co, Pennsylvania	6 Dec 1944

Displacement, tons: 1653 standard; 4080 full load
Dimensions, feet (metres): 328 × 50 × 14 *(100 × 15.2 × 4.3)*
Main machinery: 2 GM 12-567A diesels; 1800 hp *(1.34 MW)*; 2 shafts
Speed, knots: 11.6. **Range, miles:** 11 000 at 10 kts
Complement: 119 (accommodation for 266)
Military lift: 2100 tons

Guns: 7—40 mm. 2—20 mm *(Teluk Langsa)*. 6—37 mm (remainder).
   Older units and previously unarmed ships now fitted with ex-Soviet 37 mm guns.
Radars: Surface search: SPS 21 *(Teluk Tomini, Teluk Sindoro)*.
   SPS 53 *(Teluk Saleh, Teluk Bone)*. SO-1 *(Teluk Kau)*. SO-6 *(Teluk Langsa)*.

Programmes: *Teluk Bajur, Teluk Saleh* and *Teluk Bone* transferred from US in June 1961 (and purchased 22 February 1979). *Teluk Kau* and *Teluk Langsa* in July 1970.
Operational: *Teluk Bajur* and *Teluk Tomini* in Military Sealift Command and are classified as LCCs. All due to be scrapped by the end of 1994.

TELUK KAU   *3/1991, 92 Wing RAAF*

---

6 TACOMA TYPE (LST)

Name	No	Builders	Commissioned
TELUK SEMANGKA	512	Korea-Tacoma, Masan	20 Jan 1981
TELUK PENJU	513	Korea-Tacoma, Masan	20 Jan 1981
TELUK MANDAR	514	Korea-Tacoma, Masan	July 1981
TELUK SAMPIT	515	Korea-Tacoma, Masan	June 1981
TELUK BANTEN	516	Korea-Tacoma, Masan	May 1982
TELUK ENDE	517	Korea-Tacoma, Masan	2 Sep 1982

Displacement, tons: 3750 full load
Dimensions, feet (metres): 328 × 47.2 × 13.8 *(100 × 14.4 × 4.2)*
Main machinery: 2 diesels; 6860 hp(m) *(5.04 MW)*; 2 shafts
Speed, knots: 15. **Range, miles:** 7500 at 13 kts
Complement: 90 (13 officers)
Military lift: 1800 tons (including 17 MBTs); 2 LCVPs; 200 troops

Guns: 3 Bofors 40 mm/60. 2 Rheinmetall 20 mm.
Radars: Navigation: Racal Decca; I band.

Helicopters: 1 Westland Wasp; 3 NAS-332 Super Pumas can be carried in last pair.

Programmes: First four ordered in June 1979, last pair June 1981.
Structure: No hangar in *Teluk Semangka* and *Teluk Mandar*. Two hangars in *Teluk Ende*. First four ordered June 1979, last pair June 1981. The last pair differ in silhouette having drowned exhausts in place of funnels and having their LCVPs carried forward of the bridge.
Operational: Battalion of marines can be embarked if no tanks are carried. One of the class is fitted out as a hospital ship and the last pair act as Command ships.

TELUK BANTEN (command ship)   *7/1993, G Toremans*

TELUK SEMANGKA (no hangar)   *7/1993, G Toremans*

TELUK ENDE (two hangars)   *7/1993, G Toremans*

1 LST

Name	No	Builders	Commissioned
TELUK AMBOINA	503	Sasebo, Japan	June 1961

Displacement, tons: 2378 standard; 4200 full load
Dimensions, feet (metres): 327 × 50 × 15 *(99.7 × 15.3 × 4.6)*
Main machinery: 2 MAN V6V 22/30 diesels; 3425 hp(m) *(2.52 MW)*; 2 shafts
Speed, knots: 13.1. **Range, miles:** 4000 at 13.1 kts
Complement: 88
Military lift: 212 troops; 2100 tons

Guns: 6—37 mm; anti-aircraft.

Programmes: Launched on 17 March 1961 and transferred from Japan in June 1961.
Structure: A faster copy of US LST 511 class with 30 ton crane forward of bridge.
Operational: Military Sealift Command.

TELUK AMBOINA   *10/1992, van Ginderen Collection*

12 FROSCH I CLASS (TYPE 108) (LSM)

Name	No	Builders	Commissioned
TELUK GILIMANUK (ex-Hoyerswerda)	531 (ex-611)	Peenewerft, Wolgast	12 Nov 1976
TELUK CELUKAN BAWANG (ex-Hagenow)	532 (ex-632)	Peenewerft, Wolgast	1 Dec 1976
TELUK CENDRAWASIH (ex-Frankfurt/Oder)	533 (ex-613)	Peenewerft, Wolgast	2 Feb 1977
TELUK BERAU (ex-Eberswalde-Finow)	534 (ex-634)	Peenewerft, Wolgast	28 May 1977
TELUK PELENG (ex-Lübben)	535 (ex-631)	Peenewerft, Wolgast	15 Mar 1978
TELUK SIBOLGA (ex-Schwerin)	536 (ex-612)	Peenewerft, Wolgast	19 Oct 1977
TELUK MANADO (ex-Neubrandenburg)	537 (ex-633)	Peenewerft, Wolgast	28 Dec 1977
TELUK HADING (ex-Cottbus)	538 (ex-614)	Peenewerft, Wolgast	26 May 1978
TELUK PARIGI (ex-Anklam)	539 (ex-635)	Peenewerft, Wolgast	14 July 1978
TELUK LAMPUNG (ex-Schwedt)	540 (ex-636)	Peenewerft, Wolgast	7 Sep 1979
TELUK JAKARTA (ex-Eisenhüttenstadt)	541 (ex-615)	Peenewerft, Wolgast	4 Jan 1979
TELUK SANGKULIRANG (ex-Grimmen)	542 (ex-616)	Peenewerft, Wolgast	4 Jan 1979

Displacement, tons: 1950 full load
Dimensions, feet (metres): 321.5 × 36.4 × 9.2 *(98 × 11.1 × 2.8)*
Main machinery: 2 diesels; 5000 hp(m) *(3.68 MW)*; 2 shafts
Speed, knots: 18
Military lift: 600 tons
Mines: Can lay mines through stern doors.
Radars: Air/surface search: Strut Curve; F band.
Navigation: TSR 333; I band.

Comment: Former GDR ships transferred from Germany on 25 August 1993. Demilitarised with all guns removed, but it is anticipated that some form of armament is to replace the 57 mm and 30 mm twin guns. All refitted in Germany prior to sailing. First three arrived Indonesia in late 1993, remainder throughout 1994.

TELUK PELENG   *10/1993, van Ginderen Collection*

TELUK SIBOLGA   *12/1993, Hartmut Ehlers*

1 LCU TYPE

DORE 580

Displacement, tons: 182 standard; 275 full load
Dimensions, feet (metres): 125.7 × 32.8 × 5.9 *(38.3 × 10 × 1.8)*
Main machinery: 2 diesels; 600 hp(m) *(441 kW)*; 2 shafts
Speed, knots: 8
Complement: 17
Military lift: 4 light tanks or 9 trucks
Guns: 1—12.7 mm MG.

Comment: Military Sealift Command. Built by Korneuberg SY, Austria in 1968. A second of class sank in September 1992. Two of same class are civilian operated in West Irian.

3 LCUs

KUPANG 582   **DILI** 583   **NUSANTARA** 584

Displacement, tons: 400 full load
Dimensions, feet (metres): 140.7 × 29.9 × 4.6 *(42.9 × 9.1 × 1.4)*
Main machinery: 2 diesels; 2 shafts
Speed, knots: 12. **Range, miles:** 700 at 11 kts
Complement: 17
Military lift: 200 tons

Comment: Built at Naval Training Centre, Surabaya in 1978-80. Military Sealift Command.

40+ LCM 6

Displacement, tons: 62
Main machinery: 2 Gray Marine 64 HN9 diesels; 330 hp *(264 kW)*; 2 shafts
Speed, knots: 8

Comment: A programme which has continued since 1960 although some of the details may have changed. 20 were acquired from Taiwan in exchange for torpedoes.

MINE WARFARE FORCES

9 KONDOR II (TYPE 89) CLASS (MINESWEEPERS—COASTAL)

Name	No	Builders	Commissioned
PULAU ROTE (ex-Wolgast)	721 (ex-V 811)	Peenewerft, Wolgast	1 June 1971
PULAU RAAS (ex-Hettstedt)	722 (ex-353)	Peenewerft, Wolgast	22 Dec 1971
PULAU ROMANG (ex-Pritzwalk)	723 (ex-325)	Peenewerft, Wolgast	26 June 1972
PULAU RIMAU (ex-Bitterfeld)	724 (ex-332, ex-M 2672)	Peenewerft, Wolgast	7 Aug 1972
PULAU RONDO (ex-Zerbst)	725 (ex-335)	Peenewerft, Wolgast	30 Sep 1972
PULAU RUSO (ex-Oranienburg)	726 (ex-341)	Peenewerft, Wolgast	1 Nov 1972
PULAU RANGSANG (ex-Jüterbog)	727 (ex-342)	Peenewerft, Wolgast	7 Apr 1973
PULAU RAIBU (ex-Sömmerda)	728 (ex-311, ex-M 2670)	Peenewerft, Wolgast	9 Aug 1973
PULAU REMPANG (ex-Grimma)	729 (ex-336)	Peenewerft, Wolgast	10 Nov 1973

Displacement, tons: 310 full load
Dimensions, feet (metres): 186 × 24.6 × 7.9 *(56.7 × 7.5 × 2.4)*
Main machinery: 2 Russki Kolomna Type 40-DM diesels; 4408 hp(m) *(3.24 MW)* sustained; 2 shafts; cp props
Speed, knots: 17
Complement: 31 (6 officers)
Guns: 6—25 mm (3 twin).
Mines: 2 rails.
Radars: Navigation: TSR 333; I band.
Sonars: Bendix AQS 17(V) VDS; minehunting; 200 kHz or AMASS clip-on towed array.

Comment: Former GDR minesweepers transferred from Germany in Russian dockship *Trans-Shelf* in July 1993. Probably fitted with new Bendix sonars but MCM is to be a secondary role with EEZ patrol taking priority. Guns may be changed.

PULAU ROTE (and others)   *5/1993, Hartmut Ehlers*

2 PULAU RENGAT (TRIPARTITE) CLASS (MINE WARFARE VESSELS)

Name	No	Builders	Commissioned
PULAU RENGAT	711	van der Giessen-de Noord	26 Mar 1988
PULAU RUPAT	712	van der Giessen-de Noord	26 Mar 1988

Displacement, tons: 502 standard; 568 full load
Dimensions, feet (metres): 168.9 × 29.2 × 8.2 *(51.5 × 8.9 × 2.5)*
Main machinery: 2 MTU 12V 396 TC82 diesels; 2610 hp(m) *(1.92 MW)* sustained; 2 shafts; auxiliary propulsion; 3 Turbomeca gas turbine generators; 2 motors; 2400 hp(m) *(1.76 MW)*; 2 retractable Schottel propulsors; 2 bow thrusters; 150 hp(m) *(110 kW)*
Speed, knots: 15; 7 auxiliary propulsion. **Range, miles:** 3000 at 12 kts
Complement: 46 plus 4 spare berths

Guns: 2 Rheinmetall 20 mm. An additional short range missile system may be added for patrol duties or a third 20 mm gun.
Countermeasures: MCM: OD3 Oropesa mechanical sweep gear; Fiskars F-82 magnetic and SA Marine AS 203 acoustic sweeps; Ibis V minehunting system; 2 PAP 104 Mk 4 minehunting vehicles.
Combat data systems: Signaal SEWACO-RI action data automation.
Radars: Navigation: Racal Decca AC 1229C; I band.
Sonars: Thomson Sintra TSM 2022; active minehunting; high frequency.

Programmes: First ordered on 29 March 1985, laid down 22 July 1985 and launched 23 July 1987. Second ordered 30 August 1985, laid down 15 December 1985 and launched 27 August 1987. More were to have been built in Indonesia up to a total of 12 but this programme has been suspended by lack of funds.
Structure: There are differences in design between these ships and the European Tripartites, apart from their propulsion. Deck-houses and general layout are different as they will be required to act as minehunters, minesweepers and patrol ships. Hull construction is GRP shock proven Tripartite design.
Operational: Endurance, 15 days. Automatic operations, navigation and recording systems, Thomson-CSF Naviplot TSM 2060 tactical display. A 5 ton container can be shipped, stored for varying tasks—research; patrol; extended diving; drone control.

PULAU RENGAT   *8/1993, John Mortimer*

2 T 43 CLASS (MINESWEEPERS—OCEAN)

PULAU RANI 701   **PULAU RATEWO** 702

Displacement, tons: 580 full load
Dimensions, feet (metres): 190.2 × 27.6 × 6.9 *(58 × 8.4 × 2.1)*
Main machinery: 2 Kolomna 9-D-8 diesels; 2000 hp(m) *(1.6 MW)* sustained; 2 shafts
Speed, knots: 15. **Range, miles:** 3000 at 10 kts
Complement: 77
Guns: 4—37 mm/63 (2 twin). 8—12.7 mm (4 twin) MGs.
Depth charges: 2 projectors.
Radars: Navigation: Decca 110; I band.
Sonars: Stag Ear; hull-mounted; active search and attack; high frequency.

Comment: Transferred from USSR in 1964. Mostly used as patrol craft.

PULAU RANI   *1983, W Sartori*

SURVEY AND RESEARCH SHIPS

Note: There is also a 44 ton launch *Aries* built in 1960.

1 HECLA CLASS (SURVEY SHIP)

Name	No	Builders	Commissioned
DEWA KEMBAR	932	Yarrow and Co., Blythswood	5 May 1966
(ex-HMS *Hydra*)			

Displacement, tons: 1915 light; 2733 full load
Dimensions, feet (metres): 260.1 × 49.1 × 15.4 *(79.3 × 15 × 4.7)*
Main machinery: Diesel-electric; 3 Paxman 12YJCZ diesels; 3780 hp *(2.82 MW)*; 3 generators; 1 motor; 2000 hp(m) *(1.49 MW)*; 1 shaft; bow thruster
Speed, knots: 14. **Range, miles:** 12 000 at 11 kts
Complement: 123 (14 officers)
Radars: Navigation: Kelvin Hughes Type 1006; I band.
Helicopters: 1 Westland Wasp.

Comment: Transferred from UK 18 April 1986 for refit. Commissioned in Indonesian Navy 10 September 1986. SATCOM fitted. Two survey launches on davits.

DEWA KEMBAR   *9/1986, W Sartori*

3 + (1) RESEARCH SHIPS

Name	No	Builders	Commissioned
BARUNAJAYA I	—	CMN, Cherbourg	15 Sep 1989
BARUNAJAYA II	—	CMN, Cherbourg	Dec 1989
BARUNAJAYA III	—	CMN, Cherbourg	Apr 1990

Displacement, tons: 1180 full load
Dimensions, feet (metres): 198.2 × 38 × 13.8 *(60.4 × 11.6 × 4.2)*
Main machinery: 2 Niigata/SEMT-Pielstick 5 PA5 L 255 diesels; 2990 hp(m) *(2.2 MW)* sustained; 2 shafts; cp props
Speed, knots: 14. **Range, miles:** 7500 at 12 kts
Complement: 37 (8 officers) plus 26 scientists

Comment: Ordered from La Manche, Dieppe in February 1985 by the office of Technology, Ministry of Industry and Research. Badly delayed by the closing down of the original shipbuilders (ACM, Dieppe) and construction taken over by CMN at St Malo. *Barunajaya 1* is employed entirely on hydrography, the second on oceanography and the third combines both tasks. An enlarged version of 75 m is expected to be ordered in 1994.

BARUNAJAYA II   *1992, A M Nixon, RAN*

1 RESEARCH SHIP

Name	No	Builders	Commissioned
BURUJULASAD	931	Schlichting, Lübeck-Travemünde	1967

Displacement, tons: 2165 full load
Dimensions, feet (metres): 269.5 × 37.4 × 11.5 *(82.2 × 11.4 × 3.5)*
Main machinery: 4 MAN V6V 22/30 diesels; 6850 hp(m) *(5.03 MW)*; 2 shafts
Speed, knots: 19.1. **Range, miles:** 14 500 at 15 kts
Complement: 108 (15 officers) plus 28 scientists
Guns: 1—37 mm. 4—12.7 mm (2 twin) MGs.
Radars: Surface search: Decca TM 262; I band.
Helicopters: 1 Bell 47J.

Comment: *Burujulasad* was launched in August 1965; her equipment includes laboratories for oceanic and meteorological research and a cartographic room. Carries one LCVP and three surveying motor boats.

BURUJULASAD   *5/1991, 92 Wing RAAF*

1 RESEARCH SHIP

Name	No	Builders	Commissioned
JALANIDHI	933	Sasebo Heavy Industries	12 Jan 1963

Displacement, tons: 985 full load
Dimensions, feet (metres): 176.8 × 31.2 × 14.1 *(53.9 × 9.5 × 4.3)*
Main machinery: 1 MAN G6V 30/42 diesel; 1000 hp(m) *(735 kW)*; 1 shaft
Speed, knots: 11.5. **Range, miles:** 7200 at 10 kts
Complement: 87 (13 officers) plus 26 scientists
Radars: Navigation: Nikkon Denko; I band.

Comment: Launched in 1962. Oceanographic research ship with hydromet facilities. Three ton boom aft. Operated by Hydrographic Office.

JALANIDHI   *1990, Indonesian Navy*

AUXILIARIES

1 REPLENISHMENT TANKER

Name	No	Builders	Commissioned
SORONG	911	Trogir SY, Yugoslavia	Apr 1965

Measurement, tons: 5100 dwt; 4090 gross
Dimensions, feet (metres): 367.4 × 50.5 × 21.6 *(112 × 15.4 × 6.6)*
Main machinery: 1 diesel; 1 shaft
Speed, knots: 15
Cargo capacity: 4200 tons fuel; 300 tons water
Guns: 4—12.7 mm (2 twin) MGs.
Radars: Navigation: Don; I band.

Comment: Has limited underway replenishment facilities.

SORONG   *12/1992*

1 COMMAND SHIP

Name	No	Builders	Commissioned
MULTATULI	561	Ishikawajima-Harima Heavy Industries Co Ltd	Aug 1961

Displacement, tons: 3220 standard; 6741 full load
Dimensions, feet (metres): 365.3 × 52.5 × 23 *(111.4 × 16 × 7)*
Main machinery: 1 Burmeister & Wain diesel; 5500 hp(m) *(4.04 MW)*; 1 shaft
Speed, knots: 18.5. **Range, miles:** 6000 at 16 kts
Complement: 130

Guns: 6 USSR 37 mm/63 (2 twin, 2 single); 85° elevation; 160 rounds/minute to 9 km *(5 nm)*;
   weight of shell 0.7 kg.
   8—12.7 mm MGs.
Radars: Surface search: Ball End; E/F band; range 37 km *(20 nm)*.
Navigation: I band.

Helicopters: Platform for Alouette size.

Programmes: Built as a submarine tender. Launched on 15 May 1961. Delivered to Indonesia
   August 1961.
Modernisation: Original after 76 mm mounting replaced by helicopter deck.
Structure: Living and working spaces air-conditioned.
Operational: Capacity for replenishment at sea (fuel oil, fresh water, provisions, ammunition, naval
   stores and personnel). Medical and hospital facilities. Now used as fleet flagship (Eastern Force)
   and is fitted with ICS-3 communications.

MULTATULI   9/1988, 92 Wing RAAF

1 ACHELOUS CLASS (REPAIR SHIP)

Name	No	Builders	Commissioned
JAYA WIJAYA (ex-USS Askari, ex-ARL 30, ex-LST 1131)	921	Chicago Bridge and Iron Co.	15 Mar 1945

Displacement, tons: 1625 light; 4325 full load
Dimensions, feet (metres): 328 × 50 × 14 *(100 × 15.3 × 4.3)*
Main machinery: 2 GM 12-567A diesels; 1800 hp *(1.34 MW)*; 2 shafts
Speed, knots: 12. **Range, miles:** 17 000 at 7 kts
Complement: 180 (11 officers)
Cargo capacity: 300 tons; 60 ton crane

Guns: 8 Bofors 40 mm/56 (2 quad); 45° elevation; 160 rounds/minute to 11 km *(5.9 nm)*; weight
   of shell 0.9 kg.
Radars: Air/surface search: Sperry SPS 53; I/J band.
Navigation: Raytheon 1900; I/J band.
IFF: UPX 12B.

Programmes: In reserve from 1956-66. She was recommissioned and reached Vietnam in 1967
   to support River Assault Flotilla One. She was used by the US Navy and Vietnamese Navy working up the Mekong in support of the Cambodian operations in May 1970. Transferred from US on
   lease to Indonesia at Guam on 31 August 1971 and purchased 22 February 1979.
Structure: Bow doors welded shut. Carries two LCVPs.

JAYA WIJAYA   9/1988, 92 Wing RAAF

2 KHOBI CLASS (COASTAL TANKERS)

BALIKPAPAN 901   **PAKAN BARU** (ex-*Aragua*) 909

Displacement, tons: 1525 full load
Dimensions, feet (metres): 206.6 × 33 × 14.8 *(63 × 10.1 × 4.5)*
Main machinery: 2 diesels; 1600 hp(m) *(1.18 MW)*; 2 shafts
Speed, knots: 13. **Range, miles:** 2500 at 12 kts
Complement: 37 (4 officers)
Cargo capacity: 550 tons dieso
Guns: 4—12.7 mm (2 twin) MGs.
Radars: Navigation: Neptun; I band.

Comment: *Pakan Baru* transferred from USSR 1959. *Balikpapan* is a Japanese copy of a Khobi
   class.

BALIKPAPAN   6/1990, 92 Wing RAAF

1 ROVER CLASS (REPLENISHMENT TANKER)

Name	No	Builders	Commissioned
ARUN (ex-Green Rover)	903	Swan Hunter, Tyneside	15 Aug 1969

Displacement, tons: 4700 light; 11 522 full load
Dimensions, feet (metres): 461 × 63 × 24 *(140.6 × 19.2 × 7.3)*
Main machinery: 2 SEMT-Pielstick 16 PA4 diesels; 15 360 hp(m) *(11.46 MW)*; 1 shaft; cp prop;
   bow thruster
Speed, knots: 19. **Range, miles:** 15 000 at 15 kts
Complement: 49
Cargo capacity: 6600 tons fuel
Guns: 2 Oerlikon 20 mm
Radars: Navigation: Kelvin Hughes Type 1006; I band
Helicopters: Platform for Westland Sea King type

Comment: Transferred from UK in September 1992 after a refit. Small fleet tanker designed to
   replenish ships at sea with fuel, fresh water, limited dry cargo and refrigerated stores under all
   conditions while under way. No hangar but helicopter landing platform is served by a stores lift,
   to enable stores to be transferred at sea by 'vertical lift'. Capable of HIFR.

ARUN   10/1993, John Mortimer

2 FROSCH II CLASS (TYPE 109) (SUPPORT SHIPS)

Name	No	Builders	Commissioned
TELUK CIREBON (ex-Nordperd)	543 (ex-E 171)	Peenewerft, Wolgast	3 Oct 1979
TELUK SABANG (ex-Südperd)	544 (ex-E 172)	Peenewerft, Wolgast	26 Feb 1980

Displacement, tons: 1700 full load
Dimensions, feet (metres): 297.6 × 36.4 × 9.2 *(90.7 × 11.1 × 2.8)*
Main machinery: 2 diesels; 4408 hp(m) *(3.24 MW)* sustained; 2 shafts
Speed, knots: 18
Cargo capacity: 650 tons
Radars: Air/surface search: Strut Curve; F band.

Comment: Ex-GDR ships disarmed and transferred from Germany 25 August 1993. 5 ton crane
   amidships. In GDR service these ships had two twin 57 mm and two twin 25 mm guns plus Muff
   Cob fire control radar. Both still in refit at Rostock in early 1994.

TELUK CIREBON   12/1993, Reinhard Kramer

2 TISZA CLASS (SUPPORT SHIPS)

TELUK MENTAWAI 956   **KARIMATA** 960

Displacement, tons: 2400 full load
Dimensions, feet (metres): 258.4 × 35.4 × 15.1 *(78.8 × 10.8 × 4.6)*
Main machinery: 1 MAN diesel; 1000 hp(m) *(735 kW)*; 1 shaft
Speed, knots: 12. **Range, miles:** 3000 at 11 kts
Complement: 26
Cargo capacity: 875 tons dry; 11 tons liquid
Guns: 4—14.5 mm (2 twin) MGs.
Radars: Navigation: Spin Trough; I band.

Comment: Built in Hungary. Both transferred in 1963-64. Military Sealift Command since 1978. The survivors of a larger class and probably due for scrapping.

2 TRANSPORTS

TANJUNG PANDAN (ex-*Empire Orwell*) 971   **TANJUNG OISINA** (ex-*Princess Irene*) 972

Measurement, tons: 8456 grt
Dimensions, feet (metres): 459 × 61.7 × 28.9 *(139.9 × 18.8 × 8.8)*
Main machinery: 1 diesel; 8800 hp(m) *(6.47 MW)*; 1 shaft
Speed, knots: 16
Complement: 94

Comment: Details given are for *Tanjung Oisina, Pandan* is slightly bigger and is powered by steam turbines which are no longer reliable. Both ships were passenger liners built in the 1940s and purchased in 1978. Ex-Mecca pilgrim transports now used for troop transfers between islands. Unarmed. Military Sealift Command.

TANJUNG OISINA   *1992, van Ginderen Collection*

1 CABLE SHIP

Name	No	Builders	Commissioned
BIDUK	—	J & K Smit, Kinderijk	30 July 1952

Displacement, tons: 1250 standard
Dimensions, feet (metres): 213.2 × 39.5 × 11.5 *(65 × 12 × 3.5)*
Main machinery: 2 boilers; 1 triple expansion engine; 1600 ihp(m) *(1.12 MW)*; 1 shaft
Speed, knots: 12
Complement: 66

Comment: Launched on 30 October 1951. Cable layer, lighthouse tender, and multi-purpose auxiliary.

2 BUOY TENDERS

MAJANG   **MIZAN**

Displacement, tons: 2150 full load
Dimensions, feet (metres): 255.9 × 44.9 × 13.1 *(78 × 13.7 × 4)*
Complement: 70

Comment: Have three 20 ton derricks and a survey launch.

3 FLOATING DOCKS

Comment: There are three large floating docks in Surabaya which are used for naval purposes.

TRAINING SHIP

1 SAIL TRAINING SHIP

Name	No	Builders	Commissioned
DEWARUTJI	—	HC Stülcken & Sohn, Hamburg	9 July 1953

Displacement, tons: 810 standard; 1500 full load
Dimensions, feet (metres): 136.2 pp; 191.2 oa × 31.2 × 13.9 *(41.5; 58.3 × 9.5 × 4.2)*
Main machinery: 1 MAN diesel; 600 hp(m) *(441 kW)*; 1 shaft
Speed, knots: 10.5
Complement: 110 (includes 78 midshipmen)

Comment: Barquentine of steel construction. Sail area, 1305 sq yards *(1091 sq m)*. Launched on 24 January 1953.

DEWARUTJI   *5/1990, Guy Toremans*

TUGS

Note: Two BIMA VIII class of 423 tons completed in 1991 are not naval.

1 CHEROKEE CLASS

RAKATA (ex-USS *Menominee* ATF 73) 922

Displacement, tons: 1235 standard; 1640 full load
Dimensions, feet (metres): 205 × 38.5 × 17 *(62.5 × 11.7 × 5.2)*
Main machinery: Diesel-electric; 4 GM 12-278 diesels; 4400 hp *(3.28 MW)*; 4 generators; 1 motor; 3000 hp *(2.24 MW)*; 1 shaft
Speed, knots: 15. **Range, miles:** 6500 at 15 kts
Complement: 67
Guns: 1 US 3 in *(76 mm)*/50. 2 Bofors 40 mm/60 aft. 4—25 mm (2 twin) (bridge wings).
Radars: Surface search: Raytheon SPS 5B; G/H band; range 37 km *(20 nm)*.

Comment: Launched on 14 February 1942 by United Eng. Alameda. Commissioned 25 September 1942. Transferred from US at San Diego in March 1961.

Name	No	Builders	Commissioned
LAMPO BATANG	934	Ishikawajima-Harima	Sep 1961

Displacement, tons: 154 light; 280 full load
Dimensions, feet (metres): 92.3 × 23.2 × 11.3 *(28.2 × 7.1 × 3.4)*
Main machinery: 2 MAN diesels; 600 hp(m) *(441 kW)*; 2 shafts
Speed, knots: 11. **Range, miles:** 1000 at 11 kts
Complement: 13

Comment: Ocean tug. Launched in April 1961.

Name	No	Builders	Commissioned
TAMBORA (Army)	935	Ishikawajima-Harima	June 1961
BROMO	936	Ishikawajima-Harima	Aug 1961

Displacement, tons: 150 light; 250 full load
Dimensions, feet (metres): 79 × 21.7 × 9.7 *(24.1 × 6.6 × 3)*
Main machinery: 2 MAN diesels; 600 hp(m) *(441 kW)*; 2 shafts
Speed, knots: 10.5. **Range, miles:** 690 at 10.5 kts
Complement: 15

Comment: Harbour tugs.

CUSTOMS PATROL CRAFT

17 COASTAL PATROL CRAFT

BC 1001-1010   **BC 3001-3007**

Displacement, tons: 55 (1001 class); 62 (3001 class)
Dimensions, feet (metres): 92.5 × 17 × 5.3 *(28.2 × 5.2 × 1.6)*
Main machinery: 2 MTU 12V 331 TC81 diesels; 2610 hp(m) *(1.92 MW)* sustained; 2 shafts
Speed, knots: 34. **Range, miles:** 750 at 15 kts
Complement: 18
Guns: 1—20 mm (BC 3001 class). 1—12.7 mm MG (BC 1001 class).

Comment: Built by Chantiers Navals de l'Esterel. BC 1001-3 commissioned April, June and November 1975, BC 3001-2 and BC 1004-6 in 1979, BC 3003-3005 and 1007-9 in 1980, BC 3006-7 in January 1981 and BC 1010 in April 1981.

BC 3006   *10/1986, van Ginderen Collection*

7 COASTAL PATROL CRAFT

BC 2001-2007

Displacement, tons: 70.3 full load
Dimensions, feet (metres): 93.5 × 17.7 × 5.5 (28.5 × 5.4 × 1.7)
Main machinery: 2 MTU 12V 331 TC92 diesels; 2660 hp(m) (1.96 MW) sustained; 2 shafts
Speed, knots: 29.7
Guns: 1—12.7 mm MG.

Comment: Built CMN Cherbourg to Lürssen design. Ordered in January 1979. Last two commissioned 7 November 1980 (2006) and 10 February 1981 (2007).

BC 2007   1/1990, 92 Wing RAAF

48 LÜRSSEN 28 METRE TYPE

BC 4001-3, 5001-3, 6001-24, 7001-6, 8001-6, 9001-6

Displacement, tons: 68 full load
Dimensions, feet (metres): 91.8 × 17.7 × 5.9 (28 × 5.4 × 1.8)
Main machinery: 2 Deutz diesels; 2720 hp(m) (2 MW); or 2 MTU diesels; 2260 hp(m) (1.66 MW); 2 shafts
Speed, knots: 30. Range, miles: 1100 at 15 kts; 860 at 28 kts
Complement: 19 (6 officers)
Guns: 1—12.7 mm MG.

Comment: Replacements for the deleted BT series. Lürssen design, some built by Fulton Marine and Scheepswerven van Langebrugge of Belgium, some by Lürssen Vegesack and some by PT Pal Surabaya (which also assembled most of them). Programme started in 1980 and continues into the 1990s. Some of these craft are operated by the Navy, the Police and the Maritime Security Agency.

BC 8003   8/1991, 92 Wing RAAF

BC 5003   8/1991, 92 Wing RAAF

MARITIME SECURITY AGENCY

Note: Established in 1978 to control the 200 mile EEZ and to maintain navigational aids. Comes under the Military Sea Communications Command.

4 GOLOK CLASS (SAR CRAFT)

GOLOK 206	PANAN 207	PEDANG 208	KAPAK 209

Displacement, tons: 190 full load
Dimensions, feet (metres): 123 pp × 23.6 × 6.6 (37.5 × 7.2 × 2)
Main machinery: 2 MTU 16V 652 TB91 diesels; 4610 hp(m) (3.39 MW) sustained; 2 shafts
Speed, knots: 25. Range, miles: 1500 at 18 kts
Complement: 18
Guns: 1 Rheinmetall 20 mm.

Comment: All launched 5 November 1981. First pair completed 12 March 1982. Last pair completed 12 May 1982. Built by Deutsche Industrie Werke, Berlin. Fitted out by Schlichting, Travemünde.

5 KUJANG CLASS (SAR CRAFT)

KUJANG 201	CELURIT 203	BELATI 205
PARANG 202	CUNDRIK 204	

Displacement, tons: 162 full load
Dimensions, feet (metres): 125.6 × 19.6 × 6.8 (38.3 × 6 × 2.1)
Main machinery: 2 AGO SACM 195 V12 CZSHR diesels; 4410 hp(m) (3.24 MW); 2 shafts
Speed, knots: 28. Range, miles: 1500 at 18 kts
Complement: 18
Guns: 1—12.7 mm MG.

Comment: Built by SFCN, Villeneuve la Garenne. Completed April 1981 (Kujang and Parang), August 1981 (Celurit), October 1981 (Cundrik), December 1981 (Belati).

KUJANG   8/1988, 92 Wing RAAF

6 PAT CLASS

PAT 01	PAT 02	PAT 03	PAT 04	PAT 05	PAT 06

Displacement, tons: 12 full load
Dimensions, feet (metres): 40 × 14.1 × 3.3 (12.2 × 4.3 × 1)
Main machinery: 1 diesel; 260 hp(m) (191 kW); 1 shaft
Speed, knots: 14
Guns: 1—7.62 mm MG.

Comment: Built at Tanjung Priok Shipyard 1978-79.

ARMY

Note: The Army (ADRI) craft have mostly been transferred to the Military Sealift Command (Logistic Support). More LSLs are reported to be planned.

27 LANDING CRAFT LOGISTICS

ADRI XXXII-ADRI LVIII

Displacement, tons: 580 full load
Dimensions, feet (metres): 137.8 × 35.1 × 5.9 (42 × 10.7 × 1.8)
Main machinery: 2 Detroit 6-71 diesels; 348 hp(m) (260 kW) sustained; 2 shafts
Speed, knots: 10. Range, miles: 1500 at 10 kts
Complement: 15
Military lift: 122 tons equipment

Comment: Built in Tanjung Priok Shipyard 1979-82. XXXI sank in February 1993.

POLICE

Note: The police operate a large number of craft of varying sizes including 14 Bango class of 194 tons and 32 Hamilton waterjet craft of 7.9 m, 234 hp giving a speed of 28 kts. The Carpentaria class has been transferred from the Navy, and the Lürssen type (619-623) are identical to Customs craft.

POLICE 436   7/1993, G Toremans

POLICE 620   9/1991, van Ginderen Collection

10 COASTAL PATROL CRAFT

DKN 504–DKN 513

Displacement, tons: 440 full load
Dimensions, feet (metres): 157.8 × 24.6 × 9.5 *(48.1 × 7.5 × 2.9)*
Main machinery: 2 MAN V8V 22/30 diesels; 4560 hp(m) *(3.35 MW)*; 2 shafts
Speed, knots: 15. **Range, miles:** 2700 at 14 kts
Complement: 35
Guns: 1 Rheinmetall 20 mm. 2—12.7 mm MGs.

Comment: Built in Japan in the early 1960s. Can carry 70 tons equipment.

9 COASTAL PATROL CRAFT

DKN 908–DKN 916

Displacement, tons: 159 full load
Dimensions, feet (metres): 137.8 × 21.3 × 5.9 *(42 × 6.5 × 1.8)*
Main machinery: 2 MTU MD 655 diesels; 3000 hp(m) *(2.2 MW)*; 2 shafts
Speed, knots: 24.5. **Range, miles:** 1500 at 18 kts
Complement: 22
Guns: 4 Rheinmetall 20 mm.

Comment: Built by Baglietto and Riva Trigosa 1961-64.

DKN 915   7/1983

6 CARPENTARIA CLASS (COASTAL PATROL CRAFT)

Displacement, tons: 27
Dimensions, feet (metres): 51.5 × 15.7 × 4.3 *(15.7 × 4.8 × 1.3)*
Main machinery: 2 MTU 8V 331 TC92 diesels; 1770 hp(m) *(1.3 MW)* sustained; 2 shafts
Speed, knots: 29. **Range, miles:** 950 at 18 kts
Complement: 10
Guns: 1 Oerlikon 20 mm or 1—12.7 mm MG.
Radars: Surface search: Decca; I band.

Comment: Built 1976-77 by Hawker-De Havilland, Australia. Endurance, 4-5 days. Transferred from the Navy in the mid-1980s.

CARPENTARIA   1991

IRAN

Headquarters' Appointments

Commander of the Iranian Navy:
   Rear Admiral Ali Shamkhani
Deputy Commander:
   Rear Admiral Abbas Mohtaj
Commander of the Pasdaran Naval Forces:
   Hussein Alai

Personnel

(a)   1994: 16 000 officers and men (Navy)
(b)   2 years' national service

Bases

Persian Gulf: Bandar Abbas (MHQ), Boushehr (also a Dockyard),
Kharg Island, Khorramshar (Light Forces)
Indian Ocean: Chah Bahar
Caspian Sea: Bandar—Pahlavi (Training)

Strength of the Fleet

Type	Active	Building	Type	Active	Building
Submarines	2	1	Support Ships	7	—
Midget Submarines	9	—	Water Tankers	4	—
Destroyers	3	—	Tenders	13	—
Frigates	3	—			
Corvettes	2	—			
Fast Attack Craft—Missile	11	10	**Prefix to Ships' Names**		
Fast Attack Craft—Gun	3	—			
Large Patrol Craft	7	—	IS		
Coastal Patrol Craft	72	4			
Inshore Patrol Craft	71	—			
Landing Ships (Logistic)	4	—	**Mercantile Marine**		
Landing Ships (Tank)	5	2			
LCU/LCT	18	2	*Lloyd's Register of Shipping:*		
Hovercraft	14	—	431 vessels of 4 443 972 tons		
Minesweepers—Coastal	3	—			
Minesweeper—Inshore	2	—			
Replenishment Ship	1	—			
Supply Ships	2	—			
Repair Ship	1	—			

PENNANT LIST

Destroyers		Patrol Forces				Auxiliaries	
51	Damavand	201	Kaivan	P 231	Neyzeh	411	Kangan
61	Babr	202	Azadi	P 232	Tabarzin	412	Taheri
62	Palang	204	Mahvan			421	Bandar Abbas
		211	Parvin	**Mine Warfare Forces**		422	Boushehr
Frigates		212	Bahram			431	Kharg
		213	Nahid	301	Shahrokh	441	Chah Bahar
71	Alvand	P 221	Kaman	302	Simorgh	511	Hengam
72	Alborz	P 222	Zoubin	303	Karkas	512	Larak
73	Sabalan	P 223	Khadang	311	Harischi	513	Tonb
		P 226	Falakhon	312	Riazi	514	Lavan
Corvettes		P 227	Shamshir				
		P 228	Gorz				
81	Bayandor	P 229	Gardouneh				
82	Naghdi	P 230	Khanjar				

SUBMARINES

9 MIDGET SUBMARINES

Displacement, tons: 76 surfaced; 90 dived
Dimensions, feet (metres): 62.3 × 9.2 *(19 × 2.8)*
Main machinery: 2 diesels; 320 hp(m) *(236 kW)*; 1 shaft
Speed, knots: 12 surfaced; 8 dived
Range, miles: 1200 at 6 kts
Complement: 3 + 7 divers

Programmes: Initial submarine constructed in Iran and assembled at Bandar Abbas, combining Japanese and German Second World War design drawings with locally available fabrication and imported equipment. Initially completed in May 1987 but shipped to Tehran in late 1988 for modifications, as diving tests were unsuccessful. This programme seems to have been overtaken by midget submarines of North Korean (DPRK) design first delivered in June 1988 with a reported total of nine by 1993, and a possible final total of 24.
Structure: The listed characteristics are based on the Korean design. Diving depth, approx 100 m *(328 ft)*. There is a 'wet and dry' compartment for divers.

Operational: Based at Boushehr. Side cargoes can be released from inside the hull but limpet mines require a diver to exit, attach the mines to the target and then re-enter. Successful operation will require a very high level of training and support, and there is insufficient evidence that this is being achieved.

2 + 1 KILO CLASS (TYPE 877 EKM)

Name	No	Builders	Laid down	Launched	Commissioned
TAREQ	901	Admiralty Yard, St Petersburg	1988	1991	21 Nov 1992
NOOR	902	Admiralty Yard, St Petersburg	1989	1992	6 June 1993
—	903	Admiralty Yard, St Petersburg	1990	1993	1994

Displacement, tons: 2356 surfaced; 3076 dived
Dimensions, feet (metres): 242.1 × 32.5 × 21.7
(73.8 × 9.9 × 6.6)
Main machinery: Diesel-electric; 2 diesels; 3650 hp(m)
(2.68 MW); 2 generators; 1 motor; 5500 hp(m) *(4.05 MW)*; 1
economic speed motor; 130 hp(m) *(95 kW)*; 1 shaft; 2 auxiliary
propulsion motors; 204 hp(m) *(150 kW)*
Speed, knots: 17 dived; 10 surfaced
Range, miles: 6000 at 7 kts snorting; 400 at 3 kts dived
Complement: 53 (12 officers)

Torpedoes: 6—21 in *(533 mm)* tubes; combination of
TEST-71/96; wire-guided active/passive homing to 15 km
(8.1 nm) at 40 kts and 53-65; passive wake
homing to 25 km *(13.5 nm)* at 50 kts; warhead 300 kg. Total
of 18 weapons.

Mines: 24 in lieu of torpedoes.
Countermeasures: ESM: Squid Head or Brick Pulp; radar warn-
ing. Quad Loop D/F.
Radars: Surface search; Snoop Tray; I band.
Sonars: Sharks Teeth; hull-mounted; passive/active search and
attack; medium frequency.
Mouse Roar; active attack; high frequency.

Programmes: The CinC Navy revealed in 1990 that sailors were
being trained at Riga with the aim of establishing a submarine
force. The first submarine to be transferred sailed from the Baltic in October 1992 flying the Russian flag and with a predominantly Russian crew. The second sailed in June 1993. A third is
expected in late 1994.
Structure: Diving depth, 240 m *(787 ft)* normal. Has a 9700
kW/h battery. SA-N-10 SAM system may be fitted, but this is
not confirmed.

Operational: Initially based at Bandar Abbas but will eventually
move to Chah Bahar which is outside the Persian Gulf on the
northern shore of the Gulf of Oman.
Opinion: Operational effectiveness will initially depend on the
number of experienced Russian submariners retained either on
loan service or employed as mercenaries. The northern Gulf of
Oman and the few deep water parts of the Persian Gulf are
notoriously bad areas for anti-submarine warfare. These submarines will be vulnerable to attack when alongside in harbour
but could pose a severe threat to merchant shipping either
with torpedoes or mines.

NOOR   6/1993

DESTROYERS

1 BATTLE CLASS

Name	No
DAMAVAND (ex-HMS *Sluys* D 60, ex-*Artemiz*)	51

Builders	Laid down	Launched	Commissioned
Cammell Laird & Co Ltd, Birkenhead	24 Nov 1943	28 Feb 1945	30 Sep 1946

Displacement, tons: 2288 standard; 3404 full load
Dimensions, feet (metres): 379 × 40.3 × 17.1 (screws)
(115.5 × 12.3 × 5.2)
Main machinery: 2 Admiralty boilers; 2 Parsons turbines;
50 000 hp *(37 MW)*; 2 shafts
Speed, knots: 31. **Range, miles:** 3200 at 20 kts; 4400 at 12 kts
Complement: 270

Missiles: SAM: 4 GDC Pomona Standard SM-1MR box launchers
❶; command guidance; semi-active radar homing to 46 km
(25 nm) at 2 Mach; height envelope 45.7-18 288 m *(150-
60 000 ft)*; 4 missiles.
Guns: 4 Vickers 4.5 in *(114 mm)*/45 (2 twin, fwd) ❷; 80° elevation; 15 rounds/minute to 18 km *(10 nm)* anti-surface; 8 km
(4.4 nm) anti-aircraft; weight of shell 25 kg.
2 Bofors 40 mm/60 ❸; 80° elevation; 120 rounds/minute to
10 km *(5.5 nm)*; weight of shell 0.89 kg.
4 USSR 23 mm/80 (2 twin) ❹; (one replaced Seacat launcher
and one mounted forward of bridge).
A/S mortars: 1 Mk 4 3-tubed Squid ❺; range 350 m.
Countermeasures: ESM: Decca RDL 1. Racal FH 5-HF/DF.
Fire control: US Mk 25 for 4.5 in guns and MR SAM. MCS 2 for
Squid.
Radars: Air/surface search: Plessey AWS 1 ❻; E/F band; range
110 km *(60 nm)*.
Surface search: Decca 629 ❼; I band.
Fire control: Contraves Sea Hunter Mk 4 ❽; I/J band.
IFF: UK Mk 10.
Sonars: Plessey PMS 26; hull-mounted; lightweight; active
search and attack; 10 kHz.

Programmes: Transferred by UK to Iran at Southampton on 26
January 1967, and handed over to the Imperial Iranian Navy after a three-year modernisation refit by the Vosper Thornycroft
Group. Refitted again in South Africa 1976.
Operational: Standard SAM has some surface-to-surface capability. Seacat has been removed except for the optical director
and two twin 23 mm guns are mounted. Regularly seen at sea
in 1989, but not much since then.

DAMAVAND   *(Scale 1 : 1200), Ian Sturton*

DAMAVAND   3/1987

2 BABR (ALLEN M SUMNER) (FRAM II) CLASS

Name	No
BABR (ex-USS Zellers DD 777)	61
PALANG (ex-USS Stormes DD 780)	62

Builders	Laid down	Launched	Commissioned
Todd Pacific Shipyards	24 Dec 1943	19 July 1944	25 Oct 1944
Todd Pacific Shipyards	15 Apr 1944	4 Nov 1944	27 Jan 1945

Displacement, tons: 2388 standard; 3254 full load
Dimensions, feet (metres): 376.5 × 41 × 21.4
(114.8 × 12.5 × 6.5)
Main machinery: 2 Babcock & Wilcox and 2 Foster-Wheeler boilers; 600 psi *(43.3 kg/cm sq)*; 850°F *(454°C)*; 2 turbines; 60 000 hp *(45 MW)*; 2 shafts
Speed, knots: 34. **Range, miles:** 3740 at 12.5 kts
Complement: 290 (14 officers)

Missiles: SAM: 4 GDC Pomona Standard SM-1MR box launchers ❶; command guidance; semi-active radar homing to 46 km *(25 nm)* at 2 Mach; height envelope 45.7-18 288 m *(150-60 000 ft)*; 8 missiles.
Guns: 4 US 5 in *(127 mm)*/38 (2 twin) Mk 38 ❷; 85° elevation; 15 rounds/minute to 17 km *(9.3 nm)* anti-surface; 11 km *(5.9 nm)* anti-aircraft; weight of shell 25 kg.
2 USSR 23 mm/80 (twin) ❸; (replaced VDS right aft).
Torpedoes: 6—324 mm Mk 32 (2 triple) tubes ❹. Possibly Honeywell Mk 44 or 46.
Countermeasures: ESM: WLR-1; radar warning.
ECM: ULQ/6; jammers.
Fire control: Mk 37 GFCS. Mk 105 TFCS.
Radars: Air search: Westinghouse SPS 29C ❺; B/C band; range 457 km *(250 nm)*.
Surface search: Raytheon SPS 10B ❻; G band.

BABR   *(Scale 1 : 1200), Ian Sturton*

Navigation: LN 66; I band.
Fire control: Western Electric Mk 25 ❼; I/J band.
IFF: UPX-1/UPX-12.
Sonars: SQS 43 *(Babr)*, SQS 44 *(Palang)*; hull-mounted; active search and attack; medium/high frequency.

Helicopters: 1 Agusta AB 204AS ❽.

Programmes: Two FRAM II conversion destroyers of the Allen M Sumner class transferred from the US 19 March 1971 and 16 February 1972 respectively, both by sale.

Modernisation: Both ships received a full refit as well as conversion at Philadelphia NSY before sailing for Iran. This included a much-improved air-conditioning layout, the removal of B gunmount with its magazine, altered accommodation, the fitting of a Canadian telescopic hangar, the siting of the four Standard missile launchers athwartships beside the torpedo stowage between the funnels, the rigging of VDS and fitting of Hedgehogs in B position. VDS and Hedgehogs subsequently removed and a 23 mm gun fitted right aft.
Operational: Both ships reported doing regular patrols. The pennant numbers have the second digit painted out.

PALANG   7/1988

FRIGATES

3 ALVAND (VOSPER Mk 5) CLASS

Name	No
ALVAND (ex-Saam)	71
ALBORZ (ex-Zaal)	72
SABALAN (ex-Rostam)	73

Builders	Laid down	Launched	Commissioned
Vosper Thornycroft, Woolston	22 May 1967	25 July 1968	20 May 1971
Vickers, Barrow	3 Mar 1968	4 Mar 1969	1 Mar 1971
Vickers, Newcastle & Barrow	10 Dec 1967	4 Mar 1969	June 1972

Displacement, tons: 1100 standard; 1350 full load
Dimensions, feet (metres): 310 × 36.4 × 14.1 (screws)
(94.5 × 11.1 × 4.3)
Main machinery: CODOG; 2 RR Olympus TM2A gas turbines; 40 000 hp *(29.8 MW)* sustained; 2 Paxman 16YJCM diesels; 3800 hp *(2.83 MW)* sustained; 2 shafts
Speed, knots: 39 gas; 18 diesel. **Range, miles:** 3650 at 18 kts; 550 at 36 kts
Complement: 125 (accommodation for 146)

Missiles: SSM: 1 Sistel Sea Killer II quin launcher ❶; beam rider radio command or optical guidance to 25 km *(13.5 nm)* at 0.8 Mach; warhead 70 kg. May have been modified by removal of top row of cassettes to incorporate a BM-21 MRL.
Guns: 1 Vickers 4.5 in *(114 mm)*/55 Mk 8 ❷; 55° elevation; 25 rounds/minute to 22 km *(12 nm)* anti-surface; 6 km *(3.3 nm)* anti-aircraft; weight of shell 21 kg.
2 Oerlikon 35 mm/90 (twin) ❸; 85° elevation; 550 rounds/minute to 6 km *(3.3 nm)*; weight of shell 1.55 kg.
3 Oerlikon GAM-B01 20 mm ❹ (replaced 23 mm and both seaboats).
2—12.7 mm MGs.
A/S mortars: 1—3-tubed Limbo Mk 10 ❺; automatic loading; range 1000 m; warhead 92 kg.
Countermeasures: Decoys: 2 UK Mk 5 rocket flare launchers.
ESM: Decca RDL 2AC; radar warning. Racal FH 5-HF/DF.
Radars: Air/surface search: Plessey AWS 1 ❻; E/F band; range 110 km *(60 nm)*.
Surface search: Racal Decca 1226 ❼; I band.
Navigation: Decca 629; I band.
Fire control: Two Contraves Sea Hunter ❽; I/J band.
IFF: UK Mk 10.
Sonars: Graseby 174; hull-mounted; active search; medium/high frequency.
Graseby 170; hull-mounted; active attack; 15 kHz.

Programmes: It was announced on 25 August 1966 that Vosper Ltd, Portsmouth, had received an order for four Mark 5 frigates for the Iranian Navy, two of which were to be built by Vickers. *Sabalan* was towed to Barrow for completion.

ALVAND   *(Scale 1 : 900), Ian Sturton*

ALBORZ   1/1991

Modernisation: *Alvand* and *Alborz* taken in hand by HM Dockyard Devonport July/August 1975 for major refit including replacement of Mk 5 4.5 in gun by Mk 8. Completed 1977. Modifications in 1988 included replacing Seacat with a 23 mm gun and boat davits with minor armaments. By mid-1991 the 23 mm and both boats had been replaced by GAM-B01 20 mm guns.

Structure: Air-conditioned throughout. Fitted with Vosper stabilisers.
Operational: *Sahand* sunk by USN on 18 April 1988. *Sabalan* had her back broken by a laser-guided bomb in the same skirmish but was out of dock by the end of 1990 and was operational again in late 1991.

CORVETTES

2 BAYANDOR (PF 103) CLASS

Name	No
BAYANDOR (ex-US PF 103)	81
NAGHDI (ex-US PF 104)	82

Builders	Laid down	Launched	Commissioned
Levingstone Shipbuilding Co, Orange, Texas	20 Aug 1962	7 July 1963	18 May 1964
Levingstone Shipbuilding Co, Orange, Texas	12 Sep 1962	10 Oct 1963	22 July 1964

Displacement, tons: 900 standard; 1135 full load
Dimensions, feet (metres): 275.6 × 33.1 × 10.2
(84 × 10.1 × 3.1)
Main machinery: 2 Fairbanks-Morse 38TD8-1/8-9 diesels;
5250 hp *(3.92 MW)* sustained; 2 shafts
Speed, knots: 20. **Range, miles:** 2400 at 18 kts; 4800 at 12 kts
Complement: 140

Guns: 2 US 3 in *(76 mm)*/50 Mk 34 **❶**; 85° elevation; 50
rounds/minute to 12.8 km *(7 nm)*; weight of shell 6 kg.
2 Bofors 40 mm/60 (twin) **❷**; 80° elevation; 120 rounds/
minute to 10 km *(5.5 nm)*; weight of shell 0.89 kg.
2 Oerlikon GAM-B01 20 mm **❸**. 2—12.7 mm MGs.
Fire control: Mk 63 for 76 mm gun. Mk 51 for 40 mm gun.
Radars: Air/surface search: Westinghouse SPS 6C **❹**; D band;
range 146 km *(80 nm)* (for fighter).
Surface search: Racal Decca **❺**; I band.
Navigation: Raytheon 1650 **❻**; I/J band.
Fire control: Western Electric Mk 36 **❼**; I/J band.
IFF: UPX-12B.

BAYANDOR   *(Scale 1 : 900), Ian Sturton*

Sonars: EDO SQS 17A; hull-mounted; active attack; high
frequency.

Programmes: Transferred from the USA to Iran under the Mutual
Assistance programme in 1964.

Modernisation: *Naghdi* change of engines and reconstruction of
accommodation completed in mid-1988. 23 mm gun and
depth charge racks replaced by 20 mm guns in 1990.
Operational: *Milanian* and *Khanamuie* sunk in 1982 during war
with Iraq.

BAYANDOR   *9/1990*

SHIPBORNE AIRCRAFT

Numbers/Type: 7 Agusta AB 204ASW.
Operational speed: 104 kts *(193 km/h)*.
Service ceiling: 11 500 ft *(3505 m)*.
Range: 332 nm *(615 km)*.
Role/Weapon systems: Only small ship helicopter in service, mainly engaged in ASV operations in
defence of oil installations. Sensors: APS 705 search radar, dipping sonar (if carried). Weapons:
ASW; 2 × torpedoes. ASV; 2 × AS 12 missiles.

AB 204   *1987, Ralf Bendfeldt*

LAND-BASED MARITIME AIRCRAFT (FRONT LINE)

Note: The Air Force also has Su-24 Fencer fighter bombers for maritime strike.

Numbers/Type: 6 Agusta-Sikorsky ASH-3D Sea King.
Operational speed: 120 kts *(222 km/h)*.
Service ceiling: 12 200 ft *(3720 m)*.
Range: 630 nm *(1165 km)*.
Role/Weapon systems: Shore-based ASW helicopter to defend major port and oil installations.
Sensors: Selenia search radar, dipping sonar. Weapons: ASW; 4 × A244/S torpedoes or depth
bombs.

Numbers/Type: 2 Lockheed P-3F Orion.
Operational speed: 410 kts *(760 km/h)*.
Service ceiling: 28 300 ft *(8625 m)*.
Range: 4000 nm *(7410 km)*.
Role/Weapon systems: One of the remaining aircraft used for early warning and control duties for
strikes. Sensors: Search radar, sonobuoys. Weapons: ASW; various weapons can be carried.

Numbers/Type: 2 Sikorsky RH-53D.
Operational speed: 125 kts *(232 km/h)*.
Service ceiling: 11 100 ft *(3385 m)*.
Range: 405 nm *(750 km)*.
Role/Weapon systems: Mine clearance and surface search helicopter. Sensors: Weather radar.
Weapons: Unarmed.

Numbers/Type: 5 Lockheed C-130H-MP Hercules.
Operational speed: 325 kts *(602 km/h)*.
Service ceiling: 33 000 ft *(10 060 m)*.
Range: 4250 nm *(7876 km)*.
Role/Weapon systems: Long-range maritime reconnaissance role by Air Force. Sensors: Search/
weather radar. Weapons: Unarmed.

PATROL FORCES

1 OSA II CLASS (FAST ATTACK CRAFT—MISSILE)

Displacement, tons: 245 full load
Dimensions, feet (metres): 126.6 × 24.9 × 8.8 *(38.6 × 7.6 × 2.7)*
Main machinery: 3 Type M 504 diesels; 10 800 hp(m) *(7.94 MW)* sustained; 3 shafts
Speed, knots: 37. **Range, miles:** 500 at 35 kts
Complement: 30
Missiles: 4 SS-N-2B Styx; active radar or IR homing to 46 km *(25 nm)* at 0.9 Mach; warhead
513 kg.
Guns: 4—30 mm/65 (2 twin); 85° elevation; 500 rounds/minute to 5 km *(2.7 nm)*; weight of shell
0.54 kg.
Radars: Surface search/fire control: Square Tie; I band.
Fire control: Drum Tilt; H/I band.

Comment: Delivered to Iraq from USSR in the mid-1970s. Sailed to Iran in January 1991 to escape
the Gulf War and taken over by Iran. Operational in November 1991.

OSA II   *1991*

10 KAMAN (COMBATTANTE II) CLASS
(FAST ATTACK CRAFT—MISSILE)

Name	No	Builders	Commissioned
KAMAN	P 221	CMN, Cherbourg	12 Aug 1977
ZOUBIN	P 222	CMN, Cherbourg	12 Sep 1977
KHADANG	P 223	CMN, Cherbourg	15 Mar 1978
FALAKHON	P 226	CMN, Cherbourg	31 Mar 1978
SHAMSHIR	P 227	CMN, Cherbourg	31 Mar 1978
GORZ	P 228	CMN, Cherbourg	22 Aug 1978
GARDOUNEH	P 229	CMN, Cherbourg	11 Sep 1978
KHANJAR	P 230	CMN, Cherbourg	1 Aug 1981
NEYZEH	P 231	CMN, Cherbourg	1 Aug 1981
TABARZIN	P 232	CMN, Cherbourg	1 Aug 1981

Displacement, tons: 249 standard; 275 full load
Dimensions, feet (metres): 154.2 × 23.3 × 6.2 *(47 × 7.1 × 1.9)*
Main machinery: 4 MTU 16V 538 TB91 diesels; 12 280 hp(m) *(9.03 MW)* sustained; 4 shafts
Speed, knots: 37.5. **Range, miles:** 2000 at 15 kts; 700 at 33.7 kts
Complement: 31

Missiles: SSM: 4 McDonnell Douglas Harpoon or Chinese YJ-1.
Guns: 1 OTO Melara 3 in *(76 mm)*/62 compact; 85° elevation; 85 rounds/minute to 16 km *(8.7 nm)* anti-surface; 12 km *(6.6 nm)* anti-aircraft; weight of shell 6 kg; 320 rounds.
  1 Breda Bofors 40 mm/70; 90° elevation; 300 rounds/minute to 12 km *(6.6 nm)*; weight of shell 0.96 kg; 900 rounds.
Countermeasures: ESM: TMV 433 Dalia; radar intercept
ECM: Alligator; jammer.
Radars: Surface search/fire control: Signaal WM 28; I/J band.
Navigation: Racal Decca 1226; I band.
IFF: UPZ 27N/APX 72.

Programmes: Ordered in February 1974. The transfer of the last three craft was delayed by the French Government after the Iranian revolution. On 12 July 1981 France decided to hand them over. This took place on 1 August—on 2 August they sailed and soon after *Tabarzin* was seized by a pro-Royalist group off Cadiz. After the latter surrendered to the French in Toulon further problems were prevented by sending all three to Iran in a merchant ship.
Structure: The last three were not fitted with Harpoon tubes on delivery. Portable SA-7 launchers may be embarked in some. Harpoon may have been replaced by Chinese SSM.
Operational: *Peykan* was sunk in 1980 by Iraq; *Joshan* in April 1988 by the USN.

GORZ   *8/1992*

0 + 10 HEGU CLASS (FAST ATTACK CRAFT—MISSILE)

Displacement, tons: 68 standard; 79.2 full load
Dimensions, feet (metres): 88.6 × 20.7 × 4.3 *(27 × 6.3 × 1.3)*
Main machinery: 4 Type L-12V-180 diesels; 4800 hp(m) *(3.53 MW)*; 4 shafts
Speed, knots: 37.5. **Range, miles:** 400 at 30 kts
Complement: 17 (2 officers)

Missiles: SSM: 4 YJ-1 (Eagle Strike); possibly the extended range version will be fitted.
Guns: 2 USSR 25 mm/60 (twin); 85° elevation; 270 rounds/minute to 3 km *(1.6 nm)* anti-aircraft; weight of shell 0.34 kg.
Radars: Surface search: Square Tie; I band
IFF: High Pole A.

Programmes: Chinese variant of the Komar class with a steel hull which has been building since the late 1970s. Sometimes called the Hoku class. Negotiations for sale from China started in late 1991; the date of transfer may depend on whether these vessels are new or second hand. Not much progress in 1992 because of arguments over the type of missile to be fitted and still no report of delivery by early 1994. Similar craft transferred to Bangladesh, Pakistan and Egypt.

3 ZAFAR (CHAHO) CLASS (FAST ATTACK CRAFT—GUN)

Displacement, tons: 70 standard; 82 full load
Dimensions, feet (metres): 85.3 × 19 × 6.6 *(26 × 5.8 × 2)*
Main machinery: 4 Type M 50 diesels; 4400 hp(m) *(3.2 MW)* sustained; 4 shafts
Speed, knots: 40
Complement: 17
Guns: 2 USSR 23 mm/80 (twin) (aft). 2—14.5 mm (twin) MG (forward). 1 BM-21 40-barrelled rocket launcher (MRL).
Radars: Surface search: Racal Decca; I band.

Comment: Built in North Korea. Transferred to Iran in April 1987 and re-engined (type unknown) so top speed may be reduced. Called the Zafar class by the Iranians. Hull based on Soviet P 6 class.

CHAHO   *4/1988*

3 KAIVAN (CAPE) CLASS (LARGE PATROL CRAFT)

Name	No	Builders	Commissioned
KAIVAN	201	US Coast Guard, Curtis Bay, Maryland	14 Jan 1956
AZADI (ex-*Tiran*)	202	US Coast Guard, Curtis Bay, Maryland	1957
MAHVAN	204	US Coast Guard, Curtis Bay, Maryland	1959

Displacement, tons: 98 standard; 148 full load
Dimensions, feet (metres): 95 × 20.2 × 6.6 *(28.9 × 6.2 × 2)*
Main machinery: 4 Cummins NYHMS-1200 diesels; 2120 hp *(1.58 MW)*; 2 shafts
Speed, knots: 21. **Range, miles:** 460 at 20 kts; 2324 at 8 kts
Complement: 15
Guns: 1 Bofors 40 mm/60. 2 USSR 23 mm/80 (twin). 2—12.7 mm MGs.
Depth charges: 2 racks; 8—136 kg charges.
Sonars: Hull-mounted; active attack; high frequency (probably not operational).

Comment: *Mehran* (203) destroyed during war with Iraq. *Kaivan* and *Mahvan* damaged but have been made operational again. The Mk 22 Mousetrap was replaced by the USSR ZU 23 mm/80 twin mounting which may in turn have been replaced by an Oerlikon 20 mm.

1 BOGOMOL CLASS (LARGE PATROL CRAFT)

Displacement, tons: 245 full load
Dimensions, feet (metres): 127.9 × 25.6 × 5.9 *(39 × 7.8 × 1.8)*
Main machinery: 3 Type M 504 diesels; 10 800 hp(m) *(7.94 MW)* sustained; 3 shafts
Speed, knots: 37. **Range, miles:** 500 at 35 kts
Complement: 30
Guns: 1 USSR 3 in *(76 mm)*/66; 85° elevation; 120 rounds/minute to 15 km *(8 nm)*; weight of shell 7 kg.
  2 USSR 30 mm/65 (twin); 85° elevation; 500 rounds/minute to 5 km *(2.7 nm)*; weight of shell 0.54 kg.
Radars: Surface search: Pot Head; H/I band.
Fire control: Bass Tilt; H/I band.

Comment: Delivered by USSR in March 1990 to Iraq. Escaped to Iran in January 1991 and in service with the Iranian Navy in early 1993.

3 PARVIN (PGM-71) CLASS (LARGE PATROL CRAFT)

Name	No	Builders	Commissioned
PARVIN (ex-US *PGM 103*)	211	Peterson Builders Inc	1967
BAHRAM (ex-US *PGM 112*)	212	Peterson Builders Inc	1969
NAHID (ex-US *PGM 122*)	213	Peterson Builders Inc	1970

Displacement, tons: 98 standard; 148 full load
Dimensions, feet (metres): 101 × 21.3 × 8.3 *(30.8 × 6.5 × 2.5)*
Main machinery: 2 GM 6-71 diesels; 2040 hp *(1.52 MW)* sustained; 2 shafts
Speed, knots: 22. **Range, miles:** 1140 at 17 kts
Complement: 20
Guns: 1 Bofors 40 mm/60. 2 Oerlikon 20 mm. 2—12.7 mm MGs.
Depth charges: 4 racks (8 US Mk 6).
Radars: Surface search: Decca 303; I band.
Sonars: SQS 17B; hull-mounted active attack; high frequency.

Comment: The heavier 40 mm gun is mounted aft and the 20 mm forward to compensate for the large SQS 17B sonar dome under the bows.

2 + 2 MIG-S-1800 CLASS (COASTAL PATROL CRAFT)

Displacement, tons: 60 full load
Dimensions, feet (metres): 61.3 × 18.9 × 3.4 *(18.7 × 5.8 × 1.1)*
Main machinery: 2 MWM TBD 234 V12 diesels; 1646 hp(m) *(1.21 MW)*; 2 shafts
Speed, knots: 18
Complement: 10
Guns: 1 Oerlikon 20 mm. 2—7.62 mm MGs.
Radars: Surface search: I band.

Comment: Building in Iran as a general purpose patrol craft.

MIG-S-1800   *1992, IRI Marine Industries*

6 Mk II CLASS (COASTAL PATROL CRAFT)

Displacement, tons: 22.9 full load
Dimensions, feet (metres): 49.9 × 15.1 × 4.3 *(15.2 × 4.6 × 1.3)*
Main machinery: 2 GM 8V-71TI diesels; 460 hp *(343 kW)* sustained; 2 shafts
Speed, knots: 28. **Range, miles:** 750 at 26 kts
Complement: 6
Guns: 4—12.7 mm (2 twin) MGs.
Radars: Surface search: SPS 6; I band.

Comment: Twenty-six ordered from Peterson, USA in 1976-77. Six were for the Navy and the remainder for the Imperial Gendarmerie. All were built in association with Arvandan Maritime Corporation, Abadan. The six naval units operate in the Caspian Sea. Of the remaining 20, six were delivered complete and the others were only 65 per cent assembled on arrival in Iran. Some were lost when the Iraqi Army captured Kormansaar. Others have been lost at sea.

10 Mk III CLASS (COASTAL PATROL CRAFT)

Displacement, tons: 41.6 full load
Dimensions, feet (metres): 65 × 18.1 × 6 *(19.8 × 5.5 × 1.8)*
Main machinery: 3 GM 8V-71TI diesels; 690 hp *(515 kW)* sustained; 3 shafts
Speed, knots: 30. **Range, miles:** 500 at 28 kts
Complement: 5
Guns: 3—12.7 mm (1 twin, 1 single) MGs.
Radars: Surface search: RCA LN-66; I band

Comment: Twenty ordered from Marinette Marine Corp, Wisconsin, USA; the first delivered in December 1975 and the last in December 1976. A further 50 were ordered in 1976 to be shipped out and completed in Iran. It is not known how many were finally assembled. Six lost in the Gulf War, others have been scrapped.

US Mk III   *1991*

4 + 2 MIG-G-1900 CLASS (COASTAL PATROL CRAFT)

Displacement, tons: 30 full load
Dimensions, feet (metres): 64 × 13.8 × 3 *(19.5 × 4.2 × 0.9)*
Main machinery: 2 MWM TBD 234 V12 diesels; 1646 hp(m) *(1.21 MW)*; 2 shafts
Speed, knots: 36
Complement: 8
Guns: 2—12.7 mm (twin) MGs.
Radars: Surface search: I band.

Comment: Building in Iran to a modified US Mk III design.

MIG-G-1900   *1992, Iranian Marine Industries*

50 PBI TYPE (COASTAL PATROL CRAFT)

Displacement, tons: 20.1 full load
Dimensions, feet (metres): 50 × 15 × 4 *(15.2 × 4.6 × 1.2)*
Main machinery: 2 GM 8V-71TI diesels; 460 hp *(343 kW)* sustained; 2 shafts
Speed, knots: 28. **Range, miles:** 750 at 26 kts
Complement: 5 (1 officer)
Missiles: SSM: Tigercat; range 6 km *(3.2 nm)*.
Guns: 2—12.7 mm MGs.
Radars: Surface search: I band.

Comment: Ordered by Iranian Arvandan Maritime Company. First 19 completed by Petersons and remainder shipped as kits for completion in Iran. The SSM is crude and unguided. Numbers are approximate.

PBI Type   *1991*

6 ENFORCER TYPE (INSHORE PATROL CRAFT)

Displacement, tons: 4.7 full load
Dimensions, feet (metres): 30.5 × 11.2 × 3 *(9.3 × 3.4 × 0.9)*
Main machinery: 2 GM 6V-53 diesels; 296 hp *(221 kW)* sustained; 2 shafts
Speed, knots: 28. **Range, miles:** 146 at 16 kts
Complement: 4
Guns: 1—12.7 mm MG.
Radars: Surface search: Apelco AD7-7; I band.

Comment: Built by Bertram Yacht, Miami in 1972. Thirty-six units delivered; most deleted.

3 SEWART TYPE (INSHORE PATROL CRAFT)

MAHNAVI-HAMRAZ   MAHNAVI-VAHEDI   MAHNAVI-TAHERI

Displacement, tons: 9.1 full load
Dimensions, feet (metres): 40 × 12.1 × 3.3 *(12.2 × 3.7 × 1)*
Main machinery: 2 GM 6-71 diesels; 348 hp *(260 kW)* sustained; 2 shafts
Speed, knots: 31
Complement: 6
Guns: 1—12.7 mm MG.

Comment: Small launches for port duties of Sewart (USA) standard 40 ft type. Six transferred in 1970 and six in 1986. *Mardjan, Morvarid* and *Sadaf* given to Sudan in December 1975, remainder deleted.

30 BOGHAMMAR CRAFT

Displacement, tons: 6.4 full load
Dimensions, feet (metres): 41.2 × 8.6 × 2.3 *(13 × 2.7 × 0.7)*
Main machinery: 2 Volvo Penta TAMD71A diesels; 714 hp(m) *(525 kW)*; or 2 Seatek 6-4V-9 diesels; 1160 hp *(853 kW)*; 2 shafts
Speed, knots: 46. **Range, miles:** 500 at 40 kts
Complement: 5/6
Guns: 1—12.7 mm MG. 1 RPG-7 rocket launcher or 106 mm recoilless rifle. 1—12-barrelled 107 mm rocket launcher (MRL)
Radars: Surface search: Decca 170; I band

Comment: Ordered in 1983 and completed in 1984-85 for Customs Service. Total of 51 delivered. Used extensively by the Pasdaran (Islamic Revolutionary Guard) for operations against merchant vessels in the Persian Gulf. Maximum payload 450 kg. Speed is dependent on load carried. They can be transported by Amphibious Lift Ships and can operate from bases at Farsi, Sirri and Abu Musa Islands with a main base at Bandar Abbas. Being re-engined with Seatek diesels from 1991.
There are also a further 10—11 Metre craft with similar characteristics. Known as TORAGH boats.

BOGHAMMAR   *1988*

32 BOSTON WHALER CRAFT (TYPE 1)

Displacement, tons: 1.3 full load
Dimensions, feet (metres): 22.3 × 7.4 × 1.2 *(6.7 × 2.3 × 0.4)*
Main machinery: 2 outboards; 240 hp *(179 kW)*
Speed, knots: 40+
Complement: 4
Guns: Various, but can include 1—12-barrelled 107 mm MRL or 1—12.7 mm MG.

Comment: Designed for coastal law enforcement by Boston Whaler Inc, USA. GRP hulls. Numerous indigenously constructed hulls.

BOSTON WHALER   *1988*

RIVER ROADSTEAD PATROL AND HOVERCRAFT

Comment: Numerous craft used by the Revolutionary Guard include:
Type 2: Dimensions, feet (metres): 22.0 × 7.2 (6.7 × 2.2); single outboard engine; 1—12.7 mm MG.
Type 3: Dimensions, feet (metres): 16.4 × 5.2 (5.0 × 1.6); single outboard engine; small arms.
Type 4: Dimensions, feet (metres): 13.1-26.2 × 7.9 (4-8 × 1.6); two outboard engines; small arms.
Type 5: Dimensions, feet (metres): 24.6 × 9.2 (7.5 × 2.8); Damen assault craft.
Type 6: Dimensions, feet (metres): 30.9 × 11.8 (9.4 × 3.6); single outboard engine; 1—12.7 mm MG.
Dhows: Dimensions, feet (metres): 77.1 × 20 (23.5 × 6.1); single diesel engine; mine rails.
Yunus: Dimensions, feet (metres): 27.6 × 9.8 (8.4 × 3); speed 32 kts.
Ashoora: Dimensions, feet (metres): 26.6 × 7.9 (8.1 × 2.4); two outboards; speed 42 kts; 1—7.62 mm MG.

Type 4   1992, IRI Marine Industries

MINE WARFARE FORCES

3 MSC 292 and 268 CLASS (MINESWEEPERS—COASTAL)

Name	No	Builders	Commissioned
SHAHROKH (ex-MSC 276)	301	Bellingham Shipyards	1960
SIMORGH (ex-MSC 291)	302	Tacoma Boat	1962
KARKAS (ex-MSC 292)	303	Peterson Builders	1959

Displacement, tons: 376 (Shahrokh); 384 (others) full load
Dimensions, feet (metres): 145.8 × 28 × 8.3 (44.5 × 8.5 × 2.5)
Main machinery: 2 GM 8-268A diesels (Shahrokh); 880 hp (656 kW); 2 shafts
4 GM 6-71 diesels (others); 696 hp (519 kW) sustained; 2 shafts
Speed, knots: 13. **Range, miles:** 2400 at 10 kts
Complement: 40 (6 officers)
Guns: 2 Oerlikon 20 mm (twin).
Radars: Surface search: Decca; I band.

Comment: Originally class of four. Of wooden construction with mechanical, acoustic and magnetic sweeps. Transferred from the USA under MAP in 1959-62. Shahrokh in the Caspian Sea as a training ship. Karkas still active but rarely seen at sea. Simorgh paid off some years ago but reactivated in 1992.

2 CAPE CLASS (MINESWEEPERS—INSHORE)

Name	No	Builders	Commissioned
HARISCHI (ex-MSI 14)	311	Tacoma Boat	3 Sep 1964
RIAZI (ex-MSI 13)	312	Tacoma Boat	15 Oct 1964

Displacement, tons: 239 full load
Dimensions, feet (metres): 111 × 23 × 7.9 (33.9 × 7 × 2.4)
Main machinery: 4 Type 2490 8V diesels; 1300 hp (970 kW); 2 shafts
Speed, knots: 13. **Range, miles:** 1200 at 12 kts; 3500 at 8 kts
Complement: 21 (5 officers)
Guns: 1—12.7 mm MG.
Radars: Surface search: Decca 303N; I band

Comment: Delivered from US under MAP and transferred at Seattle, Washington, on 15 October 1964. Riazi is still operational with mechanical, acoustic and magnetic sweep gear. Harischi was put back in service in 1992.

RIAZI (old number)   1975, Imperial Iranian Navy

AMPHIBIOUS FORCES

Notes: (1) One Polnochny class LST escaped from Iraq in January 1991 and took shelter in Iran. Although it has been retained, no attempt had been made to make it operational by the end of 1993.
(2) Two 3600 ton LSTs are being built at Boushehr to complete in 1995/96.

3 IRAN HORMUZ 24 CLASS (LSTs)

24-26

Displacement, tons: 2014 full load
Dimensions, feet (metres): 239.8 × 46.6 × 8.2 (73.1 × 14.2 × 2.5)
Main machinery: 2 Daihatsu 6DLM-22 diesels; 2400 hp(m) (1.76 MW); 2 shafts
Speed, knots: 12
Complement: 30 plus 110 berths
Military lift: 9 tanks, 140 troops

Comment: Built by Inchon, South Korea in 1985-86 and as with the Iran Hormuz 21 class officially classed as Merchant Ships. Large bow doors. Have been used to support Pasdaran activities.

4 HENGAM CLASS (LSL)

Name	No	Builders	Commissioned
HENGAM	511	Yarrow (Shipbuilders) Ltd, Clyde	12 Aug 1974
LARAK	512	Yarrow (Shipbuilders) Ltd, Clyde	12 Nov 1974
TONB	513	Yarrow (Shipbuilders) Ltd, Clyde	21 Feb 1985
LAVAN	514	Yarrow (Shipbuilders) Ltd, Clyde	16 Jan 1985

Displacement, tons: 2540 full load
Dimensions, feet (metres): 305 × 49 × 7.3 (93 × 15 × 2.4)
Main machinery: 4 Paxman 12YJCM diesels (Hengam, Larak); 3000 hp (2.24 MW) sustained; 2 shafts
4 MTU 16V 652 TB81 diesels (Tonb, Lavan); 4600 hp(m) (3.38 MW) sustained; 2 shafts
Speed, knots: 14.5. **Range, miles:** 4000+ at 12 kts
Complement: 80
Military lift: Up to 9 tanks depending on size; 600 tons cargo; 227 troops; 10 ton crane

Guns: 4 Bofors 40 mm/60 (Hengam and Larak). 8 USSR 23 mm/80 (4 twin) (Tonb and Lavan). 2—12.7 mm MGs.
1 BM-21 multiple rocket launcher.
Countermeasures: Decoys: 2 UK Mk 5 rocket flare launchers.
Radars: Navigation: Racal Decca 1229; I band.
IFF: SSR 1520 (Hengam and Larak).
Tacan: URN 25.

Helicopters: Can embark 1 medium.

Programmes: Named after islands in the Gulf. First two ordered 25 July 1972. Four more ordered 20 July 1977. The material for the last two ships of the second order had been ordered by Yarrows when the order was cancelled in early 1979. Tonb carried out trials in October 1984 followed by Lavan later in the year and both were released by the UK in 1985 as 'Hospital Ships'.
Structure: Smaller than British Sir Lancelot design with no through tank deck.
Operational: Two LCVPs and a number of small landing craft can be carried. Can act as Depot Ships for MCMV and small craft and have been used to ferry Pasdaran small craft around the Gulf.

LAVAN   2/1991, 92 Wing RAAF

2 IRAN AJR CLASS (LSTs)

IRAN ASIR (ex-Arya Akian)   IRAN GHAYDR (ex-Arya Sahand)

Displacement, tons: 2274 full load
Measurement, tons: 1691 gross
Dimensions, feet (metres): 176 × 35.4 × 9.9 (53.7 × 10.8 × 3)
Main machinery: 2 diesels; 2200 hp(m) (1.62 MW); 2 shafts
Speed, knots: 12.5
Complement: 30
Military lift: 650 tons
Guns: 2—12.7 mm MGs.

Comment: Five built by Teraoka, Japan in 1978-79. Ro-Ro landing craft acquired by the Iranian Navy in 1980 primarily for minelaying. The Iran Ajr was captured and scuttled by the US Navy in September 1987 and two others of the class were sunk by Iraq in 1980. Probably only one is operational.

1 + 1 MIG-S-3700 CLASS (LCT)

Displacement, tons: 276 full load
Dimensions, feet (metres): 121.4 × 26.2 × 4.9 (37 × 8 × 1.5)
Main machinery: 2 MWM TBD 234 V8 diesels; 879 hp(m) (646 kW); 2 shafts
Speed, knots: 10
Complement: 8
Military lift: 140 tons of vehicles

Comment: Building in Iran by Martyr Darvishi Marine, Bandar Abbas. First one launched in 1992.

MIG-S-3700   1992, Iranian Marine Industries

3 + 1 IRAN HORMUZ 21 CLASS (LCT)

21-23

Displacement, tons: 1280 full load
Measurement, tons: 750 dwt
Dimensions, feet (metres): 213.3 × 39.4 × 8.5 *(65 × 12 × 2.6)*
Main machinery: 2 MAN V12V-12.5/14 or 2 MWM TBD 604 V12 diesels; 730 hp(m) *(537 kW);*
  2 shafts
Speed, knots: 9
Complement: 12
Military lift: 600 tons

Comment: Officially ordered for 'civilian use' and built by Ravenstein, Netherlands in 1984-85.
  Similar but slightly smaller than the Iran Ajr class. No 21 is operational but the other two are in a
  poor state of repair. A local version is being built as the MIG-S-5000.

14 ROTORK CRAFT (LCU)

Displacement, tons: 9 full load
Dimensions, feet (metres): 41.7 × 10.5 × 3 *(12.7 × 3.2 × 0.9)*
Main machinery: 2 Volvo Penta diesels; 240 hp(m) *(176 kW);* 2 shafts
Speed, knots: 28
Military lift: 30 troops
Guns: Up to 4—7.62 mm MGs.

Comment: Some are used by the Coast Guard. Some of these craft have been deleted and numbers
  are uncertain.

8 WINCHESTER (SR. N6) CLASS (HOVERCRAFT)

01-08

Displacement, tons: 10.9 full load
Dimensions, feet (metres): 48.5 × 23 × 3.9 (skirt) *(14.8 × 7 × 1.2)*
Main machinery: 1 RR Gnome Model 1050 gas turbine; 1050 hp *(783 kW)* sustained
Speed, knots: 60. **Range, miles:** 170 at 54 kts
Complement: 3
Guns: 1 or 2—12.7 mm MGs.
Radars: Surface search: Decca 202; I band.

Comment: Ordered 1970-72 and commissioned 1973-75. First three were Mk 3, remainder Mk 4.
  Some refitted in UK in 1984. Can carry 20 troops and 5 tons of cargo. Can also be fitted with four
  500 kg mines on the side decks. Probably only half are operational.

WINCHESTER 03   *1971*

6 WELLINGTON (BH.7) CLASS (HOVERCRAFT)

101-106

Displacement, tons: 53.8 full load
Dimensions, feet (metres): 78.3 × 45.6 × 5.6 (skirt) *(23.9 × 13.9 × 1.7)*
Main machinery: 1 RR Proteus 15 M/541 gas turbine; 4250 hp *(3.17 MW)* sustained
Speed, knots: 70; 30 in sea state 5 or more. **Range, miles:** 620 at 66 kts
Guns: 2 Browning 12.7 mm MGs.
Radars: Surface search: Decca 1226; I band.

Comment: First pair are British Hovercraft Corporation 7 Mk 4 commissioned in 1970-71 and the
  next four are Mk 5 craft commissioned in 1974-75. Mk 5 craft fitted for, but not with Standard
  missiles. Some refitted in UK in 1984. Can embark troops and vehicles or normal support cargoes. All were in reasonable condition in late 1992.

WELLINGTON 103   *9/1985, Michael D J Lennon*

AUXILIARIES

1 REPLENISHMENT SHIP

Name	No	Builders	Commissioned
KHARG	431	Swan Hunter Ltd, Wallsend	5 Oct 1984

Displacement, tons: 11 064 light; 33 014 full load
Measurement, tons: 9367 dwt; 18 582 gross
Dimensions, feet (metres): 679 × 86.9 × 30 *(207.2 × 26.5 × 9.2)*
Main machinery: 2 Babcock & Wilcox boilers; 2 Westinghouse turbines; 26 870 hp *(19.75 MW);*
  1 shaft
Speed, knots: 21.5
Complement: 248
Guns: 1 OTO Melara 76 mm/62 compact. 4 USSR 23 mm/80 (2 twin).
Radars: Navigation: Two Decca 1229; I band.
IFF: 955M.
Helicopters: Three can be embarked (twin hangar).

Comment: Ordered October 1974. Laid down 27 January 1976. Launched 3 February 1977. Ship
  handed over to Iranian crew on 25 April 1980 but remained in UK. In 1983 Iranian Government
  requested this ship's transfer. The British Government delayed approval until January 1984. On
  10 July 1984 began refit at Tyne Ship Repairers. Trials began 4 September 1984 and ship was
  then delivered without guns which were subsequently fitted. A design incorporating some of the
  features of the British OI class but carrying ammunition and dry stores in addition to fuel. Inmarsat fitted.

KHARG   *3/1987, Michael D J Lennon*

2 FLEET SUPPLY SHIPS

Name	No	Builders	Commissioned
BANDAR ABBAS	421	C Lühring Yard, Brake, West Germany	Apr 1974
BOUSHEHR	422	C Lühring Yard, Brake, West Germany	Nov 1974

Displacement, tons: 4673 full load
Measurement, tons: 3250 dwt; 3186 gross
Dimensions, feet (metres): 354.2 × 54.4 × 14.8 *(108 × 16.6 × 4.5)*
Main machinery: 2 MAN 6L 52/55 diesels; 12 060 hp(m) *(8.86 MW)* sustained; 2 shafts
Speed, knots: 20. **Range, miles:** 3500 at 16 kts
Complement: 59
Guns: 2 USSR 23 mm/80 (twin). 2 Oerlikon 20 mm. 8—14.5 mm (2 quad) MGs.
Radars: Navigation: Two Decca 1226; I band.
Helicopters: 1 light reconnaissance.

Comment: *Bandar Abbas* launched 11 August 1973, *Boushehr* launched 23 March 1974. Combined tankers and store-ships carrying victualling, armament and general stores. Telescopic
  hangar for Bell UH-1N size helicopter. Both carry 2 SA-7 portable SAM and 20 mm guns have
  been fitted alongside the hangar.

BOUSHEHR   *2/1990*

1 AMPHION CLASS (REPAIR SHIP)

Name	No	Builders	Commissioned
CHAH BAHAR (ex-USS *Amphion*, ex-*AR 13*)	441	Tampa Shipbuilding Co	30 Jan 1946

Displacement, tons: 8941 standard; 14 803 full load
Dimensions, feet (metres): 492 × 69.6 × 27.5 *(150.1 × 21.2 × 8.4)*
Main machinery: 2 Foster-Wheeler boilers; 435 psi *(30.6 kg/cm sq);* 2 Westinghouse turbines;
  8560 hp *(6.4 MW);* 1 shaft
Speed, knots: 18. **Range, miles:** 13 950 at 11.5 kts
Complement: 880

Comment: Launched on 15 May 1945. Transferred by US on loan to the Iran Navy on 2 October
  1971. Purchased 1 March 1977. Non-operational and based at Bandar Abbas as permanent
  repair facility. Two US 3 in (76 mm)/50 guns have been removed but navigational radar (SPS 4)
  is retained.

CHAH BAHAR (old number)   *1972, Imperial Iranian Navy*

4 KANGAN CLASS (WATER TANKERS)

KANGAN 411	SHAHID MARJANI —
TAHERI 412	AMIR —

Displacement, tons: 12 000 full load
Measurement, tons: 9430 dwt
Dimensions, feet (metres): 485.6 × 70.5 × 16.4 *(148 × 21.5 × 5)*
Main machinery: 1 MAN 7L52/55A diesel; 7385 hp(m) *(5.43 MW)* sustained; 1 shaft
Speed, knots: 15
Complement: 14
Cargo capacity: 9000 cu m of water
Guns: 2 USSR 23 mm/80 (twin). 2—12.7 mm MGs.
Radars: Navigation: Decca 1229; I band.

Comment: The first two were built in Mazagon Dock, Bombay in 1978 and 1979. The second pair to a slightly modified design were acquired in 1991/92. Some of the largest water tankers afloat and are used to supply remote coastal towns and islands. Accommodation is air-conditioned.

TAHERI   *5/1989*

13 HENDIJAN CLASS (TENDERS) (AG)

HENDIJAN	SIRIK	MOGAM	MAQAM
KALAT	SAVATAR	ROSTANI	KORAMSHAHR
KONARAK	GENO	MAYBAND	BAMREGAN
GENAVEH			

Displacement, tons: 460 full load
Dimensions, feet (metres): 166.7 × 28.1 × 11.5 *(50.8 × 8.6 × 3.5)*
Main machinery: 2 Mitsubishi S16MPTK diesels; 7600 hp(m) *(5.15 MW)*; 2 shafts
Speed, knots: 21
Complement: 15 plus 90 passengers
Cargo capacity: 40 tons on deck; 95 m³ of liquid/solid cargo space

Comment: First eight built by Damen, Netherlands 1988-91. Remainder built at Bandar Abbas under the MIG-S-4700 programme which may continue.

KONARAK   *6/1989, Gilbert Gyssels*

1 Ex-YACHT

KISH

Displacement, tons: 178 full load
Dimensions, feet (metres): 122 × 24.9 × 7.3 *(37.2 × 7.6 × 2.2)*
Main machinery: 2 MTU diesels; 2920 hp(m) *(2.15 MW)*; 2 shafts
Speed, knots: 20
Complement: 20
Radars: Navigation: I band

Comment: Completed in 1970 by Yacht und Bootswerft, West Germany. Refitted in Bandar Abbas and used for training.

10 DAMEN 1550 (PILOT CRAFT)

Displacement, tons: 25 full load
Dimensions, feet (metres): 52.5 × 15.1 × 4.6 *(16 × 4.6 × 1.4)*
Main machinery: 2 MTU diesels; 2 shafts
Speed, knots: 19
Complement: 3
Radars: Navigation: Furuno; I band.

Comment: Ordered from Damen, Gorinchen in February 1993. Steel hull and aluminium superstructure. To be used as pilot craft.

DAMEN 1550   *1993, Damen Shipyards*

7 DELVAR CLASS (SUPPORT SHIPS)

CHARAK (AK)	CHIROO (AK)	DELVAR (AE)	DILIM (AW)
SOURU (AK)	SIRJAN (AE)	DAYER (AW)	

Measurement, tons: 890 gross; 765 dwt
Dimensions, feet (metres): 210 × 34.4 × 10.9 *(64 × 10.5 × 3.3)*
Main machinery: 2 MAN G6V 23.5/33ATL diesels; 1560 hp(m) *(1.15 MW)*; 2 shafts
Speed, knots: 11
Guns: 2 USSR 23 mm/80 (twin).
Radars: Navigation: Decca 1226; I band.

Comment: All built by Karachi SY in 1980-82. *Delvar* and *Sirjan* are ammunition ships, *Dayer* and *Dilim* water carriers and the other three are general cargo ships. The water carriers have only one crane (against two on the other types), and have rounded sterns (as opposed to transoms).

45+ BARGES AND SERVICE CRAFT

Comment: Many built in Karachi 1976-79 the largest being a 260 ft *(79.2 m)* self-propelled lighter. One delivered from Iran Marine is of 1000 grt and was launched on 2 March 1987.

2 FLOATING DOCKS

400 (ex-US *ARD 29*, ex-*FD 4*)	DOLPHIN

Dimensions, feet (metres): 487 × 80.2 × 32.5 *(149.9 × 24.7 × 10) (400)*
786.9 × 172.1 × 58.4 *(240 × 52.5 × 17.8) (Dolphin)*

Comment: *400* is an ex-US ARD 12 class built by Pacific Bridge, California and transferred in 1977; lift 3556 tons. *Dolphin* built by MAN-GHH Nordenham, West Germany and completed in November 1985; lift 28 000 tons.

TUGS

14 HARBOUR TUGS

No 1 (ex-West German *Karl*)	MENAB	SEFID-RUD
No 2 (ex-West German *Ise*)	HARI-RUD	ATRAK
HAAMOON	ARAS	+5 (YTM class)
HIRMAND		

Comment: All between 70 and 90 ft in length. All but the first two (which were built in the early 1960s and acquired in June 1974) built in 1984-85.

IRAQ

Administration

Commander-in-Chief:
  Rear Admiral Abd Muhammad Abdullah
Chief of Staff:
  Commander Samad Sat Al Mufti

Bases

Basra, Umm Qasr, Az Zubayr
The UN decision on the status of Umm Qasr could deprive the Navy of its base, but leaves the commercial port still in Iraq. By early 1994 there was a small navigable channel up the Shatt-al-Arab canal to Basra. The Navy spends most of the time alongside at Az Zubayr, with occasional coastal patrols by single ships.

Mercantile Marine

Lloyd's Register of Shipping:
  121 vessels of 901 529 tons

DELETIONS

Note: Captured Kuwaiti vessels destroyed in 1991 are shown in *Kuwait* section.

Frigates

1992   *Hittin, Thi Qar, Al Qadisiya, Al Yarmouk* (retained by Italy)

Corvettes

1992   *Abdulla Ben Abi Sarh, Khalid Ibn Al Walid, Saad Ibn Abi Waccade, Salah Ad Deen Al Ayoori* (retained by Italy and two sold to Morocco in 1992/93)

Mine Warfare Forces

1991   1 Yevgenya, 1 T 43

Patrol Forces

1991   1 Osa I (to Iran), 5 Osa II (one to Iran), 6 P 6, 3 SO 1, 1 Poluchat I, 3 Zhuk, 8 PO 2, 1 Bogomol (to Iran), 3 PB 90, 1 Winchester Hovercraft, 6 Rotork Type 412
1992   3 PB 90
1993   3 Thornycroft Type (returned to Kuwait unserviceable)

Amphibious Forces

1991   3 Polnochny (one to Iran)
1993   3 Cheverton Loadmasters (returned to Kuwait unserviceable)

FRIGATES

Notes: (1) Four Modified Lupo class frigates completed between 1985 and 1988 were not transferred and are being taken on by the Italian Navy.
(2) Two Jianghu class frigates were to have been acquired from China in 1991 and this contract may be honoured in due course.

1 YUGOSLAV TYPE

Name	No	Builders	Laid down	Launched	Commissioned
IBN MARJID (ex-*Ibn Khaldoum*)	507	Uljanic, Yugoslavia	1977	1978	20 Mar 1980

Displacement, tons: 1850 full load
Dimensions, feet (metres): 317.3 × 36.7 × 14.8
(96.7 × 11.2 × 4.5)
Main machinery: CODOG; 1 RR Olympus TM3B gas turbine;
21 500 hp *(16 MW)* sustained; 2 MTU 16V 956 TB91 diesels;
7500 hp(m) *(5.5 MW)* sustained; 2 shafts
Speed, knots: 26 gas; 20 diesels. **Range, miles:** 4000 at 20 kts
Complement: 93 plus 100 trainees

Missiles: Can carry 4 Aerospatiale SSM Exocet ❶ (but not fitted).
Guns: 1 Bofors 57 mm/70 ❷. 1 Bofors 40 mm/70 ❸. 8 Oerlikon
20 mm (4 twin) ❹.
Torpedoes: Fitted for 2—21 in *(533 mm)* tubes.
Depth charges: 1 rail.
Countermeasures: ESM/ECM: Radar intercept and jammer.
Radars: Surface search/navigation: Two Racal Decca 1229 ❺;
I band.
Fire control: Philips Elektronik 9LV200 Mk 2 ❻; J band.
Sonars: Hull-mounted; active search and attack; medium
frequency.

IBN MARJID   *(Scale 1 : 900), Ian Sturton*

Structure: Near sister to Indonesian *Hajar Dewantara* but with no
helicopter deck. Training ship with frigate capability.
Operational: Mainly used as a training ship and transport during
war with Iran. Subsequently used mostly as an accommodation and supply ship and is unlikely to become operational
again as a frigate. The superstructure was badly damaged during the Gulf War in 1991. Still afloat in early 1994.

CORVETTES

2 ASSAD CLASS

Name	No	Builders	Laid down	Launched	Completed
MUSSA BEN NUSSAIR	F 210	Fincantieri, Muggiano	15 Jan 1982	22 Oct 1982	17 Sep 1986
TARIQ IBN ZIAD	F 212	Fincantieri, Muggiano	20 May 1982	8 July 1983	29 Oct 1986

Displacement, tons: 685 full load
Dimensions, feet (metres): 204.4 × 30.5 × 8
(62.3 × 9.3 × 2.5)
Main machinery: 4 MTU 20V 956 TB92 diesels; 20 120 hp(m)
(14.8 MW) sustained; 4 shafts
Speed, knots: 37. **Range, miles:** 4000 at 18 kts
Complement: 51 (without aircrew)

Missiles: SSM: 2 OTO Melara/Matra Otomat Teseo Mk 2 (fitted
for).
SAM: 1 Selenia/Elsag Albatros launcher (4 cell—2 reloads);
Aspide; semi-active radar homing to 13 km *(7 nm)* at
2.5 Mach; height envelope 15-5000 m *(49.2-16 405 ft)*; warhead 30 kg.
Guns: 1 OTO Melara 3 in *(76 mm)*/62 compact; 85° elevation;
85 rounds/minute to 16 km *(8.7 nm)* anti-surface; 12 km
(6.6 nm) anti-aircraft; weight of shell 6 kg.
2 Breda 40 mm/70 (twin) (not in helicopter ships); 85° elevation; 300 rounds/minute to 12.5 km *(6.8 nm)*; weight of shell
0.96 kg.
Countermeasures: Decoys: 2 Breda 105 mm six-tubed fixed
multi-purpose launchers; chaff to 5 km *(2.7 nm)*; illuminants to
12 km *(6.6 nm)*.
ESM: Selenia INS-3; intercept.
ECM: Selenia TQN-2; jammer.
Combat data systems: Selenia IPN-10; action data automation.
Fire control: 2 Selenia 21 (for SAM); Dardo (for guns).
Radars: Air/surface search: Selenia RAN 12L/X; D/I band; range
82 km *(45 nm)*.
Navigation: SMA SPN 703 (3 RM 20); I band; range 73 km
(40 nm).
Fire control: 2 Selenia RTN 10X; I/J band; range 40 km *(22 nm)*.
Sonars: KAe ASO 84-41; hull-mounted; active search and attack.

Helicopters: 1 Agusta AB 212 type.

Programmes: Ordered in February 1981. Formally handed over
in 1986 but without operational weapon systems. Started
trials with Iraqi crews in mid-1990 but the invasion of Kuwait
brought to a halt any prospects of final delivery until UN embargoes are lifted. Four other similar ships (but without helicopter
facilities) were not paid for and are now being sold, two to
Morocco.

TARIQ IBN ZIAD   *4/1990, van Ginderen Collection*

Structure: Flight deck and telescopic hangar, similar to Ecuadorean Esmeraldas class.
Operational: Moored at La Spezia flying the Iraqi flag and with
reduced Iraqi crews.

PATROL FORCES

Notes: (1) In addition to the vessels listed, there are two damaged SO 1 class patrol craft and three Rotork craft which may be salvaged.
One ex-Kuwaiti TNC-45 is also moored but looks to be beyond repair.
(2) Most of these craft were inactive throughout 1993.

1 OSA I CLASS (TYPE 205) (FAST ATTACK CRAFT—MISSILE)

Displacement, tons: 210 full load
Dimensions, feet (metres): 126.6 × 24.9 × 8.8 *(38.6 × 7.6 × 2.7)*
Main machinery: 3 Type M 503A diesels; 8025 hp(m) *(5.9 MW)* sustained; 3 shafts
Speed, knots: 35. **Range, miles:** 400 at 34 kts
Complement: 30
Missiles: SSM: SS-N-2A Styx; active radar or IR homing to 46 km *(25 nm)* at 0.9 Mach; warhead
513 kg.
Guns: 4—30 mm/65 (2 twin); 85° elevation; 500 rounds/minute to 5 km *(2.7 nm)*; weight of shell
0.54 kg.
Radars: Surface search/fire control: Square Tie; I band.
Fire control: Drum Tilt; H/I band.

Comment: A surprising survivor from the Gulf War but operational in late 1992. A second of class
defected to Iran together with an Osa II but only the latter has joined the Iranian Navy.

OSA I   *1989*

1 BOGOMOL CLASS (LARGE PATROL CRAFT)

Displacement, tons: 245 full load
Dimensions, feet (metres): 127.9 × 25.6 × 5.9 *(39 × 7.8 × 1.8)*
Main machinery: 3 Type M 504 diesels; 10 800 hp(m) *(7.94 MW)* sustained; 3 shafts
Speed, knots: 37. **Range, miles:** 500 at 35 kts
Complement: 30
Guns: 1 USSR 3 in *(76 mm)*/66; 85° elevation; 120 rounds/minute to 15 km *(8 nm)*; weight of shell 7 kg.
2 USSR 30 mm/65 (twin); 85° elevation; 500 rounds/minute to 5 km *(2.7 nm)*; weight of shell 0.54 kg.
Radars: Surface search: Pot Head; H/I band.
Fire control: Bass Tilt; H/I band.

Comment: Delivered by USSR in March 1990. Similar to craft delivered to Guinea and Guinea-Bissau. Another of this class defected to Iran in 1992. Doubtful operational status in 1993.

1 POLUCHAT I CLASS (LARGE PATROL CRAFT)

Displacement, tons: 70 standard; 100 full load
Dimensions, feet (metres): 97.1 × 19 × 4.8 *(29.6 × 5.8 × 1.5)*
Main machinery: 2 Type M 50 diesels; 2200 hp(m) *(1.6 MW)* sustained; 2 shafts
Speed, knots: 20. **Range, miles:** 1500 at 10 kts
Complement: 20
Guns: 2—14.5 mm (twin) MGs.
Radars: Surface search: Spin Trough; I band.

Comment: Transferred by the USSR in late 1960s. Also used for torpedo recovery.

2 ZHUK CLASS (TYPE 1400M) (COASTAL PATROL CRAFT)

Displacement, tons: 39 full load
Dimensions, feet (metres): 78.7 × 16.4 × 3.9 *(24 × 5 × 1.2)*
Main machinery: 2 Type M 401B diesels; 2200 hp(m) *(1.6 MW)* sustained; 2 shafts
Speed, knots: 30. **Range, miles:** 1100 at 15 kts
Complement: 11 (3 officers)
Guns: 4—14.5 mm (2 twin) MGs. 1—12.7 mm MG.
Radars: Surface search: Spin Trough; I band.
IFF: High Pole B.

Comment: Transferred by USSR in 1975. Survivors of a class of five. Both still in need of repair in late 1993.

ZHUK   1981

3 PB 90 CLASS (COASTAL PATROL CRAFT)

Displacement, tons: 90
Dimensions, feet (metres): 100 × 19.5 × 10 *(30.5 × 5.9 × 3.1)*
Main machinery: 3 diesels; 4290 hp(m) *(3.15 MW)*; 3 shafts
Speed, knots: 27. **Range, miles:** 800 at 20 kts
Complement: 17
Guns: 1 Bofors 40 mm/70. 4 Oerlikon 20 mm (quad). 2 twin 128 mm MRL.
Countermeasures: Decoys: 2 twin-barrelled chaff launchers.
Radars: Surface search: Decca 1226; I band.

Comment: Built by Tito, Yugoslavia. Four of the class delivered via Kuwait in July 1984 and the remainder in 1985. Six sunk in war with Iran, and three more in Desert Storm. Three more scrapped in 1992 leaving three survivors.

PB 90 Type   1986

4 SRN 6 MK 6 WINCHESTER CLASS (HOVERCRAFT)

Displacement, tons: 10.9 full load
Dimensions, feet (metres): 48.4 × 23 × 3.9 (skirt) *(14.8 × 7 × 1.2)*
Main machinery: 1 RR Gnome Model GT; 1050 hp *(783 kW)* sustained
Speed, knots: 60. **Range, miles:** 170 at 54 kts
Complement: 3
Guns: 1—12.7 mm MG.

Comment: Six built by British Hovercraft, Cowes in 1981. Can carry five tons of cargo plus 20 troops. Two destroyed in Desert Storm. These four non-operational in 1993.

70 + SAWARI CLASS (INSHORE PATROL BOATS)

Comment: This is a range of Iraqi-built boats, the largest types being Sawari 4 of 7 tons (11 × 2.5 × 0.6 m) and 22 kts and Sawari 6 of 12.5 m and 25 kts. Most have outboard engines and are capable of 25 kts in calm conditions. Used as patrol boats and landing craft armed with MGs and rocket launchers. Five exported to Djibouti in 1989.

MINE WARFARE FORCES

Note: One T 43 minesweeper is possibly still available, but in poor condition.

2 YEVGENYA CLASS (MINEHUNTERS—INSHORE)

Displacement, tons: 90 full load
Dimensions, feet (metres): 80.7 × 18 × 4.9 *(24.6 × 5.5 × 1.5)*
Main machinery: 2 Type 3-D-12 diesels; 600 hp(m) *(440 kW)* sustained; 2 shafts
Speed, knots: 11. **Range, miles:** 300 at 10 kts
Complement: 10
Guns: 2—25 mm/80 (twin).
Radars: Navigation: Spin Trough; I band.
IFF: High Pole.
Sonars: Helo type VDS (on stern); minehunting; high frequency.

Comment: GRP hulls. Delivered by USSR in January 1975 under cover-name of 'oceanographic craft'. One sunk in Desert Storm; these two damaged but have been repaired.

3 NESTIN CLASS (MINESWEEPERS—INSHORE)

Displacement, tons: 72 full load
Dimensions, feet (metres): 88.6 × 21.3 × 3.9 *(27 × 6.5 × 1.2)*
Main machinery: 2 Torpedo 12-cyl diesels; 520 hp(m) *(382 kW)*; 2 shafts
Speed, knots: 12. **Range, miles:** 860 at 11 kts
Complement: 17
Guns: 3 Hispano 20 mm (triple). 2 Hispano 20 mm.
Mines: Can lay 24.
Radars: Navigation: I band.

Comment: Built Brodotehnika, Belgrade. Transferred from Yugoslavia 1979-80. Have magnetic, acoustic and explosive sweep gear. All survived Desert Storm although one was damaged.

NESTIN   1988

AUXILIARIES

Note: One Polnochny LST was sunk in Desert Storm and one defected to Iran. The third was badly damaged but may be repaired in due course.

1 DIVING TENDER

Displacement, tons: 119 full load
Dimensions, feet (metres): 93.5 × 21 × 5.9 *(28.5 × 6.4 × 1.8)*
Main machinery: 1 MTU 8V 396 TC82 diesel; 870 hp(m) *(640 kW)*; 1 shaft
Speed, knots: 15
Complement: 6

Comment: Built in the Netherlands and completed in October 1980.

1 STROMBOLI CLASS (REPLENISHMENT TANKER)

Name	No	Builders	Commissioned
AGNADEEN	A 102	Castellamare di Stabia, Naples	29 Oct 1984

Displacement, tons: 3556 light; 8706 full load
Dimensions, feet (metres): 423.1 × 59 × 21.3 (129 × 18 × 6.5)
Main machinery: 2 GMT A 420.8 H diesels; 9400 hp(m) (6.91 MW) sustained; 1 shaft
Speed, knots: 18.5. Range, miles: 5080 at 18.5 kts
Complement: 115

Guns: 1 OTO Melara 3 in (76 mm)/62; 85° elevation; 60 rounds/minute to 16 km (8.7 nm) anti-surface; 5 km (2.7 nm) anti-aircraft; weight of shell 6 kg.
Radars: Navigation: SMA 3 RM; I band; range 73 km (40 nm).
Fire control: Selenia RTN 10X; I/J band; range 40 km (22 nm).

Programmes: Ordered 1 February 1981. Laid down 29 January 1982 under sub-contract from Fincantieri, Muggiano. Launched 22 October 1982. Completed 20 December 1983.
Structure: Underway replenishment facilities on both sides of the ship.
Operational: Laid up in Alexandria since 1986 but still capable of going to sea.

AGNADEEN   6/1993

3 TRANSPORT SHIPS

Name	No	Builders	Commissioned
AL ZAHRAA	426	Helsingør SY	21 Apr 1983
KHAWLA	428	Helsingør SY	July 1983
BALQEES	429	Helsingør SY	Oct 1983

Displacement, tons: 5800 full load
Measurement, tons: 3681 gross
Dimensions, feet (metres): 347.8 × 61.7 × 17.4 (106 × 18.8 × 5.3)
Main machinery: 2 MTU 12V 1163 TB82 diesels; 6600 hp(m) (4.85 MW) sustained; 2 shafts
Speed, knots: 15.5
Complement: 35
Military lift: 250 troops; 16 tanks

Comment: Fitted with helicopter deck. A Ro-Ro design based on civilian requirements and therefore cannot beach. Fitted with a stern ramp capable of handling 55 ton tanks to shore and launching amphibious 41 ton tanks. 55 ton lift between decks. A 1200 ton trim arrangement allows the embarkation of small landing craft. At least one of the class sails under Iraqi Line colours. Laid up in 1993: Al Zahraa in Libya, Khawla at Aqaba and Balqees at Bremerhaven.

AL ZAHRAA   1992, van Ginderen Collection

1 SPASILAC CLASS (SALVAGE SHIP)

Name	No	Builders	Commissioned
AKA	A 81 (ex-A 51)	Tito SY, Belgrade	1978

Displacement, tons: 1600 full load
Dimensions, feet (metres): 182 × 37.6 × 12.2 (55.5 × 11.5 × 3.8)
Main machinery: 2 diesels; 4340 hp(m) (3.19 MW); 2 shafts; cp props
Speed, knots: 15. Range, miles: 1700 at 12 kts
Complement: 50
Guns: 4—14.5 mm MGs.
Radars: Navigation: Racal Decca; I band.

Comment: Similar to Libyan and Yugoslav naval ships. Can carry 750 tons of equipment and liquids. Has facilities for divers. Damaged in Desert Storm but may be repaired.

AKA   1989, Peter Jones

1 POZHARNY CLASS (FIRE BOAT)

A 82

Displacement, tons: 180 full load
Dimensions, feet (metres): 114.5 × 20 × 6 (34.9 × 6.1 × 1.8)
Main machinery: 2 Type M 50 diesels; 2200 hp(m) (1.6 MW) sustained; 2 shafts
Speed, knots: 10

Comment: Built in the mid-1950s in the USSR. Survived Desert Storm but in poor repair.

A 82   1989, Peter Jones

PRESIDENTIAL YACHT

QADISSIYAT SADDAM

Displacement, tons: 1660 full load
Dimensions, feet (metres): 269 × 42.8 × 10.8 (82 × 13 × 3.3)
Main machinery: 2 MTU 12V 1163 TB82 diesels; 6600 hp(m) (4.85 MW); 2 shafts
Speed, knots: 19

Comment: Built by Helsingør SY, Denmark. Completed September 1981. Helicopter deck. Accommodation for 56 passengers.

IRELAND

Senior Appointment

Flag Officer Commanding Naval Service:
  Commodore J Kavanagh

Bases

Haulbowline Island (Cork), Headquarters, naval base and dockyard, sea-going replacement section, ship support and maintenance and communications section. Haulbowline Naval Base and Ballincollig Barracks, Cork, are the centres for all recruit and continuation training. A new training establishment is to be set up at Ringaskiddy in Cork Harbour.

Naval Requirement

If the EEZ is to be policed effectively, the OPV requirement is for 12 vessels (two at 2000 tons, six at 1000 tons and four at 500 tons).

Personnel

Establishment: 1266 (158 officers, 568 petty officers, 540 ratings)
(a) 1994: Currently under strength at 980 (129 officers)
(b) Voluntary service

Operational

All seven ships are in full commission in 1994.

Prefix to Ships' Names

LÉ (Long Éirennach = Irish Ship)

Mercantile Marine

Lloyd's Register of Shipping:
  189 vessels of 184 721 tons gross

CORVETTE

1 + (1) EITHNE CLASS

Name	No	Builders	Laid down	Launched	Commissioned
EITHNE	P 31	Verolme, Cork	15 Dec 1982	19 Dec 1983	7 Dec 1984

EITHNE   (Scale 1 : 900), Ian Sturton

Displacement, tons: 1760 standard; 1910 full load
Dimensions, feet (metres): 265 × 39.4 × 14.1
  (80.8 × 12 × 4.3)
Main machinery: 2 Ruston 12RKC diesels; 6800 hp *(5.07 MW)*
  sustained; 2 shafts
Speed, knots: 20+; 19 normal. **Range, miles:** 7000 at 15 kts
Complement: 85 (9 officers)

Guns: 1 Bofors 57 mm/70 Mk 1 ❶; 75° elevation; 200 rounds/
  minute to 17 km *(9.3 nm)*; weight of shell 2.4 kg.
  2 Rheinmetall 20 mm/20 ❷.
  2 Wallop 57 mm launchers for illuminants.
Fire control: Signaal LIOD director ❸.
Radars: Air/surface search: Signaal DA 05 Mk 4 ❹; E/F band;
  range 137 km *(75 nm)* for 2 m² target.
  Navigation: Two Racal Decca ❺; I band.
Tacan: MEL RRB transponder.
Sonars: Plessey PMS 26; hull-mounted; lightweight; active
  search and attack; 10 kHz.

Helicopters: 1 SA 365F Dauphin 2 ❻.

Programmes: Ordered 23 April 1982 from Verolme, Cork, this
  was the last ship to be built at this yard. A bid for funding a second of class has been made to the European Union.
Structure: Fitted with retractable stabilisers. Closed circuit TV for
  flight deck operations. Satellite navigation and
  communications.
Operational: Helicopter fully operational in 1993.

EITHNE   2/1993, Erik Laursen

PATROL FORCES

4 P 21 and DEIRDRE CLASSES (OFFSHORE PATROL VESSELS)

Name	No	Builders	Commissioned
DEIRDRE	P 20	Verolme, Cork	19 June 1972
EMER	P 21	Verolme, Cork	16 Jan 1978
AOIFE	P 22	Verolme, Cork	29 Nov 1979
AISLING	P 23	Verolme, Cork	21 May 1980

Displacement, tons: 972 *(Deirdre)*; 1019.5 (remainder)
Dimensions, feet (metres): 184.3 pp × 34.1 × 14.4 *(56.2 × 10.4 × 4.4) (Deirdre)*
  213.7 × 34.4 × 14 *(65.2 × 10.5 × 4.4)* (remainder)
Main machinery: 2 British Polar SF112 VS-F diesels; 4200 hp *(3.13 MW)*; 1 shaft *(Deirdre)*
  2 SEMT-Pielstick 6 PA6 L 280 diesels; 4800 hp *(3.53 MW)*; 1 shaft (remainder)
Speed, knots: 17. **Range, miles:** 4000 at 17 kts; 6750 at 12 kts
Complement: 46 (5 officers)

Guns: 1 Bofors 40 mm/60; may be uprated from 120 to 180 rounds/minute.
  2 GAMB-01 20 mm (except *Deirdre*); 60° elevation; 900 rounds/minute to 2 km.
  2—12.7 mm MGs *(Deirdre)*.
Radars: Surface search: Selesmar/Selescan 1024 or Kelvin Hughes 1007 CTD; I band.
  Navigation: Racal Decca RM 1229; I band.
Sonars: Simrad Marine; hull-mounted; active search; 34 kHz.

Programmes: *Deirdre* was the first vessel built for the Naval Service in Ireland.
Modernisation: New search radars are to be fitted in 1994/95.
Structure: All of Nevesbu design. Stabilisers fitted. *Aoife* and *Aisling* are of similar construction to
  Emer with the addition of a bow thruster and KaMeWa four-bladed skewed propeller. Satellite
  navigation and communications.
Operational: Decca Mk 53 Navigator and SATNAV. The practice of keeping one in reserve and
  rotating every six months was stopped at the end of 1990 and all have been operational since
  then.

AISLING   2/1993, Campanera i Rovira

2 P 41 PEACOCK CLASS (COASTAL PATROL VESSELS)

Name	No	Builders	Commissioned
ORLA (ex-HMS *Swift*)	P 41	Hall Russell, Aberdeen	3 May 1985
CIARA (ex-HMS *Swallow*)	P 42	Hall Russell, Aberdeen	17 Oct 1984

Displacement, tons: 712 full load
Dimensions, feet (metres): 204.1 × 32.8 × 8.9 *(62.6 × 10 × 2.7)*
Main machinery: 2 Crossley SEMT-Pielstick 18 PA6 V 280 diesels; 14 400 hp(m) *(10.58 MW)* sus-
  tained; 2 shafts; auxiliary drive; Schottel prop; 181 hp(m) *(133 kW)*
Speed, knots: 25. **Range, miles:** 2500 at 17 kts
Complement: 39 (6 officers)

Guns: 1—3 in (76 mm)/62 OTO Melara compact; 85° elevation; 85 rounds/minute to 16 km
  (8.6 nm); weight of shell 6 kg.
  2—12.7 mm MGs. 4—7.62 mm MGs.
Fire control: BAe Sea Archer (for 76 mm).
Radars: Surface search: Kelvin Hughes Type 1007 CDT; I band.
  Navigation: Kelvin Hughes 6000A; I band.

Programmes: *Orla* launched 11 September 1984 and *Ciara* 31 March 1984. Both served in Hong
  Kong from mid-1985 until early 1988. Acquired from UK and commissioned 21 November 1988.
Modernisation: New radars fitted in 1993.
Structure: Can carry Sea Rider craft. Have loiter drive. Displacement increased by the addition of
  more electronic equipment including Satellite navigation and communications.
Operational: Sprint speed is nearly 30 kts. Complement augmented by boarding party personnel.
  Two Avon Sea Riders carried.

DEIRDRE   6/1991, Stefan Terzibaschitsch

CIARA   1991, T Smith, Irish Navy

SHIPBORNE AIRCRAFT

Numbers/Type: 5 Aerospatiale SA 365F Dauphin 2.
Operational speed: 140 kts *(260 km/h)*.
Service ceiling: 15 000 ft *(4575 m)*.
Range: 410 nm *(758 km)*.
Role/Weapon systems: Embarked helicopter for MR/SAR tasks in *Eithne*; some shore land-based training by Army Air Corps and SAR. Sensors: Bendix RDR 1500 radar. Weapons: Unarmed.

DAUPHIN 2   1993, John Daly, Irish Navy

LAND-BASED MARITIME AIRCRAFT

Note: 2 civilian operated Sikorsky S-61 helicopters provide long-range SAR services.

Numbers/Type: 3 Casa CN-235.
Operational speed: 210 kts *(384 km/h)*.
Service ceiling: 24 000 ft *(7315 m)*.
Range: 2000 nm *(3218 km)*.
Role/Weapon systems: EEZ surveillance. First delivered in June 1992 with two more in 1993/94. Sensors: Search radar Bendix APS 504(V)5; FLIR. Weapons: Unarmed.

AUXILIARIES

Notes: (1) In addition there are a number of mostly civilian manned auxiliaries including: *Seabhac* a small tug acquired in 1983; *Fainleog*, *David F* (built in 1962) and *Fiachdubh* passenger craft, the last two taken over after lease in 1988 and the first in 1983; *Tailte* a Dufour 35 ft sail training yacht bought in 1979 and two elderly training yachts *Nancy Bet* and *Creidne*.
(2) *Gray Seal* (ex-*Seaforth Clansman*) and *Granuaile* are lighthouse tenders operated by the Commissioners of Irish Lights.

GRANUAILE   1993, Commissioners of Irish Lights

ISRAEL

Headquarters' Appointment

Commander-in-Chief:
  Rear Admiral Ami Ayalon

Personnel

(a) 1994: 6600 (900 officers) of whom 2500 are conscripts. Includes a Naval Commando
(b) 3 years' national service for Jews and Druzes

Note: An additional 4000 Reserves available on mobilisation.

Bases

Haifa, Ashdod, Eilat (approx seven Dabur class)
(The repair base at Eilat has a synchrolift)

Prefix to Ships' Names

INS (Israeli Naval Ship)

Strength of the Fleet

Type	Active	Building (Planned)
Patrol Submarines	3	2 (1)
Corvettes	2	1
Fast Attack Craft—Missile	19	—
Fast Attack Craft—Gun	12	4
Coastal Patrol Craft	22	—
LCTs	3	(2)
LCP	1	—
Auxiliaries	3	—

Mercantile Marine

Lloyd's Register of Shipping:
  59 vessels of 652 036 tons gross

DELETIONS

Patrol Forces

1991   1 Dvora, 10 Super Dvora (six to Chile, four to Fiji)
1992   *Shimrit, Livnit, Snapirit*
1993   *Soufa*

Amphibious Forces

1991   *Etzion Geuber, Shiqmona, Kessaraya*

Support Ship

1991   *Ma'oz*

SUBMARINES

3 GAL (VICKERS TYPE 540) CLASS

Name	No	Builders	Laid down	Launched	Commissioned
GAL	—	Vickers Ltd, Barrow	1973	2 Dec 1975	Jan 1977
TANIN	—	Vickers Ltd, Barrow	1974	25 Oct 1976	June 1977
RAHAV	—	Vickers Ltd, Barrow	1974	1977	Dec 1977

Displacement, tons: 420 surfaced; 600 dived
Dimensions, feet (metres): 146.7 × 15.4 × 12 *(45 × 4.7 × 3.7)*
Main machinery: Diesel-electric; 2 MTU 12V 483 AZ80 GA31L diesels; 1200 hp(m) *(882 kW)* sustained; 2 alternators; 810 kW; 1 motor; 1800 hp(m) *(1.32 MW)* sustained; 1 shaft
Speed, knots: 11 surfaced; 17 dived
Complement: 22

Missiles: SSM: McDonnell Douglas Sub Harpoon launched from torpedo tubes; active radar homing to 130 km *(70 nm)* at 0.9 Mach; warhead 227 kg.
Torpedoes: 8—21 in *(533 mm)* bow tubes. Honeywell NT 37E; active/passive homing to 20 km *(10.8 nm)* at 35 kts; warhead 150 kg. Total of 10 missiles and torpedoes can be embarked.
Countermeasures: ESM: Elisra NS 9034; radar warning.
Fire control: Tios System.
Radars: Surface search: Plessey; I band.
Sonars: Atlas Elektronik; hull and flank arrays; passive search and attack; medium/high frequency.

Programmes: A contract was signed by Vickers in April 1972.
Modernisation: Sub Harpoon and associated fire control equipment installed in 1983 and the NT 37E torpedoes replaced the obsolete Mk 37 in 1987-88. A local contract has been let to update sensors and fire control equipment. Atlas Elektronik is the most likely supplier of equipment.
Operational: These submarines are planned to remain in service even after the Dolphin class has commissioned. Painted blue/green to aid concealment in the central and eastern Mediterranean.

RAHAV   1988

0 + 2 (1) DOLPHIN CLASS

Displacement, tons: 1565 surfaced; 1720 dived
Dimensions, feet (metres): 188 × 22.3 × 20.3
(57.3 × 6.8 × 6.2)
Main machinery: 3 MTU 16V 396 SE 84 diesels; 4243 hp(m)
(3.12 MW) sustained; 3 alternators; 2.91 MW; 1 Siemens
motor; 3875 hp(m) *(2.85 MW)* sustained; 1 shaft; pump jet
Speed, knots: 20 dived; 11 snorting
Range, miles: 8000 at 8 kts surfaced; 420 at 8 kts dived
Complement: 30 (6 officers)

Torpedoes: 6—21 in *(533 mm)* bow tubes. 8 reloads.
Countermeasures: ESM: Radar warning.

Fire control: Atlas Elektronik ISUS 90-1 TCS.
Radars: Surface search.
Sonars: Atlas Elektronik CSU-90; hull-mounted; passive/active
search and attack.

Programmes: In mid-1988 Ingalls Shipbuilding Division of Litton
Corporation was chosen as the prime contractor for two IKL-
designed Dolphin class submarines to be built in West Germany with FMS funds by HDW in conjunction with Thyssen
Nordseewerke. Funds approved in July 1989 with an effective
contract date of January 1990 but the project was cancelled in
November 1990 due to pressures on defence funds. After the

Gulf War in April 1991 the contract was resurrected, this time
with German funding for two submarines with an option on a
third. First steel cut on 15 February 1992 at Kiel by HDW; the
hull moved to Emden for completion by TNSW starting in early
1994. The second hull is following the first by six months. Projected completion in 1997.
Structure: Diving depth, 350 m *(1150 ft)*. Similar to German
Type 212 in design but with a 'wet and dry' compartment for
underwater swimmers.
Operational: Endurance, 30 days. To be used for interdiction, surveillance and special boat operations.

CORVETTES

2 + 1 EILAT (SAAR 5) CLASS

Name	No	Builders	Laid down	Launched	Commissioned
EILAT	501	Ingalls, Pascagoula	24 Feb 1992	6 Feb 1993	Feb 1994
LAHAV	502	Ingalls, Pascagoula	25 Sep 1992	20 Aug 1993	May 1994
HANIT	503	Ingalls, Pascagoula	5 Apr 1993	May 1994	Nov 1994

Displacement, tons: 1075 standard; 1227 full load
Dimensions, feet (metres): 283.5 oa; 251.3 wl × 39 × 10.5
(86.4; 76.6 × 11.9 × 3.2)
Main machinery: CODOG; 1 GE LM 2500 gas turbine;
30 000 hp *(22.38 MW)* sustained; 2 MTU 12V 1163 TB82
diesels; 6600 hp(m) *(4.86 MW)* sustained; 2 shafts; KaMeWa
cp props
Speed, knots: 33 gas; 20 diesels. **Range, miles:** 3500 at 17 kts
Complement: 64 (16 officers) plus 10 (4 officers) aircrew

Missiles: SSM: 8 McDonnell Douglas Harpoon (2 quad) launchers ❶; active radar homing to 130 km *(70 nm)* at 0.9 Mach;
warhead 227 kg.
8 IAI Gabriel II ❷; radar or optical guidance; semi-active homing to 36 km *(19.4 nm)* at 0.7 Mach; warhead 75 kg. Probably
carry a reduced load.
SAM: 2 Israeli Industries Barak I (vertical launch) ❸; 2 × 32 cells;
command line of sight radar or optical guidance to 10 km
(5.5 nm) at 2 Mach; warhead 22 kg.
Guns: OTO Melara 3 in *(76 mm)*/62 compact ❹; 85° elevation;
85 rounds/minute to 16 km *(8.7 nm)*; weight of shell 6 kg.
The main gun is interchangeable with a Bofors 57 mm gun or
Vulcan Phalanx CIWS.
2 Sea Vulcan 25 mm CIWS ❺; range 1 km.
Torpedoes: 6—324 mm Mk 32 (2 triple) tubes ❻. Honeywell Mk
46; anti-submarine. Mounted in the superstructure.
Countermeasures: Decoys: 4 chaff launchers ❼; Nixie SLQ 25
towed torpedo decoy
ESM/ECM: Elisra NS 9003/5; intercept and jammer.
Combat data systems: ELBIT NTCCS using Elta EL/S 9000 com-
puters. Data link.
Fire control: 3 Elop MSIS optronic directors ❽.
Radars: Air search: Elta EL/M 2218S ❾; E/F band.

Surface search: Cardion SPS 55 ❿; I band.
Navigation: I band.
Fire control: 3 Elta EL/M 2221 GM STGR ⓫; I/K/J band. Only
one fitted initially.
Sonars: EDO Type 796 Mod 1; hull-mounted; search and attack;
medium frequency.
VDS or towed array (fitted for).

Helicopters: 1 Dauphin SA 366G ⓬.

Programmes: A design (QU-09-35) prepared by Israeli Shipyards, Haifa in conjunction with Ingalls Shipbuilding Division of
Litton Corporation which was authorised to act as main contractor using FMS funding. Contract awarded 8 February
1989. An option for a fourth is unlikely to be taken up. First of
class completed initial sea trials in October 1993 and was

delivered to Israel in early 1994 for combat system installation.
All are expected to be operational in 1995.
Structure: Steel hull and aluminium superstructure. Stealth features including resilient mounts for main machinery, and Prairie Masker Bubbler system. A secondary operations room is
fitted aft.
Operational: Endurance, 20 days. The main role will be to counter threats in main shipping routes. ICS-2 integrated communications system.
Opinion: The Israeli Navy wanted eight in two batches of four, so
updated versions of the Saar 4 class will replace some of the
other FAC hulls. Ton for ton *Eilat* is described as the most heavily armed ship in the world. The traditional Israeli lack of concern for topweight problems may cause difficulties in rough
weather, unless fuel tanks are kept topped up and the SSM
capacity is reduced.

EILAT   *(Scale 1 : 900), Ian Sturton*

EILAT (with Phalanx vice 76 mm gun)

10/1993, Ingalls

PATROL FORCES

Note: The *Shaldag* was launched by Israeli Shipyards on 25 December 1989. This is a 55 ton, 50 kt fast patrol boat demonstrator, which has not been taken into service by the Navy.

3 HETZ (SAAR 4.5) CLASS (FAST ATTACK CRAFT—MISSILE)

Name	Builders	Launched	Commissioned
ROMAT	Israel Shipyards, Haifa	30 Oct 1981	Oct 1981
KESHET	Israel Shipyards, Haifa	Oct 1982	Nov 1982
HETZ (ex-*Nirit*)	Israel Shipyards, Haifa	Oct 1990	Feb 1991

Displacement, tons: 488 full load
Dimensions, feet (metres): 202.4 × 24.9 × 8.2 *(61.7 × 7.6 × 2.5)*
Main machinery: 4 MTU/Bazán 16V 956 TB91 diesels; 15 000 hp(m) *(11.03 MW)* sustained;
   4 shafts
   4 MTU 16V 538 TB93 diesels; 16 600 hp(m) *(12.2 MW)*; 4 shafts *(Hetz)*
Speed, knots: 31. **Range, miles:** 3000 at 17 kts; 1500 at 30 kts
Complement: 53

Missiles: SSM: 8 McDonnell Douglas Harpoon; active radar homing to 130 km *(70 nm)* at
   0.9 Mach; warhead 227 kg.
   6 IAI Gabriel II; radar or optical guidance; semi-active radar plus anti-radiation homing to 36 km
   (19.4 nm) at 0.7 Mach; warhead 75 kg.
SAM: Israeli Industries Barak I (vertical launch); 32 cells in four 8 pack launchers; command line-of-
   sight radar or optical guidance to 10 km *(5.5 nm)* at 2 Mach; warhead 22 kg.
Guns: 1 OTO Melara 3 in *(76 mm)*/62; 85° elevation; 85 rounds/minute to 16 km *(8.7 nm)*; weight
   of shell 6 kg.
   2 Oerlikon 20 mm; 55° elevation; 800 rounds/minute to 2 km.
   1 General Electric/General Dynamics Vulcan Phalanx 6-barrelled 20 mm Mk 15; 3000 rounds/
   minute combined to 1.5 km anti-missile.
   2 or 4—12.7 mm (twin or quad) MGs.
Countermeasures: Decoys: 1—45 tube, 4—24 tube, 4 single tube chaff launchers.
ESM/ECM: Elisra NS 9003/5; intercept and jammer.
Combat data systems: IAI Reshet data link.
Fire control: Galileo OG 20 optical director; Elop MSIS optronic director.
Radars: Air/surface search: Thomson-CSF TH-D 1040 Neptune; G band.
Fire control: 2 Elta EL/M-2221 GM STGR; I/K/J band.

Programmes: *Hetz* started construction in 1984 as the fifth of the class but was not completed, as
   an economy measure. Taken in hand again in 1989 and fitted out as the trials ship for some of the
   systems installed in the Eilat class.
Modernisation: *Romat* and *Keshet* modernised to same standard as *Hetz*. One taken in hand in
   September 1991 and completed in early 1993, second completes in 1994/95.
Structure: The CIWS is mounted in the eyes of the ship replacing the 40 mm gun. The four 8 pack
   Barak launchers are fully containerised and require no deck penetration or onboard maintenance. They are fitted aft in place of two of the Gabriel launchers. The fire control system for Barak
   is fitted on the platform aft of the bridge on the port side. *Hetz* has more powerful engines which
   may have been fitted to the other two but this is unlikely.

HETZ   *1991, Israel Shipyards*

2 ALIYA (SAAR 4.5) CLASS (FAST ATTACK CRAFT—MISSILE)

Name	Builders	Launched	Commissioned
ALIYA	Israel Shipyards, Haifa	11 July 1980	Aug 1980
GEOULA	Israel Shipyards, Haifa	Oct 1980	31 Dec 1980

Displacement, tons: 498 full load
Dimensions, feet (metres): 202.4 × 24.9 × 8.2 *(61.7 × 7.6 × 2.5)*
Main machinery: 4 MTU/Bazán 16V 956 TB91 diesels; 15 000 hp(m) *(11.03 MW)* sustained;
   4 shafts
Speed, knots: 31. **Range, miles:** 3000 at 17 kts; 1500 at 30 kts
Complement: 53

Missiles: SSM: 4 McDonnell Douglas Harpoon; active radar homing to 130 km *(70 nm)* at
   0.9 Mach; warhead 227 kg.
   4 IAI Gabriel II; radar or optical guidance; semi-active radar plus anti-radiation homing to 36 km
   (19.4 nm) at 0.7 Mach; warhead 75 kg.
Guns: 2 Oerlikon 20 mm; 55° elevation; 800 rounds/minute to 2 km.
   1 General Electric/General Dynamics Vulcan Phalanx 6-barrelled 20 mm Mk 15; 3000 rounds/
   minute combined to 1.5 km anti-missile.
   2 or 4—12.7 mm (twin or quad) MGs.
Countermeasures: Decoys: 1—45 tube, 4—24 tube, 4 single tube chaff launchers.
ESM/ECM: Elisra NS 9003/5; intercept and jammer.
Combat data systems: IAI Reshet data link.
Radars: Air/surface search: Thomson-CSF TH-D 1040 Neptune; G band.
Fire control: Selenia Orion RTN-10X; I/J band.

Helicopters: 1 SA 366G Dauphin.

Programmes: First two of the class of five.
Structure: The CIWS mounted in the eyes of the ship replaced the 40 mm gun. Three others of the
   class have been extensively modernised.
Operational: The Hellstar RPV project has been cancelled.

GEOULA   *7/1993*

ALIYA   *7/1993*

8 RESHEF (SAAR 4) CLASS (FAST ATTACK CRAFT—MISSILE)

Name	Builders	Launched	Commissioned
RESHEF	Israel Shipyards, Haifa	19 Feb 1973	Apr 1973
KIDON	Israel Shipyards, Haifa	4 July 1974	Sep 1974
TARSHISH	Israel Shipyards, Haifa	17 Jan 1975	Mar 1975
YAFFO	Israel Shipyards, Haifa	3 Feb 1975	Apr 1975
NITZHON	Israel Shipyards, Haifa	10 July 1978	Sep 1978
ATSMOUT	Israel Shipyards, Haifa	3 Dec 1978	Feb 1979
MOLEDET	Israel Shipyards, Haifa	22 Mar 1979	May 1979
KOMEMIUT	Israel Shipyards, Haifa	19 July 1978	Aug 1980

Displacement, tons: 415 standard; 450 full load
Dimensions, feet (metres): 190.6 × 25 × 8 *(58 × 7.8 × 2.4)*
Main machinery: 4 MTU/Bazán 16V 956 TB91 diesels; 15 000 hp(m) *(11.03 MW)* sustained; 4 shafts
Speed, knots: 32. **Range, miles:** 1650 at 30 kts; 4000 at 17.5 kts
Complement: 45

Missiles: SSM: 2-4 McDonnell Douglas Harpoon (twin or quad) launchers; active radar homing to 130 km *(70 nm)* at 0.9 Mach; warhead 227 kg.
4-6 Gabriel II or III; radar or TV optical guidance; semi-active radar plus anti-radiation homing to 36 km *(20 nm)* at 0.7 Mach; warhead 75 kg.
Harpoons fitted with Israeli homing systems. The Gabriel II system carries a TV camera which can transmit a homing picture to the firing ship beyond the radar horizon. The missile fit currently varies in training boats—2 Harpoon, 5 Gabriel II.
Guns: 1 or 2 OTO Melara 3 in *(76 mm)*/62 compact; 85° elevation; 85 rounds/minute to 16 km *(8.7 nm)*; weight of shell 6 kg. Adapted for shore bombardment.
2 Oerlikon 20 mm; 55° elevation; 800 rounds/minute to 2 km.
1 General Electrics/General Dynamics Vulcan Phalanx 6-barrelled 20 mm Mk 15; 3000 rounds/minute combined to 1.5 km anti-missile.
2—12.7 mm MGs.
Countermeasures: Decoys: 1—45 tube, 4 or 6—24 tube, 4 single tube chaff launchers.
ESM: Elta MN-53; intercept.
ECM: Jammer.
Combat data systems: IAI Reshet data link.
Radars: Air/surface search: Thomson-CSF TH-D 1040 Neptune; G band; range 33 km *(18 nm)* for 2 m² target.
Fire control: Selenia Orion RTN 10X; I/J band; range 40 km *(22 nm)*.
Sonars: EDO 780; VDS; occasionally fitted in some of the class.

Modernisation: *Tarshish* had her after 76 mm gun removed to make way for a helicopter platform, a temporary trial in 1979. The first two being fully modernised are *Reshef* and *Tarshish*, and many of the *Hetz* modifications are included as well as the Barak SAM system. At least four others may be taken in hand sequentially when the first two complete in 1995. Gabriel III SSM did not go into production.
Operational: This very interesting class has a long range at cruising speed, two pairs having made the passage from Israel to the Red Sea via the Strait of Gibraltar and Cape of Good Hope, relying only on refuelling at sea. This is a tribute not only to their endurance but also to their seakeeping qualities. All now deployed in Mediterranean.
Sales: Eight built for South Africa in Haifa and Durban. One transferred to Chile late 1979 and one in February 1981.

YAFFO   *7/1993*

12 SUPER DVORA CLASS (FAST ATTACK CRAFT—GUN)

810-821

Displacement, tons: 54 full load
Dimensions, feet (metres): 71 × 18 × 5.9 screws *(21.6 × 5.5 × 1.8)*
Main machinery: 2 Detroit 16V-92TA diesels; 1380 hp *(1.03 MW)* sustained; 2 shafts (Mk I and II)
3 Detroit 16V-92TA diesels; 2070 hp *(1.54 MW)* sustained; 3 shafts (Mk III)
Speed, knots: 36 or 46 (Mk III). **Range, miles:** 1200 at 17 kts
Complement: 9 (1 officer)

Guns: 2 Oerlikon 20 mm/80. 2—12.7 or 7.62 mm MGs. 1—84 mm rocket launcher.
Depth charges: 2 racks.
Fire control: Elop MSIS optronic director.
Radars: Surface search: Raytheon; I band.

Programmes: A further improvement on the Dabur design ordered in March 1987 from Israel Aircraft Industries (RAMTA). First started trials in November 1988, and first two commissioned in June 1989. Remainder following at about three per year to 1993. Now only building for export.
Structure: All gun armament and improved speed and endurance compared with the prototype Dvora. SSM, depth charges, torpedoes or a 130 mm MRL can be fitted if required. The first 10 are probably fitted with twin diesels; the much faster Mk III version coming in at hull number 11. All are to be modified to take three engines in due course.
Sales: The Mk III version is being deployed to the US to bid for the USN Mk V SEALS contract planned for FY 1993. Six sold to Sri Lanka in 1988 and six more to Eritrea in 1993.

SUPER DVORA   *10/1992, Erik Laursen*

6 MIVTACH (SAAR 2) CLASS (FAST ATTACK CRAFT—MISSILE)

Name	No	Builders	Commissioned
Saar 2			
MIVTACH	311	CMN, Cherbourg	1968
MIZNAG	312	CMN, Cherbourg	1968
MIFGAV	313	CMN, Cherbourg	1968
EILATH	321	CMN, Cherbourg	1968
HAIFA	322	CMN, Cherbourg	1968
AKKO	323	CMN, Cherbourg	1968

Displacement, tons: 220 standard; 250 full load
Dimensions, feet (metres): 147.6 × 23 × 8.2 *(45 × 7 × 2.5)*
Main machinery: 4 MTU MD 16V 538 TB90 diesels; 12 000 hp(m) *(8.82 MW)* sustained; 4 shafts
Speed, knots: 40+. **Range, miles:** 2500 at 15 kts; 1600 at 20 kts; 1000 at 30 kts
Complement: 35-40 (5 officers)

Missiles: SSM: 2 or 4 McDonnell Douglas Harpoon; active radar homing to 130 km *(70 nm)* at 0.9 Mach; warhead 227 kg. Harpoon is replacing Gabriel to reduce top weight.
5 IAI Gabriel II; active radar or optical guidance; semi-active radar homing to 36 km *(19.4 nm)* at 0.7 Mach; warhead 75 kg.
Guns: 1 OTO Melara 3 in *(76 mm)*/62 DP; 85° elevation; 65 rounds/minute to 8 km *(4.4 nm)*; weight of shell 6 kg.
1-3 Breda 40 mm/70; 85° elevation; 300 rounds/minute to 4 km *(2.2 nm)* anti-aircraft; weight of shell 0.96 kg (see *Operational*).
2 or 4—12.7 mm MGs.
Torpedoes: 2 or 4—324 mm Mk 32 tubes. Honeywell Mk 46; anti-submarine; active/passive homing to 11 km *(5.9 nm)* at 40 kts; warhead 44 kg.
Countermeasures: Decoys: 6—24 tube, 4 single tube chaff launchers.
ESM: Elta MN-53; intercept.
ECM: Jammer.
Combat data systems: IAI Reshet data link.
Radars: Air/surface search: Thomson-CSF TH-D 1040 Neptune; G band; range 33 km *(18 nm)* for 2 m² target. Being replaced.
Fire control: Selenia Orion RTN 10X; I/J band; range 40 km *(22 nm)*.
Sonars: EDO 780; VDS; active search and attack; 13.7 and 5 kHz.

Programmes: Built from designs by Lürssen Werft of Bremen. Political problems caused their building in France instead of West Germany. The last of the Saar 3 class is now a museum ship, and these six Saar 2 are all expected to pay off by the end of 1994.
Structure: Steel hulls and light alloy superstructure. The class suffers from top weight problems, being alleviated to some extent by substituting Harpoon for Gabriel and fitting a lightweight radar aerial.
Operational: Armament varies from one 40 mm gun and Harpoon or Gabriel missiles to three 40 mm guns and four A/S torpedo tubes plus VDS.
Sales: *Hanit* and *Hetz* (Saar 3 class) transferred to Chile in 1988.

SAAR 2 (with VDS)   *1990*

SAAR 2 (both with VDS, one with new radar aerial)   *10/1992, Erik Laursen*

22 DABUR CLASS (COASTAL PATROL CRAFT)

Displacement, tons: 39 full load
Dimensions, feet (metres): 64.9 × 18 × 5.8 *(19.8 × 5.5 × 1.8)*
Main machinery: 2 GM 12V-71TA diesels; 840 hp *(627 kW)* sustained; 2 shafts
  About 8 have more powerful GE engines.
Speed, knots: 19; 30 (GE engines). **Range, miles:** 450 at 13 kts
Complement: 6/9 depending on armament

Guns: 2 Oerlikon 20 mm; 55° elevation; 800 rounds/minute to 2 km.
  2—12.7 mm MGs. Carl Gustav 84 mm portable rocket launchers.
Torpedoes: 2—324 mm tubes. Honeywell Mk 46; anti-submarine; active/passive homing to 11 km *(5.9 nm)* at 40 kts; warhead 44 kg.
Depth charges: 2 racks in some.
Fire control: Elop optronic director.
Radars: Surface search: Decca Super 101 Mk 3; I band.
Sonars: Active search and attack; high frequency.

Programmes: Twelve built by Sewart Seacraft USA and remainder by Israel Aircraft Industries (RAMTA) between 1973 and 1977. Final total of 34.
Structure: Aluminium hull. Several variations in the armament. Up to eight of the class are fitted with more powerful General Electric engines to increase speed to 30 kts.
Operational: Deployed in the Mediterranean and Red Sea, these craft have been designed for overland transport. Good rough weather performance. Portable rocket launchers are carried for anti-terrorist purposes. Not considered fast enough to cope with modern terrorist speedboats and some have been sold as Super Dvoras commissioned.
Sales: Four to Argentina in 1978; four to Nicaragua in 1978; two to Sri Lanka in 1984; four to Fiji and six to Chile in 1991. Five also given to Lebanon Christian Militia in 1976 but these were returned.

DABUR 882   *5/1989, Rupert Pengelley*

SHIPBORNE AIRCRAFT

Notes: (1) Sea Panther helicopters are to be acquired when funds are available.
(2) IAI Hellstar programme cancelled in 1993.

Numbers/Type: 2 Aerospatiale SA 366G Dauphin.
Operational speed: 140 kts *(260 km/h)*.
Service ceiling: 15 000 ft *(4575 m)*.
Range: 410 nm *(758 km)*.
Role/Weapon systems: SAR/MR helicopter embarked for trials; primarily SAR/MR but growing submarine threat could mean upgrading. Sensors: Israeli-designed radar/FLIR systems. Integrated Elop MSIS for OTHT targeting. Weapons: Unarmed at present but plans for ASV/ASW.

DAUPHIN   *1986, Ofer Karni*

Numbers/Type: 6 Agusta AB 206B JetRanger.
Operational speed: 115 kts *(213 km/h)*.
Service ceiling: 13 500 ft *(4115 m)*.
Range: 368 nm *(682 km)*.
Role/Weapon systems: Liaison and limited SAR helicopter. Sensors: None. Weapons: Unarmed.

LAND-BASED MARITIME AIRCRAFT

Note: Army helicopters can be used including Cobras.

Numbers/Type: 25 Bell 212.
Operational speed: 100 kts *(185 km/h)*.
Service ceiling: 13 200 ft *(4025 m)*.
Range: 224 nm *(415 km)*.
Role/Weapon systems: SAR and coastal helicopter surveillance tasks undertaken. Sensors: IAI EW systems. Weapons: Unarmed except for self-defence machine guns.

Numbers/Type: 4 Grumman E-2C Hawkeye.
Operational speed: 269 kts *(499 km/h)*.
Service ceiling: 30 800 ft *(9390 m)*.
Range: 1350 nm *(2500 km)*.
Role/Weapon systems: Airborne early warning and control aircraft; operated for air defence and strike direction by the Air Force. Sensors: APS-125 radar, various EW systems. Weapons: Unarmed.

Numbers/Type: 3 IAI 1124 Sea Scan.
Operational speed: 471 kts *(873 km/h)*.
Service ceiling: 45 000 ft *(13 725 m)*.
Range: 2500 nm *(4633 km)*.
Role/Weapon systems: Coastal surveillance tasks with long endurance; used for intelligence gathering. Sensors: Include radar, IFF, MAD and various EW systems of IAI manufacture.

AMPHIBIOUS FORCES

Notes: (1) Two new construction landing ships are planned by the Navy to transport large numbers of troops. No funds available.
(2) A Ro-Ro ship *Queset* is used for research and development. Built in Japan in 1979 and formerly used as a general purpose cargo ship.

3 ASHDOD CLASS (LCTs)

Name	No	Builders	Commissioned
ASHDOD	61	Israel Shipyards, Haifa	1966
ASHKELON	63	Israel Shipyards, Haifa	1967
ACHZIV	65	Israel Shipyards, Haifa	1967

Displacement, tons: 400 standard; 730 full load
Dimensions, feet (metres): 205.5 × 32.8 × 5.8 *(62.7 × 10 × 1.8)*
Main machinery: 3 MWM diesels; 1900 hp(m) *(1.4 MW)*; 3 shafts
Speed, knots: 10.5
Complement: 20
Guns: 2 Oerlikon 20 mm.

Comment: At least one has a helicopter deck aft. *Ashdod* is used as a trials ship for Barak VLS.

ASHDOD   *1989*

1 LCP TYPE

Displacement, tons: 24 full load
Dimensions, feet (metres): 52.5 × 14.4 × 5.6 *(16 × 4.4 × 1.7)*
Main machinery: 2 Saturn gas turbines; 2000 hp *(1.49 MW)*; 2 shafts
Speed, knots: 35
Complement: 8
Military lift: 22 troops; 1 ton equipment
Guns: 2—12.7 mm MGs.

Comment: The survivor of four transferred from US in 1968. Used for swimmer operations.

AUXILIARIES

Note: Two former merchant ships *Nir* and *Naharya* are used as alongside tenders for patrol craft in Haifa and Eilat respectively.

1 BAT SHEVA CLASS (TRANSPORT)

Name	No	Builders	Commissioned
BAT SHEVA	—	Netherlands	1967

Displacement, tons: 1150 full load
Dimensions, feet (metres): 311.7 × 36.7 × 26.9 *(95.1 × 11.2 × 8.2)*
Main machinery: 2 diesels; 2 shafts
Speed, knots: 10
Complement: 26
Guns: 4 Oerlikon 20 mm. 4—12.7 mm MGs.

Comment: Purchased from South Africa in 1968. Has a landing craft bow.

ITALY

Headquarters' Appointments

Chief of Defence Staff:
  Admiral Guido Venturoni
Chief of Naval Staff:
  Admiral Angelo Mariani
Vice Chief of Naval Staff:
  Admiral Umberto Guarnieri
Chief of Naval Personnel:
  Vice Admiral Paolo Giardini
Chief of Procurement and Technical Support:
  Engineer Admiral Alberto Pacini

Flag Officers

*Commander, Allied Naval Forces, Southern Europe (Naples) and
Commander-in-Chief Basso Tirreno:*
  Admiral Mario Angeli
Commander-in-Chief of Fleet (and Comedcent):
  Admiral Antonio Stagliano
Commander-in-Chief Alto Tirreno (La Spezia):
  Admiral Gianfranco Ginesi
Commander-in-Chief Adriatico (Ancona):
  Vice Admiral Achille Zanoni
Commander-in-Chief dello Jonio e Canale d'Otranto (Taranto):
  Admiral Alfeo Battelli
Commander Sicilian Naval Area (Messina):
  Vice Admiral Umberto Battigelli
Commander Sardinian Naval Area (La Maddalena):
  Vice Admiral Franco di Girolamo
Commander Submarine Force:
  Captain Francesco Ricci
1st Naval Division:
  Rear Admiral Piero del Bianco
2nd Naval Division:
  Rear Admiral Paolo Mancinelli
3rd Naval Division:
  Rear Admiral Elio Bolongaro
Naval Commandos and Special Naval Group (La Spezia):
  Vice Admiral Vezio Vascotto
Mine Countermeasures Force:
  Captain Franco Eccher
Naval Training Command:
  Rear Admiral Mario Lucidi
Naval Air Arm:
  Rear Admiral Filippo Pascali
Commander Marines:
  Captain Carlo Saudella

Diplomatic Representation

Naval Attaché in Bonn:
  Captain Attilio Panella-Fabrello
Naval Attaché in London:
  Rear Admiral Mario Maguolo
Naval Attaché in Moscow:
  Captain Franco Paoli
Naval Attaché in Paris:
  Captain Alessandro Valentini
Naval Attaché in Washington:
  Captain Luciano Callini

Bases

Main—La Spezia (Alto Tirreno), Taranto (Jonio e Canale d'Otranto)
Regional—Ancona (Adriatico), Naples (Basso Tirreno)
Secondary—Brindisi, Augusta, Messina, La Maddalena, Cagliari, Venice

Organisation

Name	Base	Units
First Division	La Spezia	Major warships
Second Division	Taranto	Major warships
Third Division	Brindisi	Amphibious ships; Hydrofoils
Submarine Command	Taranto	Submarines
Mine Countermeasures Command	La Spezia	MCMVs

In addition there is a 'Special Force and Underwater Swimmers (COMSUBIN)' including Commandos plus support and minor craft, located near La Spezia. The former Auxiliary Force has been disbanded.

Strength of the Fleet

Type	Active	Building (Planned)
Submarines	9	1 (2)
Light Aircraft Carrier	1	(1)
Cruisers	1	—
Destroyers	4	(2)
Frigates	14	4
Corvettes	9	—
Offshore Patrol Vessels	10	4
Hydrofoils—Missile	6	—
LPDs	3	—
LCM/LCVP	39	—
Minehunters/sweepers	10	2
Minehunters (Coastal)	5	—
Survey/Research Ships	7	(2)
Replenishment Tankers	2	1
Harbour Tankers	7	—
Fleet Support Ship	1	—
Coastal Transports	8	—
Sail Training Ships	7	—
Training Ships	5	—
Lighthouse Tenders	5	—
Salvage Ships	2	—
Repair Ships	5	—
Large Water Carriers	13	—
Tugs	51	—
Floating Docks	14	—

Personnel

(a) 1994: 44 360 (4680 officers)
(b) 1 year's national service (about 17 000 of the Navy are conscripts)

Naval Air Arm—Planned strength and deployment

2 LRMP Squadrons—Bréguet Atlantique (No 41, Catania; No 30, Cagliari/Elmas); operated by Navy with Air Force support and maintenance
2 SH-3D/H helicopter squadrons (1st and 3rd based at Luni and Catania respectively)
3 AB-212 helicopter squadrons (2nd, 4th and 5th based at Luni, Taranto and Catania respectively)
1 AV-8B Harrier II squadron at Grottaglie, Taranto (2 TAV-8B plus 16 AV-8B)

Mercantile Marine

Lloyd's Register of Shipping:
  1548 vessels of 7 030 237 tons gross

DELETIONS

Submarines

1991 *Attilio Bagnolini*
1992 *Lazzaro Mocenigo*

Cruisers

1991 *Caio Duilio*
1992 *Andrea Doria*

Destroyers

1991 *Intrepido*
1992 *Impavido*

Corvettes

1992 *Aquila, Alcione* (harbour training), *Airone* (harbour training), *Licio Visintini*
1993 *Umberto Grosso*
1994 *Salvatore Todaro*

Patrol Forces

1991 *Sparviero*

Mine Warfare Forces

1991 *Frassino, Timo, Vischio*
1992 *Loto, Alloro, Gelsomino*
1993 *Mandorlo*

Auxiliaries

1991 *Arzachena* (tug), *Ustica* (tug), *Quarto, Alicudi, MOC 1207*
1992 *MTC 1001, MTC 1006*
1993 *Mincio, Alloro, Cristoforo Colombo II* (not completed), *Tarantola* (ferry)

PENNANT LIST

Submarines

S 506	Enrico Toti
S 513	Enrico Dandolo
S 518	Nazario Sauro
S 519	Fecia di Cossato
S 520	Leonardo da Vinci
S 521	Guglielmo Marconi
S 522	Salvatore Pelosi
S 523	Giuliano Prini
S 524	Primo Longobardo
S 525	Gianfranco Gazzana
	Priaroggia (bldg)

Light Aircraft Carrier

C 551	Giuseppe Garibaldi

Cruiser

C 550	Vittorio Veneto

Destroyers

D 550	Ardito
D 551	Audace
D 560	Luigi Durand de la Penne
D 561	Francesco Mimbelli

Frigates

F 564	Lupo
F 565	Sagittario
F 566	Perseo
F 567	Orsa
F 570	Maestrale
F 571	Grecale
F 572	Libeccio
F 573	Scirocco
F 574	Aliseo
F 575	Euro
F 576	Espero
F 577	Zeffiro
F 580	Alpino
F 581	Carabiniere
F 582	Artigliere
F 583	Aviere
F 584	Bersagliere
F 585	Granatiere

Corvettes

F 550	De Cristofaro
F 551	Minerva
F 552	Urania
F 553	Danaide
F 554	Sfinge
F 555	Driade
F 556	Chimera
F 557	Fenice
F 558	Sibilla

Patrol Forces

P 401	Cassiopea
P 402	Libra
P 403	Spica
P 404	Vega
P 495	Bambù
P 496	Mango
P 497	Mogano
P 500	Palma
P —	Storione
P —	Squalo
P 421	Nibbio
P 422	Falcone
P 423	Astore
P 424	Grifone
P 425	Gheppio
P 426	Condor

Minehunters

M 5504	Castagno
M 5505	Cedro
M 5509	Gelso
M 5516	Platano
M 5550	Lerici
M 5551	Sapri
M 5552	Milazzo
M 5553	Vieste
M 5554	Gaeta
M 5555	Termoli
M 5556	Alghero
M 5557	Numana
M 5558	Crotone
M 5559	Viareggio
M 5560	Chioggia (bldg)
M 5561	Rimini (bldg)

Amphibious Forces

L 9892	San Giorgio
L 9893	San Marco
L 9894	San Giusto

Survey and Research Ships

A 5303	Ammiraglio Magnaghi
A 5305	Murena
A 5306	Mirto
A 5307	Pioppo
A 5315	Raffaele Rossetti
A 5320	Vincenzo Martellotta
P 492	Barbara

Auxiliaries

A 5301	Pietro Cavezzale
A 5302	Caroly
A 5304	Alicudi
A 5309	Anteo
A 5310	Proteo
A 5311	Palinuro
A 5312	Amerigo Vespucci
A 5313	Stella Polare
A 5316	Corsaro II
A 5317	Atlante
A 5318	Prometeo
A 5319	Ciclope
A 5322	Capricia
A 5324	Titano
A 5325	Polifemo
A 5327	Stromboli
A 5328	Gigante
A 5329	Vesuvio
A 5330	Saturno
A 5331-5	MOC 1201-5
A 5347	Gorgona
A 5348	Tremiti
A 5349	Caprera
A 5351	Pantelleria
A 5352	Lipari
A 5353	Capri
A 5354	Piave
A 5356	Basento
A 5357	Bradano
A 5358	Brenta
A 5359	Bormida
A 5364	Ponza
A 5365	Tenace
A 5366	Levanzo
A 5367	Tavolara
A 5368	Palmaria
A 5370-3	MCC 1101-4
A 5375	Simeto
A 5376	Ticino
A 5377	Tirso
A 5378	Aragosta
A 5379	Astice
A 5380	Mitilo
A 5381	Polipo
A 5382	Porpora
A 5383	Procida
Y 413	Porto Fossone
Y 416	Porto Torres
Y 417	Porto Corsini
Y 421	Porto Empedocle
Y 422	Porto Pisano
Y 423	Porto Conte
Y 425	Portoferraio
Y 426	Portovenere
Y 428	Porto Salvo
Y 436	Porto d'Ischia
Y 443	Riva Trigoso
Y 498	Mario Marino
Y 499	Alcide Pedretti

SUBMARINES

0 +(2) TYPE S 90 CLASS

Displacement, tons: 2500 surfaced; 2780 dived
Dimensions, feet (metres): 228.7 × 26.9 × 20.1
  (69.7 × 8.2 × 6.3)
Main machinery: Diesel-electric; 3 Fincantieri GMT 210.16 SM
  diesels; 6400 hp(m) *(4.7 MW)* sustained; 1 motor; 6000 hp
  (m) *(4.41 MW)*; 1 shaft
Speed, knots: 20 dived; 11 surfaced
Range, miles: 6000 at 6 kts dived
Complement: 50 (8 officers)

Torpedoes: 6—21 in *(533 mm)* bow tubes. Total of 24 missiles,
  guided and unguided torpedoes.
Radars: Navigation: I band.
Sonars: Conformal bow, flank and towed arrays.

Programmes: The programme is uncertain because overall submarine numbers have been cut from 10 to eight. The characteristics shown above are still subject to the completion of
  Project Definition in 1995. The original plan was to order in
  1993 for completion in 1998, but this has been delayed by at
  least three years.

Structure: Diving depth is expected to be about 400 m *(1300 ft)*.
  This is to be a high performance conventional submarine and
  although gaseous storage toroidal designs have been tested in
  midget submarines built by Maritalia and the concept could be
  applied to larger (2800 or 1400 ton) submarines, this technology will not be incorporated in the S 90. Some form of Air
  Independent Propulsion (AIP) is likely to be included in the
  design. The submarine will have a single periscope and an
  optronic mast.

3 + 1 IMPROVED SAURO CLASS

Name	No	Builders	Laid down	Launched	Commissioned
SALVATORE PELOSI	S 522	Fincantieri, Monfalcone	24 May 1984	29 Dec 1986	14 July 1988
GIULIANO PRINI	S 523	Fincantieri, Monfalcone	30 May 1985	12 Dec 1987	11 Nov 1989
PRIMO LONGOBARDO	S 524	Fincantieri, Monfalcone	19 Dec 1991	20 June 1992	14 Dec 1993
GIANFRANCO GAZZANA PRIAROGGIA	S 525	Fincantieri, Monfalcone	12 Nov 1992	26 June 1993	Sep 1994

Displacement, tons: 1476 (1653, S 524-5) surfaced; 1662
  (1862, S 524-5) dived
Dimensions, feet (metres): 211.2 (217.8 S 524-5) × 22.3 ×
  18.4 *(64.4 (66.4) × 6.8 × 5.6)*
Main machinery: Diesel-electric; 3 Fincantieri GMT 210.16 SM
  diesels; 6400 hp(m) *(4.7 MW)* sustained; 3 alternators;
  2.16 MW; 1 motor; 4270 hp(m) *(3.14 MW)*; 1 shaft
Speed, knots: 11 surfaced; 19 dived; 12 snorting
Range, miles: 11 000 at 11 kts surfaced; 250 at 4 kts dived
Complement: 45 (7 officers)

Missiles: Capability to launch Harpoon being considered.
Torpedoes: 6—21 in *(533 mm)* bow tubes. 12 Whitehead A184;
  dual purpose; wire-guided; active/passive homing to 25 km
  (13.7 nm) at 24 kts; 17 km *(9.2 nm)* at 38 kts; warhead
  250 kg. Swim-out discharge.
Countermeasures: ESM: Elettronica BLD-727; radar warning; 2
  aerials—1 on a mast, second in search periscope.
Fire control: SMA BSN 716(V)2; SACTIS including Link 11
  (receive only).
Radars: Search/navigation: SMA BPS 704; I band; also periscope radar for attack ranging.
Sonars: Selenia Elsag IPD 70/S; linear passive array;
  200 Hz-7.5 kHz; active and UWT transducers in bow (15 kHz).
  Selenia Elsag MD 100S; passive ranging.

PRIMO LONGOBARDO   *8/1993, Giorgio Ghiglione*

Programmes: The first two were ordered in March 1983 and the
  second pair in July 1988.
Structure: Pressure hull of HY 80 steel with a central bulkhead
  for escape purposes. Diving depth, 300 m *(985 ft)* (test) and
  600 m *(1970 ft)* (crushing). The second pair have a slightly
  longer hull.
  Periscopes: Kollmorgen; S 76 Mod 322 with laser rangefinder

and ESM—attack; S 76 Mod 323 with radar rangefinder and
ESM—search. Wave contour snort head has a very low radar
profile. The last pair have anechoic tiles and are to be fitted
with clip-on towed sonar arrays in due course.
Operational: Litton Italia PL 41 inertial navigation; Ferranti auto-
pilot Omega and Transit. Endurance, 45 days possibly
increased in second pair.

4 SAURO (TYPE 1081) CLASS

Name	No	Builders	Laid down	Launched	Commissioned
NAZARIO SAURO	S 518	Italcantieri, Monfalcone	27 June 1974	9 Oct 1976	12 Feb 1980
FECIA DI COSSATO	S 519	Italcantieri, Monfalcone	15 Nov 1975	16 Nov 1977	5 Nov 1979
LEONARDO DA VINCI	S 520	Italcantieri, Monfalcone	8 June 1978	20 Oct 1979	23 Oct 1981
GUGLIELMO MARCONI	S 521	Italcantieri, Monfalcone	23 Oct 1979	20 Sep 1980	11 Sep 1982

Displacement, tons: 1456 surfaced; 1631 dived
Dimensions, feet (metres): 210 × 22.5 × 18.9
  (63.9 × 6.8 × 5.7)
Main machinery: Diesel-electric; 3 Fincantieri GMT 210.16 NM
  diesels; 3350 hp(m) *(2.46 MW)* sustained; 3 alternators;
  2.16 MW; 1 motor; 3210 hp(m) *(2.36 MW)*; 1 shaft
Speed, knots: 11 surfaced; 19 dived; 12 snorting
Range, miles: 11 000 surfaced at 11 kts; 250 dived at 4 kts
Complement: 45 (7 officers) plus 4 trainees

Torpedoes: 6—21 in *(533 mm)* bow tubes. 12 Whitehead A184;
  dual purpose; wire-guided; active/passive homing to 25 km
  (13.7 nm) at 24 kts; 17 km *(9.2 nm)* at 38 kts; warhead
  250 kg. Swim-out discharge.
Countermeasures: ESM: Elettronica BLD 726; radar warning.
Fire control: SMA BSN 716(V)1; SACTIS data processing and
  computer-based TMA. CCRG FCS.
Radars: Search/navigation: SMA BPS 704; I band.
Sonars: Selenia Elsag IPD 70/S; linear passive array;
  200 Hz-7.5 kHz; active and UWT transducers in bow (15 kHz).
  Selenia Elsag MD 100; passive ranging.
  Thomson Sintra towed array *(Nazario Sauro)*; passive; low
  frequency.

Programmes: Two of this class were originally ordered in 1967
  but were cancelled in the following year. Reinstated in the

LEONARDO DA VINCI   *9/1993, Marina Fraccaroli*

building programme in 1972. Second pair provided for in
Legge Navale and ordered 12 February 1976.
The discrepancy in commissioning dates of *N Sauro* and *F di
Cossato* was due to problems over the main batteries. *F di Cossato* was provided with a new CGA battery which was satisfactory. *N Sauro* was then similarly fitted.
Modernisation: All modernised. *Fecia di Cossato* in 1990, *Nazario Sauro* in 1991, *Guglielmo Marconi* in 1992 and *Leonardo
da Vinci* in 1993. New batteries have greater capacity, some

auxiliary machinery replaced and habitability improved. A
clip-on towed array is being evaluated in *Nazario Sauro*.
Structure: Diving depth, 300 m *(985 ft)* (max) and 250 m
(820 ft) (normal). Periscopes: Pilkington Optronics CK 31
search and CH 81 attack.
Operational: Endurance, 35 days. Reliability improved by the
mid-life modernisation programme. *Leonardo da Vinci* damaged in a dived collision with *Ardito* in 1992.

2 TOTI (TYPE 1075) CLASS

Name	No	Builders	Laid down	Launched	Commissioned
ENRICO TOTI	S 506	Italcantieri, Monfalcone	15 Apr 1965	12 Mar 1967	22 Jan 1968
ENRICO DANDOLO	S 513	Italcantieri, Monfalcone	10 Mar 1967	16 Dec 1967	25 Sep 1968

Displacement, tons: 460 standard; 524 surfaced; 582 dived
Dimensions, feet (metres): 151.5 × 15.4 × 13.1
  (46.2 × 4.7 × 4)
Main machinery: Diesel-electric; 2 Fiat/MTU 12V 493 TY7 diesels; 2200 hp(m) *(1.62 MW)* sustained; 2 alternators;
  1.08 MW; 1 motor; 2200 hp(m) *(1.62 MW)*; 1 shaft
Speed, knots: 14 surfaced; 15 dived. **Range, miles:** 3000 at
  5 kts surfaced
Complement: 26 (4 officers)

Torpedoes: 4—21 in *(533 mm)* bow tubes. 6 Whitehead A184;
  dual purpose; wire-guided; active/passive homing to 25 km
  (13.7 nm) at 24 kts; 17 km *(9.2 nm)* at 38 kts; warhead
  250 kg.
Countermeasures: ESM: BPR-2; radar warning.
Fire control: Selenia IPD 64 TFCS.
Radars: Search/navigation: SMA 3RM 20A/SMG; I band.
Sonars: Selenia Elsag IPD 64; passive/active search and attack;
  medium frequency.
  Selenia Elsag MD 64; passive ranging.

Programmes: Italy's first indigenously built submarines after the
  Second World War. First of class paid off to reserve in July

ENRICO TOTI   *6/1993, van Ginderen Collection*

1990. Second of class *Enrico Toti* paid off in 1991 but was reactivated and taken back into service 1 April 1992, when the
fourth of the class was deleted. The two survivors will pay off in

1995 when the second pair of Improved Sauro class are fully
operational.
Structure: Diving depth, 180 m *(600 ft)*.

AIRCRAFT CARRIERS

Note: A second carrier is a high priority naval project. The design might be about 16 000 tons with twin funnels and include two VLS Aster 15 SAAM silos and three CIWS mountings. An amphibious role might also be included with extra berths for marines, two LCVPs on davits, Rigid Raiders and a stern well dock.

1 + (1) GARIBALDI CLASS

Name	No	Builders	Laid down	Launched	Commissioned
GIUSEPPE GARIBALDI	C 551	Italcantieri, Monfalcone	26 Mar 1981	4 June 1983	9 Aug 1987

Displacement, tons: 10 100 standard; 13 370 full load
Dimensions, feet (metres): 591 × 110.2 × 22
  (180 × 33.4 × 6.7)
Flight deck, feet (metres): 570.2 × 99.7 *(173.8 × 30.4)*
Main machinery: COGAG; 4 Fiat/GE LM 2500 gas turbines;
  81 000 hp *(60 MW)* sustained; 2 shafts
Speed, knots: 30. **Range, miles:** 7000 at 20 kts
Complement: 550 ship plus 230 air group (accommodation for
  825 including Flag and staff)

Missiles: SSM: 4 OTO Melara Teseo Mk 2 (TG 2) ❶; active radar
  homing to 180 km *(98.4 nm)* at 0.9 Mach; warhead 210 kg;
  sea-skimmer for last 4 km *(2.2 nm)*.
  SAM: 2 Selenia Elsag Albatros octuple launchers ❷; 48 Aspide;
  semi-active radar homing to 13 km *(7 nm)* at 2.5 Mach; height
  envelope 15-5000 m *(49.2-16 405 ft)*; warhead 30 kg.
Guns: 6 Breda 40 mm/70 (3 twin) MB ❸; 85° elevation; 300
  rounds/minute to 12.5 km *(6.8 nm)* anti-surface; 4 km
  (2.2 nm) anti-aircraft; weight of shell 0.96 kg.
Torpedoes: 6—324 mm B-515 (2 triple) tubes ❹. Honeywell Mk
  46; anti-submarine; active/passive homing to 11 km *(5.9 nm)*
  at 40 kts; warhead 44 kg. Being replaced by new A 290.
Countermeasures: Decoys: AN/SLQ 25 Nixie; noisemaker.
  2 Breda SCLAR 105 mm 20-barrelled launchers; trains and
  elevates; chaff to 5 km *(2.7 nm)*; illuminants to 12 km *(6.6 nm)*.
  ESM/ECM: Elettronica Nettuno SLQ 732; integrated intercept
  and jamming system.
Combat data systems: IPN 20 (SADOC 2) action data auto-
  mation including Links 11 and 14. SATCOM ❺.
Fire control: 3 NA 30 electro-optical backup for SAM. 3 Dardo
  NA21 for guns.
Radars: Long range air search: Hughes SPS 52C ❻; 3D; E/F
  band; range 440 km *(240 nm)*.
  Air search: Selenia SPS 768 (RAN 3L) ❼; D band; range 220 km
  (120 nm).
  SMA SPN 728; I band; range 73 km *(40 nm)*; TV indicator.
  Air/surface search: Selenia SPS 774 (RAN 10S) ❽; E/F band;
  range 155 km *(85 nm)*.
  Surface search/target indication: SMA SPS 702 UPX; 718 bea-
  con; I band.
  Navigation: SMA SPN 749(V)2; I band.
  Fire control: Three Selenia SPG 75 (RTN 30X) ❾; I/J band; range
  15 km *(8 nm)* (for Albatros).
  Three Selenia SPG 74 (RTN 20X) ❿; I/J band; range 13 km
  (7 nm) (for Dardo).
  CCA: Selenia SPN 728(V)1; I band.
  IFF: Mk XII. Tacan: SRN-15A.
Sonars: Raytheon DE 1160 LF; bow-mounted; active search;
  medium frequency.

Fixed wing aircraft: 16 AV-8B Harrier II.
Helicopters: 18 SH-3D Sea King helicopters (12 in hangar, 6 on
  deck). The total capacity is either 16 Harriers or 18 helicopters.
  In practice a combination is embarked.

Programmes: Contract awarded 21 November 1977. The design
  was changed considerably. Design work completed February
  1980 and engineering work began in March 1980. Started sea
  trials 3 December 1984. Refitted late 1986-January 1987. A
  sister ship, *Giuseppe Mazzini*, was to replace *Vittorio Veneto* in
  the mid-1990s. This project was suspended in 1990 but may
  be revived in a different design (see Note at head of page).
Structure: Six decks with 13 vertical watertight bulkheads. Fitted
  with 6.5° ski-jump and VSTOL operating equipment. Two 15
  ton lifts 18 × 10 m *(59 × 32.8 ft)*. Hangar size 110 × 15 × 6 m
  (361 × 49.2 × 19.7 ft). Has a slightly narrower flight deck than
  UK Invincible class. Two MEN class fast personnel launches
  (capacity 250) can be embarked for amphibious operations or
  disaster relief.

GIUSEPPE GARIBALDI   *8/1991, Giorgio Arra*

GIUSEPPE GARIBALDI   *8/1991, Giorgio Arra*

Operational: Fleet Flagship. The long-standing dispute between
  the Navy and the Air Force concerning the former's operation
  of fixed-wing aircraft (dating back to pre-World War II legislation) was finally resolved by legislation passed on 29 January
  1989. Embarked aircraft are operated by the Navy with the Air
  Force providing evaluation and maintenance and any
  additional pilots required. Two trainer TAV-8B aircraft acquired
  in early 1991. First operational aircraft embarked in 1993.

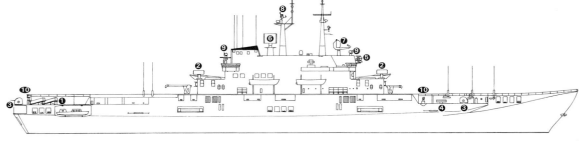

GIUSEPPE GARIBALDI   *(Scale 1 : 1200), Ian Sturton*

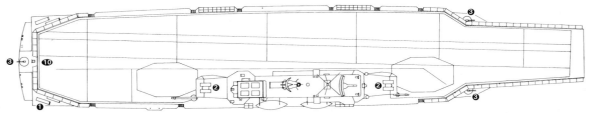

GIUSEPPE GARIBALDI   *(Scale 1 : 1200), Ian Sturton*

CRUISER

1 VITTORIO VENETO CLASS

Name	No	Builders	Laid down	Launched	Commissioned
VITTORIO VENETO	C 550	Italcantieri, Castellammare	10 June 1965	5 Feb 1967	12 July 1969

Displacement, tons: 7500 standard; 9500 full load
Dimensions, feet (metres): 589 × 63.6 × 19.7
(179.6 × 19.4 × 6)
Flight deck, feet (metres): 131 × 61 *(40 × 18.6)*
Main machinery: 4 Foster-Wheeler boilers (Ansaldo); 700 psi
(50 kg/cm sq); 850°F *(450°C)*; 2 Tosi turbines; 73 000 hp(m)
(54 MW); 2 shafts
Speed, knots: 32. **Range, miles:** 5000 at 17 kts
Complement: 550 (53 officers)

Missiles: SSM: 4 OTO Melara Teseo Mk 2 (TG 2) ❶; inertial
cruise; active radar homing to 180 km *(98.4 nm)* at 0.9 Mach;
warhead 210 kg; sea-skimmer.
SAM: GDC Pomona Standard SM-1ER; Aster twin Mk 10 Mod 9
launcher ❷; capacity for 60 missiles (including ASROC) on 3
drums; command guidance; semi-active radar homing to
64 km *(35 nm)* at 2.5 Mach.
A/S: Honeywell ASROC; inertial guidance to 1.6-10 km *(1-
5.4 nm)*; payload Mk 46 torpedo.
Guns: 8 OTO Melara 3 in *(76 mm)*/62 MMK ❸; 85° elevation;
55-65 rounds/minute to 8 km *(4.4 nm)*; weight of shell 6 kg.
6 Breda 40 mm/70 (3 twin) ❹; 85° elevation; 300 rounds/
minute to 12.5 km *(6.8 nm)* anti-surface; 4 km *(2.2 nm)* anti-
aircraft; weight of shell 0.96 kg.
Torpedoes: 6—324 mm US Mk 32 (2 triple) tubes ❺. Honeywell
Mk 46; anti-submarine; active/passive homing to 11 km
(5.9 nm) at 40 kts; warhead 44 kg.
Countermeasures: Decoys: 2 Breda SCLAR 105 mm 20-bar-
relled trainable ❻; chaff to 5 km *(2.7 nm)*; illuminants to 12 km
(6.6 nm). SLQ 25 Nixie; towed torpedo decoy.
ESM: SLR 4; intercept.
ECM: 3 SLQ-B; 2 SLQ-C; jammers.
Combat data systems: SADOC 1 action data automation;
Link 11. SATCOM.
Fire control: 4 Argo 10 systems for 76 mm guns. 2 Dardo sys-
tems for 40 mm guns.
Radars: Long range air search: Hughes SPS 52C ❼; 3D; E/F
band; range 440 km *(240 nm)*.
Air search: Selenia SPS 768 (RAN 3L) ❽; D band; range 220 km
(120 nm).
Surface search/target indication: SMA SPS 702 ❾; I band.
Navigation: SMA SPS 748; I band; range 73 km *(40 nm)*.
Fire control: Four Selenia SPG 70 (RTN 10X) ❿; I/J band; range
40 km *(22 nm)* (for Argo).

VITTORIO VENETO

1991, Camil Busquets i Vilanova

Two Selenia SPG 74 (RTN 20X) ⓫; I/J band; range 13 km
(7 nm) (for Dardo).
Two Sperry/RCA SPG 55C ⓬; G/H band; range 51 km
(28 nm) (for Standard).
IFF: Mk XII. Tacan: SRN-15A.
Sonars: Sangamo SQS 23G; bow-mounted; active search and
attack; medium frequency.

Helicopters: 6 AB 212ASW ⓭.

Programmes: Projected under the 1959-60 New Construction
Programme, but her design was recast several times. Started
trials 30 April 1969. Defined as a Guided Missile Helicopter
Cruiser.
Modernisation: In hand from 1981 to early 1984 for modernisation which included the four Teseo launchers and the three
twin Breda compact 40 mm.
Structure: Developed from the Andrea Doria class but with
much larger helicopter squadron and improved facilities for
anti-submarine operations. Fitted with two sets of stabilisers.

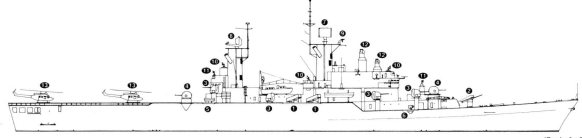

VITTORIO VENETO

(Scale 1 : 1200), Ian Sturton

VITTORIO VENETO

10/1992, C D Yaylali

VITTORIO VENETO

10/1992, C D Yaylali

DESTROYERS

Note: Italy joined the Anglo-French Horizon Project on 29 January 1993. Current requirement is for two specialised air defence ships with an option for two more. Details in France and UK sections.

2 AUDACE CLASS (DDG)

Name	No	Builders	Laid down	Launched	Commissioned
ARDITO	D 550	Italcantieri, Castellammare	19 July 1968	27 Nov 1971	5 Dec 1972
AUDACE	D 551	Fincantieri, Riva Trigoso/Muggiano	27 Apr 1968	2 Oct 1971	16 Nov 1972

Displacement, tons: 3600 standard; 4400 full load
Dimensions, feet (metres): 448 × 46.6 × 15.1
(136.6 × 14.2 × 4.6)
Main machinery: 4 Foster-Wheeler boilers; 600 psi *(43 kg/cm sq)*; 850°F *(450°C)*; 2 turbines; 73 000 hp(m) *(54 MW)*; 2 shafts
Speed, knots: 34. **Range, miles:** 3000 at 20 kts
Complement: 380 (30 officers)

Missiles: SSM: 8 OTO Melara/Matra Teseo Mk 2 (TG 2) (4 twin) **❶**; mid-course guidance; active radar homing to 180 km *(98.4 nm)* at 0.9 Mach; warhead 210 kg; sea-skimmer.
SAM: 40 GDC Pomona Standard SM-1MR; Mk 13 Mod 4 launcher **❷**; command guidance; semi-active radar homing to 46 km *(25 nm)* at 2 Mach; height envelope 45.7-18 288 m *(150-60 000 ft)*.
Selenia Albatros octuple launcher for Aspide **❸**; semi-active radar homing to 13 km *(7 nm)* at 2.5 Mach.
Guns: 1 OTO Melara 5 in *(127 mm)*/54 **❹**; 85° elevation; 45 rounds/minute to 16 km *(8.7 nm)* anti-surface; 7 km *(3.8 nm)* anti-aircraft; weight of shell 32 kg.
3 OTO Melara 3 in *(76 mm)*/62 Compact (*Ardito*) and 1 (*Ardito*) or 4 (*Audace*) Super Rapid **❺**; 85° elevation; 85 rounds/minute (Compact) or 120 rounds/minute (Super Rapid) to 16 km *(8.7 nm)* anti-surface; 12 km *(6.6 nm)* anti-aircraft; weight of shell 6 kg.
Torpedoes: 6—324 mm US Mk 32 (2 triple) tubes **❻**. Honeywell Mk 46; anti-submarine; active/passive homing to 11 km *(5.9 nm)* at 40 kts; warhead 44 kg. Transom tubes have been removed.
Countermeasures: Decoys: 2 Breda 105 mm SCLAR 20-barrelled trainable; chaff to 5 km *(2.7 nm)*; illuminants to 12 km *(6.6 nm)*. SLQ 25 Nixie; towed torpedo decoy.
ESM/ECM: Elettronica SLQ 732 Nettuno; integrated intercept and jammer.
Combat data systems: Selenia Elsag IPN-20 action data automation; Links 11 and 14. SATCOM **❼**.
Fire control: 3 Dardo E FCS (3 channels for Aspide). Selenia NA 30 optronic director.
Radars: Long range air search: Hughes SPS 52C **❽**; 3D; E/F band; range 440 km *(240 nm)*.
Air search: Selenia SPS 768 (RAN 3L) **❾**; D band; range 220 km *(120 nm)*.
Air/surface search: Selenia SPS 774 (RAN 10S) **❿**; E/F band; range 155 km *(85 nm)*.
Surface search: SMA SPQ 2D **⓫**; I band.
Navigation: SMA SPN 748; I band.
Fire control: Three Selenia SPG 76 (RTN 30X) **⓬**; I/J band; range 40 km *(22 nm)* (for Dardo E).
Two Raytheon SPG 51 **⓭**; G/I band (for Standard).
IFF: Mk XII.
Tacan: SRN-15A.
Sonars: CWE 610; hull-mounted; active search and attack; medium frequency.

Helicopters: 2 AB 212ASW **⓮**.

Programmes: It was announced in April 1966 that two new guided missile destroyers would be built. They are basically similar to, but an improvement in design on, that of the Impavido class (now deleted).

AUDACE
(Scale 1 : 1200), Ian Sturton

AUDACE
1/1992, Giorgio Ghiglione

Modernisation: B gun has been replaced by Albatros PDMS. Stern torpedo tubes removed. *Audace* fitted with four and *Ardito* one Super Rapid guns vice the 76 mm Compacts. Plans to give *Ardito* three more by 1994 have been shelved. *Ardito* completed modernisation in March 1988 and *Audace* in early 1991. Improved EW equipment also fitted.

Structure: Both fitted with stabilisers.
Operational: First deck landing trials of EH 101 helicopter were carried out on 14 May 1992.

AUDACE
9/1993, Aldo Fraccaroli

2 DE LA PENNE (ex-ANIMOSO) CLASS (DDG)

Name	No	Builders	Laid down	Launched	Commissioned
LUIGI DURAND DE LA PENNE (ex-*Animoso*)	D 560	Fincantieri, Riva Trigoso/Muggiano	20 Jan 1988	29 Oct 1989	18 Mar 1993
FRANCESCO MIMBELLI (ex-*Ardimentoso*)	D 561	Fincantieri, Riva Trigoso/Muggiano	15 Nov 1989	13 Apr 1991	18 Oct 1993

Displacement, tons: 4330 standard; 5400 full load
Dimensions, feet (metres): 487.4 × 52.8 × 16.5
  (147.7 × 16.1 × 5)
Flight deck, feet (metres): 78.7 × 42.7 *(24 × 13)*
Main machinery: CODOG; 2 Fiat/GE LM2500 gas turbines;
  54 000 hp *(40.3 MW)* sustained; 2 GMT BL 230.20 DVM die-
  sels; 12 600 hp(m) *(9.3 MW)* sustained; 2 shafts; cp props
Speed, knots: 31.5. **Range, miles:** 7000 at 18 kts
Complement: 400 approx (35 officers)

Missiles: SSM: 4 or 8 OTO Melara/Matra Teseo Mk 2 (TG 2) (2 or
  4 twin) **❶**; mid-course guidance; active radar homing to
  180 km *(98.4 nm)* at 0.9 Mach; warhead 210 kg; sea-skimmer.
  4 SSM may be replaced by 4 Milas A/S launchers.
  SAM: 40 GDC Pomona Standard SM-1MR; Mk 13 Mod 4
  launcher **❷**; command guidance; semi-active radar homing to
  46 km *(25 nm)* at 2 Mach.
  Selenia Albatros Mk 2 octuple launcher for Aspide **❸**; semi-
  active radar homing to 13 km *(7 nm)* at 2.5 Mach; 16 missiles.
  Automatic reloading.
Guns: 1 OTO Melara 5 in *(127 mm)*/54 **❹**; 85° elevation; 45
  rounds/minute to 16 km *(8.7 nm)*; weight of shell 32 kg.
  3 OTO Melara 3 in *(76 mm)*/62 Super Rapid **❺**; 85° elevation;
  120 rounds/minute to 16 km *(8.7 nm)*; weight of shell 6 kg.
Torpedoes: 6—324 mm B-515 (2 triple) tubes **❻**. Whitehead A
  290; anti-submarine.
Countermeasures: Decoys: 2 CSEE Sagaie chaff launchers **❼**. 1
  Elmer anti-torpedo system.
  ESM/ECM: Elettronica SLQ 732 Nettuno **❽**; integrated intercept
  and jamming system. SLC 705.
Combat data systems: Selenia Elsag IPN 20; Links 11 and 14.
  SATCOM.
Fire control: 4 Dardo E systems (3 channels for Aspide). Milas
  TFCS.
Radars: Long range air search: Hughes SPS 52C; 3D **❾**; E/F
  band; range 440 km *(240 nm)*.
  Air search: Selenia SPS 768 (RAN 3L) **❿**; D band; range 220 km
  (120 nm).
  Air/surface search: Selenia SPS 774 (RAN 10S) **⓫**; E/F band;
  range 155 km *(85 nm)*.
  Surface search: SMA SPS 702 **⓬**; I band.
  Fire control: Four Selenia SPG 76 (RTN 30X) **⓭**; I/J band (for
  Dardo).
  Two Raytheon SPG 51D **⓮**; G/I band (for SAM).
  Navigation: SMA SPN 703; I band.
  IFF: Mk XII. Tacan: SRN-15A.
Sonars: Raytheon DE 1164 LF-VDS; integrated bow and VDS;
  active search and attack; medium frequency (3.75 kHz (hull);
  7.5 kHz (VDS)).

Helicopters: 2 AB 212ASW **⓯**; SH-3D Sea King and EH 101
  capable.

Programmes: Order placed 9 March 1986 with Riva Trigoso. All
  ships built at Riva Trigoso are completed at Muggiano after
  launching. Names changed on 10 June 1992 to honour former
  naval heroes. Acceptance dates have been delayed by
  reduction gear radiated noise problems which have been
  resolved.

FRANCESCO MIMBELLI   *(Scale 1 : 1200), Ian Sturton*

LUIGI DURAND DE LA PENNE   *8/1993, Giorgio Ghiglione*

Structure: Kevlar armour fitted. Prairie Masker noise suppression
system. The 127 mm guns are ex-Audace class B turrets. Fully
stabilised. Hangar is 18.5 m in length.

Operational: GPS and Meteosat receivers fitted. The three Super
Rapid 76 mm guns are used as a combined medium range
anti-surface armament and CIWS against missiles.

FRANCESCO MIMBELLI   *12/1993, Giorgio Ghiglione*

FRIGATES

8 MAESTRALE CLASS

Name	No	Builders	Laid down	Launched	Commissioned
MAESTRALE	F 570	Fincantieri, Riva Trigoso	8 Mar 1978	2 Feb 1981	6 Mar 1982
GRECALE	F 571	Fincantieri, Muggiano	21 Mar 1979	12 Sep 1981	5 Feb 1983
LIBECCIO	F 572	Fincantieri, Riva Trigoso	1 Aug 1979	7 Sep 1981	5 Feb 1983
SCIROCCO	F 573	Fincantieri, Riva Trigoso	26 Feb 1980	17 Apr 1982	20 Sep 1983
ALISEO	F 574	Fincantieri, Riva Trigoso	10 Aug 1980	29 Oct 1982	7 Sep 1983
EURO	F 575	Fincantieri, Riva Trigoso	15 Apr 1981	25 Apr 1983	24 Jan 1984
ESPERO	F 576	Fincantieri, Riva Trigoso	29 July 1982	19 Nov 1983	4 May 1984
ZEFFIRO	F 577	Fincantieri, Riva Trigoso	15 Mar 1983	19 May 1984	4 May 1985

Displacement, tons: 2500 standard; 3200 full load
Dimensions, feet (metres): 405 × 42.5 × 15.1
   (122.7 × 12.9 × 4.6)
Flight deck, feet (metres): 89 × 39 *(27 × 12)*
Main machinery: CODOG; 2 Fiat/GE LM 2500 gas turbines;
   50 000 hp *(37.3 MW)* sustained; 2 GMT BL 230.20 DVM die-
   sels; 12 600 hp(m) *(9.3 MW)* sustained; 2 shafts; cp props
Speed, knots: 32 gas; 21 diesels. **Range, miles:** 6000 at 16 kts
Complement: 232 (24 officers)

Missiles: SSM: 4 OTO Melara Teseo Mk 2 (TG 2) ❶; mid-course
   guidance; active radar homing to 180 km *(98.4 nm)*; warhead
   210 kg; sea-skimmer.
   SAM: Selenia Albatros octuple launcher; 16 Aspide ❷; semi-
   active homing to 13 km *(7 nm)* at 2.5 Mach; height envelope
   15-5000 m *(49.2-16 405 ft)*; warhead 30 kg.
Guns: 1 OTO Melara 5 in *(127 mm)*/54 automatic ❸; 85° elevation; 45 rounds/minute to 16 km *(8.7 nm)* anti-surface; 7 km
   (3.8 nm) anti-aircraft; weight of shell 32 kg; fires chaff and
   illuminants.
   4 Breda 40 mm/70 (2 twin) compact ❹; 85° elevation; 300
   rounds/minute to 12.5 km *(6.8 nm)* anti-surface; 4 km
   (2.2 nm) anti-aircraft; weight of shell 0.96 kg.
   2 Oerlikon 20 mm fitted for Gulf deployments in 1990-91. 2
   Breda Oerlikon 25 mm (twin) tested in *Espero*.
Torpedoes: 6—324 mm US Mk 32 (2 triple) tubes ❺. Honeywell
   Mk 46; anti-submarine; active/passive homing to 11 km
   (5.9 nm) at 40 kts; warhead 44 kg.
   2—21 in *(533 mm)* B516 tubes in transom ❻. Whitehead
   A184; dual purpose; wire-guided; active/passive homing to
   17 km *(9.2 nm)* at 38 kts; 25 km *(13.7 nm)* at 24 kts; warhead
   250 kg.
Countermeasures: Decoys: 2 Breda 105 mm SCLAR 20-tubed
   trainable chaff rocket launchers ❼; chaff to 5 km *(2.7 nm)*;
   illuminants to 12 km *(6.6 nm)*. 2 Dagaie chaff launchers being
   fitted in all.
   SLQ 25; towed torpedo decoy. Prairie Masker; noise suppression system.
ESM: SLR-4; intercept.
ECM: 2 SLQ-D; jammers.
Combat data systems: IPN 20 (SADOC 2) action data auto-
   mation; Link 11. SATCOM ❽.
Fire control: NA 30 for Albatros and 5 in guns. 2 Dardo for
   40 mm guns.
Radars: Air/surface search: Selenia SPS 774 (RAN 10S) ❾; E/F
   band; range 155 km *(85 nm)*.
   Surface search: SMA SPS 702 ❿; I band.
   Navigation: SMA SPN 703; I band.
   Fire control: Selenia SPG 75 (RTN 30X) ⓫; I/J band (for Albatros
   and 12.7 mm gun).
   Two Selenia SPG 74 (RTN 20X) ⓬; I/J band; range 15 km
   (8 nm) (for Dardo).
IFF: Mk XII.
Sonars: Raytheon DE 1164; hull-mounted; VDS; active/passive
   attack; medium frequency. VDS can be towed at up to 28 kts.
   Maximum depth 300 m. Being modified to include mine detec-
   tion active high frequency.

Helicopters: 2 AB 212ASW ⓭.

Programmes: First six ordered December 1976 and last pair in
   October 1980. All Riva Trigoso ships completed at Muggiano
   after launch.
Modernisation: Hull and VDS sonars are being modified from
   1994 to give better shallow water performance and a mine
   detection capability.
Structure: There has been a notable increase of 34 ft in length
   and 5 ft in beam over the Lupo class to provide for the fixed
   hangar and VDS, the result providing more comfortable
   accommodation but a small loss of top speed. Fittted with
   stabilisers.
Operational: A towed passive LF array may be attached to the
   VDS body. F 576 fitted with an Oerlikon Breda 25 mm gun for
   evaluation in 1991 and 1992.

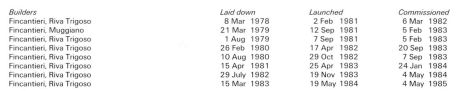

MAESTRALE   *(Scale 1 : 1200), Ian Sturton*

MAESTRALE   *9/1993, Aldo Fraccaroli*

ESPERO   *10/1993*

MAESTRALE   *9/1993, Marina Fraccaroli*

4 LUPO CLASS

Name	No	Builders	Laid down	Launched	Commissioned
LUPO	F 564	Fincantieri, Riva Trigoso	11 Oct 1974	29 July 1976	12 Sep 1977
SAGITTARIO	F 565	Fincantieri, Riva Trigoso	4 Feb 1976	22 June 1977	18 Nov 1978
PERSEO	F 566	Fincantieri, Riva Trigoso	28 Feb 1977	12 July 1978	1 Mar 1980
ORSA	F 567	Fincantieri, Muggiano	1 Aug 1977	1 Mar 1979	1 Mar 1980

Displacement, tons: 2208 standard; 2525 full load
Dimensions, feet (metres): 371.3 × 37.1 × 12.1
  (113.2 × 11.3 × 3.7)
Main machinery: CODOG; 2 Fiat/GE LM 2500 gas turbines;
  50 000 hp *(37.3 MW)* sustained; 2 GMT BL 230.20 M diesels;
  10 000 hp(m) *(7.3 MW)* sustained; 2 shafts; cp props
Speed, knots: 35 turbines; 21 diesels. **Range, miles:** 4350 at
  16 kts on diesels
Complement: 185 (16 officers)

Missiles: SSM: 8 OTO Melara Teseo Mk 2 (TG 2) ❶; mid-course
  guidance; active radar homing to 180 km *(98.4 nm)* at
  0.9 Mach; warhead 210 kg; sea-skimmer.
  SAM: Raytheon NATO Sea Sparrow Mk 29 octuple launcher ❷;
  semi-active radar homing to 14.6 km *(8 nm)* at 2.5 Mach; warhead 39 kg. 8 reloads. Updated for RIM-7M and can fire either
  Aspide or RIM-7M missiles.
Guns: 1 OTO Melara 5 in *(127 mm)*/54 ❸; 85° elevation; 45
  rounds/minute to 16 km *(8.7 nm)* anti-surface; 7 km *(3.8 nm)*
  anti-aircraft; weight of shell 32 kg.
  4 Breda 40 mm/70 (2 twin) compact ❹; 85° elevation; 300
  rounds/minute to 12.5 km *(6.8 nm)* anti-surface; 4 km
  (2.2 nm) anti-aircraft; weight of shell 0.96 kg.
  2 Oerlikon 20 mm can be fitted.
Torpedoes: 6—324 mm US Mk 32 tubes ❺. Honeywell Mk 46;
  anti-submarine; active/passive homing to 11 km *(5.9 nm)* at
  40 kts; warhead 44 kg.
Countermeasures: Decoys: 2 Breda 105 mm SCLAR 20-tubed
  trainable ❻; chaff to 5 km *(2.7 nm)*; illuminants to 12 km
  (6.6 nm).
  SLQ 25 Nixie; towed torpedo decoy.
  ESM: SLR-4; intercept.
  ECM: 2 SLQ-D; jammers.
Combat data systems: IPN 20 (SADOC 2) action data auto-
  mation; Link 11. SATCOM.
Fire control: Argo NA10 Mod 2 for missiles and 5 in gun. 2 Dardo
  for 40 mm guns.
Radars: Air search: Selenia SPS 774 (RAN 10S) ❼; E/F band;
  range 155 km *(85 nm)*.
  Surface search/target indication: SMA SPS 702 ❽; I band.
  Surface search: SMA SPQ2 F ❾; I band.
  Navigation: SMA SPN 748; I band.
  Fire control: Selenia SPG 70 (RTN 10X) ❿; I/J band; range
  40 km *(22 nm)* (for Argo).
  Two Selenia SPG 74 (RTN 20X) ⓫; I/J band; range 15 km
  (8 nm) (for Dardo).
  US Mk 95 Mod 1 (for SAM) ⓬; I band.
  IFF: Mk XII.
Sonars: Raytheon DE 1160B; hull-mounted; active search and
  attack; medium frequency.

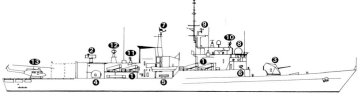

LUPO   *(Scale 1 : 1200), Ian Sturton*

SAGITTARIO   *12/1993, G Toremans*

Helicopters: 1 AB 212ASW ⓭.

Modernisation: Mid-life update started in 1991 and included low
  altitude CORA SPS 702 search radar (radome on bridge roof),
  new gyros and improved communications including SATCOM.
  All completed by early 1994.

Structure: 14 watertight compartments; fixed-fin stabilisers; telescopic hangar.
Sales: Similar ships built for Peru (4), Venezuela (6) and Iraq (4).
  Iraqi ships not delivered and transferred to the Italian Navy on
  20 January 1992 (see Artigliere class).

0 + 4 ARTIGLIERE (LUPO) CLASS (FLEET PATROL SHIPS)

Name	No	Builders	Laid down	Launched	Commissioned
ARTIGLIERE (ex-*Hittin*)	F 582 (ex-F 14)	Fincantieri, Ancona	31 Mar 1982	27 July 1983	July 1994
AVIERE (ex-*Thi Qar*)	F 583 (ex-F 15)	Fincantieri, Ancona	3 Sep 1982	19 Dec 1984	Oct 1994
BERSAGLIERE (ex-*Al Qadisiya*)	F 584 (ex-F 16)	Fincantieri, Ancona	1 Dec 1983	1 June 1985	Aug 1995
GRANATIERE (ex-*Al Yarmouk*)	F 585 (ex-F 17)	Fincantieri, Riva Trigoso	12 Mar 1984	18 Apr 1985	Nov 1995

Displacement, tons: 2208 standard; 2525 full load
Dimensions, feet (metres): 371.3 × 37.1 × 12.1
  (113.2 × 11.3 × 3.7)
Main machinery: CODOG; 2 Fiat/GE LM 2500 gas turbines;
  50 000 hp *(37.3 MW)* sustained; 2 GMT BL 230.20 M diesels;
  10 000 hp(m) *(7.3 MW)* sustained; 2 shafts; cp props
Speed, knots: 35 turbines; 21 diesels. **Range, miles:** 4350 at
  16 kts on diesels
Complement: 185 (16 officers)

Missiles: SSM: 8 OTO Melara Teseo Mk 2 (TG 2) ❶; mid-course
  guidance; active radar homing to 180 km *(98.4 nm)* at
  0.9 Mach; warhead 210 kg; sea-skimmer.
  SAM: Selenia Elsag Aspide octuple launcher ❷; semi-active radar
  homing to 14.6 km *(8 nm)* at 2.5 Mach; warhead 39 kg. 8
  reloads.
Guns: 1 OTO Melara 5 in *(127 mm)*/54 ❸; 85° elevation; 45
  rounds/minute to 16 km *(8.7 nm)* anti-surface; 7 km *(3.8 nm)*
  anti-aircraft; weight of shell 32 kg.
  4 Breda 40 mm/70 (2 twin) compact ❹; 85° elevation; 300
  rounds/minute to 12.5 km *(6.8 nm)* anti-surface; 4 km
  (2.2 nm) anti-aircraft; weight of shell 0.96 kg.
  2 Oerlikon 20 mm can be fitted.
Countermeasures: Decoys: 2 Breda 105 mm SCLAR 20-tubed
  trainable ❺; chaff to 5 km *(2.7 nm)*; illuminants to 12 km
  (6.6 nm).
  ESM/ECM: Selenia SLQ 747 (INS-3M); intercept and jammer.
Combat data systems: IPN 10 mini SADOC action data automation; Link 11. SATCOM.
Fire control: 2 Elsag Mk 10 Argo with NA 21 directors for missiles
  and 5 in gun. 2 Dardo for 40 mm guns.
Radars: Air search: Selenia SPS 774 (RAN 10S) ❻; E/F band;
  range 155 km *(85 nm)*.
  Surface search: Selenia SPQ 712 (RAN 12 L/X) ❼; I band.
  Navigation: SMA SPN 748; I band.
  Fire control: 2 Selenia SPG 70 (RTN 10X) ❽; I/J band; range
  40 km *(22 nm)* (for Argo).
  Two Selenia SPG 74 (RTN 20X) ❾; I/J band; range 15 km
  (8 nm) (for Dardo).
  IFF: Mk XII.

Helicopters: 1 AB 212 ❿.

Programmes: On 20 January 1992 it was decided to transfer the
  four ships built for Iraq to the Italian Navy. The original sale to
  Iraq was first delayed by payment problems and then cancelled in 1990 when UN embargoes were placed on military

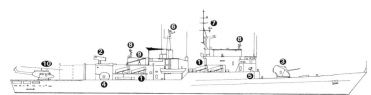

ARTIGLIERE   *(Scale 1 : 1200), Ian Sturton*

ARTIGLIERE (torpedo tubes not yet removed)   *10/1993, Italian Navy*

sales to Iraq. After several attempts by the Italian Defence
  Committee to cancel the project, finance was finally authorised in July 1993.
Modernisation: The details given are for the ships on completion
  of modernisation for Italian service. All ASW equipment
  removed, new combat and communications systems to Italian
  standards and a major upgrading of damage control and
  accommodation facilities.

Operational: The first two commission with only machinery,
  damage control and accommodation upgraded. The weapon
  systems changes are to be made during the first year in commission. The last pair will enter service fully modified. Official
  designation is Fleet Patrol Ships.

2 ALPINO CLASS

Name	No	Builders	Laid down	Launched	Commissioned
ALPINO (ex-*Circe*)	F 580	Fincantieri, Riva Trigoso	27 Feb 1963	10 June 1967	14 Jan 1968
CARABINIERE (ex-*Climene*)	F 581	Fincantieri, Riva Trigoso	9 Jan 1965	30 Sep 1967	28 Apr 1968

Displacement, tons: 2400 standard; 2700 full load
Dimensions, feet (metres): 371.7 × 43.6 × 12.7
(113.3 × 13.3 × 3.9)
Main machinery: CODAG; 2 Metrovick gas–turbines; 15 000 hp
(m) *(11.2 MW)*; 4 Tosi OTV-320 diesels; 16 800 hp(m)
(12.35 MW); 2 shafts
Speed, knots: 20 diesel; 28 diesel and gas.
Range, miles: 3500 at 18 kts
Complement: 163 (13 officers)

Missiles: SAM: Alenia/DCN 8-cell VLS for Aster 15 trials ❶ *(Cara-biniere)*; radar homing to 40 km *(21.5 nm)* at 4.5 Mach; war-head 10-15 kg.
Guns: 6 *(Alpino)* or 1 *(Carabiniere)* OTO Melara 3 in *(76 mm)*/62 ❷; 85° elevation; 60 rounds/minute to 16 km *(8.7 nm)*; weight of shell 6 kg. OTO Melara 5 in *(125 mm)*/54 to replace the 76 mm in A gun position in *Carabiniere* in due course.
Torpedoes: 6—324 mm US Mk 32 (2 triple) tubes ❸. Honeywell Mk 46; anti-submarine; active/passive homing to 11 km *(5.9 nm)* at 40 kts; warhead 44 kg.
A/S mortars: 1 Whitehead K 113 single-barrelled automatic *(Alpino)* ❹; range 900 m; warhead 160 kg. OTO Melara/Matra MILAS launcher *(Carabiniere)* ❺; command guidance to 55 km *(29.8 nm)* at Mach 0.9; payload MU 90 torpedo.
Countermeasures: Decoys: 2 Breda 105 mm SCLAR 20-tubed trainable ❻; chaff to 5 km *(2.7 nm)*; illuminants to 12 km *(6.6 nm)*.
ESM/ECM: Selenia SLQ 747; integrated intercept and jammer.
Fire control: 2 Argo 'O' for 3 in guns.
Radars: Air search: RCA SPS 12 ❼; D band; range 120 km *(65 nm)*.
Surface search: SMA SPS 702(V)3 ❽; I band.
Navigation: SMA SPN 748; I band.
Fire control: Two Selenia SPG 70 (RTN 10X) ❾; I/J band; range 40 km *(22 nm)* (for Argo).
Alenia/Marconi EMPAR SPY 790 *(Carabiniere)* ❿; for PAAMS; G band.
Sonars: Raytheon DE 1164; integrated hull and VDS; active search and attack; medium frequency.

Helicopters: 1 AB 212ASW ⓫ *(Alpino)*.

Modernisation: Both have been updated with new sonar, CCIC and EW. *Carabiniere* has been modified to replace *Quarto* as a trials ship. B gun turret and the Whitehead mortar have been replaced by MILAS launchers, and the two after 76 mm guns by the VLS for the Aster 15 SAAM system. An oil rig type mast on the flight deck carries the SAAM/PAAMS system radar SPY 790. Trial firings of the complete SAAM system are scheduled for 1996. *Alpino* is to be modified in due course as a Diver Sup-port Ship which includes removing the VDS.
Structure: Stabilisers fitted.

ALPINO   *(Scale 1 : 1200), Ian Sturton*

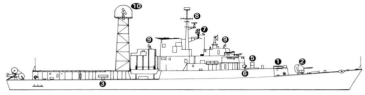

CARABINIERE   *(Scale 1 : 1200), Ian Sturton*

CARABINIERE (with EMPAR mast)   *1/1994, van Ginderen Collection*

LAND-BASED MARITIME AIRCRAFT

Numbers/Type: 18 Bréguet Atlantic 1.
Operational speed: 355 kts *(658 km/h)*.
Service ceiling: 22 800 ft *(10 000 m)*.
Range: 4855 nm *(8995 km)*.
Role/Weapon systems: Shore-based for long-range MR and shipping surveillance; wartime role includes ASW support to helicopters. Sensors: Thomson-CSF radar, ECM/ESM, MAD, sono-buoys. Weapons: ASW; 9 × torpedoes (including Mk 46 torpedoes) or depth bombs or mines.

Numbers/Type: 18 Panavia Tornado IDS.
Operational speed: Mach 2.2.
Service ceiling: 80 000 ft *(24 385 m)*.
Range: 1500 nm *(2780 km)*.
Role/Weapon systems: Swing wing strike and recce; part of a force of a total of 100 aircraft of which 18 are used for maritime operations based near Bari. Sensors: Texas instruments nav/attack systems. Weapons: ASV; 4 Kormoran missiles; 2 × 27 mm cannon. AD; 4 AIM-9L Sidewinder.

SHIPBORNE AIRCRAFT

Numbers/Type: 16/2 AV-8B/TAV-8B Harrier II Plus.
Operational speed: 562 kts *(1041 km/h)*.
Service ceiling: 50 000 ft *(15 240 m)*.
Range: 800 nm *(1480 km)*.
Role/Weapon systems: Two trainers delivered in July 1991 plus 16 front line aircraft being delivered from 1993. Eight more may be ordered in 1994. First three aircraft in service in early 1994. Sensors: Radar derived from APG-65, FLIR and ECM. Weapons: Strike and AD missiles, bombs and cannon.

Numbers/Type: 54 Agusta-Bell 212.
Operational speed: 106 kts *(196 km/h)*.
Service ceiling: 17 000 ft *(5180 m)*.
Range: 360 nm *(667 km)*.
Role/Weapon systems: ASW/ECM helicopter; mainly deployed to escorts, but also shore-based for ASW support duties and four may be used for assault. Five more acquired for ex-Iraqi frigates. Sensors: Selenia APS 705 (APS 707 in 5 ex-Iraqi aircraft) search/attack radar, AQS-13B dipping sonar or GUFO (not in Iraqi aircraft) ESM/ECM. Weapons: ASW; 2 × Mk 46 torpedoes.

SEA HARRIER   *1991, Italian Navy*

AB 212   *6/1992, Barbara Fraccaroli*

Numbers/Type: 2 Agusta/Westland EH 101 Merlin.
Operational speed: 160 kts *(296 km/h).*
Service ceiling: 15 000 ft *(4572 m).*
Range: 550 nm *(1019 km).*
Role/Weapon systems: Primary anti-submarine role with secondary anti-surface and troop carry-ing capabilities. 16 planned: 8 ASW, 4 SAR and 4 Utility. Sensors: Radar, dipping sonar, sono-buoy acoustic processor, ESM, ECM. Weapons: ASW; 4 Whitehead torpedoes. ASV; 4 Sea Killer or replacement, capability for guidance of ship-launched SSM.

Numbers/Type: 35 Agusta-Sikorsky SH-3D/H Sea King.
Operational speed: 120 kts *(222 km/h).*
Service ceiling: 12 200 ft *(3720 m).*
Range: 630 nm *(1165 km).*
Role/Weapon systems: ASW helicopter; embarked in larger ASW ships, including CVL; also shore-based for medium ASV-ASW in Mediterranean Sea; nine are fitted for ASV, 12 with ASW and EW equipment, nine transport/assault, and five are in reserve. Sensors: Selenia APS 705 search radar, AQS-13B dipping sonar, sonobuoys. ESM/ECM. Weapons: ASW; 4 × Mk 46 tor-pedoes. ASV; 2 × Marte 2 missiles.

MERLIN   *1993, Italian Navy*

SEA KING   *9/1993, Marina Fraccaroli*

CORVETTES

Note: Albatros class *Alcione* F 544 and *Airone* F 545 are used only for harbour training.

8 MINERVA CLASS

Name	No	Builders	Laid down	Launched	Commissioned
MINERVA	F 551	Fincantieri, Riva Trigoso	11 Mar 1985	3 Apr 1986	10 June 1987
URANIA	F 552	Fincantieri, Riva Trigoso	4 Apr 1985	21 June 1986	1 June 1987
DANAIDE	F 553	Fincantieri, Muggiano	26 June 1985	18 Oct 1986	9 Sep 1987
SFINGE	F 554	Fincantieri, Muggiano	2 Sep 1986	16 May 1987	13 Feb 1988
DRIADE	F 555	Fincantieri, Riva Trigoso	18 Mar 1988	11 Mar 1989	19 Apr 1990
CHIMERA	F 556	Fincantieri, Riva Trigoso	21 Dec 1988	7 Apr 1990	15 Jan 1991
FENICE	F 557	Fincantieri, Riva Trigoso	6 Sep 1988	9 Sep 1989	11 Sep 1990
SIBILLA	F 558	Fincantieri, Muggiano	16 Oct 1989	15 Sep 1990	16 May 1991

Displacement, tons: 1029 light; 1285 full load
Dimensions, feet (metres): 284.1 × 34.5 × 10.5
(86.6 × 10.5 × 3.2)
Main machinery: 2 Fincantieri GMT BM 230.20 DVM diesels; 12 600 hp(m) *(9.26 MW)* sustained; 2 shafts; cp props
Speed, knots: 24. **Range, miles:** 3500 at 18 kts
Complement: 123 (10 officers)

Missiles: SSM: Fitted for but not with 4 or 6 Teseo Otomat between the masts.
SAM: Selenia Elsag Albatros octuple launcher ❶; 8 Aspide; semi-active radar homing to 13 km *(7 nm)* at 2.5 Mach; height envel-ope 15-5000 m *(49.2-16 405 ft)*; warhead 30 kg. Capacity for larger magazine.
Guns: 1 OTO Melara 3 in *(76 mm)*/62 Compact ❷; 85° elevation; 85 rounds/minute to 16 km *(8.7 nm)* anti-surface; 12 km *(6.6 nm)* anti-aircraft; weight of shell 6 kg.
Torpedoes: 6—324 mm Whitehead B 515 (2 triple) tubes ❸. Honeywell Mk 46; active/passive homing to 11 km *(5.9 nm)* at 40 kts; warhead 44 kg. Being replaced by Whitehead A 290.
Countermeasures: Decoys: 2 Wallop Barricade double layer launchers for chaff and IR flares. SLQ 25 Nixie; towed torpedo decoy.
ESM/ECM: Selenia SLQ 747 intercept and jammer.
Combat data systems: Selenia IPN 10 Mini SADOC action data automation; Link 11. SATCOM.
Fire control: 1 Elsag Dardo E system. Selenia/Elsag Pegaso optronic director ❹. Elmer TLC system.
Radars: Air/surface search: Selenia SPS 774 (RAN 10S) ❺; E/F band; range 155 km *(85 nm)*.
Navigation: SMA SPN 728(V)2 ❻; I band.
Fire control: Selenia SPG 76 (RTN 30X) ❼; I/J band (for Albatros and gun).
Sonars: Raytheon/Elsag DE 1167; hull-mounted; active search and attack; 7.5-12 kHz.

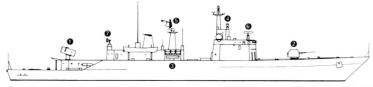

MINERVA   *(Scale 1 : 900), Ian Sturton*

DANAIDE   *5/1993, Wright & Logan*

Programmes: First four ordered in November 1982, second four in January 1987. A third four were planned, but this now seems unlikely.
Structure: The funnels remodelled to reduce turbulence and IR signature. Two fin stabilisers.

Operational: Omega transit fitted. Intended for a number of roles including EEZ patrol, fishery protection and Commanding Offi-cers' training. First four based at Augusta, Sicily.

DANAIDE   *5/1993, H M Steele*

1 DE CRISTOFARO CLASS

Name	No	Builders	Laid down	Launched	Commissioned
SALVATORE TODARO	F 550	Cantieri Ansaldo, Leghorn	21 Oct 1962	24 Oct 1964	25 Apr 1966

Displacement, tons: 850 standard; 1020 full load
Dimensions, feet (metres): 263.2 × 33.7 × 9
(80.2 × 10.3 × 2.7)
Main machinery: 2 Fiat 3012 RSS diesels; 8400 hp(m) *(6.17 MW)*; 2 shafts
Speed, knots: 23. **Range, miles:** 4000 at 16 kts
Complement: 131 (8 officers)

Guns: 2 OTO Melara 3 in *(76 mm)*/62; 85° elevation; 60 rounds/minute to 16 km *(8.7 nm)*; weight of shell 6 kg.
Torpedoes: 6—324 mm US Mk 32 (2 triple) tubes. Honeywell Mk 46; anti-submarine; active/passive homing to 11 km *(5.9 nm)*; warhead 44 kg.
A/S mortars: 1 Whitehead K 113 single-barrelled automatic; range 900 m; warhead 160 kg.
Countermeasures: ESM: Elettronica SPR; intercept.
Fire control: OG3 director for guns. DLB 1 for A/S weapons.
Radars: Air/surface search: SMA SPQ 2B; I band.
Navigation: BX 732; I band.
Fire control: Selenia Orion 7; I/J band (for OG3); range 73 km *(40 nm)*.
Sonars: EDO SQS 36; hull-mounted and VDS; active search and attack; medium frequency.

Structure: The design is an improved version of the Albatros class.
Operational: The last of the class to survive and expected to pay off in Summer 1995.

DE CRISTOFARO class (old number)   *7/1991, van Ginderen Collection*

PATROL FORCES

Note: *Saettia* P 920 is a private Fincantieri venture and is not part of the Italian Navy.

4 CASSIOPEA CLASS (OFFSHORE PATROL VESSELS)

Name	No	Builders	Laid down	Launched	Commissioned
CASSIOPEA	P 401	Fincantieri, Muggiano	16 Dec 1987	20 July 1988	6 July 1989
LIBRA	P 402	Fincantieri, Muggiano	17 Dec 1987	27 July 1988	28 Nov 1989
SPICA	P 403	Fincantieri, Muggiano	5 Sep 1988	27 May 1989	3 May 1990
VEGA	P 404	Fincantieri, Muggiano	20 June 1989	24 Feb 1990	25 Oct 1990

Displacement, tons: 1002 standard; 1475 full load
Dimensions, feet (metres): 261.8 × 38.7 × 11.5
(79.8 × 11.8 × 3.5)
Flight deck, feet (metres): 72.2 × 26.2 *(22 × 8)*
Main machinery: 2 Fincantieri/GMT BL 230.16 M diesels; 7940 hp(m) *(5.84 MW)* sustained; 2 shafts
Speed, knots: 20. **Range, miles:** 3300 at 17 kts
Complement: 78 (8 officers)

Guns: 1 OTO Melara 3 in *(76 mm)*/62; 85° elevation; 60 rounds/minute to 16 km *(8.7 nm)*; weight of shell 6 kg.
2—12.7 mm MGs.
Fire control: Argo NA 10.
Radars: Surface search: SMA SPS 702(V)2; I band.
Navigation: SMA SPN 748(V)2; I band.
Fire control: Selenia SPG 70 (RTN 10X); I/J band.

Helicopters: 1 AB 212ASW.

Programmes: Ordered in December 1986 for operations in EEZ. Officially 'pattugliatori marittimi'. Funded by the Ministry of the Merchant Navy but all operated by the Navy. The projected fifth of the class was cancelled in 1991.
Structure: Fitted for firefighting, rescue and supply tasks. Telescopic hangar. The guns and fire control radars are old stock taken from Bergamini class. There is a 500 cu m tank for storing oil polluted water.

VEGA   *12/1990, Giorgio Ghiglione*

6 SPARVIERO CLASS (HYDROFOIL—MISSILE)

Name	No	Builders	Commissioned
NIBBIO	P 421	Fincantieri, Muggiano	6 Mar 1982
FALCONE	P 422	Fincantieri, Muggiano	6 Mar 1982
ASTORE	P 423	Fincantieri, Muggiano	5 Feb 1983
GRIFONE	P 424	Fincantieri, Muggiano	5 Feb 1983
GHEPPIO	P 425	Fincantieri, Muggiano	20 Jan 1983
CONDOR	P 426	Fincantieri, Muggiano	18 Jan 1984

Displacement, tons: 60.6 full load
Dimensions, feet (metres): 80.7 × 23.1 × 14.4 *(24.6 × 7 × 4.4)* (length and beam foils extended, draught hullborne); 75.4 × 22.9 × 5.2 *(23 × 7 × 1.6)* (hull size)
Main machinery: Foilborne; 1 RR Proteus 15 M/560 gas turbine; 4250 hp *(3.17 MW)* sustained; 1 waterjet
Hullborne; 1 Isotta Fraschini ID 38 N 6V diesel; 290 hp(m) *(213 kW)* sustained; 1 retractable prop
Speed, knots: 48; 8 hullborne on diesel. **Range, miles:** 400 at 45 kts; 1200 at 8 kts
Complement: 10 (2 officers)

Missiles: SSM: 2 OTO Melara/Matra Otomat Teseo Mk 2 (TG 1); active radar homing to 80 km *(43.2 nm)* at 0.9 Mach; warhead 210 kg; sea-skimmer.
Guns: 1 OTO Melara 3 in *(76 mm)*/62 compact; 85° elevation; 85 rounds/minute to 16 km *(8.7 nm)* anti-surface; 12 km *(6.6 nm)* anti-aircraft; weight of shell 6 kg.
Fire control: Elsag NA 10 Mod 3.
Radars: Surface search: SMA SPQ 701 (3 RM 7-250 in P 420); I band; range 73 km *(40 nm)*; IFF.
Fire control: Selenia SPG 70 (RTN 10X); I/J band; range 40 km *(22 nm)*.

Modernisation: Plans to change to a more powerful GT engine have been postponed but a new diesel has been fitted.
Structure: Aluminium hull and superstructure. Payload equal to 25 per cent of displacement.
Operational: Day running capability—no sleeping accommodation. Prototype paid off in October 1991.
Sales: Six of the class being built under licence in Japan.

CONDOR   *1/1994, van Ginderen Collection*

0 + 4 COASTAL PATROL CRAFT

Displacement, tons: 160 full load
Dimensions, feet (metres): 113.8 × 24.4 × 7.5 *(34.7 × 7.5 × 2.3)*
Main machinery: 2 diesels; 3237 hp(m) *(2.38 MW)*; 2 shafts
Speed, knots: 22
Complement: 14 (3 officers)
Guns: 1 Oerlikon 20 mm. 2—7.62 mm MGs.
Radars: Surface search: 2 SPS 753B/C; I band.

Comment: Ordered from Ortona Shipyard in December 1993 for delivery from 1995. To replace the Agave class for UN patrols in the Red Sea, and for anti-illegal immigration operations in the southern Adriatic. To be based at Brindisi.

4 BAMBU (AGAVE) CLASS (OFFSHORE PATROL VESSELS)

BAMBU P 495 (ex-M 5521)   **MANGO** P 496 (ex-M 5523)
MOGANO P 497 (ex-M 5524)   **PALMA** P 500 (ex-M 5525)

Displacement, tons: 375 standard; 405 full load
Dimensions, feet (metres): 144 × 25.6 × 8.5 *(43 × 7.8 × 2.6)*
Main machinery: 2 GM 8-268A diesels; 880 hp *(656 kW)*; 2 shafts
Speed, knots: 13.5. **Range, miles:** 2500 at 10 kts
Complement: 38 (5 officers)
Guns: 2 Oerlikon 20 mm (twin).
Radars: Navigation: SPN 750; I band.

Comment: Non-magnetic minesweepers of composite wooden and alloy construction similar to those transferred from the USA but built in Italian yards; all completed November 1956-April 1957. Originally class of 19. *Mirto* now used for surveying. These four were converted for patrol duties with UN force in Red Sea, carry P numbers and are painted white. To be replaced by a new class in 1995/96.

MANGO   *7/1992, F Sadek*

2 AGGRESSIVE CLASS (OFFSHORE PATROL VESSELS)

Name	No	Builders	Commissioned	
STORIONE (ex-*MSO 506*)	(ex-M 5431)	Martinolich SB Co	23 Feb	1956
SQUALO (ex-*MSO 518*)	(ex-M 5433)	Tampa Marine Co	20 June	1957

Displacement, tons: 665 standard; 720 full load
Dimensions, feet (metres): 172 × 36 × 13.6 *(52.4 × 11 × 4.1)*
Main machinery: 4 GM 8-268A diesels; 1760 hp *(1.31 MW)*; 2 shafts; cp props
Speed, knots: 14. **Range, miles:** 2400 at 10 kts
Complement: 62 (4 officers)
Guns: 1 US/Bofors 40 mm/56.
Radars: Navigation: SMA SPN 703; I band; range 73 km *(40 nm)*.
Sonars: GE UQS-1; active mine detection; high frequency.

Comment: Built in the US. Converted to offshore patrol vessels in 1992/93. New pennant numbers allocated. All minesweeping gear removed.

STORIONE (old number)   *1990, van Ginderen Collection*

AMPHIBIOUS FORCES

3 SAN GIORGIO CLASS (LPDs)

Name	No	Builders	Laid down	Launched	Commissioned
SAN GIORGIO	L 9892	Fincantieri, Riva Trigoso	27 June 1985	25 Feb 1987	9 Oct 1987
SAN MARCO	L 9893	Fincantieri, Riva Trigoso	28 June 1986	21 Oct 1987	18 Mar 1988
SAN GIUSTO	L 9894	Fincantieri, Riva Trigoso	30 Nov 1992	2 Dec 1993	June 1994

Displacement, tons: 6687 standard; 7665 (8000 *San Giusto*) full load
Dimensions, feet (metres): 437.2 × 67.3 × 17.4 *(133.3 × 20.5 × 5.3)*
Flight deck, feet (metres): 328.1 × 67.3 *(100 × 20.5)*
Main machinery: 2 Fincantieri GMT A 420.12 diesels; 16 800 hp (m) *(12.35 MW)* sustained; 2 shafts; cp props
Speed, knots: 21. **Range, miles:** 7500 at 16 kts; 4500 at 20 kts
Complement: 170
Military lift: Battalion of 400 plus 30-36 APCs or 30 medium tanks. 3 LCMs in stern docking well. 3 LCVPs on upper deck. 1 LCPL

Guns: 1 OTO Melara 3 in *(76 mm)*/62; 85° elevation; 60 rounds/minute to 16 km *(8.7 nm)*; weight of shell 6 kg or 1 OTO Melara 3 in *(76 mm)*/62 compact *(San Giusto)*; 85 rounds/minute to 16 km *(8.7 nm)*; weight of shell 6 kg.
2 Oerlikon 20 mm. 2—12.7 mm MGs.
Countermeasures: ESM: SLR 730; intercept.
ESM/ECM: SLQ 747 *(San Giusto)*.
Combat data systems: Selenia IPN 20 *(San Giusto)*.
Fire control: Elsag NA 10.
Radars: Surface search: SMA SPS 702; I band.
Navigation: SMA SPN 748; I band.
Fire control: Selenia SPG 70 (RTN 10X); I/J band; range 40 km *(22 nm)*.

Helicopters: 3 SH-3D Sea King or 5 AB 212.

Programmes: *San Giorgio* ordered 26 November 1983, *San Marco* on 5 March 1984 and *San Giusto* 1 March 1991. Launching dates of the first two are slightly later than the 'official' launching ceremony because of poor weather and for the third because of industrial problems.
Structure: Aircraft carrier type flight deck with island to starboard. Three landing spots. Bow ramp for amphibious landings. Stern docking well 20.5 × 7 m. Fitted with a 30 ton lift and two 40 ton travelling cranes for LCMs. *San Giusto* is 300 tons heavier, of similar design except for more accommodation, a slightly longer island and different LCVP davit arrangement. Also no bow doors and therefore no beaching capability, and her davits are placed in a sponson on the port side, freeing the whole flight deck for cargo and flight operations.
Operational: *San Giorgio* replaced *Caio Duilio* for midshipmen training and amphibious squadron but is being relieved by *San Giusto* in 1994. *San Marco* was paid for by the Ministry of Civil Protection, is specially fitted for disaster relief but is run by the Navy. All are based at Brindisi and assigned to the Third Naval Division. *San Giusto* is expected to be fully operational in October 1994, and attached to the Naval Academy at Livorno during the annual three month Summer cruise.
Opinion: An imaginative but cheap and versatile design which has applications in Amphibious, ASW support or disaster relief operations. Being studied by a number of other navies.

SAN GIUSTO   *12/1993, Giorgio Ghiglione*

SAN MARCO   *1992, Ships of the World*

2 PEDRETTI CLASS (COMMANDO SUPPORT CRAFT)

Name	No	Builders	Commissioned
ALCIDE PEDRETTI	Y 499 (ex-MEN 213)	Crestitalia-Ameglia	23 Oct 1984
MARIO MARINO	Y 498 (ex-MEN 214)	Crestitalia-Ameglia	21 Dec 1984

Displacement, tons: 75.4 *(Alcide Pedretti)*, 69.5 *(Mario Marino)* full load
Dimensions, feet (metres): 86.6 × 22.6 × 3.3 *(26.4 × 6.9 × 1)*
Main machinery: 2 Isotta Fraschini ID 36 SS 12V diesels; 2640 hp(m) *(1.94 MW)* sustained; 2 shafts
Speed, knots: 25. **Range, miles:** 450 *(Alcide Pedretti)*, 250 *(Mario Marino)* at 23 kts
Complement: 6

Comment: Both laid down 8 September 1983. For use by assault swimmers of COMSUBIN. Both have decompression chambers. *Alcide Pedretti* has a floodable dock aft and is used for combat swimmers and special operations, while *Mario Marino* is fitted for underwater work and rescue missions. Based at Varignano, La Spezia. A similar but more heavily equipped vessel serves with the UAE coastguard.

ALCIDE PEDRETTI   *9/1993, Marina Fraccaroli*

5 LCMs

MTM 544-545   MTM 547-549

Displacement, tons: 56 full load
Dimensions, feet (metres): 56.1 × 14.4 × 3.9 *(17.1 × 4.4 × 1.2)*
Main machinery: 2 Gray Marine 64 NH9 diesels; 330 hp *(264 kW)*; 2 shafts
Speed, knots: 11. **Range, miles:** 130 at 10 kts
Cargo capacity: 30 tons
Guns: 2—12.7 mm MGs.

Comment: Transferred in 1953 from the US. Survivors of a much larger class.

MTM 545   *11/1988, Aldo Fraccaroli*

9 MTM 217 CLASS (LCMs)

MEN 217-222   MEN 227-228   MEN 551

Displacement, tons: 64.6 full load
Dimensions, feet (metres): 60.7 × 16.7 × 3 *(18.5 × 5.1 × 0.9)*
Speed, knots: 9. **Range, miles:** 300 at 9 kts
Complement: 3
Cargo capacity: 30 tons

Comment: First six built at Muggiano, La Spezia by Fincantieri. Three completed 9 October 1987 for *San Giorgio*, three completed 8 March 1988 for *San Marco*. Three more ordered in March 1991 from Balzamo Shipyard for *San Giusto*. Some of this class are also in service with the Army.

MEN 220   *9/1991, van Ginderen Collection*

4 LCVP TYPE

MTP 526   MTP 529   MTP 533   MTP 540

Displacement, tons: 11 full load
Dimensions, feet (metres): 36.5 × 10.8 × 3 *(11.1 × 3.3 × 0.9)*
Main machinery: 1 Gray Marine 64 HN9 diesel; 165 hp *(123 kW)*; 1 shaft
Speed, knots: 10. **Range, miles:** 110 at 9 kts
Guns: 2—12.7 mm MGs.

Comment: Italian construction but built to a basic US design. Survivors of a larger class.

17 MTP 96 CLASS (LCVP)

MDN 94-104   MDN 108-109   MDN 114-117

Displacement, tons: 14.3 full load
Dimensions, feet (metres): 44.9 × 12.5 × 2.3 *(13.7 × 3.8 × 0.7)*
Main machinery: 2 diesels; 700 hp(m) *(515 kW)*; 2 shafts or 2 waterjets
Speed, knots: 29 or 22. **Range, miles:** 100 at 12 kts
Complement: 3

Comment: Built by Technomatic Ancona in 1985 (two), Technomatic Bari in 1987/88 (six) and Technoplast Venezia 1991/94 (nine). Can carry 45 men or 4.5 tons of cargo. These craft have Kevlar armour. The most recent versions have waterjet propulsion which gives a top speed of 29 kts (22 kts fully laden). This will be backfitted to all GRP LCVPs.

SURVEY AND RESEARCH SHIPS

Note: Two 300 ton 38 m GRP hulls to be built by Intermarine, Sarzana. These ships are planned to replace *Mirto* and *Pioppo* in due course if the contract goes ahead, which is doubtful.

Name	No	Builders	Commissioned
AMMIRAGLIO MAGNAGHI	A 5303	Fincantieri, Riva Trigoso	2 May 1975

Displacement, tons: 1700 full load
Dimensions, feet (metres): 271.3 × 44.9 × 11.5 *(82.7 × 13.7 × 3.5)*
Main machinery: 2 GMT B 306 SS diesels; 3000 hp(m) *(2.2 MW)*; 1 shaft; cp prop; auxiliary motor; 240 hp(m) *(176 kW)*; bow thruster
Speed, knots: 16. **Range, miles:** 6000 at 12 kts (1 diesel); 4200 at 16 kts (2 diesels)
Complement: 148 (14 officers, 15 scientists)
Guns: 1 Breda 40 mm/70 (not fitted).
Radars: Navigation: SMA 3 RM 20; I band; range 73 km *(40 nm)*.
Helicopters: Platform only.

Comment: Ordered under 1972 programme. Laid down 13 June 1973. Launched 11 October 1974. Full air-conditioning, bridge engine controls, flume-type stabilisers. Equipped for oceanographical studies including laboratories and underwater TV. Two Qubit Trac V integrated navigation and logging systems and a Chart V data processing system installed in 1992 to augment the existing Trac 100-based HODAPS. Carries six surveying motor boats.

AMMIRAGLIO MAGNAGHI   *1/1994, van Ginderen Collection*

Name	No	Builders	Commissioned
MIRTO	A 5306	Breda, Porta Marghera	4 Aug 1956
PIOPPO	A 5307	Bellingham SY, Seattle	31 July 1954

Comment: *Mirto* of the Agave class and *Pioppo* of the Adjutant class (see *OPV* and *Mine Warfare* sections for details) have been converted for surveying duties with complement of four officers and 36 men. To be replaced by two new construction ships in due course.

MIRTO   *9/1989, Marina Fraccaroli*

4 RESEARCH SHIPS

Name	No	Builders	Commissioned
RAFFAELE ROSSETTI	A 5315	Picchiotti, Viareggio	20 Dec 1986

Displacement, tons: 320 full load
Dimensions, feet (metres): 146.3 × 25.9 × 6.9 *(44.6 × 7.9 × 2.1)*
Main machinery: 2 Fincantieri Isotta Fraschini ID 36 N 12V diesels; 1320 hp(m) *(970 kW)* sustained; 2 shafts; bow thruster
Speed, knots: 17.5. **Range, miles:** 700 at 15 kts
Complement: 17 (1 officer, 8 technicians)

Comment: Launched on 12 July 1986. Five different design torpedo tubes fitted for above and underwater testing and trials. Other equipment for research into communications, surface and air search as well as underwater weapons. There is a stern doorway which is partially submerged and the ship has a set of 96 batteries to allow 'silent' propulsion. Operated by the Permanent Commission for Experiments of War Materials at La Spezia.

RAFFAELE ROSSETTI   *9/1993, Marina Fraccaroli*

Name	No	Builders	Commissioned
VINCENZO MARTELLOTTA	A 5320	Picchiotti, Viareggio	22 Dec 1990

Displacement, tons: 340 full load
Dimensions, feet (metres): 146.3 × 25.9 × 7.5 *(44.6 × 7.9 × 2.3)*
Main machinery: 2 Fincantieri Isotta Fraschini ID 36 SS 16V diesels; 3520 hp(m) *(2.59 MW)* sustained; 2 shafts; bow thruster
Speed, knots: 17. **Range, miles:** 700 at 15 kts
Complement: 17 (1 officer)

Comment: Launched on 28 May 1988. Has one 21 in *(533 mm)* and three 12.75 in *(324 mm)* torpedo tubes and acoustic equipment to operate a 3D tracking range for torpedoes or underwater vehicles. Like *Rossetti* she is operated by the Commission at La Spezia.

V MARTELLOTTA   *6/1990, Aldo Fraccaroli*

BARBARA P 492

Displacement, tons: 195 full load
Dimensions, feet (metres): 98.4 × 20.7 × 4.9 *(30 × 6.3 × 1.5)*
Main machinery: 2 diesels; 600 hp(m) *(441 kW)*; 2 shafts
Speed, knots: 12

Comment: Built by Castracani, Ancona. A fishing vessel purchased and converted for research work in 1975. Converted in 1986 to Coastal Patrol Boat. Operates under the Technical and Scientific Council of Defence for missile testing at Perdasdefogu, Sardinia.

BARBARA   *1989, Aldo Fraccaroli*

MURENA (ex-*Scampo*) A 5305

Displacement, tons: 188 full load
Dimensions, feet (metres): 106 × 21 × 6 *(32.5 × 6.4 × 1.8)*
Main machinery: 2 Fiat/MTU MB 12V 493 TY7 diesels; 2200 hp(m) *(1.62 MW)* sustained; 2 shafts
Speed, knots: 14. **Range, miles:** 2000 at 9 kts
Complement: 16 (4 officers)

Comment: Built in 1957. Converted Aragosta class MSI used as a torpedo launching and support vessel.

MURENA   *9/1993, Marina Fraccaroli*

MINE WARFARE FORCES

Note: The Navy is studying a 'Gaeta plus' design which will include hunting, sweeping and clearance diving.

4 LERICI and 6 + 2 GAETA CLASS (MINEHUNTERS/SWEEPERS)

Name	No	Builders	Launched	Commissioned
LERICI	M 5550	Intermarine, Sarzana	3 Sep 1982	22 Mar 1985
SAPRI	M 5551	Intermarine, Sarzana	5 Apr 1984	4 June 1985
MILAZZO	M 5552	Intermarine, Sarzana	4 Jan 1985	6 Aug 1985
VIESTE	M 5553	Intermarine, Sarzana	18 Apr 1985	2 Dec 1985
GAETA	M 5554	Intermarine, Sarzana	28 July 1990	3 July 1992
TERMOLI	M 5555	Intermarine, Sarzana	15 Dec 1990	13 Nov 1992
ALGHERO	M 5556	Intermarine, Sarzana	11 May 1991	31 Mar 1993
NUMANA	M 5557	Intermarine, Sarzana	26 Oct 1991	30 July 1993
CROTONE	M 5558	Intermarine, Sarzana	11 Apr 1992	19 Jan 1994
VIAREGGIO	M 5559	Intermarine, Sarzana	3 Oct 1992	19 May 1994
CHIOGGIA	M 5560	Intermarine, Sarzana	Aug 1994	Oct 1995
RIMINI	M 5561	Intermarine, Sarzana	Dec 1994	Mar 1996

Displacement, tons: 485 standard; 502 (672, *Gaeta* onwards) full load
Dimensions, feet (metres): 164 (172.1 *Gaeta*) × 31.5 × 8.6 *(50 (52.5) × 9.6 × 2.6)*
Main machinery: 1 Fincantieri GMT BL 230.8 M diesel (passage); 1985 hp(m) *(1.46 MW)* sustained; 1 shaft; cp prop; 3 Isotta Fraschini ID 36 SS 6V diesels (hunting); 1481 hp(m) *(1.1 MW)* sustained; 3 hydraulic thrust props (1 fwd, 2 aft)
Speed, knots: 15; 7 hunting. **Range, miles:** 2500 at 12 kts
Complement: 47 (4 officers) including 7 divers

Guns: 1 Oerlikon 20 mm/70 or 2 Oerlikon 20 mm/70 (twin) (*Gaeta* onwards). 2 additional 20 mm guns added for deployments.
Countermeasures: Minehunting: 1 MIN 77 or MIN Mk 2 (*Gaeta* onwards) ROV; 1 Pluto mine destruction system; diving equipment and recompression chamber.
Minesweeping: Oropesa Mk 4 wire sweep.
Combat data systems: Motorola MRS III/GPS Eagle precision navigation system with Datamat SMA SSN-714V(2) automatic plotting and radar indicator IP-7113.
Radars: Navigation: SMA SPN 728V(3); I band; range 73 km *(40 nm)*.
Sonars: FIAR SQQ 14(IT) VDS (lowered from keel fwd of bridge); classification and route survey; high frequency.

Programmes: First four ordered 7 January 1978 under Legge Navale. Next six ordered from Intermarine 30 April 1988 and two more in 1991. From No 5 onwards ships are 2 m longer and are of an improved design. Construction of Gaetas started in 1988. The last pair delayed by budget cuts but re-ordered on 17 September 1992.
Modernisation: Improvements to Gaeta class include a better minehunting sonar system which was backfitted to the Lerici class in 1991. Other Gaeta upgrades include a third hydraulic system, improved electrical generators, ROV with better endurance and equipment, a new type of recompression chamber, and a reduced magnetic signature.
Structure: Of heavy GRP throughout hull, decks and bulkheads, with frames eliminated. All machinery is mounted on vibration dampers and main engines made of amagnetic material. Fitted with Galeazzi 2 man compression chambers and a telescopic crane for launching Callegari frogmen boats.
Operational: Endurance, 12 days. For long passages passive roll-stabilising tanks can be used for extra fuel increasing range to 4000 miles at 12 kts.
Sales: Four to Malaysia, two to Nigeria and 12 of a modified design being built by the USA.

ALGHERO   *6/1993, Giorgio Ghiglione*

MILAZZO   *9/1993, Marina Fraccaroli*

4 ADJUTANT CLASS (MINEHUNTERS—COASTAL)

CASTAGNO M 5504   **CEDRO** M 5505   **GELSO** M 5509   **PLATANO** M 5516

Displacement, tons: 378 (360, *Mandorlo*) standard; 390 full load
Dimensions, feet (metres): 144 × 27.9 × 8 *(43.9 × 8.5 × 2.4)*
Main machinery: 2 GM 8-268A diesels; 880 hp *(656 kW)*; 2 shafts
Speed, knots: 13.5. **Range, miles:** 3000 at 10 kts
Complement: 41 (3 officers)
Guns: 2 Oerlikon 20 mm (twin) (in some).
Countermeasures: Pluto remote control system (minehunting).
Radars: Navigation: SMA 3 RM 20R (SPN 703); I band.
Sonars: GE SQQ 14; VDS; mine detection; high frequency.

Comment: Wooden hulled and constructed throughout of anti-magnetic materials. All commissioned August 1953-December 1954 and transferred by the USA in 1953-54. Originally class of 18. *Pioppo* used for surveying (see *Survey Vessels*). Minehunting conversion: *Platano* in 1979, *Cedro* in 1982, *Castagno* in 1983 and *Gelso* in 1984. *Cedro* modified as a diver's support unit pays off in late 1994, to be replaced by *Castagno*. A fifth of class, *Mandorlo*, is an alongside training hulk.

CEDRO   6/1993, Giorgio Ghiglione

AUXILIARIES

0 + 1 ETNA CLASS (REPLENISHMENT TANKER)

Displacement, tons: 12 660 full load
Dimensions, feet (metres): 464.2 × 68.9 × 24.3 *(141.5 × 21 × 7.4)*
Main machinery: 2 GMT A 420.16 H diesels; 23 000 hp(m) *(16.9 MW)* sustained; 2 shafts
Speed, knots: 21. **Range, miles:** 6300 at 22 kts
Complement: 230
Cargo capacity: 5000 tons gas oil; 500 tons JP5; 2000 m³ ammunition and stores
Guns: 1 OTO Melara 76 mm/62.
Helicopters: 1 EH-101 Merlin.

Comment: Details revised in 1992 for an order in 1994. Planned in service date in 1997. The main gun may not be fitted until later, and the specification includes a CIWS on the hangar roof but no other secondary armament.

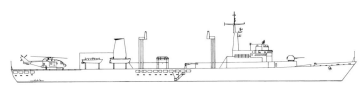

ETNA   (not to scale), Ian Sturton

1 PIAVE CLASS (WATER TANKER)

Name	No	Builders	Commissioned
PIAVE	A 5354	Orlando, Leghorn	23 May 1973

Displacement, tons: 4973 full load
Dimensions, feet (metres): 320.8 × 44 × 19.4 *(97.8 × 13.4 × 5.9)*
Main machinery: 2 diesels; 2560 hp(m) *(1.88 MW)*; 2 shafts
Speed, knots: 13. **Range, miles:** 1500 at 12 kts
Complement: 55 (7 officers)
Cargo capacity: 3500 tons
Guns: 4 Breda 40 mm/70 (2 twin) (not mounted).
Radars: Navigation: SMA SPN 748; I band.

PIAVE   4/1993, Hartmut Ehlers

2 STROMBOLI CLASS (REPLENISHMENT TANKERS)

Naame	No	Builders	Commissioned
STROMBOLI	A 5327	Fincantieri, Riva Trigoso	20 Nov 1975
VESUVIO	A 5329	Fincantieri, Muggiano	18 Nov 1978

Displacement, tons: 3556 light; 8706 full load
Dimensions, feet (metres): 423.1 × 59 × 21.3 *(129 × 18 × 6.5)*
Main machinery: 2 GMT C428 SS diesels; 9600 hp(m) *(7.06 MW)*; 1 shaft; Lips cp prop
Speed, knots: 18.5. **Range, miles:** 5080 at 18 kts
Complement: 115 (9 officers)
Cargo capacity: 3000 tons FFO; 1000 tons dieso; 400 tons JP5; 300 tons other stores
Guns: 1 OTO Melara 3 in *(76 mm)*/62.
  2 Breda 40 mm/70 (not fitted).
  4 Oerlikon 20 mm (2 twin) fitted for Gulf deployments 1987-91.
Fire control: Argo NA 10 system.
Radars: Surface search: SMA SPQ 2; I band.
Navigation: SMA SPN 748; I band.
Fire control: Selenia SPG 70 (RTN 10X); I/J band; range 40 km *(22 nm)*.
Helicopters: Flight deck but no hangar.

Comment: *Stromboli* launched 20 February 1975, *Vesuvio* 4 June 1977. *Vesuvio* was the first large ship to be built at Muggiano (near La Spezia) since the war and the first with funds under Legge Navale 1975. Beam and stern refuelling stations for fuel and stores. Also Vertrep. The two ships have different midships crane arrangements. Similar ship built for Iraq and laid up in Alexandria since 1986.

VESUVIO   9/1993, Marina Fraccaroli

3 BASENTO CLASS (WATER TANKERS)

Name	No	Builders	Commissioned
BASENTO	A 5356	Inma di La Spezia	19 July 1971
BRADANO	A 5357	Inma di La Spezia	29 Dec 1971
BRENTA	A 5358	Inma di La Spezia	18 Apr 1972

Displacement, tons: 1914 full load
Dimensions, feet (metres): 225.4 × 33.1 × 12.8 *(68.7 × 10.1 × 3.9)*
Main machinery: 2 Fiat LA 230 diesels; 1730 hp(m) *(1.27 MW)*; 2 shafts
Speed, knots: 13. **Range, miles:** 1650 at 12 kts
Complement: 24 (3 officers)
Cargo capacity: 1200 tons
Guns: 2 Oerlikon 20 mm (not fitted in all ships).

BRENTA   4/1993, Hartmut Ehlers

1 BORMIDA CLASS (WATER TANKER)

BORMIDA (ex-*GGS 1011*) A 5359

Displacement, tons: 736 full load
Dimensions, feet (metres): 131.9 × 23.6 × 10.5 *(40.2 × 7.2 × 3.2)*
Complement: 11 (1 officer)
Cargo capacity: 260 tons

Comment: Converted at La Spezia in 1974.

BORMIDA   9/1991, van Ginderen Collection

8 GGS TYPE (WATER BOATS)

GGS 185, 186, 500, 501, 502, 503, 507, 1009

Displacement, tons: 200

Comment: 185 and 502 at Taranto, 500 and 501 at Naples, 503 and 1009 at La Maddalena, 507 at Brindisi, 186 at La Spezia. GGS indicates water carriers.

GGS 186   *9/1991, van Ginderen Collection*

4 MCC 1101 CLASS (WATER TANKERS)

MCC 1101 A 5370		**MCC 1103** A 5372	
MCC 1102 A 5371		**MCC 1104** A 5373	

Displacement, tons: 898 full load
Dimensions, feet (metres): 155.2 × 32.8 × 10.8 *(47.3 × 10 × 3.3)*
Main machinery: 2 Fincantieri Isotta Fraschini ID 36 SS 6V diesels; 1320 hp(m) *(970 kW)* sustained; 2 shafts
Speed, knots: 13. **Range, miles:** 1500 at 12 kts
Complement: 12
Cargo capacity: 550 tons

Comment: Built by Ferrari, La Spezia and completed one in 1986, two in May 1987, one in May 1988.

MCC 1101   *9/1991, van Ginderen Collection*

1 BARNEGAT CLASS (SUPPORT SHIP)

Name	No	Builders	Commissioned
PIETRO CAVEZZALE (ex-USS	A 5301	Lake Washington	17 Nov 1943
Oyster Bay, ex-AGP 6, AVP 28)		Shipyard	

Displacement, tons: 1766 standard; 2800 full load
Dimensions, feet (metres): 310.8 × 41 × 13.5 *(94.7 × 12.5 × 4.1)*
Main machinery: 2 Fairbanks-Morse 38D8-1/8-10 diesels; 3540 hp *(2.64 MW)* sustained; 2 shafts
Speed, knots: 16. **Range, miles:** 10 000 at 11 kts
Complement: 114 (7 officers)
Guns: 1 US 3 in *(76 mm)*/50. 2 US/Bofors 40 mm/56.
Radars: Air search: Westinghouse SPS 6C; D band; range 146 km *(80 nm)* against fighter aircraft.
Surface search: SMA SPN 748; I band.

Comment: Former US seaplane tender (subsequently motor torpedo boat tender). Launched on 7 September 1942. Transferred to the Italian Navy on 23 October 1957. Was to have been paid off in 1991 but this has been delayed.

PIETRO CAVEZZALE   *9/1993, Aldo Fraccaroli*

3 SIMETO CLASS (WATER TANKERS)

Name	No	Builders	Commissioned
SIMETO	A 5375	Cinet, Molfetta	9 July 1988
TICINO	A 5376	Poli Shipyard, Pellestrina	Mar 1994
TIRSO	A 5377	Poli Shipyard, Pellestrina	June 1994

Displacement, tons: 1858 full load; 1968 *(Ticino* and *Tirso)* full load
Dimensions, feet (metres): 224 × 32.8 × 12.8 *(68.3 × 10 × 3.9)*
Main machinery: 2 GMT B 230.6 M diesels; 2980 hp(m) *(2.1 MW)* sustained; 2 shafts
Speed, knots: 13. **Range, miles:** 1500 at 12 kts
Complement: 27 (2 officers)
Cargo capacity: 1130 tons; 1200 *(Ticino* and *Tirso)*

Comment: Second two units of a slightly improved version.

TICINO   *(not to scale), Ian Sturton*

GRS TYPE (HARBOUR TANKERS)

Displacement, tons: 500 approx

Comment: Have GRS numbers. The old 170 series is being replaced by the 1010 series.

GRS Type   *3/1991, Giorgio Ghiglione*

6 MTC 1011 CLASS (RAMPED TRANSPORTS)

Name	No	Builders	Commissioned
GORGONA (1011)	A 5347	C N Mario Marini	23 Dec 1986
TREMITI (1012)	A 5348	C N Mario Marini	2 Mar 1987
CAPRERA (1013)	A 5349	C N Mario Marini	10 Apr 1987
PANTELLERIA (1014)	A 5351	C N Mario Marini	26 May 1987
LIPARI (1015)	A 5352	C N Mario Marini	10 July 1987
CAPRI (1016)	A 5353	C N Mario Marini	16 Sep 1987

Displacement, tons: 631 full load
Dimensions, feet (metres): 186 × 32.8 × 8.2 *(56.7 × 10 × 2.5)*
Main machinery: 2 CRM 12D/SS diesels; 1760 hp(m) *(1.29 MW)*; 2 shafts
Speed, knots: 14.5. **Range, miles:** 1500 at 14 kts
Complement: 32 (4 officers)
Guns: 1 Oerlikon 20 mm (fitted for). 2—7.62 mm MGs.
Radars: Navigation: SMA SPN 748; I band.

Comment: As well as transporting stores, oil or water they can act as support ships for Light Forces, salvage ships or minelayers. 1015 and 1016 are attached to the Italian Naval Academy at Livorno, 1011 based at La Spezia, 1012 at Ancona, 1013 at La Maddalena and 1014 at Taranto.

LIPARI   *5/1993, van Ginderen Collection*

2 MEN 215 CLASS (LCVP)

MEN 215   MEN 216

Displacement, tons: 82 full load
Dimensions, feet (metres): 89.6 × 23 × 3.6 *(27.3 × 7 × 1.1)*
Main machinery: 2 Isotta Fraschini ID 36 SS 12V diesels; 2640 hp(m) *(1.94 MW)* sustained;
  2 shafts
Speed, knots: 28. **Range, miles:** 250 at 14 kts
Complement: 4

Comment: Fast personnel launches completed in June 1986 by Crestitalia. Can also be used for
  amphibious operations or disaster relief. One is based at La Spezia and one in Taranto, where
  they are used as local ferries.

MEN 216   *9/1993, Marina Fraccaroli*

1 SAR CRAFT

Name	No	Builders	Commissioned
PAOLUCCI	—	Picchiotti, Viareggio	12 Sep 1970

Displacement, tons: 70 full load
Dimensions, feet (metres): 90.9 × 24.3 × 3.3 *(27.7 × 7.4 × 1)*
Speed, knots: 21
Complement: 8 (1 officer)

Comment: Used as an air/sea rescue and ambulance craft.

PAOLUCCI   *1991, Italian Navy*

1 MEN 212 CLASS (TRV)

MEN 212

Displacement, tons: 32 full load
Dimensions, feet (metres): 58.4 × 16.7 × 3.3 *(17.8 × 5.1 × 1)*
Main machinery: 2 HP diesels; 1380 hp(m) *(1.01 MW)*; 2 shafts
Speed, knots: 22. **Range, miles:** 250 at 20 kts
Complement: 4

Comment: Torpedo Recovery Vessel completed in October 1983 by Crestitalia. GRP construction
  with a stern ramp.

MEN 212 (and assorted harbour launches)   *9/1991, Nikolaus Sifferlinger*

1 SALVAGE SHIP

Name	No	Builders	Commissioned
PROTEO (ex-*Perseo*)	A 5310	Cantieri Navali Riuniti, Ancona	24 Aug 1951

Displacement, tons: 1865 standard; 2147 full load
Dimensions, feet (metres): 248 × 38 × 21 *(75.6 × 11.6 × 6.4)*
Main machinery: 2 Fiat diesels; 4800 hp(m) *(3.53 MW)*; 1 shaft
Speed, knots: 16. **Range, miles:** 7500 at 13 kts
Complement: 122 (8 officers)
Guns: 3 Oerlikon 20 mm.
Radars: Navigation: SMA SPN 748; I band.

Comment: Laid down at Cantieri Navali Riuniti, Ancona, in 1943. Suspended in 1944. Seized by
  Germans and transferred to Trieste. Construction re-started at Cantieri Navali Riuniti, Ancona, in
  1949. Formerly mounted one 3.9 in gun and two 20 mm. May be paid off in 1994.

PROTEO   *11/1988 Giorgio Ghiglione*

1 SALVAGE SHIP

Name	No	Builders	Commissioned
ANTEO	A 5309	C N Breda-Mestre	31 July 1980

Displacement, tons: 3200 full load
Dimensions, feet (metres): 322.8 × 51.8 × 16.7 *(98.4 × 15.8 × 5.1)*
Main machinery: 2 GMT A 230.12 diesels; 5000 hp(m) *(3.68 MW)*; 2 motors; 6000 hp(m)
  (4.41 MW); 1 shaft; 2 bow thrusters; 1000 hp(m) *(735 kW)*
Speed, knots: 20. **Range, miles:** 4000 at 14 kts
Complement: 121 (including salvage staff)
Guns: 2 Oerlikon 20 mm fitted during deployments.
Radars: Surface search: SMA SPN 751; I band.
  Navigation: SMA SPN 748; I band.
Helicopters: 1 AB 212.

Comment: Ordered mid-1977, launched 11 November 1978. Comprehensively fitted with flight
  deck and hangar, extensive salvage gear, including rescue bell, and recompression chambers.
  Carries four lifeboats of various types. Three firefighting systems. Full towing equipment. Carries
  midget submarine, *Usel,* of 13.2 tons dived with dimensions 26.2 × 6.2 × 8.9 ft *(8 × 1.9 × 2.7 m)*.
  Carries two men and can dive to 600 m. Endurance, 120 hours at 5 kts. Also has a McCann rescue chamber.

ANTEO   *7/1990, J Y Robert*

5 PONZA CLASS (LIGHTHOUSE TENDERS)

Name	No	Builders	Commissioned
PONZA	A 5364	Morini Yard, Ancona	9 Dec 1988
LEVANZO	A 5366	Morini Yard, Ancona	24 Jan 1989
TAVOLARA	A 5367	Morini Yard, Ancona	12 Apr 1989
PALMARIA	A 5368	Morini Yard, Ancona	12 May 1989
PROCIDA	A 5383	Morini Yard, Ancona	14 Nov 1990

Displacement, tons: 608 full load
Dimensions, feet (metres): 186 × 35.4 × 8.2 *(56.7 × 10.8 × 2.5)*
Main machinery: 2 Fincantieri Isotta Fraschini ID 36 SS 8V diesels; 1760 hp(m) *(1.29 MW)* sus-
  tained; 2 shafts
Speed, knots: 14.5. **Range, miles:** 1500 at 14 kts
Complement: 34
Guns: 2—7.62 mm MGs.

Comment: MTF 1304-1308. Similar to MTC 1011 class.

PALMARIA   *7/1993, Giorgio Ghiglione*

5 LCT 3 TYPE (REPAIR SHIPS)

MOC 1201 A 5331   **MOC 1203** A 5333   **MOC 1205** A 5335
MOC 1202 A 5332   **MOC 1204** A 5334

Displacement, tons: 350 standard; 640 full load
Dimensions, feet (metres): 192 × 31 × 7 *(58.6 × 9.5 × 2.1)*
Main machinery: 2 diesels; 1000 hp *(746 kW)*; 2 shafts
Speed, knots: 8
Complement: 24 (3 officers)
Guns: 2 Bofors 40 mm/70. 2 Oerlikon 20 mm.
  2 ships have 2—40 mm and 1 ship has 3—20 mm.

Comment: Built in 1943 to a British design. Originally converted as repair craft. Other duties have been taken over—*MOC 1201* is used for torpedo trials and *MOC 1203* is the minesweepers' support ship.

MOC 1203   *1990, Milpress*

MOC 1201   *4/1993, Hartmut Ehlers*

1 FERRY

CHERADI Y 402

Comment: Based at Taranto.

14 FLOATING DOCKS

Number	Date	Capacity-tons
GO 1	1942	1000
GO 5	1893	100
GO 8	1904	3800
GO 10	1900	2000
GO 11	1920	2700
GO 17	1917	500
GO 18A	1920	800
GO 18B	1920	600
GO 20	1935	1600
GO 22	1935	1000
GO 23	1935	1000
GO 51	1971	2000
GO 52	1988	6000
GO 53	1991	6000
GO 54	1993	6000

Comment: Stationed at La Spezia (*GS 52*), Augusta (*GS 53*) and Taranto (*GS 54*). Two 850 ton docks building in 1994 for Brindisi and Augusta.

TRAINING SHIPS

Note: In addition to the ships listed *San Giorgio* is used in the training role until *San Giusto* takes over in late 1994.

5 SAIL TRAINING YACHTS

Name	No	Builders	Commissioned
CAROLY	A 5302	Baglietto, Varazze	1948
STELLA POLARE	A 5313	Sangermani, Chiavari	7 Oct 1965
CORSARO II	A 5316	Costaguta, Voltri	5 Jan 1961
CAPRICIA	A 5322	Bengt-Plym	1963
AQUARIUS	—	Tencara, Venezia	June 1994

Comment: The first three are sail training yachts of between 40 and 60 tons with a crew including trainees of about 16. *Capricia* was donated by the Agnelli foundation as replacement for *Cristoforo Colombo II* which was not completed when the shipyard building her went bankrupt. *Aquarius* is a ketch of 70 tons.

1 SAIL TRAINING SHIP

Name	No	Builders	Commissioned
AMERIGO VESPUCCI	A 5312	Castellammare	15 May 1931

Displacement, tons: 3543 standard; 4146 full load
Dimensions, feet (metres): 229.5 pp; 270 oa hull; 330 oa bowsprit × 51 × 22
  (70; 82.4; 100 × 15.5 × 7)
Main machinery: Diesel-electric; 2 Fiat B 306 ESS diesel generators; 2 Marelli motors; 2000 hp(m) *(1.47 MW)*; 1 shaft
Speed, knots: 10. **Range, miles:** 5450 at 6.5 kts
Complement: 243 (13 officers)
Radars: Navigation: Two SMA SPN 748; I band.

Comment: Launched on 22 March 1930. Hull, masts and yards are of steel. Sail area, 22 604 sq ft. Extensively refitted at La Spezia Naval Dockyard in 1973 and again in 1984. Used for Naval Academy Summer cruise.

AMERIGO VESPUCCI   *8/1993, G Toremans*

5 ARAGOSTA (HAM) CLASS

ARAGOSTA A 5378   **MITILO** A 5380   **PORPORA** A 5382
ASTICE A 5379   **POLIPO** A 5381

Displacement, tons: 188 full load
Dimensions, feet (metres): 106 × 21 × 6 *(32.5 × 6.4 × 1.8)*
Main machinery: 2 Fiat-MTU 12V 493 TY7 diesels; 2200 hp(m) *(1.62 MW)* sustained; 2 shafts
Speed, knots: 14. **Range, miles:** 2000 at 9 kts
Complement: 15 (2 officers)
Radars: Navigation: BX 732; I band.

Comment: Builders: CRDA, Monfalcone: *Aragosta, Astice*. Picchiotti, Viareggio: *Mitilo*. Costaguta, Voltri: *Polipo, Porpora*.
  Similar to the late British Ham class. All constructed to the order of NATO in 1955-57. Designed armament of one 20 mm gun not mounted. Originally class of 20. Remaining five converted for training 1986. *Polipo* and *Porpora* used by the Naval Academy. *Aragosta* has large deckhouse aft as support ship for frogmen. Others of the class include *Murena* the experimental ship and GLS 501-502 ferries.

POLIPO   *9/1993, Marina Fraccaroli*

ARAGOSTA   *9/1993, Marina Fraccaroli*

1 SAIL TRAINING SHIP

Name	No	Builders	Commissioned
PALINURO	A 5311	Ch Dubigeon, Nantes	1934
(ex-*Commandant Louis Richard*)			

Displacement, tons: 1042 standard; 1450 full load
Measurement, tons: 858 gross
Dimensions, feet (metres): 193.5 × 32.8 × 15.7 *(59 × 10 × 4.8)*
Main machinery: 1 diesel; 450 hp(m) *(331 kW)*; 1 shaft
Speed, knots: 7.5. **Range, miles:** 5390 at 7.5 kts
Complement: 47

Comment: Barquentine launched in 1934. Purchased in 1951. Rebuilt in 1954-55 and commissioned in Italian Navy on 1 July 1955. Sail area, 1152 sq ft. She was one of the last two French Grand Bank cod-fishing barquentines. Owned by the Armement Glâtre she was based at St Malo until bought by Italy. Used for seamanship basic training.

PALINURO   8/1993, C D Yaylali

TUGS

Name	No	Builders	Commissioned
ATLANTE	A 5317	Visentini-Donada	14 Aug 1975
PROMETEO	A 5318	Visentini-Donada	14 Aug 1975

Displacement, tons: 750 full load
Dimensions, feet (metres): 127.9 × 32.1 × 13.4 *(39 × 9.6 × 4.1)*
Main machinery: 1 Tosi QT 320/8 SS diesel; 2670 hp(m) *(1.96 MW)*; 1 shaft; cp prop
Speed, knots: 13.5. **Range, miles:** 4000 at 12 kts
Complement: 25

PROMETEO   1990, van Ginderen Collection

9 COASTAL TUGS

PORTO EMPEDOCLE Y 421	PORTO FERRAIO Y 425	PORTO FOSSONE Y 413
PORTO PISANO Y 422	PORTO VENERE Y 426	PORTO TORRES Y 416
PORTO CONTE Y 423	PORTO SALVO Y 428	PORTO CORSINI Y 417

Displacement, tons: 412 full load
Measurement, tons: 122 dwt
Dimensions, feet (metres): 106.3 × 27.9 × 10.8 *(32.4 × 8.5 × 3.3)*
Main machinery: 2 GMT B 230.8 M diesels; 3970 hp(m) *(2.92 MW)* sustained; 2 shafts
Speed, knots: 12.7. **Range, miles:** 4000 at 12 kts
Complement: 13
Radars: Navigation: GEM BX 132; I band.
Sonars: Honeywell/Elac Type LAZ-50.

Comment: Six ordered from CN De Poli (Pellestrina) and further three from Ferbex (Naples) in 1986.
Delivery dates *Porto Salvo* (13 Sep 1985), *Porto Pisano* (22 Oct 1985), *Porto Ferraio* (20 July 1985), *Porto Conte* (21 Nov 1985), *Porto Empedocle* (19 Mar 1986), *Porto Venere* (16 May 1989), *Porto Fossone* (24 Sep 1990), *Porto Torres* (16 Jan 1991) and *Porto Corsini* (4 Mar 1991). Fitted for firefighting and anti-pollution. Carry a 1 ton telescopic crane. Based at Taranto, La Spezia, Augusta and La Maddalena.

PORTO TORRES   7/1992, Giorgio Ghiglione

CICLOPE A 5319	POLIFEMO A 5325	SATURNO A 5330
TITANO A 5324	GIGANTE A 5328	TENACE A 5365

Displacement, tons: 658 full load
Dimensions, feet (metres): 127.6 × 32.5 × 12.1 *(38.9 × 9.9 × 3.7)*
Main machinery: 2 GMT B 230.8 M diesels; 3970 hp(m) *(2.02 MW)* sustained; 2 shafts
Speed, knots: 14.5. **Range, miles:** 3000 at 14 kts
Complement: 12

Comment: Built by CN Ferrari, La Spezia. Completed *Ciclope*, 5 September 1985; *Titano*, 7 December 1985; *Polifemo*, 21 April 1986; *Gigante*, 18 July 1986; *Saturno* 5 April 1988 and *Tenace* 9 July 1988. All fitted with firefighting equipment and two portable submersible pumps. Bollard pull 45 tons.

TENACE   9/1991, van Ginderen Collection

PORTO D'ISCHIA Y 436	RIVA TRIGOSO Y 443

Displacement, tons: 296 full load
Dimensions, feet (metres): 89.5 × 23.3 × 10.8 *(27.3 × 7.1 × 3.3)*
Main machinery: Diesel; 850 hp(m) *(625 kW)*; 1 shaft; cp prop
Speed, knots: 12.1

Comment: Both launched in September 1969 by CNR, Riva Trigoso. *Porto d'Ischia* commissioned 1970 and based at La Spezia; *Riva Trigoso*, 1969 and based at Taranto.

RIVA TRIGOSO   9/1991, van Ginderen Collection

32 HARBOUR TUGS

RP 101 Y 403 (1972)	RP 113 Y 463 (1978)	RP 125 Y 478 (1983)
RP 102 Y 404 (1972)	RP 114 Y 464 (1980)	RP 126 Y 479 (1983)
RP 103 Y 406 (1974)	RP 115 Y 465 (1980)	RP 127 Y 480 (1984)
RP 104 Y 407 (1974)	RP 116 Y 466 (1980)	RP 128 Y 481 (1984)
RP 105 Y 408 (1974)	RP 118 Y 468 (1980)	RP 129 Y 482 (1984)
RP 106 Y 410 (1974)	RP 119 Y 470 (1980)	RP 130 Y 483 (1985)
RP 108 Y 452 (1975)	RP 120 Y 471 (1980)	RP 131 Y 484 (1985)
RP 109 Y 456 (1975)	RP 121 — (1984)	RP 132 Y 485 (1985)
RP 110 Y 458 (1975)	RP 122 Y 473 (1981)	RP 133 Y 486 (1985)
RP 111 Y 460 (1975)	RP 123 Y 467 (1981)	RP 134 Y 487 (1985)
RP 112 Y 462 (1975)	RP 124 Y 477 (1981)	

Comment: *RP 126* by Cantieri Navali Vittoria of Adria and *RP 121* by Baia, Naples. *RP 127-131* and *134* built by Ferrari Yard, La Spezia. *RP 132* and *133* built by CINET Yard, Molfetta. *RP 113-126* are of slightly larger dimensions and differ somewhat in appearance. *RP 127-134* are larger and slower.

RP 113   *9/1993, Marina Fraccaroli*

ARMY CRAFT

Note: The following units are operated by the 'Sile Amphibious Regiment' in the Venice Lagoons area. EIG means Italian Army Craft and is part of the hull number. Four LCM (EIG 29, 30, 31, 32), 60 tons; two LCVP (EIG 26, 27), 13 tons; four recce craft (EIG 3, 48, 49, 206), 5 tons; two command craft (EIG 208, 210), 21.5 tons; one rescue tug (EIG 209), 45 tons; one inshore tanker (EIG 44), 95 tons; one ambulance and rescue craft (EIG 28) and 15 minor craft (ferries, barges, rigid inflatable raiders).

EIG 31   *1993, Italian Army*

GOVERNMENT MARITIME FORCES

CUSTOMS (SERVIZIO NAVALE GUARDIA DI FINANZA)

Notes: (1) This force is operated by the Ministry of Finance but in time of war would come under the command of the Marina Militare. It is divided into 16 areas, 20 operational sectors and 28 squadrons. Their task is to patrol ports, lakes and rivers. The total manpower is 5300 operating 451 craft. Nearly all the larger craft are armed with a 20 mm gun or a machine gun. The first P-166 patrol aircraft was delivered by Piaggio in early 1991. A total of 10 has been ordered.
(2) Patrol craft, 2 of 210 tons; Offshore patrol craft, *Genna* G 96 (120 tons); 4 of 57 tons G 72, 75, 77, 79; 2 of 54 tons G 70-71; 56 of 40 tons G 10-G 37, G 39-G 44, G 46-G 66; Coastal patrol craft, 2 of 20.4 tons built by Intermarine, 18 of 16.4 tons GL 314-331; 2 of 13.3 tons GL 432-433; 2 of 7.1 tons GL 103, 106; Local patrol craft; 34 of 15 tons V 5800-5833; 2 of 10.5 tons V 5901-5902; 81 of 7.8 tons V 5500-5581; 15 of 6.9 tons V 4000-4014; 3 of 5.1 tons V 5300-5302; 3 of 4.9 tons V 2911-2913; 1 of 2.9 tons V 3000; 1 of 1.8 tons V 2901; Training craft, *Giorgio Cini* of 800 tons; *Gian Maria Paolini* G 95 of 348 tons.
In addition 210 small craft operate on Italian lakes and rivers.

GIAN MARIA PAOLINI   *9/1991, van Ginderen Collection*

2 + 12 CORRUBIA and 9 + 5 BIGLIANI CLASSES

BIGLIANI G 80	**MACCHI** G 83	**BUONOCORE** G 86	**CORRUBIA** G 90
CAVAGLIA G 81	**SMALTO** G 84	**SQUITIERI** G 87	**GIUDICE** G 91
GALIANO G 82	**FORUNA** G 85		

Displacement, tons: 87 full load
Dimensions, feet (metres): 86.6 × 23 × 3.6 *(26.4 × 7 × 1.1)*
Main machinery: 2 MTU 16V 396 TB94 diesels; 5800 hp(m) *(4.26 MW)* sustained; 2 shafts
Speed, knots: 40-45. **Range, miles:** 700 at 25 kts
Complement: 11
Guns: 1 Breda 30 mm. 2—7.62 mm MGs.
Fire control: Elsag Medusa optronic director.

Comment: Details given are for the Bigliani class built by Crestitalia and delivered from October 1987. G 90 and G 91 built by Cantieri Navale, Gaeta and delivered in 1990. Twelve more Corrubia class and five more Bigliani class are being built. The Corrubia class displace 81 tons and are capable of only 40 kts having slightly less powerful engines.

BIGLIANI   *9/1993, Marina Fraccaroli*

2 + 2 ANTONIO ZARA CLASS

ANTONIO ZARA P 01   **VIZZARI** P 02

Displacement, tons: 320 full load
Dimensions, feet (metres): 167 × 24.6 × 6.2 *(51 × 7.5 × 1.9)*
Main machinery: 2 GMT BL 230.12 M diesels; 5956 hp(m) *(4.38 MW)* sustained; 2 shafts
Speed, knots: 28. **Range, miles:** 2700 at 15 kts
Complement: 30 (1 officer)
Guns: 2 Breda 30 mm (twin). 2—7.62 mm MGs.
Fire control: Selenia Pegaso optronic director.

Comment: Built by Fincantieri at Muggiano, La Spezia. Similar to the Ratcharit class built for Thailand in 1976-79. Ordered in August 1987. *Antonio Zara* delivered 23 February 1990, *Vizzari* 27 April 1990. Two more to start building in 1994/95 with a modified armament of a single 30 mm gun with a Medusa optronic director. This is a second attempt by the Customs Service to create a force of high capability craft able to control the EEZ. Many years ago two 300 ton patrol boats were built and rejected as not meeting the operational requirement.

ANTONIO ZARA   *6/1993, van Ginderen Collection*

ANTONIO ZARA   *1/1990 Giorgio Ghiglione*

COAST GUARD (GUARDIA COSTIERA—CAPITANERIE DI PORTO)

Note: This is a force of 130 craft which is affiliated with the Marina Militare under whose command it would be placed in an emergency. The Coast Guard denomination was given after the Sea Protection Law in 1988. All vessels now have a red diagonal stripe painted on the hull. There are some 4700 naval personnel including 770 officers of which 2550 are doing national service.

SAR craft; 8 CP 400 class of 100 tons. *Michelle Fiorillo* CP 307 (84 tons); *Bruno Gregoretti* CP 312 (65 tons); *Dante Novaro* CP 313; CP 314-315 (43 tons); CP 301-306, 308-311 (29 tons), CP 303-304 (18 tons).

Fast patrol craft; CP 239-245 (25 tons), CP 254-256 (22.5 tons), CP 246-253 (21.5 tons), CP 226-30 (18-20 tons), CP 231-238 (14 tons), CP 257-258 (24 tons).

Coastal patrol craft; CP 2069-2081 (13 tons), CP 2049-2051, 2053-2058, 2060-2068 (12.5 tons), CP 2043-2047 (12.4 tons), CP 2033-2035 (12 tons), CP 2010-2017 (10 tons), CP 2001-2005 (9 tons), CP 207 (8 tons), CP 502-505 (6.6 tons), CP 1001-1006 (5.2 tons), CP 501, 601-605 (3 tons).

In addition there are five patrol craft of the CP 100 designation, 50 of the CP 5000 class with a speed of 25-30 kts, six inflatable rescue craft, 12 Crestitalia small patrol craft CP 6001-6012 and a new CP 801 class (29 kts) of RIB. Several of the larger craft are armed.

Aircraft include 12 Piaggio P 166 DL3 maritime patrol and four Griffon AB 412SP helicopters.

POLICE (SERVIZIO NAVALE CARABINIERI)

Notes: (1) The Carabinieri established its maritime force in 1969. This currently numbers 161 craft which operate in coastal waters within the three-mile limit and in inshore waters. The following are typical of the craft concerned;

8—700 class of 22 tons; 18—630 class of 15 tons; 25—600 class of 12 tons; 30 N 500 class of 6 tons; 3 S 500 class of 7 tons; 23—500 class of 2.6 tons; 54—400 class of 1.4 tons.

All but the 500 and 400 classes are equipped with radar and all but the N 500 class (18 kts) are capable of 20-25 kts.

(2) There is also a Sea Police Force of the State.

600 class   9/1993, Marina Fraccaroli

PS 485   9/1993, Marina Fraccaroli

CP 314   1993, Guardia Costiera

IVORY COAST

Headquarters' Appointment

Chief of Naval Staff
  Capitaine de Vaisseau C V Timité Lassana

Bases

Use made of ports at Abidjan, Sassandra, Tabou and San-Pédro

Personnel

1994: 700 (70 officers)

General

This force is primarily concerned, in conjunction with aircraft, with offshore, riverine and coastal protection. Particular emphasis is placed on environmental protection, anti-pollution operations and dealing with fires. There are also some Halter and Arcor craft which are non-naval.

Mercantile Marine

Lloyd's Register of Shipping:
  50 vessels of 103 467 tons gross

DELETIONS

1991 *Comoe*
1992 6 Arcor class

PATROL FORCES

2 PATRA CLASS (FAST ATTACK CRAFT—MISSILE)

Name	No	Builders	Commissioned
L'ARDENT	—	Auroux, Arcachon	6 Oct 1978
L'INTRÉPIDE	—	Auroux, Arcachon	6 Oct 1978

Displacement, tons: 147.5 full load
Dimensions, feet (metres): 132.5 × 19.4 × 5.2 *(40.4 × 5.9 × 1.6)*
Main machinery: 2 SACM AGO 195 V12 CZSHR diesels; 4340 hp(m) *(3.19 MW)* sustained; 2 shafts
Speed, knots: 26. **Range, miles:** 1750 at 10 kts; 750 at 20 kts
Complement: 19 (2 officers)
Missiles: SSM: 4 Aerospatiale SS 12M; wire-guided to 5.5 km *(3 nm)* subsonic; warhead 30 kg.
Guns: 1 Breda 40 mm/70. 1 Oerlikon 20 mm. 2—7.62 mm MGs.
Radars: Surface search: Racal Decca 1226; I band.

Comment: Of similar design to French Patra class. Laid down 7 July 1977 *(Intrépide)* and 7 May 1977 *(Ardent)*. Both launched 21 July 1978. Patrol endurance of five days.

2 FRANCO-BELGE TYPE (LARGE PATROL CRAFT)

Name	No	Builders	Commissioned
LE VIGILANT	—	SFCN, Villeneuve	1968
LE VALEUREUX	—	SFCN, Villeneuve	25 Oct 1976

Displacement, tons: 235 standard; 250 full load
Dimensions, feet (metres): 155.8 × 23.6 × 7.5 *(47.5 × 7 × 2.3)*
Main machinery: 2 AGO diesels; 4220 hp(m) *(3 MW)*; 2 shafts *(Valeureux)*
  2 MGO diesels; 2400 hp(m) *(1.76 MW)*; 2 shafts *(Vigilant)*
Speed, knots: 22 *(Valeureux)*; 18.5 *(Vigilant)*. **Range, miles:** 2000 at 15 kts
Complement: 34 (4 officers)
Guns: 2 Breda 40 mm/70. 2—12.7 mm MGs.
Radars: Surface search: Racal Decca; I band.

Comment: *Le Vigilant* laid down in February 1967; launched on 23 May 1967. *Le Valeureux*, laid down 20 October 1975; launched 8 March 1976. Have been reported as Exocet fitted but this is not confirmed. *Le Valeureux* received new engines in 1987.

PATRA   1989, Gilbert Gyssels

LE VIGILANT   8/1986

AUXILIARIES

1 BATRAL TYPE (LIGHT TRANSPORT)

Name	No	Builders	Commissioned
L'ÉLÉPHANT	—	A Français de l'Ouest, Grand Queville	2 Feb 1977

Displacement, tons: 750 standard; 1330 full load
Dimensions, feet (metres): 262.4 × 42.6 × 7.9 *(80 × 13 × 2.4)*
Main machinery: 2 SACM Type 195 V12 diesels; 3600 hp(m) *(2.65 MW)*; 2 shafts; cp props
Speed, knots: 16. **Range, miles:** 4500 at 13 kts
Complement: 47 (5 officers)
Military lift: 180 troops; 12 vehicles; 350 tons cargo
Guns: 2 Breda 40 mm/70. 2—81 mm mortars.
Helicopters: Platform only.

Comment: Ordered 20 August 1974. Laid down 1975.

L'ÉLÉPHANT   1983

2 LCVPs

Displacement, tons: 9 full load
Dimensions, feet (metres): 34.4 × 10.5 × 3.3 *(10.5 × 3.2 × 1.0)*
Main machinery: 1 Baudouin diesel; 1 shaft
Speed, knots: 9
Guns: 1—12.7 mm MG.

Comment: Built by DCAN, Cherbourg in 1976.

3 ROTORK TYPE 412

Displacement, tons: 9 full load
Dimensions, feet (metres): 41.7 × 10.5 × 3 *(12.7 × 3.2 × 0.9)*
Main machinery: 2 Volvo Penta AQD40A diesels; 240 hp(m) *(176 kW)*; 2 shafts
Speed, knots: 28
Military lift: 30 troops

Comment: One fast assault boat supplied in 1980. Two others supplied for civilian use at the same time have now been taken over. More are still in civilian use.

3 ARCOR TYPE

Displacement, tons: 5 full load
Dimensions, feet (metres): 31 × 11.5 × 2.6 *(9.5 × 3.5 × 0.8)*
Main machinery: 2 Baudouin diesels; 320 hp(m) *(235 kW)*; 2 shafts
Speed, knots: 20
Military lift: 30 troops

Comment: Delivered between 1982 and 1985. Six deleted so far.

JAMAICA

Defence Force Coast Guard

Jamaica, which became independent within the Commonwealth on 6 August 1962, formed the Sea Squadron on 25 August 1963 as the Maritime Arm of the Defence Force. The squadron was renamed the Defence Force Coast Guard on 1 January 1966.

Personnel

1994: (a) 182 (26 officers) Regulars
(b) 54 (16 officers) Reserve Forces

Training

(a) Officers: JDF Training depot, BRNC Dartmouth and other RN Establishments, RCN and Canadian Coast Guard, USN and US Coast Guard.
(b) Ratings: JDF Training depot, RN, RCN and Canadian Coast Guard, US Coast Guard and MTU Engineering Germany.

Headquarters' Appointment

Commanding Officer Jamaica Defence Force Coast Guard:
   Commander H M Lewin

Bases

Main: *Cagway,* Port Royal
Coastguard: Discovery Bay

Mercantile Marine

Lloyd's Register of Shipping:
   13 vessels of 11 196 tons gross

PATROL FORCES

1 FORT CLASS

Name	No	Builders	Commissioned
FORT CHARLES	P 7	Sewart Seacraft Inc, Berwick, LA, USA	Sep 1974

Displacement, tons: 130 full load
Dimensions, feet (metres): 115 × 24 × 7 *(34.5 × 7.3 × 2.1)*
Main machinery: 2 MTU 16V 538 TB90 diesels; 6000 hp(m) *(4.41 MW)* sustained; 2 shafts
Speed, knots: 32. **Range, miles:** 1500 at 18 kts
Complement: 20 (4 officers)
Guns: 1 Oerlikon 20 mm. 2—12.7 mm MGs.

Comment: Of all-aluminium construction, launched July 1974. Underwent refit at Jacksonville, FL, in 1980-81 which included extensive modifications to the bow resulting in increased length. Accommodation for 18 soldiers and may be used as 18-bed mobile hospital in an emergency.

FORT CHARLES   6/1993, JDFCG

3 BAY CLASS

Name	No	Builders	Commissioned
DISCOVERY BAY	P 4	Sewart Seacraft Inc, Berwick, LA, USA	3 Nov 1966
HOLLAND BAY	P 5	Sewart Seacraft Inc, Berwick, LA, USA	4 Apr 1967
MANATEE BAY	P 6	Sewart Seacraft Inc, Berwick, LA, USA	9 Aug 1967

Displacement, tons: 72 full load
Dimensions, feet (metres): 85 × 18 × 6 *(25.9 × 5.7 × 1.8)*
Main machinery: 3 MTU 8V 396 TC82 diesels; 2610 hp(m) *(1.92 MW)* sustained; 3 shafts
Speed, knots: 25. **Range, miles:** 800 at 15 kts
Complement: 14 (3 officers)
Guns: 3—12.7 mm MGs.

Comment: All-aluminium construction. *Discovery Bay,* the prototype, was launched in August 1966. *Holland Bay* and *Manatee Bay* were supplied under the US Military Assistance Programme. All three boats were extensively refitted and modified in 1972-73 by the builders with General Motors 12V 71 turbo-injected engines to give greater range, speed and operational flexibility. They were again re-engined and refitted at Swiftships, Louisiana, 1975-77. Between 1981 and 1984 a third engine change to MTU 396 diesels was done by Atlantic Dry Docks at Jacksonville.

MANATEE BAY   8/1993, JDFCG

1 HERO CLASS

Name	No	Builders	Commissioned
PAUL BOGLE	P 8	Lantana Boatyard Inc, FL, USA	17 Sep 1985

Displacement, tons: 93 full load
Dimensions, feet (metres): 105 × 20.6 × 7 *(32 × 6.3 × 2.1)*
Main machinery: 3 MTU 8V 396 TB93 diesels; 3270 hp(m) *(2.4 MW)* sustained; 3 shafts
Speed, knots: 30+
Complement: 20 (4 officers)
Guns: 1 Oerlikon 20 mm. 2—12.7 mm MGs.
Radars: Surface search: Furuno; I band.

Comment: Of all-aluminium construction, launched in 1984. *Paul Bogle* was originally intended for Honduras as the third of the Guardian class. Similar to patrol craft in Honduras and Grenada navies.

PAUL BOGLE   6/1993, JDFCG

3 DAUNTLESS CLASS (INSHORE PATROL CRAFT)

CG 121   CG 122   CG 123

Displacement, tons: 11 full load
Dimensions, feet (metres): 40 × 14 × 4.3 *(12.2 × 4.3 × 1.3)*
Main machinery: 2 Caterpillar 3208TA diesels; 600 hp *(448 kW)*; 2 shafts
Speed, knots: 28. **Range, miles:** 420 at 22 kts
Complement: 5
Guns: 1—7.62 mm MG.
Radars: Surface search: Raytheon; I band.

Comment: Delivered in September and November 1992 and January 1993. Built by SeaArk Marine, Monticello. Aluminium construction.

CG 102   *5/1992, JDFCG*

CG 123   *8/1993, JDFCG*

2 BOSTON WHALER TYPE (INSHORE PATROL CRAFT)

CG 091   CG 092

Displacement, tons: 2.2 full load
Dimensions, feet (metres): 27 × 10 × 1.5 *(8.2 × 3 × 0.5)*
Main machinery: 2 Johnson OMC outboards; 400 hp *(298 kW)*
Speed, knots: 35
Complement: 3
Guns: 1—7.62 mm MG.
Radars: Surface search: Raytheon; I band.

Comment: Delivered in July 1992. Built by Boston Whaler, Rockland.

3 OFFSHORE PERFORMANCE TYPE (INSHORE PATROL CRAFT)

CG 101   CG 102   CG 103

Displacement, tons: 3 full load
Dimensions, feet (metres): 33 × 8 × 1.8 *(10.1 × 2.4 × 0.6)*
Main machinery: 2 Johnson OMC outboards; 450 hp *(336 kW)*
Speed, knots: 48
Complement: 3
Guns: 1—7.62 mm MG.
Radars: Surface search: Raytheon; I band.

Comment: Delivered in April 1992. Built by Offshore Performance Marine, Miami. Used in the anti-narcotics role.

CG 092   *8/1992, JDFCG*

JAPAN (MSDF)

MARITIME SELF-DEFENCE FORCE

Naval Board

Chief of Staff, Maritime Self-Defence Force:
    Admiral Chiaki Hayashizaki
Commander-in-Chief, Self-Defence Fleet:
    Vice Admiral Makoto Yamamoto
Director, Administration, Maritime Staff Office:
    Rear Admiral Kohichi Ishigami

Senior Appointments

Commander Fleet Escort Force:
    Vice Admiral Toshio Muranaka
Commander Submarine Force:
    Vice Admiral Yoshiaki Nishimura

Diplomatic Representation

Defence (Naval) Attaché in London:
    Captain Kazuo Tohyama

Personnel

1994: 46 520 (including Naval Air) plus 3936 civilians

District Flotillas

In addition to the Escort Force there are two Submarine Flotillas (Kure and Yokosuka), two MCM Flotillas (Kure and Yokosuka) and five District Flotillas (Yokosuka, Maizuru, Ohminato, Sasebo and Kure). The District Flotillas are made up of up to six destroyers/frigates, an LST and a number of MCMV and patrol craft.

Bases

Naval—Yokosuka, Kure, Sasebo, Maizuru, Ohminato
Naval Air—Atsugi, Hachinohe, Iwakuni, Kanoya, Komatsujima, Naha, Ozuki, Ohminato, Ohmura, Shimofusa, Tateyama, Tokushima

Strength of the Fleet

Type	Active (Auxiliary)	Building (Projected)
Submarines—Patrol	15 (2)	3 (1)
Destroyers	41 (3)	5 (2)
Frigates	20	—
Fast Attack Hydrofoil—Missile	2	1 (1)
Patrol Craft—Coastal	5	—
LSTs	6	1
LSUs	2	—
Landing Craft (LCU/LSM/LCVP)	24	—
M/S Support Ships	3	(2)
Minehunters—Ocean	3	—
Minesweepers—Coastal	29	3
MSBs	4	—
Training Ships	3	1
Training Support Ships	3	—
S/M Rescue Vessels	2	—
Fleet Support Ships	4	—
Tenders	10	—
Harbour Tankers	34	1
Icebreaker	1	—
Survey and Research Ships	5	1
Cable Layer	1	—
Surtass Ships	2	—

New Construction Programme

1991 1—7200 ton DDG, 1—4400 ton DD, 1—2400 ton SS, 1—490 ton MSC.
1992 1—4400 ton DD, 1—2500 ton SS, 3—490 ton MSC, 1—50 ton PG, 1—4000 ton TV, 1—4200 ton ASE.
1993 1—7200 ton DDG, 1—2700 ton SS, 1—8900 ton LST.
1994 2—4400 ton DD, 1—2700 ton SS, 1—5600 ton MST, 2—490 ton MSC.

Fleet Air Arm

17 Air ASW Sqns: P-3C, P-2J, HSS-2, SH-60J
Six Air Training Sqns: P-3C, YS-11, TC-90, B-65, KM-2, T-5, OH-6, HSS-2, SH-60J
One Air Training Support Squadron: U-36A, EP-3
One Transport Sqn: YS-11, LC-90
One MCM Sqn: MH-53E
Air Training Command (Shimofusa)
Air Wings at Kanoya (Wing 1) (P-3C, P-2J), Hachinohe (Wing 2) (P-3C), Atsugi (Wing 4) (P-3C), Naha (Wing 5) (P-3C), Tateyama (Wing 21) (SH-60J, HSS-2B), Ohmura (Wing 22) (SH-60J), Iwakuni (Wing 31) (P-3C)
The latest 1991-95 procurement plan includes five P-3C, three EP-3, 16 SH-60J, nine UH-60J, one MH-53E and four US-1A

Mercantile Marine

Lloyd's Register of Shipping:

Organisation of the Major Surface Units of Japan (MSDF)

Four Escort Flotillas each consisting of DDH (Flagship); two Air Defence ships and two or so ASW/general purpose Divisions of up to three ships each.

Escort Force (Yokosuka)
Murakumo (DD 118) Flagship

Escort Flotilla 1 (Yokosuka)
Shirane (DDH 143)
48th Destroyer Division
Umigiri (DD 158)
Hamagiri (DD 155)
Setogiri (DD 156)
46th Destroyer Division
Yuugiri (DD 153)
Amagiri (DD 154)
61st Destroyer Division
Asakaze (DDG 169)
Hatakaze (DDG 171)

Escort Flotilla 2 (Sasebo)
Kurama (DDH 144)
47th Destroyer Division
Asagiri (DD 151)
Yamagiri (DD 152)
Sawagiri (DD 157)
44th Destroyer Division
Yamayuki (DD 129)
Matsuyuki (DD 130)
62nd Destroyer Division
Sawakaze (DDG 170)
Kongo (DDG 173)

Escort Flotilla 3 (Maizuru)
Haruna (DDH 141)
42nd Destroyer Division
Mineyuki (DD 124)
Hamayuki (DD 126)
45th Destroyer Division
Setoyuki (DD 131)
Asayuki (DD 132)
Shimayuki (DD 133)
63rd Destroyer Division
Amatsukaze (DDG 163)
Shimakaze (DD 172)

Escort Flotilla 4 (Yokosuka)
Hiei (DDH 142)
1st Destroyer Division
Takatsuki (DD 164)
Tachikaze (DDG 168)
41st Destroyer Division
Hatsuyuki (DD 122)
Shirayuki (DD 123)
Sawayuki (DD 125)
43rd Destroyer Division
Isoyuki (DD 127)
Haruyuki (DD 128)

DELETIONS and CONVERSIONS

Submarines

1991 *Kuroshio* (converted Mar)
1992 *Isoshio* (Mar), *Takashio* (converted July)
1993 *Narushio* (Mar), *Kuroshio* (Dec)

Destroyers

1991 *Yamagumo, Makigumo* (both converted June)
1993 *Teruzuki* (Sep), *Asagumo* (converted Oct), *Akizuki* (Dec)

Frigates

1991 *Mogami* (June)
1992 *Isuzu* (Mar)
1993 *Ooi* (Feb), *Kitakami* (Oct)

Patrol Forces

1991 *PT 12-13* (Oct)
1992 *PB 19-22* (Oct)
1993 *PT 14* (Mar)
1994 *PT 15*

Amphibious Forces

1992 *YF 2097-98, YF 2066-67, YF 2091, YF 2110*
1993 *YF 2068, YF 2070, YF 2071*

Mine Warfare Forces

1992 2 MSC (642, 643) (converted Mar), 2 MSB (707, 708) (Mar)
1993 3 MSC (644-646) (converted)

Auxiliaries

1991 YO 5, YW 1-2, YW 7-9, YO 7-8, YT 35, YT 34
1992 YAS 82 *(Takami)*, YAS 83 *(Iou)*, YW 10
1993 *Utone*, YAS 85 *(Awaji)*, YAS 86 *(Toushi)*, YAS 84 *(Miyaki)*, YT 38-39

PENNANT LIST

Submarines—Patrol

SS 573	Yuushio
SS 574	Mochishio
SS 575	Setoshio
SS 576	Okishio
SS 577	Nadashio
SS 578	Hamashio
SS 579	Akishio
SS 580	Takeshio
SS 581	Yukishio
SS 582	Sachishio
SS 583	Harushio
SS 584	Natsushio
SS 585	Hayashio
SS 586	Arashio
SS 587	Wakashio
SS 588	Fuyushio ((bldg)
SS 589	— (bldg)

Submarines—Auxiliary

ATSS 8004	Takashio
ATSS 8005	Yaeshio

Destroyers

DD 116	Minegumo
DD 117	Natsugumo
DD 118	Murakumo
DD 119	Aokumo
DD 120	Akigumo
DD 121	Yuugumo
DD 122	Hatsuyuki
DD 123	Shirayuki
DD 124	Mineyuki
DD 125	Sawayuki
DD 126	Hamayuki
DD 127	Isoyuki
DD 128	Haruyuki
DD 129	Yamayuki
DD 130	Matsuyuki
DD 131	Setoyuki
DD 132	Asayuki
DD 133	Shimayuki
DD 141	Haruna
DD 142	Hiei
DD 143	Shirane
DD 144	Kurama
DD 151	Asagiri
DD 152	Yamagiri
DD 153	Yuugiri
DD 154	Amagiri
DD 155	Hamagiri
DD 156	Setogiri
DD 157	Sawagiri
DD 158	Umigiri
DD 159	— (bldg)
DD 160	— (bldg)
DD 163	Amatsukaze
DD 164	Takatsuki
DD 165	Kikuzuki
DD 166	Mochizuki
DD 167	Nagatsuki
DD 168	Tachikaze
DD 169	Asakaze
DD 170	Sawakaze
DD 171	Hatakaze
DD 172	Shimakaze
DD 173	Kongo
DD 174	Kirishima (bldg)
DD 175	— (bldg)

Frigates

DE 215	Chikugo
DE 216	Ayase
DE 217	Mikuma
DE 218	Tokachi
DE 219	Iwase
DE 220	Chitose
DE 221	Niyodo
DE 222	Teshio
DE 223	Yoshino
DE 224	Kumano
DE 225	Noshiro
DE 226	Ishikari
DE 227	Yubari
DE 228	Yubetsu
DE 229	Abukuma
DE 230	Jintsu
DE 231	Ohyodo
DE 232	Sendai
DE 233	Chikuma
DE 234	Tone

Patrol Forces

923-927	PB 23-27
821-822	PG 01-02
823	PG 03 (bldg)

Minehunters/Sweepers—Ocean

MSO 301	Yaeyama
MSO 302	Tsushima
MSO 303	Hachijyo

Minesweepers—Coastal

MSC 647	Hashira
MSC 648	Iwai
MSC 649	Hatsushima
MSC 650	Ninoshima
MSC 651	Miyajima
MSC 652	Enoshima
MSC 653	Ukishima
MSC 654	Ooshima
MSC 655	Niijima
MSC 656	Yakushima
MSC 657	Narushima
MSC 658	Chichijima
MSC 659	Torishima
MSC 660	Hahajima
MSC 661	Takashima
MSC 662	Nuwajima
MSC 663	Etajima
MSC 664	Kamishima
MSC 665	Himeshima
MSC 666	Ogishima
MSC 667	Moroshima
MSC 668	Yurishima
MSC 669	Hikoshima
MSC 670	Awashima
MSC 671	Sakushima
MSC 672	Uwajima
MSC 673	Ieshima
MSC 674	Tsukishima
MSC 675	Maejima
MSC 676	Kumejima
MSC 677-678	(bldg)

Minesweeping Boats

709	Kyuu-Go
710	Jyuu-Go
711	Jyuu-Ichi-Go
712	Jyuu-Ni-Go

MCM Support Ships

MMC 951	Souya
MST 462	Hayase
MST 476	Fukue

Amphibious Forces

LST 4101	Atsumi
LST 4102	Motobu
LST 4103	Nemuro
LST 4151	Miura
LST 4152	Ojika
LST 4153	Satsuma
LSU 4171	Yura
LSU 4172	Noto
LCU 2001	Yusotei-Ichi-Go
LCU 2002	Yusotei-Ni-Go

Submarine Depot/Rescue Ships

AS 405	Chiyoda
ASR 402	Fushimi

Fleet Support Ships

AOE 421	Sagami
AOE 422	Towada
AOE 423	Tokiwa
AOE 424	Hamana

Training Ships

TV 3501	Katori
TV 3506	Yamagumo
TV 3507	Makigumo
TV 3508	Kashima

Training Support Ships

ATS 4201	Azuma
ATS 4202	Kurobe

Cable Layer

ARC 482	Muroto

Icebreaker

AGB 5002	Shirase

Survey and Research Ships

AGS 5101	Akashi
AGS 5102	Futami
AGS 5103	Suma
AGS 5104	Wakasa
ASE 6101	Kurihama
ASE 6102	— (bldg)

Surtass Ships

AOS 5201	Hibiki
AOS 5202	Harima

Tenders

ASE	(bldg)
ASU 81-85	
ASY 92	Hiyodori
ASU 7018	Asagumo
YAS 87	Teuri
YAS 88	Murotsu
YAS 89	Tashiro
YAS 90	Miyato
YAS 91	Takane
YAS 92	Muzuki
YAS 93	Yokoze
YAS 94	Sakate
YAS 95	Oumi
YAS 96	Okitsu

SUBMARINES

Note: Operational numbers are to be maintained at 14-16 hulls.

0 + 1 (1) IMPROVED HARUSHIO CLASS

Name	No	Builders	Laid down	Launched	Commissioned
—	SS 590	Kawasaki, Kobe	Dec 1993	1996	1998

Displacement, tons: 2700 standard; 3000 dived

Programmes: First of a new class approved in the 1993 budget and likely to be built at about one a year.
Structure: To be fitted with large flank sonar arrays which are reported as the reason for the increase in displacement over the Harushio class.
Opinion: Experiments have been done by Kawasaki Heavy Industries with an 800 hp Sterling engine under agreement with Kockums, with fuel cells and, on a commercial basis, with MHD propulsion. The Technical Research and Development Institute is conducting tests on the Sterling engine but it seems unlikely that it will be ready in time for the first of class.

5 + 2 HARUSHIO CLASS

Name	No	Builders	Laid down	Launched	Commissioned
HARUSHIO	SS 583	Mitsubishi, Kobe	21 Apr 1987	26 July 1989	30 Nov 1990
NATSUSHIO	SS 584	Kawasaki, Kobe	8 Apr 1988	20 Mar 1990	20 Mar 1991
HAYASHIO	SS 585	Mitsubishi, Kobe	9 Dec 1988	17 Jan 1991	25 Mar 1992
ARASHIO	SS 586	Kawasaki, Kobe	8 Jan 1990	17 Mar 1992	17 Mar 1993
WAKASHIO	SS 587	Mitsubishi, Kobe	12 Dec 1990	22 Jan 1993	1 Mar 1994
FUYUSHIO	SS 588	Kawasaki, Kobe	12 Dec 1991	16 Feb 1994	Mar 1995
—	SS 589	Mitsubishi, Kobe	24 Dec 1992	June 1995	Mar 1997

Displacement, tons: 2450 standard; 2750 (2850, SS 589) dived
Dimensions, feet (metres): 252.6 × 32.8 × 25.3 *(77 × 10 × 7.7)*
Main machinery: Diesel-electric; 2 Kawasaki 12V25/25S diesels; 5520 hp(m) *(4.1 MW)*; 2 Kawasaki alternators; 3.7 MW; 1 Fuji motor; 7200 hp(m) *(5.3 MW)*; 1 shaft
Speed, knots: 12 surfaced; 20+ dived
Complement: 75 (10 officers); 71 (10 officers) (SS 589)

Missiles: SSM: McDonnell Douglas Sub-Harpoon; active radar homing to 130 km *(70 nm)* at 0.9 Mach; warhead 227 kg (fired from torpedo tubes).
Torpedoes: 6—21 in *(533 mm)* tubes. Japanese Type 89; wire-guided (option); active/passive homing to 50 km *(27 nm)*/38 km *(21 nm)* at 40/55 kts; warhead 267 kg; depth to 900 m. Total of 20 SSM and torpedoes.
Countermeasures: ESM: ZLR 3-6; radar warning.
Radars: Surface search: JRC ZPS 6; I band.
Sonars: Hughes/Oki ZQQ 5B; hull-mounted; active/passive search and attack; medium/low frequency.
ZQR 1 towed array similar to BQR 15; passive search; very low frequency.

Programmes: First approved in 1986 estimates and one per year since then.
Structure: The slight growth in all dimensions is a natural evolution from the Yuushio class and includes more noise reduction, towed sonar and wireless aerials, as well as anechoic coating. The last of this class has a slightly larger displacement and a small cutback in the crew as a result of greater systems automation.

ARASHIO   *2/1993, Hachiro Nakai*

10 YUUSHIO CLASS

Name	No	Builders	Laid down	Launched	Commissioned
YUUSHIO	SS 573	Mitsubishi, Kobe	3 Dec 1976	29 Mar 1979	26 Feb 1980
MOCHISHIO	SS 574	Kawasaki, Kobe	9 May 1978	12 Mar 1980	5 Mar 1981
SETOSHIO	SS 575	Mitsubishi, Kobe	17 Apr 1979	10 Feb 1981	17 Mar 1982
OKISHIO	SS 576	Kawasaki, Kobe	17 Apr 1980	5 Mar 1982	1 Mar 1983
NADASHIO	SS 577	Mitsubishi, Kobe	16 Apr 1981	27 Jan 1983	6 Mar 1984
HAMASHIO	SS 578	Kawasaki, Kobe	8 Apr 1982	1 Feb 1984	5 Mar 1985
AKISHIO	SS 579	Mitsubishi, Kobe	15 Apr 1983	22 Jan 1985	5 Mar 1986
TAKESHIO	SS 580	Kawasaki, Kobe	3 Apr 1984	9 Feb 1986	3 Mar 1987
YUKISHIO	SS 581	Mitsubishi, Kobe	11 Apr 1985	23 Jan 1987	11 Mar 1988
SACHISHIO	SS 582	Kawasaki, Kobe	11 Apr 1986	17 Feb 1988	24 Mar 1989

Displacement, tons: 2200; 2250 (SS 574 and 577-582); 2300 (SS 576) standard; 2450 dived
Dimensions, feet (metres): 249.3 × 32.5 × 24.3 *(76 × 9.9 × 7.4)*
Main machinery: Diesel-electric; 2 Kawasaki-MAN V8V24/30ATL diesels; 6800 hp(m) *(5 MW)*; 1 motor; 7200 hp(m) *(5.3 MW)*; 1 shaft
Speed, knots: 12 surfaced; 20+ dived
Complement: 75 (10 officers)

Missiles: SSM: McDonnell Douglas Sub-Harpoon (SS 574, SS 577-582, others may be back-fitted); active radar homing to 130 km *(70 nm)* at 0.9 Mach; warhead 227 kg; fired from torpedo tubes.
Torpedoes: 6—21 in *(533 mm)* tubes amidships. Japanese Type 89; active/passive homing to 50 km *(27 nm)*/38 km *(21 nm)* at 40/55 kts; warhead 267 kg; depth to 900 m. Total of 20 SSM and torpedoes.
Countermeasures: ESM: ZLR 3-6; radar warning.
Radars: Surface search: JRC ZPS 6; I band.
Sonars: Hughes/Oki ZQQ 4 (or 5 in some) (modified BQS 4); bow-mounted; passive/active search and attack; medium/low frequency.
ZQR 1 towed array similar to BQR 15 (in most of the class); passive search; very low frequency.

Programmes: SS 573 approved in FY 1975, SS 574 in FY 1977, SS 575 in FY 1978, SS 576 in FY 1979, SS 577 in FY 1980, SS 578 in FY 1981, SS 579 in FY 1982, SS 580 in FY 1983, SS 581 in FY 1984 and SS 582 in FY 1985.
Modernisation: Towed sonar array fitted in *Okishio* in 1987 and now back-fitted to others in the class. ZQQ 5 is also being retrofitted.
Structure: An enlarged version of the Uzushio class with improved diving depth to 275 m *(900 ft)*. Double hull construction. The towed array is stowed in a conduit on the starboard side of the casing.
Operational: In July 1988 *Nadashio* on the surface collided with a fishing boat which caused much loss of life.

MOCHISHIO   *7/1993, Hachiro Nakai*

2 UZUSHIO CLASS

Name	No	Builders	Laid down	Launched	Commissioned
TAKASHIO	ATSS 8004 (ex-SS 571)	Mitsubishi, Kobe	6 July 1973	30 June 1975	30 Jan 1976
YAESHIO	ATSS 8005 (ex-SS 572)	Kawasaki, Kobe	14 Apr 1975	19 May 1977	7 Mar 1978

Displacement, tons: 1850 standard; 1900 surfaced; 2430 dived

Dimensions, feet (metres): 236.2 × 32.5 × 24.6
(72 × 9.9 × 7.5)

Main machinery: Diesel-electric; 2 Kawasaki-MAN V8V24/30ATL diesels; 6800 hp(m) (5 MW); 1 motor; 7200 hp(m) (5.3 MW); 1 shaft

Speed, knots: 12 surfaced; 20 dived

Complement: 80 (10 officers); 70 plus 20 trainees (ATSS)

Torpedoes: 6—21 in (533 mm) tubes amidships. 20 Japanese Type 89; active/passive homing to 50 km (27 nm)/38 km (21 nm) at 40/55 kts; warhead 267 kg; depth to 900 m.

Countermeasures: ESM: ZLR 3-6; radar warning.

Radars: Surface search: JRC ZPS 4; I band.

Sonars: Hughes/Oki ZQQ 2 (SS 572 has ZQQ 3 in lieu); bow-mounted; passive/active search and attack; medium/low frequency.

Programmes: Being paid off at one a year as new constructions commission.

Structure: Diving depth, 200 m (656 ft). Double-hull construction and 'tear-drop' form, built of high tensile steel to increase diving depth.

Operational: Takashio July 1992, and Yaeshio Dec 1993 became auxiliary training submarines. One of the class may have been fitted with a Sterling engine for trials which started in late 1991.

TAKASHIO   4/1993, Hachiro Nakai

DESTROYERS

2 HATAKAZE CLASS

Name	No	Builders	Laid down	Launched	Commissioned
HATAKAZE	DD 171	Mitsubishi, Nagasaki	20 May 1983	9 Nov 1984	27 Mar 1986
SHIMAKAZE	DD 172	Mitsubishi, Nagasaki	13 Jan 1985	30 Jan 1987	23 Mar 1988

Displacement, tons: 4600 (4650, DD 172) standard; 5500 full load

Dimensions, feet (metres): 492 × 53.8 × 15.7
(150 × 16.4 × 4.8)

Main machinery: COGAG; 2 RR Olympus TM3B gas turbines; 49 400 hp (36.8 MW) sustained; 2 RR Spey SM1A gas turbines; 26 650 hp (19.9 MW) sustained; 2 shafts; cp props

Speed, knots: 30

Complement: 260

Missiles: SSM: 8 McDonnell Douglas Harpoon ❶; active radar homing to 130 km (70 nm) at 0.9 Mach; warhead 227 kg.
SAM: 40 GDC Pomona Standard SM-1MR; Mk 13 Mod 4 launcher ❷; command guidance; semi-active radar homing to 46 km (25 nm) at 2 Mach; height envelope 45-18 288 m (150-60 000 ft).

A/S: Honeywell ASROC Mk 112 octuple launcher ❸; inertial guidance to 1.6-10 km (1-5.4 nm) at 0.9 Mach; payload Mk 46 Mod 5 Neartip. Reload capability.

Guns: 2 FMC 5 in (127 mm)/54 Mk 42 automatic ❹; 85° elevation; 20-40 rounds/minute to 24 km (13 nm) anti-surface; 14 km (7.6 nm) anti-aircraft; weight of shell 32 kg.
2 General Electric/General Dynamics 20 mm Phalanx Mk 15 CIWS ❺; 6 barrels per mounting; 3000 rounds/minute combined to 1.5 km.

Torpedoes: 6—324 mm Type 68 (2 triple) tubes ❻. Honeywell Mk 46 Mod 5 Neartip; anti-submarine; active/passive homing to 11 km (5.9 nm) at 40 kts; warhead 44 kg.

HATAKAZE   (Scale 1 : 1200), Ian Sturton

Countermeasures: Decoys: 2 Loral Hycor SRBOC 6-barrelled Mk 36 chaff launchers; range 4 km (2.2 nm).
ESM/ECM: Melco NOLQ 1/3; intercept/jammer. Fujitsu OLR 9B; intercept.

Combat data systems: OYQ-4 Mod 1 action data automation; Links 11 and 14. SATCOM ❼.

Fire control: Type 2-21C for 127 mm guns. General Electric Mk 74 Mod 13 for Standard.

Radars: Air search: Hughes SPS 52C ❽; 3D; E/F band; range 439 km (240 nm).
Melco OPS 11C ❾.

Surface search: JRC OPS 28 B ❿; G/H band.
Fire control: Two Raytheon SPG 51C ⓫; G/I band.
Melco 2-21 ⓬; I/J band. Type 2-12 ⓭; I band.
Tacan: Nec ORN-6.

Sonars: Nec OQS 4; bow-mounted; active search and attack; medium frequency.

Helicopters: Platform for 1 Mitsubishi HSS-2B Sea King or SH-60J Sea Hawk ⓮.

Programmes: DD 171 provided for in 1981 programme. DD 172 provided for in 1983 programme, ordered 29 March 1984.

HATAKAZE   4/1992, Hachiro Nakai

1 + 3 KONGO CLASS

Name	No	Builders	Laid down	Launched	Commissioned
KONGO	DD 173	Mitsubishi, Nagasaki	8 May 1990	26 Sep 1991	25 Mar 1993
KIRISHIMA	DD 174	Mitsubishi, Nagasaki	7 Apr 1992	19 Aug 1993	Mar 1995
—	DD 175	Mitsubishi, Nagasaki	8 Apr 1993	Sep 1994	Mar 1996
—	DD 176	Ishikawajima Harima, Tokyo	Apr 1995	Sep 1996	Mar 1998

KONGO   (Scale 1 : 1500), Ian Sturton

Displacement, tons: 7250 standard; 9485 full load
Dimensions, feet (metres): 528.2 × 68.9 × 20.3
  (161 × 21 × 6.2)
Main machinery: COGAG; 4 GE LM 2500 gas turbines;
  102 160 hp *(76.21 MW)* sustained; 2 shafts; cp props
Speed, knots: 30. **Range, miles:** 4500 at 20 kts
Complement: 300

Missiles: SSM: 8 McDonnell Douglas Harpoon (2 quad) ❶
  launchers; active radar homing to 130 km *(70 nm)* at
  0.9 Mach; warhead 227 kg.
  SAM: GDC Pomona Standard SM-2MR. FMC Mk 41 (29 cells) forward ❷. Martin Marietta Mk 41 VLS (61 cells) aft ❸; com-
  mand/inertial guidance; semi-active radar homing to 73 km
  (40 nm) at 2 Mach. Total of 90 Standard and ASROC weapons.
  A/S: Vertical launch ASROC; inertial guidance to 1.6-10 km
  (1-5.4 nm); payload Mk 46 Mod 5 Neartip.
Guns: 1 OTO Melara 5 in *(127 mm)*/54 Compatto ❹; 85° elevation; 45 rounds/minute to 16 km *(8.7 nm)*; weight of shell
  32 kg. 2 GE/GD 20 mm/76 Mk 15 Vulcan Phalanx ❺. 6 barrels
  per mounting; 3000 rounds/minute combined to 1.5 km.
Torpedoes: 6—324 mm (2 triple) HOS 302 tubes ❻. Honeywell
  Mk 46 Mod 5 Neartip; anti-submarine; active/passive homing
  to 11 km *(5.9 nm)* at 40 kts; warhead 44 kg.
Countermeasures: Decoys: 4 Mk 36 SRBOC ❼ 6-barrelled
  Mk 36 chaff launchers; SLQ-25 towed torpedo decoy.
  ESM/ECM: Melko NOLQ 2; intercept/jammer.
Combat data systems: Aegis NTDS with Links 11 and 14. SAT-
  COM OE-82C ❽
Fire control: 3 Mk 99 Mod 1 MFCS. Type 2-21 GFCS. Mk 116
  Mod 7 for ASW.
Radars: Air search: RCA SPY 1D ❾; 3D; E/F band.
  Surface search: JRC OPS 28C or D ❿; G/H band.
  Navigation: JRC OPS 20; I band.
  Fire control: 3 SPG 62 ⓫; 1 Mk 2/21 ⓬; I/J band.
  Tacan: UPX 29 IFF.
Sonars: Nec OQS 102 (SQS 53B/C) bow-mounted; active search
    and attack.
  Oki OQR 2 (SQR 19A (V)) TACTASS; towed array; passive; very
    low frequency.

Helicopters: Platform ⓭ and fuelling facilities for SH-60J
  Seahawk.

Programmes: Proposed in the FY 1987 programme; first one
  accepted in FY 1988 estimates, second in FY 1990, third in FY
  1991, fourth in FY 1993. Designated as destroyers but these
  ships are of cruiser size. The combination of cost and US Congressional reluctance to release Aegis technology slowed the
  programme down but the plan is to complete all four by the
  end of 1998.
Structure: This is an enlarged and improved version of the USN
  Arleigh Burke with a lightweight version of the Aegis system.
  There are two missile magazines. OQS 102 plus OQR 2 towed
  array is the equivalent of SQQ 89.
Operational: As well as air defence of the Fleet, these ships are
  planned to contribute to the air defences of mainland Japan.

KONGO   3/1993, Hachiro Nakai

KONGO   4/1993, Hachiro Nakai

KONGO   3/1993, Hachiro Nakai

2 SHIRANE CLASS

Name	No	Builders	Laid down	Launched	Commissioned
SHIRANE	DD 143	Ishikawajima Harima, Tokyo	25 Feb 1977	18 Sep 1978	17 Mar 1980
KURAMA	DD 144	Ishikawajima Harima, Tokyo	17 Feb 1978	20 Sep 1979	27 Mar 1981

KURAMA   (Scale 1 : 1500), Ian Sturton

Displacement, tons: 5200 standard
Dimensions, feet (metres): 521.5 × 57.5 × 17.5
    (159 × 17.5 × 5.3)
Main machinery: 2 IHI boilers; 850 psi *(60 kg/cm sq)*; 900°F
    (480°C); 2 IHI turbines; 70 000 hp(m) *(51.5 MW)*; 2 shafts
Speed, knots: 32
Complement: 350; 360 *(Kurama)*

Missiles: SAM: Raytheon Sea Sparrow Mk 29 octuple launcher
    ❶; semi-active radar homing to 14.6 km *(8 nm)* at 2.5 Mach;
    warhead 39 kg; 24 missiles.
    A/S: Honeywell ASROC Mk 112 octuple launcher ❷; inertial guid-
    ance to 10 km *(5.4 nm)* at 0.9 Mach; payload Mk 46 Mod 5
    Neartip.
Guns: 2 FMC 5 in *(127 mm)*/54 Mk 42 automatic ❸; 85° elev-
    ation; 20-40 rounds/minute to 24 km *(13 nm)* anti-surface;
    14 km *(7.6 nm)* anti-aircraft; weight of shell 32 kg.
    2 General Electric/General Dynamics 20 mm Phalanx Mk 15
    CIWS ❹; 6 barrels per mounting; 3000 rounds/minute com-
    bined to 1.5 km.
Torpedoes: 6—324 mm Type 68 (2 triple) tubes ❺. Honeywell
    Mk 46 Mod 5 Neartip; anti-submarine; active/passive homing
    to 11 km *(5.9 nm)* at 40 kts; warhead 44 kg.
Countermeasures: ESM/ECM: Melco NOLQ 1; intercept/jam-
    mer. Fujitsu OLR 9B; intercept.
    Prairie Masker; blade rate suppression system.
Combat data systems: OYQ-3; Links 11 and 14. SATCOM.
Fire control: Singer Mk 114 for ASROC system. Type 72-1A
    GFCS.
Radars: Air search: Nec OPS 12 ❻; 3D; D band; range 119 km
    (65 nm).
    Surface search: JRC OPS 28 ❼; G/H band.
    Navigation: Koden OFS-2D; I band.
    Fire control: Signaal WM 25 ❽; I/J band; range 46 km *(25 nm)*.
    Two Type 72-1A FCS ❾; I/J band.
    Tacan: ORN-6.
Sonars: EDO/Nec SQS 35(J); VDS; active/passive search;
    medium frequency.
    Nec OQS 101; bow-mounted; low frequency.
    EDO/Nec SQR 18A; towed array; passive; very low frequency.

Helicopters: 3 SH-60J Sea Hawk ❿.

Programmes: One each in 1975 and 1976 programmes.
Modernisation: DD 143 refit in 1989-90. Both fitted with CIWS
    and towed array sonars by mid-1990.
Structure: Fitted with Vosper Thornycroft fin stabilisers. The
    after funnel is set to starboard and the forward one to port. The
    crane is on the starboard after corner of the hangar. Bear Trap
    helicopter haul down gear.
Operational: Both ships now carry Sea Hawk helicopters. *Shi-
    rane* is the Flagship of the 1st Escort Flotilla at Yokosuka, and
    Kurama of the 2nd at Sasebo.

KURAMA   4/1993, Hachiro Nakai

2 HARUNA CLASS

Name	No	Builders	Laid down	Launched	Commissioned
HARUNA	DD 141	Mitsubishi, Nagasaki	19 Mar 1970	1 Feb 1972	22 Feb 1973
HIEI	DD 142	Ishikawajima Harima, Tokyo	8 Mar 1972	13 Aug 1973	27 Nov 1974

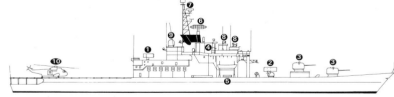

HARUNA   (Scale 1 : 1500), Ian Sturton

Displacement, tons: 4950 (5050, DD 142) standard
Dimensions, feet (metres): 502 × 57.4 × 17.1
    (153 × 17.5 × 5.2)
Main machinery: 2 Mitsubishi (DD 141) or IHI (DD 142) boilers;
    850 psi *(60 kg/cm sq)*; 900°F *(480°C)*; 2 Mitsubishi (DD 141)
    or IHI (DD 142) turbines; 70 000 hp *(51.5 MW)*; 2 shafts
Speed, knots: 31
Complement: 370 (360, DD 142) (36 officers)

Missiles: SAM: Raytheon Sea Sparrow Mk 29 octuple
    launcher ❶; semi-active radar homing to 14.6 km *(8 nm)* at
    2.5 Mach; warhead 39 kg; 24 missiles.
    A/S: Honeywell ASROC Mk 112 octuple launcher ❷; inertial guid-
    ance to 1.6-10 km *(1-5.4 nm)* at 0.9 Mach; payload Mk 46 Mod
    5 Neartip.
Guns: 2 FMC 5 in *(127 mm)*/54 Mk 42 automatic ❸; 85° elev-
    ation; 20-40 rounds/minute to 24 km *(13 nm)* anti-surface;
    14 km *(7.6 nm)* anti-aircraft; weight of shell 32 kg.
    2 General Electric/General Dynamics 20 mm Phalanx Mk 15
    CIWS ❹; 6 barrels per mounting; 3000 rounds/minute com-
    bined to 1.5 km.
Torpedoes: 6—324 mm Type 68 (2 triple) tubes ❺. Honeywell
    Mk 46 Mod 5 Neartip; anti-submarine; active/passive homing
    to 11 km *(5.9 nm)* at 40 kts; warhead 44 kg.
Countermeasures: Decoys: 4 Loral Hycor SRBOC Mk 36 multi-
    barrelled chaff launchers.
    ESM/ECM: Melco NOLQ 1; intercept/jammer. Fujitsu OLR 9;
    intercept.
Combat data systems: OYQ-6 action data automation; Links 11
    and 14. SATCOM.
Fire control: 2 Type 2-12 FCS (one for guns, one for SAM).
Radars: Air search: Melco OPS 11C ❻; D band.
    Surface search: JRC OPS 28 ❼; G/H band.
    Fire control: One Type 1A ❽; I/J band (guns).
    One Type 2-12 ❾; I/J band (SAM).
    IFF: US Mk 10.
    Tacan: Nec ORN-6.
Sonars: Sangamo/Mitsubishi OQS 3; bow-mounted; active
    search and attack; low frequency with bottom bounce.

Helicopters: 3 Mitsubishi HSS-2B Sea King ❿.

Programmes: Ordered under the third five-year defence pro-
    gramme (from 1967-71).
Modernisation: DD 141 taken in hand from 31 March 1986 to 31
    October 1987 for FRAM at Mitsubishi, Nagasaki; DD 142
    received FRAM from 31 August 1987 to 30 March 1989 at IHI,
    Tokyo; included Sea Sparrow, two CIWS and chaff launchers.

HARUNA   11/1993, Hachiro Nakai

Structure: The funnel is offset slightly to port. Fitted with fin
stabilisers. A heavy crane has been fitted on the top of the
hangar, starboard side.

Operational: Fitted with Canadian Beartrap hauldown gear.
Haruna is the Flagship of the 4th Escort Flotilla at Yokosuka
and *Hiei* of the 3rd at Maizuru.

8 ASAGIRI CLASS

Name	No	Builders	Laid down	Launched	Commissioned
ASAGIRI	DD 151	Ishikawajima Harima, Tokyo	13 Feb 1985	19 Sep 1986	17 Mar 1988
YAMAGIRI	DD 152	Mitsui, Tamano	5 Feb 1986	8 Oct 1987	25 Jan 1989
YUUGIRI	DD 153	Sumitomo, Uraga	25 Feb 1986	21 Sep 1987	28 Feb 1989
AMAGIRI	DD 154	Ishikawajima Harima, Tokyo	3 Mar 1986	9 Sep 1987	17 Mar 1989
HAMAGIRI	DD 155	Hitachi, Maizuru	20 Jan 1987	4 June 1988	31 Jan 1990
SETOGIRI	DD 156	Sumitomo, Uraga	9 Mar 1987	12 Sep 1988	14 Feb 1990
SAWAGIRI	DD 157	Mitsubishi, Nagasaki	14 Jan 1987	25 Nov 1988	6 Mar 1990
UMIGIRI	DD 158	Ishikawajima Harima, Tokyo	31 Oct 1988	9 Nov 1989	12 Mar 1991

Displacement, tons: 3500 (3550, DD 155-158) standard; 4200 full load

Dimensions, feet (metres): 449.4 × 48 × 14.6 *(137 × 14.6 × 4.5)*

Main machinery: COGAG; 4 RR Spey SM1A gas turbines; 53 300 hp *(39.8 MW)* sustained; 2 shafts; cp props

Speed, knots: 30+

Complement: 220

Missiles: SSM: 8 McDonnell Douglas Harpoon (2 quad) launchers ❶; active radar homing to 130 km *(70 nm)* at 0.9 Mach; warhead 227 kg.
SAM: Raytheon Sea Sparrow Mk 29 octuple launcher ❷; semi-active radar homing to 14.6 km *(8 nm)* at 2.5 Mach; warhead 39 kg; 20 missiles.
A/S: Honeywell ASROC Mk 112 octuple launcher ❸; inertial guidance to 1.6-10 km *(1-5.4 nm)* at 0.9 Mach; payload Mk 46 Mod 5 Neartip. Reload capability.

Guns: 1 OTO Melara 3 in *(76 mm)*/62 compact ❹; 85° elevation; 85 rounds/minute to 16 km *(8.6 nm)* anti-surface; 12 km *(6.5 nm)* anti-aircraft; weight of shell 6 kg.
2 General Electric/General Dynamics 20 mm Phalanx Mk 15 CIWS ❺; 6 barrels per mounting; 3000 rounds/minute combined to 1.5 km.

Torpedoes: 6—324 mm Type 68 (2 triple) HOS 301 tubes ❻. Honeywell Mk 46 Mod 5 Neartip; anti-submarine; active/passive homing to 11 km *(5.9 nm)* at 40 kts; warhead 44 kg.

Countermeasures: Decoys: 2 Loral Hycor SRBOC 6-barrelled Mk 36 chaff launchers ❼; range 4 km *(2.2 nm)*.
1 SLQ 51 Nixie or Type 4; towed torpedo decoy.
ESM: Nec NOLR 6C or NOLR 8 (DD 152) ❽; intercept.
ECM: Fujitsu OLT-3; jammer.

Combat data systems: OYQ-6 action data automation; Link 11. SATCOM. Helicopter datalink ❾ for SH-60J.

Radars: Air search: Melco OPS 14C (DD 151-154) ❿.
Melco OPS 24 (DD 155-158) ⓫; 3D; D band.
Surface search: JRC OPS 28C ⓬; G/H band.
Fire control: Type 2-22 (for guns) ⓭. Type 2-12E (for SAM) ⓮ (DD 151-154); Type 2-12G (for SAM) ⓯ (DD 155-158).
Tacan: ORN-6.

Sonars: Mitsubishi OQS 4A (II); hull-mounted; active search and attack; low frequency.
OQR-1; towed array; passive search; very low frequency.

Helicopters: 1 Mitsubishi HSS-2B Sea King ⓰ or SH-60J Sea Hawk ⓱.

Programmes: DD 151 in 1983 estimates, DD 152-154 in 1984, DD 155-157 in 1985 and DD 158 in 1986.

Modernisation: The last four have been fitted on build with improved air search radar, updated fire control radars and a helicopter datalink. *Umigiri* also commissioned with a sonar towed array which has been fitted to the rest of the class, as are the other improvements in due course. Sea Hawk helos are replacing the Sea Kings.

Structure: Because of the enhanced IR signature and damage to electronic systems on the mainmast caused by after funnel gases there have been modifications to help contain the problem. The mainmast is now slightly higher than originally designed and has been offset to port, more so in the last four of the class. The forward funnel is also offset slightly to port and the after funnel to the starboard side of the superstructure. The hangar structure is asymmetrical extending to the after funnel on the starboard side but only to the mainmast to port. SATCOM is fitted at the after end of the hangar roof.

Operational: Beartrap helicopter hauldown system.

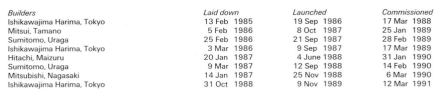

ASAGIRI   *(Scale 1 : 1200), Ian Sturton*

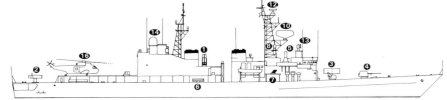

UMIGIRI   *(Scale 1 : 1200), Ian Sturton*

YUUGIRI (with OPS 14C radar)   *8/1992, Hachiro Nakai*

UMIGIRI (with OPS 24 radar)   *4/1992, Hachiro Nakai*

12 HATSUYUKI CLASS

Name	No	Builders	Laid down	Launched	Commissioned
HATSUYUKI	DD 122	Sumitomo, Uraga	14 Mar 1979	7 Nov 1980	23 Mar 1982
SHIRAYUKI	DD 123	Hitachi, Maizuru	3 Dec 1979	4 Aug 1981	8 Feb 1983
MINEYUKI	DD 124	Mitsubishi, Nagasaki	7 May 1981	19 Oct 1982	26 Jan 1984
SAWAYUKI	DD 125	Ishikawajima Harima, Tokyo	22 Apr 1981	21 June 1982	15 Feb 1984
HAMAYUKI	DD 126	Mitsui, Tamano	4 Feb 1981	27 May 1982	18 Nov 1983
ISOYUKI	DD 127	Ishikawajima Harima, Tokyo	20 Apr 1982	19 Sep 1983	23 Jan 1985
HARUYUKI	DD 128	Sumitomo, Uraga	11 Mar 1982	6 Sep 1983	14 Mar 1985
YAMAYUKI	DD 129	Hitachi, Maizuru	25 Feb 1983	10 July 1984	3 Dec 1985
MATSUYUKI	DD 130	Ishikawajima Harima, Tokyo	7 Apr 1983	25 Oct 1984	19 Mar 1986
SETOYUKI	DD 131	Mitsui, Tamano	26 Jan 1984	3 July 1985	11 Dec 1986
ASAYUKI	DD 132	Sumitomo, Uraga	22 Dec 1983	16 Oct 1985	20 Feb 1987
SHIMAYUKI	DD 133	Mitsubishi, Nagasaki	8 May 1984	29 Jan 1986	17 Feb 1987

Displacement, tons: 2950 (3050 from DD 129 onwards) standard; 3700 (3800) full load
Dimensions, feet (metres): 426.4 × 44.6 × 13.8 (14.4 from 129 onwards) *(130 × 13.6 × 4.2) (4.4)*
Main machinery: COGOG; 2 Kawasaki-RR Olympus TM3B gas turbines; 49 400 hp *(36.8 MW)* sustained; 2 RR Type RM1C gas turbines; 9900 hp *(7.4 MW)* sustained; 2 shafts; cp props
Speed, knots: 30
Complement: 195 (200, DD 124 onwards)

Missiles: SSM: 8 McDonnell Douglas Harpoon (2 quad) launchers ❶; active radar homing to 130 km *(70 nm)* at 0.9 Mach; warhead 227 kg.
SAM: Raytheon Sea Sparrow Type 3 (A-1) launcher ❷; semiactive radar homing to 14.6 km *(8 nm)* at 2.5 Mach; warhead 39 kg; 12 missiles.
A/S: Honeywell ASROC Mk 112 octuple launcher ❸; inertial guidance to 1.6-10 km *(1-5.4 nm)* at 0.9 Mach; payload Mk 46 Mod 5 Neartip.
Guns: 1 OTO Melara 3 in *(76 mm)*/62 compact ❹; 85° elevation; 85 rounds/minute to 16 km *(8.6 nm)* anti-surface; 12 km *(6.5 nm)* anti-aircraft; weight of shell 6 kg.
2 General Electric/General Dynamics 20 mm Phalanx Mk 15 CIWS ❺; 6 barrels per mounting; 3000 rounds/minute combined to 1.5 km.
Torpedoes: 6—324 mm Type 68 (2 triple) tubes ❻. Honeywell Mk 46 Mod 5 Neartip; anti-submarine; active/passive homing to 11 km *(5.9 nm)* at 40 kts; warhead 44 kg.
Countermeasures: Decoys: 2 Loral Hycor SRBOC 6-barrelled Mk 36 chaff launchers; range 4 km *(2.2 nm)*.
ESM: Nec NOLR 6C or NOLR 8 (DD 131); intercept.
ECM: Fujitsu OLT 3; jammer.
Combat data systems: OYQ-5 action data automation; Link 14 (receive only).
Radars: Air search: Melco OPS 14B ❼.
Surface search: JRC OPS 18 ❽; G/H band.
Fire control: Type 2-12 A ❾; I/J band (for SAM).
Two Type 2-21/21A ❿; I/J band (for guns).
Tacan: URN 25.
Sonars: Nec OQS 4A (II) (SQS 23 type); bow-mounted; active search and attack; low frequency.
OQR 1 TACTASS (being fitted in all); passive; low frequency.

Helicopters: 1 Mitsubishi HSS-2B Sea King ⓫.

Modernisation: *Shirayuki* retrofitted with Phalanx in early 1992; most of the class equipped by mid-1994. *Matsuyuki* first to get sonar towed array in 1990; the others are being fitted.
Structure: Fitted with fin stabilisers. Steel in place of aluminium alloy for bridge etc after DD 129 which increased displacement.
Operational: Canadian Beartrap helicopter landing aid. Improved ECM equipment in the last three of the class.

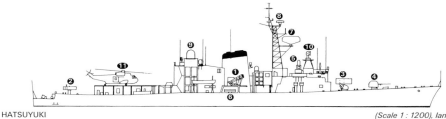

HATSUYUKI   *(Scale 1 : 1200), Ian Sturton*

SHIMAYUKI   *7/1992, John Mortimer*

SHIRAYUKI   *7/1993, Hachiro Nakai*

0 + 2 (2) MODIFIED ASAGIRI CLASS

Name	No	Builders	Laid down	Launched	Commissioned
—	DD 159	Ishikawajima Harima, Yokohama	18 Aug 1993	Aug 1994	Mar 1996
—	DD 160	Mitsui, Tamano	Aug 1994	Aug 1995	Mar 1997

Displacement, tons: 4400 standard; 5100 full load
Dimensions, feet (metres): 495.4 × 55.8 × 17.1
(151 × 17 × 5.2)
Main machinery: COGAG; 2 RR Spey SM1C gas turbines;
41 630 hp *(31 MW)* sustained; 2 GE LM 2500 gas turbines;
43 000 hp *(32.08 MW)* sustained; 2 shafts
Speed, knots: 30
Complement: 160

Missiles: SSM: 8 SSM-1B ❶ (Harpoon).
SAM: Raytheon Mk 48 VLS ❷ Sea Sparrow.
A/S: Mk 41 VL ASROC ❸. Total of 29 missiles.
Guns: 1 OTO Melara 76 mm/62 ❹; 2 Vulcan Phalanx 20 mm ❺.
Torpedoes: 6—324 mm Type 68 (2 triple) tubes ❻ Type 89 (Mk
46 Mod 5).
Countermeasures: Decoys: 4 chaff launchers ❼.
ESM/ECM: Nec NOLR 8; intercept and jammer.
Radars: Air search: Melco OPS 24 ❽; 3D; D band.
Surface search: JRC OPS 28C ❾; G/H band.
Fire control: Two Type 2-31 or Type 3 ❿.
Sonars: Mitsubishi OQS-4A; hull-mounted; active search and
attack; low frequency.
OQR-1 towed array; passive search; very low frequency.

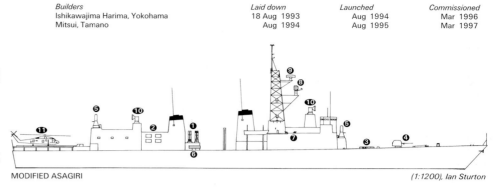

MODIFIED ASAGIRI *(1:1200), Ian Sturton*

Helicopters: 1 SH-60J Seahawk ⓫.

Programmes: First one approved in FY 1991 as an addition to the
third Aegis type destroyer. Second approved in FY 1992. Two
more approved in FY 1994. The plan is to achieve a class of
eight. The programme has been given added priority by the

Kongo class being reduced to four ships because of the cost of
Aegis.

Structure: More like a mini-Kongo than an enlarged Asagiri class,
with VLS and a much reduced complement. Stealth features
are evident in sloping sides and rounded superstructure.

4 TAKATSUKI CLASS

Name	No	Builders	Laid down	Launched	Commissioned
TAKATSUKI	DD 164	Ishikawajima Harima, Tokyo	8 Oct 1964	7 Jan 1966	15 Mar 1967
KIKUZUKI	DD 165	Mitsubishi, Nagasaki	15 Mar 1966	25 Mar 1967	27 Mar 1968
MOCHIZUKI	DD 166	Ishikawajima Harima, Tokyo	22 Nov 1966	15 Mar 1968	25 Mar 1969
NAGATSUKI	DD 167	Mitsubishi, Nagasaki	2 Mar 1968	19 Mar 1969	12 Feb 1970

Displacement, tons: 3250 standard; 3100 (DD 166, 167)
Dimensions, feet (metres): 446.1 × 44 × 14.8
(136 × 13.4 × 4.5)
Main machinery: 2 boilers; 600 psi *(60 kg/cm sq)*; 850°F
(454°C); 2 Mitsubishi turbines; 70 000 hp(m); *(51.5 MW)*;
2 shafts
Speed, knots: 31. **Range, miles:** 7000 at 20 kts
Complement: 260; 270 (DD 166, 167)

Missiles: SSM: 8 McDonnell Douglas Harpoon (2 quad) launchers (DD 164 and 165) ❶; active radar homing to 130 km
(70 nm) at 0.9 Mach; warhead 227 kg.
SAM: Raytheon Sea Sparrow Mk 29 octuple launcher (DD 164,
165) ❷; semi-active radar homing to 14.6 km *(8 nm)* at
2.5 Mach; warhead 39 kg; 16 missiles.
A/S: Honeywell ASROC Mk 112 octuple launcher ❸; inertial guidance to 10 km *(5.4 nm)* at 0.9 Mach; payload Mk 46 Mod 5
Neartip.
Guns: 1 or 2 (DD 166, 167) FMC 5 in *(127 mm)*/54 Mk 42 automatic ❹; 85° elevation; 20-40 rounds/minute to 24 km
(13 nm) anti-surface; 14 km *(7.6 nm)* anti-aircraft; weight of
shell 32 kg.
1 General Electric/General Dynamics 20 mm Phalanx CIWS
Mk 15 (DD 164, 165) ❺; 6 barrels per mounting; 3000 rounds/
minute combined to 1.5 km.
Torpedoes: 6—324 mm Type 68 (2 triple) tubes ❻. Honeywell
Mk 46 Mod 5 Neartip; anti-submarine; active/passive homing
to 11 km *(5.9 nm)* at 40 kts; warhead 44 kg.
A/S mortars: 1—375 mm Bofors Type 71 4-barrelled trainable
rocket launcher ❼; automatic loading; range 1.6 km.
Countermeasures: Decoys: 2 Loral Hycor SRBOC 6-barrelled Mk
36 chaff launchers; range 4 km *(2.2 nm)*.
ESM: Nec NOLR 6C (NOLR 9 in DD 165); intercept.
ECM: Fujitsu OLT 3; jammer.
Combat data systems: OYQ-5 (DD 164 and 165) action data
automation; Link 14. SATCOM.
Fire control: US Mk 56 or GFCS-1 for 127 mm guns. Type 2-12B
for Sea Sparrow system (DD 164, 165).
Radars: Air search: Melco OPS 11B ❽.
Surface search: JRC OPS 17 ❾; G/H band.
Fire control: Type 2-12B ❿; I/J band (DD 164, 165).
2 General Electric Mk 35 ⓫; I/J band.
Sonars: Nec SQS 35J; hull-mounted; active search and attack;
low frequency.
EDO SQR 18 TACTASS (DD 164, 165); passive; low frequency.

Modernisation: From 1 April 1984 to 31 October 1985 DD 164
taken in hand for modifications to include removal of after 5 in
gun and Dash hangar, fitting of Harpoon and Sea Sparrow, removal of VDS and its replacement by TASS, installation of
FCS-2, and fittings for one 20 mm Phalanx mounting on after
superstructure. Similar alterations carried out in DD 165 from
May 1985 to December 1986. Phalanx not fitted in DD 164
until 1989. NOLR 9 installed in DD 165 for trials in 1991/92.

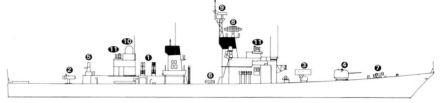

TAKATSUKI *(Scale 1 : 1200), Ian Sturton*

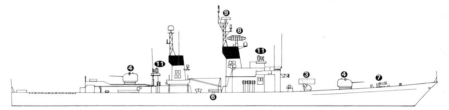

NAGATSUKI *(Scale 1 : 1200), Ian Sturton*

MOCHIZUKI (unmodified) *1/1993, Hachiro Nakai*

Operational: Two unmodified ships of the class were expected
to pay off in 1992 but have been retained in service.

TAKATSUKI (modified) *4/1993, Hachiro Nakai*

3 TACHIKAZE CLASS

Name	No	Builders	Laid down	Launched	Commissioned
TACHIKAZE	DD 168	Mitsubishi, Nagasaki	19 June 1973	17 Dec 1974	26 Mar 1976
ASAKAZE	DD 169	Mitsubishi, Nagasaki	27 May 1976	15 Oct 1977	27 Mar 1979
SAWAKAZE	DD 170	Mitsubishi, Nagasaki	14 Sep 1979	4 June 1981	30 Mar 1983

Displacement, tons: 3850 (3950, DD 170) standard
Dimensions, feet (metres): 469 × 47 × 15.4
(143 × 14.3 × 4.7)
Main machinery: 2 Mitsubishi boilers; 600 psi *(60 kg/cm sq)*;
850°F *(454°C)*; 2 Mitsubishi turbines; 70 000 hp(m);
(51.5 MW); 2 shafts
Speed, knots: 32
Complement: 250; 255 (D 170)

Missiles: SSM: 8 McDonnell Douglas Harpoon; active radar homing to 130 km *(70 nm)* at 0.9 Mach; warhead 227 kg HE.
SAM: GDC Pomona Standard SM-1MR; Mk 13 Mod 3 or 4
launcher ❶; command guidance; semi-active radar homing to
46 km *(25 nm)* at 2 Mach; height envelope 45-18 288 m *(150-
60 000 ft)*; 40 missiles (SSM and SAM combined).
A/S: Honeywell ASROC Mk 112 octuple launcher ❷; inertial guidance to 1.6-10 km *(1-5.4 nm)* at 0.9 Mach; payload Mk 46 Mod
5 Neartip. Reloads in DD 170 only.
Guns: 2 FMC 5 in *(127 mm)*/54 Mk 42 automatic ❸; 85° elevation; 20-40 rounds/minute to 24 km *(13 nm)* anti-surface;
14 km *(7.6 nm)* anti-aircraft; weight of shell 32 kg.
2 General Electric/General Dynamics 20 mm Phalanx CIWS
Mk 15 ❹; 6 barrels per mounting; 3000 rounds/minute com-
bined to 1.5 km.
Torpedoes: 6—324 mm Type 68 (2 triple) tubes ❺. Honeywell
Mk 46 Mod 5 Neartip; anti-submarine; active/passive homing
to 11 km *(5.9 nm)* at 40 kts; warhead 44 kg.
Countermeasures: Decoys: 4 Loral Hycor SRBOC Mk 36 multi-
barrelled chaff launchers.
ESM: Nec NOLR 6 (DD 168); Nec NOLQ 1 (others); intercept.
ECM: Fujitsu OLT 3; jammer.
Combat data systems: OYQ-1B (DD 168), OYQ-2B (DD 169),
OYQ-4 (DD 170) action data automation; Links 11 and 14.
SATCOM.
Fire control: 2 Mk 74 Mod 13 missile control directors. US Mk
114 ASW control. GFCS-2-21 for gun (DD 170). GFCS-72-1A for
gun (others).
Radars: Air search: Melco OPS 11 ❻.
Hughes SPS 52B ❼ or 52C (DD 170) ❼; 3D; E/F band; range
439 km *(240 nm)*.
Surface search: JRC OPS 16 ❽; D band.
JRC OPS 28 (DD 170) ❽; G/H band.
Fire control: Two Raytheon SPG 51 ❾; G/I band.
Type 2 FCS ❿; I/J band.
IFF: US Mk 10.

TACHIKAZE   *(Scale 1 : 1200), Ian Sturton*

ASAKAZE   *8/1992, Hachiro Nakai*

Sonars: Nec OQS-3A (Type 66); bow-mounted; active search and
attack; low frequency.

Modernisation: Harpoon and CIWS added to DD 168 in 1983,
DD 169 and 170 in 1987.

1 AMATSUKAZE CLASS

Name	No	Builders	Laid down	Launched	Commissioned
AMATSUKAZE	DD 163	Mitsubishi, Nagasaki	29 Nov 1962	5 Oct 1963	15 Feb 1965

Displacement, tons: 3050 standard; 4000 full load
Dimensions, feet (metres): 429.8 × 44 × 13.8
(131 × 13.4 × 4.2)
Main machinery: 2 IHI boilers 540 psi *(38 kg/cm sq)*; 820°F
(438°C); 2 IHI turbines; 60 000 hp(m) *(44 MW)*; 2 shafts
Speed, knots: 33. **Range, miles:** 7000 at 18 kts
Complement: 290

Missiles: SAM: 40 GDC Pomona Standard SM-1MR; Mk 13 Mod
0 launcher ❶; command guidance; semi-active radar homing
to 46 km *(25 nm)* at 2 Mach; height envelope 45-18 288 m
(150-60 000 ft).
A/S: Honeywell ASROC Mk 112 octuple launcher ❷; inertial guidance to 1.6-10 km *(1-5.4 nm)* at 0.9 Mach; payload Mk 46 Mod
5 Neartip.
Guns: 4 USN 3 in *(76 mm)*/50 Mk 33 (2 twin) ❸; 85° elevation;
50 rounds/minute to 12.8 km *(6.9 nm)*; weight of shell 6 kg.
Torpedoes: 6—324 mm Type 68 (2 triple) tubes ❹. Honeywell
Mk 46 Mod 5 Neartip; anti-submarine; active/passive homing
to 11 km *(5.9 nm)* at 40 kts; warhead 44 kg.
A/S mortars: 2 USN Hedgehog Mk 15 trainable rocket launch-
ers; manually loaded; range 350 m; warhead 26 kg.
Countermeasures: ESM: Nec NOLR 6; intercept.
ECM: Fujitsu OLT 3; jammer.
Fire control: Japanese Type 2-21 system for 76 mm guns.

AMATSUKAZE   *(Scale 1 : 1200), Ian Sturton*

Radars: Air search: Hughes SPS 52 ❺; 3D; E/F band.
Westinghouse SPS 29A ❻; B/C band; range 457 km
(250 nm).
Surface search: JRC OPS 17 ❼; G/H band.
Fire control: Two Raytheon SPG 51C ❽; G/I band (for Standard).
Type 2-21 ❾; I/J band.
Sonars: Sangamo SQS 23G; hull-mounted; active search and
attack; low frequency.

Programmes: Ordered under the 1960 programme.
Modernisation: Refitted in 1967 when A/S tubes and new sonar
were fitted. In 1968 equipped with ASROC launcher between
funnels. SATCOM fitted in 1991. Further planned modernisation (life extension programme) to include OTO Melara
76 mm guns and Phalanx CIWS has been cancelled and the
ship will pay off in 1995.

AMATSUKAZE   *4/1993, Hachiro Nakai*

3 YAMAGUMO CLASS

Name	No	Builders	Laid down	Launched	Commissioned
AOKUMO	DD 119	Sumitomo, Uraga	2 Oct 1970	30 Mar 1972	25 Nov 1972
AKIGUMO	DD 120	Sumitomo, Uraga	7 July 1972	23 Oct 1973	24 July 1974
YUUGUMO	DD 121	Sumitomo, Uraga	4 Feb 1976	31 May 1977	24 Mar 1978

Displacement, tons: 2150 standard
Dimensions, feet (metres): 377.2 × 38.7 × 13.1
(114.9 × 11.8 × 4)
Main machinery: 6 Mitsubishi 12UEV30/40N diesels;
21 600 hp(m) *(15.9 MW)*; 2 shafts
Speed, knots: 27. **Range, miles:** 7000 at 20 kts
Complement: 210 (19 officers)

Missiles: A/S: Honeywell ASROC Mk 112 octuple launcher ❶;
inertial guidance to 1.6-10 km *(1-5.4 nm)* at 0.9 Mach; payload
Mk 46 Mod 5 Neartip.
Guns: 4 USN 3 in *(76 mm)*/50 Mk 33 (2 twin) ❷; 85° elevation;
50 rounds/minute to 12.8 km *(6.9 nm)*; weight of shell 6 kg.
Torpedoes: 6—324 mm Type 68 (2 triple) tubes ❸. Honeywell
Mk 46 Mod 5 Neartip; anti-submarine; active/passive homing
to 11 km *(5.9 nm)* at 40 kts; warhead 44 kg.
A/S mortars: 1 Bofors 375 mm Type 71 4-barrelled trainable
rocket launcher ❹; automatic loading; range 1.6 km.
Countermeasures: ESM: Nec NOLR 6; radar intercept.
Fire control: Japanese GFCS-1 for 76 mm guns.
Radars: Air search: Melco OPS 11 ❺.
Surface search: JRC OPS 17 ❻; G/H band.
Fire control: Two General Electric Mk 35 ❼; I/J band.
IFF: US Mk 10.
Sonars: Nec OQS 3A; hull mounted; active search and attack;
medium frequency.
EDO SQS 35(J) (DD 120, 121); VDS; active/passive search;
medium frequency.

Operational: The first two of the class were converted to Training
Ships on 20 June 1991 and the third became a Submarine
Support Ship on 18 October 1993.

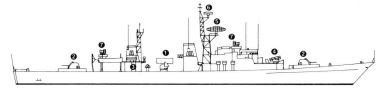

YUUGUMO   *(Scale 1 : 1200), Ian Sturton*

AOKUMO   *11/1993, Hachiro Nakai*

3 MINEGUMO CLASS

Name	No	Builders	Laid down	Launched	Commissioned
MINEGUMO	DD 116	Mitsui, Tamano	14 Mar 1967	16 Dec 1967	31 Aug 1968
NATSUGUMO	DD 117	Sumitomo, Uraga	30 June 1967	25 July 1968	15 May 1969
MURAKUMO	DD 118	Hitachi, Maizuru	19 Oct 1968	15 Nov 1969	21 Aug 1970

Displacement, tons: 2100 (2150, DD 118) standard
Dimensions, feet (metres): 373.9 (377.2, DD 118) × 38.7 × 13.1
(114 (115) × 11.8 × 4)
Main machinery: 6 Mitsubishi 12UEV30/40N diesels;
21 600 hp(m) *(15.9 MW)*; 2 shafts
Speed, knots: 27. **Range, miles:** 7000 at 20 kts
Complement: 210 (220, DD 118) (19 officers)

Missiles: A/S: Honeywell ASROC Mk 112 octuple launcher ❶;
inertial guidance to 1.6-10 km *(1-5.4 nm)* at 0.9 Mach; payload
Mk 46 Mod 5 Neartip.
Guns: 4 USN 3 in *(76 mm)*/50 Mk 33 (2 twin) (only 2 in DD 118)
❷; 85° elevation; 50 rounds/minute to 12.8 km *(6.9 nm)*;
weight of shell 6 kg.
1 FMC/OTO Melara 3 in *(76 mm)*/62 Mk 75 compact (DD 118
only) ❸; 85° elevation; 50 rounds/minute to 16 km *(8.6 nm)*
anti-surface; 12 km *(6.5 nm)* anti-aircraft; weight of shell 6 kg.
Torpedoes: 6—324 mm Type 68 (2 triple) tubes ❹. Honeywell
Mk 46 Mod 5 Neartip; anti-submarine; active/passive homing
to 11 km *(5.9 nm)* at 40 kts; warhead 44 kg.
A/S mortars: 1 Bofors 375 mm Type 71 4-barrelled trainable
rocket launcher ❺; automatic loading; range 1.6 km.
Countermeasures: ESM: Nec NOLR 5; intercept.
Fire control: Japanese Type 2 for guns.
Radars: Air search: Melco OPS 11 ❻.
Surface search: JRC OPS 17 ❼; G/H band.
Fire control: Type 2-12B ❽; I/J band.
Western Electric SPG 34 (DD 118 only).
Type 1A FCS ❾.
IFF: US Mk 10.
Sonars: Nec OQS 3; hull-mounted; active/passive; medium
frequency.
EDO SQS 36(J) (DD 118); VDS; active/passive search; medium
frequency.

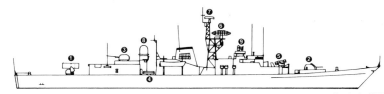

MURAKUMO   *(Scale 1 : 1200), Ian Sturton*

MINEGUMO (with SATCOM)   *3/1992, Hachiro Nakai*

Programmes: As completed the three Minegumo class had the
same basic characteristics as the early Yamagumo.
Modernisation: ASROC replaced the Dash ASW helicopter. In

1978 DD 118 was rearmed with an OTO Melara 76 mm replacing one USN Mk 33 mounting. SATCOM fitted for
deployments.

MURAKUMO (with OTO Melara gun)   *4/1993, Hachiro Nakai*

FRIGATES

6 ABUKUMA CLASS

Name	No	Builders	Laid down	Launched	Commissioned
ABUKUMA	DE 229	Mitsui, Tamano	17 Mar 1988	21 Dec 1988	12 Dec 1989
JINTSU	DE 230	Hitachi, Maizuru	14 Apr 1988	31 Jan 1989	28 Feb 1990
OHYODO	DE 231	Mitsui, Tamano	8 Mar 1989	19 Dec 1989	23 Jan 1991
SENDAI	DE 232	Sumitomo, Uraga	14 Apr 1989	26 Jan 1990	15 Mar 1991
CHIKUMA	DE 233	Hitachi, Maizuru	14 Feb 1991	22 Jan 1992	24 Feb 1993
TONE	DE 234	Sumitomo, Uraga	8 Feb 1991	6 Dec 1991	8 Feb 1993

Displacement, tons: 2050 standard; 2550 full load
Dimensions, feet (metres): 357.6 × 44 × 12.5
(109 × 13.4 × 3.8)
Main machinery: CODOG; 2 RR Spey SM1A gas turbines;
26 650 hp *(19.9 MW)* sustained; 2 Mitsubishi S12U-MTK die-
sels; 6000 hp(m) *(4.4 MW)*; 2 shafts
Speed, knots: 27
Complement: 115

Missiles: SSM: 8 McDonnell Douglas Harpoon (2 quad) launchers ❶; active radar homing to 130 km *(70 nm)* at 0.9 Mach;
warhead 227 kg.
A/S: Honeywell ASROC Mk 112 octuple launcher ❷; inertial guidance to 1.6-10 km *(1-5.4 nm)* at 0.9 Mach; payload Mk 46 Mod
5 Neartip.
Guns: 1 OTO Melara 3 in *(76 mm)*/62 compact ❸; 85° elevation;
85 rounds/minute to 16 km *(8.6 nm)* anti-surface; 12 km
(6.5 nm) anti-aircraft; weight of shell 6 kg.
1 General Electric/General Dynamics 20 mm Phalanx CIWS
Mk 15 ❹; 6 barrels per mounting; 3000 rounds/minute combined to 1.5 km.
Torpedoes: 6—324 mm Type 68 (2 triple) tubes ❺. Honeywell
Mk 46 Mod 5 Neartip; anti-submarine; active/passive homing
to 11 km *(5.9 nm)* at 40 kts; warhead 44 kg.
Countermeasures: Decoys: 2 Loral Hycor SRBOC 6-barrelled Mk
36 chaff launchers.

ESM: Nec NOLQ-6C; intercept.
ECM: Fujitsu OLT-3; jammer.
Radars: Air search: Melco OPS 14C ❻.
Surface search: JRC OPS 28 ❼; G/H band.
Fire control: Type 2-21 ❽.
Sonars: Hitachi OQS-8; hull-mounted; active search and attack;
medium frequency.
SQR 19A towed passive array in due course.

Programmes: First pair of this class approved in 1986 estimates,
ordered March 1987; second pair in 1987 estimates, ordered
February 1988; last two in 1989 estimates, ordered 24 January 1989. The name of the first of class was last used for a light
cruiser which was sunk in the battle of Leyte Gulf in October
1944.
Structure: Stealth features include non-vertical and rounded surfaces. German RAM PDMS may be fitted later and space has
been left for a towed sonar array. SATCOM fitted aft of the after
funnel.

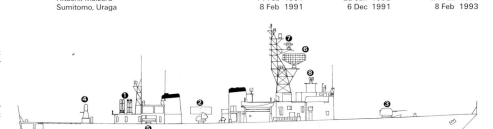

ABUKUMA   *(Scale 1 : 900), Ian Sturton*

JINTSU   *6/1993, Hachiro Nakai*

2 YUBARI CLASS

Name	No	Builders	Laid down	Launched	Commissioned
YUBARI	DE 227	Sumitomo, Uraga	9 Feb 1981	22 Feb 1982	18 Mar 1983
YUBETSU	DE 228	Hitachi, Maizuru	14 Jan 1982	25 Jan 1983	14 Feb 1984

Displacement, tons: 1470 standard; 1690 full load
Dimensions, feet (metres): 298.5 × 35.4 × 11.8
(91 × 10.8 × 3.6)
Main machinery: CODOG; 1 Kawasaki/RR Olympus TM3B gas
turbine; 24 700 hp *(18.4 MW)* sustained; 1 Mitsubishi/MAN
6DRV diesel; 4700 hp(m) *(3.45 MW)*; 2 shafts; cp props
Speed, knots: 25
Complement: 95

Missiles: SSM: 8 McDonnell Douglas Harpoon (2 quad) launchers ❶; active radar homing to 130 km *(70 nm)* at 0.9 Mach;
warhead 227 kg.
Guns: 1 OTO Melara 3 in *(76 mm)*/62 compact ❷; 85° elevation;
85 rounds/minute to 16 km *(8.6 nm)* anti-surface; 12 km
(6.5 nm) anti-aircraft; weight of shell 6 kg.
1 General Electric/General Dynamics 20 mm Phalanx CIWS
Mk 15 (not yet fitted) ❸; 6 barrels per mounting; 3000 rounds/
minute combined to 1.5 km.
Torpedoes: 6—324 mm Type 68 (2 triple) tubes ❹. Honeywell
Mk 46 Mod 5 Neartip; anti-submarine; active/passive homing
to 11 km *(5.9 nm)* at 40 kts; warhead 44 kg.
A/S mortars: 1—375 mm Bofors Type 71 4-6-barrelled trainable
rocket launcher ❺; automatic loading; range 1.6 km.
Countermeasures: Decoys: 2 Loral Hycor SRBOC 6-barrelled Mk
36 chaff launchers ❻; range 4 km *(2.2 nm)*.
ESM: Nec NOLQ 6C ❼; intercept.
ECM: Fujitsu OLT 3; jammer.
Fire control: Type 2-21 system for 76 mm guns.
Radars: Surface search: JRC OPS 28C ❽; G/H band.
Navigation: Fujitsu OPS 19B; I band.
Fire control: Type 2-21 ❾; I/J band.
Sonars: Nec SQS 36J; hull-mounted; active/passive; medium
frequency.

Programmes: The *Yubari* design is based on experience with *Ishikari* (DE 226).
Structure: The increased space for the same weapons systems
as *Ishikari* has meant improved accommodation and an
increase in fuel oil carried.

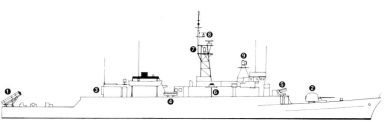

YUBARI   *(Scale 1 : 900), Ian Sturton*

YUBARI (Phalanx not fitted)   *3/1992, Hachiro Nakai*

1 ISHIKARI CLASS

Name	No	Builders	Laid down	Launched	Commissioned
ISHIKARI	DE 226	Mitsui, Tamano	17 May 1979	18 Mar 1980	28 Mar 1981

Displacement, tons: 1290 standard; 1450 full load
Dimensions, feet (metres): 278.8 × 34.7 × 11.5
(85 × 10.6 × 3.5)
Main machinery: CODOG; 1 Kawasaki/RR Olympus TM3B gas turbine; 24 700 hp (18.4 MW); 1 Mitsubishi/MAN 6DRV diesel; 4700 hp(m) (3.45 MW); 2 shafts; cp props
Speed, knots: 25
Complement: 90

Missiles: SSM: 8 McDonnell Douglas Harpoon (2 quad) launchers ❶; active radar homing to 130 km (70 nm) at 0.9 Mach; warhead 227 kg.
Guns: 1 OTO Melara 3 in (76 mm)/62 compact ❷; 85° elevation; 85 rounds/minute to 16 km (8.6 nm) anti-surface; 12 km (6.5 nm) anti-aircraft; weight of shell 6 kg.
Torpedoes: 6—324 mm Type 68 (2 triple) tubes ❸. Honeywell Mk 46 Mod 5 Neartip; anti-submarine; active/passive homing to 11 km (5.9 nm) at 40 kts; warhead 44 kg.
A/S mortars: 1—375 mm Bofors Type 71 4-barrelled trainable rocket launcher ❹; automatic loading; range 1.6 km.
Countermeasures: Decoys: 1 Loral Hycor SRBOC 6-barrelled Mk 36 chaff launcher ❺; range 4 km (2.2 nm).
ESM: Nec NOLQ 6C ❻; intercept.
ECM: Fujitsu OLT 2; jammer.
Fire control: Type 2-21 system for 76 mm gun.
Radars: Surface search: JRC OPS 28 ❼; G/H band.
Navigation: Fujitsu OPS 19B; I band.
Fire control: Type 2-21 FCS ❽; I/J band.
Sonars: Nec SQS 36D(J); hull-mounted; active/passive; low frequency.

Programmes: The Japanese had not constructed a frigate since the Chikugo class, which was designed in the mid-1960s. The development of so many new systems since that time probably dictated the need for a prototype.
Modernisation: To be fitted with Vulcan Phalanx when available.

ISHIKARI (Scale 1 : 900), Ian Sturton

ISHIKARI 11/1987, Hachiro Nakai

11 CHIKUGO CLASS

Name	No	Builders	Laid down	Launched	Commissioned
CHIKUGO	DE 215	Mitsui, Tamano	9 Dec 1968	13 Jan 1970	31 July 1970
AYASE	DE 216	Ishikawajima Harima	5 Dec 1969	16 Sep 1970	20 May 1971
MIKUMA	DE 217	Mitsui, Tamano	17 Mar 1970	16 Feb 1971	26 Aug 1971
TOKACHI	DE 218	Mitsui, Tamano	11 Dec 1970	25 Nov 1971	17 May 1972
IWASE	DE 219	Mitsui, Tamano	6 Aug 1971	29 June 1972	12 Dec 1972
CHITOSE	DE 220	Hitachi, Maizuru	7 Oct 1971	25 Jan 1973	31 Aug 1973
NIYODO	DE 221	Mitsui, Tamano	20 Sep 1972	28 Aug 1973	8 Feb 1974
TESHIO	DE 222	Hitachi, Maizuru	11 July 1973	29 May 1974	10 Jan 1975
YOSHINO	DE 223	Mitsui, Tamano	28 Sep 1973	22 Aug 1974	6 Feb 1975
KUMANO	DE 224	Hitachi, Maizuru	29 May 1974	24 Feb 1975	19 Nov 1975
NOSHIRO	DE 225	Mitsui, Tamano	27 Jan 1976	23 Dec 1976	30 June 1977

Displacement, tons: 1470 (DE 215, 217-219 and 221); 1480 (DE 216, 220); 1500 (DE 222 onwards) standard
Dimensions, feet (metres): 305 × 35.5 × 11.5
(93 × 10.8 × 3.5)
Main machinery: 4 Mitsubishi-Burmeister & Wain UEV 30/40 diesels; 16 000 hp(m) (11.8 MW) (Mitsui ships)
4 Matsui 228 V 3BU-38V diesels; 16 000 hp(m) (11.8 MW) (Hitachi ships); 2 shafts
Speed, knots: 25. **Range, miles:** 10 900 at 12 kts
Complement: 160 (12 officers)

Missiles: A/S: Honeywell ASROC Mk 112 octuple launcher ❶; inertial guidance to 1.6-10 km (1-5.4 nm) at 0.9 Mach; payload Mk 46 Mod 5 Neartip.
Guns: 2 USN 3 in (76 mm)/50 Mk 33 (twin) ❷; 85° elevation; 50 rounds/minute to 12.8 km (6.9 nm); weight of shell 6 kg.
2 Bofors 40 mm/60 Mk 1 (twin) ❸; 80° elevation; 120 rounds/minute to 10 km (5.4 nm) anti-surface; 3 km (1.6 nm) anti-aircraft; weight of shell 0.89 kg.
Torpedoes: 6—324 mm Type 68 (2 triple) tubes ❹. Honeywell Mk 46 Mod 5 Neartip; anti-submarine; active/passive homing to 11 km (5.9 nm) at 40 kts; warhead 44 kg.

TESHIO (Scale 1 : 900), Ian Sturton

Countermeasures: ESM: Nec NORL 5 ❺; intercept.
Fire control: GFCS-1 for 76 mm gun. Mk 51 GFCS for 40 mm gun.
Radars: Air search: Melco OPS 14 ❻.
Surface search: JRC OPS 16 ❼; D band.
Fire control: Type 1B ❽; I/J band.
IFF: US Mk 10.

Sonars: Hitachi OQS 3A; hull-mounted; active search and attack; medium frequency.
EDO SPS 35(J) (in last five ships only); VDS; active/passive search; medium frequency.
Structure: These are the smallest warships to mount ASROC.

YOSHINO 6/1993, Hachiro Nakai

SHIPBORNE AIRCRAFT

Numbers/Type: 70 Mitsubishi SH-3A (HSS-2B) Sea King.
Operational speed: 120 kts *(222 km/h)*.
Service ceiling: 12 200 ft *(3720 m)*.
Range: 630 nm *(1165 km)*.
Role/Weapon systems: Shipborne ASW helicopter and surface search. Production completed in 1990. 13 are earmarked for shipborne operations, the rest are land based. Sensors: Search radar, ESM ALR 66(V)1, Bendix AQS-13 dipping sonar. Weapons: ASW; 4 × Mk 46 torpedoes or depth bombs.

SEA KING   *3/1992, A Sheldon Duplaix*

Numbers/Type: 36 Sikorsky/Mitsubishi SH-60J Seahawk.
Operational speed: 135 kts *(250 km/h)*.
Service ceiling: 12 500 ft *(3810 m)*.
Range: 600 nm *(1110 km)*.
Role/Weapon systems: ASW and ASV helicopter; started replacing SH-3A/HSS-2 in July 1991; being built in Japan; prototypes fitted by Mitsubishi with Japanese avionics and mission equipment. Total of 48 authorised by the end of 1992. Plans include up to 100 plus 18 UH-60J for SAR. Sensors: Search radar; sonobuoys plus datalink; Bendix AQS 18/Nippon HQS 103 dipping sonar, ECM, HLR 108 ESM. Weapons: ASW; 2 × Mk 46 torpedoes or depth bombs. ASV; possible missile armament.

SEAHAWK   *9/1992, Hachiro Nakai*

LAND-BASED MARITIME AIRCRAFT (FRONT LINE)

Numbers/Type: 95/2 Kawasaki P-3C/EP3 Update II/III Orion.
Operational speed: 410 kts *(760 km/h)*.
Service ceiling: 28 300 ft *(8625 m)*.
Range: 4000 nm *(7410 km)*.
Role/Weapon systems: Long-range MR/ASW and surface surveillance and attack to supplement and replace P-2Js. Two EW version EP-3. The aim is a total of 103 by 1996 including four EP-3. Sensors: APS-115 radar, ASQ-81 MAD, AQA 7 processor, AQS-114 computer, IFF, ECM, ALQ 78, ESM, ALR 66, sonobuoys. Weapons: ASW; 8 × Mk 46 torpedoes, depth bombs or mines, 10 underwing stations for Harpoon and ASM-1.

ORION   *8/1993, Hachiro Nakai*

Numbers/Type: 7 Shin Meiwa US-1A.
Operational speed: 295 kts *(546 km/h)*.
Service ceiling: 29 500 ft *(9000 m)*.
Range: 2060 nm *(3817 km)*.
Role/Weapon systems: Long-range amphibian aircraft used only for SAR. To be augmented by three BAe U-125A. Sensors: Search radar. Weapons: Unarmed.

US-1A   *7/1993, Hachiro Nakai*

Numbers/Type: 6 Kawasaki P-2J.
Operational speed: 217 kts *(402 km/h)*.
Service ceiling: 30 000 ft *(9150 m)*.
Range: 2400 nm *(4450 km)*.
Role/Weapon systems: Long-range MR/ASW being phased out. Remainder to be deleted in 1994. Sensors: APS-80 search radar, ESM, ALQ 101, MAD, smoke detector, Tacan and sonobuoy processor, EW, some aircraft equipped for Elint. Weapons: ASW; Mk 46 torpedoes, depth bombs or mines.

Numbers/Type: 10 Sikorsky/Mitsubishi S-80M-1 Sea Dragon (MH53E).
Operational speed: 170 kts *(315 km/h)*.
Service ceiling: 18 500 ft *(5640 m)*.
Range: 1120 nm *(2000 km)*.
Role/Weapon systems: Improved, three-engined AMCM helicopter with mechanical, magnetic and acoustic sweep equipment; self-deployed if necessary. 11 authorised by the end of 1991 with one more to come. Sensors: None. Weapons: 2 × 12.7 mm guns for self-defence.

SEA DRAGON   *10/1992, Hachiro Nakai*

PATROL FORCES

2 + 1 (1) PG 01 (SPARVIERO) CLASS (PG)
(FAST ATTACK HYDROFOIL—MISSILE)

Name	No	Builders	Commissioned
PG 01	821	Sumitomo, Uraga	22 Mar 1993
PG 02	822	Sumitomo, Uraga	22 Mar 1993
PG 03	823	Sumitomo, Uraga	Mar 1995

Displacement, tons: 50 standard
Dimensions, feet (metres): 71.5 × 22.9 × 5.6 *(21.8 × 7 × 1.7)* (hull)
   80.7 × 23.1 × 14.4 *(24.6 × 7 × 4.4)* (foilborne)
Main machinery: 1 GE/IHI LM 500 gas turbine; 5522 hp *(4.12 MW)* sustained; 1 pumpjet (foilborne); 1 diesel; 1 retractable prop (hullborne)
Speed, knots: 46; 8 (diesel). **Range, miles:** 400 at 45 kts; 1200 at 8 kts
Complement: 11 (3 officers)
Missiles: SSM: 4 Mitsubishi SSM-1B (derivative of land-based system); range 150 km *(81 nm)*.
Guns: 1 GE 20 mm/76 Sea Vulcan; 3 barrels per mounting; 55° elevation; 1500 rounds/minute combined to 4 km *(2.2 nm)*.
Countermeasures: Decoys: 2 Loral Hycor Mk 36 SRBOC chaff launchers.
ESM/ECM: intercept and jammer.
Combat data systems: Link 11.
Radars: Surface search; I band.

Comment: First two approved in FY 1990 and both laid down 25 March 1991 and launched 17 July 1992. One more approved in FY 1992, laid down 8 March 1993 and to be launched in June 1994. Built with Italian assistance from Fincantieri. Final total expected to be six. Planned to improve the Navy's interceptor capabilities, this is an ambitious choice of vessel bearing in mind the falling popularity of the hydrofoil in the few navies (US, Italy and USSR) that have built them up to now.

PG 01   *3/1993, Sumitomo*

5 PB 19 CLASS (COASTAL PATROL CRAFT)

Name	No	Builders	Commissioned
PB 23	PB 923	Ishikawajima, Yokohama	31 Mar 1972
PB 24	PB 924	Ishikawajima, Yokohama	31 Mar 1972
PB 25	PB 925	Ishikawajima, Yokohama	29 Mar 1973
PB 26	PB 926	Ishikawajima, Yokohama	29 Mar 1973
PB 27	PB 927	Ishikawajima, Yokohama	29 Mar 1973

Displacement, tons: 18 standard
Dimensions, feet (metres): 55.8 × 14.1 × 2.3 *(17 × 4.3 × 0.7)*
Main machinery: 2 Isuzu V170T diesels; 760 hp(m) *(560 kW)*; 2 shafts
Speed, knots: 20. **Range, miles:** 400 at 20 kts
Complement: 6
Guns: 1—12.7 mm M2 MG.
Radars: Navigation: Koden OPS 29.

Comment: GRP hulls. A 12.7 mm MG has replaced the 20 mm gun. Four paid off in October 1992.

PB 23   *1993, Ships of the World*

AMPHIBIOUS FORCES

Note: It is planned to purchase two Textron Marine LCACs for the new LST.

0 + 1 LST

Name	No	Builders	Commissioned
—	—	Mitsui, Tamano	Mar 1998

Displacement, tons: 8900 standard
Dimensions, feet (metres): 557.7 × 75.5 × 24.6 *(170 × 23 × 7.5)*
Flight deck, feet (metres): 426.5 × 75.5 *(130 × 23)*
Main machinery: 2 diesels; 2 shafts; 2 bow thrusters
Speed, knots: 22
Complement: 130
Military lift: 1000 troops; 2 LCAC; 10 Type 90 tanks or equivalent in weight
Guns: 2 GE/GD 20 mm Vulcan Phalanx Mk 15.
Helicopters: C-47 type.

Comment: A 5500 ton LST was requested and not approved in the 1989 or 1990 estimates. The published design resembled the Italian San Giorgio with a large flight deck and a stern dock. No further action was taken for two years but the FY 1993 request included a larger ship showing the design of a USN LPH, although smaller in size. This vessel, with some modifications, was authorised in the 1993 estimates. The LCACs are to be purchased from Textron Marine. The project remains politically sensitive and further design changes are likely.

LST   *(not to scale), Ian Sturton*

8 LCM TYPE

YF 2075   2121   2124-25   2127-29   2132

Displacement, tons: 25 standard
Dimensions, feet (metres): 56.2 × 14 × 3.9 *(17.1 × 4.3 × 1.2)*
Main machinery: 2 Isuzu E120-MF6R diesels; 480 hp(m) *(353 kW)*; 2 shafts
Speed, knots: 10. **Range, miles:** 130 at 9 kts
Complement: 3
Military lift: 34 tons or 80 troops

Comment: Built in Japan. These are in addition to the six LCMs carried in the Miura class which do not have pennant numbers. *YF 2127-29* commissioned in March 1992 and *2132* in March 1993.

YF 2125   *10/1991, Hachiro Nakai*

3 MIURA CLASS (LSTs)

Name	No	Builders	Commissioned
MIURA	LST 4151	Ishikawajima Harima, Tokyo	29 Jan 1975
OJIKA	LST 4152	Ishikawajima Harima, Tokyo	22 Mar 1976
SATSUMA	LST 4153	Ishikawajima Harima, Tokyo	17 Feb 1977

Displacement, tons: 2000 standard
Dimensions, feet (metres): 321.4 × 45.9 × 9.8 *(98 × 14 × 3)*
Main machinery: 2 Kawasaki-MAN V8V22/30ATL diesels; 4000 hp(m) *(2.94 MW)*; 2 shafts
Speed, knots: 14
Complement: 115
Military lift: 200 troops; 2 LCMs; 2 LCVPs; 10 Type 74 main battle tanks
Guns: 2 USN 3 in *(76 mm)*/50 Mk 33 (twin); 85° elevation; 50 rounds/minute to 12.8 km *(6.9 nm)*; weight of shell 6 kg.
  2 Bofors 40 mm/70 (twin) (LST 4151-4152); 90° elevation; 300 rounds/minute to 12 km *(6.5 nm)* anti-surface; 4 km *(2.2 nm)* anti-aircraft; weight of shell 0.96 kg.
Fire control: Type 72-1B for 76 mm guns *(Miura)*; US Mk 63 for 76 mm guns (remainder). US Mk 51 for 40 mm guns.
Radars: Air search: Melco OPS 14.
Surface search: JRC OPS 16 *(Miura)*; JRS OPS 18 (remainder); D/G/H band.

Comment: Used primarily for logistic support. SATCOM fitted.

OJIKA   *8/1993, Hachiro Nakai*

3 ATSUMI CLASS (LSTs)

Name	No	Builders	Commissioned
ATSUMI	LST 4101	Sasebo Heavy Industries	27 Nov 1972
MOTOBU	LST 4102	Sasebo Heavy Industries	21 Dec 1973
NEMURO	LST 4103	Sasebo Heavy Industries	27 Oct 1977

Displacement, tons: 1480 (LST 4101), 1550 (LST 4102-4103) standard
Dimensions, feet (metres): 291.9 × 42.6 × 8.9 *(89 × 13 × 2.7)*
Main machinery: 2 Kawasaki-MAN V8V22/30ATL diesels; 4000 hp(m) *(2.94 MW)*; 2 shafts
Speed, knots: 13 (LST 4102-4103); 14 (LST 4101). **Range, miles:** 9000 at 12 kts
Complement: 100 (LST 4101); 95 (LST 4102-4103)
Military lift: 130 troops; 400 tons cargo including 5 Type 74 tanks; 2 LCVPs
Guns: 4 Bofors 40 mm/70 Mk 1 (2 twin); 90° elevation; 300 rounds/minute to 12 km *(6.5 nm)*; weight of shell 0.96 kg.
Fire control: 2 US Mk 51 for 40 mm guns.
Radars: Navigation: Fujitsu OPS 9; I band.

Comment: *Nemuro* has an electric crane at the after end of the cargo deck. SATCOM fitted.

MOTOBU   *10/1992, Hachiro Nakai*

14 LCVP TYPE

YF 2069   2072-74   2078-81   2083-87   2116

Displacement, tons: 12 full load
Dimensions, feet (metres): 35.8 × 10.5 × 3.3 *(10.9 × 3.2 × 1)*
Main machinery: 1 Yanmar 6CH-DTE diesel; 190 hp(m) *(140 kW)*; 1 shaft
Speed, knots: 9
Complement: 3
Military lift: 40 troops

Comment: Built in Japan with wooden hulls. In addition to these there are 12 more carried in the LSTs which have no pennant numbers. Some of the class deleted.

YF 2070   *2/1991, Hachiro Nakai*

2 YURA CLASS (LSU)

Name	No	Builders	Commissioned
YURA	4171	Sasebo Heavy Industries	27 Mar 1981
NOTO	4172	Sasebo Heavy Industries	27 Mar 1981

Displacement, tons: 590 standard
Dimensions, feet (metres): 190.2 × 31.2 × 5.6 *(58 × 9.5 × 1.7)*
Main machinery: 2 Fuji 6L27.5XF diesels; 3250 hp(m) *(2.39 MW)*; 2 shafts; cp props
Speed, knots: 12
Complement: 30
Military lift: 70 troops
Guns: 1 GE 20 mm/76 Sea Vulcan 20; 3 barrels per mounting; 55° elevation; 1500 rounds/minute combined to 4 km *(2.2 nm)*.

Comment: Both laid down 23 April 1980. LST 4171 launched 15 October 1980 and LST 4172 on 12 November 1980.

YURA   *7/1993, Hachiro Nakai*

2 YUSOTEI CLASS (LCU)

Name	No	Builders	Commissioned
YUSOTEI-ICHI-GO	2001	Sasebo Heavy Industries	17 Mar 1988
YUSOTEI-NI-GO	2002	Sasebo Heavy Industries	11 Mar 1992

Displacement, tons: 420 standard
Dimensions, feet (metres): 170.6 × 28.5 × 5.2 *(52 × 8.7 × 1.6)*
Main machinery: 2 Mitsubishi S16MTK diesels; 3040 hp(m) *(2.23 MW)*; 2 shafts
Speed, knots: 12
Complement: 28
Guns: 1 GE 20 mm/76 Sea Vulcan; 3 barrels per mounting; 1500 rounds/minute combined to 4 km *(2.2 nm)*.

Comment: First approved in 1986 estimates, laid down 11 May 1987, launched 9 October 1987. Second approved in FY 1990 estimates, laid down 15 May 1991, launched 7 October 1991; plans for a third have been scrapped.

YUSOTEI-NI-GO   *3/1992, Hachiro Nakai*

MINE WARFARE FORCES

Note: Two 5600 ton new Minesweeper Support Ships are in the 1991-95 ship construction plan. Complement 160; speed 22 kts; minelaying capability. To replace *Hayase* and *Souya*.

1 MCM SUPPORT SHIP (MST)

Name	No	Builders	Commissioned
FUKUE	MST 476 (ex-MSC 645)	Nippon Steel Tube Co	18 Nov 1976

Displacement, tons: 380 standard; 530 full load
Dimensions, feet (metres): 170.6 × 28.9 × 7.9 *(52 × 8.8 × 2.4)*
Main machinery: 2 Mitsubishi YV12ZC-15/20 diesels; 1440 hp(m) *(1.06 MW)*; 2 shafts
Speed, knots: 14
Complement: 38
Guns: 1 GE 20 mm/76 Sea Vulcan 20; 55° elevation; 3 barrels per mounting; 1500 rounds/minute combined to 4 km *(2.2 nm)*.
Radars: Surface search: Fujitsu OPS 9.
Sonars: Nec/Hitachi ZQS 2; hull-mounted; minehunting.

Comment: Takami class; minesweeping gear removed and fitted as MCM command ship, recommissioned February 1993 and replaced *Utone*. Used as tender for Nana-Go class MSBs.

FUKUE   *6/1993, Hachiro Nakai*

1 SOUYA CLASS (MINELAYER/SUPPORT SHIP)

Name	No	Builders	Commissioned
SOUYA	MMC 951	Hitachi, Maizuru	30 Sep 1971

Displacement, tons: 2150 standard; 3300 full load
Dimensions, feet (metres): 324.8 × 49.5 × 13.9 *(99 × 15 × 4.2)*
Main machinery: 4 Kawasaki-MAN V6V 22/30 ATL diesels; 6400 hp(m) *(4.7 MW)*; 2 shafts
Speed, knots: 18. **Range, miles:** 7500 at 14 kts
Complement: 185

Guns: 2 USN 3 in *(76 mm)*/50 Mk 33 (twin); 85° elevation; 50 rounds/minute to 12.8 km *(6.9 nm)*; weight of shell 6 kg.
  2 GE 20 mm/76 Sea Vulcan; 3 barrels per mounting; 1500 rounds/minute combined to 4 km *(2.2 nm)*.
Torpedoes: 6—324 mm Type 68 (2 triple) tubes. Honeywell Mk 46 Mod 5 Neartip; anti-submarine; active/passive homing to 11 km *(5.9 nm)* at 40 kts; warhead 44 kg.
Mines: 6 internal plus 2 external rails; 460 buoyant.
Fire control: GFCS-1 for 76 mm guns.
Radars: Air search: Melco OPS 14.
Surface search: JRC OPS 16; D band.
IFF: US Mk 10.
Sonars: SQS 11A; hull-mounted; active search and attack; medium frequency.
  ZQS 1B; bow-mounted; active search and attack; high frequency.

Helicopters: Platform for one Sea Dragon.

Operational: Dual purpose ship used as minelayer with a minesweeper support capability. Flagship for Second MCM Flotilla based at Yukosuka. SATCOM fitted.

SOUYA   *2/1990, Hachiro Nakai*

2 TAKAMI CLASS (MINEHUNTERS/SWEEPERS—COASTAL)

Name	No	Builders	Commissioned
HASHIRA	MSC 647	Nippon Steel Tube Co	28 Mar 1978
IWAI	MSC 648	Hitachi, Kanagawa	28 Mar 1978

Displacement, tons: 380 standard; 530 full load
Dimensions, feet (metres): 170.6 × 28.9 × 7.9 *(52 × 8.8 × 2.4)*
Main machinery: 2 Mitsubishi YV12ZC-15/20 diesels; 1440 hp(m) *(1.06 MW)*; 2 shafts
Speed, knots: 14
Complement: 45
Guns: 1 GE 20 mm/76 Sea Vulcan 20; 3 barrels per mounting; 55° elevation; 1500 rounds/minute combined to 4 km *(2.2 nm)*.
Radars: Surface search: Fujitsu OPS 9; I band.
Sonars: Nec/Hitachi ZQS 2 (Type 193M); hull-mounted; minehunting; high frequency.

Comment: Numbers gradually being reduced (converted to auxiliaries) as Hatsushima class complete. Wooden hulls. Fitted with wire and acoustic minesweeping gear. Also carry four clearance divers.

IWAI   *2/1993, Hachiro Nakai*

1 HAYASE CLASS (MINESWEEPER SUPPORT SHIP)

Name	No	Builders	Commissioned
HAYASE	MST 462	Ishikawajima Harima, Tokyo	6 Nov 1971

Displacement, tons: 2000 standard
Dimensions, feet (metres): 324.8 × 47.6 × 13.8 *(99 × 14.5 × 4.2)*
Main machinery: 4 Kawasaki-MAN V6V22/30ATL diesels; 6400 hp(m) *(4.7 MW)*; 2 shafts
Speed, knots: 18
Complement: 180

Guns: 2 USN 3 in *(76 mm)*/50 Mk 33 (twin); 85° elevation; 50 rounds/minute to 12.8 km *(6.9 nm)*;
    weight of shell 6 kg.
    2 GE 20 mm/76 Sea Vulcan; 3 barrels per mounting; 1500 rounds/minute combined to 4 km
    (2 nm).
Torpedoes: 6—324 mm Type 68 (2 triple) tubes. Honeywell Mk 46 Mod 5 Neartip; anti-submarine;
    active/passive homing to 11 km *(5.9 nm)* at 40 kts; warhead 44 kg.
Mines: 5 internal rails; 116 buoyant mines.
Fire control: US Mk 63 for 76 mm guns.
Radars: Air search: Melco OPS 14.
Surface search: JRC OPS 16; D band.
Fire control: Western Electric Mk 34; I/J band.
Sonars: SQS 11A; hull-mounted; active search and attack; medium frequency.

Helicopters: Platform for 1 Sea Dragon.

Operational: Flagship of historic Gulf deployment in 1991. Also flagship for First MCM Flotilla
    based at Kure. SATCOM fitted.

HAYASE   *5/1993, Hachiro Nakai*

3 YAEYAMA CLASS (MINEHUNTER/SWEEPER—OCEAN)

Name	No	Builders	Commissioned
YAEYAMA	MSO 301	Hitachi, Kanagawa	16 Mar 1993
TSUSHIMA	MSO 302	Nippon Steel Tube Co, Tsurumi	23 Mar 1993
HACHIJYO	MSO 303	Nippon Steel Tube Co, Tsurumi	10 Mar 1994

Displacement, tons: 1000 standard; 1275 full load
Dimensions, feet (metres): 219.8 × 38.7 × 10.2 *(67 × 11.8 × 3.1)*
Main machinery: 2 Mitsubishi 6NMU-TAI diesels; 2400 hp(m) *(1.76 MW)*; 2 shafts; 1 hydrojet bow
    thruster; 350 hp(m) *(257 kW)*
Speed, knots: 14
Complement: 60
Guns: 1 JM-61 20 mm/76 Sea Vulcan; 3 barrels per mounting; 1500 rounds/minute combined to
    4 km *(2.2 nm)*.
Radars: Surface search: Fujitsu OPS 39; I band.
Sonars: Raytheon SQQ 32 VDS; high frequency; active.

Comment: First two approved in 1989 estimates, third in 1990. First laid down 30 August 1990
    and launched 29 August 1991; second laid down 20 July 1990 and launched 20 September
    1991; third laid down 17 May 1991 and launched 15 December 1992. Wooden hulls. SATCOM
    fitted. Fitted with S 7 deep sea minehunting system and S 8 (SLQ 48) deep sea moored mine-
    sweeping equipment. Appears to be a derivative of the USN Avenger class. An integrated tactical
    system is to be fitted after SQQ 32 trials are completed. Second batch of three may have a Japa-
    nese sonar fitted if they are ordered.

TSUSHIMA   *9/1993, Hachiro Nakai*

23 HATSUSHIMA and 4 + 3 UWAJIMA CLASSES
(MINEHUNTERS/SWEEPERS—COASTAL)

Name	No	Builders	Commissioned
HATSUSHIMA	MSC 649	Nippon Steel Tube Co (Tsurumi)	30 Mar 1979
NINOSHIMA	MSC 650	Hitachi, Kanagawa	19 Dec 1979
MIYAJIMA	MSC 651	Nippon Steel Tube Co (Tsurumi)	29 Jan 1980
ENOSHIMA	MSC 652	Hitachi, Kanagawa	25 Dec 1980
UKISHIMA	MSC 653	Hitachi, Kanagawa	27 Nov 1980
OOSHIMA	MSC 654	Hitachi, Kanagawa	26 Nov 1981
NIIJIMA	MSC 655	Nippon Steel Tube Co (Tsurumi)	26 Nov 1981
YAKUSHIMA	MSC 656	Hitachi, Kanagawa	17 Dec 1982
NARUSHIMA	MSC 657	Hitachi, Kanagawa	17 Dec 1982
CHICHIJIMA	MSC 658	Hitachi, Kanagawa	16 Dec 1983
TORISHIMA	MSC 659	Nippon Steel Tube Co (Tsurumi)	16 Dec 1983
HAHAJIMA	MSC 660	Nippon Steel Tube Co (Tsurumi)	18 Dec 1984
TAKASHIMA	MSC 661	Hitachi, Kanagawa	18 Dec 1984
NUWAJIMA	MSC 662	Hitachi, Kanagawa	12 Dec 1985
ETAJIMA	MSC 663	Nippon Steel Tube Co (Tsurumi)	12 Dec 1985
KAMISHIMA	MSC 664	Nippon Steel Tube Co (Tsurumi)	16 Dec 1986
HIMESHIMA	MSC 665	Hitachi, Kanagawa	16 Dec 1986
OGISHIMA	MSC 666	Hitachi, Kanagawa	17 Dec 1987
MOROSHIMA	MSC 667	Nippon Steel Tube Co (Tsurumi)	17 Dec 1987
YURISHIMA	MSC 668	Nippon Steel Tube Co (Tsurumi)	15 Dec 1988
HIKOSHIMA	MSC 669	Hitachi, Kanagawa	15 Dec 1988
AWASHIMA	MSC 670	Hitachi, Kanagawa	13 Dec 1989
SAKUSHIMA	MSC 671	Nippon Steel Tube Co (Tsurumi)	13 Dec 1989
UWAJIMA	MSC 672	Nippon Steel Tube Co (Tsurumi)	19 Dec 1990
IESHIMA	MSC 673	Hitachi, Kanagawa	19 Dec 1990
TSUKISHIMA	MSC 674	Hitachi, Kanagawa	18 Mar 1993
MAEJIMA	MSC 675	Hitachi, Kanagawa	15 Dec 1993
KUMEJIMA	MSC 676	Nippon Steel Tube Co (Tsurumi)	Dec 1994
—	MSC 677	Hitachi, Kanagawa	Dec 1994
—	MSC 678	Nippon Steel Tube Co (Tsurumi)	Mar 1995

Displacement, tons: 440 (490, MSC 670 onwards) standard; 510 full load
Dimensions, feet (metres): 180.4 (189.3, MSC 670 onwards) × 30.8 × 7.9
    (55 (57.7) × 9.4 × 2.4)
Main machinery: 2 Mitsubishi YV122C-15/20 diesels (MSC 649-665); 1440 hp(m) *(1.06 MW)*; 2
    Mitsubishi 6NMU-TAI diesels (MSC 666 onwards); 1400 hp(m) *(1.03 MW)*; 2 shafts
Speed, knots: 14
Complement: 45

Guns: 1 JM-61 20 mm/76 Sea Vulcan 20; 55° elevation; 3 barrels per mounting; 1500 rounds/
    minute combined to 4 km *(2.2 nm)*.
Radars: Surface search: Fujitsu OPS 9 or OPS 39 (MSC 674 onwards); I band.
Sonars: Nec/Hitachi ZQS 2B or ZQS 3 (MSC 672 onwards); hull-mounted; minehunting; high
    frequency.

Programmes: First ordered in 1976. Last three authorised in FY 1992. Because of the new sonar
    and mine detonating equipment vessels from MSC 672 onwards are known as the Uwajima
    class. MSC 676 launched 9 December 1993.
Structure: From MSC 670 onwards the hull is lengthened by 2.7 m in order to improve the sleep-
    ing accommodation from three tier to two tier bunks. Hulls are made of wood.
Operational: Fitted with new S 4 (S 7 from MSC 672 onwards) mine detonating equipment, a
    remote-controlled counter-mine charge. Four clearance divers are carried. MSC 668, 669, 670
    and 671 formed the Minesweeper Squadron to deploy to the Gulf in 1991.

ENOSHIMA   *1/1993, Hachiro Nakai*

IESHIMA   *2/1993, Hachiro Nakai*

4 NANA-GO CLASS (MSBs)

Name	No	Builders	Commissioned
KYUU-GO	709	Nippon Steel Tube Co	28 Mar 1974
JYUU-GO	710	Nippon Steel Tube Co	29 Mar 1974
JYUU-ICHI-GO	711	Hitachi, Kanagawa	10 May 1975
JYUU-NI-GO	712	Nippon Steel Tube Co	22 Apr 1975

Displacement, tons: 58 standard
Dimensions, feet (metres): 73.8 × 17.7 × 3.3 *(22.5 × 5.4 × 1)*
Main machinery: 2 Mitsubishi 4ZV20M diesels; 480 hp(m) *(353 kW)*; 2 shafts
Speed, knots: 11
Complement: 10
Radars: Navigation: Koden OPS 29D.

Comment: Wooden hulls. *Fukue* is the depot ship. Two deleted in March 1992, remainder to go in 1994/95.

KYUU-GO   *5/1992, Hachiro Nakai*

TRAINING SHIPS

1 TRAINING SHIP

Name	No	Builders	Commissioned
KATORI	TV 3501	Ishikawajima Harima, Tokyo	10 Sep 1969

Displacement, tons: 3350 standard
Dimensions, feet (metres): 419.8 × 49.2 × 14.1 *(128 × 15 × 4.3)*
Flight deck, feet (metres): 98.4 × 42.6 *(30 × 13)*
Main machinery: 2 Ishikawajima boilers; 610 psi *(43 kg/cm sq)*; 850°F *(454°C)*; 2 Ishikawajima geared turbines; 20 000 hp(m) *(14.7 MW)*; 2 shafts; 454°C
Speed, knots: 25. **Range, miles:** 7000 at 18 kts
Complement: 463 (165 trainees)
Guns: 4 USN 3 in *(76 mm)*/50 Mk 33 (2 twin); 85° elevation; 50 rounds/minute to 12.8 km *(6.9 nm)*; weight of shell 6 kg.
Torpedoes: 6—324 mm Type 68 (2 triple) tubes. Honeywell Mk 46 Mod 5 Neartip; anti-submarine; active/passive homing to 11 km *(5.9 nm)* at 40 kts; warhead 44 kg.
A/S mortars: 1—375 mm Bofors Type 71 4-barrelled trainable rocket launcher; automatic loading; range 1.6 km.
Countermeasures: ESM: Nec NOLR 1B; radar warning.
Radars: Air search: RCA SPS 12; D band; range 119 km *(65 nm)*.
Air/surface search: JRC OPS 17; D band.
Navigation: JRC OPS 20; I band.
Sonars: Sangamo/General Electric SQS 4; hull-mounted; active; short-range; high frequency.

Comment: Provided with a large auditorium amidships and an open deck space aft which is used as a parade ground. Used for training officers. To be replaced in 1995 by *Kashima*.

KATORI   *3/1992, Hachiro Nakai*

0 + 1 KASHIMA CLASS (TRAINING SHIP)

Name	No	Builders	Commissioned
KASHIMA	TV 3508	Hitachi, Maizuru	Jan 1995

Displacement, tons: 4060 standard
Dimensions, feet (metres): 469.2 × 59.1 × 15.1 *(143 × 18 × 4.6)*
Main machinery: CODOG; 2 RR Spey SM1C gas turbines; 26 650 hp *(19.9 MW)* sustained; 2 Mitsubishi S16U diesels; 8000 hp(m) *(5.88 MW)*; 2 shafts
Speed, knots: 25. **Range, miles:** 7000 at 18 kts
Complement: 389 (includes 140 midshipmen)
Guns: 1 OTO Melara 76 mm/62. 2—40 mm saluting guns.
Torpedoes: 6—324 mm (2 triple) tubes.
Radars: Air search: E/F band.
Surface search: I band.
Sonars: Hull-mounted; active search and attack; medium frequency.
Helicopters: Platform for 1 medium.

Comment: Approved in FY 1991 as a dedicated training ship to replace *Katori* but the project postponed to FY 1992 as a budget saving measure. Laid down 20 April 1993 and launched 23 February 1994.

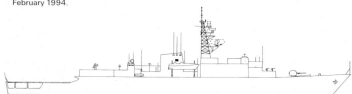

KASHIMA   *(not to scale), Ian Sturton*

3 YAMAGUMO CLASS (2 TRAINING and 1 TRAINING SUPPORT SHIPS)

Name	No	Builders	Commissioned
YAMAGUMO	TV 3506 (ex-DD 113)	Mitsui, Tamano	29 Jan 1966
MAKIGUMO	TV 3507 (ex-DD 114)	Sumitomo, Uraga	19 Mar 1966
ASAGUMO	ASU 7018 (ex-DD 115)	Hitachi, Maizuru	29 Aug 1967

Displacement, tons: 2050 standard
Dimensions, feet (metres): 373.9 × 38.7 × 13.1 *(114 × 11.8 × 4)*
Main machinery: 6 Mitsubishi 12UEV30/40 diesels; 21 600 hp(m) *(15.9 MW)*; 2 shafts
Speed, knots: 27. **Range, miles:** 7000 at 20 kts
Complement: 210 (19 officers)
Missiles: A/S: Honeywell ASROC Mk 112 octuple launcher.
Guns: 4 USN 3 in *(76 mm)*/50 Mk 33 (2 twin); 85° elevation; 50 rounds/minute to 12.8 km *(6.9 nm)*; weight of shell 6 kg.
Torpedoes: 6—324 mm Type 68 (2 triple) tubes. Honeywell Mk 46 Mod 5 Neartip; anti-submarine; active/passive homing to 11 km *(5.9 nm)* at 40 kts; warhead 44 kg.
A/S mortars: 1 Bofors 375 mm Type 71 4-barrelled trainable rocket launcher; automatic loading; range 1.6 km.
Countermeasures: ESM: Nec NOLR 1B; radar intercept.
Fire control: US Mk 56 or 63 for 76 mm guns.
Radars: Air search: Melco OPS 11.
Surface search: JRC OPS 17; G/H band.
Fire control: Two GE Mk 35; I/J band.
IFF: US Mk 10.
Sonars: Sangamo SQS 23; hull-mounted; active search and attack; low frequency.
EDO SQS 35(J); VDS; active/passive search; medium frequency.

Comment: First pair converted as training ships on 20 June 1991. Lecture room added under ASROC, chart room on the signal deck and accommodation for 16 women. *Asagumo* converted on 18 October 1993 as a training support ship for the Submarine Flotilla.

YAMAGUMO   *7/1993, Hachiro Nakai*

1 AZUMA CLASS (TRAINING SUPPORT SHIP)

Name	No	Builders	Commissioned
AZUMA	ATS 4201	Hitachi, Maizuru	26 Nov 1969

Displacement, tons: 1950 standard
Dimensions, feet (metres): 321.5 × 42.7 × 12.5 *(98 × 13 × 3.8)*
Main machinery: 2 Kawasaki-MAN V8V22/30ATL diesels; 4000 hp(m) *(2.94 MW)*; 2 shafts
Speed, knots: 18
Complement: 185
Guns: 1 USN 3 in *(76 mm)*/50; 85° elevation; 50 rounds/minute to 12.8 km *(6.9 nm)*; weight of shell 6 kg.
Torpedoes: 2—483 mm Mk 4 tubes. USN Mk 32; active/passive homing to 8 km *(4.4 nm)* at 12 kts; warhead 49 kg.
Fire control: US Mk 51 Mod 2 for 76 mm gun system.
Radars: Air/Surface search: JRC OPS 16; D band; range 146 km *(80 nm)*.
Lockheed SPS 40; E/F band; range 320 km *(175 nm)*.
Fire control: Target control and tracking system (TCATS) (for drones).
Sonars: SQS 11A; hull-mounted; active search and attack.

Comment: Drone hangar amidships and catapult on flight deck. Can operate towed target. In 1982 target control and tracking system (TCATS) fitted to work with high-speed drones. Carries 10 Northrop KD2R-5 and 4 BQM-34-AJ Chaca II drones. Training support ship for AA gunnery.

AZUMA   *6/1993, JMSDF*

1 KUROBE CLASS (TRAINING SUPPORT SHIP)

Name	No	Builders	Commissioned
KUROBE	ATS 4202	Nippon Steel Tube Co, Tsurumi	23 Mar 1989

Displacement, tons: 2270 standard; 3200 full load
Dimensions, feet (metres): 331.4 × 54.1 × 13.1 *(101 × 16.5 × 4)*
Main machinery: 4 Fuji 8L27.5XF diesels; 8700 hp(m) *(6.4 MW)*; 2 shafts; cp props
Speed, knots: 20
Complement: 156
Guns: 1 FMC/OTO Melara 3 in *(76 mm)*/62 Mk 75; 85° elevation; 85 rounds/minute to 16 km *(8.6 nm)* anti-surface; 12 km *(6.5 nm)* anti-aircraft; weight of shell 6 kg.
Radars: Air search: Melco OPS 14.
Surface search: JRC OPS 18.

Comment: Approved under 1986 estimates, laid down 31 July 1987, launched 23 May 1988. Carries four BQM-34AJ high speed drones and four Northrop Chukar II drones with two stern launchers. Used for training crews in anti-aircraft operations and evaluating the effectiveness and capability of ships' anti-aircraft missile systems.

KUROBE   *4/1992, Hachiro Nakai*

AUXILIARIES

Note: In addition to the ships and craft listed there are large numbers of service craft and small tenders. Most have YL or YT numbers.

1 CHIYODA CLASS (SUBMARINE DEPOT AND RESCUE SHIP) (AS)

Name	No	Builders	Commissioned
CHIYODA	AS 405	Mitsui, Tamano	27 Mar 1985

Displacement, tons: 3650 standard; 4450 full load
Dimensions, feet (metres): 370.6 × 57.7 × 15.1 *(113 × 17.6 × 4.6)*
Main machinery: 2 Mitsui 8L42M diesels; 10 540 hp(m) *(8.8 MW)*; 2 shafts; cp props; bow and stern thrusters
Speed, knots: 17
Complement: 120
Helicopters: Platform for up to Sea King size.

Comment: Laid down 19 January 1983, launched 7 December 1983. Carries a Deep Submergence Rescue Vehicle (DSRV), built by Kawasaki Heavy Industries, Kobe, of 40 tons, 40.7 × 10.5 × 14.1 ft *(12.4 × 3.2 × 4.3 m)* with a 30 hp(m) *(22 kW)* electric motor and speed of 4 kts, it has space for 12 people. Flagship Second Submarine Flotilla based at Yokosuka.

CHIYODA   *6/1993, van Ginderen Collection*

1 FUSHIMI CLASS (SUBMARINE RESCUE SHIP) (ASR)

Name	No	Builders	Commissioned
FUSHIMI	ASR 402	Sumitomo; Uraga	10 Feb 1970

Displacement, tons: 1430 standard
Dimensions, feet (metres): 249.5 × 41 × 12.5 *(76 × 12.5 × 3.8)*
Main machinery: 2 Kawasaki-MAN V6V22/30ATL diesels; 3200 hp(m) *(2.35 MW)*; 1 shaft
Speed, knots: 16
Complement: 100
Radars: Surface search: Fujitsu OPS 9; I band.
IFF: US Mk 10.
Sonars: SQS 11A; hull-mounted.

Comment: Laid down on 5 November 1968, launched 10 September 1969. Equipped with rescue chamber and two recompression chambers.

FUSHIMI   *7/1991, Hachiro Nakai*

3 TOWADA CLASS (FLEET SUPPORT SHIP)

Name	No	Builders	Commissioned
TOWADA	AOE 422	Hitachi, Maizuru	24 Mar 1987
TOKIWA	AOE 423	Ishikawajima Harima, Tokyo	12 Mar 1990
HAMANA	AOE 424	Hitachi, Maizuru	29 Mar 1990

Displacement, tons: 8150 standard; 15 850 full load
Dimensions, feet (metres): 547.8 × 72.2 × 26.9 *(167 × 22 × 8.2)*
Main machinery: 2 Mitsui 16V42MA diesels; 23 950 hp(m) *(17.6 MW)*; 2 shafts
Speed, knots: 22
Complement: 140
Cargo capacity: 5700 tons
Guns: 1—20 mm/76 Mk 15 Vulcan Phalanx *(Hamana)*.
Radars: Surface search: JRC OPS 18; I band.
Helicopters: Platform for 1 Sea King size.

Comment: First approved under 1984 estimates, laid down 17 April 1985, launched 25 March 1986. Second and third of class in 1987 estimates. AOE 423 laid down 12 May 1988, launched 23 March 1989. AOE 424 laid down 8 July 1988, launched 18 May 1989. Two replenishment at sea positions on each side (one fuel only, one fuel or stores). All to be fitted with Vulcan Phalanx guns in due course.

TOWADA   *4/1992, Hachiro Nakai*

1 SAGAMI CLASS (FLEET SUPPORT SHIP)

Name	No	Builders	Commissioned
SAGAMI	AOE 421	Hitachi, Maizuru	30 Mar 1979

Displacement, tons: 5000 standard; 11 600 full load
Dimensions, feet (metres): 478.9 × 62.3 × 24 *(146 × 19 × 7.3)*
Main machinery: 2 Type 12DRV diesels; 18 000 hp(m) *(13.23 MW)*; 2 shafts
Speed, knots: 22. **Range, miles:** 9500 at 18 kts
Complement: 130
Cargo capacity: 5000 tons
Radars: Surface search: JRC OPS 18; D band.
Helicopters: Platform for 1 Sea King size.

Comment: Merchant type hull. Ordered December 1976. Laid down 28 September 1977, launched 4 September 1978. Two fuel stations each side. No armament but can be fitted.

SAGAMI   *4/1992, Hachiro Nakai*

34 HARBOUR TANKERS

Comment: There are: 13 of 490 tons (YO 14, 21-27, 29-33); three of 310 tons (YW 17-19); four of 290 tons (YO 10-13); eight of 270 tons (YO 19, 28, 32 and YG 201-205); five of 160 tons (YW 12-16); one of 100 tons (YW 10). YO (oil), YW (water) and YG (avgas). Most are propelled by two diesels at about 9 kts. The latest to commission was YO 33 on 30 September 1993. One more YW of 310 tons to complete in 1994.

YW 13   *10/1991, Hachiro Nakai*

6 TAKAMI CLASS (EOD TENDERS)

TEURI (ex-*MSC 636*) YAS 87
TASHIRO (ex-*MSC 638*) YAS 89
MIYATO (ex-*MSC 639*) YAS 90

YOKOSE (ex-*MSC 642*) YAS 93
SAKATE (ex-*MSC 643*) YAS 94
OKITSU (ex-*MSC 646*) YAS 96

Displacement, tons: 380 standard; 510 full load
Dimensions, feet (metres): 170.6 × 28.9 × 7.9 *(52 × 8.8 × 2.4)*
Main machinery: 2 Mitsubishi YV12ZC-15/20 diesels; 1440 hp(m) *(1.06 MW)*; 2 shafts
Speed, knots: 14
Complement: 43
Guns: 1 Oerlikon 20 mm.

Comment: Transferred after conversion to Explosive Ordnance Disposal (EOD) Unit (Mine Hunting Diver) duties which includes removal of minesweeping gear to provide for divers' room and equipment.

TEURI   *7/1993, Hachiro Nakai*

1 CABLE LAYER

Name	No	Builders	Commissioned
MUROTO	ARC 482	Mitsubishi, Shimonoseki	27 Mar 1980

Displacement, tons: 4544 standard
Dimensions, feet (metres): 436.2 × 57.1 × 18.7 *(133 × 17.4 × 5.7)*
Main machinery: 4 Kawasaki-MAN V8V22/30ATL diesels; 8000 hp(m) *(5.88 MW)*; 2 shafts
Speed, knots: 18
Complement: 135

Comment: Ocean survey capability. Laid down 28 November 1978, launched 25 July 1979.

MUROTO   *4/1993, Hachiro Nakai*

5 81-GO CLASS

Name	Laid down	Launched	Commissioned
ASU 81	21 Oct 1967	18 Jan 1968	30 Mar 1968
ASU 82	25 Sep 1968	20 Dec 1968	31 Mar 1969
ASU 83	2 Apr 1971	24 May 1971	30 Sep 1971
ASU 84	4 Feb 1972	15 June 1972	13 Sep 1972
ASU 85	20 Feb 1973	16 July 1973	19 Sep 1973

Displacement, tons: 500 (ASU 85), 490 (ASU 82-84), 480 (ASU 81) standard
Dimensions, feet (metres): 170.6 × 32.8 × 8.3 *(52 × 10 × 2.5)*
Main machinery: 2 Akasaka diesels; 1600 hp(m) *(1.18 MW)*; 2 shafts
Speed, knots: 14
Complement: 25; 35 (ASU 81-83)
Radars: Navigation: Fujitsu OPS 19 (ASU 84/85). Oki OPS 10 (others).

Comment: Training support and rescue. The after deck crane is able to lift a helicopter. *ASU 82* and *ASU 83* can launch propeller-driven drones by catapult.

ASU 84   *2/1991, Hachiro Nakai*

1 HIYODURI CLASS

Name	No	Builders	Commissioned
HIYODORI	ASY 92 (ex-PC 320)	Sasebo Heavy Industries	28 Feb 1966

Displacement, tons: 390 standard
Dimensions, feet (metres): 197 × 23.3 × 8.3 *(60 × 7.1 × 2.5)*
Main machinery: 2 Kawasaki-MAN V8V22/30ATL diesels; 3800 hp(m) *(2.79 MW)*; 2 shafts
Speed, knots: 20
Complement: 35 (90 passengers)

Comment: Built under FY 1964 programme as large patrol craft. Reconstructed as Auxiliary Special Service Yacht (ASY) at Yokohama Yacht Co Ltd, completed 27 April 1987.

HIYODORI   *3/1993, Hachiro Nakai*

4 TAKAMI CLASS (TENDERS)

Name	No	Builders	Commissioned
MUROTSU	YAS 88 (ex-MSC 637)	Hitachi, Kanagawa	30 Mar 1972
TAKANE	YAS 91 (ex-MSC 640)	Nippon Steel Tube Co	28 Aug 1974
MUZUKI	YAS 92 (ex-MSC 641)	Hitachi, Kanagawa	28 Aug 1974
OUMI	YAS 95 (ex-MSC 644)	Hitachi, Kanagawa	18 Nov 1976

Comment: Details as for Takami class under Mine Warfare Forces. YAS 83 converted 27 March 1986, YAS 86 24 March 1987, YAS 88 23 March 1988, YAS 91 and 92 in December 1990 and YAS 95 in 1992. Various roles. YAS 95 used as noise range support ship.

MUROTSU   *4/1992, Hachiro Nakai*

HARBOUR CRAFT

Comment: Large numbers of harbour craft fly the naval ensign.

YAL 01   *4/1992, Hachiro Nakai*

SURVEY AND RESEARCH SHIPS

Notes: (1) The SES trials ship *Merguro* does not belong to the MSDF.
(2) Survey ships are also included in the Maritime Safety Agency section.

2 HIBIKI CLASS (AOS)

Name	No	Builders	Commissioned
HIBIKI	AOS 5201	Mitsui, Tamano	30 Jan 1991
HARIMA	AOS 5202	Mitsui, Tamano	10 Mar 1992

Displacement, tons: 2850 standard
Dimensions, feet (metres): 219.8 × 98.1 × 24.6 *(67 × 29.9 × 7.5)*
Main machinery: Diesel-electric; 4 Mitsubishi 6SU diesels; 6700 hp(m) *(4.93 MW)*; 4 generators; 2 motors; 3000 hp(m) *(2.2 MW)*; 2 shafts
Speed, knots: 11 (3 towing). **Range, miles:** 3800 at 10 kts
Complement: 40
Radars: Navigation: JRC OPS 16; I band.
Sonars: UQQ 2 SURTASS; passive surveillance.
Helicopters: Platform only.

Comment: First authorised 24 January 1989, laid down 28 November 1989 and launched 27 July 1990. Second approved in FY 1990, laid down 26 December 1990 and launched 11 September 1991. Total of five planned originally but subsequently reduced to two. Auxiliary Ocean Surveillance (AOS) ships to a SWATH design similar to USN TAGOS-19 class; the first of class embarks US civilians. A data collection station is based at Yokosuka Bay using WSC-6 satellite data relay to the AOS.

HARIMA   *7/1993, Hachiro Nakai*

1 SUMA CLASS (AGS)

Name	No	Builders	Commissioned
SUMA	AGS 5103	Hitachi, Maizuru	30 Mar 1982

Displacement, tons: 1180 standard
Dimensions, feet (metres): 236.2 × 42 × 11.1 *(72 × 12.8 × 3.4)*
Main machinery: 2 Fuji 6L27.5XF diesels; 3250 hp(m) *(2.39 MW)*; 2 shafts; cp props
Speed, knots: 15
Complement: 64

Comment: Laid down 24 September 1980, launched 1 September 1981. Carries an 11 m launch for surveying work.

SUMA   *10/1992, Hachiro Nakai*

2 FUTAMI CLASS (AGS)

Name	No	Builders	Commissioned
FUTAMI	AGS 5102	Mitsubishi, Shimonoseki	27 Feb 1979
WAKASA	AGS 5104	Hitachi Zosen, Maizuru	25 Feb 1986

Displacement, tons: 2050 standard; 3175 full load
Dimensions, feet (metres): 318.2 × 49.2 × 13.8 *(97 × 15 × 4.2)*
Main machinery: 2 Kawasaki-MAN V8V22/30ATL diesels; 4000 hp(m) *(2.94 MW)* (AGS 5102); 2 Fuji 6L27.5XF diesels; 3250 hp(m) *(2.39 MW)* (AGS 5104); 2 shafts; cp props; bow thruster
Speed, knots: 16
Complement: 105
Radars: Navigation: JRC OPS 18; I band.

Comment: AGS 5102 laid down 20 January 1978. Launched 9 August 1978. AGS 5104 laid down 21 August 1984, launched 21 May 1985. Built to merchant marine design. Carry an RCV-22 remote-controlled rescue/underwater survey submarine. *Wakasa* has a slightly taller funnel.

FUTAMI   *7/1992, Hachiro Nakai*

1 AKASHI CLASS (AGS)

Name	No	Builders	Commissioned
AKASHI	AGS 5101	Nippon Steel Tube Co	25 Oct 1969

Displacement, tons: 1420 standard
Dimensions, feet (metres): 242.7 × 42.2 × 14.2 *(74 × 13 × 4.3)*
Main machinery: 2 Kawasaki-MAN V6V22/30ATL diesels; 3200 hp(m) *(2.35 MW)*; 2 shafts; bow thruster
Speed, knots: 16. **Range, miles:** 16 500 at 14 kts
Complement: 65 plus 10 scientists
Countermeasures: ESM: Nec NOLR-5; radar intercept.
Radars: Navigation: Fujitsu OPS 9; I band.

Comment: Has a large number of electronic intercept aerials.

AKASHI   *1990, JMSDF*

1 KURIHAMA CLASS (ASE)

Name	No	Builders	Commissioned
KURIHAMA	ASE 6101	Sasebo Heavy Industries	8 Apr 1980

Displacement, tons: 959 standard
Dimensions, feet (metres): 223 × 37.9 × 9.8 (screws) *(68 × 11.6 × 3)*
Main machinery: 2 Fuji 6S30B diesels; 4800 hp(m) *(3.5 MW)*; 2 shafts; 2 cp props; bow thruster
Speed, knots: 15
Complement: 40 plus 12 scientists

Comment: Experimental ship built for the Technical Research and Development Institute and used for testing underwater weapons and sensors.

KURIHAMA   *5/1993, JMSDF*

0 + 1 ASE

Name	No	Builders	Commissioned
—	ASE 6102	Sumitomo, Uraga	Mar 1995

Displacement, tons: 4200 standard
Main machinery: 2 gas turbines; 2 shafts
Speed, knots: 27
Complement: 170 plus 100 scientists

Comment: Included in the FY 1992 programme. Laid down 21 April 1993, launched June 1994. For experimental and weapon systems testing.

ASE   *(not to scale), Ian Sturton*

ICEBREAKER

1 SHIRASE CLASS

Name	No	Builders	Commissioned
SHIRASE	AGB 5002	Nippon Steel Tube Co, Tsurumi	12 Nov 1982

Displacement, tons: 11 600 standard; 17 600 full load
Dimensions, feet (metres): 439.5 × 91.8 × 30.2 *(134 × 28 × 9.2)*
Main machinery: Diesel-electric; 6 Mitsui 12V42M diesels; 53 900 hp(m) *(39.6 MW)*; 6 generators; 3 motors; 30 000 hp(m) *(22 MW)*; 3 shafts
Speed, knots: 19. **Range, miles:** 25 000 at 15 kts
Complement: 174 (37 officers) plus 60 scientists
Cargo capacity: 1000 tons
Helicopters: 2 Mitsubishi S-61A; 1 Kawasaki OH-6D.

Comment: Laid down 5 March 1981 and launched 11 December 1981. Fully equipped for marine and atmospheric research. Stabilised.

SHIRASE   *8/1993, Hachiro Nakai*

SHIRASE   *5/1992, Ships of the World*

TUGS

15 OCEAN TUGS

YT 58   YT 63-74   YT 78-79

Displacement, tons: 260 standard
Dimensions, feet (metres): 93 × 28 × 8.2 *(28.4 × 8.6 × 2.5)*
Main machinery: 2 Niigata 6L25B diesels; 1800 hp(m) *(1.32 MW)*; 2 shafts
Speed, knots: 11
Complement: 10

Comment: YT 58 entered service on 31 October 1978, YT 63 on 27 September 1982, YT 64 on 30 September 1983, YT 65 on 20 September 1984, YT 66 on 20 September 1985, YT 67 on 4 September 1986, YT 68 on 9 September 1987, YT 69 on 16 September 1987, YT 70 on 2 September 1988, YT 71 on 28 July 1989, YT 72 on 27 July 1990, YT 73 on 31 July 1991, YT 74 on 30 September 1991, YT 78 in July 1994 and YT 79 in September 1994. All built by Yokohama Yacht.

YT 64   *1/1993, Hachiro Nakai*

4 COASTAL TUGS

YT 53   YT 55-57

Displacement, tons: 190 standard
Dimensions, feet (metres): 84.8 × 23 × 7.5 *(25.7 × 7 × 2.3)*
Main machinery: 2 Kubota M6D20BUCS diesels; 1500 hp(m) *(1.1 MW)*; 2 shafts
Speed, knots: 11
Complement: 10

Comment: YT 53 entered service on 8 March 1975, YT 55 on 22 August 1975, YT 56 on 13 July 1976, YT 57 on 22 August 1977.

YT 56   *3/1992, Hachiro Nakai*

7 COASTAL TUGS

YT 37, YT 40-41, YT 44-46, YT 48

Displacement, tons: 100 standard
Dimensions, feet (metres): 78.1 × 17.7 × 7.9 *(23.8 × 5.4 × 2.4)*
Main machinery: 1 diesel; 400 hp(m) *(294 kW)*; 1 shaft
Speed, knots: 10

YT 45   *8/1990, Hachiro Nakai*

13 HARBOUR TUGS

YT 42-43, YT 47, YT 49, YT 51, YT 54, YT 59-62, YT 75-77

Comment: Of varying sizes from 26-50 tons. The latest YT 77 commissioned 16 September 1993. Built by Yokohama Yacht.

YT 59   *8/1993, Hachiro Nakai*

MARITIME SAFETY AGENCY

(KAIJO HOANCHO)

Commandant of the MSA

Tsuguo Iyama

Establishment

Established in May 1948 as an external organisation of the Ministry of Transport to carry out patrol and rescue duties as well as hydrographic and navigation aids services. Since then a very considerable organisation with HQ in Tokyo has been built up. The Academy for the Agency is in Kure and the School in Maizuru. The main operational branches are the Guard and Rescue, the Hydrographic and the Aids to Navigation Departments. Regional Maritime Safety offices control the 11 districts with their location as follows (air bases in brackets): RMS 1—Otaru (Chitose, Hakodate, Kushiro); 2—Shiogama (Sendai); 3—Yokohama (Haneda); 4—Nagoya (Ise); 5—Kobe (Yao); 6—Hiroshima (Hiroshima); 7—Kitakyushu (Fukuoka); 8—Maizuru (Miho); 9—Niigata (Niigata); 10—Kagoshima (Kagoshima); 11—Naha (Naha, Ishigaki). This organisation includes, as well as the RMS HQ, 66 MS offices, 51 MS stations, 26 MS detachments, 14 MS air stations, 10 district communication centres, 3 traffic advisory service centres, 4 hydrographic observatories, 114 aids to navigation offices and 1 Special Rescue Station.

Personnel

1994: 12 163 (2615 officers)

Strength of the Fleet

Type	Active	Building
GUARD AND RESCUE SERVICE		
Patrol Vessels:		
Large with helicopter (PLH)	11	—
Large (PL)	37	1
Medium (PM)	47	—
Small (PS)	21	—
Firefighting Vessels (FL)	5	—
Patrol Craft:		
Patrol Craft (PC)	60	—
Patrol Craft (CL)	165	—
Firefighting Craft (FM)	10	—
Special Service Craft:		
Monitoring Craft (MS)	3	—
Guard Boats (GS)	2	—
Surveillance Craft (SS)	34	—
Oil Recovery Craft (OR)	5	—
Oil Skimming Craft (OS)	3	—
Oil Boom Craft (OX)	19	—
Miscellaneous (NO)	3	—

Type	Active	Building
HYDROGRAPHIC SERVICE		
Surveying Vessels:		
Large (HL)	5	—
Medium (HM)	1	—
Small (HS)	8	—
AIDS TO NAVIGATION SERVICE		
Aids to Navigation Research Vessel (LL)	1	—
Buoy Tenders:		
Large (LL)	3	—
Medium (LM)	1	—
Aids to Navigation Tenders:		
Medium (LM)	10	—
Small (LS)	60	—

DELETIONS

1991 *Ojika* PL 12 (old), *Rokko* PS 35, *Hamashio* HS 01, *Sekiun* LM 105, *Houn* LM 111

1992 *Amami* PM 62, *Takatsuki* PS 39, *Reiun* LM 102, *Kinugasa* MS 01 (old), *CL 50-51, CL 53-55, CL 66, CL 78, LS 102*

1993 *Kojima* PL 21 (old), *Genun* LM 113, *CL 65-77, Shiramine* PS 48, *Hamagiri* PC 48, *Kaiyo* HM 06, *CL 69-71, 75, 77, 83, 86, 90, 96, HS 02-10, LS 103, SS 01-02*

LARGE PATROL VESSELS

1 SHIKISHIMA CLASS

Name	No	Builders	Commissioned
SHIKISHIMA	PLH 31	Ishikawajima Harima, Tokyo	8 Apr 1992

Displacement, tons: 6500 standard
Dimensions, feet (metres): 492.1 × 55.8 × 19.7 *(150 × 17 × 6)*
Main machinery: 2 SEMT-Pielstick 16 PC2.5 V 400; 20 800 hp(m) *(15.29 MW)*; 2 shafts
Speed, knots: 25. **Range, miles:** 20 000 at 18 kts
Guns: 4 Oerlikon 35 mm/90 (2 twin). 2 JM-61 MB 20 mm Gatling.
Radars: Air/surface search: Melco Ops 14; D/E band.
Surface search: JMA 1576; I band.
Navigation: JMA 1596; I band.
Helicopter control: I band.
Helicopters: 2 Bell 212 or 2 Super Puma.

Comment: Authorised in the FY 1989 programme in place of the third Mizuho class. Laid down 24 August 1990 and launched 27 June 1991. Used to escort the plutonium transport ship. Armament and command and control systems seem barely adequate for escort duties. SATCOM fitted.

SHIKISHIMA   *5/1993, Hachiro Nakai*

SHIKISHIMA   *5/1993, Hachiro Nakai*

2 MIZUHO CLASS

Name	No	Builders	Commissioned
MIZUHO	PLH 21	Mitsubishi, Nagasaki	19 Mar 1986
YASHIMA	PLH 22	Nippon Kokan, Tsurumi	1 Dec 1988

Displacement, tons: 4900 standard; 5204 full load
Dimensions, feet (metres): 426.5 × 50.9 × 17.7 *(130 × 15.5 × 5.4)*
Main machinery: 2 SEMT-Pielstick 14 PC2.5 V 400 diesels; 18 200 hp(m) *(13.38 MW)* sustained; 2 shafts; cp props; bow thruster
Speed, knots: 23. **Range, miles:** 8500 at 22 kts
Complement: 100 plus 30 aircrew
Guns: 1 Oerlikon 35 mm/90; 85° elevation; 550 rounds/minute to 6 km *(3.2 nm)* anti-surface; 5 km *(2.7 nm)* anti-aircraft; weight of shell 1.55 kg.
1 JM-61 MB 20 mm Gatling.
Radars: Navigation: Two sets.
Helicopter control: One set.
Helicopters: 2 Fuji-Bell 212.

Comment: PLH 21 ordered under the FY 1983 programme laid down 27 August 1984 and launched 5 June 1985. PLH 22 in 1986 estimates, laid down 3 October 1987 and launched 20 January 1988. Two sets of fixed electric fin stabilisers that have a lift of 26 tons × 2 and reduce rolling by 90 per cent at 18 kts. Employed in search and rescue beyond 200 miles from the base line.

YASHIMA   *5/1993, Hachiro Nakai*

8 SOYA CLASS

Name	No	Builders	Commissioned
SOYA	PLH 01	Nippon Kokan, Tsurumi	22 Nov 1978
TSUGARU	PLH 02	IHI, Tokyo	17 Apr 1979
OOSUMI	PLH 03	Mitsui Tamano	18 Oct 1979
URAGA	PLH 04	Hitachi, Maizuru	5 Mar 1980
ZAO	PLH 05	Mitsubishi, Nagasaki	19 Mar 1982
CHIKUZEN	PLH 06	Kawasaki, Kobe	28 Sep 1983
SETTSU	PLH 07	Sumitomo, Oppama	27 Sep 1984
ECHIGO	PLH 08	Mitsui Tamano	28 Feb 1990

Displacement, tons: 3200 normal; 3744 full load
Dimensions, feet (metres): 323.4 × 51.2 × 17.1 *(98.6 × 15.6 × 5.2)* (PLH 01)
345.8 × 47.9 × 15.7 *(105.4 × 14.6 × 4.8)*
Main machinery: 2 SEMT-Pielstick 12 PC2.5 V 400 diesels; 15 604 hp(m) *(11.47 MW)* sustained; 2 shafts; cp props; bow thruster
Speed, knots: 21 (PLH 01); 22 (others). **Range, miles:** 5700 at 18 kts
Complement: 71 (PLH 01-04); 69 (others)
Guns: 1 Bofors 40 mm or Oerlikon 35 mm. 1 Oerlikon 20 mm (PLH 01, 02, 05-07).
Radars: Surface search: JMA 1576; I band.
Navigation: JMA 1596; I band.
Helicopter control: CCA Type.
Helicopters: 1 Fuji-Bell 212.

Comment: PLH 01 has an icebreaking capability while the other ships are only ice strengthened. Fitted with both fin stabilisers and anti-rolling tanks of 70 tons capacity. The fixed electric hydraulic fins have a lift of 26 tons × 2 at 18 kts which reduces rolling by 90 per cent at that speed. At slow speed the reduction is 50 per cent, using the tanks.

SOYA   *5/1993, Hachiro Nakai*

2 IZU CLASS

Name	No	Builders	Commissioned
IZU	PL 31	Hitachi, Mukaishima	31 July 1967
MIURA	PL 32	Hitachi, Maizuru	15 Mar 1969

Displacement, tons: 2081 normal
Dimensions, feet (metres): 313.3 × 38 × 12.8 *(95.5 × 11.6 × 3.9)*
Main machinery: 2 SEMT-Pielstick 12 PC2.5 V 400 diesels; 15 604 hp(m) *(11.47 MW)* sustained; 2 shafts; cp props; bow thruster
Speed, knots: 20. **Range, miles:** 6000 at 18.8 kts
Complement: 72
Guns: 1 Bofors 40 mm/70.
Radars: Surface search: JMA 1576; I band.
Navigation: JMA 1596; I band.

Comment: PL 31 was laid down in August 1966, launched in January 1967. PL 32 was laid down in May 1968, launched in October 1968. Equipped with various types of marine instruments. Ice-strengthened hull. Armament may be removed depending on employment. Based at Yokohama and employed in long-range rescue and patrol duties.

MIURA   5/1993, Hachiro Nakai

28 SHIRETOKO CLASS

Name	No	Builders	Commissioned
SHIRETOKO	PL 101	Mitsui Tamano	8 Nov 1978
ESAN	PL 102	Sumitomo	16 Nov 1978
WAKASA	PL 103	Kawasaki, Kobe	29 Nov 1978
YAHIKO	PL 104	Mitsubishi, Shimonoseki	16 Nov 1978
MOTOBU	PL 105	Sasebo	29 Nov 1978
RISHIRI	PL 106	Shikoku	12 Sep 1979
MATSUSHIMA	PL 107	Tohoku	14 Sep 1979
IWAKI	PL 108	Naikai	10 Aug 1979
SHIKINE	PL 109	Usuki	20 Sep 1979
SURUGA	PL 110	Kurushima	28 Sep 1979
REBUN	PL 111	Narasaki	21 Nov 1979
CHOKAI	PL 112	Nihonkai	30 Nov 1979
ASHIZURI	PL 113	Sanoyasu	31 Oct 1979
OKI	PL 114	Tsuneishi	16 Nov 1979
NOTO	PL 115	Miho	30 Nov 1979
YONAKUNI	PL 116	Hayashikane	31 Oct 1979
KUDAKA (ex-*Daisetsu*)	PL 117	Hakodate	31 Jan 1980
SHIMOKITA	PL 118	Ishikawajima, Kakoki	12 Mar 1980
SUZUKA	PL 119	Kanazashi	7 Mar 1980
KUNISAKI	PL 120	Kouyo	29 Feb 1980
GENKAI	PL 121	Oshima	31 Jan 1980
GOTO	PL 122	Onomichi	29 Feb 1980
KOSHIKI	PL 123	Kasado	25 Jan 1980
HATERUMA	PL 124	Osaka	12 Mar 1980
KATORI	PL 125	Tohoku	21 Oct 1980
KUNIGAMI	PL 126	Kanda	17 Oct 1980
ETOMO	PL 127	Naikai	17 Mar 1982
MASHU	PL 128	Shiikoku	12 Mar 1982

Displacement, tons: 974 normal; 1360 full load
Dimensions, feet (metres): 255.8 × 31.5 × 10.5 *(78 × 9.6 × 3.2)*
Main machinery: 2 Fuji 8S40B; 8120 hp(m) *(5.97 MW)*; or 2 Niigata 8MA40 diesels; 2 shafts; cp props
Speed, knots: 20. **Range, miles:** 4400 at 17 kts
Complement: 41
Guns: 1 Bofors 40 mm or 1 Oerlikon 35 mm. 1 Oerlikon 20 mm (PL 101-105, 127 and 128).
Radars: Navigation: One set.

Comment: Average time from launch to commissioning was about four to five months. Designed for EEZ patrol duties. PL 117 changed her name on 1 April 1988.

ESAN   5/1993, Hachiro Nakai

1 KOJIMA CLASS

Name	No	Builders	Commissioned
KOJIMA	PL 21	Hitachi, Maizuru	11 Mar 1993

Displacement, tons: 2650 normal; 2950 full load
Dimensions, feet (metres): 377.3 × 45.9 × 16.4 *(115 × 14 × 5)*
Main machinery: 2 diesels; 8000 hp(m) *(5.9 MW)*; 2 shafts
Speed, knots: 18. **Range, miles:** 7000 at 15 kts
Complement: 118
Guns: 1 Oerlikon 35 mm/90. 1—20 mm JM-61B Gatling. 1—12.7 mm MG.

Comment: Authorised in the FY 1990 programme and ordered in March 1991. Laid down 7 November 1991, launched 10 September 1992. Training ship which has replaced the old ship of the same name and pennant number.

KOJIMA   5/1993, Hachiro Nakai

4 ERIMO and DAIO CLASSES

Name	No	Builders	Commissioned
ERIMO	PL 13	Hitachi, Mukaishima	30 Nov 1965
SATSUMA	PL 14	Hitachi, Mukaishima	30 July 1966
DAIO	PL 15	Hitachi, Maizuru	28 Sep 1973*
MUROTO	PL 16	Naikai	30 Nov 1974

Displacement, tons: 1010 (1206, PL 15-16) normal
Dimensions, feet (metres): 251.3 × 30.2 × 9.9 *(76.6 × 9.2 × 3)* (PL 13-14)
251.3 × 31.5 × 10.7 *(76.6 × 9.6 × 3.3)* (PL 15-16)
Main machinery: 2 Burmeister & Wain diesels (PL 13-14); 2 Fuji 8S40B (PL 15-16); 8120 hp(m) *(5.97 MW)*; 2 shafts; cp props
Speed, knots: 20. **Range, miles:** 5000 at 18 kts (PL 13-14); 4400 at 18 kts (PL 15-16)
Complement: 72 (PL 13-14); 50 (PL 15-16)
Guns: 1 Oerlikon 20 mm. 1 Bofors 40 mm (PL 15-16). 1 Oerlikon 20 mm (PL 13-14).
Radars: Navigation: JMA 1576. JMA 1596.

Comment: PL 13's structure is strengthened against ice. Based at Kamaishi (PL 13); Kagoshima (PL 14); Kushiro (PL 15); Aburatsu (PL 16).

SATSUMA   1990, Ships of the World

1 NOJIMA CLASS

Name	No	Builders	Commissioned
NOJIMA	PL 01	Ishikawajima Harima, Tokyo	21 Sep 1989

Displacement, tons: 1500 normal
Dimensions, feet (metres): 285.4 × 34.4 × 11.5 *(87 × 10.5 × 3.5)*
Main machinery: 2 Fuji 8S40B diesels; 8120 hp(m) *(5.97 MW)*; 2 shafts
Speed, knots: 19
Guns: 1—20 mm JM-61B Gatling.
Radars: Navigation.
Helicopters: Platform for 1 Bell 212.

Comment: Laid down 16 August 1988 and launched 30 May 1989. Equipped as surveillance and rescue command ship. SATCOM fitted.

NOJIMA   5/1992, Hachiro Nakai

1 + 2 OJIKA CLASS

Name	No	Builders	Commissioned
OJIKA	PL 02	Mitsui, Tamano	31 Oct 1991
—	PL 03	Hakodate Dock	Oct 1994
—	PL 04	—	Oct 1995

Displacement, tons: 1883 normal
Dimensions, feet (metres): 299.9 × 36.1 × 11.5 *(91.4 × 11 × 3.5)*
Main machinery: 2 Fuji 8S40B diesels; 7000 hp(m) *(5.15 MW)*; 2 shafts
Speed, knots: 18. **Range, miles:** 4400 at 15 kts
Complement: 38
Guns: 1—20 mm JM-61B Gatling. 1—35 mm.
Helicopters: Platform for 1 Bell 212.

Comment: First of class launched 23 April 1991. Second ordered in October 1992 and laid down in April 1993. Third authorised in FY 1993. Equipped as SAR command ships. SATCOM fitted.

OJIKA *5/1992, Hachiro Nakai*

SHIPBORNE AIRCRAFT

Numbers/Type: 4 Aerospatiale Super Puma.
Operational speed: 151 kts *(279 km/h)*.
Service ceiling: 15 090 ft *(4600 m)*.
Range: 335 nm *(620 km)*.
Role/Weapon systems: Medium lift, support and SAR. Sensors: Search radar. Weapons: Unarmed.

SUPER PUMA *5/1993, Hachiro Nakai*

Numbers/Type: 36 Bell 212.
Operational speed: 100 kts *(185 km/h)*.
Service ceiling: 10 000 ft *(3048 m)*.
Range: 412 nm *(763 km)*.
Role/Weapon systems: Liaison, medium-range support and SAR. Sensors: Search radar. Weapons: Unarmed.

BELL 212 *5/1992, Hachiro Nakai*

LAND-BASED MARITIME AIRCRAFT (FRONT LINE)

Note: Two Sikorsky S-76C to be delivered in 1994.

Numbers/Type: 16 Beech Super King Air 200T.
Operational speed: 245 kts *(453 km/h)*.
Service ceiling: 35 000 ft *(10 670 m)*.
Range: 1460 nm *(2703 km)*.
Role/Weapon systems: Visual reconnaissance in support of EEZ. Sensors: Weather/search radar. Weapons: Unarmed.

Numbers/Type: 1 Bell 206G JetRanger.
Operational speed: 115 kts *(213 km/h)*.
Service ceiling: 10 000 ft *(3048 m)*.
Range: 312 nm *(577 km)*.
Role/Weapon systems: Liaison and training. Sensors: None. Weapons: Unarmed.

Numbers/Type: 5 NAMC YS-11A.
Operational speed: 230 kts *(425 km/h)*.
Service ceiling: 21 600 ft *(6580 m)*.
Range: 1960 nm *(3629 km)*.
Role/Weapon systems: Maritime surveillance and associated tasks. Sensors: Weather/search radar. Weapons: Unarmed.

Numbers/Type: 2 Shorts Skyvan 3.
Operational speed: 175 kts *(324 km/h)*.
Service ceiling: 10 000 ft *(3048 m)*.
Range: 847 nm *(1568 km)*.
Role/Weapon systems: Coastal patrol and support aircraft. Sensors: Weather radar. Weapons: Unarmed.

Numbers/Type: 2 Falcon 900.
Operational speed: 428 kts *(792 km/h)*.
Service ceiling: 51 000 ft *(15 544 m)*.
Range: 4170 nm *(7722 km)*.
Role/Weapon systems: Maritime surveillance. Sensors: Weather/search radar. Weapons: Unarmed.

MEDIUM PATROL VESSELS

14 TESHIO CLASS

Name	No	Builders	Commissioned
TESHIO	PM 01	Shikoku	30 Sep 1980
OIRASE	PM 02	Naikai	29 Aug 1980
ECHIZEN	PM 03	Usuki	30 Sep 1980
TOKACHI	PM 04	Narazaki	24 Mar 1981
HITACHI	PM 05	Tohoku	19 Mar 1981
OKITSU	PM 06	Usuki	17 Mar 1981
ISAZU	PM 07	Naikai	18 Feb 1982
CHITOSE	PM 08	Shikoku	15 Mar 1983
KUWANO	PM 09	Naikai	10 Mar 1983
SORACHI	PM 10	Tohoku	30 Aug 1984
YUBARI	PM 11	Usuki	28 Nov 1985
MOTOURA	PM 12	Shikoku	21 Nov 1986
KANO	PM 13	Naikai	13 Nov 1986
SENDAI	PM 14	Shikoku	1 June 1988

Displacement, tons: 630 normal; 670 full load
Dimensions, feet (metres): 222.4 × 25.9 × 6.6 *(67.8 × 7.9 × 2.7)*
Main machinery: 2 Fuji 6S32F diesels; 3650 hp(m) *(2.69 MW)*; 2 shafts
Speed, knots: 18. **Range, miles:** 3200 at 16 kts
Complement: 33
Guns: 1 JN-61B 20 mm Gatling.
Radars: Navigation: Two JMA 159B; I band.

Comment: First three built under FY 1979 programme and second three under FY 1980, seventh under FY 1981, PM 08-09 under FY 1982, PM 10 under FY 1983, PM 11 under FY 1984, PM 12-13 under FY 1985, PM 14 under FY 1987.

ISAZU *5/1992, Hachiro Nakai*

2 TAKATORI CLASS

Name	No	Builders	Commissioned
TAKATORI	PM 89	Naikai	24 Mar 1978
KUMANO	PM 94	Namura	23 Feb 1979

Displacement, tons: 634 normal
Dimensions, feet (metres): 152.5 × 30.2 × 9.3 *(46.5 × 9.2 × 2.9)*
Main machinery: 2 Niigata 6M31EX diesels; 3000 hp(m) *(2.21 MW)*; 2 shafts; cp props
Speed, knots: 15. **Range, miles:** 700 at 14 kts
Complement: 34

Comment: SAR vessels equipped for salvage and firefighting.

TAKATORI *8/1993, Hachiro Nakai*

20 BIHORO CLASS (350-M4 TYPE)

Name	No	Builders	Commissioned
BIHORO	PM 73	Tohoku	28 Feb 1974
KUMA	PM 74	Usuki	28 Feb 1974
FUJI	PM 75	Usuki	7 Feb 1975
KABASHIMA	PM 76	Usuki	25 Mar 1975
SADO	PM 77	Tohoku	7 Feb 1975
ISHIKARI	PM 78	Tohoku	13 Mar 1976
ABUKUMA	PM 79	Tohoku	30 Jan 1976
ISUZU	PM 80	Naikai	10 Mar 1976
KIKUCHI	PM 81	Usuki	6 Feb 1976
KUZURYU	PM 82	Usuki	18 Mar 1976
HOROBETSU	PM 83	Tohoku	27 Jan 1977
SHIRAKAMI	PM 84	Tohoku	24 Mar 1977
SAGAMI	PM 85	Naikai	30 Nov 1976
TONE	PM 86	Usuki	30 Nov 1976
YOSHINO	PM 87	Usuki	28 Jan 1977
KUROBE	PM 88	Shikoku	15 Feb 1977
CHIKUGO	PM 90	Naikai	27 Jan 1978
YAMAKUNI	PM 91	Usuki	26 Jan 1978
KATSURA	PM 92	Shikoku	15 Feb 1978
SHINANO	PM 93	Tohoku	23 Feb 1978

Displacement, tons: 615 normal; 636 full load
Dimensions, feet (metres): 208 × 25.6 × 8.3 *(63.4 × 7.8 × 2.5)*
Main machinery: 2 Niigata 6M31EX diesels; 3000 hp(m) *(2.21 MW)*; 2 shafts; cp props
Speed, knots: 18. **Range, miles:** 3200 at 16 kts
Complement: 34
Guns: 1 USN 20 mm/80 Mk 10.
Radars: Navigation: JMA 1596 and JMA 1576; I band.

Comment: Average time from launch to commissioning, four months. Fitted with Loran.

CHIKUGO   *2/1993, Hachiro Nakai*

7 KUNASHIRI CLASS (350-M3 TYPE)

Name	No	Builders	Commissioned
KUNASHIRI	PM 65	Hitachi, Maizuru	28 Mar 1969
MINABE	PM 66	Hitachi, Maizuru	28 Mar 1970
SAROBETSU	PM 67	Hitachi, Maizuru	30 Mar 1971
KAMISHIMA	PM 68	Usuki	31 Jan 1972
MIYAKE	PM 70	Tohoku	25 Jan 1973
AWAJI	PM 71	Usuki	25 Jan 1973
YAEYAMA	PM 72	Usuki	20 Dec 1972

Displacement, tons: 498 normal
Dimensions, feet (metres): 190.4 × 24.3 × 7.9 *(58 × 7.4 × 2.4)*
Main machinery: 2 Niigata 6MF32H or 6M31EX (PM 70-72) diesels; 2600 hp(m) *(1.91 MW)* or 3000 hp(m) *(2.21 MW)* (PM 70-72); 2 shafts
Speed, knots: 17 or 18. **Range, miles:** 3000 at 16 kts
Complement: 40
Guns: 1 USN 20 mm Mk 10.
Radars: Navigation: JMA 1576 or 1596 (PM 70-72).

Comment: The last three have slightly more powerful diesels and a top speed of 18 kts.

MINABE   *7/1992, Hachiro Nakai*

1—550 TON CLASS

Displacement, tons: 550 normal
Dimensions, feet (metres): 180.4 × 34.8 × 12.8 *(55 × 10.6 × 3.9)*
Main machinery: 2 diesels; 3600 hp(m) *(2.65 MW)*; 2 shafts
Speed, knots: 14.5
Complement: 30
Guns: 1—20 mm JM-61B Gatling; 6 barrels.

Comment: PM 97 laid down in late 1993. Carries an RIB on the stern.

2 MATSUURA CLASS (350-M2 TYPE)

Name	No	Builders	Commissioned
NATORI	PM 63	Hitachi, Mukaishima	20 Jan 1966
KARATSU	PM 64	Hitachi, Mukaishima	29 Mar 1967

Displacement, tons: 455 normal
Dimensions, feet (metres): 181.4 × 23 × 7.5 *(55.3 × 7 × 2.3)*
Main machinery: 2 Ikegai 6MSB3HS diesels (PM 63); 1800 hp(m) *(1.32 MW)*; 2 Ikegai 6MA31X diesels (PM 64); 2600 hp(m) *(1.91 MW)*; 2 shafts
Speed, knots: 17. **Range, miles:** 3500 at 13 kts
Complement: 40
Guns: 1 USN 20 mm Mk 10.
Radars: Navigation: One set.

Comment: *Natori* to be replaced by PM 97 in 1994/95.

NATORI   *1990, Ships of the World*

1 ANAMI CLASS

Name	No	Builders	Commissioned
ANAMI	PM 95	Hitachi, Kanagawa	28 Sep 1992

Displacement, tons: 230 normal
Dimensions, feet (metres): 183.7 × 24.6 × 6.6 *(56 × 7.5 × 2)*
Main machinery: 2 Fuji 8S40B diesels; 8120 hp(m) *(5.97 MW)*; 2 shafts; cp props
Speed, knots: 25
Guns: 1—20 mm JM-61B Gatling.
Radars: Navigation: I band.

Comment: Authorised in the FY 1991 programme. Laid down 22 October 1991.

ANAMI   *7/1993, van Ginderen Collection*

1 YAHAGI CLASS (350 TYPE)

Name	No	Builders	Commissioned
MISASA (ex-*Okinawa*)	PM 69	Usuki	23 Oct 1970

Displacement, tons: 376 normal
Dimensions, feet (metres): 164.9 × 24 × 7.4 *(50.3 × 7.3 × 2.3)*
Main machinery: 2 diesels; 1400 hp(m) *(1.03 MW)*; 2 shafts
Speed, knots: 15.5. **Range, miles:** 2900 at 14 kts
Complement: 44
Guns: 1 USN 20 mm Mk 10.
Radars: Navigation: One set.

Comment: Transferred to MSA in 1972. Name changed 1 April 1988.

MISASA   *1988, JMSA*

SMALL PATROL VESSELS

6 MIHASHI CLASS (180 TYPE)

Name	No	Builders	Commissioned
MIHASHI	PS 01	Mitsubishi, Shimonoseki	9 Sep 1988
SAROMA	PS 02	Hitachi, Kanagawa	24 Nov 1989
INASA	PS 03	Mitsubishi, Shimonoseki	31 Jan 1990
KIRISHIMA	PS 04	Hitachi, Kanagawa	22 Mar 1991
KAMUI	PS 05	Mitsubishi, Shimonoseki	31 Jan 1994
BIZAN	PS 06	Hitachi, Kanagawa	31 Jan 1994

Displacement, tons: 195 normal
Dimensions, feet (metres): 141.1 × 24.6 × 5.6 *(43 × 7.5 × 1.7)*
Main machinery: 2 SEMT-Pielstick 16 PA4 V 200 VGA diesels; 7072 hp(m) *(5.2 MW)*; 2 shafts
1 SEMT-Pielstick 12 PA4 V 200 VGA diesel; 2720 hp(m) *(2 MW)*; KaMeWa waterjet
Speed, knots: 35. **Range, miles:** 650 at 34 kts
Complement: 34
Guns: 1—12.7 mm MG.

Comment: First one launched 28 June 1988, second 28 June 1989 and third 20 October 1989. Fourth laid down 10 May 1990. Last pair authorised in FY 1992 programme. Capable of 15 kts on the waterjet alone.

MIHASHI   *5/1993, Hachiro Nakai*

7 AKAGI CLASS

Name	No	Builders	Commissioned
AKAGI	PS 101	Sumidagawa	26 Mar 1980
TSUKUBA	PS 102	Sumidagawa	24 Feb 1982
KONGOU	PS 103	Ishihara	16 Mar 1987
KATSURAGI	PS 104	Ishihara	24 Mar 1988
HIROMINE	PS 105	Yokohama Yacht Co	24 Mar 1988
SHIZUKI	PS 106	Sumidagawa	24 Mar 1988
TAKACHIHO	PS 107	Sumidagawa	24 Mar 1988

Displacement, tons: 115 full load
Dimensions, feet (metres): 114.8 × 20.7 × 4.3 *(35 × 6.3 × 1.3)*
Main machinery: 2 Pielstick 16 PA4 V 185 diesels; 5344 hp(m) *(3.93 MW)* sustained; 2 shafts
Speed, knots: 28. **Range, miles:** 500 at 20 kts
Complement: 22
Guns: 1 Browning 12.7 mm MG.
Radars: Navigation: One set.

Comment: Carry a 25-man inflatable rescue craft. The last four were ordered on 31 August 1987 and commissioned less than seven months later.

TSUKUBA   *5/1993, Hachiro Nakai*

2 + 2 TAKATSUKI CLASS

Name	No	Builders	Commissioned
TAKATSUKI	PS 108	Mitsubishi, Shimonoseki	23 Mar 1992
NOBARU	PS 109	Hitachi, Kanagawa	22 Mar 1993
—	PS 110	Hitachi, Kanagawa	1994
—	PS 111	Mitsubishi, Shimonoseki	1994

Displacement, tons: 115 normal; 180 full load
Dimensions, feet (metres): 114.8 × 22 × 4.3 *(35 × 6.7 × 1.3)*
Main machinery: 2 MTU 16V 396 TB94 diesels; 5200 hp(m) *(3.82 MW)*; 2 KaMeWa waterjets
Speed, knots: 35
Complement: 13
Guns: 1—12.7 mm MG.

Comment: First authorised in the FY 1991 programme, second in FY 1992. Second pair laid down in April 1993. Aluminium hulls.

NOBARU   *5/1993, Hachiro Nakai*

6 HIDAKA CLASS

Name	No	Builders	Commissioned
KUNIMI	PS 38	Hayashikane	15 Feb 1965
KAMUI	PS 41	Hayashikane	15 Feb 1966
ASHITAKA	PS 43	Usuki	10 Feb 1967
KURAMA	PS 44	Usuki	28 Feb 1967
IBUKI	PS 45	Usuki	5 Mar 1968
TOUMI	PS 46	Usuki	20 Feb 1968

Displacement, tons: 169 normal
Dimensions, feet (metres): 104 × 20.8 × 5.5 *(31.7 × 6.3 × 1.7)*
Main machinery: 1 Ikegai 6MSB31A diesel; 700 hp(m) *(515 kW)*; 1 shaft
Speed, knots: 12.5. **Range, miles:** 1000 at 12 kts
Complement: 17
Radars: Navigation: One set.

Comment: Occasionally carry a 12.7 mm MG. Being replaced by Mihashi and Takatsuki classes.

KURAMA   *1/1992, Hachiro Nakai*

COASTAL PATROL CRAFT

3 SHIMAGIRI CLASS

Name	No	Builders	Commissioned
SHIMAGIRI	PC 83	Hitachi, Kanagawa	7 Feb 1985
SETOGIRI	PC 84	Hitachi, Kanagawa	22 Mar 1985
HAYAGIRI	PC 85	Mitsubishi, Shimonoseki	22 Feb 1985

Displacement, tons: 51 normal
Dimensions, feet (metres): 75.5 × 17.4 × 6.2 *(23 × 5.3 × 1.9)*
Main machinery: 2 Ikegai 12V 175 RTC diesels; 3000 hp(m) *(2.21 MW)*; 2 shafts
Speed, knots: 30
Complement: 10
Guns: 1—12.7 mm MG (not in all).

Comment: Aluminium hulls.

SETOGIRI   *7/1992, Hachiro Nakai*

1 MATSUNAMI CLASS

Name	No	Builders	Commissioned
MATSUNAMI	PC 53	Hitachi, Kanagawa	30 Mar 1971

Displacement, tons: 59 normal
Dimensions, feet (metres): 82 × 19.7 × 7.9 *(25 × 6 × 2.4)*
Main machinery: 2 MTU MB 12V 493 TY7 diesels; 2200 hp(m) *(1.62 MW)* sustained; 2 shafts
Speed, knots: 20. **Range, miles:** 270 at 18 kts
Complement: 30

Comment: Used for Oceanographic survey and specially fitted out for the Emperor.

MATSUNAMI   *5/1993, Hachiro Nakai*

23 MURAKUMO CLASS

Name	No	Builders	Commissioned
MURAKUMO	PC 201	Mitsubishi, Shimonoseki	24 Mar 1978
KITAGUMO	PC 202	Hitachi, Kanagawa	17 Mar 1978
YUKIGUMO	PC 203	Hitachi, Kanagawa	27 Sep 1978
ASAGUMO	PC 204	Mitsubishi, Shimonoseki	21 Sep 1978
HAYAGUMO	PC 205	Mitsubishi, Shimonoseki	30 Jan 1979
AKIGUMO	PC 206	Hitachi, Kanagawa	28 Feb 1979
YAEGUMO	PC 207	Mitsubishi, Shimonoseki	16 Mar 1979
NATSUGUMO	PC 208	Hitachi, Kanagawa	22 Mar 1979
YAMAGIRI	PC 209	Hitachi, Kanagawa	29 June 1979
KAWAGIRI	PC 210	Hitachi, Kanagawa	27 July 1979
TERUZUKI	PC 211	Mitsubishi, Shimonoseki	26 June 1979
NATSUZUKI	PC 212	Mitsubishi, Shimonoseki	26 July 1979
MIYAZUKI	PC 213	Hitachi, Kanagawa	13 Mar 1980
NIJIGUMO	PC 214	Mitsubishi, Shimonoseki	29 Jan 1981
TATSUGUMO	PC 215	Mitsubishi, Shimonoseki	19 Mar 1981
HAMAYUKI	PC 216	Mitsubishi, Shimonoseki	27 Feb 1981
ISONAMI	PC 217	Mitsubishi, Shimonoseki	19 Mar 1981
NAGOZUKI	PC 218	Hitachi, Kanagawa	29 Jan 1981
YAEZUKI	PC 219	Hitachi, Kanagawa	19 Mar 1981
YAMAYUKI	PC 220	Hitachi, Kanagawa	16 Feb 1982
KOMAYUKI	PC 221	Mitsubishi, Shimonoseki	10 Feb 1982
UMIGIRI	PC 222	Hitachi, Kanagawa	17 Feb 1983
ASAGIRI	PC 223	Mitsubishi, Shimonoseki	23 Feb 1983

Displacement, tons: 85 normal
Dimensions, feet (metres): 98.4 × 20.7 × 7.2 *(30 × 6.3 × 2.2)*
Main machinery: 2 Ikegai MTU MB 16V 652 SB70 diesels; 4400 hp(m) *(3.23 MW)* sustained; 2 shafts
Speed, knots: 30. **Range, miles:** 350 at 28 kts
Complement: 13
Guns: 1 Browning 12.7 mm MG.

HAYAGUMO 5/1993, *Hachiro Nakai*

12 AKIZUKI CLASS

Name	No	Builders	Commissioned
AKIZUKI	PC 64	Mitsubishi, Shimonoseki	28 Feb 1974
SHINONOME	PC 65	Mitsubishi, Shimonoseki	25 Mar 1974
URAYUKI	PC 72	Mitsubishi, Shimonoseki	31 May 1975
ISEYUKI	PC 73	Mitsubishi, Shimonoseki	31 July 1975
HATAGUMO	PC 75	Mitsubishi, Shimonoseki	21 Feb 1976
MAKIGUMO	PC 76	Mitsubishi, Shimonoseki	19 Mar 1976
HAMAZUKI	PC 77	Mitsubishi, Shimonoseki	29 Nov 1976
ISOZUKI	PC 78	Mitsubishi, Shimonoseki	18 Mar 1977
SHIMANAMI	PC 79	Mitsubishi, Shimonoseki	23 Dec 1977
YUZUKI	PC 80	Mitsubishi, Shimonoseki	22 Mar 1979
HANAYUKI	PC 81	Mitsubishi, Shimonoseki	27 May 1981
AWAGIRI	PC 82	Mitsubishi, Shimonoseki	24 Mar 1983

Displacement, tons: 77 normal
Dimensions, feet (metres): 85.3 × 20.7 × 6.9 *(26 × 6.3 × 2.1)*
Main machinery: 3 Mitsubishi 12DM20MTK diesels; 3000 hp(m) *(2.21 MW)*; 3 shafts
Speed, knots: 22. **Range, miles:** 220 at 21.5 kts
Complement: 10
Radars: Navigation: FRA 10 Mk 2.

Comment: Aluminium hulls.

HAMAZUKI 11/1993, *Hachiro Nakai*

17 SHIKINAMI CLASS

Name	No	Builders	Commissioned
SHIKINAMI	PC 54	Mitsubishi, Shimonoseki	25 Feb 1971
TOMONAMI	PC 55	Mitsubishi, Shimonoseki	20 Mar 1971
WAKANAMI	PC 56	Mitsubishi, Shimonoseki	30 Oct 1971
ISENAMI	PC 57	Hitachi, Kanagawa	29 Feb 1972
TAKANAMI	PC 58	Mitsubishi, Shimonoseki	30 Nov 1971
MUTSUKI	PC 59	Hitachi, Kanagawa	18 Dec 1972
MOCHIZUKI	PC 60	Hitachi, Kanagawa	18 Dec 1972
HARUZUKI	PC 61	Mitsubishi, Shimonoseki	30 Nov 1972
KIYOZUKI	PC 62	Mitsubishi, Shimonoseki	18 Dec 1972
URAZUKI	PC 63	Hitachi, Kanagawa	30 Jan 1973
URANAMI	PC 66	Hitachi, Kanagawa	22 Dec 1973
TAMANAMI	PC 67	Mitsubishi, Shimonoseki	25 Dec 1973
MINEGUMO	PC 68	Mitsubishi, Shimonoseki	30 Nov 1973
KIYONAMI	PC 69	Mitsubishi, Shimonoseki	30 Oct 1973
OKINAMI	PC 70	Hitachi, Kanagawa	8 Feb 1974
WAKAGUMO	PC 71	Hitachi, Kanagawa	25 Mar 1974
ASOYUKI	PC 74	Hitachi, Kanagawa	16 June 1975

Displacement, tons: 46 normal
Dimensions, feet (metres): 69 × 17.4 × 3.3 *(21 × 5.3 × 1)*
Main machinery: 2 MTU MB 12V 493 TY7 diesels; 2200 hp(m) *(1.62 MW)* sustained; 2 shafts
Speed, knots: 26. **Range, miles:** 230 at 23.8 kts
Complement: 10
Radars: Navigation: MD 806.

Comment: Built completely of light alloy. Starting to pay off in 1994.

MINEGUMO 7/1993, *Hachiro Nakai*

3 HAYANAMI CLASS

Name	No	Builders	Commissioned
HAYANAMI	PC 11	Sumidagawa	25 Mar 1993
SHIKINAMI	PC 12	Sumidagawa	Mar 1994
MIZUNAMI	PC 13	Ishihara	Mar 1994

Displacement, tons: 110 normal; 190 full load
Dimensions, feet (metres): 114.8 × 20.7 × 7.5 *(35 × 6.3 × 2.3)*
Main machinery: 2 diesels; 4000 hp(m) *(2.94 MW)*; 2 shafts
Speed, knots: 25
Guns: 1—12.7 mm MG.

Comment: Launched 7 January 1993. Two more built in 1994.

HAYANAMI 4/1993, *Hachiro Nakai*

2 NATSUGIRI CLASS

Name	No	Builders	Commissioned
NATSUGIRI	PC 86	Sumidagawa	29 Jan 1990
SUGANAMI	PC 87	Sumidagawa	29 Jan 1990

Displacement, tons: 68 normal
Dimensions, feet (metres): 88.6 × 18.4 × 3.9 *(27 × 5.6 × 1.2)*
Main machinery: 2 diesels; 3000 hp(m) *(2.21 MW)*; 2 shafts
Speed, knots: 27

Comment: Built under FY 1988 programme. Steel hulls.

SUGANAMI 5/1990, *Hachiro Nakai*

179 COASTAL PATROL AND RESCUE CRAFT

CL 01-04, 11-33, 34-47, 79-82, 84-85, 87-89, 91-95, 97-156, 201-264

Displacement, tons: 23 *(01-04, 11-33)*, 19 *(79-156)*, 27 *(201-264)* normal
Main machinery: 2 diesels; 900 hp(m) *(01-02)*, 1400 hp(m) *(03-04)*, 1820 hp(m) *(11-33)*, 500 hp
(m) *(79-156)*, 900 hp *(201-264)*; 2 shafts
Speed, knots: 18-30
Complement: 6

Comment: This total includes five similar classes all of about 20 m in length. Some have firefighting
capability. Built by Shigi, Ishihara, Sumidagawa and Yokohama Yacht Co. CL 01-04 completed
1989-91, CL 11-17 in 1992 CL 18-33 in 1993, CL 34-43 in 1994. For coastal patrol and rescue
duties. Built of high tensile steel.

CL 12   *3/1992, Hachiro Nakai*

CL 79   *3/1991, Hachiro Nakai*

FIREFIGHTING VESSELS AND CRAFT

5 HIRYU CLASS

Name	No	Builders	Commissioned
HIRYU	FL 01	Nippon Kokan, Tsurumi	4 Mar 1969
SHORYU	FL 02	Nippon Kokan, Tsurumi	4 Mar 1970
NANRYU	FL 03	Nippon Kokan, Tsurumi	4 Mar 1971
KAIRYU	FL 04	Nippon Kokan, Tsurumi	18 Mar 1977
SUIRYU	FL 05	Yokohama Yacht Co	24 Mar 1978

Displacement, tons: 215 normal
Dimensions, feet (metres): 90.2 × 34.1 × 7.2 *(27.5 × 10.4 × 2.2)*
Main machinery: 2 Ikegai MTU MB 12V 493 TY7 diesels; 2200 hp(m) *(1.62 MW)* sustained; 2
shafts
Speed, knots: 13.2. **Range, miles:** 300 at 13 kts
Complement: 14

Comment: Catamaran type fire boats designed and built for firefighting services to large tankers.

HIRYU   *5/1992, Hachiro Nakai*

10 NUNOBIKI CLASS

Name	No	Builders	Commissioned
NUNOBIKI	FM 01	Yokohama Yacht Co	25 Feb 1974
YODO	FM 02	Sumidagawa	30 Mar 1975
OTOWA	FM 03	Yokohama Yacht Co	25 Dec 1974
SHIRAITO	FM 04	Yokohama Yacht Co	25 Feb 1975
KOTOBIKI	FM 05	Yokohama Yacht Co	31 Jan 1976
NACHI	FM 06	Sumidagawa	14 Feb 1976
KEGON	FM 07	Yokohama Yacht Co	29 Jan 1977
MINOO	FM 08	Sumidagawa	27 Jan 1978
RYUSEI	FM 09	Yokohama Yacht Co	24 Mar 1980
KIYOTAKI	FM 10	Sumidagawa	25 Mar 1981

Displacement, tons: 89 normal
Dimensions, feet (metres): 75.4 × 19.7 × 5.2 *(23 × 6 × 1.6)*
Main machinery: 1 MTU MB 12V 493 TY7 diesel; 1100 hp(m) *(810 kW)* sustained; 1 shaft
2 Nissan diesels; 500 hp(m) *(515 kW)*; 3 shafts
Speed, knots: 14. **Range, miles:** 180 at 13.5 kts
Complement: 12
Radars: Navigation: FRA 10.

Comment: Equipped for chemical firefighting.

OTOWA   *5/1992, Hachiro Nakai*

SURVEY SHIPS

Name	No	Builders	Commissioned
TAKUYO	HL 02	Nippon Kokan, Tsurumi	31 Aug 1983

Displacement, tons: 3000 normal
Dimensions, feet (metres): 314.9 × 46.6 × 15.1 *(96 × 14.2 × 4.6)*
Main machinery: 2 Fuji 6S40B diesels; 6090 hp(m) *(4.47 MW)*; 2 shafts; cp props
Speed, knots: 17. **Range, miles:** 12 000 at 16 kts
Complement: 60 (24 officers)
Radars: Navigation: Two sets.

Comment: Laid down on 14 April 1982, launched on 24 March 1983. Based at Tokyo.

TAKUYO   *8/1993, Hachiro Nakai*

Name	No	Builders	Commissioned
SHOYO	HL 01	Hitachi, Maizuru	26 Feb 1972

Displacement, tons: 2200 normal
Dimensions, feet (metres): 268 × 41.3 × 13.8 *(81.7 × 12.6 × 4.2)*
Main machinery: 2 Fuji 12VM32 H2F diesels; 4800 hp(m) *(3.53 MW)*; 1 shaft
Speed, knots: 17. **Range, miles:** 11 000 at 14 kts
Complement: 58 (23 officers)
Radars: Navigation: Two sets.

Comment: Launched 18 September 1971. Fully equipped for all types of hydrographic and
oceanographic work. Carries MX702 SATNAV and Loran. Based at Tokyo.

SHOYO   *1/1992, Hachiro Nakai*

Name	No	Builders		Commissioned
TENYO	HL 04	Sumitomo, Oppama		27 Nov 1986

Displacement, tons: 770 normal
Dimensions, feet (metres): 183.7 × 32.2 × 9.5 *(56 × 9.8 × 2.9)*
Main machinery: 2 Akasaka diesels; 1300 hp(m) *(955 kW)*; 2 shafts
Speed, knots: 13. **Range, miles:** 5400 at 12 kts
Complement: 43 (18 officers)

Comment: Laid down 11 April 1986, launched 5 August 1986. Based at Tokyo.

TENYO   *1986, Maritime Safety Agency*

Name	No	Builders	Commissioned
MEIYO	HL 03	Kawasaki, Kobe	24 Oct 1990
KAIYO	HL 05	Mitsubishi, Shimonoseki	7 Oct 1993

Displacement, tons: 550 normal
Dimensions, feet (metres): 196.9 × 34.4 × 10.2 *(60 × 10.5 × 3.1)*
Main machinery: 2 Daihatsu 6 DLM-24 diesels; 3000 hp(m) *(2.2 MW)*; 2 shafts; bow thruster
Speed, knots: 15. **Range, miles:** 5280 at 11 kts
Complement: 25 + 13 scientists

Comment: *Meiyo* laid down 24 July 1989 and launched 29 June 1990; *Kaiyo* authorised in FY 1992 programme and has taken the name of the deleted HM 06 vessel. Have anti-roll tanks and resiliently mounted main machinery. A large survey launch is carried on the port side.

MEIYO   *10/1990, Hachiro Nakai*

1 ISESHIO CLASS

KUROSHIO HS 11

Displacement, tons: 6
Dimensions, feet (metres): 32.8 *(10)* long
Main machinery: 1 Nissan UD326 diesel; 90 hp(m) *(66 kW)*; 1 shaft
Speed, knots: 8.8
Complement: 7

Comment: Completed 1972. GRP hull. Carried in *Shoyo*.

KUROSHIO   *1/1992, Hachiro Nakai*

5 AKASHI CLASS

AKASHI HS 31		**KURIHAMA** HS 34	
KERAMA HS 32		**KURUSHIMA** HS 35	
HAYATOMO HS 33			

Displacement, tons: 21
Dimensions, feet (metres): 49.2 *(15)* long
Main machinery: 1 Nissan UD626 diesel; 180 hp(m) *(132 kW)*; 1 shaft
Speed, knots: 9. **Range, miles:** 400 at 9 kts
Complement: 7

Comment: Completed 1973-77. Steel hulls.

KURIHAMA   *5/1991, Hachiro Nakai*

2 HAMASHIO CLASS

HAMASHIO HS 21   **ISOSHI** HS 22

Displacement, tons: 42 normal
Dimensions, feet (metres): 66.6 × 14.8 × 3.9 *(20.3 × 4.5 × 1.2)*
Main machinery: 3 diesels; 1015 hp(m) *(746 kW)*; 3 shafts
Speed, knots: 15
Complement: 10

Comment: *Hamashio* built by Yokohama Yacht Co and completed 25 March 1991. *Isoshi* completed 25 March 1993.

HAMASHIO   *6/1991, Ships of the World*

AIDS TO NAVIGATION SERVICE

Name	No	Builders	Commissioned
TSUSHIMA	LL 01	Mitsui, Tamano	9 Sep 1977

Displacement, tons: 1950 normal
Dimensions, feet (metres): 246 × 41 × 13.8 *(75 × 12.5 × 4.2)*
Main machinery: 1 Fuji-Sulzer 8S40C diesel; 4200 hp(m) *(3.09 MW)*; 1 shaft; cp prop; bow thruster
Speed, knots: 15.5. **Range, miles:** 10 000 at 15 kts
Complement: 54

Comment: Lighthouse Supply Ship. Fitted with tank stabilisers. Equipped with modern electronic instruments for carrying out research on electronic aids to navigation.

TSUSHIMA   *5/1993, Hachiro Nakai*

3 HOKUTO CLASS

Name	No	Builders	Commissioned
HOKUTO	LL 11	Sasebo	29 June1979
KAIO	LL 12	Sasebo	11 Mar 1980
GINGA	LL 13	Kawasaki, Kobe	18 Mar 1980

Displacement, tons: 700 normal
Dimensions, feet (metres): 180.4 × 34.8 × 8.7 *(55 × 10.6 × 2.7)*
Main machinery: 2 Asakasa MH23R diesels; 1030 hp(m) *(757 kW)*; 2 shafts
Speed, knots: 12. **Range, miles:** 3900 at 12 kts
Complement: 31

KAIO   *8/1990, Hachiro Nakai*

Name	No	Builders	Commissioned
MYOJO	LM 11	Nippon Kokan, Tsurumi	25 Mar 1974

Displacement, tons: 303 normal
Dimensions, feet (metres): 88.6 × 39.4 × 8.8 *(27 × 12 × 2.7)*
Main machinery: 2 Niigata 6M9 16HS diesels; 600 hp(m) *(441 kW)*; 2 shafts; cp props
Speed, knots: 10.5. **Range, miles:** 1360 at 10.5 kts
Complement: 18

Comment: Catamaran type buoy tender, this ship is employed in maintenance and position adjustment service to floating aids to navigation.

MYOJO   *2/1993, Hachiro Nakai*

AIDS TO NAVIGATION TENDERS

1 ZUIUN CLASS

Name	No	Builders	Commissioned
ZUIUN	LM 101	Usuki	27 July 1983

Displacement, tons: 370 normal
Dimensions, feet (metres): 146.3 × 24.6 × 7.2 *(44.6 × 7.5 × 2.2)*
Main machinery: 2 Mitsubishi-Asakasa MH23R diesels; 1030 hp(m) *(757 kW)*; 2 shafts
Speed, knots: 13.5. **Range, miles:** 1000 at 13 kts
Complement: 20

Comment: Classed as a medium tender.

ZUIUN   *1988, JMSA*

1 AYABANE CLASS

Name	No	Builders	Commissioned
AYABANE	LM 112	Shimoda	25 Dec 1972

Displacement, tons: 187 normal
Dimensions, feet (metres): 107.3 × 21.3 × 6.6 *(32.7 × 6.5 × 2)*
Main machinery: 1 diesel; 500 hp(m) *(368 kW)*; 1 shaft
Speed, knots: 12
Complement: 18

8 HAKUUN CLASS

Name	No	Builders	Commissioned
HAKUUN	LM 106	Sumidagawa	28 Feb 1978
TOUN	LM 107	Sumidagawa	14 Mar 1979
TOKUUN	LM 114	Yokohama Yacht Co	23 Mar 1981
SHOUN	LM 201	Sumidagawa	26 Mar 1986
SEIUN	LM 202	Sumidagawa	22 Feb 1989
SEKIUN	LM 203	Ishihara	12 Mar 1991
HOUUN	LM 204	Ishihara	22 Feb 1991
REIUN	LM 205	Ishihara	28 Feb 1992

Displacement, tons: 58 full load
Dimensions, feet (metres): 75.5 × 19.7 × 3.3 *(23 × 6 × 1)*
Main machinery: 2 GM 12V-71TA diesels; 840 hp *(627 kW)* sustained; 2 shafts
Speed, knots: 14. **Range, miles:** 250 at 14 kts
Complement: 9

SEIUN   *11/1993, Hachiro Nakai*

60 SMALL TENDERS

LS 105, 114, 116-118, 123, 137, 141-146, 148-149, 154-155, 157-158, 160-161, 164-170, 180-182, 185-195, 204-221

Displacement, tons: 25 full load
Dimensions, feet (metres): 54.4 × 14.1 × 2.6 *(17.5 × 4.3 × 0.9)*
Main machinery: 2 diesels; 560 hp(m) *(412 kW)*; 2 shafts
Speed, knots: 15. **Range, miles:** 230 at 14.5 kts
Complement: 8

Comment: Details given are for *LS 204-221*. Last one completed 31 January 1990. Others with varying characteristics.

LS 211   *9/1992, Hachiro Nakai*

ENVIRONMENT MONITORING CRAFT

Note: In addition there are 34 surveillance craft SS 04-35 and SS 51-52, and three oil skimmers OS 01-03.

2 KINUGASA CLASS

Name	No	Builders	Commissioned
KINUGASA	MS 01	Ishihara, Takasago	31 Jan 1992
SAIKAI	MS 02	Ishihara, Takasago	14 Jan 1994

Displacement, tons: 39 normal
Dimensions, feet (metres): 59.1 × 29.5 × 4.3 *(18 × 9 × 1.3)*
Main machinery: 2 diesels; 1000 hp(m) *(735 kW)*; 2 shafts
Speed, knots: 15
Complement: 8

Comment: Used for monitoring pollution. Replaced craft of the same name. Catamaran hulls.

KINUGASA   *8/1993, Hachiro Nakai*

1 KATSUREN CLASS

Name	No	Builders	Commissioned
KATSUREN	MS 03	Ishihara, Takasago	13 Oct 1975

Displacement, tons: 45 normal
Dimensions, feet (metres): 54.1 × 16.4 × 7.2 *(16.5 × 5 × 2.2)*
Main machinery: 2 diesels; 500 hp; 2 shafts
Speed, knots: 12
Complement: 9

Comment: Used for monitoring pollution. May be replaced in 1995 by a third of the Kinugasa class.

2 GUARD BOATS

HAYATE GS 01   **INAZUMA** GS 02

Displacement, tons: 7.9 full load
Dimensions, feet (metres): 39 × 10.5 × 4.9 *(11.9 × 3.2 × 1.5)*
Main machinery: 2 Mitsubishi S6M2 diesels; 580 hp(m) *(426 kW)*; 2 shafts
Speed, knots: 30. **Range, miles:** 150 at 28 kts

Comment: Built by Yokohama Yacht Co and commissioned 21 December 1987.

HAYATE   *7/1991, Hachiro Nakai*

5 OIL RECOVERY CRAFT

SHIRASAGI OR 01   **MIZUNANGI** OR 03   **ISOSHIGI** OR 05
SHIRATORI OR 02   **CHIDORI** OR 04

Displacement, tons: 153 normal
Dimensions, feet (metres): 72.3 × 21 × 2.6 *(22 × 6.4 × 0.9)*
Main machinery: 2 Nissan UD626 diesels; 360 hp(m) *(265 kW)*; 2 shafts
Speed, knots: 6. **Range, miles:** 160 at 6 kts
Complement: 7

Comment: Completed by Sumidagawa (OR 01), Shigi (OR 02 and 04) and Ishihara (OR 03 and 05) between 31 January 1977 and 23 March 1979.

SHIRASAGI   *5/1990, Hachiro Nakai*

JORDAN

Headquarters' Appointments	Base	Mercantile Marine

Commander Naval Forces:
Colonel Hussein Ali Mahmoud Al Khasawneh

Aqaba

Lloyd's Register of Shipping:
5 vessels of 70 751 tons gross

Organisation

The Royal Jordanian Naval Force comes under the Director of Operations at General Headquarters. There has been a considerable expansion in the years 1990-93.

Personnel

(a) 1994: 750 officers and men
(b) Voluntary service

DELETION

1992   *Ali Abdullah*

PATROL FORCES

4 FAYSAL CLASS (COASTAL PATROL CRAFT)

FAYSAL   HAN   HASAYU   MUHAMMED

Displacement, tons: 8 full load
Dimensions, feet (metres): 38 × 13.1 × 1.6 *(11.6 × 4 × 0.5)*
Main machinery: 2 diesels; 600 hp *(441 kW)*; 2 shafts
Speed, knots: 25
Complement: 8
Guns: 1—12.7 mm MG. 1—7.62 mm MG.

Comment: Acquired from Bertram, Miami in 1974. These have not been replaced by the Hawk class, and are still fully operational in 1994.

3 AL HASHIM (ROTORK) CLASS

AL HASHIM   AL FAISAL   AL HAMZA

Displacement, tons: 9 full load
Dimensions, feet (metres): 41.7 × 10.5 × 3 *(12.7 × 3.2 × 0.9)*
Main machinery: 2 diesels; 240 hp *(179 kW)*; 2 shafts
Speed, knots: 28
Military lift: 30 troops
Guns: 1—7.62 mm MG.

Comment: Delivered in late 1990 for patrolling the Dead Sea.

3 AL HUSSEIN (HAWK) CLASS (FAST ATTACK CRAFT—GUN)

AL HUSSEIN 101   **AL HUSSAN** 102   **ABDULLAH** 103

Displacement, tons: 124 full load
Dimensions, feet (metres): 100 × 22.5 × 4.9 *(30.5 × 6.9 × 1.5)*
Main machinery: 2 MTU 16V 396 TB94 diesels; 5800 hp(m) *(4.26 MW)* sustained; 2 shafts
Speed, knots: 32. **Range, miles:** 750 at 15 kts; 1500 at 11 kts
Complement: 16 (3 officers)
Guns: 2 Oerlikon GCM-A03 30 mm (twin). 1 Oerlikon GAM-B01 20 mm. 2—12.5 mm MGs.
Countermeasures: Decoys: 2 Wallop Stockade chaff launchers.
Combat data systems: Racal Cane 100.
Fire control: Radamec Series 2000 optronic for 30 mm gun.
Radars: Surface search: Kelvin Hughes 1007; I band.

Comment: Ordered from Vosper Thornycroft in December 1987. GRP structure. First one on trials
in May 1989 and completed December 1989. Second completed in March 1990 and the third in
early 1991. All transported to Aqaba in September 1991.

AL HUSSAN   7/1990, W Sartori

POLICE

2 BREMSE CLASS (INSHORE PATROL CRAFT)

SHOROUQ I (ex-G 30/GS 30)   **SHOROUQ II** (ex-G 31/GS 42)

Displacement, tons: 42 full load
Dimensions, feet (metres): 74.1 × 15.4 × 3.6 *(22.6 × 4.7 × 1.1)*
Main machinery: 2 DM 6VD 18/5 AL-1 diesels; 1020 hp(m) *(750 kW)*; 2 shafts
Speed, knots: 14
Complement: 8
Guns: 1—12.7 mm MG.
Radars: Surface search: TSR 333; I band.

Comment: Built in 1971-72 for the former GDR border guard. Transferred from Germany in 1992.
Similar craft sold to Tunisia and Malta. These ships have blue hulls with a grey superstructure.
SEA POLICE is written on the hulls. Used for anti-smuggling patrols.

BREMSE GS 42 (German colours)   4/1991, Hartmut Ehlers

KAZAKHSTAN

General

A decision was taken in June 1993 to have a naval flotilla. Two
bases are being built, and Moscow has agreed that there is some
entitlement to coastal patrol craft from the Caspian flotilla.

Bases

Fort Chevchenko (Caspian)
Aralsk (Aral Sea)

Personnel

1994: 150

KENYA

Administration

Commander, Navy:
   Major General J R E Kibwana

Personnel

(a) 1994: 1400 officers and men
(b) Voluntary service

Base

Mombasa

Customs/Police

There are some 18 Customs and Police patrol craft of between
12 and 14 metres. Mostly built by Cheverton, Performance Workboats and Fassmer in the 1980s.

Mercantile Marine

Lloyd's Register of Shipping:
   35 vessels of 16 191 tons gross

DELETIONS

1992   *Chui, Ndovu, Kiongozi* (civilian)

PATROL FORCES

Note: The Vosper type *Simba* P 3110, deleted for the second time in 1992, once again returned for
limited service in 1993.

1 MAMBA CLASS (FAST ATTACK CRAFT—MISSILE)

Name	No	Builders	Commissioned
MAMBA	P 3100	Brooke Marine, Lowestoft	7 Feb 1974

Displacement, tons: 125 standard; 160 full load
Dimensions, feet (metres): 123 × 22.5 × 5.2 *(37.5 × 6.9 × 1.6)*
Main machinery: 2 Paxman 16YJCM diesels; 4000 hp *(2.98 MW)* sustained; 2 shafts
Speed, knots: 25. **Range, miles:** 3300 at 13 kts
Complement: 25 (3 officers)

Missiles: SSM: 4 IAI Gabriel II; active radar or optical guidance; semi-active homing to 36 km
(19.4 nm) at 0.7 Mach; warhead 75 kg.
Guns: 2 Oerlikon/BMARC 30 mm GCM-A02 (twin); 85° elevation; 650 rounds/minute to 10 km
(5.4 nm) anti-surface; 3 km *(1.6 nm)* anti-aircraft; weight of shell 0.36 kg.
Radars: Navigation: Decca AC 1226; I band.
Fire control: Selenia RTN 10X; I/J band; range 40 km *(22 nm)*.

Programmes: Laid down 17 February 1972.
Modernisation: In 1982 missiles, new gunnery equipment and an optronic director fitted.
Operational: Arrived Vosper Thornycroft, Portchester on 4 May 1989 for a long refit. Returned to
Kenya with *Madaraka* as deck cargo in a transport ship leaving Portsmouth on 7 November
1990.

MAMBA (alongside *Madaraka*)   11/1990, Colin Rossiter

2 NYAYO CLASS (FAST ATTACK CRAFT—MISSILE)

Name	No	Builders	Commissioned
NYAYO	P 3126	Vosper Thornycroft	23 July 1987
UMOJA	P 3127	Vosper Thornycroft	16 Sep 1987

Displacement, tons: 310 light; 400 full load
Dimensions, feet (metres): 186 × 26.9 × 7.9 *(56.7 × 8.2 × 2.4)*
Main machinery: 4 Paxman Valenta 18CM diesels; 15 000 hp *(11.19 MW)* sustained; 4 shafts; 2
motors (slow speed patrol); 100 hp *(74.6 kW)*
Speed, knots: 40. **Range, miles:** 2000 at 18 kts
Complement: 40

Missiles: SSM: 4 OTO Melara/Matra Otomat Mk 2 (2 twin); active radar homing to 160 km
(86.4 nm) at 0.9 Mach; warhead 210 kg; sea-skimmer for last 4 km *(2.2 nm)*.
Guns: 1 OTO Melara 3 in *(76 mm)*/62; 85° elevation; 85 rounds/minute to 16 km *(8.7 nm)* anti-
surface; 12 km *(6.5 nm)* anti-aircraft; weight of shell 6 kg.
2 Oerlikon/BMARC 30 mm GCM-AO2 (twin); 85° elevation; 650 rounds/minute to 10 km
(5.4 nm) anti-surface; 3 km *(1.6 nm)* anti-aircraft; weight of shell 0.36 kg.
2 Oerlikon/BMARC 20 mm A41A; 50° elevation; 800 rounds/minute to 2 km; weight of shell
0.24 kg.
Countermeasures: Decoys: 2 Wallop Barricade 18-barrelled launchers; Stockade and Palisade
rockets.
ESM: Racal Cutlass; radar warning.
ECM: Racal Cygnus; jammer.
Fire control: CAAIS 450 including Signaal 423; action data automation.
Radars: Surface search: Plessey AWS 4; E/F band; range 101 km *(55 nm)*.
Navigation: Decca AC 1226; I band.
Fire control: Marconi/Ericsson ST802; I band.

Programmes: Ordered in September 1984. Sailed in company from the UK, arriving at Mombasa
30 August 1988. Similar to Omani Province class.
Operational: First live Otomat firing in February 1989. Form Squadron 86.

UMOJA   3/1988, van Ginderen Collection

3 MADARAKA CLASS (FAST ATTACK CRAFT—MISSILE)

Name	No	Builders	Commissioned
MADARAKA	P 3121	Brooke Marine, Lowestoft	16 June 1975
JAMHURI	P 3122	Brooke Marine, Lowestoft	16 June 1975
HARAMBEE	P 3123	Brooke Marine, Lowestoft	22 Aug 1975

Displacement, tons: 120 standard; 145 full load
Dimensions, feet (metres): 107 × 20 × 5.6 *(32.6 × 6.1 × 1.7)*
Main machinery: 2 Paxman Valenta 16CM diesels; 6650 hp *(4.96 MW)* sustained; 2 shafts
Speed, knots: 25.5. **Range, miles:** 2500 at 12 kts
Complement: 21 (3 officers)

Missiles: SSM: 4 IAI Gabriel II; active radar or optical guidance; semi-active homing to 36 km *(19.4 nm)* at 0.7 Mach; warhead 75 kg.
Guns: 2 Oerlikon/BMARC 30 mm GCM (twin); 85° elevation; 650 rounds/minute to 10 km *(5.4 nm)* anti-surface; 3 km *(1.6 nm)* anti-aircraft; weight of shell 0.36 kg.
Radars: Navigation: Decca AC 1226; I band.
Fire control: Selenia RTN 10X; I/J band; range 40 km *(22 nm)*.

Programmes: Ordered 10 May 1973. *Madaraka* launched 28 January 1975, *Jamhuri* 14 March 1975, *Harambee* 2 May 1975.
Modernisation: All received SSM, new guns and an optronic director in the early 1980s.
Operational: *Madaraka* started a long refit at Vosper Thornycroft, Portchester, on 4 May 1989 and completed in August 1990. *Harambee* refitted in Mombasa 1991-92. Form Squadron 76.

MADARAKA   *8/1990, Maritime Photographic*

TUG

NGAMIA

Measurement, tons: 298 grt
Dimensions, feet (metres): 115.8 × 30.5 × 12.8 *(35.3 × 9.3 × 3.9)*
Main machinery: 2 diesels; 1200 hp *(895 kW)*; 1 shaft
Speed, knots: 14

Comment: Tug built in 1969. Acquired from merchant marine in 1982.

HARAMBEE   *6/1991*

KIRIBATI

General

Formerly known as the Gilbert Islands. A group of about 30 atolls on the equator in mid-Pacific.

Mercantile Marine

Lloyd's Register of Shipping:
8 vessels of 4 829 tons gross

PATROL FORCES

1 PACIFIC FORUM TYPE (LARGE PATROL CRAFT)

Name	No	Builders	Commissioned
TEANOAI	301	Transfield Shipbuilding	22 Jan 1994

Displacement, tons: 165 full load
Dimensions, feet (metres): 103.3 × 26.6 × 6.9 *(31.5 × 8.1 × 2.1)*
Main machinery: 2 Caterpillar 3516TA diesels; 4400 hp *(3.28 MW)* sustained; 2 shafts
Speed, knots: 18. **Range, miles:** 2500 at 12 kts
Complement: 18 (3 officers)
Guns: Can carry 1—12.7 mm MG but is unarmed.
Radars: Navigation: Furuno; I band.

Comment: The sixteenth of this class to be built by the Australian Government for EEZ patrols of Pacific Islands. Others of the class are in service in Fiji, Papua New Guinea, Vanuatu, Cook Islands, Western Samoa, Marshall Islands, Solomon Islands, Micronesia and Tonga.

TEANOAI   *2/1994, S. Hibbert, RAN*

KOREA, NORTH
DEMOCRATIC PEOPLE'S REPUBLIC

Headquarters' Appointment

Commander of the Navy:
   Vice Admiral Kim Il-Choi

Bases

East coast: Wonsan (main), Mayang-do, Cha-ho (submarines).
Minor bases: Najin, Sanjin-dong, Kimchaek, Yohori, Songjon, Pando, Munchon-up, Namae-ri, Kosong-up.
West coast: Nampo (main), Pipa-got (submarines).
Minor bases: Yogampo-ri, Tasa-ri, Sohae-ri, Chodo, Sunwi-do, Pupo-ri, Sagon-ri.
A number of these bases has underground berthing facilities.

Personnel

(a) 1994: 60 000 officers and men plus 40 000 reserves
(b) 5 years' national service

Strength of the Fleet

Type	Active
Submarines—Patrol	25
Submarines—Midgets	48+
Frigates	3
Fast Attack Craft—Missile	39
Fast Attack Craft—Gun/Torpedo	304
Patrol Craft	55+
Amphibious Craft	131
Hovercraft (LCP)	70+
Minesweepers	29
Depot Ships for Midget Submarines	8
Survey Vessels	4

Mercantile Marine

Lloyd's Register of Shipping:
   109 vessels of 671 057 tons gross

Maritime Coastal Security Force

In addition to the Navy there is a Coastal and Port Security Police Force which would be subordinate to the Navy in war. It is reported that the strength of this force is one Sariwon class PGF, 10-15 Chong-Ju patrol craft and 130 patrol boats of the Sin Hung, Kimjin and Yongdo classes.

DELETIONS

Note: Changes to the order of battle represent the most up-to-date information available.

SUBMARINES

Notes: (1)There are also four obsolete ex-Soviet Whiskey class based at Pipa-got and used for training. Probably restricted to periscope depth when dived.
(2) 40 ex-Russian diesel patrol submarines were sold to North Korea for scrap in late 1993. It is strongly denied that any will be taken into naval service but some equipment may be used to help improve the operational state of the Romeo class.

21 + 2 ROMEO CLASS

Displacement, tons: 1475 surfaced; 1830 dived
Dimensions, feet (metres): 251.3 × 22 × 17.1
(76.6 × 6.7 × 5.2)
Main machinery: Diesel-electric; 2 Type 37-D diesels; 4000 hp
(m) *(2.94 MW)*; 2 motors; 2700 hp(m) *(1.98 MW)*; 2 creep
motors; 2 shafts
Speed, knots: 15 surfaced; 13 dived. **Range, miles:** 9000 at
9 kts surfaced
Complement: 54 (10 officers)

Torpedoes: 8—21 in *(533 mm)* tubes (6 bow, 2 stern). 14 prob-
ably SAET-60; passive homing up to 15 km *(8.1 nm)* at 40 kts;
warhead 400 kg.
Mines: 28 in lieu of torpedoes.
Radars: Surface search: Snoop Plate; I band.
Sonars: Tamir 5L; hull-mounted; active.
Feniks; hull-mounted; passive.

ROMEO   *1989*

Programmes: Two transferred from China 1973, two in 1974
and three in 1975. First three of class built in North Korea in
1975. Local building at Mayang-do and Sinpo Shipyards provided two more in 1976. Programme now seems to be running
at about one every two years. One reported sunk in February
1985. Assessed numbers are slightly down on 1993.

Operational: Most are stationed on east coast and occasionally
operate in Sea of Japan. Four ex-Chinese units are based on the
west coast. By modern standards these are basic attack submarines with virtually no anti-submarine performance or
potential.

60 MIDGET SUBMARINES

Displacement, tons: 76 surfaced; 90 dived
Dimensions, feet (metres): 62.3 × 9.2 *(19 × 2.8)*
Main machinery: 2 diesels; 320 hp(m) *(236 kW)*; 1 shaft
Speed, knots: 12 surfaced; 8 dived
Range, miles: 550 at 10 kts surfaced; 50 at 4 kts dived
Complement: 3 plus 6-7 divers

Comment: Built at Yukdaeso-ri shipyard since early 1960s. Number reported as being about 60 in
1994 and probably of more than one design. Details given are for the latest type, which have also
been exported to Iran, and have been building since 1988. Some lost on operations against
South Korea. One reported captured by South Korean Navy in 1965 or 1966. Some stationed on
Songjong peninsula. Later type imported from Yugoslavia, which began in mid-1970s. Large
scale production began in 1983. Some have two short torpedo tubes. Operate from eight merchant mother ships (see *Auxiliaries*). There are also some 50 two-man submersibles of Italian
design 4.9 × 1.4 m.

MIDGET SUBMARINE   *1990*

FRIGATES

2 NAJIN CLASS

531   631

Displacement, tons: 1500 full load
Dimensions, feet (metres): 334.6 × 32.8 × 8.9
(102 × 10 × 2.7)
Main machinery: 2 diesels; 15 000 hp(m) *(11.03 MW)*; 2 shafts
Speed, knots: 24. **Range, miles:** 4000 at 13 kts
Complement: 180

Missiles: SSM: 2 SS-N-2A Styx ❶; active radar or IR homing to
46 km *(25 nm)* at 0.9 Mach; warhead 513 kg HE. Replaced torpedo tubes on both ships.
Guns: 2—3.9 in *(100 mm)*/56 ❷; 40° elevation; 15 rounds/
minute to 16 km *(8.6 nm)*; weight of shell 13.5 kg.
4—57 mm/80 (2 twin) ❸; 85° elevation; 120 rounds/minute
to 6 km *(3.2 nm)*; weight of shell 2.8 kg.
8—25 mm/70 (2 quad) ❹; 85° elevation; 270 rounds/minute
to 3 km *(1.6 nm)*; weight of shell 0.34 kg.
8—14.5 mm (4 twin) MGs ❺; anti-aircraft.
A/S mortars: 2 RBU 1200 5-tubed fixed launchers ❻; range
1200 m; warhead 34 kg.
Depth charges: 2 projectors; 2 racks.
Mines: 30 (estimated).
Fire control: Optical director ❼.
Radars: Air search: Slim Net ❽; E/F band.
Surface search: Pot Head ❾; I band; range 37 km *(20 nm)*.
Navigation: Pot Drum; H/I band.
Fire control: Drum Tilt ❿; H/I band.
IFF: Ski Pole.
Sonars: One hull-mounted type. One VDS type.

Programmes: Built in North Korea. First completed 1973, second
completed 1975.
Structure: There is some resemblance to the ex-Soviet Kola
class, now deleted.

NAJIN   *(Scale 1 : 900), Ian Sturton*

NAJIN 631   *1990*

NAJIN 531   *5/1993, JMSDF*

1 SOHO CLASS

Displacement, tons: 1600 standard; 1845 full load
Dimensions, feet (metres): 246 × 49.2 × 12.5 *(75 × 15 × 3.8)*
Main machinery: 2 diesels; 15 000 hp(m) *(11.03 MW)*; 2 shafts
Speed, knots: 27
Complement: 190

Missiles: SSM: 4 SS-N-2A Styx; active radar or IR homing to
   46 km *(25 nm)* at 0.9 Mach; warhead 513 kg.

Guns: 1—3.9 in *(100 mm)*/56; 40° elevation; 15 rounds/minute
   to 16 km *(8.6 nm)*; weight of shell 13.5 kg.
   4—37 mm/63 (2 twin); 80° elevation; 160 rounds/minute to
   9 km *(4.9 nm)*; weight of shell 0.7 kg.
   4—25 mm/60 (quad); 85° elevation; 270 rounds/minute to
   3 km *(1.6 nm)*; weight of shell 0.34 kg.
A/S mortars: 2 RBU 1200 5-tubed fixed launchers; range
   1200 m; warhead 34 kg.

Helicopters: Platform for one medium.

Programmes: Built at Najin Shipyard; laid down 1980; commissioned 1983.
Structure: This is reported as a unique twin hull design with a
   large helicopter flight deck aft.
Operational: Little time is spent at sea so the design is probably
   unsuccessful.

CORVETTES

3 SARIWON and 2 TRAL CLASS

| 513 | 671 | 725 | 726 | 727 |

Displacement, tons: 650; 580 (Tral); full load
Dimensions, feet (metres): 203.7 × 23.9 × 7.8 *(62.1 × 7.3 × 2.4)*
Main machinery: 2 diesels; 3000 hp(m) *(2.21 MW)*; 2 shafts
Speed, knots: 21. **Range, miles:** 2700 at 18 kts
Complement: 65-70

Guns: 1 or 2—3.9 in *(100 mm)*/56; 40° elevation; 15 rounds/
   minute to 16 km *(8.6 nm)*; weight of shell 13.5 kg.
   2—37 mm/63 (Tral); 85° elevation; 160 rounds/minute to
   4 km *(2.2 nm)*; weight of shell 0.7 kg.
   12/16—14.5 mm (3/4 quad) MGs.
Depth charges: 2 rails.
Mines: 30.
Radars: Surface search: Skin Head; I band.
Navigation: I band.
IFF: Ski Pole.
Sonars: Hull-mounted; active; high frequency.

Programmes: Three Sariwon class built in Korea in the
   mid-1960s. The two Tral class were transferred from the USSR
   in the mid-1950s and were paid off in the early 1980s and
   recently returned to service.
Structure: The Sariwon design is based on the original USSR
   Fleet minelayer Tral or Fugas class in service in the mid-1930s.
   The latest picture of *671* shows armament variations including
   a 100 mm tank gun forward, and two 37 mm guns aft in place
   of the second 100 mm. Minelaying rails are visible along the
   whole of upper deck aft of the bridge superstructure. This ship
   is one of the original Tral class built in 1938 and restored to
   service.
Operational: One of the class is the Flagship of the Maritime
   Coastal Security Forces.

SARIWON 513   1991

TRAL 671   5/1993, JMSDF

PATROL FORCES

Note: A few obsolete P 4 patrol craft are still active.

6 HAINAN CLASS (LARGE PATROL CRAFT)

Displacement, tons: 375 standard; 392 full load
Dimensions, feet (metres): 192.8 × 23.6 × 6.6 *(58.8 × 7.2 × 2)*
Main machinery: 4 Kolomna/PCR Type 9-D-8 diesels; 4000 hp(m) *(2.94 MW)*; 4 shafts
Speed, knots: 30.5. **Range, miles:** 1300 at 15 kts
Complement: 69
Guns: 4—57 mm/70 (2 twin); 85° elevation; 120 rounds/minute to 8 km *(4.4 nm)*; weight of shell
   2.8 kg.
   4—25 mm/80 (2 twin); 85° elevation; 270 rounds/minute to 3 km *(1.6 nm)*; weight of shell
   0.34 kg.
A/S mortars: 4 RBU 1200 5-tubed launchers; range 1200 m; warhead 34 kg.
Depth charges: 2 projectors; 2 racks for 18 DCs.
Mines: Laying capability for 12.
Radars: Surface search: Pot Head; I band.
Sonars: Stag Ear; hull-mounted; active search and attack; high frequency.

Comment: Transferred from China in 1975 (two), 1976 (two), 1978 (two).

HAINAN (China colours)   1993

15 + 1 SOJU CLASS (FAST ATTACK CRAFT—MISSILE)

Displacement, tons: 220 full load
Dimensions, feet (metres): 141 × 24.6 × 5.6 *(43 × 7.5 × 1.7)*
Main machinery: 3 Type M 503A diesels; 8025 hp(m) *(5.9 MW)* sustained; 3 shafts
Speed, knots: 34
Missiles: SSM: 4 SS-N-2 Styx; active radar or IR homing to 46 km *(25 nm)* at 0.9 Mach; warhead 513 kg.
Guns: 4—30 mm AKM-30 (2 twin).
Radars: Surface search: Square Tie; I band.
Fire Control: Drum Tilt; H/I band.

Comment: North Korean-built and enlarged version of Osa class. First completed in 1981; building at about one per year.

8 OSA I (TYPE 205) and 4 HUANGFEN CLASSES (FAST ATTACK CRAFT—MISSILE)

Displacement, tons: 171 standard; 210 full load
Dimensions, feet (metres): 126.6 × 24.9 × 8.9 *(38.6 × 7.6 × 2.7)*
Main machinery: 3 Type M 503A diesels; 8025 hp(m) *(5.9 MW)* sustained; 3 shafts
Speed, knots: 35. **Range, miles:** 800 at 30 kts
Complement: 30

Missiles: SSM: 4 SS-N-2A Styx; active radar or IR homing to 46 km *(25 nm)* at 0.9 Mach; warhead 513 kg.
Guns: 4—30 mm/65 (2 twin); 85° elevation; 500 rounds/minute to 5 km *(2.7 nm)*; weight of shell 0.54 kg.
Radars: Surface search: Square Tie; I band.
Fire control: Drum Tilt; H/I band.
IFF: High Pole B. Square Head.

Programmes: Twelve Osa I class transferred from USSR in 1968 and four more in 1972-83. Eight deleted so far. Four Huangfen class acquired from China in 1980.

OSA I

HUANGFEN (China colours)   1993

19 SO 1 CLASS (LARGE PATROL CRAFT)

Displacement, tons: 170 light; 215 normal
Dimensions, feet (metres): 137.8 × 19.7 × 5.9 *(42 × 6 × 1.8)*
Main machinery: 3 Kolomna Type 40-D diesels; 6600 hp(m) *(4.85 MW)* sustained; 3 shafts
Speed, knots: 28. **Range, miles:** 1100 at 13 kts
Complement: 31
Guns: 1—85 mm/52; 85° elevation; 18 rounds/minute to 15 km *(8 nm)*; weight of shell 9.5 kg.
    2—37 mm/63 (twin); 80° elevation; 160 rounds/minute to 9 km *(4.9 nm)*; weight of shell 0.7 kg.
    4—25 mm/60 (2 twin); 85° elevation; 270 rounds/minute to 3 km *(1.6 nm)*; weight of shell 0.34 kg.
    4—14.5 mm/93 MGs.
A/S mortars: 2 RBU 1200 5-tubed launchers; range 1200 m; warhead 34 kg.
Radars: Surface search: Pot Head; I band; range 37 km *(20 nm)*.
Navigation: Don 2; I band.
IFF: Ski Pole or Dead Duck.
Sonars: Tamir 2; hull-mounted; active.

Comment: Eight transferred by the USSR in early 1960s, with RBU 1200 ASW rocket launchers and depth charges instead of the 85 mm and 37 mm guns. Remainder built in North Korea to modified design. Thirteen are fitted out for ASW with sonar and depth charges; the other six are used as gunboats.

SO 1 (USSR colours)   1988

10 KOMAR and 9 + 1 SOHUNG CLASSES (FAST ATTACK CRAFT—MISSILE)

Displacement, tons: 75 standard; 85 full load
Dimensions, feet (metres): 87.9 × 20.3 × 4.9 *(26.8 × 6.2 × 1.5)* (Sohung)
Main machinery: 4 Type M 50 diesels; 4400 hp(m) *(3.3 MW)* sustained; 4 shafts
Speed, knots: 40. **Range, miles:** 400 at 30 kts
Complement: 19

Missiles: SSM: 2 SS-N-2A Styx; active radar or IR homing to 46 km *(25 nm)* at 0.9 Mach; warhead 513 kg.
Guns: 2—25 mm/80 (twin); 85° elevation; 270 rounds/minute to 3 km *(1.6 nm)*; weight of shell 0.34 kg.
Radars: Surface search: Square Tie; I band.
IFF: Ski Pole. Dead Duck.

Programmes: Ten Komar class transferred by USSR, all still in service but with wood hulls replaced by steel. The Sohung class is a North Korean copy of the Komar class, first built in 1980-81 and still in production.

KOMAR

8 TAECHONG I and 4 + 1 TAECHONG II (MAYANG) CLASSES (LARGE PATROL CRAFT)

Displacement, tons: 385 standard; 410 full load (I); 425 full load (II)
Dimensions, feet (metres): 196.3 (I); 199.5 (II) × 23.6 × 6.6 *(59.8; 60.8 × 7.2 × 2)*
Main machinery: 4 Kolomna Type 40-D diesels; 8800 hp(m) *(6.4 MW)* sustained; 4 shafts
Speed, knots: 30. **Range, miles:** 2000 at 12 kts
Complement: 80
Guns: 1—3.9 in *(100 mm)*/56 (Taechong II); 40° elevation; 15 rounds/minute to 16 km *(8.6 nm)*; weight of shell 13.5 kg.
    2—57 mm/70 (twin); 90° elevation; 120 rounds/minute to 8 km *(4.4 nm)*; weight of shell 2.8 kg.
    1—37 mm/63 (Taechong I); 85° elevation; 160 rounds/minute to 4 km *(2.2 nm)*; weight of shell 0.7 kg.
    4—30 mm/65 (2 twin). 4—14.5 mm/93 (2 twin) MGs.
A/S mortars: 2 RBU 1200 5-tubed fixed launchers; range 1200 m; warhead 34 kg.
Depth charges: 2 racks.
Radars: Surface search: Pot Head; I band; range 37 km *(20 nm)*.
Fire control: Drum Tilt; H/I band.
IFF: High Pole A. Square Head.
Sonars: Stag Ear; hull-mounted; active attack; high frequency.

Comment: North Korean class of mid-1970s design, slightly larger than Hainan class. The first eight are Taechong I class. Taechong II still building at about one per year and may now be called Mayang class. They are slightly longer and are heavily armed for units of this size.

TAECHONG   (not to scale)

TAECHONG II (with *Najin*)   1988

1 SOMAN CLASS (LARGE PATROL CRAFT)

Displacement, tons: 190 full load
Dimensions, feet (metres): 91.6 × 19 × 6.2 *(27.9 × 5.8 × 1.9)*
Main machinery: 1 Kolomna Type 3-D-12 diesel; 300 hp(m) *(220 kW)*; 1 shaft
Speed, knots: 10. **Range, miles:** 1200 at 9 kts
Complement: 50 (7 officers)
Guns: 4—25 mm/60 (2 twin); 85° elevation; 270 rounds/minute to 3 km *(1.6 nm)*; weight of shell 0.34 kg.
    4—14.5 mm/93 (2 twin) MGs.
Mines: 2 rails for 16.
Radars: Surface search: Skin Head; I band.
IFF: High Pole A; Square Head.

Comment: The only one of its kind possibly used as a command gunboat or may have a secondary role as a minelayer.

13 SHANGHAI II CLASS (FAST ATTACK CRAFT—GUN)

Displacement, tons: 113 standard; 131 full load
Dimensions, feet (metres): 126.3 × 17.7 × 5.6 *(38.5 × 5.4 × 1.7)*
Main machinery: 2 Type L12-180 diesels; 2400 hp(m) *(1.76 MW)* (forward)
    2 Type 12-D-6 diesels; 1820 hp(m) *(1.34 MW)* (aft); 4 shafts
Speed, knots: 30. **Range, miles:** 700 at 16.5 kts
Complement: 34
Guns: 4—37 mm/63 (2 twin); 80° elevation; 160 rounds/minute to 9 km *(4.9 nm)*; weight of shell 0.7 kg.
    4—25 mm/60 (2 twin); 85° elevation; 270 rounds/minute to 3 km *(1.6 nm)*; weight of shell 0.34 kg.
    2—3 in *(76 mm)* recoilless rifles.
Depth charges: 8.
Mines: Rails can be fitted for 10 mines.
Radars: Surface search: Pot Head; I band or Skin Head; I band.

Comment: Acquired from China since 1967. One deleted in 1988 and one more in 1990.

SHANGHAI II

3 CHODO CLASS (FAST ATTACK CRAFT—GUN)

Displacement, tons: 130 full load
Dimensions, feet (metres): 140 × 19 × 8.5 *(42.7 × 5.8 × 2.6)*
Main machinery: 4 diesels; 6000 hp(m) *(4.41 MW)*; 2 shafts
Speed, knots: 25. **Range, miles:** 2000 at 10 kts
Complement: 40
Guns: 1—3 in *(76 mm)*/66 automatic; 85° elevation; 120 rounds/minute to 15 km *(8 nm)*; weight of shell 7 kg.
    2—37 mm/63; 85° elevation; 160 rounds/minute to 4 km *(2.2 nm)*; weight of shell 0.7 kg.
    4—25 mm/60 (2 twin); 85° elevation; 270 rounds/minute to 3 km *(1.6 nm)*; weight of shell 0.34 kg.
Radars: Surface search: Skin Head; I band.
IFF: Ski Pole.

Comment: Built in North Korea in mid-1960s.

CHODO

62 CHAHO CLASS (FAST ATTACK CRAFT—GUN)

Displacement, tons: 82 full load
Dimensions, feet (metres): 85.3 × 19 × 6.6 *(26 × 5.8 × 2)*
Main machinery: 4 Type M 50 diesels; 4400 hp(m) *(3.2 MW)* sustained; 4 shafts
Speed, knots: 40
Complement: 12
Guns: 1 BM 21 multiple rocket launcher. 2 USSR 23 mm/87 (twin). 2—14.5 mm (twin) MGs.
Radars: Surface search: Pot Head; I band.

Comment: Building in North Korea since 1974. Based on P 6 hull. Three transferred to Iran in April 1987. Four deleted in 1990/91.

CHAHO   4/1988

52 CHONG-JIN and 4 CHONG-JU CLASSES (FAST ATTACK CRAFT—GUN or TORPEDO)

Displacement, tons: 80 full load
Dimensions, feet (metres): 90.9 × 20 × 5.9 *(27.7 × 6.1 × 1.8)*
    139.4 × 22.3 × 6.2 *(42.5 × 6.8 × 1.9)* (Chong-Ju class)
Main machinery: 4 Type M 50 diesels; 4400 hp(m) *(3.2 MW)* sustained; 4 shafts
Speed, knots: 40
Complement: 12
Guns: 1—85 mm/52; 85° elevation; 18 rounds/minute to 15 km *(8 nm)*; weight of shell 9.5 kg.
    4 or 8—14.5 mm (2 or 4 twin) MGs (Chong-Jin). 1 BM 21 MRL and quad 14.5 mm (Chong-Ju).
Radars: Surface search: Pot Head; I band.
IFF: High Pole B; Square Head.

Comment: Particulars similar to Chaho class of which this is an improved version. Building began about 1975. About one third reported to be a hydrofoil development. A further class, Chong-Ju (an enlarged Chong-Jin) started building in 1985; one of these has been converted to fire torpedoes.

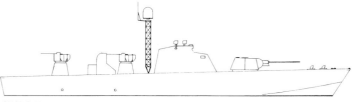

CHONG-JIN   *(not to scale), Ian Sturton*

24 P 6 CLASS (FAST ATTACK CRAFT—TORPEDO) and 21 SINPO or SINNAM CLASS (FAST ATTACK CRAFT—GUN)

Displacement, tons: 64 standard; 73 full load
Dimensions, feet (metres): 85.3 × 20 × 4.9 *(26 × 6.1 × 1.5)*
Main machinery: 4 Type M 50 diesels; 4400 hp(m) *(3.2 MW)* sustained; 4 shafts
Speed, knots: 45. **Range, miles:** 450 at 30 kts; 600 at 15 kts
Complement: 15
Guns: 4—25 mm/80 (2 twin) (original). 2—37 mm (others). 6—14.5 mm MGs (Sinpo class).
Torpedoes: 2—21 in *(533 mm)* tubes (in some). Sinpo class has no tubes.
Depth charges: 8 in some.
Radars: Surface search: Skin Head; I band (some have Furuno).
IFF: Dead Duck. High Pole.

Comment: There is a growing number of the Sinpo class with local building programme in hand of a modified form. Originally 27 P 6 class were transferred by the USSR and 15 from China. The Sinpos are replacing the P 6s.

P 6

SINPO

88 KU SONG, SIN HUNG and 37 MOD SIN HUNG CLASSES (FAST ATTACK CRAFT—TORPEDO)

Displacement, tons: 40 full load
Dimensions, feet (metres): 72.2 × 11 × 5.5 *(22 × 3.4 × 1.7)*
Main machinery: 2 Type M 50 diesels; 2200 hp(m) *(1.6 MW)* sustained; 2 shafts
Speed, knots: 40
Guns: 4—14.5 mm (2 twin) MGs.
Torpedoes: 2—18 in *(457 mm)* or 2—21 in *(533 mm)* tubes (not fitted in all).
Radars: Surface search: Skin Head; I band.
IFF: Dead Duck.

Comment: Ku Song and Sin Hung built in North Korea mid-1950s to 1970. Frequently operated on South Korean border. A modified version of Sin Hung with hydrofoils built from 1981 to 1985.

SIN HUNG (no torpedo tubes)   1991

MODIFIED FISHING VESSELS (COASTAL PATROL CRAFT)

Comment: An unknown number of fishing vessels have been converted for naval use. Two seen in 1991 include 801 which has a twin 25 mm gun forward and a twin 14.5 mm MG aft of the funnel, and 177 which was acting as a survey ship in the Sea of Japan.

801   7/1991, G Jacobs

177   7/1991, G Jacobs

10 TB 11PA AND 6 TB 40A CLASSES (INSHORE PATROL CRAFT)

Displacement, tons: 8
Dimensions, feet (metres): 36.7 × 8.6 × 3.3 *(11.2 × 2.7 × 1)*
Main machinery: 2 diesels; 520 hp(m) *(382 kW)*; 2 shafts
Speed, knots: 35. **Range, miles:** 200 at 15 kts
Complement: 4
Guns: 1—7.62 mm MG.
Radars: Surface search/navigation: Radar-24.

Comment: New construction high speed patrol boats. Reinforced fibreglass hull. Design closely resembles a number of UK/Western European commercial craft. Twenty ordered by Zaire for delivery in late 1990 but this was probably delayed by lack of funds. Larger hull design, known as 'TB 40A' also building. Both classes being operated by the MSCF.

HIGH SPEED INFILTRATION CRAFT (HSIC)

Displacement, tons: 5
Dimensions, feet (metres): 30.5 × 8.2 × 3.1 *(9.3 × 2.5 × 1)*
Main machinery: 1 diesel; 260 hp(m) *(191 kW)*; 1 shaft
Speed, knots: 35
Complement: 2
Guns: 1—7.62 mm MG.
Radars: Navigation: Furuno 701; I band.

Comment: Large numbers built for Agent infiltration and covert operations. These craft have a very low radar cross section and 'squat' at high speeds.

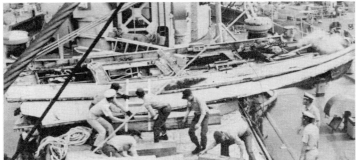

HSIC   1991, J Bermudez

AMPHIBIOUS FORCES

16 HUNGNAM AND 8 HANTAE CLASSES (LSM)

Comment: Both classes started building in 1980-82 and are capable of taking four to five medium tanks. Hungnam is slightly larger.

7 HANCHON CLASS (LCM)

Displacement, tons: 145 full load
Dimensions, feet (metres): 117.1 × 25.9 × 3.9 *(35.7 × 7.9 × 1.2)*
Main machinery: 2 Type 3-D-12 diesels; 600 hp(m) *(443 kW)* sustained; 2 shafts
Speed, knots: 10. **Range, miles:** 600 at 6 kts
Complement: 15 (1 officer)
Military lift: 2 tanks or 200 troops
Guns: 2—14.5 mm/93 (twin) MG.
Radars: Surface search: Skin Head; I band.

Comment: Built in North Korea.

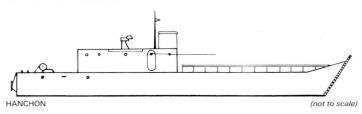

HANCHON   (not to scale)

100 NAMPO CLASS (LCP)

Displacement, tons: 80 full load
Dimensions, feet (metres): 84.2 × 20 × 6 *(27.7 × 6.1 × 1.8)*
Main machinery: 4 Type M 50 diesels; 4400 hp(m) *(3.2 MW)* sustained; 4 shafts
Speed, knots: 40. **Range, miles:** 375 at 40 kts
Complement: 19
Military lift: 20-30 troops
Guns: 4—14.5 mm (2 twin) MGs.
Radars: Surface search: Pot Head; I band.

Comment: A class of assault landing craft. Almost identical to the Chong-Jin class but with a smaller forward gun mounting and with retractable ramp in bows. Building began about 1975. Four or five have probably been deleted due to damage. Numbers uncertain. About 20 used for patrol duties with bow doors welded shut. Four sold to Madagascar in 1979.

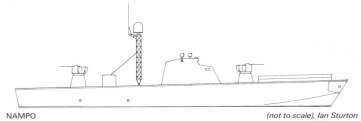

NAMPO   (not to scale), Ian Sturton

95 + SONGJONG CLASS (LCP—HOVERCRAFT)

Comment: Three types: one Type I, 31 Type II and 20 + 6 Type III. Type III is building at 6-10 per year. Length about 25 m (I) and 18 m (II). A series of high speed air-cushion landing craft first reported in 1987. Use of air-cushion technology is an adoption of commercial technology imported from the UK. Estimated to carry 35 to 55 (or more) light infantry troops. Songjong II may be called the Hwanghae class.

MINE WARFARE FORCES

19 YUKTO I and 4 YUKTO II CLASSES (COASTAL MINESWEEPERS)

Displacement, tons: 60 full load
Dimensions, feet (metres): 78.7 × 13.1 × 5.6 *(24 × 4 × 1.7)*
Main machinery: 2 diesels; 2 shafts
Speed, knots: 18
Complement: 22 (4 officers)
Guns: 1—37 mm/63 or 2—25 mm/80 (twin). 2—14.5 mm/93 (twin) MGs.
Mines: 2 rails for 4.
Radars: Surface search: Skin Head; I band.

Comment: North Korean design built in the 1980s and replaced the obsolete ex-Soviet KN-14 class. A total of four Yukto IIs was built; they are 3 m shorter (at 21 m length) overall and have no after gun. Wooden construction.

6 PIPA-GOT CLASS (INSHORE MINESWEEPERS)

Comment: A new class of MSI. No details.

SURVEY SHIPS

Note: The Hydrographic Department has four survey ships but also uses a number of converted fishing vessels.

Name	Displacement	Launched	Complement
DONGHAE 101	260 tons	1970	22 (8 officers)
DONGHAE 102	1100 tons	1979	35 (20 officers)
SOHAI 201	260 tons	1972	22 (14 officers)
SOHAI 202	300 tons	1981	26 (16 officers)

AUXILIARIES

Notes: (1) One Kowan class ASR built for submarine rescue, possibly catamaran construction. Trawlers operate as AGIs on the South Korean border where several have been sunk over the years. In addition many ocean-going commercial vessels are used for carrying weapons and ammunition worldwide in support of international terrorism.
(2) There are also eight ocean cargo ships adapted as mother ships for midget submarines. Their names are *Soo Gun-Ho, Dong Geon Ae Gook-Ho, Dong Hae-Ho, Choong Seong-Ho Number One, Choong Seong-Ho Number Two, Choong Seong-Ho Number Three, Hae Gum Gang-Ho* and the *Song Rim-Ho.*

KOREA, SOUTH
REPUBLIC

Headquarters' Appointments

Chief of Naval Operations:
    Admiral Kim Hong-Yul
Commandant Marine Corps:
    Lieutenant General Lim Jong-Rin
Commandant Naval Academy:
    Rear Admiral You Sam-Nam

Operational Commands

Commander First Fleet:
    Rear Admiral Lee Soo-Yong
Commander Second Fleet:
    Rear Admiral Yoon Kwang-Woong
Commander Third Fleet:
    Rear Admiral Choi Nak-Song

Diplomatic Representation

Defence Attaché in London:
    Captain S J Kim

Personnel

(a) 1994: 36 000 Navy, 25 000 Marine Corps
(b) 2¼ years' (Navy) national service with a proportion of ratings
     and all marines being volunteers

Pennant Numbers

Pennant numbers are changed at unspecified intervals. The numbers 0 and 4 are not used as they are unlucky.

Bases

Major: Chinhae (Fleet HQ), Pukpyong (1st Fleet)
Minor: Cheju, Mokpo, Mukho, Pohang, Inchon (2nd Fleet), Pusan (3rd Fleet)
Aviation: Pohang, Chinhae

Organisation

In 1986 the Navy was reorganised into three Fleets, each commanded by a Rear Admiral, whereas the Marines retain two Divisions and one brigade plus smaller and support units. From October 1973 the RoK Marine Force was placed directly under the RoK Navy command with a Vice Chief of Naval Operations for Marine Affairs replacing the Commandant of Marine Corps. The Marine Corps was re-established as an independent service on 1 November 1987.

1st Fleet: No 11, 12, 13 DD/FF Sqn; No 101, 102 Coastal Defence Sqn; 181, 191, 111, 121 Coastal Defence Units; 121st Minesweeper Sqn.
2nd Fleet: No 21, 22, 23 DD/FF Sqn; No 201, 202 Coastal Defence Sqn; 211, 212 Coastal Defence Units; 522nd Minesweeper Sqn.
3rd Fleet: 301, 302, 303 DD/FF Sqn; 304, 406th Coastal Defence Units.

Mercantile Marine

Lloyd's Register of Shipping:
    2085 vessels of 7 047 183 tons gross

Strength of the Fleet

Type	Active	Building (Proposed)
Submarines (Patrol)	2	4 (3)
Submarines (Midget)	11	—
Destroyers	8	(4)
Frigates	9	1 (9)
Corvettes	27	1
Fast Attack Craft—Missile	11	—
Fast Attack Craft—Patrol	107	—
Minehunters	6	(2)
Minesweepers	8	—
Minelayers	0	(1)
LSTs	8	1
LSMs	8	—
LCU/LCM	16	—
Logistic Support Ships	2	—
Salvage Ships	2 + 2 CG	1
Tankers	4	—
Survey Ships and Craft	7	—

DELETIONS

Destroyers

1993 *Inchon*

Patrol Forces

1993 Six Sea Hawk (to Philippines)
1994 Six Sea Hawk (to Philippines)

Auxiliaries

1992 *Chun Ji, Hwa Chon*

SUBMARINES

2 + 4 (3) CHANG BOGO (TYPE 209) CLASS (1200)

Name	No	Builders	Laid down	Launched	Commissioned
CHANG BOGO	061	HDW, Kiel	1989	June 1992	2 June 1993
YI CHON	062	Daewoo, Okpo	1990	14 Oct 1992	1994
CHOI MUSON	063	Daewoo, Okpo	1991	Sep 1993	1994
—	065	Daewoo, Okpo	1992	1994	1995
—	066	Daewoo, Okpo	1993	1995	1996
—	067	Daewoo, Okpo	1994	1996	1997

Displacement, tons: 1100 surfaced; 1285 dived
Dimensions, feet (metres): 183.7 × 20.3 × 18 *(56 × 6.2 × 5.5)*
Main machinery: Diesel-electric; 4 MTU 12V 396 SE diesels; 3800 hp(m) *(2.8 MW)* sustained; 4 alternators; 1 motor; 4600 hp(m) *(3.38 MW)* sustained; 1 shaft
Speed, knots: 11 surfaced/snorting; 22 dived
Range, miles: 7500 at 8 kts surfaced
Complement: 33 (6 officers)

Torpedoes: 8—21 in *(533 mm)* bow tubes. 14 SystemTechnik Nord (STN) SUT Mod 2; wire-guided; active/passive homing to 12 km *(6.6 nm)* at 35 kts; warhead 260 kg. Swim-out discharge.
Mines: 28 in lieu of torpedoes.
Countermeasures: ESM: Argo; radar warning.
Fire control: Atlas Elektronik ISUS 83 TFCS.
Radars: Navigation: I band.
Sonars: Atlas Elektronik CSU 83; hull-mounted; passive/active; medium frequency.

Programmes: First three ordered in late 1987, one built at Kiel by HDW, and two being assembled at Okpo by Daewoo from material packages transported from Germany. Key Korean personnel have been trained in Germany. Second three ordered in October 1989 and a further batch of three was to have been ordered in 1993 but this was delayed. First of class handed over in Germany on 14 October 1992. The aim of achieving a total of 18 split between the three Fleets is unlikely to be funded.
Structure: Type 1200 similar to those built for the Turkish Navy with a heavy dependence on Atlas Elektronik sensors and STN torpedoes. Air independent propulsion using a Cosworth Argo diesel is an option in some of the later hulls, which may be of a larger size.
Operational: An indigenous torpedo based on the Honeywell NP 37 may be available in due course.

CHANG BOGO   *11/1992*

3 KSS-1 TOLGORAE and 8 COSMOS CLASSES (MIDGET SUBMARINES)

051-053 (Tolgorae)

Displacement, tons: 150 surfaced; 175 dived (Tolgorae); 70 surfaced; 83 dived (Cosmos)
Dimensions, feet (metres): 82 × 6.9 *(25 × 2.1)* (Cosmos)
Main machinery: 1 diesel; 1 shaft
Speed, knots: 9 surfaced; 6 dived
Complement: 6 + 8 swimmers
Torpedoes: 2—406 mm tubes (Tolgorae). 2—533 mm tubes (Cosmos).
Sonars: Atlas Elektronik; hull-mounted; passive search; high frequency.

Comment: Tolgorae in service in 1983. Cosmos type used by Marines. Limited endurance, for use only in coastal waters. Fitted with Pilkington Optronics periscopes (CK 37 in Tolgorae and CK 41 in Cosmos). Numbers of each type were confirmed in 1993. All are based at Cheju Island.

TOLGORAE   *11/1985, G Jacobs*

DESTROYERS

Note: A new class of heavy destroyers is projected. Design work started in 1993 for an air defence ship of 7-8000 tons. Planned in-service date is 2003.

7 GEARING (FRAM I and II) CLASS

Name	No	Builders	Laid down	Launched	Commissioned
CHUNG BUK (ex-USS *Chevalier* DD 805)	DD 915	Bath Iron Works Corporation, Bath, Maine	12 June 1944	29 Oct 1944	9 Jan 1945
JEON BUK (ex-USS *Everett F Larson* DD 830)	DD 916	Bath Iron Works Corporation, Bath, Maine	4 Sep 1944	28 Jan 1945	6 Apr 1945
TAEJON (ex-USS *New* DD 818)	DD 919	Consolidated Steel Corporation	14 Apr 1945	18 Aug 1945	5 Apr 1946
KWANG JU (ex-USS *Richard E Kraus* DD 849)	DD 921	Bath Iron Works Corporation, Bath, Maine	31 July 1945	2 Mar 1946	23 May 1946
KANG WON (ex-USS *William R Rush* DD 714)	DD 922	Federal SB and DD Co, Newark	19 Oct 1944	8 July 1945	21 Sep 1945
KYONG KI (ex-USS *Newman K Perry* DD 883)	DD 923	Consolidated Steel Corporation	10 Oct 1944	17 Mar 1945	26 July 1945
JEON JU (ex-USS *Rogers* DD 876)	DD 925	Consolidated Steel Corporation	3 June 1944	20 Nov 1944	26 Mar 1945

Displacement, tons: 2425 standard; 3470 full load approx
Dimensions, feet (metres): 390.5 × 41.2 × 19
(119 × 12.6 × 5.8)
Main machinery: 4 Babcock & Wilcox boilers; 600 psi
(43.3 kg/cm sq); 850°F *(454°C)*; 2 GE turbines; 60 000 hp
(45 MW); 2 shafts
Speed, knots: 32.5. **Range, miles:** 3275 at 11 kts; 975 at 32 kts
Complement: 280

Missiles: SSM: 8 McDonnell Douglas Harpoon (2 quad) launchers **❶**(all except DD 923 and 925); active radar homing to 130 km *(70 nm)* at 0.9 Mach; warhead 227 kg.
A/S: Honeywell ASROC Mk 112 octuple launcher (DD 923 and 925); inertial guidance to 1.6-10 km *(1-6 nm)*; payload Mk 46 torpedo.
Guns: 4 or 6—5 in *(127 mm)*/38 (2 twin) Mk 38 (3 twin in DD 915-916) **❷**; 85° elevation; 15 rounds/minute to 17 km *(9 nm)* anti-surface; 11 km *(5.9 nm)* anti-aircraft; weight of shell 25 kg.
2 USN/Bofors 40 mm/56 (twin) (except DD 915 and 916); 45° elevation; 160 rounds/minute to 11 km *(5.9 nm)* anti-surface; 6 km *(3.3 nm)* anti-aircraft; weight of shell 0.9 kg.
2 General Electric/General Dynamics 20 mm Vulcan Gatling (except DD 923); 3000 rounds/minute combined to 1.5 km.
Torpedoes: 6—324 mm Mk 32 (2 triple) tubes **❸**. Honeywell Mk 46; anti-submarine; active/passive homing to 11 km *(5.9 nm)* at 40 kts; warhead 44 kg.
A/S mortars: 2 USN Hedgehog Mk 11 fixed rocket launchers (DD 915-916) **❹**; manually loaded; range 250 m; warhead 13.6 kg; 24 missiles.
Depth charges: 1 Mk IX rack.
Countermeasures: ESM: WLR-1; radar warning. WJ 1140 (DD 916).
ECM: ULQ-6; jammer.
Fire control: 1 Mk 37 GFCS. 1 Mk 51 Mod 2 (except DD 915 and 916) (for 40 mm).
Radars: Air search: Lockheed SPS 40 **❺** (DD 921 has SPS 37); E/F band; range 320 km *(175 nm)*.
Surface search: Raytheon/Sylvania SPS 10 **❻**; G band.
Fire control: Western Electric Mk 25 **❼**; I/J band.
IFF: UPX 1-12 (DD 919 and 921).
Sonars: SQS 29 (DD 915-916); hull-mounted; active search and attack; high frequency.
Sangamo SQS 23 (remainder); active search and attack; medium frequency.

Helicopters: 1 Aerospatiale SA 316B Alouette III **❽** (all except DD 923 and 925).

Programmes: First pair on loan from US on 5 July 1972 and 30 October 1972 respectively and by purchase 31 January 1977. Second pair 23 February 1977 by sale. DD 922 by sale 1 July 1978. Last pair by sale February/March 1981.
Modernisation: DD 915 and DD 916 were converted to radar picket destroyers (DDR) in 1949. All subsequently modernised under the US Navy's Fleet Rehabilitation and Modernisation (FRAM) programme—first pair to FRAM II standards, others to FRAM I. Fitted with small helicopter hangar and flight deck. Anti-ship torpedo tubes have been removed. In DD 915 and DD 919 the helicopter deck has been strengthened and in 925 two Vulcan Gatling guns have been positioned at the after end. Harpoon fitted in 1979 and some ships may still only carry two twin launchers. Most are now Tacan and SATCOM fitted.

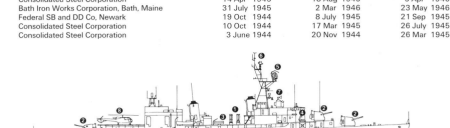
CHUNG BUK   *(Scale 1 : 1200), Ian Sturton*

KANG WON (with Harpoon and Gatling midships plus 40 mm guns forward)   *9/1988*

CHUNG BUK (with 3 twin 127 mm guns)   *9/1988*

JEON JU (ASROC and Gatling aft)   *1987*

1 ALLEN M SUMNER (FRAM II) CLASS

Name	No	Builders	Laid down	Launched	Commissioned
DAE GU (ex-USS *Wallace L Lind* DD 703)	DD 917	Bath Iron Works Corporation, Bath, Maine	Apr 1944	14 June 1944	8 Sep 1944

Displacement, tons: 2200 standard; 3320 full load
Dimensions, feet (metres): 376.5 × 40.9 × 19
(114.8 × 12.4 × 5.8)
Main machinery: 4 Babcock & Wilcox boilers; 600 psi
(43.3 kg/cm sq); 850°F *(454°C)*; 2 GE turbines; 60 000 hp
(45 MW); 2 shafts
Speed, knots: 34. **Range, miles:** 4500 at 16 kts
Complement: 235

Guns: 6 USN 5 in *(127 mm)*/38 (3 twin) Mk 38; 85° elevation; 15
rounds/minute to 17 km *(9 nm)* anti-surface; 11 km *(5.9 nm)*
anti-aircraft; weight of shell 25 kg.
2 USN/Bofors 40 mm/56 (twin); 45° elevation; 160 rounds/
minute to 11 km *(5.9 nm)* anti-surface; 6 km *(3.3 nm)* anti-
aircraft; weight of shell 0.9 kg.

1 General Electric/General Dynamics 20 mm Vulcan Gatling;
3000 rounds/minute combined to 1.5 km.
Torpedoes: 6—324 mm Mk 32 (2 triple) tubes. Honeywell Mk
46; anti-submarine; active/passive homing to 11 km *(5.9 nm)*
at 40 kts; warhead 44 kg.
A/S mortars: 2 USN Hedgehog Mk 11 fixed rocket launchers;
manually loaded; range 250 m; warhead 13.6 kg; 24 missiles.
Countermeasures: Decoys: 2 Loral-Hycor RBOC 6-barrelled Mk
33 launchers; range 4 km *(2.2 nm)*.
Fire control: USN Mk 37 for 127 mm gunnery. 2 Mk 51 for
40 mm gunnery.
Radars: Air search: Lockheed SPS 40; E/F band; range 320 km
(175 nm).
Surface search: Raytheon/Sylvania SPS 10; G band.
Fire control: Western Electric Mk 25; I/J band.

IFF: UPX 1-12.
Sonars: Sangamo SQS 23; hull-mounted; active search and
attack; medium frequency.
Litton SQA 10; VDS; active/passive search; medium
frequency.

Helicopters: 1 Aerospatiale SA 316B Alouette III.

Programmes: Transferred from US by sale December 1973.
Modernisation: Modernised under the US Navy's Fleet Rehabili-
tation and Modernisation (FRAM II) programme.
Structure: Fitted with strengthened helicopter deck and hangar.
Operational: *Inchon* paid off in 1993 and this last of the class is
likely to be scrapped soon.

SUMNER (old number)

1992

FRIGATES

0 + 1 + (9) KDX-2000 CLASS

Displacement, tons: 3900 full load
Dimensions, feet (metres): 444.2 × 46.6 × 13.8
(135.4 × 14.2 × 4.2)
Main machinery: CODOG; 2 GE LM 2500 gas turbines;
58 200 hp *(43.42 MW)* sustained; 2 MTU or SEMT-Pielstick
diesels; 8000 hp(m) *(5.88 MW)*; 2 shafts
Speed, knots: 30. **Range, miles:** 4000 at 18 kts
Complement: 170 (15 officers)

Missiles: SSM: 8 McDonnell Douglas Harpoon (2 quad) launch-
ers ❶.
SAM: Raytheon Sea Sparrow Mk 48; VLS launcher ❷ for 16 cells
RIM-7M. Mk 41 for Standard in later ships.
Guns: 1 OTO Melara 5 in *(127 mm)*/54 ❸.
2 Signaal 30 mm Goalkeeper ❹; 7 barrels per mounting.

Torpedoes: 6—324 mm (2 triple) Mk 32 tubes ❺; Mk 46 Mod 5;
anti-submarine.
Countermeasures: Decoys: 4 chaff launchers ❻. SLQ-25 Nixie
towed torpedo decoy.
ESM/ECM: Argo AR 700/APECS II; intercept and jammer.
Combat data systems: Atlas/Contraves COSYS 200. Link 11.
Radars: Air search: Raytheon SPS 49(V)5 ❼; C/D band.
Surface search: Siemens/Plessey AWS-6A Dolphin ❽; E/F band.
Fire control: Contraves TMX-KA ❾; I/J band.
Ericsson; K band.
IFF: UPX-27.
Sonars: Atlas Elektronik DSQS-23; hull-mounted active search;
medium frequency.

Helicopters: 1 Westland Super Lynx ❿.

Programmes: A much delayed programme. The first keel was to
have been laid down at Daewoo in late 1992 for completion in
1996, but definition studies extended to late 1993, when contracts started to be signed for the weapon systems. Subsequent units will be shared with Hyundai, but may not be
ordered until after first of class trials.
Structure: Later ships of the class may be fitted with vertical
launch Standard missiles and towed sonar arrays. Configuration shown in the line drawing still has some minor amendments to come and some of the weapon systems may still be
changed, including the Combat Data system.

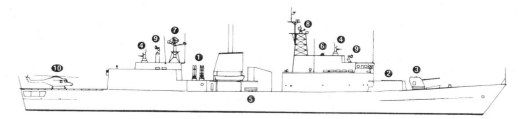

KDX-2000

(Scale 1 : 900), Ian Sturton

9 ULSAN CLASS

Name	No	Builders	Laid down	Launched	Commissioned
ULSAN	FF 951	Hyundai, Ulsan	1979	8 Apr 1980	1 Jan 1981
SEOUL	FF 952	Hyundai, Ulsan	1982	1984	30 June 1985
CHUNG NAM	FF 953	Korean SEC, Pusan	1984	1985	1 June 1986
MASAN	FF 955	Korea Tacoma	1983	26 Oct 1984	20 July 1985
KYONG BUK	FF 956	Daewoo, Okpo	1984	15 Jan 1986	30 May 1986
CHON NAM	FF 957	Hyundai, Ulsan	1986	19 Apr 1988	17 June 1989
CHE JU	FF 958	Daewoo, Okpo	1986	3 May 1988	1 Jan 1990
BUSAN	FF 959	Hyundai, Ulsan	1990	20 Feb 1992	1 Jan 1993
CHUNG JU	FF 961	Daewoo, Okpo	1990	20 Mar 1992	June 1993

Displacement, tons: 1496 light; 2180 full load (2300 for FF 957-961)
Dimensions, feet (metres): 334.6 × 37.7 × 11.5 *(102 × 11.5 × 3.5)*
Main machinery: CODOG; 2 GE LM 2500 gas turbines; 53 640 hp *(40 MW)* sustained; 2 MTU 16V 538 TB82 diesels; 5940 hp(m) *(4.37 MW)* sustained; 2 shafts; cp props
Speed, knots: 34; 18 on diesels. **Range, miles:** 4000 at 15 kts
Complement: 150 (16 officers)

Missiles: SSM: 8 McDonnell Douglas Harpoon (4 twin) launchers ❶; active radar homing to 130 km *(70 nm)* at 0.9 Mach; warhead 227 kg.
Guns: 2—3 in *(76 mm)*/62 OTO Melara compact ❷; 85° elevation; 85 rounds/minute to 16 km *(8.6 nm)* anti-surface; 12 km *(6.5 nm)* anti-aircraft; weight of shell 6 kg.
8 Emerson Electric 30 mm (4 twin) (FF 951-955) ❸; 6 Breda 40 mm/70 (3 twin) (FF 956-961) ❹.
Torpedoes: 6—324 mm Mk 32 (2 triple) tubes ❺. Honeywell Mk 46 Mod 1; anti-submarine; active/passive homing to 11 km *(5.9 nm)* at 40 kts; warhead 44 kg.
Depth charges: 12.
Countermeasures: Decoys: 4 Loral Hycor SRBOC 6-barrelled Mk 36 launchers ❻; range 4 km *(2.2 nm)*.
Nixie; towed torpedo decoy.
ESM/ECM: Intercept and jammer.
Combat data systems: Samsung/Ferranti WSA 423 action data automation (FF 957-961). Litton systems retrofitted to others.
Fire control: 1 Signaal Lirod optronic director (FF 951-956) ❼; 1 Radamec System 2400 optronic director (FF 957-961) ❽.
Radars: Air/surface search: Signaal DA 05 ❾; E/F band.
Surface search: Signaal ZW 06 (FF 951-956) ❿; Marconi S 1810 (FF 957-961) ⓫; I band.
Fire control: Signaal WM 28 (FF 951-956) ⓬; Marconi ST 1802 (FF 957-961) ⓭; I/J band.
Navigation: Raytheon SPS 10C (FF 957-961) ⓮; I band.
Tacan: SRN 15.
Sonars: Signaal PHS 32; hull-mounted; active search and attack; medium frequency.

Structure: Steel hull with aluminium alloy superstructure. There are three versions. The first five ships are the same but *Kyong Buk* has the four Emerson Electric twin 30 mm guns replaced by three Breda twin 40 mm, and the last four of the class have a built-up gun platform aft and a different combination of surface search, target indication and navigation radars. Weapon systems integration caused earlier concern and a Ferranti combat data system has been installed in the last five; it is reported that a Litton Systems CDS will be retrofitted in the earlier ships of the class.
Operational: *Che Ju* and *Chung Nam* conducted the first ever deployment of South Korean warships to Europe during a four month tour from September 1991 to January 1992. Trainees were embarked.

ULSAN   (Scale 1 : 900), Ian Sturton

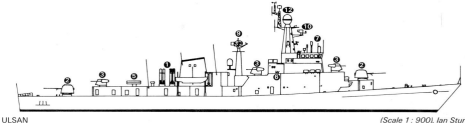

CHE JU   (Scale 1 : 900), Ian Sturton

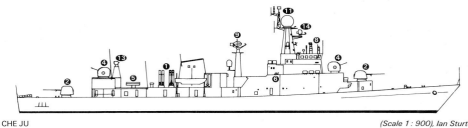

CHE JU (with Marconi FC radar and 40 mm guns)   11/1993, van Ginderen Collection

KYONG BUK (with Signaal FC radar and 40 mm guns)   11/1993, van Ginderen Collection

MASAN (with Signaal FC radar and 30 mm guns)   2/1993

CORVETTES

23 + 1 PO HANG CLASS

Name	No	Builders	Commissioned
PO HANG	756	Korea SEC, Pusan	Dec 1984
KUN SAN	757	Korea Tacoma	Dec 1984
KYONG JU	758	Hyundai, Ulsan	1986
MOK PO	759	Daewoo, Okpo	1986
KIM CHON	761	Korea SEC, Pusan	1987
CHUNG JU	762	Korea Tacoma	1987
JIN JU	763	Hyundai, Ulsan	1988
YO SU	765	Daewoo, Okpo	1988
AN DONG	766	Korea SEC, Pusan	Feb 1989
SUN CHON	767	Korea Tacoma	June 1989
YEE REE	768	Hyundai, Ulsan	June 1989
WON JU	769	Daewoo, Okpo	1989
JE CHON	771	Korea Tacoma	1989
CHON AN	772	Korea SEC, Pusan	Nov 1989
SONG NAM	773	Daewoo, Okpo	1990
BU CHON	775	Hyundai, Ulsan	1990
DAE CHON	776	Korea Tacoma	1990
JIN HAE	777	Korea SEC, Pusan	1990
SOK CHO	778	Korea Tacoma	1991
YONG JU	779	Hyundai, Ulsan	1991
NAM WON	781	Daewoo, Okpo	1991
KWAN MYONG	782	Korea SEC, Pusan	1991
—	783	Korea Tacoma	1992

Displacement, tons: 1220 full load
Dimensions, feet (metres): 289.7 × 32.8 × 9.5 *(88.3 × 10 × 2.9)*
Main machinery: CODOG; 1 GE LM 2500 gas turbine; 26 820 hp *(20 MW)* sustained; 2 MTU 12V 956 TB82 diesels; 6260 hp(m) *(4.6 MW)* sustained; 2 shafts
Speed, knots: 32. **Range, miles:** 4000 at 15 kts (diesel)
Complement: 95 (10 officers)

Missiles: SSM: 2 Aerospatiale MM 38 Exocet (756-759) ❶; inertial cruise; active radar homing to 42 km *(23 nm)* at 0.9 Mach; warhead 165 kg; sea-skimmer.
Guns: 1 or 2 OTO Melara 3 in *(76 mm)*/62 compact ❷; 85° elevation; 85 rounds/minute to 16 km *(8.6 nm)* anti-surface; 12 km *(6.5 nm)* anti-aircraft; weight of shell 6 kg.
4 Emerson Electric 30 mm (2 twin) (756-759) ❸; 4 Breda 40 mm/70 (2 twin) (761 onwards) ❹.
Torpedoes: 6—324 mm Mk 32 (2 triple) tubes (761 onwards) ❺. Honeywell Mk 46; anti-submarine; active/passive homing to 11 km *(5.9 nm)* at 40 kts; warhead 44 kg.
Depth charges: 12 (761 onwards).
Countermeasures: Decoys: 4 MEL Protean fixed launchers; 36 grenades.
2 Loral Hycor SRBOC 6-barrelled Mk 36 launchers (in some); range 4 km *(2.2 nm)*.
ESM/ECM: THORN EMI or NobelTech; intercept/jammer.
Combat data systems: Signaal Sewaco ZK (756-759); Ferranti WSA 423 (761 onwards).
Fire control: Signaal Lirod or Radamec 2400 optronic director ❻.
Radars: Surface search: Marconi 1810 ❼ and/or Raytheon SPS 64 ❽; I band.
Fire control: Signaal WM 28 ❾; I/J band; or Marconi 1802 ❿; I/J band.
Sonars: Signaal PHS 32 (761 onwards); hull-mounted; active search and attack; medium frequency.

Programmes: First laid down early 1983 by Korea SEC. The pennant number/name attribution shown above is uncertain but names and shipbuilders are correct. At least one more of the class was scheduled for completion in 1994 but the status of further orders is uncertain.
Structure: It is probable that there are three groups specialising in surface-to-surface warfare, anti-submarine and, possibly to come, air defence. The first group therefore has no ASW equipment and the second group has no SSM. The second group also has an improved combat data system with Ferranti/Radamec/Marconi fire control systems and radars as in the Ulsan class later versions.

KUN SAN (with Exocet)   *1987, Korea Tacoma*

AN DONG   *1992, Ships of the World*

PO HANG   *(Scale 1 : 900), Ian Sturton*

AN DONG   *(Scale 1 : 900), Ian Sturton*

SOK CHO   *1993, Ships of the World*

4 DONG HAE CLASS

Name	No	Builders	Commissioned
DONG HAE	751	Korea SEC, Pusan	Aug 1982
SU WON	752	Korea Tacoma	Oct 1983
KANG REUNG	753	Hyundai, Ulsan	Nov 1983
AN YANG	755	Daewoo, Okpo	Dec 1983

Displacement, tons: 1076 full load
Dimensions, feet (metres): 256.2 × 31.5 × 8.5 *(78.1 × 9.6 × 2.6)*
Main machinery: CODOG; 1 GE LM 2500 gas turbine; 26 820 hp *(20 MW)* sustained; 2 MTU 12V 956 TB82 diesels; 6260 hp(m) *(4.6 MW)* sustained; 2 shafts; cp props
Speed, knots: 31. **Range, miles:** 4000 at 15 kts (diesel)
Complement: 95 (10 officers)

Guns: 1 OTO Melara 3 in *(76 mm)*/62 compact ❶; 85° elevation; 85 rounds/minute to 16 km *(8.6 nm)*; weight of shell 6 kg.
4 Emerson Electric 30 mm (2 twin) ❷. 2 Bofors 40 mm/60 (twin) ❸.
Torpedoes: 6—324 mm Mk 32 (2 triple) tubes ❹. Honeywell Mk 46.
Depth charges: 12.
Countermeasures: Decoys: 4 MEL Protean chaff launchers.
ESM/ECM: THORN EMI or NobelTech; intercept and jammer.
Combat data systems: Signaal Sewaco ZK.
Fire control: Signaal Lirod optronic director ❺.
Radars: Surface search: Raytheon SPS 64 ❻; I band.
Fire control: Signaal WM 28 ❼; I/J band; range 46 km *(25 nm)*.
Sonars: Signaal PHS 32; hull-mounted; active search and attack; medium frequency.

Programmes: This was the first version of the corvette series, with four being ordered in 1980, one each from the four major warship building yards.
Structure: The design was almost certainly too small for the variety of different weapons which were intended to be fitted for different types of warfare and was therefore discontinued in favour of the Po Hang class.

DONG HAE   *(Scale 1 : 900), Ian Sturton*

SU WON   *1987, Korea Tacoma*

SHIPBORNE AIRCRAFT

Numbers/Type: 11 Aerospatiale SA 316B/SA 319B Alouette III.
Operational speed: 113 kts *(210 km/h)*.
Service ceiling: 10 500 ft *(3200 m)*.
Range: 290 nm *(540 km)*.
Role/Weapon systems: Marine support helicopter; operated by RoK Marine Corps. Sensors: None. Weapons: Unarmed.

ALOUETTE III   *1990*

Numbers/Type: 11 Westland Super Navy Lynx Mk 99.
Operational speed: 125 kts *(231 km/h)*.
Service ceiling: 12 000 ft *(3660 m)*.
Range: 320 nm *(593 km)*.
Role/Weapon systems: Shipborne ASV helicopter delivered in 1991 to replace Alouette III; a further order of six ASW versions is expected. Sensors: Ferranti Sea Spray Mk 3 radar and Racal ESM. Weapons: 4 BAe Sea Skua missiles. Mk 46 (Mod 5 in due course) torpedo (in ASW version).

SUPER LYNX   *1991, Westland*

LAND-BASED MARITIME AIRCRAFT (FRONT LINE)

Note: 10 UH-60 replacing UH-1H from 1993.

Numbers/Type: 14 Grumman S-2A/F Tracker.
Operational speed: 130 kts *(241 km/h)*.
Service ceiling: 25 000 ft *(7620 m)*.
Range: 1350 nm *(2500 km)*.
Role/Weapon systems: Maritime surveillance and limited ASW operations; coastal surveillance and EEZ patrol. May be upgraded to S-2T. Sensors: Search radar, ECM. Weapons: ASW; torpedoes, depth bombs and mines. ASV; underwing 127 mm rockets.

Numbers/Type: 8 Lockheed P-3C Orion.
Operational speed: 411 kts *(761 km/h)*.
Service ceiling: 28 300 ft *(8625 m)*.
Range: 4000 nm *(7410 km)*.
Role/Weapon systems: Maritime patrol aircraft ordered in December 1990 for delivery in 1995. This is the Update III version. Sensors: To include AAS-36 IR. Weapons: To include Harpoon ASM if approved.

PATROL FORCES

2 WILDCAT CLASS (FAST ATTACK CRAFT—MISSILE)

PKM 271-272

Displacement, tons: 140 full load
Dimensions, feet (metres): 108.9 × 22.6 × 7.9 *(33.9 × 6.9 × 2.4)*
Main machinery: 2 MTU MB 20V 672 TY90 (PKM 271); 5800 hp(m) *(4.26 MW)* sustained; 2 shafts
3 MTU MD 16V 538 TB90 diesels (PKM 272); 9000 hp(m) *(6.61 MW)* sustained; 3 shafts
Speed, knots: 40. **Range, miles:** 800 at 17 kts
Complement: 29 (5 officers)
Missiles: SSM: 2 Aerospatiale MM 38 Exocet; inertial cruise; active radar homing to 42 km *(23 nm)* at 0.9 Mach; warhead 165 kg; sea-skimmer.
Guns: 2 Bofors 40 mm/60; 80° elevation; 120 rounds/minute to 10 km *(5.4 nm)* anti-surface; 3 km *(1.6 nm)* anti-aircraft; weight of shell 0.89 kg.
2—12.7 mm MGs.
Radars: Surface search: Raytheon 1645; I band.
IFF: UPX 17.

Comment: Built by Korea Tacoma, Masan 1971-72. Steel hull and aluminium superstructure.

WILDCAT   *1992*

92 SEA DOLPHIN CLASS (FAST ATTACK CRAFT—PATROL)

PKM 212-358 series

Displacement, tons: 170 full load
Dimensions, feet (metres): 121.4 × 22.6 × 5.6 *(37 × 6.9 × 1.7)*
Main machinery: 2 MTU MD 16V 538 TB90 diesels; 6000 hp(m) *(4.41 MW)* sustained; 2 shafts
Speed, knots: 37. **Range, miles:** 600 at 20 kts
Complement: 31 (5 officers)
Guns: 2 Emerson Electric 30 mm (twin). 2 GE/GD 20 mm Vulcan Gatlings. 2—12.7 mm (twin) MGs.
Fire control: Optical director.
Radars: Surface search: Raytheon 1645; I band.

Comment: Built by Korea SEC, Korea Tacoma and Daewoo. First laid down 1978. The class has some gun armament variations and some minor superstructure changes in later ships of the class.

SEA DOLPHIN 292   *1991, Daewoo*

8 PAE KU (PSMM 5) CLASS (FAST ATTACK CRAFT—MISSILE)

Name	No	Builders	Commissioned
PAE KU 52	PGM 582 (ex-PGM 352)	Tacoma Boatbuilding Co, Tacoma, Wash.	14 Mar 1975
PAE KU 53	PGM 583 (ex-PGM 353)	Tacoma Boatbuilding Co, Tacoma, Wash.	14 Mar 1975
PAE KU 55	PGM 585 (ex-PGM 355)	Tacoma Boatbuilding Co, Tacoma, Wash.	1 Feb 1976
PAE KU 56	PGM 586 (ex-PGM 356)	Korea Tacoma Marine	1 Feb 1976
PAE KU 57	PGM 587 (ex-PGM 357)	Korea Tacoma Marine	1977
PAE KU 58	PGM 588 (ex-PGM 358)	Korea Tacoma Marine	1977
PAE KU 59	PGM 589 (ex-PGM 359)	Korea Tacoma Marine	1977
PAE KU 61	PGM 591 (ex-PGM 361)	Korea Tacoma Marine	1978

Displacement, tons: 268 full load
Dimensions, feet (metres): 176.2 × 23.9 × 9.5 *(53.7 × 7.3 × 2.9)*
Main machinery: 6 Avco Lycoming TF-35 gas turbines; 16 800 hp *(12.53 MW)*; 2 shafts; cp props
Speed, knots: 40+. **Range, miles:** 2400 at 18 kts
Complement: 32 (5 officers)

Missiles: SSM: 2 GDC Standard ARM launchers (PGM 582-585); anti-radiation homing to 35 km *(18.9 nm)* at 2 Mach; warhead 98 kg; 2 reloads.
4 McDonnell Douglas Harpoon (PGM 586-591); active radar homing to 130 km *(70 nm)* at 0.9 Mach; warhead 227 kg.
Guns: 1 OTO Melara 3 in *(76 mm)*/62 compact (PGM 586-591); 85° elevation; 85 rounds/minute to 16 km *(8.6 nm)* anti-surface; 12 km *(6.5 nm)* anti-aircraft; weight of shell 6 kg.
1 USN 3 in *(76 mm)*/50 Mk 34 (PGM 582-585); 85° elevation; 50 rounds/minute to 12.8 km *(6.9 nm)*; weight of shell 6 kg.
2 Emerson Electric 30 mm (twin); 80° elevation; 1200 rounds/minute combined to 6 km *(3.2 nm)*; weight of shell 0.35 kg.
2 Browning 12.7 mm MGs.
Countermeasures: Decoys: Loral RBOC 4-barrelled Mk 33 launchers; range 4 km *(2.2 nm)*.
Fire control: Mk 63 GFCS (PGM 582-585). Honeywell H 930 Mod 0 (PGM 586-591).
Radars: Air search: SPS 58; E/F band.
Surface search: Marconi Canada HC 75; I band; range 88 km *(48 nm)*.
Fire control: Western Electric SPG 50 or Westinghouse W-120; I/J band.

Programmes: Tacoma design designation was PSMM for multi-mission patrol ship.
Structure: Aluminium hulls, based on the US Navy's Asheville (PG 84) design, but appearance of Korean-built ships' superstructure differs.
Operational: The six TF 35 gas turbines turn two propeller shafts; the Asheville class ships have combination gas turbine-diesel power plants. In the South Korean units one, two, or three turbines can be selected to provide each shaft with a variety of power settings.

PAE KU 53 (with Standard) (old number)   3/1987, G Jacobs

PAE KU 58 (with Harpoon) (old number)   3/1987, G Jacobs

1 ASHEVILLE CLASS (FAST ATTACK CRAFT—MISSILE)

Name	No	Builders	Commissioned
PAE KU 51 (ex-USS *Benicia* PG 96)	PGM 581 (ex-PGM 351, ex-PGM 11, ex-PGM 101)	Tacoma Boatbuilding Co, Tacoma, Wash.	25 Apr 1970

Displacement, tons: 225 standard; 245 full load
Dimensions, feet (metres): 164.5 × 23.9 × 9.5 *(50.1 × 7.3 × 2.9)*
Main machinery: CODOG; 1 GE LM-1500 gas turbine; 13 300 hp *(9.92 MW)*; 2 Cummins VT12-875M diesels; 1450 hp *(1.08 MW)*; 2 shafts
Speed, knots: 40; 16 diesels. **Range, miles:** 1700 at 16 kts
Complement: 42 (5 officers)
Missiles: SSM: 2 GDC Standard ARM launchers; anti-radiation homing to 35 km *(18.9 nm)* at 2 Mach; warhead 98 kg; 2 reloads.
Guns: 1 USN 3 in *(76 mm)*/50 Mk 34; 85° elevation; 50 rounds/minute to 12.8 km *(6.9 nm)*; weight of shell 6 kg.
1 Bofors 40 mm/60 Mk 3; 80° elevation; 120 rounds/minute to 10 km *(5.4 nm)* anti-surface; 3 km *(1.6 nm)* anti-aircraft; weight of shell 0.89 kg.
4 Browning 12.7 mm MGs.
Fire control: USN Mk 63 Mod 29 for 76 mm gunnery.
Radars: Surface search: Raytheon 1645; I/J band.
Fire control: Western Electric SPG 50; I/J band.
IFF: APX 72.

Comment: Former US Asheville class patrol gunboat. Launched 20 December 1969; transferred on lease 15 October 1971 and arrived in South Korea in January 1972. Probably paid off in 1991.

PAE KU 51 (old number)   9/1988

15 SEA HAWK and SEA FOX CLASSES
(FAST ATTACK CRAFT—PATROL)

PK 161-189 series

Displacement, tons: 80 full load
Dimensions, feet (metres): 84.3 × 17.7 × 4.9 *(25.7 × 5.4 × 1.5)*
Main machinery: 2 MTU MD 16V 538 TB90 diesels; 6000 hp(m) *(4.41 MW)* sustained; 2 shafts
Speed, knots: 41. **Range, miles:** 600 at 17 kts; 500 at 20 kts
Complement: 15 (6 officers)
Guns: 4 Oerlikon 20 mm (2 twin). 4 Browning 12.7 mm (2 twin) MGs.

Comment: Built by Korea Tacoma Marine Industries Ltd, Korea SEC and Hyundai between 1975-1978. The term Schoolboy class was also applied to this class. Ordered in three batches: 1973, 1976, 1978. Armament varies amongst boats. Some have a US Bofors 40 mm Mk 3 forward while later boats have a Korean 40 mm mount forward. Some have two MM 38 Exocet. At least seven paid off in 1991/92. Six to the Philippines in 1993 and six more in 1994.

SEA HAWK 161   1992

MINE WARFARE FORCES

6 + (2) SWALLOW CLASS (MINEHUNTERS)

Name	No	Builders	Commissioned
KANG KYEONG	561	Kangnam Corporation	Dec 1986
KANG JIN	562	Kangnam Corporation	May 1991
KO RYEONG	563	Kangnam Corporation	Nov 1991
KIM PO	565	Kangnam Corporation	Apr 1993
KO CHANG	566	Kangnam Corporation	Oct 1993
KUM WHA	567	Kangnam Corporation	Apr 1994

Displacement, tons: 470 standard; 520 full load
Dimensions, feet (metres): 164 × 27.2 × 8.6 *(50 × 8.3 × 2.6)*
Main machinery: 2 MTU diesels; 2040 hp(m) *(1.5 MW)* sustained; 2 Voith-Schneider props; bow thruster; 102 hp(m) *(75 kW)*
Speed, knots: 15. **Range, miles:** 2000 at 10 kts
Complement: 44 (5 officers) plus 4 divers
Guns: 1 Oerlikon 20 mm. 2—7.62 mm MGs.
Countermeasures: MCM: 2 Gaymarine Pluto remote-control submersibles.
Combat data systems: Racal MAINS 500.
Radars: Navigation: Raytheon; I band.
Sonars: GEC/Marconi 193M Mod 1 or Mod 3; minehunting; high frequency.

Comment: Built to a design developed independently by Kangnam Corporation but similar to the Italian Lerici class. GRP hull. Single sweep gear deployed at 8 kts. Decca/Racal plotting system. First delivered at the end of 1986 for trials. Two more with some modifications ordered in 1988, three more in 1990. Further ships of the class are expected to be slightly larger with a variable depth sonar and a fully integrated minehunting system.

KAN KEONG   1990, Kangnam Corp

0 + (1) MINELAYER

Displacement, tons: 3300 full load
Dimensions, feet (metres): 340.6 × 49.2 × 11.2 *(103.8 × 15 × 3.4)*
Main machinery: CODAD; 4 diesels; 17 200 hp(m) *(12.64 MW)*; 2 shafts
Speed, knots: 22. **Range, miles:** 4500 at 15 kts
Complement: 160
Guns: 1 OTO Melara 3 in *(76 mm)*/62; 2 Breda 40 mm/70.
Torpedoes: 6—324 mm Mk 32 (2 triple) launchers.
Mines: 2 stern launchers.
Countermeasures: Decoys: 2 chaff launchers. ESM/ECM.
Fire control: Optronic director.
Radars: Air/surface search; Fire control; Navigation; IFF.
Sonars: Bow-mounted; active search and attack; medium frequency.
Helicopters: Platform only.

Comment: Project design contract ordered October 1991 and completed July 1993 by Hyundai. Order expected in 1994 for the first of class.

MINELAYER (model) *1993, Hyundai*

3 MSC 268 and 5 MSC 289 CLASSES
(MINESWEEPERS—COASTAL)

Name	No	Builders	Commissioned
KUM SAN (ex-US *MSC 284*)*	MSC 551	Harbour Boat Building, Terminal Island, Calif	June 1959
KO HUNG (ex-US *MSC 285*)*	MSC 552	Harbour Boat Building, Terminal Island, Calif	Aug 1959
KUM KOK (ex-US *MSC 286*)*	MSC 553	Harbour Boat Building, Terminal Island, Calif	Oct 1959
NAM YANG (ex-US *MSC 295*)	MSC 555	Peterson Builders, Wisconsin	Aug 1963
HA DONG (ex-US *MSC 296*)	MSC 556	Peterson Builders, Wisconsin	Nov 1963
SAM KOK (ex-US *MSC 316*)	MSC 557	Peterson Builders, Wisconsin	July 1968
YONG DONG (ex-US *MSC 320*)	MSC 558	Peterson Builders, Wisconsin	Oct 1975
OK CHEON (ex-US *MSC 321*)	MSC 559	Peterson Builders, Wisconsin	Oct 1975

* MSC 268 class

Displacement, tons: 320 light; 370 full load (268 class)
315 light; 380 full load (289 class)
Dimensions, feet (metres): 141.1 × 26.2 × 8.5 *(43 × 8 × 2.6)* (268 class)
145.4 × 27.2 × 12 (screws) *(44.3 × 8.3 × 2.7)* (289 class)
Main machinery: 2 GM 8-268A diesels; 880 hp *(656 kW)* (268 class); 2 shafts
4 GM 6-71 diesels; 696 hp *(519 kW)* sustained (289 class); 2 shafts
Speed, knots: 14. **Range, miles:** 2500 at 14 kts
Complement: 40
Guns: 2 Oerlikon 20 mm (twin) (268 class); 2 Oerlikon 20 mm (289 class).
3 Browning 12.7 mm MGs.
Radars: Navigation: Decca 45; I band.
Sonars: General Electric UQS 1 or Thomson Sintra; hull-mounted; minehunting; high frequency.

Comment: Built by the USA specifically for transfer under the Military Aid Programme with wooden hulls and non-magnetic metal fittings. MSC 551 transferred to South Korea in June 1959, MSC 552 in September 1959, MSC 553 in November 1959, MSC 555 in September 1963, MSC 556 in November 1963, MSC 557 in July 1968, MSC 558 and 559 on 2 October 1975. The last four may have been retrofitted with Thomson Sintra mine detection sonars. Planned to pay off as Swallow class commission.

KO HUNG *1982, G Jacobs*

AMPHIBIOUS FORCES

1 + 1 ALLIGATOR CLASS (LST)

Displacement, tons: 4200 full load
Dimensions, feet (metres): 350.7 × 50.2 × 9.8 *(106.9 × 15.3 × 3)*
Main machinery: 2 SEMT-Pielstick 16 PA6 V 280; 12 800 hp(m) *(9.41 MW)* sustained; 2 shafts
Speed, knots: 16. **Range, miles:** 10 000 at 12 kts
Complement: 120 (14 officers)
Military lift: 700 tons vehicles; 200 tons landing craft
Guns: 4 Breda 40 mm/70 (2 twin). 2 Oerlikon 20 mm.
Fire control: Optronic director.
Radars: Navigation: I band.
Helicopters: Platform for 1 medium.

Comment: Ordered in June 1990 from Korea Tacoma, Masan. Characteristics listed are for the Hyundai HDL-4000. First of class sea trials started in late 1993. The ships are similar to those built for Venezuela in the mid-1980s.

ALLIGATOR *1993*

7 LST 1-510 and 511-1152 CLASSES

Name	No	Commissioned
UN BONG (ex-USS *LST 1010*)	LST 671	25 Apr 1944
BI BONG (ex-USS *LST 218*)	LST 673	12 Aug 1943
KAE BONG (ex-USS *Berkshire County* LST 288)	LST 675	20 Dec 1943
WEE BONG (ex-USS *Johnson County* LST 849)	LST 676	16 Jan 1945
SU YONG (ex-USS *Kane County* LST 853)	LST 677	11 Dec 1945
BUK HAN (ex-USS *Lynn County* LST 900)	LST 678	28 Dec 1944
HWA SAN (ex-USS *Pender County* LST 1080)	LST 679	29 May 1945

Displacement, tons: 1653 standard; 2366 beaching; 4080 full load
Dimensions, feet (metres): 328 × 50 × 14 (screws) *(100 × 15.2 × 4.3)*
Main machinery: 2 GM 12-567A diesels; 1800 hp *(1.34 MW)*; 2 shafts
Speed, knots: 11.6
Complement: 80
Military lift: 2100 tons including 20 tanks and 2 LCVPs
Guns: 8 Bofors 40 mm (2 twin, 1 quad). 2 Oerlikon 20 mm.

Comment: Former US Navy tank landing ships. Transferred to South Korea between 1955 and 1959. All purchased 15 November 1974.

BUK HAN *1982, G Jacobs*

8 LSM 1 CLASS

Name	No
UL RUNG (ex-USS *LSM 17*)	LSM 652
—	LSM 653
KO MUN (ex-USS *LSM 30*)	LSM 655
PI AN (ex-USS *LSM 96*)	LSM 656
WOL MI (ex-USS *LSM 57*)	LSM 657
KI RIN (ex-USS *LSM 19*)	LSM 658
NUNG RA (ex-USS *LSM 84*)	LSM 659
SIN MI (ex-USS *LSM 316*)	LSM 661

Displacement, tons: 743 beaching; 1095 full load
Dimensions, feet (metres): 203.5 × 34.6 × 8.2 *(62 × 10.5 × 2.5)*
Main machinery: 2 Fairbanks-Morse 38D8-1/8-10 diesels; 3540 hp *(2.64 MW)* sustained; 2 shafts
Speed, knots: 13
Complement: 75
Guns: 2 Bofors 40 mm (twin). 4 Oerlikon 20 mm.

Comment: Former US Navy medium landing ships, built 1944-45. Transferred in 1956. All purchased 15 November 1974. Arrangement of 20 mm guns differs; some ships have two single mounts adjacent forward 40 mm mount on forecastle; other 20 mm guns along sides of cargo well.

PI AN *3/1987, G Jacobs*

6 FURSEAL CLASS (LCU)

MULKAE 72, 73, 75, 76, 77, 78

Displacement, tons: 415 full load
Dimensions, feet (metres): 134.8 × 28.8 × 5.9 *(41.1 × 8.8 × 1.8)*
Main machinery: 2 GM 6-71 diesels; 348 hp *(260 kW)* sustained; 2 Kort nozzles
Speed, knots: 13. **Range, miles:** 560 at 11 kts
Complement: 14 (2 officers)
Military lift: 200 tons including battle tanks
Guns: 2 Oerlikon 20 mm.

Comment: In service 1979-81. Built by Korea Tacoma Marine Industries Ltd based on a US design.

FURSEAL 76   *1987, Korea Tacoma*

10 LCM 8 CLASS

Displacement, tons: 115 full load
Dimensions, feet (metres): 74.5 × 21 × 4.6 *(22.7 × 6.4 × 1.4)*
Main machinery: 4 GM 6-71 diesels; 696 hp *(519 kW)* sustained; 2 shafts
Speed, knots: 11

Comment: Previously US Army craft. Transferred 1978.

LCVP TYPES

Comment: A considerable number of US type built of GRP in South Korea. In addition there are plans to build up to 30 small hovercraft for special forces.

AUXILIARIES

Notes: (1) The South Korean Navy also operates nine small harbour tugs (designated YTLs). These include one ex-US Navy craft (YTL 550) and five ex-US Army craft. There are also approximately 35 small service craft in addition to the YO-type tankers listed and the harbour tugs. These craft include open lighters, floating cranes, diving tenders, dredgers, ferries, non self-propelled fuel barges, pontoon barges, and sludge removal barges; most are former US Navy craft.
(2) The ex-US *Cavallaro* high speed transport (APD 822) was in service in 1992 and 1993.

0 + 1 SUBMARINE SALVAGE SHIP

Displacement, tons: 4300 full load
Dimensions, feet (metres): 337.3 × 53.8 × 15.1 *(102.8 × 16.4 × 4.6)*
Main machinery: Diesel-electric; 4 MAN Burmeister & Wain 16V 28/32 diesels; 11 800 hp(m) *(8.67 MW)*; 2 motors; 5440 hp(m) *(4 MW)*; 2 shafts; cp props; 3 bow and 2 stern thrusters
Speed, knots: 18. **Range, miles:** 9500 at 15 kts
Complement: 130
Guns: 1 GE/GD 20 mm Vulcan Gatling. 6—12.7 mm MGs.
Radars: Navigation: I band.
Sonars: Hull-mounted; active search; high frequency.
Helicopters: Platform for 1 light.

Comment: Ordered in 1992 from Daewoo, Okpo. Laid down in 1993 for completion in 1995. A multi-purpose salvage and rescue ship which carries a 300 m ROV as well as two LCVPs on davits plus a diving bell for nine men and a decompression chamber. Two large hydraulic cranes fore and aft and one towing winch. There are also two salvage ships which belong to the Coast Guard.

DW 4000R (model)   *1992, Daewoo*

2 CHUN JEE CLASS (LOGISTIC SUPPORT SHIPS)

Name	No	Builders	Commissioned
CHUN JEE	AO 57	Hyundai, Ulsan	Dec 1990
—	AO 53	—	1993

Displacement, tons: 7500 full load
Dimensions, feet (metres): 426.5 × 58.4 × 21.3 *(130 × 17.8 × 6.5)*
Main machinery: 2 SEMT-Pielstick 16 PA6 V 280 diesels; 12 800 hp(m) *(9.4 MW)* sustained; 2 shafts
Speed, knots: 20. **Range, miles:** 4500 at 15 kts
Cargo capacity: 4200 tons liquids; 450 tons solids
Guns: 4 Emerlec 30 mm (2 twin). 2 GE/GD 20 mm Vulcan Gatlings.
Radars: Navigation: I band.
Helicopters: 1 medium.

Comment: *Chun Jee* laid down September 1989 and launched in May 1990. Underway replenishment stations on both sides. Helicopter for Vertrep. There are three 6 ton lifts. Possibly based on Italian Stromboli class. Second of class completed in 1993.

CHUN JEE   *1991, Hyundai*

CHUN JEE   *11/1993, J Straczek*

1 TRIALS SUPPORT SHIP

Name	No	Builders	Commissioned
SUNJIN	—	Hyundai, Ulsan	Apr 1993

Displacement, tons: 310 full load
Dimensions, feet (metres): 113.2 × 49.2 × 11.5 *(34.5 × 15 × 3.5)*
Main machinery: 1 MTU 16V 396 TE74L diesel; 2680 hp(m) *(2 MW)*; 1 shaft; cp prop; 2 bow thrusters
Speed, knots: 21. **Range, miles:** 600 at 16 kts
Complement: 5 plus 20 scientists

Comment: Experimental design built by Hyundai. Ordered June 1991, laid down June 1992, launched November 1992. Aluminium SWATH hull with dynamic positioning system. Fitted with various trials equipment including an integrated navigation system and torpedo tracking pinger system. Used by the Defence Development Agency.

SUNJIN   *1993, Hyundai*

2 TONTI CLASS (TANKERS)

SO YANG (ex-*Tarland*, ex-USNS *Rincon*) AOG 55
GIN YANG (ex-*Racoon Bend*, ex-USNS *Petaluma*) AOG 56

Displacement, tons: 2100 light; 6047 full load
Dimensions, feet (metres): 325.2 × 48.2 × 19.1 *(99.1 × 14.7 × 5.8)*
Main machinery: 2 Nordberg diesels; 1400 hp *(1.04 MW)*; 1 shaft
Speed, knots: 10. **Range, miles:** 6000 at 10 kts
Complement: 41
Cargo capacity: 31 284 barrels light fuel

Comment: Launched as merchant tankers 9 August 1945 and 5 January 1945 respectively. Transferred from US 21 February 1982 on lease. Probably armed. Lease renewed 8 September 1992.

2 YO TYPE (HARBOUR TANKERS)

KU YONG (ex-USS *YO 118*) YO 1   — (ex-USS *YO 179*) YO 6

Displacement, tons: 1400 full load
Dimensions, feet (metres): 174 × 32 × 13.1 *(53 × 9.8 × 4)*
Main machinery: 1 Union diesel; 560 hp *(418 kW)*; 1 shaft
Speed, knots: 7 kts
Complement: 36
Cargo capacity: 900 tons
Guns: Several 20 mm.

Comment: Former US Navy self-propelled fuel barges. Transferred to South Korea on 3 December 1946 and 13 September 1971, respectively.

2 DIVER CLASS (SALVAGE SHIPS)

Name	No	Builders	Launched
GUMI	ARS 26	Basalt Rock Co,	18 July 1944
(ex-USS *Deliver* ARS 23)		Napa, Calif.	
CHANG WON	ARS 25	Basalt Rock Co,	22 Aug 1944
(ex-USS *Grasp* ARS 24)		Napa, Calif.	

Displacement, tons: 1530 standard; 1970 full load
Dimensions, feet (metres): 213.5 × 41 × 13 *(65.1 × 12.5 × 4)*
Main machinery: Diesel-electric; 4 Cooper Bessemer GSB8 diesels; 3420 hp *(2.55 MW)*; 4 generators; 2 motors; 3060 hp *(2.28 MW)*; 2 shafts
Speed, knots: 14.8. **Range, miles:** 9000 at 14 kts
Complement: 83
Guns: 2 Oerlikon 20 mm.
Radars: Surface search: Sperry SPS 53; I/J band.
IFF: UPX 12.

Comment: ARS 26 purchased from US 15 August 1979 and ARS 25 on 31 March 1978. Operated by Service Squadron 51. Equipped for salvage, diver support and towage.

CHANG WON   1982, G Jacobs

TUGS

2 SOTOYOMO CLASS

Name	No	Builders	Launched
YONG MUN	31 (ex-*ATA 2*)	Levingston SB Co,	17 Jan 1945
(ex-USS *Keosanqua* ATA 198)		Orange, Texas	
DO BONG	32 (ex-*ATA (S) 3*)	Gulfport Boiler & Welding	14 Dec 1944
(ex-USS *Pinola* ATA 206)		Works, Port Arthur, Texas	

Displacement, tons: 534 standard; 860 full load
Dimensions, feet (metres): 143 × 33.9 × 13 *(43.6 × 10.3 × 4)*
Main machinery: Diesel-electric; 2 GM 12-278A diesels; 2200 hp *(1.64 MW)*; 2 generators; 1 motor; 1500 hp *(1.12 MW)*; 1 shaft
Speed, knots: 13
Complement: 45
Guns: 1 USN 3 in *(76 mm)*/50. 4 Oerlikon 20 mm.

Comment: Former US Navy auxiliary ocean tugs. Both transferred to South Korea in February 1962. 32 modified for salvage work.

DO BONG   1985, G Jacobs

SURVEY SHIPS

Note: The listed craft are operated by the South Korean Hydrographic Service which is responsible to the Ministry of Transport.

7 SURVEY CRAFT

Name	Displacement, tons	Launched	Complement
PUSAN 801	494	1980	23 (8 officers)
PUSAN 802	240	1982	14 (5 officers)
PUSAN 803	125	1979	13 (5 officers)
PUSAN 805	156	1983	10 (5 officers)
CH'UNGNAM 821	65	1981	8 (3 officers)
KANGWON 831	65	1981	8 (3 officers)
PUSAN 806	22	1987	4 (2 officers)

PUSAN 801   1990, Ships of the World

COAST GUARD

Note: The South Korean Coast Guard operates a number of small ships and several hundred craft including tugs and rescue craft.

3 MAZINGER CLASS

PC 1001-PC 1003

Displacement, tons: 1200 full load
Dimensions, feet (metres): 264.1 × 32.2 × 11.5 *(80.5 × 9.8 × 3.2)*
Main machinery: 2 SEMT-Pielstick 12 PA6 V 280 diesels; 9600 hp(m) *(7.08 MW)* sustained; 2 shafts
Speed, knots: 22. **Range, miles:** 7000 at 18 kts
Complement: 69 (11 officers)
Guns: 1 Bofors 40 mm/70. 4 Oerlikon 20 mm (2 twin).

Comment: Ordered 7 November 1980 from Korea Tacoma and Hyundai. *PC 1001* delivered 29 November 1981. All welded mild steel construction. Used for offshore surveillance and general coast guard duties. *PC 1001* is reported to be the Coast Guard Command ship. Only three of this class were completed.

MAZINGER   1987, Korea Tacoma

1 HAN KANG CLASS

HAN KANG PC 1005

Displacement, tons: 1180 full load
Dimensions, feet (metres): 289.7 × 32.8 × 9.5 *(88.3 × 10 × 2.9)*
Main machinery: CODOG; 1 GE LM 2500 gas turbine; 26 820 hp *(20 MW)* sustained; 2 MTU 12V
  956 TB82 diesels; 6260 hp(m) *(4.6 MW)* sustained; 3 shafts
Speed, knots: 32. **Range, miles:** 4000 at 15 kts
Complement: 72 (11 officers)
Guns: 1 OTO Melara 76/62 compact. 1 Bofors 40 mm/70. 2 GE/GD 20 mm Vulcan Gatlings.
Fire control: Signaal LIOD optronic director.
Radars: Surface search: Raytheon SPS 64(V); I band.
  Fire control: Signaal WM 28; I/J band.

Comment: Built between May 1984 and December 1985 by Daewoo. Same hull as Po Hang class
  but much more lightly armed. Only one of the class was completed.

HAN KANG   *1989, Ships of the World*

2 HYUNDAI TYPE

402   403

Displacement, tons: 430 full load
Dimensions, feet (metres): 176.2 × 24.3 × 7.9 *(53.7 × 7.4 × 2.4)*
Main machinery: 2 MTU 16V 396 TB83 diesels; 1990 hp(m) *(1.49 MW)*; 2 shafts; cp props
Speed, knots: 19. **Range, miles:** 2100 at 17 kts
Complement: 14
Guns: 1 GD/GE 20 mm Vulcan Gatling. 4—12.7 mm MGs.

Comment: Built by Hyundai. First of class delivered in December 1991, second in 1993. Multi-
  purpose patrol craft.

402   *1992, Hyundai*

6 SEA DRAGON/WHALE CLASS

PC 501, 502, 503, 505, 506, 507

Displacement, tons: 640 full load
Dimensions, feet (metres): 200.1 × 26.2 × 8.9 *(61 × 8 × 2.7)*
Main machinery: 2 SEMT-Pielstick 12 PA6 V 280 diesels; 9600 hp(m) *(7.08 MW)* sustained; 2
  shafts
Speed, knots: 24. **Range, miles:** 6000 at 15 kts
Complement: 40 (7 officers)
Guns: 1 Bofors 40 mm. 2 Oerlikon 20 mm. 2 Browning 12.7 mm MGs.
Radars: Navigation: Two sets.

Comment: Ordered in 1980 from Hyundai, Korea SEC and Korea Tacoma. Fitted with SATNAV.
  Welded steel hull. Armament varies between ships, one 76 mm gun can be mounted on the
  forecastle.

SEA DRAGON 507   *1987, Korea Tacoma*

22 SEA WOLF/SHARK CLASS

Displacement, tons: 310 full load
Dimensions, feet (metres): 158.1 × 23.3 × 8.2 *(48.2 × 7.1 × 2.5)*
Main machinery: 2 diesels; 7320 hp(m) *(5.38 MW)*; 2 shafts
Speed, knots: 25. **Range, miles:** 2400 at 15 kts
Complement: 35 (3 officers)
Guns: 4 Oerlikon 20 mm (2 twin or 1 twin, 2 single). Some have a twin Bofors 40 mm/70 vice the
  twin Oerlikon. 2 Browning 12.7 mm MGs.

Comment: First four ordered in 1979-80 from Korea SEC (Sea Shark), Hyundai and Korea Tacoma
  (Sea Wolf). Programme terminated in 1988. Pennant numbers in 200 series up to 277.

SEA WOLF 251   *1987, Korea Tacoma*

2 BUKHANSAN CLASS

BUKHANSAN 278   **CHULMASAN** 279

Displacement, tons: 380 full load
Dimensions, feet (metres): 174.2 × 24 × 7.2 *(53.1 × 7.3 × 2.2)*
Main machinery: 2 MTU diesels; 8300 hp(m) *(6.1 MW)* sustained; 2 shafts
Speed, knots: 28. **Range, miles:** 2500 at 15 kts
Complement: 35 (3 officers)
Guns: 2 Breda 40 mm/70 (twin). 1 GE/GD 20 mm Vulcan Gatling. 2—12.7 mm MGs.
Fire control: Radamec optronic director.
Radars: Surface search: I band.

Comment: Follow on to Sea Wolf class developed by Hyundai in 1987. Ordered in 1988 from
  Hyundai and Daewoo respectively. Both in service in 1989.

CHULMASAN   *1989, Daewoo*

INSHORE PATROL CRAFT

Displacement, tons: 47 full load
Dimensions, feet (metres): 69.9 × 17.7 × 4.6 *(21.3 × 5.4 × 1.4)*
Main machinery: 2 diesels; 1800 hp(m) *(1.32 MW)*; 2 shafts
Speed, knots: 22. **Range, miles:** 400 at 12 kts
Complement: 11
Guns: 3—12.7 mm MGs.

Comment: Details are for the latest design of patrol craft. There are large numbers of this type of
  vessel used for inshore patrol work.

IPC   *1991, Kangnam Corp*

AUXILIARIES

1 SALVAGE SHIP

Name	No	Builders	Commissioned
TAE PUNG YANG	3001	Hyundai, Ulsan	Jan 1993

Displacement, tons: 3200 standard; 4300 full load
Dimensions, feet (metres): 343.5 × 49.2 × 17 *(104.7 × 15 × 5.2)*
Main machinery: 4 Ssangyoung MAN Burmeister & Wain 16V 28/32 diesels; 4800 hp(m)
(3.53 MW); 2 shafts; cp props; bow and stern thrusters
Speed, knots: 21. **Range, miles:** 8500 at 15 kts
Complement: 121
Guns: 1 GD/GE 20 mm Vulcan Gatling.
Helicopters: 1 light.

Comment: Laid down February 1991, launched October 1991. Has a helicopter deck and hangar,
an ROV capable of diving to 300 m and a firefighting capability. Dynamic positioning system.
Operates for the Coast Guard.

TAE PUNG YANG   1993, Hyundai

1 SALVAGE SHIP

Name	No	Builders	Commissioned
JACMIN	1501	Daewoo, Okpo	28 Dec 1992

Displacement, tons: 2072 full load
Dimensions, feet (metres): 254.6 × 44.3 × 13.8 *(77.6 × 13.5 × 4.2)*
Main machinery: 2 MTU diesels; 8000 hp(m) *(5.88 MW)*; 2 shafts
Speed, knots: 18. **Range, miles:** 4500 at 12 kts
Complement: 92
Guns: 1 GD/GE 20 mm Vulcan Gatling.

Comment: Ordered in 1990. Fitted with diving equipment and has a four point mooring system.

JACMIN   1992, Daewoo

KUWAIT

Headquarters' Appointment

Commander of the Navy:
Colonel Ahmed Yousuf Al Mulla

Iraq Invasion

In August 1990 Iraq invaded Kuwait. All Naval and Coast Guard
ships and aircraft were captured with the exception of two fast
attack craft. Subsequently the Iraqi Navy used the captured craft
in Operation Desert Storm and most were either sunk or damaged by Allied Forces. The majority of the survivors have been
returned, but in poor condition and unlikely to be returned to
service.

New Construction Plan

A proposed ten year reconstruction plan includes two corvettes
and two 34 m landing craft to be built in 1995. Subsequent
orders may include three minehunters, two diving support ships
and a training vessel. Eight large patrol craft are also to be
ordered in 1994, if the intention projected in August 1992 is
confirmed.

Bases

Navy: Ras Al Qalayah
Coast Guard: Shuwaikh, Umm Al-Hainan

Mercantile Marine

Lloyd's Register of Shipping:
207 vessels of 2 217 911 tons gross

DELETIONS

(Captured by Iraq in August 1990. Those that were not destroyed
in the war in 1991, were finaly returned unserviceable in 1993)

Fast Attack Craft (Missile):	5 Lürssen TNC 45 and 1 Lürssen FPB 57
Patrol Craft:	5 Seagull, 15 Thornycroft, 1 Halter Marine, 7 Magnum Sedan
Landing Craft:	4 Loadmasters, 6 Vosper Singapore Type
Miscellaneous:	10 tugs and launches
Aircraft:	12 Super Puma
Customs:	3 Azimut launches

PATROL FORCES

1 TNC 45 TYPE (FAST ATTACK CRAFT—MISSILE)

AL SANBOUK P 4505

Displacement, tons: 255 full load
Dimensions, feet (metres): 147.3 × 23 × 7.5 *(44.9 × 7 × 2.3)*
Main machinery: 4 MTU 16V 538 TB92 diesels; 13 640 hp(m) *(10 MW)* sustained; 4 shafts
Speed, knots: 41. **Range, miles:** 1800 at 16 kts
Complement: 35 (5 officers)

Missiles: SSM: 4 Aerospatiale MM 40 Exocet; inertial cruise; active radar homing to 70 km *(40 nm)*
at 0.9 Mach; warhead 165 kg; sea-skimmer.
Guns: 1 OTO Melara 3 in *(76 mm)*/62 compact; 85° elevation; 85 rounds/minute to 16 km
(8.6 nm) anti-surface; 12 km *(6.5 nm)* anti-aircraft; weight of shell 6 kg.
2 Breda 40 mm/70 (twin); 85° elevation; 300 rounds/minute to 12.5 km *(6.6 nm)*; weight of
shell 0.96 kg.
Countermeasures: Decoys: CSEE Dagaie trainable mounting; automatic dispenser; IR flares and
chaff; H/J band.
ESM: Racal Cutlass; radar intercept.
Fire control: PEAB 9LV 228 system. CSEE Lynx optical sight.
Radars: Surface search: Decca TM 1226C; I band.
Fire control: Philips 9LV 200; J band.

Programmes: Six ordered from Lürssen in 1980 and delivered in 1983/84.
Operational: *Al Sanbouk* escaped to Bahrain when the Iraqis invaded in August 1990, but the rest
of this class were taken over by the Iraqi Navy, and either sunk or severely damaged by Allied
forces in February 1991.

TNC 45 Type   1984, G Koop

1 FPB 57 TYPE (FAST ATTACK CRAFT—MISSILE)

ISTIQLAL P 5702

Displacement, tons: 410 full load
Dimensions, feet (metres): 190.6 × 24.9 × 8.9 *(58.1 × 7.6 × 2.7)*
Main machinery: 4 MTU 16V 956 TB91 diesels; 15 000 hp(m) *(11 MW)* sustained; 4 shafts
Speed, knots: 36. **Range, miles:** 1300 at 30 kts
Complement: 40 (5 officers)

Missiles: SSM: 4 Aerospatiale MM 40 Exocet; inertial cruise; active radar homing to 70 km *(40 nm)*
at 0.9 Mach; warhead 165 kg; sea-skimmer.
Guns: 1 OTO Melara 3 in *(76 mm)*/62 compact; 85° elevation; 85 rounds/minute to 16 km
(8.6 nm) anti-surface; 12 km *(6.5 nm)* anti-aircraft; weight of shell 6 kg.
2 Breda 40 mm/70 (twin); 85° elevation; 300 rounds/minute to 12.5 km *(6.6 nm)*; weight of
shell 0.96 kg.
Mines: Fitted for minelaying.
Countermeasures: Decoys: CSEE Dagaie trainable mounting; automatic dispenser; IR flares and
chaff; H/J band.
ESM: Racal Cutlass; radar intercept.
Fire control: PEAB 9LV 228 system. CSEE Lynx optical sight.
Radars: Surface search: Marconi S 810 (after radome); I band; range 43 km *(25 nm)*.
Navigation: Decca TM 1226C; I band.
Fire control: Philips 9LV 200; J band.

Programmes: Two ordered from Lürssen in 1980. In service November 1982 and March 1983.
Operational: *Istiqlal* escaped to Bahrain when the Iraqis invaded in August 1990. The second of
this class was captured and sunk in February 1991.

ISTIQLAL   6/1993

4 OPV 310 CLASS (LARGE PATROL CRAFT)

Name	No	Builders	Commissioned
INTTISAR	P 301	Australian Shipbuilding Industries	20 Jan 1993
AMAN	P 302	Australian Shipbuilding Industries	20 Jan 1993
MAIMON	P 303	Australian Shipbuilding Industries	June 1993
MOBARK	P 304	Australian Shipbuilding Industries	June 1993

Displacement, tons: 150 full load
Dimensions, feet (metres): 103.3 oa; 88.9 wl × 21.3 × 6.6 *(31.5; 27.1 × 6.5 × 2)*
Main machinery: 2 MTU 16V 396 TB94 diesels; 5800 hp(m) *(4.26 MW)* sustained; 2 shafts; 1 MTU 8V 183 TE62 diesel; 750 hp(m) *(550 kW)* maximum; 1 Hamilton 422 waterjet
Speed, knots: 28. **Range, miles:** 300 at 28 kts
Complement: 11 (3 officers)
Guns: 1 Oerlikon 20 mm. 1—12.7 mm MG.
Radars: Surface search.

Comment: First two ordered from Australian Shipbuilding Industries in 1991. Second pair ordered in July 1992. Steel hulls, aluminium superstructure. The third engine drives a small waterjet to provide a loiter capability.

COUGAR 1200 — *1991, Cougar Marine*

AMAN — *1992, Australian Shipbuilding Industries*

12 SIMMONEAU STANDARD 12 CLASS (INSHORE PATROL CRAFT)

Displacement, tons: 10 full load
Dimensions, feet (metres): 45.9 × 12.5 × 2.3 *(14 × 3.8 × 0.7)*
Main machinery: 2 Caterpillar 3208 diesels; 850 hp(m) *(625 kW)*; 2 shafts
Speed, knots: 40
Complement: 4
Guns: 1—12.7 mm MG. 1—7.62 mm MG.
Radars: Surface search: I band.

Comment: Ordered in September 1992 from Simmoneau Marine and delivered in 1993. Aluminium construction. This version has two inboard engines.

SIMMONEAU 12 — *1992, Simmoneau Marine*

17 COUGAR TYPE (INSHORE PATROL CRAFT)

Comment: Three Cat 900 (32 ft), three Cat 1000 (33 ft) and three Predator 1100 (35 ft) all powered by two Yamaha outboards (400 hp(m) *(294 kW)*). Four Type 1200 (38 ft) and four Type 1300 (41 ft) all powered by two Sabre diesels (760 hp(m) *(559 kW)*). All based on the high performance planing hull developed for racing, and acquired in 1991/92. Most have a 7.62 mm MG and a Kroden I band radar.

33 AL-SHAALI TYPE (INSHORE PATROL CRAFT)

Comment: Ten 33 ft and twenty-three 28 ft patrol craft built by Al-Shaali Marine, Dubai, and delivered in June 1992.

LAOS

General

It is reported that the Marine section of the Army has eight patrol craft, four LCMs and four service craft which are used for patrolling the Mekong river. In addition some 40 patrol boats were acquired from the USSR in 1985. Most vessels are probably USSR types but there may still be a few relics left behind by the US Navy.

Personnel

(a) 1994: 600 officers and men
(b) 18 months' national service

Bases

Luang Prabang, Chinaimo, Savanmma Khet, Pakse

Mercantile Marine

Lloyd's Register of Shipping:
2 vessels of 2 853 tons gross

LATVIA

Headquarters' Appointments

Commander Defence Forces:
Colonel Dainis Turlais
Commander of the Navy:
Captain Gaidis Zeibots

Bases

Liepāja, Riga

Personnel

1994: 557 (35 officers)
(to increase to 1100 by 1994)

Mercantile Marine

Lloyd's Register of Shipping:
317 vessels of 1 154 993 tons gross

PATROL FORCES

3 OSA I CLASS (TYPE 205) (FAST ATTACK CRAFT—GUN)

Name	No	Builders	Commissioned
— (ex-*Heinrich Dorrenbach*)	P 01 (ex-711)	Leningrad	3 Sep 1971
— (ex-*Otto Tost*)	P 02 (ex-731)	Leningrad	28 Sep 1971
— (ex-*Joseph Schares*)	P 03 (ex-753)	Leningrad	6 Oct 1971

Displacement, tons: 210 full load
Dimensions, feet (metres): 126.6 × 24.9 × 8.8 *(38.6 × 7.6 × 2.7)*
Main machinery: 3 M 503A diesels; 8025 hp(m) *(5.9 MW)* sustained; 3 shafts
Speed, knots: 35. **Range, miles:** 400 at 34 kts
Complement: 26 (3 officers)
Guns: 1—12.7 mm MG.
Radars: Surface search: I band.

Comment: Former GDR vessels paid off in 1990 and transferred from Germany on 30 August 1993. All weapon systems were removed before transfer, and the vessels were taken to Liepāja for refit and modernisation. Armament is uncertain.

P 02 (German colours) — *7/1993, Bernd Fischer*

1 SELGA CLASS

SAMS KA 04 (ex-P 101)

Displacement, tons: 147.4 standard; 174.4 full load
Dimensions, feet (metres): 78.9 × 19.6 × 7.2 *(24.08 × 6 × 2.2)*
Main machinery: 1 GNVD2B-K-2 diesel; 300 hp(m) *(221 kW)*; 1 shaft
Speed, knots: 9.5
Complement: 12 (3 officers)
Guns: 1—12.7 mm MG.
Radars: Surface search: MIUS; I band.

Comment: Ex-fishing vessel conversion in 1992.

SAMS (old number) *1992, Latvian Navy*

2 RIBNADZOR-4 CLASS

SPULGA KA 02 (ex-KA 102)   **COMETA** KA 03 (ex-KA 103)

Displacement, tons: 143 standard; 173.3 full load
Dimensions, feet (metres): 112.8 × 19 × 8 *(34.4 × 5.8 × 2.45)*
Main machinery: 1 40 DMM3 diesel; 2200 hp(m) *(1.62 MW)*; 1 shaft
Speed, knots: 15
Complement: 17 (4 officers)
Guns: 1—12.7 mm MG.
Radars: Surface search: MIUS; I band.

Comment: Ex-fishing vessels built in 1978 and converted in 1992.

SPULGA *1993, Latvian Navy*

1 COASTAL PATROL CRAFT

GAUJA KA 05

Displacement, tons: 242 full load
Dimensions, feet (metres): 118.1 × 18.4 × 3.9 *(36 × 5.6 × 1.2)*
Main machinery: 2 3D6 diesels; 450 hp(m) *(331 kW)*; 2 shafts
Speed, knots: 12.5
Complement: 11 (3 officers)
Guns: 1—14.5 mm MG.
Radars: Surface search: Donec; I band.

Comment: Acquired in 1993.

GAUJA *1993, Latvian Navy*

5 INSHORE PATROL CRAFT

KRISTAPS KA 01 (ex-*KBV 244*)   **KA 06** (ex-*KBV 249*)   **KA 08** (ex-*KBV 256*)
  KA 07 (ex-*KBV 260*)   **KA 09** (ex-*KBV 250*)

Displacement, tons: 17 full load
Dimensions, feet (metres): 63 × 13.1 × 4.3 *(19.2 × 4 × 1.3)*
Main machinery: 2 Volvo Penta TAMD120A diesels; 700 hp(m) *(515 kW)*; 2 shafts
Speed, knots: 22
Complement: 3 (1 officer)

Comment: Former Swedish Coast Guard vessel built in 1970. First one transferred in 5 March 1993, second pair 9 November 1993 and last pair in April 1994. Similar craft to Estonia and Lithuania.

KRISTAPS *1993, Latvian Navy*

4 HARBOUR PATROL CRAFT

KA 10   **KA 11**   **RK 104**   **RK 105**

Displacement, tons: 9.6 full load
Dimensions, feet (metres): 41.3 × 10.5 × 2 *(12.6 × 3.2 × 0.6)*
Main machinery: 1 3D6C diesel; 150 hp(m) *(110 kW)*; 1 shaft
Speed, knots: 14
Complement: 3
Radars: Navigation: Furuno; I band.

KA 10 *1993, Latvian Navy*

MINE WARFARE FORCES

2 KONDOR II CLASS (MINESWEEPERS)

Name	No	Builders	Commissioned
— (ex-*Kamenz*)	M 01 (ex-351)	Peenewerft, Wolgast	24 July 1971
— (ex-*Röbel*)	M 02 (ex-324)	Peenewerft, Wolgast	1 Dec 1971

Displacement, tons: 310 full load
Dimensions, feet (metres): 186 × 24.6 × 7.9 *(56.7 × 7.5 × 2.4)*
Main machinery: 2 Type 40D diesels; 4408 hp(m) *(3.24 MW)*; 2 shafts
Speed, knots: 17
Complement: 31 (6 officers)

Comment: Former GDR vessels transferred from Germany on 30 August 1993. Guns and minesweeping equipment were removed on transfer but it is planned to re-establish these ships as minesweepers.

M 01 *1993, Latvian Navy*

AUXILIARIES

1 NYRYAT 1 CLASS (DIVING SUPPORT SHIP)

LIDAKA (ex-*Gefests*) A 51 (ex-A 101)

Displacement, tons: 92 standard; 116 full load
Dimensions, feet (metres): 93.8 × 17.1 × 5.6 *(28.6 × 5.2 × 1.7)*
Main machinery: 1 6CSP 28/3C diesel; 450 hp(m) *(331 kW)*; 1 shaft
Speed, knots: 11. **Range, miles:** 1500 at 10 kts
Complement: 6 (1 officer)
Radars: Navigation: SNN-7; I band.

Comment: Ex-Russian diving tender acquired in 1992.

LIDAKA   *1993, Latvian Navy*

1 GOLIAT CLASS (TYPE 667R) (TUG)

A 18 (ex-*H 18*)

Displacement, tons: 150 full load
Dimensions, feet (metres): 70.2 × 20 × 8.5 *(21.4 × 6.1 × 2.6)*
Main machinery: 1 Buckau-Wolf 8NVD diesel; 300 hp(m) *(221 kW)*; 1 shaft
Speed, knots: 12
Complement: 12 (3 officers)

Comment: Built at Gdynia in the 1960s and transferred from Poland in December 1993.

A 18 (Polish colours)   *1992, Hartmut Ehlers*

LEBANON

Headquarters' Appointment

Naval Commander:
  Rear Admiral Alberto Ghorayeb

Personnel

1994: 705 (32 officers)

Bases

Beirut, Jounieh

Mercantile Marine

Lloyd's Register of Shipping:
  137 vessels of 249 041 tons gross

DELETIONS

1991 *Trablous* (L'Esterel craft), 1 Aztec class

PATROL FORCES

2 FRENCH EDIC CLASS (LANDING CRAFT)

Name	No	Builders	Commissioned
SOUR	21	SFCN, Villeneuve la Garonne	28 Mar 1985
DAMOUR	22	SFCN, Villeneuve la Garonne	28 Mar 1985

Displacement, tons: 670 full load
Dimensions, feet (metres): 193.5 × 39.2 × 4.2 *(59 × 12 × 1.3)*
Main machinery: 2 SACM MGO 175 V12 M1 diesels; 1200 hp(m) *(882 kW)*; 2 shafts
Speed, knots: 10. **Range, miles:** 1800 at 9 kts
Complement: 20 (2 officers)
Military lift: 33 troops; 11 trucks or 5 APCs
Guns: 2 Oerlikon 20 mm (twin). 1—81 mm mortar.

Comment: Both were damaged in early 1990 but repaired in 1991 and are fully operational.

DAMOUR   *8/1993, Lebanese Navy*

2 TRACKER Mk 2 (COASTAL PATROL CRAFT)

Displacement, tons: 31 full load
Dimensions, feet (metres): 63.3 × 16.4 × 4.9 *(19.3 × 5 × 1.5)*
Main machinery: 2 Detroit 12V-71TA diesels; 840 hp *(616 kW)* sustained; 2 shafts
Speed, knots: 25. **Range, miles:** 650 at 20 kts
Complement: 11
Guns: 2—23 mm (twin). 2—7.62 mm MGs.
Radars: Surface search: Racal Decca; I band.

Comment: Built in 1980 by Fairey Allday, UK. Both held by the Navy in 1991.

TRACKER 2   *8/1993, Lebanese Navy*

5 ATTACKER CLASS (COASTAL PATROL CRAFT)

L 01-L 05

Displacement, tons: 38 full load
Dimensions, feet (metres): 65.6 × 17 × 4.9 *(20 × 5.2 × 1.5)*
Main machinery: 2 Detroit 12V-71TA diesels; 840 hp *(616 kW)* sustained; 2 shafts
Speed, knots: 21. **Range, miles:** 650 at 14 kts
Complement: 14 (2 officers)
Guns: 1 Oerlikon 20 mm; 2—7.62 mm MGs.
Radars: Surface search: Racal Decca 1216; I band.

Comment: Built at Cowes and Southampton, and commissioned in March 1983. First three transferred from UK 17 July 1992 after serving as patrol craft for the British base in Cyprus. The other two were acquired in 1993. Former names, *Attacker, Hunter, Striker, Chaser* and *Fencer*.

ATTACKER L 02   *8/1993, Lebanese Navy*

CUSTOMS

5 AZTEC CLASS

CP 1000-1005

Displacement, tons: 5.2 full load
Dimensions, feet (metres): 29.5 × 8.5 × 1.6 *(9 × 2.6 × 0.5)*
Main machinery: 2 diesels; 320 hp(m) *(235 kW)*; 2 shafts
Speed, knots: 24

Comment: Six supplied by Crestitalia in 1979. GRP hulls. One deleted and five held by Lebanese Customs. All were damaged in 1990, but in 1991 were repaired by the Navy.

AZTEC 1003

LIBERIA

General

The Liberian National Coast Guard became the Liberian Navy in 1987. During the civil war the remaining naval vessels were taken over by rebels. One Cessna 337 aircraft was reported as under naval control in 1992.

Bases

Elijah Johnson, Monrovia;
Buchanan, Bassa;
Greenville, Sinoe;
Harper, Cape Palmas.

Mercantile Marine

Lloyd's Register of Shipping:
   1611 vessels of 53 918 534 tons gross

PATROL FORCES

1 SEA DOLPHIN CLASS (FAST ATTACK CRAFT—GUN)

Name	No	Builders	Commissioned
FARANDUGU	—	Korea Tacoma	Oct 1989

Displacement, tons: 170 full load
Dimensions, feet (metres): 108.6 × 22.6 × 8.2 *(33.1 × 6.9 × 2.5)*
Main machinery: 2 MTU MD 16V 538 TB90 diesels; 6000 hp(m) *(4.41 MW)* sustained; 2 shafts
Speed, knots: 38. **Range, miles:** 700 at 20 kts
Complement: 31
Guns: 2 Oerlikon 20 mm. 2—12.7 mm MGs.

Comment: Armament is uncertain but the hull is a variation of the South Korean Navy's Sea Dolphin class but less heavily armed. Taken over by the rebels and painted in camouflage colours. Operational status doubtful.

SEA DOLPHIN class   *1989, Korea Tacoma*

1 COASTAL PATROL CRAFT

Name	No	Builders	Commissioned
C G C ALBERT PORTE	CG 8802	Karlskrona Varvet	27 Aug 1980

Displacement, tons: 50
Dimensions, feet (metres): 87.6 × 17.1 × 3.6 *(26.7 × 5.2 × 1.1)*
Main machinery: 2 MTU 8V 331 TC82 diesels; 1740 hp(m) *(1.28 MW)* sustained; 2 shafts
Speed, knots: 25. **Range, miles:** 1000 at 18 kts
Complement: 8
Guns: 1 Browning 12.7 mm MG. 2 FN 7.62 mm MGs.
Radars: Navigation: Decca 1226C; I band.

Comment: Aluminium alloy hull. Karlskrona TV 103 design. The survivor of a class of three taken over by the rebels and painted in camouflage colours. The other two of the class were destroyed in 1990. Operational status doubtful.

TV 103 Type   *8/1986, van Ginderen Collection*

LIBYA

Headquarters' Appointments

Commander-in-Chief Libyan Armed Forces:
   Colonel Abu Bahr Yunis Jabir
Senior Officer, Libyan Navy:
   Captain Abdullah Al Latif El Shaksuki

Personnel

(a)   1994: 8000 officers and ratings, including Coast Guard
(b)   Voluntary service

Bases

Operating Ports at Tripoli, Darnah (Derna) and Benghazi.
Naval bases at Al Khums and Tobruq.
Submarine base at Ras Hilal.
Naval air station at Al Girdabiyah.
Naval infantry battalion at Sidi Bilal.

Strength of the Fleet

Type	Active
Submarines	5 (+6 small)
Frigates	3
Corvettes (Missile)	7
Minesweepers—Ocean	8
Fast Attack Craft—Missile	24
Large Patrol Craft	8
Landing Ships	5
LCTs	3
Support Ships	7
Tugs	7
Diving Tender	1
Salvage Ship	1
Floating Docks	2

Camouflage

Photographs of Libyan naval vessels taken since 1991 indicate that some ships have been painted in striped shades of green and black.

General

Specialist teams in unconventional warfare are a threat and almost any Libyan vessel can lay mines, but overall operational effectiveness is not high, not least because of poor maintenance and stores support. Sanctions imposed by the UN in April 1992 have not helped and very few vessels were seen at sea in 1993.

Mercantile Marine

Lloyd's Register of Shipping:
   148 vessels of 721 152 tons gross

DELETION

Submarines

1992   *Al Fateh*

SUBMARINES

6 R-2 MALA CLASS

Displacement, tons: 1.4 full load
Dimensions, feet (metres): 16.1 × 4.1 *(4.9 × 1.4)*
Main machinery: 1 motor; 6.2 hp(m) *(4.6 kW)*; 1 shaft
Speed, knots: 4.4
Range, miles: 18 at 4.4 kts; 23 at 3.7 kts
Complement: 2

Mines: Can carry 249 kg of limpet mines and other weapons.

Programmes: Two transferred from Yugoslavia in 1977, 1981 and 1982.
Structure: This is a free-flood craft with the main motor, battery, navigation-pod and electronic equipment housed in separate watertight cylinders. Instrumentation includes aircraft type gyro-compass, magnetic compass, depth gauge (with 0-100 m scale), echo sounder, sonar and two searchlights. Constructed of light aluminium and plexiglass, it is fitted with fore- and after-hydroplanes, the tail being a conventional cruciform with a single rudder abaft the screw. Large perspex windows give a good all-round view.
Operational: Details given are for lead-acid batteries and could be much improved by use of silver-zinc batteries. Operating depth, 60 m max. Passage to the target area can be as pick-a-back on a submarine or as deck cargo on any surface vessel with a 25-ton crane—lacking in all Libyan surface warships. However they could be floated out from *Zeltin's* dock. This class of submarine does not look very suitable for towing. Operational status doubtful, probably all are non-operational.

R-2   *12/1988, Gilbert Gyssels*

5 FOXTROT CLASS (TYPE 641)

AL BADR 311   AL MITRAQA 314   AL HUNAIN 316
AL AHAD 313   AL KHYBER 315

Displacement, tons: 1950 surfaced; 2475 dived
Dimensions, feet (metres): 299.5 × 24.6 × 19.7
(91.3 × 7.5 × 6)
Main machinery: Diesel-electric; 3 Type 37-D diesels (1 × 2700
and 2 × 1350); 6000 hp(m) *(4.4 MW)*; 3 motors; 5400 hp(m)
(3.97 MW); 3 shafts; 1 auxiliary motor; 140 hp(m) *(103 kW)*
Speed, knots: 16 surfaced; 15 dived
Range, miles: 20 000 at 8 kts surfaced; 380 at 2 kts dived
Complement: 75 (8 officers)

Torpedoes: 10—21 in *(533 mm)* (6 bow, 4 stern) tubes.
SAET-60; passive homing to 15 km *(8.1 nm)* at 40 kts; war-
head 400 kg, and SET-65E; active/passive homing to 15 km
(8.1 nm) at 40 kts; warhead 205 kg. Total of 22 torpedoes.
Mines: 44 in place of torpedoes.
Countermeasures: ESM: Stop Light; radar warning.
Radars: Surface search: Snoop Tray; I band.

AL KHYBER   *6/1992, van Ginderen Collection*

Sonars: Herkules; hull-mounted; active; medium frequency.
Feniks; hull-mounted; passive.

Programmes: Transferred from USSR from a re-activated building line in Leningrad. *Al Badr* arrived in Tripoli December 1976;
the second in February 1978, the third in March 1978, the
fourth in February 1982, the fifth in April 1982 and the sixth in
February 1983.
Structure: HF masts not fitted. Diving depth 250 m *(820 ft)*
reducing with age.

Operational: Libyan crews trained in the USSR and much of the
maintenance was done by Russian personnel. No routine
patrols have been seen since 1984. *Al Fateh* in refit in Lithuania in 1992 when UN sanctions were applied to Libya and
work stopped. She has now been abandoned and has been
deleted. Probably no more than two of the remainder are capable of going to sea.

FRIGATES
2 KONI CLASS

AL HANI F 212   AL QIRDABIYAH F 213

Displacement, tons: 1440 standard; 1900 full load
Dimensions, feet (metres): 316.3 × 41.3 × 11.5
(96.4 × 12.6 × 3.5)
Main machinery: CODAG; 1 SGW, Nikolayev, M8B gas turbine
(centre shaft); 18 000 hp(m) *(13.25 MW)* sustained; 2 Russki
B-68 diesels; 15 820 hp(m) *(11.63 MW)* sustained; 3 shafts
Speed, knots: 27 on gas; 22 on diesel. **Range, miles:** 1800 at
14 kts
Complement: 120

Missiles: SSM: 4 Soviet SS-N-2C Styx (2 twin) launchers ❶;
active radar/IR homing to 83 km *(45 nm)* at 0.9 Mach; warhead 513 kg; sea-skimmer at end of run.
SAM: SA-N-4 Gecko twin launcher ❷; semi-active radar
homing to 15 km *(8 nm)* at 2.5 Mach; altitude 9.1-3048 m
(29.5-10 000 ft); warhead 50 kg; 20 missiles.
Guns: 4 USSR 3 in *(76 mm)*/60 (2 twin) ❸; 80° elevation; 60
rounds/minute to 15 km *(8 nm)* anti-surface; 14 km *(7.6 nm)*
anti-aircraft; weight of shell 16 kg.
4 USSR 30 mm/65 (2 twin) automatic ❹; 85° elevation; 500
rounds/minute to 5 km *(2.7 nm)*; weight of shell 0.54 kg.
Torpedoes: 4—406 mm (2 twin) tubes amidships ❺. USET-95;
active/passive homing to 10 km *(5.5 nm)* at 30 kts; warhead
100 kg.
A/S mortars: 1 RBU 6000 12-tubed trainable launcher ❻; auto-
matic loading; range 6000 m; warhead 31 kg.
Depth charges: 2 racks.
Mines: Capacity for 20.
Countermeasures: Decoys: 2—16-barrelled chaff launchers.
Towed torpedo decoys.
ESM: 2 Watch Dog; radar warning.
Radars: Air search: Strut Curve ❼; F band; range 110 km *(60 nm)*
for 2 m² target.
Surface search: Plank Shave ❽; I band.
Navigation: Don 2; I band.
Fire control: Drum Tilt ❾; H/I band (for 30 mm).
Hawk Screech ❿; I band; range 27 km *(15 nm)* (for 76 mm).
Pop Group ⓫; F/H/I band (for SAM).
IFF: High Pole B. Square Head.
Sonars: Hull-mounted; active search and attack; medium
frequency.

AL HANI   *(Scale 1 : 900), Ian Sturton*

AL HANI   *7/1991, van Ginderen Collection*

Programmes: Type III Konis built at Zelenodolsk and transferred
from the Black Sea. 212 commissioned 28 June 1986 and 213
on 24 October 1987.
Structure: SSMs mounted either side of small deckhouse on
forecastle behind gun. A deckhouse amidships contains air-

conditioning machinery. Changes to the standard Koni include
SSM, four torpedo tubes, only one RBU 6000 and Plank Shave
surface search and target indication radar. Camouflage paint
applied in 1991.

1 DAT ASSAWARI (VOSPER Mk 7) CLASS

Name	No	Builders	Laid down	Launched	Commissioned
DAT ASSAWARI	F 211	Vosper Thornycroft	27 Sep 1968	Sep 1969	1 Feb 1973

Displacement, tons: 1360 standard; 1780 full load
Dimensions, feet (metres): 333 × 38.3 × 11.2
(101.5 × 11.7 × 3.4)
Main machinery: CODOG; 2 RR Olympus TM2A gas turbines;
40 000 hp *(29.8 MW)* sustained; 2 Paxman 16YJCM diesels;
3800 hp *(2.83 MW)* sustained; 2 shafts; KaMeWa cp props
Speed, knots: 37.5 gas turbines; 17 diesels. **Range, miles:** 5700
at 17 kts
Complement: 130

Missiles: SSM: 4 OTO Melara/Matra Otomat ❶; active radar
homing to 180 km *(100 nm)* at 0.9 Mach; warhead 210 kg.
SAM: 1 Selenia/Elsag Albatros quad launcher ❷; 64 Aspide;
semi-active homing to 13 km *(7 nm)* at 2.5 Mach; height envelope 15-5000 m *(49.2-16 405 ft)*; warhead 30 kg.
Guns: 1 Vickers 4.5 in *(114 mm)*/55 Mk 8 ❸; 55° elevation; 25
rounds/minute to 22 km *(11.9 nm)* anti-surface; 6 km *(3.3 nm)*
anti-aircraft; warhead 21 kg.
2 Oerlikon GDM-A 35 mm/90 (twin) ❹; 85° elevation; 550
rounds/minute to 6 km *(3.3 nm)* anti-surface; 5 km *(2.7 nm)*
anti-aircraft; weight of shell 1.55 kg.
2 Oerlikon A41A 20 mm ❺; 50° elevation; 800 rounds/minute
to 2 km; weight of shell 0.24 kg.
Torpedoes: 6—324 mm ILAS 3 (2 triple) tubes ❻. Whitehead
Motofides A244; anti-submarine; active/passive homing to
7 km *(3.8 nm)* at 33 kts; warhead 34 kg (shaped charge).
Countermeasures: ESM: Selenia INS-1; radar intercept.
Decca RDS-1. Marconi FH-12 HFD/F.
Combat data systems: Selenia IPN/10 action data automation.
Fire control: 2 Selenia Elsag NA 10 Mod 2 for guns and missiles.
Radars: Air/surface search: Selenia RAN 12 ❼; D/I band; range
82 km *(45 nm)*.
Surface search: Selenia RAN 10S ❽; E/F band; range 155 km
(85 nm).
Fire control: Two Selenia RTN 10X ❾; I/J band; range 40 km
(22 nm).

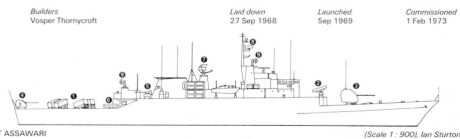

DAT ASSAWARI   *(Scale 1 : 900), Ian Sturton*

DAT ASSAWARI   *5/1984, Aldo Fraccaroli*

Sonars: Thomson Sintra TSM 2310 Diodon; hull-mounted; active
search and attack; 11-13 kHz.

Programmes: Mk 7 Frigate ordered from Vosper Thornycroft on
6 February 1968. Generally similar in design to the two Iranian
Mk 5s built by this firm, but larger and with different armament.
After trials she carried out work-up at Portland, UK, reaching
Tripoli Autumn 1973.

Modernisation: In 1979 modernisation of SAM, ASW armament
and sensors was started by CNR, Genoa but was interrupted by
onboard explosion on 29 October 1980. Completed including
trials October 1983. Returned to Italy for major engine repairs
in 1984 which completed in 1985.
Operational: In 1990 the ship was in a partly disarmed state and
back in Genoa once again. In 1992 she was in Tripoli and still
non-operational.

SHIPBORNE AIRCRAFT

Numbers/Type: 5 Aerospatiale SA 316B Alouette III.
Operational speed: 113 kts *(210 km/h).*
Service ceiling: 10 500 ft *(3200 m).*
Range: 290 nm *(540 km).*
Role/Weapon systems: Support helicopter; can be operated from amphibious warfare ships.
Sensors: None. Weapons: Unarmed.

ALOUETTE III (French colours)

LAND-BASED MARITIME AIRCRAFT

Numbers/Type: 3 Aerospatiale SA 321M Super Frelon.
Operational speed: 134 kts *(248 km/h).*
Service ceiling: 10 000 ft *(3050 m).*
Range: 440 nm *(815 km).*
Role/Weapon systems: Obsolescent helicopter; used for naval support tasks but non-operational due to lack of spares. Sensors: None. Weapons: Fitted for Exocet AM 39.

Numbers/Type: 20 Mil Mi-14 Haze A.
Operational speed: 120 kts *(222 km/h).*
Service ceiling: 15 000 ft *(4570 m).*
Range: 240 nm *(445 km).*
Role/Weapon systems: ASW and surface search helicopter. Sensors: Search radar, ECM, dipping sonar, MAD. Weapons: ASW; internal torpedoes, depth bombs or mines.

CORVETTES

3 NANUCHKA II CLASS (MISSILE CORVETTES)

TARIQ IBN ZIYAD (ex-*Ean Mara*) 416   **EAN AL GAZALA** 417   **EAN ZARA** 418

Displacement, tons: 850 full load
Dimensions, feet (metres): 194.5 × 38.7 × 8.5 *(59.3 × 11.8 × 2.6)*
Main machinery: 3 Type M 507 diesels; 21 600 hp(m) *(15.9 MW)* sustained; 3 shafts
Speed, knots: 34. Range, miles: 2500 at 12 kts; 900 at 31 kts
Complement: 60

Missiles: SSM: 4 Soviet SS-N-2C Styx launchers; auto-pilot; active radar/IR homing to 83 km *(45 nm)* at 0.9 Mach; warhead 513 kg HE; sea-skimmer at end of run.
SAM: SA-N-4 Gecko twin launcher; semi-active radar homing to 15 km *(8 nm)* at 2.5 Mach; altitude 9.1-3048 m *(29.5-10 000 ft)*; warhead 50 kg HE; 20 missiles.
Guns: 2 USSR 57 mm/80 (twin) automatic; 85° elevation; 120 rounds/minute to 6 km *(3.2 nm)*; weight of shell 2.8 kg.
Countermeasures: Decoys: 2 chaff 16-barrelled launchers.
ESM: Bell Top; radar warning.
Radars: Surface search: Square Tie; I band (Bandstand radome).
Navigation: Don 2; I band.
Fire control: Muff Cob; G/H band.
Pop Group; F/H/I band (for SAM).

Programmes: First transferred from USSR in October 1981; second in February 1983; third in February 1984; fourth in September 1985.
Structure: Camouflage paint applied in 1991.
Operational: *Ean Zaquit* (419) sunk on 24 March 1986. *Ean Mara* (416) severely damaged on 25 March 1986 by forces of the US Sixth Fleet; repaired in Leningrad and returned to Libya in early 1991 as the *Tariq Ibn Ziyad*.

TARIQ IBN ZIYAD   *7/1991, van Ginderen Collection*

4 ASSAD CLASS (MISSILE CORVETTES)

Name	No	Builders	Launched	Commissioned
ASSAD AL BIHAR	412	Fincantieri, Muggiano	29 Apr 1977	14 Sep 1979
ASSAD EL TOUGOUR	413	Fincantieri, Muggiano	20 Apr 1978	12 Feb 1980
ASSAD AL KHALI	414	Fincantieri, Muggiano	15 Dec 1978	28 Mar 1981
ASSAD AL HUDUD	415	Fincantieri, Muggiano	21 June 1979	28 Mar 1981

Displacement, tons: 670 full load
Dimensions, feet (metres): 202.4 × 30.5 × 7.2 *(61.7 × 9.3 × 2.2)*
Main machinery: 4 MTU-Bazán 16V 956 TB91 diesels; 15 000 hp(m) *(11 MW)* sustained; 4 shafts
Speed, knots: 34. Range, miles: 4400 at 14 kts
Complement: 58

Missiles: SSM: 4 OTO Melara/Matra Otomat Teseo Mk 2 (TG1); active radar homing to 80 km *(43.2 nm)* at 0.9 Mach; warhead 210 kg.
Guns: 1 OTO Melara 3 in *(76 mm)*/62 compact; 85° elevation; 85 rounds/minute to 16 km *(8.6 nm)* anti-surface; 12 km *(6.5 nm)* anti-aircraft; weight of shell 6 kg.
2 Oerlikon GDM-A 35 mm/90 (twin); 85° elevation; 550 rounds/minute to 6 km *(3.3 nm)* anti-surface; 5 km *(2.7 nm)* anti-aircraft.
Torpedoes: 6—324 mm ILAS (2 triple) tubes. Whitehead Motofides A244; anti-submarine; self-adaptive patterns to 7 km *(3.8 nm)* at 33 kts; warhead 34 kg (shaped charge).
Mines: Can lay 16 mines.
Countermeasures: ESM: Selenia INS-1; radar intercept.
Combat data systems: Selenia IPN/10 action data automation.
Fire control: Selenia Elsag NA 10 Mod 2.
Radars: Air/surface search: Selenia RAN 11X; D/I band; range 82 km *(45 nm).*
Navigation: Decca TM 1226C; I band.
Fire control: Selenia RTN 10X; I/J band; range 40 km *(22 nm).*
Sonars: Thomson Sintra TSM Diodon; hull-mounted; active search and attack; 11-13 kHz.

Programmes: Ordered in 1974. Previously Wadi class—renamed 1982-83. Similar hull to Ecuador corvettes.
Structure: Fin stabilisers and degaussing equipment fitted.
Operational: At the beginning of 1990 only one was operational with the others cannibalised for spares. By 1993 all were non-operational.

ASSAD AL HUDUD   *1986, W Magrawa*

PATROL FORCES

Notes: (1) More than 50 remote-control explosive craft acquired from Cyprus. Based on Q-Boats with Q-26 GRP hulls and speed of about 30 kts. Also reported that fifteen 31 ft craft delivered by Storebro, and 60 more built locally are similarly adapted.
(2) The 1985 order for four Improved Končar class FAC(M) from Yugoslavia was cancelled because of contract problems.
(3) 14 SAR 33 FAC(G) were reported delivered to the Customs Service by Turkey in 1986-87. In fact the order was cancelled.
(4) There is also a 37 m patrol craft *Al Kifah* 206.

9 COMBATTANTE II G CLASS (FAST ATTACK CRAFT—MISSILE)

SHARABA (ex-*Beir Grassa*) 518	**SHOULA** (ex-*Beir Ktitat*) 532
SHEHAB (ex-*Beir Gtifa*) 522	**SHAFAK** (ex-*Beir Alkrarim*) 534
WAHAG (ex-*Beir Gzir*) 524	**BARK** (ex-*Beir Alkardmen*) 536
SHOUAIAI (ex-*Beir Algandula*) 528	**RAD** (ex-*Beir Alkur*) 538
	LAHEEB (ex-*Beir Alkuefat*) 542

Displacement, tons: 311 full load
Dimensions, feet (metres): 160.7 × 23.3 × 6.6 *(49 × 7.1 × 2)*
Main machinery: 4 MTU 20V 538 TB91 diesels; 15 360 hp(m) *(11.29 MW)* sustained; 4 shafts
Speed, knots: 39. Range, miles: 1600 at 15 kts
Complement: 27

Missiles: SSM: 4 OTO Melara/Matra Otomat Mk 2 (TG1); active radar homing to 80 km *(43.2 nm)* at 0.9 Mach; warhead 210 kg.
Guns: 1 OTO Melara 3 in *(76 mm)*/62 compact; 85° elevation; 85 rounds/minute to 16 km *(8.6 nm)* anti-surface; 12 km *(6.8 nm)* anti-aircraft; weight of shell 6 kg.
2 Breda 40 mm/70 (twin); 85° elevation; 300 or 450 rounds/minute to 12.5 km *(6.8 nm)* anti-surface; 4 km *(2.2 nm)* anti-aircraft; weight of shell 0.96 kg.
Fire control: CSEE Panda director. Thomson-CSF Vega II system.
Radars: Surface search: Thomson-CSF Triton; G band; range 33 km *(18 nm)* for 2 m² target.
Fire control: Thomson-CSF Castor IIB; I band; range 15 km *(8 nm)* (associated with Vega fire control system).

Programmes: Ordered from CMN Cherbourg in May 1977. 518 completed February 1982; 522 3 April 1982; 524 29 May 1982; 528 5 September 1982; 532 29 October 1982; 534 17 December 1982; 536 11 March 1983; 538 10 May 1983; 542 29 July 1983.
Structure: Steel hull with alloy superstructure.
Operational: In 1983 an unexpected and unexplained change of names took place. *Waheed* (526) sunk on 24 March 1986 and one other severely damaged on 25 March 1986 by forces of the US Sixth Fleet. All are probably non-operational.

SHAFAK   *1993*

12 OSA II CLASS (FAST ATTACK CRAFT—MISSILE)

AL KATUM 511	AL NABHA 519	AL MOSHA 527
AL ZUARA 513	AL SAFHRA 521	AL SAKAB 529
AL RUHA 515	AL FIKAH 523	AL BITAR 531
AL BAIDA 517	AL MATHUR 525	AL SADAD 533

Displacement, tons: 245 full load
Dimensions, feet (metres): 126.6 × 24.9 × 8.8 (38.6 × 7.6 × 2.7)
Main machinery: 3 Type M 504 diesels; 10 800 hp(m) (7.94 MW) sustained; 3 shafts
Speed, knots: 37. **Range, miles:** 800 at 30 kts; 500 at 35 kts
Complement: 30

Missiles: SSM: 4 Soviet SS-N-2C Styx; active radar or IR homing to 83 km (45 nm) at 0.9 Mach; warhead 513 kg HE; sea-skimmer at end of run.
Guns: 4 USSR 30 mm/65 (2 twin) automatic; 85° elevation; 500 rounds/minute to 5 km (2.7 nm); weight of shell 0.54 kg.
Radars: Surface search: Square Tie; I band; range 73 km (45 nm).
Fire control: Drum tilt; H/I band.
IFF: Two Square Head. High Pole.

Programmes: The first craft arrived from USSR in October 1976, four more in August-October 1977, a sixth in July 1978, three in September-October 1979, one in April 1980, one in May 1980 (521) and one in July 1980 (529).
Structure: Some painted with camouflage stripes in 1991.
Operational: These are the warships most frequently seen at sea, but seldom stay out for very long.

OSA II   1993

3 SUSA CLASS (FAST ATTACK CRAFT—MISSILE)

Name	No	Builders	Commissioned
SUSA	512	Vosper Ltd, Portsmouth	23 Jan 1969
SIRTE	514	Vosper Ltd, Portsmouth	23 Jan 1969
SEBHA (ex-Sokna)	516	Vosper Ltd, Portsmouth	23 Jan 1969

Displacement, tons: 95 standard; 114 full load
Dimensions, feet (metres): 100 × 25.5 × 7 (30.5 × 7.8 × 2.1)
Main machinery: CODOG; 3 RR Proteus gas turbines; 12 750 hp (9.51 MW) sustained; 2 GM 6-71 diesels; 348 hp (260 kW) sustained; 3 shafts
Speed, knots: 54
Complement: 20

Missiles: SSM: 8 Aerospatiale SS 12M; wire-guided to 5.5 km (3 nm) subsonic; warhead 30 kg.
Guns: 2 Bofors 40 mm/60.
Fire control: Aerospatiale/Nord optical director.
Radars: Surface search: Decca 626; I band.

Programmes: The order for these three fast patrol boats was announced on 12 October 1966. They are generally similar to the RN Brave class (now deleted) and the Søløven class designed and built by Vosper for the Royal Danish Navy.
Modernisation: All three overhauled in Italy in 1977 with new electronics. Further Italian refit 1983-84.

SEBHA   Wright and Logan

3 BENINA CLASS (LARGE PATROL CRAFT)

Name	No	Builders	Commissioned
BENINA	CG 3	Vosper Thornycroft	29 Aug 1968
FARWA (ex-Homs)	CG 2	Vosper Thornycroft	early 1969
MISURATA	CG 4	Vosper Thornycroft	29 Aug 1968

Displacement, tons: 100
Dimensions, feet (metres): 100 × 21 × 5.5 (30.5 × 6.4 × 1.7)
Main machinery: 3 RR DV8TM diesels; 1740 hp (1.3 MW); 3 shafts
Speed, knots: 18. **Range, miles:** 1800 at 14 kts
Complement: 18
Guns: 1 Oerlikon 20 mm.

Comment: Welded steel construction. Two transferred to Malta in 1978. Used for Coast Guard duties.

THORNYCROFT Type   Vosper Thornycroft

4 GARIAN CLASS (LARGE PATROL CRAFT)

Name	No	Builders	Commissioned
SABRATA	611	Brooke Marine, Lowestoft	early 1970
ZLEITAN (ex-Garian)	612	Brooke Marine, Lowestoft	30 Aug 1969
KAWLAN	613	Brooke Marine, Lowestoft	30 Aug 1969
MERAWA	614	Brooke Marine, Lowestoft	early 1970

Displacement, tons: 120 standard; 159 full load
Dimensions, feet (metres): 106 × 21.2 × 5.5 (32.3 × 6.5 × 1.7)
Main machinery: 2 Paxman 12YJCM diesels; 3000 hp (2.24 MW) sustained; 2 shafts
Speed, knots: 24. **Range, miles:** 1500 at 12 kts
Complement: 15-22
Guns: 1 Bofors 40 mm/60. 1 Oerlikon 20 mm.

Comment: At least first pair refitted in Istanbul in 1984. Used for Coast Guard duties. 612 renamed after former MRC became a hulk. At least one has a 144 mm rocket launcher. All non-operational.

KAWLAN   Brooke Marine

1 POLUCHAT CLASS (LARGE PATROL CRAFT)

723

Displacement, tons: 70 standard; 100 full load
Dimensions, feet (metres): 97.1 × 19 × 4.8 (29.6 × 5.8 × 1.5)
Main machinery: 2 Type M 50 diesels; 2200 hp(m) (1.6 MW) sustained; 2 shafts
Speed, knots: 20. **Range, miles:** 1500 at 10 kts
Complement: 15
Guns: 2 (twin) MGs.
Radars: Navigation: Spin Trough; I band.

Comment: Transferred from USSR in May 1985. Used as Torpedo Recovery Vessel.

MINE WARFARE FORCES

8 NATYA CLASS (OCEAN MINESWEEPERS)

AL TIYAR (ex-Ras Hadad) 111	RAS AL FULAIJAH 117	RAS AL MASSAD 123
AL ISAR (ex-Ras El Gelais) 113	RAS AL QULA 119	RAS AL HANI 125
RAS AL HAMMAN 115	RAS AL MADWAR 121	

Displacement, tons: 770 full load
Dimensions, feet (metres): 200.1 × 31.8 × 8.9 (61 × 9.7 × 2.7)
Main machinery: 2 Type M 504 diesels; 7200 hp(m) (5.29 MW) sustained; 2 shafts
Speed, knots: 19. **Range, miles:** 4000 at 10 kts
Complement: 60

Guns: 4 USSR 30 mm/65 (2 twin) automatic; 85° elevation; 500 rounds/minute to 5 km (2.7 nm); weight of shell 0.54 kg.
4 USSR 25 mm/60 (2 twin); 85° elevation; 270 rounds/minute to 3 km (1.6 nm); weight of shell 0.34 kg.
A/S mortars: 2 RBU 1200 5-tubed fixed launchers; elevating; range 1-2 km; warhead 34 kg.
Mines: 10.
Radars: Surface search: Don 2; I band.
Fire control: Drum Tilt; H/I band.
IFF: Two Square Head. One High Pole B.
Sonars: Hull-mounted; active search; high frequency.

Programmes: First pair transferred from USSR February 1981. Second pair arrived February 1983, one in August 1983, the sixth in January 1984 the seventh in January 1985 and the eighth in October 1986.
Structure: At least one of the class painted in green striped camouflage in 1991.
Operational: Capable of magnetic, acoustic and mechanical sweeping. Mostly used for coastal patrols and never observed minesweeping.

RAS AL HANI   2/1988

AMPHIBIOUS FORCES

2 PS 700 CLASS (LSTs)

Name	No	Builders	Commissioned
IBN OUF	132	CNI de la Mediterranée	11 Mar 1977
IBN HARISSA	134	CNI de la Mediterranée	10 Mar 1978

Displacement, tons: 2800 full load
Dimensions, feet (metres): 326.4 × 51.2 × 7.9 *(99.5 × 15.6 × 2.4)*
Main machinery: 2 SEMT-Pielstick 16 PA4 V 185 diesels; 5344 hp(m) *(3.93 MW)* sustained; 2 shafts; cp props
Speed, knots: 15.4. **Range, miles:** 4000 at 14 kts
Complement: 35
Military lift: 240 troops; 11 tanks
Guns: 6 Breda 40 mm/70 (3 twin). 1—81 mm mortar.
Fire control: CSEE Panda director.
Radars: Air search: Thomson-CSF Triton; D band.
Surface search: Decca 1226; I band.
Helicopters: 1 Aerospatiale SA 316B Alouette III.

Comment: 132 laid down 1 April 1976 and launched 22 October 1976; 134 laid down 18 April 1977, launched 18 October 1977.

IBN HARISSA   *1981*

3 POLNOCHNY D CLASS (TYPE 773U) (LSMs)

IBN AL HADRAMI 112   **IBN UMAYAA** 116   **IBN AL FARAT** 118

Displacement, tons: 1305 full load
Dimensions, feet (metres): 275.3 × 31.8 × 7.9 *(83.9 × 9.7 × 2.4)*
Main machinery: 2 Type 40-D diesels; 4400 hp(m) *(3.2 MW)* sustained; 2 shafts
Speed, knots: 15. **Range, miles:** 2900 at 12 kts
Complement: 45
Military lift: 160 troops; 5 MBT or 5 APC or 5 AA guns or 8 trucks
Guns: 4 USSR 30 mm (2 twin). 2—140 mm 18-tubed rocket launchers.
Mines: 100.
Radars: Surface search: Radwar SRN-745; I band.
Fire control: Drum Tilt; H/I band.
IFF: Salt Pot A. Square Head.
Helicopters: Platform for 1 medium.

Comment: The first to be transferred from USSR arrived in November 1977. On 14 September 1978 *Ibn Qis* (fourth of the class) was burned out during a landing exercise and was a total loss. 118 and 116 delivered June 1978. All are an export variant of the standard Soviet/Polish Polnochny class but with helicopter deck added. Built at Naval Shipyard, Gdynia. Similar types built for India and Iraq (now deleted).

IBN UMAYAA   *7/1990, van Ginderen Collection*

IBN UMAYAA   *1993*

3 TURKISH TYPE (LCTs)

IBN AL IDRISI 130   **IBN MARWAN** 131   **EL KOBAYAT** 132

Displacement, tons: 280 standard; 600 full load
Dimensions, feet (metres): 183.7 × 37.8 × 3.6 *(56 × 11.6 × 1.1)*
Main machinery: 3 GM 6-71TI diesels; 930 hp *(694 kW)* maximum; 3 shafts
Speed, knots: 8.5 loaded; 10 max. **Range, miles:** 600 at 10 kts
Complement: 15
Military lift: 100 troops; 350 tons including 5 tanks
Guns: 2—30 mm (twin).

Comment: First two transferred 7 December 1979 (ex-Turkish *C130* and *C131*) from Turkish fleet. Third of class reported in 1991. Previously reported numbers were much exaggerated.

TURKISH LCT (Turkey number)   *10/1991, Harald Carstens*

TRAINING SHIP

1 VOSPER CLASS

Name	No	Builders	Commissioned
TOBRUK	C 411	Vosper Thornycroft	20 Apr 1966

Displacement, tons: 500 full load
Dimensions, feet (metres): 177.3 × 28.5 × 13 *(54 × 8.7 × 4)*
Main machinery: 2 Paxman Ventura diesels; 3800 hp *(2.83 MW)*; 2 shafts
Speed, knots: 18. **Range, miles:** 2900 at 14 kts
Complement: 63 (5 officers)
Guns: 1 Vickers 4 in *(102 mm)*/33 Mk 52; 2 Bofors 40 mm/70.
Radars: Surface search: Decca TM 1226C; I band.

Comment: Deleted as a training hulk in 1989 but was seen at sea again in 1992 and 1993. State apartments are included in the accommodation. The ship is used mostly for training.

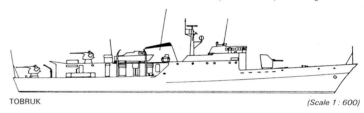

TOBRUK   *(Scale 1 : 600)*

AUXILIARIES

1 LSD TYPE

Name	No	Builders	Commissioned
ZELTIN	711	Vosper Thornycroft, Woolston	23 Jan 1969

Displacement, tons: 2200 standard; 2470 full load
Dimensions, feet (metres): 324 × 48 × 10.2 *(98.8 × 14.6 × 3.1)*; 19 *(5.8)* aft when flooded
Main machinery: 2 Paxman 16YJCM diesels; 4000 hp *(2.98 MW)*; 2 shafts
Speed, knots: 15. **Range, miles:** 3000 at 14 kts
Complement: 101 (15 officers)

Guns: 2 Bofors 40 mm/70; 90° elevation; 300 rounds/minute to 12 km *(6.5 nm)* anti-surface; 4 km *(2.2 nm)* anti-aircraft; weight of shell 0.96 kg.
Fire control: Vega II-12 for 40 mm guns.
Radars: Surface search: Thomson-CSF Triton; G band; range 33 km *(18 nm)* for 2 m² target (associated with Vega fire control).

Programmes: Ordered in January 1967; launched 29 February 1968.
Structure: Fitted with accommodation for a flag officer or a senior officer and staff. Operational and administrative base of the squadron. Workshops with a total area of approximately 4500 sq ft are situated amidships with ready access to the dock, and there is a 3 ton travelling gantry fitted with outriggers to cover ships berthed alongside up to 200 ft long.
Operational: The ship provides full logistic support, including docking maintenance and repair facilities. Craft up to 120 ft can be docked. Used as tender for Light Forces and is probably no longer capable of going to sea.

ZELTIN   *1987, van Ginderen Collection*

10 TRANSPORTS

GARYOUNIS (ex-*Mashu*)	EL TEMSAH	DERNA	GHAT
GARNATA	TOLETELA	KROL	LA GRAZIETTA
HANNA	GHARDIA		

Measurement, tons: 2412 gross
Dimensions, feet (metres): 546.3 × 80.1 × 21.3 *(166.5 × 24.4 × 6.5)*
Main machinery: 2 SEMT-Pielstick diesels; 20 800 hp(m) *(15.29 MW)*; 2 shafts; bow thruster
Speed, knots: 20

Comment: Details are for *Garyounis*, a converted Ro-Ro passenger/car ferry used as a training vessel in 1989. In addition the 117 m *El Temsah* has been refitted and is back in service, and another four of these vessels are of Ro-Ro design. All are in regular military service. All have minelaying potential.

1 SPASILAC CLASS (SALVAGE SHIP)

AL MUNJED (ex-*Zlatica*) 722

Displacement, tons: 1590 full load
Dimensions, feet (metres): 182 × 39.4 × 14.1 *(55.5 × 12 × 4.3)*
Main machinery: 2 diesels; 4340 hp(m) *(3.19 MW)*; 2 shafts; cp props; bow thruster
Speed, knots: 13. **Range, miles:** 4000 at 12 kts
Complement: 50
Guns: 4—12.7 mm MGs. Can also be fitted with 8—20 mm (2 quad) and 2—20 mm.
Radars: Surface search: Racal Decca; I band.

Comment: Transferred from Yugoslavia in 1982. Fitted for firefighting, towing and submarine rescue—carries recompression chamber. Built at Tito SY, Belgrade.

SPASILAC (old number)   *1988, Peter Jones*

2 FLOATING DOCKS

Comment: One of 5000 tons capacity at Tripoli. One of 3200 tons capacity acquired in April 1985.

1 YELVA CLASS (DIVING TENDER)

AL MANOUD VM 917

Displacement, tons: 300 full load
Dimensions, feet (metres): 134.2 × 26.2 × 6.6 *(40.9 × 8 × 2)*
Main machinery: 2 Type 3-D-12A diesels; 630 hp(m) *(463 kW)* sustained; 2 shafts
Speed, knots: 12.5
Complement: 30
Radars: Navigation: Spin trough; I band.
IFF: High Pole.

Comment: Built in early 1970s. Transferred from USSR December 1977. Carries two 1.5 ton cranes and has a portable decompression chamber.

YELVA class   *1973*

TUGS

3 COASTAL TYPE

A 33   A 34   A 35

Measurement, tons: 150 grt
Dimensions, feet (metres): 87.3 × 26 × 8.2 *(26.6 × 7.9 × 2.5)*
Main machinery: 2 diesels; 2 shafts

Comment: Built by Jonker and Stans BV Shipyard, Netherlands. First launched 16 October 1979.

4 COASTAL TYPE

Name	No	Builders	Commissioned
RAS EL HELAL	A 31	Mondego, Portugal	22 Oct 1976
AL AHWEIRIF	A 32	Mondego, Portugal	17 Feb 1977
AL KERIAT	—	Mondego, Portugal	1 July 1977
AL TABKAH	—	Mondego, Portugal	29 July 1978

Measurement, tons: 200 grt
Dimensions, feet (metres): 114 × 29.5 × 13 *(34.8 × 9 × 4)*
Main machinery: 2 diesels; 2300 hp(m) *(1.69 MW)*; 2 shafts
Speed, knots: 14

LITHUANIA

Headquarters' Appointment	General	Colours	Mercantile Marine
Commander of the Navy: Commodore Baltushka	Coast Guard Force beginning to be formed in late 1992.	There is a distinctive green and yellow diagonal stripe on all Coast Guard vessels.	*Lloyd's Register of Shipping:* 237 ships of 638 861 tons gross

FRIGATES

Note: Transfer of the last two former GDR Koni class was proposed in 1993, but was still under review in early 1994.

2 GRISHA III (ALBATROS) CLASS (TYPE 1124)

F 11   F 12

Displacement, tons: 950 standard; 1200 full load
Dimensions, feet (metres): 233.6 × 32.2 × 12.1 *(71.2 × 9.8 × 3.7)*
Main machinery: CODAG; 1 gas turbine; 15 000 hp(m) *(11 MW)*; 2 diesels; 16 000 hp(m) *(11.8 MW)*; 3 shafts
Speed, knots: 30. **Range, miles:** 2500 at 14 kts diesels; 950 at 27 kts
Complement: 48 (5 officers)

Missiles: SAM: SA-N-4 Gecko twin launcher ❶; semi-active radar homing to 15 km *(8 nm)* at 2.5 Mach; warhead 50 kg; altitude 9.1-3048 m *(30-10 000 ft)*; 20 missiles.
Guns: 2—57 mm/80 (twin) ❷; 85° elevation; 120 rounds/minute to 6 km *(3.3 nm)*; weight of shell 2.8 kg.
1—30 mm/65 ❸; 6 barrels; 85° elevation; 3000 rounds/minute combined to 2 km.
Torpedoes: 4—21 in *(533 mm)* (2 twin) tubes ❹. SET-65E; anti-submarine; active/passive homing to 15 km *(8.1 nm)* at 40 kts; warhead 205 kg and 53-65; passive wake homing to 25 km *(13.5 nm)* at 50 kts; warhead 300 kg.
A/S mortars: 2 RBU 6000 12-tubed trainable ❺; range 6000 m; warhead 31 kg.
Depth charges: 2 racks (12).
Mines: Capacity for 18 in lieu of depth charges.
Countermeasures: ESM: 2 Watch Dog.
Radars: Air/surface search: Strut Curve ❻; F band; range 110 km *(60 nm)* for 2 m² target.
Navigation: Don 2; I band.
Fire control: Pop Group ❼; F/H/I band (for SA-N-4). Bass Tilt ❽; H/I band (for guns).
IFF: High Pole A or B. Square Head. Salt Pot.
Sonars: Hull-mounted; active search and attack; high/medium frequency.
VDS; active search; high frequency. Similar to Hormone helicopter dipping sonar.

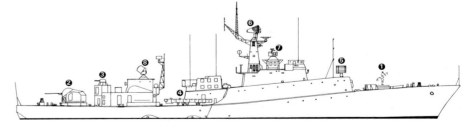

GRISHA F 11   *(Scale 1 : 600), Ian Sturton*

GRISHA F 11   *6/1993, Erik Laursen*

Programmes: Built in the early 1980s. Transferred from Russia in November 1992.

PATROL FORCES

2 TURYA CLASS (FAST ATTACK CRAFT—TORPEDO)

Displacement, tons: 190 standard; 250 full load
Dimensions, feet (metres): 129.9 × 24.9 (41 over foils) × 5.9 (13.1 over foils)
(39.6 × 7.6 (12.5) × 1.8 (4))
Main machinery: 3 Type M 504 diesels; 10 800 hp(m) *(7.94 MW)* sustained; 3 shafts
Speed, knots: 40 foilborne. **Range, miles:** 600 at 35 kts foilborne; 1450 at 14 kts hullborne
Complement: 30

Guns: 2—57 mm/80 (twin, aft); 85° elevation; 120 rounds/minute to 6 km *(3.3 nm)*; weight of shell 2.8 kg.
2—25 mm/80 (twin, fwd); 85° elevation; 270 rounds/minute to 3 km *(1.6 nm)*; weight of shell 0.34 kg.
1—14.5 mm MG.
Torpedoes: 4—21 in *(533 mm)* tubes. SET-65E; anti-submarine; active/passive homing to 15 km *(8.1 nm)* at 40 kts; warhead 205 kg and 53-65; passive wake homing to 25 km *(13.5 nm)* at 50 kts; warhead 300 kg.
Depth charges: 1 rack.
Radars: Surface search: Pot Drum; H/I band.
Fire control: Muff Cob; G/H band.
IFF: High Pole B. Square Head.
Sonars: VDS; active search and attack; high frequency. Similar to Hormone dipping sonar. This sonar is not fitted in most export versions.

Programmes: Built in the mid-1970s. Reported transferred from Russia in early 1993 but this has not been confirmed. The class has been widely sold abroad.
Structure: Single hydrofoil forward on an Osa type hull.

TURYA (Russian number)   *1992*

0 + 3 OSA I CLASS (TYPE 205)

Name	No	Builders	Commissioned
— (ex-*Paul Wieczorek*)	— (ex-754)	Leningrad	24 Sep 1965
— (ex-*Fritz Gast*)	— (ex-714)	Leningrad	29 Nov 1965
— (ex-*Albert Gast*)	— (ex-734)	Leningrad	23 Dec 1965

Displacement, tons: 210 full load
Dimensions, feet (metres): 126.6 × 24.9 × 8.8 *(38.6 × 7.6 × 2.7)*
Main machinery: 3 Type M 503A diesels; 8025 hp(m) *(5.9 MW)* sustained; 3 shafts
Speed, knots: 35. **Range, miles:** 400 at 34 kts
Complement: 26 (3 officers)
Guns: 4—30 mm/65 (2 twin).
Radars: Surface search: Square Tie; I band.
Fire control: Drum Tilt; H/I band.

Comment: Put up for transfer from Germany in 1993 but details had not been finalised in early 1994. Armament uncertain but SSM have been removed.

FRITZ GAST (German colours)   *3/1991, Hartmut Ehlers*

OSA I (no missiles—Polish colours)   *1992*

1 INSHORE PATROL CRAFT

VICTORIA 245 (ex-*KBV 245*)

Displacement, tons: 17 full load
Dimensions, feet (metres): 63 × 13.1 × 4.3 *(19.2 × 4 × 1.3)*
Main machinery: 2 Volvo Penta TAMD120A diesels; 700 hp(m) *(515 kW)*; 2 shafts
Speed, knots: 22
Complement: 5

Comment: Transferred 16 February 1993. Former Swedish Coast Guard vessel built in 1970. Similar craft transferred to Estonia and Latvia. Others may follow.

COAST GUARD TYPE (Swedish colours)   *1992, Maritime Photographic*

AUXILIARIES

1 KONDOR I CLASS (TRV)

Name	No	Builders	Commissioned
— (ex-*Libben*)	(ex-*V 662*)	Peenewerft, Wolgast	30 Mar 1971

Displacement, tons: 377 full load
Dimensions, feet (metres): 170.3 × 23.3 × 6.6 *(51.9 × 7.1 × 2)*
Main machinery: 2 diesels; 4408 hp(m) *(3.24 MW)* sustained; 2 shafts
Speed, knots: 20
Complement: 24

Comment: Former GDR patrol craft converted to a torpedo retriever. Transferred from Germany in late 1993.

LIBBEN (German colours)   *6/1992, Hartmut Ehlers*

1 VALERIAN URYVAYEV CLASS

VETRA (ex-*Rudolf Samoylovich*) 41

Displacement, tons: 1050 full load
Dimensions, feet (metres): 180.1 × 31.2 × 13.1 *(54.9 × 9.5 × 4)*
Main machinery: 1 Deutz diesel; 850 hp(m) *(625 kW)*; 1 shaft
Speed, knots: 12
Complement: 52

Comment: Built at Khabarovsk in early 1980s. Transferred from the Russian Navy in 1992 where she was used as a civilian oceanographic research vessel.

VETRA (USSR colours)   *1/1987*

MADAGASCAR

Personnel

(a) 1994: 500 officers and men (including Marine Company of 120 men)
(b) 18 months' national service

Bases

Diego-Suarez, Tamatave, Majunga, Tulear, Nossi-Be, Fort Dauphin, Manakara.

Mercantile Marine

Lloyd's Register of Shipping:
90 vessels of 34 119 tons gross

PATROL FORCES

Note: Six South Korean coast guard craft are to be transferred in 1994.

1 TYPE PR 48 (LARGE PATROL CRAFT)

Name	No	Builders	Commissioned
MALAIKA	—	Chantiers Navals Franco-Belges (SFCN)	Dec 1967

Displacement, tons: 235 light; 250 full load
Dimensions, feet (metres): 155.8 × 23.6 × 8.2 *(47.5 × 7.1 × 2.5)*
Main machinery: 2 SACM V12 CZSHR diesels; 3600 hp(m) *(2.65 MW)* sustained; 2 shafts
Speed, knots: 23. **Range, miles:** 2000 at 15 kts
Complement: 25 (3 officers)
Guns: 2 Bofors 40 mm/60; 90° elevation; 300 rounds/minute to 12 km *(6.5 nm)* anti-surface; 4 km *(2.2 nm)* anti-aircraft; weight of shell 0.89 kg.

Comment: Ordered by the French Navy for delivery to Madagascar. Laid down in November 1966, launched on 22 March 1967. Non-operational.

AMPHIBIOUS FORCES

1 BATRAM CLASS

Name	No	Builders	Commissioned
TOKY	—	Arsenal de Diego Suarez	Oct 1974

Displacement, tons: 810
Dimensions, feet (metres): 217.8 × 41 × 6.2 *(66.4 × 12.5 × 1.9)*
Main machinery: 2 MGO diesels; 2400 hp(m) *(1.76 MW)*; 2 shafts
Speed, knots: 13. **Range, miles:** 3000 at 12 kts
Complement: 43
Military lift: 250 tons stores; 30 troops or 120 troops (short range)
Missiles: SSM: 8 Aerospatiale SS 12M; wire-guided to 5.5 km *(3 nm)* subsonic; warhead 30 kg.
Guns: 1 OTO Melara 3 in *(76 mm)*. 2 Oerlikon 20 mm. 1—81 mm mortar.

Comment: Paid for by the French Government as military assistance. Fitted with a bow ramp and similar to, though larger than, the French Edic but smaller than Batral. Non-operational.

1 NAMPO CLASS

Displacement, tons: 82 full load
Dimensions, feet (metres): 84.2 × 20 × 6 *(27.7 × 6.1 × 1.8)*
Main machinery: 4 Type M 50 diesels; 4400 hp(m) *(3.2 MW)* sustained; 4 shafts
Speed, knots: 40. **Range, miles:** 375 at 38 kts
Complement: 19
Guns: 4 USSR 14.5 mm (2 twin) MGs. 1—81 mm mortar.

Comment: Assault landing craft based on Soviet P 6 hull. Four transferred from North Korea February 1979 and June 1979 but three were lost in a typhoon in April 1984. Non-operational.

1 EDIC CLASS

AINA VAO VAO (ex-*L9082*)

Displacement, tons: 250 standard; 670 full load
Dimensions, feet (metres): 193.5 × 39.2 × 4.5 *(59 × 12 × 1.3)*
Main machinery: 2 MGO diesels; 1000 hp(m) *(753 kW)*; 2 shafts
Speed, knots: 8. **Range, miles:** 1800 at 8 kts
Complement: 17
Military lift: 5 LVTs or 11 trucks
Guns: 2 Oerlikon 20 mm. 1—81 mm mortar.

Comment: Built in 1964. Transferred from France 28 September 1985 having been paid off by the French Navy in 1981. This was the only operational ship in the Navy in 1993.

EDIC   *1990, J Y Robert*

3 LCVP TYPE

FIHERENGA   MAROLA   SAMBATHRA

Comment: 14.3 m personnel launches acquired from West Germany in 1988.

TRAINING SHIP

Name	No	Builders	Commissioned
FANANTENANA (ex-*Richelieu*)	—	A G Weser, Bremen	1959

Displacement, tons: 1040 standard; 1200 full load
Dimensions, feet (metres): 206.4 × 30 × 14.8 *(62.9 × 9.2 × 4.5)*
Main machinery: 2 Deutz diesels; 2400 hp(m) *(1.76 MW)*; 1 shaft
Speed, knots: 12
Complement: 45
Guns: 2 Bofors 40 mm/60.

Comment: Trawler (691 tons gross) purchased and converted in 1966-67 for Coast Guard and as training ship/transport. Can accommodate up to 120 people as well as carrying 300 tons of cargo. Occasionally hired out to tourists.

MALAWI

Senior Appointment

Commander of the Navy:
Lieutenant Colonel M M B Gondwe

Base

Monkey Bay, Lake Malawi

Personnel

1994: 220

Mercantile Marine

Lloyd's Register of Shipping:
2 vessels of 320 tons gross

PATROL FORCES

Note: There is also one LCU and some RB 12 Zodiacs.

1 ANTARES CLASS

CHIKALA P 703

Displacement, tons: 36 full load
Dimensions, feet (metres): 68.9 × 16.1 × 4.9 *(21 × 4.9 × 1.5)*
Main machinery: 2 Poyaud 520 V12 M2 diesels; 1300 hp(m) *(956 kW)*; 2 shafts
Speed, knots: 22. **Range, miles:** 650 at 15 kts
Complement: 6
Guns: 1—12.7 mm MG.

Comment: Built in prefabricated sections by SFCN Villeneuve-la-Garenne and shipped to Malawi for assembly on 17 December 1984. Commissioned May 1985. Non-operational.

CHIKALA   *1984, van Ginderen Collection*

1 NAMACURRA CLASS

— (ex-*Y 1520*)

Displacement, tons: 5 full load
Dimensions, feet (metres): 29.5 × 9 × 2.8 *(9 × 2.7 × 0.8)*
Main machinery: 2 Yamaha outboards
Speed, knots: 32
Complement: 4
Guns: 1—12.7 mm MG. 2—7.62 mm MGs.

Comment: Delivered by South Africa on 29 October 1988.

NAMACURRA   *1988*

2 SURVEY LAUNCHES

Displacement, tons: 70 full load
Dimensions, feet (metres): 68.9 *(21)* length
Main machinery: 2 Baudouin diesels; 2 shafts
Speed, knots: 10.5

Comment: Built by SFCN Villeneuve-la-Garenne and delivered at the end of 1988 for operations on Lake Malawi.

MALAYSIA

(including Sabah)

Headquarters' Appointments

Chief of the Navy:
Vice Admiral Dato Seri Mohd Shariff Bin Ishak
Deputy Chief of Navy:
Rear Admiral Ahmad Ramli Bin Nor
Fleet Commander:
Rear Admiral Dato Yaacob Bin Haji Daud
Commander Naval Area I (Peninsula):
Commodore Dato Abu Bakar Bin Abdul Jamal
Commander Naval Area II (Sabah and Sarawak):
Commodore Hj Ahmad Bin Haron

Bases

KD *Malaya*, Lumut HQ Area 1 (West of 109°E); (Telok Muroh) Perak
Fleet Operation Command centre, main fleet base, dockyard and training centre on west coast.
KD *Pelandok*, Lumut (Training Centre)
RMN Barrack Woodlands (Training and Support), Singapore
Kuantan—an advanced base completed in 1981 on east coast
Labuan—(KD *Sri Labuan*, KD *Sri Tawau*, KD *Sri Rejang*) HQ Area 2 (East of 109°E)
Sungei Antu in Sarawak
Sitiawan, Perak; site for planned new naval air station
Kota Kinabalu; site for planned patrol boat base in East Malaysia (1995-96).

Personnel

(a) 1994: 12 500 officers and ratings
(b) Voluntary service
(c) RMNVR: Total, 1000 officers and sailors
Divisions at Penang, Selangor and Johore. Target of 7000 in 19 port divisions.

Future Plans

It is planned to build 15 small bases around the country with main emphasis on training reserves to man ships taken up in an emergency. Each base will provide a harbour for naval vessels and have up to 400 personnel.

Prefix to Ships' Names

The names of Malaysian warships are prefixed by KD (Kapal DiRaja meaning King's Ship).

Maritime Patrol Craft

There are large numbers of armed patrol craft belonging to the Police, Customs and Fisheries Departments. Details at the end of the section.

Strength of the Fleet

Type	Active	Building (Planned)
Frigates	2	2
Corvettes	2	—
Offshore Patrol Vessels	2	(4)
Logistic Support Vessels	2	—
Fast Attack Craft—Missile	8	—
Fast Attack Craft—Gun	6	—
Patrol Craft	21	—
Minehunters	4	—
Diving Tender	1	—
Survey Ships	2	(2)
LSTs	2	—
Amphibious Craft	198	—
Tugs	17	—

Mercantile Marine

Lloyd's Register of Shipping:
572 vessels of 2 165 692 tons gross

PENNANT LIST

Frigates

24	Rahmat
29	Lekiu
30	Jebat
76	Hang Tuah

Corvettes

25	Kasturi
26	Lekir

Patrol Forces

160	Musytari
161	Marikh
34	Kris

36	
37	
38	Sundang
39	Badek
40	Renchong
41	Tombak
42	Lembing
43	Serampang
44	Panah
45	Kerambit
46	Beledau
47	Kelewang
49	Rentaka
3139	Sri Perlis
3142	Sri Johor
3143	Sri Selangor
3144	Sri Kelantan

3145	Sri Trengganu
3146	Sri Sabah
3147	Sri Sarawak
3501	Sri Negri Sembilan
3502	Sri Melaka
3503	Perdana
3504	Serang
3505	Ganas
3506	Ganyang
3507	Jerong
3508	Todak
3509	Paus
3510	Yu
3511	Baung
3512	Pari
3513	Handalan
3514	Perkasa
	Pendekar
	Gempita

Mine Warfare Forces

11	Mahamiru
12	Jerai
13	Ledang
14	Kinabalu

Auxiliaries

152	Mutiara
1109	Duyong
1501	Sri Banggi
1502	Rajah Jarom
1503	Sri Indera Sakti
1504	Mahawangsa

SUBMARINES

Note: On 28 November 1990 it was announced that the government had approved a naval request to buy two new construction and two second-hand Swedish hulls at a cost of over US$500 million spread over a period of several years. In 1991 the government announced that the programme had been postponed, although in 1992 a naval staff requirement was again raised. Training is being done in Pakistan, India and Australia.

FRIGATES

1 RAHMAT CLASS

Name	No	Builders	Laid down	Launched	Commissioned
RAHMAT (ex-*Hang Jebat*)	24	Yarrow (Shipbuilders), Glasgow	Feb 1966	18 Dec 1967	31 Aug 1971

Displacement, tons: 1250 standard; 1600 full load
Dimensions, feet (metres): 308 × 34.1 × 14.8 *(93.9 × 10.4 × 4.5)*
Main machinery: CODOG; 1 Bristol Siddeley Olympus TM1B gas turbine; 20 626 hp *(15.4 MW)*; 1 Crossley Pielstick PC2.2 V diesel; 4000 hp *(2.94 MW)*; 2 shafts; cp props
Speed, knots: 26 gas; 16 diesel. **Range, miles:** 6000 at 16 kts; 1000 at 26 kts
Complement: 140

Guns: 1 Vickers 4.5 in *(114 mm)*/45 Mk 5 hand-loaded ❶; 50° elevation; 14 rounds/minute to 17 km *(9.2 nm)* anti-surface; 8 km *(4.4 nm)* anti-aircraft; weight of shell 25 kg. 103 mm rocket for illuminants on each side of mounting.
3 Bofors 40 mm/70 ❷; 90° elevation; 300 rounds/minute to 12 km *(6.5 nm)* anti-surface; 4 km *(2.2 nm)* anti-aircraft; weight of shell 0.96 kg.
A/S mortars: 1 Limbo Mk 10 3-tubed mortar ❸; automatic loading; range 900 m; warhead 92 kg.
Countermeasures: Decoys: 2 UK Mk I rail chaff launchers. ESM: UA-3; radar intercept; FH4 HF D/F.
Combat data systems: Signaal Sewaco-MA. Link Y.
Radars: Air search: Signaal LW 02 ❹; D band; range 183 km *(100 nm)*.
Surface search: Decca 626 ❺; I band.
Navigation: Kelvin Hughes MS 32; I band.
Fire control: Signaal M 22 ❻; I/J band; short range.
Sonars: Graseby Type 170B and Type 174; hull-mounted; active search and attack; 15 kHz.

Programmes: Ordered on 11 February 1966. Arrived on station 23 December 1972.
Modernisation: Seacat system removed during refit in 1982-83 and replaced by an additional Bofors gun. A fourth Bofors was mounted (lashed) on the forward part of the flight deck in July 1990 but this appears to have been a temporary arrangement. There are plans for further modernisation in 1994/95.
Operational: Can land helicopter on MacGregor hatch over Mk 10 well.

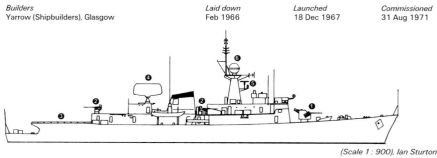

RAHMAT

(Scale 1 : 900), Ian Sturton

RAHMAT

2/1991

0 + 2 LEKIU CLASS

Name	No	Builders	Laid down	Launched	Commissioned
LEKIU	29	Yarrow (Shipbuilders), Glasgow	1993	Dec 1994	Feb 1996
JEBAT	30	Yarrow (Shipbuilders), Glasgow	1993	Mar 1995	May 1996

Displacement, tons: 1845 standard; 2270 full load
Dimensions, feet (metres): 346 oa; 319.9 wl × 42 × 11.8
(105.5; 97.5 × 12.8 × 3.6)
Main machinery: CODAD; 4 MTU 20V 1163 TB93 diesels;
33 300 hp(m) (24.5 MW) sustained; 2 shafts; cp props
Speed, knots: 28. **Range, miles:** 5000 at 14 kts
Complement: 146 (18 officers)

Missiles: SSM: 8 Aerospatiale MM 40 Exocet Block II ❶.
SAM: British Aerospace VLS Seawolf; 16 launchers ❷.
Guns: 1 Bofors 57 mm/70 SAK Mk 2 ❸.
2 MSI Defence Systems 30 mm DS 30B ❹.
Torpedoes: 6 Whitehead B 515 324 mm (2 triple) tubes ❺;
anti-submarine.
Countermeasures: Decoys: 2 Super Barricade 12-barrelled
launchers for chaff ❻; Graseby Sea Siren torpedo decoy.
ESM/ECM: AEG Telefunken/Marconi Mentor/THORN EMI
Scimitar; intercept and jammer.
Combat data systems: GEC/Marconi Nautis-F; Link Y.
Fire control: Radamec Series 2000 Optronic director ❼.
Thomson-CSF ITL 70 (for Exocet); GEC/Marconi Type V 3901
thermal imager.

LEKIU   (Scale 1 : 900), Ian Sturton

Radars: Air search: Signaal DA 08 ❽; E/F band.
Surface search: Ericsson Sea Giraffe 150HC ❾; G/H band.
Navigation: Racal; I band.
Fire control: 2 Marconi 1802 ❿; I/J band.
Sonars: Thomson Sintra Spherion; hull-mounted active search
and attack; medium frequency.

Helicopters: 1 Westland Wasp HAS 1 ⓫ or Super Lynx.

Programmes: Contract announced 31 March 1992 for two ships
originally classed as corvettes but uprated to light frigates. First
steel cut in March 1993.
Structure: GEC Naval Systems Frigate 2000 design with a modern combat data system and automated machinery control.

LEKIU (artist's impression)

1992, GEC Naval Systems

1 HANG TUAH (TYPE 41/61) CLASS

Name	No	Builders	Laid down	Launched	Commissioned
HANG TUAH (ex-HMS Mermaid)	76	Yarrow (Shipbuilders), Glasgow	1965	29 Dec 1966	16 May 1973

Displacement, tons: 2300 standard; 2520 full load
Dimensions, feet (metres): 339.3 × 40 × 16 (screws)
(103.5 × 12.2 × 4.9)
Main machinery: 8 VVS ASR 1 diesels; 12 380 hp (9.2 MW)
sustained; 2 shafts; cp props
Speed, knots: 24. **Range, miles:** 4800 at 15 kts
Complement: 210

Guns: 2 Vickers 4 in (102 mm)/45 Mk 19 (twin) ❶; 80° elevation;
16 rounds/minute to 19 km (10.3 nm) anti-surface; 13 km
(7 nm) anti-aircraft; weight of shell 16 kg.
2 Bofors 40 mm/70 ❷; 90° elevation; 300 rounds/minute to
12 km (6.5 nm) anti-surface; 4 km (2.2 nm) anti-aircraft; weight
of shell 0.96 kg.
A/S mortars: 1 RN Limbo 3-tubed Mk 10 mortar ❸; automatic
loading; range 1000 m; warhead 92 kg.
Fire control: STD Mk 1 sight for 102 mm gun.
Radars: Air/surface search: Plessey AWS 1 ❹; E/F band; range
110 km (60 nm).
Navigation: Racal Decca 45 ❺; I band.
Sonars: Graseby Type 170B and Type 174; hull-mounted; active
search and attack; 15 kHz.

Helicopters: Platform for 1 Westland Wasp HAS 1.

Programmes: Originally built for Ghana as a display ship for
ex-President Nkrumah at a cost of £5 million but put up for sale
after his departure. She was launched without ceremony on
29 December 1966 and completed in 1968. Commissioned in
Royal Navy 16 May 1973, she was based at Singapore
1974-75 returning to the UK early 1976. Transferred to Royal
Malaysian Navy May 1977 and refitted by Vosper Thornycroft
before sailing for Malaysia in August 1977.
Structure: Similar in hull and machinery to former Leopard and
Salisbury classes.
Operational: Refitted in 1991/92 to become a training ship.

HANG TUAH   (Scale 1 : 900), Ian Sturton

HANG TUAH   11/1988, Trevor Brown

SHIPBORNE AIRCRAFT

Note: New aircraft are required for the Lekiu class in due course.

Numbers/Type: 16 Westland Wasp HAS 1.
Operational speed: 96 kts (177 km/h).
Service ceiling: 12 200 ft (3720 m).
Range: 268 nm (488 km).
Role/Weapon systems: First naval air arm helicopter; six acquired in April 1988, six in 1989-90
and six more in 1991. Sensors: None. Weapons: ASW; 1 or 2 Mk 44 torpedoes, depth bombs.

LAND-BASED MARITIME AIRCRAFT

Note: Three Hercules C-130HP, formerly used for MPA, have reverted to transport duties.

Numbers/Type: 4 Beechcraft B 200T.
Operational speed: 282 kts (523 km/h).
Service ceiling: 35 000 ft (10 670 m).
Range: 2030 nm (3756 km).
Role/Weapon systems: Used for maritime surveillance. Acquired in 1993. Air Force operated.
Sensors: Search radar. Weapons: Unarmed.

CORVETTES

2 KASTURI (TYPE FS 1500) CLASS

Name	No	Builders	Laid down	Launched	Commissioned
KASTURI	25	Howaldtswerke, Kiel	3 Jan 1983	14 May 1983	15 Aug 1984
LEKIR	26	Howaldtswerke, Kiel	3 Jan 1983	14 May 1983	15 Aug 1984

Displacement, tons: 1500 standard; 1850 full load
Dimensions, feet (metres): 319.1 × 37.1 × 11.5
(97.3 × 11.3 × 3.5)
Main machinery: 4 MTU 20V 1163 TB92 diesels; 23 400 hp(m)
(17.2 MW) sustained; 2 shafts
Speed, knots: 28; 18 on 2 diesels. **Range, miles:** 3000 at 18 kts;
5000 at 14 kts
Complement: 124 (13 officers)

Missiles: SSM: 4 Aerospatiale MM 38 Exocet ❶; inertial cruise;
active radar homing to 42 km *(23 nm)* at 0.9 Mach; warhead
165 kg; sea-skimmer.
Guns: 1 Creusot-Loire 3.9 in *(100 mm)*/55 compact ❷; 80°
elevation; 20/45/90 rounds/minute to 17 km *(9.2 nm)* anti-
surface; 6 km *(3.2 nm)* anti-aircraft; weight of shell 13.5 kg.
1 Bofors 57 mm/70 ❸; 75° elevation; 200 rounds/minute to
17 km *(9.2 nm)*; weight of shell 2.4 kg. Launchers for
illuminants.
4 Emerson Electric 30 mm (2 twin) ❹; 80° elevation; 1200
rounds/minute combined to 6 km *(3.2 nm)*; weight of shell
0.35 kg.
A/S mortars: 1 Bofors 375 mm twin trainable launcher ❺; automatic loading; range 3625 m.
Countermeasures: Decoys: 2 CSEE Dagaie trainable systems;
replaceable containers for IR or chaff.
ESM: Rapids; radar intercept.
ECM: Scimitar; jammer.
Combat data systems: Signaal Sewaco-MA. Link Y.
Fire control: 2 Signaal LIOD optronic directors for gunnery.
Radars: Air/surface search: Signaal DA 08 ❻; F band; range
204 km *(110 nm)* for 2 m² target.
Navigation: Decca TM 1226C; I band.
Fire control: Signaal WM 22 ❼; I/J band; range 46 km *(25 nm)*.
IFF: US Mk 10.
Sonars: Atlas Elektronik DSQS 21C; hull-mounted; active search
and attack; medium frequency.

Helicopters: Platform for 1 Westland Wasp HAS 1 ❽.

Programmes: First two ordered in February 1981. Fabrication
began early 1982. Rated as Corvettes even though they are
bigger ships than *Rahmat*.
Modernisation: May be fitted with telescopic hangars in due
course.
Structure: Near sisters to the Colombian ships with differing
armament.

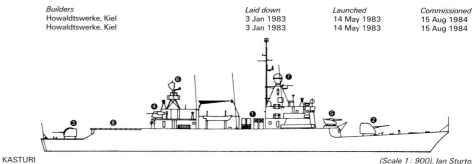

KASTURI   *(Scale 1 : 900), Ian Sturton*

KASTURI   *5/1993, John Mortimer*

KASTURI   *5/1993, John Mortimer*

PATROL FORCES

2 MUSYTARI CLASS (OFFSHORE PATROL VESSELS)

Name	No	Builders	Launched	Commissioned
MUSYTARI	160	Korea Shipbuilders, Pusan	20 July 1984	19 Dec 1985
MARIKH	161	Malaysia SB and E Co, Johore	21 Jan 1985	9 Apr 1987

Displacement, tons: 1300 full load
Dimensions, feet (metres): 246 × 35.4 × 12.1
(75 × 10.8 × 3.7)
Main machinery: 2 diesels; 12 720 hp(m) *(9.35 MW)*; 2 shafts
Speed, knots: 22. **Range, miles:** 5000 at 15 kts
Complement: 76

Guns: 1 Creusot Loire 3.9 in *(100 mm)*/55 compact; 80°
elevation; 20/45/90 rounds/minute to 17 km *(9.2 nm)* anti-
surface; 6 km *(3.2 nm)* anti-aircraft; weight of shell 13.5 kg.
2 Emerson Electric 30 mm (twin); 80° elevation; 1200 rounds/
minute combined to 6 km *(3.2 nm)*; weight of shell 0.35 kg.
Fire control: PEAB 9LV 230 optronic system.
Radars: Air/surface search: Signaal DA 05; E/F band; range
137 km *(75 nm)* for 2 m² target.
Navigation: Racal Decca TM 1226; I band.
Fire control: Philips 9LV; J band.

Programmes: Ordered in June 1983. Names translate to Jupiter
and Mars.
Structure: Flight deck suitable for Sikorsky S-61A Nuri army support helicopter.

MUSYTARI   *5/1990, John Mortimer*

0 + (4) OFFSHORE PATROL VESSELS

Displacement, tons: 1300 full load
Dimensions, feet (metres): 262.5 × 39.4 × 9.8 *(80 × 12 × 3)*
Main machinery: 2 diesels; 2 shafts
Speed, knots: 25. **Range, miles:** 6000 at 12 kts
Complement: 52 (7 officers)
Missiles: Fitted for SSM and SAM.
Guns: 1—76 mm. 2—40 mm.
Countermeasures: ESM/ECM.
Fire control: Optronic director.
Radars: Air/surface search. Fire control. Navigation.
Helicopters: 1 Lynx type.

Comment: Possible joint project with Australia. The plan is to build the first abroad and the remainder in Malaysia. Ships to be fitted for SSM (probably Exocet) and SAM (probably VL Seawolf). First one to be delivered in 1997.

21 KEDAH, SABAH and KRIS CLASSES (PATROL CRAFT)

Name	No	Builders	Commissioned
SRI SELANGOR	3139	Vosper Ltd, Portsmouth	25 Mar 1963
SRI KELANTAN	3142	Vosper Ltd, Portsmouth	12 Nov 1963
SRI TRENGGANU	3143	Vosper Ltd, Portsmouth	16 Dec 1963
SRI SABAH	3144	Vosper Ltd, Portsmouth	2 Sep 1964
SRI SARAWAK	3145	Vosper Ltd, Portsmouth	30 Sep 1964
SRI NEGRI SEMBILAN	3146	Vosper Ltd, Portsmouth	28 Sep 1964
SRI MELAKA	3147	Vosper Ltd, Portsmouth	2 Nov 1964
KRIS	34	Vosper Ltd, Portsmouth	1 Jan 1966
SUNDANG	36	Vosper Ltd, Portsmouth	29 Nov 1966
BADEK	37	Vosper Ltd, Portsmouth	15 Dec 1966
RENCHONG	38	Vosper Ltd, Portsmouth	17 Jan 1967
TOMBAK	39	Vosper Ltd, Portsmouth	2 Mar 1967
LEMBING	40*	Vosper Ltd, Portsmouth	12 Apr 1967
SERAMPANG	41	Vosper Ltd, Portsmouth	19 May 1967
PANAH	42	Vosper Ltd, Portsmouth	27 July 1967
KERAMBIT	43*	Vosper Ltd, Portsmouth	28 July 1967
BELEDAU	44*	Vosper Ltd, Portsmouth	12 Sep 1967
KELEWANG	45	Vosper Ltd, Portsmouth	4 Oct 1967
RENTAKA	46	Vosper Ltd, Portsmouth	22 Sep 1967
SRI PERLIS	47*	Vosper Ltd, Portsmouth	24 Jan 1968
SRI JOHOR	49*	Vosper Ltd, Portsmouth	14 Feb 1968

* Training

Displacement, tons: 96 standard; 109 full load
Dimensions, feet (metres): 103 × 19.8 × 5.5 *(31.4 × 6 × 1.7)*
Main machinery: 2 Bristol Siddeley or MTU MD 655/18 diesels; 3500 hp(m) *(2.57 MW)*; 2 shafts
Speed, knots: 27. **Range, miles:** 1400 (1660 Sabah class) at 14 kts
Complement: 22 (3 officers)
Guns: 2 Bofors 40 mm/60 (not in 3139, 3142-43).
Radars: Surface search: Racal Decca 616 or 707; I band.

Comment: The first six boats (of which three remain in service), constitute the Kedah class and were ordered in 1961 for delivery in 1963. The four Sabah class were ordered in 1963 for delivery in 1964. The boats of the Kris class were ordered in 1965 for delivery between 1966 and 1968. All are of prefabricated steel construction and are fitted with air-conditioning and Vosper roll damping equipment. The differences between the three classes are minor, the later ones having improved radar, communications, evaporators and engines of MTU, as opposed to Bristol Siddeley construction. *Sri Melaka* (P 3147) is on loan to Sabah. All 21 have been refitted to extend their operational lives. The three Kedah class have had their guns removed.

SRI KELANTAN   10/1993, 92 Wing RAAF

KELEWANG   5/1990, John Mortimer

4 HANDALAN (SPICA-M) CLASS (FAST ATTACK CRAFT—MISSILE)

Name	No	Builders	Commissioned
HANDALAN	3511	Karlskrona Varvet, Sweden	26 Oct 1979
PERKASA	3512	Karlskrona Varvet, Sweden	26 Oct 1979
PENDEKAR	3513	Karlskrona Varvet, Sweden	26 Oct 1979
GEMPITA	3514	Karlskrona Varvet, Sweden	26 Oct 1979

Displacement, tons: 240 full load
Dimensions, feet (metres): 142.6 × 23.3 × 7.4 (screws) *(43.6 × 7.1 × 2.4)*
Main machinery: 3 MTU 16V 538 TB91 diesels; 9180 hp(m) *(6.75 MW)* sustained; 3 shafts
Speed, knots: 34.5. **Range, miles:** 1850 at 14 kts
Complement: 40 (6 officers)

Missiles: SSM: 4 Aerospatiale MM 38 Exocet; inertial cruise; active radar homing to 42 km *(23 nm)* at 0.9 Mach; warhead 165 kg; sea-skimmer.
Guns: 1 Bofors 57 mm/70; 75° elevation; 200 rounds/minute to 17 km *(9.2 nm)*; weight of shell 2.4 kg. Illuminant launchers.
1 Bofors 40 mm/70; 90° elevation; 300 rounds/minute to 12 km *(6.5 nm)* anti-surface; 4 km *(2.2 nm)* anti-aircraft; weight of shell 0.96 kg.
Countermeasures: ECM: MEL Susie.
Fire control: 1 PEAB 9LV200 Mk 2 weapon control system with TV tracking. LME anti-aircraft laser and TV rangefinder.
Radars: Surface search: Philips 9GR 600; I band (agile frequency).
Navigation: Decca 616; I band.
Fire control: Philips 9LV 212; J band.
Sonars: Simrad; hull-mounted; active search; high frequency.

Programmes: Ordered 15 October 1976. All named in one ceremony on 11 November 1978, arriving in Port Klang on 26 October 1979.
Structure: Bridge further forward than in Swedish class to accommodate Exocet. Provision has been made for fitting 324 mm torpedo tubes.
Operational: *Handalan* acts as squadron leader.

PENDEKAR   5/1990, John Mortimer

4 PERDANA (LA COMBATTANTE II) CLASS
(FAST ATTACK CRAFT—MISSILE)

Name	No	Builders	Commissioned
PERDANA	3501	Constructions Mécaniques de Normandie	21 Dec 1972
SERANG	3502	Constructions Mécaniques de Normandie	31 Jan 1973
GANAS	3503	Constructions Mécaniques de Normandie	28 Feb 1973
GANYANG	3504	Constructions Mécaniques de Normandie	20 Mar 1973

Displacement, tons: 234 standard; 265 full load
Dimensions, feet (metres): 154.2 × 23.1 × 12.8 *(47 × 7 × 3.9)*
Main machinery: 4 MTU MB 870 diesels; 14 000 hp(m) *(10.3 MW)*; 4 shafts
Speed, knots: 36.5. **Range, miles:** 800 at 25 kts; 1800 at 15 kts
Complement: 30 (4 officers)

Missiles: SSM: 2 Aerospatiale MM 38 Exocet; inertial cruise; active radar homing to 42 km *(23 nm)* at 0.9 Mach; warhead 165 kg; sea-skimmer.
Guns: 1 Bofors 57 mm/70; 75° elevation; 200 rounds/minute to 17 km *(9.2 nm)*; weight of shell 2.4 kg.
1 Bofors 40 mm/70; 90° elevation; 300 rounds/minute to 12 km *(6.5 nm)* anti-surface; 4 km *(2.2 nm)* anti-aircraft; weight of shell 0.96 kg.
Countermeasures: Decoys: 4—57 mm chaff/flare launchers.
ESM: French type; radar warning.
Fire control: Thomson-CSF Vega optical for guns.
Radars: Air/surface search: Thomson-CSF TH-D 1040 Triton; G band; range 33 km *(18 nm)* for 2 m² target.
Navigation: Racal Decca 616; I band.
Fire control: Thomson-CSF Pollux; I/J band; range 31 km *(17 nm)* for 2 m² target.

Programmes: Left Cherbourg for Malaysia 2 May 1973.
Structure: All of basic La Combattante IID design.

PERDANA   6/1992, A M Nixon, RAN

6 JERONG CLASS (FAST ATTACK CRAFT—GUN)

Name	No	Builders	Commissioned
JERONG	3505	Hong Leong-Lürssen, Butterworth	27 Mar 1976
TODAK	3506	Hong Leong-Lürssen, Butterworth	16 June 1976
PAUS	3507	Hong Leong-Lürssen, Butterworth	16 Aug 1976
YU	3508	Hong Leong-Lürssen, Butterworth	15 Nov 1976
BAUNG	3509	Hong Leong-Lürssen, Butterworth	11 Jan 1977
PARI	3510	Hong Leong-Lürssen, Butterworth	23 Mar 1977

Displacement, tons: 244 full load
Dimensions, feet (metres): 147.3 × 23 × 8.3 *(44.9 × 7 × 2.5)*
Main machinery: 3 MTU MB 16V 538 TB90 diesels; 9000 hp(m) *(6.6 MW)* sustained; 3 shafts
Speed, knots: 32. **Range, miles:** 2000 at 14 kts
Complement: 36 (4 officers)
Guns: 1 Bofors 57 mm/70. 1 Bofors 40 mm/70.
Fire control: CSEE Naja optronic director.
Radars: Surface search: Racal Decca 626; I band.
Navigation: Kelvin Hughes MS 32.
Fire control: Signaal WM 28; I/J band; range 46 km *(25 nm)*.

Comment: Lürssen 45 type. Illuminant launchers on both gun mountings.

PARI   *5/1990, John Mortimer*

MINE WARFARE FORCES

Note: Plans for more Lerici class have been shelved in favour of Inshore minehunters in due course.

4 LERICI CLASS (MINEHUNTERS)

Name	No	Builders	Commissioned
MAHAMIRU	11	Intermarine, Italy	11 Dec 1985
JERAI	12	Intermarine, Italy	11 Dec 1985
LEDANG	13	Intermarine, Italy	11 Dec 1985
KINABALU	14	Intermarine, Italy	11 Dec 1985

Displacement, tons: 470 standard; 610 full load
Dimensions, feet (metres): 167.3 × 31.5 × 9.2 *(51 × 9.6 × 2.8)*
Main machinery: 2 MTU 12V 396 TC82 diesels (passage); 2605 hp(m) *(1.91 MW)* sustained; 2 shafts; KaMeWa cp props; 3 Fincantieri Isotta Fraschini ID 36 SS 6V diesels; 1481 hp(m) *(1.09 MW)* sustained; 2 Riva Calzoni hydraulic thrust jets
Speed, knots: 16 diesels; 7 thrust jet. **Range, miles:** 2000 at 12 kts
Complement: 42 (5 officers)
Guns: 1 Bofors 40 mm/70; 85° elevation; 300 rounds/minute to 12.5 km *(6.8 nm)*; weight of shell 0.96 kg.
Countermeasures: Thomson-CSF IBIS II minehunting system; 2 improved PAP 104 vehicles. Oropesa 'O' MIS-4 mechanical sweep.
Radars: Navigation: Racal Decca 1226; Thomson-CSF Tripartite III; I band.
Sonars: Thomson Sintra TSM 2022 with Display 2060; minehunting; high frequency.

Comment: Ordered on 20 February 1981. First (14) launched 19 March 1983; second (13) 14 July 1983; third (12) 5 January 1984; fourth (11) 23 February 1984. All arrived in Malaysia on 26 March 1986. Heavy GRP construction without frames. Snach active tank stabilisers. Draeger Duocom decompression chamber. Slightly longer than Italian sisters. Endurance, 14 days. Based at Labuan and Lumut to cover both coasts.

JERAI   *5/1990, John Mortimer*

AMPHIBIOUS FORCES

Note: Some interest shown in LCACs but no orders placed yet.

9 RCPs and 4 LCUs

RCP 1-9   LCU 1-4

Displacement, tons: 30 full load
Main machinery: 2 diesels
Speed, knots: 17
Military lift: 35 troops
Guns: 1 Oerlikon 20 mm.

Comment: Malaysian built. RCPs in service 1974. LCUs in service 1984.

2 LST 511-1152 CLASS

SRI BANGGI (ex-USS *Henry County* LST 824) 1501
RAJAH JAROM (ex-USS *Sedgewick County* LST 1123) 1502

Displacement, tons: 1653 standard; 2366 beaching; 4080 full load
Dimensions, feet (metres): 328 × 50 × 12 *(100 × 15.3 × 3.7)*
Main machinery: 2 GM 12-567A diesels; 1800 hp(m) *(1.34 MW)*; 2 shafts
Speed, knots: 11.6
Complement: 128 (11 officers)
Military lift: 2100 tons; 500 tons beaching or 125 troops
Guns: 6 Bofors 40 mm (2 twin, 2 single).
Fire control: 2 Mk 51G for guns.
Radars: Surface search: Raytheon SPS 21C (1501); G/H band; range 22 km *(12 nm)*. Sperry SPS 53 (1502); I/J band.

Comment: Built by Missouri Valley BY (1501) and Chicago Bridge Co in 1945. Transferred from US 1 August 1974, by sale 7 October 1976. Operate as harbour tenders to Light Forces and seldom go to sea.

SRI BANGGI   *5/1991, 92 Wing RAAF*

5 LCMs and 15 LCPs

LCM 1-5   LCP 1-15

Displacement, tons: 56 (LCM); 18.5 (LCVP) full load
Main machinery: 2 diesels; 330 hp *(246 kW)* (LCM); 400 hp *(298 kW)* (LCVP); 2 shafts
Speed, knots: 10 (LCM); 16 (LCVP)
Military lift: 30 tons (LCM)

Comment: Australian-built and transferred 1965-70. LCMs have light armour on sides and some have gun turrets.

LCM 3 (with gun turret)   *5/1990, van Ginderen Collection*

165 DAMEN ASSAULT CRAFT 540

Dimensions, feet (metres): 17.7 × 5.9 × 2 *(5.4 × 1.8 × 0.6)*
Main machinery: 1 outboard; 40 hp(m) *(29.4 kW)*
Speed, knots: 12
Military lift: 10 troops

Comment: First 65 built by Damen Gorinchem, Netherlands in 1986. Remainder built by Limbungan Timor SY. Army assault craft. Manportable and similar to Singapore craft.

AUXILIARIES

SABAH SUPPLY SHIPS

Comment: There are a number of Sabah supply ships which are identified by M numbers.

KURAMAH (M 48)   *9/1988, van Ginderen Collection*

2 LOGISTIC SUPPORT SHIPS

Name	No	Builders	Commissioned
SRI INDERA SAKTI	1503	Bremer Vulkan	24 Oct 1980
MAHAWANGSA	1504	Korea Tacoma	16 May 1983

Displacement, tons: 4300 (1503); 4900 (1504) full load
Dimensions, feet (metres): 328; 337.9 (1504) × 49.2 × 15.7 *(100; 103 × 15 × 4.8)*
Main machinery: 2 KHD SBV6M540 diesels; 5865 hp(m) *(4.31 MW)*; 2 shafts; cp props; bow thruster
Speed, knots: 16.5. **Range, miles:** 4000 at 14 kts
Complement: 136 (14 officers) plus accommodation for 215
Military lift: 17 tanks; 600 troops
Cargo capacity: 1300 tons dieso; 200 tons fresh water (plus 48 tons/day distillers)

Guns: 2 Bofors 57 mm Mk 1 (1 only fwd in 1503). 2 Oerlikon 20 mm.
Fire control: 2 CSEE Naja optronic directors (1 only in 1503).
Radars: Navigation: I band.

Helicopters: 1 Sikorsky S-61A Nari (army support) can be carried.

Programmes: Ordered in October 1979 and 1981 respectively.
Modernisation: 100 mm gun included in original design but used for OPVs.
Structure: Fitted with stabilising system, vehicle deck, embarkation ramps port and starboard, recompression chamber and a stern anchor. Large operations room and a conference room are provided. Transfer stations on either beam and aft, light jackstay on both sides and a 15 ton crane for replenishment at sea. 1504 has additional capacity to transport ammunition and the funnel has been removed to enlarge the flight deck.
Operational: Used as training ships for cadets in addition to main roles of long-range support of Light Forces and MCM vessels, command and communications and troop or ammunition transport.

SRI INDERA SAKTI   9/1990, G Toremans

MAHAWANGSA (no funnel)   10/1991, John Mortimer

9 COASTAL SUPPLY SHIPS AND TANKERS

LANG HINDEK	LANG KANGOK	LANG SIPUT
LANG TIRAM	ENTERPRISE	KEPAH
MELEBAN	JERNIH	TERIJAH

Comment: Various auxiliaries mostly acquired in the early 1980s.

KEPAH   5/1990, John Mortimer

1 DIVING TENDER

Name	No	Builders	Commissioned
DUYONG	1109	Kall Teck (Pte) Ltd, Singapore	5 Jan 1971

Displacement, tons: 120 standard; 140 full load
Dimensions, feet (metres): 110 × 21 × 5.8 *(33.6 × 6.4 × 1.8)*
Main machinery: 2 Cummins diesels; 500 hp *(373 kW)*; 2 shafts
Speed, knots: 12. **Range, miles:** 1000
Complement: 23
Guns: 1 Oerlikon 20 mm (not fitted).

Comment: Launched on 18 August 1970 as TRV. Carries recompression chamber. Can act as support ship for 7-10 commandos.

DUYONG   5/1990, van Ginderen Collection

SURVEY SHIPS

Notes: (1) There is also a Survey craft *Penyu* of 465 tons commissioned in 1979. Complement is 26 (2 officers).
(2) Negotiations continue for two second-hand ships.

Name	No	Builders	Commissioned
MUTIARA	152	Hong Leong-Lürssen, Butterworth	12 Jan 1978

Displacement, tons: 1905
Dimensions, feet (metres): 232.9 × 42.6 × 13.1 *(71 × 13 × 4)*
Main machinery: 2 Deutz SBA12M528 diesels; 4000 hp(m) *(2.94 MW)*; 2 shafts
Speed, knots: 16. **Range, miles:** 4500 at 16 kts
Complement: 155 (14 officers)
Guns: 4 Oerlikon 20 mm (2 twin).
Radars: Navigation: Two-Racal Decca; I band.
Helicopters: Platform only.

Comment: Ordered in early 1975. Carries satellite navigation, auto-data system and computerised fixing system. Davits for six survey launches. Painted white. She acted as the Reviewing ship for the Penang Fleet Review in May 1990.

MUTIARA   5/1990, John Mortimer

TUGS

12 HARBOUR TUGS AND CRAFT

TUNDA SATU	KETAM	KUPANG	SOTONG
BELAWKAS	KEMPONG	MANGKASA	SIPUT
TEPURUK	TERITUP	PENYU	SELAR

TUNDA SATU   5/1990, van Ginderen Collection

TRAINING SHIP

1 SAIL TRAINING SHIP

TUNAS SAMUDERA

Displacement, tons: 239 full load
Dimensions, feet (metres): 114.8 × 25.6 × 13.1 *(35 × 7.8 × 4)*
Main machinery: 2 Perkins diesels; 370 hp *(272 kW)*; 2 shafts
Speed, knots: 9
Complement: 10
Radars: Navigation: Racal Decca; I band.

Comment: Ordered from Brooke Yacht, Lowestoft. Laid down 1 December 1988, launched 4 August 1989 and completed 16 October 1989. Two-masted brig manned by the Navy but used for training all sea services.

TUNAS SAMUDERA   *8/1991, 92 Wing RAAF*

POLICE

Note: 13—21 m craft ordered from Damen, Gorinchem in December 1992.

15 LANG HITAM CLASS

LANG HITAM PZ 1	**BELIAN** PZ 6	**HARIMAU BELANG** PZ 11
LANG MALAM PZ 2	**KURITA** PZ 7	**HARIMAU AKAR** PZ 12
LANG LEBAH PZ 3	**SERANGAN BATU** PZ 8	**PERANGAN** PZ 13
LANG KUIK PZ 4	**HARIMAU BINTANG** PZ 9	**MERSUJI** PZ 14
BALONG PZ 5	**HARIMAU KUMBANG** PZ 10	**ALU-ALU** PZ 15

Displacement, tons: 230 full load
Dimensions, feet (metres): 126.3 × 22.9 × 5.9 *(38.5 × 7 × 1.8)*
Main machinery: 2 MTU 20V 538 TB92 diesels; 8530 hp(m) *(6.27 MW)* sustained; 2 shafts
Speed, knots: 35. **Range, miles:** 1200 at 15 kts
Complement: 38 (4 officers)
Guns: 1 Bofors 40 mm/70 (in a distinctive plastic turret).
1 Oerlikon 20 mm. 2 FN 7.62 mm MGs.
Radars: Navigation: Kelvin Hughes; I band.

Comment: Ordered from Hong Leong-Lürssen, Butterworth, Malaysia in 1979. First delivered August 1980, last in April 1983.

ALU-ALU   *1991, RM Police*

18 PX CLASS

MAHKOTA PX 1	**BENTARA** PX 7	**PEKAN** PX 13
TEMENGGONG PX 2	**PERWIRA** PX 8	**KELANG** PX 14
HULUBALANG PX 3	**PERTANDA** PX 9	**KUALA KANGSAR** PX 15
MAHARAJASETIA PX 4	**SHAHBANDAR** PX 10	**ARAU** PX 16
MAHARAJALELA PX 5	**SANGSETIA** PX 11	**GUMANTONG** PX 17
PAHLAWAN PX 6	**LAKSAMANA** PX 12	**LABUAN** PX 18

Displacement, tons: 86.4 full load
Dimensions, feet (metres): 87.5 × 19 × 4.9 *(26.7 × 5.8 × 1.5)*
Main machinery: 2 MTU MB 12V 493 TY7 diesels; 2200 hp(m) *(1.62 MW)* sustained; 2 shafts
Speed, knots: 25. **Range, miles:** 550 at 20 kts; 900 at 15 kts
Complement: 15
Guns: 1 Oerlikon 20 mm. 1 FN 7.62 mm MG.
Radars: Kelvin Hughes Type 19; I band; range 117 km *(64 nm)*.

Comment: Built by Vosper Thornycroft (Private) Ltd, Singapore and completed between 1963 and 1970. PX 17 and PX 18 operated by Sabah Government, remainder by Royal Malaysian Police.

BENTARA   *1991, RM Police*

6 BROOKE MARINE 29 METRE CLASS

SANGITAN PX 28	**DUNGUN** PX 30	**TUMPAT** PX 32
SABAHAN PX 29	**TIOMAN** PX 31	**SEGAMA** PX 33

Displacement, tons: 114
Dimensions, feet (metres): 95.1 × 19.7 × 5.6 *(29 × 6 × 1.7)*
Main machinery: 2 Paxman Valenta 6CM diesels; 2250 hp *(1.68 MW)* sustained; 2 shafts
Speed, knots: 36. **Range, miles:** 1200 at 24 kts
Complement: 18 (4 officers)
Guns: 2 Oerlikon 20 mm.

Comment: Ordered 1979 from Penang Shipbuilding Co. First delivery June 1981, last pair completed June 1982. Brooke Marine provided lead yard services.

SANGITAN   *1991, RM Police*

9 IMPROVED PX CLASS

ALOR SETAR PX 19	**JOHORE BAHRU** PX 22	**SRI GAYA** PX 25
KOTA BAHRU PX 20	**SRI MENANTI** PX 23	**SRI KUDAT** PX 26
KUALA TRENGGANU PX 21	**KUCHING** PX 24	**SRI TAWAU** PX 27

Displacement, tons: 92 full load
Dimensions, feet (metres): 91 × 19 × 4.9 *(27.8 × 5.8 × 1.5)*
Main machinery: 2 MTU MB 12V 493 TY7 diesels; 2200 hp(m) *(1.62 MW)* sustained; 2 shafts
Speed, knots: 25. **Range, miles:** 900 at 15 kts
Complement: 17 (2 officers)
Guns: 2 Oerlikon 20 mm.
Radars: Kelvin Hughes Type 19; I band.

Comment: Built by Vosper Thornycroft (Private) Ltd, Singapore between 1972-73.

SRI MENANTI   *1972, Yam Photos, Singapore*

122 INSHORE/RIVER PATROL CRAFT

Comment: Built in several batches and designs since 1964. Some are armed with 7.62 mm MGs. All have PA/PC/PGR/PSC numbers. The latest batch are 23 Simmoneau SM 465 type built between January 1992 and mid-1993.

PA 6 (with MG)   *1992, RM Police*

PC 2   *1991, RM Police*

6 TRANSPORT VESSELS

PENJAGA PT 1   MARGHERITA PT 2
PLC 1-4

Comment: The PLCs are landing craft built in 1980 by Pasir Gudang. The two PT craft were built in 1985 by Brooke Dockyard, Sarawak.

PENJAGA   *1991, RM Police*

CUSTOMS

Note: In addition there are 30 interceptor craft and 12 inflatable chase boats.

4 PEMBANTERAS CLASS

Dimensions, feet (metres): 94.5 × 19.4 × 6.6 *(28.8 × 5.9 × 2)*
Main machinery: 2 Deutz SBA16M816C diesels; 3140 hp(m) *(2.31 MW)*; 2 shafts
Speed, knots: 20
Complement: 8

Comment: Built at Limbungan Timor shipyard, Terengganu.

6 VOSPER 32 METRE PATROL CRAFT

| JUANG K 33 | JERAI K 35 | BAYU K 37 |
| PULAI K 34 | PERAK K 36 | HIJAU K 38 |

Displacement, tons: 143 full load
Dimensions, feet (metres): 106.2 × 23.6 × 5.9 *(32.4 × 7.2 × 1.8)*
Main machinery: 2 Paxman Valenta 16CM diesels; 6650 hp *(5 MW)* sustained; 2 shafts
   1 Cummins diesel; 575 hp *(423 kW)* on 1 shaft
Speed, knots: 27; 8 on cruise diesel. **Range, miles:** 2000 at 8 kts
Complement: 26
Guns: 1 Oerlikon 20 mm. 2—7.62 mm MGs.

Comment: Ordered February 1981 from Malaysia Shipyard and Engineering Company with technical support from Vosper Thornycroft (Private) Ltd, Singapore. Two completed 1982, the remainder in 1983-84. Names are preceded by 'Bahtera'.

HIJAU   *4/1990, 92 Wing RAAF*

23—13.7 METRE PATROL CRAFT

Comment: Some carry a 7.62 mm machine gun.

13.7 m Customs   *4/1990, 92 Wing RAAF*

1—18 METRE PATROL CRAFT

KUALA BENGKOKA KA 34

Comment: Built by Mengsina Ltd, Singapore and commissioned on 3 December 1976. Based in Sabah.

KUALA BENGKOKA   *9/1988, van Ginderen Collection*

27 PENUMPAS CLASS

Comment: 9 m fast interceptor craft capable of 65 kts. Built in 1991/92 at Penang and Johore.

FISHERIES DEPARTMENT

Note: Patrol craft have a distinctive diagonal band on the hull and have been mistaken for a Coast Guard. All have P numbers. Latest × to be built in 1992 were P 51-53 at Ironwood, Malaysia.

FISHERIES P 202   5/1991, G Toremans

FISHERIES P 25   12/1988, Hartmut Ehlers

MALDIVES

Headquarters' Appointment	Personnel	Mercantile Marine
Chief of Coast Guard: Major Hassan Naseer	1994: 400	*Lloyd's Register of Shipping:* 51 vessels of 55 191 tons gross

COAST GUARD

Note: All British craft transferred in 1976 have been scrapped as have three ex-Taiwanese trawlers. *Ufuli,* an LCM built in Singapore and delivered in 1991, is a civilian transport and not part of the Coast Guard.

4 TRACKER II CLASS

KAANI 133 (ex-11)	**MIDHILI** 151 (ex-13)
KUREDHI 142 (ex-12)	**NIROLHU** 106 (ex-14)

Displacement, tons: 38 full load
Dimensions, feet (metres): 65.6 × 17.1 × 4.9 *(20 × 5.2 × 1.5)*
Main machinery: 2 Detroit 12V-71TA diesels; 840 hp *(627 kW)* sustained; 2 shafts
Speed, knots: 25. **Range, miles:** 450 at 20 kts
Complement: 10
Guns: 1—12.7 mm MG. 1—7.62 mm MG.
Radars: Surface search: Kroden; I band.

Comment: First one ordered June 1985 from Fairey Marinteknik and commissioned in April 1987. Three more acquired July 1987 ex-UK Customs craft. GRP hulls. Seven days normal endurance. Used for fishery protection and EEZ patrols.

KUREDHI   6/1993, Maldives CG

1 CHEVERTON CLASS

BUREVI 115 (ex-7)

Displacement, tons: 24 full load
Dimensions, feet (metres): 55.8 × 14.8 × 3.9 *(17 × 4.5 × 1.2)*
Main machinery: 2 Detroit 8V-71TI diesels; 850 hp *(634 kW)* sustained; 2 shafts
Speed, knots: 22. **Range, miles:** 590 at 18 kts
Complement: 10
Guns: 1—12.7 mm MG. 1—7.62 mm MG.
Radars: Surface search: Kroden; I band.

Comment: GRP hull and aluminium superstructure. Originally built for Kiribati and subsequently sold to Maldives in 1984.

BUREVI   6/1993, Maldives CG

1 DAGGER CLASS

FUNA 124

Displacement, tons: 20 full load
Dimensions, feet (metres): 36.8 × 11.2 × 5 *(11.2 × 3.4 × 1.2)*
Main machinery: 2 Sabre diesels; 660 hp *(492 kW)*; 2 shafts
Speed, knots: 35
Complement: 6
Guns: 1—7.62 mm MG.
Radars: Surface search: Furuno; I band.

Comment: Built by Fairey Marine at Cowes, Isle of Wight and delivered in 1982.

FUNA   6/1993, Maldives CG

MALTA

General	Personnel	Mercantile Marine
A coastal patrol force of small craft was formed in 1971. It is manned by the 2nd Regiment of the Armed Forces of Malta and primarily employed as a Coast Guard.	1994: 190	*Lloyd's Register of Shipping:* 1 037 vessels of 14 163 357 tons gross

Commander, Maritime Squadron

Captain M Gatt

Pennant Numbers

In 1992 all identification numbers were changed from C to P.

DELETIONS

1991 *C 20, C 22, C 26*
1992 *C 28*
1993 *President Tito, Ganni Bonnici*

PATROL FORCES

2 KONDOR I CLASS (COASTAL PATROL CRAFT)

P 30 (ex-*Ückermünde* G 411/GS 01)   **P 31** (ex-*Pasewalk* G 423/GS 05)

Displacement, tons: 377 full load
Dimensions, feet (metres): 170.3 × 23.3 × 7.2 *(51.9 × 7.1 × 2.2)*
Main machinery: 2 Russki/Kolomna Type 40DM diesels; 4408 hp(m) *(3.24 MW)* sustained; 2 shafts
Speed, knots: 20
Complement: 20
Guns: 3—12.7 mm MGs. 4—14.5 mm ZPU-4 (quad) MG to be fitted.
Radars: Surface search: TSR 333; I band.

Comment: Built by Peenewerft, Wolgast and commissioned 1 July 1969 and 18 October 1969 respectively. Transferred from Germany with new armament and sonar removed in July 1992. A quadruple 14.5 mm gun is to be fitted. Others of the class acquired by Tunisia and Guinea Bissau.

P 31   *4/1993, Hartmut Ehlers*

2 BREMSE CLASS (INSHORE PATROL CRAFT)

P 32 (ex-*G 33/GS 20*)   **P 33** (ex-*G 22/GS 22*)

Displacement, tons: 42 full load
Dimensions, feet (metres): 74.1 × 15.4 × 3.6 *(22.6 × 4.7 × 1.1)*
Main machinery: 2 DM 6VD 18/5 AL-1 diesels; 1020 hp(m) *(750 kW)*; 2 shafts
Speed, knots: 14
Complement: 6
Guns: 1—12.7 mm MG.
Radars: Surface search: TSR 333; I band.

Comment: Built in 1971-72 for the ex-GDR GBK. Transferred from Germany in mid-1992. Others of the class acquired by Tunisia and Jordan.

P 33   *5/1993, van Ginderen Collection*

2 HARBOUR PATROL CRAFT

P 25 (ex-*1255*)   **P 26** (ex-*1257*)

Displacement, tons: 35 full load
Dimensions, feet (metres): 59 × 15 × 4 *(18 × 4.6 × 1.2)*
Main machinery: 2 GM 12V-71 diesels; 680 hp *(507 kW)* sustained; 2 shafts
Speed, knots: 20. **Range, miles:** 300 at 15 kts
Complement: 7
Guns: 2—7.62 mm MGs.

Comment: Acquired in 1991 from NOAA (US).

P 26   *4/1993, Hartmut Ehlers*

2 SWIFT CLASS (HARBOUR PATROL CRAFT)

P 23 (ex-*US C 6823*)   **P 24** (ex-*US C 6824*)

Displacement, tons: 22.5
Dimensions, feet (metres): 50 × 13 × 4.9 *(15.6 × 4 × 1.5)*
Main machinery: 2 GM 12V-71 diesels; 680 hp *(507 kW)* sustained; 2 shafts
Speed, knots: 25
Complement: 6
Guns: 3—12.7 mm M2 MGs (1 twin, 1 single). 1—81 mm mortar.
Radars: Surface search: I band.

Comment: Built by Sewart Seacraft Ltd in 1967. Bought from US in February 1971. Have an operational endurance of about 24 hours.

P 23   *6/1993, Armed Forces Malta*

3 HARBOUR PATROL CRAFT

P 34 (ex-*GL 314*)   **P 36** (ex-*GL 326*)   **P 37** (ex-*GL 316*)

Displacement, tons: 19 full load
Dimensions, feet (metres): 50.9 × 16.1 × 3.6 *(15.5 × 4.9 × 1.1)*
Main machinery: 2 Fiat SRM 828 diesels; 880 hp(m) *(649 kW)* sustained; 2 shafts
Speed, knots: 20
Complement: 7
Guns: 1—7.62 mm MG.
Radars: Surface search: I band.

Comment: Acquired from the Italian Guardia Di Finanza on 9 June 1992. First two were built by Pichiotti, and the third by Baglietto.

P 34   *4/1993, Hartmut Ehlers*

1 LCVP

L 1 (ex-*6524*)

Displacement, tons: 13.5 full load
Dimensions, feet (metres): 36 × 10.5 × 1.1 *(11 × 3.2 × 0.3)*
Main machinery: 1 Detroit 64 HN9 diesel; 225 hp *(168 kW)*; 1 shaft
Speed, knots: 10
Complement: 4

Comment: Built by Gulfstream Co, USA and acquired in January 1987.

L 1   *1989, Armed Forces Malta*

2 HARBOUR PATROL CRAFT

P 27   P 29

Comment: Malta-built 9.5 m Barberis cabin cruisers acquired in 1989 and used for SAR.

P 27   *6/1993, van Ginderen Collection*

MARSHALL ISLANDS

General	Personnel	Base	Mercantile Marine
The Marshalls are a group of five main islands which became a self governing republic on 1 May 1979, but with the United States retaining responsibility for defence. Main port is Majuro.	1994: 60 (Maritime Authority)	Majuro	*Lloyd's Register of Shipping:* 57 vessels of 2 197 961 tons gross

PATROL FORCES

Note: In addition there are two ex-US LCUs acquired in 1987 and used as ferries.

1 PACIFIC FORUM TYPE (LARGE PATROL CRAFT)

Name	*No*	*Builders*	*Commissioned*
IONMETO III	—	Australian Shipbuilding Industries	29 June 1991

Displacement, tons: 162 full load
Dimensions, feet (metres): 103.3 × 26.6 × 6.9 *(31.5 × 8.1 × 2.1)*
Main machinery: 2 Caterpillar 3516TA diesels; 4400 hp *(3.3 MW)* sustained; 2 shafts
Speed, knots: 20. **Range, miles:** 2500 at 12 kts
Complement: 17 (3 officers)
Radars: Surface search: Furuno 1011; I band.

Comment: The 14th craft to be built in this series for a number of Pacific Island Coast Guards. Ordered in 1989. Capable of mounting a 20 mm gun or 12.7 mm MG.

PACIFIC FORUM Type   *1988, Gilbert Gyssels*

1 Ex-OFFSHORE SUPPLY SHIP

IONMETO I (ex-*Southern Light*)

Displacement, tons: 110 full load
Dimensions, feet (metres): 100 × — × — *(30.5 × — × —)*
Main machinery: 2 diesels; 2 shafts
Speed, knots: 14
Complement: 12
Guns: Can carry 2—12.7 mm MGs.

Comment: Acquired in 1987 and refitted by Halter Marine for patrol duties in December 1987.

2 TRINITY MARINE CLASS (HARBOUR PATROL CRAFT)

HSPC 1-2

Dimensions, feet (metres): 40.5 × 12 × 2.5 *(12.3 × 3.6 × 0.8)*
Main machinery: 2 Merlin diesels; 800 hp *(597 kW)* sustained; 2 Arneson ASD 10 surface drives
Speed, knots: 47
Complement: 3 plus 8 troops
Guns: 1—7.62 mm MG (can be carried).
Radars: Surface search: FLIR.

Comment: Halter Marine Interceptor 41s delivered to the US Army in March 1992 for permanent basing in the Marshall Islands. Two Zodiac F 470 raiding craft embarked. Hulls of PVC/Kevlar.

HSPC 1 and 2   *3/1992, Trinity Marine*

1 CAPE CLASS (LARGE PATROL CRAFT)

Name	*No*	*Builders*	*Commissioned*
IONMETO II (ex-*Cape Small*)	—	CG Yard, Curtis Bay	1953

Displacement, tons: 98 standard; 148 full load
Dimensions, feet (metres): 95 × 20.2 × 6.6 *(28.9 × 6.2 × 2)*
Main machinery: 4 Cummins VT-12 diesels; 2340 hp *(1.75 MW)*; 2 shafts
Speed, knots: 20. **Range, miles:** 2500 at 10 kts
Complement: 15
Guns: Can carry up to 2—12.7 mm MGs.
Radars: Navigation: Raytheon SPS 64(V)1; I band.

Comment: Acquired from USCG in April 1987.

CAPE class (old number)   *1990*

MAURITANIA

Personnel	**Bases**	**Mercantile Marine**
(a) 1994: 500 (36 officers)	Port Etienne, Nouadhibou	*Lloyd's Register of Shipping:*
(b) Voluntary service	Port Friendship, Nouakchott	132 vessels of 44 244 tons gross

PATROL FORCES

0 + 1 MODIFIED GRÈBE CLASS (OPV 54) (LARGE PATROL CRAFT)

Displacement, tons: 374 full load
Dimensions, feet (metres): 177.2 × 32.8 × 7.2 *(54 × 10 × 2.2)*
Main machinery: 2 diesels; 6500 hp(m) *(4.78 MW)*; 2 shafts
Speed, knots: 24. **Range, miles:** 4500 at 12 kts
Complement: 19
Guns: 2—12.7 mm MGs.
Radars: Surface search: I band.

Comment: Ordered in September 1992 from Leroux & Lotz, Lorient, for delivery in 1994. This is the prototype of three similar craft building for the French Navy based on the Grèbe class. There is an option on a second of class.

GRÈBE (French colours)   *10/1992*

1 PATRA CLASS (LARGE PATROL CRAFT)

Name	*No*	*Builders*	*Commissioned*
EL NASR (ex-*Le Dix Juillet*, ex-*Rapière*)	P 411	Auroux, Arcachon	14 May 1982

Displacement, tons: 147.5 full load
Dimensions, feet (metres): 132.5 × 19.4 × 5.2 *(40.4 × 5.9 × 1.6)*
Main machinery: 2 SACM AGO 195 V12 CZSHR diesels; 4340 hp(m) *(3.2 MW)* sustained; 2 shafts
Speed, knots: 26.3. **Range, miles:** 1750 at 10 kts
Complement: 20 (2 officers)
Guns: 1 Bofors 40 mm/60. 1 Oerlikon 20 mm. 2—12.7 mm Browning MGs.
Radars: Surface search: Racal/Decca 1226; I band.

Comment: Originally built as a private venture by Auroux. Carried out trials with French crew as *Rapière*. Laid down February 1980, launched 3 June 1981, commissioned for trials 1 November 1981. Transferred to Mauritania in 1982. Doubtful operational status.

1 NEUSTADT CLASS

Name	*No*	*Builders*	*Launched*
Z'BAR (ex-*Uelzen*)	P 381 (ex-BG 13)	Schlichting, Travemünde	25 July 1969

Displacement, tons: 218 full load
Dimensions, feet (metres): 127.1 × 23 × 5 *(38.5 × 7 × 2.2)*
Main machinery: 2 MTU MD 16-cyl diesels; 6000 hp(m) *(4.41 MW)* 1 MWM diesel; 685 hp(m) *(503 kW)*; 3 shafts
Speed, knots: 30. **Range, miles:** 450 at 27 kts
Complement: 23 (5 officers)
Guns: 2 Bofors 40 mm/70; 90° elevation; 300 rounds/minute to 12 km *(6.5 nm)* anti-surface; 4 km *(2.2 nm)* anti-aircraft; weight of shell 0.96 kg.

Comment: Ex-West German Coast Guard vessel acquired in March 1990 and recommissioned 29 April 1990. Lürssen design larger but similar to the El Vaiz class.

NEUSTADT   *1989, Hartmut Ehlers*

4 MANDOVI CLASS (INSHORE PATROL CRAFT)

Displacement, tons: 15 full load
Dimensions, feet (metres): 49.2 × 11.8 × 2.6 *(15 × 3.6 × 0.8)*
Main machinery: 2 Deutz MWM TBD232V12 Marine diesels; 750 hp(m) *(551 kW)*; 2 Hamilton waterjets
Speed, knots: 24. **Range, miles:** 250 at 14 kts
Complement: 8
Guns: 1—7.62 mm MG.
Radars: Navigation: Furuno FR 8030; I band.

Comment: Built by Garden Reach and delivered from India in 1990. Same type acquired by Mauritius.

3 EL VAIZ (LÜRSSEN FPB 36) CLASS

Name	*No*	*Builders*	*Commissioned*
EL VAIZ	P 361	Bazán-La Carraca	16 Oct 1979
EL BEIG	P 362	Bazán-La Carraca	21 May 1979
EL KINZ	P 363	Bazán-La Carraca	3 Aug 1982

Displacement, tons: 139 full load
Dimensions, feet (metres): 118.7 × 19 × 6.2 *(36.2 × 5.8 × 1.9)*
Main machinery: 2 MTU 16V 538 TB90 diesels; 7503 hp(m) *(5.51 MW)* sustained; 2 shafts
Speed, knots: 36. **Range, miles:** 1200 at 17 kts
Complement: 19 (3 officers)
Guns: 1 Bofors 40 mm/70. 1 Oerlikon 20 mm. 2—12.7 mm MGs.
Fire control: 1 CSEE Panda optical director (made in Spain).
Radars: Surface search: Raytheon RN 1220/6XB; I band.

Comment: First pair ordered 21 July 1976—third in 1979. Doubtful operational status.

EL BEIG   *1980, Bazan*

1 JURA CLASS

N'MADI (ex-*Criscilla*, ex-*Jura*)

Displacement, tons: 1285 full load
Dimensions, feet (metres): 195.3 × 35 × 14.4 *(59.6 × 10.7 × 4.4)*
Main machinery: 2 British Polar SP 112VS-F diesels; 4200 hp *(3.13 MW)*; 1 shaft
Speed, knots: 15.5
Complement: 28

Comment: Built by Hall Russell, Aberdeen in 1975. Became a Scottish Fishery Protection vessel but was paid off in 1988 and acquired by J Marr Ltd. On lease from July 1989 for Fishery Patrol duties.

JURA (British colours)   *1982, van Ginderen Collection*

LAND-BASED MARITIME AIRCRAFT

Note: There are also two Cessna 337F and two Buffalo DHC-5D.

Numbers/Type: 2 Piper Cheyenne II.
Operational speed: 283 kts *(524 km/h)*.
Service ceiling: 31 600 ft *(9630 m)*.
Range: 1510 nm *(2796 km)*.
Role/Weapon systems: Coastal surveillance and EEZ protection acquired 1981. Sensors: Bendix 1400 weather radar; cameras. Weapons: Unarmed.

MAURITIUS

Headquarters' Appointments	**Base**	**Mercantile Marine**

Commissioner of Police:
  Marie Therese Antoine Cyril Morvan QPM, MPM, CSK
Commandant Coast Guard:
  Commander Rajiv Sehgal
	Port Louis (plus 12 manned CG stations)
	
	Personnel
	
	1994: 600
		Lloyd's Register of Shipping:
		  57 vessels of 193 580 tons gross

PATROL FORCES

Note: In 1991 tenders were invited for a 1000 ton 60 m offshore patrol vessel. An order was placed with Polar Associates, Canada in 1993. Part of the construction is being done in Chile.

1 ABHAY CLASS (LARGE PATROL CRAFT)

AMAR P 1

Displacement, tons: 120 standard; 151 full load
Dimensions, feet (metres): 117.2 × 20 × 5 *(35.7 × 6.1 × 1.5)*
Main machinery: 2 Paxman diesels; 1000 hp *(746 kW)*; 2 shafts
Speed, knots: 18. **Range, miles:** 500 at 12 kts
Complement: 20
Guns: 1 Bofors 40 mm/60.
Radars: Surface search: Racal Decca 978; I band.

Comment: The last of the old Abhay class built by Garden Reach Workshops Ltd, Calcutta 1969. Transferred April 1974. Retained original name.

AMAR   *1991, Mauritius CG*

9 MANDOVI CLASS (INSHORE PATROL CRAFT)

MARLIN	CASTOR	SIRIUS	CAPELLA	RIGEL
BARRACUDA	POLARIS	POLLUX	CANOPUS	

Displacement, tons: 15 full load
Dimensions, feet (metres): 49.2 × 11.8 × 2.6 *(15 × 3.6 × 0.8)*
Main machinery: 2 Deutz MWM TBD232V12 Marine diesels; 750 hp(m) *(551 kW)*; 2 Hamilton waterjets
Speed, knots: 24. **Range, miles:** 250 at 14 kts
Complement: 8
Guns: 1—7.62 mm MG.
Radars: Navigation: Furuno FR 8030; I band.

Comment: Ordered in 1987 from Mandovi Marine Private Ltd, courtesy of the Indian Government. First two delivered early in 1989; second batch of three with some modifications on 1 May 1990 and the last four at the end of 1990. SATNAV fitted.

MARLIN   *1990, Mauritius CG*

2 ZHUK CLASS (TYPE 1400M)

RESCUER   RETRIEVER

Displacement, tons: 39 full load
Dimensions, feet (metres): 78.7 × 16.4 × 3.9 *(24 × 5 × 1.2)*
Main machinery: 2 M 401B diesels; 2200 hp(m) *(1.6 MW)* sustained; 2 shafts
Speed, knots: 30. **Range, miles:** 1100 at 15 kts
Complement: 14
Guns: 4—14.5 mm (2 twin) MGs.
Radars: Surface search: Spin Trough; I band.

Comment: Acquired from the USSR in January 1990.

RESCUER (alongside RETRIEVER and AMAR)   *1990, Mauritius CG*

1 SDB Mk 3 CLASS (FAST ATTACK CRAFT—PATROL)

Displacement, tons: 210 full load
Dimensions, feet (metres): 124 × 24.6 × 6.2 *(37.8 × 7.5 × 1.9)*
Main machinery: 2 MTU 16V 538 TB92 diesels; 6820 hp(m) *(5 MW)* sustained; 2 shafts
Speed, knots: 30
Complement: 32
Guns: 2 Bofors 40 mm/60; 80° elevation; 120 rounds/minute to 10 km *(5.5 nm)*; weight of shell 0.89 kg.

Comment: Transferred from Indian Navy in 1993. Built by Garden Reach, Calcutta in 1984.

SDB Mk 3 (Indian colours)   *1989, G Jacobs*

32 PATROL BOATS

Comment: Two Rover 663 FPC donated by Australia and 30 Rigid Inflatable craft mostly RHIBS, AVONS and ZODIACS acquired in 1988-89.

LAND-BASED MARITIME AIRCRAFT

Numbers/Type: 1 Dornier 228 (MPCG 01).
Operational speed: 200 kts *(370 km/h)*.
Service ceiling: 28 000 ft *(8535 m)*.
Range: 940 nm *(1740 km)*.
Role/Weapon systems: EEZ surveillance and SAR; acquired from Hindustan Aeronautics in 1990.
  Sensors: MEL search radar. Weapons: Unarmed.

MEXICO

Headquarters' Appointments

Secretary of the Navy:
 Admiral Luis Carlos Ruano Angulo
Under-Secretary of the Navy:
 Admiral Omar Diaz Gonzalez
Inspector General of the Navy:
 Vice Admiral Salvador Gonzalez Santamaria
Chief of the Naval Staff:
 Vice Admiral Alejandro Maldonado Mendoza

Flag Officers

Commander in Chief, Gulf and Caribbean:
 Vice Admiral Mariano Saynez Mendoza
Commander in Chief, Pacific:
 Vice Admiral Francisco Murillo Osuna

Personnel

(a) 1994: 39 660 officers and men (including 1050 Naval Air
 Force and 10 810 Marines)
(b) Voluntary service

Naval Air Force

Naval air bases at Mexico City, Las Bajadas, Tulum, Campeche,
Chetumal, Puerto Cortes, Isla Mujeres, La Paz, Salina Cruz,
Tapachula.

Marine Force

Expanded and reorganised in 1993 to include one Marine Para-
troop Brigade of two battalions, one Presidential Guard Battalion,
18 battalions with HQs in Mexico City and each Naval Zone, plus
one weapon support company for each battalion.

Naval Bases and Commands

The Naval Command is split between the Pacific and Gulf areas
each with a Commander-in-Chief with HQs at Veracruz (Gulf) and
Acapulco (Pacific). Each area has three naval Regions which are
further sub-divided into Zones (17) and Sectors (16).
Gulf Area
North (First) Naval Region - HQ Veracruz.
 I Naval Zone - HQ Ciudad Madero (State of Tamaupilas).
  Naval Sectors - HQ Matamoros, HQ La Pesca.
 III Naval Zone - HQ Veracruz (State of Veracruz).
  Naval Sectors - HQ Tuxpan, HQ Coatzacoalcos.
East (Third) Naval Region - HQ Frontera.
 V Naval Zone - HQ Frontera (State of Tabasco).
 VII Naval Zone - HQ Lerma (State of Campeche).
  Naval Sectors - HQ Champotón, HQ Ciudad del Cármen.
Caribbean Sea (Fifth) Naval Region - HQ Chetumal.
 IX Naval Zone - HQ Yucalpeten (State of Yucatán).
 XI Naval Zone - HQ Chetumal (State of Quintana Roo).
  Naval Sectors - HQ Isla Mujeres, HQ Isla Cozumel.
Pacific Area
Northwest (Second) Naval Region - HQ Mazatlán.
 II Naval Zone - HQ Ensenada (State of Baja California Norte).
  Naval Sector - HQ San Felipe.
 IV Naval Zone - HQ La Paz (State of Baja California Sur).
  Naval Sectors - HQ Puerto Cortes, HQ Santa Rosalía, HQ San
Lucas.
 VI Naval Zone - HQ Guaymas (State of Sonora).
  Naval Sector - HQ Puerto Peñasco.
 VIII Naval Zone - HQ Mazatlán (State of Sinaloa).
  Naval Sector - HQ Topolobampo.
West (Fourth) Naval Region - HQ Lazaro Cárdenas.
 X Naval Zone - HQ San Blas (State of Nayarit).
 XII Naval Zone - HQ Puerto Vallarta (State of Jalisco).
 XIV Naval Zone - HQ Manzanillo (State of Colima).
  Naval Sector - HQ Isla Socorro.
 XVI Naval Zone - HQ Lázaro Cardenas (State of Michoacán).
Southwest (Sixth) Naval Region - HQ Acapulco.
 XVIII Naval Zone - HQ Acapulco (State of Guerrero).
  Naval Sector - HQ Ixtapa-Zihuatanejo.
 XX Naval Zone - HQ Salina Cruz (State of Oaxaca).
  Naval Sector - HQ Puerto Angel.
 XXII Naval Zone - HQ Puerto Madero (State of Chiapas).

Strength of the Fleet

Type	Active
Destroyers	3
Frigates	6
Gunships	23
Large Patrol Craft/FAC	40
Coast Guard	17
Coastal and River Patrol Craft	26
Survey Ships	5
Support Ships	11
Tankers	5
Tugs	6
Sail Training Ship	1
Floating Docks	4
Dredgers	5

General

One of the persistent problems facing the Mexican Navy is the
incursion of foreign fishery poachers, frequently highly organised
groups working from the USA. In addition there is a requirement
for patrolling the Exclusive Economic Zone including the offshore
oil fields. The drug smuggling menace is taking up more and
more of the navy's time.

Names and Pennant Numbers

Many of the ship names and pennant numbers were changed in
early 1994.

Mercantile Marine

Lloyd's Register of Shipping:
 632 vessels of 1 124 859 tons gross

DESTROYERS

1 FLETCHER CLASS

Name	No	Builders	Laid down	Launched	Commissioned
CUITLAHUAC (ex-USS *John Rodgers* DD 574)	E 01 (ex-E 02, ex-F 2)	Consolidated Steel Corporation	25 July 1941	7 May 1942	9 Feb 1943

Displacement, tons: 2100 standard; 3050 full load
Dimensions, feet (metres): 376.5 × 39.4 × 18
 (114.8 × 12 × 5.5)
Main machinery: 4 Babcock & Wilcox boilers; 600 psi
 (43.3 kg/cm sq); 850°F *(454°C)*; 2 GE turbines; 60 000 hp
 (45 MW); 2 shafts
Speed, knots: 32. **Range, miles:** 5000 at 14 kts
Complement: 197

Guns: 5 USN 5 in *(127 mm)*/38 Mk 30 ❶; 85° elevation; 15
 rounds/minute to 17 km *(9.3 nm)* anti-surface; 8 km *(4.4 nm)*
 anti-aircraft; weight of shell 25 kg.
 10 Bofors 40 mm/60 (5 twin) Mk 2 ❷; 80° elevation; 120
 rounds/minute to 10 km *(5.5 nm)*; weight of shell 0.89 kg.
Torpedoes: 5—21 in *(533 mm)* (quin) tubes ❸; anti-surface.
Fire control: Mk 37 GFCS for 127 mm guns. 5 Mk 51 GFCS for
 40 mm guns.

CUITLAHUAC

(Scale 1 : 1200), Ian Sturton

Radars: Surface search: Kelvin Hughes 17/9 ❹; I band.
Navigation: Kelvin Hughes 14/9; I band.
Fire control: Western Electric Mk 25 ❺; I/J band.

Programmes: Transferred from US in August 1970.
Operational: In spite of its age this ship still has a formidable gun
 armament and is very active in drug enforcement patrols.

CUITLAHUAC (old number)

6/1993, Mexican Navy

2 GEARING (FRAM I) CLASS

Name
ILHUICAMINA (ex-*Quetzalcoatl*, ex-USS *Vogelgesang* DD 862)
NETZAHUALCOYOTL (ex-USS *Steinaker* DD 863)

Displacement, tons: 2425 standard; 3690 full load
Dimensions, feet (metres): 390.2 × 41.9 × 15
(118.7 × 12.5 × 4.6)
Main machinery: 4 Babcock & Wilcox boilers; 600 psi
(43.3 kg/cm sq); 850°F *(454°C)*; 2 GE turbines; 60 000 hp
(45 MW); 2 shafts
Speed, knots: 32.5. **Range, miles:** 5800 at 15 kts
Complement: 300

Missiles: A/S: Honeywell ASROC Mk 112 octuple launcher **①**;
inertial guidance to 1.6-10 km *(1-5.4 nm)*; payload Mk 46
torpedo.
Guns: 4 USN 5 in *(127 mm)*/38 (2 twin) Mk 38 **②**; 85° elevation;
15 rounds/minute to 17 km *(9.3 nm)* anti-surface; 11 km
(5.9 nm) anti-aircraft; weight of shell 25 kg.
1 Bofors 57 mm/70 Mk 2 **③**; 75° elevation; 220 rounds/
minute to 17 km *(9.3 nm)*; weight of shell 2.4 kg.
Torpedoes: 6—324 mm Mk 32 (2 triple) tubes **④**. Honeywell
Mk 46; anti-submarine; active/passive homing to 11 km
(5.9 nm) at 40 kts; warhead 44 kg.
Countermeasures: ESM: WLR-1; radar warning.
Fire control: Mk 37 GFCS.

No	Builders	Laid down	Launched	Commissioned
E 10 (ex-E 03)	Bethlehem, Staten Island	3 Aug 1944	15 Jan 1945	28 Apr 1945
E 11 (ex-E 04)	Bethlehem, Staten Island	1 Sep 1944	13 Feb 1945	26 May 1945

NETZAHUALCOYOTL *(Scale 1 : 1200), Ian Sturton*

Radars: Air search: Lockheed SPS 40; E/F band (E 03); range
320 km *(175 nm)*.
Westinghouse SPS 29 **⑤**; B/C band (E 04); range 457 km
(250 nm).
Surface search: Raytheon SPS 10 **⑥**; G band.
Navigation: Marconi LN 66; I band.
Fire control: Western Electric Mk 25 **⑦**; I/J band.
Sonars: Sangamo SQS 23; hull-mounted; active search and
attack; medium frequency.

Helicopters: 1 MBB BO 105CB **⑧**.

Programmes: Transferred from US by sale 24 February 1982.
Modernisation: A Bofors 57 mm gun was mounted between the
torpedo tubes in B gun position in 1993.
Structure: The devices on top of the funnel are to reduce IR
signature.

NETZAHUALCOYOTL (old number) *10/1993, Giorgio Arra*

FRIGATES

1 EDSALL CLASS

Name
COMODORO MANUEL AZUETA PERILLOS (ex-USS *Hurst* DE 250)

Displacement, tons: 1200 standard; 1850 full load
Dimensions, feet (metres): 302.7 × 36.6 × 13
(92.3 × 11.3 × 4)
Main machinery: 4 Fairbanks-Morse 38D8-1/8-10 diesels;
7080 hp *(5.3 MW)* sustained; 2 shafts
Speed, knots: 20. **Range, miles:** 13 000 at 12 kts
Complement: 216 (15 officers)

Guns: 3 USN 3 in *(76 mm)*/50 Mk 22; 85° elevation; 20 rounds/
minute to 12 km *(6.6 nm)*; weight of shell 6 kg.
8 Bofors 40 mm/60 (1 quad, 2 twin) Mk 2 and Mk 1; 80° elevation; 120 rounds/minute to 10 km *(5.5 nm)*; weight of shell
0.89 kg.
2—37 mm saluting guns.
Fire control: Mk 52 (for 3 in); Mk 51 Mod 2 (for 40 mm).
Radars: Surface search: Kelvin Hughes Type 17; I band.
Navigation: Kelvin Hughes Type 14; I band.
Fire control: RCA/GE Mk 26; I/J band.

Programmes: Transferred from US 1 October 1973.
Operational: Employed as training ship with Gulf Area command. A/S weapons and sensors removed.

No	Builders	Laid down	Launched	Commissioned
E 30 (ex-A 06)	Brown SB Co, Houston, Texas	27 Jan 1943	14 Apr 1943	30 Aug 1943

COMODORO MANUEL AZUETA PERILLOS (old number) *1992, Mexican Navy*

2 BRONSTEIN CLASS

Name	No	Builders	Laid down	Launched	Commissioned
HERMENEGILDO GALEANA (ex-*Bronstein*)	E 42 (ex-FF 1037)	Avondale Shipyards	16 May 1961	31 Mar 1962	16 June 1963
NICOLAS BRAVO (ex-*McCloy*)	E 40 (ex-FF 1038)	Avondale Shipyards	15 Sep 1961	9 June 1962	21 Oct 1963

Displacement, tons: 2360 standard; 2650 full load
Dimensions, feet (metres): 371.5 × 40.5 × 13.5; 23 (sonar)
(113.2 × 12.3 × 4.1; 7)
Main machinery: 2 Foster-Wheeler boilers; 1 De Laval geared turbine; 20 000 hp *(14.92 MW)*; 1 shaft
Speed, knots: 25
Complement: 207 (17 officers)

Missiles: A/S: Honeywell ASROC Mk 112 octuple launcher ❶; inertial guidance to 1.6-10 km *(1-5.4 nm)*; payload Mk 46 Torpedo.
Guns: 2 USN 3 in *(76 mm)*/50 (twin) Mk 33 ❷; 85° elevation; 50 rounds/minute to 12.8 km *(7 nm)*; weight of shell 6 kg.
Torpedoes: 6—324 mm US Mk 32 (2 triple) tubes ❸. 14 Honeywell Mk 46; anti-submarine; active/passive homing to 11 km *(5.9 nm)* at 40 kts; warhead 44 kg.
Countermeasures: Decoys: 2 Loral Hycor 6-barrelled fixed Mk 33; IR flares and chaff to 4 km *(2.2 nm)*.
T—Mk 6 Fanfare; torpedo decoy system.
ESM: WLR-1; WLR-3; radar warning.
ECM: ULQ-6; jammer.
Fire control: Mk 56 GFCS. Mk 114 ASW FCS. Mk 1 target designation system.
Radars: Air search: Lockheed SPS 40D ❹; E/F band; range 320 km *(175 nm)*.
Surface search: Raytheon SPS 10F ❺; G band.
Navigation: Marconi LN 66; I band.
Fire control: General Electric Mk 35 ❻; I/J band.
Sonars: EDO/General Electric SQS 26 AXR; bow-mounted; active search and attack; medium frequency.

Helicopters: Platform and some facilities but no hangar.

Programmes: Transferred from the US to Mexico 16 November 1993 having paid off some three years earlier. These two ships are the first of the 'second generation' of post-Second World War frigates with several features such as hull design, large sonar and ASW weapons that subsequently were incorporated into the mass-produced Knox class.
Structure: Position of stem anchor and portside anchor (just forward of gun mount) necessitated by large bow sonar dome. As built, a single 3 in (Mk 34) open mount was aft of the helicopter deck; removed for installation of towed sonar which has since been taken out.

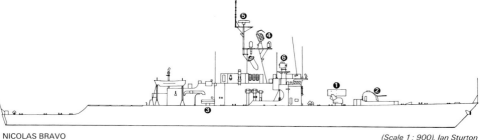

NICOLAS BRAVO

(Scale 1 : 900), Ian Sturton

NICOLAS BRAVO

12/1993, Mexican Navy

3 CHARLES LAWRENCE and CROSLEY CLASSES

Name	No	Builders	Laid down	Launched	Commissioned
MIGUEL HIDALGO (ex-*Usumacinta*, ex-USS *Don O Woods* APD 118, ex-*DE 721*)	E 20 (ex-B 06, ex-H 6)	Consolidated Steel Corporation	1 Dec 1943	19 Feb 1944	28 May 1945
VINCENTE GUERRERO (ex-*Coahuila*, ex-USS *Rednour* APD 102, ex-*DE 592*)	E 21 (ex-B 07)	Bethlehem SB Co, Hingham, Mass	9 Jan 1944	1 Mar 1944	15 Mar 1945
JOSE MARIA MORELOS Y PAVON (ex-*Chihuahua*, ex-USS *Barber* APD 57, ex-*DE 161*)	E 22 (ex-B 08)	Norfolk Navy Yard, Norfolk, Va	27 Apr 1943	20 May 1943	10 Oct 1943

Displacement, tons: 1400 standard; 2130 full load
Dimensions, feet (metres): 306 × 37 × 12.5
(93.3 × 11.3 × 3.8)
Main machinery: Turbo-electric; 2 Foster-Wheeler boilers; 435 psi *(30.6 kg/cm sq)*; 750°F *(399°C)*; 2 GE turbo generators; 12 000 hp *(9 MW)*; 2 motors; 2 shafts
Speed, knots: 18. **Range, miles:** 5000 at 15 kts
Complement: 221 plus 162 troops

Guns: 1 USN 5 in *(127 mm)*/38 Mk 30; 85° elevation; 15 rounds/minute to 17 km *(9.3 nm)*; weight of shell 25 kg.
6 Bofors 40 mm/60 (3 twin) Mk 1. 6 Oerlikon 20 mm/80.
Fire control: 3 Mk 51 GFCS for 40 mm guns.
Radars: Surface search: Kelvin Hughes 14/9; I band.

Programmes: B 06 purchased from US in December 1963, B 07 in June 1969 and B 08 in December 1969.
Structure: B 07 is the only Charles Lawrence class; the others have a tripod after mast supporting the conspicuous 10 ton boom.

VINCENTE GUERRERO (old number)

7/1993, van Ginderen Collection

MIGUEL HIDALGO (old number)

6/1993, Mexican Navy

SHIPBORNE AIRCRAFT

Note: BO 105s to be replaced by MD 900 Explorer from 1996.

Numbers/Type: 12 MBB BO 105CB.
Operational speed: 113 kts *(210 km/h)*.
Service ceiling: 9845 ft *(3000 m)*.
Range: 407 nm *(754 km)*.
Role/Weapon systems: Coastal patrol helicopter for patrol, fisheries protection and EEZ protection duties; SAR as secondary role. Sensors: Bendix search radar. Weapons: MGs or rocket pods.

Numbers/Type: 4 Aerospatiale AS 555 AF Fennec.
Operational speed: 121 kts *(225 km/h)*.
Service ceiling: 13 120 ft *(4000 m)*.
Range: 389 nm *(722 km)*.
Role/Weapon systems: Patrol helicopter for EEZ protection and SAR. Sensors: Bendix 1500 search radar. Weapons: Can carry up to 2 torpedoes, rocket pods or an MG.

LAND-BASED MARITIME AIRCRAFT (FRONT LINE)

Note: A number of confiscated drug-running aircraft are also in service, mostly Cessnas.

Numbers/Type: 9 CASA C-212 Aviocar.
Operational speed: 190 kts *(353 km/h)*.
Service ceiling: 24 000 ft *(7315 m)*.
Range: 1650 nm *(3055 km)*.
Role/Weapon systems: Acquired from 1987 and used for Maritime Surveillance. Have replaced the Albatross and Aravas. Sensors: Search radar; APS 504. Weapons: Unarmed.

BO 105CB   1993, Mexican Navy

PATROL FORCES

4 HOLZINGER CLASS (GUNSHIPS)

Name	No	Builders	Commissioned
CAPITÁN DE NAVIO SEBASTIAN JOSE HOLZINGER (ex-*Uxmal*)	C 01 (ex-GA 01)	Tampico	Nov 1991
CAPITÁN DE NAVIO BLAS GODINEZ BRITO (ex-*Mitla*)	C 02 (ex-GA 02)	Veracruz	21 Apr 1992
BRIGADIER JOSE MARIA DE LA VEGA GONZALEZ (ex-*Peten*)	C 03 (ex-GA 03)	Tampico	Apr 1993
GENERAL FELIPE B BERRIOZABAL (ex-*Anahuac*)	C 04 (ex-GA 04)	Veracruz	May 1993

Displacement, tons: 1290 full load
Dimensions, feet (metres): 244.1 × 34.4 × 11.2
(74.4 × 10.5 × 3.4)
Main machinery: 2 MTU 20V 956 TB92 diesels; 11 700 hp(m)
(8.6 MW) sustained; 2 shafts
Speed, knots: 22. **Range, miles:** 3820 at 18 kts
Complement: 75 (11 officers)

Guns: 1 Bofors 57 mm/70 Mk 2 ❶; 75° elevation; 220 rounds/minute to 17 km *(9.3 nm)*; weight of shell 2.4 kg. At least two of the class have a Bofors 40 mm/60.
Fire control: Elsag NA 18 optronic director ❷.
Radars: Surface search: Raytheon SPS 64(V)6A ❸; I band.

Helicopters: 1 MBB BO 105CB ❹.

Programmes: Originally four were ordered from Tampico and Veracruz. First laid down November 1983, second in 1984 but the whole programme has been slowed down by financial problems.
Structure: An improved variant of the Bazán Halcon (Uribe) class. C 01 and C 02 commissioned with a Bofors 40 mm/60 in lieu of the 57 mm. This is a temporary arrangement.

HOLZINGER   6/1993, Mexican Navy

6 URIBE CLASS (GUNSHIPS)

Name	No	Builders	Laid down	Launched	Commissioned
CADETE VIRGILIO URIBE ROBLES	C 11 (ex-GH 01)	Bazán, San Fernando	1 July 1981	12 Nov 1981	2 June 1982
TENIENTE JOSÉ AZUETA ABAD	C 12 (ex-GH 02)	Bazán, San Fernando	7 Sep 1981	12 Dec 1981	30 Aug 1982
CAPITAN de FRAGATA PEDRO SÁINZ de BARANDA BORREYRO	C 13 (ex-GH 03)	Bazán, San Fernando	22 Oct 1981	29 Jan 1982	20 Oct 1982
COMODORO CARLOS CASTILLO BRETÓN BARRERO	C 14 (ex-GH 04)	Bazán, San Fernando	11 Nov 1981	26 Feb 1982	4 Nov 1982
VICEALMIRANTE OTHÓN P BLANCO NUNEZ DE CACERES	C 15 (ex-GH 05)	Bazán, San Fernando	18 Dec 1981	26 Mar 1982	16 Nov 1982
CONTRALMIRANTE ANGEL ORTIZ MONASTERIO	C 16 (ex-GH 06)	Bazán, San Fernando	30 Dec 1981	4 May 1982	17 Dec 1982

Displacement, tons: 910 full load
Dimensions, feet (metres): 219.9 × 34.4 × 10.2
(67 × 10.5 × 3.1)
Main machinery: 2 MTU-Bazán 16V 956 TB91 diesels; 7500 hp
(m) *(5.52 MW)* sustained; 2 shafts
Speed, knots: 22. **Range, miles:** 5000 at 18 kts
Complement: 46 (7 officers)

Guns: 1 Bofors 40 mm/70.
Fire control: Naja optronic director.
Radars: Surface search: Decca AC 1226; I band.
Tacan: SRN 15.

Helicopters: 1 MBB BO 105CB.

Programmes: Ordered in 1980 to a Halcon class design. Contracts for a further eight of the class have been shelved. Pennant numbers changed in 1992.
Operational: Used for EEZ patrol.

BORREYRO   9/1993, Mexican Navy

1 GUANAJUATO CLASS (GUNSHIP)

Name	No	Builders	Commissioned
GUANAJUATO	C 07	SECN Ferrol	19 Mar 1936

Displacement, tons: 1950 full load
Dimensions, feet (metres): 264 × 37.8 × 13 *(80.5 × 11.5 × 4)*
Main machinery: 2 diesels; 5000 hp *(37.3 MW)*; 2 shafts
Speed, knots: 14
Complement: 140
Guns: 2 Vickers 4 in *(102 mm)*/45; 80° elevation; 16 rounds/minute to 19 km *(10.4 nm)*; weight of shell 16 kg.
  2 Bofors 40 mm/60. 2 Oerlikon 20 mm.
Radars: Surface search: I band.

Comment: Launched 29 May 1934. Originally used as a gunboat and troop transporter. Steam turbines replaced by diesels in the late 1960s.

GUANAJUATO *1990, Mexican Navy*

17 AUK CLASS (COAST GUARD

LEANDRO VALLE (ex-USS *Pioneer* MSF 105)	C 70 (ex-G-01)
GUILLERMO PRIETO (ex-USS *Symbol* MSF 123)	C 71 (ex-G-02)
MARIANO ESCOBEDO (ex-USS *Champion* MSF 314)	C 72 (ex-G-03)
MANUEL DOBLADO (ex-USS *Defense* MSF 317)	C 73 (ex-G-05)
SEBASTIAN LERDO DE TEJADA (ex-USS *Devastator* MSF 318)	C 74 (ex-G-06)
SANTOS DEGOLLADO (ex-USS *Gladiator* MSF 319)	C 75 (ex-G-07)
IGNACIO DE LA LLAVE (ex-USS *Spear* MSF 322)	C 76 (ex-G-08)
JUAN N ALVARES (ex-USS *Ardent* MSF 340)	C 77 (ex-G-09)
MANUEL GUTIERREZ ZAMORA (ex-USS *Roselle* MSF 379)	C 78 (ex-G-10)
VALENTIN GOMEZ FARIAS (ex-USS *Starling* MSF 64)	C 79 (ex-G-11)
IGNACIO MANUEL ALTAMIRANO (ex-USS *Sway* MSF 120)	C 80 (ex-G-12)
FRANCISCO ZARCO (ex-USS *Threat* MSF 124)	C 81 (ex-G-13)
IGNACIO L VALLARTA (ex-USS *Velocity* MSF 128)	C 82 (ex-G-14)
JESUS GONZALEZ ORTEGA (ex-USS *Chief* MSF 315)	C 83 (ex-G-15)
MELCHOR OCAMPO (ex-USS *Scoter* MSF 381)	C 84 (ex-G-16)
JUAN ALDAMA (ex-USS *Piloti* MSF 104)	C 85 (ex-G-18)
MARIANO MATAMOROS (ex-*Hermenegildo Galeana*, ex-USS *Sage* MSF 111)	C 86 (ex-G-19)

Displacement, tons: 1090 standard; 1250 full load
Dimensions, feet (metres): 221.2 × 32.2 × 10.8 *(67.5 × 9.8 × 3.3)*
Main machinery: Diesel-electric; 2 GM 278A diesels; 2200 hp *(1.64 MW)*; 2 generators; 2 motors; 2 shafts
Speed, knots: 18. **Range, miles:** 4300 at 10 kts
Complement: 105 (9 officers)
Guns: 1 USN 3 in *(76 mm)*/50. 4 Bofors 40 mm/56 (2 twin).
  2 Oerlikon 20 mm (in some on quarterdeck).
Radars: Surface search: Kelvin Hughes 14/9 (in most); I band.

Comment: Transferred from US six in February 1973, four in April 1973, nine in September 1973. Employed on Coast Guard duties. All built during Second World War. Variations are visible in the mid-ships section where some have a bulwark running from the break of the fo'c'sle to the quarter-deck. Minesweeping gear removed. There is a variety of diesel engines, radars and even shipbuilders for this class. Starting to be paid off. One used as a survey vessel deleted in 1988.

JUAN N ALVARES (old number) *3/1988*

SEBASTIAN LERDO DE TEJADA (old number) *6/1991*

12 ADMIRABLE CLASS (OFFSHORE PATROL VESSELS)

GENERAL MIGUEL NEGRETE (ex-*Jubilant*)	C-50 (ex-D 01)
GENERAL JUAN N MENDEZ (ex-*Execute*)	C-51 (ex-D 03)
GENERAL MANUEL E RINCON (ex-*Specter*)	C-52 (ex-D 04)
GENERAL FELIPE XICOTENCATL (ex-*Scuffle*)	C-53 (ex-D 05)
CADETE AUGUSTIN MELGAR (ex-*Device*)	C-54 (ex-D 11)
TENIENTE JUAN DE LA BARRERA (ex-*Ransom*)	C-55 (ex-D 12)
CADETE JUAN ESCUTIA (ex-*Knave*)	C-56 (ex-D 13)
CADETE FERNANDO MONTES DE OCA (ex-*Rebel*)	C-57 (ex-D 14)
GENERAL PEDRO MARIA ANAYA (ex-*Crag*)	C-58 (ex-D 15)
CADETE FRANCISCO MARQUEZ (ex-*Diploma*)	C-59 (ex-D 17)
GENERAL IGNACIO ZARAGOZA (ex-*Invade*)	C-60 (ex-D 18)
CADETE VICENTE SUAREZ (ex-*Intrigue*)	C-61 (ex-D 19)

Displacement, tons: 650 standard; 900 full load
Dimensions, feet (metres): 184.5 × 33 × 14.4 *(56.3 × 10.1 × 4.4)*
Main machinery: 2 Cooper-Bessemer GSB-8 diesels; 1710 hp *(1.28 MW)*; 2 shafts
Speed, knots: 15. **Range, miles:** 4300 at 10 kts
Complement: 104 (8 officers)
Guns: 1 USN 3 in *(76 mm)*/50 Mk 22; 85° elevation; 20 rounds/minute to 12 km *(6.5 nm)* anti-surface; 9 km *(4.9 nm)* anti-aircraft; weight of shell 6 kg.
  2 Bofors 40 mm/70; 90° elevation; 300 rounds/minute to 12 km *(6.5 nm)* anti-surface; 4 km *(2.2 nm)* anti-aircraft; weight of shell 2.4 kg.
  6 or 8 Oerlikon 20 mm; 50° elevation; 800 rounds/minute to 2 km; weight of shell 0.24 kg.
Helicopters: Platform for 1 BO 105 *(D 11-13)*.

Comment: Former US steel hulled fleet minesweepers. All completed in 1943-44. D 20 now fitted for surveying (see *Survey Vessels*). Minesweeping gear removed. Four of the class deleted in 1986. Three others, *D 11-13*, converted in 1991/93 to provide a helicopter platform aft. In these conversions the funnel has been raised. Six were given names in 1993, the others are still known by their pennant numbers.

CADETE VICENTE SUAREZ (old number) *1992, Mexican Navy*

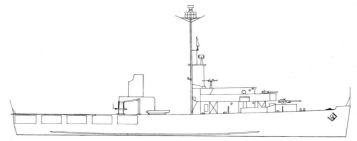

CADETE AUGUSTIN MELGAR (helo deck) *(not to scale), Ian Sturton*

3 CAPE CLASS (LARGE PATROL CRAFT)

Name	No	Builders	Recommissioned
CABO CORRIENTES	P 42	CG Yard, Curtis Bay	1 Apr 1990
(ex-*Jalisco*, ex-*Cape Carter*)			
CABO CORZO	P 43	CG Yard, Curtis Bay	21 Apr 1990
(ex-*Nayarit*, ex-*Cape Hedge*)			
CABO CATOCHE	P 44	CG Yard, Curtis Bay	18 Mar 1991
(ex-*Cape Hatteras*)			

Displacement, tons: 98 standard; 148 full load
Dimensions, feet (metres): 95 × 20.2 × 6.6 *(28.9 × 6.2 × 2)*
Main machinery: 2 GM 16V-149TI diesels; 2322 hp *(1.73 MW)* sustained; 2 shafts
Speed, knots: 20. **Range, miles:** 2500 at 10 kts
Complement: 14 (1 officer)
Guns: 2—12.7 mm MGs.
Radars: Navigation: Raytheon SPS 64; I band

Comment: Built between 1953 and 1959; have been re-engined and extensively modernised. Transferred under the FMS programme, having paid off from the US Coast Guard.

CABO CORZO *1992, Mexican Navy*

31 AZTECA CLASS (LARGE PATROL CRAFT)

Name	No	Builders	Commissioned
AZTECA (ex-*Quintana*)	P 01	Ailsa Shipbuilding Co Ltd	1 Nov 1974
GUAYCURA (ex-*Cordova*)	P 02	Scott & Sons, Bowling	22 Oct 1974
NAHUATL (ex-*Arizpe*)	P 03	Ailsa Shipbuilding Co Ltd	23 Dec 1974
TOTORAN (ex-*Izazaga*)	P 04	Ailsa Shipbuilding Co Ltd	19 Dec 1974
PAPAGO (ex-*Bautista*)	P 05	Scott & Sons, Bowling	19 Dec 1974
TARAHUMARA (ex-*Rayon*)	P 06	Ailsa Shipbuilding Co Ltd	19 Dec 1974
TEPEHUAN (ex-*Rejon*)	P 07	Ailsa Shipbuilding Co Ltd	4 July 1975
MEXICA (ex-*Fuente*)	P 08	Ailsa Shipbuilding Co Ltd	4 July 1975
ZAPOTECA (ex-*Guzman*)	P 09	Scott & Sons, Bowling	7 Apr 1975
HUASTECA (ex-*Ramirez*)	P 10	Ailsa Shipbuilding Co Ltd	17 July 1975
MAZAHUA (ex-*Mariscal*)	P 11	Ailsa Shipbuilding Co Ltd	23 Sep 1975
HUICHOL (ex-*Jara*)	P 12	Ailsa Shipbuilding Co Ltd	7 Nov 1975
SERI (ex-*Mata*)	P 13	Lamont & Co Ltd	13 Oct 1975
YAQUI (ex-*Romero*)	P 14	Scott & Sons, Bowling	23 June 1975
TLAPANECO (ex-*Lizardi*)	P 15	Ailsa Shipbuilding Co Ltd	24 Dec 1975
TARASCO (ex-*Mujica*)	P 16	Ailsa Shipbuilding Co Ltd	21 Nov 1975
ACOLHUA (ex-*Rouaix*)	P 17	Scott & Sons, Bowling	7 Nov 1975
OTOMI (ex-*Velazco*)	P 18	Lamont & Co Ltd	14 Jan 1975
MAYO (ex-*Rojas*)	P 19	Lamont & Co Ltd	3 Apr 1976
PIMAS (ex-*Macias*)	P 20	Lamont & Co Ltd	2 Sep 1976
CHICHIMECA (ex-*Calderon*)	P 21	Lamont & Co Ltd	18 June 1976
CHONTAL (ex-*Zaragoza*)	P 22	Veracruz	1 June 1976
MAZATECO (ex-*Tamaulipas*)	P 23	Veracruz	18 May 1977
TOLTECA (ex-*Yucatan*)	P 24	Veracruz	3 July 1977
MAYA (ex-*Tabasco*)	P 25	Salina Cruz	1 Dec 1978
COCHIMIE (ex-*Veracruz*)	P 26	Veracruz	1 Dec 1978
CORA (ex-*Campeche*)	P 27	Veracruz	1 Mar 1980
TOTONACA (ex-*Puebla*)	P 28	Salina Cruz	1 June 1982
MIXTECO (ex-*Maza*)	P 29	Salina Cruz	29 Nov 1976
OLMECA (ex-*Vicario*)	P 30	Veracruz	1 May 1977
TLAHUICA (ex-*Ortiz*)	P 31	Salina Cruz	1 June 1977

Displacement, tons: 148 full load
Dimensions, feet (metres): 111.8 × 28.1 × 6.8 *(34.1 × 8.6 × 2)*
Main machinery: 2 Paxman 12YJCM diesels; 3000 hp *(2.24 MW)* sustained; 2 shafts
Speed, knots: 24. **Range, miles:** 2500 at 12 kts
Complement: 24 (2 officers)
Guns: 1 Bofors 40 mm/70; 90° elevation; 300 rounds/minute to 12 km *(6.5 nm)* anti-surface;
  4 km *(2.2 nm)* anti-aircraft; weight of shell 2.4 kg.
  1 Oerlikon 20 mm; 55° elevation; 800 rounds/minute to 2 km; weight of shell 0.24 kg.

Comment: Ordered by Mexico on 27 March 1973 from Associated British Machine Tool Makers
  Ltd to a design by TT Boat Designs, Bembridge, Isle of Wight. The first 21 were modernised in
  1987 in Mexico with spare parts and equipment supplied by ABMTM Marine Division who supervised the work which included engine refurbishment and the fitting of air-conditioning. The refit
  programme was designed to extend service lives by at least 10 years. Reports that more of the
  class were to be built were not correct.

TOTORAN   *1992, Mexican Navy*

2 POINT CLASS (LARGE PATROL CRAFT)

Name	No	Builders	Recommissioned
PUNTA MORRO (ex-*Point Verde*)	P 60 (ex-P 45)	CG Yard, Curtis Bay	12 June 1991
PUNTA MASTUN (ex-*Point Herron*)	P 61 (ex-P 46)	CG Yard, Curtis Bay	21 June 1991

Displacement, tons: 67 full load
Dimensions, feet (metres): 83 × 17.2 × 5.8 *(25.3 × 5.2 × 1.8)*
Main machinery: 2 Caterpillar diesels; 1600 hp *(1.19 MW)*; 2 shafts
Speed, knots: 23. **Range, miles:** 1500 at 8 kts
Complement: 10
Guns: 2—12.7 mm MGs (can be carried).
Radars: Surface search: Raytheon SPS 64; I band.

Comment: Ex-US Coast Guard craft built in the early 1960s. Steel hulls and aluminium
  superstructures.

PUNTA MASTUN (old number)   *1992, Mexican Navy*

4 ISLA CORONADO CLASS (FAST ATTACK CRAFT)

Name	No	Builders	Commissioned
ISLA CORONADO	P 51	Equitable Shipyards	1 Sep 1993
ISLA LOBOS	P 52	Equitable Shipyards	1 Nov 1993
ISLA GUADALUPE	P 53	Equitable Shipyards	1 Feb 1994
ISLA COZUMEL	P 54	Equitable Shipyards	1 Apr 1994

Displacement, tons: 52 full load
Dimensions, feet (metres): 82 × 17.9 × 4 *(25 × 5.5 × 1.2)*
Main machinery: 3 Detroit diesels; 16 200 hp *(12.9 MW)*; 3 Arneson surface drives
Speed, knots: 50. **Range, miles:** 1200 at 30 kts
Complement: 9 (3 officers)
Guns: 1—12.7 mm MG. 2—7.62 mm MGs.
Radars: Surface search: I band.

Comment: Built by the Trinity Marine Group to an XFPB (extra fast patrol boat) design. Deep Vee
  hulls with FRP/Kevlar construction. Based at Islas Mujeres in the XI naval zone.

ISLA CORONADO   *10/1993, Mexican Navy*

7 LAGOON (ex-POLIMAR) CLASS (COASTAL PATROL CRAFT)

Name	No	Builders	Commissioned
TAMIAHUA (ex-*Poluno*)	P 70 (ex-F 01)	Astilleros de Tampico	1 Oct 1962
LAGARTOS (ex-*Poldos*)	P 71 (ex-F 02)	Icacas Shipyard, Guerrero	1968
KANA (ex-*Poltres*)	P 72 (ex-F 03)	Icacas Shipyard, Guerrero	1968
CUYUTLAN (ex-*Polcinco*)	P 73 (ex-F 05)	Astilleros de Tampico	28 July 1953
MANDINGA (ex-*Aspirante Jose V Razcon*)	P 74 (ex-F 06)	Astilleros de Tampico	18 Mar 1960
ALVARADO (ex-*Polsiete*)	P 75 (ex-F 07)	—	1985
CATEMACO (ex-*Polocho*)	P 76 (ex-F 08)	—	1986

Displacement, tons: 37 standard; 57 full load
Dimensions, feet (metres): 67.2 × 14.8 × 4.3 *(20.1 × 4.5 × 1.3)*
Main machinery: 2 diesels; 456 hp *(335 kW)*; 2 shafts
Speed, knots: 11
Guns: 1 Oerlikon 20 mm (can be carried).
Radars: Surface search: I band.

Comment: Steel construction. Details given are for the first five. The last two were transferred from
  the USN on the dates shown and may have some structural differences. All have *Laguna de* in
  front of the names.

LAGUNA DE CUYUTLAN (old number)   *1992, Mexican Navy*

5 FLUVIAL CLASS (RIVER PATROL CRAFT)

Name	No	Builders	Commissioned
LAGO DE PATZCUARO (ex-*AM 04*)	P 80 (ex-F 14)	Vera Cruz	1957
LAGO DE CHAPALA (ex-*AM 05*)	P 81 (ex-F 15)	Tampico	1959
LAGO DE TEXCOCO (ex-*AM 06*)	P 81 (ex-F 16)	Vera Cruz	1959
LAGO DE JANITZIO (ex-*AM 07*)	P 83 (ex-F 17)	Tampico	1961
LAGO DE CUITZEO (ex-*AM 08*)	P 84 (ex-F 18)	Vera Cruz	1981

Displacement, tons: 37
Dimensions, feet (metres): 56.1 × 16.4 × 8.2 *(17.1 × 5 × 2.5)*
Main machinery: 1 diesel; 1 shaft
Speed, knots: 6

Comment: Steel construction. One already deleted having been replaced by the last of the class
  which was built 20 years after the others.

LAGO DE PATZCUARO (old name)   *6/1993, Mexican Navy*

13 REEF (ex-OLMECA II) CLASS (RIVER PATROL CRAFT)

ALACRAN (ex-*AM-11*)	P-90	**LA BLANQUILLA** (ex-*AM-18*)	P-97
SISAL (ex-*AM-12*)	P-91	**ANEGADA DE ADENTRO**	P-98
TANHUIJO (ex-*AM-13*)	P-92	(ex-*AM-19*)	
CABEZO (ex-*AM-14*)	P-93	**RIZO** (ex-*AM-20*)	P-99
SANTIAGUILLO (ex-*AM-15*)	P-94	**PAJAROS** (ex-*AM-21*)	P-100
PALANCAR (ex-*AM-16*)	P-95	**DE ENMEDIO** (ex-*AM-22*)	P-101
LA GALLEGUILLA (ex-*AM-17*)	P-96	**DE HORNOS** (ex-*AM-23*)	P-102

Displacement, tons: 18 full load
Dimensions, feet (metres): 54.8 × 14.4 × 7.9 *(16.7 × 4.4 × 2.4)*
Main machinery: 2 Detroit 8V-92TA diesels; 700 hp *(562 kW)* sustained; 2 shafts
Speed, knots: 20. **Range, miles:** 460 at 15 kts
Complement: 15 (2 officers)
Guns: 1—12.7 mm MG.
Radars: Navigation: Raytheon; I band.

Comment: Built at Acapulco from 1979-83 with GRP hulls. All have *Arrecife* in front of the names.

ARRECIFE ALACRAN   *1986, Mexican Navy*

SURVEY AND RESEARCH SHIPS

2 ROBERT D CONRAD CLASS (RESEARCH SHIPS)

Name	No	Builders	Commissioned
ALTAIR (ex-*James M Gilliss*)	H 05 (ex-AGOR 4)	Christy Corp, Wisconsin	5 Nov 1962
ANTARES (ex-*S P Lee*)	H 06 (ex-AG 192)	Defoe, Bay City	2 Dec 1962

Displacement, tons: 1370 full load
Dimensions, feet (metres): 208.9 × 40 × 15.4 *(63.7 × 12.2 × 4.7)*
Main machinery: Diesel-electric; 2 Caterpillar diesel generators; 1200 hp *(895 kW)*; 2 motors; 1000 hp *(746 kW)*; 1 shaft; bow thruster
Speed, knots: 13.5. **Range, miles:** 10 500 at 10 kts
Complement: 41 plus 15 scientists
Radars: Navigation: Raytheon 1025; Raytheon R4iY; I band.

Comment: *Altair* leased from US 14 June 1983. Refitted and modernised in Mexico. Recommissioned 27 November 1984. Primarily used for oceanography. *Antares* served as an AGI with the USN until February 1974 when she transferred on loan to the Geological Survey. Acquired by sale 1 December 1992.

ALTAIR   *1989, Mexican Navy*

ANTARES   *4/1993, Mexican Navy*

1 ONJUKU CLASS (SURVEY SHIP)

ONJUKU H 04

Displacement, tons: 494 full load
Dimensions, feet (metres): 121 × 26.2 × 11.5 *(36.9 × 8 × 3.5)*
Main machinery: 1 Yanmar 6UA-UT diesel; 700 hp(m) *(515 kW)*; 1 shaft
Speed, knots: 12. **Range, miles:** 5645 at 10.5 kts
Complement: 20 (4 officers)
Radars: Navigation: I band.
Sonars: Furuno; hull-mounted; high frequency.

Comment: Launched in 1977 and commissioned in 1980.

ONJUKU   *1987, Mexican Navy*

1 ADMIRABLE CLASS (SURVEY SHIP)

ALDEBARAN (ex-DM 20, ex-USS *Harlequin* AM 365, ex-ID-20)   H 02

Comment: Details given in Admirable class under *Patrol Ships*. Now unarmed but has a complement of 62 (12 officers).

ALDEBARAN   *1990, Mexican Navy*

1 HUMBOLT CLASS (RESEARCH SHIP)

Name	No	Builders	Recommissioned
ALEJANDRO DE HUMBOLT	H 03	JG Hitzler, Elbe	22 June 1987

Displacement, tons: 585 standard; 700 full load
Dimensions, feet (metres): 140.7 × 32 × 13.5 *(42.3 × 9.6 × 4.1)*
Main machinery: 2 diesels; 2 shafts
Speed, knots: 14
Complement: 20 (4 officers)

Comment: Built in 1970. Converted in 1982 to become a hydrographical and acoustic survey ship. Based at Sinaloa.

ALEJANDRO DE HUMBOLT   *6/1993, Mexican Navy*

AUXILIARIES

Note: US planned to lease at least one Thomaston class LSD, now in reserve in Mexico, in 1991. No sign of this offer being taken up. The ship would require formation of a much larger Naval Aviation helicopter wing (UH-1Hs, and so on).

1 FABIUS CLASS (LIGHT FORCES TENDER)

Name	No	Builders	Commissioned
RIO GRIJALVA (ex-*Vicente* Guerrero, ex-USS *Megara* ARVA-6)	A 03 (ex-A 05)	American Bridge Co, Ambridge, Penn	27 June 1945

Displacement, tons: 3284 light; 4100 full load
Dimensions, feet (metres): 328 × 50 × 14 *(100 × 15.3 × 4.3)*
Main machinery: 2 GM 12-567A diesels; 1800 hp *(1.34 MW)*; 2 shafts
Speed, knots: 10.6. **Range, miles:** 6000 at 10 kts
Complement: 250
Guns: 12 Bofors 40 mm/60 (2 quad; 2 twin).
Fire control: 2 Mk 51 Mod 2 GFCS.

Comment: Ex-aircraft repair ship acquired from the US 1 October 1973. Carries two LCVPs. Armament may not be fitted.

LCVP (embarked in A 03)   1988

RIO GRIJALVA (old number)   1992, Mexican Navy

2 LST 511-1152 CLASS

Name	No	Builders	Commissioned
RIO PANUCO (ex-*Park County*)	A 01	Bethlehem Steel	8 May 1945
RIO PAPALOAPAN (ex-*Manzanillo*, ex-*Clearwater County*)	A 02	Chicago Bridge & Iron Co	31 Mar 1944

Displacement, tons: 4080 full load
Dimensions, feet (metres): 328 × 50 × 14 *(100 × 15.3 × 4.3)*
Main machinery: 2 GM 12-567A diesels; 1800 hp *(1.34 MW)*; 2 shafts
Speed, knots: 11. **Range, miles:** 6000 at 11 kts
Complement: 13
Guns: 8 Bofors 40 mm (2 twin, 4 single).

Comment: Transferred from US in 1971-72 and deployed as SAR and disaster relief ships. Were to have paid off when *Huasteco* and *Zapoteco* commissioned but have been retained in service.

RIO PANUCO   7/1991, Harald Carstens

1 LOGISTIC SUPPORT SHIP

Name	No	Builders	Recommissioned
RIO LERMA (ex-*Tarasco*, ex-*Sea Point*, ex-*Tricon*, ex-*Marika*, ex-*Arneb*)	A 22 (ex-A 25)	Solvesborg, Sweden	1 Mar 1990

Displacement, tons: 1970 full load
Dimensions, feet (metres): 282.2 × 40.7 × 16.1 *(86 × 12.4 × 4.9)*
Main machinery: 1 Kloeckner Humboldt Deutz diesel; 2100 hp(m) *(1.54 MW)*; 1 shaft
Speed, knots: 14
Cargo capacity: 778 tons

Comment: Built in 1962 as a commercial ship and taken into the Navy in 1990.

RIO LERMA (old number)   1990, Mexican Navy

2 LOGISTIC SUPPORT SHIPS

Name	No	Builders	Commissioned
RIO USUMACINTA (ex-*Huasteco*)	A 10 (ex-A 21)	Tampico, Tampa	21 May 1986
RIO COATZACOALCOS (ex-*Zapoteco*)	A 11 (ex-A 22)	Salina Cruz	1 Sep 1986

Displacement, tons: 1854 standard; 2650 full load
Dimensions, feet (metres): 227 × 42 × 18.6 *(69.2 × 12.8 × 5.7)*
Main machinery: 1 GM-EMD diesel; 3600 hp(m) *(2.65 MW)*; 1 shaft
Speed, knots: 17. **Range, miles:** 5500 at 14 kts
Complement: 85 plus 300 passengers
Guns: 1 Bofors 40/60.
Helicopters: 1 MBB BO 105C.

Comment: Can serve as troop transports, supply or hospital ships. Were to have replaced the ex-US LSTs but the latter have been retained in service.

RIO USUMACINTA (old number)   6/1992, Mexican Navy

3 TANKERS

Name	No	Builders	Recommissioned
PORTRERO DEL LLANO	A 42	Ishikawajima Harima, Nagoya	16 Nov 1993
FAJA DE ORO	A 43	Ishikawajima Harima, Nagoya	1994
TUXPAN	A 44	Ishikawajima Harima, Nagoya	1994

Displacement, tons: 27 432 full load
Dimensions, feet (metres): 560 × 74 × 31 *(170.7 × 22.6 × 9.4)*
Main machinery: 1 IHI/Sulzer diesel; 8000 hp(m) *(5.88 MW)*; 1 shaft
Speed, knots: 14.6
Complement: 30

Comment: Acquired from the Mexican Merchant Marine. Built in 1968/69.

PORTRERO DEL LLANO   12/1993, Mexican Navy

1 DURANGO CLASS (TRANSPORT)

Name	No	Builders	Commissioned
DURANGO	B 01 (ex-128)	Union Naval de Levante, Valencia	14 July 1936

Displacement, tons: 1600 standard; 2000 full load
Dimensions, feet (metres): 256.5 × 36.6 × 10.5 *(78.2 × 11.2 × 3.1)*
Main machinery: Diesel-electric; 2 Enterprise DMR-38 diesels; 5000 hp *(3.73 MW)*; 2 shafts
Speed, knots: 18. **Range, miles:** 3000 at 12 kts
Complement: 149 (24 officers)
Guns: 1—4 in *(102 mm)*. 2—57 mm. 4 Oerlikon 20 mm.

Comment: Laid down 28 October 1933 and launched 28 June 1935. Originally designed primarily as an armed transport with accommodation for 20 officers and 450 men, then reclassified as a frigate. Became non-operational in the 1970s but has since been refitted as a transport ship.

DURANGO   1992, Mexican Navy

1 LOGISTIC SUPPORT SHIP

Name	No	Builders	Recommissioned
RIO NAUTLA (ex-*Maya*)	A 20 (ex-A 23)	Isla Gran Cayman, Ru	1 June 1988

Displacement, tons: 924 full load
Dimensions, feet (metres): 160.1 × 38.7 × 16.1 *(48.8 × 11.8 × 4.9)*
Main machinery: 1 MAN diesel; 1 shaft
Speed, knots: 12
Complement: 15 (8 officers)

Comment: First launched in 1962 and acquired for the Navy in 1988. Unarmed.

RIO NAUTLA (old number)   *1989, Mexican Navy*

1 LOGISTIC SUPPORT SHIP

Name	No	Builders	Recommissioned
RIO TONALA (ex-*Progreso*)	A 21 (ex-A 24)	Angulo, Del Carmen	27 Mar 1989

Displacement, tons: 152 full load
Dimensions, feet (metres): 73.8 × 21.7 × 4.9 *(22.5 × 6.6 × 1.5)*
Main machinery: 1 diesel; 1 shaft
Speed, knots: 10
Cargo capacity: 57 tons

Comment: First commissioned 27 February 1985. Converted in 1988 and taken into the Navy in 1989.

RIO TONALA (old number)   *1992, Mexican Navy*

1 TRANSPORT VESSEL

Name	No	Builders	Recommissioned
RIO BALSAS (ex-*Plan de Iguala*, ex-*La Paz*)	A 23 (ex-A 08)	Kure Zosencho, Japan	16 Mar 1990

Displacement, tons: 4205 full load
Dimensions, feet (metres): 357.7 × 57.5 × 16.1 *(109 × 17.5 × 4.9)*
Main machinery: 2 Burmeister & Wain diesels; 5600 hp(m) *(4.1 MW)*; 2 shafts
Speed, knots: 17.5
Cargo capacity: 1227 tons

Comment: Former Ro-Ro ferry belonging to the Transport Ministry. Built in 1963.

RIO BALSAS (old number)   *1990, Mexican Navy*

4 FLOATING DOCKS

— (ex-US ARD 2)   — (ex-US ARD 11)   **AR 15** (ex-US ARD 15)   — (ex-US AFDL 28)

Comment: ARD 2 (150 × 24.7 m) transferred 1963 and ARD 11 (same size) 1974 by sale. Lift 3550 tons. Two 10 ton cranes and one 100 kW generator. ARD 15 has the same capacity and facilities—transferred 1971 by lease. AFDL 28 built in 1944, transferred 1973. Lift, 1000 tons.

5 DREDGERS

BAHIA DE BANDERAS (ex-*Chiapas*) D 01 (ex-A 30)
BAHIA TODOS SANTOS (ex-*Mazatlan*) D 02 (ex-A 31)
BAHIA MAGDALENA (ex-*Cristobal Colon*) D 03 (ex-A 32)
BAHIA ASUNCION (ex-*Isla del Carmen*) D 04 (ex-A 33)
BAHIA ALMEJAS (ex-*Isla Azteca*) D 05 (ex-A 34)

Comment: Various types.

2 YOG/YO TYPE (HARBOUR TANKERS)

Name	No	Builders	Recommissioned
LAS CHOAPAS (ex-*Aguascalientes*, ex-*YOG 6*)	A 45 (ex-A 03)	Geo H Mathis Co Ltd, Camden, NJ	Nov 1964
AMATLAN (ex-*Tlaxcala*, ex-*YO 107*)	A 46 (ex-A 04)	Geo Lawley & Son, Neponset, Mass	Nov 1964

Displacement, tons: 440 light; 1400 full load
Dimensions, feet (metres): 159.2 × 32.9 × 13.3 *(48.6 × 10 × 4.1)*
Main machinery: 1 Fairbanks-Morse diesel; 500 hp *(373 kW)*; 1 shaft
Speed, knots: 8
Complement: 26 (5 officers)
Cargo capacity: 6570 barrels
Guns: 1 Oerlikon 20 mm.

Comment: Former US self-propelled fuel oil barges built in 1943. Purchased in August 1964.

LAS CHOAPAS (old number)   *1990, Mexican Navy*

1 TRANSPORT VESSEL

Name	No	Builders	Commissioned
RIO TEHUANTEPEC (ex-*Zacatecas*)	A 24 (ex-B 02)	Ulua SY, Veracruz	1960

Displacement, tons: 785 standard
Dimensions, feet (metres): 158 × 27.2 × 10 *(48.2 × 8.3 × 2.7)*
Main machinery: 1 MAN diesel; 560 hp(m) *(412 kW)*; 1 shaft
Speed, knots: 8
Complement: 50 (13 officers)
Cargo capacity: 400 tons
Guns: 2 Bofors 40 mm/60.

Comment: Cargo ship type employed as a transport.

RIO TEHUANTEPEC (old number)   *1992, Mexican Navy*

TRAINING SHIP

1 SAIL TRAINING SHIP

Name	No	Builders	Commissioned
CUAUHTEMOC	A 07	Astilleros Talleres Calaya, SA, Bilbao	29 July 1982

Displacement, tons: 1800 full load
Dimensions, feet (metres): 296.9 (bowsprit); 220.5 wl × 39.4 × 17.7 *(90.5; 67.2 × 12 × 5.4)*
Main machinery: 1 Detroit 12V-149T diesel; 875 hp *(652 kW)* sustained; 1 shaft
Speed, knots: 17 sail; 7 diesel
Complement: 268 (20 officers, 90 midshipmen)
Guns: 2—65 mm Schneider Model 1902 saluting guns.

Comment: Launched January 1982. Has 2368 sq m of sail.

CUAUHTEMOC   *5/1993, Giorgio Arra*

TUGS

4 ABNAKI CLASS

Name	No	Builders	Commissioned
KUKULKAN (ex-*Otomi*, ex-USS *Molala* ATF 106)	A 52 (ex-A 17)	United Eng Co, Alameda, CA	29 Sep 1943
EHACATL (ex-*Yaqui*, ex-USS *Abnaki* ATF 96)	A 53 (ex-A 18)	Charleston S B and D D Co	15 Nov 1943
TONATIUH (ex-*Seri*, ex-USS *Cocopa* ATF 101)	A 54 (ex-A 19)	Charleston S B and D D Co	25 Mar 1944
CHAC (ex-*Cora*, ex-USS *Hitchiti* ATF 103)	A 55 (ex-A 20)	Charleston S B and D D Co	27 May 1944

Displacement, tons: 1640 full load
Dimensions, feet (metres): 205 × 38.5 × 17 *(62.5 × 11.7 × 5.2)*
Main machinery: Diesel-electric; 4 Busch-Sulzer BS-539 diesels; 6000 hp *(4.48 MW)*; 4 generators; 1 motor; 3000 hp(m) *(2.24 MW)*; 1 shaft
Speed, knots: 15. **Range, miles:** 6500 at 15 kts
Complement: 75
Guns: 1 US 3 in *(76 mm)*/50.
Radars: Navigation: Marconi LN 66; I band.

Comment: *Otomi* transferred from US 1 August 1978, remainder 30 September 1978. All by sale.

TONATIUH (old number) — *1990, Mexican Navy*

2 V 4 CLASS

QUEZALCOATL (ex-*Mayo*, ex-*Montauk*) A 50 (ex-A 12)
HUITILOPOCHTLI (ex-*Mixteco*, ex-*Point Vicente*) A 51 (ex-A 13)

Displacement, tons: 1863 full load
Dimensions, feet (metres): 191.3 × 37 × 18 *(58.3 × 11.3 × 5.5)*
Main machinery: 2 Nat Supply 8-cyl diesels; 2250 hp *(1.68 MW)*; 1 Kort nozzle
Speed, knots: 14. **Range, miles:** 9000 at 14 kts
Complement: 90
Guns: 1—3 in *(76 mm)*/50. 2 Oerlikon 20 mm *(Mayo)*.
Radars: Navigation: Kelvin Hughes 14/9; I band.

Comment: Part of a large class built 1943-45 by US Maritime Administration for civilian use. Not a successful design; most were laid up on completion. In 1968 six were taken from reserve and transferred by sale in June 1969. All originally unarmed—guns fitted in Mexico. *Mayo* assigned to Gulf area, *Mixteco* to Pacific area. The other four have been scrapped. *Mixteco* is unarmed.

HUITILOPOCHTLI (old number) — *1992, Mexican Navy*

MICRONESIA

Headquarters' Appointment	Bases	General	Mercantile Marine
OIC Maritime Surveillance Centre Mr Lester Ruda	Kolonia (main base), Kosral, Moen, Takatik.	Pacific Islands of the Caroline archipelago comprising the states of Kosral, Pohnpei, Truk and Yap. The Federated States became a self-governing republic on 10 May 1979. The United States maintains responsibility for defence and has leased three Cape class Coast Guard patrol craft for anti-narcotics patrols.	*Lloyd's Register of Shipping:* 18 vessels of 8559 tons gross

PATROL FORCES

2 PACIFIC FORUM TYPE (LARGE PATROL CRAFT)

Name	No	Builders	Commissioned
PALIKIR	FSM 1	Australian Shipbuilding Industries	28 Apr 1990
MICRONESIA	FSM 2	Australian Shipbuilding Industries	3 Nov 1990

Displacement, tons: 162 full load
Dimensions, feet (metres): 103.3 × 26.6 × 6.9 *(31.5 × 8.1 × 2.1)*
Main machinery: 2 Caterpillar 3516TA diesels; 4400 hp *(3.28 MW)* sustained; 2 shafts
Speed, knots: 20. **Range, miles:** 2500 at 12 kts
Complement: 17 (3 officers)
Radars: Surface search: Furuno 1011; I band.

Comment: Ordered in June 1989 from Australian Shipbuilding Industries. Training and support provided by Australia at Port Kolonia.

3 CAPE CLASS (LARGE PATROL CRAFT)

Name	No	Builders	Commissioned
— (ex-*Cape George*)	—	Coast Guard Yard, Curtis Bay	15 Mar 1958
— (ex-*Cape Cross*)	—	Coast Guard Yard, Curtis Bay	20 Aug 1958
— (ex-*Cape Corwin*)	—	Coast Guard Yard, Curtis Bay	14 Nov 1958

Displacement, tons: 148 full load
Dimensions, feet (metres): 95 × 20.2 × 6.6 *(28.9 × 6.2 × 2)*
Main machinery: 2 GM 16V-149TI diesels; 2070 hp *(1.54 MW)* sustained; 2 shafts
Speed, knots: 20. **Range, miles:** 2500 at 10 kts
Complement: 14
Guns: 2—12.7 mm MGs. 2—40 mm mortars.
Radars: Surface search: Raytheon SPS 64; I band.

Comment: Transferred from US on loan in March and September 1991. Re-engined in 1982.

MICRONESIA — *11/1990, Royal Australian Navy*

CAPE GEORGE (in USCG colours) — *1990*

MONTSERRAT

Senior Officer	Base	Mercantile Marine

Commissioner of Police:
  David H Crowther
	Plymouth	*Lloyd's Register of Shipping:*
		  1 vessel of 711 tons gross

POLICE

1 HALMATIC M160 CLASS (COASTAL PATROL CRAFT)

SHAMROCK

Displacement, tons: 18 light
Dimensions, feet (metres): 52.5 × 15.4 × 4.6 *(16 × 4.7 × 1.4)*
Main machinery: 2 Detroit 6V-92TA diesels; 520 hp *(388 kW)* sustained; 2 shafts
Speed, knots: 27. **Range, miles:** 500 at 17 kts
Complement: 6
Guns: 1—7.62 mm MG.

Comment: Delivered on 7 January 1990; identical craft acquired by Anguilla and the Turks and Caicos Islands in December 1989.

SHAMROCK

1989, Halmatic

MOROCCO

Headquarters' Appointment	Personnel	Mercantile Marine

Inspector of the Navy:
  Captain Mohamed Trikki
	(a) 1994: 8000 officers and ratings (including 1500 Marines)
	(b) 18 months' national service
		Lloyd's Register of Shipping:
		  492 vessels of 393 468 tons gross

Diplomatic Representation

Defence Attaché in London:
  Colonel Mustapha Jabrane

DELETION

1991   *Lieutenant Riffi*

Aviation

The Ministry of Fisheries operates 11 Pilatus Britten-Norman Defender maritime surveillance aircraft.

Bases

Casablanca, Safi, Agadir, Kenitra, Tangier, Dakhla, Al Hoceima

FRIGATE

Note: By early 1994 plans for more Descubierta class had been abandoned. Subject to US Congressional approval the Knox class *Valdez* (FF 1096) is to be acquired in 1994/95.

1 MODIFIED DESCUBIERTA CLASS

Name	No	Builders	Laid down	Launched	Commissioned
LIEUTENANT COLONEL ERRHAMANI	501	Bazán, Cartagena	20 Mar 1979	26 Feb 1982	28 Mar 1983

Displacement, tons: 1233 standard; 1479 full load
Dimensions, feet (metres): 291.3 × 34 × 12.5
  (88.8 × 10.4 × 3.8)
Main machinery: 4 MTU-Bazán 16V 956 TB91 diesels; 15 000 hp(m) *(11 MW)* sustained; 2 shafts; cp props
Speed, knots: 25.5. **Range, miles:** 4000 at 18 kts (1 engine)
Complement: 100

Missiles: SSM: 4 Aerospatiale MM 38 Exocet ❶; inertial cruise; active radar homing to 42 km *(23 nm)* at 0.9 Mach; warhead 165 kg; sea-skimmer. Frequently not embarked.
SAM: Selenia/Elsag Albatros octuple launcher ❷; 24 Aspide; semi-active radar homing to 13 km *(8 nm)* at 2.5 Mach; height envelope 15-5000 m *(49.2-16 405 ft)*; warhead 30 kg.
Guns: 1 OTO Melara 3 in *(76 mm)*/62 compact ❸; 85° elevation; 85 rounds/minute to 16 km *(8.6 nm)* anti-surface; 12 km *(6.5 nm)* anti-aircraft; weight of shell 6 kg.
2 Breda Meccanica 40 mm/70 ❹; 85° elevation; 300 rounds/minute to 12.5 km *(6.7 nm)*; weight of shell 0.96 kg.
Torpedoes: 6—324 mm Mk 32 (2 triple) tubes ❺. Honeywell Mk 46 Mod 1; anti-submarine; active/passive homing to 11 km *(5.9 nm)* at 40 kts; warhead 44 kg.
A/S mortars: 1 Bofors SR 375 mm twin trainable launcher ❻; range 3.6 km *(1.9 nm)*; 24 rockets.
Countermeasures: Decoys: 2 CSEE Dagaie double trainable mounting; IR flares and chaff; H/J band.
ESM/ECM: Elettronica ELT 715; intercept and jammer.
Combat data systems: Signaal SEWACO-MR action data automation.
Radars: Air/surface search: Signaal DA 05 ❼; E/F band; range 137 km *(75 nm)* for 2 m² target.
Surface search: Signaal ZW 06 ❽; I band; range 26 km *(14 nm)*.
Fire control: Signaal WM 25/41 ❾; I/J band; range 46 km *(25 nm)*.
Sonars: Raytheon DE 1160 B; hull-mounted; active/passive; medium range; medium frequency.

Programmes: Ordered 7 June 1977.
Operational: The ship is fitted to carry Exocet but the missiles are seldom embarked.

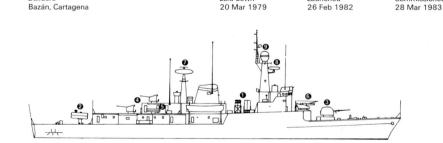

LIEUTENANT COLONEL ERRHAMANI

(Scale 1 : 900), Ian Sturton

LIEUTENANT COLONEL ERRHAMANI

3/1993, Diego Quevedo

CORVETTES

0 + 2 ASSAD CLASS

Name	No	Builders	Laid down	Launched	Completed
(ex-*Abdulla Ben Abi Sarh*)	(ex-F 214)	Fincantieri, Breda, Mestre	22 Mar 1982	5 July 1983	1987
(ex-*Khalid Ibn Al Walid*)	(ex-F 216)	Fincantieri, Breda, Mestre	3 June 1982	5 July 1983	1987

Displacement, tons: 705 full load
Dimensions, feet (metres): 204.4 × 30.5 × 8
  (62.3 × 9.3 × 2.5)
Main machinery: 4 MTU 20V 956 TB92 diesels; 20 120 hp(m)
  (14.8 MW) sustained; 4 shafts
Speed, knots: 37. **Range, miles:** 4000 at 18 kts
Complement: 47

Missiles: SSM: 6 OTO Melara/Matra Otomat Teseo Mk 2 (TG 2)
  (3 twin); active radar homing to 180 km *(98.4 nm)* at
  0.9 Mach; warhead 210 kg; sea-skimmer.
SAM: 1 Selenia/Elsag Albatros launcher (4 cell—2 reloads);
  Aspide; semi-active radar homing to 13 km *(7 nm)* at
  2.5 Mach; height envelope 15-5000 m *(49.2-16 405 ft)*; warhead 30 kg.
Guns: 1 OTO Melara 3 in *(76 mm)*/62 compact; 85° elevation;
  85 rounds/minute to 16 km *(8.7 nm)* anti-surface; 12 km
  (6.6 nm) anti-aircraft; weight of shell 6 kg.
  2 Breda 40 mm/70 (twin) (not in helicopter ships); 85° elevation; 300 rounds/minute to 12.5 km *(6.8 nm)*; weight of shell
  0.96 kg.
Torpedoes: 6—324 mm ILAS 3 (2 triple) tubes. Whitehead
  A244S; anti-submarine; active/passive homing to 6 km
  (3.3 nm); warhead 34 kg (shaped charge).
Countermeasures: Decoys: 2 Breda 105 mm six-tubed multi-
  purpose launchers; chaff to 5 km *(2.7 nm)*; illuminants to
  12 km *(6.6 nm)*.
ESM: Selenia INS-3; intercept.
ECM: Selenia TQN-2; jammer.
Combat data systems: Selenia IPN 10; action data automation.
Fire control: 2 Selenia NA 21; Dardo.
Radars: Air/surface search: Selenia RAN 12L/X; D/I band; range
  82 km *(45 nm)*.
Navigation: SMA SPN 703 (3 RM 20); I band.
Fire control: 2 Selenia RTN 10X; I/J band; range 40 km *(22 nm)*.
Sonars: Atlas Elektronik ASO 84-41; hull-mounted; active search
  and attack.

ASSAD   9/1993, Marina Fraccaroli

Programmes: Ordered in February 1981 for the Iraqi Navy and
fell foul of UN sanctions before they could either be paid for or
delivered. Subsequently maintained by Fincantieri. Two near
sister ships were paid for by Iraq and remain laid up in Italian
ports. Two of the remaining four ships bought by Morocco in
late 1992 according to Fincantieri, but up to early 1994 the

ships had still not been delivered, although both were active at
La Spezia. It now seems unlikely that a second pair will be
purchased and there is doubt about these two.
Structure: Same type as Libyan ships. NBC citadel and full air-
conditioning fitted.
Operational: All refitted for sale in 1992/93.

ASSAD   1993, Fincantieri

PATROL FORCES

2 OKBA (PR 72) CLASS (FAST ATTACK CRAFT—GUN)

Name	No	Builders	Commissioned
OKBA	302	SFCN, Villeneuve la Garenne	16 Dec 1976
TRIKI	303	SFCN, Villeneuve la Garenne	12 July 1977

Displacement, tons: 375 standard; 445 full load
Dimensions, feet (metres): 188.8 × 25 × 7.1 *(57.5 × 7.6 × 2.1)*
Main machinery: 4 SACM AGO V16 ASHR diesels; 11 040 hp(m) *(8.11 MW)*; 4 shafts
Speed, knots: 28. **Range, miles:** 2500 at 16 kts
Complement: 53 (5 officers)
Guns: 1 OTO Melara 3 in *(76 mm)*/62 compact; 85° elevation; 85 rounds/minute to 16 km
  (8.6 nm) anti-surface; 12 km *(6.5 nm)* anti-aircraft; weight of shell 6 kg.
  1 Bofors 40 mm/70; 85° elevation; 300 rounds/minute to 12.5 km *(6.7 nm)*; weight of shell
  0.96 kg.
Fire control: 2 CSEE Panda optical directors.
Radars: Surface search: Decca; I band.

Comment: Ordered June 1973. *Okba* launched 10 October 1975, *Triki* 1 February 1976. Can be
  Exocet fitted (with Vega control system).

OKBA   1992

4 LAZAGA CLASS (FAST ATTACK CRAFT—MISSILE)

Name	No	Builders	Commissioned
EL KHATTABI	304	Bazán, San Fernando	26 July 1981
COMMANDANT BOUTOUBA	305	Bazán, San Fernando	2 Aug 1982
COMMANDANT EL HARTY	306	Bazán, San Fernando	20 Nov 1981
COMMANDANT AZOUGGARH	307	Bazán, San Fernando	25 Feb 1982

Displacement, tons: 425 full load
Dimensions, feet (metres): 190.6 × 24.9 × 8.9 *(58.1 × 7.6 × 2.7)*
Main machinery: 2 MTU-Bazán 16V 956 TB91 diesels; 7500 hp(m) *(5.51 MW)* sustained; 2 shafts
Speed, knots: 30. **Range, miles:** 3000 at 15 kts
Complement: 41
Missiles: SSM: 4 Aerospatiale MM 38 Exocet; inertial cruise; active radar homing to 42 km *(23 nm)*
    at 0.9 Mach; warhead 165 kg; sea-skimmer.
Guns: 1 OTO Melara 3 in *(76 mm)*/62 compact; 85° elevation; 85 rounds/minute to 16 km
    (8.6 nm) anti-surface; 12 km *(6.5 nm)* anti-aircraft; weight of shell 6 kg.
    1 Breda Meccanica 40 mm/70; 85° elevation; 300 rounds/minute to 12.5 km *(6.7 nm)*; weight
    of shell 0.96 kg.
    2 Oerlikon 20 mm/90 GAM-BO1; 55° elevation; 800 rounds/minute to 2 km.
Fire control: CSEE Panda optical director.
Radars: Surface search: Signaal ZW 06; I band; range 26 km *(14 nm)*.
    Fire control: Signaal WM 25; I/J band; range 46 km *(25 nm)*.

Comment: Ordered from Bazán, San Fernando (Cadiz), Spain 14 June 1977.

COMMANDANT BOUTOUBA   *5/1984*

4 OSPREY MK II CLASS (LARGE PATROL CRAFT)

Name	No	Builders	Commissioned
EL HAHIQ	308	Danyard A/S, Frederickshaven	11 Nov 1987
EL TAWFIQ	309	Danyard A/S, Frederickshaven	31 Jan 1988
EL HAMISS	316	Danyard A/S, Frederickshaven	9 Aug 1990
EL KARIB	317	Danyard A/S, Frederickshaven	23 Sep 1990

Displacement, tons: 475 full load
Dimensions, feet (metres): 179.8 × 34 × 8.5 *(54.8 × 10.5 × 2.6)*
Main machinery: 2 MAN Burmeister & Wain Alpha 12V23/30-DVO diesels; 4440 hp(m)
    (3.23 MW) sustained; 2 waterjets
Speed, knots: 22. **Range, miles:** 4500 at 16 kts
Complement: 15 plus 20 spare berths
Guns: 1 Bofors 40 mm/60. 2 Oerlikon 20 mm (twin).
Radars: Surface search; Racal Decca; I band.

Comment: First two ordered in September 1986; two more on 30 January 1989 and a third pair in
    late 1990. First two were for the Customs Service and second pair for the Navy but this may have
    been reversed. There is a stern ramp with a hinged cover for launching the inspection boat.

EL HAMISS   *9/1992, H M Steele*

6 CORMORAN CLASS (LARGE PATROL CRAFT)

Name	No	Builders	Launched	Commissioned
L V RABHI	310	Bázan, San Fernando	23 Sep 1987	16 Sep 1988
ERRACHIQ	311	Bázan, San Fernando	23 Sep 1987	16 Dec 1988
EL AKID	312	Bázan, San Fernando	29 Mar 1988	4 Apr 1989
EL MAHER	313	Bázan, San Fernando	29 Mar 1988	20 June 1989
EL MAJID	314	Bázan, San Fernando	21 Oct 1988	26 Sep 1989
EL BACHIR	315	Bázan, San Fernando	21 Oct 1988	19 Dec 1989

Displacement, tons: 425 full load
Dimensions, feet (metres): 190.6 × 24.9 × 8.9 *(58.1 × 7.6 × 2.7)*
Main machinery: 2 MTU Bazán 16V 956 TB82 diesels; 8340 hp(m) *(6.13 MW)* sustained; 2 shafts
Speed, knots: 22. **Range, miles:** 6100 at 12 kts
Complement: 36 (4 officers)
Guns: 1 Bofors 40 mm/70. 2 Giat 20 mm.
Fire control: Lynx optronic director.
Radars: Surface search: Racal Decca; I band.

Comment: Three ordered from Bazán, Cadiz in October 1985 as a follow on to the Lazaga class of
    which these are a slower patrol version with a 10 day endurance. Option on three more taken up.
    Used for fishery protection.

EL MAHER   *6/1989, Bazán*

0 + 2 OPV 64 CLASS

Displacement, tons: 600 full load
Dimensions, feet (metres): 210 × 37.4 × 9.8 *(64 × 11.4 × 3)*
Main machinery: 2 diesels; 2 shafts
Speed, knots: 25

Comment: Reported ordered from Leroux and Lotz in early 1994. To be built at Lorient and
    delivered in 1997.

6 EL WACIL (P 32) CLASS (COASTAL PATROL CRAFT)

Name	No	Builders	Commissioned
EL WACIL	203	CMN, Cherbourg	9 Oct 1975
EL JAIL	204	CMN, Cherbourg	3 Dec 1975
EL MIKDAM	205	CMN, Cherbourg	30 Jan 1976
EL KHAFIR	206	CMN, Cherbourg	16 Apr 1976
EL HARIS	207	CMN, Cherbourg	30 June 1976
EL ESSAHIR	208	CMN, Cherbourg	16 July 1976

Displacement, tons: 74 light; 89 full load
Dimensions, feet (metres): 105 × 17.7 × 4.6 *(32 × 5.4 × 1.4)*
Main machinery: 2 SACM MGO 12V BZSHR diesels; 2700 hp(m) *(1.98 MW)*; 2 shafts
Speed, knots: 28. **Range, miles:** 1500 at 15 kts
Complement: 17
Guns: 1 Oerlikon 20 mm.
Radars: Surface search: Decca; I band.

Comment: Ordered in February 1974. In July 1985 a further four of this class were ordered from
    the same builders but for the Customs Service. Wooden hull sheathed in plastic.

EL WACIL   *1988*

AMPHIBIOUS FORCES

3 BATRAL CLASS

Name	No	Builders	Commissioned
DAOUD BEN AICHA	402	Dubigeon, Normandie	28 May 1977
AHMED ES SAKALI	403	Dubigeon, Normandie	Sep 1977
ABOU ABDALLAH EL AYACHI	404	Dubigeon, Normandie	Mar 1978

Displacement, tons: 750 standard; 1409 full load
Dimensions, feet (metres): 262.4 × 42.6 × 7.9 *(80 × 13 × 2.4)*
Main machinery: 2 SACM Type 195 V12 CSHR diesels; 3600 hp(m) *(2.65 MW)* sustained; 2 shafts
Speed, knots: 16. **Range, miles:** 4500 at 13 kts
Complement: 47 (3 officers)
Military lift: 140 troops; 12 vehicles
Guns: 2 Bofors 40 mm/70. 2—81 mm mortars.
Radars: Surface search: Thomson-CSF DRBN 32; I band.
Helicopters: Platform only.

Comment: Two ordered on 12 March 1975. Third ordered 19 August 1975. Of same type as the
    French *Champlain*. Vehicle-stowage above and below decks.

AHMED ES SAKALI   *8/1986, John G Callis*

1 EDIC CLASS

Name	No	Builders	Commissioned
LIEUTENANT MALGHAGH	401	Chantiers Navals Franco-Belges	1965

Displacement, tons: 250 standard; 670 full load
Dimensions, feet (metres): 193.5 × 39.2 × 4.3 *(59 × 12 × 1.3)*
Main machinery: 2 MGO diesels; 1000 hp(m) *(735 kW)*; 2 shafts
Speed, knots: 8. **Range, miles:** 1800 at 8 kts
Complement: 16 (1 officer)
Military lift: 11 vehicles
Guns: 2 Oerlikon 20 mm. 1—120 mm mortar.

Comment: Ordered early in 1963. Similar to the French landing craft of the Edic type built at the same yard.

LIEUTENANT MALGHAGH (EL KHAFIR alongside)   *1989*

AUXILIARIES

Notes: (1) There is also a yacht, *Essaouira*, 60 tons, from Italy in 1967, used as a training vessel for watchkeepers.
(2) Bazán delivered a harbour pusher tug, similar to Y 171 class, in December 1993.

2 LOGISTIC SUPPORT SHIPS

AD DAKHLA (ex-*Merc Caribe*) 405   **EL AIGH** (ex-*Merc Nordia*) 406

Measurement, tons: 1500 grt
Dimensions, feet (metres): 252.6 × 40 × 15.4 *(77 × 12.2 × 4.7)*
Main machinery: 1 Burmeister & Wain diesel; 1250 hp(m) *(919 kW)*; 1 shaft
Speed, knots: 11
Guns: 2—14.5 mm MGs.

Comment: Logistic support vessels with four 5 ton cranes. Former cargo ships built by Fredrickshavn Vaerft in 1973 and acquired in 1981.

EL AIGH   *1989*

1 TRANSPORT SHIP

ARRAFIQ (ex-*Thjelvar*, ex-*Gotland*) 407

Measurement, tons: 2990 grt, 784 dwt
Dimensions, feet (metres): 305.8 × 53.8 × 13.8 *(93.2 × 16.4 × 4.2)*
Main machinery: 4 Werkspoor 16V diesels; 8000 hp(m) *(5.88 MW)*; 4 shafts
Speed, knots: 18.5

Comment: Former Ro-Ro ferry converted as a troop transport.

ARRAFIQ   *1990*

SURVEY AND RESEARCH SHIP

1 ROBERT D CONRAD CLASS

Name	No	Builders	Commissioned
ABU EL BARAKAT AL BARBARI (ex-*Bartlett*)	(ex-T-AGOR 13)	Northwest Marine Iron Works, Portland, Oregon	31 Mar 1969

Displacement, tons: 1200 light; 1370 full load
Dimensions, feet (metres): 208.9 × 40 × 15.3 *(63.7 × 12.2 × 4.7)*
Main machinery: Diesel-electric; 2 Caterpillar D 378 diesel generators; 1 motor; 1000 hp *(746 kW)*; 1 shaft; bow thruster
Speed, knots: 13.5. **Range, miles:** 12 000 at 12 kts
Complement: 41 (9 officers, 15 scientists)
Radars: Navigation: TM 1660/12S; I band.

Comment: Leased from the US on 26 July 1993. Fitted with instrumentation and laboratories to measure gravity and magnetism, water temperature, sound transmission in water, and the profile of the ocean floor. Special features include 10 ton capacity boom and winches for handling over-the-side equipment; bow thruster; 620 hp gas turbine (housed in funnel structure) for providing 'quiet' power when conducting experiments; can propel the ship at 6.5 kts.
Ships of this class are in service with Brazil, Mexico, New Zealand, Chile and Tunisia.

ABU EL BARAKAT AL BARABARI (US colours)   *12/1991, Giorgio Arra*

CUSTOMS/COAST GUARD/POLICE

4 P 32 TYPE (COASTAL PATROL CRAFT)

Name	No	Builders	Commissioned
ERRAID	209	CMN, Cherbourg	18 Mar 1988
ERRACED	210	CMN, Cherbourg	15 Apr 1988
EL KACED	211	CMN, Cherbourg	17 May 1988
ESSAID	212	CMN, Cherbourg	4 July 1988

Displacement, tons: 89 full load
Dimensions, feet (metres): 105 × 17.7 × 4.6 *(32 × 5.4 × 1.4)*
Main machinery: 2 SACM MGO 12V BZSHR diesels; 2700 hp(m) *(1.98 MW)*; 2 shafts
Speed, knots: 28. **Range, miles:** 1500 at 15 kts
Complement: 17
Guns: 1 Oerlikon 20 mm.
Radars: Navigation: Decca; I band.

Comment: Almost identical to the El Wacil class listed under Light Forces. Ordered in July 1985.

P 32 TYPE   *1988*

18 ARCOR 46 CLASS (COASTAL PATROL CRAFT)

D01-D18

Displacement, tons: 15 full load
Dimensions, feet (metres): 47.6 × 13.8 × 4.3 *(14.5 × 4.2 × 1.3)*
Main machinery: 2 Uni Diesel UD18 V8 M5; 1010 hp(m) *(742 kW)* sustained; 2 shafts
Speed, knots: 32
Complement: 6
Guns: 2 Browning 12.7 mm MGs.
Radars: Surface search: Racal Decca; I band.

Comment: Ordered from Arcor, La Teste in June 1985. GRP hulls. Delivered in groups of three from April to September 1987. Used for patrolling the Mediterranean coastline.

ARCOR 46   *1987, Arcor*

15 ARCOR 53 CLASS (COASTAL PATROL CRAFT)

Displacement, tons: 17 full load
Dimensions, feet (metres): 52.5 × 13 × 3.9 *(16 × 4 × 1.2)*
Main machinery: 2 diesels; 2 shafts
Speed, knots: 35
Complement: 6
Guns: 1—12.7 mm MG.
Radars: Surface search: Racal Decca; I band.

Comment: Ordered from Arcor, La Teste in 1990 for the Police Force. Delivered at one a month from October 1992.

3 SAR CRAFT

HAOUZ   ASSA   TARIK

Displacement, tons: 40 full load
Dimensions, feet (metres): 63.6 × 15.7 × 4.3 *(19.4 × 4.8 × 1.3)*
Main machinery: 2 diesels; 1400 hp(m) *(1.03 MW)*; 2 shafts
Speed, knots: 20
Complement: 6

Comment: Rescue craft built by Schweers, Bardenfleth, and delivered in 1991.

ARCOR 53   *1992, Arcor*

MOZAMBIQUE

General

The 14 year civil war ended in October 1992, although there have been frequent violations since then. Apart from a Halmatic 44 ft pilot craft ordered in January 1993, none of the former naval craft were operational by the end of 1993. It is possible that some of the vessels listed under *Deletions* may be recoverable in 1994 with UN assistance. There may also be some 18 m patrol craft built in India.

Bases

Maputo (Naval HQ); Nacala; Beira; Pemba (Porto Amelia); Metangula (Lake Malawi).

Mercantile Marine

Lloyd's Register of Shipping:
  103 vessels of 36 105 tons gross

DELETIONS

1991-92   2 SO 1 class, 2 Jupiter class, 1 Alfange class
1992-93   3 Zhuk class, 2 Yevgenya class

NAMIBIA

General

A Coast Guard is slowly being established for Fisheries Patrol. The vessels listed are those in service in early 1994. The *Globe* lease expired in 1993, and *Benguella* is a small vessel used only for Fisheries research.

Base

Walvis Bay

Mercantile Marine:

Lloyd's Register of Shipping:
  76 vessels of 35 837 tons gross

PATROL FORCES

1 OSPREY FV 710 CLASS

Name	No	Builders	Commissioned
HAVØRNEN	—	Frederikshavn Vaerft	July 1979

Displacement, tons: 505 full load
Dimensions, feet (metres): 164 × 34.5 × 9 *(50 × 10.5 × 2.8)*
Main machinery: 2 Burmeister & Wain Alpha 16V23L diesels; 4640 hp(m) *(3.41 MW)*; 2 shafts; cp props
Speed, knots: 20
Complement: 15 plus 20 spare
Radars: Navigation: Furuno FRM 64; I band.

Comment: Leased from Denmark in late 1993, retaining some Danish crew. The helicopter deck can handle up to Lynx size aircraft and there is a slipway on the stern for launching an RIB. Similar ships in service in Greece, Morocco and Senegal.

1 PATROL SHIP

Name	No	Builders	Commissioned
ORYX (ex-*S to S*)	—	Bremen, Germany	1975

Displacement, tons: 406 full load
Dimensions, feet (metres): 149.9 × 28.9 × 7.9 *(45.7 × 8.8 × 2.4)*
Main machinery: 1 Deutz diesel; 2000 hp(m) *(1.47 MW)*; 1 shaft
Speed, knots: 14. **Range, miles:** 4100 at 11 kts
Complement: 20 (6 officers)
Guns: 1—12.7 mm MG.
Radars: Surface search: Furuno ARPA FR 1525; I band.
Navigation: Furuno FR 805D; I band.

Comment: Built for the Nautical Investment Company, Panama and used as a yacht by the Managing Director of Fiat. Acquired in 1993 by Namibia.

HAVØRNEN   *1993, Royal Danish Navy*

ORYX   *10/1993*

1 PATROL SHIP

Name	No	Builders	Commissioned
CUITO CUANAVALE (ex-*Oetind*)	—	Eikefjord, Norway	1988

Measurement, tons: 78 grt
Dimensions, feet (metres): 80.7 × 18.7 × 8.5 *(24.6 × 5.7 × 2.6)*
Main machinery: 2 GM diesels; 1920 hp *(1.43 MW)*; 2 shafts
Speed, knots: 27. **Range, miles:** 900 at 11 kts
Complement: 10 (5 officers)
Guns: 1—12.7 mm MG.
Radars: Surface search: Furuno ARPA FR 1510; I band.
Navigation: Koden MDC 431; I band.

Comment: Built as an ambulance ship for Svein Magne Hausen, then used as a ferry by Agasoester Boat Service. Sold to Namibia in 1993 with a largely Norwegian crew. The ship has a very short range.

CUITO CUANAVALE   *10/1993*

NATO

Note: The NATO frigate project NFR 90 died a predictable death as participating countries pulled out at the end of 1989. A number of bilateral projects are now being considered and some of these are taking advantage of the work done on NFR 90. For example Britain, France and Italy are collaborating, as are Germany, Netherlands and Spain, for new air defence escorts.

1 RESEARCH SHIP

Name	No	Builders	Commissioned
ALLIANCE	A1456	Fincantieri, Muggiano	6 May 1988

Displacement, tons: 2466 standard; 3180 full load
Dimensions, feet (metres): 305.1 × 49.9 × 16.7 *(93 × 15.2 × 5.1)*
Main machinery: Diesel-electric; 2 Fincantieri GMT B 230.12 M diesels; 6079 hp(m) *(4.47 MW)* sustained; 2 AEG CC 3127 generators; 2 AEG motors; 5100 hp(m) *(3.75 MW)*; 2 shafts; bow thruster
Speed, knots: 16. **Range, miles:** 8000 at 12 kts
Complement: 27 (10 officers) plus 23 scientists

Comment: Built at La Spezia and launched 9 July 1986. NATO's first wholly owned ship is a Public Service vessel of the German Navy with a German, British and Italian crew. Designed for oceanography and acoustic research, replacing the *Maria Paolina*. Based at La Spezia and operated by SACLANT Undersea Research Centre. Facilities include extensive laboratories, position location systems, silent propulsion, and overside deployment equipment. Can tow a 20 ton load at 12 kts. A Kongsberg gas turbine on 02 deck provides silent propulsion power at 1945 hp *(1.43 MW)* up to speeds of 12 kts. Hydrosweep side scan echo sounder fitted in 1993.

ALLIANCE   *9/1992, H M Steele*

NETHERLANDS

Headquarters' Appointments

Chief of the Naval Staff:
    Vice Admiral N W G Buis
Vice Chief of the Naval Staff:
    Rear Admiral C van Duyvendijk
Director, Material (Navy):
    Rear Admiral T J N van der Voort
Director, Personnel (Navy):
    Rear Admiral J L A van Aalst

Commands

Admiral Netherlands Fleet Command:
    Vice Admiral L Kroon
Commander Netherlands Task Group:
    Rear Admiral G G Hooft
Commandant General Royal Netherlands Marine Corps:
    Major-General R Spiekerman van Weezelenburg
Flag Officer Netherlands Antilles:
    Brigadier F E van Kappen
Hydrographer:
    Commodore E Bakker

Diplomatic Representation

Naval Attaché in London and Dublin:
    Captain W F L van Leeuwen
Naval Attaché in Madrid:
    Captain D T Notten
Naval Attaché in Paris and Lisbon:
    Captain W H Hoek
Naval Attaché in Washington and NLR SACLANT:
    Rear Admiral A van der Sande
Naval Attaché in Oslo, Copenhagen, Stockholm and Helsinki:
    Colonel C Receveur

Personnel

(a) 1994: 15 400 officers and ratings (including the Navy Air Service, 2965 Royal Netherlands Marine Corps and 850 female personnel) plus 5000 civilians
(b) 12 months' national service

Bases

Naval HQ: The Hague
Main Base: Den Helder
Minor Bases: Flushing and Curacao
Fleet Air Arm: NAS Valkenburg (LRMP),
NAS De Kooy (helicopters)
R Neth Marines: Rotterdam, Doorn and Texel
Training Base (Technical and Logistic): Amsterdam

Naval Air Arm (see *Shipborne Aircraft* section)

Personnel: 1500

Squadron	Aircraft	Task
7	Lynx (SH-14)	Utility and Transport/ SAR
320/321	P-3C Orion	LRMP
860	Lynx (SH-14)	Embarked

Royal Netherlands Marine Corps

Four (one in reserve) Marine battalions; one combat support battalion and one logistic battalion. Based at Doorn and in the Netherlands Antilles and Aruba.

Prefix to Ships' Names

Hr Ms

Strength of the Fleet

Type	Active (Reserve)	Building (Projected)
Submarines (Patrol)	6	—
Frigates	17	2
Mine Hunters	15	—
Minesweepers—Coastal	2 (4)	—
Submarine Support Ship	1	—
Amphibious Transport Ship (LPD)	—	1
Landing Craft	12	—
Survey Ships	3	—
Combat Support Ships	2	1
Training Ships	3	—
Tugs	12	—
Auxiliaries (Major)	9	—

Planned Fleet Disposition

(1) Two Task Groups, each with two air defence frigates, four Karel Doormans, two Kortanaers, one AOR, two SSK, 10 helicopters and six or seven MPA.
(2) One amphibious transport ship.
(3) MCMV of 15 Alkmaar class.
(4) Marine force of two battalions (arctic trained), one battalion for Antilles and Aruba, one battalion in reserve.
(5) Two hydrographic and one oceanographic vessels.

Mercantile Marine

Lloyd's Register of Shipping:
    1006 vessels of 3 085 644 tons gross

DELETIONS

Submarines

1991 *Tonijn* (museum)
1992 *Potvis* (trials)

Frigates

1992 *Banckert, Callenburgh, Van Kinsbergen* (all to Greece in 1993, 1994 and 1995 respectively)

Minesweepers

1992 *Hoogezand, Giethoorn, Venlo, Hoogeveen, Gemert*
1993 *Naaldwijk, Abcoude, Drachten, Ommen* (all in reserve)

Miscellaneous

1992 *Nautilus* (old), *Hydra* (old), *L 9512-9515, L 9518, Triton*
1993 *Wielingen*

PENNANT LIST

Submarines		F 829	Willem van der Zaan	Coastal Minesweepers		A 875	Regge
		F 830	Tjerk Hiddes			A 876	Hunze
S 802	Walrus	F 831	Van Amstel	M 823	Naarden	A 877	Rotte
S 803	Zeeleeuw	F 832	Abraham van der Hulst	M 830	Sittard	A 880	Bulgia
S 806	Zwaardvis	F 833	Van Nes			A 886	Cornelis Drebbel
S 807	Tijgerhaai	F 834	Van Galen (bldg)			A 887	Thetis
S 808	Dolfijn			Amphibious Forces		A 900	Mercuur
S 810	Bruinvis	Mine Hunters				A 903	Zeefakkel
				L 800	Rotterdam (bldg)	A 904	Buyskes
Frigates		M 850	Alkmaar	L 9530-35		A 905	Blommendal
		M 851	Delfzyl	L 9536-41		A 906	Tydeman
F 801	Tromp	M 852	Dordrecht			Y 8001	Van Speijk (old)
F 806	De Ruyter	M 853	Haarlem	Auxiliary Ships		Y 8018	Breezand
F 807	Kortenaer	M 854	Harlingen			Y 8019	Balgzand
F 811	Piet Heyn	M 855	Scheveningen	A 801	Pelikaan	Y 8050	Urania
F 812	Jacob van Heemskerck	M 856	Maassluis	A 832	Zuiderkruis	Y 8055	Schelde
F 813	Witte de With	M 857	Makkum	A 835	Poolster	Y 8056	Wierbalg
F 816	Abraham Crijnssen	M 858	Middelburg	A 836	Amsterdam (bldg)	Y 8057	Malzwin
F 823	Philips van Almonde	M 859	Hellevoetsluis	A 851	Cerberus	Y 8058	Zuidwal
F 824	Bloys van Treslong	M 860	Schiedam	A 852	Argus	Y 8059	Westwal
F 825	Jan van Brakel	M 861	Urk	A 853	Nautilus	Y 8500	Tax
F 826	Pieter Florisz	M 862	Zierikzee	A 854	Hydra		
F 827	Karel Doorman	M 863	Vlaardingen	A 872	Westgat		
F 828	Van Speijk (new) (bldg)	M 864	Willemstad	A 874	Linge		

SUBMARINES

Note: The Moray class is a private design by Rotterdam Drydock with the government giving limited financial support on condition that the company collaborates with developers of air independent systems (AIP). The old *Zeehond* hull is being used as a test platform for air independent propulsion by RDM with support from the Navy.

2 ZWAARDVIS CLASS

Name	No	Builders	Laid down	Launched	Commissioned
ZWAARDVIS	S 806	Rotterdamse Droogdok Mij, Rotterdam	14 July 1966	2 July 1970	18 Aug 1972
TIJGERHAAI	S 807	Rotterdamse Droogdok Mij, Rotterdam	14 July 1966	25 May 1971	20 Oct 1972

Displacement, tons: 2350 surfaced; 2640 dived
Dimensions, feet (metres): 216.5 × 27.6 × 23.3
  (66 × 8.4 × 7.1)
Main machinery: Diesel-electric; 3 Werkspoor RUB 215X12 diesels; 4200 hp(m) *(3.1 MW)*; 1 motor; 5100 hp(m) *(3.75 MW)*; 1 shaft
Speed, knots: 13 surfaced; 20 dived
Range, miles: 10 000 at 9 kts snorting
Complement: 67 (8 officers)

Missiles: SSM: McDonnell Douglas Sub-Harpoon; fitted for but not with.
Torpedoes: 6—21 in *(533 mm)* bow tubes. Honeywell Mk 48 Mod 4; wire-guided; active/passive homing to 38 km *(20.5 nm)* active at 55 kts; 50 km *(27 nm)* passive at 40 kts; warhead 267 kg and Honeywell NT 37D; wire-guided; active/passive homing to 20 km *(10.8 nm)* at 35 kts; warhead 150 kg; 20 torpedoes or missiles carried. Two torpedoes can be launched simultaneously.
Countermeasures: ESM: Radar warning.
Fire control: Signaal M8 digital system.
Radars: Surface search: RN Type 1001; I band.
Sonars: Thomson Sintra Eledone; hull-mounted; passive/active search and attack; medium frequency.
  GEC Avionics Type 2026; towed array; passive search; very low frequency.

Programmes: In the 1964 Navy Estimates a first instalment was approved for the construction of two conventionally powered submarines of tear-drop design. Planned to pay off for sale in 1996 when the last Walrus class is fully operational.
Modernisation: Mid-life conversion carried out in 1988 *(Tijgerhaai)* and 1989-91 *(Zwaardvis)*. New Thomson Sintra Eledone sonar, Signaal fire control and GEC Avionics Type 2026 towed array plus other minor improvements including a quieter propulsion drive unit and shaft.
Structure: Diving depth, 200 m *(656 ft)*.

ZWAARDVIS
4/1993, van Ginderen Collection

ZWAARDVIS
7/1993, J L M van der Burg

4 WALRUS CLASS

Name	No
WALRUS	S 802
ZEELEEUW	S 803
DOLFIJN	S 808
BRUINVIS	S 810

Builders	Laid down	Launched	Commissioned
Rotterdamse Droogdok Mij, Rotterdam	11 Oct 1979	28 Oct 1985 (13 Sep 1989)	25 Mar 1992
Rotterdamse Droogdok Mij, Rotterdam	24 Sep 1981	20 June 1987	25 Apr 1990
Rotterdamse Droogdok Mij, Rotterdam	12 June 1986	25 Apr 1990	29 Jan 1993
Rotterdamse Droogdok Mij, Rotterdam	14 Apr 1988	25 Apr 1992	July 1994

Displacement, tons: 1900 standard; 2465 surfaced; 2800 dived
Dimensions, feet (metres): 223.1 × 27.6 × 21.6 *(67.7 × 8.4 × 6.6)*
Main machinery: Diesel-electric; 3 SEMT-Pielstick 12 PA4 200 VG diesels; 6300 hp(m) *(4.63 MW)*; 3 alternators; 2.88 MW; 1 Holec motor; 6910 hp(m) *(5.1 MW)*; 1 shaft; 7-bladed propeller
Speed, knots: 13 surfaced; 20 dived
Range, miles: 10 000 at 9 kts snorting
Complement: 52 (7 officers)

Missiles: SSM: McDonnell Douglas Sub-Harpoon; active radar homing to 130 km *(70 nm)* at 0.9 Mach; warhead 227 kg.
Torpedoes: 4—21 in *(533 mm)* tubes. Honeywell Mk 48 Mod 4; wire-guided; active/passive homing to 38 km *(20.5 nm)* active at 55 kts; 50 km *(27 nm)* passive at 40 kts; warhead 267 kg and Honeywell NT 37D; wire-guided; active/passive homing to 20 km *(10.8 nm)* at 35 kts; warhead 150 kg; 20 torpedoes or missiles carried. Mk 19 Turbine ejection pump. Mk 67 water-ram discharge.
Mines: 40 in lieu of torpedoes.
Countermeasures: ESM: ARGOS 700; radar warning.
Fire control: Signaal SEWACO VIII action data automation. Signaal Gipsy data system. GTHW integrated Harpoon and Torpedo FCS.
Radars: Surface search: Signaal/Racal ZW 07; I band; range 29 km *(16 nm)* surfaced.
Sonars: Thomson Sintra TSM 2272 Eledone Octopus; hull-mounted; passive/active search and attack; medium frequency.
GEC Avionics Type 2026; towed array; passive search; very low frequency.
Thomson Sintra DUUX 5; passive ranging and intercept.

Programmes: In the 1975 Navy Estimates money was set aside for design work on this class and a contract for the building of the first was signed 16 June 1979, the second was on 17 December 1979. In 1981 various changes to the design were made which resulted in a delay of one to two years. *Dolfijn* and *Bruinvis* ordered 16 August 1985; prefabrication started late 1985. Completion of *Walrus* delayed by serious fire 14 August 1986; hull undamaged but cabling and computers destroyed. *Walrus* re-launched 13 September 1989.

BRUINVIS   *9/1993, Diego Quevedo*

Structure: These are improved Zwaardvis class with similar dimensions and silhouettes except for X stern. Use of H T steel increases the diving depth by some 50 per cent. New Gipsy fire control and electronic command system fitted and automation reduces the crew from 65 to 50. Diving depth, 300 m *(984 ft)*. Pilkington Optronics CK 24 search and CH 74 attack periscopes.
Operational: Weapon systems evaluations completed 1990-93.

DOLFIJN   *7/1993, J L M van der Burg*

FRIGATES

0 + (2) AIR DEFENCE SHIPS

Displacement, tons: 4500 full load
Main machinery: CODOG or CODAD; 2 shafts
Speed, knots: 28-30 kts
Complement: 200

Missiles: SSM: 8 Harpoon ❶.
SAM: Mk 41 (40 cell) VLS ❷; for Standard SM2-MR and Evolved Sea Sparrow.
Guns: 2 Bofors 120 mm/50 ❸.
Goalkeeper 30 mm CIWS ❹.
Torpedoes: 4—324 mm (2 twin) Mk 32 Mod 9 fixed launchers ❺.
Countermeasures: Decoys: Chaff launchers.
ESM/ECM: Argo APECS II; intercept/jammer.
Combat data systems: SEWACO FD; Link; SATCOMs.
Fire control: Sirius IRST optronic director ❻.
Radars: Air search: SMART-L ❼; 3D.
Air/surface search: APAR (phased array) ❽.
Navigation: I band.
Sonars: Bow-mounted; active search and attack; medium frequency.

Helicopters: 1 NH-90 ❾.

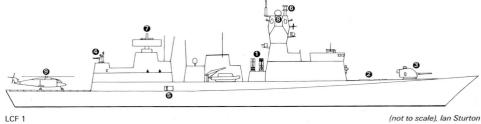

LCF 1   *(not to scale), Ian Sturton*

Programmes: It is planned to order two air defence frigates (LCF project) in 1996 in collaboration with Germany and Spain to an enlarged Karel Doorman design. Shipyards in the three countries are co-operating in the design. Project definition was awarded to Royal Schelde on 15 December 1993. Contract is expected for the first of class in 1995/96 with trials to start in 2001. These ships are to replace the Tromp class.
Structure: Details shown represent preliminary ideas and may be changed during project definition.

2 TROMP CLASS

Name	No	Builders	Laid down	Launched	Commissioned
TROMP	F 801	Koninklijke Maatschappij De Schelde, Flushing	4 Aug 1971	2 June 1973	3 Oct 1975
DE RUYTER	F 806	Koninklijke Maatschappij De Schelde, Flushing	22 Dec 1971	9 Mar 1974	3 June 1976

Displacement, tons: 3665 standard; 4308 full load
Dimensions, feet (metres): 454 × 48.6 × 15.1
(138.4 × 14.8 × 4.6)
Main machinery: COGOG; 2 RR Olympus TM3B gas turbines;
50 880 hp *(37.9 MW)* sustained;
2 RR Tyne RM 1C gas turbines; 9900 hp *(7.4 MW)* sustained;
2 shafts
Speed, knots: 30. **Range, miles:** 5000 at 18 kts
Complement: 306 (34 officers)

Missiles: SSM: 8 McDonnell Douglas Harpoon (2 quad) launchers ❶; active radar homing to 130 km *(70 nm)* at 0.9 Mach;
warhead 227 kg; 16 missiles.
SAM: 40 GDC Pomona Standard SM-1MR; Mk 13 Mod 4
launcher ❷; command guidance; semi-active radar homing to
46 km *(25 nm)* at 2 Mach.
Raytheon Sea Sparrow Mk 29 octuple launcher ❸; semi-active
radar homing to 14.6 km *(8 nm)* at 2.5 Mach; warhead 39 kg;
16 missiles.
Guns: 2 Bofors 4.7 in *(120 mm)*/50 (twin) ❹; 85° elevation; 42
rounds/minute to 20 km *(10.8 nm)* anti-surface; 12 km
(6.5 nm) anti-aircraft; weight of shell 24 kg.
Signaal SGE-30 Goalkeeper with GE 30 mm ❺; 7-barrelled;
4200 rounds/minute combined to 2 km.
2 Oerlikon 20 mm.
Torpedoes: 6—324 mm US Mk 32 (2 triple) tubes ❻. Honeywell
Mk 46 Mod 5; anti-submarine; active/passive homing to 11 km
(5.9 nm) at 40 kts; warhead 44 kg.

DE RUYTER (Scale 1 : 1200), Ian Sturton

Countermeasures: Decoys: 2 Loral Hycor SRBOC ❼; IR flares
and chaff.
ESM/ECM: Ramses; intercept and jammer.
Combat data systems: Signaal SEWACO I action data auto-
mation; Links 10 and 11. Scot SATCOM ❽.
Fire control: Signaal WM 25 for guns and missiles.
Radars: Air/surface search: Signaal MTTR/SPS 01 ❾; 3D; F
band.
Navigation: Two Decca 1226; I band.
Fire control: Two Raytheon SPG 51C ❿; G/I band.
Signaal WM 25 ⓫; I/J band; range 46 km *(25 nm)*.
Sonars: CWE 610; hull-mounted; active search and attack;
medium frequency.

Helicopters: 1 Westland SH-14B Lynx ⓬.

Programmes: First design allowance was voted for in 1967 estimates. The intention is to replace both ships towards the end
of the century in collaboration with other European navies
needing similar ships in the same timescale.
Modernisation: Modernisation plans cancelled in 1988 as an
economy measure but partially resurrected in 1990.
Structure: Goalkeeper is fitted on the starboard side of the
hangar roof.
Operational: Fitted as Flagships.

DE RUYTER 10/1992, W Sartori

TROMP 3/1993, J L M van der Burg

2 JACOB VAN HEEMSKERCK CLASS

Name	No
JACOB VAN HEEMSKERCK	F 812
WITTE DE WITH	F 813

Builders	Laid down	Launched	Commissioned
Koninklijke Maatschappij De Schelde, Flushing	21 Jan 1981	5 Nov 1983	15 Jan 1986
Koninklijke Maatschappij De Schelde, Flushing	15 Dec 1981	25 Aug 1984	17 Sep 1986

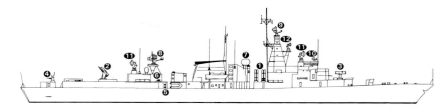

JACOB VAN HEEMSKERCK   (Scale 1 : 1200), Ian Sturton

Displacement, tons: 3750 full load approx

Dimensions, feet (metres): 428 × 47.9 × 14.1 (20.3 screws)
(130.5 × 14.6 × 4.3 (6.2))

Main machinery: COGOG; 2 RR Olympus TM3B gas turbines;
50 880 hp (37.9 MW) sustained;
2 RR Tyne RM1C gas turbines; 9900 hp (7.4 MW) sustained;
2 shafts; cp props

Speed, knots: 30. **Range, miles:** 4700 at 16 kts on Tynes

Complement: 197 (23 officers)

Missiles: SSM: 8 McDonnell Douglas Harpoon (2 quad) launchers ❶; active radar homing to 130 km (70 nm) at 0.9 Mach;
warhead 227 kg.
SAM: 40 GDC Pomona Standard SM-1MR; Mk 13 Mod 1
launcher ❷; command guidance; semi-active radar homing to
46 km (25 nm) at 2 Mach.
Raytheon Sea Sparrow Mk 29 octuple launcher ❸; semi-active
radar homing to 14.6 km (8 nm) at 2.5 Mach; warhead 39 kg;
24 missiles.

Guns: 1 Signaal SGE-30 Goalkeeper ❹ with General Electric
30 mm 7-barrelled; 4200 rounds/minute combined to 2 km.
2 Oerlikon 20 mm.

Torpedoes: 4—324 mm US Mk 32 (2 twin) tubes ❺. Honeywell
Mk 46 Mod 5; anti-submarine; active/passive homing to 11 km
(5.9 nm) at 40 kts; warhead 44 kg.

Countermeasures: Decoys: 2 Loral Hycor Mk 36 SRBOC 6-tubed
fixed quad launchers ❻; IR flares and chaff to 4 km (2.2 nm).
ESM/ECM: Ramses; intercept and jammer.

Combat data systems: Signaal SEWACO VI action data automation; Link 11. SATCOM ❼.

Radars: Air search: Signaal LW 08 ❽; D band; range 264 km
(145 nm) for 2 m² target.
Air/surface search: Signaal DA 05 ❾; E/F band; range 137 km
(75 nm) for 2 m² target. To be replaced in refit by Signaal
Smart; 3D.
Surface search: Signaal ZW 06 ❿; I band; range 26 km (14 nm).
Fire control: Two Signaal STIR 240 ⓫; I/J/K band; range
140 km (76 nm) for 1 m² target.
Signaal STIR 180 ⓬; I/J/K band.

Sonars: Westinghouse SQS 509; hull-mounted; active search
and attack; medium frequency.

Programmes: Ordered as replacements for the two Kortenaer
class frigates sold to Greece. Same hull and engines.

Modernisation: Capability upkeep programme (CUP) planned
between 1999 and 2002. Twin SATCOM terminals fitted in
1993 to F 812, and is to be fitted in F 813 in 1994/95. The SHF
system is based on the USN WSC-6, with twin aerials providing
a 360° coverage even at high latitudes.

Operational: Air defence frigates with command facilities for a
task group commander and his staff.

JACOB VAN HEEMSKERCK   10/1993, H M Steele

7 KORTENAER CLASS

Name	No
KORTENAER	F 807
PIET HEYN	F 811
ABRAHAM CRIJNSSEN	F 816
PHILIPS VAN ALMONDE	F 823
BLOYS VAN TRESLONG	F 824
JAN VAN BRAKEL	F 825
PIETER FLORISZ (ex-Willem van der Zaan)	F 826

Builders	Laid down	Launched	Commissioned
Koninklijke Maatschappij De Schelde, Flushing	8 Apr 1975	18 Dec 1976	26 Oct 1978
Koninklijke Maatschappij De Schelde, Flushing	28 Apr 1977	3 June 1978	14 Apr 1981
Koninklijke Maatschappij De Schelde, Flushing	25 Oct 1978	16 May 1981	27 Jan 1983
Dok en Werfmaatschappij Wilton-Fijenoord	3 Oct 1977	11 Aug 1979	2 Dec 1981
Dok en Werfmaatschappij Wilton-Fijenoord	27 Apr 1978	15 Nov 1980	25 Nov 1982
Koninklijke Maatschappij De Schelde, Flushing	16 Nov 1979	16 May 1981	14 Apr 1983
Koninklijke Maatschappij De Schelde, Flushing	21 Jan 1981	8 May 1982	1 Oct 1983

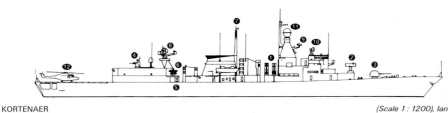

KORTENAER   (Scale 1 : 1200), Ian Sturton

Displacement, tons: 3050 standard; 3630 full load

Dimensions, feet (metres): 428 × 47.9 × 14.1; 20.3 (screws)
(130.5 × 14.6 × 4.3; 6.2)

Main machinery: CODOG; 2 RR Olympus TM3B gas turbines;
50 880 hp (37.9 MW) sustained;
2 RR Tyne RM1C gas turbines; 9900 hp (7.4 MW) sustained;
2 shafts; cp props

Speed, knots: 30. **Range, miles:** 4700 at 16 kts on Tynes

Complement: 176 (18 officers) plus 24 spare berths

Missiles: SSM: 8 McDonnell Douglas Harpoon (2 quad) launchers ❶; active radar homing to 130 km (70 nm) at 0.9 Mach;
warhead 227 kg.
SAM: Raytheon Sea Sparrow Mk 29 octuple launcher ❷; semi-
active radar homing to 14.6 km (8 nm) at 2.5 Mach; warhead
39 kg; 24 missiles.

Guns: 1 OTO Melara 3 in (76 mm)/62 compact ❸; 85° elevation;
85 rounds/minute to 16 km (8.6 nm) anti-surface; 12 km
(6.5 nm) anti-aircraft; weight of shell 6 kg. New 100 rounds/
minute version to be fitted.
Signaal SGE-30 Goalkeeper with General Electric 30 mm ❹;
7-barrelled; 4200 rounds/minute combined to 2 km.
2 Oerlikon 20 mm.

Torpedoes: 4—324 mm US Mk 32 (2 twin) tubes ❺. Honeywell
Mk 46 Mod 5; anti-submarine; active/passive homing to 11 km
(5.9 nm) at 40 kts; warhead 44 kg.

Countermeasures: Decoys: 2 Loral Hycor SRBOC Mk 36 6-tubed
launchers ❻; chaff distraction or centroid modes.
ESM/ECM: Ramses ❼; intercept and jammer.

Combat data systems: Signaal SEWACO II action data automation; Link 11. SATCOM.

Radars: Air search: Signaal LW 08 ❽; D band; range 264 km
(145 nm) for 2 m² target.
Surface search: Signaal ZW 06 ❾; I band; range 26 km (14 nm).
Fire control: Signaal STIR ❿; I/J band; range 140 km (76 nm) for
1 m² target.
Signaal WM 25 ⓫; I/J band; range 46 km (25 nm).

Sonars: Westinghouse SQS 505 (F 807, 811 and 816); SQS 509
(F 823-F 826); bow-mounted; active search and attack;
medium frequency.

Helicopters: 2 Westland SH-14B Lynx ⓬.

Modernisation: During refit in 1985-86 Pieter Florisz was
adapted for a limited number of female crew (about 25); others
similarly converted. Goalkeeper has replaced the 40 mm gun
on the hangar roof. Plans to fit SMART fire control radars have

PHILIPS VAN ALMONDE   3/1993, Giorgio Arra

been cancelled. The last four are to be fitted with same SAT-
COM twin aerial as in the Karel Doorman class.

Structure: Although only one Lynx is carried there is hangar
accommodation for two. TACTASS is not planned except that
the last two ships had a temporary fit prior to the completion of
the first of the Karel Doorman class. Jan Van Brakel had the
trials SMART radar fitted on her hangar roof in 1990 with the
control room in the hangar.

Sales: Two sold to Greece during construction, mid-1980 and
mid-1981. Banckert to Greece 14 May 1993, Callenburg 30
March 1994 and Van Kinsbergen 1 February 1995. Sale agreed
for all three on 11 November 1992, including refits by De
Schelde, Flushing and the removal of Goalkeeper CIWS. Piet
Heyn, Abraham Crijnssen and Kortenaer are planned to be sold
in 1996.

6 + 2 KAREL DOORMAN CLASS

Name	No	Builders	Laid down	Launched	Commissioned
KAREL DOORMAN	F 827	Koninklijke Maatschappij De Schelde, Flushing	26 Feb 1985	20 Apr 1988	31 May 1991
WILLEM VAN DER ZAAN	F 829	Koninklijke Maatschappij De Schelde, Flushing	6 Nov 1985	21 Jan 1989	28 Nov 1991
TJERK HIDDES	F 830	Koninklijke Maatschappij De Schelde, Flushing	28 Oct 1986	9 Dec 1989	3 Dec 1992
VAN AMSTEL	F 831	Koninklijke Maatschappij De Schelde, Flushing	3 May 1988	19 May 1990	27 May 1993
ABRAHAM VAN DER HULST	F 832	Koninklijke Maatschappij De Schelde, Flushing	8 Feb 1989	7 Sep 1991	15 Dec 1993
VAN NES	F 833	Koninklijke Maatschappij De Schelde, Flushing	10 Jan 1990	16 May 1992	2 June 1994
VAN GALEN	F 834	Koninklijke Maatschappij De Schelde, Flushing	7 June 1990	21 Nov 1992	Dec 1994
VAN SPEIJK	F 828	Koninklijke Maatschappij De Schelde, Flushing	1 Oct 1991	26 Mar 1994	Sep 1995

Displacement, tons: 3320 full load
Dimensions, feet (metres): 401.1 × 47.2 × 14.1
(122.3 × 14.4 × 4.3)
Main machinery: CODOG; 2 RR Spey SM1C; 33 800 hp
(25.2 MW) sustained (early ships of the class will initially only
have SM1A gas generators and 30 800 hp *(23 MW)* sustained
available); 2 Stork-Wärtsilä 12SW280 diesels; 8700 hp
(6.4 MW) sustained; 2 shafts; cp props
Speed, knots: 30 (Speys); 21 (diesels). **Range, miles:** 5000 at
18 kts
Complement: 156 (16 officers) (accommodation for 163)

Missiles: SSM: 8 McDonnell Douglas Harpoon (2 quad) launchers ❶; active radar homing to 130 km *(70 nm)* at 0.9 Mach;
warhead 227 kg.
SAM: Raytheon Sea Sparrow Mk 48 vertical launchers ❷; semi-
active radar homing to 14.6 km *(8 nm)* at 2.5 Mach; warhead
39 kg; 16 missiles. Canisters mounted on port side of hangar.
Guns: 1—3 in *(76 mm)*/62 OTO Melara compact Mk 100 ❸; 85°
elevation; 100 rounds/minute to 16 km *(8.6 nm)* anti-surface;
12 km *(6.5 nm)* anti-aircraft; weight of shell 6 kg. This is the latest version with an improved rate of fire.
1 Signaal SGE-30 Goalkeeper with General Electric 30 mm
7-barrelled ❹; 4200 rounds/minute combined to 2 km.
2 Oerlikon 20 mm; 55° elevation; 800 rounds/minute to 2 km.
Torpedoes: 4—324 mm US Mk 32 (2 twin) tubes (mounted
inside the after superstructure) ❺. Honeywell Mk 46 Mod 5;
anti-submarine; active/passive homing to 11 km *(5.9 nm)* at
40 kts; warhead 44 kg.
Countermeasures: Decoys: 2 Loral Hycor SRBOC 6-tubed fixed
Mk 36 quad launchers; IR flares and chaff to 4 km *(2.2 nm)*.
ESM/ECM: Argo APECS II (includes AR 700 ESM); intercept and
jammers.
Combat data systems: Signaal SEWACO VIIB action data auto-
mation; Link 11. SATCOM ❻.
Fire control: Signaal IRSCAN infra-red detector (fitted in F 829
for trials).
Radars: Air/surface search: Signaal SMART ❼; 3D; F band.
Air/surface search: Signaal LW 08 ❽; D band.
Navigation: Racal Decca 1226; I band.
Fire control: Two Signaal STIR ❾; I/J/K band; range 140 km
(76 nm) for 1 m² target.
Sonars: Signaal PHS 36; hull-mounted; active search and attack;
medium frequency.
Thomson Sintra Anaconda DSBV 61; towed array; low
frequency.

Helicopters: 1 Westland SH-14 Lynx ❿.

Programmes: This class is designed to be interoperable with the
Kortenaer class frigates. Declaration of intent signed on
29 February 1984 although the contract was not signed until

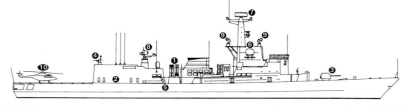

KAREL DOORMAN   *(Scale 1 : 1200), Ian Sturton*

VAN AMSTEL   *3/1993, G Toremans*

29 June 1985 by which time the design had been completed.
A further four ordered 10 April 1986. Because the trials ship
Van Speijk is still operational, names have been shuffled to
make the new *Van Speijk* the last of the class but she has
retained her allocated pennant number.
Modernisation: SEWACO VII(A) operational from January 1992
and VII(B) from mid-1994. By 1994 all fitted with APECS II EW
system and DSBV 61 towed array. IRSCAN infra-red detector

fitted on hangar roof in *Willem van der Zaan* for trials in 1993.
SHF SATCOM based on the USN WSC-6, with twin aerials providing a 360° coverage even at high latitudes.
Structure: The VLS SAM is similar to Canadian Halifax and Greek
MEKO classes. The ship is designed to reduce radar and IR signatures and has extensive NBCD arrangements. Full automation and roll stabilisation fitted.

ABRAHAM VAN DER HULST   *9/1993, van Ginderen Collection*

KAREL DOORMAN   *7/1993, J L M van der Burg*

SHIPBORNE AIRCRAFT

Numbers/Type: 22 Westland Lynx Mks 25B/27A/81A.
Operational speed: 125 kts *(232 km/h)*.
Service ceiling: 12 500 ft *(3810 m)*.
Range: 320 nm *(590 km)*.
Role/Weapon systems: ASW, SAR and utility helicopter series all being converted to SH-14D type. Mk 25B, Mk 27A and Mk 81A can all be embarked for ASW duties in escorts. Sensors: Ferranti Sea Spray radar, Alcatel DUAV-4 dipping sonar, FLIR Model 2000; Ferranti AWARE-3 ESM (being fitted). Weapons: 2 × Mk 46 torpedoes or depth bombs.

LYNX

6/1992, Stefan Terzibaschitsch

LAND-BASED MARITIME AIRCRAFT

Numbers/Type: 2 Fokker F27 Maritime.
Operational speed: 250 kts *(463 km/h)*.
Service ceiling: 29 500 ft *(8990 m)*.
Range: 2700 nm *(5000 km)*.
Role/Weapon systems: Netherlands Antilles for ocean surveillance; operated by Air Force with naval observers. Sensors: APS-504 search radar, LAPADS processor. Weapons: ASW; 4 × Mk 46 torpedoes, 6 × underwing points. ASV; has provision for missiles.

Numbers/Type: 13 Lockheed P-3C/Update II Orion.
Operational speed: 410 kts *(760 km/h)*.
Service ceiling: 28 300 ft *(8625 m)*.
Range: 4000 nm *(7410 km)*.
Role/Weapon systems: Long-range MR and NATO area ocean surveillance, particularly for ASW/ASV operations. Update planned for 1997-2001. Sensors: APS-115 radar, FLIR Model 2000HP; AQS-81 MAD, AQA 7 processor, AQS-114 computer, IFF, ECM/ESM, sonobuoys. Weapons: ASW; 8 × Mk 46 torpedoes, depth bombs or mines. Underwing stations for Harpoon missiles for which procurement has been suspended.

MINE WARFARE FORCES

Note: The decision taken on 12 January 1993 to cancel the new minesweeper programme has been confirmed.

15 ALKMAAR (TRIPARTITE) CLASS (MINEHUNTERS)

Name	No	Laid down	Launched	Commissioned
ALKMAAR	M 850	30 Jan 1979	18 May 1982	28 May 1983
DELFZYL	M 851	29 May 1980	29 Oct 1982	17 Aug 1983
DORDRECHT	M 852	5 Jan 1981	26 Feb 1983	16 Nov 1983
HAARLEM	M 853	16 June 1981	6 May 1983	12 Jan 1984
HARLINGEN	M 854	30 Nov 1981	9 July 1983	12 Apr 1984
SCHEVENINGEN	M 855	24 May 1982	2 Dec 1983	18 July 1984
MAASSLUIS	M 856	7 Nov 1982	5 May 1984	12 Dec 1984
MAKKUM	M 857	25 Feb 1983	27 Sep 1984	13 May 1985
MIDDELBURG	M 858	11 July 1983	23 Feb 1985	10 Dec 1986
HELLEVOETSLUIS	M 859	12 Dec 1983	18 July 1985	20 Feb 1987
SCHIEDAM	M 860	6 May 1984	20 Dec 1985	9 July 1986
URK	M 861	1 Oct 1984	2 May 1986	10 Dec 1986
ZIERIKZEE	M 862	25 Feb 1985	4 Oct 1986	7 May 1987
VLAARDINGEN	M 863	6 May 1986	4 Aug 1988	15 Mar 1989
WILLEMSTAD	M 864	3 Oct 1986	27 Jan 1989	20 Sep 1989

Displacement, tons: 562 standard; 595 full load
Dimensions, feet (metres): 168.9 × 29.2 × 8.5 *(51.5 × 8.9 × 2.6)*
Main machinery: 1 Brons-Werkspoor A-RUB 215X-12 diesel; 1860 hp(m) *(1.35 MW)* sustained; 1 shaft; Lips cp prop; 2 active rudders; 2 motors; 240 hp(m) *(179 kW)*; 2 bow thrusters
Speed, knots: 15 diesel; 7 electric. **Range, miles:** 3000 at 12 kts
Complement: 29-42 depending on task

Guns: 1 Giat 20 mm (an additional short-range missile system may be added for patrol duties).
Countermeasures: MCM: 2 PAP 104 remote-controlled submersibles. Mechanical minesweeping gear and OD 3.
Combat data systems: Signaal Sewaco IX. SATCOM.
Radars: Navigation: Racal Decca TM 1229C; I band.
Sonars: Thomson Sintra DUBM 21A; hull-mounted; minehunting; 100 kHz (± 10 kHz).

Programmes: The two Indonesian ships ordered in 1985 took the place of M 863 and 864 whose laying down was delayed as a result. This class is the Netherlands' part of a tripartite co-operative plan with Belgium and France for GRP hulled minehunters. The whole class built by van der Giessen-de Noord. Ships were launched virtually ready for trials.
Modernisation: Conversions start in 1995 for three of the class to become Troika control ships operating four drones each. The remainder are to have minehunting capability upgrades including a new mine disposal system. Four of the class will also be fitted with propelled variable depth sonars (PVDS). The drones are to be based on the German type, developed by Signaal.
Structure: A 5 ton container can be shipped, stored for varying tasks—research; patrol; extended diving; drone control.
Operational: Endurance, 15 days. Automatic radar navigation system. Automatic data processing and display. EVEC 20. Decca Hi-fix positioning system. Alcatel dynamic positioning system. One of the class is to be converted for use as a survey vessel but can be restored as a minehunter at three months notice.
Sales: Two of a modified design to Indonesia, completed March 1988.

2 DOKKUM CLASS (MINESWEEPERS—COASTAL)

Name	No	Builders	Commissioned
NAARDEN	M 823	Wilton-Fijenoord Niestern Shipbuilders	18 May 1956
SITTARD	M 830	Wilton-Fijenoord Niestern Shipbuilders	19 Dec 1956

Displacement, tons: 373 standard; 453 full load
Dimensions, feet (metres): 152.9 × 28.9 × 7.5 *(46.6 × 8.8 × 2.3)*
Main machinery: 2 Fijenoord MAN V64 diesels; 2500 hp(m) *(1.84 MW)*; 2 shafts
Speed, knots: 16. **Range, miles:** 2500 at 10 kts
Complement: 27-36 depending on task
Guns: 1 or 2 Oerlikon 20 mm.
Radars: Navigation: Racal Decca TM 1229C; I band.

Comment: 32 Western Union type coastal minesweepers were built in the Netherlands, 18 were under offshore procurement as the Dokkum class, with MAN engines. All launched in 1954-56 and completed in 1955-56. This class was subject to a fleet rehabilitation and modernisation programme completed by 1977 and a 'life prolonging' refit from the mid-1980s to 1991 for the last six. Included in the refit was additional accommodation in the form of a deckhouse. Five unmodernised vessels were scrapped in 1993. *Naaldwijk* M 809, *Abcoude* M 810, *Drachten* M 812 and *Ommen* M 813 were all put in reserve in 1993 but could be reactivated in emergency. The ex-*Dokkum* is a trials ship.

SITTARD

7/1993, Harald Carstens

AMPHIBIOUS FORCES

0 + 1 AMPHIBIOUS TRANSPORT SHIP (LPD)

Name	No	Builders	Commissioned
ROTTERDAM	L 800	Royal Schelde	1997

Displacement, tons: 12 000 full load
Dimensions, feet (metres): 492.1 × 82 × 19.3 *(150 × 25 × 5.9)*
Main machinery: 4 diesels (possibly diesel-electric); 2 shafts
Speed, knots: 20. **Range, miles:** 6000 at 14 kts
Complement: 115 plus 12 spare
Military lift: 600 troops; 170 APCs or 33 MBTs. 3 LCVP and 2 LCU/LCM or 6 LCVP
Guns: 2 Signaal Goalkeeper 30 mm. 4 Oerlikon 20 mm.
Combat data systems: SATCOM; Link 11.
Fire control: Signaal IRSCAN infra-red detector.
Radars: Air/surface search. Navigation.
Helicopters: 6 NH 90 or equivalent; or 4 EH 101 or equivalent.

Comment: Collaborative project with Spain. First steel cut in February 1994 with completion in 1997 by Royal Schelde. Can be used to transport a fully equipped battalion of Marines. Docking facilities for landing craft and a two-spot helicopter flight deck. Alternative employment as an SAR ship for environmental and disaster relief tasks.

ROTTERDAM

(not to scale), Royal Netherlands Navy

URK

9/1993, Hartmut Ehlers

6 LCVP Mk II

L 9530-9535

Displacement, tons: 17.5
Dimensions, feet (metres): 52.5 × 13.9 × 3.5 *(16 × 4.3 × 1.1)*
Main machinery: 1 DAF DKS 1160 M diesel; 300 hp(m) *(220 kW)* sustained; Schottel prop
Speed, knots: 11. Range, miles: 220 at 11 kts
Complement: 3
Military lift: 35 troops; 1 Land Rover or BV 202E Snowcat
Guns: 1 FN FAL 7.62 mm MG.
Radars: Navigation: Racal Decca 110; I band.

Comment: L 9530-9541 plus two extra ordered 27 October 1981 from Rijkswerf, Willemsoord and Schottel, Netherlands. First pair completed 1984, next three in 1985, last one in 1986. The rest were cancelled in favour of the Mk III design.

L 9535   *6/1993, van Ginderen Collection*

6 LCVP Mk III

L 9536-9541

Displacement, tons: 30 full load
Dimensions, feet (metres): 55.4 × 15.7 × 3.6 *(16.9 × 4.8 × 1.1)*
Main machinery: 2 diesels; 750 hp(m) *(551 kW)*; 2 shafts
Speed, knots: 14 (full load); 16.5 (light). Range, miles: 200 at 12 kts
Complement: 3
Military lift: 34 troops or 7 tons or 2 Land Rovers or 1 Snowcat
Guns: 1—7.62 mm MG.
Radars: Navigation: Racal Decca; I band.

Comment: Ordered from van der Giessen-de Noord 10 December 1988. First one laid down 10 August 1989, commissioned 16 October 1990. Last one commissioned 19 October 1992. These are an improvement over the Mk II type which did not come up to expectations.

L 9540   *7/1993, M Nitz*

SURVEY SHIPS

Note: There are also four survey boats 8901-8904 completed in 1989-90; dimensions 9.5 × 3.8 m; 1 Volvo Penta diesel of 170 hp(m) *(125 kW)*. The first two are carried by A 904 and A 905 respectively.

1 TYDEMAN CLASS (HYDROGRAPHIC/OCEANOGRAPHIC SHIP)

Name	No	Builders	Commissioned
TYDEMAN	A 906	Merwede, Hardinxveld, Giessendam	10 Nov 1976

Displacement, tons: 2977 full load
Dimensions, feet (metres): 295.9 × 47.2 × 15.7 *(90.2 × 14.4 × 4.8)*
Main machinery: Diesel-electric; 3 Stork-Werkspoor 8-FCHD-240 diesel generators; 3690 hp(m) *(2.71 MW)*; 1 motor; 2730 hp(m) *(2 MW)*; 1 shaft
1 Paxman diesel; 485 hp(m) *(356 kW)*; 1 active rudder; 300 hp(m) *(220 kW)*; bow thruster; 450 hp(m) *(330 kW)*
Speed, knots: 15. Range, miles: 15 700 at 10.3 kts; 10 300 at 13.5 kts
Complement: 62 (8 officers) plus 15 scientists
Radars: Navigation: Racal Decca; I band.
Sonars: Atlas-Deco 10 echo-sounders with Edig digitisers. KAe Deso 25 replacements.
Kelvin Hughes; hull-mounted; side-scan. Klein; towed; side-scan.
Elac; bow-mounted; wreck search; trainable in sectors on either bow.
Helicopters: 1 Westland UH-14A Lynx.

Comment: Ordered in October 1974. Laid down 29 April 1975, launched 18 December 1975. Able to operate oceanographic cables down to 7000 m. Has six laboratories and two container spaces each for 20 ft standard container. Has forward working deck with wet-hall, midships and after working decks, one 10 ton crane, one 4 ton crane and frames. Diving facilities. Passive stabilisation tank. Decca Hi-fix 6; Digital PDP computer; COMPLOT plotting system. Normally operates in the Atlantic and between March 1991 and March 1992 tested a derivative of the Thomson Sintra DUBM 41 towed sonar for the detection of mines buried up to 2 m deep. Major refit from April to November 1992 by van der Giessen-de Noord. The present plan is to pay off the ship in 2000 when hydrographic duties will be taken over by one of the Alkmaar class.

TYDEMAN   *7/1993, Harald Carstens*

2 BUYSKES CLASS

Name	No	Builders	Commissioned
BUYSKES	A 904	Boele's Scheepswerven en Machinefabriek BV, Bolnes	9 Mar 1973
BLOMMENDAL	A 905	Boele's Scheepswerven en Machinefabriek BV, Bolnes	22 May 1973

Displacement, tons: 967 standard; 1033 full load
Dimensions, feet (metres): 196.6 × 36.4 × 12 *(60 × 11.1 × 3.7)*
Main machinery: Diesel-electric; 3 Paxman 12 RPH diesel generators; 2100 hp *(1.57 MW)*; 1 motor; 1400 hp(m) *(1.03 MW)*; 1 shaft
Speed, knots: 13.5. Range, miles: 3000 at 11.5 kts
Complement: 43 (6 officers)
Radars: Navigation: Racal Decca; I band.
Sonars: Side-scanning and wreck-search.

Comment: Both designed primarily for hydrographic work but have also limited oceanographic and meteorological capability. They operate mainly in the North Sea. A data logging system is installed as part of the automatic handling of hydrographic data. HYDRAUT logging system; wire-drags. Marconi Bathyscan swath sounders. Atlas Elektronik Deso 25 echo sounders. They carry two 22 ft survey launches capable of 15 kts and two work-boats normally used for sweeping. Major refits in 1988-89.

BLOMMENDAL   *2/1993, Gilbert Gyssels*

AUXILIARIES

Note: In addition to vessels listed below, non self-propelled craft include Y 8514, floating crane built in 1974 and about 40 others including tank-cleaning vessels, barges, berthing pontoons (Y 8594-8617), diving pontoons (Y 8579-92). Other small craft include general purpose harbour and dockyard craft (Y 8351-2) (Y 8200-03) (Y 8012), four diving craft attached to *Thetis* (Y 8579-82), seven targets (Y 8694-99, Y 8704), four small transports (Y 8343-46) and eight fuel lighters (Y 8347-52, Y 8536, Y 8538).

1 SUBMARINE SUPPORT SHIP and TORPEDO TENDER

Name	No	Builders	Commissioned
MERCUUR	A 900	Koninklijke Maatschappij de Schelde	21 Aug 1987

Displacement, tons: 1400 full load
Dimensions, feet (metres): 212.6 × 39.4 × 14.1 *(64.8 × 12 × 4.3)*
Main machinery: 2 Brons 61-20/27 diesels; 1100 hp(m) *(808 kW)*; 2 shafts; bow thruster
Speed, knots: 14
Complement: 39
Guns: 2 Oerlikon 20 mm.
Torpedoes: 3—324 mm (triple) tubes. 1—21 in *(533 mm)* underwater tube.
Mines: Can lay mines.
Sonars: SQR 01; hull-mounted; passive search.

Comment: Replacement for previous ship of same name. Ordered 13 June 1984. Laid down 6 November 1985. Floated out 25 October 1986. Can launch training and research torpedoes above and below the waterline. Services, maintains and recovers torpedoes.

MERCUUR   *10/1992, Camil Busquets i Vilanova*

0 + 1 AMSTERDAM CLASS (FAST COMBAT SUPPORT SHIP)

Name	No	Builders	Laid down	Launched	Commissioned
AMSTERDAM	A 836	Merwede, Hardinxveld, and Royal Schelde, Vlissingen	21 May 1992	11 Sep 1993	June 1995

Displacement, tons: 17 040 full load
Dimensions, feet (metres): 544.6 × 72.2 × 26.2
(166 × 22 × 8)
Main machinery: 2 MAN 16V 40/45 diesels; 26 330 hp(m)
(19.36 MW); 1 shaft; cp prop
Speed, knots: 20. **Range, miles:** 13 440 at 20 kts
Complement: 160 (23 officers) including 24 aircrew
Cargo capacity: 6700 tons dieso; 1660 tons aviation fuel; 500
tons solids

Guns: 2 Oerlikon 20 mm. 1 Goalkeeper 30 mm CIWS.
Countermeasures: Decoys: 4 chaff launchers. Nixie towed
torpedo decoy.
ESM: Ferranti AWARE-4; radar warning.
Fire control: Signaal IRSCAN infra-red detector.
Radars: 2 navigation; I band (includes helo control).

Helicopters: 4 Lynx or 3 NH 90 or 2 EH-101.

Programmes: NP/SP AOR 90 replacement for *Poolster* ordered
14 October 1991. Close co-operation between Dutch Nevesbu
and Spanish Bazán has led to this design which has maintenance workshops as well as four abeam and one stern RAS/FAS
station, and one Vertrep supply station. Built to merchant ship
standards but with military NBC damage control. Hull built by
Merwede, with fitting out by Royal Schelde from October
1993. Second of class required to replace *Zuiderkruis* after
2000. An identical ship is building for the Spanish Navy.

AMSTERDAM (model)   *1991, Royal Netherlands Navy*

2 POOLSTER CLASS (FAST COMBAT SUPPORT SHIPS)

Name	No	Builders	Laid down	Launched	Commissioned
ZUIDERKRUIS	A 832	Verolme Shipyards, Alblasserdam	16 July 1973	15 Oct 1974	27 June 1975
POOLSTER	A 835	Rotterdamse Droogdok Mij	18 Sep 1962	16 Oct 1963	10 Sep 1964

Displacement, tons: 16 800 (16 900, *Zuiderkruis*) full load
Measurement, tons: 10 000 dwt
Dimensions, feet (metres): 552.2 × 66.6 × 26.9
(168.3 × 20.3 × 8.2) (Poolster)
556 × 66.6 × 27.6 *(169.6 × 20.3 × 8.4) (Zuiderkruis)*
Main machinery: 2 boilers; 2 turbines; 22 000 hp(m) *(16.2 MW);*
1 shaft *(Poolster)*
2 Stork-Werkspoor TM410 diesels; 21 000 hp(m) *(15.4 MW);*
1 shaft *(Zuiderkruis)*
Speed, knots: 21
Complement: 200 (17 officers) *(Poolster);* 266 (17 officers)
(Zuiderkruis)
Cargo capacity: 10 300 tons including 8-9000 tons oil fuel

Guns: 1 Signaal SGE-30 Goalkeeper with GE 30 mm 7-barrelled;
4200 rounds/minute combined to 2 km. Fitted for operational
deployments.
2 Bofors 40 mm *(Poolster)*. 5 Oerlikon 20 mm *(Zuiderkruis)*.
Countermeasures: Decoys: 2 Loral Hycor SRBOC Mk 36 fixed
6-barrelled launchers; IR flares and chaff.
ESM: Ferranti AWARE-4; radar warning.
Fire control: Signaal IRSCAN *(Zuiderkruis)*.
Radars: Air/surface search: Racal Decca 2459; F/I band.
Navigation: Two Racal Decca TM 1226C *(Zuiderkruis);* I band.
Racal Decca TM 1229C *(Poolster);* I band.
Sonars: Signaal CWE 10 *(Poolster);* hull-mounted; active search;
medium frequency.

Helicopters: 1 Westland UH-14A Lynx.

Structure: Helicopter deck aft. Funnel heightened by 4.5 m
(14.8 ft). Additional 20 mm guns, containerised Goalkeeper
CIWS and SATCOM, fitted for operational deployments.
Operational: Capacity for five helicopters. Both ships carry A/S
weapons for helicopters. Two fuelling stations each side for
underway replenishment.
Sales: *Poolster* offered for sale in 1995 when her replacement is
scheduled to enter service.

POOLSTER   *5/1993, Erik Laursen*

ZUIDERKRUIS (with Goalkeeper)   *7/1993, J L M van der Burg*

3 ACCOMMODATION SHIPS

CORNELIS DREBBEL A 886   **THETIS** A 887   **TAX** Y 8500

Displacement, tons: 775 *(Cornelis Drebbel)*; 800 *(Thetis)*
Dimensions, feet (metres): 206.7 × 38.7 × 3.6 *(63 × 11.8 × 1.1) (Cornelis Drebbel)*
223 × 39.4 × 5.3 *(68 × 12 × 1.6) (Thetis)*

Comment: *Cornelis Drebbel* built by Scheepswerf Voorwaarts at Hoogezand in 1971. Serves as accommodation vessel for crews of ships building and refitting at private yards in the Rotterdam area. *Thetis* built by Koninklijke Maatschappij De Schelde, Flushing; completed 14 March 1985 and commissioned 27 June 1985; accommodation for 106. Stationed at Den Helder, she provides harbour training for divers and underwater swimmers. *Tax* built in 1953 as a small cargo ship and converted in 1988.

1 SUPPORT SHIP

Name	No	Builders	Commissioned
PELIKAAN (ex-*Kilindoni*)	A 801	Vinholmen, Arendal	1984

Displacement, tons: 505 full load
Dimensions, feet (metres): 151.6 × 34.8 × 9.2 *(46.2 × 10.6 × 2.8)*
Main machinery: 2 Caterpillar 3412T diesels; 1080 hp *(806 kW)* sustained; 2 shafts
Speed, knots: 10
Complement: 15
Guns: 2—12.7 mm MGs.

Comment: Ex-oil platform supply ship acquired 28 May 1990 after being refitted in Curaçao. Has taken over from the deleted *Woerden* as tender and transport for marines in the Antilles. Capacity for 40 marines in five accommodation units.

PELIKAAN   *11/1990, Hartmut Ehlers*

1 EXPERIMENTAL SHIP

VAN SPEIJK (ex-*Dokkum*) Y 8001

Comment: For data see Dokkum class in Mine Warfare Forces. Weapon systems removed and converted by Wilton Fijenoord, Schiedam in November 1986 for testing fuels. Renamed because there has to be a *Van Speijk* in commission in the Navy.

VAN SPEIJK   *7/1992, Gilbert Gyssels*

4 CERBERUS CLASS (DIVING TENDERS)

Name	No	Builders	Commissioned
CERBERUS	A 851	Visser, Den Helder	28 Feb 1992
ARGUS	A 852	Visser, Den Helder	2 June 1992
NAUTILUS	A 853	Visser, Den Helder	18 Sep 1992
HYDRA	A 854	Visser, Den Helder	20 Nov 1992

Displacement, tons: 223 full load
Dimensions, feet (metres): 89.9 × 27.9 × 4.9 *(27.4 × 8.5 × 1.5)*
Main machinery: 2 Volvo Penta TAMD122A diesels; 760 hp(m) *(560 kW)*; 2 shafts
Speed, knots: 12
Complement: 8 (2 officers)

Comment: Ordered 29 November 1990. Capable of maintaining 10 kts in sea state 3. Can handle a 2 ton load at 4 m from the ship's side. Have replaced the Triton class.

HYDRA   *7/1993, J L M van der Burg*

TRAINING SHIPS

Name	No	Builders	Commissioned
BULGIA	A 880 (ex-P 803)	Rijkswerf, Willemsoord	20 Sep 1954

Displacement, tons: 150 standard; 163 full load
Dimensions, feet (metres): 119.1 × 20.2 × 6.3 *(36.3 × 6.2 × 1.9)*
Main machinery: 2 Werkspoor RUB 612 diesels; 1050 hp(m) *(772 kW)*; 2 shafts
Speed, knots: 15. **Range, miles:** 1000 at 13 kts
Complement: 28
Radars: Navigation: Decca; I band.

Comment: Non-commissioned training tender to the Naval College since November 1986. Armament removed.

BULGIA   *3/1993, J L M van der Burg*

Name	No	Builders	Commissioned
ZEEFAKKEL	A 903	J & K Smit, Kinderdijk	16 Mar 1951

Displacement, tons: 355 standard; 384 full load
Dimensions, feet (metres): 149 × 24.6 × 7.2 *(45.4 × 7.5 × 2.2)*
Main machinery: 2 Smit-MAN diesels; 640 hp(m) *(470 kW)*; 2 shafts
Speed, knots: 12
Complement: 26
Radars: Navigation: Racal Decca; I band.

Comment: Laid down 28 November 1949, launched 21 July 1950. Former surveying vessel. Now used as local training ship at Den Helder. Re-engined 1980.

ZEEFAKKEL   *7/1993, M Nitz*

Name	No	Builders	Commissioned
URANIA (ex-*Tromp*)	Y 8050	Haarlem	23 Apr 1938

Displacement, tons: 76
Dimensions, feet (metres): 78.4 × 17.4 × 10.5 *(23.9 × 5.3 × 3.2)*
Main machinery: 1 diesel; 65 hp(m) *(48 kW)*; 1 shaft
Speed, knots: 5 diesel; 10 sail
Complement: 17

Comment: Schooner used for training in seamanship.

URANIA   *7/1990, Wright and Logan*

TUGS

Name	No	Builders	Commissioned
WESTGAT	A 872	Rijkswerf, Willemsoord	10 Jan 1968

Displacement, tons: 206
Dimensions, feet (metres): 89.2 × 23 × 7.7 (27.2 × 7 × 2.3)
Main machinery: 1 Bolnes diesel; 720 hp(m) (529 kW); 1 shaft
Speed, knots: 12
Complement: 9
Guns: 2 Oerlikon 20 mm (not fitted).

Comment: Equipped with salvage pumps and firefighting equipment. Stationed at Den Helder. One of the class deleted in 1992.

WESTGAT *7/1993, J L M van der Burg*

Name	No	Builders	Commissioned
LINGE	A 874	Delta SY, Sliedrecht	20 Feb 1987
REGGE	A 875	Delta SY, Sliedrecht	6 May 1987
HUNZE	A 876	Delta SY, Sliedrecht	20 Oct 1987
ROTTE	A 877	Delta SY, Sliedrecht	20 Oct 1987

Displacement, tons: 200 approx
Dimensions, feet (metres): 90.2 × 27.2 × 8.9 (27.5 × 8.3 × 2.7)
Main machinery: 2 Stork-Werkspoor diesel; 1600 hp(m) (1.18 MW); 2 shafts
Speed, knots: 11
Complement: 7

Comment: Order placed in 1986. Based at Den Helder.

ROTTE *7/1993, J L M van der Burg*

7 HARBOUR TUGS

BREEZAND Y 8018	SCHELDE Y 8055	ZUIDWAL Y 8058
BALGZAND Y 8019	WIERBALG Y 8056	WESTWAL Y 8059
MALZWIN Y 8057		

Dimensions, feet (metres): 54.2 × 17.5 × 5.9 (16.5 × 5.3 × 1.8) (Y 8018/19)
35.4 × 12.5 × 4.3 (10.8 × 3.8 × 1.3) (remainder)
Main machinery: 2 diesels; 760 hp(m) (559 kW); 2 shafts (Y 8018/19)
1 DAF diesel; 115 hp(m) (85 kW); 1 shaft (remainder)

Comment: *Breezand* completed December 1989, *Balgzand* January 1990. The others are smaller pusher tugs and were completed December 1986 to February 1987. All built by Delta Shipyard.

BALGZAND *8/1992, van Ginderen Collection*

ARMY

Note: In addition there are three patrol boats with a limited coastal capability and 15 vessels for inland waters.

1 TANK LANDING CRAFT

RV 40

Displacement, tons: 815
Dimensions, feet (metres): 150.3 × 31.2 × 8.2 (45.8 × 9.5 × 2.5)
Main machinery: 2 diesels; 654 hp(m) (481 kW); 2 shafts
Speed, knots: 9.4
Complement: 4

Comment: Built by Grave BV and completed 22 November 1979.

RV 40 *1988, Royal Netherlands Army*

1 DIVING VESSEL

RV 50

Dimensions, feet (metres): 121.4 × 29.5 × 4.9 (37 × 9 × 1.5)
Main machinery: 2 diesels; 476 hp(m) (350 kW); 2 shafts
Speed, knots: 9
Complement: 21
Radars: Navigation: AP Mk 4; I band.

Comment: Built by Vervako as a diving training ship. There is a moonpool aft with a 50 m diving bell, and a decompression chamber.

RV 50 *1990, Vervako*

COAST GUARD (KUSTWACHT)

Note: In 1987 many of the separate maritime services were merged to form a Coast Guard with its own distinctive colours. Included are some of the 70 police craft, 23 customs vessels and over 320 assorted craft of the Ministry of Transport and Public Works. Many of these vessels would come under naval control in an emergency.

BREEVEERTIEN *7/1993, J L M van der Burg*

P 93 (Police) *10/1993, van Ginderen Collection*

NEW ZEALAND

Headquarters' Appointments

Chief of Defence Force:
  Vice Admiral S F Teagle, ADC
Chief of Naval Staff:
  Rear Admiral J Welch
Deputy Chief of Naval Staff:
  Commodore K R Moen
Maritime Commander:
  Commodore K F Wilson, CBE, LVO

Diplomatic Representation

Head of Defence Liaison Staff, London:
  Commodore J G Peddie
Naval Adviser, Canberra:
  Captain M N Franklin
Naval Technical Liaison Officer, London:
  Commander M I Louisson
Naval Technical Liaison Officer, Washington:
  Commander P C Redman

Personnel

(a) 1994: 2340
(b) Reserve: 458 RNZNVR officers and ratings

Shore Establishments

Naval Staff: HMNZS Wakefield (Wellington)
Fleet Support: HMNZS Philomel (Auckland)
Training: HMNZS Tamaki (Auckland)
Ship Repair: HMNZ Dockyard (Auckland)

RNZNVR Divisions

Auckland: HMNZS *Ngapona*
Wellington: HMNZS *Olphert*
Christchurch: HMNZS *Pegasus*
Dunedin: HMNZS *Toroa*

Prefix to Ships' Names

HMNZS

Mercantile Marine

Lloyd's Register of Shipping:
  135 vessels of 217 854 tons gross

Strength of the Fleet

Type	Active (Reserve)	Building (Projected)
Frigates	4	2
Inshore Patrol Craft	4	—
Survey Vessels	3	—
Fleet Supply Ship	1	—
Military Sealift Ship	—	(1)
Research Vessel	1	—
Training Craft	1	—
Tugs	2	—
Diving Support Vessel	1	—

DELETIONS

Patrol Forces

1991 *Pukaki, Rotoiti, Taupo, Hawea*

FRIGATES

2 LEANDER (BROAD-BEAMED) CLASS

Name	No	Builders	Laid down	Launched	Commissioned
WELLINGTON (ex-HMS *Bacchante*)	F 69	Vickers Armstrong Ltd, Newcastle	27 Oct 1966	29 Feb 1968	17 Oct 1969
CANTERBURY	F 421	Yarrow Ltd, Clyde	12 Apr 1969	6 May 1970	22 Oct 1971

Displacement, tons: 2474 standard; 2945 full load
Dimensions, feet (metres): 372 × 43 × 18
  (113.4 × 13.1 × 5.5)
Main machinery: 2 Babcock & Wilcox boilers; 550 psi
(38.7 kg/cm sq); 850°F *(454°C)*; 2 White-English Electric turbines; 30 000 hp *(22.4 MW)*; 2 shafts
Speed, knots: 28. **Range, miles:** 5500 at 15 kts
Complement: 245 (15 officers) *(Canterbury)*; 260 (19 officers) *(Wellington)*

Guns: 2 Vickers 4.5 in *(114 mm)*/45 Mk 6 (twin) (except *Southland*) **①**; 80° elevation; 20 rounds/minute to 19 km *(10.3 nm)* anti-surface; 6 km *(3.2 nm)* anti-aircraft; weight of shell 25 kg.
1 GE/GD 20 mm Vulcan Phalanx 6-barrelled Mk 15 **②**; 3000 rounds/minute combined to 1.5 km. Replacing Seacat.
4 or 6—12.7 mm MGs.
Torpedoes: 6—324 mm US Mk 32 Mod 5 (2 triple) tubes **③**. Honeywell/Marconi Mk 46 Mod 5; anti-submarine; active/passive homing to 11 km *(5.9 nm)* at 40 kts; warhead 44 kg.
Countermeasures: Decoys: 2 Loral Hycor SRBOC Mk 36 6-barrelled trainable launchers. Graseby Type 182; towed torpedo decoy.
ESM: Argo Phoenix. Telegon PST 1288 HVU.
ECM: Type 668/669; jammer.
Combat data systems: Plessey/Marconi Nautis F; Link 11.
Fire control: RCA R-76C5 GFCS.
Radars: Air search: Signaal LW08 **④**; D band; range 265 km *(145 nm)* for 2 m² target.
Air/surface search: Plessey Type 993 **⑤**; E/F band.

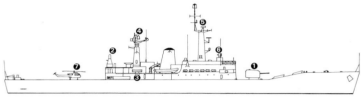

CANTERBURY (with Phalanx)   *(Scale 1 : 1200), Ian Sturton*

Navigation: Kelvin Hughes Type 1006; I band.
Fire control: RCA TR 76 **⑥**; I band.
IFF: Cossor Mk XII.
Sonars: Graseby Type 750; hull-mounted; active search and attack; medium frequency.
Kelvin Hughes Type 162M; hull-mounted; bottom classification; 50 kHz.
Ferranti FMS 15/2 TACTASS may be fitted in due course.

Helicopters: 1 Westland Wasp HAS 1 **⑦**. Probably to be replaced by Lynx.

Programmes: *Canterbury* ordered in August 1968, arrived in New Zealand in August 1972. *Wellington* transferred on 1 October 1982, arriving in New Zealand December 1982.

Modernisation: Since 1984 new equipment includes LW08 radar, Telegon HF-DF, Phoenix ESM, a modern gunnery fire control system, G750 hull-mounted sonar, Mk 32 torpedo tubes, Nautis-F system, computer-aided message handling, Mk 36 chaff launchers and replacement ships' boats. Upgrades started in November 1993 include a Whittaker Track Management system, IFF Mk 12, Link 11 and replacement of the HF communications system. Seacat is obsolete and being removed in 1994. Plans for fitting Phalanx and enlarging the hangar are in hand.
Structure: Referred to as 'broad-beamed' Leanders in RN service.
Operational: Both ships are scheduled to remain operational and compatible to the Anzacs until 2005. Flight decks are being modified to take a Lynx size helicopter. *Canterbury* started long refit November 1993.

WELLINGTON (with Seacat)

1993, RNZN

2 LEANDER CLASS

Name	No	Builders	Laid down	Launched	Commissioned
WAIKATO	F 55	Harland & Wolff Ltd, Belfast	10 Jan 1964	18 Feb 1965	16 Sep 1966
SOUTHLAND (ex-HMS *Dido*)	F 104	Yarrow & Co Ltd, Scotstoun	2 Dec 1959	22 Dec 1961	18 Sep 1963

Displacement, tons: 2580 standard; 3035 full load
Dimensions, feet (metres): 372 × 41 × 18
(113.4 × 12.5 × 5.5)
Main machinery: 2 Babcock & Wilcox boilers; 550 psi
(38.7 kg/cm sq); 850°F *(454°C)*; 2 White-English Electric
turbines; 30 000 hp *(22.4 MW)*; 2 shafts
Speed, knots: 28. **Range, miles:** 3000 at 15 kts
Complement: 243 (16 officers) *(Waikato)*

Guns: 2 Vickers 4.5 in *(114 mm)*/45 Mk 6 (twin) *(Waikato)* ❶;
80° elevation; 20 rounds/minute to 19 km *(10.3 nm)* anti-
surface; 6 km *(3.2 nm)* anti-aircraft; weight of shell 25 kg.
2 Bofors 40 mm/60 Mk 9 *(Southland)*; 80° elevation; 120
rounds/minute to 10 km *(5.4 nm)* anti-surface; 3 km *(1.6 nm)*
anti-aircraft; weight of shell 0.89 kg.
4 or 6—12.7 mm MGs.
Torpedoes: 6—324 mm US Mk 32 Mod 5 (2 triple) tubes ❷.
Honeywell/Marconi Mk 46 Mod 2; anti-submarine; active/
passive homing to 11 km *(5.9 nm)* at 40 kts; warhead 44 kg.
Countermeasures: Decoys: Graseby Type 182; towed torpedo
decoy.
ESM: Argo Phoenix; intercept.
ECM: Type 668/669; jammer.
Combat data systems: ADAWS 5 action data automation; Link
10 *(Southland)*.
Fire control: MRS 3 for 114 mm *(Waikato)*.
Radars: Air search: Marconi Type 965 AKE-1 *(Waikato)* ❸; A
band.
Air/surface search: Plessey Type 993 ❹ or Plessey Type 994
(Southland); E/F band.
Navigation: Kelvin Hughes Type 1006; I band.
Fire control: Plessey 903 ❺ *(Waikato)* (for 114 mm guns).
Sonars: Graseby Type 184 or Type 177 *(Waikato)*; hull-mounted;
active search and attack; medium frequency.

Helicopters: 1 Westland Wasp HAS 1 ❻.

Programmes: *Waikato*, ordered on 14 June 1963, arrived in New
Zealand in May 1967. *Southland* transferred on 18 July 1983.
She then had a refit at Vosper Thornycroft, commissioned 21
December, sailing for New Zealand on completion.
Modernisation: Both completed limited refits in 1990 and 1991.
Structure: *Waikato* has an enlarged hangar for Lynx helicopters.
Operational: The Ikara system, including the GWS 41 fire control
director in *Southland* is non-operational. The Seacat system is
obsolete and is being removed in 1994. *Southland* has a limited operational capability and has only half her normal complement, supplemented if necessary. She will be replaced by the
first Anzac, or may even be paid off in 1994 if *Tobruk* is
acquired from Australia.

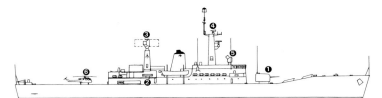

WAIKATO

(Scale 1 : 1200), Ian Sturton

WAIKATO (alongside *Southland*)

11/1993, Nikolaus Sifferlinger

0 + 2 ANZAC CLASS

Name	No	Builders	Laid down	Launched	Commissioned
—	F 77	Transfield Amecon, Williamstown	Sep 1994	Oct 1995	Mar 1997
—	F 111	Transfield Amecon, Williamstown	July 1996	July 1997	Nov 1998

Displacement, tons: 3600 full load
Dimensions, feet (metres): 387.1 oa; 357.6 wl × 48.6 × 14.3
(118; 109 × 14.8 × 4.4)
Main machinery: CODOG; 1 GE LM 2500 gas turbine;
30 172 hp *(22.5 MW)* sustained; 2 MTU 12V 1163 TB83 die-
sels; 8840 hp(m) *(6.5 MW)* sustained; 2 shafts; cp props
Speed, knots: 27. **Range, miles:** 6000 at 18 kts
Complement: 163

Missiles: SAM: Raytheon Sea Sparrow RIM-7P; Mk 41 Mod 5
octuple cell vertical launcher ❶.
Guns: 1 FMC 5 in *(127 mm)*/54 Mk 45 Mod 2 ❷.
Torpedoes: 6—324 mm US Mk 32 Mod 5 (2 triple) tubes ❸;
Mk 46 Mod 5.
Countermeasures: Decoys: Sea Gnat/SRBOC Mk 36 Mod 1
chaff launcher ❹. Torpedo decoy system.

ESM: Telefunken Telegon 10; THORN EMI Sceptre A; intercept.
Combat data systems: CelsiusTech 9LV 453 Mk 3. Link 11.
Fire control: CelsiusTech 9LV 453 optronic director ❺.
Raytheon CWI Mk 73 Mod 1 (for SAM).
Radars: Air search: Raytheon SPS 49(V)8 ❻; C/D band.
Air/surface search: CelsiusTech 9LV 453 TIR (Ericsson Tx/Rx) ❼;
G band.
Navigation: Atlas Elektronik 9600 ARPA; I band.
Fire control: CelsiusTech 9LV 453 ❽; J band.
IFF: Cossor Mk XII.
Sonars: Thomson Sintra Spherion B; hull-mounted; active search
and attack; medium frequency.
Provision for towed array; passive; very low frequency.

Helicopters: 1 light ASW (to be decided) ❾.

Programmes: Contract signed with Amecon consortium on 19
November 1989 to build eight Blohm & Voss-designed MEKO
200 ANZ frigates for Australia and two for New Zealand, which
has an option for two more. Modules being constructed at
Newcastle, Australia and Whangarei, New Zealand, and shipped to Melbourne for final assembly. The two New Zealand
ships are the second and fourth of the class. First steel cut on F
77 on 11 February 1993.
Structure: The ships include space and weight provision for considerable enhancement including canister-launched SSM,
CIWS, an additional fire control channel and ECM. Mk 32 torpedo tubes will be fitted in New Zealand as soon as the ships
are delivered. Signature suppression features are incorporated
in the design. All steel construction. Fin stabilisers. McTaggert
Scott helicopter recovery system. Two RHIBs are carried.

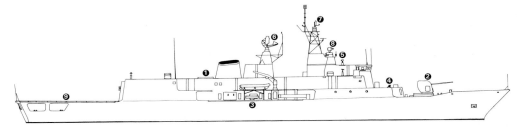

ANZAC

(Scale 1 : 900), Ian Sturton

SHIPBORNE AIRCRAFT

Note: Replacement helicopters are urgently needed. Sensors are to be optimised for surface
surveillance.

Numbers/Type: 6 Westland Wasp HAS Mk 1.
Operational speed: 96 kts *(177 km/h)*.
Service ceiling: 12 200 ft *(3720 m)*.
Range: 263 nm *(488 km)*.
Role/Weapon systems: ASW helicopter; low time aircraft procured from UK. Flown by Navy,
maintained by Air Force. Were to have been paid off in 1992 but lives extended. Sensors: None.
Weapons: ASW; 1 × Mk 46 torpedo or depth bomb.

WESTLAND WASP

1986, Paul Beaver

LAND-BASED MARITIME AIRCRAFT

Numbers/Type: 6 Lockheed P-3K Orion.
Operational speed: 410 kts *(760 km/h)*.
Service ceiling: 28 300 ft *(8625 m)*.
Range: 4000 nm *(7410 km)*.
Role/Weapon systems: Long-range surveillance and ASW patrol; update 1981-84 and to Phase II standard 1988-92. Operated by RNZAF. Sensors: APS-134 radar, ASQ-10 MAD, AQH5/AQA1 processor, 3 AYK 14 computers, IFF, ESM, SQ 41/47/SSQ 46 sonobuoys. Weapons: ASW: 8 × Mk 46 torpedoes, depth bombs or mines, 10 × underwing stations for weapons.

PATROL FORCES

4 MOA CLASS (INSHORE PATROL CRAFT)

Name	No	Builders	Commissioned
MOA	P 3553	Whangarei Engineering and Construction Co Ltd	28 Nov 1983
KIWI	P 3554	Whangarei Engineering and Construction Co Ltd	2 Sep 1984
WAKAKURA	P 3555	Whangarei Engineering and Construction Co Ltd	26 Mar 1985
HINAU	P 3556	Whangarei Engineering and Construction Co Ltd	4 Oct 1985

Displacement, tons: 91.5 standard; 105 full load
Dimensions, feet (metres): 88 × 20 × 7.2 *(26.8 × 6.1 × 2.2)*
Main machinery: 2 Cummins KT-1105M diesels; 710 hp *(530 kW)*; 2 shafts
Speed, knots: 12. **Range, miles:** 1000 at 11 kts
Complement: 18 (5 officers (4 training))
Guns: 1 Browning 12.7 mm MG.
Radars: Surface search: Racal Decca 916; I band.
Sonars: Klein 595 Tracpoint; sidescan; active high frequency.

Comment: On 11 February 1982 the New Zealand Cabinet approved the construction of four inshore patrol craft. The four IPC are operated by the Reserve Divisions, *Moa* with *Toroa* (Dunedin), *Kiwi* with *Pegasus* (Christchurch), *Wakakura* with *Olphert* (Wellington), *Hinau* with *Ngapona* (Auckland). Same design as Inshore Survey and Training craft *Kahu* but with a modified internal layout. MCM system fitted in 1993/94. Sidescan sonar and MCAIS data system fitted to *Hinau* in 1993; the remainder by December 1994.

MOA 10/1991, Guy Toremans

SURVEY AND RESEARCH SHIPS

1 SURVEY SHIP

Name	No	Builders	Commissioned
MONOWAI (ex-*Moana Roa*)	A 06	Grangemouth DY	Aug 1960

Displacement, tons: 3903 full load
Dimensions, feet (metres): 298 × 46 × 17 *(90.8 × 14 × 5.2)*
Main machinery: 2 Clark-Sulzer 7-cyl diesels; 3640 hp(m) *(2.68 MW)*; 2 shafts; bow thruster
Speed, knots: 14. **Range, miles:** 12 000 at 12 kts
Complement: 136 (11 officers)
Guns: 2 Oerlikon 20 mm.
Radars: Navigation: Racal Decca 1290A/9; ARPA 1690S; I band.
Helicopters: 1 Wasp HAS Mk 1 (not always embarked).

Comment: Previously owned by the New Zealand Government department of Maori and Island Affairs and employed on the Cook Islands service. Taken over 1974 for conversion by Scott Lithgow which included an up-rating of the engines, provision of a helicopter deck and hangar and fitting of cp propellers and a bow thruster. Commissioned into RNZN 4 October 1977. Racal System 960 automated data acquisition and processing system (RNZN Hadlaps) fitted in 1991. New radar and communications equipment fitted during 1988 modernisation which included the installation of a reverse osmosis plant and a rigid hull inflatable boat. The ship is white with a yellow funnel. Inmarsat comms fitted.

MONOWAI 10/1991, John Mortimer

---

2 SURVEY SHIPS

Name	No	Builders	Commissioned
TAKAPU	A 07	Whangarei Engineering and Construction Co Ltd	8 July 1980
TARAPUNGA	A 08	Whangarei Engineering and Construction Co Ltd	9 Apr 1980

Displacement, tons: 91.5 standard; 104.9 full load
Dimensions, feet (metres): 88 × 20 × 7.2 *(26.8 × 6.1 × 2.2)*
Main machinery: 2 Cummins KT-1150M diesels; 710 hp *(530 kW)*; 2 shafts
Speed, knots: 12. **Range, miles:** 1000 at 12 kts
Complement: 11 (2 officers)
Radars: Navigation: Racal Decca 916; I band.

Comment: Equipment has been specifically designed to work with *Monowai*. Same hull design as Inshore Patrol and Training craft *Kahu* with modified internal layout. Survey equipment: Magnavox MX1102 GPS; Atlas Deso 20 echo-sounders; Del Norte Trisponder position fixing; EG and G 135 (*Tarapunga*) and Klein 531T (*Takapu*) side scan sonars; fitted for but not with Decca Hi-Fix/6. Fitted with two Omega power control gearboxes for slow speed running. Racal System 960 (Hadlaps) fitted in 1991.

TARAPUNGA 10/1991, Guy Toremans

1 ROBERT D CONRAD CLASS (RESEARCH SHIP)

Name	No	Builders	Commissioned
TUI (ex-USS *Charles H Davis, T-AGOR 5*)	A 05	Christy Corporation, Sturgeon Bay, Wis.	25 Jan 1963

Displacement, tons: 1432 full load
Dimensions, feet (metres): 208.9 × 40 × 15.3 *(63.7 × 12.2 × 4.7)*
Main machinery: Diesel-electric; 2 Caterpillar D 398B diesel generators; 1 twin motor; 1000 hp *(746 kW)*; 1 shaft; bow thruster; 175 hp *(130 kW)*
Speed, knots: 13. **Range, miles:** 14 800 at 12 kts
Complement: 45 (5 officers, 15 scientists)
Radars: Navigation: SPN 7A and LR 880; I band.

Comment: Oceanographic research ship. Laid down on 15 June 1961, launched on 30 June 1962. On loan from the USA since 10 August 1970. Commissioned in the RNZN on 11 September 1970. Operates for NZ Defence Scientific Establishment on acoustic research. Port after gallows removed—gallows at stern—cable reels on quarter-deck and amidships—light cable-laying gear over bow. Ferranti FMS 15/2 towed sonar array for trial 1989-91. Fitted with Inmarsat.

TUI 2/1993, John Mortimer

AUXILIARIES

Note: In addition to vessels listed below there are four 12 m sail training craft used for seamanship training: *Paea II, Mako II, Manga II, Haku II* (sail nos 6911-6914).

MILITARY SEALIFT SHIP

Comment: Project Definition Study completed in Autumn 1989 for a logistic support ship to carry equipment and stores for the Army's Ready Reaction Force. The design solution produced by British Maritime Technology Defence Services was shelved but after a second successive disaster in Samoa in 1991, the project has a new lease of life as a Sealift Ship for the Army as well as for disaster relief. The conversion of a commercially built ship is currently being considered, as is the lease of HMAS *Tobruk* for a period, while a more long term solution is worked out.

1 REPLENISHMENT TANKER

Name	No	Builders	Commissioned
ENDEAVOUR	A 11	Hyundai, South Korea	6 Apr 1988

Displacement, tons: 12 390 full load
Dimensions, feet (metres): 453.1 × 60 × 23 *(138.1 × 18.4 × 7.3)*
Main machinery: 1 MAN-Burmeister & Wain 12V32/36 diesel; 5780 hp(m) *(4.25 MW)* sustained;
  1 shaft
Speed, knots: 14. **Range, miles:** 8000 at 14 kts
Complement: 30 (6 officers)
Cargo capacity: 7500 tons dieso; 100 tons Avcat; 100 tons water
Radars: Navigation: Racal Decca 1290A/9; ARPA 1690S; I band.
Helicopters: 1 Westland Wasp HAS Mk 1 (not always embarked).

Comment: Ordered July 1986, laid down April 1987 and launched 14 August 1987. Completion
  delayed by engine problems but arrived in New Zealand in May 1988. Two abeam RAS rigs (one
  QRC, one Probe) and one astern refuelling rig. Fitted with Inmarsat. Standard merchant design
  modified on building to provide a relatively inexpensive replenishment tanker.

ENDEAVOUR   *7/1993, Maritime Photographic*

1 MOA CLASS (TRAINING SHIP)

Name	No	Builders	Commissioned
KAHU (ex-*Manawanui*)	A 04 (ex-A 09)	Whangarei Engineering and Construction Co Ltd	28 May 1979

Displacement, tons: 91.5 standard; 105 full load
Dimensions, feet (metres): 88 × 20 × 7.2 *(26.8 × 6.1 × 2.2)*
Main machinery: 2 Cummins KT-1150M diesels; 710 hp *(530 kW)*; 2 shafts
Speed, knots: 12. **Range, miles:** 1000 at 11 kts
Complement: 16
Radars: Navigation: Racal Decca 916; I band.

Comment: Same hull design as Inshore Survey Craft and Patrol Craft. Formerly a Diving Tender,
  now used for navigation and seamanship training.

KAHU   *10/1991, Guy Toremans*

1 DIVING TENDER

Name	No	Builders	Commissioned
MANAWANUI (ex-*Star Perseus*)	A 09	Cochrane, Selby	May 1979

Displacement, tons: 911 full load
Dimensions, feet (metres): 143 × 31.2 × 10.5 *(43.6 × 9.5 × 3.2)*
Main machinery: 2 Caterpillar diesels; 1130 hp *(843 kW)*; 2 shafts; bow thruster
Speed, knots: 10.7. **Range, miles:** 5000 at 10 kts
Complement: 24 (2 officers)
Sonars: Klein 595 Tracpoint; sidescan; active high frequency.

Comment: North Sea Oil Rig Diving support vessel commissioned into the RNZN on 5 April 1988.
  Completed conversion in December 1988 and has replaced the previous ship of the same name
  which proved to be too small for the role. Equipment includes two Phantom HDX remote-
  controlled submersibles, a decompression chamber (to 250 ft), wet diving bell and 13 ton crane.
  Fitted with Inmarsat. MCAIS data system, sidescan sonar and GPS fitted in 1994.

MANAWANUI   *10/1991, John Mortimer*

TUGS

Note: Floating crane *Hikinui* purchased from Auckland Harbour Board in 1991.

ARATAKI (ex-*Aorangi*) A 10

Displacement, tons: 180 full load
Dimensions, feet (metres): 74.8 × 19 × 8.2 *(22.8 × 5.8 × 2.5)*
Main machinery: Ruston 6 ARM diesel; 1100 hp *(821 kW)*; 1 shaft; bow thruster
Speed, knots: 12

Comment: Bollard pull, 16.3 tons. Purchased in November 1984 from Timaru Harbour Board by
  the RNZFA to replace previous tug of same name. Based at Devonport, Auckland.

ARATAKI   *10/1991, John Mortimer*

WAITANGI

Displacement, tons: 410 full load
Dimensions, feet (metres): 105 × 28 × 14.6 *(32 × 8.5 × 4.5)*
Main machinery: 2 Veiten diesels; 1720 hp(m) *(1.3 MW)*; 2 shafts
Speed, knots: 12. **Range, miles:** 2500 at 12 kts
Complement: 4

Comment: Bollard pull, 21 tons. Leased from Northland Harbour Board and still wears NHB
  colours.

WAITANGI   *10/1991, van Ginderen Collection*

NICARAGUA

Headquarters' Appointment	General	Mercantile Marine
Head of Navy: Major Manuel Rivas Guatemala	All craft operated by Marina de Guerra Sandinista. Pennant numbers: odd—Atlantic; even—Pacific.	*Lloyd's Register of Shipping:* 25 vessels of 3784 tons gross
Personnel	**Bases**	**DELETIONS**
1994: 800 officers and men	Corinto, Puerto Cabezas, El Bluff, San Juan del Sur	1991 1 Zhuk class, 1 Sin Hung class

PATROL FORCES

3 YEVGENYA CLASS (MINEHUNTERS—INSHORE)

501   508   510

Displacement, tons: 77 standard; 90 full load
Dimensions, feet (metres): 80.7 × 18 × 4.9 *(24.6 × 5.5 × 1.5)*
Main machinery: 2 Type 3-D-12 diesels; 600 hp(m) *(440 kW)* sustained; 2 shafts
Speed, knots: 11. **Range, miles:** 300 at 10 kts
Complement: 10
Guns: 2 USSR 25 mm/80 (twin).
Radars: Surface search/navigation: Don 2; I band.
Sonars: A small sonar is lifted over stern on crane.

Comment: Transferred from USSR in 1984 and 1986 via Algeria and Cuba. All four refitted in Cuba in 1987-88 but one then sank in the hurricane of 1989 and was subsequently scrapped. Have GRP hulls. Tripod mast. Used as patrol craft but probably non-operational.

YEVGENYA 508   *1989*

4 K8 CLASS (MINESWEEPING BOATS)

500   502   504   506

Displacement, tons: 26 full load
Dimensions, feet (metres): 55.4 × 10.5 × 3.9 *(16.9 × 3.2 × 1.2)*
Main machinery: 2 Type 3-D-6 diesels; 300 hp(m) *(220 kW)* sustained; 2 shafts
Speed, knots: 18. **Range, miles:** 300 at 10 kts
Complement: 6
Guns: 2 USSR 14.5 mm (twin) MGs.

Comment: Transferred from USSR in 1984. Built in Poland in late 1950s. Non-operational in 1993.

K8 502   *1988*

7 ZHUK CLASS

304   305   307   309   311   315   317

Displacement, tons: 39 full load
Dimensions, feet (metres): 78.7 × 16.4 × 3.9 *(24 × 5 × 1.2)*
Main machinery: 2 Type M 401B diesels; 2200 hp(m) *(1.6 MW)* sustained; 2 shafts
Speed, knots: 30. **Range, miles:** 1100 at 15 kts
Complement: 12
Guns: 4 USSR 14.5 mm (2 twin) MGs.
Radars: Surface search: Spin Trough; I band.

Comment: First transferred April 1982, having previously been sent to Algeria in May 1981. Second transferred 24 July 1983, third in 1984, two more early 1986 and three in late 1986/early 1987 via Cuba. Two more of this class were transferred via Cuba in December 1989 to replace two sunk in the hurricane of October 1989. No more than three were seaworthy in 1992/93.

ZHUK 304   *1988*

8 SIN HUNG CLASS

400-404   406   408-410

Displacement, tons: 40 full load
Dimensions, feet (metres): 72.2 × 11 × 5.5 *(22 × 3.4 × 1.7)*
Main machinery: 2 diesels; 2400 hp(m) *(1.76 MW)*; 2 shafts
Speed, knots: 40
Guns: 4 USSR 14.5 mm (2 twin) MGs.

Comment: Two transferred from North Korea June 1984, one in August 1988, five in December 1988, and two in 1989. Torpedo tubes have been removed. Two deleted so far, one of which sank in the 1989 hurricane. About three operational in 1992/93.

SIN HUNG 404 and 406   *1989*

2 KIMJIN CLASS

306   308

Displacement, tons: 25 full load
Dimensions, feet (metres): 66.6 × 11 × 5.5 *(20.3 × 3.4 × 1.7)*
Main machinery: 2 diesels; 2400 hp(m) *(1.76 MW)*; 2 shafts
Speed, knots: 42. **Range, miles:** 220 at 20 kts
Complement: 10
Guns: 4 USSR 14.5 mm (2 twin) MGs.

Comment: A smaller version of the Sin Hung class transferred from North Korea in the early 1980s, causing some confusion over numbers. Non-operational in 1992/93.

2 DABUR CLASS

231   235

Displacement, tons: 39 full load
Dimensions, feet (metres): 64.9 × 18 × 5.8 *(19.8 × 5.5 × 1.8)*
Main machinery: 2 GM 12V-71TA; 840 hp *(626 kW)* sustained; 2 shafts
Speed, knots: 19. **Range, miles:** 450 at 13 kts
Complement: 6
Guns: 2 Oerlikon 20 mm. 2 Browning 12.7 mm (twin) MGs.

Comment: Delivered by Israel April 1978 (first pair), May 1978 (second pair). One lost by gunfire in 1985; a second was severely damaged in 1987 and has been deleted. Original armament may have been replaced by Soviet 14.5 mm MGs. Non-operational in 1992/93.

DABUR (Israel number)   *1989*

2 VEDETTE TYPE

300   302

Displacement, tons: 57 full load
Dimensions, feet (metres): 92.5 × 17.1 × 5.2 *(28.2 × 5.2 × 1.6)*
Main machinery: 2 Poyaud 520 V12 M25 diesels; 1520 hp(m) *(1.12 MW)*; 2 shafts
Speed, knots: 24. **Range, miles:** 800 at 15 kts
Guns: 2 USSR 14.5 mm (twin) MGs.

Comment: Built by Ch N de l'Esterel. Ordered December 1981 from France and completed 24 June 1983. Oerlikon 20 mm replaced by MG. Both in service during 1993.

VEDETTE 300   *1990*

2 EL TUYACAN CLASS

301   303

Comment: 105 ft ex-transport craft taken over and used as Presidential yachts. Fitted with twin 37 mm/63 guns. Probably now hulks without propulsion.

EL TUYACAN 301   *5/1988*

NIGERIA

Headquarters' Appointments

Chief of the Naval Staff:
    Rear Admiral Allison Madueke
Chief of Personnel:
    Rear Admiral J Ayinla
Chief of Logistics:
    Commodore O Dada
Chief of Operations:
    Rear Admiral S O Oloko

Personnel

(a) 1994: 5200 (560 officers)
(b) Voluntary service

Bases

Apapa—Lagos: Western Naval Command; Dockyard (Wilmot Point, Victoria Island, Lagos)
Calabar: Eastern Naval Command (Naval schools at Lagos, Port Harcourt, Apapa (NNS *Quorra*) and Calabar)
Okemimi, Port Harcourt

Prefix to Ships' Names

NNS

Port Security Police

A separate force of 1600 officers and men.

Mercantile Marine

Lloyd's Register of Shipping:
    279 vessels of 514 971 tons gross

DELETIONS

Corvettes

1993   *Otobo* (scrap)

FRIGATES

1 OBUMA CLASS

Name	No	Builders	Laid down	Launched	Commissioned
OBUMA (ex-*Nigeria*)	F 87	Wilton-Fijenoord NV, Netherlands	9 Apr 1964	12 Apr 1965	16 Sep 1965

Displacement, tons: 1724 standard; 2000 full load
Dimensions, feet (metres): 360.2 × 37 × 11.5
    (109.8 × 11.3 × 3.5)
Main machinery: 4 MAN Burmeister & Wain V9V24/30B; 16 000 hp(m) *(11.8 MW)* sustained; 2 shafts
Speed, knots: 26. **Range, miles:** 3500 at 15 kts
Complement: 216

Guns: 2 Vickers 4 in *(102 mm)*/45 (twin); 80° elevation; 16 rounds/minute to 19 km *(10.4 nm)*; weight of shell 16 kg.
    2 Bofors 40 mm/70 (fitted for but not with).
    2 Oerlikon 20 mm.
Fire control: Optical director for 102 mm guns.
Radars: Surface search: Plessey AWS 4; E/F band; range 101 km *(55 nm)*.
Navigation: Decca; I band.

Helicopters: Platform for 1 Lynx Mk 89.

Programmes: Refitted at Birkenhead, 1973. Further refit completed at Schiedam October 1977.
Modernisation: Various plans to improve armament not yet realised. Squid A/S mortar non-operational and sonar removed.
Operational: Used as a training ship. Probably non-operational.

OBUMA   *6/1983, Hartmut Ehlers*

1 MEKO TYPE 360

Name	No	Builders	Laid down	Launched	Commissioned
ARADU (ex-*Republic*)	F 89	Blohm & Voss, Hamburg	1 Dec 1978	25 Jan 1980	20 Feb 1982

Displacement, tons: 3360 full load
Dimensions, feet (metres): 412 × 49.2 × 19 (screws)
(125.6 × 15 × 5.8)
Main machinery: CODOG; 2 RR Olympus TM3B gas turbines;
50 880 hp *(37.9 MW)* sustained; 2 MTU 20V 956 TB92 diesels; 10 420 hp(m) *(7.71 MW)* sustained; 2 shafts; 2 KaMeWa
cp props
Speed, knots: 30.5. **Range, miles:** 6500 at 15 kts
Complement: 195 (26 officers) plus 35 midshipmen

Missiles: SSM: 8 OTO Melara/Matra Otomat Mk 1 ❶; active
radar homing to 80 km *(43.2 nm)* at 0.9 Mach; warhead
210 kg.
SAM: Selenia Elsag Albatros octuple launcher ❷; 24 Aspide;
semi-active radar homing to 13 km *(7 nm)* at 2.5 Mach; height
envelope 15-5000 m *(49.2-16 405 ft)*; warhead 30 kg.
Guns: 1 OTO Melara 5 in *(127 mm)*/54 ❸; 85° elevation; 45
rounds/minute to 16 km *(8.7 nm)*; weight of shell 32 kg.
8 Breda Bofors 40 mm/70 (4 twin) ❹; 85° elevation; 300
rounds/minute to 12.5 km *(6.8 nm)* anti-surface; weight of
shell 0.96 kg.
Torpedoes: 6—324 mm Plessey STWS-1B (2 triple) tubes ❺. 18
Whitehead A244S; anti-submarine; active/passive homing to
7 km *(3.8 nm)* at 33 kts; warhead 34 kg (shaped charge).
Depth charges: 1 rack.
Countermeasures: Decoys: 2 Breda 105 mm SCLAR 20-tubed
trainable; chaff to 5 km *(2.7 nm)*; illuminants to 12 km
(6.6 nm).
ESM: Decca RDL-2; intercept.
ECM: RCM-2; jammer.
Combat data systems: Sewaco-BV action data automation.
Fire control: M20 series GFCS. Signaal Vesta ASW.
Radars: Air/surface search: Plessey AWS 5 ❻; E/F band; range
155 km *(85 nm)* for 4 m² target.
Navigation: Racal Decca 1226; I band.
Fire control: Signaal STIR ❼; I/J/K band; range 140 km *(76 nm)*
for 1 m² target.
Signaal WM 25 ❽; I/J band; range 46 km *(25 nm)*.
IFF/SIF: Two Decca.

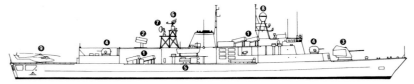

ARADU   (Scale 1 : 1200), Ian Sturton

ARADU   9/1987, Hartmut Ehlers

Sonars: Atlas Elektronik EA80; hull-mounted; active search and
attack; medium frequency.

Helicopters: 1 Lynx Mk 89 ❾.

Programmes: Originally named *Republic*; renamed *Aradu*
1 November 1980.
Modernisation: Refit started at Wilmot Point, Lagos with Blohm
& Voss assistance in 1991. In late 1992 the ship was still in

dock with little work being done. No equipment changes have
been reported.
Structure: This design shows the flexibility of the modular
approach: the Argentinian Meko 360 ships have an all-gas tur-
bine propulsion and two helicopters; containerised armament. This is the first class with
Operational: Had two groundings and a major collision in 1987.

CORVETTES

Note: *Dorina* is a training hulk.

2 Mk 9 VOSPER THORNYCROFT TYPE

Name	No	Builders	Commissioned
ERINOMI	F 83	Vosper Thornycroft Ltd	29 Jan 1980
ENYIMIRI	F 84	Vosper Thornycroft Ltd	2 May 1980

Displacement, tons: 680 standard; 780 full load
Dimensions, feet (metres): 226 × 31.5 × 9.8 *(69 × 9.6 × 3)*
Main machinery: 4 MTU 20V 956 TB92 diesels; 22 140 hp(m) *(16.27 MW)* sustained; 2 shafts; 2
KaMeWa cp props
Speed, knots: 27. **Range, miles:** 2200 at 14 kts
Complement: 90 (including Flag Officer)

Missiles: SAM: Short Bros Seacat triple launcher ❶; optical/radar or TV guidance to 5 km *(2.7 nm)*;
warhead 10 kg; 12 missiles.
Guns: 1 OTO Melara 3 in *(76 mm)*/62 Mod 6 compact ❷; 85° elevation; 85 rounds/minute to
16 km *(8.7 nm)*; weight of shell 6 kg.
1 Breda Bofors 40 mm/70 Type 350 ❸; 85° elevation; 300 rounds/minute to 12.5 km *(6.8 nm)*;
weight of shell 0.96 kg.
2 Oerlikon 20 mm ❹; 50° elevation; 800 rounds/minute to 2 km.
A/S mortars: 1 Bofors 375 mm twin launcher ❺; range 1600 m or 3600 m (depending on type of
projectile).
Countermeasures: ESM: Decca Cutlass; radar warning.
Fire control: Signaal WM 20 series.
Radars: Air/surface search: Plessey AWS 2 ❻; E/F band; range 110 km *(60 nm)*.
Navigation: Racal Decca TM 1226; I band.
Fire control: Signaal WM 24 ❼; I/J band; range 46 km *(25 nm)*.
Sonars: Plessey PMS 26; lightweight; hull-mounted; active search and attack; 10 kHz.

Programmes: Ordered from Vosper Thornycroft 22 April 1975.
Modernisation: Proposals for refits in Lagos submitted in 1991 but no progress so far.
Operational: Much of the armament is non-operational. *Enyimiri* in refit in early 1994.

ERINOMI   (Scale 1 : 900), Ian Sturton

ENYIMIRI   7/1985, Hartmut Ehlers

SHIPBORNE AIRCRAFT

Numbers/Type: 2 Westland Lynx Mk 89.
Operational speed: 125 kts *(232 km/h)*.
Service ceiling: 12 500 ft *(3810 m)*.
Range: 320 nm *(590 km)*.
Role/Weapon systems: Coastal patrol and ASW helicopter; embarked and shore-based for frigate
ASW and SAR duties. Sensors: RCA 5000 radar. Weapons: ASW; 2 × 244/S torpedoes. ASV; 1 ×
7.62 mm door-mounted machine gun.

LAND-BASED MARITIME AIRCRAFT

Numbers/Type: 18 Dornier Do 128-6MPA.
Operational speed: 165 kts *(305 km/h)*.
Service ceiling: 32 600 ft *(9335 m)*.
Range: 790 nm *(1460 km)*.
Role/Weapon systems: Coastal surveillance and EEZ protection duties; anti-smuggling tasks.
Sensors: Weather radar, cameras. Weapons: Unarmed.

Numbers/Type: 3 Fokker F27 Maritime.
Operational speed: 250 kts *(463 km/h)*.
Service ceiling: 25 000 ft *(7620 m)*.
Range: 2700 nm *(5000 km)*.
Role/Weapon systems: Long-range MR and offshore surveillance of vital oil and fishing grounds.
Sensors: Search radar, MAD, provision for sonobuoys. Weapons: ASW; 2 × torpedoes, depth
bombs or mines. ASV; 4 × 127 mm rockets.

Numbers/Type: 15 MBB BO 105C.
Operational speed: 113 kts *(210 km/h)*.
Service ceiling: 9845 ft *(3000 m)*.
Range: 407 nm *(754 km)*.
Role/Weapon systems: Onshore, coastal and inshore search and rescue helicopter; limited com-
mando assault tasks and other fleet support duties. Sensors: None. Weapons: Unarmed but
could be provided with machine gun or cannon pods.

PATROL FORCES

5 VAN MILL TYPE (COASTAL PATROL CRAFT)

P 215   P 216   P 217   P 218   P 219

Displacement, tons: 45 full load
Dimensions, feet (metres): 66.3 × 17.4 × 5.9 *(20.2 × 5.3 × 1.8)*
Main machinery: 3 Detroit 12V-71TA diesels; 1260 hp *(939 kW)* sustained; 3 shafts *(P 215-216)*
2 MTU diesels; 2200 hp(m) *(1.61 MW)*; 2 shafts *(P 217-220)*
Speed, knots: 35. **Range, miles:** 950 at 25 kts
Complement: 12 (2 officers)
Guns: 1 Rheinmetall 20 mm. 2—7.62 mm MGs.

Comment: Built by Van Mill, Netherlands. Completed between July 1985 and end 1986. Sixth of
class given to Equatorial Guinea in June 1986. One operational in early 1994.

3 LÜRSSEN FPB-57 CLASS (FAST ATTACK CRAFT—MISSILE)

Name	No	Builders	Commissioned
EKPE	P 178	Lürssen, Vegesack	Aug 1980
DAMISA	P 179	Lürssen, Vegesack	Apr 1981
AGU	P 180	Lürssen, Vegesack	Apr 1981

Displacement, tons: 444 full load
Dimensions, feet (metres): 190.6 × 24.9 × 10.2 *(58.1 × 7.6 × 3.1)*
Main machinery: 4 MTU 16V 956 TB92 diesels; 17 700 hp(m) *(13 MW)* sustained; 2 shafts
Speed, knots: 42. **Range, miles:** 670 at 36 kts; 2000 at 16 kts
Complement: 40

Missiles: SSM: 4 OTO Melara/Matra Otomat Mk 1; active radar homing to 80 km *(43.2 nm)* at 0.9 Mach; warhead 210 kg.
Guns: 1 OTO Melara 3 in *(76 mm)*/62; 85° elevation; 60 rounds/minute to 16 km *(8.7 nm)*; weight of shell 6 kg.
   2 Breda 40 mm/70 (twin); 85° elevation; 300 rounds/minute to 12.5 km *(6.8 nm)*; weight of shell 0.96 kg.
   4 Emerson Electric 30 mm (2 twin); 80° elevation; 1200 rounds/minute combined to 6 km *(3.3 nm)*; weight of shell 0.35 kg.
Countermeasures: ESM: Decca RDL; radar intercept.
Radars: Surface search/navigation: Racal Decca TM 1226; I band.
Fire control: Signaal WM 28; I/J band; range 46 km *(25 nm)*.

Programmes: Ordered in late 1977. All three sailed in company for Nigeria on 21 August 1981 and completed major refit at building yard in February 1984.
Operational: Not regular sea-going but two of the class took part in the 1987 fleet exercise 'Odion'.

AGU (alongside DAMISA)   11/1983, G Koop

3 COMBATTANTE IIIB CLASS (FAST ATTACK CRAFT—MISSILE)

Name	No	Builders	Commissioned
SIRI	P 181	CMN, Cherbourg	19 Feb 1981
AYAM	P 182	CMN, Cherbourg	11 June 1981
EKUN	P 183	CMN, Cherbourg	18 Sep 1981

Displacement, tons: 385 standard; 430 full load
Dimensions, feet (metres): 184 × 24.9 × 7 *(56.2 × 7.6 × 2.1)*
Main machinery: 4 MTU 16V 956 TB92 diesels; 17 700 hp(m) *(13 MW)* sustained; 2 shafts
Speed, knots: 41. **Range, miles:** 2000 at 15 kts
Complement: 42

Missiles: SSM: 4 Aerospatiale MM 38 Exocet; inertial cruise; active radar homing to 42 km *(23 nm)* at 0.9 Mach; warhead 165 kg; sea-skimmer.
Guns: 1 OTO Melara 3 in *(76 mm)*/62; 85° elevation; 60 rounds/minute to 16 km *(8.7 nm)*; weight of shell 6 kg.
   2 Breda 40 mm/70 (twin); 85° elevation; 300 rounds/minute to 12.5 km *(6.8 nm)*; weight of shell 0.96 kg.
   4 Emerson Electric 30 mm (2 twin); 80° elevation; 1200 rounds/minute combined to 6 km *(3.3 nm)*; weight of shell 0.35 kg.
Countermeasures: ESM: Decca RDL; radar intercept.
Fire control: Thomson-CSF Vega system. 2 CSEE Panda optical directors.
Radars: Air/surface search: Thomson-CSF Triton (TRS 3033); G band; range 33 km *(18 nm)* for 2 m² target.
Navigation: Racal Decca TM 1226; I band.
Fire control: Thomson-CSF Castor II (TRS 3203); I/J band; range 15 km *(8 nm)* for 1 m² target.

Programmes: Ordered in late 1977. Finally handed over in February 1982 after delays caused by financial problems.
Modernisation: Major refit and repairs carried out at Cherbourg from March to December 1991.

EKUN (Siri behind)   12/1985, Hartmut Ehlers

4 BROOKE MARINE TYPE (LARGE PATROL CRAFT)

Name	No	Builders	Commissioned
MAKURDI	P 167	Brooke Marine, Lowestoft	14 Aug 1974
HADEJIA	P 168	Brooke Marine, Lowestoft	14 Aug 1974
JEBBA	P 171	Brooke Marine, Lowestoft	29 Apr 1977
OGUTA	P 172	Brooke Marine, Lowestoft	29 Apr 1977

Displacement, tons: 115 standard; 143 full load
Dimensions, feet (metres): 107 × 20 × 11.5 *(32.6 × 6.1 × 3.5)*
Main machinery: 2 Paxman Ventura 12CM diesels; 3000 hp *(2.24 MW)* sustained; 2 shafts
Speed, knots: 20.5
Complement: 21 (4 officers)
Guns: 4 Emerson Electric 30 mm (2 twin). 2 rocket flare launchers.
Radars: Surface search: Racal Decca TM 1226; I band.

Comment: First pair ordered in 1971. Second pair ordered 30 October 1974. Modifications to *Makurdi* and *Hadejia* were carried out by Brooke Marine in 1981-82. This included provision of new engines and Emerlec guns. The second pair similarly refitted in Nigeria. Operational status doubtful.

HADEJIA   1982, Brooke Marine

4 ABEKING AND RASMUSSEN TYPE (LARGE PATROL CRAFT)

Name	No	Builders	Commissioned
ARGUNGU	P 165	Abeking & Rasmussen	Aug 1973
YOLA	P 166	Abeking & Rasmussen	Aug 1973
BRAS	P 169	Abeking & Rasmussen	Mar 1976
EPE	P 170	Abeking & Rasmussen	Mar 1976

Displacement, tons: 90
Dimensions, feet (metres): 95.1 × 18 × 5.2 *(29 × 5.5 × 1.6)*
Main machinery: 2 MTU diesels; 2200 hp(m) *(1.62 MW)*; 2 shafts
Speed, knots: 20
Complement: 25
Guns: 4 Emerson Electric 30 mm (2 twin).
Radars: Surface search: Racal Decca TM 1229; I band.

Comment: *Yola* and *Bras* rearmed in 1978, the remainder in 1982. Operational status doubtful.

YOLA   8/1983, Hartmut Ehlers

2 WATERCRAFT P-2000 TYPE (COASTAL PATROL CRAFT)

OKRIKA P 225   **ABONNEMA** P 226

Displacement, tons: 49 full load
Dimensions, feet (metres): 68.2 × 19 × 9.8 *(20.8 × 5.8 × 3)*
Main machinery: 2 MTU 8V 396 TB93 diesels; 2180 hp(m) *(1.6 MW)* sustained; 2 shafts
Speed, knots: 33. **Range, miles:** 660 at 22 kts
Guns: 1 Rheinmetall 20 mm. 2—7.62 mm MGs.

Comment: Delayed by Watercraft's insolvency until 1988. GRP hulls.

6 SIMMONEAU 500 TYPE (COASTAL PATROL CRAFT)

P 233   P 234   P 235   P 236   P 237   P 238

Displacement, tons: 22 full load
Dimensions, feet (metres): 51.8 × 15.7 × 5.9 *(15.8 × 4.8 × 1.8)*
Main machinery: 2 MTU 6V 396 TC82 diesels; 1300 hp(m) *(956 kW)* sustained; 2 shafts
Speed, knots: 33. **Range, miles:** 375 at 25 kts
Complement: 6
Guns: 2—7.62 mm MGs (interchangeable with 20 mm if required).
Radars: Surface search: Racal Decca 976; I band.

Comment: First two commissioned October 1986, remainder by early 1987. Built by Simmoneau Fontenay-le-Comte, France. Aluminium hulls.

P 234   *1987, Simmoneau*

6 DAMEN 1500 TYPE (COASTAL PATROL CRAFT)

P 227   P 228   P 229   P 230   P 231   P 232

Displacement, tons: 16 full load
Dimensions, feet (metres): 49.5 × 14.8 × 4.9 *(15.1 × 4.5 × 1.5)*
Main machinery: 2 MTU diesels; 2250 hp(m) *(1.65 MW)*; 2 shafts
Speed, knots: 34
Complement: 6
Guns: 1—7.62 mm MG.

Comment: Built by Damen, Netherlands. First three completed April 1986, second three June 1986. Aluminium hulls. Two operational in early 1994.

14 INTERMARINE TYPE (COASTAL PATROL CRAFT)

ABEOKUTA P 200	IKEJA P 205	MAIDUGURI P 210
AKURE P 201	ILORIN P 206	MINNA P 211
BAUCHI P 202	JOS P 207	OWERRI P 212
BENIN CITY P 203	KADUNA P 208	SOKOTO P 214
ENUGU P 204	KANO P 209	

Displacement, tons: 22 full load
Dimensions, feet (metres): 55.1 × 14.8 × 3.3 *(16.8 × 4.5 × 1)*
Main machinery: 2 MTU 8V 331 TC82 diesels; 1740 hp(m) *(1.28 MW)* sustained; 2 waterjets
Speed, knots: 32. **Range, miles:** 400 at 28 kts
Complement: 6
Guns: 1 Oerlikon 20 mm. 2—7.62 mm (twin) MGs.

Comment: GRP hulls. Last of class delivered April 1982. Built by Intermarine, Sazana, Italy. Most are not operational and are on cradles ashore as in the picture. P 213 sank in 1984.

ENUGU   *9/1987, Hartmut Ehlers*

4 ROTORK SEA TRUCKS

P 239   P 240   P 241   P 242

Dimensions, feet (metres): 47.6 × 14.4 × 2.9 *(14.5 × 4.4 × 0.9)*
Main machinery: 2 MTU diesels; 600 hp(m) *(441 kW)*; 2 shafts
Speed, knots: 20
Complement: 8
Guns: 1—7.62 mm MG.

Comment: Delivered in 1986. P 242 used for survey work.

ROTORK P 242   *12/1985, Hartmut Ehlers*

4 SWIFTSHIPS TYPE (COASTAL PATROL CRAFT)

ISEYIN P 221   AFIKTO P 223
ERUWA P 222   ABA P 224

Displacement, tons: 36 full load
Dimensions, feet (metres): 65.6 × 18.4 × 4.9 *(20 × 5.6 × 1.5)*
Main machinery: 2 MTU 8V 396 TB93 diesels; 2180 hp(m) *(1.6 MW)* sustained; 2 shafts
Speed, knots: 32. **Range, miles:** 500 at 18 kts
Complement: 6
Guns: 1 Rheinmetall 20 mm. 2—7.62 mm MGs.

Comment: Delivered by Swiftships, USA in 1986. Aluminium hulls.

MINE WARFARE FORCES

2 LERICI CLASS (MINEHUNTERS/SWEEPERS)

Name	No	Builders	Commissioned
OHUE	M 371	Intermarine SY, Italy	28 May 1987
MARABAI	M 372	Intermarine SY, Italy	25 Feb 1988

Displacement, tons: 540 full load
Dimensions, feet (metres): 167.3 × 31.5 × 9.2 *(51 × 9.6 × 2.8)*
Main machinery: 2 MTU 12V 396 TB83 diesels; 3120 hp(m) *(2.3 MW)* sustained; 2 waterjets
Speed, knots: 15.5. **Range, miles:** 2500 at 12 kts
Complement: 50 (5 officers)
Guns: 2 Emerson Electric 30 mm (twin); 80° elevation; 1200 rounds/minute combined to 6 km *(3.3 nm)*; weight of shell 0.35 kg.
2 Oerlikon 20 mm GAM-BO1.
Countermeasures: Fitted with 2 Pluto remote-controlled submersibles, Oropesa 'O' Mis 4 and Ibis V control system.
Radars: Navigation: Racal Decca 1226; I band.
Sonars: Thomson Sintra TSM 2022; hull-mounted; mine detection; high frequency.

Comment: Ohue ordered in April 1983 and Marabai in January 1986 with an option for a third which has not been taken up. Ohue laid down 23 July 1984 and launched 22 November 1985, Marabai laid down 11 March 1985, launched 6 June 1986. GRP hulls but, unlike Italian and Malaysian versions they do not have separate hydraulic minehunting propulsion. Carry Galeazzi 2-man decompression chambers. Endurance, 14 days.

OHUE   *7/1987, Marina Fraccaroli*

AMPHIBIOUS FORCES

2 FDR TYPE RO-RO 1300 (LSTs)

Name	No	Builders	Commissioned
AMBE	LST 1312	Howaldtswerke, Hamburg	Apr 1979
OFIOM	LST 1313	Howaldtswerke, Hamburg	July 1979

Displacement, tons: 1470 standard; 1860 full load
Dimensions, feet (metres): 285.4 × 45.9 × 7.5 *(87 × 14 × 2.3)*
Main machinery: 2 MTU 16V 956 TB92 diesels; 8850 hp(m) *(6.5 MW)* sustained; 2 shafts
Speed, knots: 17. **Range, miles:** 5000 at 10 kts
Complement: 56 (6 officers)
Military lift: 460 tons and 220 troops long haul; 540 troops or 1000 troops seated short haul; can carry 5—40 ton tanks
Guns: 1 Breda 40 mm/70; 85° elevation; 300 rounds/minute to 12.5 km *(6.8 nm)*; weight of shell 0.96 kg.
2 Oerlikon 20 mm.
Radars: Navigation: Racal Decca 1226; I band.

Comment: Ordered September 1976. Built to a design prepared for the FGN. Have a 19 m bow ramp and a 4 m stern ramp. Reported that Ambe's bow ramp is welded shut. One of the class inadvertently grounded in 1992 and may not be recoverable.

AMBE   *5/1986, Michael D J Lennon*

SURVEY SHIP

Name	No	Builders	Commissioned
LANA	A 498	Brooke Marine, Lowestoft	15 July 1976

Displacement, tons: 800 standard; 1088 full load
Dimensions, feet (metres): 189 × 37.5 × 12 *(57.8 × 11.4 × 3.7)*
Main machinery: 4 Lister-Blackstone ERS-8M diesels; 2640 hp *(1.97 MW)*; 2 shafts
Speed, knots: 16. **Range, miles:** 4500 at 12 kts
Complement: 52 (12 officers)
Guns: 2 Oerlikon 20 mm.
Radars: Navigation: Racal Decca; I band.

Comment: Ordered in late 1973, laid down 5 April 1974, launched 4 March 1976. Sister to Bulldog class.

LANA   *8/1983, Hartmut Ehlers*

TUGS

Note: Two 46 ft pusher tugs delivered by Damen in 1986 for use in Lagos.

3 COASTAL TUGS

Displacement, tons: 200 full load
Dimensions, feet (metres): 90.5 × 25.5 × 11.3 *(27.6 × 7.8 × 3.5)*
Main machinery: 2 GM diesels; 2400 hp *(1.79 MW)*; 2 shafts
Speed, knots: 12.5

Comment: Built by Alblas (Krimpen A/D, Rijn). First launched 9 October 1981.

Name	No	Builders	Commissioned
COMMANDER APAYI JOE	A 499	SY de Wiel BV, Asperen, Netherlands	Sep 1983

Displacement, tons: 310 full load
Dimensions, feet (metres): 76.1 × 23.6 × 9.5 *(23.2 × 7.2 × 2.9)*
Main machinery: 2 MAN diesels; 1510 hp(m) *(1.11 MW)*; 2 shafts

Comment: A second of class *Commander Rudolf* was not paid for and therefore not delivered.

COMMANDER APAYI JOE   *11/1983, Hartmut Ehlers*

2 TUGS

DOLPHIN MIRA   **DOLPHIN RIMA**

Comment: Based at Apapa.

TRAINING SHIP

Name	No	Builders	Commissioned
RUWAN YARO (ex-*Ogina Brereton*)	A 497	Van Lent, Netherlands	1976

Displacement, tons: 400 full load
Dimensions, feet (metres): 144.6 × 26.2 × 12.8 *(44.2 × 8 × 3.9)*
Main machinery: 2 Deutz BA12M528 diesels; 3000 hp(m) *(2.2 MW)*; 1 shaft; cp prop; bow thruster
Speed, knots: 17. **Range, miles:** 3000 at 15 kts
Complement: 42 (11 midshipmen)
Radars: Navigation: Racal Decca TM 1626; I band.

Comment: Originally built in 1975 as a yacht. Used as navigational training vessel.

RUWAN YARO   *12/1983, Hartmut Ehlers*

POLICE

Note: Mostly used to patrol Niger River and Lake Chad. In addition to the craft listed there are some 60 light launches and five small hovercraft, many of which are non-operational.

1 P 1200 TYPE (COASTAL PATROL CRAFT)

Displacement, tons: 9.5
Dimensions, feet (metres): 39 × 13.4 × 3.5 *(11.9 × 4.1 × 1.1)*
Main machinery: 2 Detroit 8V-7ITA diesels; 460 hp *(343 kW)* sustained; 2 shafts
Speed, knots: 27. **Range, miles:** 240 at 25 kts

Comment: GRP hull. Delivered February 1981 by Watercraft Ltd, Shoreham, Sussex.

P 1200   *1981, Watercraft*

8 VOSPER THORNYCROFT TYPE (COASTAL PATROL CRAFT)

Displacement, tons: 15
Dimensions, feet (metres): 34 × 10 × 2.8 *(10.4 × 3.1 × 0.9)*
Main machinery: 2 diesels; 290 hp *(216 kW)*; 2 shafts
Speed, knots: 19
Complement: 6
Guns: 1—12.7 mm MG.

Comment: Ordered for Nigerian Police in March 1971, completed 1971-72. GRP hulls.

NORWAY

Headquarters' Appointments

Chief of Naval Staff:
Rear Admiral K A Prytz
Commander Naval Material Command:
Rear Admiral H K Svensholt
Deputy Chief of Naval Staff:
Commodore R H Christensen
Inspector Coast Artillery:
Commodore K M Aam
Inspector Coast Guard:
Commodore T M Nikolaisen
Commander Coast Fleet and Commodore Sea Training:
Commodore J G Jaeger

Diplomatic Representation

Defence Attaché in Bonn:
Colonel J H Skaar (AF)
Defence Attaché in Helsinki:
Colonel A Mørch (A)
Defence Attaché in London:
Colonel Per Johan Aunaas (A)
Defence Attaché in Moscow:
Colonel J W Smedsrud (AF)
Defence Attaché in Paris:
Captain T Ubbe
Defence Attaché in Stockholm:
Captain Erik Langum
Defence Attaché in Washington and Ottawa:
Major General Olav F Aamoth (AF)

Personnel

(a) 1994: 7000 officers and ratings (including 1400 Coast Artillery)
(b) 9-12 months' national service

Naval Home Guard

The Naval Home Guard numbers some 7000 men and women on mobilisation, assigned to eight naval districts and manning 400 craft.

Coast Artillery

Numerous coastal forts, all with co-ordinated radar stations and guns for air defence, and some with torpedo batteries and/or controlled minefields. The most modern are equipped with RB 70 SAM missiles and 120 mm guns.

Coast Guard

Founded April 1977 with operational command held by Norwegian Defence Command. Main bases at Sortland (North) and Haakonsvern (South).

Bases

Karl Johansvern (Horten)—HQ Østlandet District
Haakonsvern (Bergen)—HQ Vestlandet District
Laksevag (Bergen)—Submarine Repair and Maintenance
Ramsund—Supply/Repair/Maintenance
Olavsvern (Tromsø)—HQ Tromsø District

Air Force Squadrons (see *Shipborne* and *Land-based Aircraft* section)

Aircraft (Squadron)	Location	Duties
Sea King Mk 43 (330)	Bodø, Banak, Sola, Ørland	SAR
Orion P3B/C (333)	Andøya	LRMP
Lynx (337)	Coast Guard vessels/ Bardufoss	MP
Bell 412 (719, 339 & 720)	Bodø, Rygge, Bardufoss	Army Transport

Strength of the Fleet

Type	Active	Building (Projected)
Submarines—Coastal	12	—
Frigates	4	—
Fast Attack Craft—Missile	30	(12)
Minelayers	3	—
Minesweepers/Hunters	5	9
LCTs	5	—
Depot Ship	1	—
Auxiliaries	4	—
Naval District Auxiliaries	39	—
Coast Guard Vessels	13	—
Survey Vessels	7	—

Prefix to Ships' Names

KNM (Naval)
K/V (Coast Guard)

Mercantile Marine

Lloyd's Register of Shipping:
1514 vessels of 2 152 258 tons gross

DELETIONS

Frigate

1994   *Oslo*

Submarines

1991   *Utsira* (old), *Utstein* (old)
1992   *Kaura, Kinn*

Corvettes

1992   *Sleipner, Aeger*

Patrol Forces

1990-91   *Sev, Hval, Laks, Knurr, Skrei, Hai, Lyr, Delfin*
1991-92   *Glimt, Arg, Brann, Tross, Traust, Brott, Odd, Rokk*

Minesweepers

1992   *Sira, Vosso, Glomma*

Amphibious Forces

1991   *Kvalsund, Raftsund*

Survey Vessels

1992   *Sjøvern, Sjøfalk, Sjøskvett, Sjødrev, Sverdrup*
1994   *Marjata* (old), *Sjørokk*

Coast Guard

1992   *Malene Østervold*

PENNANT LIST

Note: Naval District Auxiliaries are listed on page 466.

Submarines

S 300	Ula
S 301	Utsira
S 302	Utstein
S 303	Utvaer
S 304	Uthaug
S 305	Uredd
S 306	Skolpen
S 308	Stord
S 309	Svenner
S 314	Sklinna
S 318	Kobben
S 319	Kunna

Frigates

F 301	Bergen
F 302	Trondheim
F 303	Stavanger
F 304	Narvik

Minesweepers/Hunters

M 313	Tana
M 314	Alta
M 331	Tista
M 332	Kvina
M 334	Utla
M 340	Oksøy
M 341	Karmøy
M 342	Maløy
M 343	Hinnøy
M 350	Alta
M 351	Otra
M 352	Rauma
M 353	Orkla
M 354	Glomma

Minelayers

N 51	Borgen
N 52	Vidar
N 53	Vale

Patrol Forces

P 358	Hessa
P 359	Vigra
P 961	Blink
P 963	Skjold
P 964	Trygg
P 965	Kjekk
P 966	Djerv
P 967	Skudd
P 969	Steil
P 972	Hvass
P 977	Brask
P 979	Gnist
P 980	Snögg
P 981	Rapp
P 982	Snar
P 983	Rask
P 984	Kvikk
P 985	Kjapp
P 986	Hauk
P 987	Ørn
P 988	Terne
P 989	Tjeld
P 990	Skarv
P 991	Teist
P 992	Jo
P 993	Lom
P 994	Stegg
P 995	Falk
P 996	Ravn
P 997	Gribb
P 998	Geir
P 999	Erle

Amphibious Forces

L 4502	Reinøysund
L 4503	Sørøysund
L 4504	Maursund
L 4505	Rotsund
L 4506	Borgsund

Auxiliaries

A 530	Horten
A 531	Sarpen
A 532	Draug
A 533	Norge

Coast Guard

W 300	Nornen
W 301	Farm
W 302	Heimdal
W 312	Kim
W 314	Stålbas
W 315	Nordsjøbas
W 316	Volstad Jr
W 317	Lafjord
W 318	Garpeskjaer
W 319	Grimsholm
W 320	Nordkapp
W 321	Senja
W 322	Andenes

SUBMARINES

6 ULA CLASS (TYPE P 6071 (Ex-210))

Name	No
ULA	S 300
UREDD	S 305
UTVAER	S 303
UTHAUG	S 304
UTSTEIN	S 302
UTSIRA	S 301

Builders	Laid down	Launched	Commissioned
Thyssen Nordseewerke, Emden	29 Jan 1987	28 July 1988	27 Apr 1989
Thyssen Nordseewerke, Emden	23 June 1988	22 Sep 1989	3 May 1990
Thyssen Nordseewerke, Emden	8 Dec 1988	19 Apr 1990	8 Nov 1990
Thyssen Nordseewerke, Emden	15 June 1989	18 Oct 1990	7 May 1991
Thyssen Nordseewerke, Emden	6 Dec 1989	25 Apr 1991	14 Nov 1991
Thyssen Nordseewerke, Emden	15 June 1990	21 Nov 1991	30 Apr 1992

Displacement, tons: 1040 surfaced; 1150 dived
Dimensions, feet (metres): 193.6 × 17.7 × 15.1
(59 × 5.4 × 4.6)
Main machinery: Diesel-electric; 2 MTU 16V 396 SB83 diesels;
2700 hp(m) (1.98 MW) sustained; 1 Siemens motor; 6000 hp
(m) (4.41 MW); 1 shaft
Speed, knots: 11 surfaced; 23 dived
Range, miles: 5000 at 8 kts
Complement: 18-20 (3 officers)

Torpedoes: 8—21 in (533 mm) bow tubes. 14 AEG DM 2A3
Seeal; dual purpose; wire-guided; active/passive homing to
28 km (15 nm) at 23 kts; 13 km (7 nm) at 35 kts; warhead
260 kg.
Countermeasures: ESM: Racal Sealion; radar warning.
Fire control: Kongsberg MSI-90(U); command and weapon con-
trol system.
Radars: Surface search: Kelvin Hughes 1007; I band.
Sonars: Atlas Elektronik CSU83; active/passive intercept search
and attack; medium frequency.
Thomson Sintra; flank array; passive; low frequency.

Programmes: Contract signed on 30 September 1982. This was
a joint West German/Norwegian effort known as Project 210
in Germany and is the most expensive ever undertaken by the
Norwegian Navy. Although final assembly was at Thyssen a
number of pressure hull sections were provided by Norway.

UTHAUG   6/1991, Stefan Terzibaschitsch

Structure: Diving depth, 250 m (820 ft). The basic command
and weapon control systems are Norwegian, the attack sonar
is German but the flank array, based on piezoelectric polymer
antenna technology, has been developed in France and sub-
stantially reduces flow noise. Calzoni Trident modular system
of non-penetrating masts has been installed.

UTSIRA   6/1992, van Ginderen Collection

6 MODERNISED KOBBEN CLASS (TYPE 207)

Name	No
SKLINNA	S 314 (ex-S 305)
SKOLPEN	S 306
STORD	S 308
SVENNER	S 309
KOBBEN	S 318
KUNNA	S 319

Builders	Laid down	Launched	Commissioned
Rheinstahl-Nordseewerke, Emden	17 Aug 1965	21 Jan 1966	27 May 1966
Rheinstahl-Nordseewerke, Emden	1 Nov 1965	24 Mar 1966	17 Aug 1966
Rheinstahl-Nordseewerke, Emden	1 Apr 1966	2 Sep 1966	14 Feb 1967
Rheinstahl-Nordseewerke, Emden	8 Sep 1966	27 Jan 1967	12 June 1967
Rheinstahl-Nordseewerke, Emden	9 Dec 1963	25 Apr 1964	17 Aug 1964
Rheinstahl-Nordseewerke, Emden	3 Mar 1964	16 July 1964	29 Oct 1964

Displacement, tons: 459 standard; 524 dived
Dimensions, feet (metres): 155.5 × 15 × 14 (47.4 × 4.6 × 4.3)
Main machinery: Diesel-electric; 2 MTU 12V 493 AZ80 GA31L
diesels; 1200 hp(m) (880 kW) sustained; 1 motor; 1800 hp(m)
(1.32 MW) sustained; 1 shaft
Speed, knots: 12 surfaced; 18 dived. **Range, miles:** 5000 at
8 kts (snorting)
Complement: 18 (17 Svenner) (5 officers)

Torpedoes: 8—21 in (533 mm) bow tubes. 8 mix of (a) FFV Type
61; anti-surface; wire-guided; passive homing to 25 km
(13.7 nm) at 45 kts; warhead 240 kg and (b) Honeywell
NT37C; dual purpose; wire-guided; active/passive homing to
20 km (10.8 nm) at 35 kts; warhead 150 kg.
Countermeasures: ESM: Argo radar warning.
Fire control: Kongsberg MSI-90(U) TFCS.
Radars: Surface search: Kelvin Hughes 1007; I band.
Sonars: Atlas Elektronik or Simrad; passive search and attack;
medium/high frequency.

Programmes: It was announced in July 1959 that the USA and
Norway would share equally the cost of these submarines.
They are a development of IKL Type 205 (West German U4-
U8) with increased diving depth. Kobben was the name of the
first submarine in the Royal Norwegian Navy. Commissioned
on 28 November 1909.
Modernisation: These six modernised at Urivale Shipyard, Bergen, to a similar standard to the three sold to Denmark including lengthening and new communications, navigation and fire
control equipment. The remainder phased out with some taken
on by the USN for trials. Modernisation completion programme was S 314 January 1989, S 306 October 1989,
S 308 August 1990, S 318 May 1991, S 319 December
1991, S 309 April 1992.
Structure: Diving depth, 200 m (650 ft). Svenner's second periscope for COs training operations is a metre longer. Pilkington
Optronics CK 30 search periscope.

KOBBEN   5/1988, W Sartori

Sales: Utvaer, Uthaug and Kya sold to Denmark and modernised
to the same standard as the Norwegian programme. Kaura has
also been sold to Denmark to be cannibalised to repair Saelen,
which was flooded after conversion.

FRIGATES

Note: It is intended to tender for new frigates in 1996.

4 OSLO CLASS

Name	No
BERGEN	F 301
TRONDHEIM	F 302
STAVANGER	F 303
NARVIK	F 304

Builders	Laid down	Launched	Commissioned
Marinens Hovedverft, Horten	1964	23 Aug 1965	15 June 1967
Marinens Hovedverft, Horten	1963	4 Sep 1964	2 June 1966
Marinens Hovedverft, Horten	1965	4 Feb 1966	1 Dec 1967
Marinens Hovedverft, Horten	1964	8 Jan 1965	30 Nov 1966

Displacement, tons: 1450 standard; 1745 full load
Dimensions, feet (metres): 317 × 36.8 × 18 (screws)
(96.6 × 11.2 × 5.5)
Main machinery: 2 Babcock & Wilcox boilers; 600 psi
(42.18 kg/cm sq); 850°F *(454°C)*; 1 set De Laval Ljungstrom
PN20 geared turbines; 20 000 hp(m) *(14.7 MW)*; 1 shaft
Speed, knots: 25+. **Range, miles:** 4500 at 15 kts
Complement: 150 (11 officers)

Missiles: SSM: 4 Kongsberg Penguin Mk 2 ❶; IR homing to
27 km *(14.6 nm)* at 0.8 Mach; warhead 120 kg.
SAM: Raytheon NATO RIM-7M Sea Sparrow Mk 29 octuple
launcher ❷; semi-active radar homing to 14.6 km *(8 nm)* at
2.5 Mach; warhead 39 kg; 24 cell magazine.
Guns: 2 US 3 in *(76 mm)*/50 Mk 33 (twin) ❸; 85° elevation; 50
rounds/minute to 12.8 km *(7 nm)*; weight of shell 6 kg.
1 Bofors 40 mm/70 ❹; 90° elevation; 300 rounds/minute to
12 km *(6.6 nm)*; weight of shell 0.96 kg
2 Rheinmetall 20 mm/20 (not in all); 55° elevation; 1000
rounds/minute to 2 km.
Torpedoes: 6—324 mm US Mk 32 (2 triple) tubes ❺. Marconi
Stingray; anti-submarine; active/passive homing to 11 km
(5.9 nm) at 45 kts; warhead 32 kg (shaped charge); depth to
750 m *(2460 ft)*.
A/S mortars: Kongsberg Terne III 6-tubed trainable ❻; range pattern from 400-5000 m; warhead 70 kg. Automatic reloading
in 40 seconds.
Mines: Laying capability.
Countermeasures: Decoys: 2 chaff launchers.
ESM/ECM: Argo intercept and jammer.
Combat data systems: NFT MSI-3100 action data automation;
capability for Link 11 and 14. SATCOM ❼.
Fire control: Mk 91 MFCS. TVT 300 tracker ❽; MPDR 45/1.
Radars: Air search: Thomson-CSF DRBV 22 ❾; D band; range
366 km *(200 nm)*. To be replaced by Siemens/Plessey AWS-9
in 1994/95.
Surface search: Racal Decca TM 1226 ❿; I band.
Fire control: NobelTech 9LV 200 Mk 2 ⓫; I band (includes
search).
Raytheon Mk 95 ⓬, I/J band (for Sea Sparrow).
Navigation: Decca; I band.
Sonars: Thomson Sintra/Simrad TSM 2633; combined hull and
VDS; active search and attack; medium frequency.
Simrad Terne III; active attack; high frequency.

Programmes: Built under the five-year naval construction programme approved by the Norwegian Storting (Parliament) late
in 1960. Although all the ships of this class were constructed in
the Norwegian Naval Dockyard, half the cost was borne by
Norway and the other half by the USA.
Modernisation: All ships modernised with improvements in
weapons control and habitability; new countermeasures
equipment includes two chaff launchers; Spherion TSM-2633
sonar (with VDS) (a joint Thomson Sintra/Simrad-Subsea (Norway) project); the after 76 mm mounting replaced by a Bofors
40 mm/70; and MSI 3100 action data automation. Modernisation completion programme: F 302 30 November 1987, F
304 21 October 1988, F 303 5 June 1989, F 301 4 April 1990.
Structure: The hull and propulsion design of these ships is based
on that of the Dealey class destroyer escorts (now deleted) of
the US Navy, but considerably modified to suit Norwegian
requirements.
Operational: The fifth of class *Oslo* sank under tow south of Bergen in January 1994, after an engine failure had caused her to
run aground in heavy weather. Although recoverable she is
unlikely to be put back in service.

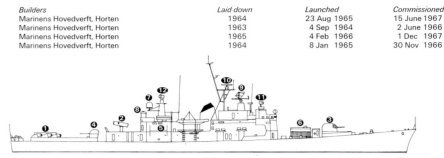

TRONDHEIM
(Scale 1 : 900), Ian Sturton

TRONDHEIM
5/1993, Camil Busquets i Vilanova

TRONDHEIM
8/1993, Diego Quevedo

BERGEN
7/1992, Maritime Photographic

SHIPBORNE AIRCRAFT

Numbers/Type: 6 Westland Lynx Mk 86.
Operational speed: 125 kts *(232 km/h)*.
Service ceiling: 12 500 ft *(3810 m)*.
Range: 320 nm *(590 km)*.
Role/Weapon systems: Helicopter, operated by Air Force on behalf of the Coast Guard for fishery protection, offshore oil protection and SAR; embarked in CG vessels and shore-based. Sensors: Search radar, ESM. Weapons: Generally unarmed.

LYNX   *1993, Royal Norwegian Navy*

LAND-BASED MARITIME AIRCRAFT

Numbers/Type: 2/4 Lockheed P-3B/C Orion.
Operational speed: 410 kts *(760 km/h)*.
Service ceiling: 28 300 ft *(8625 m)*.
Range: 4000 nm *(7410 km)*.
Role/Weapon systems: Long-range MR and oceanic surveillance duties in peacetime, with ASW added as a war role; P-3Bs used by Coast Guard. Sensors: APS-115 radar, ASQ-81 MAD, processor and computer, IFF, ECM/ESM, sonobuoys. Weapons: ASW; 8 MUSL Stingray torpedoes, depth bombs or mines. ASV; possible arming with Penguin missile.

Numbers/Type: 10 Westland Sea King Mk 43/43B.
Operational speed: 125 kts *(232 km/h)*.
Service ceiling: 10 500 ft *(3200 m)*.
Range: 630 nm *(1165 km)*.
Role/Weapon systems: SAR, surface search and surveillance helicopter; supplemented by civil helicopters in wartime. Two 43B to be delivered in 1995/96; remainder to be updated to 43B standard. Sensors: FLIR 2000 and dual Bendix radars RDR 1500 and RDR 1300. Weapons: Generally unarmed.

PATROL FORCES

Note: 12 new FAC planned by 2000. Air cushion design of 125 tons capable of 52 kts.

14 HAUK CLASS (FAST ATTACK CRAFT—MISSILE)

Name	No	Builders (see *Programmes*)	Commissioned
HAUK	P 986	Bergens Mek Verksteder	17 Aug 1977
ØRN	P 987	Bergens Mek Verksteder	19 Jan 1979
TERNE	P 988	Bergens Mek Verksteder	13 Mar 1979
TJELD	P 989	Bergens Mek Verksteder	25 May 1979
SKARV	P 990	Bergens Mek Verksteder	17 July 1979
TEIST	P 991	Bergens Mek Verksteder	11 Sep 1979
JO	P 992	Bergens Mek Verksteder	1 Nov 1979
LOM	P 993	Bergens Mek Verksteder	15 Jan 1980
STEGG	P 994	Bergens Mek Verksteder	18 Mar 1980
FALK	P 995	Bergens Mek Verksteder	30 Apr 1980
RAVN	P 996	Westamarin A/S, Alta	20 May 1980
GRIBB	P 997	Westamarin A/S, Alta	10 July 1980
GEIR	P 998	Westamarin A/S, Alta	16 Sep 1980
ERLE	P 999	Westamarin A/S, Alta	10 Dec 1980

Displacement, tons: 120 standard; 148 full load
Dimensions, feet (metres): 120 × 20 × 5 *(36.5 × 6.1 × 1.5)*
Main machinery: 2 MTU 16V 538 TB92 diesels; 6820 hp(m) *(5 MW)* sustained; 2 shafts
Speed, knots: 32. **Range, miles:** 440 at 30 kts
Complement: 22 (6 officers)

Missiles: SSM: Up to 6 Kongsberg Penguin Mk 2 Mod 5; IR homing to 27 km *(14.6 nm)* at 0.8 Mach; warhead 120 kg.
SAM: Twin Simbad launcher for Matra Mistral being fitted from late 1994.
Guns: 1 Bofors 40 mm/70; 90° elevation; 300 rounds/minute to 12 km *(6.6 nm)*; weight of shell 0.96 kg.
1 Rheinmetall 20 mm/20; 55° elevation; 1000 rounds/minute to 2 km.
Torpedoes: 2—21 in *(533 mm)* tubes. FFV Type 613; passive homing to 27 km *(14.5 nm)* at 45 kts; warhead 240 kg.
Fire control: Kongsberg MSI-80S TV optronic tracker and laser rangefinder.
Radars: Surface search/navigation: Two Racal Decca TM 1226; I band.
Sonars: Simrad; active search; high frequency.

Programmes: Ordered 12 June 1975. Westamarin is the former Westermoen shipyard (see *Storm* class).
Modernisation: Simbad twin launchers for SAM being fitted from 1994.
Structure: Very similar to *Snögg* class with improved fire control.

TERNE   *5/1993, Erik Laursen*

FALK   *4/1993, Antonio Moreno*

10 STORM CLASS (FAST ATTACK CRAFT—MISSILE)

Name	No	Builders	Commissioned
BLINK	P 961	Bergens Mek. Verksteder	18 Dec 1965
SKJOLD	P 963	Westermoen, Mandal	1966
TRYGG	P 964	Bergens Mek Verksteder	1966
KJEKK	P 965	Bergens Mek Verksteder	1966
DJERV	P 966	Westermoen, Mandal	1966
SKUDD	P 967	Bergens Mek Verksteder	1966
STEIL	P 969	Westermoen, Mandal	1967
HVASS	P 972	Westermoen, Mandal	1967
BRASK	P 977	Bergens Mek Verksteder	1967
GNIST	P 979	Bergens Mek Verksteder	1968

Displacement, tons: 100 standard; 135 full load
Dimensions, feet (metres): 120 × 20 × 5 *(36.5 × 6.1 × 1.5)*
Main machinery: 2 MTU MB 16V 538 TB90 diesels; 6000 hp(m) *(4.41 MW)* sustained; 2 shafts
Speed, knots: 32
Complement: 22 (6 officers)

Missiles: SSM: Up to 6 Kongsberg Penguin Mk 1 Mod 7; IR homing to 20 km *(10.8 nm)* at 0.7 Mach; warhead 120 kg.
Guns: 1 Bofors 3 in *(76 mm)*/50; 30° elevation; 30 rounds/minute to 13 km *(7 nm)* surface fire only; weight of shell 5.9 kg.
1 Bofors 40 mm/70; 90° elevation; 300 rounds/minute to 12 km *(6.6 nm)*; weight of shell 0.96 kg.
Fire control: TVT 300 optronic tracker and laser rangefinder.
Radars: Surface search: Racal Decca TM 1226; I band.
Fire control: Signaal WM 26; I/J band.

Programmes: Originally a class of 20. *Storm* (P 960) used as a trials vessel.
Modernisation: The introduction of Penguin surface-to-surface guided missile launchers started in 1970, in addition to originally designed armament, although all boats do not carry full complement at all times. Further modernisation of the surviving 10 of the class was intended but has been cancelled.
Structure: Depth charge rails can still be fitted. The optronic tracker is fitted aft of the mainmast.

BLINK   *5/1993, Erik Laursen*

GNIST   *5/1993, Erik Laursen*

6 SNÖGG CLASS (FAST ATTACK CRAFT—MISSILE)

Name	No	Builders	Commissioned
SNÖGG (ex-Lyr)	P 980	Båtservice, Mandal	1970
RAPP	P 981	Båtservice, Mandal	1970
SNAR	P 982	Båtservice, Mandal	1970
RASK	P 983	Båtservice, Mandal	1971
KVIKK	P 984	Båtservice, Mandal	1971
KJAPP	P 985	Båtservice, Mandal	1971

Displacement, tons: 100 standard; 135 full load
Dimensions, feet (metres): 120 × 20 × 5 (36.5 × 6.1 × 1.5)
Main machinery: 2 MTU 16V 538 TB92 diesels; 6820 hp(m) (5 MW) sustained; 2 shafts
Speed, knots: 32
Complement: 22 (6 officers)

Missiles: SSM: Up to 4 Kongsberg Penguin Mk 1; IR homing to 20 km (10.8 nm) at 0.7 Mach; warhead 120 kg.
Guns: 1 Bofors 40 mm/70; 90° elevation; 300 rounds/minute to 12 km (6.6 nm); weight of shell 0.96 kg.
Torpedoes: 4—21 in (533 mm) tubes. T1 mod 1; anti-surface; wire-guided; passive homing to 18 km (9.8 nm) at 45 kts; warhead 240 kg.

Fire control: PEAB TORC1 system.
Radars: Surface search: Racal Decca 1626; I band.

Programmes: Steel hulled fast attack craft, started coming into service in 1970.
Modernisation: Modernisation of fire control and electronics to be done in due course and may include installation of a Simbad SAM twin launcher.
Structure: Hulls are similar to those of the Storm class.

KJAPP   5/1992, Antonio Moreno

MINE WARFARE FORCES

0 + 9 OKSØY/ALTA CLASS (MINEHUNTERS/SWEEPERS)

Name	No	Builders	Commissioned
Hunters			
OKSØY	M 340	Kvaerner Mandal	June 1994
KARMØY	M 341	Kvaerner Mandal	June 1995
MALØY	M 342	Kvaerner Mandal	Dec 1995
HINNØY	M 343	Kvaerner Mandal	Feb 1996
Sweepers			
ALTA	M 350	Kvaerner Mandal	May 1996
OTRA	M 351	Kvaerner Mandal	Nov 1996
RAUMA	M 352	Kvaerner Mandal	Feb 1997
ORKLA	M 353	Kvaerner Mandal	June 1997
GLOMMA	M 354	Kvaerner Mandal	Dec 1997

Displacement, tons: 367 full load
Dimensions, feet (metres): 181.1 × 44.6 × 7.5 (2.76 cushion) (55.2 × 13.6 × 2.3 (0.84))
Main machinery: 2 MTU 12V 396 TE84 diesels; 3700 hp(m) (2.72 MW) sustained; 2 Kvaerner Eureka waterjets; 2 MTU 8V 396 TE54 diesels; 1740 hp(m) (1.28 MW/60 Hz) sustained; lift engines
Speed, knots: 25. **Range, miles:** 1200 at 22 kts
Complement: 37 (14 officers)

Guns: 2 Rheinmetall 20 mm. 2—12.7 mm MGs.
Countermeasures: MCMV: 2 Pluto submersibles (minehunter); mechanical and influence sweeping equipment (minesweepers).
Radars: Navigation: 2 Racal Decca; I band.
Sonars: Thomson Sintra/Simrad TSM 2023N; hull-mounted (minehunters); high frequency.
Simrad Subsea SA 950; hull-mounted (minesweepers); high frequency.

Programmes: Orders for nine placed with Kvaerner on 9 November 1989. Four will be minehunters, the remainder minesweepers. Option on a tenth of class will not be taken up. Oksøy launched on 8 March 1993.
Structure: Design developed by the Navy in Bergen with the Defence Research Institute and Norsk Veritas and uses an air-cushion created by the surface effect between two hulls. The hull is built of Fibre Reinforced Plastics (FRP) in sandwich configuration.
Operational: Simrad Albatross tactical system including mapping; Cast/Del Norte mobile positioning system with GPS. The catamaran design is claimed to give higher transit speeds with lesser installed power than a traditional hull design. Other advantages are lower magnetic and acoustic signatures, more comfortable motion, clearer water for sonar operations, and less susceptibility to shock.
Opinion: There is some scepticism amongst international naval architects as to whether this design will live up to expectations. It is certainly a very bold choice by the Norwegian Navy.

2 VIDAR CLASS (COASTAL MINELAYERS)

Name	No	Builders	Commissioned
VIDAR	N 52	Mjellem and Karlsren, Bergen	21 Oct 1977
VALE	N 53	Mjellem and Karlsren, Bergen	10 Feb 1978

Displacement, tons: 1500 standard; 1673 full load
Dimensions, feet (metres): 212.6 × 39.4 × 13.1 (64.8 × 12 × 4)
Main machinery: 2 Wichmann 7AX diesels; 4200 hp(m) (3.1 MW); 2 shafts; auxiliary motor; 425 hp(m) (312 kW); bow thruster
Speed, knots: 15
Complement: 50

Guns: 2 Bofors 40 mm/70; 90° elevation; 300 rounds/minute to 12 km (6.6 nm); weight of shell 0.96 kg.
Torpedoes: 6—324 mm US Mk 32 (2 triple) tubes. Honeywell Mk 46; anti-submarine; active/passive homing to 11 km (5.9 nm) at 40 kts; warhead 44 kg.
Mines: 300-400 (dependent on type) on 3 decks with an automatic lift between. Loaded through hatches fwd and aft, each served by 2 cranes.
Radars: Surface search: Racal Decca TM 1226; I band.
Sonars: Simrad; hull-mounted; search and attack; medium/high frequency.

Programmes: Ordered 11 June 1975.
Operational: Versatile ships that can perform a number of roles in addition to minelaying.

VIDAR   8/1991, van Ginderen Collection

OKSØY   8/1993, Royal Norwegian Navy

1 CONTROLLED MINELAYER

Name	No	Builders	Commissioned
BORGEN	N 51	Marinens Hovedverft, Horten	1961

Displacement, tons: 282 standard
Dimensions, feet (metres): 102.5 × 26.2 × 11 *(31.2 × 8 × 3.4)*
Main machinery: 2 GM 3-71 diesels; 660 hp *(492 kW)*; 2 Voith-Schneider props
Speed, knots: 9
Guns: 1 Rheinmetall 20 mm.
Mines: 2 rails.
Radars: Navigation: I band.

Comment: Launched 29 April 1960. Has two derricks used for mine placement. Planned to be replaced in mid-1994 by a new construction dual purpose amphibious vessel but this has been postponed.

BORGEN   *1990, Royal Norwegian Navy*

5 ADJUTANT/SAUDA CLASS (MSC 60)
(MINESWEEPERS—COASTAL)

Name	No	Builders	Commissioned
TANA (ex-*Roeselare* M 914, ex-*MSC 103*)	M 313	Hodgeson Bros, Gowdy & Stevens, Maine	Sep 1953
ALTA (ex-*Arlon* M 915, ex-*MSC 104*)	M 314	Hodgeson Bros, Gowdy & Stevens, Maine	Oct 1953
TISTA	M 331	Forende Båtbyggerier, Risör	27 Apr 1955
KVINA	M 332	Båtservice, Mandal	12 July 1955
UTLA	M 334	Båtservice, Mandal	15 Nov 1955

Displacement, tons: 333 standard; 384 full load
Dimensions, feet (metres): 144 × 28 × 8.5 *(44 × 8.5 × 2.6)*
Main machinery: 2 GM 8-268A diesels; 880 hp *(656 kW)*; 2 shafts
Speed, knots: 13.5. **Range, miles:** 2500 at 10 kts
Complement: 38; 39 *Tana*

Guns: 2 Rheinmetall 20 mm/20; 55° elevation; 1000 rounds/minute to 2 km.
Countermeasures: Thomson-CSF Ibis III minehunting system including 2 PAP 104 *(Tana* only).
Radars: Navigation: Racal Decca TM 1226; I band.
Sonars: UQS-1; hull-mounted; minehunting; high frequency. Plessey 193M *(Tana).*

Programmes: Five coastal minesweepers were built in Norway with US engines. *Alta* and *Tana* were taken over from the Royal Belgian Navy in 1966.
Modernisation: *Tana* converted as a minehunter in 1977. All have been given 20 mm guns.
Operational: To be replaced by the Alta class.

ALTA   *5/1992, Wright & Logan*

SURVEY AND RESEARCH SHIPS

6 SURVEY SHIPS

Name	Displacement tons	Launched	Officers	Crew
LANCE	960	1978	7	8
OLJEVERN 01-04	200	1978	2	6
GEOFJORD	364	1958	2	6

Comment: Under control of Ministry of Environment based at Stavanger. *Oljevern 01* and *03* work for the Pollution Control Authority.

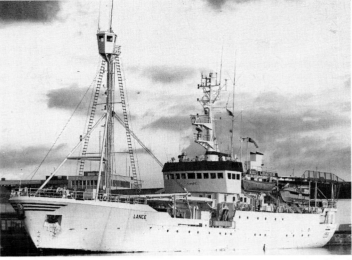

LANCE   *10/1988, Gilbert Gyssels*

OLJEVERN 01   *5/1993, van Ginderen Collection*

1 RESEARCH SHIP (AGI)

Name	No	Builders	Launched	Commissioned
MARJATA	—	Tangern Verft AS	18 Dec 1992	July 1994

Displacement, tons: 7560 full load
Dimensions, feet (metres): 267.4 × 130.9 × 47.6 *(81.5 × 39.9 × 14.5)*
Main machinery: Diesel-electric; 2 MTU Siemens 16V 396 TE diesels; 7072 hp(m) *(5.2 MW)*; 2 Dresser Rand/Siemens gas turbine generators; 9792 hp(m) *(7.2 MW)*; 2 Siemens motors; 8160 hp(m) *(6 MW)*; 2 Schottel thrusters. 1 Siemens motor; 2720 hp(m); *(2 MW)*; 1 Schottel thruster (forward)
Speed, knots: 15
Complement: 14 plus 31 scientists

Comment: Ordered in February 1992 from Langsten Slip og Batbyggeri to replace the old ship of the same name. Called Project Minerva. Design developed by Ariel A/S, Horten. The three main superstructure mounted cupolas (not fitted in the photograph) contain ELINT and SIGINT equipment. Hull-reinforced to allow operations in fringe ice. Equipment includes Sperry radars and Elac sonars, and a fully equipped helicopter flight deck. The unconventional hull which gives the ship an extraordinary length to beam ratio of 2:1 is said to give great stability and dynamic qualities.

MARJATA (without domes)   *1993, Royal Norwegian Navy*

AMPHIBIOUS FORCES

Note: Replacements in the late 1990s will have a minelaying capability, if they are funded.

5 REINØYSUND CLASS (LCTs)

Name	No	Builders	Commissioned
REINØYSUND	L 4502	Mjellem & Karlsen, Bergen	Jan 1972
SØRØYSUND	L 4503	Mjellem & Karlsen, Bergen	May 1972
MAURSUND	L 4504	Mjellem & Karlsen, Bergen	Sep 1972
ROTSUND	L 4505	Mjellem & Karlsen, Bergen	Nov 1972
BORGSUND	L 4506	Mjellem & Karlsen, Bergen	Feb 1973

Displacement, tons: 595 full load
Dimensions, feet (metres): 171 × 33.8 × 5.9 (52.1 × 10.3 × 1.8)
Main machinery: 2 MTU MD diesels; 1350 hp(m) (992 kW); 2 shafts
Speed, knots: 11.5
Complement: 10 (2 officers)
Military lift: 7 tanks; 200 troops
Guns: 3 Rheinmetall 20 mm/20.

Comment: Same design as deleted Kvalsund class.

MAURSUND   3/1992, Jürg Kürsener

BORGSUND   5/1991, Royal Norwegian Navy

AUXILIARIES

1 DEPOT SHIP

Name	No	Builders	Commissioned
HORTEN	A 530	A/S Horten Verft	Apr 1978

Displacement, tons: 2530 full load
Dimensions, feet (metres): 287 × 42.6 × 16.4 (87.5 × 13 × 5)
Main machinery: 2 Wichmann 7AX diesels; 4200 hp(m) (3.1 MW); 2 shafts; bow thruster
Speed, knots: 16.5
Complement: 86
Guns: 2 Bofors 40 mm/70.
Helicopters: Platform only.

Comment: Contract signed 30 March 1976. Laid down 28 January 1977; launched 12 August 1977. Serves both submarines and fast attack craft. Quarters for 45 extra and can cater for 190 extra.

HORTEN   8/1991, van Ginderen Collection

2 DIVING TENDERS

Name	No	Builders	Commissioned
SARPEN	A 531	Nielsen, Harstad	1972
DRAUG	A 532	Nielsen, Harstad	1972

Displacement, tons: 250 full load
Dimensions, feet (metres): 95 × 22 × 8.2 (29 × 6.8 × 2.5)
Main machinery: 1 diesel; 530 hp(m) (389 kW); 1 shaft
Speed, knots: 12

Comment: Small depot ships for frogmen and divers.

SARPEN   1992, Royal Norwegian Navy

NAVAL DISTRICT COASTAL VESSELS

Note: A large number of coastal vessels are attached to the eight naval districts. They have bow numbers prefaced by three letters: HSD (Harstad), NSD (Narvik), ROS (Ramsund naval base), RSD (Rogaland), SSD (Sørlandet), TRSD (Tromsø), VSD (Vertlandet), OSD (Ostlandet). All are less than 300 tons displacement. Names on 1 January 1994:

Name	No	Speed, knots	Commissioned	Role
GARSØY	HSD-12	30	1988	Cargo (6 tons)/Passengers (78)
KRØTTØY	HSD-15	11	1978	Cargo (100 tons)/Passengers (50)
MAAGØY	HSD-10	20	1989	Cargo (—) /Passengers (12)
—	NSD-34	25	1978	Cargo (—) /Passengers (28)
ROTVÆR	NSD-35	10	1978	Cargo (80 tons)/Passengers (35)
—	ROS-27	9	1979	Cargo (—) /Passengers (—)
—	ROS-28	10	1988	Cargo (—) /Passengers (—)
—	ROS-24	8	1975	Passengers (—)
KJEØY	ROS-22	10.7	1969	Cargo (80 tons)/Passengers (30)
BRIMSE	RSD-23	16	1982	Passengers (25)
FJØLØY	RSD-22	17.5	1985	Passengers (23)
MERMAID	RSD-29	17	1990	Passengers (—)
ROGIN	RSD-28	20	1989	Passengers (6)
AGDER	SSD-1	22	1975	Passengers (17)
GLEODDEN	SSD-3	9	1958	Cargo (3 tons)/Passengers (88)
VARODDEN	SSD-4	9	1969	Cargo (5 tons)
ARNØY	TRSD-5	13.5	1978	Passengers (55)
FISK	TRSD-2	9	1973	TRV/Cargo (10 tons)/Passengers (6)
KARLSØY	TRSD-4	11.5	1978	Cargo (87 tons)/Passengers (31)
TAUTRA	TSD-5	12	1978	Cargo (—) /Passengers (5)
TITRAN	TSD-1	25	1992	Cargo (5 tons)/Passengers (56)
—	VSD-20	9	1980	Passengers (—)
—	VSD-3	10	1973	TRV
—	VSD-18	18	1977	Passengers (10)
—	VSD-22	22	1985	Passengers (12)
BOGØY	VSD-10	10.5	1992	Tug
KNAPPEN	VSD-19	22	1987	Passengers (12)
KVARVEN	VSD-2	11.5	1986	Tug/Passengers (12)
TORPEN	VSD-4	12	1977	Cargo (—)
TUG	VSD-8	10	1967	Tug
VERNØY	VSD-1	14	1978	TRV
VIKEN	VSD-5	12	1977	Diving Tender/Passengers (60)
OSCARSBURG	ØSD-11	10	1968	Passengers (55)
—	ØSD-8	8	1985	Cargo (—) /Passengers (12)
FOLDEN	ØSD-14	12	1974	Cargo (3 tons)/Passengers (80)
NORDEP	ØSD-15	12.5	1987	Cargo (6 tons)/Passengers (60)
ODIN	ØSD-6	17	1989	Cargo (—) /Passengers (9)
WELDING	ØSD-1	17	1974	Cargo (—) /Passengers (14)
WISTING	ØSD-2	12	1978	Cargo (150 tons)/Passengers (75)

GARSØY   8/1990, T Gander

TRAINING SHIPS

Name	No	Builders	Commissioned
HESSA (ex-Hitra, ex-Marsteinen)	P 358	Fjellstrand, Omastrand	Jan 1978
VIGRA (ex-Kvarven)	P 359	Fjellstrand, Omastrand	July 1978

Displacement, tons: 39 full load
Dimensions, feet (metres): 77 × 16.4 × 3.5 (23.5 × 5 × 1.1)
Main machinery: 2 GM diesels; 1800 hp (1.34 MW); 2 shafts
Speed, knots: 20
Complement: 5
Guns: 1—12.7 mm Browning MG.

Comment: The vessels are designed for training students at the Royal Norwegian Naval Academy in navigation, manoeuvring and seamanship. All-welded aluminium hulls. Also equipped with an open bridge and a blind pilotage position below deck. 18 berths.

HESSA   1992, Royal Norwegian Navy

ROYAL YACHT

Name	No	Builders	Commissioned
NORGE (ex-Philante)	A 533	Camper & Nicholson's Ltd, Southampton	1937

Displacement, tons: 1786 full load
Dimensions, feet (metres): 263 × 38 × 15.2 (80.2 × 11.6 × 4.6)
Main machinery: 2 Bergen KRMB-8 diesels; 4850 hp(m) (3.6 MW) sustained; 2 shafts
Speed, knots: 17
Complement: 50 (18 officers)

Comment: Built to the order of the late T O M Sopwith as an escort and store vessel for the yachts *Endeavour I* and *Endeavour II*. Launched on 17 February 1937. Served in the Royal Navy as an anti-submarine escort during the Second World War, after which she was purchased by the Norwegian people for King Haakon and reconditioned as a Royal Yacht at Southampton. Can accommodate about 50 people in addition to crew. Repaired after serious fire on 7 March 1985.

NORGE   4/1993, Maritime Photographic

COAST GUARD

1 NORNEN CLASS

Name	No	Builders	Commissioned
NORNEN	W 300	Mjellem & Karlsen, Bergen	1963

Displacement, tons: 1030 full load
Dimensions, feet (metres): 201.8 × 32.8 × 15.8 (61.5 × 10 × 4.8)
Main machinery: 4 diesels; 3500 hp(m) (2.57 MW); 1 shaft
Speed, knots: 17
Complement: 32
Guns: 1 Bofors 40 mm/70.

Comment: Launched 20 August 1962. Modernised in 1978 with increased tonnage.

NORNEN   1988, Royal Norwegian Navy

3 NORDKAPP CLASS

Name	No	Builders	Commissioned
NORDKAPP	W 320	Bergens Mek Verksteder	25 Apr 1981
SENJA	W 321	Horten Verft	6 Mar 1981
ANDENES	W 322	Haugesund Mek Verksted	30 Jan 1982

Displacement, tons: 3240 full load
Dimensions, feet (metres): 346 × 47.9 × 16.1 (105.5 × 14.6 × 4.9)
Main machinery: 4 Wichmann 9AXAG diesels; 16 163 hp(m) (11.9 MW); 2 shafts
Speed, knots: 23. **Range, miles:** 7500 at 15 kts
Complement: 52 (6 aircrew)

Missiles: SSM: Fitted for 6 Kongsberg Penguin II but not embarked.
Guns: 1 Bofors 57 mm/70 ❶; 75° elevation; 200 rounds/minute to 17 km (9.3 nm); weight of shell 2.4 kg.
4 Rheinmetall 20 mm/20 ❷; 55° elevation; 1000 rounds/minute to 2 km.
Torpedoes: 6—324 mm US Mk 32 (2 triple) tubes ❸. Honeywell Mk 46; anti-submarine; active/passive homing to 11 km (5.9 nm) at 40 kts; warhead 44 kg. Mountings only in peacetime.
Depth charges: 1 rack.
Countermeasures: Decoys: 2 chaff launchers.
Combat data systems: Navkis action data automation. SATCOM can be carried ❹.
Radars: Air/surface search: Plessey AWS 5 ❺; E/F band; range 155 km (85 nm) for 4 m² target.
Navigation: Two Racal Decca 1226; I band.
Fire control: Philips 9LV 200 Mk 2 ❻; J band.
Sonars: Simrad SS 105; hull-mounted; active search and attack; 14 kHz.

Helicopters: 1 Westland Lynx Mk 86 ❼.

Programmes: In November 1977 the Coast Guard budget was cut resulting in a reduction of the building programme from seven to three ships.
Structure: Strengthened for ice. Fitted for firefighting, anti-pollution work, all with two motor cutters and a Gemini-type dinghy. SATCOM fitted for Gulf deployment.
Operational: Bunks for 109. War complement increases to 76.

ANDENES   (Scale 1 : 1200), Ian Sturton

NORDKAPP   1992, Royal Norwegian Navy

2 FARM CLASS

Name	No	Builders	Commissioned
FARM	W 301	Ankerlokken Verft	1962
HEIMDAL	W 302	Bolsones Verft, Molde	1962

Measurement, tons: 600 gross
Dimensions, feet (metres): 177 × 26.2 × 16.1 (54.3 × 8.2 × 4.9)
Main machinery: 2 Wichmann 9ACAT diesels; 2400 hp(m) (1.76 MW); 1 shaft; cp prop
Speed, knots: 16
Complement: 29
Guns: 1 Bofors 40 mm/70.

Comment: *Farm* modernised by Bergens Mekaniske Verksteder in 1979 and *Heimdal* by same firm in 1980.

FARM   6/1991, van Ginderen Collection

7 CHARTERED SHIPS

Name	No	Tonnage	Completion
KIM	W 313	493	1955
STÅLBAS	W 314	498	1955
NORDSJØBAS	W 315	814	1978
VOLSTAD JR	W 316	598	1950
LAFJORD	W 317	814	1978
GARPESKJAER	W 318	1122	1956
GRIMSHOLM	W 319	1189	1978

Comment: *Stålbas* and *Volstad Jr* chartered in 1977; *Lafjord, Nordsjøbas* and *Grimsholm* in 1980; *Garpeskjaer* in 1986 and *Kim* (modernised in 1985) in 1991. All armed with one 40 mm/60 gun.

GARPESKJAER   8/1990, T J Gander

VOLSTAD JR   5/1992, Erik Laursen

OMAN

Senior Officers

Commander Royal Navy of Oman:
Rear Admiral (Liwaa Bahry) H H Sayyid Shihab bin Tarik bin Taimur al Said
Assistant Commander Royal Navy of Oman:
Commodore (Ameed) Hilal bin Mohammad bin Rashid al Rashdy
Commander Coast Guard:
Captain (Aqeed Bahry) Hamdan bin Marhoon al Mamary
Commander Royal Yacht Squadron:
Commodore (Ameed) J M Knapp

Bases

Qa'Adat Said Bin Sultan Albahria, Wudam (main base, dockyard and shiplift)
Mina Raysut (advanced naval base), Salalah
Jazirat Ghanam (advanced naval base), Musandam
Muaskar al Murtafa'a (headquarters)

Personnel

(a) 1994: 3600 officers and men
(b) Voluntary service

Future Plans

The main deficiency in this force is in the MCMV category and plans for a limited capability seem to have been postponed.

Mercantile Marine

Lloyd's Register of Shipping:
21 vessels of 15 648 tons gross

FRIGATES

0 + 1 KNOX CLASS

Name	No	Builders	Laid down	Launched	Commissioned
— (ex-*Miller*)	— (ex-FF 1091)	Avondale Shipyard	6 Aug 1971	3 June 1972	30 June 1973

Displacement, tons: 3011 standard; 4260 full load
Dimensions, feet (metres): 439.6 × 46.8 × 15; 24.8 (sonar) *(134 × 14.3 × 4.6; 7.8)*
Main machinery: 2 Combustion Engineering/Babcock & Wilcox boilers; 1200 psi *(84.4 kg/cm sq)*; 950°F *(510°C)*; 1 turbine; 35 000 hp *(26 MW)*; 1 shaft
Speed, knots: 27. **Range, miles:** 4000 at 22 kts on 1 boiler
Complement: 288 (17 officers)

Missiles: SSM: 8 McDonnell Douglas Harpoon; active radar homing to 130 km *(70 nm)* at 0.9 Mach; warhead 227 kg.
A/S: Honeywell ASROC Mk 16 octuple launcher with reload system (has 2 cells modified to fire Harpoon) ❶; inertial guidance to 1.6-10 km *(1-5.4 nm)*; payload Mk 46 Mod 5.
Guns: 1 FMC 5 in *(127 mm)*/54 Mk 42 Mod 9 ❷; 85° elevation; 20-40 rounds/minute to 24 km *(13 nm)* anti-surface; 14 km *(7.7 nm)* anti-aircraft; weight of shell 32 kg.
1 General Electric/General Dynamics 20 mm/76 6-barrelled Mk 15 Vulcan Phalanx ❸; 3000 rounds/minute combined to 1.5 km.
Torpedoes: 4—324 mm Mk 32 (2 twin) fixed tubes ❹. 22 Honeywell Mk 46 Mod 5; anti-submarine; active/passive homing to 11 km *(5.9 nm)* at 40 kts; warhead 44 kg.
Countermeasures: Decoys: 2 Loral Hycor SRBOC 6-barrelled fixed Mk 36 ❺; IR flares and chaff to 4 km *(2.2 nm)*. T Mk-6 Fanfare/SLQ-25 Nixie; torpedo decoy. Prairie Masker hull and blade rate noise suppression.
ESM/ECM: SLQ 32(V)2 ❻; radar warning. Sidekick modification adds jammer and deception system.
Combat data systems: Link 14 receive only.
Fire control: SWG-1A Harpoon LCS. Mk 68 GFCS. Mk 114 ASW FCS. Mk 1 target designation system. MMS target acquisition sight (for mines, small craft and low flying aircraft).
Radars: Air search: Lockheed SPS 40B ❼; E/F band; range 320 km *(175 nm)*.
Surface search: Raytheon SPS 10 or Norden SPS 67 ❽; G band.
Navigation: Marconi LN 66; I band.
Fire control: Western Electric SPG 53A/D/F ❾; I/J band.
Tacan: SRN 15. IFF: UPX-12.
Sonars: EDO/General Electric SQS 26 CX; bow-mounted; active search and attack; medium frequency.
EDO SQR 18A(V)1; passive towed array; very low frequency.

Helicopters: 1 medium ❿.

Programmes: Lease agreed in December 1993 subject to approval by US Congress. Planned to arrive in Oman in mid-1994. Ships of this class have been transferred to Greece, Taiwan and Turkey and transfers are planned for Brazil, Egypt, Morocco, Spain, Thailand and Venezuela in 1994/95.
Modernisation: Vulcan Phalanx replaced Sea Sparrow SAM in the mid-1980s.
Structure: Four torpedo tubes are fixed in the midship superstructure, two to a side, angled out at 45°. A lightweight

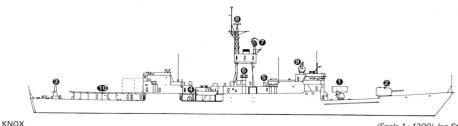

KNOX   (Scale 1 : 1200), Ian Sturton

KNOX (US colours)   10/1993, Wright & Logan

anchor is fitted on the port side and an 8000 lb anchor fits in to the after section of the sonar dome.

Operational: The ship carried a medium helicopter in USN service.

CORVETTES

0 + 2 MUHEET PROJECT TYPE 83

Name	No	Builders	Laid down	Launched	Commissioned
—	—	Vosper Thornycroft	21 May 1993	Sep 1994	Dec 1995
—	—	Vosper Thornycroft	Apr 1994	Aug 1995	Nov 1996

Displacement, tons: 1420 full load
Dimensions, feet (metres): 274.6 oa; 249.3 wl × 37.7 × 11.5 *(83.7; 76 × 11.5 × 3.5)*
Main machinery: CODAD; 4 Crossley SEMT-Pielstick 16 PA6 V 280 STC; 28 160 hp(m) *(20.7 MW)* sustained; 2 shafts; cp props
Speed, knots: 25
Complement: 76 (14 officers)

Missiles: SSM: 8 Aerospatiale MM 40 Exocet ❶.
SAM: Thomson CSF Crotale NG octuple launcher ❷; 8 VT1 (no reloads).
Guns: 1 OTO Melara 3 in *(76 mm)*/62 Super Rapid ❸.
2 Oerlikon/BMARC 20 mm GAM-B01 ❹.
Countermeasures: Decoys: 2 Barricade chaff launchers ❺.
ESM/ECM: Thomson CSF DR 3000; intercept and jammer.
Combat data systems: Signaal SEWACO-FD with Thomson CSF TACTICOS; Link Y; SATCOM.
Fire control: Signaal STING optronic tracker ❻; two optical directors.
Radars: Air/surface search: Signaal MW 08 ❼; G band.
Fire control: Signaal STING ❽; I/J band.
Navigation: Kelvin Hughes 1007; I band.
Sonars: Thomson Sintra/BAe Sema ATAS; towed array; active search; 3 kHz (may be fitted).

Helicopters: Platform for 1 medium ❾.

Programmes: Vosper Thornycroft signed the contract on 5 April 1992. First steel cut 23 September 1992.
Structure: The ship is based on the Vigilance class design. It is possible a bow sonar may be fitted, as may lightweight torpedo tubes. The towed array adds another 8 tons on the stern but does not affect the helicopter deck.

MUHEET PROJECT Type 83   *(Scale 1 : 900), Ian Sturton*

MUHEET PROJECT (artist's impression)   *1993*

Opinion: The rapid progression from Dhow to high technology corvette has taken just 20 years. The effectiveness of these ships will depend on retaining close links with western technology.

PATROL FORCES

4 DHOFAR (PROVINCE) CLASS (FAST ATTACK CRAFT—MISSILE)

Name	No	Builders	Commissioned
DHOFAR	B 10	Vosper Thornycroft	7 Aug 1982
AL SHARQIYAH	B 11	Vosper Thornycroft	5 Dec 1983
AL BAT'NAH	B 12	Vosper Thornycroft	18 Jan 1984
MUSSANDAM	B 14	Vosper Thornycroft	31 Mar 1989

Displacement, tons: 311 light; 394 full load
Dimensions, feet (metres): 186 × 26.9 × 7.9 *(56.7 × 8.2 × 2.4)*
Main machinery: 4 Paxman Valenta 18CM diesels; 15 000 hp *(11.2 MW)* sustained; 4 shafts; auxiliary propulsion; 2 motors; 200 hp *(149 kW)*
Speed, knots: 38. **Range, miles:** 2000 at 18 kts
Complement: 45 (5 officers) plus 14 trainees

Missiles: SSM: 8 or 6 (B 10) Aerospatiale MM 40 Exocet; inertial cruise; active radar homing to 70 km *(40 nm)* at 0.9 Mach; warhead 165 kg; sea-skimmer.
Guns: 1 OTO Melara 3 in *(76 mm)*/62 compact; 85° elevation; 85 rounds/minute to 16 km *(8.7 nm)*; weight of shell 6 kg.
2 Breda 40 mm/70 (twin); 85° elevation; 300 rounds/minute to 12.5 km *(6.8 nm)*; weight of shell 0.96 kg.
2—12.7 mm MGs.
Countermeasures: Decoys: 2 Wallop Barricade fixed triple barrels; 4 modes of fire for chaff and IR deception.
ESM: Racal Cutlass; radar warning.
ECM: Scorpion; jammer.
Fire control: Sperry Sea Archer (B 10). Philips 9LV 307 (remainder).
Radars: Air/surface search: Plessey AWS 4 (B 10) or AWS 6 (remainder); E/F band.
Navigation: Racal Decca TM 1226C; I band.

Programmes: First ordered in 1980, launched 14 October 1981 and sailed from Portsmouth for Oman 21 October 1982. Two more ordered in January 1981 and sailed for Oman on 16 May 1984. Fourth ordered January 1986, launched 19 March 1988 and sailed for Oman 1 May 1989.
Structure: Similar to Kenyan Nyayo class.

AL SHARQIYAH   *10/1992, Hartmut Ehlers*

0 + 3 PROJECT MAWJ (P 400) CLASS
(FAST ATTACK CRAFT—GUN)

Displacement, tons: 475 full load
Dimensions, feet (metres): 178.6 × 26.2 × 8.9 *(54.5 × 8 × 2.7)*
Main machinery: 2 SEMT-Pielstick 16 PA4 V 200 diesels; 8000 hp(m) *(5.88 MW)* sustained; 2 shafts; cp props
Speed, knots: 24.5. **Range, miles:** 4200 at 15 kts
Complement: 26 (3 officers) plus 20 spare
Guns: 1 OTO Melara 76/62 compact. 2—30 mm.
Fire control: Optronic director.
Radars: Surface search; I band.

Comment: Order for three, with an option on five more, reported in September 1993. To be built by CMN, Cherbourg to the same design as the French P 400 class which has been modified with twin funnels replacing submerged exhausts. The first ship is planned to leave Cherbourg in 1995 for weapon systems to be fitted in Muscat dockyard. The 76 mm guns may be taken from the Al Waafi class, which these ships are to replace.

DHOFAR (with 6 Exocet and AWS 4 radar)   *1989, Royal Navy of Oman*

P 400 class (French colours)   *1/1993, van Ginderen Collection*

1 PATROL SHIP

Name	No	Builders	Commissioned
AL MABRUKAH (ex-Al Said)	A 1	Brooke Marine, Lowestoft	1971

Displacement, tons: 900 full load
Dimensions, feet (metres): 203.4 × 35.1 × 9.8 *(62 × 10.7 × 3)*
Main machinery: 2 Paxman Valenta 12CM diesels; 5000 hp *(3.73 MW)* sustained; 2 shafts
Speed, knots: 12
Complement: 39 (7 officers)
Guns: 1 Bofors 40 mm/70. 2 Oerlikon 20 mm A41A.
Countermeasures: Decoys: Wallop Barricade 18-barrelled chaff launcher.
ESM: Radar warning.
Radars: Surface search: Racal Decca TM 1226; I band.
Helicopters: Platform only.

Comment: Built by Brooke Marine, Lowestoft. Launched 7 April 1970 as a yacht for the Sultan of Oman. Carried on board is one Rotork landing craft. Converted to training ship/patrol ship in 1983 with enlarged helicopter deck.

AL MABRUKAH   10/1993, 92 Wing RAAF

4 AL WAAFI (BROOKE MARINE) CLASS
(FAST ATTACK CRAFT—GUN)

Name	No	Builders	Commissioned
AL WAAFI	B 4	Brooke Marine, Lowestoft	24 Mar 1977
AL FULK	B 5	Brooke Marine, Lowestoft	24 Mar 1977
AL MUJAHID	B 6	Brooke Marine, Lowestoft	20 July 1977
AL JABBAR	B 7	Brooke Marine, Lowestoft	6 Oct 1977

Displacement, tons: 135 standard; 153 full load
Dimensions, feet (metres): 123 × 22.5 × 6 *(37.5 × 6.9 × 1.8)*
Main machinery: 2 Paxman 16YJCM diesels; 3000 hp *(2.24 MW)* sustained; 2 shafts
Speed, knots: 25. **Range, miles:** 3300 at 15 kts
Complement: 27 (3 officers)
Guns: 1 OTO Melara 3 in *(76 mm)*/62 compact; 85° elevation; 85 rounds/minute to 16 km *(8.7 nm)*; weight of shell 6 kg.
1 Oerlikon 20 mm. 2—7.62 mm MGs.
Fire control: Laurence Scott optical director and Sperry Sea Archer system.
Radars: Surface search/navigation: Racal Decca 1226; Racal Decca 1229; I band.

Comment: Ordered 26 April 1974. To be replaced by the Project Mawj class starting in 1996.

AL WAAFI   10/1992, Hartmut Ehlers

AL FULK   1989, Royal Navy of Oman

4 SEEB (VOSPER 25) CLASS (INSHORE PATROL CRAFT)

Name	No	Builders	Commissioned
SEEB	B 20	Vosper Private, Singapore	15 Mar 1981
SHINAS	B 21	Vosper Private, Singapore	15 Mar 1981
SADH	B 22	Vosper Private, Singapore	15 Mar 1981
KHASSAB	B 23	Vosper Private, Singapore	15 Mar 1981

Displacement, tons: 60.7
Dimensions, feet (metres): 82.8 × 19 × 5.2 *(25 × 5.8 × 1.6)*
Main machinery: 2 MTU 12V 331 TC92 diesels; 2660 hp(m) *(1.96 MW)* sustained; 2 shafts
1 Cummins N-855M diesel for slow cruising; 189 hp *(141 kW)* sustained; 1 shaft
Speed, knots: 25; 8 (Cummins diesel). **Range, miles:** 750 at 14 kts
Complement: 13
Guns: 1 Oerlikon 20 mm. 2—7.62 mm (twin) MGs.

Comment: Arrived in Oman on 19 May 1981 having been ordered one month earlier. The craft were built on speculation and completed in 1980.

KHASSAB   1989, Royal Navy of Oman

SHINAS   10/1992, Hartmut Ehlers

1 TYLER-VORTEX TYPE (INSHORE PATROL CRAFT)

Q 2

Dimensions, feet (metres): 42.7 × 11.8 × 4.6 *(13 × 3.6 × 1.4)*
Main machinery: 2 diesels; 1000 hp *(746 kW)*; 2 shafts
Speed, knots: 30
Guns: 1—12.7 mm MG.
Radars: Surface search: I band.

Comment: A quick reaction boat of Tyler-Vortex design. A second of class Q 1 was scrapped after grounding.

Q 2   10/1992, Hartmut Ehlers

AMPHIBIOUS FORCES

1 LANDING SHIP—LOGISTIC

Name	No	Builders	Commissioned
NASR AL BAHR	L 2	Brooke Marine, Lowestoft	6 Feb 1985

Displacement, tons: 2500 full load
Dimensions, feet (metres): 305 × 50.8 × 8.5 *(93 × 15.5 × 2.6)*
Main machinery: 2 Paxman Valenta 18 CM diesels; 7500 hp *(5.6 MW)* sustained; 2 shafts
Speed, knots: 16. **Range, miles:** 5000 at 15 kts
Complement: 81 (13 officers)
Military lift: 7 MBT or 400 tons cargo; 240 troops; 2 LCVPs
Guns: 4 Breda 40 mm/70 (2 twin). 2 Oerlikon 20 mm. 2—12.7 mm MGs.
Countermeasures: Decoys: Wallop Barricade double layer chaff launchers.
Fire control: PEAB 9LV 200 GFCS and CSEE Lynx optical sight.
Radars: Surface search/navigation: Two Racal Decca; I band.
Helicopters: Platform for Super Puma.

Comment: Ordered 18 May 1982. Launched 16 May 1984. Carries one 16 ton crane. Bow and stern ramps. Full naval command facilities. The forward ramp is of two sections measuring length 59 ft (when extended) × 16.5 ft breadth *(18 × 5 m)*, and the single section stern ramp measures 14 × 16.5 ft *(4.3 × 5 m)*. Both hatches can support a 60 ton tank. The tank deck side bulkheads extend 7.5 ft *(2.25 m)* above the upper deck between the forecastle and the forward end of the superstructure, and provide two hatch openings to the tank deck below. Positioned between the hatches is a two ton crane with athwartship travel.

NASR AL BAHR   *4/1993, van Ginderen Collection*

1 LANDING SHIP—LOGISTIC

Name	No	Builders	Commissioned
AL MUNASSIR	L 1	Brooke Marine, Lowestoft	31 Jan 1979

Displacement, tons: 2000
Dimensions, feet (metres): 276 × 49 × 7.3 *(84.1 × 14.9 × 2.3)*
Main machinery: 2 Mirrlees Blackstone ESL 8MGR diesels; 2440 hp *(1.82 MW)*; 2 shafts
Speed, knots: 12. **Range, miles:** 1000 at 12 kts
Complement: 45 (9 officers)
Military lift: 8 MBTs or 550 tons cargo; 188 troops; 2 Rotork LCPs
Radars: Navigation: Racal Decca TM 1229; I band.
Helicopters: Platform for 1 medium.

Comment: This ship is in reserve but is used for harbour training. Armament has been removed including the OTO Melara 76 mm gun.

AL MUNASSIR (disarmed)   *10/1992, Hartmut Ehlers*

3 LCMs

Name	No	Builders	Commissioned
SABA AL BAHR	C 8	Vosper Private, Singapore	17 Sep 1981
AL DOGHAS	C 9	Vosper Private, Singapore	10 Jan 1983
AL TEMSAH	C 10	Vosper Private, Singapore	12 Feb 1983

Displacement, tons: 230 full load
Dimensions, feet (metres): 108.2 (83.6, C 8) × 24.3 × 4.3 *(33 (25.5) × 7.4 × 1.3)*
Main machinery: 2 Caterpillar 3408TA diesels; 1880 hp *(1.4 MW)* sustained; 2 shafts
Speed, knots: 8. **Range, miles:** 1400 at 8 kts
Complement: 11
Military lift: 100 tons

Comment: C 8 launched 30 June 1981. C 9 and C 10, similar but not identical ships, ordered 8 May 1982.

AL TEMSAH   *10/1992, Hartmut Ehlers*

1 LCU

Name	No	Builders	Commissioned
AL NEEMRAN	C 7	Lewis Offshore, Stornoway	1979

Displacement, tons: 130 full load (C 4)
Measurement, tons: 45 (C 4), 85 (C 7) dwt
Dimensions, feet (metres): 60 × 20 × 3.6 *(18.3 × 6.1 × 1.1)* (C 4)
   84 × 24 × 6 *(25.5 × 7.4 × 1.8)* (C 7)
Main machinery: 2 diesels; 300 hp *(220 kW)*; 2 shafts
Speed, knots: 7/8

Comment: Second of class deleted in 1993.

LCU   *1975, Roger Smith*

AUXILIARIES

Notes: (1) A 700 ton Survey Ship has been funded and put out to tender in October 1993. To be ordered in 1995/96.
(2) In addition to the listed vessels there are four 12 m Cheverton Workboats (W 41-W 44) and eight 8 m Workboats (W 4-W 11).

1 SUPPLY SHIP

Name	No	Builders	Commissioned
AL SULTANA	A 2	Conoship, Groningen	4 June 1975

Measurement, tons: 1380 dwt
Dimensions, feet (metres): 215.6 × 35 × 13.5 *(65.7 × 10.7 × 4.2)*
Main machinery: 1 Mirrlees Blackstone diesel; 1120 hp(m) *(835 kW)*; 1 shaft
Speed, knots: 11
Complement: 20

Comment: Major refit in 1992.

AL SULTANA   *6/1993, Royal Navy of Oman*

1 SURVEY CRAFT

AL RAHMANNIYA H 1

Displacement, tons: 23.6 full load
Dimensions, feet (metres): 50.8 × 13.1 × 4.3 *(15.5 × 4 × 1.3)*
Main machinery: 2 Volvo TMD120A diesels; 604 hp(m) *(444 kW)* sustained; 2 shafts
Speed, knots: 13.5. **Range, miles:** 500 at 12 kts

Comment: Built by Watercraft, Shoreham, England in 1980.

AL RAHMANNIYA   *1988, Royal Navy of Oman*

1 DIVING CRAFT

R 1

Displacement, tons: 13 full load
Dimensions, feet (metres): 59 × 12.4 × 3.6 *(18 × 3.8 × 1.1)*
Main machinery: 2 Volvo Penta diesels; 430 hp(m) *(316 kW)* sustained; 2 shafts
Speed, knots: 20
Complement: 4
Guns: 2—7.62 mm MGs.

Comment: Rotork type acquired in 1991. Used as a diver's boat. Similar to Police craft also used for divers.

R 1   *10/1992, Hartmut Ehlers*

2 HARBOUR CRAFT

T 2   T 3

Comment: Van Damen Pushy Cat 1500 type of 15 m acquired in 1990/91. Used as general purpose craft as well as tugs.

T 2   *10/1992, Hartmut Ehlers*

TRAINING SHIP

1 SAIL TRAINING SHIP

Name	No	Builders	Recommissioned
SHABAB OMAN	S 1	Herd and Mackenzie,	1979
(ex-*Captain Scott*)		Buckie, Scotland	

Displacement, tons: 386
Dimensions, feet (metres): 144.3 × 27.9 × 15.1 *(44 × 8.5 × 4.6)*
Main machinery: 2 Caterpillar auxiliary diesels; 1 shaft
Complement: 20 (5 officers) plus 3 officers and 24 trainees

Comment: Topsail schooner taken over from Dulverton Trust in 1977 used for sail training.

SHABAB OMAN   *12/1991, Giorgio Ghiglione*

ROYAL YACHTS

Note: There is also a Royal Dhow *Zinat Al Bihar*.

Name	No	Builders	Commissioned
AL SAID	—	Picchiotti SpA, Viareggio	1982

Displacement, tons: 3800 full load
Dimensions, feet (metres): 340.5 × 53.2 × 16.4 *(103.8 × 16.2 × 5)*
Main machinery: 2 GMT A 420.6 H diesels; 8400 hp(m) *(6.17 MW)* sustained; 2 shafts; cp props; bow thruster
Speed, knots: 18
Complement: 156 (16 officers)
Radars: Navigation: Decca TM 1226C; ACS 1230C; I band.

Comment: This ship is an independent command and not part of the Omani Navy. Fitted with helicopter deck and fin stabilisers. Carries three Puma C service launches and one Rotork beach landing craft.

AL SAID   *1991, van Ginderen Collection*

Name	No	Builders	Commissioned
FULK AL SALAMAH	—	Bremer-Vulkan	3 Apr 1987
(ex-*Ghubat Al Salamah*)			

Measurement, tons: 10 864 grt; 5186 net
Dimensions, feet (metres): 447.5 × 68.9 × 19.7 *(136.4 × 21 × 6)*
Main machinery: 4 Fincantieri GMT A 420.6 H diesels; 16 800 hp(m) *(12.35 MW)* sustained; 2 shafts
Speed, knots: 19.5
Helicopters: Up to 2 AS 332C Super Puma.

Comment: Support ship and transport with side doors for heavy loading. Part of the Royal Yacht Squadron and the old pennant number L 3 has been removed.

FULK AL SALAMAH   *8/1990, Maritime Photographic*

POLICE

Note: In addition to the vessels listed below there are several harbour craft including a Cheverton 8 m workboat *Zahra 24* and a fireboat pennant number *10*.

3 CG 29 TYPE (COASTAL PATROL CRAFT)

HARAS VII   HARAS IX   HARAS X

Displacement, tons: 84
Dimensions, feet (metres): 94.8 × 17.7 × 4.3 *(28.9 × 5.4 × 1.3)*
Main machinery: 2 MTU 12V 331 TC92 diesels; 2660 hp(m) *(1.96 MW)* sustained; 2 shafts
Speed, knots: 25. **Range, miles:** 600 at 15 kts
Complement: 13
Guns: 2 Oerlikon 20 mm.

Comment: Built by Karlskrona Varvet. Commissioned in 1981-82. GRP Sandwich hulls.

HARAS X   10/1992, Hartmut Ehlers

1 P 1903 TYPE (COASTAL PATROL CRAFT)

HARAS VIII

Displacement, tons: 26
Dimensions, feet (metres): 63 × 15.7 × 5.2 *(19.2 × 4.8 × 1.6)*
Main machinery: 2 MTU 8V 331 TC92 diesels; 1770 hp(m) *(1.3 MW)*; 2 shafts
Speed, knots: 30. **Range, miles:** 1650 at 17 kts
Complement: 10
Guns: 2—12.7 mm MGs.

Comment: Built by Le Comte, Netherlands. Commissioned August 1981. Type 1903 Mk III.

HARAS VIII   10/1992, Hartmut Ehlers

1 P 2000 TYPE (COASTAL PATROL CRAFT)

DHEEB AL BAHAR I

Displacement, tons: 80
Dimensions, feet (metres): 68.2 × 19 × 5 *(20.8 × 5.8 × 1.5)*
Main machinery: 2 MTU 12V 396 TB93 diesels; 3260 hp(m) *(2.4 MW)* sustained; 2 shafts
Speed, knots: 40. **Range, miles:** 423 at 36 kts; 700 at 18 kts
Guns: 1—12.7 mm MG.
Radars: Surface search: Furuno 701; I band.

Comment: Delivered January 1985 by Watercraft Ltd, Shoreham, England. GRP hull. Carries SATNAV.

DHEEB AL BAHAR I (with *Dheeb Al Bahar II*)   10/1992, Hartmut Ehlers

1 CG 27 TYPE (COASTAL PATROL CRAFT)

HARAS VI

Displacement, tons: 53
Dimensions, feet (metres): 78.7 × 18 × 6.2 *(24 × 5.5 × 1.9)*
Main machinery: 2 MTU 12V 331 TC92 diesels; 2660 hp(m) *(1.96 MW)* sustained; 2 shafts
Speed, knots: 25
Complement: 11
Guns: 1 Oerlikon 20 mm.

Comment: Completed in 1980 by Karlskrona Varvet. GRP hull.

HARAS VI   10/1992, Hartmut Ehlers

5 VOSPER THORNYCROFT 75 ft TYPE (COASTAL PATROL CRAFT)

HARAS I-V

Displacement, tons: 50
Dimensions, feet (metres): 75 × 20 × 5.9 *(22.9 × 6.1 × 1.8)*
Main machinery: 2 Caterpillar D 348 diesels; 1450 hp *(1.08 MW)* sustained; 2 shafts
Speed, knots: 24.5. **Range, miles:** 600 at 20 kts; 1000 at 11 kts
Complement: 11
Guns: 1 Oerlikon 20 mm.

Comment: First four completed 22 December 1975 by Vosper Thornycroft. GRP hulls. *Haras V* commissioned November 1978.

HARAS II   1984, N Overington

2 D 59116 TYPE (COASTAL PATROL CRAFT)

DHEEB AL BAHAR II and III

Displacement, tons: 65
Dimensions, feet (metres): 75.5 × 17.1 × 3.9 *(23 × 5.2 × 1.2)*
Main machinery: 2 MTU 12V 396 TB93 diesels; 3260 hp(m) *(2.4 MW)* sustained; 2 shafts
Speed, knots: 36. **Range, miles:** 420 at 30 kts
Complement: 11
Guns: 1—12.7 mm MG.
Radars: Surface search: Furuno 711-2; Furuno 2400; I band.

Comment: Built by Yokohama Yacht Co, Japan. Commissioned in 1988.

DHEEB AL BAHAR II   1988, Royal Oman Police

3 WATERCRAFT TYPE and 2 EMSWORTH TYPE
(INSHORE PATROL CRAFT)

ZAHRA 14   ZAHRA 15   ZAHRA 17   ZAHRA 18   ZAHRA 21

Displacement, tons: 16; 18 (*Zahra 18* and *21*)
Dimensions, feet (metres): 45.6 × 14.1 × 4.6 *(13.9 × 4.3 × 1.4)*
  52.5 × 13.8 × 7.5 *(16 × 4.2 × 2.3)* (*Zahra 18* and *21*)
Main machinery: 2 Cummins VTA-903M diesels; 643 hp *(480 kW)*; 2 shafts
Speed, knots: 36. **Range, miles:** 510 at 22 kts
Complement: 5-6
Guns: 1 or 2—7.62 mm MGs.

Comment: *Zahra 14, 15* and *17* built by Watercraft, Shoreham, England and completed in 1981. *Zahra 18* and *21* completed by Emsworth SB in 1987 to a different design.

1 DIVING CRAFT

ZAHRA 27

Displacement, tons: 13 full load
Dimensions, feet (metres): 59 × 12.4 × 3.6 *(18 × 3.8 × 1.1)*
Main machinery: 2 Volvo Penta AQD70D diesels; 430 hp(m) *(316 kW)* sustained; 2 shafts
Speed, knots: 20
Complement: 4
Guns: 2—7.62 mm MGs.

Comment: Rotork Type, the last of several logistic support craft, now used as a diving boat. Similar craft used by the Navy.

ZAHRA 18   10/1992, Hartmut Ehlers

ZAHRA 27   10/1992, Hartmut Ehlers

PAKISTAN

Headquarters' Appointment

Chief of the Naval Staff:
  Admiral Saeed M Khan, NI(M), S. Bt

Flag Officers

Commander, Karachi:
  Vice Admiral Khalid Mir, HI(M), S. Bt
Commander Pakistan Fleet:
  Rear Admiral Abaidullah Khan, SJ, SI(M), S. Bt

Diplomatic Representation

Naval Adviser in London:
  Commodore M Jameel Akhtar, T. Bt
Naval Attaché in Paris:
  Captain Najam-ul-Hasnain
Naval Attaché in Washington:
  Captain M Nishat Rafi

Personnel

(a) 1994: 22 000 (2200 officers) including 750 (65 officers) seconded to the MSA
(b) Voluntary service

Bases

Karachi, Gwadar (shore base), Port Qasim

Prefix to Ships' Names

PNS

Maritime Security Agency

Set up in 1986 with four Shanghai II class and Fokker reconnaissance aircraft as its assets. Main purpose is to patrol the EEZ in co-operation with the Navy and the Army-manned Coast Guard. The obsolete destroyer *Badr* has been replaced as the HQ ship by *Nazim* (ex-*Tariq*), and Chinese-built Barkat class patrol craft have replaced the Shanghai IIs. A Norman Defender aircraft acquired in early 1993 has replaced the Fokker aircraft which have been returned to the Army.

Marines

A Marine Commando and Special Service Unit of about 150 men was formed at PNS *Iqbal*, Karachi in 1991.

Strength of the Fleet

Type	Active	Building
Submarines—Patrol	6	(3)
Submarines—Midget	3	—
Destroyers	3	—
Frigates	8	—
Fast Attack Craft—Missile	8	—
Fast Attack Craft—Gun	4	—
Large Patrol Craft	1	—
Minehunters	1	2
Minesweepers—Coastal	2	—
Minesweepers—Drones	5	—
Survey Ship	1	—
Tankers	4	—
Tugs	7	—
Auxiliaries	7	—
Customs Service	22	—
Coast Guard	5	—
Maritime Security Agency		
Destroyers	1	—
Large Patrol Craft	4	1
Fast Attack Craft—Gun	4	—

Mercantile Marine

Lloyd's Register of Shipping:
  67 vessels of 360 132 tons gross

DELETIONS

Destroyers

1992 *Shahjahan* (old)
1993 *Babur* (old), *Tippu Sultan* (old)

Frigates

1993 *Badr* (old), *Khaibar* (old), *Hunain, Aslat* (lease expired)
1994 *Saif, Tabuk, Harbah, Siqqat* (lease expired)

Patrol Forces

1992 *HDF 01-04* (sold), *Lahore, Baluchistan, Kalat*
1993 *Mardan, Sukkur, Bannu, Sind, Sarhad*

Minesweepers

1992 *Mukhtar*

Auxiliaries

1991 *Bholu* (old), *Gama* (old)
1993 *Madadgar*
1994 *Moawin* (lease expired)

PENNANT LIST

Submarines						
		F 183	Khaibar	P 144	Gilgit	1063	Vehdat

Submarines

S 131	Hangor
S 132	Shushuk
S 133	Mangro
S 134	Ghazi
S 135	Hashmat
S 136	Hurmat

Destroyers

D 160	Alamgir
D 166	Taimur
D 167	Tughril

Frigates

F 181	Tariq
F 182	Babur

F 183	Khaibar
F 184	Badr
F 185	Shahjahan
F 186	Tippu Sultan
F 262	Zulfiquar
F 263	Shamsher

Minesweepers

M 166	Munsif
M 167	Muhafiz (bldg)
M 160	Mahmood
M 164	Mujahid
MSI 02-03, 06-08	

Patrol Forces

P 140	Rajshahi

P 144	Gilgit
P 145	Pishin
P 149	Bahawalpur
P 197	Punjab
P 1021	Haibat
P 1022	Jalalat
P 1023	Jurat
P 1024	Shujaat
P 1025	Azmat
P 1026	Dehshat
P 1027	Himmat
P 1028	Quwwat

Maritime Security Agency

D 156	Nazim
1060	Barkat
1061	Rehmat
1062	Nusrat

1063	Vehdat
—	Sabqat
—	Rafaqat
P 67	Rahat
P 69	Sadaqat

Service Forces

A 21	Kalmat
A 40	Attock
A 41	Dacca
A 44	Bholu
A 45	Gama
A 46	Zum Zum
A 47	Nasr
A 49	Gwadar
A 260	Orwell

SUBMARINES

Note: Tenders put out in 1993 with France, China and Sweden for three submarines.

2 HASHMAT (AGOSTA) CLASS

Name	No	Builders	Laid down	Launched	Commissioned
HASHMAT (ex-SAS *Astrant*)	S 135	Dubigeon Normandie, Nantes	15 Sep 1976	14 Dec 1977	17 Feb 1979
HURMAT (ex-SAS *Adventurous*)	S 136	Dubigeon Normandie, Nantes	18 Sep 1977	1 Dec 1978	18 Feb 1980

Displacement, tons: 1230 standard; 1490 surfaced; 1740 dived
Dimensions, feet (metres): 221.7 × 22.3 × 17.7 *(67.6 × 6.8 × 5.4)*
Main machinery: Diesel-electric; 2 SEMT-Pielstick 16 PA4 V 185 VG diesels; 3600 hp(m) *(2.65 MW)*; 2 Jeumont Schneider alternators; 1.7 MW; 1 motor; 4600 hp(m) *(3.4 MW)*; 1 cruising motor; 32 hp(m) *(23 kW)*; 1 shaft
Speed, knots: 12 surfaced; 20 dived
Range, miles: 8500 at 9 kts snorting; 350 at 3.5 kts dived
Complement: 54 (7 officers)

Missiles: SSM: McDonnell Douglas Sub Harpoon; active radar homing to 130 km *(70 nm)* at 0.9 Mach; warhead 227 kg.
Torpedoes: 4—21 in *(533 mm)* bow tubes. Up to 20 ECAN F17P or AEG SUT; wire-guided; active/passive homing; water ram discharge gear.
Mines: Stonefish.
Countermeasures: ESM: ARUD; intercept and warning.
Radars: Surface search: Thomson-CSF DRUA 33; I band.
Sonars: Thomson Sintra DSUV 2H; passive search; medium frequency.
DUUA 2A/2B; active/passive search and attack; 8 kHz active.
DUUX 2A; hull-mounted; passive ranging.
DUUA 1D; active; high frequency.

Programmes: Purchased from France in mid-1978 after United Nations' ban on arms sales to South Africa. *Hashmat* arrived Karachi 31 October 1979, *Hurmat* arrived 11 August 1980. A provisional order for three more of the class was reported in September 1992 but this was not confirmed. More of the class must be a strong contender when funds become available for the additional three submarines (see *Note* above).
Structure: Diving depth, 300 m *(985 ft)*. Probably equipped with SSM in 1985 although there is some doubt about this.
Operational: Endurance, 45 days.

HASHMAT   *1990, G Jacobs*

4 HANGOR (DAPHNE) CLASS

Name	No	Builders	Laid down	Launched	Commissioned
HANGOR	S 131	Arsenal de Brest	1 Dec 1967	28 June 1969	12 Jan 1970
SHUSHUK	S 132	CN Ciotat, Le Trait	1 Dec 1967	30 July 1969	12 Jan 1970
MANGRO	S 133	CN Ciotat, Le Trait	8 July 1968	7 Feb 1970	8 Aug 1970
GHAZI (ex-*Cachalote*)	S 134	Dubigeon, Normandie, Nantes	12 May 1967	23 Sep 1968	1 Oct 1969

Displacement, tons: 700 standard; 869 surfaced; 1043 dived
Dimensions, feet (metres): 189.6 × 22.3 × 15.1 *(57.8 × 6.8 × 4.6)*
Main machinery: Diesel-electric; 2 SEMT-Pielstick 12 PA4 V 185 diesels; 2450 hp(m) *(1.8 MW)*; 2 Jeumont Schneider alternators; 1.7 MW; 2 motors; 2600 hp(m) *(1.9 MW)*; 2 shafts
Speed, knots: 13 surfaced; 15.5 dived
Range, miles: 4500 at 5 kts
Complement: 45 (5 officers)

Missiles: SSM: McDonnell Douglas Sub Harpoon; active radar homing to 130 km *(70 nm)* at 0.9 Mach; warhead 227 kg.
Torpedoes: 12—21.7 in *(550 mm)* (8 bow, 4 stern). 12 ECAN L5 Mod 3 or AEG SUT; dual purpose; active/passive homing. No reloads.
Mines: Stonefish.
Countermeasures: ESM: ARUD; intercept and warning.
Radars: Surface search: Thomson-CSF DRUA 31; I band.
Sonars: Thomson Sintra DSUV 1; hull-mounted; passive search; medium frequency.
DUUA 1; active/passive search and attack.

Programmes: The first three were built in France. The Portuguese Daphne class *Cachalote* was bought by Pakistan in December 1975.
Structure: They are broadly similar to the submarines built in France for Portugal and South Africa and the submarines constructed to the Daphne design in Spain, but slightly modified internally to suit Pakistan requirements and naval conditions. Diving depth 300 m *(985 ft)*. SSM capability added in late 1980s.
Operational: *Hangor* in collision in September 1990 and badly damaged but back in service in 1992.

GHAZI   *10/1991, G Jacobs*

3 MIDGET SUBMARINES

Displacement, tons: 118 dived
Dimensions, feet (metres): 91.2 × 18.4 *(27.8 × 5.6)*
Speed, knots: 7 dived
Range, miles: 1200 surfaced; 60 dived
Complement: 6 + 8 swimmers
Torpedoes: 2—21 in *(533 mm)* tubes; AEG SUT; wire-guided; active homing to 12 km *(6.5 nm)* at 35 kts; passive homing to 28 km *(15 nm)* at 23 kts; warhead 250 kg.
Mines: 8 Mk 414 Limpet type.

Comment: MG 110 type built in Pakistan under supervision by Cosmos. These are enlarged SX 756 of Italian Cosmos design and have replaced the SX 404 which were acquired in 1972. Diving depth of 150 m and can carry eight swimmers with two tons of explosives as well as two CF2 FX 60 SDVs (swimmer delivery vehicles). Pilkington Optronics CK 39 periscopes. Reported as having a range of 1000 nm and an endurance of 20 days.

MIDGET SUBMARINE   *1993*

DESTROYERS

3 GEARING (FRAM I) CLASS

Name	No	Builders	Laid down	Launched	Commissioned
ALAMGIR (ex-USS *Cone* DD 866)	D 160	Bethlehem, Staten Island	30 Nov 1944	10 May 1945	18 Aug 1945
TAIMUR (ex-USS *Epperson* DD 719)	D 166	Todd Pacific Shipyards	20 June 1945	29 Dec 1945	19 Mar 1949
TUGHRIL (ex-USS *Henderson* DD 785)	D 167	Todd Pacific Shipyards	27 Oct 1944	28 May 1945	4 Aug 1945

Displacement, tons: 2425 standard; 3500 full load
Dimensions, feet (metres): 390.5 × 41.2 × 19
(119 × 12.6 × 5.8)
Main machinery: 4 Babcock & Wilcox boilers; 600 psi
(43.3 kg/cm sq); 850°F *(454°C)*; 2 GE turbines; 60 000 hp
(45 MW); 2 shafts
Speed, knots: 32. **Range, miles:** 4500 at 16 kts
Complement: 274 (27 officers)

Missiles: SSM: 6 McDonnell Douglas Harpoon (3 twin) launchers
❶; active radar homing to 130 km *(70 nm)* at 0.9 Mach; warhead 227 kg.
A/S: Honeywell ASROC Mk 112 octuple launcher ❷; 8 reloads;
inertial guidance to 1.6-10 km *(1-5.4 nm)*; payload Mk 46
torpedo.
Guns: 2 US 5 in *(127 mm)*/38 (twin) Mk 38 ❸; 85° elevation; 15
rounds/minute to 17 km *(9.3 nm)* anti-surface; 11 km *(5.9 nm)*
anti-aircraft; weight of shell 25 kg.
General Electric/General Dynamics 20 mm 6-barrelled Vulcan
Phalanx Mk 15 ❹; 3000 rounds/minute combined to 1.5 km.
8—23 mm/87 (2 quad) ❺.
Torpedoes: 6—324 mm US Mk 32 (2 triple) tubes ❻. Honeywell
Mk 46; anti-submarine; active/passive homing to 11 km
(5.9 nm) at 40 kts; warhead 44 kg.
Countermeasures: Decoys: 2 Plessey Shield 6-barrelled fixed
launchers; chaff and IR flares in distraction, decoy or centroid
modes.
ESM/ECM: Argo APECS II includes AR 700 intercept and
jammer.
Fire control: Mk 37 for 5 in guns. OE 2 SATCOM.
Radars: Air search: Lockheed SPS 40 ❼; E/F band; range
320 km *(175 nm)*.
Surface search: Raytheon/Sylvania ❽; SPS 10; G band.
Navigation: Racal Decca TM 1226; I band.
Fire control: Western Electric Mk 25 ❾; I/J band.
Sonars: Sangamo SQS 23D with Raytheon Solid State transmit-
ters; hull-mounted; active search and attack; medium
frequency.

Helicopters: Facilities for 1 SA 319B Alouette III seldom used ❿.

Programmes: Two transferred from US 30 September 1980;
Alamgir on 1 October 1982.
Modernisation: Modernised with Harpoon and Vulcan Phalanx
fitted in place of Y gun turret, improved EW equipment and the
addition of two 23 mm quadruple mountings at the base of the
foremast.
Operational: Form 25 Destroyer Squadron. *Tughril* is able to
launch Banshee target drones. One of the class *Tariq* was converted to an MSA HQ ship in early 1990 (see MSA section).

TUGHRIL

(Scale 1 : 1200), Ian Sturton

TUGHRIL

9/1993, van Ginderen Collection

ALAMGIR

12/1993, G Toremans

FRIGATES

6 TARIQ (AMAZON) CLASS (TYPE 21)

Name	No	Builders	Laid down	Launched	Commissioned
BABUR (ex-*Amazon*)	F 182 (ex-F 169)	Vosper Thornycroft, Woolston	6 Nov 1969	26 Apr 1971	11 May 1974
SHAHJAHAN (ex-*Active*)	F 185 (ex-F 171)	Vosper Thornycroft, Woolston	23 July 1971	23 Nov 1972	17 June 1977
TARIQ (ex-*Ambuscade*)	F 181 (ex-F 172)	Yarrow Shipbuilders, Glasgow	1 Sep 1971	18 Jan 1973	5 Sep 1975
KHAIBAR (ex-*Arrow*)	F 183 (ex-F 173)	Yarrow Shipbuilders, Glasgow	28 Sep 1972	5 Feb 1974	29 July 1976
BADR (ex-*Alacrity*)	F 184 (ex-F 174)	Yarrow Shipbuilders, Glasgow	5 Mar 1973	18 Sep 1974	2 July 1977
TIPPU SULTAN (ex-*Avenger*)	F 186 (ex-F 185)	Yarrow Shipbuilders, Glasgow	30 Oct 1974	20 Nov 1975	19 July 1978

Displacement, tons: 3100 standard; 3600 full load
Dimensions, feet (metres): 384 oa; 360 wl × 41.7 × 19.5 (screws) *(117; 109.7 × 12.7 × 5.9)*
Main machinery: COGOG; 2 RR Olympus TM3B gas turbines; 50 000 hp *(37.3 MW)* sustained; 2 RR Tyne RM1C gas turbines (cruising); 9900 hp *(7.4 MW)* sustained; 2 shafts; cp props
Speed, knots: 30; 18 on Tynes. **Range, miles:** 4000 at 17 kts; 1200 at 30 kts
Complement: 175 (13 officers) (accommodation for 192)

Missiles: SSM: 4 McDonnell Douglas Harpoon ❶ (may be fitted).
Guns: 1 Vickers 4.5 in *(114 mm)*/55 Mk 8 ❷; 55° elevation; 25 rounds/minute to 22 km *(11.9 nm)* anti-surface; 6 km *(3.3 nm)* anti-aircraft; weight of shell 21 kg.
    1 GE/GD 20 mm 6-barrelled Vulcan Phalanx Mk 15 ❸; 3000 rounds/minute combined to 1.5 km. To replace Seacat.
    2 or 4 Oerlikon 20 mm Mk 7A ❹; 50° elevation; 800 rounds/minute to 2 km; weight of shell 0.24 kg.
Torpedoes: 6—324 mm Plessey STWS Mk 2 (2 triple) tubes ❺. Only in *Badr* and *Shahjahan*; the others may be fitted in due course.
Countermeasures: Decoys: Graseby Type 182; towed torpedo decoy.
    2 Vickers Corvus 8-tubed trainable launchers ❻; chaff to 1 km.
ESM: Thomson-CSF DR 3000; intercept.
Combat data systems: CAAIS combat data system with Ferranti FM 1600B computers. Links 10 and 14 (receive).
Fire control: Ferranti WSA-4 digital fire control system.
Radars: Air/surface search: Marconi Type 992R ❼; E/F band.
Navigation: Kelvin Hughes Type 1006; I band.
Fire control: Two Selenia Type 912 ❽; I/J band; range 40 km *(22 nm)*.
Sonars: Graseby Type 184P; hull-mounted; active search and attack; medium frequency.
    Kelvin Hughes Type 162M; hull-mounted; bottom classification; 50 kHz.

Helicopters: 1 Westland Lynx HAS 3 ❾.

Programmes: *Tariq* handed over by the UK 28 July 1993, *Babur* 30 September 1993. *Khaibar* and *Badr* transferred 1 March 1994 and last pair planned for 23 September 1994. *Tariq* arrived in Karachi 1 November 1993 and the last one is scheduled to arrive in October 1994. These ships replace the Garcia and Brooke classes.
Modernisation: Exocet, torpedo tubes and Lynx helicopter facilities were all added in RN service, but torpedo tubes were subsequently removed in all but *Badr* and *Shahjahan* and may be retrofitted by Pakistan. The Seacat SAM system is to be replaced by Vulcan Phalanx guns taken from the County and Gearing class destroyers and new EW equipment has been installed. Other equipment upgrades are projected and include Harpoon (also from the Gearings), a new search radar, and

TARIQ   *(Scale 1 : 1200), Ian Sturton*

TARIQ (still with Seacat launcher)   *8/1993, van Ginderen Collection*

BAe/Thomson Sintra ATAS towed active sonar array. The hull-mounted sonar may also be updated.
Structure: Due to cracking in the upper deck structure large strengthening pieces have been fixed to the ships' side at the top of the steel hull as shown in the illustration. The addition of permanent ballast to improve stability has increased displacement by about 350 tons. Further hull modifications to reduce noise and vibration started in 1988 and completed in all of the class by 1992.
Operational: Lynx helicopters are being purchased separately.

TARIQ (still with Exocet launchers)   *8/1993, H M Steele*

2 LEANDER CLASS

Name	No	Builders	Laid down	Launched	Commissioned
ZULFIQUAR (ex-HMS *Apollo*)	F 262	Yarrows, Glasgow	1 May 1969	15 Oct 1970	28 May 1972
SHAMSHER (ex-HMS *Diomede*)	F 263	Yarrows, Glasgow	30 Jan 1968	15 Apr 1969	2 Apr 1971

Displacement, tons: 2500 standard; 2962 full load
Dimensions, feet (metres): 360 wl; 372 oa × 43 × 14.8 (keel); 18 (screws) *(109.7; 113.4 × 13.1 × 4.5; 5.5)*
Main machinery: 2 Babcock & Wilcox boilers; 550 psi *(38.7 kg/cm sq)*; 850°F *(454°C)*; 2 White/English Electric turbines; 30 000 hp *(22.4 MW)*; 2 shafts
Speed, knots: 28. **Range, miles:** 4000 at 15 kts
Complement: 235 (15 officers)

Missiles: SAM: Short Bros Seacat GWS 22 quad launcher ❶; optical/radar guidance to 5 km *(2.7 nm)*; warhead 10 kg.
Guns: 2 Vickers 4.5 in *(114 mm)*/45 Mk 6 (twin) ❷; 80° elevation; 20 rounds/minute to 19 km *(10.3 nm)* anti-surface; 6 km *(3.3 nm)* anti-aircraft; weight of shell 25 kg.
2 Oerlikon 20 mm/70 ❸; 50° elevation; 800 rounds/minute to 2 km; weight of shell 0.24 kg.
1 Oerlikon/BMARC 20 mm GAM-BO1 (on after end of flight deck when fitted) ❹; 55° elevation; 1000 rounds/minute to 2 km.
A/S mortars: 3-barrelled UK MoD Mortar Mk 10 ❺; automatic loading; range 1 km; warhead 92 kg.
Countermeasures: Decoys: Graseby Type 182; towed torpedo decoy.
2 Vickers Corvus 8-barrelled trainable launchers ❻; chaff to 1 km.
ESM: UA-8/9/13; radar warning.
ECM: Type 668; jammer.
Fire control: MRS 3 system for 114 mm guns.
Radars: Air search: Marconi Type 966 ❼; A band; AKE-1; long range.
Surface search: Plessey Type 993 ❽; E/F band.
Navigation: Kelvin Hughes Type 1006; I band.
Fire control: Two Plessey Type 904 (for Seacat and 114 mm guns) ❾; I/J band.
Sonars: Kelvin Hughes Type 162M; hull-mounted; bottom classification; 50 kHz.
Graseby Type 170B; hull-mounted; active search and attack; 15 kHz.
Graseby Type 184P; hull-mounted; active search and attack; 6-9 kHz.

SHAMSHER

(Scale 1 : 1200), Ian Sturton

SHAMSHER

10/1991, G Jacobs

Helicopters: 1 SA 319B Alouette III ❿.

Programmes: Transferred from UK 15 July 1988 (*Shamsher*) and 14 October 1988 (*Zulfiquar*). Both ships are from the Batch 3B broad-beamed group of this class.

Structure: No equipment changes made on transfer except the replacement of the Wasp helicopter by an Alouette III.
Operational: Both ships sailed for Pakistan in August and December 1988 respectively. Extensive refits carried out 1991-93.

SHIPBORNE AIRCRAFT

Numbers/Type: 3 Westland Lynx HAS 3.
Operational speed: 120 kts *(222 km/h)*.
Service ceiling: 10 000 ft *(3048 m)*.
Range: 320 nm *(593 km)*.
Role/Weapon systems: To be acquired from UK by mid-1995 with a second batch of three more to follow. Sensors: Ferranti Sea Spray radar, Orange Crop ESM. Weapons: ASW; 2 Type 244/S torpedoes. ASV; 4 × Sea Skua missiles; 2—12.7 mm MG pods.

LYNX (British colours)

1992, H M Steele

Numbers/Type: 6 Westland Sea King Mk 45.
Operational speed: 125 kts *(232 km/h)*.
Service ceiling: 10 500 ft *(3200 m)*.
Range: 630 nm *(1165 km)*.
Role/Weapon systems: ASVW helicopter with all ASW gear removed. Plans are to fit GEC-Marconi Type 2069 dipping sonar and AQS-928G acoustic processors from 1995. Sensors: MEL search radar. Weapons: ASW; none. ASV; 1 × AM 39 Exocet missile.

SEA KING

1990, Pakistan Navy

Numbers/Type: 4 Aerospatiale SA 319B Alouette III.
Operational speed: 113 kts *(210 km/h)*.
Service ceiling: 10 500 ft *(3200 m)*.
Range: 290 nm *(540 km)*.
Role/Weapon systems: Reconnaissance helicopter; one embarked in County class DLG and can be carried in the Frigates for reconnaissance, support and SAR. Sensors: Weather/search radar. Weapons: Generally unarmed.

ALOUETTE III

1988

LAND-BASED MARITIME AIRCRAFT

Note: Three P-3C Orion were completed in May 1991 but have been embargoed in the USA under the Pressler amendment.

Numbers/Type: 4 Breguet Atlantic 1.
Operational speed: 355 kts *(658 km/h)*.
Service ceiling: 32 800 ft *(10 000 m)*.
Range: 4855 nm *(8995 km)*.
Role/Weapon systems: Long-range MR/ASW cover for Arabian Sea; ex-French and Dutch stock. Upgraded in 1992/93. Two aircraft to be fitted with Thomson-CSF Ocean Master radar and Sadang 1C sonobuoy signal processor in 1994. Sensors: Thomson-CSF radar, ECM/ESM, MAD, sonobuoys. Weapons: ASW; 9 × Mk 46 or 244/S torpedoes, depth bombs, mines. ASV; 2 × AS 12 or AM 39 Exocet missiles.

Numbers/Type: 5 AMD-BA Mirage 5.
Operational speed: 750 kts *(1390 km/h)*.
Service ceiling: 59 055 ft *(18 000 m)*.
Range: 740 nm *(1370 km)*.
Role/Weapon systems: Maritime strike aircraft operated by the Air Force. Sensors: Thomson-CSF radar. Weapons: ASVW; 2 × AM 39 Exocet; 2 × 30 mm DEFA.

Numbers/Type: 3 Fokker F27 MPA Friendship.
Operational speed: 250 kts *(463 km/h)*.
Service ceiling: 25 000 ft *(7620 m)*.
Range: 2700 nm *(5000 km)*.
Role/Weapon systems: Visual reconnaissance and coastal surveillance aircraft (ex-Airline) used by the Maritime Security Agency. Possibly one more to come. One to be fitted with Ocean Master radar and DR 3000A ESM. Sensors: Weather radar and visual means only. Weapons: Limited armament.

PATROL FORCES

4 HUANGFEN CLASS (FAST ATTACK CRAFT—MISSILE)

AZMAT P 1025   **DEHSHAT** P 1026   **HIMMAT** P 1027   **QUWWAT** P 1028

Displacement, tons: 171 standard; 205 full load
Dimensions, feet (metres): 110.2 × 24.9 × 8.9 (33.6 × 7.6 × 2.7)
Main machinery: 3 Type M 503 diesels; 8025 hp(m) (5.4 MW) sustained; 3 shafts
Speed, knots: 35. **Range, miles:** 800 at 30 kts
Complement: 28
Missiles: SSM: 4 Hai Ying 2 (C 201); active radar or IR homing to 95 km (51 nm) at 0.9 Mach; warhead 513 kg.
Guns: 4 Norinco 25 mm/80 (2 twin); 85° elevation; 270 rounds/minute to 3 km (1.6 nm); weight of shell 0.34 kg.
Radars: Surface search/target indication: Square Tie; I band.

Comment: Transferred from China April 1984. Chinese version of the Soviet Osa II class.

HIMMAT   1989, Pakistan Navy

4 HAIBAT (HEGU) CLASS (FAST ATTACK CRAFT—MISSILE)

HAIBAT P 1021   **JALALAT** P 1022   **JURAT** P 1023   **SHUJAAT** P 1024

Displacement, tons: 68 standard; 79.2 full load
Dimensions, feet (metres): 88.6 × 20.7 × 4.3 (27 × 6.3 × 1.3)
Main machinery: 4 Type L-12V-180 diesels; 4800 hp(m) (3.53 MW); 4 shafts
Speed, knots: 37.5. **Range, miles:** 400 at 30 kts
Complement: 17
Missiles: SSM: 2 SY 1; active radar or IR homing to 45 km (24.3 nm) at 0.9 Mach; warhead 513 kg.
Guns: 2 Norinco 25 mm/80 (twin); 85° elevation; 270 rounds/minute to 3 km (1.6 nm); weight of shell 0.34 kg.
Radars: Surface search: Pot Head; I band.

Comment: Two transferred in May and two in October 1981. Steel hull version of Komar class.

JALALAT   1992, Pakistan Navy

1 SIND (HAINAN) CLASS (FAST ATTACK CRAFT—GUN)

PUNJAB P 197

Displacement, tons: 375 standard; 392 full load
Dimensions, feet (metres): 192.8 × 23.6 × 6 (58.8 × 7.2 × 2.2)
Main machinery: 4 PCR/Kolomna Type 9-D-8 diesels; 4000 hp(m) (2.94 MW) sustained; 4 shafts
Speed, knots: 30.5. **Range, miles:** 1300 at 15 kts
Complement: 70
Guns: 4 Norinco 57 mm/70 (2 twin); 85° elevation; 120 rounds/minute to 12 km (6.5 nm); weight of shell 6.3 kg.
4 Norinco 25 mm/80 (2 twin); 85° elevation; 270 rounds/minute to 3 km (1.6 nm); weight of shell 0.34 kg.
A/S mortars: 4 RBU 1200 5-tubed fixed; range 1200 m; warhead 34 kg.
Depth charges: 2 projectors; 2 racks. 18 DCs.
Mines: Rails fitted for 12.
Radars: Surface search: Pot Head; I band.
Sonars: Stag Ear; hull-mounted; active attack; high frequency.

Comment: First pair transferred from China mid-1976, second pair in April 1980. This is the sole survivor, the others being used for spares.

PUNJAB   1990, Pakistan Navy

3 SHANGHAI II CLASS (FAST ATTACK CRAFT—GUN)

GILGIT P 144   **PISHIN** P 145   **BAHAWALPUR** P 149

Displacement, tons: 113 standard; 131 full load
Dimensions, feet (metres): 127.3 × 17.7 × 5.6 (38.8 × 5.4 × 1.7)
Main machinery: 2 Type L12-180 diesels; 2400 hp(m) (1.76 MW) (forward); 2 Type 12-D-6 diesels; 1820 hp(m) (1.34 MW) (aft); 4 shafts
Speed, knots: 30. **Range, miles:** 700 at 16.5 kts
Complement: 34
Guns: 4—37 mm/63 (2 twin). 4—25 mm/80 (2 twin).
Depth charges: 2 projectors; 8 weapons.
Mines: Fitted with mine rails for approx 10 mines.
Radars: Surface search: Skin Head; I band.

Comment: Acquired from China between 1972 and 1976. Four were transferred to the Maritime Security Agency, and five others have been used for spares to keep both these and the MSA craft operational.

PISHIN   1/1994, van Ginderen Collection

1 TOWN CLASS (LARGE PATROL CRAFT)

Name	No	Builders	Commissioned
RAJSHAHI	P 140	Brooke Marine	1965

Displacement, tons: 115 standard; 143 full load
Dimensions, feet (metres): 107 × 20 × 6.9 (32.6 × 6.1 × 2.1)
Main machinery: 2 MTU 12V 538 diesels; 3400 hp(m) (2.5 MW); 2 shafts
Speed, knots: 24
Complement: 19
Guns: 2 Bofors 40 mm/70. 2—12.7 mm MGs.

Comment: The last survivor in Pakistan of a class of four built by Brooke Marine in 1965. Steel hull and aluminium superstructure.

RAJSHAHI   1989, Pakistan Navy

MARITIME SECURITY AGENCY

Notes: (1) All ships are painted white with a distinctive diagonal blue band and MSA on each side.
(2) One 200 ton patrol craft reported building at Karachi in 1992.
(3) One Britten-Norman Maritime Defender acquired in 1993. Based near Karachi with 93 Squadron. Second ordered in February 1994.

1 GEARING (FRAM 1) CLASS

Name	No	Builders	Commissioned
NAZIM (ex-Tariq, ex-Wiltsie)	D 156 (ex-D 165, ex-DD 716)	Federal SB & DD Co	12 Jan 1946

Comment: Transferred from the Navy on 25 January 1990 and has replaced the old Badr as the MSA Flagship. All details as for the Gearing class (see Destroyers) except that ASROC and Torpedo Tubes have been removed, there is a quadruple 14.5 mm gun mounting on each side of the foremast and no Phalanx aft.

NAZIM (with two Barkat class)   1/1994, van Ginderen Collection

4 BARKAT CLASS (LARGE PATROL CRAFT)

Name	No	Builders	Commissioned
BARKAT	1060 (ex-P 60)	China Shipbuilding Corp	29 Dec 1989
REHMAT	1061 (ex-P 61)	China Shipbuilding Corp	29 Dec 1989
NUSRAT	1062 (ex-P 62)	China Shipbuilding Corp	13 June 1990
VEHDAT	1063 (ex-P 63)	China Shipbuilding Corp	13 June 1990

Displacement, tons: 435 full load
Dimensions, feet (metres): 190.3 × 24.9 × 7.5 *(58 × 7.6 × 2.3)*
Main machinery: 4 MTU 16V 396 TB93 diesels; 8720 hp(m) *(6.4 MW)* sustained; 4 shafts
Speed, knots: 27. Range, miles: 1500 at 12 kts
Complement: 50 (5 officers)
Guns: 2—37 mm/63 (twin); 4—25 mm/80 (2 twin).
Radars: Surface search: 2 Fujitsu Ops 9; I band.

Comment: Type P58A patrol craft built in China for the MSA. First two arrived in Karachi at the end of January 1990, second pair in August 1990.

BARKAT (old number)   *1990, CSSC*

4 SHANGHAI II CLASS (FAST ATTACK CRAFT—GUN)

SABQAT   RAFAQAT   RAHAT P 67   SADAQAT P 69

Comment: Four of the class were transferred from the Navy in 1986 and were reported as scrapped in 1990. These four are either the same ships brought back into service, or some of the others of the class which have subsequently been paid off by the Navy. Details in naval section.

MINE WARFARE FORCES

2 MAHMOOD (MSC 268) CLASS (MINESWEEPERS—COASTAL)

MAHMOOD (ex-*MSC 267*) M 160   MUJAHID (ex-*MSC 261*) M 164

Displacement, tons: 330 light; 390 full load
Dimensions, feet (metres): 144 × 27.9 × 8.5 *(43.9 × 8.5 × 2.6)*
Main machinery: 2 GM 8-268A diesels; 880 hp *(656 kW)*; 2 shafts
Speed, knots: 13.5. Range, miles: 3000 at 10.5 kts
Complement: 39
Guns: 4 USSR 23 mm (quad) or 1 Oerlikon 20 mm.
Radars: Navigation: Decca 45; I band.

Comment: Transferred by the USA under MAP. *Mahmood* in May 1957, *Mujahid* in November 1956. *Mujahid* paid off in 1990 but back in service in 1991.

MAHMOOD   *1991, Pakistan Navy*

5 FUTI CLASS (TYPE 312) (DRONE MINESWEEPERS)

MSI 01-02   MSI 06-08

Displacement, tons: 47 standard
Dimensions, feet (metres): 68.6 × 12.8 × 6.9 *(20.9 × 3.9 × 2.1)*
Main machinery: Diesel-electric; 1 Type 12V 150C diesel; 300 hp(m) *(220 kW)*; 1 motor; cp prop
Speed, knots: 12. Range, miles: 144 at 12 kts
Complement: 3

Comment: Acquired from China in 1991. Fitted to carry out magnetic and acoustic sweeping under remote control up to 5 km *(2.7 nm)* from shore control station.

FUTI (Chinese colours)   *1988, CSSC*

1 + 2 MUNSIF (ÉRIDAN) CLASS (MINEHUNTERS)

Name	No	Builders	Commissioned
MUNSIF (ex-*Sagittaire*)	M 166	Lorient Dockyard	27 July 1989
MUHAFIZ	M 167	Lorient Dockyard	1995
—	M 168	Lorient/Karachi	1996

Displacement, tons: 562 standard; 595 full load
Dimensions, feet (metres): 168.9 × 29.2 × 8.2 *(51.5 × 8.9 × 2.5)*
Main machinery: 1 Brons Werkspoor A-RUB 215X-12 diesel; 1860 hp(m) *(1.37 MW)* sustained; 1 shaft; Lips cp prop; Auxiliary propulsion; 2 motors; 240 hp(m) *(179 kW)*; 2 active rudders; 2 bow thrusters
Speed, knots: 15; 7 on auxiliary propulsion. Range, miles: 3000 at 12 kts
Complement: 46 (5 officers)
Guns: 1 GIAT 20F2 20 mm; 1—12.7 mm MG.
Countermeasures: MCM; 2 PAP 104 Mk 5 systems; mechanical sweep gear. AP-4 acoustic sweep.
Radars: Navigation: Racal Decca 1229; I band.
Sonars: Thomson Sintra DUBM 21B; hull-mounted; active; high frequency; 100 kHz (±10 kHz). Thomson Sintra TSM 2054 MCM towed array may be included.

Comment: Contract signed with France 17 January 1992. The first recommissioned into the Pakistan Navy on 24 September 1992 after active service in the Gulf in 1991. Sailed for Pakistan in November 1992. The second is building at Lorient Dockyard and the third hull will be shipped to Karachi for fitting out.

MUNSIF   *11/1992, Selim San*

SURVEY SHIP

Note: Two Griffon Type 1000-TD survey hovercraft delivered in March 1993. Probably for civilian use.

Name	No	Builders	Commissioned
BEHR PAIMA	—	Ishikawajima, Japan	17 Dec 1982

Measurement, tons: 1183 gross
Dimensions, feet (metres): 200.1 × 38.7 × 12.1 *(61 × 11.8 × 3.7)*
Main machinery: 2 Daihatsu diesels; 2000 hp(m) *(1.47 MW)*; 2 shafts
Speed, knots: 13.7
Complement: 84 (16 officers)

Comment: Ordered in November 1981. Laid down 16 February 1982. There is a second survey ship *Jatli* under civilian control.

BEHR PAIMA   *1989, G Jacobs*

AUXILIARIES

1 DEGAUSSING VESSEL

Displacement, tons: 250
Dimensions, feet (metres): 115.5 × 23 × 7.9 *(35.2 × 7 × 2.4)*
Main machinery: 1 diesel; 375 hp(m) *(276 kW)*; 1 shaft
Speed, knots: 10

Comment: Built at Karachi with French assistance 1981-82.

1 SUPPLY TENDER

ORWELL   A 260

Comment: Patrol craft supply tender and berthing hulk based at Gwadar.

1 MISSION CLASS (AOR)

Name	No	Builders	Commissioned
DACCA (ex-USNS *Mission Santa* *Cruz* AO 132)	A 41	Marinship Corp, California	21 June 1944

Displacement, tons: 5730 light; 22 380 full load
Dimensions, feet (metres): 524 × 68 × 31 *(159.7 × 20.7 × 9.5)*
Main machinery: Turbo-electric; 2 Babcock & Wilcox boilers; 600 psi *(42.3 kg/cm sq)*; 825°F *(440°C)*; 2 GE turbo generators; 10 000 hp(m) *(7.46 MW)*; 1 motor; 1 shaft
Speed, knots: 16
Complement: 160 (15 officers)
Cargo capacity: 20 000 tons fuel
Guns: 8—35 mm (4 twin).

Comment: Handed over from the USA on 17 January 1963 after being fitted with underway replenishment rigs on both sides. Purchased 31 May 1974.

DACCA *1990, Pakistan Navy*

1 FUQING CLASS (AOR)

Name	No	Builders	Commissioned
NASR (ex-X-350)	A 47	Dalian Shipyard	27 Aug 1987

Displacement, tons: 7500 standard; 21 750 full load
Dimensions, feet (metres): 561 × 71.5 × 30.8 *(171 × 21.8 × 9.4)*
Main machinery: 1 Sulzer 8RLB66 diesel; 13 000 hp(m) *(9.56 MW)*; 1 shaft
Speed, knots: 18. **Range, miles:** 18 000 at 14 kts
Complement: 130 (during visit to Australia in October 1988 carried 373 (23 officers) including 100 cadets)
Cargo capacity: 10 550 tons fuel; 1000 tons dieso; 200 tons feed water; 200 tons drinking water
Radars: Navigation: Two Decca 1006; I band.
Helicopters: 1 SA 319B Alouette III.

Comment: Similar to Chinese ships of the same class. Two replenishment at sea positions on each side for liquids and one for solids.

NASR *10/1988, G Toremans*

2 HARBOUR TANKERS

Name	No	Builders	Commissioned
GWADAR	A 49	Karachi Shipyard	1984
KALMAT	A 21	Karachi Shipyard	29 Aug 1992

Displacement, tons: 831 gross
Dimensions, feet (metres): 206 × 37.1 × 9.8 *(62.8 × 11.3 × 3)*
Main machinery: 1 Sulzer diesel; 550 hp(m) *(404 kW)*; 1 shaft
Speed, knots: 10

Comment: Second of class launched 6 June 1991. One used for oil and one for water.

GWADAR *1987*

2 UTILITY CRAFT

427   428

Measurement, tons: 57 gross
Dimensions, feet (metres): 65.6 × 16.4 × 4.9 *(20 × 5 × 1.5)*
Main machinery: 2 Detroit 8V-71TI diesels; 1360 hp *(1 MW)*; 2 shafts
Speed, knots: 12

Comment: Built by Karachi Shipyard and completed in 1991.

2 WATER BARGES

ZUM ZUM A 46   **ATTOCK** A 40

Displacement, tons: 1200 full load
Dimensions, feet (metres): 177.2 × 32.3 × 15.1 *(54 × 9.8 × 4.6)*
Main machinery: 2 diesels; 800 hp(m) *(276 kW)*; 2 shafts
Speed, knots: 8
Cargo capacity: 550 tons
Guns: 2 Oerlikon 20 mm.

Comment: Built in Italy in 1957 under MDAP.

ATTOCK *1990*

2 OIL BARGES

JANBAZ   KALMAT

Measurement, tons: 282 gross
Dimensions, feet (metres): 114.8 × 30.5 × 11.5 *(35 × 9.3 × 3.5)*
Main machinery: 2 Niigata diesels; 2 shafts

Comment: Built by Karachi Shipyard in 1990 and 1992.

2 FLOATING DOCKS

PESHAWAR (ex-US *ARD 6*)   **FD II**

Comment: *Peshawar* transferred June 1961, 3000 tons lift. *FD II* built 1974, 1200 tons lift.

TUGS

Note: There are three more general purpose tugs plus two harbour tugs *Goga* and *Jhara*.

2 COASTAL TUGS

Name	No	Builders	Commissioned
BHOLU	A 44	Giessendam Shipyard, Netherlands	Apr 1991
GAMA	A 45	Giessendam Shipyard, Netherlands	Apr 1991

Displacement, tons: 265 full load
Dimensions, feet (metres): 85.3 × 22.3 × 9.5 *(26 × 6.8 × 2.9)*
Main machinery: 2 Cummins KTA38-M diesels; 1836 hp *(1.26 MW)* sustained; 2 shafts
Speed, knots: 12
Complement: 6

Comment: Ordered from Damen in 1990. Have replaced the two old tugs of the same name and pennant numbers.

BHOLU *1991, Pakistan Navy*

COAST GUARD AND CUSTOMS SERVICE

Note: Unlike the Maritime Security Agency which comes under the Defence Ministry, the official Coast Guard was set up in 1985 and is manned by the Army and answerable to the Ministry of the Interior.

1 SWALLOW CRAFT

SAIF

Displacement, tons: 30 full load
Dimensions, feet (metres): 65.6 × 14.4 × 4.3 *(20 × 4.4 × 1.3)*
Main machinery: 2 diesels; 1800 hp(m) *(1.3 MW)*; 2 shafts
Speed, knots: 27. **Range, miles:** 500 at 20 kts
Complement: 8
Guns: 2—12.7 mm MGs.

Comment: Built in South Korea in 1986.

22 CRESTITALIA 16.5 METRE CRAFT

P 551-568 (Customs)   **SADD   SHABAZ   VAQAR   BURQ**

Displacement, tons: 23 full load
Dimensions, feet (metres): 54.1 × 17.1 × 2.9 *(16.5 × 5.2 × 0.9)*
Main machinery: 2 diesels; 1600 hp(m) *(1.18 MW)*; 2 shafts
Speed, knots: 30. **Range, miles:** 425 at 25 kts
Complement: 5
Guns: 1—14.5 mm MG.

Comment: Acquired 1979-80 from Crestitalia, Italy. The four named craft belong to the Coast Guard.

PANAMA

Senior Appointment

Commander of the Navy:
Major Jose Rosas

General

A force which became a naval service in 1983 and is split between both coasts. Aircraft are all Air Force operated. During the US invasion in December 1989, half the fleet was sunk and most of the others damaged. In 1990 virtually all the officers were dismissed so recovery is going to take time. The US Coast Guard is assisting the re-training and is providing replacement patrol craft and a buoy tender. Much repair work was started in 1992 and some of the damaged vessels are being refitted.

Personnel

(a) 1994: 280
(b) Voluntary service

Bases

Flamenco Island

Mercantile Marine

Lloyd's Register of Shipping:
5564 ships of 57 618 623 tons gross

PATROL FORCES

Note: In addition to the vessels listed below, there are three Boston Whalers acquired in mid-1991 and one confiscated motor yacht. *Macho de Monte 2* back in service in 1992.

1 POINT CLASS (LARGE PATROL CRAFT)

TRES DE NOVIEMBRE (ex-*Point Barrow*) P 204

Displacement, tons: 67 full load
Dimensions, feet (metres): 83 × 17.2 × 5.8 *(25.3 × 5.2 × 1.8)*
Main machinery: 2 Caterpillar diesels; 1600 hp *(1.19 MW)*; 2 shafts
Speed, knots: 23. **Range, miles:** 1500 at 8 kts
Complement: 10 (1 officer)
Guns: 2—12.7 mm MGs.
Radars: Navigation: Raytheon SPS 64; I band.

Comment: Built at Coast Guard Yard, Maryland in early 1960s. Transferred from US 7 June 1991.

POINT class (USCG colours)   *4/1992, van Ginderen Collection*

1 MSB 29 CLASS (LARGE PATROL CRAFT/MINESWEEPER)

ex-*MSB 29*

Displacement, tons: 80 full load
Dimensions, feet (metres): 87 × 19 × 5.5 *(26.5 × 5.8 × 1.7)*
Main machinery: 2 Packard 2D850 diesels; 600 hp *(448 kW)*; 2 shafts
Speed, knots: 11
Complement: 11 (2 officers)
Guns: 1—12.7 mm MG.
Radars: Surface search: Raytheon 1900; I band.
Sonars: Hydroscan Mk 24; active; high frequency.

Comment: Built in 1954 as an enlarged MSB 5 design by John Trumpy, Annapolis. Paid off in 1992 and transferred from US to Panama in March 1993 after refit. Wooden hull.

Ex-MSB 29   *1986, US Navy*

2 VOSPER TYPE (LARGE PATROL CRAFT)

Name	No	Builders	Commissioned
PANQUIACO	P 301 (ex-GC 10)	Vospers, Portsmouth	Mar 1971
LIGIA ELENA	P 302 (ex-GC 11)	Vospers, Portsmouth	Mar 1971

Displacement, tons: 96 standard; 123 full load
Dimensions, feet (metres): 103 × 18.9 × 5.8 *(31.4 × 5.8 × 1.8)*
Main machinery: 2 Paxman 12YJCM diesels; 5000 hp *(3.73 MW)* sustained; 2 shafts
Speed, knots: 24
Complement: 23
Guns: 2 Oerlikon 20 mm.
Radars: Surface search: Decca 916; I band.

Comment: *Panquiaco* launched on 22 July 1970, *Ligia Elena* on 25 August 1970. Hull of welded mild steel and upperworks of welded or buck-bolted aluminium alloy. Vosper fin stabiliser equipment. Both vessels undergoing major repairs in a Panama shipyard from September 1992. Should be back in service in 1993/94.

PANQUIACO   *1987*

3 MSB 5 CLASS (COASTAL PATROL CRAFT/MINESWEEPERS)

ex-*MSB 25*   ex-*MSB 28*   ex-*MSB 41*

Displacement, tons: 44 full load
Dimensions, feet (metres): 57.2 × 15.5 × 4 *(17.4 × 4.7 × 1.2)*
Main machinery: 2 Packard 2D850 diesels; 600 hp *(448 kW)*; 2 shafts
Speed, knots: 12
Complement: 6
Guns: 1—12.7 mm MG.
Radars: Surface search: Raytheon 1900; I band.
Sonars: Hydroscan Mk 24; active; high frequency.

Comment: Built between 1952 and 1956. Served in the canal area until 1992 and were transferred from US to Panama in March 1993 after refits. Wooden hulls.

Ex-MSB 41   *1988, Giorgio Arra*

1 SWIFTSHIPS 65 ft TYPE (COASTAL PATROL CRAFT)

Name	No	Builders	Commissioned
COMANDANTE TORRIJOS	P 201 (ex-GC 16)	Swiftships Inc, USA	July 1982

Displacement, tons: 35 full load
Dimensions, feet (metres): 65 × 18.5 × 6 *(19.8 × 5.6 × 1.8)*
Main machinery: 2 Detroit 12V-71TA diesels; 840 hp *(627 kW)* sustained; 2 shafts
Speed, knots: 21
Complement: 8
Guns: 1—12.7 mm MG.
Radars: Surface search: Decca 110; I band.

Comment: Aluminium hull. Second of class sunk in 1989.

TORRIJOS   1988

1 WORK BOAT

FLAMENCO (ex-*Scheherazade*) P 304 (ex-WB 831)

Comment: Transferred from US to Panama 22 July 1992.

4 LCM 8 CLASS

COIBA   CEBACO   BASTIMENTO   SAN MIGUEL

Displacement, tons: 118 full load
Dimensions, feet (metres): 73.5 × 21 × 5.2 *(22.4 × 6.4 × 1.6)*
Main machinery: 4 GM 6-71 diesels; 348 hp *(260 kW)* sustained; 2 shafts
Speed, knots: 10
Complement: 6

Comment: Used for patrol and logistic duties with converted superstructure and bows giving increased berthing, thereby extending endurance. Unarmed. Three transferred from US 1972, one deleted in 1986, two more acquired. Two badly damaged in December 1989 (one was sunk) but both have been salvaged and repaired.

LCM 8 (converted)   1989

AUXILIARIES

Note: There is also a support ship *Carlos Guzman Baules*, commissioned in March 1992.

1 SUPPORT CRAFT

NAOS (ex-*Erline*) P 303 (ex-RV 821)

Displacement, tons: 120 full load
Dimensions, feet (metres): 105 × 20.7 × 5.9 *(32 × 6.3 × 1.8)*
Main machinery: 2 diesels; 2 shafts
Speed, knots: 10. **Range, miles:** 1100 at 10 kts

Comment: Built by Equitable, New Orleans in 1965. Served as a support/research craft at the US Underwater Systems establishment at Bermuda. Transferred from US in July 1992.

LAND-BASED MARITIME AIRCRAFT

Numbers/Type: 4 CASA C-212 Aviocar.
Operational speed: 190 kts *(353 km/h)*.
Service ceiling: 24 000 ft *(7315 m)*.
Range: 1650 nm *(3055 km)*.
Role/Weapon systems: Coastal patrol aircraft for EEZ protection and anti-smuggling duties. Sensors: APS-128 radar, limited ESM. Weapons: ASW; 2 × Mk 44/46 torpedoes. ASV; 2 × rocket or machine gun pods.

Numbers/Type: 1 Pilatus Britten-Norman Islander.
Operational speed: 150 kts *(280 km/h)*.
Service ceiling: 18 900 ft *(5760 m)*.
Range: 1500 nm *(2775 km)*.
Role/Weapon systems: Coastal surveillance duties. Sensors: Search radar. Weapons: Unarmed.

PAPUA NEW GUINEA

Senior Officers

Commander Defence Forces:
  Brigadier Robert Dadimo
Director Maritime Operations:
  Lieutenant Colonel P Molean

Personnel

(a) 1994: 430
(b) Voluntary

Bases

Port Moresby (HQ PNGDF and PNGDF Landing Craft Base); Lombrum (Manus) (being improved with Australian assistance) Buka and Alotau (one Pacific Forum Patrol Craft at each)

Prefix to Ships' Names

HMPNGS

Mercantile Marine

Lloyd's Register of Shipping:
  90 vessels of 47 474 tons gross

DELETION

1992 *Madang*

PATROL FORCES

4 PACIFIC FORUM TYPE (LARGE PATROL CRAFT)

Name	No	Builders	Commissioned
TARANGAU	01	Australian Shipbuilding Industries	16 May 1987
DREGER	02	Australian Shipbuilding Industries	31 Oct 1987
SEEADLER	03	Australian Shipbuilding Industries	29 Oct 1988
BASILISK	04	Australian Shipbuilding Industries	1 July 1989

Displacement, tons: 162 full load
Dimensions, feet (metres): 103.3 × 26.6 × 6.9 *(31.5 × 8.1 × 2.1)*
Main machinery: 2 Caterpillar 3516TA diesels; 4400 hp *(3.3 MW)* sustained; 2 shafts
Speed, knots: 20. **Range, miles:** 2500 at 12 kts
Complement: 17 (3 officers)
Guns: 1 GAM-BO1 20 mm. 2—7.62 mm MGs.
Radars: Surface search: Furuno 1011; I band.

Comment: Contract awarded in 1985 to Australian Shipbuilding Industries (Hamilton Hill, West Australia) under Australian Defence co-operation. These are the first, third, sixth and seventh of the class and the only ones to be armed. Training and support provided by the Australian Navy. Others of the class belong to Vanuatu, Western Samoa, Solomon Islands, Cook Islands, Micronesia, Tonga and Marshall Islands.

DREGER   12/1990, James Goldrick

AUXILIARIES

2 LANDING CRAFT (LCH)

Name	No	Builders	Commissioned
SALAMAUA	31	Walkers Ltd, Maryborough	19 Oct 1973
BUNA	32	Walkers Ltd, Maryborough	7 Dec 1973

Displacement, tons: 310 light; 503 full load
Dimensions, feet (metres): 146 × 33 × 6.5 *(44.5 × 10.1 × 1.9)*
Main machinery: 2 GM diesels; 2 shafts
Speed, knots: 10. **Range, miles:** 3000 at 10 kts
Complement: 15 (2 officers)
Military lift: 150 tons approx
Guns: 2—12.7 mm MGs.
Radars: Navigation: Racal Decca RM 916; I band.

Comment: Transferred from Australia in 1975. Underwent extensive refits 1985-86.

SALAMAUA   *12/1990, James Goldrick*

2 LANDING CRAFT (LCVP)

01   02

Displacement, tons: 12 full load
Dimensions, feet (metres): 39.7 × 13.1 × 3 *(12.1 × 4 × 0.9)*
Main machinery: 2 diesels; 150 hp *(110 kW)*; 2 shafts
Speed, knots: 9

Comment: Acquired from Australia in 1975.

LCVP 01   *12/1990, James Goldrick*

LAND-BASED MARITIME AIRCRAFT

Numbers/Type: 6 GAF N22B Missionmaster.
Operational speed: 168 kts *(311 km/h)*.
Service ceiling: 21 000 ft *(6400 m)*.
Range: 730 nm *(1352 km)*.
Role/Weapon systems: Coastal surveillance and transport duties. Sensors: Search radar. Weapons: Unarmed.

Missionmaster   *1991*

GOVERNMENT CRAFT

1 BUOY TENDER

SEPURA

Displacement, tons: 944
Speed, knots: 12

Comment: Built by Sing Koon Seng Yard, Singapore. Completed 14 December 1982. Government owned, civilian manned.

SEPURA   *1990, van Ginderen Collection*

4 LANDING CRAFT

BURTIDE   BURCREST   BURSEA   BURWAVE

Displacement, tons: 725 full load
Dimensions, feet (metres): 122 × 29.5 × 7.9 *(37.2 × 9 × 2.4)*
Main machinery: 2 Deutz MWM BA6M816 diesels; 930 hp(m) *(684 kW)* sustained; 2 shafts
Speed, knots: 9. **Range, miles:** 1800 at 9 kts
Complement: 18

Comment: Built at Sing Koon Seng Yard, Singapore. Completed April-September 1981. Government owned, civilian manned. Not part of PNGDF, but occasionally used by the Armed Forces. Can carry about 500 tons cargo.

2 PILOT/PATROL CRAFT

DAVARA   NANCY DANIEL

Comment: Pilot craft of 12 and 8.2 m built by FBM Marine and delivered in March 1989.

PARAGUAY

Headquarters' Appointments

Commander-in-Chief of the Navy:
  Vice Admiral Eduardo González Petit
Chief of the Naval Staff:
  Rear Admiral Flavio Alcibiades Abadie Gaona

Personnel

(a) 1994: 3680 including Coast Guard and 500 marines (50 per cent conscripts)
(b) 12 months' national service

Training

Specialist training is done with Argentina (Operation Sirena), Brazil (Operation Ninfa) and USA (Operation Unitas).

Bases

Base Naval de Bahía Negra (BNBN) (on upper Paraguay river)
Base Aeronaval de Pozo Hondo (BANPH) (on upper Pilcomayo river)
Base Naval de Saltos del Guairá (BNSG) (on upper Parana river)
Base Naval de Ciudad del Este (BNCE) (on Parana river)
Base Naval de Encarnación (BNE) (on Parana river)
Base Naval de Ita-Piru (BNIP) (on Parana river)

Marine Corps

BIM 1 (COMIM). BIM 2 (Bahía Negra). BIM 3 (Cuartel Gral del Comando de la Armada). BIM 4 (Prefectura Gral Naval). BIM 5 (BNBN - BANPH - BNIP). BIM 8 (BNSG - BNCE - BNE).

Coast Guard

Prefectura General Naval

Prefix to Ships' Names

Type designators only used

Mercantile Marine

Lloyd's Register of Shipping:
  31 vessels of 31 344 tons gross

PATROL FORCES

2 RIVER DEFENCE VESSELS

Name	No	Builders	Commissioned
PARAGUAY	C 1	Odero, Genoa	May 1931
HUMAITA	C 2	Odero, Genoa	May 1931

Displacement, tons: 636 standard; 865 full load
Dimensions, feet (metres): 231 × 35 × 5.3 *(70 × 10.7 × 1.7)*
Main machinery: 2 boilers; 2 Parsons turbines; 3800 hp *(2.83 MW)*; 2 shafts
Speed, knots: 17. **Range, miles:** 1700 at 16 kts
Complement: 86
Guns: 4—4.7 in *(120 mm)*. 3—3 in *(76 mm)*. 2—40 mm. 2—20 mm *(Paraguay only)*.
Mines: 6.
Radars: Navigation *(Paraguay)*; I band.

Comment: Both refitted in 1975. Have 0.5 in side armour plating and 0.3 in on deck.

HUMAITA   *9/1993*

PARAGUAY   *5/1991, Paraguay Navy*

1 ITAIPÚ CLASS (RIVER DEFENCE VESSEL)

Name	No	Builders	Commissioned
ITAIPÚ	P 05 (ex-P 2)	Arsenal de Marinha, Rio de Janeiro	2 Apr 1985

Displacement, tons: 365 full load
Dimensions, feet (metres): 151.9 × 27.9 × 4.6 *(46.3 × 8.5 × 1.4)*
Main machinery: 2 MAN V6V16/18TL diesels; 1920 hp(m) *(1.41 MW)*; 2 shafts
Speed, knots: 14. **Range, miles:** 6000 at 12 kts
Complement: 40 (9 officers)
Guns: 1 Bofors 40 mm/60. 2—81 mm mortars. 6—12.7 mm MGs.
Radars: Navigation: I band.
Helicopters: Platform for 1 HB 350B or equivalent.

Comment: Ordered late 1982. Launched 16 March 1984. Same as Brazilian Roraima class.

ITAIPÚ   *6/1990, Paraguay Navy*

3 BOUCHARD CLASS (PATROL SHIPS)

Name	No	Builders	Commissioned
NANAWA (ex-*Bouchard* M 7)	P 02 (ex-P 01, ex-M 1)	Rio Santiago Naval Yard	27 Jan 1937
CAPITAN MEZA (ex-*Seaver* M 12)	P 03 (ex-P 02, ex-M 2)	Hansen, San Fernando	20 May 1939
TENIENTE FARINA (ex-*Py* M 10)	P 04 (ex-P 03, ex-M 3)	Rio Santiago Naval Yard	1 July 1939

Displacement, tons: 450 standard; 620 normal; 650 full load
Dimensions, feet (metres): 197 × 24 × 8.5 *(60 × 7.3 × 2.6)*
Main machinery: 2 sets MAN 2-stroke diesels; 2000 hp(m) *(1.47 MW)*; 2 shafts
Speed, knots: 16. **Range, miles:** 6000 at 12 kts
Complement: 70
Guns: 4 Bofors 40 mm/60 (2 twin). 2—12.7 mm MGs.
Mines: 1 rail.
Radars: Navigation: I band.

Comment: Former Argentinian minesweepers of the Bouchard class. Launched on 20 March 1936, 24 August 1938, 31 March 1938 respectively. Transferred from the Argentine Navy to the Paraguayan Navy; *Nanawa* commissioned 14 March 1964; *Teniente Farina* and *Capitan Meza*, 6 May 1968.

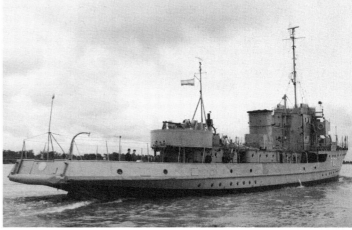

CAPITAN MEZA   *8/1992*

NANAWA   *6/1990, Paraguay Navy*

1 RIVER PATROL CRAFT

Name	No	Builders	Commissioned
CAPITAN CABRAL (ex-*Triunfo*)	P 01 (ex-P 04, ex-A 1)	Werf-Conrad, Haarlem	1908

Displacement, tons: 180 standard; 206 full load
Dimensions, feet (metres): 107.2 × 23.5 × 9.8 *(32.7 × 7.2 × 3)*
Main machinery: 1 Caterpillar 3408 diesel; 360 hp *(269 kW)*; 1 shaft
Speed, knots: 9
Complement: 47
Guns: 1 Bofors 40 mm/60. 2 Oerlikon 20 mm. 2—12.7 mm MGs.

Comment: Former tug. Launched in 1907. Of wooden construction and with a single boiler and steam reciprocating engine. Stationed on Upper Paraña River and still in excellent condition. Vickers guns were replaced, and a diesel engine fitted by Arsenal de Marina in 1984.

CAPITAN CABRAL   *6/1990, Paraguay Navy*

9 + 2 RIVER PATROL CRAFT

P 07-P 17

Displacement, tons: 18 full load
Dimensions, feet (metres): 48.2 × 10.2 × 4.6 *(14.7 × 3.1 × 1.4)*
Main machinery: 1 diesel; 200 hp(m) *(147 kW)*; 1 shaft
Speed, knots: 12
Complement: 4
Guns: 2—12.7 mm MGs.

Comment: Built by Arsenal de Marina, Paraguay. One launched in 1989, then two each year up to 1994.

P 08   *3/1991, Paraguay Navy*

6 TYPE 701 CLASS (RIVER PATROL CRAFT)

P 101   102   103   104   105   106

Displacement, tons: 15 full load
Dimensions, feet (metres): 42.5 × 12.8 × 3 *(13 × 3.9 × 0.9)*
Main machinery: 2 GM diesels; 500 hp *(373 kW)*; 2 shafts
Speed, knots: 20
Complement: 7
Guns: 2—12.7 mm MGs.

Comment: Built by Sewart Inc, Berwick. Transferred by USA, two in December 1967, three in September 1970 and one in March 1971.

P 104   *6/1992, Paraguay Navy*

LAND-BASED MARITIME AIRCRAFT (FRONT LINE)

Numbers/Type: 5 Cessna U 206.
Operational speed: 167 kts *(309 km/h)*.
Service ceiling: 20 000 ft *(6100 m)*.
Range: 775 nm *(1435 km)*.
Role/Weapon systems: Fixed-wing MR for short-range operations. Sensors: Visual reconnaissance. Weapons: Unarmed.

Numbers/Type: 2 Helibras HB 350B Esquilo
Operational speed: 125 kts *(232 km/h)*.
Service ceiling: 10 000 ft *(3050 m)*.
Range: 390 nm *(720 km)*.
Role/Weapon systems: Support helicopter for riverine patrol craft. Delivered in July 1985.

AUXILIARIES

1 LSM 1 CLASS (CONVERTED TENDER)

Name	No	Builders	Commissioned
BOQUERON (ex-Argentinian Corrientes, ex-US LSM 86)	BC 1	Brown SB Co, Houston	13 Oct 1944

Displacement, tons: 1095 full load
Dimensions, feet (metres): 203.5 × 33.8 × 8 *(62 × 10.3 × 2.4)*
Main machinery: 2 Fairbanks-Morse 38D8-1/8-10 diesels; 3540 hp *(2.64 MW)*; 2 shafts
Speed, knots: 13. **Range, miles:** 4100 at 12 kts
Complement: 66
Guns: 2 Bofors 40 mm (twin). 4 Oerlikon 20 mm.
Helicopters: Platform for 1 medium support type.

Comment: Converted at Navyard, Buenos Aires during 1968. Transferred as a gift from Argentina 13 January 1972. Light Forces Tender with helicopter deck added aft.

BOQUERON   *1990, Paraguay Navy*

1 TRAINING SHIP/TRANSPORT

Name	No	Builders	Commissioned
GUARANI	—	Tomas Ruiz de Velasco, Bilbao	Feb 1968

Measurement, tons: 714 gross; 1047 dwt
Dimensions, feet (metres): 240.3 × 36.3 × 11.9 *(73.6 × 11.1 × 3.7)*
Main machinery: 1 MWM diesel; 1300 hp(m) *(956 kW)*; 1 shaft
Speed, knots: 13
Complement: 21
Cargo capacity: 1000 tons

Comment: Refitted in 1975 after a serious fire in the previous year off the coast of France. Used to spend most of her time acting as a freighter on the Asunción-Europe run, commercially operated for the Paraguayan Navy. Since 1991 she has only been used for river service Asunción-Montevideo.

GUARANI   *3/1988, van Ginderen Collection*

1 RIVER TRANSPORT

TENIENTE HERREROS (ex-*Presidente Stroessner*) T 1

Displacement, tons: 150 full load
Dimensions, feet (metres): 124 × 29.5 × 7.2 *(37.8 × 9 × 2.2)*
Main machinery: 2 MWM diesels; 330 hp(m) *(243 kW)*
Speed, knots: 10
Military lift: 120 tons

Comment: Built by Arsenal de Marina in 1964.

TENIENTE HERREROS   *5/1991, Paraguay Navy*

1 SURVEY VESSEL

LANCHA ECOGRAFA

Comment: Built in 1957. Displacement 50 tons with a crew of seven.

2 LCU 501 CLASS

BT 1 (ex-US *YFB 82*)   **BT 2** (ex-US *YFB 86*)

Displacement, tons: 309 full load
Main machinery: 3 Gray Marine 64 YTL diesels; 675 hp *(504 kW)*; 3 shafts
Speed, knots: 10
Military lift: 120 tons

Comment: Built in 1944 and converted in 1958-60. Leased by the US in June 1970 and by sale 11 February 1977. Used as ferries.

BT 1   *1991, Paraguay Navy*

4 DREDGERS

Name	No	Displacement	Launched	Officers	Crew
ASUNCIÓN	RP 1	107 tons	1908	1	27
PROGRESO	D 1	140 tons	1907	2	28
DRAGA (ex-*Teniente O C Saguier*)	D 2	110 tons	1957	2	17
—	—	550 tons	1988	2	35

Comment: *Draga* is also used for survey work.

1 FLOATING DOCK

DF 1 (Ex-US *AFDL 26*)

Comment: Built 1944, leased March 1965. Purchased 11 February 1977. Lift 1000 tons.

TUGS

4 COASTAL TUGS

R 2   R 4   R 6   R 7

Displacement, tons: 70 full load
Dimensions, feet (metres): 65 × 16.4 × 7.5 *(19.8 × 5 × 2.3)*
Main machinery: 1 Caterpillar 3408 diesel; 360 hp *(269 kW)*; 1 shaft
Speed, knots: 9

Comment: Harbour tugs transferred under MAP in the 1960s and 1970s. Details given are for *R 4*. The others are smaller 20 ton vessels.

1 YTL TUG

ANGOSTURA R 5 (ex-YTL 211)

Displacement, tons: 82 full load
Dimensions, feet (metres): 64 × 16.4 × 9.2 *(19.5 × 5 × 2.8)*
Main machinery: 1 Scania DSI 14 M03 diesel; 357 hp *(266 kW)*; 1 shaft
Speed, knots: 9

Comment: Built by Robert Jacob Inc in 1942. Sold to Paraguay 11 February 1977. Refitted at Arsenal de Marina in 1992.

ANGOSTURA   *4/1992, Paraguay Navy*

PERU

Headquarters' Appointments

Commander of the Navy:
  Admiral Alfredo Arnaiz Ambrosiani
Chief of the Naval Staff:
  Vice Admiral Ricardo Villaran Tapia
Chief of Naval Operations:
  Vice Admiral Rolando Rabines Cardoso
Flag Officer Commanding Marines:
  Rear Admiral Carlos Zagazeta Martinez

Personnel

(a) 1994: 26 500 (2500 officers)
(b) 2 years' national service

Bases and Organisation

There are Five Naval Zones: 1st Piura, 2nd Callao, 3rd Arequipa, 4th Puerto Maldonado, 5th Iquitos
Pacific Naval Force (HQ Callao)
Amazon River Force (HQ Iquitos)
Lake Titicaca Patrol Force (HQ at Puno)
Callao—Main naval base; dockyard with shipbuilding capacity, 1 dry dock, 3 floating docks, 1 floating crane; training schools
Iquitos—River base for Amazon Flotilla; small building yard, repair facilities, floating dock
La Punta (naval academy), San Lorenzo (submarine base), Chimbote, Paita, Talara, Puno (Lake Titicaca), Madre de Dios (river base), Piura, El Salto, Bayovar, Pimental, Pacasmayo, Salavenry, Mollendo, Matarani, Ilo, Puerto Maldonado, Inapari, Pucallpa and Estrecha.

Marines

There is one brigade of 3000 men, armed with amphibious vehicles (twin Oerlikon, 88 mm rocket launchers) and armoured cars. Headquarters at Ancon. First Battalion—Guarnicion de Marina; Second Battalion—Guardia Chalaca.

Strength of the Fleet

Type	Active
Submarines—Patrol	8
Cruisers	1 (1)
Destroyer	1
Frigates	4
Fast Attack Craft—Missile	6
Patrol Craft	5
River Gunboats	4
Landing Ships	4
Transports	2
Oil Tankers	8
Survey and Research Ships	6
Tugs	11
Water Tanker	1
Hospital Craft	2
Torpedo Recovery Vessel	1
Floating Docks	5
Coast Guard	16

Prefix to Ships' Names

BAP (Buque Armada Peruana). PC (Coastal Patrol). PL (Lake Patrol). PP (Port Patrol). PF (River Patrol).

Coast Guard

A separate service set up in 1975 with a number of light forces transferred from the Navy.

Mercantile Marine

Lloyd's Register of Shipping:
  640 vessels of 410 934 tons gross

DELETIONS

Submarines

1992 *La Pedrera*
1993 *Iquique*

Destroyers

1991 *Diez Canseco, Villar, Galvez*
1992 *Quiñones*
1993 *Palacios*

Patrol Forces

1993 *Rio Inambari, Rio Manu*

Auxiliaries

1991 *Independencia, Franco*
1993 *Parinas, ABA 330*

Coast Guard

1993 *Rio Majes*

PENNANT LIST

Submarines		Patrol Forces		Auxiliaries		Coast Guard	
SS 31	Casma	CF 11	Amazonas	ACA 110	Mantilla	PC 223	Rio Chira
SS 32	Antofagasta	CF 12	Loreto	ACA 111	Colayeras	PC 225	Rio Pativilca
SS 33	Pisagua	CF 13	Marañon	ACP 118	Noguera	PC 227	Rio Locumba
SS 34	Chipana	CF 14	Ucayali	ACP 119	Gauden	PC 241	Rio Tumbes
SS 35	Islay	CM 21	Velarde	ARB 120	Mejia	PC 242	Rio Piura
SS 36	Arica	CM 22	Santillana	ARB 121	Huerta	PC 243	Rio Nepeña
SS 41	Dos de Mayo	CM 23	De los Heros	ARB 123	Rios	PC 244	Rio Tambo
SS 42	Abtao	CM 24	Herrera	ARB 124	Franco	PC 245	Rio Ocoña
		CM 25	Larrea	ARB 126	Duenas	PC 246	Rio Huarmey
		CM 26	Sanchez Carrillon	ARB 128	Olaya	PC 247	Rio Zaña
Cruisers		PF 274	Rio Tambopata	ARB 129	Selendon	PP 230	La Punta
		PL 290	Rio Ramis	ATC 131	Ilo	PP 231	Rio Chillon
CH 81	Almirante Grau	PL 291	Rio Ilave	ATC 132	Matarina	PP 232	Rio Santa
CH 84	Aguirre	PL 292	Rio Azangaro	ATP 150	Bayovar	PP 235	Rio Viru
		MP 147	Lagarto	ATP 152	Talara	PP 236	Rio Lurin
Destroyer				ATP 158	Zorritos	PP 237	Rio Surco
				ATP 159	Lobitos		
DM 74	Ferré			AMB 160	Unanue		
				AH 172	Stiglich		
				AH 175	Carrillo		
Frigates		**Amphibious Forces**		AH 176	Melo		
				ABH 302	Morona		
FM 51	Meliton Carvajal	DT 141	Paita	ABH 306	Puno		
FM 52	Manuel Villavicencio	DT 142	Pisco	ART 322	San Lorenzo		
FM 53	Montero	DT 143	Callao				
FM 54	Mariategui	DT 144	Eten				

SUBMARINES

6 CASMA (TYPE 209) CLASS (TYPE 1200)

Name	No	Builders	Laid down	Launched	Commissioned
CASMA	SS 31	Howaldtswerke, Kiel	15 July 1977	31 Aug 1979	19 Dec 1980
ANTOFAGASTA	SS 32	Howaldtswerke, Kiel	3 Oct 1977	19 Dec 1979	20 Feb 1981
PISAGUA	SS 33	Howaldtswerke, Kiel	15 Aug 1978	19 Oct 1980	12 July 1983
CHIPANA	SS 34	Howaldtswerke, Kiel	1 Nov 1978	19 May 1981	20 Sep 1982
ISLAY	SS 35	Howaldtswerke, Kiel	15 Mar 1971	11 Oct 1973	29 Aug 1974
ARICA	SS 36	Howaldtswerke, Kiel	1 Nov 1971	5 Apr 1974	21 Jan 1975

Displacement, tons: 1185 surfaced; 1290 dived
Dimensions, feet (metres): 183.7 × 20.3 × 17.9
  (56 × 6.2 × 5.5)
Main machinery: Diesel-electric; 4 MTU 12V 493 AZ80 GA31L
  diesels; 2400 hp(m) *(1.76 MW)* sustained; 4 Siemens alter-
  nators; 1.7 MW; 1 Siemens motor; 4600 hp(m) *(3.38 MW)*
  sustained; 1 shaft
Speed, knots: 11 surfaced/snorting; 21.5 dived
Range, miles: 240 at 8 kts
Complement: 35 (5 officers) *(Islay* and *Arica);* 31 (others)

Torpedoes: 8—21 in *(533 mm)* tubes. 14 Whitehead A184; dual
  purpose; wire-guided; active/passive homing to 25 km
  (13.7 nm) at 24 kts; 17 km *(9.2 nm)* at 38 kts; warhead
  250 kg. Swim-out discharge.
Countermeasures: ESM: Radar warning.
Fire control: Sepa Mk 3 or Signaal Sinbad M8/24 *(Casma* and
  Antofagasta).
Radars: Surface search: Thomson-CSF Calypso; I band.
Sonars: Atlas Elektronik CSU 3; active/passive search and
  attack; medium/high frequency.
  Thomson Sintra DUUX 2C or Atlas Elektronik PRS 3; passive
  ranging.

Programmes: First pair ordered 1969. Two further boats ordered
  12 August 1976 and two more ordered 21 March 1977.
  Designed by Ingenieurkontor, Lübeck for construction by
  Howaldtswerke, Kiel and sale by Ferrostaal, Essen all acting as
  a consortium.
Modernisation: Sepa Mk 3 fire control fitted progressively from
  1986. A184 torpedoes supplied from 1990.
Structure: A single-hull design with two ballast tanks and forward and after trim tanks. Fitted with snort and remote
  machinery control. The single screw is slow revving, very high
  capacity batteries with GRP lead-acid cells and battery cooling—by Wilh Hagen and VARTA. Fitted with two periscopes
  and Omega receiver. Foreplanes retract. Diving depth, 250 m
  (820 ft).
Operational: Endurance, 50 days.

ANTOFAGASTA   *1993, Peruvian Navy*

2 ABTAO CLASS

Name	No	Builders	Laid down	Launched	Commissioned
DOS DE MAYO (ex-*Lobo*)	SS 41	General Dynamics (Electric Boat), Groton, Connecticut	12 May 1952	6 Feb 1954	14 June 1954
ABTAO (ex-*Tiburon*)	SS 42	General Dynamics (Electric Boat), Groton, Connecticut	12 May 1952	27 Oct 1953	20 Feb 1954

Displacement, tons: 825 standard; 1400 dived
Dimensions, feet (metres): 243 × 22 × 14 *(74.1 × 6.7 × 4.3)*
Main machinery: Diesel-electric; 2 GM 12-278A diesels;
  2400 hp *(1.8 MW)*; 2 motors; 2 shafts
Speed, knots: 16 surfaced; 10 dived
Range, miles: 5000 at 10 kts surfaced
Complement: 40

Guns: 1—5 in *(127 mm)*/25; manual control; line of sight range.
Torpedoes: 6—21 in *(533 mm)* (4 bow, 2 stern) tubes. West-
  inghouse Mk 37 Type; typically active/passive homing to 8 km
  (4.4 nm) at 24 kts; warhead 150 kg.
Countermeasures: ESM: Radar warning.
Radars: Navigation: SS-2A; I band.
Sonars: Thomson Sintra Eledone 1102/5; active/passive inter-
  cept search and attack; medium frequency.

Programmes: They are of modified US Mackerel class. One
  deleted in 1990 and a second in 1993.
Modernisation: New batteries shipped in 1981. Since then
  engineering and electrical systems have been modernised and
  Eledone sonar fitted.
Operational: Used for training; reduced diving depth.

ABTAO   *1992, Peruvian Navy*

CRUISERS

2 DE RUYTER CLASS

Name	No	Builders	Laid down	Launched	Commissioned
ALMIRANTE GRAU (ex-HrMs *De Ruyter*)	CH 81	Wilton-Fijenoord, Schiedam	5 Sep 1939	24 Dec 1944	18 Nov 1953
AGUIRRE (ex-HrMs *De Zeven Provinciën*)	CH 84	Rotterdamse Droogdok Maatschappij	19 May 1939	22 Aug 1950	17 Dec 1953

Displacement, tons: 9529 standard; 12 165 full load *(Grau)*
9850 standard; 12 250 full load *(Aguirre)*
Dimensions, feet (metres): 609 × 56.7 × 22
(185.6 × 17.3 × 6.7) (length 624.5 *(190.3)* *(Grau)*)
Flight deck, feet (metres): 115 × 56 *(35 × 17)* *(Aguirre)*
Main machinery: 4 Werkspoor-Yarrow boilers; 2 De Schelde-Parsons turbines; 85 000 hp *(62.5 MW)*; 2 shafts
Speed, knots: 32. **Range, miles:** 7000 at 12 kts
Complement: 953 (49 officers)

Missiles: SSM: 8 Aerospatiale MM 38 Exocet *(Grau only)* ❶; inertial cruise; active radar homing to 42 km *(23 nm)* at 0.9 Mach; warhead 165 kg; sea-skimmer.
Guns: 8 Bofors 6 in *(152 mm)*/53 (4 twin) (4 in *Aguirre*) ❷; 60° elevation; 15 rounds/minute to 26 km *(14 nm)*; weight of shell 46 kg.
6 Bofors 57 mm/60 (3 twin) ❸ (these guns removed from *Grau*); 90° elevation; 130 rounds/minute to 14 km *(7.7 nm)*; weight of shell 2.6 kg.
6 Bofors 40 mm/70 (4 in *Aguirre*) ❹; 90° elevation; 300 rounds/minute to 12 km *(6.6 nm)*; weight of shell 0.96 kg. Removed from *Grau* during modernisation—reported still not back at the end of 1991.
Depth charges: 2 racks.
Countermeasures: Decoys: 2 Dagaie and 1 Sagaie chaff launchers *(Grau)*.
Combat data systems: Signaal Sewaco PE *(Grau)*.
Fire control: 2 *(Grau)* or 1 *(Aguirre)* Lirod 8 optronic directors ❺.
Radars: Air search: Signaal LW 08 *(Grau)* ❻; D band. Signaal LW 02 *(Aguirre)* ❼; D band.
Surface search/target indication: Signaal DA 08 *(Grau)* ❽; E/F band. Signaal DA 02 *(Aguirre)* ❾; E/F band.
Navigation: Signaal ZW 03 *(Aguirre)*; I/J band. Racal Decca 1226 *(Grau)*; I band.
Fire control: Signaal WM25 *(Grau)* ❿; I/J band (for 6 in guns); range 46 km *(25 nm)*.
Two Signaal M45 *(Aguirre)* ⓫; I/J band. One Signaal M25 *(Aguirre)* ⓬; I/J band.
Signaal STIR *(Grau)* ⓭; I/J/K band; range 140 km *(76 nm)* for 1 m² target.
Sonars: CWE 10N *(Aguirre)*; CWE 610 *(Grau)*; hull-mounted; active search; medium frequency.

Helicopters: 3 Agusta ASH-3D Sea Kings *(Aguirre)* ⓮.

Programmes: *Grau* transferred by purchase from Netherlands 7 March 1973 and *Aguirre* bought August 1976. *Grau* commissioned in Peruvian Navy 23 May 1973. After sale *Aguirre* was taken in hand by her original builders for conversion to a helicopter cruiser. Conversion completed 31 October 1977. In 1986 *Aguirre* assumed the name *Almirante Grau* and the former *Almirante Grau* became *Proyecto 01*, while refitting in Amsterdam. Former names were resumed as soon as *Grau* started sea trials in November 1987.
Modernisation: *Grau* taken in hand for a two and a half year modernisation at Amsterdam Dry Dock Co in March 1985. This was to include reconditioning of mechanical and electrical engineering systems, fitting of SSM and SAM, replacement of electronics and fitting of one CSEE Sagaie and two Dagaie launchers. In 1986 financial constraints limited the work but much had been done to update sensors and fire control equipment. *Grau* sailed for Peru 23 January 1988 without her secondary gun armament, to be completed at Sima Yard, Callao, but lack of funds has so far prevented further work. *Aguirre* had her boilers retubed and underwent major refit completing in mid-1986. In 1994 the plan is to retrofit Exocets from the Daring class into *Grau* to replace the Otomat launchers.

AGUIRRE (Scale 1 : 1800), Ian Sturton

ALMIRANTE GRAU (Scale 1 : 1800), Ian Sturton

ALMIRANTE GRAU 1993, Peruvian Navy

Structure: *Aguirre* Terrier missile system replaced by hangar (67 × 54 ft) and flight deck built from midships to the stern. Second landing spot on hangar roof.

Operational: *Aguirre* helicopters carry AM 39 Exocet missiles. *Aguirre* was in reserve in 1992/93 with only a caretaker crew, but is still listed in the operational Fleet in 1994.

AGUIRRE 1987

DESTROYER

1 DARING CLASS

Name	No	Builders	Laid down	Launched	Commissioned
FERRÉ (ex-*Decoy*)	DM 74	Yarrow, Glasgow	22 Sep 1946	29 Mar 1949	28 Apr 1953

Displacement, tons: 2800 standard; 3600 full load
Dimensions, feet (metres): 390 × 43 × 18
   (118.9 × 13.1 × 5.5)
Main machinery: 2 Foster-Wheeler boilers; 650 psi *(45.7 kg/ cm sq)*; 850°F *(454°C)*; 2 English Electric turbines; 54 000 hp *(40 MW)*; 2 shafts
Speed, knots: 32. **Range, miles:** 3000 at 20 kts
Complement: 297

Missiles: SSM: 8 Aerospatiale MM 38 Exocet ❶; inertial cruise; active radar homing to 42 km *(23 nm)* at 0.9 Mach; warhead 165 kg; sea-skimmer.
Guns: 6 (3 twin) *(Ferré)* ❷ or 4 (2 twin) *(Palacios)* Vickers 4.5 in *(114 mm)*/45 Mk 6; 80° elevation; 20 rounds/minute to 19 km *(10.4 nm)*; weight of shell 25 kg.
   4 Breda 40 mm/70 (2 twin) ❸; 85° elevation; 300 rounds/ minute to 12.5 km *(6.8 nm)*; weight of shell 0.96 kg.
Radars: Air/surface search: Plessey AWS 1 ❹; E/F band; range 110 km *(60 nm)*.
   Navigation: Decca; I band.
   Fire control: TSF forward; Signaal aft ❺; I/J band.

Helicopters: Platform only.

Programmes: Purchased from UK in 1969 and refitted by Cammell Laird, Birkenhead.
Modernisation: A helicopter deck was fitted in the 1970s.
Operational: One of the class deleted in 1993. The Exocet missiles are to be fitted in *Almirante Grau*.

FERRÉ   (Scale 1 : 1200), Ian Sturton

FERRÉ   2/1988

FRIGATES

4 MELITON CARVAJAL (LUPO) CLASS

Name	No	Builders	Laid down	Launched	Commissioned
MELITON CARVAJAL	FM 51	Fincantieri, Riva Trigoso	8 Aug 1974	17 Nov 1976	5 Feb 1979
MANUEL VILLAVICENCIO	FM 52	Fincantieri, Riva Trigoso	6 Oct 1976	7 Feb 1978	25 June 1979
MONTERO	FM 53	SIMA, Callao	Oct 1978	8 Oct 1982	25 July 1984
MARIATEGUI	FM 54	SIMA, Callao	1979	8 Oct 1984	10 Oct 1987

Displacement, tons: 2208 standard; 2500 full load
Dimensions, feet (metres): 371.3 × 37.1 × 12.1
   (113.2 × 11.3 × 3.7)
Main machinery: CODOG; 2 GE/Fiat LM 2500 gas turbines; 50 000 hp *(37.3 MW)* sustained; 2 GMT A 230.20 M diesels; 8000 hp(m) *(5.88 MW)* sustained; 2 shafts; cp props
Speed, knots: 35. **Range, miles:** 3450 at 20.5 kts
Complement: 185 (20 officers)

Missiles: SSM: 8 OTO Melara/Matra Otomat Mk 2 (TG 1) ❶; active radar homing to 80 km *(43.2 nm)* at 0.9 Mach; warhead 210 kg; sea-skimmer for last 4 km *(2.2 nm)*.
SAM: Selenia Elsag Albatros octuple launcher ❷; 8 Aspide; semi-active radar homing to 13 km *(7 nm)* at 2.5 Mach; height envelope 15-5000 m *(49.2-16 405 ft)*; warhead 30 kg.
Guns: 1 OTO Melara 5 in *(127 mm)*/54 ❸; 85° elevation; 45 rounds/minute to 16 km *(8.7 nm)*; weight of shell 32 kg.
   4 Breda 40 mm/70 (2 twin) ❹; 85° elevation; 300 rounds/ minute to 12.5 km *(6.8 nm)*; weight of shell 0.96 kg.
Torpedoes: 6—324 mm ILAS (2 triple) tubes ❺. Probably White-head A244; anti-submarine; active/passive homing to 7 km *(3.8 nm)* at 33 kts; warhead 34 kg (shaped charge).
Countermeasures: Decoys: 2 Breda 105 mm SCLAR 20-barrelled trainable launchers ❻; multi-purpose; chaff to 5 km *(2.7 nm)*; illuminants to 12 km *(6.6 nm)*; HE bombardment.
ESM: Radar intercept.
Combat data systems: Selenia IPN-10 action data automation.

MONTERO   (Scale 1 : 1200), Ian Sturton

Fire control: 2 Elsag Mk 10 Argo with NA-21 directors. Dardo system for 40 mm.
Radars: Air search: Selenia RAN 10S ❼; E/F band; range 155 km *(85 nm)*.
Surface search: Selenia RAN 11LX ❽; D/I band; range 82 km *(45 nm)*.
Navigation: SMA 3 RM 20R; I band; range 73 km *(40 nm)*.
Fire control: Two RTN 10X ❾; I/J band.
   Two RTN 20X ❿; I/J band; range 12.8 km *(7 nm)* (for Dardo).
Sonars: EDO 610E; hull-mounted; active search and attack; medium frequency.

Helicopters: 1 Agusta AB 212ASW ⓫.

Programmes: *Montero* and *Mariategui* were the first major warships to be built on the Pacific Coast of South America, although some equipment was provided by Fincantieri.
Structure: In the design for the pair built by Servicios Industriales de la Marina, Callao (SIMA) the two 40 mm guns are mounted higher and reloading of the Albatros is by hand not power. Also the hangar is fixed and the flight deck does not come flush to the stern of the ship.
Operational: Helicopter provides an over-the-horizon targeting capability for SSM. HIFR facilities fitted in 1989 allow refuelling of Sea King helicopters.

MONTERO   1993, Peruvian Navy

SHIPBORNE AIRCRAFT

Note: There are also six Agusta 109A and four Bell 206B assault helicopters for Marines.

Numbers/Type: 6 Agusta AB 212ASW.
Operational speed: 106 kts *(196 km/h)*.
Service ceiling: 14 200 ft *(4330 m)*.
Range: 230 nm *(425 km)*.
Role/Weapon systems: ASW and surface search helicopter for smaller escorts. Sensors: Selenia search radar, Bendix ASQ-18 dipping sonar, ECM. Weapons: ASW; 2 × Mk 46 or 244/S torpedoes or depth bombs.

AB 212   *8/1993, N Sifferlinger*

Numbers/Type: 3 Agusta-Sikorsky ASH-3D Sea King.
Operational speed: 120 kts *(222 km/h)*.
Service ceiling: 12 200 ft *(3720 m)*.
Range: 630 nm *(1165 km)*.
Role/Weapon systems: ASW helicopter; embarked in *Aguirre*. Sensors: Selenia search radar, ASQ-18 dipping sonar, sonobuoys. Weapons: ASW; 4 × Mk 46 or 244/S torpedoes or depth bombs or mines. ASV; 2 × AM 39 Exocet missiles.

LAND-BASED MARITIME AIRCRAFT (FRONT LINE)

Notes: (1) There are also three MI-8T transport helicopters.
(2) Three EMB-111 maritime surveillance aircraft ordered in 1993.

Numbers/Type: 5 Beechcraft Super King Air 200T.
Operational speed: 282 kts *(523 km/h)*.
Service ceiling: 35 000 ft *(10 670 m)*.
Range: 2030 nm *(3756 km)*.
Role/Weapon systems: Coastal surveillance and EEZ patrol duties. Sensors: Search radar, cameras. Weapons: Unarmed.

PATROL FORCES

6 VELARDE (PR-72P) CLASS (FAST ATTACK CRAFT—MISSILE)

Name	No	Builders	Launched	Commissioned
VELARDE	CM 21	SFCN, France	16 Sep 1978	25 July 1980
SANTILLANA	CM 22	SFCN, France	11 Sep 1978	25 July 1980
DE LOS HEROS	CM 23	SFCN, France	20 May 1979	17 Nov 1980
HERRERA	CM 24	SFCN, France	16 Feb 1979	10 Feb 1981
LARREA	CM 25	SFCN, France	12 May 1979	16 June 1981
SANCHEZ CARRILLON	CM 26	SFCN, France	28 June 1979	14 Sep 1981

Displacement, tons: 470 standard; 560 full load
Dimensions, feet (metres): 210 × 27.4 × 5.2 *(64 × 8.4 × 2.6)*
Main machinery: 4 SACM AGO 240 V16 M7 diesels; 22 200 hp(m) *(16.32 MW)* sustained; 4 shafts
Speed, knots: 37. **Range, miles:** 2500 at 16 kts
Complement: 36 (accommodation for 46)

Missiles: SSM: 4 Aerospatiale MM 38 Exocet; inertial cruise; active radar homing to 42 km *(23 nm)* at 0.9 Mach; warhead 165 kg; sea-skimmer.
Guns: 1 OTO Melara 3 in *(76 mm)*/62; 85° elevation; 85 rounds/minute to 16 km *(8.7 nm)*; weight of shell 6 kg.
2 Breda 40 mm/70 (twin); 85° elevation; 300 rounds/minute to 12.5 km *(6.8 nm)*; weight of shell 0.96 kg.
Fire control: CSEE Panda director. Vega system.
Radars: Surface search: Thomson-CSF Triton; G band; range 33 km *(18 nm)* for 2 m² target.
Navigation: Racal Decca 1226; I band.
Fire control: Thomson-CSF/Castor II; I/J band; range 15 km *(8 nm)* for 1 m² target.

Programmes: Ordered late 1976. Hulls of *Velarde*, *De Los Heros*, *Larrea* sub-contracted to Lorient Naval Yard, the others being built at Villeneuve-la-Garenne. Classified as corvettes.

HERRERA   *1987, Peruvian Navy*

2 MARAÑON CLASS (RIVER GUNBOATS)

Name	No	Builders	Commissioned
MARAÑON	CF 13 (ex-CF 401)	John I Thornycroft & Co Ltd	July 1951
UCAYALI	CF 14 (ex-CF 402)	John I Thornycroft & Co Ltd	June 1951

Displacement, tons: 365 full load
Dimensions, feet (metres): 154.8 wl × 32 × 4 *(47.2 × 9.7 × 1.2)*
Main machinery: 2 British Polar M 441 diesels; 800 hp *(597 kW)*; 2 shafts
Speed, knots: 12. **Range, miles:** 6000 at 10 kts
Complement: 40 (4 officers)
Guns: 2—3 in *(76 mm)*/50. 1 Bofors 40 mm/60. 4 Oerlikon 20 mm (2 twin).

Comment: Ordered early in 1950 and both laid down in early 1951. Employed on police duties in Upper Amazon. Superstructure of aluminium alloy. Based at Iquitos.

UCAYALI   *1993, Peruvian Navy*

MARAÑON   *1987, Peruvian Navy*

2 LORETO CLASS (RIVER GUNBOATS)

Name	No	Builders	Commissioned
AMAZONAS	CF 11 (ex-CF 403)	Electric Boat Co, Groton	1935
LORETO	CF 12 (ex-CF 404)	Electric Boat Co, Groton	1935

Displacement, tons: 250 standard
Dimensions, feet (metres): 145 × 22 × 4 *(44.2 × 6.7 × 1.2)*
Main machinery: 2 diesels; 750 hp(m) *(551 kW)*; 2 shafts
Speed, knots: 15. **Range, miles:** 4000 at 10 kts
Complement: 35 (5 officers)
Guns: 2—3 in *(76 mm)*. 4 Bofors 40 mm/60. 1 Oerlikon 20 mm.

Comment: Launched in 1934. In Upper Amazon Flotilla, based at Iquitos.

LORETO   *1987, Peruvian Navy*

3 LAKE PATROL CRAFT

Name	No	Builders	Commissioned
RIO RAMIS	PL 290	American SB&D, Miami	15 Sep 1982
RIO ILAVE	PL 291	American SB&D, Miami	20 Nov 1982
RIO AZANGARO	PL 292	American SB&D, Miami	4 Feb 1983

Displacement, tons: 5 full load
Dimensions, feet (metres): 32.8 × 11.2 × 2.6 *(10 × 3.4 × 0.8)*
Main machinery: 2 Perkins diesels; 480 hp *(358 kW)*; 2 shafts
Speed, knots: 29. **Range, miles:** 450 at 28 kts
Complement: 4
Guns: 1—12.7 mm MG.
Radars: Surface search: Raytheon 2800; I band.

Comment: On Lake Titicaca. GRP hulls.

2 RIVER PATROL CRAFT

LAGARTO MD 147   **RIO TAMBOPATA PF 274**

Comment: Based at Madre de Dios. Commissioned in 1975. Armed with one MG and capable of 18 kts. Two others of the class deleted.

AMPHIBIOUS FORCES

Note: Reported that orders may be placed for up to three 300 ft LSLs to be locally built.

4 PAITA (TERREBONNE PARISH) CLASS (LSTs)

Name	No	Builders	Commissioned
PAITA (ex-USS *Walworth County* LST 1164)	DT 141	Ingalls SB	26 Oct 1953
PISCO (ex-USS *Waldo County* LST 1163)	DT 142	Ingalls SB	17 Sep 1953
CALLAO (ex-USS *Washoe County* LST 1165)	DT 143	Ingalls SB	30 Nov 1953
ETEN (ex-USS *Traverse County* LST 1160)	DT 144	Bath Iron Works	19 Dec 1953

Displacement, tons: 2590 standard; 5800 full load
Dimensions, feet (metres): 384 × 55 × 17 *(117.1 × 16.8 × 5.2)*
Main machinery: 4 GM 16-278A diesels; 6000 hp *(4.48 MW)*; 2 shafts
Speed, knots: 15. **Range, miles:** 15 000 at 9 kts
Complement: 116
Military lift: 2000 tons; 395 troops
Guns: 6 Bofors 40 mm/60 (3 twin).
Radars: Surface search: Raytheon SPS 10; G band.
Navigation: I band.

Comment: All transferred from US on loan 7 August 1984, recommissioned 4 March 1985. Have small helicopter platform. Original 3 inch guns replaced by 40 mm. *Pisco* is non-operational providing spares for the others. Lease extended to 1994.

PAITA   *9/1991, Giorgio Arra*

SURVEY AND RESEARCH SHIPS

Note: The converted fish factory ship *Humboldt* is a civilian fisheries research ship.

1 SOTOYOMO CLASS

Name	No	Builders	Commissioned
UNANUE (ex-USS *Wateree* ATA 174)	AMB 160 (ex-AH 170)	Levingston SB Co, Orange, Texas	20 July 1944

Displacement, tons: 534 standard; 860 full load
Dimensions, feet (metres): 143 × 33.9 × 13 *(43.6 × 10.3 × 4)*
Main machinery: Diesel-electric; 2 GM 12-278A diesels; 2200 hp *(1.64 MW)*; 2 generators; 1 motor; 1500 hp *(1.12 MW)*; 1 shaft
Speed, knots: 13
Complement: 31 (3 officers)

Comment: Former US auxiliary ocean tug. Laid down on 5 October 1943, launched on 18 November 1943. Purchased from the USA in November 1961 under MAP. Refitted in 1985 for operation in the Antarctic.

2 VAN STRAELEN CLASS

Name	No	Builders	Commissioned
CARRILLO (ex-*van Hamel*)	AH 175	De Vries, Amsterdam	14 Oct 1960
MELO (ex-*van der Wel*)	AH 176	De Vries, Amsterdam	6 Oct 1961

Displacement, tons: 169 full load
Dimensions, feet (metres): 108.6 × 18.2 × 5.2 *(33.1 × 5.6 × 1.6)*
Main machinery: 2 GM diesels; 1100 hp(m) *(808 kW)* sustained; 2 shafts
Speed, knots: 13
Complement: 17 (2 officers)

Comment: Both built as inshore minesweepers. Acquired 23 February 1985 for conversion with new engines and survey equipment.

MELO   *1989, Peruvian Navy*

1 RIVER SURVEY VESSEL

Name	No	Builders	Commissioned
STIGLICH	AH 172	McLaren, Niteroi	1981

Displacement, tons: 230 full load
Dimensions, feet (metres): 112.2 × 25.9 × 5.6 *(34.2 × 7.9 × 1.7)*
Main machinery: 2 Detroit 12V-71TA diesels; 840 hp *(616 kW)* sustained; 2 shafts
Speed, knots: 15
Complement: 28 (2 officers)

Comment: Based at Iquitos for survey work on the Upper Amazon.

STIGLICH   *1992, Peruvian Navy*

2 INSHORE SURVEY CRAFT

Name	No	Builders	Commissioned
—	EH 173	SIMA, Chimbote	June 1979
MACHA	EH 174	SIMA, Chimbote	Apr 1982

Displacement, tons: 23 *(EH 173)*; 53 *(EH 174)* full load
Dimensions, feet (metres): 64.9 × 17.1 × 3 *(19.8 × 5.2 × 0.9) (EH 174)*
Speed, knots: 13
Complement: 8 (2 officers) *(EH 174)*; 4 (1 officer) *(EH 173)*

Comment: *Macha* has a side scan sonar for plotting bottom contours. EH (Embarcacion Hidrográfica) 173 may be non-operational.

AUXILIARIES

Note: All auxiliaries may be used for commercial purposes if not required for naval use.

1 ILO CLASS (TRANSPORT)

Name	No	Builders	Commissioned
ILO	ATC 131	SIMA, Callao	Dec 1971

Displacement, tons: 18 400 full load
Measurement, tons: 13 000 dwt
Dimensions, feet (metres): 507.7 × 67.3 × 27.2 *(154.8 × 20.5 × 8.3)*
Main machinery: 1 Burmeister & Wain 6K47 diesel; 11 600 hp(m) *(8.53 MW)*; 1 shaft
Speed, knots: 15.6
Complement: 60
Cargo capacity: 13 000 tons

Comment: Sister ship *Rimac* is on permanent commercial charter.

ILO   *12/1990, Hartmut Ehlers*

1 MATARINA CLASS (TRANSPORT)

Name	No	Builders	Commissioned
MATARINA (ex-*Amazonas*)	ATC 132	SIMA, Callao	1975

Displacement, tons: 15 297 full load
Measurement, tons: 10 430 dwt
Dimensions, feet (metres): 597.8 × 75.1 × 45.2 *(182.2 × 22.9 × 13.8)*
Main machinery: 1 Sulzer 6RND-76/2 diesel; 1 shaft
Speed, knots: 16.5
Complement: 65
Cargo capacity: 10 430 tons

Comment: Acquired in 1993.

1 TALARA CLASS (REPLENISHMENT TANKER)

Name	No	Builders	Commissioned
TALARA	ATP 152	SIMA, Callao	23 Jan 1978

Displacement, tons: 30 000 full load
Measurement, tons: 25 000 dwt
Dimensions, feet (metres): 561.5 × 82 × 31.2 *(171.2 × 25 × 9.5)*
Main machinery: 2 Burmeister & Wain 6K47EF diesels; 12 000 hp(m) *(8.82 MW)*; 1 shaft
Speed, knots: 15.5
Cargo capacity: 35 662 cu m

Comment: Capable of underway replenishment at sea. *Talara* laid down 1975, launched 9 July 1976. *Bayovar* of this class laid down 9 July 1976, launched 18 July 1977 having been originally ordered by Petroperu (State Oil Company) and transferred to the Navy while building. Sold back to Petroperu in 1979 and renamed *Payavacu*. A third, *Trompeteros*, of this class has been built for Petroperu.

1 FREIGHTING TANKER

Name	No	Builders	Commissioned
BAYOVAR (ex-*Loreto II*, ex-*St Vincent*)	ATP 150	Ch N de la Ciotat	1976

Displacement, tons: 15 175 light; 107 320 full load
Dimensions, feet (metres): 821.9 × 116.5 × 63.7 *(250.5 × 35.5 × 19.4)*
Main machinery: 1 Sulzer 7RND90 diesel; 20 300 hp(m) *(14.92 MW)*; 1 shaft
Speed, knots: 16

Comment: Launched in 1976. Acquired by Peruvian Navy from Peruvian civilian company in 1986. Sold in 1992 but chartered back until further notice.

BAYOVAR   *1986, Peruvian Navy*

2 SECHURA CLASS (SUPPORT TANKERS)

Name	No	Builders	Commissioned
ZORRITOS	ATP 158	SIMA, Callao	1959
LOBITOS	ATP 159	SIMA, Callao	1966

Displacement, tons: 8700 full load
Measurement, tons: 4300 gross; 6000 dwt
Dimensions, feet (metres): 385 × 52 × 21.2 *(117.4 × 15.9 × 6.4)*
Main machinery: 1 Burmeister & Wain 562-VTF-115 diesels; 2400 hp(m) *(1.76 MW)*; 1 shaft
Speed, knots: 12
Radars: Navigation: Decca; I band.

Comment: Alongside at sea refuelling capability. Two Scotch boilers with Thornycroft oil burners for cargo tank cleaning.

ZORRITOS   *5/1986, Surgeon Lieutenant P J Buxton RN*

4 HARBOUR TANKERS (FUEL/WATER)

MANTILLA ACA 110 (ex-US *YW 122*)   NOGUERA ACP 118 (ex-US *YO 221*)
COLAYERAS ACA 111 (ex-US *YW 128*)   GAUDEN ACP 119 (ex-US *YO 171*)

Displacement, tons: 1235 full load
Dimensions, feet (metres): 174 × 32 × 13.3 *(52.3 × 9.8 × 4.1)*
Main machinery: 1 GM diesel; 560 hp *(418 kW)*; 1 shaft
Speed, knots: 8
Cargo capacity: 200 000 gal

Comment: YW 122 transferred to Peru July 1963; YO 221 January 1975; YO 171 20 January 1981; YW 128 26 January 1985.

GAUDEN   *1988, Peruvian Navy*

1 TORPEDO RECOVERY VESSEL

Name	No	Builders	Commissioned
SAN LORENZO	ART 322	Lürssen/Burmeister	Sep 1981

Displacement, tons: 58 standard; 65 full load
Dimensions, feet (metres): 82.7 × 18.4 × 5.6 *(25.2 × 5.6 × 1.7)*
Main machinery: 2 MTU 8V 396 TC82 diesels; 1740 hp(m) *(1.28 MW)* sustained; 2 shafts
Speed, knots: 19. **Range, miles:** 500 at 15 kts
Complement: 9

Comment: Can carry four long or eight short torpedoes.

SAN LORENZO   *9/1981, Lürssen Werft*

1 RIVER HOSPITAL CRAFT

Name	No	Builders	Commissioned
MORONA	ABH 302	SIMA, Iquitos	1976

Displacement, tons: 150
Dimensions, feet (metres): 98.4 × 19.6 × 1.5 *(30 × 6 × 0.5)*
Speed, knots: 12

Comment: For service on Peruvian rivers. Two more projected but not built.

MORONA   *1989, Peruvian Navy*

1 LAKE HOSPITAL CRAFT

Name	No	Builders	Commissioned
PUNO (ex-*Yapura*)	ABH 306	Cammell Laird, Birkenhead	1873

Comment: Stationed on Lake Titicaca. 500 grt and has a diesel engine. Sadly the second of the class was finally paid off in 1990 after 119 years service.

PUNO   *1993, Peruvian Navy*

1 WATER TANKER

ABA 332 (ex-113)

Comment: 'Barcasa Cisterna de Aqua' built in Peru 1972. Attached to Amazon Flotilla. Capacity 300 tons.

5 FLOATING DOCKS

ADF 106-110

Displacement, tons: 1900 (*106*); 5200 (*107*); 600 (*108*); 18 000 (*109*); 4500 tons (*110*)

Comment: *106* (ex-US *AFDL 33*) transferred 1959; *107* (ex-US *ARD 8*) transferred 1961; *108* built in 1951; *109* built in 1979; *110* built in 1991.

TUGS

Note: There are also three small harbour tugs *Mejia* ARB 120, *Huertas* ARB 121 and *Duenas* ARB 126.

1 CHEROKEE CLASS (SALVAGE TUG)

Name	No	Builders	Commissioned
GUARDIAN RIOS (ex-USS *Pinto* ATF 90)	ARB 123	Cramp, Philadelphia	1 Apr 1943

Displacement, tons: 1235 standard; 1640 full load
Dimensions, feet (metres): 205 × 38.5 × 17 *(62.5 × 11.7 × 5.2)*
Main machinery: Diesel-electric; 4 GM 12-278 diesels; 4400 hp *(3.28 MW)*; 4 generators; 1 motor; 3000 hp *(2.24 MW)*; 1 shaft
Speed, knots: 16.5. **Range, miles:** 6500 at 16 kts
Complement: 99

Comment: Transferred from US on loan in 1960, sold 17 May 1974. Fitted with powerful pumps and other salvage equipment.

GUARDIAN RIOS   *1993, Peruvian Navy*

Name	No	Builders	Commissioned
OLAYA	ARB 128	Ruhrorter, SW Duisburg	1967
SELENDON	ARB 129	Ruhrorter, SW Duisburg	1967

Measurement, tons: 80 gross
Dimensions, feet (metres): 61.3 × 20.3 × 7.4 *(18.7 × 6.2 × 2.3)*
Main machinery: 1 diesel; 600 hp(m) *(441 kW)*; 1 shaft
Speed, knots: 10

COAST GUARD

Note: Six 40 ft river patrol boats may be provided by the US for drug interdiction.

5 RIO CANETE CLASS (LARGE PATROL CRAFT)

Name	No	Builders	Commissioned
RIO NEPEÑA	PC 243	SIMA, Chimbote	1 Dec 1981
RIO TAMBO	PC 244	SIMA, Chimbote	1982
RIO OCOÑA	PC 245	SIMA, Chimbote	1983
RIO HUARMEY	PC 246	SIMA, Chimbote	1984
RIO ZAÑA	PC 247	SIMA, Chimbote	12 Feb 1985

Displacement, tons: 300 full load
Dimensions, feet (metres): 164 × 24.8 × 5.6 *(50 × 7.4 × 1.7)*
Main machinery: 4 Bazán MAN V8V diesels; 5640 hp(m) *(4.15 MW)*; 2 shafts
Speed, knots: 25. **Range, miles:** 3050 at 17 kts
Complement: 39
Guns: 1 Bofors 40 mm/60. 1 Oerlikon 20 mm.
Radars: Surface search: Decca 1226; I band.

Comment: Have aluminium alloy superstructures. The prototype craft was scrapped in 1990.

RIO TAMBO   *1989, Peruvian Navy*

2 VOSPER TYPE (LARGE PATROL CRAFT)

Name	No	Builders	Commissioned
RIO PATIVILCA	PC 225	Vosper Ltd, Portsmouth	1965
RIO LOCUMBA	PC 227	Vosper Ltd, Portsmouth	1965

Displacement, tons: 100 standard; 130 full load
Dimensions, feet (metres): 109.7 × 21 × 5.7 *(33.5 × 6.4 × 1.7)*
Main machinery: 2 Napier Deltic T38-37 diesels; 6200 hp *(4.62 MW)*; 2 shafts
Speed, knots: 30. **Range, miles:** 1100 at 15 kts
Complement: 25 (4 officers)
Guns: 2 Bofors 40 mm.
Radars: Surface search: Decca 707; I band.

Comment: Of all-welded steel construction with aluminium upperworks. Equipped with Vosper roll damping fins, Decca Type 707 true motion radar, comprehensive radio, up-to-date navigation aids and air-conditioning. A twin rocket projector can be fitted forward instead of gun.

RIO LOCUMBA (old pennant number)   *Peruvian Navy*

1 PGM 71 CLASS (LARGE PATROL CRAFT)

Name	No	Builders	Commissioned
RIO CHIRA (ex-US *PGM 111*)	PC 223 (ex-PC 12)	SIMA, Callao	June 1972

Displacement, tons: 130 standard; 147 full load
Dimensions, feet (metres): 101 × 21 × 6 *(30.8 × 6.4 × 1.8)*
Main machinery: 2 GM diesels; 1450 hp *(1.08 MW)*; 2 shafts
Speed, knots: 18.5. **Range, miles:** 1500 at 10 kts
Complement: 15
Guns: 1 Bofors 40 mm/60. 2 Oerlikon 20 mm. 2—12.7 mm MGs.
Radars: Surface search: Raytheon 1500; I band.

Comment: Transferred from the Navy in 1975.

RIO CHIRA   *1987, Peruvian Navy*

2 RIVER PATROL CRAFT

Name	No	Builders	Commissioned
RIO TUMBES	PC 241 (ex-P 251)	Viareggio, Italy	5 Sep 1960
RIO PIURA	PC 242 (ex-P 252)	Viareggio, Italy	5 Sep 1960

Displacement, tons: 37 full load
Dimensions, feet (metres): 65.7 × 17 × 3.2 *(20 × 5.2 × 1)*
Main machinery: 2 GM 8V-71 diesels; 460 hp *(344 kW)* sustained; 2 shafts
Speed, knots: 18
Guns: 2 Bofors 40 mm.

Comment: Ordered in 1959.

RIO PIURA   *1975, Peruvian Navy*

6 PORT PATROL CRAFT

LA PUNTA PP 230	RIO SANTA PP 232	RIO LURIN PP 236
RIO CHILLON PP 231	RIO VIRU PP 235	RIO SURCO PP 237

Displacement, tons: 43 full load
Dimensions, feet (metres): 61 × 17.3 × 5.6 *(18.6 × 5.3 × 1.7)*
Main machinery: 2 GM 12V-71TA diesels; 840 hp *(616 kW)* sustained; 2 shafts
Speed, knots: 25
Guns: 2 Oerlikon 20 mm.

Comment: Built by McLaren, Niteroi in 1980-82. PP 231 transferred to the Navy as a survey craft but has been returned.

PHILIPPINES

Headquarters' Appointments

Flag Officer-in-Command:
Vice Admiral Virgilio Q Marcelo
Vice Commander:
Commodore Plaridel C Garcia
Chief of Naval Staff:
Commodore Jose P Divinagracia
Commander Fleet:
Commodore Dario T Fajardo
Commandant Coast Guard:
Commodore Carlos L Agustin Jr
Commandant Marines:
Brigadier Eduardo T Cabanlig

Diplomatic Representation

Defence Attaché in London:
Colonel C P Garcia, Jr

Personnel

1994: 13 560 Navy; 3391 Coast Guard; 7500 Marines

Organisation

The Navy is organised into three major commands: Fleet, Coast Guard and Marines. There are seven Naval districts, eight Coast Guard districts, within which there are 42 stations and 148 detachments. Coast Guard units are under operational control of Naval district commanders when conducting counter-insurgency operations. The Navy and the Coast Guard are interchangeable and often share duties. In addition there are three Naval construction battalions and 26 SEAL teams deployed in Naval districts.

Marine Corps

Marines comprise three tactical brigades composed of ten tactical battalions, one support brigade, composed of a guard and an admin battalion, deployed as follows: six battalions in Luzon, seven in Mindanao and one in Palawan.

Naval Bases

Main: Cavite, Mactan (under construction).
Stations: Zamboanga, Poro, Cebu, Davao, Legaspi, Bonifacio, Tacloban, San Miguel.

Prefix to Ships' Names

BRP: Barko Republika Pilipinas

Strength of the Fleet (1 January 1994)

Type	Active	Building
Frigates	1	—
Corvettes	9	—
Fast Attack Craft	—	(6)
Large Patrol Craft	5	4
Coastal Patrol Craft	20	10
LST/LSV Transports	8	1
LCM/LCU/RUC/LCVP	38	—
Command Ship	1	—
Repair Ship	1	—
Tankers	4	—
Survey and Research Ships	5	1
Coast Guard		
Tenders	5	—
Patrol Craft	59	—

New Construction

By 1996 it is planned to acquire six FAC missile/gun, 35 PCF 70 class, two PSMH and four LSMs. An MCM programme of four vessels will begin in FY 1997. There are also intentions to build a frigate and three corvettes by the end of the century.

Mercantile Marine

Lloyd's Register of Shipping:
1469 vessels of 8 466 171 tons gross

DELETIONS

Frigate

1993 *Andres Bonifacio*

Corvette

1994 *Quezon*

Patrol Craft

1991 *PCF 304* (sunk)
1992 *Negros Oriental*
1993 *Mount Samat*

Amphibious Ships (Transports)

1991 *Samar Oriental* (sunk), 1 LCM 6 (sunk)
1992 *Ilocos Norte, Tawi-Tawi*
1993 *Northern Samar, South Cotobato*

Auxiliaries

1991 *Bataan, Narra, Explorer*
1994 *Mactan*

PENNANT LIST

Frigate

PF 11	Rajah Humabon

Corvettes

PS 19	Miguel Malvar
PS 20	Magat Salamat
PS 22	Sultan Kudarat
PS 23	Datu Marikudo
PS 28	Cebu
PS 29	Negros Occidental
PS 31	Pangasinan
PS 32	Iloilo
PS 74	Rizal

Patrol Forces

PG 101	Kagitingan
PG 102	Bagong Lakas
PG 104	Bagong Silang
PG 140	Emilo Aguinaldo
PG 141	General Antonio Luna
PG 840	Conrado Yap
PG 844	Jose Artiaga Jr
PG 845	Leon Tadina
PG 847	Leopoldo Regis
PG 849	Loreto Danipog
PG 853	Sulpicio Hernandez

Auxiliaries

LT 57	Sierra Madre
LT 86	Zamboanga Del Sur
LT 501	Laguna
LT 504	Lanao Del Norte
LT 507	Benguet
LT 516	Kalinga Apayao
LC 550	Bacolod City
LC 551	Cagayan De Oro City
AT 25	Ang Pangulo
AW 33	Lake Bulusan
AW 34	Lake Paoay
AF 72	Lake Taal
TP 77	Ang Pinuno
AF 78	Lake Buhi
AP 617	Yakal

Coast Guard

AE 46	Cape Bojeador
AE 59	Badjao
PG 61	Agusan
PG 62	Catanduanes
PG 63	Romblon
PG 64	Palawan
AT 71	Mangyan
AU 75	Bessang Pass
AE 79	Limasawa
AG 89	Kalinga
AU 100	Tirad Pass

FRIGATES

Note: *Rajah Lakandula*, paid off in 1988, is still afloat as an alongside HQ and depot ship where she is planned to remain until the end of the century.

1 CANNON CLASS

Name	No	Builders	Laid down	Launched	Commissioned
RAJAH HUMABON (ex-*Hatsuhi* DE 263, ex-USS *Atherton* DE 169)	PF 11 (ex-PF 78)	Norfolk Navy Yard, Portsmouth, VA	14 Jan 1943	27 May 1943	29 Aug 1943

Displacement, tons: 1390 standard; 1750 full load
Dimensions, feet (metres): 306 × 36.6 × 14
(93.3 × 11.2 × 4.3)
Main machinery: Diesel-electric; 4 GM 16-278A diesels; 6000 hp *(4.5 MW)*; 4 generators; 2 motors; 2 shafts
Speed, knots: 18. **Range, miles:** 10 800 at 12 kts
Complement: 165

Guns: 3 US 3 in *(76 mm)*/50 Mk 22; 85° elevation; 20 rounds/ minute to 12 km *(6.6 nm)*; weight of shell 6 kg.
6 US/Bofors 40 mm/56 (3 twin); 45° elevation; 160 rounds/ minute to 11 km *(5.9 nm)*; weight of shell 0.9 kg.
2 Oerlikon 20 mm/70; 50° elevation; 800 rounds/minute to 2 km.
A/S mortars: 1 Hedgehog Mk 10; range 250 m; warhead 13.6 kg; 24 rockets.
Depth charges: 8 K-gun Mk 6 projectors; range 160 m; warhead 150 kg; 1 rack.
Fire control: Mk 52 GFCS with Mk 51 rangefinder for 3 in guns. 3 Mk 51 Mod 2 GFCS for 40 mm.
Radars: Surface search: Raytheon SPS 5; G/H band; range 37 km *(20 nm)*.
Navigation: RCA/GE Mk 26; I band.
Sonars: SQS 17B; hull-mounted; active search and attack; medium/high frequency.

Programmes: *Hatsuhi* originally transferred by the USA to Japan 14 June 1955 and paid off June 1975 reverting to US Navy. Transferred to Philippines 23 December 1978. Towed to South Korea 1979 for overhaul and modernisation. Recommissioned 27 February 1980. A sister ship *Datu Kalantiaw* lost during Typhoon Clara 20 September 1981.

RAJAH HUMABON

1993, Philippine Navy

CORVETTES

1 AUK CLASS

Name	No	Builders	Commissioned
RIZAL (ex-USS *Murrelet* MSF 372)	PS 74 (ex-PS 69)	Savannah Machine & Foundry Co, GA	21 Aug 1945

Displacement, tons: 1090 standard; 1250 full load
Dimensions, feet (metres): 221.2 × 32.2 × 10.8 *(67.4 × 9.8 × 3.3)*
Main machinery: Diesel-electric; 2 GM 12-278 diesels; 2200 hp *(1.64 MW)*; 2 generators; 2 motors; 2 shafts
Speed, knots: 18. **Range, miles:** 5700 at 16 kts
Complement: 80 (5 officers)

Guns: 2 US 3 in *(76 mm)*/50 Mk 26; 85° elevation; 20 rounds/minute to 12 km *(6.6 nm)*; weight of shell 6 kg.
4 US/Bofors 40 mm/56 (2 twin); 45° elevation; 160 rounds/minute to 11 km *(5.9 nm)*; weight of shell 0.9 kg.
4 Oerlikon 20 mm (2 twin); 50° elevation; 800 rounds/minute to 2 km.
Torpedoes: 3—324 mm US Mk 32 (triple) tubes. Honeywell Mk 44; anti-submarine; active homing to 5.5 km *(3 nm)* at 30 kts; warhead 34 kg.
A/S mortars: 1 Hedgehog Mk 10; range 250 m; warhead 13.6 kg; 24 rockets.
Depth charges: 2 Mk 9 racks.
Radars: Surface search: Raytheon SPS 5C; G/H band.
Navigation: DAS 3; I band.
Sonars: SQS 17B; hull-mounted; active search and attack; high frequency.

Programmes: Transferred from the US to the Philippines on 18 June 1965.
Structure: Upon transfer the minesweeping gear was removed and a second 3 in gun fitted aft; additional anti-submarine weapons also fitted. To be deleted in late 1994.

RIZAL   *1993, Philippine Navy*

8 PCE 827 CLASS

Name	No	Builders	Commissioned
MIGUEL MALVAR (ex-*Ngoc Hoi*, ex-USS *Brattleboro* PCER 852)	PS 19	Pullman Standard Car Co, Chicago	26 May 1944
MAGAT SALAMAT (ex-*Chi Lang II*, ex-USS *Gayety* MSF 239)	PS 20	Winslow Marine Co, Seattle	14 June 1944
SULTAN KUDARAT (ex-*Dong Da II*, ex-USS *Crestview* PCER 895)	PS 22	Willamette Iron & Steel Corporation, Portland	30 Oct 1943
DATU MARIKUDO (ex-*Van Kiep II*, ex-USS *Amherst* PCER 853)	PS 23	Pullman Standard Car Co, Chicago	16 June 1944
CEBU (ex-USS *PCE 881*)	PS 28	Albina E and M Works, Portland, Oregon	31 July 1944
NEGROS OCCIDENTAL (ex-USS *PCE 884*)	PS 29	Albina E and M Works, Portland, Oregon	30 Mar 1944
PANGASINAN (ex-USS *PCE 891*)	PS 31	Willamette Iron & Steel Corporation, Portland	15 June 1944
ILOILO (ex-USS *PCE 897*)	PS 32	Willamette Iron & Steel Corporation, Portland	6 Jan 1945

Displacement, tons: 640 standard; 914 full load
Dimensions, feet (metres): 184.5 × 33.1 × 9.5 *(56.3 × 10.1 × 2.9)*
Main machinery: 2 GM 12-278A diesels; 2200 hp *(1.64 MW)*; 2 shafts
Speed, knots: 15. **Range, miles:** 6600 at 11 kts
Complement: 85 (8 officers)

Guns: 1 US 3 in *(76 mm)*/50; 85° elevation; 20 rounds/minute to 12 km *(6.6 nm)*; weight of shell 6 kg.
2 to 6 US/Bofors 40 mm/56 (single or 1-3 twin); 45° elevation; 160 rounds/minute to 11 km *(5.9 nm)*; weight of shell 0.9 kg.
4 Oerlikon 20 mm/70; 50° elevation; 800 rounds/minute to 2 km.
Radars: Surface search: SPS 50 (PS 23). SPS 21D (PS 19). CRM-NIA-75 (PS 29, 31, 32). SPS 53A (PS 20).
Navigation: RCA SPN 18; I/J band.

Programmes: Five transferred from the US to the Philippines in July 1948 (PS 28-32); PS 22 to South Vietnam from US Navy on 29 November 1961, PS 20 in April 1962, PS 19 on 11 July 1966, and PS 23 in June 1970. PS 19, 20 and 22 to Philippines November 1975 and PS 23 5 April 1976.
Modernisation: PS 19, 22, 31 and 32 refurbished in 1990-91, PS 23 and 28 in 1992, and the last pair in 1993 if funds are available.
Structure: First three were originally fitted as rescue ships (PCER). A/S equipment has now been removed or is inoperable. PS 20 has some minor structural differences having been built as an Admirable class MSF.

PANGASINAN   *10/1989, Mel Back*

CEBU   *1991*

SHIPBORNE AIRCRAFT

Numbers/Type: 8 PADC (MBB) BO 105C.
Operational speed: 145 kts *(270 km/h)*.
Service ceiling: 17 000 ft *(5180 m)*.
Range: 355 nm *(657 km)*.
Role/Weapon systems: Sole shipborne helicopter; some shore-based for SAR; some commando support capability. Purchased at the rate of one per year up to 1992. Sensors: Some fitted with search radar. Weapons: Unarmed.

BO 105C   *1990*

LAND-BASED MARITIME AIRCRAFT

Note: In addition there are two L 4 training aircraft and one Cessna transport.

Numbers/Type: 5 PADC (Pilatus Britten-Norman) Islander.
Operational speed: 150 kts *(280 km/h)*.
Service ceiling: 18 900 ft *(5760 m)*.
Range: 1500 nm *(2775 km)*.
Role/Weapon systems: Short-range MR and SAR aircraft. Purchased at the rate of one per year to 1992. Three more belonging to the Air Force are used for coastal surveillance. Sensors: Search radar, cameras. Weapons: Unarmed.

PATROL FORCES

Note: The Navy operates two Mk 1 (50 ft) and two Mk 3 (65 ft) coastal patrol craft. Details under identical craft operated by the Coast Guard.

0 + (3) LAUNCESTON TYPE (FAST ATTACK CRAFT—GUN)

Displacement, tons: 396 full load
Dimensions, feet (metres): 187 × 27 × 8 *(57 × 8.2 × 2.4)*
Main machinery: 3 MTU 16V 956 TB91 diesels; 11 250 hp(m) *(8.27 MW)* sustained; 3 shafts; cp props
Speed, knots: 30. **Range, miles:** 3500 at 18 kts
Guns: 1 OTO Melara 76 mm/62. 2 Breda 40 mm/70 (twin) compact. 2 Oerlikon 25 mm.
Radars: Surface search/fire control: Signaal WM 22.

Comment: Agreement signed in April 1990 with Launceston Marine, Tasmania for six of the class. Negotiations were then taken over by the Australia Submarine Corporation (ASC) which signed a contract on 21 October 1991 to build three of the craft. The contract is subject to Australian Government approval and financial support, as well as credit guarantees from the weapons systems manufacturers. By early 1994 the contract had been endorsed by the AFP to the Defence Department. The plan is to build the vessels (or at least the first) at ASC Newcastle, which is the former Carrington Slipways, to be delivered by 1996. The propulsion details have changed since the original CODAG proposals.

LAUNCESTON TYPE   *(not to scale), Ian Sturton*

0 + (3) CORMORAN CLASS (FAST ATTACK CRAFT—MISSILE)

Displacement, tons: 384 full load
Dimensions, feet (metres): 185.7 × 24.7 × 6.5 *(56.6 × 7.5 × 2)*
Main machinery: 3 Bazán-MTU 16V 956 TB91 diesels; 11 250 hp(m) *(8.27 MW)* sustained; 3 shafts
Speed, knots: 34
Complement: 32 (5 officers)
Missiles: SSM: 4 Aerospatiale Exocet MM 40.
Guns: 1 OTO Melara 76 mm/62. 2 Breda 40 mm/70 (twin).
Fire control: Alenia NA 21.

Comment: Contract signed with Bazán on 30 September 1991. First of class to be built at San Fernando, Spain and delivered by 1996, the other two to be built at Cavite Shipyard. The contract is subject to Spanish Government approval and financial support, as well as credit guarantees from weapon systems manufacturers. Construction had not started by early 1994 but expenditure had been endorsed by the AFP to the Defence Department.

CORMORAN (Spanish number)   1991

2 + 4 AGUINALDO CLASS (LARGE PATROL CRAFT)

Name	No	Builders	Commissioned
EMILIO AGUINALDO	PG 140	Cavite, Sangley Point	21 Nov 1990
GENERAL ANTONIO LUNA	PG 141	Cavite, Sangley Point	Mar 1994
—	PG 142	Cavite, Sangley Point	Sep 1995
—	PG 143	Cavite, Sangley Point	Mar 1997
—	PG 144	Cavite, Sangley Point	Sep 1998
—	PG 145	Cavite, Sangley Point	Mar 2000

Displacement, tons: 279 full load
Dimensions, feet (metres): 144.4 × 24.3 × 5.2 *(44 × 7.4 × 1.6)*
Main machinery: 4 Detroit 12V-92TA diesels; 2040 hp *(1.52 MW)* sustained; 2 shafts
Speed, knots: 25. **Range, miles:** 1100 at 18 kts
Complement: 58 (6 officers)
Guns: 2 Bofors 40 mm/60. 2 Oerlikon 20 mm. 4—12.7 mm MGs.

Comment: First of class launched 23 June 1984 but only completed in 1990. Second laid down 2 December 1990 and launched in September 1992, and the keel laid of PG 142 in early 1993. The plan is one more every 18 months to a total of six. Steel hulls of similar design to *Tirad Pass* (see Coast Guard). The intention is to upgrade the armament in due course to include a SAM and an OTO Melara 76 mm/62 gun.

EMILIO AGUINALDO   *1993, Philippine Navy*

3 KAGITINGAN CLASS (LARGE PATROL CRAFT)

Name	No	Builders	Commissioned
KAGITINGAN	P 101	Hamelin SY, Germany	9 Feb 1979
BAGONG LAKAS	PG 102 (ex-P 102)	Hamelin SY, Germany	9 Feb 1979
BAGONG SILANG	PG 104 (ex-P 104)	Hamelin SY, Germany	1979

Displacement, tons: 132 full load
Dimensions, feet (metres): 100.3 × 18.6 × 5 *(30.6 × 5.7 × 1.5)*
Main machinery: 2 MTU MB 12V 493 TZ60 diesels; 1360 hp(m) *(1 MW)* sustained; 2 shafts
Speed, knots: 16
Complement: 30 (4 officers)
Guns: 2—30 mm (twin). 4—12.7 mm MGs. 2—7.62 mm MGs.
Radars: Surface search: I band.

Comment: Based at Cavite. P 103 paid off and used for spares.

BAGONG LAKAS   *1993, Philippine Navy*

8 + 10 PCF 70 (HALTER) CLASS (COASTAL PATROL CRAFT)

DF 370-372   DF 374-378

Displacement, tons: 56 full load
Dimensions, feet (metres): 78 × 20 × 5.8 *(23.8 × 6.1 × 1.8)*
Main machinery: 2 Detroit 16V-92TA diesels; 1380 hp *(1.03 MW)* sustained; 2 shafts
Speed, knots: 28. **Range, miles:** 1200 at 12 kts
Complement: 8 (1 officer)
Guns: 1 Breda 25 mm (not fitted).
4—12.7 mm Mk 26 MGs. 2—7.62 mm M60 MGs.
Radars: Surface search: Raytheon; I band.

Comment: First five ordered from Halter Marine in August 1989, a second batch of three in September 1990. Built at Equitable Shipyard, New Orleans. First completed in August 1990, second in December 1990 and then delivered at a rate of one about every three weeks. Ten more are programmed to be built in the Philippines. The aim is for 35 craft (probably now includes Hawk class) divided into five squadrons each based on a support ship and spread through the archipelago. Built to Coast Guard standards with an aluminium hull and superstructure. The main gun may be fitted in due course.

DF 370   *1992, Philippine Navy*

12 SEA HAWK/KILLER (TYPE PK 181) CLASS (COASTAL PATROL CRAFT)

CONRADO YAP PG 840	LEOPOLDO REGIS PG 847	PG 842-3
JOSE ARTIAGA JR PG 844	LORETO DANIPOG PG 849	PG 846
LEON TADINA PG 845	SULPICIO FERNANDEZ PG 853	PG 848
		PG 851-2

Displacement, tons: 74.5 full load
Dimensions, feet (metres): 83.7 × 17.7 × 6.2 *(25.5 × 5.4 × 1.9)*
Main machinery: 2 MTU 16V 638 TB96 diesels; 7200 hp(m) *(5.29 MW)*; 2 shafts
Speed, knots: 41. **Range, miles:** 500 at 20 kts
Complement: 15 (3 officers)
Guns: 1 Bofors 40 mm/60. 2 Oerlikon 20 mm (twin) Mk 16.
Radars: Surface search: I band.

Comment: Built by Korea Tacoma and Hyundai 1975-1978. All transferred from South Korea 19 June 1993. There may be some armament variations. All are to be named in due course.

SEA HAWK PG 852   *1993, Philippine Navy*

AUXILIARIES

Note: All LSTs, LSVs, LCMs and LCUs are classified as Transports.

6 LST 512-1152 CLASS (TRANSPORT SHIPS)

Name	No	Commissioned
ZAMBOANGA DEL SUR (ex-*Cam Ranh*, ex-USS *Marion County* LST 975)	LT 86	3 Feb 1945
LAGUNA (ex-*USNS T-LST 230*)	LT 501	3 Nov 1943
LANAO DEL NORTE (ex-*USNS T-LST 566*)	LT 504	29 May 1944
BENGUET (ex-*USNS Davies County* T-LST 692)	LT 507	10 May 1944
SIERRA MADRE (ex-*Dumagat*, ex-*My Tho*, ex-USS *Harnett County*, AGP 821, ex-*LST 821*)	LT 57 (ex-AL 57)	14 Jan 1944
KALINGA APAYAO (ex-*Can Tho*, ex-USS *Garrett County* AGP 786, ex-LST 786)	LT 516 (ex-AE 516)	28 Aug 1944

Displacement, tons: 1620 standard; 2472 beaching; 4080 full load
Dimensions, feet (metres): 328 × 50 × 14 *(100 × 15.2 × 4.3)*
Main machinery: 2 GM 12-567A diesels; 1800 hp *(1.34 MW)*; 2 shafts
Speed, knots: 10
Complement: Varies—approx 60 to 110 (depending upon employment)
Military lift: 2100 tons. 16 tanks or 10 tanks plus 200 troops

Guns: 6 US/Bofors 40 mm (2 twin, 2 single). 4 Oerlikon 20 mm (in refitted ships).
Radars: Navigation: SPS 53 (LT 87); RCA CR 107 or SPS 21D (remainder).

Programmes: Transferred from US Navy in 1976 with exception of LT 57 and LT 516 which were used as light craft repair ships in South Vietnam and have retained amphibious capability (transferred to Vietnam 1970 and to Philippines 1976, acquired by purchase 5 April 1976). LT 86 transferred (grant aid) 17 November 1975. LT 501 and 504 commissioned in Philippine Navy 8 August 1978 and LT 507 on 18 October 1978.
Modernisation: Several have had major refits including replacement of frames and plating as well as engines and electrics and provision for four 20 mm guns.
Structure: Some of the later ships have tripod masts, others have pole masts.
Operational: All are used for general cargo work in Philippine service. Fourteen were deleted in 1989 and one sank in 1991. Two paid off in 1992 and two in 1993.

LANAO DEL NORTE
1993, Philippine Navy

38 LCM/LCU (TRANSPORT CRAFT)

Comment: Ex-US minor landing craft mostly transferred in the mid-1970s. 11 LCM 6, six LCM 8, eight LCU, 11 RUC and two LCVP. More LCVP may be building at Cavite.

1 ACHELOUS CLASS (REPAIR SHIP)

Name	No	Commissioned
YAKAL (ex-USS *Satyr* ARL 23, ex-*LST 852*)	AP 617 (ex-AR 517)	20 Nov 1944

Displacement, tons: 4342 full load
Dimensions, feet (metres): 328 × 50 × 14 *(100 × 15.2 × 4.3)*
Main machinery: 2 GM 12-567A diesels; 1800 hp *(1.34 MW)*; 2 shafts
Speed, knots: 11.6
Complement: 220 approx
Guns: 4 US/Bofors 40 mm (quad). 10 Oerlikon 20 mm (5 twin).

Comment: Transferred from the US to the Philippines on 24 January 1977 by sale. (Originally to South Vietnam 30 September 1971.) Converted during construction. Extensive machine shop, spare parts stowage, supplies, etc. Second of class paid off in 1992.

ACHELOUS class (old number)
1968, Philippine Navy

2 BACOLOD CITY (FRANK S BESSON) CLASS (LSV TRANSPORTS)

Name	No	Builders	Commissioned
BACOLOD CITY	LC 550	Moss Point Marine	1 Dec 1993
CAGAYAN DE ORO CITY	LC 551	Moss Point Marine	Mar 1994

Displacement, tons: 4265 full load
Dimensions, feet (metres): 272.8 × 60 × 12 *(83.1 × 18.3 × 3.7)*
Main machinery: 2 GM EMD 16-645E2 diesels; 3900 hp *(2.9 MW)* sustained; 2 shafts; bow thruster; 250 hp *(187 kW)*
Speed, knots: 11.6. **Range, miles:** 6000 at 11 kts
Complement: 30 (6 officers)
Military lift: 2280 tons (900 for amphibious operations) of vehicles, containers or cargo, plus 150 troops
Radars: Surface search/navigation: I band.
Helicopters: Platform for 1 light.

Comment: Contract announced by Trinity Marine 3 April 1992 for two ships with an option on a third. Ro-Ro design with 10 500 sq ft of deck space for cargo. Capable of beaching with 4 ft over the ramp on a 1 : 30 offshore gradient with a 900 ton cargo. Similar to US Army vessels but with only a bow ramp. The stern ramp space is used for accommodation for 150 troops and a helicopter platform is fitted over the stern.

BACOLOD CITY
9/1993, Trinity Marine

0 + 1 CHINESE TYPE (LSV)

Displacement, tons: 1560 full load
Dimensions, feet (metres): 279.5 × 44 × 15.1 *(85.2 × 13.4 × 4.6)*
Main machinery: 2 diesels; 2 shafts
Speed, knots: 16
Complement: 45 (5 officers)

Comment: Contract signed in September 1991 with China Shipbuilding Corporation for one LSV with an option on a second. To be built at Guangzhou shipyard. The project has been delayed by lack of funds but was endorsed in 1993 by the AFP to the Defence Department. The original delivery date of 1994 may not be achieved.

1 TRANSPORT VESSEL

Name	No	Builders	Commissioned
ANG PANGULO (ex-*The President*, ex-*Roxas*, ex-*Lapu-Lapu*)	AT 25 (ex-TP 777)	Ishikawajima, Japan	1959

Displacement, tons: 2239 standard; 2727 full load
Dimensions, feet (metres): 257.6 × 42.6 × 21 *(78.5 × 13 × 6.4)*
Main machinery: 2 Mitsui DE642/VBF diesels; 5000 hp(m) *(3.68 MW)*; 2 shafts
Speed, knots: 18. **Range, miles:** 6900 at 15 kts
Complement: 81 (8 officers)
Guns: 2 Oerlikon 20 mm/70 Mk 4 (twin).
Radars: Navigation: RCA CRMN-1A-75; I band.

Comment: Built as war reparation; launched in 1958. Was used as presidential yacht and command ship with accommodation for 50 passengers. Originally named *Lapu-Lapu* after the chief who killed Magellan; renamed *Roxas* on 9 October 1962 after the late Manuel Roxas, the first President of the Philippines Republic, renamed *The President* in 1967 and *Ang Pangulo* in 1975. One 15 ton crane. In early 1987 she was in Hong Kong with a full crew, having not returned to Cavite after the banishment of ex-President Marcos, but since then has been taken on as an attack transport.

ANG PANGULO
1988, Gilbert Gyssels

1 BATAAN CLASS (COMMAND SHIP)

Name	No	Builders	Commissioned
ANG PINUNO	AM 701 (ex-TP 77)	Vosper (Private) Ltd, Singapore	Dec 1975

Displacement, tons: 150 full load
Dimensions, feet (metres): 124.3 × 23.6 × 12.5 *(37.9 × 7.2 × 3.8)*
Main machinery: 3 MTU 12V 538 TB91 diesels; 4600 hp(m) *(3.38 MW)* sustained; 3 shafts
Speed, knots: 30
Complement: 32

Comment: Used as a command ship and has been used before 1986 as a presidential yacht. Sister ship *Bataan* deleted in 1991.

BATAAN   *1984, Gilbert Gyssels*

2 YW TYPE (WATER TANKERS)

LAKE BULUSAN AW 33 (ex-US YW 111, ex-YW 33)
LAKE PAOAY AW 34 (ex-US YW 130, ex-YW 34)

Displacement, tons: 1237 full load
Dimensions, feet (metres): 174 × 32.7 × 13.2 *(53 × 10 × 4)*
Main machinery: 2 GM 8-278A diesels; 1500 hp *(1.12 MW)*; 2 shafts
Speed, knots: 7.5
Complement: 29
Cargo capacity: 200 000 gal
Guns: 1 Bofors 40/60. 1 Oerlikon 20 mm.

Comment: Basically similar to YOG type but adapted to carry fresh water. Transferred from the US to the Philippines on 16 July 1975.

LAKE PAOAY   *1993, Philippine Navy*

2 YOG TYPE (TANKERS)

Name	No	Commissioned
LAKE BUHI (ex-US YOG 73)	AF 78 (ex-YO 78)	1944
LAKE TAAL (ex-US YOG)	AF 72 (ex-YO 72)	1945

Displacement, tons: 447 standard; 1400 full load
Dimensions, feet (metres): 174 × 32.7 × 13.2 *(53 × 10 × 4)*
Main machinery: 2 GM 8-278A diesels; 1500 hp *(1.12 MW)*; 2 shafts
Speed, knots: 8
Complement: 28
Cargo capacity: 6570 barrels dieso and gasoline
Guns: 2 Oerlikon 20 mm/70 Mk 4.

Comment: Former US Navy gasoline tankers. Transferred in July 1967 on loan and by purchase 5 March 1980.

LAKE BUHI   *1993, Philippine Navy*

3 FLOATING DOCKS

YD 200 (ex-*AFDL 24*)   **YD 204** (ex-*AFDL 20*)   **YD 205** (ex-*AFDL 44*)

Comment: Floating steel dry docks built in the USA; all are former US Navy units with YD 200 transferred in July 1948, YD 204 in October 1961 (sale 1 August 1980) and YD 205 in September 1969.
Capacities: YD 205, 2800 tons; YD 200 and YD 204, 1000 tons. In addition there are two floating cranes, YU 206 and YU 207, built in USA in 1944 and capable of lifting 30 tons.

TUGS

4 YTL 422 CLASS

IGOROT (ex-*YTL 572*) YQ 222   **ILONGOT** (ex-*YTL 427*) YQ 225
TAGBANUA (ex-*YTL 429*) YQ 223   **TASADAY** (ex-*YTL 425*) YQ 226

Displacement, tons: 71
Main machinery: 1 diesel; 240 hp *(179 kW)*; 1 shaft
Speed, knots: 10

Comment: Former US Navy 66 ft harbour tugs. YTL 748 was to be transferred but sank on passage. YQ 225 and 226 acquired by sale 1 August 1980.

SURVEY AND RESEARCH SHIPS

Notes: (1) Operated by Coast and Geodetic Survey of Ministry of National Defence.
(2) An 83 m hydrographic ship ordered in April 1990 from Japan. Operated by Mines and Geoscience Bureau.

Name	No	Builders	Commissioned
ARLUNUYA	—	Walkers, Maryborough, Australia	1964
ARINYA	—	Walkers, Maryborough, Australia	1962

Displacement, tons: 255 full load
Dimensions, feet (metres): 101 × 22 × 8 *(30.8 × 6.7 × 2.4)*
Main machinery: 2 GM 6-71 diesels; 348 hp *(260 kW)* sustained; 2 shafts
Speed, knots: 10
Complement: 33 (6 officers)

Comment: Survey ships of same design as Australian *Banks* and *Bass*.

ARLUNUYA TYPE (Australian number)   *1983*

1 SURVEY SHIP

Name	No	Builders	Commissioned
ATYIMBA	—	Walkers, Maryborough, Australia	1969

Displacement, tons: 611 standard; 686 full load
Dimensions, feet (metres): 161 × 33 × 12 *(49.1 × 10 × 3.7)*
Main machinery: 2 Paxman diesels; 1452 hp *(1.08 MW)*; 2 shafts
Speed, knots: 11. **Range, miles:** 5000 at 8 kts
Complement: 54 (8 officers)
Guns: 2 Oerlikon 20 mm.

Comment: Survey ship similar to HMAS *Flinders* with differences in displacement and use of davits aft instead of cranes. Guns may be removed.

ATYIMBA   *1981, van Ginderen Collection*

2 RESEARCH SHIPS

FORT SAN ANTONIO AM 700   **FORT ABAD** AM 701

Comment: Acquired in 1993.

COAST GUARD

Notes: (1) Some of the PCF craft listed are manned by the Navy.
(2) The Coast Guard also operates one LCM 6 (BM 270), one LCU (B 124), one LCVP (BV 182) and a River Utility Craft VU 463.

1 BALSAM CLASS (TENDER)

Name	No	Builders	Commissioned
KALINGA (ex-USCGC *Redbud*, *WAGL 398*, ex-USNS *Redbud*, *T-AKL 398*)	AG 89	Marine Iron & Shipbuilding Co, Duluth	2 May 1944

Displacement, tons: 950 standard; 1041 full load
Dimensions, feet (metres): 180 × 37 × 13 *(54.8 × 11.3 × 4)*
Main machinery: Diesel-electric; 2 Cooper-Bessemer GSB-8 diesels; 1710 hp *(1.28 MW)*; 2 generators; 1 motor; 1200 hp *(895 kW)*; 1 shaft
Speed, knots: 12. **Range, miles:** 3500 at 7 kts
Complement: 53
Guns: 2—12.7 mm MGs.
Radars: Navigation: Sperry SPS 53; I/J band.

Comment: Originally US Coast Guard buoy tender (WAGL 398). Transferred to US Navy on 25 March 1949 as AG 398 and then to the Philippine Navy 1 March 1972. One 20 ton derrick.

KALINGA   *10/1977, Giorgio Arra*

4 BUOY TENDERS

Name	No
CAPE BOJEADOR (ex-US Army *FS 203*)	AE 46 (ex-TK 46)
LIMASAWA (ex-USCGC *Nettle* WAK 129, ex-US Army *FS 169*)	AE 79 (ex-TK 79)
BADJAO (ex-Japanese, ex-US Army *FS 524*)	AE 59 (ex-AS 59)
MANGAYAN (ex-Japanese, ex-US Army *FS 408*)	AT 71 (ex-AE 71, ex-AS 71)

Displacement, tons: 470 standard; 950 full load
Dimensions, feet (metres): 180 × 32 × 10 *(54.9 × 9.8 × 3)*
Main machinery: 2 GM 6-278A diesels; 1120 hp *(836 kW)*; 2 shafts
Speed, knots: 10. **Range, miles:** 4150 at 10 kts
Complement: 50
Cargo capacity: 400 tons
Guns: 12.7 mm (TK 79). 7.62 mm MGs (TK 79).
Radars: Navigation: RCA CRMN 1A 75; I band.

Comment: Former US Army FS 381 Type freight and supply ships. First three are employed as tenders for buoys and lighthouses. *Mangayan* transferred 24 September 1976 by sale. *Limasawa* acquired by sale 31 August 1978. One 5 ton derrick. *Cape Bojeador* paid off in 1988 but was back in service in 1991 after a major overhaul. *Mangayan* reclassified AT in 1993. Masts and superstructures have minor variations.

CAPE BOJEADOR   *1993, Philippine Navy*

2 LARGE PATROL CRAFT (SAR)

Name	No	Builders	Commissioned
TIRAD PASS	AU 100 (ex-SAR 100)	Sumidagawa, Japan	1974
BESSANG PASS	AU 75 (ex-SAR 99)	Sumidagawa, Japan	1974

Displacement, tons: 279 full load
Dimensions, feet (metres): 144.3 × 24.3 × 4.9 *(44 × 7.4 × 1.5)*
Main machinery: 2 diesels; 800 hp(m) *(588 kW)*; 2 shafts
Speed, knots: 27.5
Complement: 32
Guns: 4—12.7 mm (2 twin) MGs.

Comment: Paid for under Japanese war reparations. Similar type building for the Navy as the Aguinaldo class.

TIRAD PASS   *1992, Phillippine Navy*

4 PGM-39 CLASS (LARGE PATROL CRAFT)

Name	No	Builders	Commissioned
AGUSAN (ex-*PGM 39*)	PG 61	Tacoma Boatbuilding Co, Washington	Mar 1960
CATANDUANES (ex-*PGM 40*)	PG 62	Tacoma Boatbuilding Co, Washington	Mar 1960
ROMBLON (ex-*PGM 41*)	PG 63	Peterson Builders, Wisconsin	June 1960
PALAWAN (ex-*PGM 42*)	PG 64	Tacoma Boatbuilding Co, Washington	June 1960

Displacement, tons: 124 full load
Dimensions, feet (metres): 100.3 × 18.6 × 6.9 *(30.6 × 5.7 × 2.1)*
Main machinery: 2 MTU MB 12V 493 TY57 diesels; 2200 hp(m) *(1.6 MW)* sustained; 2 shafts
Speed, knots: 17. **Range, miles:** 1400 at 11 kts
Complement: 26-30
Guns: 2—20 mm. 2—12.7 mm MGs. 1—81 mm mortar.
Radars: Surface search: Alpelco DFR-12; I/J band.

Comment: Steel-hulled craft built under US military assistance programmes. Assigned US PGM-series numbers while under construction. Transferred upon completion. These craft are lengthened versions of the US Coast Guard 95 ft Cape class patrol boat design.

CATANDUANES   *10/1977, Giorgio Arra*

16 PCF 46 CLASS (COASTAL PATROL CRAFT)

DF 326	DB 411	DB 419	DB 429
DF 328	DB 413	DB 422	DB 431-435
DF 330-331	DB 417	DB 427	

Displacement, tons: 15 full load
Dimensions, feet (metres): 45.9 × 14.5 × 3.3 *(14 × 4.4 × 1)*
Main machinery: 2 Cummins diesels; 740 hp *(552 kW)*; 2 shafts
Speed, knots: 25. **Range, miles:** 1000 at 15 kts
Complement: 8
Guns: 2—12.7 mm MGs. 1—7.62 mm M60 MG.
Radars: Surface search: Kelvin Hughes 17; I band.

Comment: Survivors of a class built by De Havilland Marine, Sydney NSW between 20 November 1974 and 8 February 1975 (DF series). In August 1975 further craft of this design (DB series) were ordered from Marcelo Yard, Manila to be delivered 1976-78 at the rate of two per month. By the end of 1976, 25 more had been completed but a serious fire in the shipyard destroyed 14 new hulls and halted production. Some deleted.

DB 435   *1993, Philippine Navy*

12 CUTTERS

CGC 103	CGC 110	CGC 128-130
CGC 107	CGC 115	CGC 132-136

Displacement, tons: 13 full load
Dimensions, feet (metres): 40 × 13.6 × 3 *(12.2 × 4.1 × 0.9)*
Main machinery: 2 Detroit diesels; 560 hp *(418 kW)*; 2 shafts
Speed, knots: 28
Guns: 1—12.7 mm MG. 1—7.62 mm MG.

Comment: Built at Cavite Yard from 1984.

10 PCF 65 (SWIFT Mk 3) CLASS (COASTAL PATROL CRAFT)

DF 325-332   **DF 353-354**

Displacement, tons: 29 standard; 37 full load
Dimensions, feet (metres): 65 × 16 × 3.4 *(19.8 × 4.9 × 1)*
Main machinery: 3 GM 12V-71TI diesels; 840 hp *(616 kW)* sustained; 3 shafts
Speed, knots: 25
Complement: 8
Guns: 2—12.7 mm (twin) MGs. 2—7.62 mm MGs.
Radars: Surface search: Marconi Canada LN 66; I band.

Comment: Improved Swift type inshore patrol boats built by Sewart for the Philippine Navy. Delivered 1972-1976. *DF 353-354* belong to the Navy.

DF 352   *1984, Gilbert Gyssels*

15 PCF 50 (SWIFT Mk 1 and Mk 2) CLASS (COASTAL PATROL CRAFT)

DF 300-303   **DF 305**   **DF 307-316**

Displacement, tons: 22.5 full load
Dimensions, feet (metres): 50 × 13.6 × 4 *(15.2 × 4.1 × 1.2)* (Mk 1) 51.3 × 13.6 × 4 *(15.6 × 4.1 × 1.2)* (Mk 2)
Main machinery: 2 GM 12-71 diesels; 680 hp *(504 kW)* sustained; 2 shafts
Speed, knots: 28. **Range, miles:** 685 at 16 kts
Complement: 6
Guns: 2—12.7 mm (twin) MGs. 2 M-79 40 mm grenade launchers.
Radars: Surface search: Decca 202; I band.

Comment: Most built in the USA. Built for US military assistance programmes and transferred in the late 1960s. Some built in 1970 in the Philippines (ferro-concrete) with enlarged superstructure. *DF 303, 308, 309, 311* and *312* belong to the Navy.

DF 303   *1993, Philippine Navy*

POLAND

Headquarters' Appointments

Commander-in-Chief:
Vice Admiral Romuald Waga
Chief of the Naval Staff:
Rear Admiral Ryszard Lukasik

Diplomatic Representation

Naval Attaché in London:
Captain R Szlegier

Personnel

(a) 1994: 19 110 (including 6000 conscripts, 4100 coastal defence)
(b) 18 months national service

Prefix to Ships' Names

ORP, standing for *Okręt Rzeczypospolitej Polskiej*

Maritime Frontier Guard (MOSG)

A para-naval force, subordinate to the Minister of the Interior, which could be integrated into the navy in a crisis.

Strength of the Fleet

Type	Active	Building
Submarines—Patrol	3	—
Destroyer	1	—
Frigates	1	(4)
Corvettes	5	2
Fast Attack Craft—Missile	7	—
Large Patrol Craft	8	—
Coastal Patrol Craft	11	—
Minesweepers—Ocean	7	—
Minesweepers—Coastal	15	—
Minehunters—Coastal	3	—
LCTs	6	—
LCUs	3	—
Survey and Research Ships	5	—
AGIs	2	—
Training Ships	6	—
Salvage Ships and Craft	7	—
Tankers	4	—
TRVs	2	—
DGVs	3	—
Icebreaker	1	—

Bases

Gdynia (3rd Flotilla), Hel (9th Flotilla), Swinoujscie (8th Flotilla), Kolobrzeg, Ustka, Gdansk (Frontier Guard)

Coastal Defence

This branch is formed into several battalions with SS-C-3 missiles and a number of gun batteries covering approaches to naval bases and major commercial ports.

Mercantile Marine

Lloyd's Register of Shipping:
591 vessels of 2 645 716 tons gross

DELETIONS

Mine Warfare Forces

1991 *Bizon, Bobr, Tur* (ex-AGI)
1993 *Pelikan*

Amphibious Forces

1991 14 Polnochny class, 1 Eichstaden class
1992 *Glogow*

Auxiliaries

1991 *Z 5, Z 7,* 3 Goliat class (civilian)
1993 *Z 6, H 18, H 19, M 6, M 8, M 33*

PENNANT LIST

Submarines

291	Orzel
292	Wilk
293	Dzik

Destroyer

| 271 | Warszawa |

Frigate

| 240 | Kaszub |

Corvettes

421	Orkan
422	Piorun
423	Huragan
434	Gornik
435	Hutnik
436	Metalowiec
437	Rolnik

Patrol Forces

| 351 | Grozny |

352	Wytrwaly
353	Zreczny
354	Zwinny
355	Zwrotny
356	Zawziety
357	Nieugiety
358	Czujny
427	Puck
428	Ustka
429	Oksywie
430	Darlowo
431	Swinoujscie
432	Dziwnów
433	Wladyslawowo

Mine Warfare Forces

616	Kormoran
618	Albatros
620	Tukan
621	Flamingo
622	Rybitwa
623	Mewa
624	Czajka
630	Goplo
631	Gardno
632	Bukowo
633	Dabie
634	Jamno
635	Mielno

636	Wicko
637	Resko
638	Sarbsko
639	Necko
640	Naklo
641	Druzno
642	Hancza
643	Mamry
644	Wigry
645	Sniardwy

Amphibious Forces

811	Grunwald
821	Lublin
822	Gniezno
823	Krakow
824	Poznan
825	Torun

Survey Ships

261	Kopernik
262	Navigator
263	Hydrograf
265	Heweliusz
266	Arctowski

Auxiliaries

251	Wodnik
252	Gryf
711	Podchorazy
712	Kadet
713	Elew
281	Piast
282	Lech
R 11	Gniewko
R 12	Bolko
R 13	Semko
R 14	Zbyszko
R 15	Macko
K 18	Bryza

Maritime Frontier Guard

301	Gdynia
302	Szczecin
303	Elblag
304	Kolobrzeg
311	Kaper I
312	Kaper II
321	Fala
322	Szkwal
323	Zefir
324	Zorza
325	Tecza

SUBMARINES

1 KILO CLASS (TYPE 877E)

ORZEL 291

Displacement, tons: 2325 surfaced; 3076 dived
Dimensions, feet (metres): 242.1 × 32.5 × 21.7
  (73.8 × 9.9 × 6.6)
Main machinery: Diesel-electric; 2 diesels; 3650 hp(m)
  (2.68 MW); 2 generators; 1 motor; 5500 hp(m) *(4.05 MW)*; 1
  shaft
Speed, knots: 10 surfaced; 17 dived; 9 snorting
Range, miles: 6000 at 7 kts snorting; 400 at 3 kts dived
Complement: 52

Torpedoes: 6—21 in *(533 mm)* tubes. Combination of 53-65;
  anti-surface; passive/wake homing to 25 km *(13.5 nm)* at
  50 kts; warhead 300 kg and TEST-71; anti-submarine; active/
  passive homing to 15 km *(8.1 nm)* at 40 kts; warhead 205 kg.
  Total of 18 torpedoes.
Mines: 24 in lieu of torpedoes.
Countermeasures: ESM: Brick Group; radar warning; Quad Loop
  HF D/F.
Radars: Surface search: Snoop Tray; I band.
Sonars: Shark Teeth; hull-mounted; passive search and attack
  (some active capability); low/medium frequency.
  Whale series; passive search; medium frequency.

Programmes: Built in Leningrad (Sudomekh), transferred from
  USSR 21 June 1986. This was the second transfer of this
  class, the first being to India and others have since gone to
  Romania, Algeria and Iran. It was expected that more than one
  would be acquired as part of an exchange deal with the USSR
  for Polish-built amphibious ships, but this class is considered
  too large for Baltic operations and subsequent transfers have
  been of the Foxtrot class.
Structure: Diving depth, 240 m *(787 ft)*. Some of this class have
  two torpedo tubes modified for wire guiding anti-submarine
  torpedoes and a SAM system in the fin.

ORZEL   *6/1992, A Smigielski*

2 FOXTROT CLASS (TYPE 641)

WILK 292   **DZIK** 293

Displacement, tons: 1952 surfaced; 2475 dived
Dimensions, feet (metres): 299.5 × 24.6 × 19.7
  (91.3 × 7.5 × 6)
Main machinery: Diesel-electric; 3 Type 37-D diesels; 6000 hp
  (m) *(4.4 MW)*; 3 motors; 5400 hp(m) (1 × 2700 and 2 × 1350)
  (3.97 MW); 3 shafts; 1 auxiliary motor; 140 hp(m) *(103 kW)*
Speed, knots: 16 surfaced; 15 dived; 9 snorting
Range, miles: 20 000 at 8 kts surfaced; 380 at 2 kts dived
Complement: 75

Torpedoes: 10—21 in *(533 mm)* (6 bow, 4 stern) tubes. Combination of SAET-60; anti-surface; passive homing to 15 km
  (8.1 nm) at 40 kts; warhead 400 kg and SET-65E; anti-submarine; active/passive homing to 15 km *(8.1 nm)* at 40 kts;
  warhead 205 kg. Total of 22 weapons.
Mines: 44 in lieu of torpedoes.
Countermeasures: ESM: Stop Light; radar warning.
Radars: Surface search: Snoop Tray; I band.
Sonars: Hull-mounted; passive/active search and attack; high
  frequency.

Programmes: *Wilk* commissioned 3 November 1987; *Dzik* on
  10 December 1988. Both originally leased from the former
  USSR and purchased outright in 1993.
Structure: Diving depth, 250 m (820 ft).
Operational: The Polish Navy considers that this is about the
  largest practical size of submarine for Baltic operations. *Wilk*
  given a six month refit in 1993.

DZIK   *3/1993, Erik Laursen*

WILK   *8/1993, van Ginderen Collection*

DESTROYER

1 MODIFIED KASHIN CLASS (TYPE 61MP) (DDG)

Name	No	Builders	Laid down	Launched	Commissioned
WARSZAWA (ex-Smely)	271	Nikolaev 61	1967	1969	1973

Displacement, tons: 4010 standard; 4974 full load
Dimensions, feet (metres): 479.7 × 51.8 × 15.7
(146.2 × 15.8 × 4.8)
Main machinery: 4 gas turbines; 72 000 hp(m) (53 MW); 2 shafts
Speed, knots: 35. **Range, miles:** 2600 at 30 kts
Complement: 280 (25 officers)

Missiles: SSM: 4 SS-N-2C Styx ❶; active radar or IR homing to 83 km (45 nm) at 0.9 Mach; warhead 513 kg; sea-skimmer at end of run; no reloads.
SAM: 2 SA-N-1 Goa twin launchers ❷; command guidance to 31.5 km (17 nm) at 2 Mach; warhead 60 kg; 32 missiles. Some SSM capability.
Guns: 4—3 in (76 mm)/60 AK 726 (2 twin) ❸; 80° elevation; 90 rounds/minute to 15 km (8 nm); weight of shell 6.8 kg.
4—30 mm/65 AK 630; 6 barrels per mounting ❹; 85° elevation; 3000 rounds/minute combined to 2 km.
Torpedoes: 5—21 in (533 mm) (quin) tubes ❺. SET-65E; active/passive homing to 15 km (8.1 nm) at 40 kts; warhead 205 kg.
A/S mortars: 2 RBU 6000 12-tubed trainable ❻; range 6000 m; warhead 31 kg; 120 rockets.
Countermeasures: Decoys: 4—16-tubed chaff launchers. 2 towed torpedo decoys.
ESM/ECM: 2 Bell Shroud. 2 Bell Squat.
Fire control: 2 Tee Plinth and 4 Tilt Pot optronic directors.
Radars: Air/surface search: Big Net ❼; C band.
Head Net C; 3D; E band ❽; range 128 km (70 nm).
Navigation: Two SRN 7453; I band.
Fire control: Two Peel Group ❾; H/I band (for SA-N-1). Two Bass Tilt ❿; H/I band (for 30 mm). Two Owl Screech ⓫; G band (for guns).
IFF: Salt Pot.
Sonars: Bull Horn; hull-mounted; active search and attack; medium frequency.
Mare Tail VDS; active search; medium frequency.

Helicopters: Platform for 1 medium.

Programmes: Converted in the mid-1970s. Transferred from the USSR to the Polish Navy on 9 January 1988 at the port of Oksywie after a lengthy refit in St Petersburg. Purchased outright in 1993.
Structure: No changes were made to the armament before the transfer, except that Polish navigation radars were fitted.
Operational: The Flagship of the Polish Navy.

WARSZAWA
(Scale 1 : 1200), Ian Sturton

WARSZAWA
1993

WARSZAWA
10/1993, G. Toremans

WARSZAWA
1993

FRIGATES

1 + (4) KASZUB CLASS (TYPE 620)

Name	No	Builders	Laid down	Launched	Commissioned
KASZUB	240	Northern Shipyard, Gdansk	11 May 1985	4 Oct 1986	23 Nov 1988

KASZUB   *(Scale 1 : 900), Ian Sturton*

Displacement, tons: 1051 standard; 1183 full load
Dimensions, feet (metres): 270 × 32.8 × 10.2
   (82.3 × 10 × 3.1)
Main machinery: CODAD; 4 Cegielski-Sulzer AS 16V 25/30 diesels; 16 900 hp(m) *(12.42 MW)*; 2 shafts
Speed, knots: 26. **Range, miles:** 2000 at 18 kts
Complement: 87

Missiles: SAM: 2 SA-N-5 quad launchers ❶; IR homing to 10 km *(5.5 nm)* at 1.5 Mach.
Guns: 1 USSR 3 in *(76 mm)*/66 ❷; 85° elevation; 120 rounds/minute to 15 km *(8 nm)*; weight of shell 7 kg.
   6 ZU-23-2M Wrobel 23 mm/87 (3 twin) ❸; 400 rounds/minute combined to 2 km; to be replaced by 30 mm/65 AK 630.
Torpedoes: 4—21 in *(533 mm)* (2 twin) tubes ❹. SET-65E; active/passive homing to 15 km *(8.1 nm)* at 40 kts; warhead 205 kg.
A/S mortars: 2 RBU 6000 12-tubed trainable ❺; range 6000 m; warhead 31 kg; 120 rockets.
Depth charges: 2 rails.
Countermeasures: 2 PK 16 chaff launchers ❻.
Radars: Air/surface search: Strut Curve ❼; F band.
Surface search: Tamirio RN 231 ❽; I band.
IFF: Square Head.
Sonars: Stern-mounted dipping type mounted on the transom; active; high frequency.

Programmes: Second of class cancelled in 1989 but a class of four more ships based on the Kaszub hull and specialised for anti-submarine warfare is scheduled to start construction in 1994.
Structure: Design appears to be based on Grisha class but with many alterations. The 76 mm gun was fitted in late 1991. The 23 mm guns are to be replaced by Gatlings in due course. There is also space for a fire control director on the bridge roof.
Operational: Finally achieved operational status in 1990. Based at Hel with the Border Guard in 1990 but returned to the Navy in 1991.

KASZUB   *7/1993, G Toremans*

KASZUB   *5/1992, W Sartori*

CORVETTES

4 GORNIK (TARANTUL I) CLASS (TYPE 1241)

Name	No	Builders	Commissioned
GORNIK	434	Volodyarski Yard	Dec 1983
HUTNIK	435	Volodyarski Yard	Apr 1984
METALOWIEC	436	Volodyarski Yard	Jan 1988
ROLNIK	437	Volodyarski Yard	Jan 1989

Displacement, tons: 455 full load
Dimensions, feet (metres): 184.1 × 37.7 × 8.2 *(56.1 × 11.5 × 2.5)*
Main machinery: COGOG; 2 Type NK-12MV gas turbines; 20 400 hp(m) *(15 MW)* sustained; 2 gas turbines with reversible gearbox; 8000 hp(m) *(5.88 MW)*; 2 shafts
Speed, knots: 35. **Range, miles:** 2300 at 18 kts
Complement: 34 (5 officers)

Missiles: SSM: 4 SS-N-2C Styx (2 twin) launchers; active radar or IR homing to 83 km *(45 nm)* at 0.9 Mach; warhead 513 kg; sea-skimmer in terminal flight.
SAM: SA-N-5 Grail quad launcher; manual aiming; IR homing to 6 km *(3.2 nm)* at 1.5 Mach; warhead 1.5 kg.
Guns: 1—3 in *(76 mm)*/60 automatic; 85° elevation; 120 rounds/minute to 15 km *(8 nm)*; weight of shell 7 kg.
   2—30 mm/65 6-barrelled type; 85° elevation; 3000 rounds/minute combined to 2 km.
Countermeasures: Decoys: 2 chaff launchers.
Radars: Air/surface search: Plank Shave; E band.
Navigation: Krivach; I band.
Fire control: Bass Tilt; H/I band.
IFF: Square Head.

Programmes: Transferred from the USSR. Plans to take two more from the former GDR stock have been cancelled.
Structure: Similar to others of the class exported to India, Yemen and Romania.

METALOWIEC   *7/1993, Marek Twardowski*

1 + 2 ORKAN (SASSNITZ) CLASS (TYPE 660 (ex-151))

Name	No	Builders	Commissioned
ORKAN	421	Peenewerft/Northern Shipyard, Gdansk	18 Sep 1992
PIORUN	422	Peenewerft/Northern Shipyard, Gdansk	1994
HURAGAN	423	Peenewerft/Northern Shipyard, Gdansk	1994

Displacement, tons: 296 standard; 326 full load
Dimensions, feet (metres): 160.4 oa; 147.6 wl × 28.5 × 7.2 *(48.9; 45 × 8.7 × 2.2)*
Main machinery: 3 Type M 520T diesels; 14 670 hp(m) *(10.78 MW)* sustained; 3 shafts
Speed, knots: 36. **Range, miles:** 1530 at 14 kts
Complement: 34 (6 officers)

Missiles: SSM: 8 (2 quad) launchers Type 152; missiles to be fitted in due course.
SAM: SA-N-5 Grail quad launcher; manual aiming; IR homing to 6 km *(3.2 nm)* at 1.5 Mach; warhead 1.5 kg.
Guns: 1 USSR 3 in *(76 mm)*/66 AK 176; 85° elevation; 120 rounds/minute to 15 km *(8 nm)*; weight of shell 7 kg.
1—30 mm/65 ADG 630; 6 barrels; 3000 rounds/minute combined to 2 km.
Countermeasures: Decoys: 8—12-tubed chaff and IR launchers.
Radars: Air/surface search: NUR-27XA; E/F band.
Fire control: Bass Tilt; H/I band.
Navigation: SRN 443; I band.
IFF: Square Head; Salt Pot.

Programmes: Originally six of this former GDR Sassnitz class were to be built at Peenewerft for Poland. The future of the programme is uncertain but so far three units have been acquired for completion at Stocznia Polnocna Gdansk. Programme delayed by lack of funds.
Structure: The prototype vessel had two quadruple SSM launchers with an Exocet type (SS-N-25) of missile and the plan is to fit eight SSM in due course. Plank Shave radar has been replaced by a Polish set. Unlike the German Coast Guard vessels of the same class, these ships have retained three engines.

ORKAN   9/1993, Erik Laursen

LAND-BASED MARITIME AIRCRAFT (FRONT LINE)

Notes: (1) In addition there are two AN-28 patrol and 15 TS-11R reconnaissance aircraft.
(2) 36 MiG-21 with ASMs allocated to the maritime role.

Numbers/Type: 10/4 Mil Mi-14PL/PS Haze A.
Operational speed: 120 kts *(222 km/h).*
Service ceiling: 15 000 ft *(4570 m).*
Range: 240 nm *(445 km).*
Role/Weapon systems: PL for ASW, PS for SAR. PL operates in co-operation with surface units; supported by five Mi-2 Hoplite helicopters in same unit. Can be carried in *Warszawa*. Sensors: Search radar, MAD, sonobuoys. Weapons: ASW; internal torpedoes, depth bombs and mines.

Numbers/Type: 10 PZL Swidnik W-3 Sokol/W-3RM Anakonda.
Operational speed: 119 kts *(220 km/h).*
Service ceiling: 15 256 ft *(4650 m).*
Range: 335 nm *(620 km).*
Role/Weapon systems: Planned to replace the Haze in due course. Total of 18 planned for SAR and a variant for ASW (W-3UI Alligator).

SOKOL ANAKONDA   1992, Swidnik

PATROL FORCES

7 PUCK (OSA I) CLASS (TYPE 205)
(FAST ATTACK CRAFT—MISSILE)

PUCK 427	OKSYWIE 429	SWINOUJSCIE 431	WLADYSLAWOWO 433
USTKA 428	DARLOWO 430	DZIWNÓW 432	

Displacement, tons: 171 standard; 210 full load
Dimensions, feet (metres): 126.6 × 24.9 × 8.8 *(38.6 × 7.6 × 2.7)*
Main machinery: 3 Type M 503A diesels; 8025 hp(m) *(5.9 MW)* sustained; 3 shafts
Speed, knots: 35. **Range, miles:** 800 at 30 kts
Complement: 30

Missiles: SSM: 4 SS-N-2A Styx; active radar or IR homing to 46 km *(25 nm)* at 0.9 Mach; warhead 513 kg.
Guns: 4—30 mm/65 (2 twin) automatic; 85° elevation; 500 rounds/minute to 5 km *(2.7 nm)*; weight of shell 0.54 kg.
Radars: Surface search: Square Tie; I band.
Fire control: Drum Tilt; H/I band.

Programmes: All date from early to mid-1960s and are running out of operational life.
Structure: Pennant numbers are carried on side-boards on the bridge. By the end of 1992 four (423, 425, 426 and 424) had been transferred to Frontier Guard ships with SSM and after gun removed and the forward gun replaced by a twin 25 mm 2M3M. More may be converted in due course.

DARLOWO   8/1992

---

8 MODIFIED OBLUZE CLASS (TYPE 912M)
(LARGE PATROL CRAFT)

GROZNY 351	ZRECZNY 353	ZWROTNY 355	NIEUGIETY 357
WYTRWALY 352	ZWINNY 354	ZAWZIETY 356	CZUJNY 358

Displacement, tons: 237 full load
Dimensions, feet (metres): 135.5 × 20.7 × 6.6 *(41.3 × 6.3 × 2)*
Main machinery: 2 Type 40-D diesels; 4400 hp(m) *(3.23 MW)* sustained; 2 shafts
Speed, knots: 24. **Range, miles:** 600 at 18 kts
Complement: 28
Guns: 4—30 mm/65 (2 twin) automatic; 85° elevation; 500 rounds/minute to 5 km *(2.7 nm)*; weight of shell 0.54 kg.
Depth charges: 2 racks.
Radars: Surface search: Tamirio RN 231; I band.
Fire control: Drum Tilt; H/I band.
IFF: Two Square Head. High Pole.
Sonars: Hull-mounted; active attack; high frequency.

Comment: Modified Obluze class. Completed 1969-72 at the Naval Shipyard, Gdynia.

ZAWZIETY   6/1993, Erik Laursen

---

11 PILICA CLASS (TYPE 918) (COASTAL PATROL CRAFT)

166-176

Displacement, tons: 87 full load
Dimensions, feet (metres): 95.1 × 18.4 × 4.6 *(29 × 5.6 × 1.4)*
Main machinery: 3 M 50F diesels; 6610 hp(m) *(4.86 MW)*; 3 shafts
Speed, knots: 30
Complement: 15
Guns: 2 ZU-23-2M Wrobel 23 mm/87 (twin); 400 rounds/minute to 2 km.
Torpedoes: 2—21 in *(533 mm)* tubes; anti-surface.
Radars: Surface search: Tamirio RN 231; I band.
Sonars: Dipping VDS aft.

Comment: Built at Naval Shipyard, Gdynia from 1973 to 1982. Based at Kolobrzeg and Gdansk. First batch of five, without torpedo tubes are part of the Maritime Frontier Guard.

PILICA 170   3/1992, Erik Laursen

MINE WARFARE FORCES

7 KROGULEC CLASS (TYPE 206F) (MINESWEEPERS—OCEAN)

Name	No	Builders	Commissioned
KORMORAN	616	Naval Shipyard, Gdynia	1963
ALBATROS	618	Naval Shipyard, Gdynia	1964
TUKAN	620	Naval Shipyard, Gdynia	1966
FLAMINGO	621	Naval Shipyard, Gdynia	1966
RYBITWA	622	Naval Shipyard, Gdynia	1966
MEWA	623	Naval Shipyard, Gdynia	1967
CZAJKA	624	Naval Shipyard, Gdynia	1967

Displacement, tons: 474 full load
Dimensions, feet (metres): 190.9 × 25.3 × 6.9 *(58.2 × 7.7 × 2.1)*
Main machinery: 2 Fiat A-230S diesels; 3750 hp(m) *(2.76 MW)*; 2 shafts
Speed, knots: 18. **Range, miles:** 2000 at 17 kts
Complement: 48 (6 officers)
Guns: 6—25 mm/60 (3 twin) or 4—23 mm (2 twin) and 2—25 mm/60 (twin).
Depth charges: 2 racks.
Mines: 2 rails.
Radars: Surface search: Tamirio RN 231; I band.
Sonars: Hull-mounted; minehunting; high frequency.

Comment: Armament varies with some having 23 mm guns aft instead of the 25 mm guns. Five deleted so far.

TUKAN *7/1993, G Toremans*

13 GOPLO (NOTEC) CLASS (TYPE 207P) (MINESWEEPERS—COASTAL)

GOPLO 630	JAMNO 634	RESKO 637	NAKLO 640
GARDNO 631	MIELNO 635	SARBSKO 638	DRUZNO 641
BUKOWO 632	WICKO 636	NECKO 639	HANCZA 642
DABIE 633			

Displacement, tons: 208 standard; 225 full load
Dimensions, feet (metres): 125.7 × 23.6 × 5.9 *(38.3 × 7.2 × 1.8)*
Main machinery: 2 M 40-1A diesels; 1874 hp(m) *(1.38 MW)*; 2 shafts
Speed, knots: 14. **Range, miles:** 1100 at 9 kts
Complement: 24 (4 officers)
Guns: 2 Wrobel ZU-23-2M 23 mm (twin); 400 rounds/minute combined to 2 km.
Radars: Navigation: Tamirio RN 231; I band.

Comment: *Goplo* launched April 1981 as an experimental prototype numbered 207D. Built at about one per year, with the last one commissioning 1 March 1991. The 23 mm guns have replaced the original 25 mm. GRP hulls. Some carry divers for minehunting work. Named after Lakes.

GOPLO *6/1993, Erik Laursen*

3 MAMRY (NOTEC II) CLASS (TYPE 207M) (MINEHUNTERS—COASTAL)

Name	No	Builders	Launched	Commissioned
MAMRY	643	Naval Shipyard, Gdynia	20 Sep 1991	25 Sep 1992
WIGRY	644	Naval Shipyard, Gdynia	28 Nov 1992	1994
SNIARDWY	645	Naval Shipyard, Gdynia	20 June 1993	1994

Displacement, tons: 262 full load
Dimensions, feet (metres): 142.7 × 25.3 × 5.9 *(43.5 × 7.7 × 1.8)*
Main machinery: 2 M 401A diesels; 1605 hp(m) *(1.18 MW)*; 2 shafts; 2 auxiliary motors; 816 hp(m) *(60 kW)*
Speed, knots: 13. **Range, miles:** 790 at 12 kts
Complement: 24 (4 officers)
Missiles: SAM/Guns: 2 ZU-23-2MR 23 mm Wrobel II (twin); combination of 2 SA-N-5 missiles; IR homing to 6 km *(3.2 nm)* at 1.5 Mach; warhead 1.5 kg and guns; 400 rounds/minute combined to 2 km.
Mines: 6-24 depending on type.
Radars: Navigation: RN 231 Tamirio; I band.
Sonars: Atlas Elektronik; active search; high frequency.

Comment: This is a minehunter variant of the Goplo class designed to deal with magnetic and acoustic mines. Five of the class were planned but this has been reduced to three.

WIGRY *6/1993, Erik Laursen*

2 LENIWKA CLASS (TYPE 410S) (MINESWEEPERS—COASTAL)

625   626

Displacement, tons: 245 full load
Dimensions, feet (metres): 84.6 × 23.6 × 8.9 *(25.8 × 7.2 × 2.7)*
Main machinery: 1 Puck-Sulzer 6AL20/24 diesel; 570 hp(m) *(420 kW)*; 1 shaft
Speed, knots: 11. **Range, miles:** 3100 at 8 kts

Comment: Project 410S modified stern trawlers built at Ustka Shipyard in 1982/83. Sweeping is done by using strung-out charges. The ships can carry 40 tons of cargo or 40 people.

LENIWKA 625 *9/1992, Hartmut Ehlers*

AMPHIBIOUS FORCES

Note: The following ships and craft plus a number of civilian Ro-ro ships are for use by the 7th Coastal Defence Brigade (ex-Sea Landing Division) (5000 men) based in the Gdansk area.

1 MODIFIED POLNOCHNY C CLASS (TYPE 776) (LCTs)

Name	No	Builders	Commissioned
GRUNWALD	811	Northern Shipyard, Gdansk	1973

Displacement, tons: 1253 full load
Dimensions, feet (metres): 246.1 × 31.5 × 7.5 *(75 × 9.6 × 2.3)*
Main machinery: 2 Type 40-D diesels; 4400 hp(m) *(3.2 MW)* sustained; 2 shafts
Speed, knots: 18. **Range, miles:** 1000 at 18 kts
Complement: 45 plus 54 flag staff
Military lift: 2 light trucks
Guns: 2 or 4—30 mm (1 or 2 twin). 2—140 mm rocket launchers.
Radars: Navigation: Don 2; I band.
Fire control: Drum Tilt; H/I band.
IFF: Square Head. High Pole.

Comment: A modified Group C ship converted to an amphibious command vessel. Command and electronic equipment fitted on the vehicle deck leaving a small area behind the bow doors for two light trucks or jeeps. The remainder of this class have been deleted.

GRUNWALD *10/1993, G. Toremans*

5 LUBLIN CLASS (TYPE 767) (LCT/MINELAYER)

Name	No	Builders	Launched	Commissioned
LUBLIN	821	Northern Shipyard, Gdansk	12 July 1988	12 Oct 1989
GNIEZNO	822	Northern Shipyard, Gdansk	7 Dec 1988	23 Feb 1990
KRAKOW	823	Northern Shipyard, Gdansk	7 Mar 1989	27 June 1990
POZNAN	824	Northern Shipyard, Gdansk	5 Jan 1990	8 Mar 1991
TORUN	825	Northern Shipyard, Gdansk	8 June 1990	24 May 1991

Displacement, tons: 1089 standard; 1745 full load
Dimensions, feet (metres): 313 × 35.4 × 6.6 *(95.4 × 10.8 × 2)*
Main machinery: 3 Cegielski 6ATL25D diesels; 5390 hp(m) *(3.96 MW)* sustained; 3 shafts
Speed, knots: 16. **Range, miles:** 1400 at 16 kts
Complement: 37 (5 officers)
Military lift: 5 MBT or 9 APC or 7 amphibious tanks. 135 troops plus equipment
Missiles: SAM/Guns: 8 ZU-23-2MR 23 mm Wrobel II (4 twin); combination of 2 SA-N-5 missiles; IR
 homing to 6 km *(3.2 nm)* at 1.5 Mach; warhead 1.5 kg and guns; 400 rounds/minute combined
 to 2 km.
Depth charges: 9 throwers for counter-mining.
Mines: 50-134.
Countermeasures: Decoys: 2 chaff launchers.
Radars: 2 navigation: SRN 7455 and SRN 433XTA; I band.

Comment: Designed with a through deck from bow to stern and can be used as minelayers as well
 as for amphibious landings. Folding bow and stern ramps and a stern anchor are fitted. The ship
 has a pressurised citadel for NBC defence and an upper deck washdown system.

LUBLIN   *1992, MoD Bonn*

KRAKOW   *3/1993, Erik Laursen*

3 DEBA CLASS (TYPE 716) (LCU)

851   852   853

Displacement, tons: 176 full load
Dimensions, feet (metres): 122 × 23.3 × 5.6 *(37.2 × 7.1 × 1.7)*
Main machinery: 3 Type M 401A diesels; 3000 hp(m) *(2.2 MW)*; 3 shafts
Speed, knots: 20. **Range, miles:** 430 at 16 kts
Complement: 10
Military lift: 2 small tanks or 3 vehicles up to 15 tons or 50 troops
Guns: 2 ZU-23-2M Wrobel 23 mm (twin).
Radars: Surface search: SRN 207A; I band.

Comment: Built at Navy Yard, Gdynia. First one commissioned 16 June 1988, second in 1990 and
 third in 1991. The plan was to build 12 but the programme was suspended at three through lack
 of funds and is unlikely to be resumed. Can carry up to six launchers for strung-out charges.
 Mostly used as patrol craft.

DEBA 851   *9/1993, Marek Twardowski*

INTELLIGENCE VESSELS (AGIs)

2 MODIFIED MOMA CLASS (TYPE 863)

Name	No	Builders	Commissioned
NAVIGATOR	262	Northern Shipyard, Gdansk	June 1975
HYDROGRAF	263	Northern Shipyard, Gdansk	June 1975

Displacement, tons: 1680 full load
Dimensions, feet (metres): 240.5 × 39.4 × 12.8 *(73.3 × 12 × 3.9)*
Main machinery: 2 Zgoda-Sulzer 6TD48 diesels; 3300 hp(m) *(2.43 MW)* sustained; 2 shafts
Speed, knots: 17. **Range, miles:** 9000 at 12 kts
Complement: 65 (10 officers)

Comment: Much altered in the upperworks and unrecognisable as Momas. The fo'c'sle in *Hydrograf* is longer than in *Navigator* and one deck higher. Both fitted for but not with two twin 25 mm
 gun mountings. Forward radomes replaced by a cylindrical type and after ones removed on both
 ships in 1987.

HYDROGRAF   *3/1993, Erik Laursen*

NAVIGATOR   *3/1993, Erik Laursen*

SURVEY AND RESEARCH SHIPS

2 MODIFIED FINIK 2 CLASS (TYPE 874)

Name	No	Builders	Commissioned
HEWELIUSZ	265	Northern Shipyard, Gdansk	27 Nov 1982
ARCTOWSKI	266	Northern Shipyard, Gdansk	27 Nov 1982

Displacement, tons: 1135 full load
Dimensions, feet (metres): 202.1 × 36.7 × 10.8 *(61.6 × 11.2 × 3.3)*
Main machinery: 2 Cegielski-Sulzer 6AL25/30 diesels; 1920 hp(m) *(1.4 MW)*; 2 auxiliary motors;
 204 hp(m) *(150 kW)*; 2 shafts; cp props; bow thruster
Speed, knots: 13. **Range, miles:** 3000 at 13 kts
Complement: 55 (10 officers)

Comment: Sister ships to Russian class which were built in Poland, except that *Heweliusz* and
 Arctowski have been modified and have no buoy handling equipment. Two sister ships, *Zodiak*
 and *Planeta*, are civilian operated.

HEWELIUSZ   *8/1993*

1 MOMA CLASS (TYPE 861K)

Name	No	Builders	Commissioned
KOPERNIK	261	Northern Shipyard, Gdansk	20 Feb 1971

Displacement, tons: 1240 standard; 1580 full load
Dimensions, feet (metres): 240.5 × 36.8 × 12.8 (73.3 × 11.2 × 3.9)
Main machinery: 2 Zgoda-Sulzer 6TD48 diesels; 3300 hp(m) (2.43 MW) sustained; 2 shafts
Speed, knots: 17. **Range, miles:** 9000 at 12 kts
Complement: 41 (8 officers) plus 40 scientists

Comment: Forward crane removed in 1983.

KOPERNIK   7/1993

2 KHK 121 CLASS (SURVEY CRAFT)

K 20   K 21

Displacement, tons: 12.3 standard
Dimensions, feet (metres): 29.5 × 9.8 × 2.6 (9 × 3 × 0.8)
Main machinery: 2 diesels; 800 hp(m) (588 kW); 2 shafts
Speed, knots: 8. **Range, miles:** 85 at 8 kts
Complement: 8

Comment: Survey craft built by Rzeczna Shipyard, Wroclawska in 1989-90.

TRAINING SHIPS

Note: The sloop *Dar Mlodziezy* is civilian owned and operated but also takes naval personnel for training.

2 WODNIK CLASS (TYPE 888)

Name	No	Builders	Commissioned
WODNIK	251	Northern Shipyard, Gdansk	27 May 1976
GRYF	252	Northern Shipyard, Gdansk	26 Sep 1976

Displacement, tons: 1697 standard; 1820 full load
Dimensions, feet (metres): 234.3 × 38.1 × 12.8 (71.4 × 11.6 × 3.9)
Main machinery: 2 Zgoda-Sulzer 6TD48 diesels; 3300 hp(m) (2.43 MW) sustained; 2 shafts
Speed, knots: 16. **Range, miles:** 7200 at 11 kts
Complement: 75 plus 101 midshipmen
Guns: 4—30 mm (2 twin). 4 ZU-23-2M Wrobel 23 mm (2 twin).
Radars: Navigation: Two RN 231; I band.
Fire control: Drum Tilt; H/I band.

Comment: *Wodnik* launched 29 November 1975, *Gryf* 13 March 1976. Sisters to former GDR *Wilhelm Pieck* and two Russian ships. *Wodnik* converted to a hospital ship (150 beds) in 1990 for deployment to the Gulf. Armament removed as part of the conversion but restored in 1992. *Wodnik* has a helicopter platform.

WODNIK (guns restored)   5/1992, Maritime Photographic

GRYF   5/1992, H M Steele

1 BRYZA and 3 ELEW (TYPE OS 1) CLASSES

Name	No	Builders	Commissioned
BRYZA	K 18	Wisla Shipyard, Gdansk	8 Oct 1965
PODCHORAZY	711	Wisla Shipyard, Gdansk	30 Nov 1974
KADET	712	Wisla Shipyard, Gdansk	19 July 1975
ELEW	713	Wisla Shipyard, Gdansk	8 Apr 1976

Displacement, tons: 180 (167, *Bryza*) full load
Dimensions, feet (metres): 94.5 × 21.7 × 6.4 (28.8 × 6.6 × 2)
Main machinery: 2 Wola diesels; 300 hp(m) (220 kW); 2 shafts
Speed, knots: 10. **Range, miles:** 1100 at 10 kts
Complement: 11 plus 26 cadets
Radars: Navigation: Two RN 231; I band.

Comment: *Bryza* has a lighter superstructure than remainder but is built on the same hull. The class is similar to Russian vessels used for naval and merchant marine training.

PODCHORAZY   6/1993, Mikael Laursen

BRYZA   4/1989, Marek Twardowski

1 SAIL TRAINING SHIP

Name	No	Builders	Commissioned
ISKRA	253	Northern Shipyard, Gdansk	11 Aug 1982

Displacement, tons: 498 full load
Dimensions, feet (metres): 160.8 × 26.6 × 12.1 (49 × 8.1 × 3.7)
Main machinery: 1 Wola 68H12 diesel; 310 hp(m) (228 kW); 1 auxiliary shaft
Speed, knots: 10 (diesel)
Complement: 62 (5 officers, 45 cadets)

Comment: Type B79 sloop with 1040 m² of sail. Used by the Naval Academy for training with a secondary survey role.

ISKRA   5/1993, Marek Twardowski

AUXILIARIES

1 BALTYK CLASS (TYPE ZP 1200) (TANKER)

Name	No	Builders	Commissioned
BALTYK	Z 1	Naval Shipyard, Gdynia	11 Mar 1991

Displacement, tons: 2918 standard; 2974 full load
Dimensions, feet (metres): 278.2 × 43 × 15.4 *(84.8 × 13.1 × 4.7)*
Main machinery: 2 Cegielski diesels; 4025 hp(m) *(2.96 MW)*; 2 shafts
Speed, knots: 15. **Range, miles:** 4250 at 12 kts
Complement: 32
Guns: 4 ZU-23-2M Wrobel 23 mm (2 twin).
Radars: Navigation: SRN-443; I band.

Comment: Beam replenishment stations, one each side. First of a projected class of four, of which the others have been cancelled.

BALTYK   *1992, Polish Navy*

3 MOSKIT CLASS (TYPE B 199) (TANKERS)

KRAB Z 3   **MEDUZA** Z 8   **SLIMAK** Z 9

Displacement, tons: 1200 full load
Dimensions, feet (metres): 189.3 × 31.2 × 11.2 *(57.7 × 9.5 × 3.4)*
Main machinery: 2 Sulzer diesels; 850 hp(m) *(625 kW)*; 2 shafts
Speed, knots: 11. **Range, miles:** 1200 at 10 kts
Complement: 18
Cargo capacity: 656 tons
Guns: 4 ZU-23-2MR Wrobel 23 mm (2 twin).
Radars: Navigation: RN-231; I band.

Comment: Built in Poland in 1971-72 by Rzeczna Shipyard, Wroclawska. First two carry oil, the other one water. Names are unofficial.

KRAB   *10/1992, Erik Laursen*

2 KORMORAN CLASS (TRVs)

K 8   **K 11**

Displacement, tons: 149 full load
Dimensions, feet (metres): 114.8 × 19.7 × 5.2 *(35 × 6 × 1.6)*
Main machinery: 2 Type M 50 diesels; 2200 hp(m) *(1.6 MW)*; 2 shafts
Speed, knots: 21. **Range, miles:** 550 at 15 kts
Complement: 18
Guns: 2 ZU-23-2M Wrobel 23 mm (twin).

Comment: Built at Naval Shipyard, Gdynia in 1970. Armament updated in 1993.

K 8   *1992, Polish Navy*

3 MROWKA CLASS (TYPE B 208) (DEGAUSSING VESSELS)

WRONA SD 11   **RYS** SD 12   **SD 13**

Displacement, tons: 600 full load
Dimensions, feet (metres): 145.3 × 26.6 × 7.5 *(44.3 × 8.1 × 2.3)*
Main machinery: 1 diesel; 335 hp(m) *(246 kW)*; 1 shaft
Speed, knots: 9.5
Guns: 2—25 mm (twin) (SD 13); 2 ZU-23-2M Wrobel 23 mm (twin) (SD 12).

Comment: Completed in 1971-72 by Naval Yard, Gdynia. Names are unofficial.

SD 13   *6/1993, Erik Laursen*

2 PIAST CLASS (TYPE 570) (SALVAGE SHIPS)

Name	No	Builders	Commissioned
PIAST	281	Northern Shipyard, Gdansk	26 Jan 1974
LECH	282	Northern Shipyard, Gdansk	30 Nov 1974

Displacement, tons: 1732 full load
Dimensions, feet (metres): 238.5 × 38.1 × 13.1 *(72.7 × 11.6 × 4)*
Main machinery: 2 Zgoda-Sulzer 6TD48 diesels; 3300 hp(m) *(2.43 MW)* sustained; 2 shafts
Speed, knots: 15. **Range, miles:** 3000 at 12 kts
Complement: 52 (6 officers) plus 15 spare
Guns: 8—25 mm (4 twin) (can be fitted).

Comment: Basically a Moma class hull with towing and firefighting capabilities. Ice-strengthened hulls. Wartime role as hospital ships. Carry three-man diving bells capable of 100 m depth and a decompression chamber.

PIAST   *6/1993, Erik Laursen*

2 ZBYSZKO CLASS (TYPE B 823) (SALVAGE SHIPS)

Name	No	Builders	Commissioned
ZBYSZKO	R 14	Uskta Shipyard	Sep 1991
MACKO	R 15	Uskta Shipyard	Dec 1991

Displacement, tons: 380 full load
Dimensions, feet (metres): 114.8 × 26.2 × 9.8 *(35 × 8 × 3)*
Main machinery: 1 Sulzer 6AL20/24D; 750 hp(m) *(551 kW)*; 1 shaft
Speed, knots: 11. **Range, miles:** 3000 at 10 kts
Radars: Navigation: SRN 402X; I band.

Comment: Type B-823 ordered 30 May 1988. Carries a decompression chamber and two divers. Mobile gantry crane on the stern.

ZBYSZKO   *7/1993, van Ginderen Collection*

3 PLUSKWA CLASS (TYPE R-30) (SALVAGE TUGS)

Name	No	Builders	Commissioned
GNIEWKO	R 11	Navy Yard, Gdynia	25 July 1981
BOLKO	R 12	Navy Yard, Gdynia	7 Nov 1982
SEMKO	R 13	Navy Yard, Gdynia	9 May 1987

Displacement, tons: 365 full load
Dimensions, feet (metres): 105 × 29.2 × 10.2 *(32 × 8.9 × 3.1)*
Main machinery: 1 Cegielski-Sulzer diesel; 1470 hp(m) *(1.08 MW)*; 1 shaft
Speed, knots: 12. **Range, miles:** 4000 at 7 kts

BOLKO   *9/1992, Hartmut Ehlers*

3 DIVING TENDERS

K 1   K 7   K 14

Comment: Similar to M 27 but modified as diving tenders.

DIVING TENDER (old number)   *8/1991, Marek Twardowski*

7 HARBOUR LIGHTERS and 15 PATROL CRAFT

B 5-7, B 11-13, W 2
M 5, M 12, M 21-22, M 25-30, M 81-85

Comment: M numbers are patrol launches; B numbers are freighters and oil lighters; W 2 is a water lighter.

B 12   *6/1993, Erik Laursen*

ICEBREAKER

PERKUN

Measurement, tons: 1152 gross; 272 net
Dimensions, feet (metres): 185 × 46 × — *(56.5 × 14 × —)*
Main machinery: Diesel-electric; 4 diesel generators; 3680 hp(m) *(2.7 MW)*; 4 motors; 3000 hp(m) *(2.2 MW)*; 2 shafts
Speed, knots: 10

Comment: Built by PK Harris and Sons Ltd, Appledore, Devon in 1963. Civilian owned, naval operated and manned.

TUGS

Note: In addition there are a number of small berthing tugs with M numbers.

2 H 820 CLASS

H 9   H 10

Displacement, tons: 230 full load
Dimensions, feet (metres): 72.2 × 20.7 × 6.9 *(22 × 6.3 × 2.1)*
Main machinery: 2 Delfin SW-680 diesels; 242 hp(m) *(178 kW)*; 2 shafts
Speed, knots: 9. **Range, miles:** 500 at 9 kts
Complement: 6

Comment: Commissioned in 1993.

1 GOLIAT CLASS (TYPE 667R)

H 16

Displacement, tons: 150 full load
Dimensions, feet (metres): 70.2 × 20 × 8.5 *(21.4 × 6.1 × 2.6)*
Main machinery: 1 8NVD 36 diesel; 300 hp(m) *(221 kW)*; 1 shaft
Speed, knots: 12

Comment: Built at Gdynia in the 1960s. Remainder of class sold for civilian use in 1991 except for one which transferred to Latvia in December 1993.

GOLIAT (old number)   *9/1992, Hartmut Ehlers*

5 H 900 and 2 H 800 CLASSES

H 3, 4, 5, 6, 7   H 1, 2

Displacement, tons: 218 full load
Dimensions, feet (metres): 84 × 22.3 × 11.5 *(25.6 × 6.8 × 3.5)*
Main machinery: 1 Cegielski-Sulzer 6AL20/24H diesel; 935 hp(m) *(687 kW)*; 1 shaft
Speed, knots: 10
Complement: 17

Comment: Similar designs. *H 1* and *H 2* built in 1970, the remainder in the early 1980s. Have fire-fighting capability.

H 6   *5/1993, Marek Twardowski*

2 MOTYL CLASS (TYPE 1500)

H 12, 20

Displacement, tons: 439 full load
Dimensions, feet (metres): 103.7 × 27.6 × 11.5 *(31.6 × 8.4 × 3.5)*
Main machinery: 1 Sulzer 5TD48 diesel; 1500 hp(m) *(1.1 MW)*; 1 shaft
Speed, knots: 12. **Range, miles:** 1500 at 12 kts
Complement: 22

Comment: Built at Gdansk in 1964.

H 12   *4/1993, Marek Twardowski*

MARITIME FRONTIER GUARD (MOSG)

Headquarters' Appointments

Commandant MOSG:
Captain Stanislaw Lisak
Deputy Commandant (Operations):
Commander Miroslaw Kursa
Deputy Commandant (Technical):
Commander Ignacy Wajs

Bases

Gdansk (HQ and Kaszubski Division)
Kolobrzeg (Baltycki Division)
Swinoujscie (Pomorski Division)

General

MOSG (Morski Oddzial Strazy Graniczna) formed on 12 June 1991. Vessels have blue hulls with red and yellow striped insignia. Superstructures are painted white.

---

4 OSA I CLASS (TYPE 205) (FAST ATTACK CRAFT—GUN)

GDYNIA 301 (ex-423)   **ELBLAG** 303 (ex-426)
SZCZECIN 302 (ex-425)   **KOLOBRZEG** 304 (ex-424)

Comment: Built in the USSR 1965-67. Three transferred from the Navy in 1991 and one in 1992. Details under *Patrol Forces* except that all armament and fire control radar has been removed, leaving only a twin 25 mm 2M3M gun forward. *Kolobrzeg* still unconverted in late 1993 and may be scrapped.

ELBLAG   *1992, MOSG*

5 OBLUZE CLASS (TYPE 912) (LARGE PATROL CRAFT)

FALA 321   **ZEFIR** 323   **TECZA** 325
SZKWAL 322   **ZORZA** 324

Displacement, tons: 236 full load
Dimensions, feet (metres): 135.5 × 21.3 × 7 *(41.3 × 6.5 × 2.1)*
Main machinery: 2 DM 40 diesels; 8078 hp(m) *(5.94 MW)* sustained; 2 shafts
Speed, knots: 24
Complement: 34
Guns: 4 AK 230 30 mm (2 twin). Some have after mounting removed.
Depth charges: 2 internal racks.
Radars: Surface search: Tamirio RN 231; I band.
Sonars: Hull-mounted; active attack; high frequency.

Comment: Built at Naval Shipyard, Gdynia in 1965-67.

FALA   *7/1993, van Ginderen Collection*

2 KAPER CLASS (TYPE SKS-40) (LARGE PATROL CRAFT)

KAPER I 311   **KAPER II** 312

Displacement, tons: 376 full load
Dimensions, feet (metres): 139.4 × 27.6 × 9.2 *(42.5 × 8.4 × 2.8)*
Main machinery: 2 Sulzer 8ATL25/30 diesels; 4720 hp(m) *(3.47 MW)*; 2 shafts
Speed, knots: 17. **Range, miles:** 2800 at 14 kts
Complement: 11 plus 7 spare
Radars: Surface search: E/F band.
Navigation: I band.

Comment: *Kaper I* completed at Wisla Yard, Gdansk in January 1991, *Kaper II* in November 1991. Have fish finding sonars fitted. Used for Fishery Protection. More may be built.

KAPER I   *1992, MOSG*

12 WISLOKA CLASS (TYPE 90) (COASTAL PATROL CRAFT)

SG 141-152

Displacement, tons: 45 full load
Dimensions, feet (metres): 69.6 × 14.8 × 5.2 *(21.2 × 4.5 × 1.6)*
Main machinery: 2 Wola ZM diesels; 1000 hp(m) *(735 kW)*; 2 shafts
Speed, knots: 18. **Range, miles:** 300 at 18 kts
Complement: 9
Guns: 2—12.7 mm MGs (twin) and 1 ZM rocket launcher.

Comment: Built at Wisla Shipyard, Gdansk between 1973 and 1977.

SG 142   *7/1993, Marek Twardowski*

5 PILICA CLASS (TYPE 918) (COASTAL PATROL CRAFT)

SG 161-165

Displacement, tons: 87 full load
Dimensions, feet (metres): 95.1 × 18.4 × 4.3 *(29 × 5.6 × 1.3)*
Main machinery: 3 M 50 diesels; 6610 hp(m) *(4.86 MW)*; 3 shafts
Speed, knots: 28
Complement: 15
Guns: 2 ZU-23-2M Wrobel 23 mm (twin).
Radars: Surface search: Tamiro RN 231; I band.

Comment: Same as naval craft but without the torpedo tubes and sonar. Built in 1973-74 by Naval Shipyard, Gdynia.

SG 161   *1992, MOSG*

SG 165   *9/1992, Hartmut Ehlers*

4 B 306 CLASS

SG 81-83   85

Displacement, tons: 41 full load
Dimensions, feet (metres): 50 × 13.8 × 4.9 *(15.3 × 4.2 × 1.5)*
Main machinery: 2 Wola diesels; 2754 hp(m) *(2.03 MW);* 2 shafts
Speed, knots: 10
Complement: 4

Comment: Built in 1971-73.

SG 81   *1993, MOSG*

5 SZKWAL CLASS (TYPE S-12) (INSHORE PATROL CRAFT)

SG 111-115

Dimensions, feet (metres): 38.4 × 15.1 × 3 *(11.7 × 4.6 × 0.9)*
Main machinery: 2 diesels; 2000 hp(m) *(1.47 MW);* 2 shafts
Speed, knots: 38
Complement: 4
Guns: 1—7.62 mm MG.
Radars: Surface search: I band.

Comment: Built at Wisla, Gdansk between 1986 and 1990. Fast pursuit boats possibly taken over from the Police. There may be up to 14 of this class but some are still used by the Police.

SG 113   *9/1992, Hartmut Ehlers*

INSHORE PATROL CRAFT

Comment: There are at least two other classes of harbour patrol craft. Overall numbers not known.

SG 14   *6/1993, Erik Laursen*

PORTUGAL

Headquarters' Appointments

Chief of Naval Staff:
    Admiral António Carlos Fuzeta da Ponte
Deputy Chief of Naval Staff:
    Vice Admiral Fernando Manuel Palla Machado da Silva
Naval Commander:
    Vice Admiral Narciso Augusto do Carmo Duro
Azores Maritime Zone Commander:
    Rear Admiral Pedro Manuel de Vasconcelos Caeiro
Madeira Maritime Zone Commander:
    Captain Luis Filipe Vidigal Aragão
Marine Corps Commander:
    Captain José Luis Pereira de Almeida Viegas
Submarine Squadron Commander:
    Captain Luis Sebastião Delgado de Rodrigues Nascimento

Diplomatic Representation

Naval Attaché in London:
    Commander Rui Cardoso de Telles Palhinha
Naval Attaché in Paris, Brussels and Hague:
    Commander José Manuel de Fonseca Alvarenga Rua
Naval Attaché in Washington, Ottawa and NLR SACLANT:
    Captain Jose Luis Lopes Celestino da Silva
Defence Attaché in Bissau, Dakar and Conakry:
    Commander Antonio Joao Carreiro e Silva
Defence Attaché in Rabat and Tunis:
    Commander José Manuel Fernandez de Barros Braz Mimoso
Defence Attaché in Brasilia:
    Captain José Manuel Castanho Paes

Personnel

(a)   1994: 11 248 (1603 officers) including 1660 marines
(b)   12 months national service

Strength of the Fleet

Type	Active (Reserve)	Building (Projected)
Submarines (Patrol)	3	(3)
Frigates	17	—
Large Patrol Craft	15	—
Coastal/River Patrol Craft	12	5
Minesweepers	—	(4)
LCTs	3	—
LCMs	7	—
Survey Ships and Craft	9	—
Sail Training Ships	4	—
Replenishment Tanker	1	—
Harbour Tankers	1 (2)	—
Buoy Tender	1	—
Diving Tender	1	—

Bases

Main Base: Lisbon—Alfeite
Dockyard: Arsenal do Alfeite
Fleet Support: Porto, Portimão, Funchal, Ponta Delgada
Air Base: Montijo (Lisbon)

Naval Air

The helicopter squadron was formally activated on 8 June 1993 at Montigo air force base, Lisbon. Operational and logistic procedures are similar to the air force.

Prefix to Ships' Names

NRP

Mercantile Marine

Lloyd's Register of Shipping:
    307 vessels of 285 596 tons gross

DELETIONS

Patrol Forces

1992   *São Roque*

Amphibious Forces

1993   *LDM 406, LDM 401, LDM 119 (to Guinea Bissau)*

Auxiliaries

1993   *São Gabriel, São Miguel*

PENNANT LIST

Submarines

S 163	Albacora
S 164	Barracuda
S 166	Delfim

Frigates

F 330	Vasco da Gama
F 331	Alvares Cabral
F 332	Corte Real
F 471	Antonio Enes
F 475	João Coutinho
F 476	Jacinto Candido
F 477	Gen Pereira d'Eça
F 480	Comandante João Belo
F 481	Comandante Hermenegildo Capelo
F 482	Comandante Roberto Ivens
F 483	Comandante Sacadura Cabral
F 484	Augusto de Castilho
F 485	Honorio Barreto
F 486	Baptista de Andrade
F 487	João Roby
F 488	Afonso Cerqueira
F 489	Oliveira E Carmo

Patrol Forces

P 370	Rio Minho
P 1140	Cacine
P 1141	Cunene
P 1142	Mandovi
P 1143	Rovuma
P 1144	Cuanza
P 1145	Geba
P 1146	Zaire
P 1147	Zambeze
P 1148	Dom Aleixo
P 1149	Dom Jeremias
P 1150	Argos
P 1151	Dragão
P 1152	Escorpião
P 1153	Cassiopeia
P 1154	Hidra
P 1160	Limpopo
P 1161	Save
P 1162	Albatroz
P 1163	Açor
P 1164	Andorinha
P 1165	Aguia
P 1167	Cisne
UAM 630	Condor

Amphibious Forces

LDG 201	Bombarda
LDG 202	Alabarda
LDG 203	Bacamarte
LDM 120-121	
LDM 418, 420, 422, 423	

Service Forces

A 520	Sagres
A 521	Schultz Xavier
A 527	Almeida Carvalho
A 5201	Vega
A 5203	Andromeda
A 5204	Polar
A 5205	Auriga
A 5207	Ribeira Grande
A 5210	Berrio

SUBMARINES

Note: Replacements for the Daphne class are being studied with the aim of placing an order by 1996.

3 ALBACORA (DAPHNE) CLASS

Name	No	Builders	Laid down	Launched	Commissioned
ALBACORA	S 163	Dubigeon-Normandie, Nantes	6 Sep 1965	13 Oct 1966	1 Oct 1967
BARRACUDA	S 164	Dubigeon-Normandie, Nantes	19 Oct 1965	24 Apr 1967	4 May 1968
DELFIM	S 166	Dubigeon-Normandie, Nantes	14 May 1967	23 Sep 1968	1 Oct 1969

Displacement, tons: 869 surfaced; 1043 dived
Dimensions, feet (metres): 189.6 × 22.3 × 17.1
  (57.8 × 6.8 × 5.2)
Main machinery: Diesel-electric; 2 SEMT-Pielstick 12 PA4 V 185 diesels; 2450 hp(m) *(1.8 MW)*; 2 Jeumont Schneider alternators; 1.7 MW; 2 motors; 2600 hp(m) *(1.9 MW)*; 2 shafts
Speed, knots: 13.5 surfaced; 16 dived
Range, miles: 2710 at 12.5 kts surfaced; 2130 at 10 kts snorting
Complement: 55 (8 officers)

Torpedoes: 12—21.7 in *(550 mm)* (8 bow, 4 stern) tubes. ECAN E14/15; anti-surface; passive homing to 12 km *(6.6 nm)* at 25 kts; warhead 300 kg or ECAN L3; anti-submarine; active homing to 5.5 km *(3 nm)* at 25 kts; warhead 200 kg. No reloads.
Countermeasures: ESM: ARUR; radar warning.
Fire control: DLT D3 torpedo control.
Radars: Surface search: Kelvin Hughes KH 1007; I band.
Sonars: Thomson Sintra DSUV 2; passive search and attack; medium frequency.
  DUUA 2; active search and attack; 8.4 kHz.

Programmes: Basically similar to the French Daphne type, but slightly modified to suit Portuguese requirements.
Modernisation: Similar to French Daphne class but without the external modification to the hull. New radar fitted in 1993/94.
Structure: Diving depth, 300 m *(984 ft)*. Crushing depth, 575 m *(1885 ft)*.
Sales: *Cachalote* transferred to Pakistan as *Ghazi* in 1975.

DELFIM   *10/1993, Diego Quevedo*

FRIGATES

4 BAPTISTA DE ANDRADE CLASS

Name	No	Builders	Laid down	Launched	Commissioned
BAPTISTA DE ANDRADE	F 486	Empresa Nacional Bazán, Cartagena	1 Sep 1972	13 Mar 1973	19 Nov 1974
JOÃO ROBY	F 487	Empresa Nacional Bazán, Cartagena	1 Dec 1972	3 June 1973	18 Mar 1975
AFONSO CERQUEIRA	F 488	Empresa Nacional Bazán, Cartagena	10 Mar 1973	6 Oct 1973	26 June 1975
OLIVEIRA E CARMO	F 489	Empresa Nacional Bazán, Cartagena	1 June 1973	22 Feb 1974	28 Oct 1975

Displacement, tons: 1203 standard; 1380 full load
Dimensions, feet (metres): 277.5 × 33.8 × 10.2
  (84.6 × 10.3 × 3.1)
Main machinery: 2 OEW Pielstick 12 PC2.2 V 400 diesels; 12 000 hp(m) *(8.82 MW)* sustained; 2 shafts
Speed, knots: 22. **Range, miles:** 5900 at 18 kts
Complement: 122 (11 officers) plus marine detachment

Guns: 1 Creusot Loire 3.9 in *(100 mm)*/55 Mod 1968 ❶; 80° elevation; 80 rounds/minute to 17 km *(9 nm)* anti-surface; 8 km *(4.4 nm)* anti-aircraft; weight of shell 13.5 kg.
2 Bofors 40 mm/70 ❷; 90° elevation; 300 rounds/minute to 12 km *(6.6 nm)*; weight of shell 0.96 kg.
Torpedoes: 6—324 mm US Mk 32 (2 triple) tubes ❸. Honeywell Mk 46; anti-submarine; active/passive homing to 11 km *(5.9 nm)* at 40 kts; warhead 44 kg.
Fire control: Vega GFCS.
Radars: Air/surface search: Plessey AWS 2 ❹; E/F band; range 110 km *(60 nm)*.
Navigation: Decca RM 316P; I band.

BAPTISTA DE ANDRADE   *(Scale 1 : 900), Ian Sturton*

Fire control: Thomson-CSF Pollux ❺; I/J band; range 31 km *(17 nm)* for 2 m² target.
Sonars: Thomson Sintra Diodon; hull-mounted; active search and attack; 11, 12 or 13 kHz.

Helicopters: Platform for 1 Lynx.

Modernisation: Planned programme to include PDMS Sea Sparrow and SSM has been shelved although space and weight allowance is available for two SSM. Communications equipment updated 1988-91.

JOÃO ROBY   *8/1993, van Ginderen Collection*

3 VASCO DA GAMA (MEKO 200) CLASS

Name	No	Builders	Laid down	Launched	Commissioned
VASCO DA GAMA	F 330	Blohm & Voss, Hamburg	1 Feb 1989	26 June 1989	18 Jan 1991
ALVARES CABRAL	F 331	Howaldtswerke, Kiel	2 June 1989	6 June 1990	24 May 1991
CORTE REAL	F 332	Howaldtswerke, Kiel	24 Nov 1989	6 June 1990	22 Nov 1991

Displacement, tons: 2700 standard; 3300 full load
Dimensions, feet (metres): 380.3 oa; 357.6 pp × 48.7 × 20
(115.9; 109 × 14.8 × 6.1)
Main machinery: CODOG; 2 GE LM 2500 gas turbines;
53 000 hp (39.5 MW) sustained; 2 MTU 12V 1163 TB83 diesels; 8840 hp(m) (6.5 MW); 2 shafts; cp props
Speed, knots: 32 gas; 20 diesel. **Range, miles:** 4900 at 18 kts;
9600 at 12 kts
Complement: 182 (23 officers) (including air crew of 16 (4 officers)) plus 16 Flag Staff

Missiles: SSM: 8 McDonnell Douglas Harpoon (2 quad) launchers ❶; active radar homing to 130 km (70 nm) at 0.9 Mach;
warhead 227 kg.
SAM: Raytheon Sea Sparrow Mk 29 Mod 1 octuple launcher ❷;
RIM-7M; semi-active radar homing to 14.6 km (8 nm) at
2.5 Mach; warhead 39 kg. Space left for VLS Sea Sparrow ❸.
Guns: 1 Creusot Loire 3.9 in (100 mm)/55 Mod 68 CADAM ❹;
80° elevation; 60 rounds/minute to 17 km (9 nm) anti-surface;
8 km (4.4 nm) anti-aircraft; weight of shell 13.5 kg.
1 General Electric/General Dynamics Vulcan Phalanx 20 mm
Mk 15 Mod 11 ❺; 6 barrels per mounting; 3000 rounds/
minute combined to 1.5 km.
Torpedoes: 6—324 mm US Mk 32 (2 triple) tubes ❻. Honeywell
Mk 46 Mod 5; anti-submarine; active/passive homing to 11 km
(5.9 nm) at 40 kts; warhead 44 kg.
Countermeasures: Decoys: 2 Loral Hycor Mk 36 SRBOC 6-
barrelled chaff launchers ❼.
SLQ 25 Nixie; towed torpedo decoy.
ESM/ECM: Argo AR 700/APECS II; intercept and jammer.
Combat data systems: Signaal SEWACO action data auto-
mation with STACOS tactical command; Link 11 and 14. SAT-
COMs (from 1994).
Fire control: SWG 1A(V) for SSM. Vesta Helo transponder with
data link for OTHT.
Radars: Air search: Signaal MW 08 (derived from Smart 3D) ❽;
3D; G band.
Air/surface search: Signaal DA 08 (fitted with IFF Mk 12 Mod 4)
❾; F band.
Navigation: Kelvin Hughes Type 1007; I band.
Fire control: 2 Signaal STIR ❿; I/J/K band; range 140 km
(76 nm) for 1 m² target.
Sonars: Computing Devices (Canada) SQS 510(V); hull-mounted;
active search and attack; medium frequency.

Helicopters: 2 Super Sea Lynx Mk 95 ⓫.

Programmes: The contract for all three was signed on 25 July
1986. These are Meko 200 type ordered from a consortium of
builders. As well as Portugal, which is bearing 40 per cent of
the cost, assistance has been given by Germany and NATO
with some missile, CIWS and torpedo systems being provided
by the USA.
Structure: All-steel construction. Stabilisers fitted. Full RAS facilities. Space has been left for a sonar towed array and for VLS
Sea Sparrow.
Operational: Designed primarily as ASW ships.

VASCO DA GAMA   (Scale 1 : 1200), Ian Sturton

ALVARES CABRAL   3/1993, Giorgio Arra

ALVARES CABRAL   7/1993, van Ginderen Collection

CORTE REAL   11/1993, H M Steele

4 COMANDANTE JOÃO BELO CLASS

Name	No	Builders	Laid down	Launched	Commissioned
COMANDANTE JOÃO BELO	F 480	At et Ch de Nantes	6 Sep 1965	22 Mar 1966	1 July 1967
COMANDANTE HERMENEGILDO CAPELO	F 481	At et Ch de Nantes	13 May 1966	29 Nov 1966	26 Apr 1968
COMANDANTE ROBERTO IVENS	F 482	At et Ch de Nantes	13 Dec 1966	8 Aug 1967	23 Nov 1968
COMANDANTE SACADURA CABRAL	F 483	At et Ch de Nantes	18 Aug 1967	15 Mar 1968	25 July 1969

Displacement, tons: 1750 standard; 2250 full load
Dimensions, feet (metres): 336.9 × 38.4 × 14.4
(102.7 × 11.7 × 4.4)
Main machinery: 4 SEMT-Pielstick 12 PC2.2 V 400 diesels;
16 000 hp(m) *(11.8 MW)* sustained; 2 shafts
Speed, knots: 25. **Range, miles:** 7500 at 15 kts
Complement: 201 (15 officers)

Guns: 3 Creusot Loire 3.9 in *(100 mm)*/55 Mod 1953 ❶; 80°
elevation; 60 rounds/minute to 17 km *(9 nm)* anti-surface;
8 km *(4.4 nm)* anti-aircraft; weight of shell 13.5 kg.
2 Bofors 40 mm/60 ❷; 90° elevation; 300 rounds/minute to
12 km *(6.6 nm)*; weight of shell 0.89 kg.
Torpedoes: 6—21.7 in *(550 mm)* (2 triple) tubes ❸ or
6—324 mm US Mk 32 Mod 5 (2 triple) tubes (after modernisation); ECAN L3 being replaced by Honeywell Mk 46 Mod 5
(after modernisation).
A/S mortars: 1 Mortier 305 mm 4-barrelled ❹; automatic loading; range 2700 m; warhead 227 kg. To be removed during
modernisation.
Countermeasures: Decoys: 2 Loral Hycor Mk 36 SRBOC 6-
barrelled chaff launchers.
SLQ-25 Nixie; towed torpedo decoy.
ESM: ARBR-10 or Argo 700 DF (after modernisation); radar
warning.
Fire control: C T Analogique. Sagem DMA optical director.
Radars: Air search: Thomson-CSF DRBV 22A ❺; D band; range
366 km *(200 nm)*.
Surface search: Thomson-CSF DRBV 50 ❻; G band; range 29 km
(16 nm).
Navigation: Kelvin Hughes KH 1007; I band.
Fire control: Thomson-CSF DRBC 31D ❼; I band.
Sonars: CDC SQS 510 (after modernisation); hull-mounted;
active search and attack; medium frequency.
Thomson Sintra DUBA 3A; hull-mounted; active search; high
frequency.

Modernisation: Modernisation of external communications, sensors and electronics completed 1987-90. Chaff launchers
installed in 1989. In 1993-96 the hull sonar is being replaced,
torpedo tubes updated, the A/S mortar removed, towed torpedo decoy installed and ESM equipment changed. It is also
planned to add a combat data system with Link 11 compatible
with the Vasco da Gama class. The plan to have one or both
after guns replaced either by flight deck and hangar for helicopter or by SSM has been shelved but X turret is to be
removed in at least three of the class. *Roberto Ivens* may
become a training ship.
Structure: They are generally similar to the French Commandant
Rivière class.
Operational: Designed for tropical service but being modernised
primarily for the ASW role.

COMANDANTE JOÃO BELO

(Scale 1 : 900), Ian Sturton

COMANDANTE HERMENEGILDO CAPELO

10/1992, A Campanera i Rovira

COMANDANTE JOÃO BELO

7/1993, van Ginderen Collection

6 JOÃO COUTINHO CLASS

Name	No	Builders	Laid down	Launched	Commissioned
ANTONIO ENES	F 471	Empresa Nacional Bazán, Cartagena	10 Apr 1968	16 Aug 1969	18 June 1971
JOÃO COUTINHO	F 475	Blohm & Voss AG, Hamburg	24 Dec 1968	2 May 1969	28 Feb 1970
JACINTO CANDIDO	F 476	Blohm & Voss AG, Hamburg	10 Feb 1969	16 June 1969	29 May 1970
GENERAL PEREIRA D'EÇA	F 477	Blohm & Voss AG, Hamburg	21 Apr 1969	26 July 1969	10 Oct 1970
AUGUSTO DE CASTILHO	F 484	Empresa Nacional Bazán, Cartagena	15 Oct 1968	4 July 1969	14 Nov 1970
HONORIO BARRETO	F 485	Empresa Nacional Bazán, Cartagena	20 Feb 1968	11 Apr 1970	15 Apr 1971

Displacement, tons: 1203 standard; 1380 full load
Dimensions, feet (metres): 277.5 × 33.8 × 10.8
(84.6 × 10.3 × 3.3)
Main machinery: 2 OEW Pielstick 12 PC2.2 V 400 diesels;
12 000 hp(m) *(8.82 MW)* sustained; 2 shafts
Speed, knots: 22. **Range, miles:** 5900 at 18 kts
Complement: 77 (9 officers)

Guns: 2 US 3 in *(76 mm)*/50 (twin) Mk 33 ❶; 85° elevation; 50
rounds/minute to 12.8 km *(7 nm)*; weight of shell 6 kg.
2 Bofors 40 mm/60 (twin) ❷; 90° elevation; 300 rounds/
minute to 12 km *(6.6 nm)*; weight of shell 0.89 kg.
Fire control: Mk 51 GFCS for 40 mm. Mk 63 for 76 mm.
Radars: Air/surface search: Kelvin Hughes ❸; I band.
Navigation: Racal Decca RM 1226C; I band.
Fire control: Western Electric SPG 34 ❹; I/J band.

Modernisation: A programme for this class to include SSM and
PDMS has been shelved. In 1989-91 the main radar was

JOÃO COUTINHO   *(Scale 1 : 900), Ian Sturton*

updated and JATCOMS installed. Also fitted with SIFICAP
which is a Fishery Protection data exchange system by satellite
to the main database ashore.

Structure: Helicopter platform only.
Operational: A/S equipment no longer operational and laid apart
on shore. Crew reduced by 23 as a result.

HONORIO BARRETO   *7/1993, van Ginderen Collection*

SHIPBORNE AIRCRAFT

Numbers/Type: 5 Westland Super Navy Lynx Mk 95.
Operational speed: 125 kts *(231 km/h)*.
Service ceiling: 12 000 ft *(3660 m)*.
Range: 320 nm *(593 km)*.
Role/Weapon systems: Ordered 2 November 1990 for MEKO 200 frigates; two are updated HAS
3 and three are new aircraft, all delivered in 1993. Sensors: Bendix 1500 radar; Bendix AQS-18
dipping sonar; Racal RNS 252 data link. Weapons: Mk 46 torpedoes.

SUPER LYNX   *8/1993, Portuguese Navy*

LAND-BASED MARITIME AIRCRAFT

(All Air Force manned)

Numbers/Type: 10 Aerospatiale SA 330C Puma.
Operational speed: 151 kts *(280 km/h)*.
Service ceiling: 15 090 ft *(4600 m)*.
Range: 343 nm *(635 km)*.
Role/Weapon systems: For SAR and surface search. Sensors: Omera search radar. Weapons:
Unarmed except for pintle-mounted machine guns.

Numbers/Type: 6/2 CASA C-212 Aviocar.
Operational speed: 190 kts *(353 km/h)*.
Service ceiling: 24 000 ft *(7315 m)*.
Range: 1650 nm *(3055 km)*.
Role/Weapon systems: The first six are for short-range SAR support and transport operations. The
last pair were ordered in February 1993 for maritime patrol and fisheries surveillance off the
Azores and Madeira. Sensors: Search radar and MAD. FLIR and data link (last pair). Weapons:
Unarmed.

Numbers/Type: 5 Lockheed C-130H Hercules.
Operational speed: 325 kts *(602 km/h)*.
Service ceiling: 33 000 ft *(10 060 m)*.
Range: 4250 nm *(7880 km)*.
Role/Weapon systems: MR is a secondary role for the Air Force transport aircraft assigned to
NATO. Sensors: Search radar. Weapons: Unarmed.

Numbers/Type: 6 Lockheed P-3B Orion.
Operational speed: 410 kts *(760 km/h)*.
Service ceiling: 28 300 ft *(8625 m)*.
Range: 4000 nm *(7410 km)*.
Role/Weapon systems: Long-range surveillance and ASW patrol aircraft; acquired with NATO
funding from RAAF update programme and modernised by Lockheed starting in 1987. Progress
is slow. Sensors: APS-115 radar, ASQ-81 MAD, AQS-901 sonobuoy processor, AQS-114 computer, IFF, ECM/ESM. Weapons: ASW; 8 × Mk 46 torpedoes, depth bombs or mines; ASV; 10 ×
underwing stations for ASMs.

PATROL FORCES

Note: Up to 12 offshore patrol vessels are required. Orders may be placed from 1996, or older ships acquired sooner.

10 CACINE CLASS (LARGE PATROL CRAFT)

Name	No	Builders	Commissioned
CACINE	P 1140	Arsenal do Alfeite	May 1969
CUNENE	P 1141	Arsenal do Alfeite	June 1969
MANDOVI	P 1142	Arsenal do Alfeite	Sep 1969
ROVUMA	P 1143	Arsenal do Alfeite	Nov 1969
CUANZA	P 1144	Estaleiros Navais do Mondego	May 1970
GEBA	P 1145	Estaleiros Navais do Mondego	May 1970
ZAIRE	P 1146	Estaleiros Navais do Mondego	Nov 1970
ZAMBEZE	P 1147	Estaleiros Navais do Mondego	Jan 1971
LIMPOPO	P 1160	Arsenal do Alfeite	Apr 1973
SAVE	P 1161	Arsenal do Alfeite	May 1973

Displacement, tons: 292.5 standard; 310 full load
Dimensions, feet (metres): 144 × 25.2 × 7.1 *(44 × 7.7 × 2.2)*
Main machinery: 2 MTU 12V 538 TB80 diesels; 3750 hp(m) *(2.76 MW)* sustained; 2 shafts
Speed, knots: 20. **Range, miles:** 4400 at 12 kts
Complement: 33 (3 officers)
Guns: 1 Bofors 40 mm/60. 1 Oerlikon 20 mm/65.
Radars: Surface search: Kelvin Hughes Type 1007; I/J band.

Comment: Originally mounted a second Bofors aft but most have been removed as has the 37 mm rocket launcher. Have SIFICAP satellite data handling system for Fishery Protection duties. Two of the class are based at Madeira.

ROVUMA
7/1993, van Ginderen Collection

ZAIRE
5/1993, van Ginderen Collection

5 ARGOS CLASS (COASTAL PATROL CRAFT)

Name	No	Builders	Commissioned
ARGOS	P 1150	Arsenal do Alfeite	2 July 1991
DRAGÃO	P 1151	Arsenal do Alfeite	18 Oct 1991
ESCORPIÃO	P 1152	Arsenal do Alfeite	26 Nov 1991
CASSIOPEIA	P 1153	Conafi	11 Nov 1991
HIDRA	P 1154	Conafi	18 Dec 1991

Displacement, tons: 84 standard; 94 full load
Dimensions, feet (metres): 89.2 × 19.4 × 4.6 *(27.2 × 5.9 × 1.4)*
Main machinery: 2 MTU 12V 396 TE84 diesels; 3700 hp(m) *(2.73 MW)* sustained; 2 shafts
Speed, knots: 28. **Range, miles:** 1350 at 15 kts; 200 at 28 kts
Complement: 9 (1 officer)
Guns: 2—12.7 mm MGs.
Radars: Navigation: Furuno 1505 DA; I band.

Comment: Ordered in 1989 and 50 per cent funded by the EC. Capable of full speed operation up to sea state 3. Carries a semi-rigid boat with a 37 hp outboard engine. The boat is recoverable via a stern well at up to 10 kts. *Cassiopeia* is based at Madeira.

CASSIOPEIA
5/1993, van Ginderen Collection

2 DOM ALEIXO CLASS (COASTAL PATROL CRAFT)

Name	No	Builders	Commissioned
DOM ALEIXO	P 1148	S Jacinto Aveiro	7 Dec 1967
DOM JEREMIAS	P 1149 (ex-A 5202)	S Jacinto Aveiro	22 Dec 1967

Displacement, tons: 62.6 standard; 67.7 full load
Dimensions, feet (metres): 82.1 × 17 × 5.2 *(25 × 5.2 × 1.6)*
Main machinery: 2 Cummins diesels; 1270 hp *(947 kW)*; 2 shafts
Speed, knots: 16
Complement: 10 (2 officers)
Gun: 1 Oerlikon 20 mm/65.
Radars: Surface search: Decca 303; I band.

Comment: *Dom Jeremias* has been used as a survey craft but reverted to being a patrol craft in 1989.

DOM JEREMIAS
3/1991, van Ginderen Collection

6 ALBATROZ CLASS (COASTAL PATROL CRAFT)

Name	No	Builders	Commissioned
ALBATROZ	P 1162	Arsenal do Alfeite	9 Dec 1974
AÇOR	P 1163	Arsenal do Alfeite	9 Dec 1974
ANDORINHA	P 1164	Arsenal do Alfeite	20 Dec 1974
AGUIA	P 1165	Arsenal do Alfeite	28 Feb 1975
CISNE	P 1167	Arsenal do Alfeite	31 Mar 1976
CONDOR	UAM 630 (ex-P 1166)	Arsenal do Alfeite	23 Apr 1975

Displacement, tons: 45 full load
Dimensions, feet (metres): 77.4 × 18.4 × 5.2 *(23.6 × 5.6 × 1.6)*
Main machinery: 2 Cummins diesels; 1100 hp *(820 kW)*; 2 shafts
Speed, knots: 20. **Range, miles:** 2500 at 12 kts
Complement: 8 (1 officer)
Guns: 1 Oerlikon 20 mm/65. 2—12.7 mm MGs.
Radars: Surface search: Decca RM 316P; I band.

Comment: *Condor* is now used for harbour patrol duties.

ALBATROZ
8/1993, Portuguese Navy

1 RIO MINHO CLASS (RIVER PATROL CRAFT)

Name	No	Builders	Commissioned
RIO MINHO	P 370	Arsenal do Alfeite	1 Aug 1991

Displacement, tons: 72 full load
Dimensions, feet (metres): 73.5 × 19.7 × 2.6 *(22.4 × 6 × 0.8)*
Main machinery: 2 KHD-Deutz diesels; 664 hp(m) *(488 kW)*; 2 Schottel pump jets
Speed, knots: 9.5. **Range, miles:** 420 at 7 kts
Complement: 8 (1 officer)
Guns: 1—7.62 mm MG.
Radars: Navigation: Furuno FR 1505DA; I band.

Comment: River patrol craft which has replaced *Atria* on the River Minho.

RIO MINHO
1991, Arsenal do Alfeite

MINE WARFARE FORCES

0 + (4) NEW MINESWEEPER (COASTAL)

Displacement, tons: 620 full load
Dimensions, feet (metres): 171.9 oa; 157.5 wl × 34.1 × 10.2 *(52.4; 48 × 10.4 × 3.1)*
Speed, knots: 15; 10 (sweeping). **Range, miles:** 3000 at 12 kts
Complement: 25 plus 5 spare

Guns: 1 DCN 20 mm/20.
Radars: Navigation: I band.

Programmes: Memorandum of Understanding signed 6 April 1989 for a joint Belgium/Netherlands minesweeper project. Design contract awarded November 1990 to van der Giessen-de Noord Marinebouw in a joint venture with Beliard Polyship NV, completed in August 1992 when Portugal joined the project. Netherlands withdrew in 1993 and Belgium now intends to build only four of the class. Because of these problems, Portugal has now put replacement submarines as a higher priority.
Operational: The ship is to be equipped with a newly developed magnetic sweeping gear, 'Sterne M', by Thomson Sintra. This development, ordered by the joint navies, is based upon the concept of 'target simulation' and consists of six bodies, towed in array, each carrying two coils. By automatically computed coil settings a simulated ship's signature is generated without any assumption concerning the mine itself. In addition, proven acoustic and mechanic sweeping capabilities are installed. The requirement is to be able to sweep bottom mines which have sunk so far into soft sand that they are not detected by hunters.

AMPHIBIOUS FORCES

3 BOMBARDA CLASS LDG (LCT)

Name	No	Builders	Commissioned
BOMBARDA	LDG 201	Estaleiros Navais do Mondego	1969
ALABARDA	LDG 202	Estaleiros Navais do Mondego	1970
BACAMARTE	LDG 203	Arsenal do Alfeite	1985

Displacement, tons: 652 full load
Dimensions, feet (metres): 184.3 × 38.7 × 6.2 *(56.2 × 11.8 × 1.9)*
Main machinery: 2 MTU MB diesels; 910 hp(m) *(669 kW)*; 2 shafts
Speed, knots: 9.5. **Range, miles:** 2600 at 9 kts
Complement: 21 (3 officers)
Military lift: 350 tons
Guns: 2 Oerlikon 20 mm.
Radars: Navigation: Decca RM 316P; I band.

Comment: Similar to French EDIC.

BACAMARTE   *4/1992, Hartmut Ehlers*

4 LDM 400 CLASS (LCM)

LDM 418   LDM 420   LDM 422   LDM 423

Displacement, tons: 48 full load
Dimensions, feet (metres): 58.3 × 15.8 × 3.3 *(17.3 × 4.8 × 1)*
Main machinery: 2 Cummins diesels; 400 hp *(298 kW)*; 2 shafts
Speed, knots: 10

Comment: Built 1967-68. Two paid off in 1993.

LDM 421 (old number)   *3/1992, van Ginderen Collection*

2 LDM 100 CLASS (LCM)

LDM 120   LDM 121

Displacement, tons: 50 full load
Dimensions, feet (metres): 50 × 14.4 × 3.6 *(15.3 × 4.4 × 1.1)*
Main machinery: 2 GM diesels; 450 hp *(336 kW)*; 2 shafts
Speed, knots: 9

Comment: Built at the Estaleiros Navais do Mondego in 1965.

SURVEY SHIPS

Note: A sister ship is needed for *Almeida Carvalho* to aid work on behalf of Portuguese-speaking African countries. An ex-US Robert D Conrad class is a possibility.

1 KELLAR CLASS

Name	No	Builders	Commissioned
ALMEIDA CARVALHO	A 527	Marietta Shipbuilding Co	31 Jan 1969
(ex-USNS *Kellar*, T-AGS 25)			

Displacement, tons: 1297 standard; 1327 full load
Dimensions, feet (metres): 209 × 37.1 × 15.1 *(63.7 × 11.3 × 4.6)*
Main machinery: Diesel-electric; 2 Caterpillar diesel generators; 1 motor; 1300 hp *(970 kW)*; 1 shaft
Speed, knots: 15. **Range, miles:** 1200 at 11 kts
Complement: 47 (7 officers) plus 10 scientists
Radars: Surface search: Kelvin Hughes Type 1007; I band.
Navigation: Racal Decca TM 829; I band.

Comment: Leased from the US Navy on 21 January 1972. Transferred finally in 1988. Started building in 1962 but sank alongside during a typhoon in 1965, and so took a long time to complete.

ALMEIDA CARVALHO   *8/1993, Portuguese Navy*

2 ANDROMEDA CLASS

Name	No	Builders	Commissioned
ANDROMEDA	A 5203	Arsenal do Alfeite	1 Feb 1987
AURIGA	A 5205	Arsenal do Alfeite	1 July 1987

Displacement, tons: 230 full load
Dimensions, feet (metres): 103.3 × 25.4 × 8.2 *(31.5 × 7.7 × 2.5)*
Main machinery: 1 MTU 12V 396 TC62 diesel; 1200 hp(m) *(880 kW)* sustained; 1 shaft
Speed, knots: 12. **Range, miles:** 1980 at 10 kts
Complement: 17 (3 officers)
Radars: Navigation: Decca RM 914C; I band.

Comment: Both ordered in January 1984. *Auriga* has a research submarine ROV Phantom S2 and a Klein side scan sonar.

ANDROMEDA   *1987, Arsenal do Alfeite*

6 SURVEY CRAFT

CORAL UAM 801	**ACTINIA** UAM 803	**FISALIA** UAM 805
ATLANTA (ex-*Hidra*) UAM 802	**SICANDRA** UAM 804	**SAVEL** UAM 830

Comment: 801, 802 and 805 are of 36 tons and were launched in 1980. 803 and 804 are converted fishing vessels (803 of 90 tons, 804 of 70 tons) of different designs mostly used as lighthouse tenders. 830 is of 7 tons and was built by Conafi in 1992/93.

FISALIA   *4/1992, Hartmut Ehlers*

TRAINING SHIPS

Name	No	Builders	Commissioned
SAGRES (ex-*Guanabara*, ex-*Albert Leo Schlageter*)	A 520	Blohm & Voss, Hamburg	10 Feb 1938

Displacement, tons: 1725 standard; 1940 full load
Dimensions, feet (metres): 231 wl; 295.2 oa × 39.4 × 17 *(70.4; 90 × 12 × 5.2)*
Main machinery: 2 MTU 12V 183 TE92 auxiliary diesels; 1 shaft
Speed, knots: 10.5. **Range, miles:** 5450 at 7.5 kts on diesel
Complement: 162 (12 officers)

Comment: Former German sail training ship launched 30 October 1937. Sister of US Coast Guard training ship *Eagle* (ex-German *Horst Wessel*) and Soviet *Tovarisch* (ex-German *Gorch Fock*). Taken by the USA as a reparation after the Second World War in 1945 and sold to Brazil in 1948. Purchased from Brazil and commissioned in the Portuguese Navy on 2 February 1962 at Rio de Janeiro and renamed *Sagres*. Sail area, 20 793 sq ft. Height of main-mast, 142 ft. Phased refits 1987-88 and again in 1991-92 which included new engines, improved accommodation, a hydraulic crane and updated navigation equipment.

SAGRES   *4/1992, Hartmut Ehlers*

Name	No	Builders	Commissioned
CREOULA	UAM 201	Lisbon Shipyard	1937

Displacement, tons: 818 standard; 1055 full load
Dimensions, feet (metres): 221.1 × 32.5 × 13.8 *(67.4 × 9.9 × 4.2)*
Main machinery: 1 MTU 8V 183 TE92 auxiliary diesel; 665 hp(m) *(490 kW)*; 1 shaft

Comment: Ex-deep sea sail fishing ship used off the coast of Newfoundland for 36 years. Bought by Fishing Department in 1976 to turn into a museum ship but because she was still seaworthy it was decided to convert her to a training ship. Recommissioned in the Navy in 1987. Refit completed in 1992 including a new engine and improved accommodation.

CREOULA   *9/1991, van Ginderen Collection*

VEGA (ex-*Arreda*) A 5201   **POLAR** (ex-*Anne Linde*) A 5204

Displacement, tons: 70 (60, *Vega*)
Dimensions, feet (metres): 75 × 16 × 8.2 *(22.9 × 4.9 × 2.5)* *(Polar)*
65 × 14.1 × 8.2 *(19.8 × 4.3 × 2.5)* *(Vega)*

AUXILIARIES

1 SÃO ROQUE CLASS (DIVING TENDER)

Name	No	Builders	Commissioned
RIBEIRA GRANDE	A 5207 (ex-M 402)	CUF Shipyard, Lisbon	8 Feb 1957

Displacement, tons: 394.4 standard; 451.9 full load
Dimensions, feet (metres): 153 × 27.7 × 8.2 *(46.3 × 8.5 × 2.5)*
Main machinery: 2 Mirrlees JVSS-12 diesels; 2500 hp *(1.87 MW)*; 2 shafts
Speed, knots: 15. **Range, miles:** 2400 at 12 kts
Complement: 46 (3 officers)
Guns: 1 Oerlikon 20 mm/65.
Radars: Navigation: I band.

Comment: Same style as British Ton class coastal minesweepers. 40 mm gun removed 1972, as was the minesweeping gear. Neither the equipment nor the trained personnel are available for mine warfare operations. This ship has replaced *São Roque* as the diver support vessel in 1993 and has a recompression chamber.

RIBEIRA GRANDE   *8/1993, Portuguese Navy*

1 ROVER CLASS (REPLENISHMENT TANKER)

Name	No	Builders	Commissioned
BERRIO (ex-*Blue Rover*)	A 5210 (ex-A 270)	Swan Hunter	15 July 1970

Displacement, tons: 4700 light; 11 522 full load
Dimensions, feet (metres): 461 × 63 × 24 *(140.6 × 19.2 × 7.3)*
Main machinery: 2 SEMT-Pielstick 16 PA4 185 diesels; 5344 hp(m) *(3.93 MW)*; 1 shaft; cp prop; bow thruster
Speed, knots: 19. **Range, miles:** 15 000 at 15 kts
Complement: 54 (7 officers)
Cargo capacity: 6600 tons fuel
Guns: 2 Oerlikon 20 mm.
Countermeasures: Decoys: 2 Vickers Corvus launchers. 2 Plessey Shield launchers. 1 Graseby Type 182; towed torpedo decoy.
Radars: Navigation: Kelvin Hughes Type 1006; I band.
Helicopters: Platform for 1 medium.

Comment: Transferred from UK 31 March 1993. Small fleet tanker designed to replenish oil and aviation fuel, fresh water, limited dry cargo and refrigerated stores under all conditions while under way. Full refit in 1990/91 gives a service life expectancy until about 2004. No hangar but helicopter landing platform is served by a stores lift, to enable stores to be transferred at sea by 'vertical lift'. Capable of HIFR. Can pump fuel at 600 cu m/h.

BERRIO   *6/1993, Portuguese Navy*

3 HARBOUR TANKERS

ODELEITE UAM 301   **ODIVELAS** UAM 302   OEIRAS UAM 303 (ex-BC 3, ex-YO 3)

Comment: Cargo capacity: First two, 674 tons; *Oeiras*, 924 tons. *Oeiras* and *Odivelas* placed in reserve in 1993 as a result of a new fuel delivery system installed at the Alfeite naval base.

OEIRAS   *5/1987, Hartmut Ehlers*

1 BUOY TENDER (RIVER)

Name	No.	Builders	Commissioned
GUIA	UAM 676	S Jacinto, Aveiro	30 Jan 1985

Displacement, tons: 70
Dimensions, feet (metres): 72.2 × 25.9 × 7.2 *(22 × 7.9 × 2.2)*
Main machinery: 1 Deutz MWM SBA6M816 diesel; 465 hp(m) *(342 kW)* sustained; Schottel Navigator prop
Speed, knots: 8.5 (3.5 on auxiliary engine)

GUIA   *5/1993, van Ginderen Collection*

HARBOUR PATROL CRAFT AND FERRIES

SURRIADA UAM 602	**BONANCA** UAM 612	**TUFAO** UAM 639
MARETA UAM 605	**MAR CHAO** UAM 613	**VASCAO** UAM 912
MARESIA UAM 608	**LEVANTE** UAM 631	**ZEZERE** UAM 913
BOLINA UAM 611	**VENTANTE** UAM 636	

Displacement, tons: 9
Dimensions, feet (metres): 39 × 11.8 × 3.3 *(11.8 × 3.6 × 1)*
Main machinery: 2 Volvo Penta diesels; 426 hp(m) *(313 kW)*; 2 shafts
Speed, knots: 20
Complement: 4

Comment: Large numbers of harbour craft of similar characteristics to those listed. 912 and 913 are ferries. Some have *Marinha* on the side, others of the same type have *Guarda Fiscal*. Up to 24 craft are required to assist in controlling drug runners.

ZEZERE   *4/1992, Hartmut Ehlers*

MAR CHAO   *3/1992, van Ginderen Collection*

COURA   *4/1992, van Ginderen Collection*

ALBACORA II   *3/1993, van Ginderen Collection*

8 CALMARIA CLASS

CALMARIA UAM 642	**MONCÃO** UAM 645	**PREIA-MAR** UAM 648
CIRRO UAM 643	**SUÃO** UAM 646	**BAIXA-MAR** UAM 649
VENDAVAL UAM 644	**MACAREO** UAM 647	

Displacement, tons: 12 full load
Dimensions, feet (metres): 39 × 12.5 × 2.3 *(11.9 × 3.8 × 0.7)*
Main machinery: 2 Bazán MAN 2866 LXE diesels; 881 hp(m) *(648 kW)*; 2 waterjets
Speed, knots: 32. **Range, miles:** 275 at 20 kts
Complement: 3
Guns: 1—7.62 mm MG.
Radars: Surface search: Furuno 1830; I band.

Comment: Similar to Spanish Guardia Civil del Mar Saetta II craft. Ordered from Bazán, Cadiz on 8 January 1993. First pair completed 30 November 1993, third one on 18 January 1994. Remainder to be delivered between August and December 1994. GRP hulls.

CALMARIA   *12/1993, Portuguese Navy*

TUG

1 OCEAN TUG

Name	No	Builders	Commissioned
SCHULTZ XAVIER	A 521	Alfeite Naval Yard	14 July 1972

Displacement, tons: 900
Dimensions, feet (metres): 184 × 33 × 12.5 *(56 × 10 × 3.8)*
Main machinery: 2 diesels; 2400 hp(m) *(1.76 MW)*; 2 shafts
Speed, knots: 14.5. **Range, miles:** 3000 at 12.5 kts
Complement: 54 (4 officers)

SCHULTZ XAVIER   *3/1991, van Ginderen Collection*

QATAR

Senior Appointment	Personnel	Bases	Mercantile Marine
Commander Naval Force: Colonel Said Al Suweidi	(a) 1994: 850 officers and men (including Marine Police) (b) Voluntary service	Doha (main); Halul Island (secondary)	*Lloyd's Register of Shipping:* 59 vessels of 430 542 tons gross

PATROL FORCES

0 + 4 VITA CLASS (FAST ATTACK CRAFT—MISSILE)

Displacement, tons: 376 full load
Dimensions, feet (metres): 185.7 × 29.5 × 7.5 *(56.3 × 9 × 2.3)*
Main machinery: 4 MTU 20V 538 TB93 diesels; 18 740 hp(m) *(13.8 MW)* sustained; 4 shafts
Speed, knots: 35. **Range, miles:** 1800 at 12 kts
Complement: 47 (7 officers)

Missiles: SSM: 4 or 8 Aerospatiale MM 40 Exocet ❶.
SAM: Matra Sadral sextuple launcher for Mistral ❷.
Guns: 1 OTO Melara 76 mm/62 Super Rapid ❸.
  1 Signaal Goalkeeper 30 mm ❹ or Thomson-CSF Crotale. 2—12.7 mm MGs.
Countermeasures: Decoys: CSEE Dagaie Mk 2 for chaff ❺.
ESM: Thomson-CSF DR 3000S; intercept.
ECM: Dassault ARBB 33; jammer.
Combat data systems: Signaal SEWACO FD with Thomson-CSF TACTICOS; Link Y.
Fire control: Signaal STING optronic director. IRSCAN electro-optical tracker ❻.
Radars: Air/surface search; 3D; ❼; E/F band.
Navigation: I band.
Fire control: Signaal STING ❽; I/J band.

Programmes: Order announced on 4 June 1992 by Vosper Thornycroft. First steel cut 20 July 1993. Expected launch of first of class in February 1995 for completion in November 1995. Remainder to commission at six month intervals.
Structure: Described as a Vita design derivative. There are few officially released facts so some of the details listed are subject to change. It is reported that a CSEE Sidewind EW management system is to be installed and that a THORN EMI data distribution system is to be used.

VITA   *(not to scale), Ian Sturton*

3 DAMSAH (COMBATTANTE III M) CLASS
(FAST ATTACK CRAFT—MISSILE)

Name	No	Builders	Commissioned
DAMSAH	Q 01	CMN, Cherbourg	10 Nov 1982
AL GHARIYAH	Q 02	CMN, Cherbourg	10 Feb 1983
RBIGAH	Q 03	CMN, Cherbourg	11 May 1983

Displacement, tons: 345 standard; 395 full load
Dimensions, feet (metres): 183.7 × 26.9 × 7.2 *(56 × 8.2 × 2.2)*
Main machinery: 4 MTU 20V 538 TB93 diesels; 18 740 hp(m) *(13.8 MW)* sustained; 4 shafts
Speed, knots: 38.5. **Range, miles:** 2000 at 15 kts
Complement: 41 (6 officers)

Missiles: SSM: 8 Aerospatiale MM 40 Exocet; inertial cruise; active radar homing to 70 km *(40 nm)* at 0.9 Mach; warhead 165 kg; sea-skimmer.
Guns: 1 OTO Melara 3 in *(76 mm)*/62; 85° elevation; 60 rounds/minute to 16 km *(8.7 nm)*; weight of shell 6 kg.
  2 Breda 40 mm/70 (twin); 85° elevation; 300 rounds/minute to 12.5 km *(6.8 nm)*; weight of shell 0.96 kg.
  4 Oerlikon 30 mm/75 (2 twin); 85° elevation; 650 rounds/minute to 10 km *(5.5 nm)*; weight of shell 1 kg or 0.36 kg.
Countermeasures: Decoys: CSEE Dagaie trainable single launcher; 6 containers; IR flares and chaff; H/J band.
ESM/ECM: Racal Cutlass/Cygnus.
Fire control: Vega system. 2 CSEE Naja directors.
Radars: Surface search: Thomson-CSF Triton; G band.
Navigation: Racal Decca 1226; I band.
Fire control: Thomson-CSF Castor II; I/J band; range 15 km *(8 nm)* for 1 m² target.

Programmes: Ordered in 1980 and launched in 1982. All arrived at Doha July 1983.

RBIGAH   *1993*

6 BARZAN CLASS (LARGE PATROL CRAFT)

Name	No	Builders	Commissioned
BARZAN	Q 11	Vosper Thornycroft Ltd	13 Jan 1975
HWAR	Q 12	Vosper Thornycroft Ltd	30 Apr 1975
THAT ASSUARI	Q 13	Vosper Thornycroft Ltd	3 Oct 1975
AL WUSAIL	Q 14	Vosper Thornycroft Ltd	28 Oct 1975
FATEH-AL-KHAIR	Q 15	Vosper Thornycroft Ltd	22 Jan 1976
TARIQ	Q 16	Vosper Thornycroft Ltd	1 Mar 1976

Displacement, tons: 120 full load
Dimensions, feet (metres): 110 × 21 × 5.5 *(33.5 × 6.4 × 1.6)*
Main machinery: 2 Paxman Valenta 16CM diesels; 6703 hp(m) *(5 MW)* sustained; 2 shafts
Speed, knots: 27
Complement: 25
Guns: 4 Oerlikon 30 mm/75 (2 twin).
Radars: Surface search: Racal Decca; I band.

Comment: Ordered in 1972-73. To be replaced by the Vita class.

BARZAN   *1993*

6 DAMEN POLYCAT 1450 CLASS (COASTAL PATROL CRAFT)

Q 31-36

Displacement, tons: 18 full load
Dimensions, feet (metres): 47.6 × 15.4 × 4.9 *(14.5 × 4.7 × 2.1)*
Main machinery: 2 Detroit 12V-71TA diesels; 840 hp *(627 kW)* sustained; 2 shafts
Speed, knots: 26
Complement: 11
Guns: 1 Oerlikon 20 mm.
Radars: Navigation: Racal Decca; I band.

Comment: Delivered February-May 1980. May have been transferred to the Marine Police.

Q 33   *3/1980, Damen SY*

25 FAIREY MARINE SPEAR CLASS (COASTAL PATROL CRAFT)

Q 71-Q 95

Displacement, tons: 4.3
Dimensions, feet (metres): 29.8 × 9 × 2.8 *(9.1 × 2.8 × 0.9)*
Main machinery: 2 diesels; 290 hp *(216 kW)*; 2 shafts
Speed, knots: 26
Complement: 4
Guns: 3—7.62 mm MGs.

Comment: First seven ordered early 1974 and delivered June 1974 to February 1975. Contract for further five signed December 1975. Third contract for three fulfilled with delivery of two on 30 June 1975 and one on 14 July 1975. Fourth order for 10 (four Mk 1, six Mk 2) received October 1976 and delivery effected April 1977. These craft belong to the Navy, not the Police.

AUXILIARIES

Note: There are a number of amphibious craft including an LCT *Rabha* of 160 ft *(48.8 m)* with a capacity for three tanks and 110 troops, acquired in 1986-87. Also four Rotork craft and 30 Sea Jeeps in 1985. It is not clear how many of the smaller craft are for civilian use.

LAND-BASED MARITIME AIRCRAFT

Numbers/Type: 6 Westland Commando Mk 3.
Operational speed: 125 kts *(230 km/h)*.
Service ceiling: 10 500 ft *(3200 m)*.
Range: 630 nm *(1165 km)*.
Role/Weapon systems: Form No 8 Anti-surface Vessel Squadron for coastal surveillance and anti-shipping operations. Sensors: MEL ARI 5955 radar. Weapons: ASV; 1 × AM 39 Exocet ASM, carried by two helicopters only; general purpose machine guns carried; door-mounted.

POLICE

2 KEITH NELSON TYPE (COASTAL PATROL CRAFT)

Displacement, tons: 13
Dimensions, feet (metres): 44 × 12.3 × 3.8 *(13.5 × 3.8 × 1.1)*
Main machinery: 2 Caterpillar diesels; 800 hp *(597 kW)*; 2 shafts
Speed, knots: 26
Complement: 6
Guns: 1—12.7 mm MG. 2—7.62 mm MGs.

Comment: The third of this group has been converted into a pilot cutter.

KEITH NELSON TYPE   9/1990

4 CRESTITALIA MV-45 CLASS (COASTAL PATROL CRAFT)

Displacement, tons: 17 full load
Dimensions, feet (metres): 47.6 × 12.5 × 2.6 *(14.5 × 3.8 × 0.8)*
Main machinery: 2 diesels; 1270 hp *(933 kW)*; 2 shafts
Speed, knots: 32. **Range, miles:** 275 at 29 kts
Complement: 6
Guns: 1 Oerlikon 20 mm. 2—7.62 mm MGs.

Comment: Built by Crestitalia and delivered in mid-1989. GRP construction.

MV-45   *1989, Crestitalia*

5 WATERCRAFT P 1200 TYPE (COASTAL PATROL CRAFT)

Displacement, tons: 12.7
Dimensions, feet (metres): 39 × 13.4 × 3.6 *(11.9 × 4.1 × 1.1)*
Main machinery: 2 Wizeman Mercedes 400 diesels; 660 hp(m) *(485 kW)*; 2 shafts
Speed, knots: 29
Complement: 4
Guns: 2—7.62 mm MGs.

Comment: Built by Watercraft, Shoreham, England in 1980. Two have been deleted.

ROMANIA

General

Up to the overthrow of President Ceaucescu in December 1989 the Fleet was undermanned and seldom went to sea mostly because sailors were used for civilian tasks. At the end of 1990 it was reported that due to financial problems work had stopped on all new construction and major refits. There was more activity in 1991 and in August 1992 a Naval Review was held. In 1993 exercises were being held at regular intervals.

Headquarters' Appointments

Commander-in-Chief of the Navy:
 Vice Admiral Gheorghe Anghelescu

Strength of the Fleet

Type	Active	Building
Submarine	1	—
Destroyer	1	—
Frigates	5	1
Corvettes	10	—
River Monitors	6	—
Fast Attack Craft (Missile)	6	—
Fast Attack Craft (Gun and Patrol)	21(4)	—
Fast Attack Craft (Torpedo)	36	—
River Patrol Craft	18	—
Minelayer/MCM Support	2	—
Minesweepers (Coastal and River)	41	—
Training Ship	1	—
Survey Ships	2	—
Auxiliaries	23	—
Tugs	3	1

Personnel

1994: 7000 regulars plus 6900 conscripts.

Bases

Black Sea—Mangalia (HQ and Training); Constanta (Coastal Defence and Naval Aviation)
Danube—Giurgiu (HQ), Sulina, Galati, Dulcea

Mercantile Marine

Lloyd's Register of Shipping:
 443 vessels of 2 866 962 tons gross

SUBMARINES

1 KILO CLASS (TYPE 877E)

DELFINUL   521

Displacement, tons: 2325 surfaced; 3076 dived
Dimensions, feet (metres): 243.8 × 32.8 × 21.7 *(74.3 × 10 × 6.6)*
Main machinery: Diesel-electric; 2 diesels; 3650 hp(m) *(2.68 MW)*; 2 generators; 1 motor; 5900 hp(m) *(4.34 MW)*; 1 shaft
Speed, knots: 10 surfaced; 20 dived; 9 snorting
Range, miles: 6000 at 7 kts surfaced; 400 at 3 kts dived
Complement: 45

Torpedoes: 6—21 in *(533 mm)* tubes. Combination of Russian 53-65; anti-surface; passive wake homing to 25 km *(13.5 nm)* at 50 kts; warhead 300 kg or TEST-71; anti-submarine; active/passive (optional wire-guided) homing to 15 km *(8.1 nm)* warhead 205 kg. Total of 18 weapons.
Mines: 24 in lieu of torpedoes.
Countermeasures: ESM: Brick Group; radar warning. Quad Loop D/F.
Radars: Surface search: Snoop Tray; I band.
Sonars: Shark Teeth; hull-mounted; passive search and attack; medium frequency.
 Mouse Roar; active attack; high frequency.

Programmes: Transferred from USSR in December 1986. Second one planned but funds not available.
Structure: Diving depth, 240 m *(785 ft)*. Two torpedo tubes probably capable of firing wire-guided torpedoes.

DELFINUL   5/1990

DESTROYER

1 MUNTENIA CLASS

Name	No	Builders	Laid down	Launched	Commissioned
MARASESTI (ex-*Muntenia*)	111	Mangalia Shipyard	1979	1982	3 June 1985

Displacement, tons: 5790 full load
Dimensions, feet (metres): 474.4 × 48.6 × 23
  (144.6 × 14.8 × 7)
Main machinery: 4 diesels; 32 000 hp(m) *(23.5 MW)*; 4 shafts
Speed, knots: 27
Complement: 270 (25 officers)

Missiles: SSM: 8 SS-N-2C Styx ❶; active radar or IR homing to
  83 km *(45 nm)* at 0.9 Mach; warhead 513 kg.
Guns: 4 USSR 3 in *(76 mm)*/60 (2 twin) ❷; 80° elevation; 90
  rounds/minute to 15 km *(8 nm)*; weight of shell 6.8 kg.
  4—30 mm/65 AK 630 ❸; 6 barrels per mounting; 3000
  rounds/minute to 2 km.
Torpedoes: 6—21 in *(533 mm)* (2 triple) tubes ❹. Russian 53-65;
  passive/wake homing to 25 km *(13.5 nm)* at 50 kts; warhead
  300 kg.
A/S mortars: 2 RBU 6000 ❺; 12 tubed trainable; range 6000 m;
  warhead 31 kg.
Radars: Air/surface search: Strut Curve ❻; F band.
Fire control: Two Drum Tilt ❼; H/I band.
  Hawk Screech ❽; I band.
Navigation: Spin Trough; I band.
IFF: High Pole B.
Sonars: Hull-mounted; active search and attack; medium
  frequency.

Helicopters: 2 IAR-316 Alouette III type ❾ and 1 IAR-330.

Modernisation: Attempts have been made to modernise some of
  the electronic equipment. Also topweight problems have been
  addressed by reducing the height of the mast structures and
  lowering the Styx missile launchers by one deck. RBU 6000
  has replaced the RBU 1200.
Structure: A distinctive Romanian design. Originally thought to
  be powered by gas turbines but a diesel configuration including four shafts is now confirmed.
Operational: Deactivated in June 1988 due to manpower and
  fuel shortages but modernisation work was done from 1990 to
  1992 and sea trials started in mid-1992. Carried out a major
  naval exercise in September 1993. Reported to be available for
  sale.

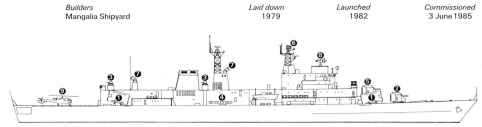

MARASESTI (modernised)   (Scale 1 : 1200), Ian Sturton

MARASESTI   1991, Romanian Navy

FRIGATES

4 TETAL CLASS

Name	No	Builders	Launched	Commissioned
ADMIRAL PETRE BARBUNEANU	260	Mangalia Shipyard	1981	4 Feb 1983
VICE ADMIRAL VASILE SCODREA	261	Mangalia Shipyard	1982	3 Jan 1984
VICE ADMIRAL VASILE URSEANU	262	Mangalia Shipyard	1983	3 Jan 1985
VICE ADMIRAL EUGENIU ROSCA	263	Mangalia Shipyard	1985	23 Apr 1987

Displacement, tons: 1440 full load
Dimensions, feet (metres): 303.1 × 38.4 × 9.8
  (95.4 × 11.7 × 3)
Main machinery: 4 diesels; 13 000 hp(m) *(9.6 MW)* 4 shafts
Speed, knots: 24
Complement: 98

Guns: 4 USSR 3 in *(76 mm)*/60 (2 twin) ❶; 80° elevation; 90
  rounds/minute to 15 km *(8 nm)*; weight of shell 6.8 kg.
  4 USSR 30 mm/65 (2 twin) ❷; 85° elevation; 500 rounds/
  minute to 4 km *(2.2 nm)*; weight of shell 0.54 kg.
  2—14.5 mm MGs.
Torpedoes: 4—21 in *(533 mm)* (2 twin) tubes ❸. Russian 53-65;
  passive/wake homing to 25 km *(13.5 nm)* at 50 kts; warhead
  300 kg.
A/S mortars: 2 RBU 2500 16-tubed trainable ❹; range 2500 m;
  warhead 21 kg.
Countermeasures: ESM: 2 Watch Dog; radar warning.
Radars: Air/surface search: Strut Curve ❺; F band.

ADMIRAL PETRE BARBUNEANU   (Scale 1 : 900), Ian Sturton

Fire control: Drum Tilt ❻; H/I band (for 30 mm). Hawk Screech ❼;
  I band (for 76 mm).
IFF: High Pole.
Sonars: Hull-mounted; active search and attack; medium
  frequency.

Programmes: Building terminated in 1987 in favour of the
  improved design with a helicopter platform.
Structure: A modified Soviet Koni design. There is an unidenti-
  fied launcher forward of the Drum Tilt radar, probably for chaff.

VICE ADMIRAL VASILE SCODREA   1991, Romanian Navy

1 + 1 IMPROVED TETAL CLASS

Name	No	Builders	Launched	Commissioned
CONTRE ADMIRAL EUSTATIU SEBASTIAN	264	Mangalia Shipyard	1988	30 Dec 1989
—	265	Mangalia Shipyard	1992	1994

Displacement, tons: 1500 full load
Dimensions, feet (metres): 303.1 × 38.4 × 10
(92.4 × 11.7 × 3.1)
Main machinery: 4 diesels; 13 000 hp(m) *(9.6 MW)*; 4 shafts
Speed, knots: 24
Complement: 95
Guns: 1 USSR 3 in *(76 mm/60)* ❶; 85° elevation; 120 rounds/
minute to 15 km *(8 in)*; weight of shell 6.8 kg.
2—30 mm/65 AK 630 ❷; 6 barrels per mounting; 3000
rounds/minute to 2 km.
2—30 mm/65 AK 306 ❸; 6 barrels per mounting; 3000
rounds/minute to 2 km.
Torpedoes: 4—21 in *(533 mm)* (2 twin) tubes ❹. Russian 53-65;
passive/wake homing to 25 km *(13.5 nm)* at 50 kts; warhead
300 kg.
A/S mortars: 2 RBU 6000 ❺; 12-tubed trainable; range 6000 m;
warhead 31 kg.
Radars: Air/surface search; Strut Curve ❻; F band.

CONTRE ADMIRAL EUSTATIU SEBASTIAN
(Scale 1 : 900), Ian Sturton

Fire-control: Drum Tilt ❼; H/I band.
Navigation: Spin Trough; I band.
IFF: High Pole.
Sonars: Hull-mounted; active search and attack; medium
frequency.

Helicopters: 1 IAR-316 Aloutte III ❾.

Programmes: Follow on to Tetal class.
Structure: As well as improved armament and a helicopter deck,
there are superstructure changes from the original Tetals.

SHIPBORNE AIRCRAFT

Numbers/Type: 6 IAR 316B Alouette III.
Operational speed: 113 kts *(210 km/h)*.
Service ceiling: 10 500 ft *(3200 m)*.
Range: 290 nm *(540 km)*.
Role/Weapon systems: ASW helicopter. Sensors: Nose-mounted search radar(?) Weapons: ASW;
2 × lightweight torpedoes.

ALOUETTE III
1993, van Ginderen Collection

CORVETTES

3 ZBORUL (TARANTUL I) CLASS (TYPE 1241)

Name	No	Builders	Commissioned
ZBORUL	188	Petrovsky Shipyard	Dec 1990
LASTUNUL	189	Petrovsky Shipyard	Feb 1992
PESCARUSUL	190	Petrovsky Shipyard	Feb 1992

Displacement, tons: 385 standard; 450 full load
Dimensions, feet (metres): 184.1 × 37.7 × 8.2 *(56.1 × 11.5 × 2.5)*
Main machinery: CODOG; 2 Type NK-12MV gas turbines; 20 400 hp(m) *(15 MW)* sustained; 2 die-
sels; 8000 hp(m) *(5.88 MW)*; 2 shafts
Speed, knots: 36. **Range, miles:** 2000 at 20 kts; 400 at 36 kts
Complement: 41 (5 officers)

Missiles: 4 SS-N-2C Styx (2 twin); active radar or IR homing to 83 km *(45 nm)* at 0.9 Mach; war-
head 513 kg.
Guns: 1 USSR 3 in *(76 mm)*/60; 85° elevation; 120 rounds/minute to 15 km *(8 nm)*; weight of shell
7 kg.
2—30 mm/65 AK 630; 6 barrels per mounting; 3000 rounds/minute to 2 km.
Countermeasures: 2—16 barrelled chaff launchers.
ESM: 2 Watch Dog; radar intercept.
Fire control: Hood Wink optronic director.
Radars: Air/surface search: Plank Shave; E band.
Fire control: Bass Tilt; H/I band.
Navigation: Spin Trough; I band.
IFF: Square Head. High Pole.

Programmes: Built in 1985 and later transferred from the USSR.
Structure: Export version similar to those built for Poland, India, Yemen and former GDR.

TARANTUL I
1991, Stefan Terzibaschitsch

3 POTI CLASS

Name	No	Builders	Commissioned
CONTRE ADMIRAL NICOLAE CRISTESCU	31	Zelonodolsk Shipyard	5 Dec 1968
CONTRE ADMIRAL NICOLAE NEGRU	32	Zelonodolsk Shipyard	1 Apr 1969
CONTRE ADMIRAL IRIMESCU	33	Zelonodolsk Shipyard	20 Oct 1969

Displacement, tons: 545 full load
Dimensions, feet (metres): 196.8 × 26.2 × 6.6 *(60 × 8 × 2)*
Main machinery: CODAG; 2 gas turbines; 30 000 hp(m) *(22 MW)*; 2 Type M 503A diesels;
5350 hp(m) *(3.91 MW)* sustained; 2 shafts
Speed, knots: 32. **Range, miles:** 3000 at 18 kts; 500 at 32 kts
Complement: 78

Guns: 2 USSR 57 mm/80 (twin); 85° elevation; 120 rounds/minute to 6 km *(3.3 nm)*; weight of
shell 2.8 kg.
Torpedoes: 2—21 in *(533 mm)* tubes. Russian Type SET 65E; anti-submarine; active/passive hom-
ing to 15 km *(8.1 nm)* at 40 kts; warhead 205 kg.
A/S mortars: 2 RBU 2500 16-tubed trainable; range 2500 m; warhead 21 kg.
Radars: Air/surface search: Strut Curve; F band.
Navigation: Spin Trough; I band.
Fire control: Muff Cob; G/H band.
IFF: High Pole B.
Sonars: Hull-mounted; active search and attack; medium/high frequency.

Programmes: Transferred from the USSR as new construction hulls.
Structure: Differ from Bulgarian ships of the same class, because of the different ASW weapons.

CONTRE ADMIRAL IRIMESCU

4 M 40 CLASS (Ex-MINESWEEPERS)

Name	No	Builders	Commissioned
VICE ADMIRAL MIHAI GAVRILESCU (ex-Democratia)	13	Galatzi Shipyard	1954
VICE ADMIRAL IOAN BALANESCU (ex-Descatusaria)	14	Galatzi Shipyard	1954
VICE ADMIRAL EMIL GRECESCU (ex-Desrobirea)	15	Galatzi Shipyard	1955
VICE ADMIRAL IOAN GEORGESCU (ex-Dreptatea)	16	Galatzi Shipyard	1956

Displacement, tons: 543 standard; 775 full load
Dimensions, feet (metres): 206.5 × 28 × 7.5 *(62.3 × 8.5 × 2.3)*
Main machinery: 2 diesels; 2400 hp(m) *(1.76 MW)*; 2 shafts
Speed, knots: 15. **Range, miles:** 1400 at 10 kts
Complement: 80
Guns: 4—37 mm (2 twin). 1—37 mm . 4—14.5 mm (2 twin) MGs.
A/S mortars: 2 RBU 1200; 5-tubed fixed; range 1200 m; warhead 34 kg.
Radars: Navigation: Don 2; I band.

Comment: German M Boote class originally designed as coal-burning minesweepers. The
appearance of this class changed drastically during refits at Mangalia Shipyard between 1976
and 1983. Referred to locally as Corvettes. All minesweeping gear removed. A small helicopter
platform has been fitted aft.

VICE ADMIRAL IOAN GEORGESCU
1991, Romanian Navy

LAND-BASED MARITIME AIRCRAFT

Numbers/Type: 5 Mil Mi-14PL Haze A.
Operational speed: 124 kts *(230 km/h)*.
Service ceiling: 15 000 ft *(4570 m)*.
Range: 432 nm *(800 km)*.
Role/Weapon systems: Medium range ASW helicopter. Sensors: Search radar, dipping sonar, MAD, sonobuoys. Weapons: ASW; internally stored torpedoes, depth mines and bombs.

PATROL FORCES

Note: Three 27 ft Boston Whalers were presented by the US in March 1993 for Customs/Police patrols on the Danube in support of UN sanctions operations.

6 BRUTAR CLASS (RIVER MONITORS)

Name	No	Builders	Commissioned
GRIVITA	94	Mangalia Shipyard	21 Nov 1986
RAHOVA	95	Mangalia Shipyard	14 Apr 1988
OPANEZ	177	Mangalia Shipyard	24 July 1990
SMIRDAN	178	Mangalia Shipyard	24 July 1990
—	179	Mangalia Shipyard	14 May 1992
—	180	Mangalia Shipyard	30 June 1993

Displacement, tons: 320 full load
Dimensions, feet (metres): 150 × 26.4 × 4.9 *(45.7 × 8 × 1.5)*
Main machinery: 2 diesels; 2700 hp(m) *(2 MW)*; 2 shafts
Speed, knots: 16
Guns: 1—100 mm (tank turret). 2—30 mm (twin). 10—14.5 mm (2 quad, 2 single) MGs. 2—122 mm BM-21 rocket launchers; 40-tubed trainable.
Radars: Navigation; I band.

Comment: Operational with the Danube Flotilla.

6 OSA I CLASS (TYPE 205)
(FAST ATTACK CRAFT—MISSILE)

Name	No	Builders	Commissioned
SOIMUL	194	USSR	3 Nov 1964
VULTURUL	195	USSR	3 Nov 1964
ULIUL	196	USSR	31 Dec 1964
ACVILA	197	USSR	27 Dec 1964
ERETELE	198	USSR	1 Jan 1965
ALBATROSUL	199	Mangalia Shipyard	25 Feb 1981

Displacement, tons: 171 standard; 210 full load
Dimensions, feet (metres): 126.6 × 24.9 × 8.8 *(38.6 × 7.6 × 2.7)*
Main machinery: 3 Type M 503A diesels; 8025 hp *(5.9 MW)* sustained; 3 shafts
Speed, knots: 35. **Range, miles:** 400 at 34 kts
Complement: 30

Missiles: SSM: 4 SS-N-2 Styx; active radar or IR homing to 46 km *(25 nm)* at 0.9 Mach; warhead 513 kg.
Guns: 4 USSR 30 mm/65 (2 twin); 85° elevation; 500 rounds/minute to 5 km *(2.7 nm)*; weight of shell 0.54 kg.
Radars: Surface search: Square Tie; I band.
Fire control: Drum Tilt; H/I band.
IFF: High Pole. Square Head.

Programmes: Six transferred by the USSR in 1964. One deleted and replaced in 1981 by a locally built vessel.

VULTURUL   *6/1993*

24 HUCHUAN CLASS
(FAST ATTACK CRAFT—TORPEDO)

51-74   320-325

Displacement, tons: 39 standard; 45 full load
Dimensions, feet (metres): 71.5 × 20.7 oa; 11.8 hull × 3.3 *(21.8 × 6.3; 3.6 × 1)*
Main machinery: 3 Type M 50 diesels; 3000 hp(m) *(2.4 MW)* sustained; 3 shafts
Speed, knots: 50 foilborne. **Range, miles:** 500 at 30 kts
Complement: 11
Guns: 4—14.5 mm (2 twin) MGs.
Torpedoes: 2—21 in *(533 mm)* tubes; anti-surface.

Comment: Hydrofoils of the same class as the Chinese. Three imported from China have been deleted. *51-74* built at Mangalia Shipyard 1974-1983. *320-325* was a repeat order also built at Mangalia 1988-1990. Two more are listed under Auxiliaries.

HUCHUAN 55   *6/1993*

21 (+ 4 RESERVE) SHANGHAI CLASS
(FAST ATTACK CRAFT—GUN and PATROL)

20-40   41-44

Displacement, tons: 113 standard; 131 full load
Dimensions, feet (metres): 127.3 × 17.7 × 5.6 *(38.8 × 5.4 × 1.7)*
Main machinery: 2 L12-180 diesels (forward); 2400 hp(m) *(1.76 MW)*; 2 L12-180Z diesels (aft); 1820 hp(m) *(1.34 MW)*; 4 shafts
Speed, knots: 30. **Range, miles:** 700 at 17 kts
Complement: 34

Guns: 4 China 37 mm/63 (2 twin) *(20-40)*; 85° elevation; 180 rounds/minute to 8.5 km *(4.6 nm)*; weight of shell 1.42 kg.
1 China 37 mm/63 *(41-44)*. 4—14.5 mm MGs *(41-44)*.
A/S mortars: 2 RBU 1200 5-tubed fixed *(41-44)*; range 1200 m; warhead 34 kg.
Depth charges: 2 racks *(41-44)*.
Radars: Surface search: Don 2; I band.
Sonars: Hull-mounted; active attack; high frequency *(41-44)*.

Programmes: Built at Mangalia since 1973 in a programme of about two a year (which is now complete) with the exception of 22, 24 and 25 which were imported from China. V numbers have been removed.
Structure: Variants of the Shanghai class. The 57 mm gun has been replaced by a second twin 37 mm in the *20-40* type.
Operational: *20-40* serve with Border Guard, *41-44* are used for anti-submarine patrols. Two more of the class are listed under auxiliaries. Four of the class are non-operational and being cannibalised for spares.

SHANGHAI 29   *1991, Romanian Navy*

12 EPITROP CLASS (FAST ATTACK CRAFT—TORPEDO)

Name	No	Builders	Commissioned
NALUCA	201	Mangalia Shipyard	19 May 1979
SMEUL	202	Mangalia Shipyard	25 Oct 1979
VIFORUL	203	Mangalia Shipyard	14 Jan 1980
VIJELIA	204	Mangalia Shipyard	7 Feb 1980
VISCOLUL	205	Mangalia Shipyard	30 Apr 1980
VIRTEJUL	206	Mangalia Shipyard	1 Sep 1980
FULGERUL	207	Mangalia Shipyard	30 Dec 1980
VINTUL	208	Mangalia Shipyard	25 May 1981
VULCANUL	209	Mangalia Shipyard	26 Oct 1981
FURTUNA	210	Mangalia Shipyard	13 Jan 1982
TRASNETUL	211	Mangalia Shipyard	15 June 1982
TORNADA	212	Mangalia Shipyard	5 Oct 1982

Displacement, tons: 215 full load
Dimensions, feet (metres): 120.7 × 24.9 × 5.9 *(36.8 × 7.6 × 1.8)*
Main machinery: 3 Type M 503A diesels; 8025 hp *(5.9 MW)* sustained; 3 shafts
Speed, knots: 36. **Range, miles:** 500 at 35 kts
Guns: 4—30 mm/65 (2 twin).
Torpedoes: 4—21 in *(533 mm)* tubes; anti-surface.
Radars: Surface search: Pot Drum; H/I band.
Fire control: Drum Tilt; H/I band.
IFF: High Pole A.

Comment: Based on the Osa class hull.

FURTUNA   *1991, Romanian Navy*

18 MONITORS (RIVER PATROL CRAFT)

76-93

Displacement, tons: 127 full load
Dimensions, feet (metres): 106.3 × 15.8 × 3 *(32.4 × 4.8 × 0.9)*
Main machinery: 2 diesels; 1700 hp(m) *(1.25 MW)*; 2 shafts
Speed, knots: 17
Complement: 25
Guns: 1—76 mm. 4—14.5 mm (2 twin). 1—81 mm mortar.

Comment: Built in Mangalia Shipyard from 1974-1977. Belong to Danube Flotilla.

RIVER MONITOR 76

MINE WARFARE FORCES

2 COSAR CLASS (MINELAYER/MCM SUPPORT SHIPS)

Name	No	Builders	Commissioned
VICE ADMIRAL IOAN MURGESCU	271	Mangalia Shipyard	30 Dec 1980
VICE ADMIRAL CONSTANTIN BALESCU	274	Mangalia Shipyard	16 Nov 1981

Displacement, tons: 1450 full load
Dimensions, feet (metres): 259.1 × 34.8 × 11.8 *(79 × 10.6 × 3.6)*
Main machinery: 2 diesels; 6400 hp(m) *(4.7 MW)*; 2 shafts
Speed, knots: 19
Complement: 75
Guns: 1—57 mm. 4—30 mm/65 (2 twin). 8—14.5 mm (2 quad) MGs.
A/S mortars: 2 RBU 1200 5-tubed fixed; range 1200 m; warhead 34 kg.
Mines: 200.
Countermeasures: ESM: Watch Dog; radar warning.
Radars: Air/surface search: Strut Curve; F band.
Navigation: Don 2; I band.
Fire control: Muff Cob; G/H band. Drum Tilt; H/I band.
Sonars: Hull-mounted; active search; high frequency.

Comment: 271 has a helicopter platform for one IAR-316 Alouette III. 274 has a crane on the after deck.

VICE ADMIRAL IOAN MURGESCU   *1991, Romanian Navy*

4 MUSCA CLASS (MINESWEEPERS—COASTAL)

Name	No	Builders	Commissioned
LIEUTENANT REMUS LEPRI	24	Mangalia Shipyard	23 Apr 1987
LIEUTENANT LUPU DINESCU	25	Mangalia Shipyard	6 Jan 1989
LIEUTENANT DIMITRIE NICOLESCU	29	Mangalia Shipyard	7 Dec 1989
SUB LIEUTENANT ALEXANDRU AXENTE	30	Mangalia Shipyard	7 Dec 1989

Displacement, tons: 790 full load
Dimensions, feet (metres): 199.4 × 31.1 × 9.2 *(60.8 × 9.5 × 2.8)*
Main machinery: 2 diesels; 4800 hp(m) *(3.5 MW)*; 2 shafts
Speed, knots: 17
Guns: 4—30 mm/65 (2 twin). 16—14.5 mm (4 quad) MGs.
A/S mortars: 2 RBU 1200 5-tubed fixed; range 1200 m; warhead 34 kg.
Radars: Surface search: Krivach; I band.
Fire control: Drum Tilt; H/I band.
Sonars: Hull-mounted; active search; high frequency.

Comment: Reported as having a secondary mining capability but this is not confirmed.

LIEUTENANT REMUS LEPRI   *1991, Romanian Navy*

25 RIVER MINESWEEPERS

141-165

Displacement, tons: 97 full load
Dimensions, feet (metres): 109 × 15.7 × 2.8 *(33.3 × 4.8 × 0.9)*
Main machinery: 2 diesels; 870 hp(m) *(640 kW)*; 2 shafts
Speed, knots: 13
Guns: 4—14.5 mm (2 twin) MGs.
Mines: 6.

Comment: Built in Romania at Dobreta Severin Shipyard 1976-1984.

MINESWEEPER 144   *1979*

12 T 301 CLASS (MINESWEEPERS—COASTAL)

Name	No	Builders	Commissioned
CAPTAIN CONSTANTIN DUMITRESCU	4	Galatzi Shipyard	1956
LIEUTENANT CONSTANTIN VIRTOSU	5	Galatzi Shipyard	1957
LIEUTENANT GHEORGHE NICULESCU	6	Galatzi Shipyard	1957
LIEUTENANT MOISE PAUTA	7	Galatzi Shipyard	1957
LIEUTENANT NICOLAE STOICESCU	8	Galatzi Shipyard	1957
LIEUTENANT ALEXANDRU POMPILIAN	9	Galatzi Shipyard	1958
COMMODORE DUMITRU LUPASCU	17	Galatzi Shipyard	1958
COMMODORE VASILE TOESCU	18	Galatzi Shipyard	1959
COMMODORE CONSTANTIN MICOESCU	19	Galatzi Shipyard	1959
CAPTAIN ADRIAN VASILIU	26	Galatzi Shipyard	1960
CAPTAIN CONSTANTIN ISTRATE	27	Galatzi Shipyard	1960
CAPTAIN ALEXANDRU CONSTANTINESCU	28	Galatzi Shipyard	1960

Displacement, tons: 170 full load
Dimensions, feet (metres): 124.6 × 18.7 × 5.2 *(38 × 5.7 × 1.6)*
Main machinery: 3 diesels; 900 hp(m) *(661 kW)*; 3 shafts
Speed, knots: 14.5
Complement: 25
Guns: 2—37 mm /63; 4—14.5 mm (2 twin) MGs.
Mines: 18.

Comment: Transferred from the USSR as new construction. Laid up in the mid-1980s but modernisation refits started at Mangalia Shipyard in 1986 and most are now back in service.

SURVEY AND RESEARCH SHIPS

Name	No	Builders	Commissioned
GRIGORE ANTIPA	—	Mangalia Shipyard	25 May 1980

Displacement, tons: 1450 full load
Dimensions, feet (metres): 259.1 × 34.8 × 11.8 *(79 × 10.6 × 3.6)*
Main machinery: 2 diesels; 6400 hp(m) *(4.7 MW)*; 2 shafts
Speed, knots: 19
Complement: 75

Comment: Large davits aft for launching submersible. Used mostly as an AG1.

GRIGORE ANTIPA   *1991, Romanian Navy*

Name	No	Builders	Commissioned
EMIL RACOVITA	—	Drobeta Severin Shipyard	30 Oct 1977

Displacement, tons: 1900 full load
Dimensions, feet (metres): 229.9 × 32.8 × 12.7 *(70.1 × 10 × 3.9)*
Main machinery: 1 diesel; 3285 hp(m) *(2.4 MW)*; 1 shaft
Speed, knots: 11
Complement: 80

Comment: Modernised in the mid-1980s. Used mostly as an AGI.

TRAINING SHIP

Note: Neptun belongs to the Merchant Navy.

Name	No	Builders	Commissioned
MIRCEA	—	Blohm & Voss, Hamburg	29 Mar 1939

Displacement, tons: 1604 full load
Dimensions, feet (metres): 206; 266.4 (with bowsprit) × 39.3 × 16.5 *(62.8; 81.2 × 12 × 5.2)*
Main machinery: Auxiliary diesel; 1000 hp(m) *(735 kW)*; 1 shaft
Speed, knots: 6
Complement: 83 plus 140 midshipmen for training

Comment: Refitted at Hamburg in 1966. Sail area, 5739 sq m *(18 830 sq ft)*.

MIRCEA   *6/1993*

AUXILIARIES

2 CROITOR CLASS (LOGISTIC SUPPORT SHIPS)

Name	No	Builders	Commissioned
CONSTANTA	281	Braila Shipyard	15 Sep 1980
MIDIA	283	Braila Shipyard	26 Feb 1982

Displacement, tons: 2850 full load
Dimensions, feet (metres): 354.3 × 44.3 × 12.5 *(108 × 13.5 × 3.8)*
Main machinery: 2 diesels; 6500 hp(m) *(4.8 MW)*; 2 shafts
Speed, knots: 16
Missiles: SAM: 2 SA-N-5 Grail quad launchers; manual aiming; IR homing to 6 km *(3.2 nm)* at 1.5 Mach; warhead 1.5 kg.
Guns: 2—57 mm/70 (twin). 4—30 mm/65 (2 twin). 8—14.5 mm (2 quad) MGs.
A/S mortars: 2 RBU 1200 5-tubed fixed; range 1200 m; warhead 34 kg.
Radars: Air/surface search: Strut Curve; F band.
Navigation: Krivach; I band.
Fire control: Muff Cob; G/H band. Drum Tilt; H/I band.
Helicopters: 1 IAR-316 Alouette III type.

Comment: These ships are a scaled down version of Soviet Don class. Forward crane for ammunition replenishment. Some ASW escort capability. Can carry Styx missiles and torpedoes.

MIDIA   *6/1993*

4 DIVING SUPPORT CRAFT

Name	No	Builders	Commissioned
SATURN	—	Mangalia Shipyard	19 Oct 1978
VENUS	—	Mangalia Shipyard	5 Dec 1978
MARTE	—	Mangalia Shipyard	10 Oct 1979
JUPITER	—	Mangalia Shipyard	14 Jan 1980

Comment: The first two are converted Shanghai class (see *Patrol Forces*) and the second pair are converted Huchuan class (see *Patrol Forces*). The only armament is a twin 14.5 mm MG and the Huchuans have no hydrofoils.

2 FRIPONNE CLASS (SUPPLY SHIPS)

LIEUTENANT COMMANDER EUGEN STIHI (ex-*Mignonne*) 112
SUB LIEUTENANT ION GHICULESCU (ex-*Impatiente*) 113

Displacement, tons: 440 full load
Dimensions, feet (metres): 200.1 × 23 × 8.2 *(61 × 7 × 2.5)*
Main machinery: 2 Sulzer diesels; 1800 hp(m) *(1.32 MW)*; 2 shafts
Speed, knots: 12. **Range, miles:** 3000 at 10 kts
Complement: 50
Guns: 1—37 mm/63. 4—14.5 mm (2 twin) MGs.
A/S mortars: 2 RBU 1200 5-tubed fixed; range 1200 m; warhead 34 kg.
Radars: Navigation: Two sets.
Sonars: Hull-mounted; active attack; high frequency.

Comment: Originally built at Brest and Lorient in 1916-17 as French minesweepers. The armament listed above reflects the latest conversion which also included a smoother bridge form.

SUB LIEUTENANT ION GHICULESCU   *1991, Romanian Navy*

1 TANKER

532

Displacement, tons: 2170 full load
Dimensions, feet (metres): 250.4 × 41 × 16.4 (76.3 × 12.5 × 5)
Main machinery: 2 diesels; 4800 hp(m) *(3.5 MW)*; 2 shafts
Speed, knots: 16
Cargo capacity: 1200 tons oil
Guns: 2—30 mm (twin). 4—14.5 mm (2 twin) MGs.

Comment: Built by Tulcea Shipyard and commissioned 24 December 1992.

6 BRAILA CLASS (RIVER TRANSPORTS)

C 414-C 419

Displacement, tons: 240 full load
Dimensions, feet (metres): 125.7 × 28.2 × 3.3 *(38.3 × 8.6 × 1)*
Main machinery: 2 diesels; 300 hp(m) (220 kW); 2 shafts
Speed, knots: 4
Cargo capacity: 160 tons

Comment: Used by civilian as well as naval authorities. Built at Braila Shipyard 1967-1970.

BRAILA 419   *1987*

2 COASTAL TANKERS

530   531

Displacement, tons: 1042 full load
Dimensions, feet (metres): 181.2 × 30.9 × 13.4 *(55.2 × 9.4 × 4.1)*
Main machinery: 2 diesels; 1800 hp(m) *(1.3 MW)*; 2 shafts
Speed, knots: 12.5
Cargo capacity: 500 tons oil
Guns: 1—37 mm. 2—12.7 mm MGs.

Comment: Built by Braila Shipyard and both commissioned 15 June 1971.

2 HARBOUR TANKERS

131   132

Displacement, tons: 190 full load
Dimensions, feet (metres): 97.3 × 22.6 × 8.2 *(29.6 × 6.9 × 2.5)*
Main machinery: 2 diesels; 300 hp(m) *(221 kW)*; 2 shafts
Speed, knots: 10
Cargo capacity: 80 tons oil

Comment: Built at Braila Shipyard and both completed 22 September 1986.

4 DEGAUSSING SHIPS

Name	No	Builders	Commissioned
AUTOMATICA	—	Braila Shipyard	9 Dec 1972
ELECTRONICA	—	Braila Shipyard	6 Aug 1973
ENERGETICA	—	Braila Shipyard	20 Oct 1973
MAGNETICA	—	Mangalia Shipyard	18 Dec 1989

Displacement, tons: 299 full load
Dimensions, feet (metres): 134 × 21.6 × 10.7 *(40.8 × 6.6 × 3.2)*
Main machinery: diesel-electric; 1 diesel generator; 600 kW; 1 shaft
Speed, knots: 12.5
Guns: 2—14.5 mm (twin) MGs. 2—12.7 mm MGs.

Comment: Built for degaussing ships up to 3000 tons displacement.

TUGS

1 OCEAN TUG

GROZAVU 500

Displacement, tons: 3600 full load
Dimensions, feet (metres): 212.6 × 47.9 × 18 *(64.8 × 14.6 × 5.5)*
Main machinery: 2 diesels; 5000 hp(m) *(3.7 MW)*; 2 shafts
Speed, knots: 12
Guns: 2—30 mm (twin). 8—14.5 mm (2 quad) MGs.

Comment: Built at Oltenitza Shipyard and commissioned 29 June 1993. A second of class is building.

2 ROSLAVL CLASS

VITEAZUL 101   **VOINICUL 116**

Displacement, tons: 620 full load
Dimensions, feet (metres): 146 × 27.5 × 10.8 *(44.5 × 8.4 × 3.3)*
Main machinery: Diesel-electric; 2 diesel generators; 1 motor; 1200 hp(m) *(882 kW)*; 1 shaft
Speed, knots: 13
Complement: 28
Guns: 1—37 mm/63. 4—14.5 mm (2 twin) MGs.

Comment: Built in Galatzi shipyard 1953-54.

RUSSIA
AND
ASSOCIATED STATES

Headquarters' Appointments

Commander-in-Chief and Deputy Minister of Defence:
　Admiral F N Gromov
1st Deputy Commander-in-Chief:
　Admiral I V Kasatonov
Chief of Main Naval Staff:
　Admiral V Y Selivanov
1st Deputy Chief of the Main Naval Staff:
　Vice Admiral Y A Kaysin
Deputy Commander-in-Chief (Operational Training):
　Vice Admiral A V Gorbunov
Deputy Commander-in-Chief (Technical Readiness and New Construction):
　Vice Admiral V P Yeremin
Commander of Naval Aviation:
　Colonel General V P Potapov
1st Deputy Commander Naval Aviation:
　Lieutenant General V V Budeyev
Chief of Navigation and Oceanography:
　Vice Admiral Y I Zheglov
Commander, Coastal Defence Forces:
　Colonel General I S Skuratov

Northern Fleet

Commander:
　Admiral O A Yerofeyev
1st Deputy Commander and Chief of Staff:
　Vice Admiral I I Nalyotov
Deputy Commander (Combat Training):
　Vice Admiral V A Poroshin
Commander Naval Aviation:
　Lieutenant General V Deyneka
Deputy Commander (Rear Services):
　Rear Admiral N I Radetsky

Pacific

Commander:
　Admiral G N Gurinov
1st Deputy Commander:
　Vice Admiral I N Khmelnov
Commander Naval Aviation:
　Lieutenant General V Y Bumatin
Deputy Commander (Combat Training):
　Vice Admiral B F Prikhodko

Black Sea

Commander:
　Admiral E D Baltin
1st Deputy Commander and Acting Commander:
　Vice Admiral V P Larionov
Chief of Staff:
　Vice Admiral P G Svyatashov
Deputy Commander (Rear Services):
　Vice Admiral L A Vasiliev
Commander Naval Aviation:
　Major General N N Fadeyev

Baltic

Commander:
　Admiral V G Yegorov
Chief of Staff:
　Vice Admiral V V Grishanov
Commander Naval Aviation:
　Lieutenant General V Proskurin
Deputy Commander (Combat Training):
　Vice Admiral V I Litvinov
Deputy Commander (Rear Services):
　Vice Admiral I I Ryabinin

Caspian Flotilla

Commander:
　Vice Admiral B M Zinin

Personnel

(a) 1994: 300 000 officers and ratings (including 60 000 naval aviation and 25 000 naval infantry/coastal defence)
(b) Approximately 30 per cent volunteers (officers and senior ratings)—remainder two years' national service (18 months if ashore) since 1991 (or three years if volunteered)
(c) Deployed: Northern 75 000, Baltic 65 000, Black Sea 67 000, Pacific 75 000, elsewhere 18 000.

Associated States

The Soviet Union was dissolved in December 1991. In 1992 a Commonwealth of Independent States was formed from the Republics of the former Union, but without the Baltic States. The two major Fleets in the North and Pacific are wholly Russian based. In the Baltic the Russian flotilla had withdrawn from the former East German and Polish ports by 1993 but still retained some vessels in the Baltic republics which are also forming their own Coast Guards (see Estonia, Latvia and Lithuanian sections). The Caspian flotilla divided with about one third going to Azerbaijan, and some patrol craft to Kazakhstan, but the permanence of this arrangement is in doubt. In the Black Sea an uneasy coalition has been formed between Russia and Ukraine until 1995.

Main Bases (Russian unless indicated otherwise)

North: Severomorsk (HQ), Motovsky Gulf, Polyarny, Severodvinsk, Gremika, Nerpichya, Yagelnaya, Olenya
Baltic: Kaliningrad (HQ), St Petersburg, Kronshtadt, Baltiysk
Black Sea: Sevastopol (HQ) (Crimea), Tuapse, Poti (Georgia), Balaklava (Crimea), Odessa (Ukraine), Nikolayev (Ukraine), Novorssiysk
Caspian: Astrakhan (HQ), Baku (Azerbaijan), Fort Chevnenko (Kazakhstan)
Pacific: Vladivostok (HQ), Sovetskaya Gavan, Magadan, Petropavlovsk, Komsomolsk

Operational

Since 1991 a shortage of funds to pay for dockyard repairs and spare parts has meant that some major units have not been to sea, and few have operated away from their local exercise areas.

Pennant Numbers

The Navy has changes of pennant numbers as a matter of routine every three years and when ships change fleet. The last major overall change of numbers took place in May 1990 and the Pacific and Northern fleets changed again in May 1993. Such a list has therefore been omitted in this section as it is of little use identifying ships over any lengthy period.

Class and Weapon Systems Names

Most Russian ship class names differ from those allocated by NATO. In such cases the Russian name is placed in brackets after the NATO name. Type or Project numbers are also placed in brackets. Weapon systems retain their NATO name, with the Russian name, when known, placed in brackets. The release of the Russian names has inevitably caused some confusion as the same equipment now has three names - NATO, Russian Navy and Russian export.

Building Programme

Submarines
SSGN—Oscar class at one a year.
SSN—Akula class at one or two a year. New conbuilding.
SS—Kilo class at two or three a year.

Aircraft Carriers
One Kuznetsov class fitting out slowly.

Cruisers
Fourth Kirov class fitting out. Fourth Slava fitting out.

Destroyers
Two Sovremenny class fitting out, more building.
One Udaloy II class fitting out.

Frigates
Two Neustrashimy class building.
Grisha V class continues.
Gepard class, building.

Light Forces

Tarantul III class continues, some for export.
Pauk class continues for export.
Zhuk class coastal patrol craft continue, some for export.
Svetlyak class continues.

Mine Warfare Forces

Natya class continues for export.
Sonya class (MSC) continues including for export.
Lida class (MSI) building.

Air Cushion Vehicles

Pomornik and Tsaplya classes continue.

Auxiliaries

Sorum class ocean tugs continue.

Strength of the Fleet (includes Ukraine, Georgia, Azerbaijan and Kazakhstan)

Type	Active (Reserve)	Building
Submarines (SSBN)	48	—
Submarines (SSGN)	22	1 (1)
Submarines (SSG)	5	—
Submarines (SSN)	53	5
Submarines (SS)	65	1
Auxiliary Submarines (SSA(N))	15	—
Aircraft Carriers (CV)	2	1
Helicopter Cruisers (CHG)	1	—
Battle Cruisers (CGN)	3	1
Cruisers (CG)	10	1
Destroyers (DDG)	33	4
Frigates (FFG)	32	4
Frigates (FF and FFL)	107	2
Corvettes	82	3
Patrol Ships/Radar Pickets	5	—
Fast Attack Craft	214	3
Hydrofoils (Missile)	13	—
Coastal Patrol Craft	34	2
River Patrol Craft	126	—
Minelayers	3	—
Minehunters—Ocean	2	—
Minesweepers—Ocean	58	—
Minesweepers—Coastal	90	2
Minesweepers—Inshore/Drones	64	3
Minesweeping Boats	5 (10)	—
LPDs	3	—
LSTs	40	—
LSMs	29	—
Hovercraft (Amphib)	49 (6)	2
Depot, Support and Repair Ships	79	2
Intelligence Collectors (AGI)	55	—
Survey and Research Ships	133 + 102 civilian	—
Missile Range Ships	11	—
Training Ships	32	—
Cable Ships	13	—
Replenishment Tankers	27	—
Support Tankers	19+	—
Special Tankers	13	—
Hospital Ships	5	—
Salvage and Mooring Vessels	47	—
Submarine Rescue Ships	17	—
Transports and Cargo Ships	56+	—

Mercantile Marine

Lloyd's Register of Shipping:
　5674 vessels of 17 618 313 tons gross

Fleet Disposition on 1 January 1994

Type	Northern	Baltic	Black Sea	Pacific	Caspian
SSBN	30	—	—	18	—
SSGN	13	—	—	9	—
SSG	—	4	1	—	—
SSN	36	—	—	17	—
SS	23	14	9	19	—
SSAN, SSA	8	1	4	2	—
CV	2	—	—	—	—
CHG	—	—	1	—	—
CGN	2	—	—	1	—
CG	1	1	5	4	—
DDG	14	4	5	10	—

Type	Northern	Baltic	Black Sea	Pacific	Caspian
FFG	6	8	6	10	—
FF and FFL	31	14	20	23	2
Corvettes, FAC, CPC, RPC	13	55	127	95	7
MCM Forces	44	67	48	48	22
LPD	1	—	—	2	—
LST	8	10	9	13	—
LSM	6	5	6	2	10
Hovercraft	5	11	14	13	6
Depot, Repair and Support Ships	26	11	14	28	—
Underway Replenishment Ships	7	3	7	10	—
Support Tankers	8	3	5	3	—

DELETIONS

Note: Some of the ships listed are still theoretically 'in reserve' but none will go to sea again and a realistic scrapping policy continues with the aim of having 65 per cent of operational ships less than 20 years old.

Submarines

1991	1 Yankee I (SSBN), 1 Yankee II (SSBN), 2 Charlie I (SSGN), 3 Echo II (SSGN), 1 Victor I (SSN), 3 Juliett (SSG), 2 Mod Golf (SSQ), 15 Foxtrot (SS), 18 Whiskey (SS)
1992	4 Yankee I (SSBN), 1 Delta I (SSBN), 1 Charlie II (SSGN), 3 Charlie I (SSGN), 5 Echo II (SSGN), 7 Juliett (SSG), 10 Foxtrot (SS)
1993	3 Delta I (SSBN), 3 Yankee I (SSBN), 2 Charlie II (SSGN), 2 Charlie I (SSGN), 5 Echo II (SSGN), 2 Juliett (SSG), 4 Alfa (SSN), 4 Victor II (SSN), 9 Victor I (SSN), 6 Foxtrot (SS), 1 Bravo (SSA)

Aircraft Carriers

1992	*Ulyanovsk, Minsk, Leningrad*
1993	*Novorossiysk*
1994	*Kiev*

Cruisers

1991	2 Kresta I *(V A Drozd, Vladivostok)*
1992	3 Kresta II *(Kronstadt, A Nakhimov, A Isachenkov),* 1 Kynda *(Grozny)*
1993	2 Kara *(Nikolayev, Tashkent),* 5 Kresta II *(A Isakov, A Makarov, Khabarovsk, M Timoshenko, A Yumashev)*
1994	1 Kynda *(Admiral Fokin)*
1994	2 Kresta II *(A Oktyabrsky, Vasily Chapayev)*

Destroyers

1991	3 Kashin (DDG)
1992	3 Kashin (DDG)
1993	1 Udaloy *(A Zakharov),* 3 Kashin *(Obraztsovy, Smyshlenny, Sposobny)*

Frigates

1991-92	5 Riga, 7 Mirka, 5 Petya
1992	1 Krivak I (FFG), 3 Grisha I, 2 Grisha III (to Lithuania), 5 Riga, 3 Mirka II
1993	1 Krivak I *(Doblestny),* 1 Grisha I, 1 Petya I, 5 Petya II

Corvettes (Missile)

1992	3 Matka, 4 Osa I, 5 Osa II
1993	2 Nanuchka I

Patrol Forces

1991-92	8 Osa, 3 Shershen, 29 Poti; 3 SO 1, 5 Stenka, 12 T 58/PGF
1992	6 Poti, 2 Zhuk, 2 Yaz, 3 Vosh, 16 Schmel, 4 TR 40
1993	2 Turya (to Lithuania), 3 SO 1, 8 Osa I, 30 Osa II, 6 Stenka, 2 TR40

Mine Warfare Vessels

1991-92	12 Yurka, 10 T 43, 2 Zhenya, 20 Vanya, 3 Ilyusha, 1 Olya
1992	2 Natya I, 1 T 43, 4 Vanya, 1 Sasha
1993	3 Natya I, 10 Yurka, 4 T 43, 3 Sonya, 4 Vanya, 2 Pelikan, 10 Yevgenya

Amphibious Forces

1991-92	15 SMB 1
1992	2 Alligator
1993	3 Polnochny A

Hovercraft

1991	10 Gus
1992	3 Lebed
1993	4 Aist, 4 Gus

AGIs

1991	4 Mirny, 2 Lentra
1993	3 Okean, 1 Lentra

Survey and Research Ships

1992	5 Melitopol, *Otto Schmidt* (sold), *A I Voeykov, Arnold Veimer* (to Estonia), *Lev Titov* (to Lithuania)
1993	*Sirocco*

Auxiliaries

1991	*Nevelsky,* 5 Telnovsk, *Petr Lebedev, Sergey Vavilov, Chukotka,* 1 Ugra, *Polyarnik, Indiga, Ural, Ishim*
1992	1 Ugra, 1 Don, 1 Amur I, 1 Altay, 5 Khobi, 5 Neptun, 2 Valday, 1 Chulym, 10 Lentra, 1 MP 6, 4 Khabarov, 1 Vikhr (to Syria), 1 Sekstan, 5 Okhtensky
1993	*Alatyr, Soyana,* 2 Orel, *Vladimir Trefolev, Kazbek,* 2 MP 4, 4 Telnovsk, 9 Khabarov, 14 Vikhr (civilian), 1 Voda, *Kiev, Moskva* (both icebreakers), *Stroptivy* (icebreaker to Lithuania), 7 Okhtenskiy
1994	1 Ugra *(Tobol)*

NAVAL AVIATION

Overall totals: 1300 front-line, transport and training aircraft in early 1994.

Anti-ship missile firers: 160 Backfire and Badger ASM carriers deployed as follows: Northern 40, Black Sea 40, Pacific 80.

Fighters and fighter/ground attack: 325 Flanker, Frogfoot, Fitter, Fencer, Flogger, deployed as follows: Northern 115, Baltic 135, Black Sea 45, Pacific 30.

Reconnaissance: 90 Badger, Blinder, Bear D, Fencer, Cub, Coot, Curl, deployed as follows: Northern 30, Baltic 15, Black Sea 10, Pacific 35.

Fixed-wing ASW: 180 Bear F/J, May, Mail, deployed as follows: Northern 80, Baltic 12, Black Sea 22, Pacific 66.

Helicopter ASW: 270 Helix A, Hormone A, Haze A, deployed as follows: Northern 55, Baltic 30, Black Sea 100, Pacific 85.

Mine warfare: About 25 Haze B.

Training aircraft: All types - 125.

Fixed-wing transports: All types - 125.

TORPEDOES

Note: There are several torpedo types in service. The following table lists broad characteristics.

Type/Designator	Diameter/Length	Role	Launch Platform	Propulsion	Speed/Range	Guidance	Warhead	Remarks
35	35 cm/3.7 m	ASW	1. Aircraft 2. Helicopters	Rocket	62 kts/2 km	Active/passive	100 kg	Export as APR-2E
SAET-40	40 cm/4.5 m	ASW/ASV	1. Submarines 2. Escorts	Electric	30 kts/10 km	Active/passive	100 kg	USET-95 (see Note 1)
40	40 cm/3.8 m	ASW	1. Aircraft 2. Helicopters 3. SS-N-14 4. SS-N-15 5. SS-N-16	Electric	45 kts/15 km	Active/passive	60 kg	Export as APSET-95
45	45 cm/3.9 m	ASW	1. Aircraft 2. Helicopters	Electric	30 kts/15 km	Active/passive	100 kg	
E53-72	53 cm/4.7 m	ASW	1. Aircraft 2. Helicopters 3. SS-N-14	Electric	40 kts/10 km	Active/passive	150 kg	Alternative to Type 40
SAET-60	53 cm/7.8 m	ASV	1. Submarines 2. Surface ships	Electric	40 kts/15 km	Passive	400 kg	Nuclear variant available
ET80-67 (see Note 2)	53 cm/7.8 m	ASW	1. Submarines 2. Surface ships	Electric	40 kts/15 km	Active/passive	205 kg	Export as SET-65E
TEST-71 (see Note 3)	53 cm/7.9 m	ASW	Submarines	Electric	40 kts/15 km	Active/passive Wire-guided	205 kg	Export as TEST-71ME
53-65	53 cm/7.8 m	ASV	1. Submarines 2. Surface ships	Turbine	50 kts/25 km	Passive/wake	300 kg	Nuclear variant available
65	65 cm/11 m	ASV	Submarines (Victor III, Akula, Sierra)	Turbine	50 kts/50 km	Wake	450 kg	Nuclear variant available. Export as DT or DST

Notes: (1) Export USET-95 may have ASV wake homing option.
(2) ET80-67 superseded by torpedo promoted for export as SET-92K (53 cm/7.8 m, ASW, active/passive).
(3) TEST-71 superseded by torpedo promoted for export as TEST-96 (53 cm/8 m, ASW/ASV, wire-guided, active/passive/wake homing) (submarines and surface ships).

SUBMARINES
Strategic Missile Submarines

Note: In the late 1960s the SS-N-8 was first tested and this was fitted in the Delta I class in 1972 and subsequently the Delta II in 1975. In the latter half of the 1970s the SS-N-18 appeared in the Delta III class and comes in three versions. Mod 1 and Mod 3 have three and seven MIRV respectively. Mod 2 has a single RV. In early 1980 a new type of solid-fuelled SLBM, SS-N-20, was tested. This is larger than SS-N-18, carries a seven to ten MIRV head and is in the Typhoon class. SS-N-20 is in turn being replaced by SS-N-24/26 which has improved accuracy. In 1983 testing of SS-N-23 began; this missile is carried in the Delta IV class. Operational in 1986 with seven to ten MIRV. With both Delta IV and Typhoon programmes terminated a new class of SSBN is expected in due course to maintain an operational force of about 25 hulls on a one for one replacement basis. If this plan is maintained, the first of the new class will not be in service until all the remaining Yankee, Delta I and Delta II submarines have paid off. However, at least two types of new ballistic missile are being developed and may be retrofitted to existing classes, as well as being available for new classes, including possibly a Delta IV variant. The revised Fleet Plan released in late 1993 suggests a further reduction in submarine numbers during the next decade, with all but the Typhoon and Delta IV classes being paid off early.

In addition to the ballistic missiles a sea-launched cruise missile (SLCM), the SS-N-21, is operational. Its primary role is nuclear strike against land targets. Its size is compatible with submarine torpedo tubes and it can be carried in all modern classes of SSN. A larger missile of this type, SS-NX-24, was under test in 1989/90 in a modified Yankee SSN but this programme has been abandoned.

6 TYPHOON CLASS (TYPE 941)

Displacement, tons: 21 500 surfaced; 26 500 dived
Dimensions, feet (metres): 562.7 oa; 541.3 wl × 80.7 × 42.7
(171.5; 165 × 24.6 × 13)
Main machinery: Nuclear; 2 PWR; 320 MW; 2 turbines;
81 600 hp(m) *(60 MW)*; 2 shafts; shrouded props
Speed, knots: 26 dived; 19 surfaced
Complement: 175 (55 officers). 2 crews

Missiles: SLBM: 20 SS-N-20 Sturgeon; three-stage solid fuel
rocket; stellar inertial guidance to 8300 km *(4500 nm)*; warhead nuclear 6-9 MIRV each of 100 kT; CEP 500 m. 2 missiles
fired from the first of class in 15 seconds. Being modified to
take an improved version of the Sturgeon (SS-N-24/26) which
has improved accuracy.
SAM: There are suggestions that this class may have a SAM
capability.
A/S: SS-N-15 fired from 21 in *(533 mm)* tubes; inertial flight to
37 km *(20 nm)*; warhead nuclear 200 kT.
SS-N-16 fired from 25.6 in *(650 mm)* tubes; inertial flight to
120 km *(65 nm)*; payload Type 40 torpedo; active/passive
homing to 15 km *(8.1 nm)* at 45 kts; warhead 60 kg. There is
also a 16B version with a nuclear warhead.
Torpedoes: 2—21 in *(533 mm)* and 4—25.6 in *(650 mm)* tubes.
Combination of 53 and 65 cm torpedoes (see table at front of
section). The weapon load includes a total of 36 torpedoes and
A/S missiles.

Mines: Could be carried in lieu of torpedoes.
Countermeasures: ESM: Rim Hat; radar warning. Park Lamp
D/F.
Radars: Surface search: Snoop Pair; I/J band.
Sonars: Shark Gill; hull-mounted; passive/active search and
attack; low/medium frequency.
Mouse Roar; hull-mounted; active attack; high frequency.

Programmes: This is the largest type of submarine ever built. The
first was begun in 1977 and launched at Severodvinsk in September 1980 (in service 1982) and the second in September
1982 entering service in late 1983. The third was commissioned in late 1984, the fourth followed a year later, the
fifth in 1987 and the sixth in 1989. Statements by senior officers indicate disenchantment with these very large submarines and no more of this class are to be completed. One is
called *Miskiy Komsomolets*.
Modernisation: The class is being modernised to take an
SS-N-20 follow-on missile which has improved accuracy. This
is a very slow programme.
Structure: Two separate 8.5 m diameter hulls covered by a

single outer free-flood hull with anechoic Cluster Guard tiles
plus separate 6 m diameter pressure-tight compartments in
the fin and fore-ends. There is a large separation between the
outer and inner hulls along the sides. The unique features of
Typhoon are her enormous size and the fact that the missile
tubes are mounted forward of the fin. The positioning of the
launch tubes means a fully integrated weapons area in the bow
section leaving space abaft the fin for the provision of two nuclear reactors, one in each hull—probably needed to achieve a
reasonable speed with this huge hull. The fin configuration
indicates a designed capability to break through ice cover
possibly up to 3 m thick; the retractable forward hydroplanes,
the rounded hull and the shape of the fin are all related to
under-ice operations. Diving depth, 1000 ft *(300 m)*.
Operational: Strategic targets are within range from anywhere in
the world. Two VLF/ELF communication buoys are fitted. VLF
navigation system for under-ice operations. Pert Spring SAT-
COM mast, Cod Eye radiometric sextant and Kremmny 2 IFF.
All are based in the Northern Fleet at Nerpichya. One reported
damaged by fire during a missile loading accident and may
have to be scrapped.

TYPHOON   *1991, S Breyer*

TYPHOON   *5/1991*

TYPHOON   *1992*

TYPHOON   *1990*

7 DELTA IV (DELFIN) CLASS (TYPE 667BDRM)

Displacement, tons: 10 750 surfaced; 12 150 dived
Dimensions, feet (metres): 544.6 oa; 518.4 wl × 39.4 × 28.5
(166; 158 × 12 × 8.7)
Main machinery: Nuclear; 2 PWR; 160 MW; 2 turbines;
37 400 hp(m) *(27.5 MW)* 2 shafts
Speed, knots: 24 dived; 19 surfaced
Complement: 130

Missiles: SLBM: 16 SS-N-23 Skiff; three-stage liquid fuel rocket;
stellar inertial guidance to 8300 km *(4500 nm)*; warhead nuc-
lear 10 MIRV each of 100 kT; CEP 500 m. Same diameter as
SS-N-18 but longer.
Torpedoes: 4—21 in *(533 mm)* and 2—25.6 in *(650 mm)* tubes.
Combination of 53 and 65 cm torpedoes (see table at front of
section). Total of 18 weapons.
Countermeasures: ESM: Brick Pulp/Group; radar warning. Park
Lamp D/F.
Radars: Surface search: Snoop Tray; I band.
Sonars: Shark Gill; hull-mounted; passive/active search and
attack; low/medium frequency.
Mouse Roar; hull-mounted; active attack; high frequency.

Programmes: First of class launched February 1984 and commissioned later that year. All built at Severodvinsk and
launched at the rate of about one per year. This programme
completed in late 1990. A follow-on class is expected in the
mid-1990s.
Structure: A slim fitting is sited on the after fin which is remi-
niscent of a similar tube in one of the November class in the
early 1980s. This may be a form of dispenser for a buoyant
communications wire aerial. The other distinguishing feature,
apart from the size being greater than Delta III, is the pressure-
tight fitting on the after end of the missile tube housing, which
may be a TV camera to monitor communications buoy and
wire retrieval operations. Unfortunately this is not fitted in all of
the class. Also there are two 650 mm torpedo tubes. Diving

DELTA IV   10/1993

depth, 1000 ft *(300 m)*. The outer casing has a continuous
acoustic coating and fewer free flood holes than the Delta III.
Operational: Two VLF/ELF communication buoys. Navigation
systems include SATNAV, SINS, Cod Eye. Pert Spring

SATCOM. A modified and more accurate version of SS-N-23
was tested at sea in 1988 bringing the CEP down from 900 m
to 500 m. All based in the Northern Fleet at Olenya.

DELTA IV   1992

14 DELTA III (KALMAR) CLASS (TYPE 667BDR)

Displacement, tons: 10 000 surfaced; 11 700 dived
Dimensions, feet (metres): 524.9 oa; 498.7 wl × 39.4 × 28.5
(160; 152 × 12 × 8.7)
Main machinery: Nuclear; 2 PWR; 160 MW; 2 turbines;
37 400 hp(m) *(27.5 MW)*; 2 shafts
Speed, knots: 24 dived; 19 surfaced
Complement: 130

Missiles: SLBM: 16 SS-N-18 Stingray; two stage liquid fuel
rocket with post boost vehicle (PBV); stellar inertial guidance;
3 variants:
Mod 1; range 6500 km *(3500 nm)*; warhead nuclear 3 MIRV
each of 200 kT; CEP 900 m.
Mod 2; range 8000 km *(4320 nm)*; warhead nuclear 450 kT;
CEP 900 m.
Mod 3; range 6500 km *(3500 nm)*; warhead nuclear 7 MIRV
100 kT; CEP 900 m.
Mods 1 and 3 are the first MIRV SLBMs in Soviet service.
SS-N-23 retrofitted in some (see Delta IV for details).
Torpedoes: 6—21 in *(533 mm)* tubes. Combination of 53 cm
torpedoes (see table at front of section). Total of 18.
Countermeasures: ESM: Brick Pulp/Group; radar warning. Park
Lamp D/F.

Radars: Surface search: Snoop Tray; I band.
Sonars: Shark Teeth; hull-mounted; passive/active search and
attack; low/medium frequency.
Mouse Roar; hull-mounted; active attack; high frequency.

Programmes: Built at Severodvinsk 402. Completed
1976-1982.
Modernisation: SS-N-23 Skiff has been retrofitted in some. Also
the dispenser tube on the after fin has now been fitted to most
of the class.
Structure: The missile casing is higher than in Delta II class to
accommodate SS-N-18 missiles which are longer than the
SS-N-8 of the Delta II class. The outer casing has a continuous
'acoustic' coating but is less streamlined and has more free
flood holes than the Delta IV. Diving depth, 1000 ft *(300 m)*.
Operational: ELF/VLF communications with floating aerial and
buoy; UHF and SHF aerials. Navigation equipment includes
Cod Eye radiometric sextant, SATNAV, SINS and Omega. Pert
Spring SATCOM. Kremmny 2 IFF. Nine of the class are based in
the Pacific and five in the Northern Fleet.

DELTA III   5/1993   DELTA III   1992

4 DELTA II (MURENA-M) CLASS (TYPE 667BD)

Displacement, tons: 9700 surfaced; 11 300 dived
Dimensions, feet (metres): 508.4 oa; 498.7 wl × 39.4 × 28.5 *(155; 152 × 12 × 8.7)*
Main machinery: Nuclear; 2 PWR; 160 MW; 2 turbines; 37 400 hp(m) *(27.5 MW)*; 2 shafts
Speed, knots: 24 dived; 19 surfaced
Complement: 130

Missiles: SLBM: 16 SS-N-8 Sawfly; 2-stage liquid fuel rocket; stellar inertial guidance; 2 variants:
    Mod 1; range 7800 km *(4210 nm)*; warhead nuclear 1.2 MT; CEP 400 m.
    Mod 2; range 9100 km *(4910 nm)*; warhead nuclear 2 MIRV each of 800 kT; CEP 400 m.
Torpedoes: 6—21 in *(533 mm)* bow tubes. Combination of 53 cm torpedoes (see table at front of section). Total of 18.
Countermeasures: ESM: Brick Pulp/Group; radar warning.
Radars: Surface search: Snoop Tray; I band.
Sonars: Shark Teeth; hull-mounted; passive/active search and attack; low/medium frequency.
    Mouse Roar; hull-mounted; active attack; high frequency.

Programmes: Building yard—Severodvinsk. First appeared in 1976. Further construction cancelled with the advent of SS-N-18 and the Delta III class.
Structure: A larger edition of Delta I designed to carry four extra missile tubes and suffering a speed reduction as a result. Has a straight run on the after part of the missile casing. The outer casing has a continuous 'acoustic' coating. Diving depth, 1000 ft *(300 m)*.
Operational: ELF/VLF communications with floating aerial and buoy; UHF and SHF aerials. Navigation equipment includes SATNAV, SINS, Omega, Cod Eye radiometric sextant. Pert Spring SATCOM. Kremmny 2 IFF. All based in the Northern Fleet at Yagelnaya.

DELTA II   *1992*

14 DELTA I (MURENA) CLASS (TYPE 667B)

Displacement, tons: 8700 surfaced; 10 200 dived
Dimensions, feet (metres): 459.3 oa; 446.2 wl × 39.4 × 28.5 *(140; 136 × 12 × 8.7)*
Main machinery: Nuclear; 2 PWR; 160 MW; 2 turbines; 37 400 hp(m) *(27.5 MW)*; 2 shafts
Speed, knots: 25 dived; 19 surfaced
Complement: 120

Missiles: SLBM: 12—SS-N-8 Sawfly; 2-stage liquid fuel rocket; stellar inertial guidance; 2 variants:
    Mod 1; range 7800 km *(4210 nm)*; warhead nuclear 1.2 MT; CEP 400 m.
    Mod 2; range 9100 km *(4910 nm)*; warhead nuclear 2 MIRV each of 800 kT; CEP 400 m.
Torpedoes: 6—21 in *(533 mm)* bow tubes. 18 Type 53; dual purpose; pattern active/passive homing up to 20 km *(10.8 nm)* at up to 45 kts; warhead 400 kg or low yield nuclear.
Countermeasures: ESM: Brick Pulp/Group; radar warning. Park Lamp D/F.
Radars: Surface search: Snoop Tray; I band.
Sonars: Shark Teeth; hull-mounted; passive/active search and attack; low/medium frequency.
    Mouse Roar; hull-mounted; active attack; high frequency.

Programmes: The first of this class, an advance on the Yankee class SSBNs, was laid down at Severodvinsk in 1969 and completed in 1972. Programme completed 1972-77. Building yards—Severodvinsk 402 (10) and Komsomolsk (8).
Structure: The longer-range SS-N-8 missiles are of greater length than the SS-N-6s and, as this length cannot be accommodated below the keel, they stand several feet proud of the after-casing. At the same time the need to compensate for the additional top-weight would seem to be the reason for the reduction to 12 missiles in this class. The outer casing has a continuous 'acoustic' coating. Diving depth, 1000 ft *(300 m)*.
Operational: ELF/VLF communications with floating aerial and buoy; UHF and SHF aerials. Cod Eye radiometric sextant.

DELTA I   *1990*

Kremmny 2 IFF. In common with all the Delta class variations, this submarine is ill-designed for under-ice operations. Seven based in the North, seven in the Pacific. First of this class paid off in 1992, three more in 1993.

3 YANKEE I (NAVAGA) CLASS (TYPE 667A)

Displacement, tons: 8000 surfaced; 9450 dived
Dimensions, feet (metres): 426.4 × 38 × 26.2 *(130 × 11.6 × 8)*
Main machinery: Nuclear; 2 PWR; 160 MW; 2 turbines; 37 400 hp(m) *(27.5 MW)*; 2 shafts
Speed, knots: 26.5 dived; 20 surfaced
Complement: 120

Missiles: SLBM: 16 SS-N-6 Serb; single-stage liquid fuel rocket; inertial guidance; 2 variants:
    Mod 1; range 2400 km *(1300 nm)*; warhead nuclear 1 MT; CEP 1300 m.
    Mod 3; range 3000 km *(1620 nm)*; warhead 2 MRV each of 500 kT; CEP 1300 m.
Launch rate for a full salvo is reported as less than 2 minutes.
Torpedoes: 6—21 in *(533 mm)* tubes. Combination of 53 cm torpedoes (see table at front of section). Total of 18.
Countermeasures: ESM: Brick Group; radar warning. Park Lamp D/F.
Radars: Surface search: Snoop Tray; I band.
Sonars: Shark Teeth; hull-mounted; passive/active search and attack; low/medium frequency.
    Mouse Roar; hull-mounted; active attack; high frequency

Programmes: The first of the class was laid down in 1963-64 and delivered late 1967 and the programme then accelerated with output rising to six to eight a year in the period around 1970. The last one was completed in 1974. Construction took place at Severodvinsk 402 (first laid down in 1965) and Komsomolsk. Of the total of 34 built, these last three are all fitted with SS-N-6. In the last 15 years some of this class had their missile tubes removed to remain within SALT 1 limits, and are still in service as SSN/SSGN/SSAN.
Structure: Design is similar to USS *Ethan Allen* (now deleted) with vertical tubes in two rows of eight and fin-mounted fore-

YANKEE I   *1990*

planes; the first time the Navy had used this arrangement. The outer casing has a continuous 'acoustic' coating. Diving depth, 1000 ft *(300 m)*.
Operational: Fitted for ELF communications with floating aerial and VLF buoy. VHF and SHF aerials. Navigation equipment includes SATNAV, SINS, Omega and Cod Eye radiometric sex-

tant. Pert Spring SATCOM. Kremmny 2 IFF. One Yankee I sank in Western Atlantic after an internal explosion 6 October 1986 while patrolling 600 miles north of Bermuda. The single Yankee II paid off in 1991. In early 1994 one was in the Northern Fleet and two in the Pacific. All are expected to be withdrawn from service in 1994.

Cruise Missile Submarines

Note: The Echo II nuclears and the conventional Juliett class were built over the same period (1961-68), armed with eight and four SS-N-3A missiles respectively as a counter to the threat of the US carriers with their nuclear strike capability. The SS-N-3As were replaced by SS-N-12 in about 14 of the Echo II class. By 1968 both production lines had stopped when the first Charlie class appeared with underwater launch capability for its SS-N-7 missiles. The problem which had faced all the earlier boats, that

of having to surface to launch, had been overcome. An improved design of Charlie I (Charlie II) and the single unit of the Papa class (since deleted) appeared in the early 1970s with SS-N-9 missiles to be followed by the launch of the giant Oscar in 1980 with 24 SS-N-19 supersonic missiles.

The arrival of SS-N-21, a sea-launched land attack cruise missile with an estimated range of 1600 nm and a tube-launch capability for all modern classes of SSN, changed the balance of

cruise missile submarines. A larger land attack missile, SS-NX-24 was fitted in a converted Yankee class for trials in 1989 but this programme was abandoned in 1991.

All these submarines, with the exception of Echo II and Juliett classes, are coated with Cluster Guard anechoic tiles. All are capable of laying mines from their torpedo tubes.

3 CHARLIE II (TYPE 670M) and 3 CHARLIE I (TYPE 670) CLASSES

Displacement, tons: 4500 surfaced; 5550 dived (5000 Charlie I)
Dimensions, feet (metres): 334.6; 308.3 (Charlie I) × 32.5 × 25.6
(102; 94 × 9.9 × 7.8)
Main machinery: Nuclear; 1 PWR; 65 MW; 1 turbine; 20 00 hp(m) *(15 MW)*; 1 shaft
Speed, knots: 25 dived; 15 surfaced
Complement: 90

Missiles: SSM: 8 SS-N-9 Siren (Charlie II); IR and active radar homing to 110 km *(60 nm)* at 0.9 Mach; warhead nuclear 250 kT or HE 500 kg.
8 SS-N-7 (Charlie I); active radar homing to 64 km *(35 nm)* at 0.9 Mach; warhead nuclear 200 kT or HE 500 kg.

A/S: SS-N-15 fired from 21 in *(533 mm)* tubes; inertial flight to 37 km *(20 nm)*; warhead nuclear 200 kT.
Torpedoes: 6—21 in *(533 mm)* tubes. Combination of 53 cm torpedoes (see table at front of section). Total of 14 tube-launched weapons.
Countermeasures: ESM: Stop Light and Brick Spit/Pulp; intercept. Park Lamp D/F.
Radars: Surface search: Snoop Tray; I band.
Sonars: Shark Fin; hull-mounted; passive/active search and attack; low/medium frequency.
Mouse Roar; hull-mounted; active attack; high frequency.

Programmes: Built at Gorky from 1973-80 (Charlie II) and 1967-72 (Charlie I).
Structure: The first Soviet SSGNs capable of launching SSMs

without having to surface. Although similar in some respects to the Victor class, visible differences include the bulge at the bow, the almost vertical drop of the forward end of the fin, a slightly lower after casing and a different arrangement of free-flood holes in the casing. Some of this class have a raised platform around the forward part of the fin as well as a similar addition around the stern fin. This may be designed to smooth the flow of water in these areas. There is single improved reactor design vice the two in the Victor class resulting in a loss of some five knots. Diving depth, 1000 ft *(300 m)*.
Operational: VLF communications buoy. Pert Spring SATCOM. Kremmny 2 IFF. Charlie IIs based in the Northern Fleet, Charlie Is in the Pacific, and all rapidly being paid off.
Sales: One Charlie I leased to India from January 1988 to January 1991.

CHARLIE II   7/1992

4 ECHO II CLASS (TYPE 675M)

Displacement, tons: 4800 surfaced; 5800 dived
Dimensions, feet (metres): 390.4 × 30.2 × 22.6
(119 × 9.2 × 6.9)
Main machinery: Nuclear; 2 PWR; 17 500 hp(m) *(13 MW)*; 2 turbines; 30 000 hp(m) *(22 MW)*; 2 shafts
Speed, knots: 24 dived; 18 surfaced
Complement: 90

Missiles: SSM: 8 SS-N-12 Sandbox; inertial guidance with command update; active radar homing to 550 km *(300 nm)* at 1.7+ Mach; warhead nuclear 350 kT or HE 1000 kg; altitude 10 668 m *(35 000 ft)*.
Torpedoes: 6—21 in *(533 mm)* bow and 4—16 in *(406 mm)* stern tubes. Combination of 53 and 40 cm torpedoes (see table at front of section). Total of 20 torpedoes carried.
Countermeasures: ESM: Stop Light and Brick Pulp or Squid Head; radar warning. Quad Loop D/F.
Radars: Surface search: Snoop Tray/Snoop Slab; I band.
Fire control: Front Piece/Front Door; F band (for SS-N-3A midcourse guidance).
Sonars: Hull-mounted; passive/active search and attack; medium frequency.

Programmes: Built at Severodvinsk and Komsomolsk between 1961 and 1967.
Structure: A large radome Punch Bowl, used for satellite missile targeting, is housed in the fin and raised like any other mast. At the after end of the fin there is a hinged communications aerial which stows in a depression in the casing. There is no acoustic coating. Diving depth, 650 ft *(200 m)*.

ECHO II   1992

Operational: Based in the Northern and Pacific Fleets. For a time one acted as a mother ship for the X-Ray class trials submarine. The only reason for keeping these submarines is so that they

can fire missiles to act as targets for air defence systems. All the SS-N-3C firers have been paid off, and all are expected to go by the end of 1994.

1 YANKEE SIDECAR CLASS (conversion) (SSGN)

(see also Yankee Notch class in *Attack Submarine* section)

Displacement, tons: 13 650 dived
Dimensions, feet (metres): 501.8 × 49.2 × 26.2
(153 × 15 × 8)
Main machinery: Nuclear; 2 PWR; 160 MW; 2 turbines; 37 400 hp(m) *(27.5 MW)*; 2 shafts
Speed, knots: 22 dived
Complement: 120

Missiles: SLCM: 12 SS-NX-24; inertial guidance; terrain following to 4000 km *(2200 nm)* at 2 Mach; warhead nuclear 1 MT. 6 tubes are sited on either side abaft the fin, inclined and built in outside the pressure hull.
Torpedoes: 6—21 in *(533 mm)* bow tubes.
Countermeasures: ESM: Brick Pulp; intercept.
Radars: Surface search: Snoop Tray; I band.
Sonars: Shark Fin; hull-mounted; passive/active search and attack; low/medium frequency.

Programmes: Completed conversion in 1983 as the trials submarine for SSN-X-24, a new long-range SLCM. Trials were cancelled in 1991 but the submarine remains operational presumably in the hope of resumption at some future date.
Structure: A lengthened section of some 23 m added in place of original SLBM tubes. The configuration of the SLCM launchers has also increased the beam dimensions and the fin is rounder in appearance.

9 + 1 (1) OSCAR II (ANTYEY) (TYPE 949A) and 2 OSCAR I (GRANIT) (TYPE 949) CLASSES

Displacement, tons: 10 200 surfaced; 12 500 dived (Oscar I);
10 700 surfaced; 13 500 dived (Oscar II)

Dimensions, feet (metres): 469.2; 505.2 (Oscar II) × 59.7
× 29.5
(143; 154 × 18.2 × 9)

Main machinery: Nuclear; 2 PWR; 200 MW; 2 turbines;
75 000 hp(m) *(55 MW)*; 2 shafts; 2 spinners

Speed, knots: 30; 28 (Oscar II) dived; 19 surfaced

Complement: 135

Missiles: SSM: 24 SS-N-19 Shipwreck (improved SS-N-12 with
lower flight profile); inertial with command update guidance;
active radar homing to 20-550 km *(10.8-300 nm)* at 1.6 Mach;
warhead 750 kg HE or nuclear.
 A/S: SS-N-15 fired from 21 in *(533 mm)* tubes; inertial flight to
37 km *(20 nm)*; warhead nuclear 200 kT.
 SS-N-16 fired from 25.6 in *(650 mm)* tubes; inertial flight to
120 km *(65 nm)*; payload Type 40 torpedo; active passive
homing to 15 km *(8.1 nm)* at 45 kts; warhead 60 kg. There is
also a 16B version with a nuclear warhead.

Torpedoes: 4—21 in *(533 mm)* and 4—25.6 in *(650 mm)* tubes.
Combination of 65 and 53 cm torpedoes (see table at front of
section). Total of 24 weapons including tube-launched A/S
missiles.

Countermeasures: ESM: Bald Head/Rim Hat; intercept. Park
Lamp D/F.

Fire control: Punch Bowl for third party targeting.

Radars: Surface search: Snoop Head/Pair; I band.

Sonars: Shark Gill; hull-mounted; passive/active search and
attack; low/medium frequency.
 Mouse Roar; hull-mounted; active attack; high frequency.

Programmes: First Oscar I class laid down at Severodvinsk in
1978 and launched in Spring 1980. Second completed in
1982. The first Oscar II completed in 1985, a second in 1986,
a third in 1988, a fourth in 1989, two more in 1990, one in
1991, one in 1992, and the ninth was doing sea trials in late
1993. Still building at one a year.

Structure: SSM missile tubes are in banks of 12 either side and
external to the 8.5 m diameter pressure hull; they are inclined
at 40° with one hatch covering each pair, the whole resulting
in the very large beam. The position of the missile tubes provides a large gap of some 3 m between the outer and inner
hulls. The Oscar II has a hull lengthened by 36.1 ft *(11 m)* and
an increased displacement of 1400 tons, presumably as the
result of some deficiency found in first of class trials, which
could not have been corrected in time to change hull number
two. Alternatively it could have something to do with incorporating an SS-N-24 weapon system in due course. Diving depth,
1000 ft *(300 m)*.

Operational: ELF/VLF communications buoy. All but the first of
class have a tube on the rudder fin as in Delta IV which may be
used for dispensing a VLF floating aerial. Pert Spring SATCOM.
Based in both Northern and Pacific Fleets.

OSCAR II   7/1992

OSCAR II   7/1993

OSCAR II   1990

OSCAR I   1989

5 JULIETT CLASS (TYPE 651)

JULIETT   7/1993, Hartmut Ehlers

Displacement, tons: 3150 surfaced; 3850 dived
Dimensions, feet (metres): 285.4 × 32.8 × 23
  (87 × 10 × 7)
Main machinery: Direct drive or diesel-electric; 2 Type D-43 diesels; 4000 hp(m) *(2.94 MW)*; 2 motors; 4000 hp(m) *(2.94 MW)*; 2 shafts
Speed, knots: 19 surfaced; 11 dived; 8 snorting
Range, miles: 9000 at 8 kts snorting
Complement: 79

Missiles: SSM: 4 SS-N-12 Sandbox; inertial guidance with command update; active radar homing to 550 km *(300 nm)* at 1.7 Mach; warhead nuclear 350 kT or HE 1000 kg; altitude 10 668 m *(35 000 ft)* or 4 SS-N-3C Shaddock; command guidance; active radar or IR homing to 460 km *(250 nm)* at 1.1 Mach; warhead nuclear 350 kT or HE 1000 kg. The tubes elevate to 20°.
Torpedoes: 6—21 in *(533 mm)* bow and 4—15.7 in *(400 mm)* stern tubes. 18—53 cm and 4—40 cm torpedoes (see table at front of section).
Countermeasures: ESM: Stop Light; radar warning. Quad Loop D/F.
Radars: Surface search: Snoop Slab; I band.

Fire control: Front Door; F band (for SSM mid-course guidance).
Sonars: Pike Jaw; hull-mounted; passive/active search and attack; medium/high frequency.

Programmes: Completed between 1961 and 1968 at Gorky.
Structure: At least one has the large Punch Bowl radome in the fin similar to Echo II. This is a receiver for satellite targeting information for an SS-N-12 retrofit. Diving depth, 650 ft *(200 m)*.
Operational: In 1980-81 three were transferred from the Northern Fleet to the Baltic Fleet establishing a pattern of patrols in that area. Two more were transferred in 1989 but operational patrols have now stopped and the class began paying off in 1990. Two are based in the Black Sea.

Attack Submarines

Note: The use of nuclear power for marine propulsion was developed from 1950 onwards, the first submarine reactor being put in hand in 1953 probably about the same time as a larger reactor for the icebreaker *Lenin* was under construction.

No prototype was produced before series production of the November class began and this was also true for the Victor class which followed after a four year pause in 1967. Since the early November class provided sea experience of this new form of submarine some years of redesign were therefore available before the first Victor was laid down. The ability to produce hydrodynamically advanced hull forms was further proved by the efficiency of the Victor and her near sister the Charlie. Five years after the first Victor came the Victor II, an enlarged edition whose increase in size may be due to the fitting of the new tube-launched ASW system, SS-N-15, probably similar to the Subroc of the US Navy. This again was followed six years later by the Victor III, slightly longer than the Victor II.

The Alfa class was a new concept of attack submarine built in 1970-83 with a length/beam ratio very different from its predecessors, much improved propulsion plant with high speeds and a very deep diving depth. This was probably an extended research and development project with a limited production run. Some of this technology was reflected in the Mike and Sierra classes which appeared in 1983. The Akula class which is a more traditional design successor of the Victor III class, appeared first in 1984, and by 1994 was the only class in series production. According to Admiral Gromov the first of a new class was started in 1993 and laid down at Severodvinsk Shipyard early in 1994, with an expected operational date of 1998. First reports indicate a smaller hull than Akula, and the use of steel in construction. The single Mike was sunk in an accident in April 1989 and subsequent Soviet official statements indicated a diving depth of 1000 m with a titanium-reinforced hull and the use of explosive charges to blow main ballast tanks at great depths. Attempts to salvage the Mike have so far been defeated by lack of funds.

A significant change in the capability of the fleet submarines has resulted from the introduction of SS-N-21, a tube-launched land attack cruise missile with a 1600 nm range. The stern pod on the rudder of the Victor III, Sierra, Akula and one converted Yankee is a towed array dispenser which has taken several years to become operational, and may not be very effective.

The last of the November class paid off in mid-1991. All Fleet submarines are coated with Cluster Guard anechoic tiles. All submarines are capable of laying mines from their torpedo tubes. Newer classes are increasingly being fitted with environmental sensors for measuring discontinuities caused by the passage of a submarine in deep water.

11 + 5 AKULA (BARS) CLASS (TYPE 971)

BARS	PANTERA	VOLK	+ 5
LEOPARD	PUMA	TIGR	

Displacement, tons: 7500 surfaced; 9100 dived
Dimensions, feet (metres): 360.1 oa; 337.9 wl × 45.9 × 34.1
  (110; 103 × 14 × 10.4)
Main machinery: Nuclear; 2 PWR; 200 MW; 2 turbines; 47 600 hp(m) *(35 MW)*; 1 shaft; 2 spinners
Speed, knots: 32 dived; 18 surfaced
Complement: 85

Missiles: SLCM: SS-N-21 Sampson fired from 21 in *(533 mm)* tubes; land-attack; inertial/terrain following to 3000 km *(1620 nm)* at 0.7 Mach; warhead nuclear 200 kT. CEP 150 m. Flies at a height of about 200 m.
A/S: SS-N-15 fired from 21 in *(533 mm)* tubes; inertial flight to 37 km *(20 nm)*; warhead nuclear 200 kT.
SS-N-16 fired from 25.6 in *(650 mm)* tubes; inertial flight to 120 km *(65 nm)*; payload Type 40 torpedo; active/passive homing to 15 km *(8.1 nm)* at 45 kts; warhead 60 kg. There is also a 16B version with a nuclear warhead.
Torpedoes: 4—21 in *(533 mm)* and 4—25.6 in *(650 mm)* tubes. Combination of 53 and 65 cm torpedoes (see table at front of section). Tube liners can be used to reduce the larger diameter tubes to 533 mm.
Countermeasures: ESM: Amber Light; Rim Hat; intercept. Park Lamp D/F.
Radars: Surface search: Snoop Pair with back-to-back aerials on same mast as ESM.
Sonars: Shark Gill; hull-mounted; passive/active search and attack; low/medium frequency.
Mouse Roar; hull-mounted; active attack; high frequency.

Programmes: First of class launched July 1984 at Komsomolsk and operational at the end of 1985. The class is in series production at Severodvinsk with a construction rate of one or two per year. The fifth or sixth and subsequent hulls are sometimes referred to as the Akula II class. There are no dimensional changes but better sensors and improved acoustic quieting have been reported. The most recent to be launched was named *Tigr* on 9 July 1993.
Structure: The very long fin is particularly notable. Has the same broad hull as Sierra and has reduced radiated noise levels by comparison with Victor III of which she is the traditional follow-on design. A number of prominent water environment sensors appear on the fin leading edge and on the forward casing. These are similar to devices tested on a Hotel II class from the early 1980s. The engineering standards around the bridge and

AKULA II (with casing sensors)   6/1993

casing are noticeably to a higher quality than other classes. Diving depth, 1300 ft *(400 m)*.
Operational: A multi-role SSN following the Victor III class. Pert Spring SATCOM. Based in both Northern and Pacific Fleets.

AKULA I   10/1993

2 SIERRA II (BARACUDA II) CLASS (TYPE 945B)

OREL   KASATKA

Displacement, tons: 7200 surfaced; 8200 dived
Dimensions, feet (metres): 364.2 × 46.6 × 28.9
  (111 × 14.2 × 8.8)
Main machinery: Nuclear; 2 PWR; 200 MW; 2 turbo alternators;
  95 000 hp(m) *(70 MW)*; 1 shaft; 2 spinners
Speed, knots: 32 dived; 18 surfaced
Complement: 72

Missiles: SLCM: SS-N-21 Sampson fired from 21 in *(533 mm)*
  tubes; land-attack; inertial/terrain following to 3000 km
  (1620 nm) at 0.7 Mach; warhead nuclear 200 kT. CEP 150 m.
  Flies at a height of about 200 m.
  A/S: SS-N-15 fired from 21 in *(533 mm)* tubes; inertial flight to
  37 km *(20 nm)*; warhead nuclear 200 kT.
  SS-N-16 fired from 25.6 in *(650 mm)* tubes; inertial flight to
  120 km *(65 nm)*; payload Type 40 torpedo; active/passive
  homing to 15 km *(8.1 nm)* at 45 kts; warhead 60 kg. There is
  also a 16B version with a nuclear warhead.
Torpedoes: 8—25.6 in *(650 mm)* tubes. Combination of 65 and
  53 cm torpedoes (see table at front of section). Tube liners are
  used for 21 in *(533 mm)* weapons.
Mines: Up to 50 or 60 in lieu of torpedoes.
Countermeasures: ESM: Rim Hat; intercept. Park Lamp D/F.
Radars: Surface search: Snoop Pair with back-to-back ESM
  aerial.
Sonars: Shark Gill; hull-mounted; passive/active search and
  attack; low/medium frequency.
  Mouse Roar; hull-mounted; active attack; high frequency.

Programmes: Built at Gorky. First launched in July 1989 and on
  trials in 1990. Second launched July 1992 and in service in
  1993. A third of class was scrapped before completion in July
  1992.
Structure: A follow-on class to the Sierra I. Apart from larger
  overall dimensions the Sierra II has a longer fin by some 16.5 ft
  (5 m) and an almost flat surface at the leading edge. The towed
  communications buoy has been recessed. A ten point environmental sensor is fitted at the front end of the fin. The stand-off
  distance between hulls is considerable and has obvious advantages for radiated noise reduction and damage resistance. Diving depth, 2100 ft *(650 m)*.
Operational: Pert Spring SATCOM.

SIERRA II   1992

SIERRA II   1992

2 SIERRA I (BARACUDA I) CLASS (TYPE 945A)

Displacement, tons: 7000 surfaced; 7900 dived
Dimensions, feet (metres): 351 × 41 × 28.9 *(107 × 12.5 × 8.8)*
Main machinery: Nuclear; 2 PWR; 200 MW; 2 turbo alternators; 95 000 hp(m) *(70 MW)*; 1 shaft; 2 spinners
Speed, knots: 34 dived; 18 surfaced
Complement: 72

Missiles: SLCM: SS-N-21 Sampson fired from 21 in *(533 mm)* tubes; land-attack; inertial/terrain following to 3000 km *(1620 nm)* at 0.7 Mach; warhead nuclear 200 kT. CEP 150 m. Probably flies at a height of about 200 m.
A/S: SS-N-15 fired from 21 in *(533 mm)* tubes; inertial flight to 37 km *(20 nm)*; warhead nuclear 200 kT.
SS-N-16 fired from 25.6 in *(650 mm)* tubes; inertial flight to 120 km *(65 nm)*; payload Type 40 torpedo; active/passive homing to 15 km *(8.1 nm)* at 45 kts; warhead 60 kg. There is also a 16B version with a nuclear warhead.
Torpedoes: 8—25.6 in *(650 mm)* tubes. Combination of 65 and 53 cm torpedoes (see table at front of section). Tube liners are used for 21 in *(533 mm)* weapons.
Mines: Up to 50 or 60 in lieu of torpedoes.
Countermeasures: ESM: Rim Hat; intercept. Park Lamp D/F.
Radars: Surface search: Snoop Pair with back-to-back ESM aerial.
Sonars: Shark Gill; hull-mounted; passive/active search and attack; low/medium frequency.
Mouse Roar; hull-mounted; active attack; high frequency.

Programmes: First launched in August 1983 at Gorky, and fitted out at Severodvinsk. In service for trials in late 1984. Second launched July 1986 and on trials in early 1987.
Structure: Similar to the late Mike in having a strengthened hull which makes it much more expensive than Akula and a logical successor to the Alfa class. The pod on the after fin is larger than that in Victor III. The stand-off distance between hulls is considerable and has obvious advantages for radiated noise

SIERRA I (Unit 2)   *1989*

reduction and damage resistance. The second unit picture shows the V-shaped casing on the port side of the fin which covers the releasable escape chamber. This submarine also has a bulbous casing at the after end of the fin for a towed communications buoy. Diving depth, 2100 ft *(650 m)*.
Operational: Pert Spring SATCOM.

SIERRA I (Unit 1)   *1984*

1 ALFA (ALPHA) CLASS (TYPE 705)

Displacement, tons: 2700 surfaced; 3600 dived
Dimensions, feet (metres): 267.4 oa; 246.1 wl × 31.2 × 24.6 *(81.5; 75 × 9.5 × 7.5)*
Main machinery: Nuclear; 2 PWR; 170 MW; 2 turbo alternators; 50 000 hp(m) *(37 MW)*; 1 shaft; 2 spinners
Speed, knots: 40 dived; 20 surfaced
Complement: 40

Torpedoes: 6—21 in *(533 mm)* fwd tubes. Combination of 53 cm torpedoes (see table at front of section). Can carry 20 torpedoes or a mixed equivalent load.
Mines: Up to 40 in lieu of torpedoes.
Countermeasures: ESM: Bald Head and Brick Group; radar warning. Park Lamp D/F.

Radars: Surface search: Snoop Head (on same mast as ESM); I band.
Sonars: Shark Gill; hull-mounted; passive/active search and attack; low/medium frequency.
Mouse Roar; hull-mounted; active attack; high frequency.

Programmes: The first of this class was laid down in mid-1960s and completed in 1970 at Sudomekh, Leningrad. The building time was very long in comparison with normal programmes and it seems most likely that this was a prototype. This boat was scrapped in 1974. Six more were then built between 1979 and 1983 at Sudomekh and Severodvinsk.
Structure: The reduction of the length combined with the high speed indicated considerable progress in hydrodynamic

design and laminar flow techniques. A greater diving depth, down to 2500 ft *(700 m)* has been achieved by use of titanium alloy for the hull. This also results in a much reduced magnetic signature. The sound profile of this class is, however, high, reflecting the fact that this is a design now over 25 years old.
Operational: Small complement indicates a high level of automation. Navigation systems include SINS, SATNAV, Loran and Omega. High levels of speed dependent noise, much quieter when slow. One was scrapped in 1988 and one recommissioned in late 1989 as a trials boat, having been in refit for five years. The rest of the class were defuelled in 1992/93 and are probably to be scrapped.

ALFA   *5/1990*

26 VICTOR III (KEFAL III) CLASS (TYPE 671RTM)

Displacement, tons: 4850 surfaced; 6300 dived
Dimensions, feet (metres): 351.1 × 34.8 × 24.3
(107 × 10.6 × 7.4)
Main machinery: Nuclear; 2 PWR; 130 MW; 2 turbines;
30 000 hp(m) *(22 MW)*; 1 shaft; 2 spinners
Speed, knots: 30 dived; 18 surfaced
Complement: 70 (17 officers)

Missiles: SLCM: SS-N-21 Sampson fired from 21 in *(533 mm)*
tubes; land-attack; inertial/terrain following to 3000 km
(1620 nm) at 0.7 Mach; warhead nuclear 200 kT. CEP 150 m.
Probably flies at a height of about 200 m.
A/S: SS-N-15 fired from 21 in *(533 mm)* tubes; inertial flight to
37 km *(20 nm)*; warhead nuclear 200 kT.
SS-N-16 A/B fired from 25.6 in *(650 mm)* tubes; inertial flight
to 120 km *(65 nm)*; payload Type 40 torpedo; active/passive
homing to 15 km *(8.1 nm)* at 45 kts; warhead 60 kg. There is
also a 16B version with a nuclear warhead.
Torpedoes: 2—21 in *(533 mm)* and 4—25.6 in *(650 mm)* tubes:
Combination of 53 and 65 cm torpedoes (see table at front of
section). Can carry up to 24 torpedoes. Liners can be used to
reduce 650 mm tubes to 533 mm.
Mines: Can carry 36 in lieu of torpedoes.
Countermeasures: ESM: Brick Group (Brick Spit and Brick Pulp);
intercept. Park Lamp D/F.
Radars: Surface search: Snoop Tray; I band.
Sonars: Shark Gill; hull-mounted; passive/active search and
attack; low/medium frequency.
Mouse Roar; hull-mounted; active attack; high frequency.

Programmes: An improvement on Victor II, the first of class
being completed at Komsomolsk in 1978. With construction
also being carried out at Admiralty Yard, Leningrad, there was
a very rapid building programme up to the end of 1984. Since
then construction continued only at Leningrad and at a rate of
about one per year which terminated in 1991. The last of the
class completed sea trials in October 1992.
Structure: The streamlined pod on the stern fin is now described
as a towed sonar array dispenser. Water environment sensors
are being mounted at the front of the fin and on the forward
casing as in the Akula and Sierra classes. One of the class has
the trials SS-N-21 SLCM mounted on the forward casing. Diving depth, 1000 ft *(300 m)*.

VICTOR III (sensors at front of the fin)   6/1992

Operational: VLF communications buoy. VHF/UHF aerials. Navigation equipment includes SINS and SATNAV. Pert Spring
SATCOM. Kremmny 2 IFF. Much improved acoustic quietening
puts the radiated noise levels at the upper limits of the USN Los
Angeles class. Based in Northern and Pacific Fleets.

VICTOR III   8/1993

VICTOR III   6/1992

3 VICTOR II (KEFAL II) CLASS (TYPE 671RT)

VICTOR II   *6/1992*

Displacement, tons: 4700 surfaced; 5800 dived
Dimensions, feet (metres): 337.9 oa; 315 wl × 34.8 × 24.3
(103; 96 × 10.6 × 7.4)
Main machinery: Nuclear; 2 PWR; 130 MW; 2 turbines;
30 000 hp(m) *(22 MW)*; 1 shaft; 2 spinners
Speed, knots: 30 dived; 18 surfaced
Complement: 70 (17 officers)

Missiles: A/S: SS-N-15 fired from 21 in *(533 mm)* tubes; inertial
flight to 37 km *(20 nm)*; warhead nuclear 200 kT.
SS-N-16 A/B fired from 25.6 in *(650 mm)* tubes; inertial flight
to 120 km *(65 nm)*; payload Type 40 torpedo. There is also a
16B version with a nuclear warhead.
Torpedoes: 2—21 in *(533 mm)* and 4—25.6 in *(650 mm)* tubes.
Combination of 53 and 65 cm torpedoes (see table at front of
section). Can carry up to 24 torpedoes.
Mines: Up to 48 in lieu of torpedoes.
Countermeasures: ESM: Brick Group (Brick Spit and Brick Pulp);
radar warning. Park Lamp D/F.
Radars: Surface search: Snoop Tray; I band.
Sonars: Shark Teeth; hull-mounted; passive/active search and
attack; low/medium frequency.
Mouse Roar; hull-mounted; active attack; high frequency.

Programmes: First appeared in 1972, class completed 1978.
Built at Admiralty Yard, Leningrad and Gorky.
Structure: An enlarged Victor I design, 9 m longer to provide
more space for torpedo stowage. Diving depth, 1000 ft
(300 m) approx.
Operational: VLF communications buoy. VHF and UHF aerials.
Navigation equipment includes SINS and SATNAV. Kremmny
2 IFF. These three survivors are based in the Northern Fleet and
rapidly being paid off.

5 VICTOR I (KEFAL I) CLASS (TYPE 671T)

VICTOR I   *7/1993*

Displacement, tons: 4400 surfaced; 5300 dived
Dimensions, feet (metres): 308.4 oa; 282.2 wl × 34.4 × 24
(94; 86 × 10.5 × 7.3)
Main machinery: Nuclear; 2 PWR; 130 MW; 2 turbines;
30 000 hp(m) *(22 MW)*; 1 shaft; 2 spinners
Speed, knots: 32 dived; 18 surfaced
Complement: 70 (17 officers)

Missiles: A/S: SS-N-15 fired from 21 in *(533 mm)* tubes; inertial
flight to 37 km *(20 nm)*; warhead nuclear 200 kT.
Torpedoes: 6—21 in *(533 mm)* bow tubes. Type 53; dual pur-
pose; pattern active/passive homing up to 20 km *(10.8 nm)* at
up to 45 kts; warhead 400 kg or low yield nuclear. Can carry
up to 24 torpedoes.
Mines: In lieu of torpedoes.
Countermeasures: ESM: Brick Group; radar warning. Park
Lamp D/F.
Radars: Surface search: Snoop Tray; I band.
Sonars: Shark Teeth; hull-mounted; passive/active search and
attack; low/medium frequency.
Mouse Roar; hull-mounted; active attack; high frequency.

Programmes: The first of class laid down in 1965 entering service in 1967-68—class completed 1974 at a building rate of
two per year. Superseded by the Victor II programme. Built at
Admiralty Yard, Leningrad.
Structure: This was the first Soviet submarine with an Albacore
hull-form and a new reactor system, a new generation design
shared by the Charlie class. Is of double-hulled form but, unlike
Charlie, has two reactors giving an enhanced speed. Diving
depth, 1000 ft *(300 m)* approx.
Operational: Three with the Northern Fleet, two are with the
Pacific Fleet. Becoming unreliable and of the original 16 units
at least 11 have been withdrawn from service, one as a result
of a reactor refuelling accident in August 1985.

3 YANKEE NOTCH CLASS (SSN, ex-SSBN)

YANKEE NOTCH   *1990*

Displacement, tons: 8500 surfaced; 10 300 dived
Dimensions, feet (metres): 464.2 × 38.1 × 26.6
(141.5 × 11.6 × 8.1)
Main machinery: Nuclear; 2 PWR; 160 MW; 2 turbines;
37 400 hp(m) *(27.5 MW)*; 2 shafts
Speed, knots: 26 dived; 16 surfaced
Complement: 109 (18 officers)

Missiles: SLCM: 35 approx SS-N-21 Sampson fired from 21 in
(533 mm) tubes; land attack; inertial/terrain following to
3000 km *(1620 nm)* at 0.7 Mach; warhead nuclear 200 kT.
CEP 150 m. Flies at a height of about 200 m.
Torpedoes: 6—21 in *(533 mm)* tubes; combination of 53 cm tor-
pedoes (see table at front of section).
Countermeasures: ESM: Brick Group; intercept. Park Lamp D/F.
Radars: Surface search: Snoop Tray; I band.
Sonars: Shark Gill; hull-mounted; passive/active search and
attack; low/medium frequency.
Mouse Roar; hull-mounted; active attack; high frequency.

Programmes: The SALT limits of 62 SSBNs and 950 SLBMs
were adhered to by the Soviet Navy and this resulted in the
conversion of Yankee class as well as the deleted Hotel and
Golf classes. The Yankee conversion to SSN was first seen in
1983. The conversion takes about two years and it seemed to
be the intention to convert about 10 of the class until the programme fell victim to financial cuts in 1989-90. See also *Auxiliary Submarine* section.
Structure: In spite of the removal of the ballistic missile section
the overall length of the hull has increased by 39.4 ft *(12 m)*
with the insertion of a 'notch waisted' central section. This new
section houses three tubes amidships on each side and it is
likely that the magazine holds up to 20 SS-N-21s or additional
torpedoes and mines. There may also have been a rearrangement of torpedo tubes to include some at 26.5 in *(650 mm)*.
Diving depth, 1000 ft *(300 m)*.

Patrol Submarines

Note: The Foxtrot class was built from 1958-71 with 62 completed for the Soviet Navy, and a further 17, last in 1983, for client countries. In 1972 came the Tango class, with a total of 18, produced at the rate of two a year. The Kilo class, built at Komsomolsk, appeared in the late 1970s and was initially produced at the rate of one a year. This rate increased with production at Gorky and St Petersburg. The latter two yards are most concerned with exports, the first clients being Poland, Romania, India, Algeria and Iran. There are incremental modifications to the original Kilo design. Non-nuclear submarine construction continues, probably with a follow-on to the Kilo class as its 1970s technology has severe limitations by modern Western standards. The new class is expected to have a form of air independent propulsion (AIP). In addition certain specialised submarines have been built—the four Bravo class target boats in the late 1960s, the two India class rescue submarines and the single Lima research submarine in the late 1970s, Beluga in 1987 and others.

Kilo and Tango classes are coated with Cluster Guard anechoic tiles and both have a minelaying capability from their torpedo tubes. In 1992 a Tango was fitted with a towed array.

23 + 1 KILO (GRANAY) CLASS (TYPE 877/877K/877M)

Displacement, tons: 2325 surfaced; 3076 dived
Dimensions, feet (metres): 242.1 × 32.5 × 21.7
  (73.8 × 9.9 × 6.6)
Main machinery: Diesel-electric; 2 diesels; 3650 hp(m) *(2.68 MW)*; 2 generators; 1 motor; 5900 hp(m) *(4.34 MW)*; 1 shaft; 2 auxiliary motors; 204 hp(m) *(150 kW)*; 1 economic speed motor; 130 hp(m) *(95 kW)*
Speed, knots: 17 dived; 10 surfaced
Range, miles: 6000 at 7 kts snorting; 400 at 3 kts dived.
Complement: 52

Torpedoes: 6—21 in *(533 mm)* tubes. 18 combinations of 53 cm torpedoes (see table at front of section). Wire-guided in the 877M version.
Mines: 24 in lieu of torpedoes.
Countermeasures: ESM: Squid Head or Brick Pulp; radar warning. Quad Loop D/F.
Radars: Surface search: Snoop Tray; I band.
Sonars: Shark Teeth; hull-mounted; passive/active search and attack; medium frequency.
  Mouse Roar; hull-mounted; active attack; high frequency.

Programmes: First launched in 1979 at Komsomolsk. Construction is taking place at St Petersburg as well as at Komsomolsk. The building rate at the beginning of 1994 was about three a year, Soviet numbers depending on the export rate.
Structure: Has a better hull form than the Foxtrot or Tango but is still fairly basic by comparison with modern Western designs. Diving depth, 820 ft *(250 m)* normal. Battery has a 9700 kW/h capacity. The basic Kilo is the Type 877; 877K has an improved fire-control system and 877M includes wire-guided torpedoes, but not necessarily from all tubes.
Operational: There is evidence of trials carried out with a SAM launcher fitted on the fin. Probably SA-N-8; IR homing from 600 m to 6000 m; warhead 2 kg.
Sales: The Kilo programme replaced the Foxtrot export stream and the class has so far been exported to Poland (one), Romania (one), India (eight), Algeria (two), Iran (two). Further transfers are expected to Iran, and Syria is also likely to become a customer. China is expected to build or acquire the class. Export versions have the letter E after the type or project designator. The latest export version is referred to as the Type 636 and has improved accommodation, upgraded fire-control systems and possibly more powerful propulsion.

KILO (with anechoic tiles)   6/1993

KILO   6/1992

18 TANGO CLASS (TYPE 641B)

TANGO (with towed array)   8/1992

Displacement, tons: 3000 surfaced; 3800 dived
Dimensions, feet (metres): 298.6 × 29.9 × 23.6
  (91 × 9.1 × 7.2)
Main machinery: Diesel-electric; 3 diesels; 5475 hp(m) (4 MW);
  3 motors; 6256 hp(m) (4.6 MW); 3 shafts
Speed, knots: 16 dived; 13 surfaced
Complement: 62

Torpedoes: 6—21 in (533 mm) bow tubes. Combination of 18—
  53 cm torpedoes (see table at front of section). There are no
  stern tubes.
Mines: 24 in lieu of torpedoes.
Countermeasures: ESM: Squid Head or Stop Light; radar warning. Quad Loop D/F.
Radars: Surface search: Snoop Tray; I band.
Sonars: Shark Teeth; hull-mounted; passive/active search and
  attack; medium frequency. There is a large array mounted
  above the torpedo tubes as well as a bow-mounted dome.

Programmes: This class was first seen at the Sevastopol Review
  in July 1973 and, immediately succeeding the Foxtrot class,
  showed a continuing commitment to non-nuclear-propelled
  boats. The building rate rose to two a year at Gorky and the programme finished in 1982.
Structure: There is a marked increase in the internal capacity of
  the hull used to improve battery capacity and habitability compared with Foxtrot. Diving depth, 820 ft (250 m) normal. The
  casing and fin have a continuous acoustic coating. One Northern Fleet unit was fitted with a towed array stern tube and a
  reel mounted in the casing forward of the fin in 1992. There
  are no stern torpedo tubes.
Operational: Long-range operational capability as shown by
  deployments to the Mediterranean and to West Africa. All
  except one are based in the Northern Fleet with refits at Kronstadt in the Baltic. One of the class is in the Black Sea.

24 FOXTROT CLASS (TYPE 641)

FOXTROT   7/1993, Hartmut Ehlers

Displacement, tons: 1952 surfaced; 2475 dived
Dimensions, feet (metres): 299.5 × 24.6 × 19.7
  (91.3 × 7.5 × 6)
Main machinery: Diesel-electric; 3 Type 37-D diesels; 6000
  hp(m) (4.4 MW); 3 motors (1 × 2700 and 2 × 1350); 5400
  hp(m) (3.97 MW); 3 shafts; 1 auxiliary motor; 140 hp(m)
  (103 kW)
Speed, knots: 16 surfaced; 15 dived; 9 snorting
Range, miles: 20 000 at 8 kts surfaced; 380 at 2 kts dived
Complement: 75

Torpedoes: 10—21 in (533 mm) (6 bow, 4 stern) tubes. Combi-
  nation of 22—53 cm torpedoes (see table at front of section).
Mines: 44 in lieu of torpedoes.
Countermeasures: ESM: Stop Light; radar warning. Quad
  Loop D/F.
Radars: Surface search: Snoop Tray or Snoop Plate; I band.
Sonars: Herkules/Feniks; hull-mounted; passive/active search
  and attack; high frequency.

Programmes: Built between 1958 and 1971 at Sudomekh. Production continued until 1984 for transfer to other countries ie
  Cuba, India, Libya. A follow-on of the Zulu class. Only 60 out of
  a total programme of 160 were completed as the changeover
  to nuclear boats took effect. A most successful class which has
  been deployed worldwide, forming the bulk of the submarine
  force in the Mediterranean in the 1960s and 1970s.
Operational: This class is now progressively being withdrawn
  from front-line service, with Northern Fleet units being
  redeployed to the Baltic and Black Sea. Diving depth was
  820 ft (250 m) but this is reducing with age.
Sales: All new construction (except those for Poland): Cuba: One
  in February 1979, one in March 1980, one in February 1984.
  India: One in April 1968, one in March 1969, one in November
  1969, one in February 1970, one in November 1973, one in
  December 1973, one in October 1974, one in February 1975.
  Libya: One in December 1976, two in February 1978, one in
  February 1981, one in January 1982 and one in February
  1983. One to Poland in 1987 and a second in 1988. Some of
  these have been deleted.

Auxiliary Submarines

Note: In addition to those listed, the last of the Alfa class SSN is used for trials, and there is an elderly Romeo class diesel submarine with two large experimental torpedo type tubes fitted on the casing at
the bow.

1 BELUGA CLASS

BELUGA   10/1991

Displacement, tons: 1900 dived
Dimensions, feet (metres): 213.3 × 28.5 × 19.7
  (65 × 8.7 × 6)
Main machinery: 1 motor; 5440 hp (4 MW); 1 shaft
Speed, knots: 10 surfaced; 22 dived

Comment: Built at St Petersburg, launched in 1985 and completed in February 1987. A single experimental unit with a fin
  similar to the Alfa class. Stated by the Russians to be for marine
  and biological research and probably used for hydrodynamic
  tests including hull forms, propulsors and boundary layer control methods. One report suggests there is no power source
  other than main batteries and therefore the submarine has to
  return alongside to recharge. It seems more likely that an AIP
  system is involved. Unarmed but there is probably a standard
  Snoop Tray radar, Brick Group ESM and Shark Teeth and
  Mouse Roar sonars. Based in the Black Sea. Has the number
  SS 533.

2 LOSOS (PYRANJA) CLASS (TYPE 865)

Displacement, tons: 218 surfaced
Dimensions, feet (metres): 95.8 × 16.4 × 12.8
    (29.2 × 5 × 3.9)
Main machinery: 1 diesel generator; 160 kW; 1 motor; 82 hp(m)
    (60 kW); 1 shaft
Speed, knots: 6.5. **Range, miles:** 1000 at 4 kts

Complement: 4

Comment: Built at Admiralty Yard, St Petersburg and launched in
mid-1986. Based at Kronstadt and claimed by Sweden to be
the type of submarine responsible for violating Swedish territorial waters. Can carry up to six divers or torpedoes or mines.

There are two outboard pressurised containers for special
equipment, and two outboard tubes for mines or torpedoes.
The main battery has a capacity of 1200 kilowatt hours. Sonar
and radar can be fitted. Capable of diving to 200 m. Endurance
reported as 10 days. Reported in reserve in 1993.

PYRANJA

1992, Russian Navy

2 UNIFORM CLASS

Displacement, tons: 1390 dived
Dimensions, feet (metres): 224.4 × 20 × 17.1
    (68.4 × 6.1 × 5.2)
Main machinery: Nuclear; 1 PWR; 65 MW; 2 turbines; 2 shafts
Speed, knots: 10 surfaced

Complement: 35

Comment: Research and development nuclear-powered submarines. The first launched at Sudomekh, St Petersburg in
November 1982 and entered service in July 1983. The second

launched April 1988 and in service November 1989. Both
have single hulls and what look like 'wheel' arches either side
of the fin. There are very deep diving submarines based in the
Northern Fleet, and are probably used mainly for ocean bed
operations. One has the number AS-15.

UNIFORM

1992

1 LIMA CLASS (TYPE 1840)

Displacement, tons: 1700 surfaced; 2100 dived
Dimensions, feet (metres): 282.2 × 25.9 × 23
    (86 × 7.9 × 7)
Main machinery: Diesel-electric; 2 diesels; 1 motor; 2500 hp(m)
    (1.8 MW); 1 shaft
Speed, knots: 12 surfaced; 12 dived
Complement: 70
Radars: Navigation: Snoop Tray; I band.
Sonars: Hull-mounted; passive/active search and attack; high
    frequency.

Comment: Built at Sudomekh Yard and launched in August
1978. A bulge at the forward end of the fin is similar to that
used for the German Balkon sonar in the early 1940s but could
be a tower for exit/re-entry trials. The most conspicuous feature is that some of the masts are non-retractable. Returned to
St Petersburg from the Black Sea to start refit in 1990 and was
still there in late 1993. Has the number BS 555.

LIMA

1990

1 YANKEE POD and 1 YANKEE STRETCH CLASS (ex-SSBN)

Displacement, tons: 9800 surfaced
Dimensions, feet (metres): 440.6 × 38 × 26.6
(134.3 × 11.6 × 8.1)
Main machinery: Nuclear; 2 PWR; 160 MW; 2 turbines;
37 400 hp(m) *(27.5 MW)*; 2 shafts
Speed, knots: 26 dived; 20 surfaced
Complement: 120

Comment: As well as the Yankee SSGN and Yankee Notch SSN
conversions, two other hulls have been converted for research
and development roles. The dimensions given are for the so-
called Yankee Pod which has been used as a trials platform for
the towed array pod on the stern since about 1984. There are
also two prominent bulges either side of the fin and other trials
sonars have been fitted including those from homing torpedoes. This submarine was in refit in 1993 and may be
scrapped. The other conversion is a Yankee Stretch which has
a lengthened central section extending the hull to some 525 ft
(160 m) and is used for unspecified underwater research
which may include submarine rescue operations. Based in the
Northern Fleet.

YANKEE STRETCH   *1993*

1 PALTUS CLASS and 1 X-RAY CLASS (TYPE 1916)

Displacement, tons: 520 dived
Dimensions, feet (metres): 154.2 × 13.1 × 13.1
(47 × 4 × 4)

Comment: Details given are for the X-Ray which is a very small
research submarine built at Sudomekh Yard, St Petersburg in
1984. Originally thought to be nuclear-powered. Based in the
Northern Fleet and probably associated with deep diving
seabed operations associated with an Echo II SSGN. Paltus is
of a similar size and was launched at Sudomekh in April 1991.
Also originally thought to be nuclear-powered and is associated in seabed operations with the Yankee Stretch SSAN. The
picture shows yet another small auxiliary submarine, one of
many used for special operations and various research
projects.

SSA   *1992, B Lemachko*

2 INDIA CLASS (TYPE 666)

Displacement, tons: 4000 surfaced; 4800 dived
Dimensions, feet (metres): 354.3 oa; 344.5 wl × 32.8 × 23
(108; 105 × 10 × 7)
Main machinery: 2 diesels; 3800 hp(m) *(2.79 MW)*; 2 motors;
3000 hp *(2 MW)*; 2 shafts; bow thruster
Speed, knots: 15 surfaced; 10 dived

Countermeasures: ESM: Stop Light/Squid Head; radar warning.
Quad Loop D/F.
Radars: Navigation: Snoop Tray; I band.
Sonars: Hull-mounted; passive/active search; high frequency.

Programmes: Built at Komsomolsk. First launched in 1975, second in 1979.
Structure: Designed for rescue work and carry two 12.1 m
DSRVs on the after casing. The overall silhouette is similar to
Delta class SSBNs. Both DSRVs have access hatches in the hull
and probably have an operating depth of about 2000 m, although this would be reduced to 600-700 m for actual submarine rescue operations. It seems unlikely that these submarines
carry any armament.
Operational: One is in service in the Pacific and one in the Northern Fleet. Both reported in poor condition.

INDIA with DSRVs   *7/1987*

3 BRAVO CLASS (TYPE 600) (TARGET SUBMARINES)

Displacement, tons: 2250 surfaced; 2750 dived
Dimensions, feet (metres): 239.5 oa; 219.8 wl × 32.1 × 26.2
(73; 67 × 9.8 × 8)
Main machinery: Diesel-electric; 2 diesels; 3970 hp(m)
(2.9 MW); 2 generators; 1 motor; 5900 hp(m) *(4.34 MW)*;
1 shaft
Speed, knots: 14 dived
Complement: 60

Torpedoes: 6—21 in *(533 mm)* bow tubes. Type 53; dual purpose; pattern active/passive homing up to 20 km *(10.8 nm)* at
up to 45 kts; warhead 400 kg or low yield nuclear.
Countermeasures: ESM: Brick Group; radar warning.
Radars: Navigation: Snoop Tray; I band.
Sonars: Hull-mounted; passive; medium frequency and active
search and attack; high frequency.

Programmes: Completed at Komsomolsk 1967-70.
Structure: The beam-to-length ratio is larger than normal in a diesel submarine which would account in part for the large displacement for a comparatively short hull. Diving depth 1000 ft
(300 m).
Operational: Act as 'padded targets' for ASW exercises and
weapon firings. One in the Pacific Fleet deleted in 1993, the
other three reported to be all in the Black Sea.

BRAVO   *1986*

AIRCRAFT CARRIERS

Note: Work on the *Ulyanovsk* stopped on 5 February 1992 when the ship was within a few months of being launched. She has been dismantled for sale as scrap in spite of strong protests by the Russian Navy. This ship was to be the first nuclear-powered, steam catapult-fitted aircraft carrier, following on from the Kuznetsov design.

1 MODIFIED KIEV CLASS (TYPE 1143.4) (CVG)

Name	Builders	Laid down	Launched	Commissioned
ADMIRAL GORSHKOV (ex-*Baku*)	Nikolayev South (Nosenko, 444)	Dec 1978	17 Apr 1982	Jan 1987

Displacement, tons: 44 500 full load
Dimensions, feet (metres): 899 oa; 818.6 wl × 167.3 oa; 107.3 wl × 32.8 (screws) *(274; 249.5 × 51; 32.7 × 10)*
Flight deck, feet (metres): 640 × 68 *(195 × 20.7)*
Main machinery: 8 boilers; 4 turbines; 200 000 hp(m) *(147 MW)*; 4 shafts
Speed, knots: 32. **Range, miles:** 13 500 at 18 kts; 4000 at 31 kts
Complement: 1200 plus aircrew

Missiles: SSM: 12 SS-N-12 Sandbox (6 twin) launchers ❶; inertial guidance with command update; active radar homing to 550 km *(300 nm)* at 1.7 Mach; warhead nuclear 350 kT or HE 1000 kg; 24 reloads.
SAM: 4 SA-N-9 Gauntlet (Kynshal) sextuple vertical launchers ❷; command guidance; active radar homing to 45 km *(24.4 nm)* at 2 Mach; warhead 15 kg; altitude 3.4-12 192 m *(10-40 000 ft)*; 24 magazines; 192 missiles; four channels of fire.
Guns: 2—3.9 in *(100 mm)*/59 ❸; 85° elevation; 60 rounds/minute to 15 km *(8.2 nm)*; weight of shell 16 kg.
8—30 mm/65 ❹; 6 barrels per mounting; 85° elevation; 3000 rounds/minute combined to 2 km.
A/S mortars: 2 RBU 12 000 ❺; 10 tubes per launcher; range 12 000 m; warhead 80 kg.
Countermeasures: Decoys: 2 twin chaff launchers. Towed torpedo decoy.
ESM/ECM: 4 Wine Flask (intercept); 8 Foot Ball; 4 Bell Nip; 4 Bell Thump. 2 Cage Pot.
Fire control: 3 Tin Man optronic trackers ❻. 2 Punch Bowl SAT-COM for SSM data link. 2 Low Ball SATNAV. 1 Bob Tail.
Radars: Air search: Sky Watch; 4 Planar phased array ❼; 3D.
Air/surface search: Plate Steer ❽; E band.
Surface search: Two Strut Pair ❾; F band.
Navigation: Three Palm Frond; I band.
Fire control: Trap Door (for SS-N-12) ❿. Kite Screech ⓫; H/I/K band (for 100 mm). Four Bass Tilt ⓬; H/I band (for Gatlings). Four Cross Sword ⓭; K band (for SA-N-9).
Aircraft control: Fly Trap; G/H band. Cake Stand ⓮.
IFF: 2 Salt Pot A and B. 1 Long Head.
Sonars: Horse Jaw; hull-mounted; active search and attack; low/medium frequency.
Horse Tail; VDS; active search; medium frequency.

Fixed wing aircraft: 12 VSTOL ⓯; (see *Operational*).
Helicopters: 19 Ka-27 Helix A ⓰; 3 Ka-25 Hormone B (OTHT).

Programmes: The fourth and last of the Kiev class much delayed by the planar radar development. Full name is *Admiral Flota Sovietskogo Sojuza Gorshkov*.
Structure: Major differences with *Kiev* include 12 SSMs, 2—100 mm guns, 24 SA-N-9 magazines, planar 3D radar and a 30.5 × 19.7 ft *(9 × 6 m)* cupola at the top of the mast. The *Kiev's* torpedo armament has been removed. Many of these innovations have been incorporated in *Kuznetsov*.
Operational: *Gorshkov* is based in the Northern Fleet. The Sky Watch radar should allow full control of the air battle when it finally becomes operational. The withdrawal of Forger aircraft from service in 1992 has reduced the ship to a Helicopter Carrier. Not operational in 1993 but has not yet been paid off, and it is reported that the deleted *Kiev* is to provide spares to keep this ship alive if possible. This objective cannot have been helped by a boiler room explosion and subsequent fire on 2 February 1994.

ADMIRAL GORSHKOV   11/1990

ADMIRAL GORSHKOV   6/1989

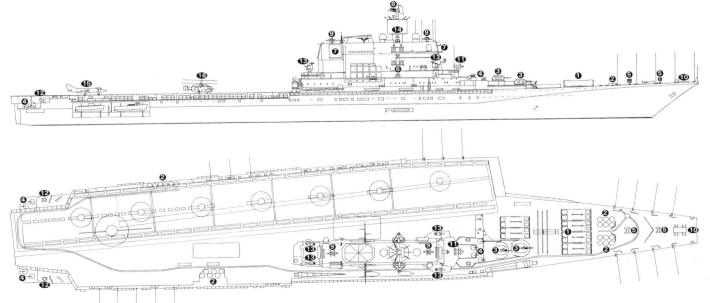

ADMIRAL GORSHKOV

(Scale 1 : 1500), Ian Sturton

1 + 1 KUZNETSOV CLASS (TYPE 1143.5) (CV)

Name	Builders	Laid down	Launched	Commissioned
ADMIRAL KUZNETSOV (ex-*Tbilisi*, ex-*Leonid Brezhnev*)	Nikolayev South, Ukraine	22 Feb 1983	5 Dec 1985	21 Jan 1991
VARYAG (ex-*Riga*)	Nikolayev South, Ukraine	8 Dec 1985	28 Nov 1988	—

ADMIRAL KUZNETSOV

1993

Displacement, tons: 55 000 standard; 67 500 full load
Dimensions, feet (metres): 999 oa; 918.6 wl × 229.7 oa; 121.4 wl × 34.4 *(304.5; 280 × 70; 37 × 10.5)*
Flight deck, feet (metres): 999 × 229.7 *(304.5 × 70)*
Main machinery: 8 boilers; 4 turbines; 200 000 hp(m) *(147 MW)*; 4 shafts
Speed, knots: 30
Complement: 1700 (200 officers)

Missiles: SSM: 12 SS-N-19 Shipwreck launchers (flush mounted) **❶**; inertial guidance with command update; active radar homing to 20-450 km *(10.8-243 nm)* at Mach 1.6; warhead 500 kT nuclear or 750 kg HE.
SAM: 4 SA-N-9 Gauntlet (Kynshal) sextuple vertical launchers (192 missiles) **❷**; command guidance and active radar homing to 45 km *(24.4 nm)* at 2 Mach; warhead 15 kg. 24 magazines; 192 missiles; four channels of fire.
SAM/Guns: 8 CADS-N-1 (Kashtan) **❸**; each has a twin 30 mm Gatling combined with 8 SA-N-11 and Hot Flash/Hot Spot fire-control radar/optronic director. Laser beam riding guidance for missiles to 8 km *(4.4 nm)*; 4500 rounds/minute combined to 2 km (for guns).
Guns: 6—30 mm/65 **❹** AK 630; 6 barrels per mounting; 85° elevation; 3000 rounds/minute combined to 2 km. Probably controlled by Hot Flash/Hot Spot on CADS-N-1.
A/S mortars: 2 RBU 12 000 **❺**; range 12 000 m; warhead 80 kg.
Countermeasures: Decoys: chaff launchers.
ESM/ECM: 2 Bell Push. 8 Foot Ball. 2 Wine Flask (intercept). 2 Flat Track.
Fire control: 4 Tin Man optronic trackers. 2 Punch Bowl SATCOM data link **❻**. 2 Low Ball SATNAV **❼**. 2 Bell Crown data link.
Radars: Air search: Sky Watch; four Planar phased arrays **❽**; 3D.
Air/surface search: Top Plate **❾**; D/E band.
Surface search: Two Strut Pair **❿**; F band.
Navigation: Three Palm Frond; I band.
Fire control: Four Cross Sword (for SAM) **⓫**; K band.
Aircraft control: Fly Trap B; G/H band.
Tacan: Cake Stand **⓬**.
IFF: Four Watch Guard.
Sonars: Horse Jaw; hull-mounted; active search and attack; medium/low frequency.

Fixed wing aircraft: 20 Su-27K (Su-33) Flanker D; 4 Su-25 UTG Frogfoot (see *Shipborne Aircraft* section).
Helicopters: 15 Ka-27 Helix. 2 Ka-29 RLD Helix AEW.

Programmes: This is a logical continuation of the Kiev class and a basic component of a task force including the nuclear-propelled Kirov class battle cruisers. *Varyag* was between 70 and 80 per cent complete by early 1993 and made little progress by early 1994. The Russian Navy wants her and is trying to spread the payments. Nonetheless the future is uncertain. Names were changed in 1990 because the Navy was unhappy about ships being called after the cities of independent republics. The full name of *Kuznetsov* is *Admiral Flota Sovietskogo Sojuza Kuznetsov*.
Structure: The hangar is approximately 610 × 98 × 25 ft and can hold up to 18 Flanker aircraft. There are two starboard side lifts,

a ski-jump of 12° and an angled deck of 7°. There are four arrester wires. The SSM system is in the centre of the flight deck forward with flush deck covers. The class has some 16.5 m of freeboard (13 m in *Kiev*). There is no Bass Tilt radar and the ADG guns are probably controlled by CADS-N-1 fire-control system.
Operational: AEW, ASW and reconnaissance tasks undertaken by Helix helicopters. Flanker and Frogfoot aircraft conducted extensive deck landings throughout the second half of 1993. The aircraft complement listed is based on the number which might be embarked for peacetime operations but the Russians claim a top limit of sixty.

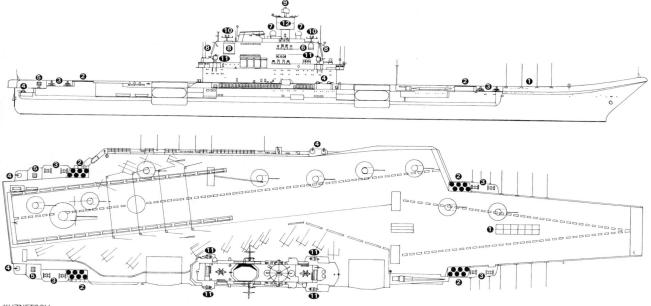

ADMIRAL KUZNETSOV

(Scale 1 : 1800), Ian Sturton

ADMIRAL KUZNETSOV

1992

ADMIRAL KUZNETSOV 1993

ADMIRAL KUZNETSOV 12/1991

ADMIRAL KUZNETSOV 12/1991

ADMIRAL KUZNETSOV 6/1991

ADMIRAL KUZNETSOV 6/1991

BATTLE CRUISERS

3 + 1 KIROV CLASS (TYPE 1144)

Name	Builders	Laid down	Launched	Commissioned
ADMIRAL USHAKOV (ex-*Kirov*)	Baltic Yard 189, Leningrad	June 1973	26 Dec 1977	July 1980
ADMIRAL LAZAREV (ex-*Frunze*)	Baltic Yard 189, Leningrad	26 Dec 1977	23 May 1981	Nov 1983
ADMIRAL NAKHIMOV (ex-*Kalinin*)	Baltic Yard 189, Leningrad	May 1983	26 Apr 1986	Oct 1988
PYOTR VELIKIY (ex-*Yuri Andropov*)	Baltic Yard 189, St Petersburg	25 Apr 1986	29 Apr 1989	1994

Displacement, tons: 19 000 standard; 24 300 full load
Dimensions, feet (metres): 826.8; 754.6 wl × 93.5 × 29.5 *(252; 230 × 28.5 × 9.1)*
Main machinery: Nuclear; 2 PWR; 2 oil-fired boilers; 2 turbines; 108 800 hp(m) *(80 MW)*; 2 shafts
Speed, knots: 30. **Range, miles:** 14 000 at 30 kts
Complement: 692 (82 officers)

Missiles: SSM: 20 SS-N-19 Shipwreck (improved SS-N-12 with lower flight profile) ❶; inertial guidance with command update; active radar homing to 20-450 km *(10.8-243 nm)* at 1.6 Mach; warhead 350 kT nuclear or 750 kg HE; no reloads.
SAM: 12 SA-N-6 Grumble (Rif) vertical launchers ❷; 8 rounds per launcher; command guidance; semi-active radar homing to 100 km *(54 nm)*; warhead 90 kg (or nuclear?); altitude 27 432 m *(90 000 ft)*.
2 SA-N-4 Gecko twin launchers ❸; semi-active radar homing to 15 km *(8 nm)* at 2.5 Mach; warhead 50 kg; altitude 9.1-3048 m *(30-10 000 ft)*; 40 missiles.
2 SA-N-9 Gauntlet (Kynshal) octuple vertical launchers (not in *Kirov*); command guidance; active radar homing to 45 km *(24.4 nm)* at 2 Mach; warhead 15 kg; altitude 3.4-12 192 m *(10-40 000 ft)*; 128 missiles; four channels of fire.
SAM/Guns: 6 CADS-N-1 (Kashtan) *(Nakhimov)* ❼; each has a twin 30 mm Gatling combined with 8 SA-N-11 and Hot Flash/Hot Spot fire-control radar/optronic director. Laser beam riding guidance for missiles to 8 km *(4.4 nm)*; 4500 rounds/minute combined to 2 km (for guns).
A/S: 1 twin SS-N-14 Silex launcher *(Ushakov)* ❹; command guidance to 55 km *(30 nm)* at 0.95 Mach; payload nuclear or Type 53 torpedo; active/passive homing to 15 km *(8.1 nm)* at 40 kts; warhead 150 kg; 14 missiles. SSM version; range 35 km *(19 nm)*; warhead 500 kg.
SS-N-15 (not in *Ushakov*); inertial flight to 120 km *(65 nm)*; payload Type 45 torpedo or nuclear warhead; fired from fixed torpedo tubes behind shutters in the superstructure.
Guns: 2—3.9 in *(100 mm)*/59 *(Ushakov)* ❺; 85° elevation; 60 rounds/minute to 15 km *(8.2 nm)*; weight of shell 16 kg.
2—130 mm/70 (twin) (not in *Ushakov*) ❻; 85° elevation;

35/45 rounds/minute to 29 km *(16 nm)*; weight of shell 27 kg.
8—30 mm/65 *(Ushakov* and *Lazarev)* ❻; 6 barrels per mounting; 85° elevation; 3000 rounds/minute combined to 2 km. *Lazarev* guns controlled by CADS-N-1 system.
Torpedoes: 10—21 in *(533 mm)* (2 quin) tubes. Combination of 53 cm torpedoes (see table at front of section). Mounted in the hull adjacent to the RBU 1000s on both quarters. Fixed tubes behind shutters (not in *Ushakov*) can fire either SS-N-15 (see *Missiles A/S*) or Type 40 torpedoes.
A/S mortars: 1 RBU 6000 12-tubed trainable fwd *(Ushakov* and *Lazarev)* ❽; range 6000 m; warhead 31 kg.
1 RBU 12 000 *(Lazarev)* ❾; 10 tubes per launcher; range 12 000 m; warhead 80 kg.
2 RBU 1000 6-tubed aft ❿; range 1000 m; warhead 55 kg.
Countermeasures: Decoys: 2 twin 150 mm chaff launchers. Towed torpedo decoy.
ESM/ECM: 8 Side Globe (jammers) *(Ushakov)*. 8 Foot Ball (not in *Ushakov*). 4 Rum Tub (intercept) (not in *Ushakov*). 8 Bell Bash. 4 Bell Nip. Half Cup (laser intercept).
Fire control: 4 Tin Man optronic trackers. 2 Punch Bowl SAT-COM ⓫. 4 Low Ball SATNAV.
Radars: Air search: Top Pair (Top Sail + Big Net) ⓬; 3D; C/D band; range 366 km *(200 nm)* for bomber, 183 km *(100 nm)* for 2 m² target.
Air/surface search: Top Steer ⓭ (Top Plate in *Lazarev* ⓮); 3D; D/E band.
Navigation: Three Palm Frond; I band.
Fire control: Two Eye Bowl *(Ushakov* only) ⓯; F band (for SS-N-14). Cross Sword (not in *Ushakov*) ⓰; K band (for SA-N-9). Two Top Dome ⓱; J band (for SA-N-6). Two Pop Group, F/H/I band (for SA-N-4) ⓲. Kite Screech ⓳; H/I/K band (for main guns). Four Bass Tilt ⓴; H/I band (for Gatlings (not in *Lazarev*)).
Aircraft control: Flyscreen A *(Ushakov)* or B; I band.
IFF: Salt Pot A and B.
Tacan: 2 Round House B.
Sonars: Horse Jaw; hull-mounted; active search and attack; low/medium frequency.

Horse Tail; VDS; active search; medium frequency. Depth to 150-200 m *(492.1-656.2 ft)* depending on speed.

Helicopters: 3 Ka-25 Hormone ㉑ or Ka-27 Helix ㉒.

Programmes: Type name is *atomny raketny kreyser* meaning nuclear-powered missile cruiser. In 1989-90 Baltic Yard started to build eight Kronstadt Ro-Ro ships for civilian use, which confirmed statements that only four Kirovs were to be built. All renamed in 1992. *Pyotr Velikiy* (Peter the Great) is making very slow progress to completion.
Structure: The first surface warships with nuclear propulsion. In addition to the nuclear plant a unique maritime combination with an auxiliary oil-fuelled system has been installed. This provides a superheat capability, boosting the normal steam output by some 50 per cent. The SS-N-19 tubes are set at an angle of about 45 degrees. *Lazarev* and subsequent ships of the class have a modified superstructure and armament although the SS-N-19 and SA-N-6 missile fits are the same. *Lazarev* has an SA-N-9 octuple launcher in place of *Ushakov's* SS-N-14 and another one aft in place of 4—30 mm guns which have been moved to a lengthened after deckhouse. *Nakhimov* and *Pyotr Velikiy* have CADS-N-1 with a central fire-control radar on six mountings, each of which has two cannon and eight missile launchers. Two are mounted either side of the SS-N-19 forward and four on the after superstructure. All except *Ushakov* have the same A/S system as the frigate *Neustrashimy* with fixed torpedo tubes in ports behind shutters in the superstructure for firing SS-N-15 or Type 45 torpedoes. These ships are reported as carrying about 500 SAM of different types.
Operational: The CIWS in *Nakhimov* is an attempt further to improve inadequate hard-kill air defences in *Ushakov*, following the installation of SA-N-9 in *Lazarev*. Over-the-horizon targeting for SS-N-19 provided by SATCOM or helicopter. *Ushakov* and *Nakhimov* are in the Northern Fleet, *Lazarev* in the Pacific and *Pyotr Velikiy* may start sea trials in the Baltic in 1995. *Ushakov* has been inactive in Murmansk since a propulsion accident in late 1990. These ships are expensive to man and maintain and spend little time at sea.

ADMIRAL USHAKOV   *(Scale 1 : 1500), Ian Sturton*

ADMIRAL NAKHIMOV   *(Scale 1 : 1500), Ian Sturton*

ADMIRAL NAKHIMOV   *6/1991*

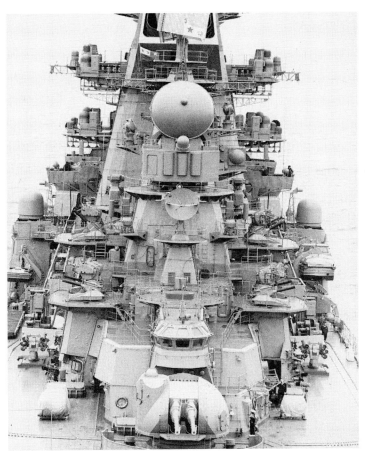

ADMIRAL NAKHIMOV   5/1990

ADMIRAL NAKHIMOV   5/1990

ADMIRAL USHAKOV   6/1990

HELICOPTER CRUISERS

1 MOSKVA CLASS (TYPE 1123)

Name	Builders	Laid down	Launched	Commissioned
MOSKVA	Nikolayev South	1963	1965	May 1967

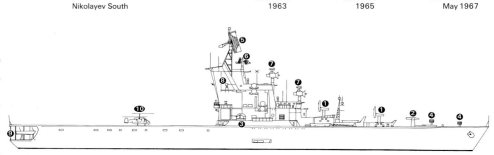

MOSKVA   (Scale 1 : 1500), Ian Sturton

Displacement, tons: 14 900 standard; 17 500 full load
Dimensions, feet (metres): 626.6 oa; 587.3 wl × 115.5 oa; 75.5 wl × 28.5 *(191 oa; 179 wl × 34; 23 × 8.7)*
Flight deck, feet (metres): 265.7 × 111.5 *(81 × 34)*
Main machinery: 4 boilers; 2 turbines; 100 000 hp(m) *(73.5 MW)*; 2 shafts
Speed, knots: 31. **Range, miles:** 9000 at 18 kts; 4500 at 29 kts
Complement: 840 plus aircrew

Missiles: SAM: 2 SA-N-3 Goblet twin launchers ❶; semi-active radar homing to 55 km *(30 nm)* at 2.5 Mach; warhead 80 kg; altitude 91.4-22 860 m *(300-75 000 ft)*; 48 missiles.
A/S: SUW-N-1 twin launcher ❷; 18 Fras 1A or 1B; inertial flight to 29 km *(16 nm)*; warhead nuclear 5 kT or Type 45 torpedo. Probably non-operational.
Guns: 4—57 mm/80 (2 twin) ❸; 85° elevation; 120 rounds/minute to 6 km *(3.3 nm)*; weight of shell 2.8 kg.
A/S mortars: 2 RBU 6000 12-tubed trainable ❹; range 6000 m; warhead 31 kg.
Countermeasures: Decoys: 2 twin chaff launchers.
ESM/ECM: 8 Side Globe (jammers). 2 Bell Clout. 2 Bell Slam. 2 Bell Tap. 2 Top Hat.
Fire control: 2 Tee Plinth and 3 Tilt Pot optronic directors.
Radars: Air search: Top Sail ❺; 3D; D band; range 555 km *(300 nm)*.
Head Net C ❻; E band; range 128 km *(70 nm)*.
Surface search: Two Don 2; I band.
Fire control: Two Head Light A ❼; F/G/H band (for SA-N-3). Two Muff Cob ❽; G/H band (for 57 mm).
IFF: 2 High Pole.
Sonars: Moose Jaw; hull-mounted; active search and attack; medium/low frequency.
Mare Tail; VDS ❾; active search; medium frequency.

Helicopters: 14 Ka-25 Hormone A ASW ❿.

Programmes: Type name is *protivolodochny kreyser* meaning anti-submarine cruiser.
Structure: In early 1973 *Moskva* was seen with a landing pad on the after end of the flight deck for flight tests of VTOL aircraft. Since removed. Main hangar, 67 × 25 m *(219.8 × 82 ft)*. There is also a small hangar 41 × 12 m *(134.5 × 39.4 ft)* in the superstructure. Two 10 ton lifts. Has Bell Crown data link antennas.
Operational: General-purpose capability including command, air defence and ASW. Based in the Black Sea and kept in service in a Flagship role. Sister ship *Leningrad* was scrapped in 1992.

MOSKVA   4/1992, van Ginderen Collection

CRUISERS

1 KRESTA I CLASS (TYPE 1134)

Name	Builders	Laid down	Launched	Commissioned
ADMIRAL ZOZULYA	Zhdanov, Leningrad	Feb 1964	Oct 1965	Mar 1967

ADMIRAL ZOZULYA   (Scale 1 : 1500), Ian Sturton

Displacement, tons: 6140 standard; 7700 full load
Dimensions, feet (metres): 510 × 55.7 × 19.7 *(155.5 × 17 × 6)*
Main machinery: 4 boilers; 2 turbines; 90 000 hp(m) *(66.15 MW)*; 2 shafts
Speed, knots: 35. **Range, miles:** 10 500 at 14 kts; 2400 at 32 kts
Complement: 360

Missiles: SSM: 4 SS-N-3B Sepal (2 twin) launchers ❶; command guidance; active radar homing to 460 km *(250 nm)* at 1.1 Mach; warhead 350 kT or HE 1000 kg; no reloads.
SAM: 2 SA-N-1 Goa twin launchers ❷; command guidance to 31.5 km *(17 nm)* at 2 Mach; warhead 60 kg; altitude 91.4-22 860 m *(300-75 000 ft)*; 32 missiles.
Guns: 4—57 mm/80 (2 twin) ❸; 85° elevation; 120 rounds/minute to 6 km *(3.3 nm)*; weight of shell 2.8 kg.
4—30 mm/65 AK 630 ❹; 6 barrels per mounting; 3000 rounds/minute to 2 km.
Torpedoes: 10—21 in *(533 mm)* (2 quin) tubes ❺. Combination of 53 cm torpedoes (see table at front of section).
A/S mortars: 2 RBU 6000 12-tubed trainable ❻; range 6000 m; warhead 31 kg.
2 RBU 1000 6-tubed ❼; range 1000 m; warhead 55 kg.
Countermeasures: Decoys: 2 twin chaff launchers.
ESM/ECM: 8 Side Globe (jammers). Bell Clout. 2 Bell Slam. 2 Bell Tap. 2 Bell Strike.
Fire control: 2 Tee Plinth optronic directors ❽. 2 Bell Crown data link.
Radars: Air search: Big Net ❾; C band; range 183 km *(100 nm)* for 2 m² target.
Air/surface: Head Net C ❿; 3D; E band; range 128 km *(70 nm)*.
Navigation: Two Palm Frond; I band.
Fire control: Scoop Pair ⓫; E band (for SS-N-3). Two Peel Group ⓬; H/I band (for SA-N-1). Two Muff Cob ⓭; G/H band (for 57 mm). Two Bass Tilt ⓮; H/I band (for 30 mm).
IFF: High Pole B.
Sonars: Herkules; hull-mounted; active search and attack; medium frequency.

Helicopters: 1 Ka-25 Hormone B ⓯.

Programmes: Designed for surface warfare, the successor to the Kynda class. Type name *bolshoy protivolodochny korabl*, meaning large anti-submarine ship. Changed in 1977-78 to *raketny kreyser*, meaning missile cruiser.
Modernisation: 30 mm guns and fire-control radars were added during refit at Kronstadt from 1985 to November 1991.

ADMIRAL ZOZULYA   6/1993

Structure: Provided with a helicopter landing deck and hangar aft. This gives an enhanced carried-on-board target-location facility for the SS-N-3B system. The Kresta I was therefore the first missile cruiser free to operate alone and without targeting assistance from shore-based aircraft.

Operational: Baltic Fleet Flagship. The remainder of the class have been paid off, as have all the Kresta IIs.

3 + 1 SLAVA CLASS (TYPE 1164)

Name	Builders	Laid down	Launched	Commissioned
SLAVA	Nikolayev North (61 Kommuna)	1976	July 1979	Aug 1982
MARSHAL USTINOV	Nikolayev North (61 Kommuna)	1978	Sep 1982	Apr 1986
CHERVONA UKRAINA	Nikolayev North (61 Kommuna)	1979	July 1983	Jan 1990
VILNA UKRAINA (ex-*Admiral Lobov*) (Ukraine)	Nikolayev North (61 Kommuna)	1984	15 Aug 1990	1995

Displacement, tons: 9800 standard; 11 200 full load
Dimensions, feet (metres): 610.2 × 68.2 × 24.9
(186 × 20.8 × 7.6)
Main machinery: COGAG; 4 gas-turbines; 108 800 hp(m)
(80 MW); 2 gas-turbines, 13 600 hp(m) *(10 MW)*; 2 shafts
Speed, knots: 32. **Range, miles:** 2500 at 30 kts; 6000 at 15 kts
Complement: 454 (38 officers)

Missiles: SSM: 16 SS-N-12 (8 twin) Sandbox launchers ❶; inertial
guidance with command update; active radar homing to
550 km *(300 nm)* at 1.7 Mach; warhead nuclear 350 kT or HE
1000 kg.
SAM: 8 SA-N-6 Grumble (Rif) vertical launchers ❷; 8 rounds per
launcher; command guidance; semi-active radar homing to
100 km *(54 nm)*; warhead 90 kg (or nuclear?); altitude
27 432 m *(90 000 ft)*.
2 SA-N-4 Gecko twin launchers ❸; semi-active radar homing to
15 km *(8 nm)* at 2.5 Mach; warhead 50 kg; altitude 9.1-
3048 m *(30-10 000 ft)*; 40 missiles.
Guns: 2—130 mm/70 (twin) ❹; 35/45 rounds/minute to 29 km
(16 nm); weight of shell 27 kg.
6—30 mm/65; 6 barrels per mounting; 85° elevation; 3000
rounds/minute to 2 km.
Torpedoes: 10—21 in *(533 mm)* (2 quin) tubes ❺. Combination
of 53 cm torpedoes (see table at front of section).
A/S mortars: 2 RBU 6000 12-tubed trainable ❻; range 6000 m;
warhead 31 kg.
Countermeasures: Decoys: 2 twin 12-tubed chaff launchers.
ESM/ECM; 8 Side Globe (jammers). 4 Rum Tub (intercept). Bell
series. IR surveillance.
Fire control: 2 Tee Plinth and 3 Tilt Pot optronic directors. 2
Punch Bowl satellite data receiving/targeting systems. Bell
Crown data link.
Radars: Air search: Top Pair (Top Sail + Big Net) ❼; 3D; C/D band;
range 366 km *(200 nm)* for bomber, 183 km *(100 nm)* for 2 m²
target.

Air/surface search: Top Steer ❽ or Top Plate *(Chervona Ukraina*
and *Vilna Ukraina)*; 3D; D/E band.
Navigation: Three Palm Frond; I band.
Fire control: Front Door ❾; F band (for SS-N-12). Top Dome ❿; J
band (for SA-N-6). Two Pop Group ⓫; F/H/I band (for SA-N-4).
Three Bass Tilt ⓬; H/I band (for Gatlings). Kite Screech ⓭;
H/I/K band (for 130 mm).
IFF: Salt Pot A and B. 2 Long Head.
Sonars: Bull Horn; hull-mounted; active search and attack; low/
medium frequency.
Mare Tail; VDS; active search; medium frequency.

Helicopters: 1 Ka-25 Hormone B ⓮.

Programmes: Building at the same yard that built the Kara class.
This is a smaller edition of the dual-purpose surface warfare/
ASW *Kirov*, designed as a conventionally powered back-up for
that class. The last of the class was renamed in 1992 and was
80 per cent complete in early 1994. Ukraine plans to complete
her as the Flagship of the Ukrainian Navy.
Structure: The notable gap abaft the twin funnels (SA-N-6 area)
is traversed by a large crane which stows between the funnels.
The hangar is recessed below the flight deck with an inclined
ramp. The torpedo tubes are behind shutters in the hull below
the Top Dome radar director aft. Air-conditioned citadels for
NBCD. There is a bridge periscope.
Operational: The SA-N-6 system effectiveness is diminished by
having only one radar director. Over-the-horizon targeting for
SS-N-12 provided by helicopter or SATCOM. *Slava* is based in
the Black Sea Fleet, *Marshal Ustinov* deployed to the Northern
Fleet on a permanent basis in March 1987. *Chervona Ukraina*
started sea trials in August 1989 and transferred to the Pacific
in October 1990.

MARSHAL USTINOV 6/1993

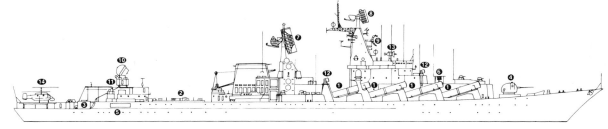

SLAVA (Scale 1 : 1200), Ian Sturton

CHERVONA UKRAINA (with Top Plate) 10/1990, 92 Wing RAAF

MARSHAL USTINOV 6/1993

5 KARA CLASS (TYPE 1134B/1136B)

Name	Builders	Laid down	Launched	Commissioned
OCHAKOV	Nikolayev North (61 Kommuna)	Mar 1970	June 1971	Mar 1973
KERCH	Nikolayev North (61 Kommuna)	June 1971	July 1972	Sep 1974
AZOV	Nikolayev North (61 Kommuna)	Aug 1972	Sep 1973	Nov 1975
PETROPAVLOVSK	Nikolayev North (61 Kommuna)	Nov 1973	Dec 1974	Nov 1976
VLADIVOSTOK (ex-*Tallinn*)	Nikolayev North (61 Kommuna)	Dec 1975	Mar 1977	Apr 1980

Displacement, tons: 8000 standard; 9900 full load
Dimensions, feet (metres): 568 × 61 × 22
(173.2 × 18.6 × 6.7)
Main machinery: COGAG; 4 gas-turbines; 108 800 hp(m)
(80 MW); 2 gas-turbines; 13 600 hp(m) (10 MW); 2 shafts
Speed, knots: 34. **Range, miles:** 9000 at 15 kts cruising turbines; 3000 at 32 kts
Complement: 540 (30 officers)

Missiles: SAM: 2 SA-N-3 Goblet twin launchers (1 launcher in *Azov*) ❶; semi-active radar homing to 55 km (30 nm) at 2.5 Mach; warhead 80 kg; altitude 91.4-22 860 m (300-75 000 ft); 72 missiles.
6 SA-N-6 Grumble (Rif) vertical launchers (*Azov* only); 4 rounds per launcher; command guidance; semi-active radar homing to 100 km (54 nm); warhead 90 kg (or nuclear?); altitude 27 432 m (90 000 ft).
2 SA-N-4 Gecko twin launchers ❷; semi-active radar homing to 15 km (8 nm) at 2.5 Mach; warhead 50 kg; altitude 9.1-3048 m (30-10 000 ft); 40 missiles.
A/S: 2 SS-N-14 Silex quad launchers ❸; command guidance to 55 km (30 nm) at 0.95 Mach; payload nuclear or Type E53 torpedo; active/passive homing to 15 km (8.1 nm) at 40 kts; warhead 150 kg. SSM version; range 35 km (19 nm); warhead 500 kg.
In addition to the Kresta II armament of eight tubes for the SS-N-14 A/S system (probably with a surface-to-surface capability) and the pair of twin launchers for SA-N-3 system with Goblet missiles, Kara class mounts the SA-N-4 system in 2 silos, either side of the mast. The SA-N-3 system has only 2 loading doors per launcher and a larger launching arm. *Azov* was the trials ship for the SA-N-6 SAM system designed for subsequent classes. This replaces the after SA-N-3, after RBUs and torpedo tubes of a standard Kara.
Guns: 4—3 in (76 mm)/60 (2 twin) ❹; 80° elevation; 90 rounds/minute to 15 km (8 nm); weight of shell 6.8 kg.
4—30 mm/65 ❺; 6 barrels per mounting; 85° elevation; 3000 rounds/minute combined to 2 km.
The siting of both main and secondary armament on either beams in the waist follows the precedent of both Kresta classes, although the weight of the main armament is increased.
Torpedoes: 10 or 4—21 in (533 mm) (2 quin) (2 twin in *Azov*) tubes ❻. Combination of 53 cm torpedoes (see table at front of section).
A/S mortars: 2 RBU 6000 12-tubed trainable ❼; range 6000 m; warhead 31 kg.
2 RBU 1000 6-tubed (aft) (not in *Petropavlovsk*) ❽; range 1000 m; warhead 55 kg.
Countermeasures: Decoys: 2 twin chaff launchers. 1 BAT-1 torpedo decoy.
ESM/ECM: 8 Side Globe (jammers). 2 Bell Slam. 1 Bell Clout and 2 Bell Tap (in *Ochakov*). 4 Rum Tub (intercept) (fitted on mainmast in *Kerch*).

Fire control: 2 Tee Plinth (*Azov*) and 4 Tilt Pot optronic directors.
Radars: Air search: Top Sail ❾; 3D; D band; or Flat Screen; E/F band.
Air/surface search: Head Net C ❿; 3D; E band; range 128 km (70 nm).
Navigation: Two Don Kay; I band. Don 2 (not in *Azov*); I band.
Fire control: Two Head Light B or C (one in *Azov*) ⓫; F/G/H band (for SA-N-3 and SS-N-14). Two Pop Group ⓬; F/H/I band (for SA-N-4). Top Dome (aft in *Azov* in place of one Head Light C); J band (for SA-N-6). Two Owl Screech ⓭; G band (for 76 mm). Two Bass Tilt ⓮; H/I band (for 30 mm).
Tacan: Fly Screen A (not in all). Two Round House (*Petropavlovsk*).
IFF: High Pole A. High Pole B.
Sonars: Bull Nose; hull-mounted; active search and attack; low/medium frequency.
Mare Tail; VDS ⓯; active search; medium frequency.

Helicopters: 1 Ka-25 Hormone A ⓰.

Programmes: Apart from the specialised Moskva class this was the first class of large cruisers to join the Soviet Navy since the Sverdlov class—designed specifically for ASW. Type name is *bolshoy protivolodochny korabl*, meaning large anti-submarine ship. *Azov* is the Type 1136B.
Modernisation: The Flat Screen air search radar, first seen in *Kerch*, was to have been retrofitted in all of the class.
Structure: *Azov* is of a modified design as the SA-N-6 trials ship and emerged from the Black Sea only in June 1986. All are fitted with stabilisers. *Petropavlovsk* has a higher hangar with two Round House Tacan on each side. The helicopter is raised to flight deck level by a lift in all of the class.
Operational: Two others of the class started refits in July 1987 and have been put up for sale or scrap by the Ukraine.

KERCH (with Flat Screen)   3/1990

KARA class   (Scale 1 : 1200), Ian Sturton

AZOV (with Top Dome and one Head Light)   9/1993

1 KYNDA CLASS (TYPE 58)

Name ADMIRAL GOLOVKO	Builders Zhdanov, Leningrad	Laid down Dec 1960	Launched Apr 1963	Commissioned July 1964

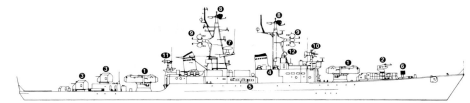

ADMIRAL GOLOVKO   (Scale 1 : 1200), Ian Sturton

Displacement, tons: 4400 standard; 5550 full load
Dimensions, feet (metres): 468.2 × 52.5 × 13.5
  (142.7 × 16 × 4.1)
Main machinery: 4 boilers; 2 turbines; 90 000 hp(m)
  (66.15 MW); 2 shafts
Speed, knots: 34. **Range, miles:** 6000 at 14.5 kts; 1500 at
  34 kts
Complement: 304 (25 officers)

Missiles: SSM: 8 SS-N-3B Sepal (2 quad) launchers ❶; inertial
  guidance; active radar homing to 460 km (250 nm) at
  1.1 Mach; warhead nuclear 350 kT or HE 1000 kg; 8 reloads.
SAM: SA-N-1 Goa twin launcher ❷; command guidance to
  31.5 km (17 nm) at 2 Mach; warhead 60 kg; altitude 91.4-
  22 860 m (300-75 000 ft); 16 missiles. Some SSM capability.
Guns: 4—3 in (76 mm)/60 (2 twin) ❸; 80° elevation; 90 rounds/
  minute to 15 km (8 nm); weight of shell 6.8 kg.
  4—30 mm/65 ❹; 6 barrels per mounting; 85° elevation; 3000
  rounds/minute combined to 2 km.
Torpedoes: 6—21 in (533 mm) (2 triple) tubes ❺. Combination of
  53 cm torpedoes (see table at front of section).
A/S mortars: 2 RBU 6000 12-tubed trainable ❻; range 6000 m;
  warhead 31 kg.
Countermeasures: ESM/ECM: 4 Top Hat. Bell Clout. Bell Tap.
  Bell Slam.
Fire control: 2 Tee Plinth; 2 Plinth Net ❼ optronic directors.
Radars: Air search: Two Head Net A ❽; E band.
  Surface search and Navigation: Two Don 2; I band.
  Fire control: Two Scoop Pair ❾; E band (for SS-N-3B). Peel Group
    ❿; H/I band (for SS-N-1). Owl Screech ⓫; G band (for
    76 mm). Two Bass Tilt ⓬; H/I band (for 30 mm).
IFF: High Pole B.
Sonars: Herkules; hull-mounted; active search and attack;
  medium frequency.

Helicopters: Platform only.

Programmes: This class was designed for surface warfare and
  was the first class of missile cruisers built. The role made it the
  successor of the Sverdlov class. Type name is *raketny kreyser*
  meaning missile cruiser.

KYNDA   7/1985

Modernisation: Modernised in the early 1980s, including the
  four 30 mm Gatling mounts with two associated Bass Tilt
  radars and a twin level deckhouse abaft the forward funnel.

Operational: *Golovko* based in the Black Sea. One of the class
  deleted in 1990, one in 1992, one in 1993. The last of class is
  expected to be scrapped in 1994.

DESTROYERS

Note: The Navy has indicated that the Sovremenny follow-on class will have a single type of VLS launcher for all weapons.

0 + 1 UDALOY II CLASS (TYPE 1155.1)

Name ADMIRAL BASISTY (ex-*Vice Admiral Chebanenko*)	Builders Yantar, Kaliningrad 820	Laid down 1989	Launched 12 Dec 1992	Commissioned 1994

ADMIRAL BASISTY   7/1993, Hartmut Ehlers

Displacement, tons: 7700 standard; 8900 full load
Dimensions, feet (metres): 536.4 × 63.3 × 24.6
  (163.5 × 19.3 × 7.5)
Main machinery: COGAG; 2 gas-turbines; 48 600 hp(m)
  (35.72 MW); 2 gas-turbines; 24 200 hp(m) (17.79 MW);
  2 shafts
Speed, knots: 30. **Range, miles:** 4000 at 18 kts
Complement: 250 (29 officers)

Missiles: SSM: 8 SS-N-22 Sunburn (2 quad) ❶; active/passive
  radar homing to 160 km (87 nm) at 2.5 Mach (4.5 for attack);
  warhead nuclear or HE 300 kg; sea-skimmer.
SAM: 8 SA-N-9 Gauntlet (Kynshal) vertical launchers ❷; command guidance; active radar homing to 45 km (24.4 nm) at 2
  Mach; warhead 15 kg. 64 missiles; four channels of fire.
SAM/Guns: 2 CADS-N-1 (Kashtan) ❸; each with twin 30 mm Gatling; combined with 8 SA-N-11 and Hot Flash/Hot Spot fire-
  control radar/optronic director. Laser beam guidance for missiles to 8 km (4.4 nm); 4500 rounds/minute combined to
  1.5 km for guns.
Guns: 2—130 mm/70 (twin) ❹; 85° elevation; 35-45 rounds/
  minute to 29.5 km (16 nm); weight of shell 27 kg.
Torpedoes: 10—21 in (533 mm) (2 quin tubes) ❺. Combination
  of 53 cm torpedoes (see table at front of section). The tubes
  are protected by flaps in the superstructure.
A/S mortars: 2 RBU 6000 ❻. 12-tubed trainable; range 6000 m;
  warhead 31 kg.
Countermeasures: 8—10-barrelled chaff launchers ❼.
ESM/ECM: 2 Wine Glass (intercept). 2 Bell Shroud. 2 Bell Squat.
  4 Half Cup laser warner. Light Bulb.
Fire control: M 145 radar and optronic system. 2 Bell Crown data
  link.
Radars: Air Search: Strut Pair ❽; F band.
  Top Plate ❾; 3D; D/E band.
  Surface Search: Two Palm Frond ❿; I band.
  Fire Control: Band Stand ⓫; D/E/F band (for SS-N-22). Two
    Cross Swords ⓬; K band (for SA-N-9). Kite Screech ⓭; H/I/K
    band (for 100 mm gun).
CCA: Fly Screen B ⓮.
Sonars: Horse Jaw; hull-mounted; active search and attack;
  medium/low frequency.
  Horse Tail; VDS; active search; medium frequency.

Helicopters: 2 Ka-27 Helix A ⓯.

Programmes: Follow-on class from the Udaloys. NATO designator Balcom 12. Progress is very slow and only one of the
  class may be completed.
Structure: Similar size to the Udaloy and has the same propulsion machinery. Improved combination of weapon systems

owing something to both the Sovremenny and the Neustrashimy classes. The distribution of SA-N-9 launchers may be the
same as Udaloy class. The torpedo tubes are protected by a
hinged flap in the superstructure.

ADMIRAL BASISTY   (Scale 1 : 1200), Ian Sturton

11 UDALOY CLASS (TYPE 1155)

Name	Builders	Laid down	Launched	Commissioned
UDALOY	Yantar, Kaliningrad 820	1977	Feb 1980	Nov 1980
VITSE-ADMIRAL KULAKOV	Zhdanov Yard, Leningrad 190	1977	Apr 1980	Sep 1981
MARSHAL VASILEVSKY	Yantar, Kaliningrad 820	1979	Jan 1982	June 1983
ADMIRAL SPIRIDONOV	Yantar, Kaliningrad 820	1980	Nov 1983	Sep 1984
ADMIRAL TRIBUTS	Zhdanov Yard, Leningrad 190	1980	Apr 1983	Aug 1985
MARSHAL SHAPOSHNIKOV	Yantar, Kaliningrad 820	1982	Jan 1985	Oct 1985
SIMFEROPOL (ex-Marshal Buokenny)	Yantar, Kaliningrad 820	1982	Feb 1985	Dec 1986
ADMIRAL LEVCHENKO	Zhdanov Yard, Leningrad 190	1982	Mar 1985	Jan 1988
ADMIRAL VINOGRADOV	Yantar, Kaliningrad 820	1985	June 1987	Oct 1988
ADMIRAL KHARLAMOV	Yantar, Kaliningrad 820	1985	June 1988	Sep 1989
ADMIRAL PANTELEYEV	Yantar, Kaliningrad 820	1987	Feb 1990	July 1991

Displacement, tons: 6700 standard; 8700 full load
Dimensions, feet (metres): 536.4 × 63.3 × 24.6
   (163.5 × 19.3 × 7.5)
Flight deck, feet (metres): 65.6 × 59 *(20 × 18)*
Main machinery: COGAG; 2 gas-turbines; 55 500 hp(m)
(40.8 MW); 2 gas-turbines, 13 600 hp(m) *(10 MW)*; 2 shafts
Speed, knots: 30. **Range, miles:** 2600 at 30 kts; 4000 at 18 kts
Complement: 249 (29 officers)

Missiles: SAM: 8 SA-N-9 Gauntlet (Kynshal) vertical launchers ❶;
command guidance; active radar homing to 45 km *(24.4 nm)*
at 2 Mach; warhead 15 kg; altitude 3.4-12 192 m *(10-
40 000 ft)*; 64 missiles; four channels of fire.
   The launchers are set into the ships' structures with 6 ft diameter cover plates—four on the fo'c'sle, two between the torpedo tubes and two at the forward end of the after deckhouse
between the RBUs.
A/S: 2 SS-N-14 Silex quad launchers ❷; command guidance to
55 km *(30 nm)* at 0.95 Mach; payload nuclear or Type E53 torpedo; active/passive homing to 15 km *(8.1 nm)* at 40 kts; warhead 150 kg. SSM version; range 35 km *(19 nm)*; warhead
500 kg.
Guns: 2—3.9 in *(100 mm)*/59 ❸; 85° elevation; 60 rounds/
minute to 15 km *(8.2 nm)*; weight of shell 16 kg.
   4—30 mm/65 ❹; 6 barrels per mounting; 85° elevation; 3000
rounds/minute combined to 2 km.
Torpedoes: 8—21 in *(533 mm)* (2 quad) tubes ❺. Combination of
53 cm torpedoes (see table at front of section).
A/S mortars: 2 RBU 6000 12-tubed trainable ❻; range 6000 m;
warhead 31 kg.
Mines: Rails for 30 mines.
Countermeasures: Decoys: 8 ten-barrelled chaff launchers. US
Masker type noise reduction.
ESM/ECM: 2 Bell Squat. 2 Foot Ball (not in all). 2 Wine Glass
(intercept). 4 Half Cup laser warner.
Fire control: MP 145 radar and optronic system. 2 Bell Crown
data link.
Radars: Air search: One or two (*Udaloy* and *Kulakov*) Strut Pair ❼;
F band.
   Top Plate (not *Udaloy* and *Kulakov*) ❽; 3D; D/E band.
Surface search: Three Palm Frond ❾; I band.
Fire Control: Two Eye Bowl ❿; F band (for SS-N-14). Two Cross
Sword ⓫; K band (for SA-N-9). Kite Screech ⓬; H/I/K band
(for 100 mm guns). Two Bass Tilt ⓭; H/I/K band (for 30 mm
guns).
IFF: Salt Pot A and B.
Tacan: Two Round House.
CCA: Fly Screen B (by starboard hangar) ⓮.
Sonars: Horse Jaw; hull-mounted; active search and attack; low/
medium frequency.
   Horse Tail; VDS; active search; medium frequency.

Helicopters: 2 Ka-27 Helix A ⓯.

Programmes: Successor to Kresta II class but based on Krivak
class design. Type name is *bolshoy protivolodochny korabl*
meaning large anti-submarine ship.
Structure: The two hangars are set side by side with inclined elevating ramps to the flight deck. Has pre-wetting NBCD equip-

ADMIRAL VINOGRADOV   *12/1993, G Toremans*

ADMIRAL KHARLAMOV   *6/1993*

ment and replenishment at sea gear. Initially SA-N-9 was not
operational and the first three of the class commissioned without the Cross Sword fire-control radars. There also seemed to
be a shortage of Strut Pair radars and numbers three to seven
initially had no air search radar on their foremasts on commissioning. These deficiencies are slowly being made good.
Active stabilisers are fitted. The chaff launchers are fitted on
both sides of the foremast and inboard of the torpedo tubes.

Operational: A general purpose ship with the emphasis on ASW
and complementary to Sovremenny class. Good sea-keeping
and endurance have been reported. Based as follows: Northern
Fleet—*Udaloy, Vasilevsky, Simferopol, Kharlamov* and *Lev-
chenko*; Pacific Fleet—*Spiridonov, Tributs, Shaposhnikov, Pan-
teleyev* and *Vinogradov. Kulakov* returned to the Baltic from the
Northern Fleet for repairs in 1992. The fourth of class, *Admiral
Zakharov* has been paid off after a fire in March 1992.

ADMIRAL SPIRIDONOV   *(Scale 1 : 1200), Ian Sturton*

ADMIRAL TRIBUTS   *10/1993, 92 Wing RAAF*

4 KASHIN (TYPE 61A) and 1 MODIFIED KASHIN (TYPE 61MR) CLASSES

KRASNY-KAVKAZ   **SDERZHANNY***
KRASNY-KRYM   **SKORY**
                         SMETLIVY

* Modified

Displacement, tons: 4010 standard; 4750 full load (Kashin);
  4974 (mod Kashin)
Dimensions, feet (metres): 472.4 (479.7 mod) × 51.8 × 15.4
  (144 (146.2) × 15.8 × 4.7)
Main machinery: COGAG; 4 gas-turbines; 72 000 hp(m)
  (52.9 MW); 2 shafts
Speed, knots: 35. **Range, miles:** 4000 at 20 kts; 2600 at 30 kts
Complement: 280 (20 officers, unmodified), (25 officers,
  modified)

Missiles: SSM: 4 SS-N-2C Styx (modified) ❶; active radar or IR
  homing to 83 km *(45 nm)* at 0.9 Mach; warhead 513 kg; sea-
  skimmer at end of run; no reloads.
SAM: 2 SA-N-1 Goa twin launchers ❷; command guidance to
  31.5 km *(17 nm)* at 2 Mach; warhead 60 kg; altitude 91.4-
  22 860 m *(300-75 000 ft)*; 32 missiles. Some SSM capability.
Guns: 4—3 in *(76 mm)*/60 (2 twin) ❸; 80° elevation; 90 rounds/
  minute to 15 km *(8 nm)*; weight of shell 6.8 kg.
  4—30 mm/65 (modified) ❹; 6 barrels per mounting; 85° elevation; 3000 rounds/minute combined to 2 km.
Torpedoes: 5—21 in *(533 mm)* (quin) tubes ❺. Combination of
  53 cm torpedoes (see table at front of section).
A/S mortars: 2 RBU 6000 12-tubed trainable ❻; range 6000 m;
  warhead 31 kg; 120 rockets.
  2 RBU 1000 6-tubed (not in modified) ❼; range 1000 m; war-
  head 55 kg.
Mines: Laying capability (unmodified only) for up to 20.
Countermeasures: Decoys: 4—16-tubed chaff launchers (modi-
  fied). 2 towed torpedo decoys.
  ESM/ECM: 2 Bell Shroud. 2 Bell Squat (modified). 2 Watch Dog
  (remainder).
Fire control: 3 Tee Plinth and 4 Tilt Pot optronic directors.
Radars: Air/surface search: Head Net C ❽; 3D; E band.
  Big Net ❾; C band.
  Navigation: Two Don 2/Don Kay/Palm Frond; I band.
  Fire control: Two Peel Group ❿; H/I band (for SA-N-1). Two Owl
  Screech ⓫; G band (for guns). Two Bass Tilt (modified) ⓬;
  H/I band (for 30 mm).
IFF: High Pole B (Modified ships).
Sonars: Bull Horn or Bull Nose; hull-mounted; active search and
  attack; medium frequency.
  Mare Tail; VDS (modified plus *Smetlivy*); search; medium
  frequency.

Helicopters: Platform only ⓭ (modified).

Programmes: The first class of warships in the world to rely
  entirely on gas-turbine propulsion. The remaining ships of the
  class were built from 1962-1972 at Kommuna (North) Yard,
  Nikolayev (1962-72). *Sderzhanny*, last of the class, was the
  only one to be built to the modified design. Type name is
  bolshoy protivolodochny korabl, meaning large anti-submarine
  ship.
Modernisation: In order to bring this class up to date with SSM
  and VDS a conversion programme was started in 1972 to the
  same pattern as set in *Sderzhanny*. This conversion consisted
  of lengthening the hull by 7.3 ft *(2.2 m)*, shipping four SS-N-2
  (C) launchers (SSM), four Gatling close range weapons, a VDS
  under a new stern helicopter platform and removing the after
  RBUs.
Operational: One sank in the Black Sea in 1974. The class is now
  being paid off at the rate of about three a year. *Smetlivy* has
  been in refit in the Black Sea since 1987 and is unlikely to
  return to service.
Sales: Additional ships of a modified design built for India. First
  transferred September 1980, the second in June 1982, the
  third in 1983, the fourth in August 1986 and the fifth and last in
  January 1988. All are fitted with helicopter hangars. *Smely*
  transferred to Poland 9 January 1988.

KRASNY-KRYM   *(Scale 1 : 1200), Ian Sturton*

KRASNY-KRYM   *6/1991, van Ginderen Collection*

SKORY   *4/1992, van Ginderen Collection*

SMYSHLENNY   *(Scale 1 : 1200), Ian Sturton*

SDERZHANNY (modified)   *6/1992, van Ginderen Collection*

17 + 3 SOVREMENNY CLASS (TYPE 956/956A)

Name	Builders	Laid down	Launched	Commissioned
SOVREMENNY	Zhdanov Yard, Leningrad	1977	Nov 1978	Aug 1980
OTCHYANNY	Zhdanov Yard, Leningrad	1977	Apr 1980	May 1982
OTLICHNNY	Zhdanov Yard, Leningrad	1978	Apr 1981	May 1983
OSMOTRITELNY	Zhdanov Yard, Leningrad	1979	Apr 1982	June 1984
BEZUPRECHNY	Zhdanov Yard, Leningrad	1980	Aug 1983	June 1985
BOYEVOY	Zhdanov Yard, Leningrad	1981	Aug 1984	June 1986
STOYKY	Zhdanov Yard, Leningrad	1982	Aug 1985	Sep 1986
OKRYLENNY	Zhdanov Yard, Leningrad	1983	June 1986	Sep 1987
BURNY	Zhdanov Yard, Leningrad	1984	Feb 1987	Aug 1988
GREMYASHCHY	Zhdanov Yard, Leningrad	1984	June 1987	Nov 1988
BYSTRY	Zhdanov Yard, Leningrad	1985	Dec 1987	Feb 1989
RASTOROPNY	Zhdanov Yard, Leningrad	1986	June 1988	Dec 1989
BEZBOYAZNENNY	Zhdanov Yard, Leningrad	1986	Mar 1989	Sep 1990
BEZUDERZHNY	Zhdanov Yard, Leningrad	1987	Oct 1990	Feb 1991
BESPOKOINY	Zhdanov Yard, Leningrad	1987	June 1990	Nov 1991
NASTOYCHIVY	North Yard, St Petersburg	1987	June 1991	30 Mar 1993
BESSTRASHNY	North Yard, St Petersburg	1987	Dec 1991	Feb 1994
VAZHNY	North Yard, St Petersburg	1988	1994	1995
VDUMCHIVY	North Yard, St Petersburg	1989	1994	1996
—	North Yard, St Petersburg	1990	1995	1997

Displacement, tons: 6500 standard; 7300 full load
Dimensions, feet (metres): 511.8 × 56.8 × 21.3
(156 × 17.3 × 6.5)
Main machinery: 4 boilers; 2 turbines; 102 000 hp(m) *(75 MW)*;
2 shafts; bow thruster
Speed, knots: 32. **Range, miles:** 2400 at 32 kts; 6500 at 20 kts;
14 000 at 14 kts
Complement: 296 (25 officers)

Missiles: SSM: 8 SS-N-22 Sunburn (2 quad) launchers ❶; active/
passive radar homing to 110 km *(60 nm)* at 2.5 (4.5 for attack)
Mach; warhead nuclear or HE 300 kg; sea-skimmer. From *Bespokoiny* onwards the launchers are longer and fire a modified
missile with a range of 160 km *(87 nm)*.
SAM: 2 SA-N-7 Gadfly (Uragan) ❷; command/semi-active radar
and IR homing to 25 km *(13.5 nm)* at 3 Mach; warhead 70 kg;
altitude 15-14 020 m *(50-46 000 ft)*; 44 missiles. Multiple
channels of fire. From *Bespokoiny* onwards the same launcher
is used for the SA-X-17 Grizzly (Smertch).
Guns: 4—130 mm/70 (2 twin) ❸; 85° elevation; 35-45 rounds/
minute to 29.5 km *(16 nm)*; weight of shell 27 kg.
4—30 mm/65 ADG 630 ❹; 6 barrels per mounting; 85° elevation; 3000 rounds/minute combined to 2 km.
Torpedoes: 4—21 in *(533 mm)* (2 twin) tubes ❺. Combination of
53 cm torpedoes (see table at front of section).
A/S mortars: 2 RBU 1000 6-barrelled ❻; range 1000 m; warhead 55 kg; 120 rockets carried.
Mines: Have mine rails for up to 40.
Countermeasures: Decoys: 8 ten-barrelled chaff launchers.
ESM/ECM: 4 Foot Ball (some variations including 2 Bell Shroud
and 2 Bell Squat). Half Cup laser warner.
Fire control: 1 Squeeze Box optronic director and laser range-
finder ❼. 2 Shot Dome. Optical director for SAM.
Radars: Air search: Top Steer (in first three). Plate Steer (in 4th
and 5th ships). Top Plate (remainder) ❽; 3D; D/E band.
Surface search: Three Palm Frond ❾; I band.
Fire control: Band Stand ❿; D/E/F band (for SS-N-22). Six Front
Dome ⓫; F band (for SA-N-7/17). Kite Screech ⓬; H/I/K
band (for 130 mm guns). Two Bass Tilt ⓭; H/I band (for
30 mm guns).
IFF: Salt Pot A and B. High Pole A and B. Long Head.
Tacan: Two Light Bulb.
Sonars: Bull Horn and Steer Hide; hull-mounted; active search
and attack; medium frequency.

Helicopters: 1 Ka-25 Hormone B or Ka-27 Helix ⓮.

Programmes: Zhdanov was renamed North Yard in 1989. Type
name is *eskadrenny minonosets* meaning destroyer. Building
rate has slowed down to about one a year. From *Bespokoiny*
onwards the class is known as 956A. Total of 28 of the class is
currently planned.
Structure: Telescopic hangar. The fully automatic 130 mm gun
was first seen in 1976. Chaff launchers are fitted on both sides
of the foremast and either side of the after SAM launcher. A
longer-range version of SS-N-22 has been introduced in the
Type 956A. This has slightly longer launch tubes. Also the
SAM system has been improved to take the SS-N-17. There are
also some variations in the EW fit.

Operational: A specialist surface warfare ship complementing
the ASW-capable Udaloy class. Based as follows: Northern
Fleet—*Sovremenny, Otchyanny, Otlichnny, Bezuprechny, Okry-
lenny, Gremyashchy, Rastoropny* and *Bezuderzhny*. Pacific
Fleet—*Osmotritelny, Boyevoy, Stoyky, Burny, Bystry,* and *Bez-
boyaznenny. Bespokoiny* started trials in the Baltic in early
1992 but after a fire in August 1992 has been alongside in Kaliningrad; *Nastoychivy* has remained in the Baltic; *Besstrashny*
started trials in November 1993.

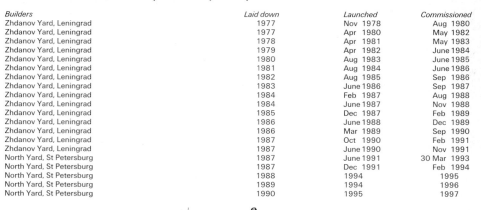

BOYEVOY

(Scale 1 : 1200), Ian Sturton

NASTOYCHIVY (Type 956A)

10/1993, G Toremans

NASTOYCHIVY (Type 956A)

6/1993, Antonio Moreno

BEZUDERZHNY   *6/1993*

RASTOROPNY   *8/1993*

GREMYASHCHY   *6/1993, H M Steele*

FRIGATES

1 + 2 NEUSTRASHIMY CLASS (TYPE 1154)

Name	Builders	Laid down	Launched	Commissioned
NEUSTRASHIMY	Yantar, Kaliningrad	Apr 1986	May 1988	24 Jan 1993
NEPRISTUPNY	Yantar, Kaliningrad	May 1988	May 1991	1994
—	Yantar, Kaliningrad	Sep 1990	July 1993	—

Displacement, tons: 4100 full load
Dimensions, feet (metres): 423.2 oa; 403.5 wl × 50.9 × 15.7 *(129; 123 × 15.5 × 4.8)*
Main machinery: COGAG; 2 gas-turbines; 48 600 hp(m) *(35.72 MW)*; 2 gas-turbines; 24 200 hp(m) *(17.79 MW)*; 2 shafts
Speed, knots: 32. **Range, miles:** 4500 at 16 kts
Complement: 200

Missiles: SSM: 8 SS-N-25 ❶ active radar homing to 130 km *(70.2 nm)* at 0.9 Mach; warhead 145 kg; sea-skimmer (not yet fitted - see *Structure*).
SAM: 4 SA-N-9 Gauntlet (Kynshal) sextuple vertical launchers ❷; command guidance; active radar homing to 45 km *(24.4 nm)* at 2 Mach; warhead 15 kg.
SAM/Guns: 2 CADS-N-1 (Kashtan) ❸; each has a twin 30 mm Gatling combined with 8 SA-N-11 and Hot Flash/Hot Spot fire-control radar/optronic director. Laser beam guidance for missiles to 8 km *(4.4 nm)*; 4500 rounds/minute (combined) to 1.5 km (for guns).
A/S: SS-N-15 type; inertial flight to 120 km *(65 nm)*; payload Type 40 torpedo or nuclear warhead; fired from torpedo tubes.
Guns: 1—3.9 in *(100 mm)*/59 ❹; 85° elevation; 60 rounds/minute to 15 km *(8.2 nm)*; weight of shell 16 kg.
Torpedoes: 6—21 in *(533 mm)* tubes combined with A/S launcher ❺; can fire SS-N-15 missiles with Type 40 anti-submarine torpedoes or 53 cm torpedoes (see table at front of section).
A/S mortars: 1 RBU 12 000 ❻; 10-tubed trainable; range 12 000 m; warhead 80 kg.
Mines: 2 rails.
Countermeasures: Decoys: 2—10-barrelled chaff launchers.
ESM/ECM: Intercept and jammers. 2 Foot Ball; 2 Half Hat; 3 Cage Flask.
Fire control: 2 Bell Crown data link.
Radars: Air/surface search: Top Plate ❼; 3D; D/E band.
Navigation: 2 Palm Frond; I band.
Fire control: Cross Sword ❽ (for SAM); K band. Kite Screech ❾ (for SSM and guns); I band.
IFF: 2 Salt Pot.
Sonars: Bull Nose; hull-mounted; active search and attack.
Steer Hide VDS ❿ or towed sonar array.

Helicopters: 1 Ka-27 Helix ⓫.

Programmes: The first of class started sea trials in the Baltic in December 1990. Second of class was still fitting out in early 1994 and the third was launched with only the hull completed. It is possible the building programme may transfer to St Petersburg.
Structure: This ship is slightly larger than the Krivak and has a helicopter which is a standard part of the armament of modern Western frigates. There are three horizontal launchers at main deck level on each side of the ship, angled at 18° from forward. These double up for A/S missiles of the SS-N-15 type and normal torpedoes. Similar launchers are behind shutters in the last

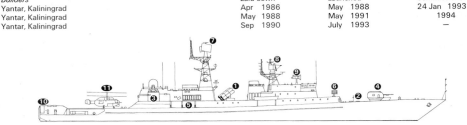

NEUSTRASHIMY   *(Scale 1 : 1200), Ian Sturton*

NEUSTRASHIMY   *7/1993, Hartmut Ehlers*

three of the Kirov class. The helicopter deck extends across the full width of the ship. The after funnel is unusually flush decked but both funnels have been slightly extended after initial sea trials. The SS-N-25 launchers as shown may not be fitted if

SSM missiles can also be fired from the midships combined torpedo launchers. Attempts have been made to incorporate stealth features. Main propulsion is the same as the Udaloy II class.

NEUSTRASHIMY   *7/1993, Hartmut Ehlers*

NEUSTRASHIMY   *4/1991, MoD Bonn*

11 GRISHA I (TYPE 1124), 12 GRISHA II (TYPE 1124P), 28 GRISHA III (TYPE 1124M) and 30 + 2 GRISHA V (TYPE 1124EM) (ALBATROS) CLASSES

AMETYST, BRILLIANT, IZUMRUD, PREDANNY, IZMAIL, DNEPR, RESITELNY, PRIMERNY RUBIN, SAPFIR, ZHEMCHUG, PROVORNY
(All Grisha II class (Border Guard))

Displacement, tons: 950 standard; 1200 full load
Dimensions, feet (metres): 233.6 × 32.2 × 12.1
(71.2 × 9.8 × 3.7)
Main machinery: CODAG; 1 gas-turbine; 15 000 hp(m) *(11 MW)*;
2 diesels; 16 000 hp(m) *(11.8 MW)*; 3 shafts
Speed, knots: 30. **Range, miles:** 2500 at 14 kts; 1750 at 20 kts
diesels; 950 at 27 kts
Complement: 70 (5 officers) (Grisha III); 60 (Grisha I)

Missiles: SAM: SA-N-4 Gecko twin launcher (Grisha I, III and V
classes) ❶; semi-active radar homing to 15 km *(8 nm)* at
2.5 Mach; warhead 50 kg; altitude 9.1-3048 m *(30-10 000 ft)*;
20 missiles (see *Structure* for SA-N-9).
Guns: 2—57 mm/80 (twin) (2 twin in Grisha II class) ❷; 85° elevation; 120 rounds/minute to 6 km *(3.3 nm)*; weight of shell
2.8 kg.
1—3 in *(76 mm)*/60 (Grisha V) ❸; 85° elevation; 120 rounds/
minute to 15 km *(8 nm)*; weight of shell 7 kg.
1—30 mm/65 (Grisha III and V classes) ❹; 6 barrels; 85° elevation; 3000 rounds/minute combined to 2 km.
Torpedoes: 4—21 in *(533 mm)* (2 twin) tubes ❺. Combination of
53 cm torpedoes (see table at front of section).
A/S mortars: 2 RBU 6000 12-tubed trainable ❻; range 6000 m;
warhead 31 kg. (Only 1 in Grisha Vs).
Depth charges: 2 racks (12).
Mines: Capacity for 18 in lieu of depth charges.
Countermeasures: ESM: 2 Watch Dog. 1—10-barrelled chaff
launcher (Grisha V).
Radars: Air/surface search: Strut Curve (Strut Pair in early Grisha
Vs) ❼; F band; range 110 km *(60 nm)* for 2 m² target.
Half Plate Bravo (in later Grisha Vs); E/F band.
Navigation: Don 2; I band.
Fire control: Pop Group (Grisha I, III and V) ❽; F/H/I band (for
SA-N-4). Muff Cob (except in Grisha III and V) ❾; G/H band
(for 57 mm). Bass Tilt (Grisha III and V) ❿; H/I band (for
57/76 mm and 30 mm).
IFF: High Pole A or B. Square Head. Salt Pot.
Sonars: Hull-mounted; active search and attack; high/medium
frequency.
VDS ⓫; active search; high frequency. Similar to Hormone
helicopter dipping sonar.

Programmes: Grisha I series production 1968-75; Grisha II
1973-84; Grisha III 1973-85; Grisha V 1982 onwards. All were
built or are building at Kiev, Kharbarovsk and Zelenodolsk
except Grisha II which were only built at Zelenodolsk. Type
name is *maly protivolodochny korabl* meaning small anti-submarine ship (Grisha I, III and V) or *pogranichny storozhevoy
korabl* meaning border patrol ship (Grisha II). Last two Grisha V
should complete in 1994.
Structure: SA-N-4 launcher mounted on the fo'c'sle in all but
Grisha II. This is replaced by a second twin 57 mm in Grisha II
class. Grisha III class has Muff Cob radar removed, Bass Tilt and
30 mm ADG (fitted aft), and Rad-haz screen removed from
abaft funnel as a result of removal of Muff Cob. Grisha V is simi-

lar to Grisha III with the after twin 57 mm mounting replaced
by a single Tarantul type 76 mm gun. One Grisha III in the Black
Sea was modified as the trials unit for the SA-N-9/Cross
Swords SAM system in the early 1980s and is sometimes
known as Grisha IV (Type 1124K).

Operational: Grisha II and six Grisha III are Border Guard ships
and have names. Some Grisha III and V may have two SA-N-5
launchers. Grisha I are beginning to pay off.
Sales: Two Grisha III to Lithuania in November 1992. At least one
Grisha V claimed by Ukraine.

GRISHA I

(Scale 1 : 900), Ian Sturton

GRISHA II

(Scale 1 : 900), Ian Sturton

GRISHA III

(Scale 1 : 900), Ian Sturton

GRISHA V

(Scale 1 : 900), Ian Sturton

GRISHA I   *5/1990*

GRISHA III   *7/1991*

GRISHA II   *8/1993*

GRISHA V   *8/1993*

19 KRIVAK I (TYPE 1135), 11 KRIVAK II (TYPE 1135M) and 9 KRIVAK III (TYPE 1135MP) (BUREVESTNIK) CLASSES

KRIVAK I (Kaliningrad)	KRIVAK I (Zhdanov, Leningrad*) (Kamysh-Burun (Kerch))	KRIVAK II (Kaliningrad)	KRIVAK III (Zaliv (Kerch))
BDITELNY	LEGKY* (ex-Leningradsky Komsomolets)	BESSMENNY	MENZHINSKY
BODRY	LETUCHY*	GORDELIVY	DZERZHINSKY
DRUZHNY	PYLKY*	GROMKY	OREL (ex-Imeni XXVII Sezda KPSS)
RAZUMNY	RETIVY*	GROZYASHCHY	IMENI LXX LETIYA VCHK-KGB
SILNY	ZADORNY*	NEUKROTIMY (ex-Komsomolets Litvii)	IMENI LXX LETIYA POGRANVOYSK
STOROZHEVOY	ZHARKY*	PYTLIVY	KEDROV
SVIREPY	BEZZAVETNY	RAZITELNY	VOROVSKY
	BEZUKORIZNENNY	REVNOSTNY	HETMAN DOROSENKO (Ukraine)
	DOSTOYNY	REZKY	HETMAN PETR SAGADACHNY (Ukraine)
	DEYATELNY	REZVY	
	LADNY	RYANNY	
	PORYVISTY		

Displacement, tons: 3100 standard; 3600 full load
Dimensions, feet (metres): 405.2 × 46.9 × 16.4 *(123.5 × 14.3 × 5)*
Main machinery: COGAG; 2 gas-turbines; 55 500 hp(m) *(40.8 MW)*; 2 gas-turbines, 13 600 hp(m) *(10 MW)*; 2 shafts
Speed, knots: 32. **Range, miles:** 4600 at 20 kts; 1600 at 30 kts
Complement: 180 (18 officers)

Missiles: SSM: 8 SS-N-25 (2 quad) ❶; (Krivak I after modernisation); active radar homing to 130 km *(70.2 nm)* at 0.9 Mach; warhead 145 kg; sea-skimmer.
SAM: 2 SA-N-4 Gecko twin launchers (1 in Krivak III) ❷; semi-active radar homing to 15 km *(8 nm)* at 2.5 Mach; warhead 50 kg; altitude 9.1-3048 m *(30-10 000 ft)*; 40 missiles (20 in Krivak III). The launcher retracts into the mounting for stowage and protection, rising to fire and retracting to reload. The two mountings are forward of the bridge and abaft the funnel.
A/S: SS-N-14 Silex quad launcher (not in Krivak III) ❸; command guidance to 55 km *(30 nm)* at 0.95 Mach; payload nuclear or Type E53 torpedo; active/passive homing to 15 km *(8.1 nm)* at 40 kts; warhead 150 kg. SSM version; range 35 km *(19 nm)*; warhead 500 kg.
Guns: 4—3 in *(76 mm)*/60 (2 twin) (Krivak I) ❹; 80° elevation; 90 rounds/minute to 15 km *(8 nm)*; weight of shell 6.8 kg.
2—3.9 in *(100 mm)*/59 (Krivak II) (1 in Krivak III) ❺; 85° elevation; 60 rounds/minute to 15 km *(8.2 nm)*; weight of shell 16 kg.
2—30 mm/65 (Krivak III) ❻; 6 barrels per mounting; 3000 rounds/minute combined to 2 km.
Torpedoes: 8—21 in *(533 mm)* (2 quad) tubes ❼. Combination of 53 cm torpedoes (see table at front of section).
A/S mortars: 2 RBU 6000 12-tubed trainable ❽; (not in modernised Krivak I); range 6000 m; warhead 31 kg.
Mines: Capacity for 20.
Countermeasures: Decoys: 4 chaff launchers (16 tubes per launcher) or 10 (10 tubes per launcher). Towed torpedo decoy.
ESM/ECM: 2 Bell Shroud. 2 Bell Squat.
Radars: Air search: Head Net C ❾; 3D; E band; range 128 km *(70 nm)*. Top Plate (*Imeni XXVII* and later and some Krivak I after modernisation) ❿.
Surface search: Don Kay or Palm Frond or Don 2 or Spin Trough ⓫; I band.
Peel Cone ⓬; I band (Krivak III).
Fire control: Two Eye Bowl (not in Krivak III) ⓭; F band (for SS-N-14). Two Pop Group (one in Krivak III) ⓮; F/H/I band (for SA-N-4). Owl Screech (Krivak I) ⓯; G band. Kite Screech (Krivak II and III) ⓰; H/I/K band. Bass Tilt (Krivak III) ⓱; H/I band.
IFF: High Pole B. Salt Pot (Krivak III).
Sonars: Bull Nose; hull-mounted; active search and attack; medium frequency.
Mare Tail or Steer Hide (*Zharky, Bditelny, Leningradsky Komsomolets* and other Krivak Is after modernisation); VDS ⓲; active search; medium frequency.

Helicopters: 1 Ka-25 Hormone or Ka-27 Helix (Krivak III) ⓳.

Programmes: The Krivak I class built from 1969-1981, Krivak II from 1976-81 and Krivak III from 1984-1993. Type name was originally *bolshoy protivolodochny korabl*, meaning large anti-submarine ship. Changed in 1977-78 to *storozhevoy korabl* meaning escort ship. Most of the Krivak III names seem certain to be changed. The last pair have been given Ukrainian names.
Modernisation: Krivak Is are being modernised with SS-N-25 quadruple launchers replacing RBU mountings forward of the bridge. Top Plate radar is replacing Head Net and a more modern VDS is also being fitted. Ships converted by early 1994 included *Legky, Silny* and *Pylky*.
Structure: Krivak II class has X-gun mounted higher and the break to the quarter-deck further aft apart from other variations noted. Krivak III class built for the former KGB but now under naval control. The removal of SS-N-14 and one SA-N-4 mounting compensates for the addition of a hangar and flight deck.
Operational: First Krivak I paid off in 1992 in the Pacific, second in 1993. Apart from the two Ukrainian ships, all the Krivak IIIs are in the Pacific Fleet. *Petr Sagadachny* commissioned on 5 July 1993.

KRIVAK I (mod)   *(Scale 1 : 1200), Ian Sturton*

KRIVAK II   *(Scale 1 : 1200), Ian Sturton*

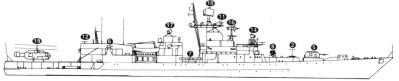

KRIVAK III   *(Scale 1 : 1200), Ian Sturton*

LEGKY (with SS-N-25 launchers)   *6/1993*

LEGKY (Krivak I)   *7/1993, C D Yaylali*

BESSMENNY (Krivak II)   *5/1993*

VOROVSKY (Krivak III)   *10/1991*

DRUZHNY (Krivak I)   *7/1993*

1 + 2 GEPARD CLASS

Displacement, tons: 1900 full load
Dimensions, feet (metres): 334.6 × 44.6 × 14.4
(102 × 13.6 × 4.4)
Main machinery: CODOG; 2 gas-turbines; 2 diesels; 2 shafts;
cp props
Speed, knots: 26 (18 on diesels). **Range, miles:** 3500 at 18 kts
Complement: 110 plus 21 spare

Missiles: SSM: 8 SS-N-25 (2 quad) ❶; IR or radar homing to
130 km *(70.2 nm)* at 0.9 Mach; warhead 145 kg; sea-skimmer.
SAM: 1 SA-N-4 Gecko twin launcher ❷; semi-active radar homing
to 15 km *(8 nm)* at 2.5 Mach; warhead 50 kg.
Guns: 1—3 in *(76 mm)*/60 ❸; 85° elevation; 120 rounds/minute
to 15 km *(8 nm)*; weight of shell 7 kg.
2—30 mm/65 ADG 630 ❹; 6 barrels per mounting; 85° elev-
ation; 3000 rounds/minute combined to 2 km.
Torpedoes: 4—21 in *(533 mm)* (2 twin) tubes ❺. Combination of
53 cm torpedoes (see table at front of section).
A/S mortars: 1 RBU 6000 12-tubed trainable ❻; range 6000 m;
warhead 31 kg.
Mines: 2 rails.
Countermeasures: Decoys: 4 chaff launchers.
ESM/ECM: 2 Bell Shroud. 3 Cage Flask. Intercept and jammers.
Fire control: 2 Light Bulb data link.
Radars: Air/surface search: Cross Dome ❼; E/F band.
Band Stand ❽; D/E/F band.
Fire control: Bass Tilt ❾; H/I band (for guns and SSM). Pop Group
❿; F/H/I band (for SAM).
Navigation: Nayada; I band.
IFF: 2 Square Head. 1 Salt Pot B.
Sonars: Hull-mounted; active search and attack; medium
frequency.
VDS ⓫; active search and attack; medium frequency.

Programmes: Successor to the Koni class being built at Zelenodolsk, Kazan. First of class trials in 1993. Available for export.
Structure: A logical development of existing light frigate classes
with the addition of SS-N-25. Steel hull with aluminium superstructure. Stealth features are claimed and the ship has roll
stabilisers and air-conditioned spaces.

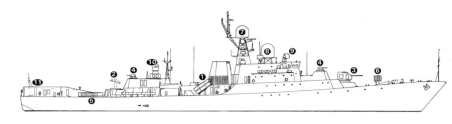

GEPARD

(Scale 1 : 900), Ian Sturton

GEPARD (artist's impression)

1/1993

12 PARCHIM II CLASS (FFL)

MPK 67, 99, 105, 192, 205, 213, 219, 224, 228, 229, 216, JUNGA

Displacement, tons: 769 standard; 1200 full load
Dimensions, feet (metres): 246.7 × 32.2 × 14.4
(75.2 × 9.8 × 4.4)
Main machinery: 3 Type M 504A diesels; 10 812 hp(m)
(7.95 MW) sustained; 3 shafts
Speed, knots: 28
Complement: 60

Missiles: SAM: 2 SA-N-5 Grail quad launchers ❶; manual aiming;
IR homing to 6 km *(3.2 nm)* at 1.5 Mach; altitude to 2500 m
(8000 ft); warhead 1.5 kg.
Guns: 1—3 in *(76 mm)*/66 ❷; 85° elevation; 120 rounds/minute
to 15 km *(8 nm)*; weight of shell 7 kg.
1—30 mm/65 ❸; 6 barrels; 85° elevation; 3000 rounds/
minute combined to 2 km.
Torpedoes: 4—21 in *(533 mm)* (2 twin) tubes ❹. Combination of
53 cm torpedoes (see table at front of section).
A/S mortars: 2 RBU 6000 12-tubed trainable ❺; range 6000 m;
warhead 31 kg.
Depth charges: 2 racks.
Mines: Rails fitted.
Countermeasures: Decoys: 2—16 barrelled chaff launchers.
ESM: 2 Watch Dog.
Radars: Air/surface search: Cross Dome ❻; E/F band.
Navigation: TSR 333; I band.
Fire control: Bass Tilt ❼; H/I band.

PARCHIM II

(Scale 1 : 600), Ian Sturton

Sonars: Hull-mounted; active search and attack; medium
frequency.
Helicopter type VDS; high frequency.

Programmes: Built in the GDR at Peenewerft, Wolgast for the
USSR. First one commissioned 19 December 1986 and the last
on 6 April 1990.

Structure: Similar design to the ex-GDR Parchim I class but some
armament differences.
Operational: All operate in the Baltic.

PARCHIM II

7/1993, Hartmut Ehlers

1 MODIFIED PETYA I (TYPE 159), 3 PETYA II (TYPE 159A) and 1 MODIFIED PETYA II CLASSES

Displacement, tons: 950 standard; 1180 full load
Dimensions, feet (metres): 268.3 (270.6, Mod Petya II) × 29.9 × 9.5 *(81.8 (82.5) × 9.1 × 2.9)*
Main machinery: CODAG; 2 gas-turbines; 30 000 hp(m) *(22 MW)*; 1 Type 61V-3 diesel; 5400 hp(m) *(3.97 MW)* sustained (centre shaft); 3 shafts
Speed, knots: 32. **Range, miles:** 4870 at 10 kts; 450 at 29 kts
Complement: 98

Guns: 4—3 in *(76 mm)*/60 (2 twin); (1 twin in Mod Petya I); 80° elevation; 90 rounds/minute to 15 km *(8 nm)*; weight of shell 6.8 kg.
Torpedoes: 10 (Petya II) or 5 (Mod Petya I) 16 in *(406 mm)* (2 or 1 quin) tubes. SAET-40; anti-submarine; active/passive homing to 10 km *(5.4 nm)* at 30 kts; warhead 100 kg.
A/S mortars: 2 (Mod Petya I) RBU 2500 16-tubed trainable; range 2500 m; warhead 21 kg.
2 RBU 6000 12-tubed trainable (Petya II and Mod Petya II); range 6000 m; warhead 31 kg.
Depth charges: 2 racks (not in Mod Petya II and some Mod Petya I).
Mines: Capacity for 22 (not in Mod Petya I).
Countermeasures: ESM: 2 Watch Dog; radar warning.
Radars: Air/surface search: Slim Net (Mod Petya I); E/F band. Strut Curve (Petya II); F band; range 110 km *(60 nm)* for 2 m² target.
Navigation: Don 2; I band.
Fire control: Hawk Screech; I band; range 27 km *(15 nm)*.
IFF: High Pole B.
Sonars: Hull-mounted; active search and attack; high/medium frequency.
VDS (in some); active search; high frequency.

PETYA II   9/1991

Programmes: The first ship was built in 1960-61 at Kaliningrad. Construction continued there and at Komsomolsk until about 1970.
Structure: Mod Petya I—carry towed sonar in a deckhouse on the stern.
Petya II—extra quin torpedo tubes vice after RBUs.
Mod Petya II—first seen in 1978. After torpedo tubes removed and with a deckhouse built abaft the after 3 in *(76 mm)* gun to contain the towed trials equipment. There is a space either side for mine rails.
Operational: Numbers represent operational hulls in early 1994. More are being scrapped. One Petya II 'defected' to Ukraine in

July 1992; two more were under Azerbaijan control from November 1992. One of this class was also used as the trials ship for the SUWN-1 A/S launcher.
Sales: Petya III (sales version)—ten to India, two to Syria and two to Vietnam December 1978. Some of these have been deleted including one Indian ship which sank in 1990. These export versions are on Petya II hulls but fitted with one triple 21 in *(533 mm)* torpedo tube mounting in place of the two 16 in *(406 mm)* mountings and four RBU 2500s in place of two RBU 6000s. In addition other Petya IIs have been transferred: to Ethiopia—one in July 1983, second in March 1984, and to Vietnam—two in December 1983 and one in December 1984.

SHIPBORNE AIRCRAFT

Note: All Yak-38 Forger aircraft were out of service by 1992. The MiG-29 Fulcrum D has been abandoned by the Navy and the Ka-34 Hokum is not in production.

Numbers/Type: 15/25 Sukhoi Su-27K (Su-33) Flanker B/D.
Operational speed: 1345 kts *(2500 km/h)*.
Service ceiling: 59 000 ft *(18 000 m)*.
Range: 2160 + nm *(4000 km)*.
Role/Weapon systems: Fleet air defence fighter. Sensors: Track-while-scan pulse Doppler radar, IR scanner. Weapons: 1 × 30 mm cannon, 10 × AAMs (AA-12, AA-11, AA-8).

FLANKER   8/1992, Linda Jackson

Numbers/Type: 65/6 Sukhoi Su-25UT Frogfoot A/B.
Operational speed: 526 kts *(975 km/h)*.
Service ceiling: 22 965 ft *(7000 m)*.
Range: 675 nm *(1250 km)*.
Role/Weapon systems: The UTG version is the two seater ground attack aircraft used for deck trials in the carrier *Kuznetsov*. Most of these aircraft are ex-Air Force. Sensors: Laser rangefinder, ESM, ECM. Weapons: 1 × 30 mm cannon, AAMs (AA-8), rockets, bombs.

FROGFOOT   1992

Numbers/Type: 1 Yakovlev Yak-41 Freestyle.
Operational speed: 984 kts *(1800 km/h)*.
Service ceiling: 49 200 ft *(15 000 m)*.
Range: 1150 nm *(2100 km)*.
Role/Weapon systems: Follow-on to the Forger. STOVL development which has poor handling characteristics and may be cancelled unless export orders are achieved. Sensors: Search radar, ESM. Weapons: 1 × 30 mm cannon, 2 × R 27, 2 × R 73, 4 × AAM, 4 × ASM.

FREESTYLE   8/1991

Numbers/Type: 170 Kamov Ka-27/Ka-29 Helix A/B/RLD.
Operational speed: 135 kts *(250 km/h)*.
Service ceiling: 19 685 ft *(6000 m)*.
Range: 432 nm *(800 km)*.
Role/Weapon systems: ASW helicopter; successor to 'Hormone' with greater ASW potential; three main versions—'A' for ASW, 'B' for assault, 'C' for SAR/utility; deployed to surface ships and some shore stations. There are also two RLD Helix B AEW aircraft with a solid-state radar under the fuselage. Sensors: Search radar, dipping sonar, sonobuoys, MAD, ECM. Weapons: ASW; 3 × torpedoes, nuclear or conventional depth bombs or mines. Assault type: 2 UV-57 rocket pods (2 × 32).

HELIX   8/1992

Numbers/Type: 35 Mil Mi-14BT Haze B.
Operational speed: 124 kts *(230 km/h)*.
Service ceiling: 15 000 ft *(4570 m)*.
Range: 432 nm *(800 km)*.
Role/Weapon systems: Minesweeping and possible minelaying helicopter; seen in action in Red Sea in 1985. Sensors: Search radar, sweep gear. Weapons: Unarmed.

HAZE   6/1989

Numbers/Type: 65 Kamov Ka-25 Hormone.
Operational speed: 119 kts *(220 km/h)*.
Service ceiling: 11 500 ft *(3500 m)*.
Range: 350 nm *(650 km)*.
Role/Weapon systems: First Soviet successful shipborne ASW helicopter (being replaced by 'Helix'); 'A' version for ASW, 'B' for recce (called REB) and 'C' for utility; 25 Ka-25B versions reported. Sensors: Puff Ball search radar, dipping sonar, sonobuoys, MAD, ECM (A), EW equipment and Big Bulge search radar (B), Radar only (C). Weapons: ASW; 2 × torpedoes, nuclear or conventional depth bombs (A). ASV; 2 or 4 × missiles or rocket launchers (A).

HORMONE   8/1992

LAND-BASED MARITIME AIRCRAFT (FRONT LINE)

Note: All Mi-8 Hip aircraft out of service by late 1992.

Numbers/Type: 80 Beriev Be-12 Mail.
Operational speed: 328 kts *(608 km/h)*.
Service ceiling: 37 000 ft *(11 280 m)*.
Range: 4050 nm *(7500 km)*.
Role/Weapon systems: Long-range ASW/MR amphibian in arctic waters, Baltic and Black Sea areas; to be replaced by mid-1990s. Sensors: Search/weather radar, sonobuoys, MAD, EW. Weapons: ASW; 5 tons of depth bombs, mines or torpedoes, nuclear-capable. ASV; limited missile and rocket armament.

MAIL   5/1992

Numbers/Type: 3 Ilyushin Il-20 Coot A.
Operational speed: 364 kts *(675 km/h)*.
Service ceiling: 32 800 ft *(10 000 m)*.
Range: 3508 nm *(6500 km)*.
Role/Weapon systems: Long-range Elint and MR for naval forces' intelligence gathering, especially in European waters. Sensors: SLAR, weather radar, cameras, Elint equipment. Weapons: Unarmed.

Numbers/Type: 8 Antonov An-12 Cub ('Cub B/C/D') ('Cub C/D' ECM/ASW).
Operational speed: 419 kts *(777 km/h)*.
Service ceiling: 33 500 ft *(10 200 m)*.
Range: 3075 nm *(5700 km)*.
Role/Weapon systems: Used either for intelligence gathering (B) or electronic warfare (C, D); is versatile with long range; operated by and for all Soviet Fleets and in support of client states. Sensors: Search/weather radar, 3 × EW blisters (B), tail-mounted EW/Elint equipment in addition (C/D). Weapons: Self-defence; 2 × 23 mm cannon (B and D only).

Numbers/Type: 45 Ilyushin Il-38 May.
Operational speed: 347 kts *(645 km/h)*.
Service ceiling: 32 800 ft *(10 000 m)*.
Range: 3887 nm *(7200 km)*.
Role/Weapon systems: Long-range MR and ASW over Atlantic, Indian and Mediterranean Sea areas. Sensors: Wet Eye search/weather radar, MAD, sonobuoys. Weapons: ASW; internal storage for 6 tons weapons.

MAY   5/1992

Numbers/Type: 70 Mil Mi-14PL/BT/PS Haze A/C.
Operational speed: 124 kts *(230 km/h)*.
Service ceiling: 15 000 ft *(4570 m)*.
Range: 432 nm *(800 km)*.
Role/Weapon systems: ASW (A) and assault (C) helicopters for medium-range operations. Sensors: Search radar, dipping sonar, sonobuoys, MAD, EW (A only). Weapons: ASW; 4 × torpedoes, nuclear or conventional depth bombs or mines (A); self-defence weapons (B).

Numbers/Type: 130 Sukhoi Su-17 Fitter C/D.
Operational speed: Mach 2.09.
Service ceiling: 59 050 ft *(18 000 m)*.
Range: 700 nm *(1300 km)*.
Role/Weapon systems: Anti-ship and support strike aircraft. Being placed in reserve. Sensors: Attack radar, ECM. Weapons: ASV; 2 × 30 mm cannon and 3.5 tons of underwing stores, including rockets and missiles. Self-defence; can mount AAMs.

Numbers/Type: 30 Tupolev Tu-16 Badger.
Operational speed: 535 kts *(992 km/h)*.
Service ceiling: 40 350 ft *(12 300 m)*.
Range: 2605 nm *(4800 km)*.
Role/Weapon systems: Medium-range operations in the strike/attack role. Now only in the Pacific Fleet. Other variants include reconnaissance, tanker and electronic warfare support role. Large numbers scrapped. Sensors: Puff Ball or Short Horn search/weather radar, EW. Weapons: Self-defence; 2 × 23 mm cannon. ASV; 2 × Kipper, Kelt and Kingfish ASMs or 9 tons of nuclear/conventional bombs.

Numbers/Type: 20 Tupolev Tu-22 Blinder.
Operational speed: 800 kts *(1480 km/h)*.
Service ceiling: 60 000 ft *(18 300 m)*.
Range: 3100 nm *(5740 km)*.
Role/Weapon systems: Limited number in service for Fleet reconnaissance, intelligence gathering and EW tasks, now only in the Black Sea. Sensors: Short Horn search/attack radar, EW, cameras. Weapons: ASV; 'iron' bombs or stand-off weapons. Self-defence; 1 × 23 mm cannon.

Numbers/Type: 130 Tupolev Tu-22 M Backfire B/C.
Operational speed: Mach 2.0.
Service ceiling: 60 000 ft *(18 300 m)*.
Range: 2500 nm *(4630 km)*.
Role/Weapon systems: Medium-range nuclear/conventional strike and reconnaissance. Sensors: Down Beat search/Fan Tail attack radars, EW. Weapons: ASV; 12 tons of 'iron' bombs or stand-off missiles including 'Kitchen'. Self-defence; 2 × 23 mm cannon.

Numbers/Type: 20/40/15 Tupolev Tu-95/Tu-142 Bear D/F/J.
Operational speed: 500 kts *(925 km/h)*.
Service ceiling: 60 000 ft *(18 300 m)*.
Range: 6775 nm *(12 550 km)*.
Role/Weapon systems: Multi-mission long-range aircraft (reconnaissance, ASW and communications variants); seen over all oceans of the world. There are also some 20 Bear G in the Pacific Air Force which have same ASV armament as Backfire. Sensors: Big Bulge and Short Horn (in Bear D) or Wet Eye (Bear F/J) search radars, ECM (D); search radar, sonobuoys, ECM, MAD (F), ELINT systems (J). Weapons: ASW; various torpedoes, depth bombs and/or mines (F). ASV; none (D), (J). Self-defence; some have 2 × 23 mm or more cannon.

BEAR   8/1992

CORVETTES

0 + 1 NEW CORVETTE

Displacement, tons: 1560 full load
Dimensions, feet (metres): 282.2 × 36.1 × 9.8 *(86 × 11 × 3)*
Main machinery: 2 diesels; 16 000 hp(m) *(11.76 MW)*; 2 shafts
Speed, knots: 25. **Range, miles:** 5000 at 14 kts
Complement: 90

Missiles: SSM: 4 SS-N-25 (2 twin).
SAM: 1 SA-N-4 Gecko twin launcher.
Guns: 1—3 in *(76 mm)*/60. 1—30 mm/65 ADG 630.
Torpedoes: 4—21 in *(533 mm)* (2 twin tubes).
Countermeasures: Decoys: 4 chaff launchers.
Radars: Air/surface search. Navigation. Fire control.
Sonars: Bow-mounted; active search and attack.

Helicopters: 1 Helix.

Programmes: A smaller version of Gepard class designed by the Northern Design Bureau for export. A prototype may be completed as a demonstrator.

14 NANUCHKA I (BURYA) (TYPE 1234), 18 NANUCHKA III (VETER) (TYPE 1234.1) and 1 NANUCHKA IV NAKAT (TYPE 1234.2) CLASSES

Nanuchka I:	GRAD	RADUGA	SKVAL	STORM	TAIFUN	ZYKLON	METL	ZARNITSA	GROM	MOLNIJA	MUSSON	VICHR	BORA BRIZ
Nanuchka III:	METEOR	ZYB	TUCHA	PRILIV BURUN		URAGAN	LIVEN	PASSAT	PRIBOY ZARYA	SMERCH	MIRAS	GROSA	SHTYL VETER +3
Nanuchka IV:	NAKAT												

Displacement, tons: 850 full load
Dimensions, feet (metres): 194.5 × 38.7 × 8.5
(59.3 × 11.8 × 2.6)
Main machinery: 3 Type M 507 diesels; 21 600 hp(m)
(15.9 MW) sustained; 3 shafts
Speed, knots: 36. **Range, miles:** 2500 at 12 kts; 900 at 31 kts
Complement: 42 (7 officers)

Missiles: SSM: 6 SS-N-9 Siren (2 triple) launchers ❶; command
guidance and IR and active radar homing to 110 km *(60 nm)* at
0.9 Mach; warhead nuclear 250 kT or HE 500 kg. Nanuchka IV
has 2 sextuple launchers for a possible improved version of
SS-N-9 or a new longer-range missile.
SAM: SA-N-4 Gecko twin launcher ❷; semi-active radar homing
to 15 km *(8 nm)* at 2.5 Mach; warhead 50 kg; altitude 9.1-
3048 m *(30-10 000 ft)*; 20 missiles. Some anti-surface
capability.
Guns: 2—57 mm/80 (twin) (Nanuchka I) ❸; 85° elevation; 120
rounds/minute to 6 km *(3.3 nm)*; weight of shell 2.8 kg.
1—3 in *(76 mm)*/60 (Nanuchka III and IV) ❹; 85° elevation;
120 rounds/minute to 7 km *(3.8 nm)*; weight of shell 7 kg.
1—30 mm/65 (Nanuchka III and IV) ❺; 6 barrels; 3000
rounds/minute combined to 2 km.
Countermeasures: Decoys: 2—16 or 10 (Nanuchka III) barrelled
chaff launchers ❻.
ESM: Bell Tap or other Bell series. 4 radomes.
Fire control: Two Fish Bowl or Light Bulb (data links).
Radars: Air/surface search: Band Stand (also associated with SS-
N-9 fire-control) ❼; D/E/F band. Plank Shave in later Nanuchka
III units.
Surface search: Peel Pair ❽; I band (in early units).
Fire control: Muff Cob (Nanuchka I) ❾; G/H band. Bass Tilt
(Nanuchka III) ❿; H/I band. Pop Group ⓫; F/H/I band (for
SA-N-4).
IFF: High Pole. Square Head. Spar Stump.

Programmes: Built from 1969 onwards at Petrovsky, Leningrad
and in the Pacific (Nanuchka III only). Nanuchka III, first seen in
1978. Nanuchka IV completed in 1987 as a trials ship. Programme terminated when *Liven* was commissioned in November 1991. A follow-on class is expected. Type name is *maly
raketny korabl* meaning small missile ship.

Structure: The Nanuchka IV is similar in detail to Nanuchka III
except that she is the trials vehicle for a possible 300 km range
version of SS-N-9 or its successor.
Operational: Probably mainly intended for deployment in coastal
waters although formerly deployed in the Mediterranean (in
groups of two or three), North Sea and Pacific. Nanuchka Is
beginning to be scrapped.

Sales: Three of a modified version of Nanuchka I (Nanuchka II)
with four SS-N-2B missiles have been supplied to India in
1977-78, three to Algeria in 1980-82, one to Libya in 1981, a
second in February 1983, a third in February 1984 and a fourth
in September 1985.

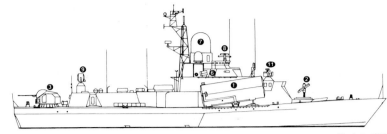

NANUCHKA I *(Scale 1 : 600), Ian Sturton*

NANUCHKA III *(Scale 1 : 600), Ian Sturton*

NANUCHKA I *4/1992, van Ginderen Collection*

NANUCHKA IV (2 sextuple launchers) *5/1990*

NANUCHKA III *8/1992*

2 DERGACH (SIVUCH) (TYPE 1239) CLASS

BORA (MRK 27)   **SAMUM** (MRK 17)

Displacement, tons: 750 full load
Dimensions, feet (metres): 211.6 × 55.8 × 7.9
     (64.5 × 17 × 2.4)
Main machinery: 3 gas-turbines; 36 300 hp(m) *(26.68 MW)*;
     2 hydroprops; 2 auxiliary diesels; 2 props on retractable pods
Speed, knots: 45. **Range, miles:** 2000 at 12 kts (hull); 80 at
     40 kts (air cushion)
Complement: 60

Missiles: SSM: 8 SS-N-22 (2 quad) Sunburn launchers ❶; active
     radar homing to 110 km *(60 nm)* at 2.5 Mach; warhead
     nuclear or HE; sea-skimmer.
     SAM: SA-N-4 Gecko twin launcher ❷; semi-active radar homing
     to 15 km *(8 nm)* at 2.5 Mach; warhead 50 kg; 20 missiles.
Guns: 1—3 in *(76 mm)*/60 ❸; 85° elevation; 120 rounds/minute
     to 7 km *(3.8 nm)*; weight of shell 16 kg.
     2—30 mm/65 AK 630 ❹; 6 barrels per mounting; 3000
     rounds/minute combined to 2 km.
Countermeasures: Decoys: 2—10-barrelled launchers.
     ESM/ECM: 2 Foot Ball A.
Fire control: 2 Light Bulb data link ❺.
Radars: Air/surface search: Band Stand ❻; D/E/F band.
     Surface search: Cross Dome ❼; E/F band.
     Fire control: Bass Tilt ❽; H/I band (for guns).
        Pop Group ❾; F/H/I band (for SAM).
IFF: Square Head. Salt Pot.

Programmes: Built at Zelenodolsk 340; first one launched in
     1987, second in 1992. Classified as a PGGA (Guided Missile
     Patrol Air Cushion Vessels).
Structure: Twin-hulled surface effect design.
Operational: Based in the Black Sea at Sevastopol.

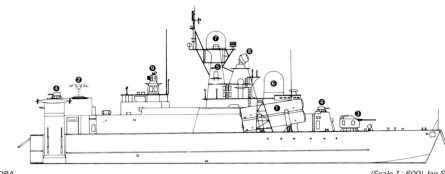

BORA   *(Scale 1 : 600), Ian Sturton*

BORA   *1993*

2 TARANTUL I (TYPE 1241.1), 18 TARANTUL II (TYPE 1241.1M) and 27 + 2 TARANTUL III (TYPE 1241.1MP) (MOLNIYA) CLASSES

Displacement, tons: 385 standard; 455 full load
Dimensions, feet (metres): 184.1 × 37.7 × 8.2 *(56.1 × 11.5 × 2.5)*
Main machinery: COGOG; 2 Nikolayev Type DR 77 gas-turbines; 16 016 hp(m) *(11.77 MW)* sus-
     tained; 2 Nikolayev Type DR 76 gas-turbines with reversible gearboxes; 4993 hp(m) *(3.67 MW)*
     sustained; 2 shafts or CODOG with 2 diesels; 8000 hp(m) *(5.88 MW)*; replacing second pair of
     gas-turbines
Speed, knots: 36. **Range, miles:** 400 at 36 kts; 1650 at 14 kts
Complement: 34 (5 officers)

Missiles: SSM: 4 SS-N-2C/D Styx (2 twin) launchers (Tarantul I and Tarantul II); active radar or IR
     homing to 83 km *(45 nm)* at 0.9 Mach; warhead 513 kg; sea-skimmer at end of run.
     4 SS-N-22 Sunburn (2 twin) launchers (Tarantul III); active radar homing to 110 km *(60 nm)* at
     2.5 Mach; warhead nuclear or HE 300 kg; sea-skimmer. Modified version in one of the class.
     SAM: SA-N-5 Grail quad launcher; manual aiming; IR homing to 6 km *(3.2 nm)* at 1.5 Mach; altitude
     to 2500 m *(8000 ft)*; warhead 1.5 kg.
     SAM/Guns: 1 CADS-N-1 (Kashtan) (one Tarantul II only); twin 30 mm Gatling combined with 8 SA-
     N-11 and Hot Flash/Hot Spot fire-control radar/optronic director; laser beam guidance for
     missiles to 8 km *(4.4 nm)*; 4500 rounds/minute combined to 1.5 km (for guns).
Guns: 1—3 in *(76 mm)*/60; 85° elevation; 120 rounds/minute to 15 km *(8 nm)*; weight of shell
     7 kg.
     2—30 mm/65; 6 barrels per mounting; 3000 rounds/minute to 2 km (not in CADS-N-1 Tarantul
     II).
Countermeasures: Decoys: 2—16 or 10 (Tarantul III) barrelled chaff launchers.
     ESM: 2 Foot Ball, 2 Half Hat (in some).
Fire control: Hood Wink optronic director. Light Bulb data link.
Radars: Air/surface search: Plank Shave (Tarantul I); I band. Band Stand (with Plank Shave) (Taran-
     tul II and III); E band.
     Navigation: Spin Trough or Kivach II; I band.
     Fire control: Bass Tilt; H/I band.
IFF: Square Head. High Pole B.

Programmes: The first Tarantul I was completed in 1978 at Petrovsky, Leningrad. A single experi-
     mental Tarantul III with four SS-N-22 was completed at Petrovsky in 1981. Tarantul II were built
     at Kolpino, Petrovsky, Leningrad and in the Pacific in 1980-86. A second Tarantul I without Band
     Stand is retained to train foreign crews. Current production is of Tarantul III class for Russia and
     Tarantul I for export. Type name is *raketny kater* meaning missile cutter.
Modernisation: One Tarantul III is serving as a trials platform for a modified version of SS-N-22 with
     a longer range; the missile is distinguished by end caps on the launcher doors. A Tarantul II
     served as a trials platform for the CADS-N-1 air defence system in the Black Sea.
Structure: Basically same hull as Pauk class, without extension for sonar. Tarantul I and II have
     SS-N-2 launchers and Tarantul III SS-N-22.

TARANTUL I   *7/1992, Jürg Kürsener*

TARANTUL II   *7/1993, Hartmut Ehlers*

Sales: Tarantul I class—one to Poland 28 December 1983, second in April 1984, third in March
     1988 and fourth in January 1989. One to GDR in September 1984, second in December 1984,
     third in September 1985, fourth in January 1986 and fifth in November 1986 (all deleted or sold
     including one which is doing trials with the US Navy). One to India in April 1987, second in Janu-
     ary 1988, third in December 1988, fourth in November 1989 and fifth in January 1990. Two to
     Yemen in November 1990 and January 1991. One to Romania in December 1990, two more in
     February 1992. One Tarantul II to Bulgaria in March 1990.

TARANTUL III   *7/1993, Hartmut Ehlers*

PATROL FORCES

Note: At least one Alpinist class (see AGIs) has been modified as a patrol craft.

13 MATKA CLASS (TYPE 206MP)
(FAST ATTACK CRAFT—MISSILE HYDROFOIL)

Displacement, tons: 225 standard; 260 full load
Dimensions, feet (metres): 129.9 × 24.9 (41 over foils) × 6.9 (13.1 over foils)
   (39.6 × 7.6 (12.5) × 2.1 (4))
Main machinery: 3 Type M 504 diesels; 10 800 hp(m) *(7.94 MW)* sustained; 3 shafts
Speed, knots: 40. **Range, miles:** 600 at 35 kts foilborne; 1500 at 14 kts hullborne
Complement: 33

Missiles: SSM: 2 SS-N-2C Styx; active radar or IR homing to 83 km *(45 nm)* at 0.9 Mach; warhead 513 kg; sea-skimmer at end of run.
   8 SS-N-25 (in one of the class); radar homing to 130 km *(70.2 nm)* at 0.9 Mach; warhead 145 kg; sea-skimmer.
Guns: 1—3 in *(76 mm)*/60; 85° elevation; 120 rounds/minute to 15 km *(8 nm)*; weight of shell 7 kg.
   1—30 mm/65 AK 630; 6 barrels per mounting; 3000 rounds/minute to 2 km.
Countermeasures: Decoys: 2—16-barrelled chaff launchers.
ESM: Radar warning.
Radars: Air/surface search: Plank Shave; E band.
   Navigation: Cheese Cake; I band.
   Fire control: Bass Tilt; H/I band.
IFF: High Pole B or Salt Pot B and Square Head.

Programmes: In early 1978 the first of class was seen. Built at Kolpino Yard, Leningrad. Production stopped in 1983 being superseded by Tarantul class. Type name is *raketny kater* meaning missile cutter.
Structure: Similar hull to the Osa class with similar single hydrofoil system to Turya class. The combination has produced a better sea-boat than the Osa class. One of the class is the trials craft for the SS-N-25 first seen in 1988 in the German prototype Sassnitz class but removed when the GDR was reunited with Germany. Also being fitted in modernised Krivak Is, Neustrashimy and Udaloy II classes.
Operational: Based in the Baltic and Black Seas. Some may be fitted with quadruple SA-N-5 systems. Three deleted in 1992.

MATKA   7/1993, Hartmut Ehlers

6 OSA I (TYPE 205) and 12 OSA II (TYPE 205M) CLASSES
(FAST ATTACK CRAFT—MISSILE)

Displacement, tons: 210 (245, Osa II) full load
Dimensions, feet (metres): 126.6 × 24.9 × 8.8 *(38.6 × 7.6 × 2.7)*
Main machinery: 3 Type M 503A diesels; 8025 hp(m) *(5.9 MW)* sustained; 3 shafts (Osa I)
   3 Type M 504 diesels; 10 800 hp(m) *(7.94 MW)* sustained; 3 shafts (Osa II)
Speed, knots: 35 (Osa I); 37 (Osa II). **Range, miles:** 400 at 34 kts (Osa I); 500 at 35 kts (Osa II)
Complement: 26 (3 officers)

Missiles: SSM: 4 SS-N-2A/B (Osa I); 4 SS-N-2B/C (Osa II); active radar or IR homing to 46 km *(25 nm)* at 0.9 Mach; warhead 513 kg. C has a range of 83 km *(45 nm)* and is a sea-skimmer at end of run.
   SAM: SA-N-5 Grail quad launcher (some Osa II); manual aiming; IR homing to 6 km *(3.2 nm)* at 1.5 Mach; altitude to 2500 m *(8000 ft)*; warhead 1.5 kg.
Guns: 4—30 mm/65 (2 twin); 85° elevation; 500 rounds/minute to 5 km *(2.7 nm)*; weight of shell 0.54 kg.
Radars: Surface search/fire control: Square Tie; I band.
   Fire control: Drum Tilt; H/I band.
IFF: High Pole A or B. Square Head.

Programmes: Osa I class built in first half of the 1960s and Osa II class in the latter half at a number of yards. Type name is *raketny kater* meaning missile cutter.
Structure: This class was a revolution in naval shipbuilding leading to a whole generation of fast missile patrol craft being built worldwide.
Operational: Although confined by their size and range to coastal operations the lethality and accuracy of the Styx missile were first proved by the sinking of the Israeli destroyer *Eilat* on 21 October 1967 by an Egyptian Komar class vessel. Nine deleted in 1988-89, 25 in 1990, eight in 1991, nine in 1992 and 11 in 1993.
Sales: Osa I: Algeria (three), Bulgaria (three), Cuba (five), Egypt (12—eight remaining), East Germany (15), India (eight), Iraq (four), North Korea (eight), Poland (14), Romania (six), Syria (six), Yugoslavia (10).
   Osa II: Algeria (nine), Angola (six), Bulgaria (three), Cuba (13), Ethiopia (four), Finland (four), India (eight), Iraq (eight), Libya (12), Somalia (two), Syria (10—six remaining), North Yemen (two) (subsequently returned), South Yemen (eight), Vietnam (eight). Many of both types have been deleted.

OSA II   1992, MoD Bonn

OSA I   7/1991

29 TURYA CLASS (TYPE 206M)
(FAST ATTACK CRAFT—TORPEDO HYDROFOIL)

Displacement, tons: 190 standard; 250 full load
Dimensions, feet (metres): 129.9 × 24.9 (41 over foils) × 5.9 (13.1 over foils)
   (39.6 × 7.6 (12.5) × 1.8 (4))
Main machinery: 3 Type M 504 diesels; 10 800 hp(m) *(7.94 MW)* sustained; 3 shafts
Speed, knots: 40 foilborne. **Range, miles:** 600 at 35 kts foilborne; 1450 at 14 kts hullborne
Complement: 30

Guns: 2—57 mm/80 (twin, aft); 85° elevation; 120 rounds/minute to 6 km *(3.3 nm)*; weight of shell 2.8 kg.
   2—25 mm/80 (twin, fwd); 85° elevation; 270 rounds/minute to 3 km *(1.6 nm)*; weight of shell 0.34 kg.
   1—14.5 mm MG.
Torpedoes: 4—21 in *(533 mm)* tubes. Type 53; dual purpose; pattern active/passive homing up to 20 km *(10.8 nm)* at up to 45 kts; warhead 400 kg or low yield nuclear.
Depth charges: 1 rack.
Radars: Surface search: Pot Drum; H/I band.
   Fire control: Muff Cob; G/H band.
IFF: High Pole B. Square Head.
Sonars: VDS; active search and attack; high frequency. Similar to Hormone dipping sonar. This sonar is not fitted in most export versions.

Programmes: The second class of hydrofoil with single foil forward (after Matka class). Has a naval orientation rather than the earlier Pchela class of the Border Guard. Entered service from 1972 to 1978—built at Petrovsky, Kolpino, Leningrad and Vladivostok. Basically Osa hull. Type name is *torpedny kater* meaning torpedo cutter. Production ended in 1987.
Operational: Some of the class have had the foils removed.
Sales: Two to Cuba 9 February 1979, two in February 1980, two in February 1981, two in January 1983 and one in November 1983; one to Ethiopia in early 1985 and one in March 1986; one to Kampuchea in mid-1984 and one in early 1985; one to Seychelles in April 1986 (no tubes or sonar); two to Vietnam in mid-1984, one in late 1984 and two in early 1986. Two to be transferred to Lithuania in 1993.

TURYA   8/1988, van Ginderen Collection

TURYA (foils removed)   7/1993, Hartmut Ehlers

2/3 T 58 PGF/PGR CLASS (PATROL SHIPS)

Displacement, tons: 790 standard; 860 full load
Dimensions, feet (metres): 229.9 × 29.5 × 7.9 *(70.1 × 9 × 2.4)*
Main machinery: 2 diesels; 4000 hp(m) *(2.94 MW)*; 2 shafts
Speed, knots: 17. **Range, miles:** 2500 at 13 kts
Complement: 82

Guns: 4—57 mm/70 (2 twin); 90° elevation; 120 rounds/minute to 8 km *(4.4 nm)*; weight of shell 2.8 kg.
4—25 mm/80 (2 twin) (in some); 85° elevation; 270 rounds/minute to 3 km *(1.6 nm)*; weight of shell 0.34 kg.
A/S mortars: 2 RBU 1200 5-tubed fixed; range 1200 m; warhead 34 kg (in PGF type).
Depth charges: 2 projectors.
Countermeasures: ESM: 2 Watch Dog.
Radars: Air search: Big Net; C band (PGR type).
Surface search: Spin Trough or Strut Curve; I band.
Navigation: One or two Don 2; I band.
Fire control: Muff Cob; G/H band.
IFF: Two Square Head. High Pole A or B.
Sonars: Tamir II; hull-mounted; active search and attack; high frequency.

Programmes: Built from 1957 to 1963, conversion to patrol ships in about 1975 with sweep winches, magnetic sweep cable reel and stern davit retained but without associated minesweeping gear. Originally fleet minesweepers with steel hulls. Of this class 16 were completed as submarine rescue ships with armament and sweeping gear removed, see later page (Valday class).
Modernisation: Three converted to radar pickets with Big Net radar in late 1970s and early 1980s. These ships had the A/S systems removed and have two SA-N-5 quad launchers fitted.
Operational: From a total of 18 in 1988, these are the survivors in 1994.

T 58/PGR   5/1990

32 PAUK I (TYPE 1241P) and 2 PAUK II (TYPE 1241PE) CLASSES (FAST ATTACK CRAFT—PATROL)

Displacement, tons: 520 full load
Dimensions, feet (metres): 195.2 × 33.5 × 10.8 *(59.5 × 10.2 × 3.3)*
Main machinery: 2 Type M 507 diesels; 14 400 hp(m) *(10.6 MW)* sustained; 2 shafts
Speed, knots: 32. **Range, miles:** 2400 at 14 kts
Complement: 32

Missiles: SAM: SA-N-5 Grail quad launcher; manual aiming; IR homing to 6 km *(3.2 nm)* at 1.5 Mach; altitude to 2500 m *(8000 ft)*; warhead 1.5 kg; 8 missiles.
Guns: 1—3 in *(76 mm)*/60; 85° elevation; 120 rounds/minute to 15 km *(8 nm)*; weight of shell 7 kg.
1—30 mm/65 AK 630; 6 barrels; 3000 rounds/minute combined to 2 km.
Torpedoes: 4—16 in *(406 mm)* (Pauk I) or 4—21 in *(533 mm)* (Pauk II) tubes. For torpedo details see table at front of section.
A/S mortars: 2 RBU 1200 5-tubed fixed; range 1200 m; warhead 34 kg.
Depth charges: 2 racks (12).
Countermeasures: Decoys: 2—16-barrelled chaff launchers.
ESM: Radar warning.
Radars: Air/surface search: Peel Cone (Pauk I) or Positive E (Pauk II); E/F band.
Surface search: Kivach; I band.
Fire control: Bass Tilt; H/I band.
Sonars: Rat Tail; VDS (mounted on transom); active attack; high frequency.

Programmes: First laid down in 1977 and completed in 1979. Replacement for Poti class. In series production at Yaroslavl in the Black Sea and at Vladivostok until 1988 when the Svetlyak class took over. Type name is *maly protivolodochny korabl* meaning small anti-submarine ship. Overall numbers increased by two Pauk IIs, reported to be wearing Russian colours, perhaps while sales are still expected.
Structure: This appears to be an ASW version of the Tarantul class having the same hull form with a 1.8 m extension for dipping sonar. First three of class have a lower bridge than successors. A modified version (Pauk II) has a longer superstructure, two twin 533 mm torpedo tubes and a radome similar to the Parchim class built primarily for export.
Operational: 25 of the craft are operated by the Border Guard.
Sales: All Pauk II: First one to India in March 1989, second in January 1990, third in December 1990 and fourth in February 1991. One Pauk I to Bulgaria in September 1989 and a second in December 1990.

PAUK I   7/1993, Hartmut Ehlers

1 BABOCHKA (SOKOL) (TYPE 1141) and 2 MUKHA (TYPE 1145) CLASSES (FAST ATTACK CRAFT—PATROL HYDROFOIL)

ALEKSANDR KUNACHOVICH   + 2

Displacement, tons: 400 full load
Dimensions, feet (metres): 164 × 27.9 (33.5 over foils) × 13.1 (19.4 foils) *(50 × 8.5 (10.2.) × 4 (5.9))*
Main machinery: CODOG; 3 Type NK-12M gas-turbines; 23 046 hp(m) *(16.95 MW)* sustained; 2 diesels; 3 shafts
Speed, knots: 45
Complement: 45

Guns: 1—3 in *(76 mm)*/60 (in one only); 85° elevation; 120 rounds/minute to 15 km *(8 nm)*; weight of shell 7 kg.
2—30 mm/65 AK 630; 6 barrels per mounting; 3000 rounds/minute combined to 2 km.
Torpedoes: 8—16 in *(406 mm)* (2 quad) tubes. SAET-40; anti-submarine; active/passive homing to 10 km *(5.4 nm)* at 30 kts; warhead 100 kg.
Countermeasures: Decoys: 2—16-barrelled chaff launchers.
ESM: Radar warning.
Radars: Surface search: Peel Cone; E band.
Navigation: Don 2; I band.
Fire control: Bass Tilt; H/I band.
Sonars: Dipping sonar.

Programmes: First sighted 1977 in the Black Sea. Probably used for research and development. Two more of a modified type were completed in 1986 and 1987 at Feodosiya.
Structure: Features include a hydrofoil arrangement with a single fixed foil forward, large gas-turbine exhausts aft, and trainable torpedo mountings forward in Babochka and aft in Mukha.

BABOCHKA   1991

MUKHA   1990, S Breyer

18 + 3 SVETLYAK (TYPE 1041Z) CLASS (FAST ATTACK CRAFT—PATROL)

Displacement, tons: 370 full load
Dimensions, feet (metres): 164 × 29.5 × 11.5 *(50 × 9 × 3.5)*
Main machinery: 3 diesels; 20 000 hp(m) *(14.7 MW)*; 3 shafts
Speed, knots: 32. **Range, miles:** 2200 at 30 kts
Complement: 55
Missiles: SAM: SA-N-5 Grail quad launcher; manual aiming; IR homing to 6 km *(3.2 nm)* at 1.5 Mach; warhead 1.5 kg.
Guns: 1—3 in *(76 mm)*/60; 85° elevation; 120 rounds/minute to 15 km *(8 nm)*; weight of shell 7 kg.
1—30 mm/65 AK 630; 6 barrels; 3000 rounds/minute combined to 2 km.
Torpedoes: 2—16 in *(406 mm)* tubes; SAET-40; anti-submarine; active/passive homing to 10 km *(5.4 nm)* at 30 kts; warhead 100 kg.
Radars: Air/surface search: Peel Cone; E band.
Fire control: Bass Tilt; H/I band.
IFF: High Pole B; Square Head.

Comment: A class of attack craft for the Border Guard building at Vladivostok, St Petersburg and Yaroslavl. It complements the Pauks in the Pacific in place of the less seaworthy Muravey class. Series production after first of class trials in 1989, has risen to about three a year.

SVETLYAK   7/1993, Hartmut Ehlers

14 MURAVEY (TYPE 133) CLASS
(FAST ATTACK CRAFT—PATROL HYDROFOIL)

Displacement, tons: 180 standard; 230 full load
Dimensions, feet (metres): 126.6 × 24.9 × 6.2; 14.4 (foils) *(38.6 × 7.6 × 1.9; 4.4)*
Main machinery: 2 gas-turbines; 8000 hp(m) *(5.88 MW)*; 2 shafts
Speed, knots: 40. **Range, miles:** 950 at 28 kts
Guns: 1—3 in *(76 mm)*/60; 85° elevation; 120 rounds/minute to 15 km *(8 nm)*; weight of shell 7 kg.
1—30 mm/65 AK 630; 6 barrels; 3000 rounds/minute combined to 2 km.
Torpedoes: 2—16 in *(406 mm)* tubes; SAET-40; anti-submarine; active/passive homing to 10 km *(5.4 nm)* at 30 kts; warhead 100 kg.
Depth charges: 6.
Radars: Surface search: Peel Cone; E band.
Fire control: Bass Tilt; H/I band.
IFF: High Pole B; Square Head.
Sonars: VDS: active attack; high frequency; dipping sonar.

Comment: Built at Feodosya. First seen in 1983. Programme terminated in 1988 in favour of the Mukha class. Assigned to Border Guard.

MURAVEY   *1/1989, MoD Bonn*

MURAVEY   *9/1992*

98 STENKA (TYPE 205P) CLASS (FAST ATTACK CRAFT—PATROL)

Displacement, tons: 211 standard; 253 full load
Dimensions, feet (metres): 129.3 × 25.9 × 8.2 *(39.4 × 7.9 × 2.5)*
Main machinery: 3 Type M 517 diesels; 14 100 hp(m) *(10.36 MW)*; 3 shafts
Speed, knots: 37. **Range, miles:** 800 at 24 kts; 500 at 35 kts
Complement: 25 (5 officers)
Guns: 4—30 mm/65 (2 twin) AK 230.
Torpedoes: 4—16 in *(406 mm)* tubes.
Depth charges: 2 racks.
Radars: Surface search: Pot Drum or Peel Cone; H/I or E band.
Fire control: Drum Tilt; H/I band.
IFF: High Pole. 2 Square Head.
Sonars: VDS; high frequency; Hormone type dipping sonar.

Comment: Based on the hull design of the Osa class. Construction started in 1967 and continued at a rate of about five a year at Petrovsky, Leningrad and Vladivostok for the Border Guard. Programme terminated in 1989 at a total of 133 hulls. Type name is *pogranichny storozhevoy korabl* meaning border patrol ship. Some are beginning to be paid off.
Transfers include: Cuba, two in February 1985 and one in August 1985. Four to Cambodia in October 1985 and November 1987. Six transferred to Azerbaijan control in November 1992.

STENKA   *7/1993, Hartmut Ehlers*

34 + 2 ZHUK (TYPE 1400) CLASS (COASTAL PATROL CRAFT)

Displacement, tons: 39 full load
Dimensions, feet (metres): 78.7 × 16.4 × 3.9 *(24 × 5 × 1.2)*
Main machinery: 2 Type M 401B diesels; 2200 hp(m) *(1.6 MW)* sustained; 2 shafts
Speed, knots: 30. **Range, miles:** 1100 at 15 kts
Complement: 11 (3 officers)
Guns: 2—14.5 mm (twin, fwd) MGs. 1—12.7 mm (aft) MG.
Radars: Surface search: Spin Trough; I band.

Comment: Under construction since 1970. Building at three a year. Manned by the Border Guard. Export versions have twin (over/under) 14.5 mm aft.
Transfers: Algeria (one in 1981), Angola (one in 1977), Benin (four in 1978-80), Bulgaria (five in 1977), Cape Verde (one in 1980), Congo (three in 1982), Cuba (40 in 1971-88), Equatorial Guinea (three in 1974-75), Ethiopia (two in October 1982 and two in June 1990), Guinea (two in July 1987), Iraq (five in 1974-75), Kampuchea (three in 1985-87), Mauritius (two in January 1990), Mozambique (five in 1978-80), Nicaragua (eight in 1982-86), Seychelles (one in 1981, one in October 1982), Somalia (one in 1974), Syria (six in 1981-84), Vietnam (nine in 1978-88 (at least one passed on to Cambodia), five in 1990), North Yemen (five in 1978-87), South Yemen (two in 1975). Some have been deleted.

ZHUK   *7/1993, Hartmut Ehlers*

RIVER PATROL FORCES

Note: Attached to Black Sea and Pacific Fleets for operations on the Danube, Amur and Usuri Rivers, and to the Caspian Flotilla. Belong to the Maritime Border Guard.

23 YAZ (TYPE 1208) CLASS

Displacement, tons: 400 full load
Dimensions, feet (metres): 180.4 × 29.5 × 4.9 *(55 × 9 × 1.5)*
Main machinery: 2 diesels; 2 shafts
Speed, knots: 15. **Range, miles:** 1000 at 10 kts
Complement: 60
Guns: 2—115 mm tank guns (TB 62). Twin barrel rocket launcher on after deckhouse.
2—30 mm/65 AK 630; 6 barrels per mounting.
Mines: Laying capability.
Radars: Surface search: Square Tie; I band.
Fire control: Bass Tilt; H/I band.
Navigation: Don 2; I band.
IFF: High Pole B. Square Head.

Comment: First entered service in Amur Flotilla 1978. Building at Chabarovsk until 1987.

YAZ   *2/1991, A Pavlov*

8 VOSH CLASS

Displacement, tons: 190 full load
Dimensions, feet (metres): 140.1 × 20.7 × 3.3 *(42 × 6.3 × 1)*
Main machinery: 2 diesels; 2 shafts
Speed, knots: 18
Guns: 1—3 in *(76 mm)*/48 (tank turret). 1—30 mm/65 AK 630.
Countermeasures: 1 twin barrel decoy launcher.

Comment: Built in Pacific yards 1980-84.

VOSH   *1992, B Lemachko*

10 PIYAVKA CLASS

Displacement, tons: 150 full load
Dimensions, feet (metres): 126.3 × 20.7 × 2.9 *(38.5 × 6.3 × 0.9)*
Main machinery: 2 diesels; 2 shafts
Speed, knots: 14
Guns: 1—30 mm/65 AK 630; 6 barrels. 2—14.5 mm (twin) MG.

Comment: Built at Khabarovsk from 1979 to 1984. Amur Flotilla.

PIYAVKA   *1992, B Lemachko*

84 SHMEL (TYPE 1204) CLASS

Displacement, tons: 77 full load
Dimensions, feet (metres): 90.9 × 14.1 × 3.9 *(27.7 × 4.3 × 1.2)*
Main machinery: 2 Type M 50 diesels; 2200 hp(m) *(1.6 MW)* sustained; 2 shafts
Speed, knots: 25. **Range, miles:** 600 at 12 kts
Complement: 12 (4 officers)
Guns: 1—3 in *(76 mm)*/48 (tank turret). 2—25 mm/70 (twin) (later ships). 2—14.5 mm (twin) MGs (earlier ships). 5—7.62 mm MGs. 1 BP 6 rocket launcher; 18 barrels.
Mines: Can lay 9.
Radars: Surface search: Spin Trough; I band.

Comment: Completed at Kerch and Khabarovsk 1967-74. Some of the later ships also mount one or two multi-barrelled rocket launchers amidships. The 7.62 mm guns fire through embrasures in the superstructure with one mounted on the 76 mm. Can be carried on land transport. Type name is *artillerisky kater* meaning artillery cutter. Some have been scrapped.
Transfers: Four to Cambodia (1984-85).

SHMEL   *1992, B Lemachko*

1 COMMAND SHIP

SSV-10

Displacement, tons: 340 full load
Dimensions, feet (metres): 129.3 × 23 × 3.9 *(39.4 × 7 × 1.2)*
Speed, knots: 12
Guns: 2—40 mm saluting guns. 6—14.5 mm MGs (3 twin).

Comment: Support ship on the Danube for the river patrols. Built in 1940. May now belong to Ukraine.

SSV-10   *6/1991, van Ginderen Collection*

MINE WARFARE FORCES

Notes: (1) Some 40-50 craft of various dimensions, some with cable reels, some self-propelled and unmanned, some towed and unmanned are reported including the 8 m Kater and Volga unmanned mine-clearance craft. Some are attached to the Polnochny (MCM) ships, others may be used for wide deployment of magnetic sweeps. Both Mi-8 'Hip' and Mi-14 'Haze B' helicopters have carried out what may be acoustic and magnetic sweeping with small craft of the Volga type towed by a cable.
(2) The two experimental air cushion Pelikan class have been scrapped.

MINE CLEARANCE SWEEPS   *1990*

3 ALESHA (TYPE 317) CLASS (MINELAYERS)

PRIPYAT   VYCHEGDA   PECHORA

Displacement, tons: 3860 full load
Dimensions, feet (metres): 324.8 × 44.3 × 17.7 *(99 × 13.5 × 5.4)*
Main machinery: 4 diesels; 30 000 hp(m) *(22.4 MW)*; 2 shafts
Speed, knots: 24. **Range, miles:** 4000 at 16 kts
Complement: 150
Guns: 4—45 mm/70 (quad, fwd).
Mines: 400.
Radars: Surface search: Strut Curve; F band.
Navigation: Don 2; I band.
Fire control: Muff Cob; G/H band.
IFF: High Pole B.

Comment: In service since 1967. Fitted with four mine tracks to provide stern launchings. Also have a capability in general support role. Can act as netlayers. Type name is *zagraditel minny* meaning minelayer and the Russian name is the Alyosha Popovich class. One in each of the Northern, Pacific and Black Sea Fleets. *Vychegda* sighted in the Pacific in 1991 with Elint vans fitted forward of the bridge. Fitted with Army surplus guns.

VYCHEGDA   *12/1989, G Jacobs*

4 POLNOCHNY A (TYPE 770) and B (TYPE 771) CLASSES

Comment: Four of this class of LSMs (see *Amphibious Warfare* section for details) have been converted to carry large counter-mining charges on long chutes discharging over the stern on either side. These charges are laid in lines using a radio-controlled MCM craft to tow the charges into position before detonation. In one case these craft are carried on davits amidships and the remainder carry them on chutes aft.

POLNOCHNY B (MCM)   *1984, JMSDF*

2 GORYA (TYPE 1260) CLASS (MINEHUNTERS—OCEAN)

ZHELEZNYAKOV   + 1

Displacement, tons: 1130 full load
Dimensions, feet (metres): 216.5 oa; 200.1 wl × 36.1 × 10.8 *(66; 61 × 11 × 3.3)*
Main machinery: 2 diesels; 5000 hp(m) *(3.7 MW)*; 2 shafts
Speed, knots: 17
Complement: 80

Missiles: 2 SA-N-5 Grail quad launchers; IR homing to 6 km *(3.2 nm)* at 1.5 Mach; warhead 1.5 kg.
Guns: 1—3 in *(76 mm)*/60; 85° elevation; 120 rounds/minute to 15 km *(8 nm)*; weight of shell 7 kg.
1—30 mm/65 AK 630; 6 barrels; 3000 rounds/minute to 2 km.
Countermeasures: Decoys: 2—16-barrelled chaff launchers.
ESM: Cross Loop; Long Fold.
Radars: Surface search: Palm Frond; I band.
Navigation: Nayada; I band.
Fire control: Bass Tilt; H/I band.
IFF: Salt Pot C. 2 Square Head.
Sonars: Hull-mounted; active search; high frequency.

Programmes: Both completed at Kolpino Yard, Leningrad, first in late 1986 and second in 1991.
Structure: Appears to carry mechanical, magnetic and acoustic sweep gear and may have accurate positional fixing equipment. A remote-controlled submersible is housed behind the sliding doors in the superstructure below the ADG gun mounting.
Operational: *Zheleznyakov* is conducting trials and training in the Black Sea. The second of class was reported to have conducted sea trials in 1992 and has remained in the Baltic.

ZHELEZNYAKOV   *8/1989*

30 NATYA I (TYPE 266M) and 1 NATYA II (TYPE 266ME) (MINER) CLASSES (MINESWEEPERS—OCEAN)

DIZELIST	MINER	STARSHKIY	SNAYPR
ELEKTRIK	MOTORIST	SIGNALSHIK	TURBINIST
POLEMETCHIK	RULEVOY	ZAPAL	ZENITCHIK
RADIST	DOBROTAY	ZARYAD	ARTILLERIST
NAVODCHIK	PARAVAN	TRAL	NAVODCHIK + 11

Displacement, tons: 770 full load
Dimensions, feet (metres): 200.1 × 31.8 × 8.9 *(61 × 9.7 × 2.7)*
Main machinery: 2 Type M 504 diesels; 7200 hp(m) *(5.3 MW)* sustained; 2 shafts
Speed, knots: 19. **Range, miles:** 4000 at 10 kts
Complement: 65

Missiles: SAM: 2 SA-N-5 Grail quad launchers (in some); manual aiming; IR homing to 6 km *(3.2 nm)* at 1.5 Mach; altitude to 2500 m *(8000 ft)*; warhead 1.5 kg; 16 missiles.
Guns: 4—30 mm/65 (2 twin); 85° elevation; 500 rounds/minute to 5 km *(2.7 nm)*; weight of shell 0.54 kg or 2—30 mm/65 AK 630; 6 barrels per mounting; 3000 rounds/minute combined to 2 km.
4—25 mm/80 (2 twin) (Natya I); 85° elevation; 270 rounds/minute to 3 km *(1.6 nm)*; weight of shell 0.34 kg.
A/S mortars: 2 RBU 1200 5-tubed fixed (Natya I); range 1200 m; warhead 34 kg.
Mines: 10.
Countermeasures: MCM: Carries two contact, two influence and one mechanical sweeps.
Radars: Surface search: Don 2 or Low Trough; I band.
Fire control: Drum Tilt; H/I band (not in all).
IFF: Two Square Head. High Pole B.
Sonars: Hull-mounted; active minehunting; high frequency.

Programmes: First reported in 1970, as successor to the Yurka class. Built at Kolpino and Khabarovsk. Construction for Soviet Navy ended in 1980 with Natya II although Natya I building continues for export. Type name is *morskoy tralshchik* meaning seagoing minesweeper.
Structure: Some have hydraulic gantries aft. Have aluminium/steel alloy hulls. Natya II was built without minesweeping gear to make way for a lengthened superstructure, the transom has been cut away amidships to take a 5 ft sheave. This is believed to be a minehunting version for research and development. Some have Gatling 30 mm guns and a different radar configuration without Drum Tilt.
Operational: Usually operate in home waters but have deployed to the Mediterranean, Indian Ocean and West Africa.
Sales: India (two in 1978, two in 1979, two in 1980, one in August 1986, one in 1987, three in 1988). Libya (two in 1981, two in February 1983, one in August 1983, one in January 1984, one in January 1985, one in October 1986). Syria (one in 1985). Yemen (one in 1991). Ethiopia (one in 1991).

NATYA I   6/1992

NATYA I   8/1992

NATYA II   5/1986, US Navy

20 YURKA (TYPE 266) CLASS (MINESWEEPERS—OCEAN)

GAFEL	NAVODCHIK	EVGENIY NIKONOV	SEMEN ROSAL	+ 16

Displacement, tons: 460 full load
Dimensions, feet (metres): 171.9 × 30.8 × 8.5 *(52.4 × 9.4 × 2.6)*
Main machinery: 2 Type M 503 diesels; 5350 hp(m) *(3.91 MW)* sustained; 2 shafts
Speed, knots: 17. **Range, miles:** 1500 at 12 kts
Complement: 60

Missiles: SAM: 2 SA-N-5 Grail quad launchers (in some); manual aiming; IR homing to 6 km *(3.2 nm)* at 1.5 Mach; altitude to 2500 m *(8000 ft)*; warhead 1.5 kg; 16 missiles.
Guns: 4—30 mm/65 (2 twin); 85° elevation; 500 rounds/minute to 5 km *(2.7 nm)*; weight of shell 0.54 kg.
Mines: 10.
Countermeasures: Fitted for wire, magnetic and acoustic sweeping. ESM: Watch Dog.
Radars: Surface search: Don 2 or Spin Trough; I band.
Fire control: Drum Tilt; H/I band.
IFF: Two Square Head. High Pole B.
Sonars: Stag Ear; hull-mounted; active minehunting; high frequency.

Programmes: A class of medium fleet minesweepers with aluminium/steel alloy hull. Completed from 1963 to 1972 at Kolpino and Khabarovsk. Type name is *morskoy tralshchik* meaning sea-going minesweeper.
Operational: One sank in the Black Sea after an explosion in August 1989. Being scrapped at about 10 per year.
Sales: Four to Egypt (1969), two to Vietnam (1979).

YURKA   7/1992

5 T 43 (TYPE 254) CLASS (MINESWEEPERS—OCEAN)

Displacement, tons: 500 standard; 580 (600 for 60 m ships) full load
Dimensions, feet (metres): 190.2 × 27.6 × 6.9 *(58 × 8.4 × 2.1)* (older units)
196.8 × 27.6 × 7.5 *(60 × 8.4 × 2.3)* (in later ships)
Main machinery: 2 Kolomna Type 9-D-8 diesels; 2000 hp(m) *(1.47 MW)* sustained; 2 shafts
Speed, knots: 15. **Range, miles:** 3000 at 10 kts; 2000 at 14 kts
Complement: 65

Guns: 4—37 mm/63 (2 twin); 85° elevation; 160 rounds/minute to 9 km *(5 nm)*; weight of shell 0.7 kg.
2 or 4—14.5 mm (1 or 2 twin) MGs.
Depth charges: 2 projectors.
Mines: 16.
Radars: Surface search: Ball End; E/F band.
Navigation: Don 2 or Spin Trough; I band.
IFF: Square Head. High Pole A.
Sonars: Stag Ear; hull-mounted; active minehunting; high frequency.

Programmes: Built in 1948-57 in shipyards throughout the Soviet Union. A number of this class was converted into radar pickets. Of the 200+ hulls built a number were also used as diving ships, tenders and patrol ships. Type name is *morskoy tralshchik* meaning seagoing minesweeper.
Structure: Steel hulls. The later version *(60 m* long) carries the additional four 25 mm guns and has a double-level bridge instead of the straight-up type in earlier ships.
Operational: Most of the survivors are in the Caspian Sea.
Sales: Algeria (two), Albania (two), Bulgaria (three), China (two), Egypt (seven), Indonesia (six), Iraq (two), Syria (two), 12 built in Poland for Polish Navy; one converted to a radar picket in late 1970s. Many of these had the 58 m hull and double-level bridges. Most deleted.

T 43   1981

2 ANDRYUSHA (TYPE 1256) (TOPAZ) CLASS
(MINESWEEPERS—COASTAL SPECIAL)

ALTAYSKIY   ESTONIY

Displacement, tons: 380 full load
Dimensions, feet (metres): 154.2 × 27.9 × 6.5 *(47 × 8.5 × 2)*
Main machinery: 2 diesels; 2200 hp(m) *(1.6 MW)*; 2 shafts
Speed, knots: 15. **Range, miles:** 3000 at 10 kts
Complement: 40
Guns: None.
Radars: Surface search: Spin Trough or Don 2; I band.
IFF: High Pole B.

Comment: First entered service in 1975. Probably built at Kolpino. Specially designed, possibly
with GRP hulls, for deep water magnetic sweeping. Possibly carry a gas-turbine generator. May
be trials ships as no more have been built and one has been paid off.

ALTAYSKIY   *9/1984, G Jacobs*

72 + 2 SONYA (TYPE 1265) CLASS
(MINESWEEPERS—HUNTERS/COASTAL)

Displacement, tons: 450 full load
Dimensions, feet (metres): 157.4 × 28.9 × 6.6 *(48 × 8.8 × 2)*
Main machinery: 2 Kolomna Type 9-D-8 diesels; 2000 hp(m) *(1.47 MW)* sustained; 2 shafts
Speed, knots: 15. **Range, miles:** 3000 at 10 kts
Complement: 43
Missiles: SAM: 2 quad SA-N-5 launchers (in some).
Guns: 2—30 mm/65 AK 630 or 2—30 mm/65 (twin) and 2—25 mm/80 (twin).
Mines: 8.
Radars: Surface search: Don 2; I band.
IFF: Two Square Head. High Pole B.

Comment: Wooden hull with GRP sheath. Still in series production at about two a year in St Petersburg and at Ulis, Vladivostok (Pacific). First reported 1973. Type name is *bazovy tralshchik* meaning base minesweeper. Some have two twin 30 mm Gatling guns, others one 30 mm/65 (twin)
plus one 25 mm (twin). Early models are being scrapped while new construction continues.
Transfers: Bulgaria, four in 1981-85. Cuba, four in 1980-85. Syria, one in 1986. Vietnam, one in
February 1987, one in February 1988, one in July 1989 and one in February 1990. Ethiopia, one
in February 1991.

SONYA (new guns)   *5/1990, MoD Bonn*

SONYA (old guns)   *1991, Ships of the World*

13 VANYA (TYPE 257D) and 2 MODIFIED VANYA (TYPE 257DM/DT) CLASSES (MINESWEEPERS—HUNTERS/COASTAL)

Displacement, tons: 250 full load
Dimensions, feet (metres): 131.2 × 23.9 × 5.9 *(40 × 7.3 × 1.8)*
Main machinery: 2 Kolomna Type 9-D-8 diesels; 2000 hp(m) *(1.47 MW)* sustained; 2 shafts
Speed, knots: 16. **Range, miles:** 1400 at 14 kts; 2400 at 10 kts
Complement: 30
Guns: 2—30 mm/65 (twin). 2—25 mm/80 (twin) (in conversions in place of 30 mm).
Mines: 8 (12 in Vanya II).
Radars: Surface search: Don 2. Don Kay (in conversions).
IFF: Square Head (unmodified). High Pole B.

Comment: A coastal class with wooden hulls of a type suitable for series production built from
1961-73. The normal Vanya class can act as minehunters. Three have been modified with superstructure extended forward, with 25 mm mounting on fo'c'sle in place of 30 mm, lattice mast at
break amidships and two boats stowed on quarter-deck. Guidance ships for Ilyusha class. Type
name is *bazovy tralshchik* meaning base minesweeper. Some 50 deleted since 1988. Remainder
in reserve.
Transfers: Six to Bulgaria (1970-85), two to Syria (1973) and one to Vietnam (November 1986).

VANYA (under tow)   *6/1992*

1 BALTIKA CLASS (MINESWEEPER—COASTAL)

Displacement, tons: 210 full load
Dimensions, feet (metres): 83.3 × 22.3 × 10.8 *(25.4 × 6.8 × 3.3)*
Main machinery: 1 ChISP 18/22 diesel; 300 hp(m) *(220 kW)*; 1 shaft; cp prop
Speed, knots: 9. **Range, miles:** 1400 at 9 kts
Complement: 10
Guns: 2—14.5 mm MGs (twin).
Radars: Navigation: Spin Trough; I band.

Comment: A trawler acquired in 1983 and converted for some form of MCM operations probably
to test the feasibility of rapid conversion of trawlers to the minesweeping role.

35 YEVGENYA (TYPE 1258) CLASS (MINEHUNTERS—INSHORE)

Displacement, tons: 77 standard; 90 full load
Dimensions, feet (metres): 80.7 × 18 × 4.9 *(24.6 × 5.5 × 1.5)*
Main machinery: 2 Type 3-D-12 diesels; 600 hp(m) *(440 kW)* sustained; 2 shafts
Speed, knots: 11. **Range, miles:** 300 at 10 kts
Complement: 10
Guns: 2—14.5 mm (twin) MGs or 2—25 mm/80 (twin) (in some later ships).
Radars: Surface search: Spin Trough; I band.
IFF: High Pole.
Sonars: A small sonar is lifted over stern on crane; a TV system may also be used.

Comment: GRP hulls. Production started in 1967 and completed in 1988 at Kolpino. Type name is
reydny tralshchik meaning roadstead minesweeper. 10 deleted so far. Some are painted a blue/
grey colour.
Transfers: Two to Angola (September 1987), three to Bulgaria (1976-77), 10 to Cuba (1977-82),
six to India (1983-84), three to Iraq (1975), three to Mozambique (1985-86), eight to Nicaragua
(1984-88), five to Syria (1978-86), three to North Yemen (May 1982-November 1987), three to
Vietnam (December 1986-November 1987), three to South Yemen in March 1990. Some
deleted.

YEVGENYA   *1991*

9 + 3 LIDA (TYPE 1075) CLASS (MINEHUNTERS—INSHORE)

Displacement, tons: 135 full load
Dimensions, feet (metres): 103.3 × 21.3 × 5.2 *(31.5 × 6.5 × 1.6)*
Main machinery: 3 diesels; 900 hp(m) *(690 kW)*; 3 shafts
Speed, knots: 12. **Range, miles:** 650 at 10 kts
Complement: 14
Guns: 2—30 mm/54 AK 230 (twin).
Countermeasures: MCM: Two acoustic and one contact sweeps; towed underwater TV.
Radars: Surface search: I band.
Sonars: Minehunting; high frequency.

Comment: A follow-on to the Yevgenya class started construction in 1989 at Kolpino Yard, Leningrad. Similar in appearance to Yevgenya. Building rate was about three a year to 1992 but has since slowed down. Some are painted a blue/grey colour.

LIDA   *5/1993*

10 OLYA (TYPE 1259) CLASS (MINESWEEPERS—INSHORE)

Displacement, tons: 64 full load
Dimensions, feet (metres): 84.6 × 14.9 × 3.3 *(25.8 × 4.5 × 1)*
Main machinery: 2 Type 3D 6S11/235 diesels; 471 hp(m) *(364 kW)*; 2 shafts
Speed, knots: 12. **Range, miles:** 500 at 10 kts
Complement: 15
Guns: 2—25 mm/80 (twin).
Radars: Surface search: Spin Trough; I band.

Comment: Built in mid-1970s. Type name is *reydny tralshchik* meaning roadstead minesweeper. One deleted in 1988-89 and one in 1991. Remainder based in the Baltic. Two to Bulgaria in mid-1970s.

OLYA   *8/1991, MoD Bonn*

3 TANYA CLASS (MINESWEEPERS—DRONES)

Displacement, tons: 73 full load
Dimensions, feet (metres): 87 × 13 × 5 *(26.5 × 4 × 1.5)*
Main machinery: 1 diesel; 270 hp(m) *(200 kW)*; 1 shaft
Speed, knots: 10
Radars: Surface search: Spin Trough; I band.

Comment: Built at Kolpino Yard. First operational in 1987, second and third in 1989/90. Probably designed to replace the Ilyusha class as radio-controlled drones but the programme seems to have stopped at three hulls.

TANYA   *1991*

7 ILYUSHA (TYPE 1376) CLASS (MINESWEEPERS—DRONES)

Displacement, tons: 85 full load
Dimensions, feet (metres): 86.6 × 19.4 × 4.6 *(26.4 × 5.9 × 1.4)*
Main machinery: 2 diesels; 500 hp(m) *(367 kW)*; 2 shafts
Speed, knots: 12. **Range, miles:** 300 at 10 kts
Complement: 10
Radars: Navigation: Spin Trough; I band.

Comment: First reported in 1966. Large foremast carrying electronic arrays. Capable of operating unmanned and radio controlled. (See Vanya class.) Three left in the Baltic and four in the Black Sea; the remainder scrapped.

ILYUSHA   *1980*

15 K 8 CLASS (MINESWEEPING BOATS)

Displacement, tons: 26 full load
Dimensions, feet (metres): 55.4 × 10.5 × 3.9 *(16.9 × 3.2 × 1.2)*
Main machinery: 2 Type 3-D-6 diesels; 300 hp(m) *(220 kW)* sustained; 2 shafts
Speed, knots: 18. **Range, miles:** 300 at 10 kts
Complement: 6
Guns: 2—14.5 mm (twin) MGs.

Comment: Built in Poland between 1954-59. Being deleted. Over half in reserve.
   Transfers: Two to Egypt (late 1960s), four to Nicaragua (1984), five to Vietnam (October 1980).

K 8

AMPHIBIOUS FORCES

9 VYDRA (TYPE 106K) CLASS (LCUs)

Displacement, tons: 550 full load
Dimensions, feet (metres): 179.7 × 25.3 × 6.6 *(54.8 × 7.7 × 2)*
Main machinery: 2 Type 3-D-12 diesels; 600 hp(m) *(440 kW)* sustained; 2 shafts
Speed, knots: 12. **Range, miles:** 2500 at 10 kts
Complement: 20
Military lift: 3 MBTs or 200 tons or 100 troops
Radars: Navigation: Don 2; I band.

Comment: Built from 1967-69 to a German MFP design. No armament.
   Transfers: 19 to Bulgaria, 10 to Egypt. Some employed as YF transports.

VYDRA   *5/1993, Alexander Mladenov*

3 IVAN ROGOV (TYPE 1174) CLASS (LPDs)

IVAN ROGOV   ALEKSANDR NIKOLAEV   MITROFAN MOSKALENKO

Displacement, tons: 12 600 full load
Dimensions, feet (metres): 518.2 × 80.2 × 21.2 (27.8 flooded)
(158 × 24.5 × 6.5 (8.5))
Main machinery: 2 gas-turbines; 48 000 hp(m) *(35.3 MW)*;
2 shafts
Speed, knots: 25. **Range, miles:** 4000 at 18 kts
Complement: 250
Military lift: 522 troops (battalion); 20 tanks or equivalent weight
of APCs and trucks; 2 Lebed class ACVs and 1 Ondatra class
LCM in docking bay

Missiles: SAM: SA-N-4 Gecko twin launcher ❶; semi-active radar
homing to 15 km *(8 nm)* at 2.5 Mach; warhead 50 kg; altitude
9.1-3048 m *(30-10 000 ft)*; 20 missiles.
2 SA-N-5 Grail quad launchers; manual aiming; IR homing to
6 km *(3.2 nm)* at 1.5 Mach; warhead 1.5 kg.
Guns: 2—3 in *(76 mm)*/60 (twin) ❷; 80° elevation; 60 rounds/
minute to 15 km *(8 nm)*; weight of shell 6.8 kg.
1—122 mm BM-21 (naval); 2 × 20-barrelled rocket launcher;
range 9 km *(5 nm)*.
4—30 mm/65 AK 630 ❸; 6 barrels per mounting; 3000
rounds/minute combined to 2 km.
Countermeasures: Decoys: 4—10-barrelled chaff launchers.
ESM: 2 Bell Squat. 2 Bell Shroud.
Fire control: 2 Squeeze Box optronic directors ❹.
Radars: Air/surface search: Head Net C (first two); Half Plate
(third) ❺; 3D; E band.
Navigation: 2 Don Kay or 2 Palm Frond; I band.
Fire control: Owl Screech ❻; G band (for 76 mm). Two Bass Tilt
❼; H/I band (for 30 mm). Pop Group ❽; F/H/I band (for
SA-N-4).
CCA: Fly Screen ❾; I band.
IFF: High Pole B. Salt Pot B.
Tacan: 2 Round House ❿.

Helicopters: 4 Ka-29 Helix B ⓫.

Programmes: First launched in July 1977 having been built at
Kaliningrad. Second launched April 1982; third launched in
July 1989 and completed trials in March 1991. No more are to
be built. Type name is *bolshoy desantny korabl* meaning large
landing ship.
Structure: Has bow ramp with beaching capability leading from
a tank deck 200 ft long and 45 ft wide. Stern doors open into a
docking bay 250 ft long and 45 ft wide. A helicopter spot for-

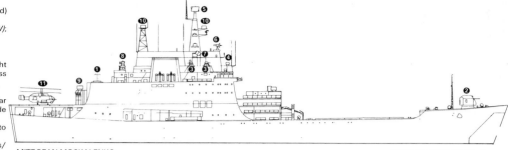

MITROFAN MOSKALENKO   *(Scale 1 : 1200), Ian Sturton*

MITROFAN MOSKALENKO   *10/1992*

ward has a flying-control station and the after helicopter deck
and hangar is similarly fitted. Helicopters can enter the hangar
from both front and rear. Positions arranged on main superstructure for replenishment of both fuel and solids.

Operational: First two are based in the Pacific and the last one in
the Northern Fleet.

25 ROPUCHA I (TYPE 775) and 3 ROPUCHA II (TYPE 775M) CLASSES (LSTs)

ALEKSANDR SHABALIN   KONSTANTIN OLSHANSKIY   TSESAR KUNIKOV   BOBRUISK

Displacement, tons: 4080 full load
Dimensions, feet (metres): 369.1 × 49.2 × 12.1
(112.5 × 15 × 3.7)
Main machinery: 2 Zgoda-Sulzer 16ZVB40/48 diesels;
19 230 hp(m) *(14.14 MW)* sustained; 2 shafts
Speed, knots: 17.5. **Range, miles:** 3500 at 16 kts; 6000 at
12 kts
Complement: 98
Military lift: 10 MBT plus 190 troops or 24 AFVs plus 170 troops
or mines

Missiles: SAM: 4 SA-N-5 Grail quad launchers (in at least two
ships); manual aiming; IR homing to 6 km *(3.2 nm)* at
1.5 Mach; altitude to 2500 m *(8000 ft)*; warhead 1.5 kg; 32
missiles.
Guns: 4—57 mm/80 (2 twin) (Ropucha I); 85° elevation; 120
rounds/minute to 6 km *(3.3 nm)*; weight of shell 2.8 kg.
1—76 mm/60 (Ropucha II); 2—30 mm/65 AK 630
(Ropucha II).
2—122 mm BM-21 (naval) (in some). 2 × 20-barrelled rocket
launchers; range 9 km *(5 nm)*.
Mines: 92 contact type.
Fire Control: 2 Squeeze Box optronic directors.
Radars: Air/surface search: Strut Curve or Cross Dome (Ropucha
II); F band.
Navigation: Don 2 or Kivach; I band.
Fire control: Muff Cob (Ropucha I); G/H band.
Bass Tilt (Ropucha II); H/I band.
IFF: Two High Pole A or Salt Pot A.

Programmes: Ropucha Is completed at Northern Shipyard,
Gdansk, Poland in two spells from 1974-78 (12 ships) and
1980-88. Ropucha IIs started building in 1987 with the first
one commissioning in May 1990. The third and last of the class
completed in January 1992. Type name is *bolshoy desantny
korabl* meaning large landing ship.
Structure: A 'roll-on-roll-off' design with a tank deck running the
whole length of the ship. All have very minor differences in
appearance. These ships have a higher troop-to-vehicle ratio
than the Alligator class. At least five of the class have rocket

ROPUCHA II (with 76 mm gun and 30 mm ADGs)   *12/1992, 92 Wing RAAF*

launchers at the after end of the forecastle. The second type
have a 76 mm gun forward in place of one twin 57 mm and an
ADG aft instead of the second. Radar and EW suites are also
different. The after mast has been replaced by a solid extension
to the superstructure. One Ropucha II has a masthead radome
possibly with a Positive E radar underneath it.

Operational: Distributed between the four Fleets. Only four
appear to show names.
Sales: One to South Yemen in 1979, returned to Russia in late
1991 for refit and was back in Aden in 1993.

ROPUCHA I (with 57 mm guns)   *5/1993*

12 ALLIGATOR (TYPE 1170/1171) CLASS (LSTs)

Type 1	Type 2	Type 3	Type 4
KRIMSKY KOMSOMOLETS	SERGEY LAZO	ALEKSANDR TORTSEV	NIKOLAY FILCHENKOV
TOMSKY KOMSOMOLETS	+ 1	PETR ILICHEV	NIKOLAY VILKOV
VORONEZHSKY KOMSOMOLETS		50 LET SHEFTSVA VLKSM	
KOMSOMOLETS KARELY		ILYA AZAROV	

Displacement, tons: 3400 standard; 4700 full load
Dimensions, feet (metres): 370.7 × 50.8 × 14.7
  (113 × 15.5 × 4.5)
Main machinery: 2 diesels; 9000 hp(m) *(6.6 MW)*; 2 shafts
Speed, knots: 18. **Range, miles:** 10 000 at 15 kts
Complement: 100
Military lift: 300 troops; 1700 tons including about 20 tanks and
  various trucks; 40 AFVs

Missiles: SAM: 3 SA-N-5 Grail twin launchers with 24 missiles in
  all ships except *Komsomolets Karely, Sergey Lazo* and *Donet-
  sky Shakhter.*
  2 SA-N-5 Grail twin launchers *(Petr Ilichev)*; manual aiming; IR
  homing to 6 km *(3.2 nm)* at 1.5 Mach; altitude to 2500 m
  (8000 ft); warhead 1.5 kg; 16 missiles.
Guns: 2—57 mm/70 (twin); 85° elevation; 120 rounds/minute
  to 8 km *(4.4 nm)*; weight of shell 2.8 kg.
  4—25 mm/80 (2 twin) (Type 4); 85° elevation; 270 rounds/
  minute to 3 km *(1.6 nm)*; weight of shell 0.34 kg.
  1—122 mm BM-21; 2 × 20-barrelled rocket launchers (in last
  seven); range 9 km *(5 nm).*
Fire control: 1 Squeeze Box optronic director (Types 3 and 4).
Radars: Surface search: Two Don 2 or Don 2 and Spin Trough (in
  two Type 1); I band.
  Don 2 *(Krimsky Komsomolets)*; I band.

Programmes: First ship commissioned in 1966 at Kaliningrad.
  Last of class completed in 1976. Type name is *bolshoy
  desantny korabl* meaning large landing ship.
Structure: These ships have ramps on the bow and stern. There
  are four variations of rig. In Type 1 two cranes are carried—
  other types have only one crane. In Type 3 the bridge structure
  has been raised and a forward deck house has been added to
  accommodate shore bombardment rocket launchers. Type 4 is
  similar to Type 3 with the addition of two twin 25 mm gun
  mountings on centre-line abaft the bridge superstructure. As
  well as a tank deck 300 ft long stretching right across the hull
  there are two smaller deck areas and a hold.
Operational: In the 1980s the class operated regularly off West
  Africa, in the Mediterranean and in the Indian Ocean, usually
  with Naval Infantry units embarked. Two of the Type 3s were
  deleted in 1992. At least one unit was in the Baltic in 1993.

NIKOLAY VILKOV (Type 4)   *1993, Ships of the World*

SERGEY LAZO (Type 2)   *1991, Ships of the World*

29 POLNOCHNY CLASS (10 GROUP A (TYPE 770), 16 GROUP B (TYPE 771), 3 GROUP C (TYPE 773)) (LSMs)

Displacement, tons: 750 standard; 800 full load (Group A)
  760 standard; 834 full load (Group B)
  1120 standard; 1150 full load (Group C)
Dimensions, feet (metres): 239.5 × 27.9 × 5.8
  (73 × 8.5 × 1.8) (Group A)
  246.1 × 31.5 × 7.5 *(75 × 9.6 × 2.3)* (Group B)
  266.7 × 31.8 × 7.9 *(81.3 × 9.7 × 2.4)* (Group C)
Main machinery: 2 Kolomna Type 40-D diesels; 4400 hp(m)
  (3.2 MW) sustained; 2 shafts
Speed, knots: 19; 18 (Group C). **Range, miles:** 1000 at 18 kts
  (Groups A and B); 900 at 17 kts (Group C); 2000 at 12 kts
  (Group C)
Complement: 40-42
Military lift: 180 troops; 350 tons including 6 tanks

Missiles: SAM: 2 SA-N-5 Grail quad launchers (Group A); manual
  aiming; IR homing to 6 km *(3.2 nm)* at 1.5 Mach; altitude to
  2500 m *(8000 ft)*; warhead 1.5 kg; 16 missiles.
  4 SA-N-5 Grail quad launchers (Groups B and C); manual aiming; IR homing to 6 km *(3.2 nm)* at 1.5 Mach; altitude to
  2500 m *(8000 ft)*; warhead 1.5 kg; 32 missiles.
Guns: 2—30 mm (twin) (in one ship) (Group A).
  2 or 4—30 mm (1 or 2 twin) (Group B). 4—30 mm (2 twin)
  (Group C).
  2—140 mm rocket launchers (Groups A, B and C); 18 barrels.
Fire control: PED-1 system.
Radars: Surface search: Spin Trough; I band.
  Fire control: Drum Tilt; H/I band (for 30 mm guns).
IFF: High Pole A. Square Head.

Programmes: All Soviet ships built in Poland, Group A in
  1963-68, Group B in 1968-70 and Group C in 1970-74. Many
  of Group A are unarmed. Group D are export models for Iraq,

POLNOCHNY A   *1991, MoD Bonn*

Libya and India built later than the others. Soviet type name is
stredny desantny korabl meaning medium landing ship.
Another four of the class (probably from Group B) have been
converted for MCM operations (see *Mine Warfare* section).
Structure: Have bow ramps only. Tank decks vary considerably
in size between groups—Group A, 36.9 × 5.2 m *(120 × 17 ft)*;
Group B, 45.7 × 5.2 m *(150 × 17 ft)*; Group C, 53.3 × 6.7 m
(175 × 22 ft). Group D have a helicopter landing platform
amidships.

Operational: Many of the earlier units are being paid off.
Sales: From Navy: Algeria (one), Angola (three), Bulgaria (two),
  Cuba (two), Egypt (three), Ethiopia (two), Somalia (one), Syria
  (three), Vietnam (three), Yemen (three). All Type A or B. From
  Poland: India (eight), Indonesia (one), Iraq (four), Libya (four).
  All Type D. Of these some have been deleted. In addition 23
  built for the Polish Navy, most of which have been scrapped.

POLNOCHNY C   *4/1992*

14 ONDATRA (TYPE 1176) CLASS (LCMs)

Displacement, tons: 145 full load
Dimensions, feet (metres): 78.7 × 16.4 × 4.9 *(24 × 5 × 1.5)*
Main machinery: 1 diesel; 300 hp(m) *(220 kW)*
Speed, knots: 10. **Range, miles:** 500 at 5 kts
Military lift: 1 MBT

Comment: First completed in 1979—associated with *Ivan Rogov*. Tank deck of 45 × 13 ft. Two to
    Yemen in 1983.

ONDATRA   *7/1993, Hartmut Ehlers*

8 + 2 POMORNIK (ZUBR) (TYPE 1232) CLASS (ACV)

Displacement, tons: 550 full load
Dimensions, feet (metres): 189 × 70.5 *(57.6 × 21.5)*
Main machinery: 5 Type NK-12MV gas-turbines; 2 for lift, 23 672 hp(m) *(17.4 MW)* nominal; 3 for
    drive, 35 508 hp(m) *(26.1 MW)* nominal
Speed, knots: 60. **Range, miles:** 300 at 55 kts
Complement: 31
Military lift: 3 MBT or 10 APC plus 310 troops (total 130 tons)
Missiles: SAM: 2 SA-N-5 Grail quad launchers; manual aiming; IR homing to 6 km *(3.2 nm)* at
    1.5 Mach; altitude to 2500 m *(8000 ft)*; warhead 1.5 kg.
Guns: 2—30 mm/65 AK 630; 6 barrels per mounting; 3000 rounds/minute combined to 2 km.
    2 retractable 122 mm rocket launchers (not in first of class).
Fire control: Quad Look (modified Squeeze Box) optronic director.
Radars: Air/surface search: Kivach II or Cross Dome; I band.
Fire control: Bass Tilt; H/I band.
IFF: Salt Pot A/B; High Pole A.

Comment: First of class delivered 1986, commissioned in 1988. Produced at St Petersburg and at
    Feodosiya. Bow and stern ramps for ro-ro working. Split between the Black Sea and Baltic Fleets.
    The Black Sea units have a different radar, and at least one (third of class *Donets*) is claimed by
    Ukraine.

POMORNIK (with Cross Dome)   *7/1993, Hartmut Ehlers*

POMORNIK (with Kivach II and rocket launchers raised)   *1992, S S Breyer*

9 TSAPLYA (TYPE 1206.1) CLASS (ACV)

Displacement, tons: 150 full load
Dimensions, feet (metres): 102.4 × 42.6 *(31.2 × 13)*
Main machinery: 2 gas-turbines; 8000 hp(m) *(5.88 MW)*; 2 shafts
Speed, knots: 55. **Range, miles:** 200 at 55 kts
Complement: 6
Military lift: 1 MBT plus 80 troops or 24 tons plus 160 troops
Guns: 2—30 mm/65 AK 630. 8—14.5 mm MGs (4 twin).

Comment: Prototype built at Feodosiya entered service in 1982, second in 1987, and then at about
    one a year. Follow-on to the Lebed class and has replaced the Gus class. Embarked in Ivan Rogov
    class.

TSAPLYA   *1989*

16 LEBED (KALMAR) (TYPE 1206) CLASS (ACV)

Displacement, tons: 87 full load
Dimensions, feet (metres): 80.1 × 36.7 *(24.4 × 11.2)*
Main machinery: 2 Ivchenko AI-20K gas-turbines for lift and propulsion; 8000 hp(m) *(5.88 MW)*
Speed, knots: 50. **Range, miles:** 100 at 50 kts
Complement: 6 (2 officers)
Military lift: 2 light tanks or 40 tons cargo or 120 troops
Guns: 2—30 mm (twin) MGs.
Radars: Navigation: Kivach; I band.

Comment: First entered service 1975. At least two can be carried in Ivan Rogov class. Have a bow
    ramp with gun on starboard side and the bridge to port. Three scrapped in 1992. The Russian
    name for the class is shared with the Delta III SSBN.

LEBED   *9/1991*

2 UTENOK (TYPE 1209) CLASS (ACV)

Displacement, tons: 70 full load
Dimensions, feet (metres): 75.4 × 36.1 *(23 × 11)*
Main machinery: 1 gas-turbine; 530 hp(m) *(390 kW)*; 2 airscrews
Speed, knots: 65
Military lift: 1 MBT or 24 tons plus 80 troops
Guns: 2—30 mm/65 (twin).
Radars: Surface search: Kivach; I band.

Comment: Completed at Feodosiya in 1980-81.

UTENOK   *1990, B Lemachko*

6 GUS (SKAT) (TYPE 1205) CLASS (ACV)

Displacement, tons: 27 full load
Dimensions, feet (metres): 67.6 × 24 *(20.6 × 7.3)*
Main machinery: 2 TVD-10 marine gas-turbines; 1560 hp(m) *(1.15 MW)* (propulsion); 1 TVD-10
    marine gas-turbine; 780 hp(m) *(573 kW)* (lift)
Speed, knots: 60. **Range, miles:** 230 at 43 kts; 185 at 50 kts
Complement: 6
Military lift: 70 tons or 25 troops and equipment

Comment: Completed 1969-1974. This is a naval version of a passenger carrying design *(Skate)*.
    Built for Naval Infantry. Deployed to all fleets except Northern. Probably non-operational and in
    reserve.

GUS   *9/1981, Royal Danish Navy*

14 AIST (DZHEYRAN) (TYPE 1232) CLASS (ACV)

Displacement, tons: 275 full load
Dimensions, feet (metres): 155.2 × 58.4 *(47.3 × 17.8)*
Main machinery: 2 Type NK-12M gas turbines driving four axial lift fans and four propeller units for propulsion; 19 200 hp(m) *(14.1 MW)* nominal
Speed, knots: 70. **Range, miles:** 120 at 50 kts
Complement: 10
Military lift: 80 tons or 4 light tanks plus 50 troops or 2 medium tanks plus 200 troops or 3 APCs plus 100 troops
Guns: 4—30 mm/65 (2 twin) AK 630; 6 barrels per mounting; 3000 rounds/minute combined to 2 km.
Radars: Surface search: Kivach; I band.
Fire control: Drum Tilt; H/I band.
IFF: High Pole B. Square Head.

Comment: First produced at Leningrad in 1970, subsequent production at rate of about six every four years. The first large hovercraft for naval use. Similar to British SR. N4. Type name is *maly desantny korabl na vozdushnoy podushke* meaning small ACV. Modifications have been done to the original engines and some units have been reported carrying two SA-N-5 quadruple SAM systems and chaff launchers. One scrapped in the Baltic in 1988, four more in 1993.

AIST   *7/1993, Hartmut Ehlers*

AIST   *7/1993, Hartmut Ehlers*

1 UTKA (LON) and 3 ORLAN (ORLENOK) (TYPE 904) CLASSES
(WING-IN-GROUND EFFECT CRAFT)

Displacement, tons: 125 full load
Dimensions, feet (metres): 190.3 × 103.3 *(58 × 31.5)*
Main machinery: 1 NK-12 gas turbine; 12 000 hp(m) *(8.82 MW)* (propulsion); 2 NK-8 gas turbines (lift)
Speed, knots: 250. **Range, miles:** 1200 at 250 kts
Complement: 5
Military lift: 28 tons or 150 troops with equipment

Comment: Details given are for the Orlan class which is an amphibious transporter. This type of craft takes advantage of the lift created between a wide wing and the ground at low altitude. On take-off the forward engines are angled down to generate initial lift. The first experimental craft dates back to the 1960s followed by two prototypes completed in 1982. *Utka* is 246 ft *(75 m)* in length and has a wing span of 134.5 ft *(41 m)*. Weight is 400 tons and has an operational radius of 1000 nm flying at an altitude of 5 m. There are eight turbofan engines and the craft is armed with six SS-N-22 anti-ship missiles. In service in 1989. This was an ambitious programme which is reported to have failed mainly because of corrosion problems associated with flying only 3-4 m above the sea surface. All these craft, and the associated technology, are for sale and have been demilitarised for civilian transport. One Orlan crashed during testing and a second was scrapped after an accident in the Black Sea in August 1992.

ORLAN   *1990*

INTELLIGENCE VESSELS (AGIs)

Notes: (1) About half the AGIs are fitted with SA-N-5 (Grail).
(2) SSV in pennant numbers of some AGIs is a contraction of *sudno svyazy* meaning communications vessel.
(3) GS in pennant numbers of some AGIs is a contraction of *gidrograficheskoye sudno* meaning survey ship.
(4) One Keyla class *(Ritsa)* converted to AGI in 1987. Details under Keyla class.
(5) Since 1991 activity has been largely confined to an area from the Baltic approaches to the Mediterranean, and occasional excursions to the South China Seas.

7 VISHNYA (TYPE 864) CLASS

SSV 169, SSV 175, SSV 201, SSV 208, SSV 231, SSV 520, SSV 535

Displacement, tons: 3470 full load
Dimensions, feet (metres): 309.7 × 47.9 × 14.8 *(94.4 × 14.6 × 4.5)*
Main machinery: 2 Zgoda 12AV25/30 diesels; 4406 hp(m) *(3.24 MW)* sustained; 2 auxiliary electric motors; 286 hp(m) *(210 kW)*; 2 shafts; cp props
Speed, knots: 16. **Range, miles:** 7000 at 14 kts
Complement: 146
Missiles: SAM: 2 SA-N-5 Grail quad launchers; manual aiming; IR homing to 6 km *(3.2 nm)* at 1.5 Mach; altitude to 2500 m *(8000 ft)*; warhead 1.5 kg.
Guns: 2—30 mm/65 AK 630; 6 barrels per mounting. 2—72 mm four-tubed rocket launchers.

Comment: Built in Poland. First of class entered service in July 1986, the last had completed by July 1988. *SSV 231* and *520* based in the Baltic, *SSV 175* and *201* in the Black Sea, *SSV 169* in the Northern Fleet and *SSV 208* and *535* in the Pacific. NBC pressurised citadels. Ice strengthened hulls.

SSV 169   *9/1993*

SSV 231   *3/1993*

4 BALZAM (ASIA) CLASS

SSV 80   SSV 493   SSV 516   SSV 571

Displacement, tons: 4000 standard; 5400 full load
Dimensions, feet (metres): 344.5 × 50.9 × 16.4 *(105 × 15.5 × 5)*
Main machinery: 2 diesels; 18 000 hp(m) *(13.2 MW)*; 2 shafts
Speed, knots: 20. **Range, miles:** 7000 at 16 kts
Complement: 200
Missiles: SAM: 2 SA-N-5 Grail quad launchers; manual aiming; IR homing to 6 km *(3.2 nm)* at 1.5 Mach; altitude to 2500 m *(8000 ft)*; warhead 1.5 kg; 16 missiles.
Guns: 1—30 mm/65 AK 630; 6 barrels per mounting.

Comment: All built at Kaliningrad. First of class completed in 1980, second in 1981, third in 1984 and last in 1987. Notable for twin radomes. The first class of AGI to be armed. *SSV 80* and *493* based in Pacific, the other two in the Northern Fleet.

SSV 493   *10/1991, G Jacobs*

6 PRIMORYE (TYPE 394) CLASS

ZABAYKALYE SSV 464	**ZAKARPATYE** SSV 502
PRIMORYE SSV 465	**KRYM** SSV 590
ZAPOROZHYE SSV 501	**KAVKAZ** SSV 591

Displacement, tons: 3400 standard; 5000 full load
Dimensions, feet (metres): 278 × 46 × 23 (84.7 × 14 × 7)
Main machinery: 2 diesels; 2000 hp(m) (1.47 MW); 2 shafts
Speed, knots: 12. **Range, miles:** 10 000 at 10 kts
Complement: 120
Missiles: SAM: 2 SA-N-5 Grail quad launchers (SSV 464, 501 and 591); manual aiming; IR homing to 6 km (3.2 nm) at 1.5 Mach; altitude to 2500 m (8000 ft); warhead 1.5 kg; 16 missiles. SSV 590 has 1 launcher.

Comment: The first custom-built class of AGIs and the first to have an onboard analysis capability. First unit built 1968-70 to the same hull design as the Mayakovsky class of stern trawlers. Mast arrangements and electronic fits vary between ships. SSV 464 and 465 in the Pacific, 501 and 502 in the North and 590 and 591 in the Black Sea. SSV 501 has a Mad Hack active phased array radar for the collection of missile related data and telemetry.

PRIMORYE   9/1992, Hachiro Nakai

ZAPOROZHYE   5/1992

ZAKARPATYE   1986, US Navy

KAVKAZ   6/1993

3 NIKOLAY ZUBOV CLASS

GAVRIL SARYCHEV (mod) SSV 468	**KHARITON LAPTEV** (mod) SSV 503
SEMEN CHELYUSKIN SSV 469	

Displacement, tons: 2674 standard; 3021 full load
Dimensions, feet (metres): 294.2 × 42.7 × 15 (89.7 × 13 × 4.6)
Main machinery: 2 Zgoda 8TD48 diesels; 4400 hp(m) (3.23 MW) sustained; 2 shafts
Speed, knots: 16.5. **Range, miles:** 11 000 at 14 kts
Complement: 85
Missiles: SAM: 3 SA-N-5 Grail quad launchers (SSV 468 and 469); manual aiming; IR homing to 6 km (3.2 nm) at 1.5 Mach; altitude to 2500 m (8000 ft); warhead 1.5 kg; 24 missiles.

Comment: Built in Poland. Similar class operates as research ships. SSV 468 and SSV 503 now have additional superstructure and a flush deck from bow to stern. Operational in 1965. SSV 468 and 469 in the Pacific, 503 in the Northern Fleet.

SEMEN CHELYUSKIN   8/1991, G Jacobs

1 MODIFIED PAMIR CLASS

PELENG (ex-Arban) SSV 477

Displacement, tons: 1443 standard; 2240 full load
Dimensions, feet (metres): 256 × 42 × 13.5 (78 × 12.8 × 4.1)
Main machinery: 2 MAN Giot 40/60 diesels; 4200 hp(m) (3.1 MW); 2 shafts; cp props
Speed, knots: 18. **Range, miles:** 21 000 at 12 kts
Complement: 60
Missiles: SAM: 3 SA-N-5 Grail quad launchers; manual aiming; IR homing to 6 km (3.2 nm) at 1.5 Mach; altitude to 2500 m (8000 ft); warhead 1.5 kg; 24 missiles.

Comment: Built in Sweden 1959-60. Originally a salvage tug and has higher deckhouse abaft bridge than other ships of class. Converted to AGI by 1965. Based in the Pacific.

PELENG   1985

3 LENTRA CLASS

GS 41	**GS 43** (mod)	**GS 55**

Displacement, tons: 250 standard; 480 (600, GS 43 and 55) full load
Dimensions, feet (metres): 128.6 × 24.3 × 9.2 (39.2 × 7.4 × 2.8)
  141.7 × 24.9 × 9.5 (43.2 × 7.6 × 2.9) (GS 43 and 55)
Main machinery: 1 diesel; 330 hp(m) (243 kW) (450 hp(m) (331 kW) in GS 43 and 55); 1 shaft
Speed, knots: 11. **Range, miles:** 6000 at 9 kts
Complement: 35; 45 (GS 43 and 55)

Comment: Built in USSR 1957-63. These last three are in the Black Sea and were inactive in 1992/93.

LENTRA   3/1988

9 MOMA (TYPE 861) CLASS

EKVATOR	**SSV 472** (ex-*Ilmen*) (mod)	**SSV 509** (ex-*Pelorus*) (mod)
YUPITER (mod)	**SSV 474** (ex-*Vega*) (mod)	**SSV 512** (ex-*Arkhipelag*) (mod)
KILDIN (mod)	**SSV 506** (ex-*Nakhodka*)	**SSV 514** (ex-*Seliger*) (mod)

Displacement, tons: 1240 standard; 1600 full load
Dimensions, feet (metres): 240.5 × 36.8 × 12.8 *(73.3 × 11.2 × 3.9)*
Main machinery: 2 Zgoda-Sulzer 6TD48 diesels; 3300 hp(m) *(2.43 MW)* sustained; 2 shafts
Speed, knots: 17. **Range, miles:** 9000 at 11 kts
Complement: 85
Missiles: SAM: 2 SA-N-5 Grail quad launchers (*SSV 472, 474, 514, Kildin* and *Yupiter*); manual aiming; IR homing to 6 km *(3.2 nm)* at 1.5 Mach; altitude to 2500 m *(8000 ft)*; warhead 1.5 kg; 16 missiles.

Comment: The six modernised versions have a foremast in the fore well-deck and a new, low superstructure before the bridge. Non-modernised ships retain their cranes in the forward well-deck. Similar class operates as survey ships. Built at Gdansk, Poland between 1968-72. *SSV 472* and *474* in the Pacific, named ships in the Black Sea, remainder Northern Fleet.

EKVATOR   *5/1991*

YUPITER   *1986, US Navy*

SSV 512   *7/1993*

5 ALPINIST CLASS

GS 7 (mod)	**GS 8**	**GS 19** (mod)	**GS 21** (mod)	**GS 39** (mod)

Displacement, tons: 1260 full load
Dimensions, feet (metres): 177.1 × 34.4 × 13.1 *(54 × 10.5 × 4)*
Main machinery: 1 SKL 8 NVD 48 A2U diesel; 1320 hp(m) *(970 kW)* sustained; 1 shaft; bow thruster
Speed, knots: 13. **Range, miles:** 7000 at 13 kts
Complement: 50
Missiles: SAM: 1 SA-N-5 Grail quad launcher *(GS 39)*; manual aiming; IR homing to 6 km *(3.2 nm)* at 1.5 Mach; altitude to 2500 m *(8000 ft)*; warhead 1.5 kg.
Guns: 2—25 mm M3 (twin) *(GS 21)*.
Torpedoes: 4—16 in *(406 mm)* tubes *(GS 21)*.
A/S mortars: 2 RBU 1200 *(GS 21)*.

Comment: Similar to Alpinist stern-trawlers which have been built at about 10 a year at the Leninskaya Kuznitsa yard at Kiev and at the Volvograd shipyard. These AGIs could come from either yard. In 1987 and 1988 *GS 7, GS 39* and *GS 19* forecastle was extended further aft and the electronics fit upgraded. In 1992 *GS 21* was fitted with guns, torpedo tubes and A/S mortars, and clearly has an ASW role. *GS 7* and *GS 8* in the Pacific, the other three in the Baltic.

GS 19   *7/1993, Hartmut Ehlers*

GS 21 (armed)   *7/1993, Hartmut Ehlers*

8 MAYAK CLASS

KHERSONES	**GS 239**
KURS	**GS 242**
KURSOGRAF	**GIRORULEVOY** (GS 536)
LADOGA	**ANEROID**

Displacement, tons: 914 full load
Dimensions, feet (metres): 178.1 × 30.5 × 11.8 *(54.3 × 9.3 × 3.6)*
Main machinery: 1 SKL 8 NVD 48 2U diesel; 880 hp(m) *(647 kW)* sustained; 1 shaft
Speed, knots: 16. **Range, miles:** 9500 at 7.5 kts
Complement: 75
Missiles: SAM: 2 SA-N-5 Grail quad launchers (in all except *GS 239, Girorulevoy* and *Khersones*); manual aiming; IR homing to 6 km *(3.2 nm)* at 1.5 Mach; altitude to 2500 m *(8000 ft)*; warhead 1.5 kg; 16 missiles.
Guns: 4—14.5 mm (2 twin) MGs (*Kursograf* only).

Comment: Built in the USSR from 1965. All ships except *Aneroid* have had additional accommodation built on the well-deck. The port side of the superstructure is enclosed while the starboard is open. *Kursograf* and *Aneroid* are in the Pacific, *GS 239, Kurs* and *Ladoga* in the Black Sea and remainder in the Baltic. More ships of the class are in the *Transports* section. This class may be about to be scrapped.

KHERSONES   *9/1992*

KURS   *5/1990*

9 OKEAN CLASS

EKHOLOT	LOTLIN (mod)*	TEODOLIT
KRENOMETR	REDUKTOR (mod)*	TRAVERZ
LINZA (mod)*	REPITER	ZOND (mod)*
* No missiles		

Displacement, tons: 750 full load
Dimensions, feet (metres): 167.3 × 28.9 × 12.1 *(51 × 8.8 × 3.7)*
Main machinery: 1 diesel; 540 hp(m) *(397 kW)*; 1 shaft
Speed, knots: 13. **Range, miles:** 7900 at 11 kts
Complement: 70
Missiles: SAM: 2 SA-N-5 Grail quad launchers (in some ships); manual aiming; IR homing to 6 km *(3.2 nm)* at 1.5 Mach; altitude to 2500 m *(8000 ft)*; warhead 1.5 kg; 16 missiles.

Comment: Built in East Germany from 1959 to mid-1960s. Have the same unbalanced superstructure with the port side closed in and the starboard side open as in the Mayak class, although there are many variations. Modified ships have additional accommodation on the well-deck. Three of the class scrapped in 1990-91, three more in 1993. *Lotlin, Reduktor* and *Zond* in the Baltic, and the remainder in Northern Fleet. More are due to be scrapped.

REDUKTOR (mod)   10/1992

LOTLIN (mod)   10/1992

SURVEY AND RESEARCH SHIPS

Note: Research submarines are listed at the end of the Submarine section.

2 SIBIRIYAKOV (TYPE 865) CLASS (AGS)

SIBIRIYAKOV	ROMAULD MUKLEVITCH

Displacement, tons: 3422 full load
Dimensions, feet (metres): 281.2 × 49.2 × 16.4 *(85.7 × 15 × 5)*
Main machinery: 2 Cegielski-Sulzer 12AS25 diesels; 6480 hp(m) *(4.44 MW)* sustained; 2 shafts; cp props
Speed, knots: 14. **Range, miles:** 11 000 at 14 kts
Complement: 58 plus 12 scientists
Guns: 1—30 mm (not carried).
Radars: 2 navigation: I band.

Comment: Built in Northern Shipyard, Gdansk 1990-92. Has a pressurised citadel for NBC defence, and a degaussing installation. Six separate laboratories for hydrographic and geophysical research.

SIBIRIYAKOV   6/1993, Erik Laursen

6 AKADEMIK KRYLOV (TYPE 856) CLASS (AGOR)

ADMIRAL VLADIMIRSKY	IVAN KRUZENSHTERN	LEONID DEMIN
AKADEMIK KRYLOV	LEONID SOBOLEV	MIKHAIL KRUPSKY

Displacement, tons: 9100 full load
Dimensions, feet (metres): 482.3 × 60.7 × 20.3 *(147 × 18.5 × 6.2)*
Main machinery: 2 diesels; 14 500 hp(m) *(10.7 MW)*; 2 shafts
Speed, knots: 20. **Range, miles:** 23 000 at 15 kts
Complement: 90
Radars: Navigation: Two Don 2; I band.
Helicopters: 1 Hormone.

Comment: Built in Szczecin 1974-79. Carry two survey launches and have 26 laboratories. *Krupsky* has a large radome abaft the foremast.

AKADEMIK KRYLOV   1992

4 ABKHAZIYA CLASS (AGOR)

ABKHAZIYA	ADZHARIYA	BASHKIRIYA	MOLDAVIA

Displacement, tons: 7500 full load
Dimensions, feet (metres): 409.2 × 56 × 21.1 *(124.8 × 17.1 × 6.4)*
Main machinery: 2 MAN K62 57/80 diesels; 10 500 hp(m) *(7.72 MW)*; 2 shafts; 2 bow thrusters
Speed, knots: 17. **Range, miles:** 20 000 at 16 kts
Complement: 105
Helicopters: 1 Hormone (not normally carried).

Comment: Built by Mathias Thesen Werft at Wismar. A modified Akademik Kurchatov class. Fitted telescopic hangar aft. Completed: 1971, *Abkhaziya;* 1972, *Adzhariya;* 1973, other two. Two survey launches are usually embarked. Vee Cone communications. Endurance, 60 days.

MOLDAVIA   7/1993, Hartmut Ehlers

3 POLYUS CLASS (KOVEL TYPE) (AGOR)

BAYKAL (mod)	BALKHASH (mod)	POLYUS

Displacement, tons: 6700 full load
Measurement, tons: 3897 gross; 1195 net
Dimensions, feet (metres): 365.8 × 46.2 × 20.7 *(111.6 × 14.1 × 6.3)*
Main machinery: Diesel-electric; 4 diesel generators; 1 motor; 3000 hp(m) *(2.2 MW) (Polyus)*, 3700 hp(m) *(2.72 MW)* (remainder); 1 shaft
Speed, knots: 14. **Range, miles:** 25 000 at 12 kts
Complement: 120

Comment: These ships are a part of the Andizhan class of some 45 ships. They were converted while building by Schiffswerft Neptun of Rostock. *Polyus* in 1962 and the other two in 1964. Oceanographic research ships. First two ships have modified superstructure with two king-posts on the fo'c'sle and several A-frame davits down each side. *Polyus* has been used to escort Kilo class submarines from the Baltic to Iran and may be transferred to Iran as a submarine depot ship in due course.

POLYUS   6/1993

1 MODIFIED DOBRYNYA NIKITICH CLASS (AGS)

VLADIMIR KAVRAYSKY

Displacement, tons: 3900 full load
Dimensions, feet (metres): 239.4 × 59.4 × 20 *(73 × 18.1 × 6.1)*
Main machinery: Diesel-electric; 3 Type 13-D-100 diesel generators; 2 motors; 5400 hp(m) *(3.97 MW)*; 2 shafts
Speed, knots: 14. **Range, miles:** 8000 at 13 kts
Complement: 60

Comment: One of a numerous class of icebreakers built at Leningrad since the early 1960s and built for polar research in 1970. Has helicopter deck aft, 8 ton crane on the after well-deck and two 3 ton derricks. Carries a survey launch. Has nine laboratories.

VLADIMIR KAVRAYSKY   1982

8 NIKOLAY ZUBOV (TYPE 850) CLASS (AGS)

ALEKSEY CHIRIKOV	FADDEY BELLINSGAUSEN	SEMEN DEZHNEV
ANDREY VILKITSKY	FEDOR LITKE	VASILY GOLOVNIN
BORIS DAVIDOV	NIKOLAY ZUBOV	

Displacement, tons: 2674 standard; 3021 full load
Dimensions, feet (metres): 294.2 × 42.7 × 15 *(89.7 × 13 × 4.6)*
Main machinery: 2 Zgoda-Sulzer 8TD48 diesels; 4400 hp(m) *(3.23 MW)* sustained; 2 shafts
Speed, knots: 16.5. **Range, miles:** 11 000 at 14 kts
Complement: 50

Comment: Oceanographic research ships built at Szczecin Shipyard, Poland in 1964-68. Also employed on navigational, sonar and radar trials. Have nine laboratories and small deck aft for hydromet-balloon work. Carry two to four survey launches. Ships of same class act as AGIs. The whole class varies marginally in appearance from ship to ship.

BORIS DAVIDOV   5/1993

18 YUG (TYPE 862) CLASS (AGS/AGI)

V ADM VORONTSOV (ex-*Briz*)	MANGYSHLAK	PLUTON	TAYGA
DONUZLAV	MARSHAL GELOVANI	SENEZH	VIZIR
GALS	NIKOLAY MATUSEVICH	STRELETS	ZODIAK
GIDROLOG	PEGAS	STVOR	SSV 704
GORIZONT	PERSEY		(ex-*SSV 328*)

Displacement, tons: 2500 full load
Dimensions, feet (metres): 270.6 × 44.3 × 13.1 *(82.5 × 13.5 × 4)*
Main machinery: 2 Zgoda-Sulzer Type 6TD48 diesels; 3300 hp(m) *(2.43 MW)* sustained; 2 auxiliary motors; 272 hp(m) *(200 kW)*; 2 shafts; cp props; bow thruster; 300 hp *(220 kW)*
Speed, knots: 15. **Range, miles:** 9000 at 12 kts
Complement: 46 (8 officers) plus 20 scientists
Guns: 6—25 mm/80 (3 twin) (fitted for but not with).

Comment: Built at Northern Shipyard, Gdansk 1977-83. Have a 4 ton davit at the stern and two survey craft. *Zodiak* has a large gantry aft. Others have minor variations around the stern area. *704* was converted in 1989 and now serves in the Northern Fleet as an AGI.

PLUTON   10/1992

1 MOD SORUM CLASS (AGE)

OS 572

Displacement, tons: 1660 full load
Dimensions, feet (metres): 190.2 × 41.3 × 15.1 *(58 × 12.6 × 4.6)*
Main machinery: Diesel-electric; 2 type 5-2-DW2 diesel generators; 1 motor; 2000 hp(m) *(1.47 MW)*; 1 shaft
Speed, knots: 14. **Range, miles:** 6750 at 13 kts
Complement: 35
Radars: Navigation: Two Nayada; I band.

Comment: A Sorum class tug built in 1987 at Yaroslavl and converted for acoustic trials. The built-up stern houses a winch and cable drum for a lengthy acoustic array which is deployed through the stern doors.

OS 572   1988, CHOD Norway

20 MOMA (TYPE 861) CLASS (AGS/AGE/AGI)

ALTAIR	ARKTIKA	KOLGUEV (AGE)	OKEAN (AGE)
ANADYR	ASKOLD	KRILON	RIBACHI (AGE)
ANDROMEDA	BEREZAN	LIMAN (AGI)	SEVER (AGE)
ANTARES	CHELEKEN	MARS	TAYMYR
ANTARKTYDA	ELTON	MORZHOVETS	ZAPOLYARYE

Displacement, tons: 1550 full load
Dimensions, feet (metres): 240.5 × 36.8 × 12.8 *(73.3 × 11.2 × 3.9)*
Main machinery: 2 Zgoda-Sulzer 6TD48 diesels; 3300 hp(m) *(2.43 MW)* sustained; 2 shafts; cp props
Speed, knots: 17. **Range, miles:** 9000 at 11 kts
Complement: 55
Radars: Navigation: Two Don 2; I band.
IFF: High Pole A.

Comment: Built at Northern Shipyard, Gdansk from 1967 to 1972. Some of the class are particularly active in ASW research associated operations. Four laboratories. One survey launch and a 7 ton crane. *Rybachi* has no crane but has an additional deckhouse forward. She also carries two twin 12.7 mm MG mountings and two SA-N-5 launchers. The AGEs are fitted with bow probes. *Liman* is used as an AGI and also has a bow probe. Ships of this class serve in the Bulgarian, Polish and Yugoslav navies.

RIBACHI (mod)   2/1992

CHELEKEN   9/1992, van Ginderen Collection

13 SAMARA (TYPE 860) CLASS (AGS)

AZIMUT	GLUBOMYR	TROPIK
DEVIATOR	GRADUS	VOSTOK
GIGROMETR	KOMPAS	VAYGACH (mod)
MOSKOVSKY UNIVERSITET	PAMYAT MERKURYIA	ZENIT
(ex-*Gorizont*) (mod)	RUMB	

Displacement, tons: 1000 standard; 1270 full load
Dimensions, feet (metres): 193.5 × 34.4 × 12.5 *(59 × 10.5 × 3.8)*
Main machinery: 2 Zgoda-Sulzer Type 6TD48 diesels; 3300 hp(m) *(2.43 MW)* sustained; 2 shafts;
cp props
Speed, knots: 15. **Range, miles:** 6200 at 10 kts
Complement: 45

Comment: Built at Northern Shipyard, Gdansk, 1962-64 for hydrographic surveying and research.
Have laboratories and one survey launch and a 5 ton crane. *Vaygach* has additional accommodation around the base of the crane and has been fitted with a bow probe. *Moskovsky Universitet*
is subordinated to the Academy of Sciences and has an extended superstructure forward and no
crane.

PAMYAT MERKURYIA   *4/1992, van Ginderen Collection*

2 MUNA CLASS (AGS)

GIROSCOP   UGLOMER

Displacement, tons: 690 full load
Dimensions, feet (metres): 165 × 26.9 × 9.5 *(50.3 × 8.2 × 2.9)*
Main machinery: 1 diesel; 300 hp(m) *(220 kW)*; 1 shaft
Speed, knots: 10. **Range, miles:** 3000 at 10 kts
Complement: 40

Comment: Converted transport ships. Others of the class in service as Auxiliaries.

GIROSCOP   *7/1993, Hartmut Ehlers*

24 FINIK (TYPE 872) CLASS (AGS/AGE)

GS 44, 47, 84, 86, 87, 260, OS 265, 270, 272, 278, 296, 297, 301, 388, 392, 397-405

Displacement, tons: 1200 full load
Dimensions, feet (metres): 201.1 × 35.4 × 10.8 *(61.3 × 10.8 × 3.3)*
Main machinery: 2 Cegielski-Sulzer 6AL25/30 diesels; 1920 hp(m) *(1.4 MW)*; auxiliary propul-
sion; 2 motors; 204 hp(m) *(150 kW)*; 2 shafts; cp props; bow thruster
Speed, knots: 13. **Range, miles:** 3000 at 13 kts
Complement: 26 (5 officers) plus 9 scientists

Comment: Improved Biya class. Built at Northern Shipyard, Gdansk 1978-83. Fitted with 7 ton
crane for buoy handling. Can carry two self-propelled pontoons and a boat on well-deck. Ships of
same class serve in the Polish Navy. *265* was redesignated *OS 265* in March 1990 and serves as
an AGE.

FINIK OS 265   *1991*

16 BIYA (TYPE 871) CLASS (AGS)

GS 182, 192, 193, 194, 198, 200, 202, 204, 206, 208, 210, 212, 214, 271, 273, 275

Displacement, tons: 750 full load
Dimensions, feet (metres): 180.4 × 32.1 × 8.5 *(55 × 9.8 × 2.6)*
Main machinery: 2 diesels; 1200 hp(m) *(882 kW)*; 2 shafts; cp props
Speed, knots: 13. **Range, miles:** 4700 at 11 kts
Complement: 25
Radars: Navigation: Don 2; I band.

Comment: Built at Northern Shipyard, Gdansk 1972-76. With laboratory and one survey launch
and a 5 ton crane.
  Transfers: One to Cuba in November 1980 (from Poland); one to Cape Verde in 1979.

GS 271   *3/1991, van Ginderen Collection*

13 KAMENKA (TYPE 870) CLASS (AGS)

GS 66, 74, 78, 82, 103, 107, 108 (ex-*Vernier*), 113 (ex-*Belbeck*), 118, 199 (ex-*Sima*), 207, 211,
ASTRONOM (mod)

Displacement, tons: 700 full load
Dimensions, feet (metres): 175.5 × 29.8 × 8.5 *(53.5 × 9.1 × 2.6)*
Main machinery: 2 diesels; 1800 hp(m) *(1.32 MW)*; 2 shafts; cp props
Speed, knots: 14. **Range, miles:** 4000 at 10 kts
Complement: 25
Radars: Navigation: Don 2; I band.
IFF: High Pole.

Comment: Built at Northern Shipyard, Gdansk 1968-72. A 5 ton crane forward. They do not carry a
survey launch but have facilities for handling and stowing buoys. In *Astronom* the deckhouse
below the crane is twice the length of that in other ships of the class.

GS 107   *6/1984*

2 DESNA CLASS (MISSILE RANGE SHIPS)

CHAZHMA (ex-*Dangara*)   CHUMIKAN (ex-*Dolgeschtschelje*)

Displacement, tons: 5300 light; 13 600 full load
Dimensions, feet (metres): 457.7 × 59 × 25.9 *(139.6 × 18 × 7.9)*
Main machinery: 1 MAN diesel; 5200 hp(m) *(3.8 MW)*; 1 shaft
Speed, knots: 15. **Range, miles:** 20 000 at 13 kts
Complement: 240
Countermeasures: ESM: 2 Watch Dog; radar warning.
Radars: Missile tracker: Ship Globe.
Air search: Head Net B; E band.
Navigation: Don 2; I band.
Helicopters: 1 Ka-25 'Hormone C'.

Comment: Formerly bulk ore-carriers of the Dshankoy class (7265 tons gross) built at Warnemunde. Range Instrumentation Ships. Active since 1963. Based in the Pacific. Two Vee Cone
communications aerials.

CHAZHMA   *7/1989, G Jacobs*

2 VINOGRAD CLASS (AGOR)

GS 525   GS 526

Displacement, tons: 980 full load
Dimensions, feet (metres): 108.3 × 23 × 6.6 *(33 × 7 × 2)*
Main machinery: 2 diesels; 2 motors; 1200 hp(m) *(882 kW)*; 2 trainable props
Speed, knots: 11.5
Complement: 30

Comment: Built by Rauma-Repola 1985-87 as hydrographic research ships.

NYRYAT 1 and 2 CLASSES

Comment: A number of these 120 and 55 ton classes (see *Auxiliaries* section for details) were built for inshore survey work using Nyryat hull and machinery. They carry GPB pennant numbers which are also used in the 7 ton survey launches carried in the larger ships.

2 SIBIR CLASS (MISSILE RANGE SHIPS)

SAKHALIN   SPASSK (ex-*Suchan*)

Displacement, tons: 7400 full load
Dimensions, feet (metres): 354 × 49.2 × 20 *(108 × 15 × 6.1)*
Main machinery: 2 boilers; Compound reciprocating engine; 2500 ihp(m) *(1.84 MW)*; 1 shaft
Speed, knots: 12. **Range, miles:** 9800 at 12 kts
Complement: 200
Radars: Air search: Head Net C; E band.
   Three smaller trackers forward of the bridge.
Navigation: Two Don 2; I band.
Helicopters: 1 Ka-25 'Hormone C' (no hangar).

Comment: Converted bulk ore-carriers employed as Missile Range Ships in the Pacific. *Sakhalin* has three radomes forward and aft. Launched in 1957-59. Formerly freighters of the Polish B 31 type (Donbas class). One of the class *Sibir* deleted in 1990 and *Chukotka* in 1991.

SAKHALIN   *11/1992, 92 Wing RAAF*

3 MARSHAL NEDELIN CLASS (2 MISSILE RANGE SHIPS and 1 AGOR)

MARSHAL NEDELIN   MARSHAL KRYLOV   AKADEMIK NICOLAI PILYUGIN

Displacement, tons: 24 000 full load
Dimensions, feet (metres): 695.5 × 88.9 × 25.3 *(212 × 27.1 × 7.7)*
Main machinery: 2 gas-turbines; 54 000 hp(m) *(40 MW)*; 2 shafts
Speed, knots: 20. **Range, miles:** 22 000 at 16 kts
Complement: 500
Radars: Air search: Strut Pair *(Nedelin)*; Top Plate *(Krylov)*.
Navigation: Three Palm Frond; I band.
Helicopter control: Fly Screen B; I band.
Space trackers: End Tray (balloons). Quad Leaf. Three Quad Wedge. Four smaller aerials.
Tacan: Two Round House.
Helicopters: 2-4 Ka-32 'Helix C'.

Comment: First completed at Admiralty Yard, Leningrad in 1983, second in 1989 and third was due to complete in 1993 but has been delayed. Fitted with a variety of space and missile associated electronic systems. Fitted for but not with six twin 30 mm/65 ADG guns and three Bass Tilt fire-control radars. Naval subordinated, the task is monitoring missile tests with a war time role of command ship. The Ship Globe radome is for SATCOM. The third ship of the class is to work for the Academy of Sciences under civilian control and has a different appearance from the other two.

MARSHAL NEDELIN   *3/1992*

2 KAMCHATKA CLASS (AGH)

KAMCHATKA SSV 679 (ex-391)   **SLAVUTICH** SSV 189

Displacement, tons: 6000 full load
Dimensions, feet (metres): 350.1 × 52.5 × 19.7 *(106.7 × 16 × 6)*
Main machinery: 2 diesels; 6100 hp(m) *(4.5 MW)*; 2 shafts
Speed, knots: 16
Complement: 178
Missiles: SAM: 2 SA-N-5 Grail quad launchers; manual aiming; IR homing to 6 km *(3.2 nm)* at 1.5 Mach; altitude to 2500 m *(8000 ft)*; warhead 1.5 kg.
Guns: 2—30 mm/65 AK 630. 6 barrels per mounting.
Radars: Navigation: 3 Palm Frond; 2 Shot Dome; I band.
CCA: Fly Screen; I band.
Tacan: 2 Round House.
Helicopters: 2 Ka-25 'Hormone C'.

Comment: *Kamchatka* launched at Nikolayev in August 1985, started trials in the Black Sea in September 1987 and then sailed for the Pacific at the end of the year. AGE stands for Auxiliary General Experimental. Pennant number indicates intelligence collection and as the large tower could house an acoustic device for lowering below the hull, this ship is most probably involved in VLF bi-static sonar trials similar to the type being tested in major Western navies. *Slavutich* was laid down in 1988 and commissioned in a still uncompleted state as the Ukrainian Flagship on 28 July 1992. The ship is similar to *Kamchatka* but had no tower on commissioning.

KAMCHATKA   *11/1987*

SLAVUTICH   *1993*

1 KAPUSTA CLASS

URAL SSV 33

Displacement, tons: 36 000 full load
Dimensions, feet (metres): 866.1 × 98.1 × 31.5 *(264 × 29.9 × 9.6)*
Main machinery: CONAS; nuclear; 2 PWR; 2 boilers; 4 turbines; 75 000 hp(m) *(55 MW)*; 4 shafts
Speed, knots: 27
Complement: 940
Missiles: SAM: 4 SA-N-10 mountings each with 4 IR-guided missiles derived from SA-16.
Guns: 2—3 in *(76 mm)*/60. 4—30 mm/65 AK 630. 8—14.5 mm (4 twin) MGs.
Countermeasures: ESM: Trawl Net; 2 Soup Cup; Cage Box; Cake Tin.
Fire control: 4 Tin Man and 4 Spot Pot optronic directors.
Radars: Air search: Top Plate; 3D; D/E band.
Air/surface search: 4 Mad Hack planar arrays.
Navigation: 3 Palm Frond; I band.
Fire control: Two Bass Tilt. Six Owl Perch (missile telemetry and tracking).
CCA: Fly Screen B.
Tacan: Two Round House.
IFF: 1 Long Head; 2 Salt Pot.
Sonars: Hull-mounted active/passive sonar; medium frequency.
Helicopters: 1 or 2 Ka-27 'Helix D'.

Comment: Laid down in May 1981 and launched in May 1983 at Baltic Yard, Leningrad. Did trials in the Baltic in 1987 and 1988, commissioning in August 1989 and sailing for the Pacific in September 1989. Has an extensive space associated electronic fit including Ship Globe (satellite tracking) and 1 Quad Leaf, 2 Low Ball and Punch Bowl for SATCOMs. Naval manned and heavily armed, the official description is *sudno suyazyy* meaning communications ship. As well as being a missile range control ship and having an intelligence gathering role monitoring other countries' missile tests, it also has obvious potential as a Flagship. The fourth planar array is mounted horizontally on the deck aft and to starboard of the midship's mast. Probable Kirov class hull. There is some doubt about the name.

URAL   *9/1989, 92 Wing RAAF*

CIVILIAN RESEARCH SHIPS

Notes: (1) There are some 180 ships ranging downward from 3200 tons engaged on fishery research worldwide. The larger ships are of the Mayakovsky, Tropik, Atlantik, Leskov and Luchegorsk classes of 3200-2400 tons. Two of the Mayakovsky class carry submersibles.
Research ships (also tugs, cargo ships, training ships) operating on behalf of the fishery ministries carry a form of pennant number. This usually consists of two letters followed by four numbers. The first letter indicates the port or area where the vessel is based, the second, the type of vessel and the numerals indicate a specific ship and are usually allocated consecutively to a particular class.
(2) In addition to the classes listed below there are several more, although some are converted trawler designs. New classes include Iscatel II and Svetlomar which are for civilian use.
(3) Some classes are not included because they are associated only with geophysical research. These include Bavenit, Tropik, Pulkovsky Meridian, Agat, Akademik Orbeli and Zarya.
(4) Activity since 1991 has been resource related with the Academy of Science ships looking for contract work. The Atlantic is the major operating area, with some ships being used to carry cargo or even to relay fishing crews.

Known letter allocations:

1st Letter		2nd Letter	
A/M	Murmansk	A	Fish factory
B	Novorossiysk	B/b	Large ST/FF
K	Kaliningrad	H	Tanker
L	Klaypeda	M	Fish factory-mother ship
M	Vladivostok	R	Fish carrier (small)
Q	Kerch/Sevastopol	T	Fish carrier (large)
C	Korsakov	Y	Tugs, rescue ship, icebreakers
		X	Cargo ship
		G	Large stern trawler
		W	Tuna factory ship

1 A A KRYLOV and 2 A N ANDREYEV CLASSES

AKADEMIK ALEKSEY KRYLOV   AKADEMIK NIKOLAY ANDREYEV
AKADEMIK BORIS KONSTANTINOV

Displacement, tons: 9920 full load
Dimensions, feet (metres): 406.7 × 55.8 × 23 *(124 × 17 × 7)*
Main machinery: 2 Type 58-D-6R diesels; 9000 hp(m) *(6.6 MW)*; 2 shafts; cp props
Speed, knots: 16. **Range, miles:** 10 000 at 16 kts
Complement: 117 plus 32 scientists *(Krylov)*; 90 plus 40 scientists *(remainder)*

Comment: Built at Nikolayev, *Krylov* for the Institute of Shipbuilding, *Andreyev* and *Konstantinov* for the Institute of Acoustics. *Krylov* carries a submersible in an internal compartment with doors in the port side and sailed on her maiden voyage in December 1982. *Andreyev* entered service in October 1986 and *Konstantinov* in March 1989; they have a different superstructure shape from *Krylov*. *Konstantinov* has a large stern door for streaming towed devices and with *Andreyev* has replaced the two Lebedev class ships for oceanographic acoustic research.

AKADEMIK BORIS KONSTANTINOV   *6/1993, van Ginderen Collection*

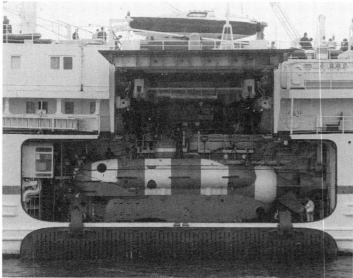

AKADEMIK ALEKSEY KRYLOV (Research Submarine)   *9/1990, Harald Carstens*

2 AKADEMIK SERGEI VAVILOV CLASS

AKADEMIK SERGEI VAVILOV   AKADEMIK IOFFE

Displacement, tons: 6600 full load
Dimensions, feet (metres): 383.9 × 59.7 × 19.4 *(117 × 18.2 × 5.9)*
Main machinery: 2 SEMT-Pielstick diesels; 7000 hp(m) *(15.15 MW)*; 2 shafts; cp props; bow thruster
Speed, knots: 15. **Range, miles:** 20 000 at 14 kts
Complement: 128

Comment: Built by Hollming, Rauma, Finland for hydrophysical/biological/chemical research. *Vavilov* launched on 16 December 1986 and completed 17 February 1988; *Ioffe* launched on 29 August 1987 and completed sea trials in February 1989. Low speed manoeuvrability is achieved by an Aquamatic propulsion unit aft and bow thruster forward. *Ioffe* has two rigid sails which stow horizontally on the superstructure. The sails minimise self noise during acoustic research operations. Both have extensive acoustic trials equipment including multi-beam echo-sounders and low frequency sidescan sonars. Sonar transducers are compact and ice resistant. *Ioffe* has been used as a ferry in the Baltic since 1992.

AKADEMIK IOFFE   *7/1993*

AKADEMIK SERGEI VAVILOV   *10/1992, Hartmut Ehlers*

3 VITYAZ CLASS

AKADEMIK ALEKSANDR NESMEYANOV   VITYAZ
AKADEMIK ALEKSANDR VINOGRADOV

Displacement, tons: 6000 full load
Dimensions, feet (metres): 364.1 × 54.5 × 18.7 *(111 × 16.6 × 5.7)*
Main machinery: 2 Zgoda-Sulzer 6ZL140/48 diesels; 6500 hp(m) *(4.78 MW)*; 2 shafts; cp props
Speed, knots: 17. **Range, miles:** 16 000 at 16 kts
Complement: 60 plus 65 scientists

Comment: Built at Szczecin, Poland. First completed in 1981, second in 1982 and third in 1983. Operate for Academy of Scientists. Capabilities for a wide range of oceanographical and meteorological studies and have excellent diver support facilities. Carry Argus submersible; 8 tons displacement; diving to 600 m *(1968.6 ft)* with endurance of eight hours; has a complement of three. *Vityaz* based at Novorossiysk, *A A Nesmeyanov* and *A A Vinogradov* at Vladivostok.

AKADEMIK ALEXANDR VINOGRADOV   *12/1991, 92 Wing RAAF*

1 AKADEMIK M KELDYSH CLASS

AKADEMIK MSTISLAV KELDYSH

Displacement, tons: 5500
Dimensions, feet (metres): 400.2 × 59 × 19.7 *(122 × 18 × 6)*
Main machinery: 4 Wärtsilä Vasa 824TS diesels; 5820 hp(m) *(3.88 MW)*; 2 shafts; bow thruster
Speed, knots: 16
Complement: 50 plus 80 scientists

Comment: Built by Hollming Yard, Rauma, Finland. Commissioned December 1980. One of the most sophisticated oceanographic research ships in the world. Under the Academy of Sciences. Has 17 laboratories and can carry two MIR manned submersibles which can dive to 6000 m *(19 686 ft)*. Two garage structures have been added aft of the funnel. Fitted with a rotatable stern propulsor. Based at Kaliningrad. Treasure hunting for Mexico in 1993.

AKADEMIK MSTISLAV KELDYSH   *4/1993, van Ginderen Collection*

1 AKADEMIK FEDOROV CLASS

AKADEMIK FEDOROV

Measurement, tons: 7600 dwt; 10 000 gross
Dimensions, feet (metres): 462.6 × 77 × 28 *(141 × 23.5 × 8.5)*
Main machinery: Diesel-electric; 2 Wärtsilä diesel generators; 18 700 hp(m) *(13.74 MW)*; 1 motor; 1 shaft
Speed, knots: 16
Complement: 90 plus 160 scientists
Helicopters: 1 Mi-8 Hip.

Comment: Built by Rauma-Repola, Finland and completed 10 September 1987 as a Polar Research and Support Ship. Comes under the Arctic and Antarctic Research Institute and is used for servicing Antarctic bases. Ice-strengthened and has a transverse omni-thruster. To replace *Mikhail Somov* in due course.

AKADEMIK FEDOROV   *7/1993*

1 AMGUEMA CLASS

MIKHAIL SOMOV

Displacement, tons: 15 100 full load
Measurement, tons: 8445 dwt; 7714 gross; 3113 net
Dimensions, feet (metres): 436.4 × 62.3 × 28.2 *(133 × 19 × 8.6)*
Main machinery: Diesel-electric; 4 diesel generators; 2 motors; 7200 hp(m) *(5.3 MW)*; 2 shafts
Speed, knots: 15
Complement: 58
Radars: Navigation: Two Don 2; I band.
Helicopters: Platform only.

Comment: Built at Kherson SY 1975. Ice-strengthened. Operates under Arctic and Antarctic Research Institute for research duties and Antarctic support. To be replaced by *Akademik Fedorov* in due course.

MIKHAIL SOMOV   *4/1992, Robert Pabst*

7 AKADEMIK KURCHATOV CLASS

AKADEMIK KOROLEV   **DMITRY MENDELEYEV**
AKADEMIK KURCHATOV   **PROFESSOR ZUBOV**
AKADEMIK SHIRSHOV   **PROFESSOR VIEZE**
AKADEMIK VERNADSKY

Displacement, tons: 6681 full load
Measurement, tons: 1986 dwt; 5460 gross; 1387 net
Dimensions, feet (metres): 400.3-406.8 × 56.1 × 15 *(122.1-124.1 × 17.1 × 4.6)*
Main machinery: 2 Halberstadt-MAN 6KZ57/60 diesels; 8000 hp(m) *(5.88 MW)*; 2 shafts; 2 bow thrusters; 360 hp(m) *(264 kW)*
Speed, knots: 20. **Range, miles:** 20 000 at 18 kts

Comment: All built by Mathias Thesen Werft at Wismar, East Germany between 1966 and 1968. All have a hull of the same design as the Mikhail Kalinin class of merchant vessels. There are variations in mast and aerial rig. *Professor Vieze* is similar to *A Shirshov* while *A Kurchatov*, *A Vernadsky* and *D Mendeleyev* are the same. *Kurchatov* and *Mendeleyev* have launched submersibles from a specially fitted crane.
Employment: Hydromet (Vladivostok): *A Korolev*, *A Shirshov*. Institute of Oceanology (Baltic): *A Kurchatov*. Institute of Oceanology (Vladivostok): *D Mendeleyev*. Ukraine Institute of Oceanology: *A Vernadsky*. Hydromet (Baltic): *P Vieze*, *P Zubov*.

AKADEMIK SHIRSHOV   *6/1993*

1 KOLOMNA CLASS

MIKHAIL LOMONOSOV

Displacement, tons: 5470 full load
Measurement, tons: 3897 gross; 1195 net
Dimensions, feet (metres): 336 × 47.2 × 22 *(102.5 × 14.4 × 6.7)*
Main machinery: 1 Liebknecht reciprocating engine; 2450 ihp(m) *(1.8 MW)*; 1 shaft
Speed, knots: 13

Comment: Built by Neptun, Rostock, in 1957 from the hull of a freighter of the Kolomna class. Operated for the Academy of Sciences by Ukraine Institute of Oceanology, Black Sea. Equipped with 16 laboratories.

MIKHAIL LOMONOSOV   *9/1986, van Ginderen Collection*

IZUMRUD

Displacement, tons: 5170 full load
Measurement, tons: 3862 gross; 465 net
Dimensions, feet (metres): 326 × 46 × 15.5 *(99.4 × 14 × 4.7)*
Main machinery: Diesel-electric; 4 diesel generators; 1 motor; 1 shaft
Speed, knots: 13.8

Comment: A research ship built in 1970 at Nikolayev. Used for structural and material tests. Owned by Ministry of Shipping. Operated by Naval Institute of Shipbuilding, Black Sea, and flies the Ukraine ensign.

IZUMRUD   *6/1992*

9 PASSAT CLASS (B 88 TYPE)

ERNST KRENKEL (ex-*Vikhr*)	OKEAN	PRILIV
GEORGY USHAKOV (ex-*Schkval*)	PASSAT	VIKTOR BUGAYEV (ex-*Poriv*)
MUSSON	PRIBOY	VOLNA

Displacement, tons: 4145 full load
Measurement, tons: 3280 (3311, *E Krenkel* and *V Bugayev*) gross
Dimensions, feet (metres): 318.5 × 45.6 × 15.4 *(97.1 × 13.9 × 4.7)*
328 × 48.5 × 15.4 *(100 × 14.8 × 4.7)* (*E Krenkel* and *V Bugayev*)
Main machinery: 2 Cegielski Sulzer diesels; 4800 hp(m) *(3.53 MW)*; 2 shafts
Speed, knots: 16
Complement: 110

Comment: Hydromet ships built at Szczecin, Poland. 1968: *Musson, Passat, Volna;* 1969: *Okean, Priboy;* 1970: *Priliv;* 1971: *G Ushakov, E Krenkel, V Bugayev*. Most are based in the Black Sea and are claimed by Ukraine but *Okean, Priboy,* and *Priliv* are at Vladivostok.

VOLNA
9/1993, C D Yaylali

8 AKADEMIK FERSMAN CLASS (B 93 TYPE)

AKADEMIK FERSMAN	AKADEMIK LAZAREV	AKADEMIK NALIVKIN
AKADEMIK SHATSKY	ZEPHYR (ex-*Akademik*	AKADEMIK NAMYOTKIN
AKADEMIK SELSKIY	*Gubkin*)	AKADEMIK KREPS

Displacement, tons: 3500 full load
Dimensions, feet (metres): 269 × 49.2 × 16.4 *(82 × 15 × 5)*
Main machinery: 1 Sulzer diesel; 4200 hp(m) *(3.1 MW)*; 1 Kort nozzle
Speed, knots: 15. **Range, miles:** 12 000 at 15 kts
Complement: 65

Comment: First pair completed at Szczecin, Poland in 1986, next five in 1987 and last one in 1988. Three more ordered in August 1988 but have not been completed. Fitted for gravimetric and geophysical research with towed seismic array and bow thruster. Ice-strengthened. *Shatsky* has been working under contract for Western geophysical research companies and has been renamed. *Shatsky* has a helo deck aft. One deleted in 1993.

AKADEMIK SHATSKY (helo deck)
7/1992

9 AKADEMIK SHULEYKIN CLASS

AKADEMIK GAMBURTSEV*	PROFESSOR GOLITSYN*
AKADEMIK SHULEYKIN	PROFESSOR KHROMOV
AKADEMIK SHOKALSKY	PROFESSOR PAVEL MOLCHANOV
GEOLOG DIMITRI NALIVKIN*	PROFESSOR MULTANOVSKY
	PROFESSOR POLSHKOV*

* Second group

Displacement, tons: 2000 (first four); 2554 (second five)
Dimensions, feet (metres): 236.2 × 42.6 × 15.4 *(72 × 13 × 4.7)* (first four)
244.3 × 48.3 × 14.8 *(74.5 × 14.7 × 4.5)* (second five)
Main machinery: 2 Gorkiy G-74 diesels; 3060 hp(m) *(2.25 MW)*; 2 shafts (first four)
2 SEMT-Pielstick 6 PC2.5 L 400 diesels; 7020 hp(m) *(5.16 MW)* sustained; 2 shafts (second five)
Speed, knots: 14
Complement: 70 (including scientists)

Comment: Built by Laivateollisuus, Turku, Finland. Ice-strengthened. First two entered service in 1982, next pair in 1983. *A Shuleykin* based at St Petersburg, *A Shokalsky* at Vladivostok, *Professor P Molchanov* at Murmansk, *Professor Khromov* in Pacific, *Professor Multanovsky* at St Petersburg. All hydromet ships work for Hydromet Service. Four more built for Academy of Sciences and Ministry of Geology. Completion December 1983 to October 1984. *Nalivkin* has a Qubit TRAC IV integrated navigation and data logging system for work in the Norwegian Sea under contract to a Western company. Tenth of class ex-*Arnold Veimer* belongs to Estonia. The second group * have a broader funnel and additional superstructure aft.

GEOLOG DIMITRI NALIVKIN
6/1993

7 VADIM POPOV CLASS

VADIM POPOV	VASILIY LOMINADZE
VIKTOR BUINITSKIY	IGOR MAKSIMOV
PAVEL GORDIYENKO	VLADIMIR PARSHIN
	IVAN PETROV

Displacement, tons: 927 full load
Dimensions, feet (metres): 164 × 33 × 12 *(49.9 × 10 × 3.6)*
Main machinery: 1 diesel; 1340 hp(m) *(985 kW)*; 1 shaft
Speed, knots: 13
Complement: 35

Comment: Small hydromet ships built at Laivateollisuus, Turku, the first of which entered service 6 October 1986. *Buinitskiy* is based at Murmansk, *Lominadze* in the Caspian, and three others are based in the Pacific. *Ivan Petrov* was the last to enter service, in 1991.

VLADIMIR PARSHIN
6/1992

4 AKADEMIK BORIS PETROV CLASS

AKADEMIK BORIS PETROV	AKADEMIK M A LAVRENTYEV
AKADEMIK N STRAKHOV	AKADEMIK OPARIN

Displacement, tons: 2550 full load
Dimensions, feet (metres): 247.6 × 48.2 × 15.4 *(75.5 × 14.7 × 4.7)*
Main machinery: 2 Russkiy SEMT-Pielstick 6 PC2.5 L 400 diesels; 7020 hp(m) *(5.16 MW)* sustained; 1 shaft; cp prop
Speed, knots: 15
Complement: 74
Radars: Navigation: Okean; I band. Don; I band.

Comment: Built by Hollming, Finland. Data similar to second group of Akademik Shuleykin class. *Petrov* and *Lavrentyev* completed June and October 1984, *Strakhov* on 14 May 1985 and *Oparin* launched 1 February 1985. May be used for sea-bed coring as part of programme of geophysical and hydrophysical research for Academy of Sciences.

AKADEMIK N STRAKHOV
7/1993, Hartmut Ehlers

3 ALEKSEY MARYSHEV CLASS

ALEKSEY MARYSHEV	GRIGORY MIKHEYEV	PETR KOTSOV

Comment: Built by Hollming, Rauma, Finland in 1990/91. Ice-strengthened, designed for survey work on the arctic coast and in the Siberian rivers. Owned by the Ministry of Transport. Of 1763 gross tons. So far used only for carrying timber.

PETR KOTSOV
6/1993, van Ginderen Collection

3 MODIFIED ALPINIST CLASS

GIDROBIOLOG   GIDRONAVT   RIFT

Displacement, tons: 1140 full load
Dimensions, feet (metres): 177.1 × 34.4 × 13.1 *(54 × 10.5 × 4)*
Main machinery: 1 SKL 8 NVD 48 A-2U diesel; 1320 hp(m) *(970 kW)* sustained; 1 shaft; cp prop
Speed, knots: 13. **Range, miles:** 7000 at 13 kts
Complement: 26 plus 12 scientists

Comment: Of the same stern-trawler design as the Alpinist AGIs. Modified to carry and operate a manned submersible (*Rift*—Pisces; others—Argus) from the gantry crane. Completed 1982-83.

RIFT   1987

20 VALERIAN URYVAYEV CLASS

CHAYVO   KERN
DALNIE ZELENTSY   POISK
ELM   PROFESSOR FEDYINSKY
GEOFIZIK   VALERIAN URYVAYEV*
ISKATEL   VEKTOR
VLADIMIR OBRUCHEV   ISSLEDOVATEL
VSEVOLOD BEREZKIN* MODUL
VULKANOLOG   MORSKOY GEOFIZIK
VYACHESLAV FROLOV* ZOND
YAKOV GAKKEL*   PROFESSOR GAGARINSKY
* Hydromet ships.

Displacement, tons: 1050 full load
Measurement, tons: 350 dwt; 697 gross; 85 net
Dimensions, feet (metres): 180.1 × 31.2 × 13.1 *(54.9 × 9.5 × 4)*
Main machinery: 1 Deutz diesel; 850 hp(m) *(625 kW)*; 1 shaft
Speed, knots: 12
Complement: 40 plus 12 scientists

Comment: Built at Khabarovsk between 1974 and 1990. *Vetra* (ex-*Lev Titov*) transferred to Lithuania in 1992.
Bases: Murmansk; *V Berezkin, D Zelentsy, Chayvo, Geofizik, Kern*. Black Sea; *Modul, Vektor, Issledovatel, Y Gakkel*. Caspian; *Elm*. Pacific; Remainder.
Tasks: Hydromet; *D Zelentsy, Elm*, Marine Biology; *Modul, Vektor*, Hydro-acoustics; *Issledovatel*, General Oceanography; Remainder, geology and geophysics.

VEKTOR   10/1990

ZOND   11/1993, Harald Carstens

19 DMITRY OVTSYN CLASS

DMITRY LAPTEV   PROFESSOR BOGOROV
DMITRY OVTSYN   PROFESSOR KURENTSOV
DMITRY STERLEGOV   PROFESSOR SHTOKMAN
E TOLL   PROFESSOR VODYANITSKY
FEDOR MATISEN   SERGEY KRAKOV
GEORGY MAKSIMOV   STEFAN MALYGIN
IVAN KIREYEV   VALERIAN ALBANOV
NIKOLAI KOLOMEYTSEV V SUKHOTSKY
NIKOLAI YEVGENOV   YAKOV SMIRNITSKY
PAVEL BASHMAKOV

Displacement, tons: 1800 full load
Dimensions, feet (metres): 220 × 39 × 15 *(67.1 × 11.9 × 4.6)*
Main machinery: 1 Deutz RBV6M 358 diesel; 2200 hp(m) *(1.62 MW)*; 1 shaft; bow thruster
Speed, knots: 16. **Range, miles:** 9000 at 13.5 kts
Complement: 52 (including 20 scientists)
Radars: Navigation: Okean or Don 2 or Decca 626; I band.

Comment: Built by Laivateollisuus, Åbo, Finland except *P Bogorov* at Turku, Finland. Fitted with eight laboratories. Employed largely on geological research oceanographic work and survey in the Arctic. Completed between 1974 and 1978. Average time from launch to completion, seven months. Owned by Ministry of Merchant Marine except for the four Professors which are subordinated to the Academy of Sciences. Have ice-strengthened bows.

PROFESSOR SHTOKMAN   6/1993

1 GAGARIN CLASS

KOSMONAUT YURY GAGARIN

Displacement, tons: 53 500
Measurement, tons: 32 291 gross; 5247 net
Dimensions, feet (metres): 760 × 101.7 × 30.2 *(232 × 31 × 9.2)*
Main machinery: 2 boilers; 2 turbines; 19 000 hp(m) *(14 MW)*; 1 shaft; bow and stern thrusters
Speed, knots: 17
Radars: Navigation: Don Kay and Okean; I band.

Comment: Design based on the Sofia or Akhtyuba (ex-Hanoi) class steam tanker. Built at Leningrad by Baltic SB & Eng Works in 1970, completed in 1971. Used for investigation into conditions in the upper atmosphere, and the control of space vehicles. She is the largest research vessel. Communications fit includes two Ship Shell (the largest dishes), two Ship Bowl, four Quad Ring and two Vee Cone (alongside funnel). With all four aerials vertical and facing forward she experiences a loss in speed of 2 kts. Based in Black Sea and claimed by Ukraine.

KOSMONAUT YURY GAGARIN   6/1993

1 KOROLEV CLASS

AKADEMIK SERGEY KOROLEV

Displacement, tons: 21 250
Measurement, tons: 17 114 gross; 2158 net
Dimensions, feet (metres): 596.6 × 82 × 25.9 *(181.9 × 25 × 7.9)*
Main machinery: 1 Bryansk Burmeister & Wain diesel; 12 000 hp(m) *(8.8 MW)*; 1 shaft
Speed, knots: 17
Radars: Navigation: Two Inayada; I band.

Comment: Built at Chernomorsky Shipyard, Nikolayev in 1970, completing in 1971. Space associated communications include four Quad Rings, two Ship Bowl and one Ship Globe. Based in the Baltic.

AKADEMIK SERGEY KOROLEV   3/1989

4 KOSMONAUT VLADISLAV VOLKOV CLASS

KOSMONAUT VLADISLAV VOLKOV   **KOSMONAUT PAVEL BELYAYEV**
KOSMONAUT GEORGY DOBROVOLSKY   **KOSMONAUT VIKTOR PATSAYEV**

Displacement, tons: 8920 full load
Dimensions, feet (metres): 400.3 × 55.1 × 22.3 *(122.1 × 16.8 × 6.8)*
Main machinery: 1 Bryansk Burmeister & Wain diesel; 5200 hp(m) *(3.82 MW)*; 1 shaft
Speed, knots: 15
Radars: Navigation: Don 2; I band.

Comment: Former freighters of Vytegrales class rebuilt as space associated research ships at Leningrad 1977-78. Space associated communications include one Quad Spring and three smaller aerials. Have Kite Screech fire-control radars.

KOSMONAUT GEORGY DOBROVOLSKY   *4/1993, van Ginderen Collection*

TRAINING SHIPS

2 UGRA II (TYPE 1889-U) CLASS (AXT)

BORODINO   **GANGUT**

Displacement, tons: 6750 standard; 7000 full load
Dimensions, feet (metres): 462.6 × 57.7 × 23 *(141 × 17.6 × 7)*
Main machinery: Diesel-electric; 4 Kolomna Type 2-D-42 diesel generators; 2 motors; 8000 hp(m) *(5.88 MW)*; 2 shafts
Speed, knots: 17. **Range, miles:** 21 000 at 10 kts; 9500 at 16 kts
Complement: 250 plus 400 instructors and trainees
Missiles: SAM: 2 SA-N-5 Grail quad launchers; manual aiming; IR homing to 6 km *(3.2 nm)* at 1.5 Mach; altitude to 2500 m *(8000 ft)*; warhead 1.5 kg.
Guns: 8—57 mm/70 (4 twin).
Radars: Air/surface search: Strut Curve; F band; range 110 km *(60 nm)* for 2 m² target.
Navigation: Three Don 2; I band.
Fire control: Two Muff Cob; G/H band.
IFF: Two Square Head. One High Pole B.
Sonars: Hull-mounted; active search; medium frequency (for training).

Comment: These are the last two of this class built, the remainder being submarine depot ships. Built at Nikolayev in 1971-72. Have large deckhouse aft in place of helicopter deck. No bow lift. One 10 ton and two 3.2 ton cranes.

GANGUT   *6/1992*

3 SMOLNY (TYPE 887) CLASS (AXT)

KHASAN   **PEREKOP**   **SMOLNY**

Displacement, tons: 9150 full load
Dimensions, feet (metres): 452.8 × 53.1 × 21.3 *(138 × 16.2 × 6.5)*
Main machinery: 2 Zgoda Sulzer 12ZV 40/48 diesels; 15 000 hp(m) *(11 MW)*; 2 shafts
Speed, knots: 20. **Range, miles:** 12 000 at 15 kts
Complement: 150 plus 350 cadets
Guns: 4—3 in *(76 mm)*/60 (2 twin). 4—30 mm/65 (2 twin).
A/S mortars: 2 RBU 2500.
Countermeasures: ESM: 2 Watch Dog; radar warning.
Radars: Air/surface search: Head Net C; 3D; E band; range 128 km *(70 nm)*.
Navigation: Four Don 2; I band. Don Kay *(Perekop)*; I band.
Fire control: Owl Screech; G band. Drum Tilt; H/I band.
IFF: Two High Pole A. Square Head.
Sonars: Hull-mounted; active search and attack; medium frequency.

Comment: Built at Szczecin, Poland. *Smolny* completed in 1976, *Perekop* in 1977 and *Khasan* in 1978. Have considerable combatant potential. *Khasan* collided with and sank a Turkish Kartal class FAC in the Bosphorus in October 1985.

KHASAN   *5/1993, Camil Busquets i Vilanova*

2 WODNIK II (TYPE 888-R) CLASS (AXT)

LUGA   **OKA**

Displacement, tons: 1820 full load
Dimensions, feet (metres): 234.3 × 38.1 × 12.8 *(71.4 × 11.6 × 3.9)*
Main machinery: 2 Zgoda-Sulzer 6TD48 diesels; 3600 hp(m) *(2.65 MW)* sustained; 2 shafts; cp props
Speed, knots: 17. **Range, miles:** 7200 at 11 kts
Complement: 60 plus 100 instructors and cadets
Radars: Navigation: Two Don 2; I band.
IFF: High Pole A.

Comment: Built at Northern Shipyard, Gdansk, Poland in 1976-77. Of same general design as Polish ships with an extra deck in the bridge and a larger superstructure. No armament. *Oka* is in the Caspian.

LUGA   *6/1991, MoD Bonn*

20 PETRUSHKA CLASS

MIERNYK   **ORSON**   **+ 18**

Displacement, tons: 335 full load
Dimensions, feet (metres): 129.3 × 27.6 × 7.2 *(39.4 × 8.4 × 2.2)*
Main machinery: 2 Wola H12 diesels; 756 hp(m) *(556 kW)*; 2 shafts
Speed, knots: 11. **Range, miles:** 1000 at 11 kts
Complement: 13 plus 30 cadets

Comment: Training vessels built at Wisla Shipyard, Poland; first one commissioned in 1989. Used for seamanship and navigation training. There is also a smaller version used as an auxiliary.

PETRUSHKA 317   *2/1991, MoD Bonn*

5 SAIL TRAINING SHIPS (TYPE B810)

MIR   **DRUZJBA**   **KHERSONES**   **PALLADA**   **NADHEZHDA**

Measurement, tons: 2996 gross
Dimensions, feet (metres): 346.1 × 45.9 × 19.7 *(105.5 × 14 × 6)*
Main machinery: 1 Sulzer 8AL20/24 diesel; 1500 hp(m) *(1.1 MW)*; 1 shaft
Speed, knots: 17
Complement: 55 plus 144 cadets

Comment: Three masted ship rig. Ordered from Northern Shipyard, Gdansk in July 1985. First launched 30 December 1986, second 31 March 1987, third 10 June 1988, fourth 30 July 1989, fifth June 1992. Not all are naval manned.

PALLADA   *2/1992, 92 Wing RAAF*

AUXILIARIES

4 UGRA (TYPE 1886) CLASS (SUBMARINE DEPOT SHIPS)

IVAN KOLYSHKIN   IVAN KUCHERENKO   IVAN VAKHRAMEEV   VOLGA

Displacement, tons: 6750 standard; 9650 full load
Dimensions, feet (metres): 462.6 × 57.7 × 23
(141 × 17.6 × 7)
Main machinery: Diesel-electric; 4 Kolomna Type 2-D-42 diesel
generators; 2 motors; 8000 hp(m) *(5.88 MW)*; 2 shafts
Speed, knots: 17. **Range, miles:** 21 000 at 10 kts; 9500 at
16 kts
Complement: 450

Missiles: SAM: 2 SA-N-5 Grail quad launchers; manual aiming; IR
homing to 6 km *(3.2 nm)* at 1.5 Mach; altitude to 2500 m
(8000 ft); warhead 1.5 kg; 16 missiles (in some ships).
Guns: 8—57 mm/70 (4 twin).
Countermeasures: ESM: 2 Watch Dog.
Radars: Air/surface search: Strut Curve; F band.
Navigation: Two Don 2; I band.
Fire control: Two Muff Cob; G/H band.
IFF: Two Square Head. High Pole B.

Helicopters: Platform (hangar in *Ivan Kolyshkin*) for 1 light.

Programmes: Built at Nikolayev from 1962 to 1970. Type name
is *plavuchaya baza* meaning floating base.
Structure: Improved versions of the Don class with the superstructure stretching aft to the funnel. Equipped with workshops. Provided with a helicopter platform and, in *Ivan
Kolyshkin* (last of class), a hangar. Has mooring points in hull
about 100 ft apart, and has baggage ports for coastal craft and
submarines. Two 10 ton and two 5 ton cranes. *Volga* and some
others have lattice mainmast with Vee Cone HF antenna.
Operational: Two scrapped in 1991, one in 1994. The last pair of
this class were completed as training ships (*Borodino* and
Gangut).
Sales: *Amba*, (sixth of class) which has 76 mm guns, was transferred to India in 1969.

VOLGA (with Vee Cone)   8/1993

5 DON (BATOOR) (TYPE 310) CLASS (SUBMARINE DEPOT SHIPS)

FEDOR VIDYAYEV   KAMCHATSKY KOMSOMOLETS (ex-*Mikhail Tukhachevsky*)   MAGOMET GADZHIEV
VIKTOR KOTELNIKOV   MAGADANSKY KOMSOMOLETS

Displacement, tons: 5100 standard; 6850 full load
Dimensions, feet (metres): 459.3 × 57.7 × 17.7
(140 × 17.6 × 5.4)
Main machinery: Diesel-electric; 4 diesel generators; 2 motors;
8000 hp(m) *(5.88 MW)*; 2 shafts
Speed, knots: 17. **Range, miles:** 21 000 at 10 kts; 9500 at
16 kts
Complement: 300 plus 450 submariners

Guns: 4—3.9 in *(100 mm)*/56 (2 in *Viktor Kotelnikov*, none
mounted in *Magadansky Komsomolets*).
8—57 mm/70 (4 twin).
8—25 mm/80 (4 twin) (mounted in *K. Komsomolets* and *Fedor
Vidyayev*).
Countermeasures: ESM: 2 Watch Dog.
Radars: Surface search: Slim Net; E/F band. Strut Curve (in
some); F band.
Navigation: Two Don 2; I band. Snoop Plate (in some); I band.
Fire control: Two Hawk Screech (not in *M. Komsomolets*); I band.
IFF: Two Square Head. High Pole A.

Helicopters: Platform *(Magadansky Komsomolets* and *Viktor
Kotelnikov).*

Programmes: Originally seven ships were built in 1957 to 1962,
all in Nikolayev. Type name is *plavuchaya baza* meaning float-
ing base.
Structure: Have a 100 ton bow lift and two 10 ton and two 5 ton
cranes.
Operational: Used as Flagships. Vee Cone fitted in *Fedor
Vidyayev* for long-range communications. One scrapped in the
Black Sea in 1991 and *Fedor Vidyayev* is probably
non-operational.
Sales: One to Indonesia in 1962.

VIKTOR KOTELNIKOV   11/1990

1 + 1 ALEKSANDR BRYKIN (TYPE 1826) CLASS (MISSILE SUPPORT SHIP)

ALEKSANDR BRYKIN

Displacement, tons: 14 350 full load
Dimensions, feet (metres): 511.8 × 76.1 × 26.2
(156 × 23.2 × 8)
Main machinery: Diesel-electric; 2 diesel generators; 1 motor;
26 000 hp(m) *(19 MW)*; 1 shaft; bow thruster
Speed, knots: 16
Complement: 140
Missiles: SAM: 4 SA-N-5 Grail quad launchers; manual aiming; IR
homing to 6 km *(3.2 nm)* at 1.5 Mach; altitude to 2500 m
(8000 ft); warhead 1.5 kg.
Guns: 4—30 mm/65 AK 630.
Countermeasures: ESM: 2 Bell Shroud; 2 Bell Squat.
Radars: Surface search: Half Plate Alpha; E/F band.
Navigation: 2 Nayhda; I band.
Fire control: Two Bass Tilt; H/I band.
IFF: Salt Pot. Longhead.

Comment: First of class completed in Leningrad in 1986. A second of class was launched in 1991, laid up, and may be completed in due course. Missile supply ship for submarine ballistic
missiles including SS-N-20, carried in the Typhoon class.
A 75 ton crane plumbs 16 vertical storage holds forward of the
funnel. First one transferred to Northern Fleet in 1987.

ALEKSANDR BRYKIN   5/1987

3 AMGA (TYPE 1791) CLASS (MISSILE SUPPORT SHIPS)

AMGA   VETLUGA   DAUGAVA

Displacement, tons: 5750 *(Amga)*, 6100 *(Vetluga)*, 6400 *(Daugava)* full load
Dimensions, feet (metres): 334.6 × 59 × 14.8
(102 × 18 × 4.5) (Amga) (see *Comment*)
Main machinery: 2 diesels; 9000 hp(m) *(6.6 MW)*; 2 shafts
Speed, knots: 16. **Range, miles:** 4500 at 14 kts
Complement: 210
Guns: 4—25 mm/80 (2 twin).
Radars: Surface search: Strut Curve; F band; range 110 km
(60 nm) for 2 m² target.
Navigation: Don 2; I band.
IFF: High Pole B.

Comment: Built at Gorkiy. Ships with similar duties to the Lama
class. Fitted with a large 55 ton crane forward and thus capable of handling much larger missiles than their predecessors.
Each ship has a different length and type of crane to handle
later types of missiles. Designed for servicing submarines, particularly those armed with SS-N-6, 8 and 18 missiles. First
appeared in December 1972, the second *Vetluga* (6 m longer
than *Amga*) in 1976 and third *Daugava* (11 m longer than
Amga) in 1981. *Amga* in the North, *Vetluga* and *Daugava* in the
Pacific.

DAUGAVA   6/1992

2 PINEGA CLASS (NUCLEAR SUBMARINE SUPPORT SHIPS)

AMUR   PINEGA

Displacement, tons: 6500 full load
Dimensions, feet (metres): 393.7 × 55.8 × 18 *(120 × 17 × 5.5)*
Main machinery: 2 diesels; 6800 hp(m) *(5 MW)*; 2 shafts
Speed, knots: 16
Complement: 100

Comment: Built at Vyborg. *Amur* completed in 1986 and went to the Northern Fleet. *Pinega* completed in 1987 and transferred to the Pacific in 1989. Both used for the dispersal of low level
radioactive waste.

PINEGA   10/1991, G Jacobs

2 MODIFIED ANDIZHAN CLASS (MISSILE SUPPORT SHIPS)

VENTA   VILYUY

Displacement, tons: 6700 full load
Dimensions, feet (metres): 341.1 × 47.2 × 21.6 *(104 × 14.4 × 6.6)*
Main machinery: 2 diesels; 2500 hp(m) *(1.84 MW)*; 2 shafts
Speed, knots: 14. **Range, miles:** 6000 at 13 kts
Complement: 60
Radars: Navigation: Don 2; I band.
IFF: Square Head. High Pole.

Comment: Cargo ships built in late 1950s at Rostock. Converted to support ships 1974-75. Have
one main crane forward, two smaller cranes aft and a helicopter platform. Can carry 10 SS-N-9
missiles as well as 20 SA-N-3. Type name is *voyenny transport* meaning military transport. *Venta*
in the Pacific, *Vilyuy* in the Black Sea.

VENTA   1980

3 + 1 MALINA CLASS (NUCLEAR SUBMARINE SUPPORT SHIPS)

PM 63   PM 74   PM 12   PM 16

Displacement, tons: 10 500 full load
Dimensions, feet (metres): 449.5 × 68.9 × 18.4 *(137 × 21 × 5.6)*
Main machinery: 4 gas-turbines; 60 000 hp(m) *(44 MW)*; 2 shafts
Speed, knots: 17
Complement: 260
Radars: Navigation: Two Palm Frond; I band.

Comment: Built at Nikolayev. First deployed to the Northern Fleet in October 1984, second to
Pacific in 1986, and third to the Northern Fleet in 1991. A fourth of class launched early in 1992,
may be claimed by Ukraine. Designed to support nuclear-powered submarines and surface ships.
Carry two 15 ton cranes.

PM 74   1990

7 LAMA CLASS (MISSILE SUPPORT SHIPS)

GENERAL RYABAKOV (877)   918   872   873   874   + 2

Displacement, tons: 4600 full load
Dimensions, feet (metres): 370 × 49.2 × 14.4 *(112.8 × 15 × 4.4)*
Main machinery: 2 diesels; 4800 hp(m) *(3 MW)*; 2 shafts
Speed, knots: 14. **Range, miles:** 6000 at 10 kts
Complement: 200
Missiles: SAM: 4 SA-N-5 Grail quad launchers (in four); manual aiming; IR homing to 6 km *(3.2 nm)*
at 1.5 Mach; altitude to 2500 m *(8000 ft)*; warhead 1.5 kg.
Guns: 4 or 8—57 mm/70 (quad, on the fo'c'sle or 2 or 4 twin).
4—25 mm/80 (in some).
Radars: Surface search: Slim Net; E/F band or Strut Curve; F band.
Navigation: Don 2; I band.
Fire control: Two Hawk Screech or Owl Screech; I band or Muff Cob; G/H band.
IFF: Two Square Head. High Pole A.

Comment: Built between 1963 and 1972 at Nikolayev with seventh ship in 1979. The engines are
sited aft to allow for a very large and high hangar or hold amidships for carrying missiles or weapons' spares for submarines, surface ships and missile craft. This is about 12 ft high above the
main deck. There are doors at the forward end with rails leading in and a raised turntable gantry
or 20 ton travelling cranes for armament supply. Variations in armament may reflect differences
in missile stowage. The well-deck is about 40 ft long, enough for most missiles to fit horizontally
before being lifted for loading. There are several differences in midships superstructure in these
ships, those specifically designed for missile craft having a longer missile store, two 10 ton
cranes and a shorter forward well-deck. Type name is *plavuchaya masterskaya* meaning floating
workshop. PM numbers have been removed. *918* and *872* are in the North; *873, 874* and *877* in
the Black Sea; the other pair are in the Pacific.

LAMA 872   6/1989

23 AMUR I (TYPE 304) and 5 AMUR II CLASS (REPAIR SHIPS)

AMUR I
PM 9, PM 10, PM 37, PM 49, PM 56, PM 75, PM 138, PM 161, PM 163
5, 15, 30, 34, 40, 52, 64, 73, 81, 82, 129, 139, 140, 156
AMUR II
59, 69, 86, 92, 97

Displacement, tons: 5500 full load
Dimensions, feet (metres): 400.3 × 55.8 × 16.7 *(122 × 17 × 5.1)*
Main machinery: 1 diesel; 3000 hp(m) *(2.2 MW)*; 1 shaft
Speed, knots: 12. **Range, miles:** 13 000 at 8 kts
Complement: 145
Radars: Navigation: Don 2; I band.

Comment: Amur I class general-purpose depot and repair ships completed 1968-83 in Szczecin, Poland. Successors to the Oskol class. Carry two 5 ton cranes and have accommodation for 200 from ships alongside. Amur II class similar in design. Built at Szczecin 1983-85. *PM 94* scrapped in the Baltic in 1992.

PM 138 (Amur I)   *1992*

PM 97 (Amur II)   *9/1991, G Jacobs*

12 OSKOL (TYPE 300/301) CLASS (REPAIR SHIPS)

PM 2, PM 21, PM 24, PM 26, PM 42, PM 147, PM 148
20, 21, 51, 68, 146

Displacement, tons: 2550 (3500, Oskol IV) full load
Dimensions, feet (metres): 300.1 × 40 × 13.1 *(91.5 × 12.2 × 4)*
Main machinery: 2 diesels; 2500 hp(m) *(1.84 MW)*; 1 shaft
Speed, knots: 12. **Range, miles:** 8000 at 10 kts
Complement: 100
Radars: Navigation: Don 2; I band.
IFF: High Pole.

Comment: Four series: Oskol I class, well-decked hull, no armament; Oskol II class, well-decked hull, open promenade deck aft and twin 14.5 mm MGs forward; Oskol III class, well-decked hull, armed with two 57 mm guns (one twin forward) and four 25 mm guns (2 twin aft); Oskol IV class, flush-decked hull with no armament and a bridge one deck higher than other types. General purpose tenders and repair ships with one or two 3.5 ton cranes. Built from 1963 to 1970 in Poland. Type name is *plavuchaya masterskaya* meaning floating workshop. *PM 21* to South Yemen in 1988 but returned in 1991.

OSKOL III PM 24 (with twin 57 mm gun)   *4/1991*

8 BOLVA 1, 30 BOLVA 2 and 10 BOLVA 3 CLASSES (BARRACKS SHIPS)

Displacement, tons: 6500
Dimensions, feet (metres): 560.9 × 45.9 × 9.8 *(110 × 14 × 3)*
Cargo capacity: 350-400 tons

Comment: All built by Valmet Oy, Helsinki between 1960-74. Used for accommodation of ships' companies during refit etc. The Bolva 2 and 3 have a helicopter pad. Have alongside berthing facilities for about 400. Have no means of propulsion but can be steered. In addition there are several other types of Barracks Ships including five ex-Atrek class depot ships as well as converted merchant ships and large barges.

4 TOMBA (TYPE 305) CLASS (SUPPORT SHIPS)

244, 254, 348, 357

Displacement, tons: 5200 full load
Dimensions, feet (metres): 351 × 55.8 × 16.4 *(107 × 17 × 5)*
Main machinery: Diesel-electric; 3 diesel generators; 1 motor; 5500 hp(m) *(4 MW)*; 1 shaft
Speed, knots: 18. **Range, miles:** 7000 at 14 kts
Complement: 50
Radars: Navigation: Don 2 and Spin Trough; I band.
IFF: High Pole B.

Comment: Built at Szczecin, Poland. First completed 1974. *254* and *244* deployed in Northern Fleet, and *348* and *357* in the Pacific. There is a donkey funnel on fo'c'sle. Two 3 ton cranes. Type name is *elektrostantsiye nalivatelnoye sudno* meaning electricity supply ship.

TOMBA   *10/1982*

8 VYTEGRALES (TYPE 596P) CLASS (SUPPORT SHIPS)

APSHERON (ex-*Vagales*)	**DONBAS** (ex-*Vostok 4*)
BASKUNCHAK (ex-*Kirishi*)	**SEVAN** (ex-*Siverles*)
DAURIYA (ex-*Vyborgles*)	**TAMAN** (ex-*Suzdal*)
DIKSON (ex-*Vostok 3*)	**YAMAL** (ex-*Tosnoles*)

Displacement, tons: 6150 full load
Dimensions, feet (metres): 400.3 × 55.1 × 22.3 *(122.1 × 16.8 × 6.8)*
Main machinery: 1 Burmeister & Wain 950VTBF diesel; 5200 hp(m) *(3.82 MW)*; 1 shaft
Speed, knots: 15
Complement: 150
Radars: Air search: Big Net; C band (*Donbas* only).
Navigation: Two Don 2; I band.
Helicopters: 1 Ka-25 'Hormone C'.

Comment: Standard timber carriers of a class of 27. These eight ships were modified for naval use in 1966-68 with helicopter flight deck. Built at Zhdanov Yard, Leningrad between 1963 and 1966. *Sevan* and *Taman* fitted as squadron Flagships in support of Indian Ocean detachments. Variations exist between ships of this class; *Baskunchak* and *Dauriya* have a deckhouse over the aft hold and *Donbas* has a large air-search radar aerial on the central mast. All have two Vee Cone communications aerials. The first of class, completed in 1962, was originally *Vytegrales*, but this was later changed to *Kosmonaut Pavel Belyayev* and, with three other ships of this class, converted to Space Support Ships. Four others (*Borovichi* etc) received a different conversion for the same purpose. *Dikson* which is a Black Sea Fleet trials ship was laid up in 1992. The eight civilian-manned ships together with these eight naval ships are often incorrectly called Vostok or Baskunchak class.

SEVAN   *2/1993, van Ginderen Collection*

5 MOD ALTAY CLASS (REPLENISHMENT TANKERS)

ELNYA   ILIM   KOLA   PRUT   YEGORLIK

Displacement, tons: 7250 full load
Dimensions, feet (metres): 348 × 51 × 22 *(106.2 × 15.5 × 6.7)*
Main machinery: 1 Burmeister & Wain BM550VTBN110 diesel; 3200 hp(m) *(2.35 MW)*; 1 shaft
Speed, knots: 14. **Range, miles:** 8600 at 12 kts
Complement: 60
Cargo capacity: 4400 tons oil fuel
Radars: Navigation: Two Don 2; I band.

Comment: Built from 1967-72 by Rauma-Repola, Finland. All modified for alongside replenishment. This class is part of 38 ships, being the third group of Rauma types built in Finland in 1967. Some have armament fittings similar to the Uda class with 25 mm guns. A sixth of the class *Izhora* sunk in Vladivostok after an explosion in July 1991. *Elnya* claimed by Ukraine in April 1993.

ELNYA   *2/1992*

1 BEREZINA (TYPE 1859) CLASS (REPLENISHMENT SHIP)

BEREZINA

Displacement, tons: 35 000 full load
Dimensions, feet (metres): 695.5 × 85.3 × 38.7
(212 × 26 × 11.8)
Main machinery: 2 diesels; 47 500 hp(m) *(35 MW)*; 2 shafts
Speed, knots: 22. **Range, miles:** 15 000 at 16 kts
Complement: 600
Cargo capacity: Approx 16 000 tons fuel (including Avgas);
2000 tons provisions; 500 tons fresh water

Missiles: SAM: SA-N-4 Gecko twin launcher (abaft funnel); semi-
active radar homing to 15 km *(8 nm)* at 2.5 Mach; warhead
50 kg; altitude 9.1-3048 m *(30-10 000 ft)*; 20 missiles.
Guns: 4—57 mm/80 (2 twin); 85° elevation; 120 rounds/minute
to 6 km *(3.3 nm)*; weight of shell 2.8 kg.
4—30 mm/65; 6 barrels per mounting; 3000 rounds/minute
combined to 2 km.
A/S mortars: 2 RBU 1000 6-tubed; range 1000 m; warhead
55 kg
Countermeasures: Decoys: 2—16-barrelled Chaff launchers.
ESM: 2 Bell series.
Radars: Air/surface search: Strut Curve; F band; range 110 km
(60 nm) for 2 m² target.
Navigation: Two Don Kay; I band. Two Don 2; I band.
Fire control: Pop Group; F/H/I band (for SA-N-4). Muff Cob; G/H
band (for 57 mm). Two Bass Tilt; H/I band (for 30 mm).
IFF: Two High Pole B. Two Square Head.
Sonars: Hull-mounted; active search and attack; medium
frequency.

Helicopters: 2 Ka-25 'Hormone C'.

Programmes: Laid down in 1973; launched in 1975. Built at
Nikolayev (61 Kommuna) and completed in 1977.
Structure: Two storing gantries (apparently with moving high-
points); four 10 ton cranes and one other; liquid fuelling gantry
(amidships); stern refuelling. The weight of her armament is
notable in comparison with Western practice. This is the first
replenishment ship to be fitted with SAM missiles and Gatling
guns as well as carrying helicopters and mounting RBUs. This
gives her a considerable AA capability and, if the helicopters
have an ASW as well as Vertrep role, some self-sufficiency in
anti-submarine operations. This is the only ship to site the RBU
1000 forward of the bridge.
Operational: Can replenish two ships at a time or refuel three.
Based in the Black Sea and rarely deploys even to the
Mediterranean.

BEREZINA   8/1991

6 BORIS CHILIKIN (TYPE 1559) CLASS (REPLENISHMENT SHIPS)

BORIS BUTOMA	GENRICH GASANOV
BORIS CHILIKIN	IVAN BUBNOV
DNESTR	VLADIMIR KOLECHITSKY

Displacement, tons: 23 400 full load
Dimensions, feet (metres): 531.5 × 70.2 × 33.8
(162.1 × 21.4 × 10.3)
Main machinery: 1 diesel; 9600 hp(m) *(7 MW)*; 1 shaft
Speed, knots: 17. **Range, miles:** 10 000 at 16 kts
Complement: 75 (without armament)
Cargo capacity: 13 000 tons oil fuel and dieso; 400 tons ammu-
nition; 400 tons spares; 400 tons victualling stores; 500 tons
fresh water

Guns: 4—57 mm/80 (2 twin). Most are fitted for but not with the
guns.
Radars: Air/surface search/fire-control: Strut Curve (fitted for
but not with).
Muff Cob (fitted for but not with).
Navigation: Two Don Kay (plus Don 2 in *V Kolechitsky*); I band.
IFF: High Pole B.

Programmes: Based on the Veliky Oktyabr merchant ship tanker
design, *Boris Chilikin* was built at the Baltic Yard, Leningrad
completing in 1971. Last of class *Boris Butoma* completed in
1978.
Structure: This is the only class of purpose-built underway fleet
replenishment ships for the supply of both liquids and solids.
The removal of both fire-control radar and armament is in contrast to the considerable weight of such items carried in *Berezina*. Although most operate in merchant navy paint schemes,
all wear naval ensigns.
Operational: Earlier ships can supply solids on both sides forward. Later ships supply solids to starboard, liquids to port forward. All can supply liquids either side aft and astern. *Dnestr*
and *Gasanov* are based in the North, *Bubnov* in the Black Sea,
Butoma and *Kolechitsky* in the Pacific.

DNESTR   5/1993

4 DUBNA CLASS (REPLENISHMENT TANKERS)

DUBNA	PECHENGA
IRKUT	SVENTA

Displacement, tons: 11 500 full load
Dimensions, feet (metres): 426.4 × 65.6 × 23.6
(130 × 20 × 7.2)
Main machinery: 1 Russkiy 8DRPH23/230 diesel; 6000 hp(m)
(4.4 MW); 1 shaft
Speed, knots: 16. **Range, miles:** 7000 at 16 kts
Complement: 70
Cargo capacity: 7000 tons fuel; 300 tons fresh water; 1500 tons
stores

Radars: Navigation: One or two Don 2; I band.

Programmes: *Dubna* completed 1974, *Irkut* December 1975,
both at Rauma-Repola, Finland. *Pechenga* commissioned end
1978, *Sventa* completed April 1979.
Structure: Have 1 ton replenishment stations forward. Normally
painted in merchant navy colours.
Operational: Can refuel on either beam and astern. *Dubna* in
North, *Sventa* in Black Sea, remainder in Pacific.

DUBNA   6/1993

2 MOD KAZBEK CLASS (REPLENISHMENT TANKERS)

DESNA   **VOLKHOV**

Displacement, tons: 16 250 full load
Measurement, tons: 12 000 dwt; 8230 gross; 3942 net
Dimensions, feet (metres): 477.2 × 62.9 × 26.9 *(145.5 × 19.2 × 8.2)*
Main machinery: 1 Russkiy Dizel diesel; 4000 hp(m) *(2.94 MW)*; 1 shaft
Speed, knots: 15. **Range, miles:** 18 000 at 12 kts
Complement: 46
Cargo capacity: 10 500 tons oil fuel
Radars: Navigation: Two Don 2; I band.
IFF: High Pole A.

Comment: Former Leningrad class merchant fleet tankers taken over by the Navy. Built at Leningrad and Nikolayev from 1951 to 1961. Eight others—*Karl Marx, Kazbek, Dzerzhinsk, Grodno, Cheboksary, Liepaya, Zhitomir* and *Buguzuslan*—have acted in support of naval operations. The original class numbered 64. Both modified for alongside replenishment. The naval ships of this class can be distinguished by the A-frame before the bridge, the two forward kingposts and the cat-walks. One scrapped in 1993.

DESNA   *5/1992*

6 UDA CLASS (REPLENISHMENT TANKERS)

DUNAY (mod)   **KOIDA**   **LENA** (mod)   **TEREK** (mod)   **VISHERA** (mod)
SHEKSNA (mod)

Displacement, tons: 5500 standard; 7110 full load
Dimensions, feet (metres): 400.3 × 51.8 × 20.3 *(122.1 × 15.8 × 6.2)*
Main machinery: 2 diesels; 9000 hp(m) *(6.6 MW)*; 2 shafts
Speed, knots: 17. **Range, miles:** 4000 at 15 kts
Complement: 85
Cargo capacity: 3000 tons oil fuel
Guns: Positions for 8—57 mm/70 (2 quad); 6—25 mm/80 (3 twin) (landed in peacetime).
Radars: Navigation: Two Don 2; I band.
Fire control: Two Muff Cob (when guns are fitted); G/H band.
IFF: High Pole A.

Comment: All have a beam replenishment capability. May retain fitting for a quadruple 57 mm or three twin 25 mm guns. Built in 1961-67. *Koida* was first Soviet ship refitted in Greek Orion shipyard. Modified ships have a second A-frame amidships thus providing two alongside refuelling positions. Three transferred to Indonesia 1963-64 and since deleted. One deleted in error in 1991.

LENA   *6/1993, Marek Twardowski*

LENA (with Krivak I)   *6/1993*

2 MANYCH CLASS (WATER TANKERS)

MANYCH   **TAGIL**

Displacement, tons: 7700 full load
Dimensions, feet (metres): 380.5 × 51.5 × 23 *(116 × 15.7 × 7)*
Main machinery: 2 diesels; 9000 hp(m) *(6.6 MW)*; 2 shafts
Speed, knots: 18. **Range, miles:** 7500 at 16 kts
Complement: 90
Cargo capacity: 4400 tons
Guns: 4—57 mm/70 (2 twin) (not normally fitted).
Radars: Air/surface search: Strut Curve; F band.
Navigation: Two Don Kay; I band.
Fire control: Two Muff Cob (not in *Tagil*); G/H band.
IFF: High Pole B.

Comment: Completed 1972 and 1976 in Vyborg. The high point on the single gantry is very similar to that on *Boris Chilikin*'s third gantry. Both ships in use as distilled water-carriers with armament removed. Have underway abeam replenishment capability.

MANYCH   *2/1990*

12 VODA CLASS (WATER TANKERS)

ABAKAN   **SURA**
MVT 6, 9, 10, 16, 17, 18, 20, 24, 136, 138

Displacement, tons: 3000 full load
Dimensions, feet (metres): 267.3 × 37.7 × 13.2 *(81.5 × 11.5 × 4)*
Main machinery: 2 diesels; 1600 hp(m) *(1.18 MW)*; 2 shafts
Speed, knots: 12. **Range, miles:** 3000 at 10 kts
Complement: 40
Cargo capacity: 1500 tons
Radars: Navigation: Don 2; Spin Trough; I band.
IFF: High Pole A.

Comment: Built in 1956 onwards. No armament. Some lack the catwalk forward of the bridge. Astern replenishment only. One deleted in 1992, one in 1993.

SURA   *6/1992*

3 OLEKMA CLASS (REPLENISHMENT TANKERS)

OLEKMA (mod)   **IMAN**   **ZOLOTOY ROG**

Displacement, tons: 4000 standard; 6700 full load
Dimensions, feet (metres): 344.5 × 47.9 × 22 *(105.1 × 14.6 × 6.7)*
Main machinery: 1 Burmeister & Wain diesel; 2900 hp(m) *(2.13 MW)*; 1 shaft
Speed, knots: 14. **Range, miles:** 8000 at 14 kts
Complement: 40
Cargo capacity: 4500 tons oil fuel
Radars: Navigation: Don 2 and Spin Trough; I band.

Comment: Part of the second group of 34 tankers built by Rauma-Repola, Finland between 1960 and 1966. *Olekma* is modified for replenishment with refuelling rig abaft the bridge as well as astern refuelling. The other two can only refuel astern. *Zolotoy Rog* has a square sided funnel and is more correctly referred to as a Pevek class tanker.

OLEKMA   *10/1992*

2 KALININGRADNEFT CLASS (SUPPORT TANKERS)

ARGUN   **VYAZMA**

Displacement, tons: 8600 full load
Dimensions, feet (metres): 380.5 × 56 × 21 *(116 × 17 × 6.5)*
Main machinery: 1 Russkiy Burmeister & Wain 5DKRP50/110-2 diesel; 3850 hp(m) *(2.83 MW)*;
  1 shaft
Speed, knots: 14. **Range, miles:** 5000 at 14 kts
Complement: 32
Cargo capacity: 5400 tons oil fuel and other liquids
Radars: Navigation: Okean; I band.

Comment: Built by Rauma-Repola, Finland in 1982. Can refuel alongside or astern. At least an
  additional 20 of this class operate with the fishing fleets.

ARGUN   11/1991, G Jacobs

1 SOFYA CLASS (SUPPORT TANKER)

AKHTYUBA (ex-*Hanoi*)

Displacement, tons: 62 600 full load
Dimensions, feet (metres): 757.9 × 100.4 × 38 *(231.2 × 30.6 × 11.6)*
Main machinery: 2 boilers; 1 turbine; 21 000 hp(m) *(15.4 MW)*; 1 shaft
Speed, knots: 17. **Range, miles:** 10 000 at 17 kts
Complement: 75
Cargo capacity: 45 000 tons oil fuel.
Radars: Navigation: Two Don 2; I band.

Comment: Built as the merchant tanker *Hanoi* in 1963 at Leningrad, she was taken over by the
  Navy in 1969 and renamed *Akhtyuba*. The hull type was used in the construction of the space
  associated ship *Kosmonaut Yury Gagarin*. Astern refuelling. Active in the South China Sea.

AKHTYUBA   8/1993, van Ginderen Collection

3 KONDA CLASS (SUPPORT TANKERS)

KONDA   **ROSSOSH**   **YAKHROMA**

Displacement, tons: 2090 full load
Dimensions, feet (metres): 226.3 × 33 × 14.1 *(69 × 10.1 × 4.3)*
Main machinery: 1 diesel; 1600 hp(m) *(1.18 MW)*; 1 shaft
Speed, knots: 12. **Range, miles:** 2200 at 11.5 kts
Complement: 36
Cargo capacity: 1000 tons oil fuel
Radars: Navigation: Don 2; I band. Spin Trough; I band.

Comment: Originally of the Iskra class of merchant tankers built in 1955. Have a stern refuelling
  capability. Icebreaker bow. One scrapped in 1993.

KONDA   5/1990

2 NERCHA CLASS (SUPPORT TANKERS)

NARA   **KLYAZMA**

Displacement, tons: 1850 full load
Dimensions, feet (metres): 208.3 × 33 × 14.1 *(63.5 × 10.1 × 4.3)*
Main machinery: 1 diesel; 1000 hp(m) *(735 kW)*; 1 shaft
Speed, knots: 11. **Range, miles:** 2000 at 10 kts
Complement: 25
Cargo capacity: 700 tons oil fuel
Radars: Navigation: Don 2; I band.

Comment: Built in Finland 1952-55 as part of class of 12. Renamed in naval service. Have astern
  refuelling capability. Strengthened for ice.

8 KHOBI CLASS (SUPPORT TANKERS)

| CHEREMSHAN | ORSHA | SEIMA | SOSVA |
| SYSOLA | LOVAT | METAN | SHACHA |

Displacement, tons: 700 light; 1500 full load
Dimensions, feet (metres): 206.6 × 33 × 14.8 *(63 × 10.1 × 4.5)*
Main machinery: 2 diesels; 1600 hp(m) *(1.18 MW)*; 2 shafts
Speed, knots: 13. **Range, miles:** 2500 at 12 kts
Complement: 35 (4 officers)
Cargo capacity: 500 tons oil fuel
Radars: Navigation: Don 2 and Spin Trough; I band.

Comment: Built from 1957 to 1959. Survivors of a class of 25. Can refuel while being towed. Now
  being deleted. Transfers: Two to Albania; one to Hungary (deleted); three to Indonesia (two
  deleted).

LOVAT   7/1993 Hartmut Ehlers

1 IRTYSH CLASS (SUPPORT TANKER)

NARVA

Displacement, tons: 1700 full load
Dimensions, feet (metres): 224.7 × 34.1 × 14.1 *(68.5 × 10.4 × 4.3)*
Main machinery: 1 diesel; 880 hp(m) *(647 kW)*; 1 shaft
Speed, knots: 12. **Range, miles:** 2000 at 10 kts
Complement: 40
Cargo capacity: 1170 tons oil fuel
Radars: Navigation: Neptun or Spin Trough; I band.

NARVA   11/1985, van Ginderen Collection

2 BASKUNCHAK CLASS (SUPPORT TANKERS)

IVAN GOLUBETS   **SOVIETSKY POGRANICHNIK**

Displacement, tons: 2280 full load
Dimensions, feet (metres): 272.6 × 39.4 × 15.7 *(83.1 × 12 × 4.8)*
Main machinery: 1 Bryansk Type 8DR34/61VI diesel; 2000 hp(m) *(1.47 MW)*; 1 shaft
Speed, knots: 13. **Range, miles:** 5000 at 12 kts
Complement: 30
Cargo capacity: 1500 tons oil fuel

Comment: Last of a large class. These two support Border Guard units in the Pacific.

SOVIETSKY POGRANICHNIK   11/1991, G Jacobs

TOPLIVO SERIES (HARBOUR TANKERS)

Comment: There are three versions under this name. Toplivo 1, built in Poland, are of 420 tons full load and 34.4 m long. Toplivo 2, some of which were built in Egypt but the majority in the USSR, are of 1200 tons full load and 53 m long. Toplivo 3, built in the USSR, are of 1300 tons full load and 52.7 m long with a very different appearance from Toplivo 2. These ships are used in many bases for the transport of all forms of liquids.

TOPLIVO 3   5/1992, van Ginderen Collection

6 LUZA CLASS (SPECIAL TANKERS)

ALAMBAI   **BARGUZIN**   **KAMA**
ARAGVI   **DON**   **SELENGA**

Displacement, tons: 1900 full load
Dimensions, feet (metres): 205 × 35.1 × 14.1 (62.5 × 10.7 × 4.3)
Main machinery: 1 diesel; 1000 hp(m) (735 kW); 1 shaft
Speed, knots: 12. **Range, miles:** 2000 at 11 kts
Complement: 60
Radars: Navigation: Don 2; I band. Spin Trough; I band.
IFF: High Pole B.

Comment: Completed at Kolpino 1962-70. Used for transporting special liquids such as missile fuel.

DON   8/1991, van Ginderen Collection

7 VALA CLASS (SPECIAL TANKERS)

VALA   **TNT 11**   **TNT 27**   **12**   **19**   **25**   **29**

Displacement, tons: 2030 full load
Dimensions, feet (metres): 239.8 × 42.3 × 15.7 (73.1 × 12.9 × 4.8)
Main machinery: 1 diesel; 1000 hp(m) (735 kW); 1 shaft
Speed, knots: 14. **Range, miles:** 2000 at 11 kts
Complement: 30
Guns: 4—14.5 mm (2 twin) MGs (in some).
Radars: Navigation: Spin Trough; I band.

Comment: Completed 1964-71. Used for transporting radiological liquids and nuclear waste, and for dumping them at sea.

VALA 27   1993, Ships of the World

4 OB (TYPE 320) CLASS (HOSPITAL SHIPS) (AH)

OB   **YENISEI**   **SVIR**   **IRTYSH**

Displacement, tons: 11 300 full load
Dimensions, feet (metres): 499.7 × 63.6 × 20.5 (152.3 × 19.4 × 6.3)
Main machinery: 2 Zgoda-Sulzer 12ZV40/48; 15 600 hp(m) (11.47 MW) sustained; 2 shafts; cp props
Speed, knots: 19. **Range, miles:** 10 000 at 18 kts
Complement: 124 plus 83 medical staff
Radars: Navigation: Three Don 2; I band.
IFF: High Pole A.
Helicopters: 1 Ka-25 'Hormone C'.

Comment: Built at Szczecin, Poland. Ob completed in 1980 and transferred to the Pacific in September 1980. Yenisei completed 1981 and is based in the Black Sea. Svir completed in early 1989 and transferred to the Northern Fleet in September 1989. Irtysh completed in June 1990, was stationed in the Gulf in 1990-91 and is now based in the Pacific. A fifth of the class was cancelled. Have 100 beds and seven operating theatres. The first purpose-built hospital ships in the Navy, a programme which may have been prompted by the use of several merchant ships off Angola for Cuban casualties in the 'war of liberation.' NBC pressurised citadel. Ship stabilisation system. Decompression chamber.

SVIR   7/1992

3 EMBA I and 2 EMBA II CLASSES

Group I: **EMBA, NEPRYADVA, SETUN**
Group II: **BIRIUSA, KEMJ**

Displacement, tons: 2050 full load (Group I); 2400 (Group II)
Dimensions, feet (metres): 249 × 41.3 × 9.8 (75.9 × 12.6 × 3) (Group I)
   282.4 × 41.3 × 9.9 (86.1 × 12.6 × 3) (Group II)
Main machinery: Diesel-electric; 2 Wärtsilä Vasa 6R22 diesel alternators; 2350 kVA 60 Hz; 2 motors; 1360 hp(m) (1 MW); 2 shafts (Group I)
   2 Wärtsilä Vasa 8R22 diesel alternators; 3090 kVA 60 Hz; 2 motors; 2180 hp(m) (1.6 MW); 2 shafts (Group II)
   The two turnable propulsion units can be inclined to the ship's path giving, with a bow thruster, improved turning movement
Speed, knots: 11
Complement: 40
Radars: Navigation: Two Spin Trough; I band.

Comment: Emba completed by Wärtsilä in 1980, second pair in 1981. Designed for shallow water cable-laying. Carry 380 tons of cable. Order placed with Wärtsilä in January 1985 for two larger (Group II) ships; Biriusa delivered 4 July 1986 and Kemj on 23 October 1986. Can lay about 600 tons of cable. Designed for use off Vladivostok but also capable of operations in inland waterways.

SETUN (Emba I)   1981, Wärtsilä

KEMJ (Emba II)   1986, Wärtsilä

8 KLASMA CLASS (CABLE SHIPS)

DONETS	INGUL*	INGURI	KATUN
TAVDA	TSNA	YANA*	ZEYA

*Type I

Displacement, tons: 6000 standard; 6900 full load
Measurement, tons: 3400 dwt; 5786 gross
Dimensions, feet (metres): 427.8 × 52.5 × 19 *(130.5 × 16 × 5.8)*
Main machinery: Diesel-electric; 5 Wärtsilä Sulzer 624TS diesel generators (4 in *Ingul* and *Yana*); 5000 hp(m) *(3.68 MW)*; 2 motors; 2150 hp(m) *(1.58 MW)*; 2 shafts
Speed, knots: 14. **Range, miles:** 12 000 at 14 kts
Complement: 85
Radars: Navigation: Two Don 2; I band.

Comment: *Ingul* and *Yana* were built by Wärtsilä, Helsingforsvarvet, Finland in 1962; *Donets* and *Tsna* at the Wärtsilä, Åbovarvet in 1968-69; *Zeya* in 1970. *Donets, Tsna* and *Zeya* are of slightly modified design. *Tavda* completed 1977; *Inguri* in 1978. All are ice-strengthened and can carry 1650 miles of cable. Type II can be distinguished by gantry right aft.

TSNA   9/1993, van Ginderen Collection

4 MIKHAIL RUDNITSKY CLASS
(SALVAGE AND MOORING VESSELS)

MIKHAIL RUDNITSKY	GEORGY KOZMIN	GEORGY TITOV	SAYANY

Displacement, tons: 10 700 full load
Dimensions, feet (metres): 427.4 × 56.7 × 23.9 *(130.3 × 17.3 × 7.3)*
Main machinery: 1 S5DKRN62/140-3 diesel; 6100 hp(m) *(4.48 MW)*; 1 shaft
Speed, knots: 16. **Range, miles:** 12 000 at 15.5 kts
Complement: 70
Radars: Navigation: Palm Frond; Nayada; I band.

Comment: Built at Vyborg, based on Moskva Pionier class merchant ship hull. First completed 1979, second in 1980, third in 1983 and fourth in 1984. Fly flag of Salvage and Rescue Service. Have two 40 ton and one 20 ton lift with cable fairleads forward and aft. This lift capability would be adequate for handling small submersibles, one of which is carried in the centre hold. *Sayany* is also described as a research ship. *Rudnitsky* based in the Black Sea, *Titov* in the Northern Fleet and the other two in the Pacific.

GEORGY TITOV   10/1993, van Ginderen Collection

2 PAMIR CLASS (SALVAGE TUGS)

AGATAN	ALDAN

Displacement, tons: 2050 full load
Dimensions, feet (metres): 256 × 42 × 13.5 *(78 × 12.8 × 4.1)*
Main machinery: 2 MAN G10V40/60 diesels; 4200 hp(m) *(3.1 MW)*; 2 shafts; cp props
Speed, knots: 17. **Range, miles:** 15 000 at 17 kts
Complement: 77
Radars: Navigation: Two Don 2; I band.
IFF: High Pole A.

Comment: Salvage tugs built at AB Gävle Varv, Sweden in 1959-60. Equipped with one 10 ton and two 1.5 ton derricks, powerful pumps, air compressors, diving gear, recompression chambers, firefighting apparatus and electric generators. Have rather less cluttered bridge area than the two of this class converted to AGIs. Both based in the North.

ALDAN   2/1983

4 INGUL (TYPE 1452) CLASS (SALVAGE TUGS)

PAMIR	MASHUK	ALATAU	ALTAY (ex-*Karabakh*)

Displacement, tons: 4050 full load
Dimensions, feet (metres): 304.4 × 50.5 × 19 *(92.8 × 15.4 × 5.8)*
Main machinery: 2 Type 58-D-4R diesels; 6000 hp(m) *(4.4 MW)*; 2 shafts; cp props
Speed, knots: 20. **Range, miles:** 9000 at 19 kts
Complement: 35 plus salvage party of 18
Guns: Positions for 2—57 mm/70 (twin) and 4—25 mm/80 (2 twin) (not fitted).
Radars: Navigation: Two Palm Frond; I band.
IFF: High Pole. Square Head.

Comment: Built at Admiralty Yard, Leningrad in 1975-84. NATO class-name the same as one of the Klasma class cable-ships. Naval-manned arctic salvage and rescue tugs. Two more, *Yaguar* (Murmansk) and *Bars* (Vladivostok), operate with the merchant fleet. Carry salvage pumps, diving and firefighting gear as well as a high-line for transfer of personnel. *Pamir* and *Karabakh* in the North, the other pair in the Pacific.

ALTAY   7/1993

4 SLIVA CLASS (SALVAGE TUGS)

SB 406	SB 408	SB 921	SHAKHTER SB 922

Displacement, tons: 3050 full load
Dimensions, feet (metres): 227 × 50.5 × 16.7 *(69.2 × 15.4 × 5.1)*
Main machinery: 2 Russkiy SEMT-Pielstick 6 PC2.5 L 400 diesels; 7020 hp(m) *(5.2 MW)* sustained; 2 shafts; bow thruster
Speed, knots: 16
Complement: 43 plus 10 salvage party
Radars: Navigation: Nayada; I band.

Comment: Built at Rauma-Repola, Finland. *SB 406* completed 20 February 1984. *SB 408* completed 5 June 1984. Second pair ordered 1984 *SB 921* completed 5 July 1985 and *SB 922* on 20 December 1985. *SB 922* named *Shakhter* in 1989. *SB 408* was sold illegally to a Greek company in March 1993 and the Navy is trying to reclaim it.

SB 406   9/1992

8 KASHTAN (TYPE 141) CLASS (BUOY TENDERS)

KIL 926	KIL 143	KIL 164	KIL 498
KIL 927	KIL 158	KIL 140	KIL 168

Displacement, tons: 4600 full load
Dimensions, feet (metres): 313.3 × 56.4 × 16.4 *(95.5 × 17.2 × 5)*
Main machinery: 4 Wärtsilä diesels; 29 000 hp(m) *(2.31 MW)*; 2 shafts
Speed, knots: 13.5
Complement: 51 plus 20 spare berths
Radars: Navigation: Nayada; I band.

Comment: Enlarged Sura class built at the Neptun Shipyard, Rostock. Ordered 29 August 1986; *926* handed over in June 1988 and is in the Baltic; *927* to the Pacific in July 1989; *143* to the North in July 1989; *158* to the Black Sea in November 1989; *164* to the North in January 1990; *140* to the Baltic in May 1990; *498* to the Pacific in November 1990 and *168* to the Pacific in mid-1991. Lifting capacity: one 130 ton lifting frame, one 100 ton derrick, one 12.5 ton crane and one 10 ton derrick.

KIL 140   7/1993, Hartmut Ehlers

10 SURA CLASS (BUOY TENDERS)

KIL 1, 2, 21, 22, 25, 27, 29, 31, 32, 33

Displacement, tons: 2370 standard; 3150 full load
Dimensions, feet (metres): 285.4 × 48.6 × 16.4 *(87 × 14.8 × 5)*
Main machinery: Diesel-electric; 4 diesel generators; 2 motors; 2240 hp(m) *(1.65 MW)*; 2 shafts
Speed, knots: 12. **Range, miles:** 2000 at 11 kts
Complement: 40
Cargo capacity: 900 tons cargo; 300 tons fuel for transfer
Radars: Navigation: Two Don 2; I band.

Comment: Heavy lift ships built as mooring and buoy tenders at Rostock in East Germany between 1965 and 1976. Lifting capacity: one 65 ton derrick and one 65 ton stern cage. Have been seen to carry 12 m DSRVs.

KIL 29   *3/1992, Erik Laursen*

9 KATUN I and 2 KATUN II CLASSES (SALVAGE TUGS)

Katun I: **PZHS 96, 98, 123, 124, 209, 273, 279, 282, 551**
Katun II: **PZHS 64, 92**

Displacement, tons: 920 full load
Dimensions, feet (metres): 205.3 × 33.1 × 11.5 *(62 × 10.1 × 3.5)* (Katun I)
Main machinery: 2 diesels; 5000 hp(m) *(3.68 MW)*; 2 shafts
Speed, knots: 17. **Range, miles:** 2000 at 17 kts
Complement: 30
Radars: Navigation: Spin Trough or Kivach (Katun II); I band.
IFF: High Pole A.

Comment: Katun I built in USSR 1970-78. Equipped for firefighting and rescue. PZHS 64 and 92, both Katun II, were completed in 1982—3 m *(9.8 ft)* longer than Katun I with an extra bridge level and lattice masts. Some may have a PDS prefix to their pennant numbers.

KATUN 123   *8/1991, van Ginderen Collection*

4 NEPTUN CLASS

KIL 6, 9, 15, 17

Displacement, tons: 1240 full load
Dimensions, feet (metres): 187.9 × 37.4 × 10.8 *(57.3 × 11.4 × 3.3)*
Main machinery: 2 boilers; 2 steam reciprocating engines; 1000 ihp(m) *(735 kW)*; 2 shafts
Speed, knots: 12. **Range, miles:** 1000 at 10 kts
Complement: 28

Comment: Mooring tenders similar to Western boom defence vessels. Built in 1957-60 by Neptun, Rostock. Have a crane of 75 tons lifting capacity on the bow. Several of the class scrapped since 1989.

NEPTUN   *1973*

3 ELBRUS (TYPE 537) CLASS (SUBMARINE RESCUE SHIPS)

ELBRUS   ALAGEZ   AYU-DAG (Ukraine)

Displacement, tons: 19 000 standard; 22 500 full load
Dimensions, feet (metres): 562.7 × 80.4 × 27.9 *(171.5 × 24.5 × 8.5)*
Main machinery: Diesel-electric; 4 diesel generators; 2 motors; 24 500 hp(m) *(18 MW)*; 2 shafts
Speed, knots: 17. **Range, miles:** 14 500 at 15 kts
Complement: 420
Guns: 4—30 mm/65 (2 twin).
Radars: Navigation: Don 2 and two Don Kay; I band.
Helicopters: 1 Ka-25 Hormone C.

Comment: Very large submarine rescue and salvage ships with icebreaking capability, possibly in view of under-ice capability of some SSBNs. Built at Nikolayev. First seen 1981. Second one completed 1989. Can carry two submersibles in store abaft the funnel which are launched from telescopic gantries. *Elbrus* is based in the Black Sea, *Alagez* in the Pacific. A third of class launched in 1992 and taken over by Ukraine.

ALAGEZ   *9/1991, G Jacobs*

1 NEPA (TYPE 530) CLASS (SUBMARINE RESCUE SHIP)

KARPATY

Displacement, tons: 6100 full load
Dimensions, feet (metres): 424.9 × 62 × 21 *(129.5 × 18.9 × 6.4)*
Main machinery: Diesel-electric; 4 diesel generators; 2 motors; 8000 hp(m) *(5.88 MW)*; 2 shafts
Speed, knots: 16. **Range, miles:** 8000 at 14 kts
Complement: 270
Radars: Navigation: Two Don 2; I band.
IFF: High Pole B.

Comment: Completed 1968 at Nikolayev. Submarine rescue and salvage ship with a special high stern which extends out over the water for rescue manoeuvres. Has two 750 ton lifts which can work in tandem. Also one 100 ton lift, one 60 ton derrick and two 10 ton derricks. Carries a rescue bell, two submersibles and a number of recompression chambers. Based in the Baltic since November 1988.

KARPATY   *1972, A Nubert*

6 PRUT (TYPE 527) CLASS (RESCUE TUGS)

ALTAY (ex-*SS 22*)   BESHTAU   SS 21
ZHIGULI (ex-*SS 25*)   EPRON (ex-*SS 26*)   SS 83

Displacement, tons: 2120 standard; 2800 full load
Dimensions, feet (metres): 295.9 × 46.9 × 18 *(90.2 × 14.3 × 5.5)*
Main machinery: Diesel-electric; 4 diesel generators; 2 motors; 10 000 hp(m) *(7.35 MW)*; 2 shafts
Speed, knots: 20. **Range, miles:** 9000 at 16 kts
Complement: 130
Guns: 4—57 mm/70 (2 quad) (not fitted).
Radars: Navigation: Two Don 2; I band.
Sonars: Tamir; hull-mounted; active search; high frequency.

Comment: Large rescue vessels. Built 1960-66. Carry two heavy-duty derricks, submersible recompression chambers, rescue chambers and bells. Four marker buoys stowed abaft mainmast. All except *Altay* and *Zhiguli* have been modernised with quadruped foremasts and smaller marker buoys. One scrapped in 1987, a second in 1993.

EPRON   *6/1991, van Ginderen Collection*

7 VALDAY (TYPE 532-A) CLASS (Ex-T 58 CLASS)
(SUBMARINE RESCUE SHIPS)

KHIBINY   VALDAY   ZANGEZUR   PULKOVO (ex-*SS 38*)
SS 30, 35, 47

Displacement, tons: 725 standard; 930 full load
Dimensions, feet (metres): 236.2 × 29.5 × 9.9 *(72 × 9 × 3)*
Main machinery: 2 diesels; 4000 hp(m) *(2.94 MW)*; 2 shafts
Speed, knots: 17. **Range, miles:** 2500 at 12 kts
Complement: 100
Radars: Navigation: Don; I band.
IFF: High Pole, Square Head or Dead Duck.
Sonars: Tamir; hull-mounted; active search; high frequency.

Comment: Basically of similar design to that of the T 58 class fleet minesweepers, but they were completed as emergency salvage vessels and submarine rescue ships at Leningrad in 1961-62. Equipped with diving bell, recompression chamber and emergency medical ward. Have stern lift of 10 tons and rescue chamber aft. One transferred to India (*Nistar* ex-SS 48) in 1971. Two scrapped in 1990, two more in 1992 and one in 1993.

VALDAY SS 30   *3/1992, Hartmut Ehlers*

1 MARINA TSVETAYEVA (TYPE B 961) CLASS (TRANSPORT)

MARINA TSVETAYEVA

Measurement, tons: 1500 gross
Dimensions, feet (metres): 291.3 × 56.4 × 16.4 *(88.8 × 17.2 × 5)*
Main machinery: 1 Zgoda-Sulzer 6ZL40/48 diesel; 4350 hp(m) *(3.2 MW)*; 1 shaft
Speed, knots: 14. **Range, miles:** 2000 at 14 kts
Complement: 34

Comment: Built at Gdynia in 1990/91. Capable of taking up to 240 troops. Based in the Pacific. More of the class may be built for offshore supply tasks.

MARINA TSVETAYEVA   *7/1991, 92 Wing RAAF*

1 ANADYR CLASS (AK)

ANADYR

Displacement, tons: 27 000 full load
Dimensions, feet (metres): 741.5 × 98.4 × 21.3 *(226 × 30 × 6.5)*
Main machinery: 4 Wärtsilä Vasa 16V32 diesels; 32 200 hp(m) *(23.7 MW)* sustained; 2 shafts
Speed, knots: 20
Complement: 70
Cargo capacity: 10 500 tons
Radars: Navigation: Two Spin Trough; I band.
Helicopters: 2 medium.

Comment: Ro-flo ship built at Wärtsilä, Finland and completed in 1988. Handed over to the Navy and transferred to the Pacific via the Northern Sea route in August 1990. The ship's well-deck is 150 m in length.

ANADYR   *10/1991, G Jacobs*

1 ANGARA CLASS (AGF)

ANGARA (ex-*Hela*)

Displacement, tons: 2520 full load
Dimensions, feet (metres): 327.4 × 41.7 × 13.5 *(99.8 × 12.7 × 4.1)*
Main machinery: 2 MAN diesels; 8360 hp(m) *(6.14 MW)*; 2 shafts
Speed, knots: 19. **Range, miles:** 2000 at 15 kts
Complement: 224
Radars: Navigation: Spin Trough; I band

Comment: Acts as a yacht for the Commander-in-Chief of the Navy. Stationed in the Black Sea. Built by Stülcken of Hamburg and launched 29 December 1938. Passed to USSR as partial reparation. Refit in Greece in 1983. Little change seen except improved electronics.

ANGARA   *5/1990, S Breyer*

1 AMGUEMA CLASS (TRANSPORT)

YAUZA

Displacement, tons: 15 000 full load
Dimensions, feet (metres): 436.4 × 62.3 × 29.7 *(133 × 19 × 9)*
Main machinery: Diesel-electric; 4 diesel generators; 1 motor; 7200 hp(m) *(5.29 MW)*; 1 shaft
Speed, knots: 16. **Range, miles:** 7000 at 15 kts
Cargo capacity: 6500 tons
Radars: Navigation: Two Don 2; I band.

Comment: Built in Kherson in 1974. Ice-strengthened. Similar class operates in merchant fleet. Based in the Northern Fleet.

YAUZA   *1985*

2 ANDIZAN CLASS (TRANSPORTS)

ONDA   POSYET

Displacement, tons: 6550 full load
Dimensions, feet (metres): 341.1 × 47.6 × 21.7 *(104 × 14.5 × 6.6)*
Main machinery: 2 diesels; 2500 hp(m) *(1.84 MW)*; 1 shaft
Speed, knots: 14. **Range, miles:** 6000 at 13 kts
Complement: 43
Cargo capacity: 4000 tons
Radars: Navigation: Don 2; I band.

Comment: Part of a class of about 50 merchant ships, built at Neptun, Rostock 1960-61. *Onda* in the North, *Posyet* in the Pacific.

ONDA   *7/1987*

1 KALININ CLASS (TRANSPORT)

KUBAN (ex-*Nadeshda-Krupskaya*)

Displacement, tons: 6400 full load
Dimensions, feet (metres): 401 × 52.5 × 16.4 *(122.2 × 16 × 5)*
Main machinery: 2 MAN diesels; 8000 hp(m) *(5.88 MW)*; 2 shafts
Speed, knots: 17. **Range, miles:** 8200 at 17 kts
Complement: 120 plus 350 passengers
Cargo capacity: 1000 tons
Radars: Navigation: Two Don 2; I band.

Comment: Built in 1958 by Mathias Thesen Werft, Wismar, East Germany. Part of Mikhail Kalinin class of merchant ships originally to have been 24 ships of which only 19 were completed 1958-64. Name changed on transfer to naval service. In the 1980s was employed under naval command as personnel support ship for the Mediterranean Squadron. May have reverted to civilian owners.

KUBAN   *1987, Selçuk Emre*

10 ANTONOV CLASS (TRANSPORTS)

IVAN ANTONOV	NIKOLAY SIPYAGIN	NICOLAY STARSHINOV
IVAN LEDNEV	VICTOR DENISOV	IVAN YEVTEYEV
DVINA	MIKHAIL KONOVALOV	SERGEY SUDETSKY
IRBIT		

Displacement, tons: 5600 full load
Dimensions, feet (metres): 311.7 × 48.2 × 21.3 *(95 × 14.7 × 6.5)*
Main machinery: 2 diesels; 7000 hp(m) *(5. 15 MW)*; 2 shafts
Speed, knots: 17. **Range, miles:** 8500 at 13 kts
Complement: 40
Capacity: 2500 tons
Missiles: SAM: 2 SA-N-5 Grail twin launchers; manual aiming; IR homing to 6 km *(3.2 nm)* at 1.5 Mach; altitude to 2500 m *(8000 ft)*; warhead 1.5 kg.
Guns: 2—30 mm/65 (twin). 4—14.5 mm (2 twin) MGs.
Radars: Navigation: Don Kay; Spin Trough; I band.

Comment: Ten of the class built at Nikolayev in 1975-early 1980s. All but *Irbit* (Pacific Fleet) and *Dvina* (Northern Fleet) operated by the Border Guard in the Pacific. Have two small landing craft aft. Armament is not normally mounted.

SERGEY SUDETSKY *1/1992, van Ginderen Collection*

4 PARTIZAN CLASS (TRANSPORTS)

PECHORA	TURGAY	UFA	V ADM FOMIN (ex-*Pinega*) (mod)

Displacement, tons: 2150 full load
Dimensions, feet (metres): 291.3 × 42.3 × 16.4 *(88.8 × 12.9 × 5)*
Main machinery: 1 Sulzer diesel; 2080 hp(m) *(1.53 MW)*; 1 shaft
Speed, knots: 13. **Range, miles:** 4000 at 12 kts
Complement: 35
Cargo capacity: 3150 tons
Radars: Navigation: Don 2 or Palm Frond; I band.

Comment: Built at Turnu Severin SY, Romania 1975-76. Have two 10 ton and one 20 ton derricks. Basically small container ships with 20 similar in merchant fleet. *Fomin* is an ammunition transport and is armed with SA-N-5 missiles and two twin MG mountings.

PECHORA *9/1988*

10 KEYLA CLASS (TRANSPORTS)

MEZEN	ONEGA	PONOI
RITSA (AGI)	TERIBERKA	TULOMA
TVERTSA	UNZA	USSURY
YERUSLAN		

Displacement, tons: 2440 full load
Dimensions, feet (metres): 257.5 × 34.8 × 14.8 *(78.5 × 10.6 × 4.5)*
Main machinery: 1 diesel; 1000 hp(m) *(735 kW)*; 1 shaft
Speed, knots: 14. **Range, miles:** 3000 at 11 kts
Complement: 26
Cargo capacity: 1195 tons
Radars: Navigation: Spin Trough or Neptun (plus Don 2 in some); I band.

Comment: Built 1959-61 in Budapest. Cargo ships. *Ritsa* has a deckhouse forward of the bridge, several communications type aerials, and has been used for intelligence gathering. *Teriberka* and *Ussury*, of original design, have one 15 ton and six 2.5 ton derricks. The remainder have one 10 ton and six 5 ton derricks.

PONOI *9/1991, G Jacobs*

13 MUNA CLASS (TRANSPORTS)

VTR 28, 48, 81-86, 91-94, 148

Displacement, tons: 690 full load
Dimensions, feet (metres): 165 × 26.9 × 9.5 *(50.3 × 8.2 × 2.9)*
Main machinery: 1 diesel; 300 hp(m) *(220 kW)*; 1 shaft
Speed, knots: 10. **Range, miles:** 3000 at 10 kts
Complement: 40
Radars: Navigation: Two Spin Trough; I band.

Comment: Torpedo and ammunition transports with large crane amidships. Most have VTR prefix to their pennant numbers. Some act as experimental ships. Two more of this class are listed under *Survey Ships*.

MUNA *8/1991, G Jacobs*

8 MAYAK CLASS (TRANSPORTS)

BUZULUK, ISHIM, LAMA, MIUS, NEMAN, RIONI, ULMA, VYTEGRA

Displacement, tons: 920 full load
Dimensions, feet (metres): 178.1 × 30.5 × 11.8 *(54.3 × 9.3 × 3.6)*
Main machinery: 1 diesel; 1000 hp(m) *(735 kW)*; 1 shaft
Speed, knots: 12. **Range, miles:** 11 000 at 11 kts
Cargo capacity: 240 tons refrigerated stores
Radars: Navigation: Spin Trough; I Band.

Comment: Converted trawlers. Refrigerated stores ships.

LAMA *7/1992*

4 MP 6 CLASS

BIRA	VOLOGDA	IRGIZ	VTR 412

Displacement, tons: 2130 full load
Dimensions, feet (metres): 246 × 37.1 × 14.4 *(75 × 11.3 × 4.4)*
Main machinery: 2 diesels; 800 hp(m) *(588 kW)*; 2 shafts
Speed, knots: 11. **Range, miles:** 3000 at 10 kts
Cargo capacity: 1000 tons
Guns: 6—37 mm/63 (3 twin) (not always fitted).
Radars: Navigation: Don 2 and Spin Trough; I band.

Comment: Ex-amphibious craft. Bow doors now welded shut. One 10 ton derrick on some; six 2.5 ton derricks in all. Two of the class are used as ammunition transports.

BIRA *3/1992, Hartmut Ehlers*

4 POTOK CLASS (TORPEDO EXPERIMENTAL SHIPS)

OS-100   OS-138   OS-145   OS-225

Displacement, tons: 850 full load
Dimensions, feet (metres): 236.5 × 30.8 × 8.2 *(72.1 × 9.4 × 2.5)*
Main machinery: 2 diesels; 4000 hp(m) *(2.94 MW)*; 2 shafts
Speed, knots: 17. **Range, miles:** 2500 at 12 kts
Torpedoes: 1—21 in *(533 mm)* tube. 1—16 in *(406 mm)* tube.

Comment: Used for torpedo trials in Black Sea. Torpedo tubes fitted on fo'c'sle with large recovery crane aft. Built since 1977. Type name is *opytnoye sudno* meaning experimental ship. Two scrapped in 1988-89.

OS-225   1978

20 SHELON CLASS (TRVs)

Displacement, tons: 270 full load
Dimensions, feet (metres): 150.9 × 19.7 × 6.6 *(46 × 6 × 2)*
Main machinery: 2 diesels; 10 000 hp(m) *(7.35 MW)*; 2 shafts
Speed, knots: 26
Complement: 20
Radars: Navigation: Spin Trough or Kivach; I band.

Comment: Built 1978-84. Built-in weapon recovery ramp aft.

SHELON   5/1992

70 POLUCHAT I, II and III CLASSES (TRVs)

Displacement, tons: 70 standard; 100 full load
Dimensions, feet (metres): 97.1 × 19 × 4.8 *(29.6 × 5.8 × 1.5)*
Main machinery: 2 M 50 diesels; 2200 hp(m) *(1.6 MW)* sustained; 2 shafts
Speed, knots: 20. **Range, miles:** 1500 at 10 kts
Complement: 15
Guns: 2—14.5 mm (twin) MGs (in some).
Radars: Navigation: Spin Trough; I band.

Comment: Employed as specialised or dual purpose torpedo recovery vessels and/or patrol boats. They have a stern slipway. Several exported as patrol craft. Some used by the Border Guard. Transfers: Algeria, Angola, Congo (three), Ethiopia (one), Guinea-Bissau, India, Indonesia (three), Iraq (two), Mozambique, Somalia (six), Syria, Tanzania, Vietnam (five), North Yemen (two), South Yemen. Many deleted.

POLUCHAT III   6/1989

16 OSA I (TYPE 205) CLASS

Comment: Details as in Light Forces (Osa) but with no armament. Half used as control craft and remainder as target vessels. Control craft use Square Tie radar while the targets carry radar reflectors and heat generators. In addition there is a large number of immobile target barges fitted with infra-red sources and radar reflectors as well as a number of P 6 class.

OSA Target   5/1990

4 KOMANDOR CLASS (FISHERY CONTROL SHIPS)

KOMANDOR   SHKIPER GYEK   HERLUF BIDSTRUP   +1

Displacement, tons: 2435 full load
Dimensions, feet (metres): 289.7 × 44.6 × 15.4 *(88.3 × 13.6 × 4.7)*
Main machinery: 2 Russkiy SEMT-Pielstick 6 PC2.5 L 400 diesels; 7020 hp(m) *(5.2 MW)* sustained; 1 shaft; bow thruster; 1500 hp(m) *(1.1 MW)*
Speed, knots: 19. **Range, miles:** 7000 at 19 kts
Complement: 42
Radars: Navigation: Furuno; I band.
Helicopters: 2 Helix type for SAR.

Comment: Built by Danyard A/S for the Ministry of Fisheries. Contract signed in December 1987 and the ships were completed between August 1989 and April 1990. The hull is ice strengthened. The helicopter deck has a lift serving the double hangar below. There are considerable command and control facilities and these vessels have obvious military potential.

HERLUF BIDSTRUP   5/1992, 92 Wing RAAF

16 ONEGA CLASS (AGS)

GKS 52	SFP 95	SFP 173	SFP 224	SFP 240	GKS 244	SFP 283	GKS 286
SFP 295	SFP 322	SFP 340	SFP 372	SFP 511	SFP 542	SFP 562	SFP 177

Displacement, tons: 2150 full load
Dimensions, feet (metres): 265.7 × 36 × 13.7 *(81 × 11 × 4.2)*
Main machinery: 2 gas-turbines; 8000 hp(m) *(5.88 MW)*; 1 shaft
Speed, knots: 20
Complement: 45
Radars: Navigation: Neptun or Spin Trough; I band.

Comment: First seen in September 1973. Helicopter platform but no hangar in earlier ships of the class but in later hulls the space is taken up with more laboratory accommodation. Used as hydroacoustic monitoring ships.

ONEGA GKS   7/1993, Hartmut Ehlers

SFP 173   5/1991

18 T 43 CLASS (AGS)

GKS 11, 12-24, 26, 37, 45, 62

Comment: Details under *Mine Warfare Forces*. Fitted with davits aft for laying hydroacoustic buoys for measuring ships' noise signatures. Unarmed but can carry one 37 mm/63 on fo'c'sle.

GKS 17   *4/1992, van Ginderen Collection*

FLAMINGO CLASS (TENDERS)

Displacement, tons: 42 full load
Dimensions, feet (metres): 72.8 × 12.8 × 4.6 *(22.2 × 3.9 × 1.4)*
Main machinery: 1 Type 3-D-12 diesel; 300 hp(m) *(220 kW)* sustained; 1 shaft
Speed, knots: 12
Complement: 8

Comment: Successor to Nyryat II as a diving tender and for miscellaneous harbour duties by the Border Guard.

FLAMINGO   *7/1993, Hartmut Ehlers*

PO 2 and NYRYAT 2 CLASSES (TENDERS)

Displacement, tons: 56 full load
Dimensions, feet (metres): 70.5 × 11.5 × 3.3 *(21.5 × 3.5 × 1)*
Main machinery: 1 Type 3-D-12 diesel; 300 hp(m) *(220 kW)* sustained; 1 shaft
Speed, knots: 12
Complement: 8
Guns: Some carry 1—12.7 mm MG on the fo'c'sle.

Comment: This 1950s design of hull and machinery has been used for a wide and diverse number of adaptations. Steel hull. Nyryat 2 have the same characteristics but are used as diving tenders and inshore survey craft.
Transfers: Albania, Bulgaria, Cuba, Guinea, Iraq. Many deleted.

NYRYAT 2   *3/1992*

NYRYAT I CLASS (TENDERS)

Displacement, tons: 120 full load
Dimensions, feet (metres): 93 × 18 × 5.5 *(28.4 × 5.5 × 1.7)*
Main machinery: 1 diesel; 450 hp(m) *(331 kW)*; 1 shaft
Speed, knots: 12.5. **Range, miles:** 1500 at 10 kts
Complement: 15
Guns: 1—12.7 mm MG (in some).

Comment: Built from 1955. Can operate as patrol craft or diving tenders with recompression chamber. Similar hull and propulsion used for inshore survey craft. Some have BGK, VM or GBP numbers.
Transfers: Albania, Algeria, Cuba, Egypt, Iraq, North Yemen. Many deleted.

NYRYAT I   *3/1992*

25 SK 620 CLASS (TENDERS)

Displacement, tons: 236 full load
Dimensions, feet (metres): 108.3 × 24.3 × 6.9 *(33 × 7.4 × 2.1)*
Main machinery: 2 56ANM30-H12 diesels; 620 hp(m) *(456 kW)* sustained; 2 shafts
Speed, knots: 12. **Range, miles:** 1000 at 12 kts
Complement: 14 plus 3 spare

Comment: Built at Wisla Shipyard, Poland as a smaller version of the Petrushka class training ship. Mostly used as a hospital tender capable of carrying 15 patients.

SK 620   *7/1993, Hartmut Ehlers*

1 DALDYN CLASS (TENDER)

DALDYN

Displacement, tons: 360
Dimensions, feet (metres): 103.6 × 23.9 × 9.2 *(31.7 × 7.3 × 2.8)*
Main machinery: 1 SKL 6 VD 36/24-1U diesel; 305 hp(m) *(224 kW)* sustained; 1 shaft
Speed, knots: 9
Complement: 13

Comment: First seen in May 1973. Of Kareliya class trawler design with a high bridge. Used for MCM trials.

DALDYN   *1973*

12 YELVA CLASS (DIVING TENDERS)

VM 143, 146, 154, 266, 268, 413, 414, 416, 420, 425, 907, 909

Displacement, tons: 300 full load
Dimensions, feet (metres): 134.2 × 26.2 × 6.6 *(40.9 × 8 × 2)*
Main machinery: 2 Type 3-D-12A diesels; 630 hp(m) *(463 kW)* sustained; 2 shafts
Speed, knots: 12.5
Complement: 30
Radars: Navigation: Spin Trough; I band.

Comment: Diving tenders built in early 1970s. Carry a 1 ton crane and diving bell. Some have submersible recompression chamber. Ice-strengthened. One to Cuba 1973, one to Libya 1977.

YELVA 413   *7/1992, van Ginderen Collection*

9 IVA (MORKOV) (TYPE 1461.3) CLASS (FIRE/PATROL CRAFT)

PZHK 415, 900, 1514, 1544, 1547, 1859   **+ 3**

Displacement, tons: 320 full load
Dimensions, feet (metres): 119.8 × 25.6 × 7.2 *(36.5 × 7.8 × 2.2)*
Main machinery: 2 diesels; 1040 hp(m) *(764 kW)*; 2 shafts
Speed, knots: 12.5
Complement: 20

Comment: Carry four water monitors. Completed in 1984-86. Can be used for patrol/towage.

IVA 900   *7/1993, van Ginderen Collection*

40 POZHARNY I CLASS (FIREFIGHTING CRAFT)

Displacement, tons: 180 full load
Dimensions, feet (metres): 114.5 × 20 × 6 *(34.9 × 6.1 × 1.8)*
Main machinery: 2 Type M 50 diesels; 2200 hp(m) *(1.6 MW)* sustained; 2 shafts
Speed, knots: 10
Guns: 4—12.7 mm (2 twin) MGs (in some).

Comment: Built in the mid-1950s. Harbour fire boats but can be used for patrol duties. One transferred to Iraq.

POZHARNY I   *7/1993, Hartmut Ehlers*

HARBOUR CRAFT

Comment: There are numerous types of harbour launches, training cutters and trials vessels (including a converted Kola class frigate) in all of the major Fleet bases.

HARBOUR CRAFT   *7/1993, Hartmut Ehlers*

23 PELYM (TYPE 1799) CLASS (DEGAUSSING SHIPS)

SR 26	SR 70	SR 111	SR 179	SR 180	SR 188	SR 191
SR 203	SR 215	SR 218	SR 221	SR 222	SR 233	SR 241
SR 276	SR 280	SR 281	SR 334	SR 344	SR 407	SR 409
SR 455						

Displacement, tons: 1370 full load
Dimensions, feet (metres): 214.8 × 38 × 11.2 *(65.5 × 11.6 × 3.4)*
Main machinery: 2 diesels; 2400 hp(m) *(1.76 MW)*; 2 shafts
Speed, knots: 14. **Range, miles:** 4500 at 13 kts
Complement: 70

Comment: First completed in 1971. Earlier ships have stump mast on funnel, later ships a tripod main mast and a platform deck extending to the stern. Type name is *sudno razmagnichivanya* meaning degaussing ship. One to Cuba 1982.

PELYM SR 409   *5/1979*

19 BEREZA (TYPE 130) CLASS (DEGAUSSING SHIPS)

SR 23	SR 28	SR 59	SR 74	SR 120	SR 137	SR 188
SR 216	SR 245	SR 370	SR 478	SR 479	SR 541	SR 548
SR 568	SR 569	SR 936	SR 938	SR 939		

Displacement, tons: 1850 standard; 2051 full load
Dimensions, feet (metres): 228 × 45.3 × 13.1 *(69.5 × 13.8 × 4)*
Main machinery: 2 Zgoda-Sulzer 8AL25/30 diesels; 2938 hp(m) *(2.16 MW)* sustained
Speed, knots: 14. **Range, miles:** 1000 at 14 kts
Complement: 48
Radars: Navigation: Kivach; I band.

Comment: First completed at Northern Shipyard, Gdansk in 1984. One transferred to Bulgaria in 1988. Have NBC citadels and three laboratories. Two laid up in 1993.

BEREZA SR 568 (with Kilo)   *10/1991, van Ginderen Collection*

2 LARGE FLOATING DOCKS

PD 41   PD 50

Displacement, tons: 80 000
Dimensions, feet (metres): 1082.4 × 232.9 (inertial beam) × 49.2 (over blocks) *(330 × 71 × 15) (PD 41)*
1000.4 × 226.3 (inertial beam) × 49.2 (over blocks) *(305 × 69 × 15) (PD 50)*
Complement: 175

Comment: Amongst the largest independently supported dry docks in the world. *PD 41* built by Ishikawajima Heavy Industries, Japan and towed to Vladivostok in October 1978. *PD 50* built by Götaverken Arendal, Sweden. Two 30 ton cranes *(PD 41)* and two 50 ton *(PD 50)*.

30 SEKSTAN CLASS (DEGAUSSING SHIPS)

Displacement, tons: 528 full load
Dimensions, feet (metres): 136.2 × 29.9 × 9.8 *(41.5 × 9.1 × 3)*
Main machinery: 1 diesel; 400 hp(m) *(294 kW)*; 1 shaft
Speed, knots: 10

Comment: Most have SR numbers in the 100 series.

150 FLOATING DOCKS

Comment: There is a dock of some 35-40 000 tons capacity in Vladivostok in addition to the 80 000 ton dock above. At least six of 30 000 tons capacity have been built in Yugoslavia and another six of about 28 000 tons capacity have been delivered from Sweden. The 20 or so various types of docks which are in use throughout the Russian naval bases may total about 150 of which about half have a capacity of 5000 tons to 25 000 tons. There are also numerous floating cranes, barges and workshops.

ICEBREAKERS

Note: All these ships are operated by Ministry of Merchant Marine and civilian manned except for the seven Dobrynya Nikitich class shown as being naval manned. All are an indispensable part of many naval operations not only in the Baltic, Northern and Pacific Fleet areas but also on rivers, lakes and canals.

2 TAMYR CLASS

Name	Builders	Launched	Commissioned
TAMYR	Wärtsilä, Helsinki	10 Apr 1987	7 Apr 1988
VAYGACH	Wärtsilä, Helsinki	26 Feb 1988	8 Mar 1989

Displacement, tons: 23 500 full load
Dimensions, feet (metres): 492 × 93.8 × 26.2 *(150 × 28.6 × 8)*
Main machinery: Nuclear; 2 PWR; 3 turbines; 52 000 hp(m) *(38 MW)*; 3 shafts
Speed, knots: 18.5
Complement: 138 plus 12 spare bunks
Radars: Navigation: 3 Okean; I band.
Helicopters: 1 Ka-32 Helix C.

Comment: Ordered 12 November 1984. Both ships had to spend over a year in the Baltic Yard, Leningrad for installation of nuclear reactors. The design is a combined Finnish/USSR effort, the requirement being for comparatively shallow draught ships to operate in Siberian estuaries in temperatures down to −50°C. *Tamyr* joined the Northern Fleet in July 1989, *Vaygach* in late 1990.

TAMYR   *8/1991, Bryan Hird*

5 + 1 ARKTIKA CLASS

Name	Builders	Launched	Commissioned
ARKTIKA	Baltic Yard, Leningrad	Dec 1972	Dec 1974
SIBIR	Baltic Yard, Leningrad	Feb 1976	Nov 1977
ROSSIYA	Baltic Yard, Leningrad	2 Nov 1983	Feb 1986
SOVETSKIY SOYUZ	Baltic Yard, Leningrad	31 Oct 1986	Jan 1990
YAMAL (ex-*Oktyabryskaya Revolutsiya*)	Baltic Yard, Leningrad	4 Oct 1989	Oct 1992
URAL	Baltic Yard, Leningrad	31 Dec 1993	1996

Displacement, tons: 19 300 standard; 23 460 full load
Dimensions, feet (metres): 485.4 × 98.4 × 36.4 *(148 × 30 × 11.1)*
Main machinery: Nuclear; 2 PWR; 3 turbines; 67 500 hp(m) *(49.6 MW)*; 3 shafts
Speed, knots: 22
Complement: 144 (49 officers)
Guns: 4—3 in *(76 mm)*/60 (2 twin) (fitted for but not with). 2—30 mm/65 AK 630.
Radars: Air/surface search: Head Net C (first two); Flat Screen (remainder); 3D; E band.
Navigation: Don 2 or Palm Frond; I band.
Helicopters: 2 Ka-32 Helix C.

Comment: *Ural* laid down in October 1989. *Arktika* was renamed *L I Brezhnev* in 1982 but reverted to original name in 1986. Can be fitted with guns and fire-control radars. Some superstructure differences between the first two and the newer ships. The purpose of these ships is to extend the Arctic passage navigational season beyond the present June to October period, but according to a former Captain of *Arktika* the ships would need twice the power to achieve this aim, and it is reported that *Ural* may have an increased power output of 90 000 bhp. 2.3 m ice can be broken at 3 kts and ridges up to 8 m have been broken. Double hull construction with water ballast. The outer hull is 55 mm thick at ice levels, with the cast steel prow 2 m thick at its strongest point.

ROSSIYA   *7/1992*

SOVETSKIY SOYUZ   *7/1992*

3 YERMAK CLASS

Name	Builders	Launched	Commissioned
YERMAK	Wärtsilä, Helsinki	7 Sep 1973	30 June 1974
ADMIRAL MAKAROV	Wärtsilä, Helsinki	26 Apr 1974	2 June 1975
KRASIN	Wärtsilä, Helsinki	18 Apr 1975	28 Apr 1976

Displacement, tons: 20 241 full load
Dimensions, feet (metres): 442.8 × 85.3 × 36.1 *(135 × 26 × 11)*
Main machinery: Diesel-electric; 9 Wärtsilä-Sulzer 12ZA40 diesels; 88 344 hp(m) *(65 MW)*; 9 Oy Strömberg Ab generators; 3 Strömberg motors; 36 000 hp(m) *(26.5 MW)*; 3 shafts
Speed, knots: 19.5. **Range, miles:** 40 000 at 15 kts
Complement: 118 plus 28 spare berths
Radars: Navigation: Okean and Don 2; I band.
Helicopters: Platform only.

Comment: Ordered on 29 April 1970 from Wärtsilä Shipyard, Helsinki, for delivery in 1974, 1975 and 1976. These are the first vessels to be fitted with Wärtsilä mixed-flow air-bubbling system to decrease friction between hull and ice. Can maintain 2 kts in 6 ft ice.
There is also a former icebreaker built in 1917 called *Krasin* which is still afloat and occasionally goes to sea.

KRASIN   *3/1992*

3 MOSKVA CLASS

Name	Builders	Launched	Commissioned
LENINGRAD	Wärtsilä, Helsinki	24 Oct 1959	Sep 1960
MURMANSK	Wärtsilä, Helsinki	14 July 1967	May 1968
VLADIVOSTOK	Wärtsilä, Helsinki	28 May 1968	Apr 1969

Displacement, tons: 13 290 standard; 15 360 full load
Dimensions, feet (metres): 400.7 × 80.3 × 34.5 *(122.2 × 24.5 × 10.5)*
Main machinery: Diesel-electric; 8 Wärtsilä-Sulzer 9MH51 diesels; 8 generators; 26 000 hp(m) *(19.1 MW)* (*Murmansk* and *Vladivostok*); 22 000 hp(m) *(16.2 MW)* (remainder); 1 motor (centre shaft); 11 000 hp(m) *(8.1 MW)*; 2 motors (wing shafts); 5500 hp(m) *(4 MW)*; 3 shafts
Speed, knots: 18. **Range, miles:** 20 000 at 14 kts
Complement: 100
Helicopters: 2 Ka-32 Helix C.

Comment: Designed to stay at sea for a year without returning to base. The concave embrasure in the ship's stern is a housing for the bow of a following vessel when additional power is required. Becoming increasingly unreliable and two were scrapped in 1993.

LENINGRAD   *3/1992*

4 KAPITAN SOROKIN CLASS

Name	Builders	Commissioned
KAPITAN SOROKIN (mod)	Wärtsilä, Helsinki	14 July 1977
KAPITAN NIKOLAYEV	Wärtsilä, Helsinki	31 Jan 1978
KAPITAN DRANITSYN	Wärtsilä, Helsinki	2 Dec 1980
KAPITAN KHLEBNIKOV	Wärtsilä, Helsinki	1 Dec 1981

Displacement, tons: 14 917 full load; 17 150 (conversion) full load
Dimensions, feet (metres): 424.5; 463.9 (conversion) × 86.9; 102 (conversion) × 27.9
(129.4; 141.4 × 26.5; 31.1 × 8.5)
Main machinery: Diesel-electric; 6 Wärtsilä-Sulzer 9ZL40/48 diesels; 24 800 hp(m) *(18.2 MW)*; 6 alternators; 22 000 hp(m) *(16.2 MW)*; 3 motors; 3 shafts
Speed, knots: 19. **Range, miles:** 10 500 at 16 kts
Complement: 76 (16 spare berths)
Helicopters: Platform only.

Comment: Shallow draught polar icebreakers fitted with Wärtsilä bubbling system. Fitted with single cabins (except spare berths), sauna, swimming pool, gymnasium, library, cinema and hospital. They are used for North Siberian operations in shallow deltas at ambient temperatures down to −50°C. As a result of *Mudyug's* successful conversion, the first two of this class are being given similar treatment with major extensions to bow and stern. *Sorokin* completed 18 November 1990 at Thyssen-Nordseewerke, Emden. *Nikolayev* is planned to be similarly converted in due course. After conversion the hull is 17 per cent wider, has an increased displacement of 15 per cent and, as well as cutting a wider channel, has an icebreaking performance increased by 48 per cent to 2.15 m thick.

KAPITAN KHLEBNIKOV   *11/1992, Robert Pabst*

KAPITAN SOROKIN (modified)   *7/1992*

21 DOBRYNYA NIKITICH CLASS

AFANASY NIKITIN (ex-*Ledokol 2*) (1962)
BURAN (1966)*
DOBRYNYA NIKITICH (1960)*
FEDOR LITKE (1970)
GEORGY SEDOV (1967)**
ILYA MUROMETS (1966)*
IVAN MOSKVITIN (1971)
IVAN KRUZENSHTERN (ex-*Ledokol 6*)(1964)
KHARITON LAPTEV (ex-*Ledokol 3*) (1962)
P PAKHTUSOV (1966)**
PERESVET (1969)*
YURY LISYANSKY (ex-*Ledokol 9*) (1965)
PURGA (1961)*
SADKO (1968)*
SEMEN CHELYUSKIN (ex-*Ledokol 8*) (1965)
SEMEN DEZHNEV (1971)
VASILY POYARKOV (ex-*Ledokol 4*) (1963)
VLADIMIR RUSANOV (ex-*Ledokol 7*)(1964)
VYUGA (1961)* (ex-*Ledokol 5*) (1963)
YEROFEI KHABAROV
PLUG (1961)
    * Naval manned.
    ** Occasionally used for hydrographic work in the Arctic.

Displacement, tons: 2995 full load
Measurement, tons: 2254 gross; 1118 dwt; 50 net
Dimensions, feet (metres): 222.1 × 59.4 × 20 *(67.7 × 18.1 × 6.1)*
Main machinery: Diesel-electric; 3 Type 13-D-100 diesel generators; 3 motors; 5400 hp(m) *(4 MW)*; 3 shafts (1 fwd, 2 aft)
Speed, knots: 14.5. **Range, miles:** 5500 at 12 kts
Complement: 45
Guns: 2—57 mm/70 (twin). 2—37 mm/63 (fitted for but not with in *Dobrynya Nikitich* and *Vyuga*). 2—25 mm/80 (twin) *(Sadko)* (fitted for but not with in remainder). Non-naval ships unarmed.
Radars: Navigation: Two Don 2; I band.

Comment: All built at Admiralty Yard, Leningrad between 1960 (first ship, *Dobrynya Nikitich*) and 1971 (last ship, *Semen Dezhnev*). Divided between the Baltic, Black Sea and Pacific. One scrapped in 1989.

AFANASY NIKITIN   *7/1992*

3 MUDYUG CLASS

Name	Builders	Launched	Commissioned
MUDYUG	Wärtsilä, Helsinki	16 Apr 1982	29 Oct 1982
MAGADAN	Wärtsilä, Helsinki	16 Apr 1982	29 Dec 1982
DIKSON	Wärtsilä, Helsinki	16 Apr 1982	17 Mar 1983

Displacement, tons: 6210; 7775 *(Mudyug)*
Dimensions, feet (metres): 290.7 × 69.6 × 19.7 *(88.6 × 21.2 × 6)*
365.5 × 72.8 × 21.3 *(111.4 × 22.2 × 6.5)* *(Mudyug)*
Main machinery: 4 Wärtsilä Vasa 8R32 diesels; 16 100 hp(m) *(11.83 MW)* sustained; 2 shafts; cp props
Speed, knots: 16.5. **Range, miles:** 15 000 at 16 kts
Complement: 43
Radars: Navigation: Okean and Nyada; I band.

Comment: Ordered on 3 April 1980. For use in Barents Sea, the Baltic and the Sea of Okhotsk. Fitted with Wärtsilä bubbling gear. *Mudyug* fitted with a new ice-breaking bow and longer stern by Thyssen-Nordseewerke, Emden. This means a power saving of about 65 per cent when breaking ice. Completed 30 October 1986.

DIKSON   *8/1989*

MUDYUG (modified)   *1992*

3 KAPITAN IZMAYLOV CLASS

Name	Builders	Launched	Commissioned
KAPITAN M IZMAYLOV	Wärtsilä, Helsinki	11 Dec 1975	15 June 1976
KAPITAN KOSOLAPOV	Wärtsilä, Helsinki	13 Feb 1976	14 July 1976
KAPITAN A RADZABOV	Wärtsilä, Helsinki	9 Mar 1976	5 Oct 1976

Displacement, tons: 2045 full load
Dimensions, feet (metres): 185.3 × 51.5 × 13.8 *(56.5 × 15.7 × 4.2)*
Main machinery: Diesel-electric; 4 Wärtsilä Vasa 824TS diesel generators; 5820 hp(m) *(3.83 MW)*; 2 Strömberg motors; 3400 hp(m) *(2.5 MW)*; 2 shafts
Speed, knots: 13. **Range, miles:** 5000 at 12 kts
Complement: 25
Radars: Navigation: Low Trough; I band.

Comment: Contract signed with Wärtsilä, Helsinki on 22 March 1974 for the building of these three icebreakers for delivery in 1976. All fitted with Wärtsilä air-bubbling system.

KAPITAN A RADZABOV   *7/1986, Ralf Bendfeldt*

3 KAPITAN BELOUSOV CLASS

Name	Builders	Launched	Commissioned
KAPITAN BELOUSOV	Wärtsilä, Helsinki	1954	1955
KAPITAN MELEKHOV	Wärtsilä, Helsinki	1955	1957
KAPITAN VORONIN	Wärtsilä, Helsinki	1956	1956

Displacement, tons: 4375-4415 standard; 5350 full load
Dimensions, feet (metres): 273 × 63.7 × 23 (83.3 × 19.4 × 7)
Main machinery: Diesel-electric; 6 Polar diesel generators; 4 motors; 10 500 hp(m) (7.72 MW); 4 shafts (2 fwd, 2 aft)
Speed, knots: 14.9. **Range, miles:** 10 000 at 14 kts
Complement: 75

Comment: Used for harbour ice clearance.

KAPITAN BELOUSOV   1970, Michael D J Lennon

6 KAPITAN CHECHKIN CLASS

Name	Builders	Launched	Commissioned
KAPITAN CHECHKIN	Wärtsilä, Helsinki	29 Apr 1977	6 Nov 1977
KAPITAN PLAKHIN	Wärtsilä, Helsinki	8 Aug 1977	30 Dec 1977
KAPITAN CHADAYEV	Wärtsilä, Helsinki	13 Oct 1977	7 Apr 1978
KAPITAN KRUTOV	Wärtsilä, Helsinki	11 Jan 1978	6 June 1978
KAPITAN BUKAYEV	Wärtsilä, Helsinki	3 Mar 1978	29 Sep 1978
KAPITAN ZARUBIN	Wärtsilä, Helsinki	13 May 1978	10 Nov 1978

Displacement, tons: 2240 full load
Dimensions, feet (metres): 254.5 × 53.5 × 10.7 (77.6 × 16.3 × 3.3)
Main machinery: Diesel-electric; 3 Wärtsilä Vasa 12V22 diesel generators; 6.3 MW sustained; 3 motors; 3877 hp(m) (2.85 MW); 3 shafts
Speed, knots: 14
Complement: 28

Comment: Ordered 16 May 1975. Designed for service on Volga-Baltic waterways and Siberian rivers. Fitted with three rudders, air-bubbling system and an automatic lowering system for masts, radar and aerials.

KAPITAN CHADAYEV (operating bubbling equipment)   1978, Wärtsilä

8 KAPITAN YEVDOKIMOV CLASS

Name	Builders	Commissioned
KAPITAN YEVDOKIMOV	Wärtsilä, Helsinki	31 Mar 1983
KAPITAN BABICHEV	Wärtsilä, Helsinki	30 June 1983
KAPITAN CHUDINOV	Wärtsilä, Helsinki	9 Sep 1983
KAPITAN BORODKIN	Wärtsilä, Helsinki	18 Nov 1983
AVRAMIY ZAVENYAGIN (ex-Kapitan Krylov)	Wärtsilä, Helsinki	1 Dec 1983
KAPITAN METSAYK	Wärtsilä, Helsinki	21 Aug 1984
KAPITAN DEMIDOV	Wärtsilä, Helsinki	22 Nov 1984
KAPITAN MOSHKIN	Wärtsilä, Helsinki	14 May 1986

Displacement, tons: 2150 full load
Dimensions, feet (metres): 250.9 × 54.4 × 8.2 (76.5 × 16.6 × 2.5)
Main machinery: Diesel-electric; 3 Wärtsilä Vasa 12V22 diesel generators; 6.3 kVA 60 Hz; 4 Strömberg motors; 5170 hp(m) (3.8 MW); 4 shafts
Speed, knots: 13.5
Complement: 25

Comment: Contract for first seven signed in December 1980 for completion by 1984. One more ordered in 1983. This design is unique, having a draught shallower than any previous icebreaker. Designed for service in temperatures of −50°C on Siberian rivers and deltas.

KAPITAN YEVDOKIMOV   1990, van Ginderen Collection

6 STROPTIVY CLASS

Name	Builders	Commissioned
STAKHANOVETS	Wärtsilä, Helsinki	29 Feb 1980
SIBIRSKY	Wärtsilä, Helsinki	2 July 1980
SPRAVEDLIVY	Wärtsilä, Helsinki	1982
SUVOROVETS	Wärtsilä, Helsinki	1982
FOBOS	Wärtsilä, Helsinki	29 Apr 1983
DEYMOS	Wärtsilä, Helsinki	31 May 1983

Displacement, tons: 4200 full load
Dimensions, feet (metres): 238.5 × 59 × 21.3 (72.7 × 18 × 6.5)
Main machinery: 2 Wärtsilä SEMT-Pielstick 6 PC2.5 L 400 diesels; 7020 hp(m) (5.2 MW) sustained; 2 shafts; cp props; bow thruster
Speed, knots: 15
Complement: 40 plus 12 spare berths

Comment: Designed as icebreaking salvage vessels, serving in support of Arctic fishing fleets. Can carry out repair, firefighting, salvage and towing. Have two 5 ton and two 3 ton cranes, four foam generators, a diving centre with oxy-acetylene equipment, TV monitors and a hospital. First of class Jupiteris (ex-Stroptivy) transferred to Lithuania for civilian use in November 1992.

FOBOS   4/1993

8 IVAN SUSANIN CLASS (ARMED ICEBREAKERS/PATROL SHIPS)

AISBERG	NEVA
DUNAY	RUSLAN
IMENI XXVI SYEZDA KPSS	VOLGA
IVAN SUSANIN	IMENI XXV SYEZDA KPSS

Displacement, tons: 2720 full load
Dimensions, feet (metres): 229.7 × 59.4 × 21 (70 × 18.1 × 6.4)
Main machinery: Diesel-electric; 3 Type 13-D-150 diesel generators; 3 motors; 5400 hp(m) (4 MW); 3 shafts (1 fwd, 2 aft)
Speed, knots: 14.5. **Range, miles:** 5500 at 12.5 kts
Guns: 2—3 in (76 mm)/60 (twin). 2—30 mm/65 AK 630 (not in all).
Radars: Surface search: Strut Curve; F band.
Navigation: 2 Don Kay; I band.
Fire control: Hawk Screech; I band.
Helicopters: Platform only.

Comment: Generally similar to Dobrynya Nikitich class though larger with a tripod mast and different superstructure. Operated by the Border Guard primarily as patrol ships. Only Ruslan is used mainly as an icebreaker. Armament sometimes removed.

AISBERG   8/1991, Bryan Hird

TUGS

Notes: (1) SB means *Spasatelny Buksir* or Salvage Tug. MB means *Morskoy Buksir* or Seagoing Tug.
(2) MB 86 of Priboy class is still in service at Baltiysk.

2 BAKLAZHAN CLASS

NIKOLAI CHIKER SB 131   **FEODOR KRYLOV** SB 135

Displacement, tons: 7000 full load
Dimensions, feet (metres): 324.8 × 64 × 23.6 *(99 × 19.5 × 7.2)*
Main machinery: 4 Wärtsilä Vasa 12V32 diesels; 24 160 hp(m) *(17.76 MW)*; 2 shafts; bow thruster; 1360 hp(m) *(1 MW)*
Speed, knots: 18. **Range, miles:** 11 000 at 16 kts
Complement: 51 plus 20 spare berths
Radars: Navigation: Nyada; I band.

Comment: Built by Hollming (Rauma), Helsinki and completed 12 April 1989 and 30 June 1989 respectively. These are the largest salvage tugs in the world with a 250 ton bollard pull on each of two towing winches with a third 60 ton winch. The crew includes two divers and there are two decompression chambers. Four firefighting foam/water guns are fitted on the bridge/mast. Designed to operate in extreme temperatures. *Krylov* was sold illegally in March 1993 and renamed *Tsavliris Giant*. The Russian Navy is attempting to get the ship back.

NIKOLAI CHIKER   *10/1991*

13 GORYN CLASS

MB 15	MB 36	MB 119	SB 522 (ex-*MB 62*)	SB 931 (ex-*MB 18*)
MB 32	MB 38	SB 365 (ex-*MB 29*)	SB 523 (ex-*MB 64*)	
MB 35	MB 105	SB 521 (ex-*MB 61*)	SB 524 (ex-*MB 108*)	

Displacement, tons: 2240 standard; 2600 full load
Dimensions, feet (metres): 208.3 × 46.9 × 16.7 *(63.5 × 14.3 × 5.1)*
Main machinery: 2 Russkiy SEMT-Pielstick 6 PC2.5 L 400 diesels; 7020 hp(m) *(5.2 MW)* sustained; 2 shafts; cp props; bow thruster
Speed, knots: 15
Complement: 43 plus 16 spare berths
Radars: Navigation: Two Don 2; I band.

Comment: Built by Rauma-Repola 1977-83. Have sick-bay. First ships have goal-post mast with 10 ton and 5 ton derricks and bollard pull of 35 tons. Remainder have an A-frame mast with a 15 ton crane and bollard pull of 45 tons. SB number indicates a 'rescue' tug. Four in the North, five in the Pacific, two each in Black and Baltic Seas.

GORYN SB 523   *12/1992*

MB 15 (with goalposts)   *5/1990*

2 NEFTEGAZ CLASS

ILGA   **KALAR**

Displacement, tons: 2800 full load
Dimensions, feet (metres): 267.4 × 53.5 × 14.8 *(81.5 × 16.3 × 4.5)*
Main machinery: 2 Sulzer diesels; 7200 hp(m) *(5.29 MW)*; 2 shafts; bow thruster
Speed, knots: 15
Complement: 25

Comment: Built by Warski, Szczecin in 1983. Can carry 600 tons cargo or be used as a tug or for firefighting. These naval units are mostly used in a range monitoring role, *Ilga* in the North, *Kalar* in the Pacific. Others of the class in civilian use.

KALAR   *4/1992, 92 Wing RAAF*

41 SORUM CLASS

AMUR	PRIMORYE	MB 4	MB 31	MB 110
BREST	SAKHALIN	MB 6	MB 37	MB 147
BUG	TAYMIR	MB 13	MB 56	MB 148
BURYA	URAL	MB 19	MB 58	MB 196
CHUKOTKA	VICTOR KINGSEPP	MB 25	MB 61	MB 236
KAMCHATKA	YAN BERZIN	MB 26	MB 76	MB 304
KARELIA	YENISEY	MB 28	MB 99	MB 307
LADOGA	ZABAYKALYE	MB 30	MB 106	
NEMAN	ZAPOLARYE			

Displacement, tons: 1660 full load
Dimensions, feet (metres): 190.2 × 41.3 × 15.1 *(58 × 12.6 × 4.6)*
Main machinery: Diesel-electric; 2 Type 5-2-DW2 diesel generators; 2900 hp(m) *(2.13 MW)*; 1 motor; 2000 hp(m) *(1.47 MW)*; 1 shaft
Speed, knots: 14. **Range, miles:** 3500 at 13 kts
Complement: 35
Guns: 4—30 mm/65 (2 twin) (all fitted for, but only Border Guard ships carry them).
Radars: Navigation: Two Don 2 or Nayada; I band.
IFF: High Pole B.

Comment: A class of ocean tugs with firefighting and diving capability. Named ships are used as patrol vessels and are Border Guard operated. Built in Yaroslavl and Oktyabskoye since 1973 to a similar design used for Ministry of Fisheries rescue tugs.

MB 4 (Tug)   *7/1993, Hartmut Ehlers*

LADOGA (Patrol ship)   *8/1992*

38 OKHTENSKY CLASS

LOKSA	ORION	SATURN
NEPTUN	POCHETNY	TYULEN

Displacement, tons: 930 full load
Dimensions, feet (metres): 156.1 × 34 × 13.4 *(47.6 × 10.4 × 4.1)*
Main machinery: Diesel-electric; 2 BM diesel generators; 1 motor; 1500 hp(m) *(1.1 MW)*; 1 shaft
Speed, knots: 13. **Range, miles:** 8000 at 7 kts; 6000 at 13 kts
Complement: 40
Guns: 2—57 mm/70 (twin) or 2—25 mm/80 (twin) (Border Guard only).
Radars: Navigation: One or two Don 2 or Spin Trough; I band.
IFF: High Pole B.

Comment: Ocean-going salvage and rescue tugs. First completed 1958. Fitted with powerful pumps and other apparatus for salvage. The six named ships are manned by the Border Guard and are armed; others have either SB or MB numbers. Some scrapped in both 1992 and 1993.

OKHTENSKY   *3/1993*

10 ROSLAVL CLASS

MB 50, MB 94, MB 95, MB 102, MB 125, MB 145-147, SB 41, SB 46

Displacement, tons: 750 full load
Dimensions, feet (metres): 146 × 31.2 × 10.8 *(44.5 × 9.5 × 3.3)*
Main machinery: Diesel-electric; 2 diesel generators; 1 motor; 1200 hp(m) *(882 kW)*; 1 shaft
Speed, knots: 12. **Range, miles:** 6000 at 11 kts
Complement: 30
Radars: Navigation: Don 2; I band.

Comment: First completed in 1953. Some of the same class are in the merchant fleet.

MB 94   *3/1992, Hartmut Ehlers*

16 ZENIT CLASS

Displacement, tons: 800 full load
Dimensions, feet (metres): 157.1 × 32.8 × 15.3 *(47.9 × 10 × 4.3)*
Main machinery: 2 boilers; 1 steam reciprocating engine; 800 ihp(m) *(588 kW)*; 1 shaft
Speed, knots: 11. **Range, miles:** 10 000 at 8 kts
Complement: 25
Radars: Navigation: Don 2; I band.

Comment: Have icebreaking capability. Survivors in the navy of a large class of naval and merchant tugs built by Wärtsilä in 1950s.

ZENIT   *1991, van Ginderen Collection*

BERTHING TUGS

Displacement, tons: 350 full load
Dimensions, feet (metres): 114.1 × 27.9 × 9.2 *(34.8 × 8.5 × 2.8)*
Main machinery: 1 diesel; 1 shaft
Speed, knots: 11

Comment: Large numbers built in 1970s by Edgar Andre, Magdeburg, East Germany. All originally numbered MB 70 *et seq.* Some renamed.

BERTHING TUGS   *7/1993, Hartmut Ehlers*

HARBOUR TUGS

Displacement, tons: 189 full load
Dimensions, feet (metres): 98.4 × 21.3 × 9.8 *(30 × 6.5 × 3)*
Main machinery: 1 RGDV 148 K10 diesel; 1 shaft
Speed, knots: 10

Comment: Details given are for the Scholle class. There are numerous other types.

HARBOUR TUGS   *7/1993, Hartmut Ehlers*

35 TUGUR CLASS (HARBOUR TUGS)

Displacement, tons: 300 full load
Dimensions, feet (metres): 100.7 × 25.3 × 7.5 *(30.7 × 7.7 × 2.3)*
Main machinery: 2 boilers; 1 steam reciprocating engine; 500 ihp(m) *(367 kW)*; 1 shaft
Speed, knots: 10

Comment: Numerous class (over 200 built) with tall funnel built in 1950s in Finland. Two transferred to Albania.

TUGUR   *3/1991, Erik Laursen*

22 SIDEHOLE 1 and 2 CLASSES (HARBOUR TUGS)

Displacement, tons: 183 (Sidehole 1); 197 (Sidehole 2)
Dimensions, feet (metres): 80 × 23 × 6.9 *(24.4 × 7 × 2.1)*
Main machinery: 2 diesels; 600 hp(m) *(441 kW)* (Sidehole 1), 900 hp(m) *(661 kW)* (Sidehole 2);
  2 shafts
Speed, knots: 9 (Sidehole 1); 10 (Sidehole 2)
Complement: 12
Radars: Navigation: Spin Trough; I band.

Comment: Built at Leningrad in 1960s (Sidehole 1) and 1970s (Sidehole 2). About 15 are Sidehole 2s.

SIDEHOLE 2   4/1992

MARITIME BORDER GUARD

Notes: (1) The Border Guard operates a considerable fleet of warships which would be integrated
with naval operations in a crisis. Formerly run by the KGB, the force came under the Ministry of Defence in October 1991 and some of the vessels will be devolved to the individual Republics with
coastal regions. The OOB of this group on 1 January 1994 is listed here for convenience—details of
the classes are in the sections preceding.
(2) From 1993 the Border Guard has started to fly its own ensign which is the St Andrews Cross on
a white border with a green background. Diagonal stripes are painted on the hull in white/blue/
red. So far these colours have only been seen in the Baltic.

Frigates	*Patrol Forces*	*Armed Icebreakers*
7 Krivak III class	25 Pauk class	8 Ivan Susanin class
12 Grisha II class	98 Stenka class	
6 Grisha III class	14 Muravey class	*Auxiliaries*
	34 Zhuk class	8 Antonov class
River Monitors	18 Svetlyak class	2 Baskunchak class
10 Piyavka class	18 Sorum clas	Flamingo class
8 Vosh class	6 Okhtensky class	
23 Yaz class		
84 Schmel class		

ZHUK (Border Guard colours)   7/1993, Hartmut Ehlers

ST KITTS-NEVIS

Senior Appointments	Base	Personnel	Mercantile Marine
		1994: 36	
Commissioner of Police:	Basseterre		*Lloyd's Register of Shipping:*
Stanley V Franks			1 vessel of 300 tons
Commanding Officer:			
Inspector Ivor Blake			

COAST GUARD

1 SWIFTSHIPS 110 ft PATROL CRAFT

STALWART C 253

Displacement, tons: 99.1 normal
Dimensions, feet (metres): 116.5 × 25 × 7 *(35.5 × 7.6 × 2.1)*
Main machinery: 4 Detroit 12V-71TA diesels; 1680 hp *(1.25 MW)* sustained; 4 shafts
Speed, knots: 21. **Range, miles:** 1800 at 15 kts
Complement: 11
Guns: 2—12.7 mm MGs. 2—7.62 mm MGs.

Comment: Built by Swiftships, Morgan City, and delivered August 1985. Aluminium alloy hull and
  superstructure.

STALWART   4/1992, van Ginderen Collection

1 FAIREY MARINE SPEAR CLASS

RANGER I

Displacement, tons: 4.3 full load
Dimensions, feet (metres): 29.8 × 9.5 × 2.8 *(9.1 × 2.8 × 0.9)*
Main machinery: 2 Ford Mermaid diesels; 360 hp *(268 kW)*; 2 shafts
Speed, knots: 30
Complement: 2
Guns: Mountings for 2—7.62 mm MGs.

Comment: Ordered for the police in June 1974—delivered 10 September 1974. Refitted 1986.

RANGER I   1992, St Kitts-Nevis Police

2 BOSTON WHALERS

ROVER I C 087   **ROVER II** C 088

Displacement, tons: 3 full load
Dimensions, feet (metres): 22 × 7.5 × 2 *(6.7 × 2.3 × 0.6)*
Main machinery: 1 Johnson outboard; 223 hp *(166 kW)*
Speed, knots: 35. **Range, miles:** 70 at 35 kts
Complement: 2

Comment: Delivered in May 1988.

ROVER I   1990, St Kitts-Nevis Police

ST LUCIA

Senior Appointments	Base	Personnel	Mercantile Marine

Comptroller of Customs and Excise:
  M J Scholar
Coast Guard Commander:
  Lieutenant Commander N Hawkyard
	Castries	1994: 39	*Lloyd's Register of Shipping:*
			  7 vessels of 2014 tons gross

COAST GUARD

1 INSHORE PATROL CRAFT

VIGILANT II P 06

Displacement, tons: 5 full load
Dimensions, feet (metres): 29 × 10 × 2.4 *(8.8 × 3.1 × 0.7)*
Main machinery: 2 Volvo Turbo diesels; 400 hp(m) *(294 kW)*; 2 shafts
Speed, knots: 30

Comment: Completed in May 1990 by Phoenix Marine Enterprises, Hialeah, Florida. Has replaced *Vigilant I.*

2 BOSTON WHALERS

P 03   P 04

Displacement, tons: 3
Dimensions, feet (metres): 22 × 6.8 × 2 *(6.7 × 2 × 0.6)*
Main machinery: 1 V6-2500CC Johnson outboard
Speed, knots: 36

Comment: Acquired in July 1988.

1 SWIFT 65 ft CLASS

DEFENDER P 02

Displacement, tons: 42 full load
Dimensions, feet (metres): 64.9 × 18.4 × 6.6 *(19.8 × 5.6 × 2)*
Main machinery: 2 Detroit 12V-71 diesels; 680 hp *(507 kW)* sustained; 2 shafts
Speed, knots: 22. **Range, miles:** 1200 at 18 kts
Complement: 5

Comment: Ordered from Swiftships, Morgan City in November 1983. Completed 1985. Similar to craft supplied to Antigua and Dominica.

DEFENDER   *11/1993, Maritime Photographic*

ST VINCENT AND THE GRENADINES

Senior Appointments	Base	Personnel	Mercantile Marine

Commissioner of Police:
  William Harry
Coast Guard Commander:
  Lieutenant D V Robin
	Calliaqua	1994: 50	*Lloyd's Register of Shipping:*
			  961 vessels of 5 287 171 tons gross

COAST GUARD

1 SWIFTSHIPS 120 ft PATROL CRAFT

CAPTAIN MULZAC SVG 01

Displacement, tons: 101
Dimensions, feet (metres): 120 × 25 × 7 *(36.6 × 7.6 × 2.1)*
Main machinery: 4 Detroit 12V-71TA diesels; 1360 hp *(1.01 MW)* sustained; 4 shafts
Speed, knots: 21. **Range, miles:** 1800 at 15 kts
Complement: 13
Guns: 2—12.7 mm MGs. 2—7.62 mm MGs.
Radars: Surface search: Furuno 1411 Mk II; I/J band.

Comment: Built by Swiftships, Morgan City and delivered in June 1987.

CAPTAIN MULZAC   *1993, St Vincent Coastguard*

1 VOSPER THORNYCROFT 75 ft PATROL CRAFT

GEORGE McINTOSH SVG 05

Displacement, tons: 70
Dimensions, feet (metres): 75 × 19.5 × 8 *(22.9 × 6 × 2.4)*
Main machinery: 2 Caterpillar D 348 diesels; 1450 hp *(1.08 MW)* sustained; 2 shafts
Speed, knots: 24.5. **Range, miles:** 1000 at 11 kts; 600 at 20 kts
Complement: 11
Guns: 1 Oerlikon 20 mm.
Radars: Surface search: Furuno 1411 Mk III; I/J band.

Comment: Handed over 23 March 1981. GRP hull.

GEORGE McINTOSH   *1992, St Vincent Coastguard*

2 BUHLER TYPE (INSHORE PATROL CRAFT)

LARIKAI SVG 06   **BRIGHTON** SVG 07

Displacement, tons: 6 full load
Dimensions, feet (metres): 27 × 6.8 × 2.4 *(8.2 × 2.1 × .73)*
Main machinery: 2 outboard engines; 2 props
Speed, knots: 23

Comment: Locally built by Buhler's Yachts Ltd. Converted to outboard engines in 1990-91.

BRIGHTON   *1991, St Vincent Coastguard*

SAUDI ARABIA

Senior Appointments

Chief of Naval Staff:
   Vice Admiral Talal Salem Al Mofadhi
Commander Eastern Fleet:
   Rear Admiral Badr Saleh Al-Saleh
Commander Western Fleet:
   Rear Admiral Muhammad Abdullah Al-Ajalen

Personnel

(a) 1994: 11 400 officers and men (including 1200 marines)
(b) Voluntary service

Bases

Naval HQ: Riyadh
Main bases: Jiddah, Al Jubail, Aziziah (Coast Guard)
Minor bases (Naval and Coast Guard): Ras Tanura, Al Dammam, Yanbo, Ras al-Mishab, Al Wajh, Al Qatif, Haqi, Al Sharmah, Qizan, Duba

Strength of the Fleet

Type	Active	Building
Frigates	4	(3)
Corvettes—Missile	—	—
Fast Attack Craft—Missile	9	—
Fast Attack Craft—Torpedo	2 (1)	—
Patrol Craft	57	—
Minehunters	2	1 (3)
Minesweepers—Coastal	4	—
Replenishment Tankers	2	—
LCMs	4	—
LCUs	4	—
Tugs	14	—
Royal Yacht	1	—
Hydrofoil	1	—

Coast Guard

Fast Attack Craft—Missile	2
Large Patrol Craft	8
Coastal Patrol Craft	38
Hovercraft	31
Inshore Patrol Craft	653
Royal Yachts	2
Training Ships	2
Tankers	3
Firefighting Craft	3
Tugs	3

General

Funding for the Navy has the lowest defence service priority. New programmes are slow to come forward, and spares and maintenance are suffering as well.

Command and Control

The United States is providing an update of command and control capabilities during the period 1991-95, including a commercial datalink to improve interoperability.

Coast Guard

Part of the Frontier Force under the Minister of the Interior. 5500 officers and men in January 1994. It is not always clear which ships belong to the Navy and which to the Coast Guard.

Mercantile Marine

Lloyd's Register of Shipping:
   267 vessels of 997 701 tons gross

SUBMARINES

Notes: (1) Orders for patrol submarines are unlikely until mid-1990s although training is being done in France and Pakistan. One possibility is the lease of the UK Upholder class.
(2) Previous reports of Midget Submarines being acquired are not correct, although there is much interest.

FRIGATES

Note: A provisional order for three La Fayette class was signed with France on 11 June 1989. This had still not been confirmed by early 1994, and other designs have been looked at including the Canadian Halifax class. The emphasis has shifted from air defence to ASW because of Iran's acquisition of submarines.

4 MADINA (TYPE F 2000S) CLASS

Name	No	Builders	Laid down	Launched	Commissioned
MADINA	702	Lorient (DTCN)	15 Oct 1981	23 Apr 1983	4 Jan 1985
HOFOUF	704	CNIM, Seyne-sur-Mer	14 June 1982	24 June 1983	31 Oct 1985
ABHA	706	CNIM, Seyne-sur-Mer	7 Dec 1982	23 Dec 1983	4 Apr 1986
TAIF	708	CNIM, Seyne-sur-Mer	1 Mar 1983	25 May 1984	29 Aug 1986

Displacement, tons: 2000 standard; 2870 full load
Dimensions, feet (metres): 377.3 × 41 × 16 (sonar)
   (115 × 12.5 × 4.9)
Main machinery: CODAD; 4 SEMT-Pielstick 16 PA6 280V BTC diesels; 38 400 hp(m) *(28 MW)* sustained; 2 shafts
Speed, knots: 30. **Range, miles:** 8000 at 15 kts; 6500 at 18 kts
Complement: 179 (15 officers)

Missiles: SSM: 8 OTO Melara/Matra Otomat Mk 2 (2 quad) **❶**; active radar homing to 160 km *(86.4 nm)* at 0.9 Mach; warhead 210 kg; sea-skimmer for last 4 km *(2.2 nm)*. ERATO system allows mid-course guidance by ship's helicopter.
SAM: Thomson-CSF Crotale Naval octuple launcher **❷**; command line-of-sight guidance; radar/IR homing to 13 km *(7 nm)* at 2.4 Mach; warhead 14 kg; 26 missiles.
Guns: 1 Creusot Loire 3.9 in *(100 mm)*/55 compact **❸**; 80° elevation; 20/45/90 rounds/minute to 17 km *(9.3 nm)* anti-surface; 6 km *(3.3 nm)* anti-aircraft; weight of shell 13.5 kg.
4 Breda 40 mm/70 (2 twin) **❹**; 85° elevation; 300 rounds/minute to 12.5 km *(6.8 nm)*; weight of shell 0.96 kg.
Torpedoes: 4—21 in *(533 mm)* tubes **❺**. ECAN F17P; anti-submarine; wire-guided; active/passive homing to 20 km *(10.8 nm)* at 40 kts; warhead 250 kg.
Countermeasures: Decoys: CSEE Dagaie double trainable mounting **❻**; IR flares and chaff; H/J band.
ESM: Thomson-CSF DR 4000; intercept; HF/DF.
ECM: Janet; jammer.
Combat data systems: Thomson-CSF TAVITAC action data automation; capability for Link 11.
Fire control: Vega system. 3 CSEE Naja optronic directors. DLT for torpedoes.
Radars: Air/surface search/IFF: Thomson-CSF Sea Tiger (DRBV 15) **❼**; E/F band; range 110 km *(60 nm)* for 2 m² target.
Navigation: Racal Decca TM 1226; I band.
Fire control: Thomson-CSF Castor IIB **❽**; I/J band; range 15 km *(8 nm)* for 1 m² target.
Thomson-CSF DRBC 32 **❾**; I/J band (for SAM).
Sonars: Thomson Sintra Diodon TSM 2630; hull-mounted; active search and attack with integrated Sorel VDS **❿**; 11, 12 or 13 kHz.

Helicopters: 1 SA 365F Dauphin 2 **⓫**.

Programmes: Ordered in 1980, the major part of the Sawari contract. Agreement for France to provide supplies and technical help.
Modernisation: All of the class are to be upgraded starting in 1995. The work is to be done by DCN at Toulon and is expected to take five years. An A/S missile is being considered. Possibly Matra Milas with a range of 55 km *(29.8 nm)* with a torpedo payload.
Structure: Fitted with Snach/Saphir folding fin stabilisers.
Operational: Navigation: CSEE Sylosat. Helicopter can provide mid-course guidance for SSM. All based at Jiddah. Only a few weeks a year are spent at sea. *Madina* had a severe engine-room fire in August 1991 which has not yet been repaired.

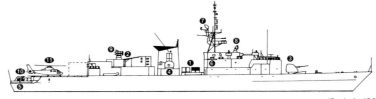

MADINA
(Scale 1 : 1200), Ian Sturton

ABHA
4/1988, A Sheldon Duplaix

TAIF
9/1989, G Jacobs

CORVETTES

4 BADR CLASS

Name	No	Builders	Laid down	Launched	Commissioned
BADR	612	Tacoma Boatbuilding Co, Tacoma	6 Oct 1979	26 Jan 1980	30 Nov 1980
AL YARMOOK	614	Tacoma Boatbuilding Co, Tacoma	3 Jan 1980	13 May 1980	18 May 1981
HITTEEN	616	Tacoma Boatbuilding Co, Tacoma	19 May 1980	5 Sep 1980	3 Oct 1981
TABUK	618	Tacoma Boatbuilding Co, Tacoma	22 Sep 1980	18 June 1981	10 Jan 1983

Displacement, tons: 870 standard; 1038 full load
Dimensions, feet (metres): 245 × 31.5 × 8.9
(74.7 × 9.6 × 2.7)
Main machinery: CODOG; 1 GE LM 2500 gas-turbine; 23 000
hp *(17.2 MW)* sustained; 2 MTU 12V 652 TB91 diesels; 3470
hp(m) *(2.55 MW)* sustained; 2 shafts; cp props
Speed, knots: 30 gas; 20 diesels. **Range, miles:** 4000 at 20 kts
Complement: 58 (7 officers)

Missiles: SSM: 8 McDonnell Douglas Harpoon (2 quad) launchers ❶; active radar homing to 130 km *(70 nm)* at 0.9 Mach; warhead 227 kg.
Guns: 1 FMC/OTO Melara 3 in *(76 mm)*/62 Mk 75 Mod 0 ❷; 85° elevation; 85 rounds/minute to 16 km *(8.7 nm)*; weight of shell 6 kg.
1 General Electric/General Dynamics 20 mm 6-barrelled Vulcan Phalanx ❸; 3000 rounds/minute combined to 2 km.
2 Oerlikon 20 mm/80 ❹; 55° elevation; 800 rounds/minute to 2 km anti-aircraft.
1—81 mm mortar. 2—40 mm Mk 19 grenade launchers.
Torpedoes: 6—324 mm US Mk 32 (2 triple) tubes ❺. Honeywell Mk 46; anti-submarine; active/passive homing to 11 km *(5.9 nm)* at 40 kts; warhead 44 kg.
Countermeasures: Decoys: 2 Loral Hycor SRBOC 6-barrelled fixed Mk 36 ❻; IR flares and chaff to 4 km *(2.2 nm)*.
ESM: SLQ 32(V)1 ❼; intercept.
Fire control: Mk 24 optical director ❽. Mk 309 for torpedoes. Mk 92 Mod 5 GFCS.
Radars: Air search: Lockheed SPS 40B ❾; E/F band; range 320 km *(175 nm)*.
Surface search: ISC Cardion SPS 55 ❿; I/J band.
Fire control: Sperry Mk 92 ⓫; I/J band.
Sonars: Raytheon SQS 56 (DE 1164); hull-mounted; active search and attack; medium frequency.

Modernisation: A five year programme started in 1988.
Structure: Fitted with fin stabilisers.
Operational: All based at Al Jubail on the east coast.

BADR *(Scale 1 : 600), Ian Sturton*

BADR *1989, van Ginderen Collection*

SHIPBORNE AIRCRAFT

Numbers/Type: 20/4 Aerospatiale SA 365F/N Dauphin 2.
Operational speed: 140 kts *(260 km/h)*.
Service ceiling: 15 000 ft *(4575 m)*.
Range: 410 nm *(758 km)*.
Role/Weapon systems: SA 365F is the ASV/ASW helicopter; procured for embarked naval aviation force; surface search/attack is the primary role. Sensors: Thomson-CSF Agrion 15, Crouzet MAD. Weapons: ASV; 4 × AS/15TT missiles. ASW; 2 Mk 46 torpedoes. SA 365N is for SAR. Sensors: Omera ORB 32 search radar. Weapons: Unarmed.

DAUPHIN 2

LAND-BASED MARITIME AIRCRAFT

Note: 6 P3-C Orion may be acquired in due course.

Numbers/Type: 21 Aerospatiale AS 332SC Super Puma.
Operational speed: 150 kts *(280 km/h)*.
Service ceiling: 15 090 ft *(4600 m)*.
Range: 335 nm *(620 km)*.
Role/Weapon systems: Two delivered in August 1989 then one per month to a total of 21 by the end of 1990. Sensors: Twelve have Omera search radar. Weapons: Nine have Giat 20 mm cannon; twelve have AM39 Exocet or Sea Eagle ASM.

SUPER PUMA

PATROL FORCES

9 AL SIDDIQ CLASS (FAST ATTACK CRAFT—MISSILE)

Name	No	Builders	Commissioned
AL SIDDIQ	511	Peterson Builders, Wisconsin	15 Dec 1980
AL FAROUQ	513	Peterson Builders, Wisconsin	22 June 1981
ABDUL AZIZ	515	Peterson Builders, Wisconsin	3 Sep 1981
FAISAL	517	Peterson Builders, Wisconsin	23 Nov 1981
KAHLID	519	Peterson Builders, Wisconsin	11 Jan 1982
AMYR	521	Peterson Builders, Wisconsin	21 June 1982
TARIQ	523	Peterson Builders, Wisconsin	11 Aug 1982
OQBAH	525	Peterson Builders, Wisconsin	18 Oct 1982
ABU OBAIDAH	527	Peterson Builders, Wisconsin	6 Dec 1982

Displacement, tons: 425 standard; 478 full load
Dimensions, feet (metres): 190.5 × 26.5 × 6.6 *(58.1 × 8.1 × 2)*
Main machinery: CODOG; 1 GE LM 2500 gas-turbine; 23 000 hp *(17.2 MW)* sustained; 2 MTU 12V 652 TB91 diesels; 3470 hp(m) *(2.55 MW)* sustained; 2 shafts; cp props
Speed, knots: 38 gas; 25 diesel. **Range, miles:** 2900 at 14 kts
Complement: 38 (5 officers)

Missiles: SSM: 4 McDonnell Douglas Harpoon (2 twin) launchers; active radar homing to 130 km *(70 nm)* at 0.9 Mach; warhead 227 kg.
Guns: 1 FMC/OTO Melara 3 in *(76 mm)*/62 Mk 75 Mod 0; 85° elevation; 85 rounds/minute to 16 km *(8.7 nm)*; weight of shell 6 kg.
1 General Electric/General Dynamics 20 mm 6-barrelled Vulcan Phalanx; 3000 rounds/minute combined to 2 km.
2 Oerlikon 20 mm/80; 55° elevation; 800 rounds/minute to 2 km anti-aircraft.
2—81 mm mortars. 2—40 mm Mk 19 grenade launchers.
Countermeasures: Decoys: 2 Loral Hycor SRBOC 6-barrelled fixed Mk 36; IR flares and chaff to 4 km *(2.2 nm)*.
ESM: SLQ 32(V)1; intercept.
Fire control: Mk 92 mod 5 GFCS.
Radars: Surface search: ISC Cardion SPS 55; I/J band.
Fire control: Sperry Mk 92; I/J band.

Modernisation: There is a planned modernisation programme but the Gulf conflict caused it to be postponed.
Operational: *Amyr* and *Tariq* operate from Jiddah, the remainder are based at Al Jubail. *Faisal* has been non-operational since being damaged in the Gulf war in 1991.

AL SIDDIQ *1992, G Toremans*

3 JAGUAR CLASS (FAST ATTACK CRAFT—TORPEDO)

Name	No	Builders	Commissioned
DAMMAM	90 (ex-190)	Lürssen, Vegesack	1969
KHABAR	50 (ex-192)	Lürssen, Vegesack	1969
MACCAH	10 (ex-194)	Lürssen, Vegesack	1969

Displacement, tons: 160 standard; 190 full load
Dimensions, feet (metres): 139.4 × 23 × 7.9 *(42.5 × 7 × 2.4)*
Main machinery: 4 Maybach 16-cyl diesels; 12 000 hp(m) *(8.82 MW)*; 4 shafts
Speed, knots: 42. **Range, miles:** 1000 at 30 kts
Complement: 33 (3 officers)
Guns: 2 Bofors 40 mm/70; 90° elevation; 300 rounds/minute to 12 km *(6.6 nm)*; weight of shell 0.96 kg.
Torpedoes: 4—21 in *(533 mm)* tubes; anti-surface.

Comment: Refitted by Lürssen Werft, West Germany in 1976. Two are used for training, mostly alongside, and one is in reserve. All based at Al Jubail.

JAGUAR   1989

17 HALTER TYPE (COASTAL PATROL CRAFT)

Displacement, tons: 56 full load
Dimensions, feet (metres): 78 × 20 × 5.8 *(23.8 × 6.1 × 1.8)*
Main machinery: 2 Detroit 16V-92TA diesels; 1380 hp *(1.03 MW)* sustained; 2 shafts
Speed, knots: 28. **Range, miles:** 1200 at 12 kts
Complement: 8 (2 officers)
Guns: 2—12.7 mm MGs. 2—7.62 mm MGs (can be carried).

Comment: Ordered from Halter Marine 17th February 1991. Last delivered in late 1992. Same type for Philippines, Ecuador and Panama. These may be Coast Guard craft.

HALTER TYPE   8/1990, Trinity Marine

40 SIMMONEAU 51 TYPE (INSHORE PATROL CRAFT)

Displacement, tons: 22
Dimensions, feet (metres): 51.8 × 15.7 × 5.9 *(15.8 × 4.8 × 1.8)*
Main machinery: 2 outboards; 2400 hp(m) *(1.76 MW)*
Speed, knots: 33. **Range, miles:** 375 at 25 kts
Guns: 1 GIAT 20 mm. 2—7.62 mm MGs.
Radars: Surface search: Furuno; I band.

Comment: First 20 ordered from France in June 1988 and delivered in 1989-90. A second batch of 20 ordered in 1991. Used by naval commandos. These craft were also reported as Panhards.

SIMMONEAU TYPE   1989, Simmoneau Marine

2 + 1 (3) SANDOWN CLASS (MINEHUNTERS—COASTAL)

Name	No	Builders	Launched	Commissioned
AL JAWF	420	Vosper Thornycroft	2 Aug 1989	12 Dec 1991
SHAQRA	422	Vosper Thornycroft	15 May 1991	7 Feb 1993
AL KHARJ	424	Vosper Thornycroft	8 Feb 1993	1994
ONAIZAH	426	Vosper Thornycroft	—	—
AL RAAS	428	Vosper Thornycroft	—	—
AL BAHAN	430	Vosper Thornycroft	—	—

Displacement, tons: 450 standard; 480 full load
Dimensions, feet (metres): 172.9 × 34.4 × 6.9 *(52.7 × 10.5 × 2.1)*
Main machinery: 2 Paxman 6RP200E diesels; 1500 hp *(1.12 MW)* sustained; Voith-Schneider propulsion; 2 shafts; 2 Schottel bow thrusters
Speed, knots: 13 diesels; 6 electric drive. **Range, miles:** 3000 at 12 kts
Complement: 34 (7 officers) plus 6 spare berths
Guns: 2 Emmerson Electric 30 mm (twin); 80° elevation; 1200 rounds/minute combined to 6 km *(3.3 nm)*; weight of shell 0.35 kg.
Countermeasures: Decoys: 2 Loral Hycor SRBOC Mk 36 Mod 1 6-barrelled chaff launchers.
ESM: Thomson-CSF Shiploc; intercept.
MCM: ECA mine disposal system; 2 PAP 104 Mk 5.
Combat data systems: Plessey Nautis M action data automation.
Fire control: Contraves TMEO optronic director (Seahawk Mk 2).
Radars: Navigation: Kelvin Hughes Type 1007; I band.
Sonars: Plessey/MUSL Type 2093; VDS; high frequency.

Comment: Three ordered 2 November 1988 from Vosper Thornycroft with option for three more which had not been taken up by early 1994. GRP hulls. Combines vectored thrust units with bow thrusters and Remote Controlled Mine Disposal System (RCMDS). Some of the hulls have been reallocated from the RN production line.

AL JAWF   7/1993, Maritime Photographic

SHAQRA   5/1993, Wright & Logan

MINE WARFARE FORCES

4 MSC 322 CLASS (MINESWEEPERS/HUNTERS—COASTAL)

Name	No	Builders	Commissioned
ADDRIYAH	MSC 412	Peterson Builders, Wisconsin	6 July 1978
AL QUYSUMAH	MSC 414	Peterson Builders, Wisconsin	15 Aug 1978
AL WADEEAH	MSC 416	Peterson Builders, Wisconsin	7 Sep 1979
SAFWA	MSC 418	Peterson Builders, Wisconsin	2 Oct 1979

Displacement, tons: 320 standard; 407 full load
Dimensions, feet (metres): 153 × 26.9 × 8.2 *(46.6 × 8.2 × 2.5)*
Main machinery: 2 Waukesha L1616 diesels; 1200 hp *(895 kW)*; 2 shafts
Speed, knots: 13
Complement: 39 (4 officers)
Guns: 1 Oerlikon 20 mm.
Radars: Surface warning: ISC Cardion SPS 55; I/J band.
Sonars: GE SQQ 14; VDS; active minehunting; high frequency.

Comment: Ordered on 30 September 1975 under the International Logistics Programme. Wooden structure.
Fitted with fin stabilisers, wire and magnetic sweeps and also for minehunting. *Addriyah* based at Jiddah, the remainder at Al Jubail.

SAFWA   1984, van Ginderen Collection

AUXILIARIES

2 MOD DURANCE CLASS (REPLENISHMENT SHIPS)

Name	No	Builders	Commissioned
BORAIDA	902	C du N et de la Méditerranée, La Ciotat	29 Feb 1984
YUNBOU	904	C du N et de la Méditerranée, La Ciotat	29 Aug 1985

Displacement, tons: 10 500
Dimensions, feet (metres): 442.9 × 61.3 × 22.9 *(135 × 18.7 × 7)*
Main machinery: 2 SEMT-Pielstick 14 PC2.5 V 400 diesels; 18 200 hp(m) *(13.4 MW)* sustained; 2 shafts; cp props
Speed, knots: 20.5. **Range, miles:** 7000 at 15 kts
Complement: 129 plus 11 trainees
Cargo capacity: 4350 tons diesel; 350 tons AVCAT; 140 tons fresh water; 100 tons victuals; 100 tons ammunition; 70 tons spares

Guns: 4 Breda Bofors 40 mm/70 (2 twin); 85° elevation; 300 rounds/minute to 12.5 km *(6.8 nm)*; weight of shell 0.96 kg.
Fire control: 2 CSEE Naja optronic directors. 2 CSEE Lynx optical sights.
Radars: Navigation: Two sets; I band.

Helicopters: 2 SA 365 F Dauphin or 1 AS 332SC Super Puma.

Programmes: Contract signed October 1980 as part of Sawari programme.
Modernisation: Both to be upgraded by DCN at Toulon starting in 1995.
Structure: Refuelling positions: Two alongside, one astern.
Operational: Also serve as training ships and as depot and maintenance ships. Helicopters can have ASM or ASW armament. Both based at Jiddah.

YUNBOU   6/1993

BORAIDA   11/1987, G Toremans

4 LCU 1610 CLASS (TRANSPORTS)

AL QIAQ (ex-*SA 310*) 212   AL ULA (ex-*SA 312*) 216
AL SULAYEL (ex-*SA 311*) 214   AFIF (ex-*SA 313*) 218

Displacement, tons: 200 light; 375 full load
Dimensions, feet (metres): 134.9 × 29 × 6.1 *(41.1 × 8.8 × 1.9)*
Main machinery: 4 GM diesels; 1000 hp *(746 kW)*; 2 Kort nozzles
Speed, knots: 11. **Range, miles:** 1200 at 8 kts
Complement: 14 (2 officers)
Military lift: 170 tons; 20 troops
Guns: 2—12.7 mm MGs.
Radars: Surface search: Marconi LN 66; I band.

Comment: Built by Newport Shipyard, Rhode Island. Transferred from US June/July 1976. Based at Al Jubail.

4 LCM 6 CLASS (TRANSPORTS)

DHEBA 220   AL LEETH 224
UMLUS 222   AL QUONFETHA 226

Displacement, tons: 62 full load
Dimensions, feet (metres): 56.2 × 14 × 3.9 *(17.1 × 4.3 × 1.2)*
Main machinery: 2 GM diesels; 450 hp *(336 kW)*; 2 shafts
Speed, knots: 9. **Range, miles:** 130 at 9 kts
Complement: 5
Military lift: 34 tons or 80 troops
Guns: 2—40 mm grenade launchers.

Comment: Four transferred July 1977 and four in July 1980. The first four have been cannibalised for spares. Based at Jiddah.

TUGS

1 SALVAGE TUG (ARS)

JIDDAH 13

Displacement, tons: 350
Dimensions, feet (metres): 112.8 × — × — *(34.4 × — × —)*
Main machinery: 2 diesels; 800 hp(m) *(588 kW)*; 2 shafts
Speed, knots: 12

Comment: Built at Hayashikane, Shimonoseki. Laid down 19 August 1977.

3 OCEAN TUGS (ATA)

RADHWA 12, 16, 17

Displacement, tons: 680
Dimensions, feet (metres): 142.7 × 44.9 × 18.4 *(43.5 × 13.7 × 5.6)*
Main machinery: 2 Fuji diesels; 5600 hp(m) *(4.12 MW)*; 2 shafts
Speed, knots: 12

Comment: First launched 16 October 1982, second 17 May 1983 and third 24 June 1983.

10 HARBOUR TUGS (ATB/YTB)

RADHWA 1-6, 14-15   TUWAIG 111   DAREEN 112

Measurement, tons: 350 gross
Dimensions, feet (metres): 118 × 42 × 15 *(35.9 × 12.8 × 4.6)*
Main machinery: 2 Fuji 8L32X diesels; 6250 hp(m) *(4.6 MW)* sustained; 2 shafts
Speed, knots: 15

Comment: Details given are for the Radhwa type. Builders Hitachi Robin DY, Singapore (for 1-3), Jonker and Stans, Netherlands (4-6) and Damen, Netherlands (14-15). All commissioned between 1981 and 1983. *Tuwaig* and *Dareen* are ex-US YTB transferred in October 1975. These two are used to tow targets for weapons firing exercises and are based at Al Jubail and Damman respectively.

YTB TYPE (US colours)   9/1992, Jürg Kürsener

ROYAL YACHTS

Note: A second yacht *Al Yamamah* has been reported. This may be similar to the Omani *Al Said*.

Name	No	Builders	Commissioned
AL RIYADH	—	Van Lent (de Kaag), Netherlands	Jan 1978

Displacement, tons: 670 full load
Dimensions, feet (metres): 228 × 34.4 × 10.8 *(69.5 × 10.5 × 3.3)*
Main machinery: 2 MTU 16V 956 TB91 diesels; 7500 hp(m) *(5.51 MW)* sustained; 2 shafts; Schottel bow thruster
Speed, knots: 26
Complement: 26 (accommodation for 18 passengers)
Radars: Navigation: Decca 1216 and Decca 916; I band.

Comment: Ordered 12 December 1975. Laid down 6 May 1976. Launched 17 December 1977. Fittings include helicopter pad, sauna, swimming pool, hospital with intensive care unit. Steel hull fitted with stabilisers. Based at Damman.

1 PEGASUS CLASS (HYDROFOIL)

Displacement, tons: 115 full load
Dimensions, feet (metres): 89.9 × 29.9 × 6.2 *(27.4 × 9.1 × 1.9)*
Main machinery: 2 Allison 501-KF20A gas-turbines; 8660 hp *(6.46 MW)* sustained; 2 waterjets (foilborne); 2 Detroit 8V92 diesels; 606 hp *(452 kW)* sustained; 2 shafts (hullborne)
Speed, knots: 46. **Range, miles:** 890 at 42 kts
Guns: 2 General Electric 20 mm Sea Vulcan.

Comment: Ordered in 1984 from Boeing, Seattle; delivered in August 1985. Mostly used as a tender to the Royal Yacht.

COAST GUARD

2 LARGE PATROL CRAFT

BADR   YARMOUK

Displacement, tons: 65 full load
Dimensions, feet (metres): 95.1 × 22 × 4.9 *(29 × 6.7 × 1.5)*
Main machinery: 2 GM 16V-149 diesels; 2 shafts
Speed, knots: 25. **Range, miles:** 1000 at 22 kts
Complement: 17
Guns: 2—12.7 mm MGs.
Radars: Surface search: Racal Decca RM 1690; I band.

Comment: Built by Bayerische, Germany in the 1970s. Aluminium hulls. Both based at Aziziah.

2 SEA GUARD CLASS (FAST ATTACK CRAFT—MISSILE)

AL RIYADH   ZULURAB

Displacement, tons: 53 standard
Dimensions, feet (metres): 73.8 × 18.4 × 5.6 *(22.5 × 5.6 × 1.7)*
Main machinery: 2 MTU 12V 331 TC92 diesels; 2920 hp(m) *(21.46 MW)*; 2 shafts
Speed, knots: 35
Complement: 10
Missiles: SSM: 2 Aerospatiale AS 15TT (twin); radar guidance to 15 km *(8.1 nm)* at 0.8 Mach; warhead 30 kg; sea-skimmer.
Guns: 2—12.7 mm MGs.
Radars: Surface search: Racal Decca; I band.
Fire control: Thomson-CSF Agrion; J band.

Comment: Built by Simonneau Marine and delivered by SOFREMA in April 1992. Aluminium construction. Both based at Jiddah.

ZULURAB   *1992, Simonneau Marine*

4 LARGE PATROL CRAFT

AL JOUF 351   **TURAIF** 352   **HAIL** 353   **NAJRAN** 354

Displacement, tons: 210 full load
Dimensions, feet (metres): 126.6 × 26.2 × 6.2 *(38.6 × 8 × 1.9)*
Main machinery: 3 MTU 16 V 538 TB93 diesels; 11 265 hp(m) *(8.28 MW)* sustained; 3 shafts
Speed, knots: 38. **Range, miles:** 1700 at 15 kts
Complement: 20
Guns: 2 Oerlikon GAM-BO1 20 mm. 2—12.7 mm MGs.
Radars: Surface search: Racal S 1690; I band.
Navigation: Racal RM 1290A; I band.

Comment: Ordered on 18 October 1987 from Blohm & Voss. First two completed 15 June 1989; second pair 20 August 1989. Steel hulls with aluminium superstructure. *Hail* and *Najran* based at Jiddah in the Red Sea and the others at Aziziah.

AL JOUF   *6/1989, Blohm & Voss*

2 LARGE PATROL CRAFT

AL JUBATEL   SALWA

Displacement, tons: 95 full load
Dimensions, feet (metres): 86 × 19 × 6.9 *(26.2 × 5.8 × 2.1)*
Main machinery: 2 MTU 16V 396 TB94 diesels; 5800 hp(m) *(4.26 MW)* sustained; 2 shafts
Speed, knots: 34. **Range, miles:** 1100 at 25 kts
Complement: 12
Guns: 1 Oerlikon/GAM-B01 20 mm. 2—12.7 mm MGs.
Radars: Surface search: Racal Decca AC 1290; I band.

Comment: Built by Abeking & Rasmussen, completed in April 1987. Smaller version of Turkish SAR 33 Type. One based at Jizan and one at Al Wajh.

AL JUBATEL   *1987, Abeking and Rasmussen*

25 SKORPION CLASS (COASTAL PATROL CRAFT)

139-164

Displacement, tons: 33 full load
Dimensions, feet (metres): 55.8 × 16.1 × 4.6 *(17 × 4.9 × 1.4)*
Main machinery: 2 Detroit 12V-71TA diesels; 840 hp *(627 kW)* sustained; 2 shafts
Speed, knots: 25. **Range, miles:** 200 at 20 kts
Complement: 7
Guns: 2—7.62 mm MGs.
Radars: Surface search: Decca 914C; I band.

Comment: Twenty built by Bayerische SY, Erlenbach am Main. 139-148 shipped to Jiddah in October 1979. Last 10 built by Arminias Werft, Bodenwerder in 1980. Some deleted. Spread around all six Coast Guard bases.

SKORPION 144   *10/1979, van Ginderen Collection*

1 COASTAL PATROL CRAFT

Displacement, tons: 72 full load
Dimensions, feet (metres): 69.9 × 19 × 5.2 *(21.3 × 5.8 × 1.6)*
Main machinery: 2 Deutz SBF 12M 716 diesels; 724 hp(m) *(532 kW)*; 2 shafts
Speed, knots: 12
Guns: 1—12.7 mm MG.
Radars: Surface search: Decca 110; I band.

Comment: Built by Whittingham and Mitchell in the 1970s. Steel hull. Based at Jiddah.

12 RAPIER CLASS (COASTAL PATROL CRAFT)

127-138

Displacement, tons: 26 full load
Dimensions, feet (metres): 50 × 15.1 × 4.6 *(15.2 × 4.6 × 1.4)*
Main machinery: 2 Detroit 12V-71TA diesels; 840 hp *(627 kW)* sustained; 2 shafts
Speed, knots: 28. **Range, miles:** 290 at 24 kts
Complement: 9 (1 officer)
Guns: 2—7.62 mm MGs.
Radars: Surface search: Decca 101; I band.

Comment: Three completed 1976, remainder in 1977 by Halter Marine, New Orleans. Steel hulls. Three based at Jiddah, five at Al Wajh, four at Aziziah.

7 SR N6 Mod 4 HOVERCRAFT

Displacement, tons: 10.9 normal
Dimensions, feet (metres): 48.5 × 23 × 3.9 (skirt) *(14.8 × 7 × 1.2)*
Main machinery: 1 Rolls-Royce Gnome 1050 gas-turbine; 900 hp *(671 kW)* sustained
Speed, knots: 60. **Range, miles:** 170 at 54 kts
Complement: 3
Military lift: 20 troops plus 5 tons equipment
Guns: 1—7.62 mm MG.

Comment: First eight acquired from British Hovercraft Corporation, between February and December 1970. Eight more ordered in 1980 of which two delivered in 1981, four in 1982 and two in 1983. First nine have been scrapped.

SR N6 Hovercraft   *11/1981, G S Long*

8 SR N6 Mod 8 HOVERCRAFT

Displacement, tons: 17 normal
Dimensions, feet (metres): 60 × 27.9 × 5.2 *(18.3 × 8.5 × 1.6)*
Main machinery: 1 RR Gnome 1060 gas-turbine; 1060 hp *(791 kW)*
Speed, knots: 55
Military lift: 30 troops plus equipment
Guns: 1—7.62 mm MG.

Comment: Acquired in the mid-1980s from the British Hovercraft Corporation. Five based at Aziziah, three at Jiddah.

16 SLINGSBY SAH 2200 HOVERCRAFT

Dimensions, feet (metres): 34.8 × 13.8 *(10.6 × 4.2)*
Main machinery: 1 Deutz BF6L913C diesel; 190 hp(m) *(140 kW)* sustained; lift and propulsion
Speed, knots: 40. **Range, miles:** 500 at 40 kts
Military lift: 2.2 tons or 24 troops
Guns: 1—7.62 mm MG.

Comment: First three supplied from UK in 1990. Final total could be up to 30 for coastal defence and oil rig protection. Have Kevlar armour.

SLINGSBY 2200   *1991*

653 INSHORE PATROL CRAFT

Number	Builder/Type	Date	Speed
4	Lambro, Greece, 14 m	1974	12
8	LCVP, 14 m	1970s	8
10	Cytra, Germany, 12.8 m	1970s	38
2	Enforcer, USA, 9.4 m	1980s	30
30	Simonneau SM 331, 9.3 m	1992	40
60	Boston Whalers, 8.3 m	1980s	30
50	Cytra, Greece, 6.5 m	1970s	30
8	Catamarans, 6.4 m	1977	30
475	Task Force Boats, 5.25 m	1976	20
4	Viper, 5.1 m	1980s	25
2	Cobra, 3.9 m	1984	40

Comment: Many are based at Jiddah with the rest spread around the other bases. Most are armed with MGs and the larger craft have I band radars.

SIMONNEAU SM 331   *1992, Simonneau Marine*

1 ROYAL YACHT

AL DERYAH

Displacement, tons: 112 full load
Dimensions, feet (metres): 91.2 × 20 × 6.9 *(27.8 × 6.1 × 2.1)*
Main machinery: 2 MTU 16V diesels; 2 shafts
Speed, knots: 16. **Range, miles:** 550 at 14 kts
Radars: Navigation: Decca 370; I band.

Comment: Based at Aziziah.

1 ROYAL YACHT

Name	No	Builders	Commissioned
ABDUL AZIZ	—	Halsingør Waerft, Denmark	12 June 1984

Displacement, tons: 5000 full load
Measurement, tons: 1450 dwt
Dimensions, feet (metres): 482.2 × 59.2 × 16.1 *(147 × 18 × 4.9)*
Main machinery: 2 Lindholmen-Pielstick 12 PC2.5 V diesels; 15 600 hp(m) *(11.47 MW)* sustained; 2 shafts
Speed, knots: 22.5
Complement: 65 plus 4 Royal berths and 60 spare
Helicopters: 1 Bell 206B JetRanger type.

Comment: Completed March 1983 for subsequent fitting out at Vosper's Ship Repairers, Southampton. Helicopter hangar set in hull forward of bridge—covers extend laterally to form pad. Swimming pool. Stern ramp leading to garage. Based at Jiddah.

ABDUL AZIZ   *6/1984, W Sartori*

1 TRAINING SHIP

TABBOUK

Displacement, tons: 585 full load
Dimensions, feet (metres): 196.8 × 32.8 × 5.8 *(60 × 10 × 1.8)*
Main machinery: 2 MTU MD 16V 538 TB80 diesels; 5000 hp(m) *(3.68 MW)* sustained; 2 shafts
Speed, knots: 20. **Range, miles:** 3500 at 12 kts
Complement: 24 plus 36 trainees
Guns: 1 Oerlikon GAM-BO1 20 mm.
Radars: Surface search: Racal Decca TM 1226; I band.
Navigation: Racal Decca 2690BT; I band.

Comment: Built by Bayerische, Germany and commissioned 1 December 1977. Based at Jiddah.

1 TRAINING YACHT

AL TAIF

Displacement, tons: 75 full load
Dimensions, feet (metres): 70.2 × 19 × 5.6 *(21.4 × 5.8 × 1.7)*
Main machinery: 2 Deutz SBF 12M716 diesels; 2 shafts
Speed, knots: 15
Radars: Navigation: Decca 101; I band.

Comment: Based at Jiddah.

3 SMALL TANKERS

AL FORAT   DAJLAH   AL NIL

Displacement, tons: 233 full load
Dimensions, feet (metres): 94.2 × 21.3 × 6.9 *(28.7 × 6.5 × 2.1)*
Main machinery: 2 Caterpillar D343 diesels; 2 shafts
Speed, knots: 12. **Range, miles:** 500 at 12 kts
Radars: Navigation: Decca 110; I band.

Comment: *Al Nil* based at Aziziah, the others at Jiddah.

4 FIREFIGHTING CRAFT

JUBAIL   JIDDAH   DAMMAM   AZIZIAH

Displacement, tons: 82 full load
Dimensions, feet (metres): 80.4 × 24.9 × 7.5 *(24.5 × 7.6 × 2.3)*
Main machinery: 2 GM 16V-92; 2 shafts
Speed, knots: 19. **Range, miles:** 350 at 14 kts

Comment: Built by Brooke Marine in 1979. Two based at Jiddah, two at Aziziah.

3 HARBOUR TUGS

Displacement, tons: 210 full load
Dimensions, feet (metres): 84.3 × 23.6 × 9.5 *(25.7 × 7.2 × 2.9)*
Main machinery: 1 Deutz SBA 16M 816 diesel; 1 shaft
Speed, knots: 13. **Range, miles:** 1200 at 12 kts

Comment: Two based at Jiddah and one at Aziziah.

SENEGAL

Political

On 1 February 1982 the two countries of Senegal and The Gambia united to form the confederation of Senegambia, which included merging the armed forces. Confederation was cancelled on 30 September 1989 and the forces again became national and independent of each other.

Head of Navy:
Captain Alexandre Diam

Personnel

(a) 1994: 700 officers and men
(b) 2 years' conscript service

Bases

Dakar, Casamance

Mercantile Marine

Lloyd's Register of Shipping:
172 vessels of 66 123 tons gross

DELETIONS

Amphibious Forces

1993   *La Faleme, Diombos, Diou Loulou*

LAND-BASED MARITIME AIRCRAFT

Note: In addition there are six F27-400M aircraft.

Numbers/Type: 1 de Havilland Canada DHC-6 Twin Otter.
Operational speed: 168 kts *(311 km/h)*.
Service ceiling: 23 200 ft *(7070 m)*.
Range: 1460 nm *(2705 km)*.
Role/Weapon systems: MR for coastal surveillance but effectiveness limited. Backed up by a French Navy Breguet Atlantique based at Dakar. Sensors: Search radar. Weapons: Unarmed.

PATROL FORCES

1 IMPROVED OSPREY 55 CLASS (LARGE PATROL CRAFT)

Name	No	Builders	Commissioned
FOUTA	—	Danyard A/S, Fredrikshavn	1 June 1987

Displacement, tons: 470 full load
Dimensions, feet (metres): 180.5 × 33.8 × 8.5 *(55 × 10.3 × 2.6)*
Main machinery: 2 MAN Burmeister & Wain Alpha 12V23/30-DVO diesels; 4400 hp(m) *(3.23 MW)* sustained; 2 shafts; cp props
Speed, knots: 20. **Range, miles:** 4000 at 16 kts
Complement: 38 (4 officers) plus 8 spare berths
Guns: 1 Hispano Suiza 30 mm.
Radars: Surface search: Furuno FR 1411; I band.
Navigation: Furuno FR 1221; I band.

Comment: Ordered in 1985. Intended for patrolling the EEZ rather than as a warship, hence the modest armament. A 25 knot rigid inflatable boat can be launched from a stern ramp which has a protective hinged door. Similar vessels built for Morocco and Greece.

FOUTA   *1992, Ships of the World*

1 PR 72M CLASS

Name	No	Builders	Commissioned
NJAMBUUR	P 773	SFCN, Villeneuve-la-Garenne	1983

Displacement, tons: 375 standard; 451 full load
Dimensions, feet (metres): 192.5 × 24.9 × 7.2 *(58.7 × 7.6 × 2.2)*
Main machinery: 4 SACM AGO 195 V16 RVR diesels; 11 760 hp(m) *(8.64 MW)* sustained; 4 shafts
Speed, knots: 29. **Range, miles:** 2500 at 16 kts
Complement: 39 plus 7 passengers
Guns: 2 OTO Melara 3 in *(76 mm)* compact.
2 Oerlikon 20 mm F2.
Fire control: 2 CSEE Naja optronic directors.
Radars: Surface search: Racal Decca 1226; I band

Comment: Ordered in 1979. Completed September 1981 for shipping of armament at Lorient.

NJAMBUUR   *1983*

3 P 48 CLASS (LARGE PATROL CRAFT)

Name	No	Builders	Commissioned
SAINT LOUIS	—	SFCN, Villeneuve-la-Garenne	1 Mar 1971
POPENGUINE	—	SFCN, Villeneuve-la-Garenne	10 Aug 1974
PODOR	—	SFCN, Villeneuve-la-Garenne	13 July 1977

Displacement, tons: 250 full load
Dimensions, feet (metres): 156 × 23.3 × 8.1 *(47.5 × 7.1 × 2.5)*
Main machinery: 2 SACM AGO V12 CZSHR diesels; 4340 hp(m) *(3.2 MW)*; 2 shafts
Speed, knots: 23. **Range, miles:** 2000 at 16 kts
Complement: 33 (3 officers)
Guns: 2 Bofors 40 mm/70.

Comment: Sisters to *Malaika* of Madagascar, *Le Vigilant* and *Le Valeureux* of Ivory Coast and Bizerte class of Tunisian Navy. *Podor* ordered August 1975.

P 48 class   *1989, van Ginderen Collection*

3 INTERCEPTOR CLASS (COASTAL PATROL CRAFT)

Name	No	Builders	Commissioned
SÉNÉGAL II	—	Les Bateaux Turbec Ltd, Sainte Catherine, Canada	Feb 1979
SINE-SALOUM II	—	Les Bateaux Turbec Ltd, Sainte Catherine, Canada	16 Nov 1979
CASAMANCE II	—	Les Bateaux Turbec Ltd, Sainte Catherine, Canada	Aug 1979

Displacement, tons: 62 full load
Dimensions, feet (metres): 86.9 × 19.3 × 5.2 *(26.5 × 5.8 × 1.6)*
Main machinery: 2 diesels; 2700 hp *(2.01 MW)*; 2 shafts
Speed, knots: 32.5
Guns: 2 Oerlikon 20 mm.

Comment: Used for EEZ patrol. Doubtful operational status.

CASAMANCE II   *9/1979, van Ginderen Collection*

2 FAIREY MARINE TRACKER 2 CLASS (COASTAL PATROL CRAFT)

Name	No	Builders	Commissioned
CHALLENGE	P 3	Fairey Marine, UK	1978
CHAMPION	P 4	Fairey Marine, UK	1978

Displacement, tons: 34
Dimensions, feet (metres): 65.7 × 17 × 4.8 *(20 × 5.2 × 1.5)*
Main machinery: 2 Detroit 12V-71TA diesels; 820 hp *(612 kW)* sustained; 2 shafts
Speed, knots: 24. **Range, miles:** 650 at 20 kts
Complement: 11
Guns: 1 Oerlikon 20 mm. 2—7.62 mm MGs.
Radars: Surface search: Racal Decca; I band.

Comment: Hull and superstructure of GRP. Air-conditioned accommodation. The third of the class belongs to Gambia.

TRACKER 2 class (Gambia number)   *1/1990, E Grove*

AMPHIBIOUS FORCES

1 EDIC 700 CLASS (LCT)

Name	No	Builders	Commissioned
KARABANE	841	SFCN, Villeneuve-la-Garenne	30 Jan 1987

Displacement, tons: 736 full load
Dimensions, feet (metres): 193.5 × 39 × 5.6 *(59 × 11.9 × 1.7)*
Main machinery: 2 SACM MGO 175 V12 ASH diesels; 1200 hp(m) *(882 kW)* sustained; 2 shafts
Speed, knots: 12. **Range, miles:** 1800 at 10 kts
Complement: 18 (33 spare billets)
Military lift: 12 trucks; 340 tons equipment
Guns: Fitted for 2 Oerlikon 20 mm.

Comment: Ordered May 1985, delivered 23 June 1986 from France. Replaced similar LCT *Damour*.

EDIC 700   *1991, G Toremans*

TUGS

2 TUGS

IBIS   AIGRETTE

Displacement, tons: 56
Dimensions, feet (metres): 60.4 × 18.7 × 8.2 *(18.4 × 5.7 × 2.5)*
Main machinery: 1 SACM Poyaud diesel; 250 hp(m) *(184 kW)*; 1 shaft
Speed, knots: 9. **Range, miles:** 1700 at 9 kts

Comment: Lent by France in 1990.

1 TENDER

CRAME JEAN (ex-*Raymond Sarr*)

Comment: An 18 ton fishing boat used as training craft since 1979.

CUSTOMS

2 TYPE DS-01 (COASTAL PATROL CRAFT)

Displacement, tons: 22
Dimensions, feet (metres): 52.5 × 15.1 × 7.5 *(16 × 4.6 × 2.3)*
Main machinery: 2 GM diesels; 970 hp *(724 kW)*; 2 shafts
Speed, knots: 20
Complement: 8
Guns: 1—12.7 mm MG.

Comment: Ordered A T Celaya, Bilbao March 1981. Delivered 9 February 1982.

4 LVI 85 S CLASS (INSHORE PATROL CRAFT)

DJIBRIL   N'DIAYE   GORÉE   DJILOR

Displacement, tons: 3.4
Speed, knots: 18

Comment: Ordered from Aresa, Barcelona and delivered in mid-1987 after long delays.

ARESA patrol craft   *1980, Aresa*

SEYCHELLES

Senior Appointment

Commander of the Navy:
  Major Paul Hodoul

Base

Port Victoria, Mahé

Personnel

1994:   200 officers and men

Mercantile Marine

Lloyd's Register of Shipping:
  9 vessels of 4465 tons gross

DELETION

Patrol Forces

1993   *Junon*

PATROL FORCES

1 TURYA CLASS

ZOROASTER

Displacement, tons: 190 standard; 250 full load
Dimensions, feet (metres): 129.9 × 24.9 × 5.9 *(39.6 × 7.6 × 1.8)*
Main machinery: 3 Type M 504 diesels; 10 800 hp *(7.94 MW)* sustained; 3 shafts
Speed, knots: 18. **Range, miles:** 1450 at 14 kts
Complement: 30
Guns: 2—57 mm/70 (twin). 2—25 mm/80 (twin).
Depth charges: 1 rack.
Radars: Surface search: Pot Drum; H/I band.
Fire control: Muff Cob; G/H band.
Sonars: Helicopter type VDS; active search and attack; high frequency.

Comment: Craft presented by USSR 21 June 1986. Same as Turya class except torpedo tubes and hydrofoils removed. Seychelles crew trained in USSR. Russian Commanding Officer and Executive Officer returned to USSR in August 1986. The retention of the sonar is unusual in the export version as is the removal of the hydrofoils. Non-operational since 1992.

ZOROASTER   *1988*

1 TYPE FPB 42 (LARGE PATROL CRAFT)

Name	No	Builders	Commissioned
ANDROMACHE	— (ex-605)	Picchiotti, Viareggio	10 Jan 1983

Displacement, tons: 268 full load
Dimensions, feet (metres): 137.8 × 26 × 8.2 *(41.8 × 8 × 2.5)*
Main machinery: 2 Paxman Valenta 16 CM diesels; 6650 hp *(5 MW)* sustained; 2 shafts
Speed, knots: 26. **Range, miles:** 3000 at 16 kts
Complement: 22 (3 officers)
Guns: 1 Oerlikon 25 mm. 2—7.62 mm MGs.
Radars: Navigation: Furuno; I band.

Comment: Ordered from Inma, La Spezia in November 1981. Pennant numbers no longer worn. A second of class reported ordered in 1991.

ANDROMACHE   *1988, PDFS*

2 ZHUK (TYPE 1400M) CLASS (COASTAL PATROL CRAFT)

CONSTANT   FORTUNE

Displacement, tons: 39 full load
Dimensions, feet (metres): 78.7 × 16.4 × 3.9 *(24 × 5 × 1.2)*
Main machinery: 2 Type M 401B diesels; 2200 hp *(1.6 MW)* sustained; 2 shafts
Speed, knots: 30. **Range, miles:** 1100 at 15 kts
Complement: 12 (3 officers)
Guns: 4—14.5 mm (2 twin) MGs.
Radars: Surface search: Furuno; I band.

Comment: Transferred from USSR on 11 October 1981 and 6 November 1982 respectively.

CONSTANT   *1990*

1 SIRIUS CLASS (LARGE PATROL CRAFT)

TOPAZ (ex-*Croix du Sud*)

Displacement, tons: 440 full load
Dimensions, feet (metres): 152 × 28 × 8.2 *(46.4 × 8.6 × 2.5)*
Main machinery: 2 SEMT-Pielstick diesels; 2000 hp(m) *(1.47 MW)*; 2 shafts
Speed, knots: 15. **Range, miles:** 3000 at 10 kts
Complement: 38
Guns: 1 Bofors 40 mm/60. 1 Oerlikon 20 mm.

Comment: Ex-French minesweeper built in 1956 and transferred without sweep gear in January 1979. Paid off in 1987 but brought back into service in late 1990. Not in good repair.

AUXILIARY

1 LANDING CRAFT (TANK)

Name	No	Builders	Commissioned
CINQ JUIN	—	La Perrière, France	11 Jan 1979

Displacement, tons: 855 full load
Dimensions, feet (metres): 186.8 × 38 × 6 *(56.9 × 11.6 × 1.9)*
Main machinery: 2 Poyaud A12 150M diesels; 880 hp(m) *(647 kW)*; 2 shafts
Speed, knots: 9. **Range, miles:** 2000 at 8 kts
Military lift: 300 tons plus 1 LCP

Comment: Ordered 12 December 1977. Although government-owned, this ship is commercially operated except for occasional exercises.

CINQ JUIN   *1986, PDFS*

LAND-BASED MARITIME AIRCRAFT

Numbers/Type: 1 Fairchild Merlin IIIB.
Operational speed: 309 kts *(571 km/h)*.
Service ceiling: 31 400 ft *(9570 m)*.
Range: 2468 nm *(4574 km)*.
Role/Weapon systems: Reconnaissance aircraft for coastal patrol. Sensors: Search radar. Weapons: Unarmed.

Numbers/Type: 2 HAL (Aerospatiale) Chetak (Alouette III).
Operational speed: 113 kts *(210 km/h)*.
Service ceiling: 10 500 ft *(3200 m)*.
Range: 290 nm *(540 km)*.
Role/Weapon systems: Support helicopter; used for police and anti-smuggler patrols. Sensors: None. Weapons: 2 × 7.62 mm machine guns can be fitted.

Numbers/Type: 1 Pilatus Britten-Norman Maritime Defender.
Operational speed: 150 kts *(280 km/h)*.
Service ceiling: 18 900 ft *(5760 m)*.
Range: 1500 nm *(2775 km)*.
Role/Weapon systems: Coastal surveillance and surface search aircraft. Sensors: Search radar. Weapons: Provision for rockets or guns.

SIERRA LEONE

Senior Appointment	Base	
Commander of Navy: Lieutenant Commander Alimany Sesay	Freetown	

DELETIONS

Patrol Forces

1992   *Maritime Protector* (charter ended), *Pompoli, Gulama, Kailondo*
1993   Halmatic Type (Port Authority)

Personnel

(a)   1994: 140 officers and men
(b)   Voluntary service

Mercantile Marine

Lloyd's Register of Shipping:
    61 vessels of 25 898 tons gross

PATROL FORCES

1 SWIFT 105 FT CLASS (LARGE PATROL CRAFT)

FARANDUGU

Displacement, tons: 103 full load
Dimensions, feet (metres): 105 × 22 × 7 *(31.5 × 6.7 × 2.1)*
Main machinery: 4 MTU 12V 331 TC92 diesels; 5320 hp(m) *(3.92 MW)* sustained; 4 shafts
Speed, knots: 25. **Range, miles:** 1200 at 12 kts
Complement: 19
Guns: 2—12.7 mm MGs. 2—7.62 mm MGs.

Comment: Laid down under FMS funding by Swiftships in October 1987 and delivered in December 1989. Carries a RIB.

SWIFT 105 FT (different armament)   *1991*

2 SHANGHAI II CLASS (FAST ATTACK CRAFT—GUN)

MOA   NAIMBANA

Displacement, tons: 113 standard; 131 full load
Dimensions, feet (metres): 127.3 × 17.7 × 5.6 *(38.8 × 5.4 × 1.7)*
Main machinery: 2 Type L12-180 diesels; 2400 hp(m) *(1.76 MW)* (forward); 2 Type L12-180Z diesels; 1820 hp(m) *(1.34 MW)* (aft); 4 shafts
Speed, knots: 30. **Range, miles:** 700 at 16.5 kts
Complement: 34
Guns: 2 China 37 mm/63 (twin); 85° elevation; 180 rounds/minute to 8.5 km *(4.6 nm)*; weight of shell 1.42 kg.
   4 USSR 25 mm/60 (2 twin); 85° elevation; 270 rounds/minute to 3 km *(1.6 nm)* anti-aircraft; weight of shell 0.34 kg.
Mines: Mine rails can be fitted for 10 mines.
Radars: Surface search: Skin Head or Pot Head; I band.

Comment: Delivered in March 1987. Chinese technicians were loaned for maintenance work and training. These craft only have one twin 37 mm gun (forward) vice two in Chinese craft. Both re-engined in 1993 and fully operational.

SHANGHAI II   1990

2 CAT 900S CLASS (INSHORE PATROL CRAFT)

Displacement, tons: 7.4 full load
Dimensions, feet (metres): 34.1 × 9.5 × 2.6 *(10.4 × 2.9 × 0.8)*
Main machinery: 2 Volvo Penta TAMD41A diesels; 400 hp(m) *(294 kW)* maximum; 2 shafts
Speed, knots: 30
Complement: 4

Comment: Built by Cougar Holdings Ltd, Hamble and completed in May 1988. Catamaran hulls. Both unserviceable by 1992 but back in operation in early 1994 after being refitted.

SINGAPORE

Headquarters' Appointment

Chief of the Navy:
   Commodore Kwek Siew Jin

Personnel

(a)   1994: 4500 officers and men including 1800 conscripts
(b)   National Service: two and a quarter years for Corporals and above; two years for the remainder
(c)   4500 reservists

Base

Pulau Brani, Tuas (Jurong)

Prefix to Ships' Names

RSS

Organisation

First Flotilla: Squadrons 188 (six Victory), 185 (six Lürssen), 182 (six Vosper Type A and B)
Third Flotilla: Squadrons 191 (five LSTs), 194 *(Jupiter and Endeavour),* 195 (LCVPs), 192 and 193 (Civil Reserve)
Coastal Patrol Squadrons (COPAS): 183 and 186 (8 Swift, 12 IPC)
Naval Logistics Command

Strength of the Fleet

Type	Active	Building (Projected)
Submarines	—	(2)
Missile Corvettes	6	—
Fast Attack Craft—Missile	6	6 (6)
Fast Attack Craft—Gun	6	—
Coastal Patrol Craft	8	—
Inshore Patrol Craft	12	—
Minehunters	—	4
LSTs/LSL	5 (1)	(4)
LCMs	10	—
LHC	1	—
Diving Support Ships	2	—

Maritime Air

The navy has no separate air arm but the Air Force has Grumman E 2C Hawkeyes (see *Land-based Maritime Aircraft* section) and several reconnaissance aircraft. In addition the Air Force has more than 50 A4 Skyhawks, (possibly with Harpoon when modernised), and eight F16 A/B.

Mercantile Marine

Lloyd's Register of Shipping:
   1129 vessels of 11 034 831 tons gross

DELETIONS

Patrol Forces

1991   *Panglima*
1993   4 Swift class (to Police)

Auxiliary

1993   *Mercury*

SUBMARINES

Note: Two submarines of about 800 tons are to be leased, with four new construction built by the end of the decade. Sales depend on full government/builder support to develop all aspects of creating and operating a submarine flotilla. A consortium of UK/Netherlands, Australia/Sweden, and Germany are all interested.

CORVETTES

6 VICTORY CLASS

Name	No	Builders	Launched	Commissioned
VICTORY	P 88	Lürssen Werft, Bremen	8 June 1988	18 Aug 1990
VALOUR	P 89	Singapore SB and Marine	10 Dec 1988	18 Aug 1990
VIGILANCE	P 90	Singapore SB and Marine	27 Apr 1989	18 Aug 1990
VALIANT	P 91	Singapore SB and Marine	22 July 1989	25 May 1991
VIGOUR	P 92	Singapore SB and Marine	1 Dec 1989	25 May 1991
VENGEANCE	P 93	Singapore SB and Marine	23 Feb 1990	25 May 1991

Displacement, tons: 550 full load
Dimensions, feet (metres): 204.7 oa; 190.3 wl × 27.9 × 10.2 *(62.4; 58 × 8.5 × 3.1)*
Main machinery: 4 MTU 16V 538 TB93 diesels; 15 020 hp(m) *(11 MW)* sustained; 4 shafts
Speed, knots: 35. **Range, miles:** 4000 at 18 kts
Complement: 49 (8 officers)

Missiles: SSM: 8 McDonnell Douglas Harpoon; active radar homing to 130 km *(70 nm)* at 0.9 Mach; warhead 227 kg.
   SAM: Rafael Barak I to be fitted aft in due course.
Guns: 1 OTO Melara 3 in *(76 mm)*/62 Super Rapid; 85° elevation; 120 rounds/minute to 16 km *(8.7 nm)*; weight of shell 6 kg.
Torpedoes: 6—324 mm Whitehead B 515 (2 triple) tubes. Whitehead A 244S; anti-submarine; active/passive homing to 7 km *(3.8 nm)* at 33 kts; warhead 34 kg (shaped charge).
Countermeasures: Decoys: 2 Plessey Shield 12-barrelled chaff launchers.
   ESM/ECM: Rafael RAN 1101 intercept and jammer.
Combat data systems: Elbit command system.
Fire control: BEAB 9LV 200 Mk 3
Radars: Surface search: Ericsson/Radamec Sea Giraffe 150HC; G/H band.
   Navigation: Racal Decca; I band.
   Fire control: Bofors Electronic 9LV 200; I/J band.
Sonars: Thomson Sintra TSM 2064; VDS; active search and attack.

Programmes: Ordered in June 1986 to a Lürssen MGB 62 design similar to Bahrain and UAE vessels.
Structure: Close range armament is to include Barak I CIWS in due course. Trials are being done on stabilisers to try and improve roll characteristics. It is possible that the mast may have to be rebuilt and reduced in size.
Operational: Form Squadron 188.

VIGILANCE   5/1993, John Mortimer

PATROL FORCES

Note: Ten 12 m craft are to be ordered for Special Forces in 1995.

0 + 6 (6) FAST ATTACK CRAFT (MISSILE)

Displacement, tons: 300 full load
Dimensions, feet (metres): 164 × 23.6 × 7.9 *(50 × 7.2 × 2.4)*
Main machinery: 4 diesels; 4 shafts
Speed, knots: 35
Complement: 40 (6 officers)

Missiles: SSM: Harpoon/Gabriel II (may be fitted).
Guns: 1—76 mm/62.
Torpedoes: 3 or 6—324 mm (1 or 2 triple tubes).
Countermeasures: Decoys: Plessey Shield III chaff launchers.
Radars: Surface search. Fire control.

Programmes: Ordered from Singapore Shipbuilding and Engineering in December 1993. To be built in Singapore in two batches of six to replace the Vosper Types first, and then the FPB 45s.

6 LÜRSSEN FPB 45 CLASS (FAST ATTACK CRAFT—MISSILE)

Name	No	Builders	Commissioned
SEA WOLF	P 76	Lürssen Werft, Vegesack	1972
SEA LION	P 77	Lürssen Werft, Vegesack	1972
SEA DRAGON	P 78	Singapore SBEC	1974
SEA TIGER	P 79	Singapore SBEC	1974
SEA HAWK	P 80	Singapore SBEC	1975
SEA SCORPION	P 81	Singapore SBEC	29 Feb 1976

Displacement, tons: 226 standard; 254 full load
Dimensions, feet (metres): 147.3 × 23 × 7.5 *(44.9 × 7 × 2.3)*
Main machinery: 4 MTU 16V 538 TB92 diesels; 13 640 hp(m) *(10 MW)* sustained; 4 shafts
Speed, knots: 38. **Range, miles:** 950 at 30 kts; 1800 at 15 kts
Complement: 36 (6 officers)

Missiles: SSM: 4 McDonnell Douglas Harpoon (2 twin); active radar homing to 130 km *(70 nm)* at 0.9 Mach; warhead 227 kg.
2 IAI Gabriel I launchers; radar or optical guidance; semi-active radar homing to 20 km *(10.8 nm)* at 0.7 Mach; warhead 75 kg.
Guns: 1 Bofors 57 mm/70 (not in all); 75° elevation; 200 rounds/minute to 17 km *(9.3 nm)*; weight of shell 2.4 kg.
1 Bofors 40 mm/70; 90° elevation; 300 rounds/minute to 12 km *(6.6 nm)*; weight of shell 0.96 kg.
Countermeasures: Decoys: 4 Mk 36 SRBOC chaff launchers.
ESM/ECM: Racal intercept and jammer.
Radars: Surface search: Racal Decca; I band.
Fire control: Signaal WM 28/5; I/J band; range 46 km *(25 nm)*.

Programmes: Designed by Lürssen Werft which built the first pair.
Modernisation: *Sea Hawk* was the first to complete refit in January 1988 with two sets of twin Harpoon launchers replacing the triple Gabriel launcher. The remainder were converted by December 1990 with the exception of *Sea Wolf* which finished refit in Spring 1991. ECM equipment has also been fitted on a taller mast. SATCOM and GPS installed. The Bofors 40 mm gun may be replaced with a Matra Simbad SAM launcher if trials are successful.

SEA TIGER   *1/1993, A M Nixon, RAN*

3 VOSPER TYPE A (FAST ATTACK CRAFT—GUN)

Name	No	Builders	Commissioned
INDEPENDENCE	P 69	Vosper Thornycroft Ltd, Gosport	8 July 1970
FREEDOM	P 70	Vosper Thornycroft Private Ltd, Singapore	11 Jan 1971
JUSTICE	P 72	Vosper Thornycroft Private Ltd, Singapore	23 Apr 1971

Displacement, tons: 112 standard; 142 full load
Dimensions, feet (metres): 109.6 × 21 × 5.6 *(33.5 × 6.4 × 1.8)*
Main machinery: 2 MTU MD 16V 538 TB90 diesels; 3580 hp(m) *(2.63 MW)* sustained; 2 shafts
Speed, knots: 32. **Range, miles:** 1000 at 14 kts
Complement: 19-22 (3 officers)
Guns: 1 Bofors 40 mm/70 fwd; 90° elevation; 300 rounds/minute to 12 km *(6.6 nm)*; weight of shell 0.96 kg.
1 Oerlikon 20 mm/80 aft; 55° elevation; 800 rounds/minute to 2 km.
Radars: Surface search: Racal Decca; I band.
Navigation: Decca 626; I band.

Comment: Ordered on 21 May 1968. To be replaced by new class in 1995/96.

JUSTICE   *4/1990, 92 Wing RAAF*

3 VOSPER TYPE B (FAST ATTACK CRAFT—GUN)

Name	No	Builders	Commissioned
SOVEREIGNTY	P 71	Vosper Thornycroft Ltd, Gosport	Feb 1971
DARING	P 73	Vosper Thornycroft Private Ltd, Singapore	18 Sep 1971
DAUNTLESS	P 74	Vosper Thornycroft Private Ltd, Singapore	July 1971

Displacement, tons: 112 standard; 142 full load
Dimensions, feet (metres): 109.6 × 21 × 5.6 *(33.5 × 6.4 × 1.8)*
Main machinery: 2 MTU MD 16V 538 TB90 diesels; 3580 hp(m) *(2.63 MW)* sustained; 2 shafts
Speed, knots: 32. **Range, miles:** 1000 at 14 kts
Complement: 19 (3 officers)
Guns: 1 Bofors 3 in *(76 mm)*/50; 30° elevation; 30 rounds/minute to 13 km *(7 nm)* surface fire only; weight of shell 5.9 kg.
1 Oerlikon 20 mm/80; 55° elevation; 800 rounds/minute to 2 km.
Radars: Surface search: Racal Decca; I band.
Fire control: Signaal WM 26; I/J band; range 46 km *(25 nm)*.

Comment: Steel hulls of round bilge form. Aluminium alloy superstructure. To be replaced in 1995/96.

DARING   *5/1992, G Toremans*

8 SWIFT CLASS (COASTAL PATROL CRAFT)

SWIFT KNIGHT P 11		SWIFT CAVALIER P 20
SWIFT WARRIOR P 15		SWIFT CONQUEROR P 21
SWIFT WARLORD P 17		SWIFT CENTURION P 22
SWIFT CHALLENGER P 19		SWIFT CHIEFTAIN P 23

Displacement, tons: 45.7 full load
Dimensions, feet (metres): 74.5 × 20.3 × 5.2 *(22.7 × 6.2 × 1.6)*
Main machinery: 2 Deutz BA16M816 diesels; 2680 hp(m) *(1.96 MW)* sustained; 2 shafts
Speed, knots: 32. **Range, miles:** 550 at 20 kts; 900 at 10 kts
Complement: 12 (3 officers)
Guns: 1 Oerlikon 20 mm. 2—7.62 mm MGs.
Radars: Surface search: Decca 1226; I band.

Comment: Delivered by Singapore SBEC 20 October 1981. Fitted for but not with two Gabriel SSMs. P12, P14, P16 and P18 transferred to the Police on 15 February 1993, others may follow.

SWIFT CHALLENGER   *5/1992, G Toremans*

12 INSHORE PATROL CRAFT

FB 31-42

Displacement, tons: 20 full load
Dimensions, feet (metres): 47.6 × 13.8 × 3.6 *(14.5 × 4.2 × 1.1)*
Main machinery: 2 MTU 12V 183 TC91 diesels; 1200 hp(m) *(882 kW)*; 2 Hamilton waterjets
Speed, knots: 30
Complement: 4
Guns: 1—7.62 mm MG.
Radars: Surface search: Racal Decca; I band.

Comment: Built by Singapore SBEC and delivered in 1990/91. Based at Brani.

FB 42   *1991, Singapore Shipbuilding and Engineering*

LAND-BASED MARITIME AIRCRAFT

Note: A squadron of four Fokker F50 Maritime Enforcer II aircraft to be formed in 1994.

Numbers/Type: 4 Grumman E-2C Hawkeye.
Operational speed: 323 kts *(598 km/h).*
Service ceiling: 30 800 ft *(9390 m).*
Range: 1000 nm *(1850 km).*
Role/Weapon systems: Delivered in 1987 for surveillance of shipping in sea areas around Singapore and South China Sea; understood to have priority assistance from US Government. Sensors: APS-125 radar; data link for SSM targeting; later aircraft will have APS-138 radar. Weapons: Unarmed.

MINE WARFARE FORCES

0 + 4 LANDSORT CLASS (MINEHUNTERS)

Name	No	Builders	Commissioned
BEDOK	M 47	Kockums/Karlskrona	1994
KALLANG	M 48	Singapore Shipbuilding	1995
KATONG	M 49	Singapore Shipbuilding	1995
PUNGGOL	M 50	Singapore Shipbuilding	1996

Displacement, tons: 360 full load
Dimensions, feet (metres): 155.8 × 31.5 × 7.3 *(47.5 × 9.6 × 2.2)*
Main machinery: 4 Saab Scania diesels; 1592 hp(m) *(1.17 MW);* coupled in pairs to 2 Voith Schneider props
Speed, knots: 15. **Range, miles:** 2000 at 12 kts
Complement: 26 (8 officers)

Guns: 1 Bofors 40 mm/70. 2—7.62 mm MGs.
Fire control: Thomson-CSF TSM 2061 Mk II minehunting system. Signaal WM 20 director.
Radars: Navigation: I band.
Sonars: Thomson-CSF TSM 2022; hull-mounted; minehunting; high frequency.

Programmes: Kockums/Karlskrona design ordered in February 1991. *Bedok* launched 24 June 1993, started trials in Sweden in December 1993, and was shipped to Singapore in early 1994 to complete. Prefabrication work done for the other three in Sweden with assembly and fitting out in Singapore at Benoi Basin. *Kallang* launched 29 January 1994.
Structure: GRP hulls. Two PAP Mk V ROVs embarked.

BEDOK (old number)   *12/1993, Karlskronavarvet*

AMPHIBIOUS FORCES

Note: The plan is to order up to four LPDs in 1994/95. Requirements include two spot helo deck and air cushion landing craft.

1 SIR LANCELOT CLASS (LSL)

Name	No	Builders	Commissioned
PERSEVERANCE (?) (ex-*Sir Lancelot*)	— (ex-L 3029)	Fairfield, Glasgow	16 Jan 1964

Displacement, tons: 3270 light; 5674 full load
Dimensions, feet (metres): 412.1 × 59.8 × 13 *(125.6 × 18.2 × 4)*
Main machinery: 2 Mirrlees 10-ALSSDM diesels; 9400 hp *(7.01 MW);* 2 shafts; bow thruster
Speed, knots: 17. **Range, miles:** 8000 at 15 kts
Complement: 65
Military lift: 340 troops (534 hard lying); 16 MBTs; 34 mixed vehicles; 120 tons POL; 30 tons ammunition; 1—20 ton crane; 2—4.5 ton cranes.
Guns: 2 Bofors 40 mm/70. 2—12.7 mm MGs.
Radars: Navigation: Kelvin Hughes Type 1006; I band.
Helicopters: Platform for 2 medium.

Comment: Paid off from the British Navy in 1989 and used commercially for survey work. Acquired by Singapore in late 1992 and being refitted to upgrade accommodation and fit 40 mm guns. Fitted for bow and stern loading with drive-through facilities and deck-to-deck ramps. Facilities provided for onboard maintenance of vehicles and for laying out pontoon equipment. Mexeflote self-propelled floating platforms can be strapped one on each side. Carries 850 tons oil fuel.

LSL (British colours)   *1988*

---

5 LST 511-1152 CLASS (LSTs)

Name	No	Builders	Commissioned
ENDURANCE (ex-USS *Holmes County* LST 836)	L 201 (ex-A 82)	American Bridge Co	25 Nov 1944
EXCELLENCE (ex-US *LST 629*)	L 202 (ex-A 81)	Chicago Bridge & Iron Co	28 July 1944
INTREPID (ex-US *LST 579*)	L 203 (ex-A 83)	Missouri Valley B and I Co	21 July 1944
RESOLUTION (ex-US *LST 649*)	L 204 (ex-A 84)	Chicago Bridge & Iron Co	26 Oct 1944
PERSISTENCE (ex-US *LST 613*)	L 205 (ex-A 85)	Chicago Bridge & Iron Co	19 May 1944

Displacement, tons: 1653 light; 4100-4150 full load (modernised)
Dimensions, feet (metres): 328 × 50 × 14 *(100 × 15.2 × 4.3)*
Main machinery: 2 GM 12-567ATL diesels; 1800 hp *(1.34 MW);* 2 shafts
Speed, knots: 11.6. **Range, miles:** 19 000 at 10.5 kts
Complement: 120 (15 officers)
Military lift: 1500 tons general; 500 tons beaching; 440 m² tank deck; 500 m² main deck storage; can carry 125 troops on long haul; 2—5 ton cranes; 2 LCVPs on davits

Guns: 1 or 3 *(Endurance)* Bofors 40 mm/60; 80° elevation; 120 rounds/minute to 10 km *(5.5 nm);* weight of shell 0.89 kg.
2—7.62 mm MGs.
Radars: Navigation: Decca 626; I band.
IFF: UPX 12.

Helicopters: Platform only.

Programmes: *Endurance* loaned from the US Navy on 1 July 1971 and bought on 5 December 1975. Remainder transferred 4 June 1976. One of the class *Perseverence* has been cannibalised for spares.
Modernisation: This class has been modernised since 1977. This includes new electrics, new communications, an enclosed bridge and updated command facilities. A goal-post derrick has been fitted forward of the bridge (except in *Endurance*) and the lattice mast replaced by a pole mast. *Excellence* has a helicopter pad aft, others have a landing spot amidships. Most have been re-engined and service life extensions continue.
Operational: Used as Command ships and in support of the Army. *Resolution* is in reserve. *Persistence* is used for occasional training cruises.

EXCELLENCE (with helo platform aft)   *5/1990, G Toremans*

ENDURANCE   *10/1991, John Mortimer*

6 RPL TYPE (LCM)

RPL 60-RPL 65

Displacement, tons: 151
Dimensions, feet (metres): 120.4 × 28 × 5.9 *(36.7 × 8.5 × 1.8)*
Main machinery: 2 MAN D2540MLE diesels; 860 hp(m) *(632 kW);* 2 Schottel props
Speed, knots: 10.7
Complement: 6
Military lift: 2 tanks or 450 troops or 110 tons cargo (fuel or stores)

Comment: First pair built at North Shipyard Point, second pair by Singapore SBEC. First two launched August 1985, next two in October 1985. Cargo deck 86.9 × 21.6 ft *(26.5 × 6.6 m).* Bow ramp suitable for beaching. Third pair reported built by Singapore SBEC and completed in 1993. These may be of a slightly modified design.

RPL 61   *1/1989, Hartmut Ehlers*

4 AYER CHAWAN CLASS (LCM)

AYER CHAWAN RPL 54	AYER MERBAN RPL 55	RPL 56	RPL 57

Displacement, tons: 60 light; 150 full load
Dimensions, feet (metres): 88.5 × 22 × 4 *(27 × 6.9 × 1.2)*
Main machinery: 2 diesels; 650 hp(m) *(478 kW)*; 2 shafts
Speed, knots: 10. **Range, miles:** 300 at 10 kts
Complement: 9
Military lift: 40 tons general or 20 tons fuel or 1 medium tank.

Comment: Built by Vosper Thornycroft Private Ltd, Singapore 1968-69.

AYER CHAWAN   *1/1989, Hartmut Ehlers*

LANDING CRAFT (LCVP)

EP series

Displacement, tons: 4 full load
Dimensions, feet (metres): 44.6 × 12.1 × 2 *(13.6 × 3.7 × 0.6)*
Main machinery: 2 MAN D2866 LE diesels; 816 hp(m) *(600 kW)*; 2 Hamilton 362 waterjets
Speed, knots: 20. **Range, miles:** 100 at 20 kts
Complement: 3
Military lift: 4 tons

Comment: Fast Craft, Equipment and Personnel (FCEP), built by Singapore SBEC, are used to transport troops around the Singapore archipelago. They have a single bow ramp and can carry a rifle platoon. More than 100 are in service and more of a stretched version FCU (fast craft utility) are being built. Form part of 195 Squadron.

LCVPs   *9/1992, van Ginderen Collection*

1 TIGER 40 HOVERCRAFT (LHC)

Displacement, tons: 12
Dimensions, feet (metres): 54.1 × 19.7 *(16.5 × 6)*
Main machinery: 4 Deutz diesels; 760 hp(m) *(559 kW)* (for lift and propulsion)
Speed, knots: 35. **Range, miles:** 175 at 35 kts
Military lift: 30 troops or 2.6 tons equipment
Guns: 2—12.7 mm MGs.

Comment: Delivered by Singapore SBEC in 1987 for trials as a logistic support craft. More may be ordered in due course.

TIGER 40 class   *3/1987, Singapore Shipbuilding and Engineering*

450 ASSAULT CRAFT

Dimensions, feet (metres): 17.7 × 5.9 × 2.3 *(5.4 × 1.8 × 0.7)*
Main machinery: 1 outboard; 50 hp(m) *(37 kW)*
Speed, knots: 12
Military lift: 12 troops

Comment: Built by Singapore SBEC. Manportable craft which can carry a section of troops in the rivers and creeks surrounding Singapore island.

AUXILIARIES

1 DIVING SUPPORT SHIP

Name	No	Builders	Commissioned
JUPITER	A 102	Singapore SBEC	June 1990

Displacement, tons: 170 full load
Dimensions, feet (metres): 117.5 × 23.3 × 7.5 *(35.8 × 7.1 × 2.3)*
Main machinery: 2 Deutz MWM TBD234V12 diesels; 1360 hp(m) *(1 MW)* sustained; 2 shafts; bow thruster
Speed, knots: 14. **Range, miles:** 200 at 14 kts
Complement: 33 (5 officers)
Guns: 1 Oerlikon 20 mm.
Radars: Navigation: Racal Decca; I band.

Comment: Designed for underwater search and salvage operations and built to German naval standards. Secondary role of surveying. Equipped with a precise navigation system, towed sidescan sonar, and a remotely operated vehicle (ROV). The ship's diving support equipment comprises two high pressure compressors, a two-man decompression chamber, a rubber dinghy with 40 hp outboard motor and a 1.5 ton SWL crane.

JUPITER   *9/1991, G Toremans*

1 DIVING TRAINING SHIP

Name	No	Builders	Commissioned
ENDEAVOUR	P 75	Schiffswerft Oberwinter, Germany	30 Sep 1970

Displacement, tons: 250 full load
Dimensions, feet (metres): 135 × 25 × 8 *(40.9 × 7.6 × 2.4)*
Main machinery: 2 MTU MD diesels; 2600 hp(m) *(1.91 MW)*; 2 shafts
Speed, knots: 20. **Range, miles:** 800 at 8 kts
Complement: 24
Guns: 2 Oerlikon 20 mm.
Radars: Navigation: Racal Decca; I band.

Comment: Training ship for divers.

ENDEAVOUR   *1976, Singapore Navy*

POLICE

4 SWIFT CLASS

SWIFT LANCER (ex-P 12)	SWIFT ARCHER (ex-P 16)
SWIFT SWORDSMAN (ex-P 14)	SWIFT COMBATANT (ex-P 18)

Comment: Details under Swift class in naval section. Transferred from the Navy on 15 February 1993.

SWIFT   *1993, Ships of the World*

24 PATROL CRAFT

PX 10-33

Displacement, tons: 11
Dimensions, feet (metres): 37 × 10.5 × 1.6 *(11 × 3.2 × 0.5)*
Main machinery: 2 MTU diesels; 770 hp(m) *(566 kW)*; 2 shafts
Speed, knots: 30

Comment: Completed 1981 by Sembawang SY.

PX 14   *6/1990, F Sadek*

23 PATROL CRAFT

PT 1-23

Displacement, tons: 20 full load
Dimensions, feet (metres): 47.6 × 13.8 × 3.9 *(14.5 × 4.2 × 1.2)*
Main machinery: 2 MAN D2542MLE diesels; 1076 hp(m) *(791 kW)*; or MTU 12V 183 TC91 diesels; 1200 hp(m) *(882 kW)* maximum; 2 shafts
Speed, knots: 30. **Range, miles:** 310 at 22 kts
Complement: 4 plus 8 spare berths
Guns: 1—7.62 mm MG.

Comment: First 13 completed by Singapore SBEC between January and August 1984, two more completed February 1987 and eight more (including two Command Boats) in 1989. Of aluminium construction. Four more operated by Customs and Excise. There are differences in the deck houses between earlier and later vessels.

PT 13   *1984, Singapore Shipbuilding and Engineering*

34 PATROL CRAFT

PC 32-51   **PC 52-65**

Comment: First 20 were of 21.3 ft *(6.5 m)*, 35 kt craft from Vosper Thornycroft Private Ltd, built in 1978-79. Second series built in the 1980s. Some used by the Navy. All have twin Johnson outboard engines.

PC 61   *4/1990, F Sadek*

PILOT and CUSTOMS CRAFT

Note: Customs Craft include CE 1-4 and CE 5-8, the latter being sisters to PT 1 Police Craft. Pilot craft have GP numbers and include GP 40-57 built in 1989-90 by Cheoy Lee, Kowloon.

CE 2   *1/1989, Hartmut Ehlers*

SOLOMON ISLANDS

Control

Tulagi is operated by the Department of Fisheries. SIPV *Lata* and *Savo* are operated by the maritime wing of the Royal Solomon Islands Police Force.

Senior Officer

Commissioner of Police:
  F Soaks

Personnel

1994:   30 (6 officers)

Prefix to Ships' Names

RSIPV

Mercantile Marine

Lloyd's Register of Shipping:
  32 vessels of 7417 tons gross

PATROL FORCES

2 PACIFIC FORUM TYPE

Name	No	Builders	Commissioned
LATA	03	Australian Shipbuilding Industries	3 Sep 1988
AUKI	04	Australian Shipbuilding Industries	2 Nov 1991

Displacement, tons: 162 full load
Dimensions, feet (metres): 103.3 × 26.6 × 6.9 *(31.5 × 8.1 × 2.1)*
Main machinery: 2 Caterpillar 3516TA diesels; 4400 hp *(3.28 MW)* sustained; 2 shafts
Speed, knots: 20. **Range, miles:** 2500 at 12 kts
Complement: 14 (1 officer)
Guns: 3—12.7 mm MGs (not always mounted).
Radars: Surface search: Furuno 1011; I band.

Comment: Built under the Australian Defence Co-operation Programme. Training, operational and technical assistance provided by the Royal Australian Navy. Aluminium construction. Nominal endurance of 10 days.

LATA   *5/1992, van Ginderen Collection*

1 PATROL CRAFT

SAVO 02

Dimensions, feet (metres): 82 × 25.8 × 6.2 *(25 × 7.9 × 1.9)*
Main machinery: 2 Caterpillar 3516TA diesels; 4400 hp *(3.28 MW)* sustained; 2 shafts
Speed, knots: 36. **Range, miles:** 3000 at 12 kts

Comment: Built by ASI, Western Australia in 1984 as a prototype for the Pacific Forum class.

SAVO   5/1992, van Ginderen Collection

2 TUGS

SOLOMAN ATU   SOLOMAN KARIQUA

Comment: Acquired in 1981. 140 tons and capable of 9 kts.

1 CARPENTARIA CLASS

TULAGI 01

Displacement, tons: 27 full load
Dimensions, feet (metres): 51.5 × 15.7 × 4.3 *(15.7 × 4.8 × 1.3)*
Main machinery: 2 Detroit 12V-71TA diesels; 840 hp *(626 kW)* sustained; 2 shafts
Speed, knots: 28. **Range, miles:** 950 at 18 kts
Complement: 10
Guns: 1—7.62 mm MG.
Radars: Surface search: Racal Decca; I band.

Comment: Built by De Havilland Marine, Homebush Bay, Australia. Launched December 1978. Arrived Solomon Islands 4 May 1979.

TULAGI   1984, van Ginderen Collection

2 LANDING CRAFT

LIGOMO 3   ULUSAGE

Measurement, tons: 105 dwt
Main machinery: 2 diesels; 2 shafts
Speed, knots: 9

Comment: Built by Carpenter BY, Suva in 1981. 27 m in length.

SOMALIA

General

After the revolution in January 1991, the Navy effectively ceased to exist. The only vessels which were not sunk were one Polnochny LST and four Mol class attack craft. All were ransacked with every fixture and fitting removed by mid-1991, and two of the Mol class sank in 1992.

Bases

Berbera, Mogadishu and Kismayu

Mercantile Marine

Lloyd's Register of Shipping:
29 vessels of 17 767 tons gross

SOUTH AFRICA

Headquarters' Appointments

Chief of the Navy:
Vice Admiral R C Simpson-Anderson
Chief of Naval Support:
Rear Admiral H J M Trainor
Chief of Naval Operations:
Rear Admiral J F Retief

Bases

Pretoria: Headquarters and Command Centre
Durban: Minister class
Simonstown: Remainder of the Fleet
Saldanha Bay (basic training), Gordon's Bay (officer training).

Personnel

1994: 4100 (all volunteer)

Prefix to Ships' Names

SAS (South African Ship/Suid Afrikaanse Skip)

Marine Corps

The Marine Branch was re-established in 1979 after its earlier stand-down in 1957. Disbanded again in 1990 as part of the defence cuts.

Mercantile Marine

Lloyd's Register of Shipping:
190 vessels of 345 502 tons gross

DELETION

Auxiliary

1993   *Tafelberg*

SUBMARINES

3 DAPHNE CLASS

Name	No	Builders	Laid down	Launched	Commissioned
MARIA VAN RIEBEECK	S 97	Dubigeon—Normandie, Nantes-Chantenay	14 Mar 1968	18 Mar 1969	22 June 1970
EMILY HOBHOUSE	S 98	Dubigeon—Normandie, Nantes-Chantenay	18 Nov 1968	24 Oct 1969	25 Jan 1971
JOHANNA VAN DER MERWE	S 99	Dubigeon—Normandie, Nantes-Chantenay	24 Apr 1969	21 July 1970	21 July 1971

Displacement, tons: 869 surfaced; 1043 dived
Dimensions, feet (metres): 189.6 × 22.3 × 15.1 *(57.8 × 6.8 × 4.6)*
Main machinery: Diesel-electric; 2 SEMT-Pielstick 12 PA4 V 185 diesels; 2450 hp(m) *(1.8 MW)*; 2 Jeumont Schneider alternators; 1.7 MW; 2 motors; 2600 hp(m) *(1.9 MW)*; 2 shafts
Speed, knots: 13.5 surfaced; 16 dived
Range, miles: 4500 at 5 kts snorting; 2700 at 12.5 kts surfaced
Complement: 47 (6 officers)

Torpedoes: 12—21.7 in *(550 mm)* (8 bow, 4 stern) tubes. ECAN E15; dual purpose; passive homing to 12 km *(6.6 nm)* at 25 kts; warhead 300 kg; or ECAN L4/L5 to 9.5 km *(5.1 nm)*. No reloads.
Countermeasures: ESM: ARUD; radar warning.
Fire control: Trivetts-UEC weapon control system.
Radars: Surface search: Thomson-CSF Calypso II; I band; range 31 km *(17 nm)* for 10 m² target.
Sonars: Thomson Sintra DUUA 2; hull-mounted; active/passive search and attack; 8.4 kHz active.
Thomson Sintra DUUX 2; passive range finding.
Thomson Sintra DSUV 2; passive search; medium frequency.

Programmes: Ordered from France in 1967. Feasibility studies have been done to evaluate replacements.

MARIA VAN RIEBEECK   10/1992, Robert Pabst

Modernisation: Weapon systems upgrading (including sonar) as well as improved habitability as part of a mid-life improvement programme. *Emily Hobhouse* completed in July 1988, *Van der Merwe* in late 1990, *Maria van Riebeeck* in mid-1993.

Structure: French Daphne design, similar to those built in France for that country, Pakistan and Portugal and also built in Spain. Diving depth, 300 m *(985 ft)*.

PATROL FORCES

Note: The plan is to order four 1500-3000 ton offshore patrol vessels in 1994. This would restore ASW capability and provide more robust patrol ships than the existing Minister class. One solution would be to buy the hulls from Russia or Ukraine and fit them out in South Africa.

9 MINISTER CLASS (FAST ATTACK CRAFT—MISSILE)

Name	No	Builders	Commissioned
JAN SMUTS	P 1561	Haifa Shipyard	18 July 1977
P W BOTHA	P 1562	Haifa Shipyard	2 Dec 1977
FREDERIC CRESSWELL	P 1563	Haifa Shipyard	6 Apr 1978
JIM FOUCHÉ	P 1564	Sandock Austral, Durban	22 Dec 1978
FRANS ERASMUS	P 1565	Sandock Austral, Durban	27 July 1979
OSWALD PIROW	P 1566	Sandock Austral, Durban	4 Mar 1980
HENDRIK MENTZ	P 1567	Sandock Austral, Durban	11 Feb 1983
KOBIE COETSEE	P 1568	Sandock Austral, Durban	11 Feb 1983
MAGNUS MALAN	P 1569	Sandock Austral, Durban	4 July 1986

Displacement, tons: 430 full load
Dimensions, feet (metres): 204 × 25 × 8 *(62.2 × 7.8 × 2.4)*
Main machinery: 4 Maybach MTU 16V 965 TB91 diesels; 15 000 hp(m) *(11 MW)* sustained; 4 shafts
Speed, knots: 32. **Range, miles:** 1500 at 30 kts; 3600+ at economical speed
Complement: 47 (7 officers)

Missiles: SSM: 8 Skerpioen; active radar or optical guidance; semi-active radar homing to 36 km *(19.4 nm)* at 0.7 Mach; warhead 75 kg. Another pair may be mounted. Skerpioen is an Israeli Gabriel II built under licence in South Africa.
Guns: 2 OTO Melara 3 in *(76 mm)*/62 compact; 85° elevation; 85 rounds/minute to 16 km *(8.7 nm)*; weight of shell 6 kg; 500 rounds per gun.
2 Oerlikon 20 mm. 2—12.7 mm MGs.
Countermeasures: Decoys: 4 launchers for chaff.
ESM: Elta; radar warning.
Combat data systems: Mini action data automation with Link.
Radars: Air/surface search: Thomson-CSF Triton; G band; range 33 km *(18 nm)* for 2 m² target.
Fire control: Selenia RTN 10X; I/J band; range 40 km *(22 nm)*.

Programmes: Contract signed with Israel in late 1974 for this class, similar to Saar 4 class. Three built in Haifa and reached South Africa in July 1978. The ninth craft launched late March 1986. Three more improved vessels of this class were ordered but subsequently cancelled. The last of the class was finally christened in March 1992.
Modernisation: *P W Botha* recommissioned 3 November 1986 after modernisation; *Kobie Coetsee* in July 1988; *Oswald Pirow* in May 1989. The cancellation of the corvette replacements in 1991 has led to the expansion of the upgrade programme into a major ship-life extension. This includes a new communications refit, improvements to sensors, a third-generation target designation assembly, a computer-assisted action information system served by data links, improvements to fire-control, a complete overhaul of the Skerpioen missiles, and a new engine room monitoring system. *Frederic Cresswell* is the first to undergo this upgrade and should complete in 1994. Others are to follow.

P W BOTHA   1/1993, Peter Humphries

28 NAMACURRA CLASS (INSHORE PATROL CRAFT)

Y 1501-1519   Y 1521-1529

Displacement, tons: 5 full load
Dimensions, feet (metres): 29.5 × 9 × 2.8 *(9 × 2.7 × 0.8)*
Main machinery: 2 Yamaha outboards
Speed, knots: 32
Complement: 4
Guns: 1—12.7 mm MG. 2—7.62 mm MGs.
Depth charges: 1 rack.

Comment: Built in South Africa in 1980-81. Can be transported by road. One transferred to Malawi in October 1988 and one has sunk at sea.

NAMACURRA   3/1993, Nikolaus Sifferlinger

NAMACURRA (with guns)   1993, South African Navy

OSWALD PIROW   3/1992, Peter Humphries

3 T 2212 COASTGUARD CLASS (INSHORE PATROL CRAFT)

Displacement, tons: 23 full load
Dimensions, feet (metres): 72.2 × 23 × 3 *(22 × 7 × 0.9)*
Main machinery: 2 ADE 444 TI 12V diesels; 2000 hp *(1.5 MW)*; 2 Castoldi waterjets
Speed, knots: 37. **Range, miles:** 530 at 30 kts
Complement: 4 (1 officer)
Guns: 1 MG-151 20 mm. 6—107 mm mortars.
Fire control: Hesis optical director.
Radars: Surface search: I band.

Comment: Twin hulled catamarans of GRP sandwich construction. Built by T Craft International, Cape Town. Capable of carrying up to 15 people. First three ordered in mid-1991.

COASTGUARD   *1991, T Craft International*

SHIPBORNE AIRCRAFT

Note: Super Frelon and Wasp helicopters paid off in 1990.

Numbers/Type: 10 Aerospatiale SA 330E/H/J Puma.
Operational speed: 139 kts *(258 km/h).*
Service ceiling: 15 750 ft *(4800 m).*
Range: 297 nm *(550 km).*
Role/Weapon systems: Support helicopter; allocated by SAAF for naval duties and can be embarked in both AORs and in *Agulhas*. Sensors: Doppler navigation, some with search radar. Weapons: Unarmed but can mount Armscor 30 mm Ratler.

LAND-BASED MARITIME AIRCRAFT

Note: Albatross aircraft were withdrawn from service in 1990.

Numbers/Type: 20 Douglas Turbodaks.
Operational speed: 161 kts *(298 km/h).*
Service ceiling: 24 000 ft *(7315 m).*
Range: 1390 nm *(2575 km).*
Role/Weapon systems: A number of Dakotas has been converted for MR/SAR and other tasks. Additional fuel tanks extend the range to 2620 nm *(4800 km)*. Sensors: Search radar and navigation aids. Weapons: Unarmed.

MINE WARFARE FORCES

4 TON CLASS (MINESWEEPERS)

Name	No	Builders	Commissioned
KIMBERLEY (ex-HMS *Stratton*)	M 1210	Dorset Yacht Co	1958
WALVISBAAI (ex-HMS *Packington*)	M 1214	Harland & Wolff, Belfast	1959
EAST LONDON (ex-HMS *Chilton*)	M 1215	Cook Welton and Gemmell	1958
WINDHOEK	M 1498	Thornycroft, Southampton	1959

Displacement, tons: 360 standard; 440 full load
Dimensions, feet (metres): 153 × 28.9 × 8.2 *(46.6 × 8.8 × 2.5)*
Main machinery: 2 Paxman Deltic 18A-7A diesels; 3000 hp *(2.24 MW)*; 2 shafts
Speed, knots: 15. **Range, miles:** 2300 at 13 kts
Complement: 27
Guns: 1 Bofors 40 mm/60; 80° elevation; 120 rounds/minute to 10 km *(5.5 nm)*; weight of shell 0.89 kg.
1 Oerlikon 20 mm. 2—7.62 mm MGs.
Radars: Navigation: Racal Decca; I band.

Comment: The last four survivors of a class of 10. Six were paid off in 1987 because of a shortage of trained personnel. Two year major modernisation started in 1991 with a new MCM control system and a major renewal of decks and frames. *Kimberley* converted to minehunter 1977-78 but has now reverted to minesweeping duties. *Walvisbaai* completed modernisation 13 April 1993 and is considered to be good for another 20 years. Second of class started in mid-1993.

WINDHOEK   *4/1992, Peter Humphries*

---

4 RIVER CLASS (COASTAL MINEHUNTERS)

Name	No	Builders	Commissioned
UMKOMAAS (ex-*Navors I*)	M 1499	Abeking & Rasmussen/ Sandock Austral	13 Jan 1981
UMGENI (ex-*Navors II*)	M 1213	Abeking & Rasmussen/ Sandock Austral	1 Mar 1981
UMZIMKULU (ex-*Navors III*)	M 1142	Sandock Austral	30 Oct 1981
UMHLOTI (ex-*Navors IV*)	M 1212	Sandock Austral	15 Dec 1981

Displacement, tons: 380 full load
Dimensions, feet (metres): 157.5 × 27.9 × 8.2 *(48 × 8.5 × 2.5)*
Main machinery: 2 MTU 12V 652 TB81 diesels; 4515 hp(m) *(3.32 MW)*; 2 Voith Schneider props
Speed, knots: 16. **Range, miles:** 2000 at 13 kts
Complement: 40 (7 officers)
Guns: 1 MG151 20 mm. 2—12.7 mm MGs.
Countermeasures: MCM: 2 PAP 104 remote-controlled submersibles.
Radars: Navigation: Decca; I band.
Sonars: Klein VDS; sidescan; high frequency.

Comment: Ordered in 1978 as Research Vessels to be operated by the Navy for the Department of Transport. The lead ship *Navors I* was shipped to Durban from Germany in the heavy lift ship *Uhenfels* in June 1980 for fitting out, shortly followed by the second. The last pair were built in Durban. The vessels were painted blue with white upperworks and formed the First Research Squadron. Painted grey and renamed in 1982 but continued to fly the national flag and not the naval ensign. The prefix RV was only changed to SAS on 3 February 1988 when they were formally accepted as naval ships. Minehunting capability could be enhanced by substituting the diving container on the after deck with lightweight mechanical and acoustic sweeping gear.

UMKOMAAS   *10/1993, van Ginderen Collection*

SURVEY SHIP

1 HECLA CLASS

Name	No	Builders	Commissioned
PROTEA	A 324	Yarrow (Shipbuilders) Ltd	23 May 1972

Displacement, tons: 2733 full load
Dimensions, feet (metres): 260.1 × 49.1 × 15.6 *(79.3 × 15 × 4.7)*
Main machinery: Diesel-electric; 3 Paxman 12YJCM diesels; 3840 hp *(2.68 MW)* sustained; 3 generators; 1 motor; 2000 hp *(1.49 MW)*; 1 shaft; cp prop; bow thruster
Speed, knots: 14. **Range, miles:** 12 000 at 11 kts
Complement: 114 (10 officers)
Helicopters: 1 Alouette III.

Comment: Laid down 20 July 1970. Launched 14 July 1971. Equipped for hydrographic survey with limited facilities for the collection of oceanographical data and for this purpose fitted with special communications equipment, naval surveying gear, survey launches and facilities for helicopter operations. Hull strengthened for navigation in ice and fitted with a passive roll stabilisation system.

PROTEA   *10/1993, van Ginderen Collection*

AUXILIARIES

8 DELTA 80 CLASS (LCU)

Displacement, tons: 5.5 full load
Dimensions, feet (metres): 27.2 × 10.2 × 3 *(8.3 × 3.1 × 0.9)*
Main machinery: 2 outboards; 350 hp *(261 kW)*
Speed, knots: 37. **Range, miles:** 150 at 35 kts
Complement: 5

Comment: Two each can be carried in *Drakensberg* and *Outeniqua*.

DELTA 80   *1993, South African Navy*

1 FLEET REPLENISHMENT SHIP

Name	No	Builders	Commissioned
OUTENIQUA (ex-*Juvent*, ex-*Aleksander Sledzyuk*)	A 302	Kherson Shipyard, Ukraine	3 Apr 1992

Displacement, tons: 21 025 full load
Dimensions, feet (metres): 545.6 × 74.1 × 29.5 *(166.3 × 22.6 × 9)*
Main machinery: 1 MAN Burmeister & Wain 8DKRN-60/195 diesel; 17 512 hp(m) *(12.87 MW)*; 1 shaft
Speed, knots: 17. **Range, Miles:** 8000 at 15 kts
Complement: 126 (17 officers) including aircrew
Military lift: 2 Delta 80 LCU; 10 vehicles; 600 troops
Guns: 2 Oerlikon 20 mm.
Helicopters: 1 SA 330H/J Puma.

Comment: Launched on 6 September 1991 as the *Aleksander Sledzyuk* and renamed *Juvent* on 4 April 1992 when ownership was transferred to a shipping company. This company operated her until 26 February 1993 when she was bought by the Navy, through Armscor and recommissioned 8 July 1993. Built as an Arctic supply vessel with an icebreaking capability of 1 m thick ice at a constant speed of 2 kts. Refit in 1994 to allow alterations to flight deck and hangars, and to fit light armament and RAS gear. Planned to be back in service in 1995.

OUTENIQUA (before conversion)   *10/1993, Robert Pabst*

OUTENIQUA (before conversion)   *9/1993, C D Yaylali*

1 FLEET REPLENISHMENT SHIP

Name	No	Builders	Commissioned
DRAKENSBERG	A 301	Sandock Austral, Durban	11 Nov 1987

Displacement, tons: 6000 light; 12 500 full load
Dimensions, feet (metres): 482.3 × 64 × 25.9 *(147 × 19.5 × 7.9)*
Main machinery: 2 diesels; 16 320 hp(m) *(12 MW)*; 1 shaft; cp prop; bow thruster
Speed, knots: 20+
Complement: 96 (10 officers)
Cargo capacity: 5500 tons fuel; 750 tons ammunition and dry stores; 2 Delta 80 LCUs
Guns: 4 Oerlikon 20 mm.
Helicopters: 2 SA 330H/J Puma.

Comment: The largest ship built in South Africa and the first naval vessel to be completely designed in that country. In addition to her replenishment role she is employed on SAR, patrol and surveillance with a considerable potential for disaster relief. Laid down in August 1984 and launched 24 April 1986. Two abeam positions and astern fuelling, jackstay and vertrep. Two helicopter landing spots. Can be used as a mother ship for small craft and for troop transport and commando insertion operations.

DRAKENSBERG   *5/1993, Wright & Logan*

DRAKENSBERG   *1/1993, Robert Pabst*

1 ANTARCTIC SURVEY AND SUPPLY VESSEL

S A AGULHAS

Measurement, tons: 5353 gross
Dimensions, feet (metres): 358.3 × 59 × 19 *(109.2 × 18 × 5.8)*
Main machinery: 2 Mirrlees-Blackstone K6 major diesels; 6600 hp *(4.49 MW)*; 1 shaft; bow and stern thrusters
Speed, knots: 14. **Range, miles:** 8200 at 14 kts
Complement: 40 plus 92 spare berths
Radars: Navigation: Racal Decca; I band.
Helicopters: 2 SA 330J Puma.

Comment: Built by Mitsubishi, Shimonoseki and commissioned 31 January 1978. Red hull and white superstructure. A Department of Transport vessel, civilian manned. Major refit March to October 1992; 25 ton crane moved forward, transverse thrusters and roll damping fitted, improved navigation and communications equipment. A hinged hatch has been fitted at the stern to recover towed equipment. All scientific spaces improved.

S A AGULHAS   *10/1992, Robert Pabst*

1 DIVING SUPPORT SHIP

Name	No	Builders	Commissioned
FLEUR	P 3148	Dorman Long, Durban	3 Dec 1969

Displacement, tons: 220 standard; 257 full load
Dimensions, feet (metres): 121.5 × 27.5 × 11.1 *(37 × 8.4 × 3.4)*
Main machinery: 2 Paxman 6YJCM diesels; 1400 hp *(1.04 MW)* sustained; 2 shafts
Speed, knots: 14
Complement: 22 (4 officers)
Radars: Navigation: Decca; I band.

Comment: Combined torpedo recovery vessel and diving tender with recompression chamber.

FLEUR   *12/1993, Robert Pabst*

1 KRÖGERWERFT TYPE (SAR LAUNCH)

P 1551

Displacement, tons: 82 full load
Dimensions, feet (metres): 96 × 19 × 4 *(29.3 × 5.8 × 1.2)*
Main machinery: 2 MTU MD diesels; 4480 hp(m) *(3.29 MW)*; 2 shafts
Speed, knots: 30. **Range, miles:** 1000 at 30 kts
Complement: 12

Comment: Built by Krögerwerft, Rendsburg and commissioned in 1961. Can carry a 12.7 mm MG. Sister ship was wrecked in Saldanha Bay in 1988. More of this class may have been acquired.

P 1551   *4/1992, Robert Pabst*

1 FAIREY MARINE TRACKER CLASS (SAR LAUNCH)

P 1555

Displacement, tons: 26
Dimensions, feet (metres): 64 × 16 × 5 *(19.5 × 4.9 × 1.5)*
Main machinery: 2 GM diesels; 1120 hp *(836 kW)*; 2 shafts
Speed, knots: 28. **Range, miles:** 650 at 18 kts
Complement: 11

Comment: Built by Groves and Gutteridge, Cowes and commissioned in 1973.

TUGS

1 COASTAL TUG

DE MIST

Displacement, tons: 275
Dimensions, feet (metres): 111.5 × 29.5 × 9.8 *(34 × 9 × 3)*
Main machinery: 2 Lister-Blackstone diesels; 2400 hp *(1.79 MW)*; 2 Voith-Schneider props
Speed, knots: 12

Comment: Completed by Dorman Long, Durban in December 1978.

2 HARBOUR TUGS

DE NEYS   DE NOORDE

Displacement, tons: 170 full load
Dimensions, feet (metres): 94 × 26.5 × 15.7 *(28.7 × 8.7 × 4.8)*
Main machinery: 2 Lister-Blackstone diesels; 1216 hp *(907 kW)*; 2 Voith-Schneider props
Speed, knots: 9
Complement: 10

Comment: Details given are for *De Neys* built by Globe Engineering, Cape Town and commissioned 23 July 1969. *De Noorde* is slightly longer at 31.9 m but has the same propulsion machinery and was delivered by Globe in December 1961.

DE NEYS

3/1992, Peter Humphries

SPAIN

Headquarters' Appointments

Chief of the Naval Staff:
Admiral Juan J Romero Caramelo
Second Chief of the Naval Staff:
Vice Admiral Eduardo Liberal Lucini
Chief of Fleet Support:
Admiral Eduardo Liberal

Commands

Commander-in-Chief of the Fleet:
Admiral Pedro Regalado Aznar
Commander-in-Chief, Cantabrian Zone:
Admiral Francisco J Lopez de Arenosa Diaz
Commander-in-Chief, Straits Zone:
Vice Admiral José Antonio Serrano Punyed
Commander-in-Chief, Mediterranean Zone:
Admiral Miguel J Garcia de Lomas Ristori
Commander-in-Chief, Canarias Zone:
Vice Admiral Gabriel Portal Anton
Commander-in-Chief, Central Zone:
Vice Admiral Justino Antón Pérez-Pardo
Commandant General, Marines:
Major General José Manuel Estévez Ons

Diplomatic Representation

Naval Attaché in Bonn:
Commander Luis Delgado Bañón
Naval Attaché in Brasilia:
Commander Pedro Mackinlay Leiciaga
Naval Attaché in Buenos Aires:
Commander Francisco J Fontán Suances
Naval Attaché in Lisbon:
Captain José Samaniego Oviedo
Naval Attaché in London:
Captain José Maria Pery Paredes
Naval Attaché in Paris:
Commander Vicente Rubio Peral
Naval Attaché in Rome:
Commander Santiago Zárate y López de Roda
Naval Attaché in Santiago:
Captain Pedro L Diaz Leante
Naval Attaché in Washington:
Captain Miguel Fernández Fernández
Naval Attaché in The Hague:
Captain José Carlos Manzano Gutiérrez
Naval Attaché in Morocco:
Commander Ramón López Alemany

Bases

Ferrol: Cantabrian Zone HQ—Ferrol arsenal, support centre at La Graña, naval school at Marín, Pontevedra, electronics school at Vigo, Pontevedra
Cadiz: Straits Zone HQ—La Carraca arsenal, fleet command HQ and naval air base at Rota, amphibious base at Puntales, Tarifa small ships' base
Cartagena: Mediterranean Zone HQ—Cartagena arsenal, underwater weapons and divers school at La Algameca; support base at Mahón, Minorca and at Porto Pi, Majorca, submarine weapons schools at La Algameca and Porto Pi base, Majorca
Las Palmas: Canaries Zone HQ—Las Palmas arsenal

Naval Air Service (see *Shipborne Aircraft* section)

Type	Escuadrilla
AB 212ASW (with AS-12 missiles)	3
Twin Comanche ⎫	4
Cessna Citation ⎭	
Sikorsky SH-3D/G Sea King (with AS-12 missiles) ⎫	5
Sikorsky SH-3E Sea King (AEW) ⎭	
Hughes 500M (Training)	6
Matador AV-8A (Harrier) ⎫	8
Matador TAV-8A (Harrier) ⎭	
EAV-8B Bravo	9
Sikorsky SH-60B Seahawk	10

Marine Corps

This consists of four 'Tercios' (intermediate between a Regiment and a Brigade) based at Ferrol, Cartagena and Cádiz (two). Two Groups (intermediate between a Battalion and a Regiment) are based in Madrid and Las Palmas (Canary Islands). These Tercios and Groups are charged with the protection of their naval bases and establishments.
The Tercio de Armada is based at San Fernando, Cádiz and is the landing force available for immediate embarkation. The Tercio de Armada, brigade-sized, consists of two landing battalions plus a special operations unit (UOE) of 170 men, a support logistic battalion, a communications company, a tank company (with 17 M-48E and one M-88 recovery vehicle, plus 17 Scorpion light tanks), one amphibious tractors company (19 LVT-7 in three versions, possibly to be replaced by the VMA Pegaso 8331), one artillery battalion (six M109A2 with six M-992 ammunition vehicles, 12 towed OTO Melara 105 mm L14 howitzers), one anti-tank company with 12 TOW and 16/18 Dragon missile launchers. Infantry support weapons include 106 mm M40 recoilless rifles, 120, 81 and 60 mm ECIA mortars, Instalaza 90 mm and LAWS 72 mm anti-tank rocket launchers, Rasura infantry locating radars. Also armoured Pegaso BLR-400 infantry carriers (not in Tercio de Armada) and Pegaso 3550 three ton amphibious trucks.
There is a Fuerza de Intervencion Rápida (FIR). This includes Marines and Group Delta amphibious ships.

Fleet Deployment

1.   Flota
  (a) Grupo Aeronaval Alfa: (based at Rota)
     Principe de Asturias with appropriate escorts
  (b) Escuadrillas de Escoltas:
     21st Squadron; 6 Descubierta class (based at Cartagena)
     31st Squadron; 5 Baleares class (based at Ferrol)
     41st Squadron; 4 Santa Maria class (based at Rota)
  (c) Grupo Anfibio Delta: (based at Puntales, Cádiz)
     All Amphibious Forces
  (d) Fuerza de Medidas contra Minas: (based at Cartagena from September 1990)
     8 MSCs and 4 MSOs
  (e) Flotilla de Submarinos: (based at Cartagena)
     All submarines
2.   Support units, Cantabrian Zone:
    1 Ocean Tug, 2 Water-boats, 8 Tugs, 4 Patrol Ships, 5 Large Patrol Craft, 7 Coastal Patrol Craft, 3 Sail Training Ships, 5 Training Craft
3.   Support units, Straits Zone:
    6 Oceanographic Ships, 1 Sail Training Ship, 4 Fast Attack Craft, 1 Transport, 1 Ocean Tug, 7 Tugs, 2 Water-boats
4.   Support units, Mediterranean Zone:
    4 Fast Attack Craft, 1 Boom Defence Vessel, 1 Water-boat, 7 Tugs, 1 Frogman Support Ship
5.   Support units, Canaries Zone:

Personnel

(a) 1994: Navy: 27 900 (2600 officers)
          Marines: 4580 (440 officers)
(b) 9 months' national service (approx half of the total numbers)

Guardia Civil del Mar

Started operations in 1992. For details, see end of section.

Strength of the Fleet

Type	Active	Building (Planned)
Submarines—Patrol	8	(4)
Aircraft Carrier	1	—
Frigates	18	1 (4)
Corvettes	4	—
Offshore Patrol Vessels	4	—
Fast Attack Craft—Gun	7	—
Large Patrol Craft	11	—
Coastal Patrol Craft	8	—
Inshore Patrol Craft	2	—
Attack Transports	2	—
LPDs	—	1 (1)
LSTs	2	(2)
LCTs	3	—
LCU/LCM/LCP	55	—
Hovercraft	1	—
Minesweepers	12	(4)
Minehunters	—	4
Survey Ships	8	—
Replenishment Tankers	1	1
Tankers	18	—
Transport Ship	1	—
Training Ships	9	—

Mercantile Marine

Lloyd's Register of Shipping:
1885 vessels of 1 745 793 tons gross

DELETIONS

Destroyers

1991 *Gravina, Blas de Lezo*
1992 *Méndez Núñez, Lángara*

Patrol Forces

1991 *Princesa, Nautilus*
1992 *Atrevida, Villa de Bilbao*
1993 *Lazaga, Alsedo, Cadarso, Villamil, Bonifaz, Recalde, Nalón, Ulla, Turia, P 311-313,* 20 P 101 class, *P 124,* 5 P 231 class, 23 P 202 class

Auxiliaries

1991 *Y 234* (tanker)
1992 *Y 322, Y 332, Y 112, Y 233, Y 136*
1993 *Hispania, Cíclope, Cádiz, Maquinista Macías, Torpedista Hernández, Sansón*

PENNANT LIST

Submarines		F 83	Numancia		P 81	Toralla		A 32	Tofiño
		F 84	Reina Sofía		P 82	Formentor		A 33	Hesperides
S 61	Delfin	F 85	Navarra		P 201	Cabo Fradera		A 111	Alerta
S 62	Tonina	F 86	Canarias (bldg)						
S 63	Marsopa				**Amphibious Forces**			**Auxiliaries**	
S 64	Narval	**Patrol Forces**							
S 71	Galerna				L 11	Velasco		A 01	Contramaestre Casado
S 72	Siroco	P 11	Barceló		L 12	Martin Alvarez		A 11	Marqués de la Ensenada
S 73	Mistral	P 12	Laya		L 21	Castilla		A 12	Poseidón
S 74	Tramontana	P 13	Javier Quiroga		L 22	Aragón		A 14	Patiño
		P 14	Ordóñez					A 41	Cartagena
Aircraft Carrier		P 15	Acevedo		**Mine Warfare Forces**			A 43	Ferrol
		P 16	Cándido Pérez					A 51	Mahón
R 11	Principe de Asturias	P 21	Anaga		M 21	Júcar		A 52	Las Palmas
		P 22	Tagomago		M 22	Ebro		A 61	Contramaestre Castelló
Frigates		P 23	Marola		M 23	Duero		A 64	Fogonero Bañobre
		P 24	Mouro		M 24	Tajo		A 65	Marinero Jaranoa
F 31	Descubierta	P 25	Grosa		M 25	Genil		A 66	Condestable Zaragoza
F 32	Diana	P 26	Medas		M 26	Odiel		A 71	Juan Sebastian de Elcano
F 33	Infanta Elena	P 27	Izaro		M 27	Sil		A 72	Arosa
F 34	Infanta Cristina	P 28	Tabarca		M 28	Miño		A 74	La Graciosa
F 35	Cazadora	P 29	Deva		M 41	Guadalete		A 75	Giralda
F 36	Vencedora	P 30	Bergantin		M 42	Guadalmedina		A 81	Guardiamarina Barrutia
F 71	Baleares	P 31	Conejera		M 43	Guadalquivir		A 82	Guardiamarina Salas
F 72	Andalucia	P 32	Dragonera		M 44	Guadiana		A 83	Guardiamarina Godínez
F 73	Cataluña	P 33	Espalmador					A 84	Guardiamarina Rull
F 74	Asturias	P 34	Alcanada		**Survey Ships**			A 85	Guardiamarina Chereguini
F 75	Extremadura	P 41	Cormoran					A 101	Mar Caribe
F 76	—	P 61	Chilreu		A 21	Castor		A 102	Mar Rojo
F 77	—	P 71	Serviola		A 22	Pollux		Y 562	Nereida
F 81	Santa Maria	P 72	Centinela		A 23	Antares		Y 563	Proserpina
F 82	Victoria	P 73	Vigia		A 24	Rigel			
		P 74	Atalaya		A 31	Malaspina			

SUBMARINES

Note: Four Scorpene class (S 80) are planned to start construction in 1999. Being developed with DCN, France. Probably about 2000 tons and 300 m with a complement of 35.

4 GALERNA (AGOSTA) CLASS

Name	No	Builders	Laid down	Launched	Commissioned
GALERNA	S 71	Bazán, Cartagena	5 Sep 1977	5 Dec 1981	22 Jan 1983
SIROCO	S 72	Bazán, Cartagena	27 Nov 1978	13 Nov 1982	5 Dec 1983
MISTRAL	S 73	Bazán, Cartagena	30 May 1980	14 Nov 1983	5 June 1985
TRAMONTANA	S 74	Bazán, Cartagena	10 Dec 1981	30 Nov 1984	27 Jan 1986

Displacement, tons: 1490 surfaced; 1740 dived
Dimensions, feet (metres): 221.7 × 22.3 × 17.7
(67.6 × 6.8 × 5.4)
Main machinery: Diesel-electric; 2 SEMT-Pielstick 16 PA4 V 185
VG diesels; 3600 hp(m) *(2.7 MW)*; 2 Jeumont Schneider alternators; 1.7 MW; 1 motor; 4600 hp(m) *(3.4 MW)*; 1 cruising
motor; 32 hp(m) *(23 kW)*; 1 shaft
Speed, knots: 12 surfaced; 20 dived; 17.5 sustained
Range, miles: 8500 snorting at 9 kts; 350 dived on cruising
motor at 3.5 kts
Complement: 54 (6 officers)

Torpedoes: 4—21 in *(533 mm)* tubes. 20 combination of (a)
ECAN L5 Mod 3/4; dual purpose; active/passive homing to
9.5 km *(5.1 nm)* at 35 kts; warhead 150 kg; depth to 550 m
(1800 ft).
(b) ECAN F17 Mod 2; wire-guided; active/passive homing to
20 km *(10.8 nm)* at 40 kts; warhead 250 kg; depth 600 m
(1970 ft).
Mines: 19 can be carried if torpedo load is reduced to 9.
Countermeasures: ESM: THORN EMI/Inisel Manta; radar
warning.
Radars: Surface search: Thomson-CSF DRUA 33C; I band.
Sonars: Thomson Sintra DSUV 22; passive search and attack;
medium frequency.
Thomson Sintra DUUA 2A/2B; active search and attack; 8 or
8.4 kHz active.
DUUX 2A (S 71-72) or DUUX-5 (S 73-74); passive; range finding. Eledone; intercept.

SIROCO   6/1993, Diego Quevedo

Thomson Sintra DSUV-62 towed passive array (S 72-73); trials
in 1991.

Programmes: First two ordered 9 May 1975 and second pair
29 June 1977. Built with some French advice. About 67 per
cent of equipment and structure from Spanish sources.
Modernisation: All to be modernised by the mid-1990s with
improved torpedo fire-control, towed array sonars, new ESM

and IR enhanced periscopes. New main batteries to be
installed with central control monitoring. *Galerna* started in
April 1993 to complete in May 1994. The plan to fit SSM may
have been cancelled.
Structure: Diving depth, 300 m *(984 ft)*.
Operational: Endurance, 45 days.

4 DELFIN (DAPHNE) CLASS

Name	No	Builders	Laid down	Launched	Commissioned
DELFIN	S 61	Bazán, Cartagena	13 Aug 1968	25 Mar 1972	3 May 1973
TONINA	S 62	Bazán, Cartagena	2 Mar 1970	3 Oct 1972	10 July 1973
MARSOPA	S 63	Bazán, Cartagena	19 Mar 1971	15 Mar 1974	12 Apr 1975
NARVAL	S 64	Bazán, Cartagena	24 Apr 1972	14 Dec 1974	22 Nov 1975

Displacement, tons: 869 surfaced; 1043 dived
Dimensions, feet (metres): 189.6 × 22.3 × 15.1
(57.8 × 6.8 × 4.6)
Main machinery: Diesel-electric; 2 SEMT-Pielstick 12 PA4 V 185
diesels; 2450 hp(m) *(1.8 MW)*; 2 Jeumont Schneider alternators; 1.7 MW; 2 motors; 2600 hp(m) *(1.9 MW)*; 2 shafts
Speed, knots: 13.2 surfaced; 15.5 dived
Range, miles: 4300 snorting at 7.5 kts; 2710 surfaced at
12.5 kts
Complement: 47 (6 officers)

Torpedoes: 12—21.7 in *(550 mm)* (8 bow, 4 stern) tubes. 12
combination of (a) ECAN L5 Mod 3/4; dual purpose; active/
passive homing to 9.5 km *(5.1 nm)* at 35 kts; warhead 150 kg;
depth to 550 m *(1800 ft)*.
(b) ECAN F17 Mod 2; wire-guided; active/passive homing to
20 km *(10.8 nm)* at 40 kts; warhead 250 kg; depth 600 m
(1970 ft).
Mines: 12 in lieu of torpedoes.
Countermeasures: ESM: THORN EMI Manta; radar warning.
Radars: Surface search: Thomson-CSF DRUA 31 or 33A; I band.
Sonars: Thomson Sintra DSUV 22; passive search and attack;
medium frequency.
Thomson Sintra DUUA 2A; active search and attack; 8 or
8.4 kHz active.

NARVAL   2/1993, Diego Quevedo

Programmes: First pair ordered 26 December 1966 and second
pair in March 1970. Identical to the French Daphne class and
built with extensive French assistance.
Modernisation: The class has been taken in hand since 1983 for
modernisation of sonar (DUUA 2A for DUUA 1), updating of
fire-control and torpedo handling. It is possible that torpedo

tubes were also linered to 21 in *(533 mm)*. Last one completed
at the end of 1988. ESM updated in 1990-91. Torpedo fire-
control is being updated for the F17 wire-guided weapons
starting with *Marsopa* in 1994.
Structure: Diving depth, 300 m *(984 ft)*.

AIRCRAFT CARRIER

Name	No	Builders	Laid down	Launched	Commissioned
PRINCIPE DE ASTURIAS (ex-*Almirante Carrero Blanco*)	R 11	Bazán, Ferrol	8 Oct 1979	22 May 1982	30 May 1988

Displacement, tons: 17 188 full load
Dimensions, feet (metres): 642.7 oa; 615.2 pp × 79.7 × 30.8 *(195.9; 187.5 × 24.3 × 9.4)*
Flight deck, feet (metres): 575.1 × 95.1 *(175.3 × 29)*
Main machinery: 2 GE LM 2500 gas-turbines; 46 400 hp *(34.61 MW)* sustained; 1 shaft; cp prop; 2 motors; 1600 hp(m) *(1.18 MW)*; retractable prop
Speed, knots: 26 (4.5 on motors). **Range, miles:** 6500 at 20 kts
Complement: 555 (90 officers) plus 208 (Flag Staff (7 officers) and Air Group)

Guns: 4 Bazán Meroka 12-barrelled 20 mm/120 ❶; 85° elevation; 3600 rounds/minute combined to 2 km.
2 Rheinmetall 37 mm saluting guns.
Countermeasures: Decoys: 4 Loral Hycor SRBOC 6-barrelled fixed Mk 36; IR flares and chaff to 4 km *(2.2 nm)*.
SLQ 25 Nixie; towed torpedo decoy.
US Prairie/Masker; hull noise/blade rate suppression.
ESM/ECM: Elettronica Nettunel; intercept and jammers.
Combat data systems: Tritan Digital Command and Control System NTDS; Links 11 and 14. Saturn SATCOM ❷.
Fire control: Four Selenia directors (for Meroka). Radamec 2000 series.
Radars: Air search: Hughes SPS 52 C/D ❸; 3D; E/F band; range 439 km *(240 nm)*.
Surface search: ISC Cardion SPS 55 ❹; I/J band.
Aircraft control: ITT SPN 35 A ❺; J band.
Fire control: Four Sperry VPS 2 ❻; I band (for Meroka).
RTN 11L/X; I/J band; missile warning.
Selenia RAN 12L (target designation); I/J band.

Fixed wing aircraft: 6-12 AV 8B Bravo (see *Shipborne Aircraft* section).
Helicopters: 6-10 SH-3 Sea Kings; 2-4 AB 212ASW/EW; 2 SH-60B Seahawks.

Programmes: Ordered on 29 June 1977. Associated US firms were Gibbs and Cox, Dixencast, Bath Iron Works and Sperry

PRINCIPE DE ASTURIAS   *10/1993, Giorgio Ghiglione*

SM. Commissioning delays caused by changes to command and control systems and the addition of a Flag Bridge.
Modernisation: After two years service some modifications were made to the port after side of the island, to improve briefing rooms and provide sheltered parking space for FD vehicles. Also improved accommodation has been added on for six officers and 50 specialist ratings.
Structure: Based on US Navy Sea Control Ship design. 12 degree ski-jump of 46.5 m. Two flight deck lifts, one right aft. Two LCVPs carried. Two pairs of fin stabilisers. The hangar is 24 748 sq ft *(2300 m²)*. The Battle Group Commander occupies the lower bridge. Two saluting guns have been mounted on the port quarter.
Operational: Three Sea Kings have Searchwater AEW radar. Aircraft complement could be increased to 37 (parking on deck) in an emergency but maximum operational number is 24. A typical air wing includes 10 Matador IIs and 10 Sea Hawks/Sea Kings (including two AEW). Ship is based at Rota.

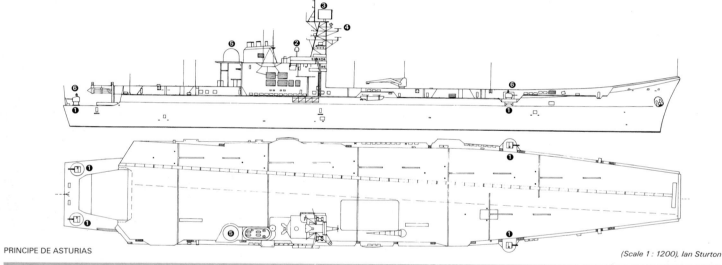

PRINCIPE DE ASTURIAS   *(Scale 1 : 1200), Ian Sturton*

PRINCIPE DE ASTURIAS   *10/1993, Spanish Navy*

FRIGATES

0 + (4) F 100 CLASS

Displacement, tons: 4400 full load
Dimensions, feet (metres): 419.3 × 50.9 × 15.4
(127.8 × 15.5 × 4.7)
Main machinery: CODOG; 2 gas-turbines; 2 diesels; 2 shafts;
cp props
Speed, knots: 28. **Range, miles:** 4500 at 18 kts
Complement: 200

Missiles: SSM: 8 McDonnell Douglas Harpoon ❶.
SAM: Aster or Evolved Sea Sparrow; VLS ❷.
Guns: 1 FMC 5 in *(127 mm)*/54 Mk 45 ❸.
2 Bazán 20 mm/120 Meroka ❹; possibly including a SAM
combination.
Torpedoes: 4 fixed tubes ❺.
Countermeasures: Decoys: 4 chaff launchers ❻. ESM/ECM.
Combat data systems: Link. SATCOM ❼.
Fire control: 2 optronic directors.
Radars: Air search ❽.
Surface search ❾.
Fire control ❿. Thomson-CSF Anabel.

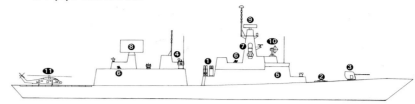

F 100   *(Scale 1 : 1200), Ian Sturton*

Sonars: Hull-mounted; active search and attack; medium frequency. Possible active towed sonar.

Helicopters: 1 SH-60B LAMPS III ⓫.

Programmes: Project definition from September 1992. Design
collaboration with German and Netherlands shipyards started

in January 1994. First of class in service date has slipped to
2001.
Structure: The VLS system is to have four channels of fire.
Stealth features are to be an important part of the design.
Many of the weapon systems details are still to be decided.

5 + 1 SANTA MARÍA (FFG 7) CLASS

Name	No
SANTA MARÍA	F 81
VICTORIA	F 82
NUMANCIA	F 83
REINA SOFÍA (ex-*América*)	F 84
NAVARRA	F 85
CANARIAS	F 86

Builders	Laid down	Launched	Commissioned
Bazán, Ferrol	23 May 1982	24 Nov 1984	12 Oct 1986
Bazán, Ferrol	16 Aug 1983	23 July 1986	11 Nov 1987
Bazán, Ferrol	8 Jan 1986	30 Jan 1987	8 Nov 1988
Bazán, Ferrol	12 Dec 1987	19 July 1989	18 Oct 1990
Bazán, Ferrol	15 Apr 1991	23 Oct 1992	June 1994
Bazán, Ferrol	15 Apr 1992	21 June 1993	Dec 1994

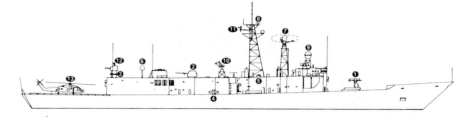

SANTA MARÍA   *(Scale 1 : 1200), Ian Sturton*

Displacement, tons: 3610 standard; 4017 full load
Dimensions, feet (metres): 451.2 × 46.9 × 24.6
(137.7 × 14.3 × 7.5)
Main machinery: 2 GE LM 2500 gas-turbines; 41 000 hp
(30.59 MW) sustained; 1 shaft; cp prop; 2 motors; 1600 hp(m)
(1.18 MW); 1 retractable prop
Speed, knots: 29; 4.5 on auxiliary. **Range, miles:** 4500 at 20 kts
Complement: 223 (13 officers)

Missiles: SSM: 8 McDonnell Douglas Harpoon; active radar homing to 130 km *(70 nm)* at 0.9 Mach; warhead 227 kg.
SAM: 32 GDC Pomona Standard SM-1MR; Mk 13 Mod 4
launcher ❶; command guidance; semi-active radar homing to
46 km *(25 nm)* at 2 Mach.
Both missile systems share a common magazine.
Guns: 1 OTO Melara 3 in *(76 mm)*/62 ❷; 85° elevation; 85
rounds/minute to 16 km *(8.7 nm)*; weight of shell 6 kg.
1 Bazán 20 mm/120 12-barrelled Meroka Mod 2A or 2B ❸;
85° elevation; 3600 rounds/minute combined to 2 km.
Torpedoes: 6—324 mm US Mk 32 (2 triple) tubes ❹. Honeywell
Mk 46 Mod 5; anti-submarine; active/passive homing to 11 km
(5.9 nm) at 40 kts; warhead 44 kg.
Countermeasures: Decoys: 2 Loral Hycor SRBOC 6-barrelled
fixed Mk 37 Mod 1 ❺; IR flares and chaff to 4 km *(2.2 nm)*.
Prairie/Masker: hull noise/blade rate suppression.
SLQ 25 Nixie; torpedo decoy.
ESM/ECM: Elettronica Nettunel or Mk 3000 (F 84-86); intercept
and jammer.
Combat data systems: IPN 10 action data automation; Link 11.
SSQ 28 LAMPS III helo data link. Saturn SATCOM ❻.
Fire control: Mk 92 Mod 2 (Mod 6 with CORT in F 85 and 86).
Optronic tracker for Meroka.
Radars: Air search: Raytheon SPS 49(V)5 ❼; C/D band; range
457 km *(250 nm)*.
Surface search: Raytheon SPS 55 ❽; I band.
Navigation: Raytheon 1650/9; I/J band.
Fire control: RCA Mk 92 Mod 2/6 (F 81-84) ❾; I/J band. 1 or 2
(F 85-86) Signaal STIR ❿; I/J band.
Selenia RAN 30L/X (RAN 12L + RAN 30X) ⓫; I band (for
Meroka). Sperry VPS 2 ⓬ (for Meroka); I band.
Tacan: URN-25.
Sonars: Raytheon SQS 56 (DE 1160); hull-mounted; active
search and attack; medium frequency.
Gould SQR 19(V)2; tactical towed array (TACTASS); passive;
very low frequency.

Helicopters: 2 Sikorsky S-70L Seahawk ⓭ (only one normally
embarked).

SANTA MARÍA   *5/1993, Camil Busquets i Vilanova*

Programmes: Three ordered 29 June 1977. The execution of
this programme was delayed due to the emphasis placed on
the carrier construction. The fourth ship was ordered on 19
June 1986, and numbers five and six on 26 December 1989.
The original plan to build four more has been shelved and the
last two have been delayed by a shortage of funds.

Modernisation: All are being modified with a combined RAN 12L
and RAN 30X fire-control radar for Meroka. The combined system is called RAN 30L/X. Last two are fitted with Meroka Mod
2B.
Structure: Based on the US FFG 7 Oliver Perry class although
broader in the beam and therefore able to carry more top-

weight. Fin stabilisers fitted. RAST helicopter handling system.
Navarra and *Canarias* have an indigenous combat data system
thereby increasing national inputs to 75 per cent. They also
have improved fire-control systems.
Operational: All based at Rota as the 41st Squadron.

VICTORIA   *7/1992, F Gámez*

0 + 2 KNOX CLASS

Name	No	Builders	Laid down	Launched	Commissioned
— (ex-*Aylwin*)	F 76 (ex-FF 1081)	Avondale Shipyard	13 Nov 1969	29 Aug 1970	18 Sep 1971
— (ex-*Pharris*)	F 77 (ex-FF 1094)	Avondale Shipyard	11 Feb 1972	16 Dec 1972	26 Jan 1974

Displacement, tons: 3011 standard; 4260 full load
Dimensions, feet (metres): 439.6 × 46.8 × 15; 24.8 (sonar)
(134 × 14.3 × 4.6; 7.8)
Main machinery: 2 Combustion Engineering/Babcock & Wilcox
boilers; 1200 psi *(84.4 kg/cm sq)*; 950°F *(510°C)*; 1 turbine;
35 000 hp *(26 MW)*; 1 shaft
Speed, knots: 27. **Range, miles:** 4000 at 22 kts on 1 boiler
Complement: 288 (17 officers)

Missiles: SSM: 8 McDonnell Douglas Harpoon; active radar homing to 130 km *(70 nm)* at 0.9 Mach; warhead 227 kg.
A/S: Honeywell ASROC Mk 16 octuple launcher with reload system (has 2 cells modified to fire Harpoon) ❶; inertial guidance
to 1.6-10 km *(1-5.4 nm)*; payload Mk 46 Mod 5.
Guns: 1 FMC 5 in *(127 mm)*/54 Mk 42 Mod 9 ❷; 85° elevation;
20-40 rounds/minute to 24 km *(13 nm)* anti-surface; 14 km
(7.7 nm) anti-aircraft; weight of shell 32 kg.
1 General Electric/General Dynamics 20 mm/76 6-barrelled
Mk 15 Vulcan Phalanx ❸; 3000 rounds/minute combined to
1.5 km.
Torpedoes: 4—324 mm Mk 32 (2 twin) fixed tubes ❹. 22 Honeywell Mk 46 Mod 5; anti-submarine; active/passive homing to
11 km *(5.9 nm)* at 40 kts; warhead 44 kg.
Countermeasures: Decoys: 2 Loral Hycor SRBOC 6-barrelled
fixed Mk 36 ❺; IR flares and chaff to 4 km *(2.2 nm)*. T Mk-6
Fanfare/SLQ-25 Nixie; torpedo decoy. Prairie Masker hull and
blade rate noise suppression.
ESM/ECM: SLQ 32(V)2 ❻; radar warning. Sidekick modification
adds jammer and deception system.
Combat data systems: Link 14 receive only. Link 11 may be fitted in due course.

Fire control: SWG-1A Harpoon LCS. Mk 68 GFCS. Mk 114 ASW
FCS. Mk 1 target designation system. MMS target acquisition
sight (for mines, small craft and low flying aircraft).
Radars: Air search: Lockheed SPS 40B ❼; E/F band; range
320 km *(175 nm)*.
Surface search: Raytheon SPS 10 or Norden SPS 67 ❽; G band.
Navigation: Marconi LN 66; I band.
Fire control: Western Electric SPG 53A/D/F ❾; I/J band.
Tacan: SRN 15. IFF: UPX-12.
Sonars: EDO/General Electric SQS 26 CX; bow-mounted; active
search and attack; medium frequency.
EDO SQR 18A(V)1; passive towed array; very low frequency.

Helicopters: 1 AB 212ASW ❿.

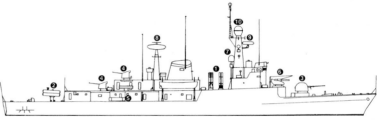

KNOX   *(Scale 1 : 1200), Ian Sturton*

Programmes: Lease agreed from US in December 1993 subject
to approval by Congress. Both ships planned to arrive in Spain
in mid-1994. Ships of this class have been transferred to
Greece, Taiwan and Turkey and transfers are planned for Brazil,
Egypt, Morocco, Oman, Thailand and Venezuela in 1994/95.
Modernisation: Vulcan Phalanx replaced Sea Sparrow SAM in
the mid-1980s.
Structure: Four torpedo tubes are fixed in the midship superstructure, two to a side, angled out at 45°. A lightweight
anchor is fitted on the port side and an 8000 lb anchor fits in to
the after section of the sonar dome.
Operational: The ship carried a medium helicopter in USN
service.

6 DESCUBIERTA CLASS

Name	No	Builders	Laid down	Launched	Commissioned
DESCUBIERTA	F 31	Bazán, Cartagena	16 Nov 1974	8 July 1975	18 Nov 1978
DIANA	F 32	Bazán, Cartagena	8 July 1975	26 Jan 1976	30 June 1979
INFANTA ELENA	F 33	Bazán, Cartagena	26 Jan 1976	14 Sep 1976	12 Apr 1980
INFANTA CRISTINA	F 34	Bazán, Cartagena	11 Sep 1976	25 Apr 1977	24 Nov 1980
CAZADORA	F 35	Bazán, Ferrol	14 Dec 1977	17 Oct 1978	20 July 1982
VENCEDORA	F 36	Bazán, Ferrol	1 June 1978	27 Apr 1979	18 Mar 1983

Displacement, tons: 1233 standard; 1666 full load
Dimensions, feet (metres): 291.3 × 34 × 12.5
(88.8 × 10.4 × 3.8)
Main machinery: 4 MTU-Bazán 16V 956 TB91 diesels;
15 000 hp(m) *(11 MW)* sustained; 2 shafts; cp props
Speed, knots: 25. **Range, miles:** 4000 at 18 kts; 7500 at 12 kts
Complement: 118 (10 officers) plus 30 marines

Missiles: SSM: 8 McDonnell Douglas Harpoon (2 quad) launchers ❶; active radar homing to 130 km *(70 nm)* at 0.9 Mach;
warhead 227 kg. Normally only 2 pairs are embarked.
SAM: Selenia Albatros octuple launcher ❷; 24 Raytheon Sea
Sparrow; semi-active radar homing to 14.6 km *(8 nm)* at
2.5 Mach; height envelope 15-5000 m *(49.2-16 405 ft)*;
warhead 39 kg.
Guns: 1 OTO Melara 3 in *(76 mm)*/62 compact ❸; 85° elevation;
85 rounds/minute to 16 km *(8.7 nm)*; weight of shell 6 kg.
1 or 2 Bofors 40 mm/70 ❹; 85° elevation; 300 rounds/minute
to 12.5 km *(6.8 nm)*; weight of shell 0.96 kg.
Torpedoes: 6—324 mm US Mk 32 (2 triple) tubes ❺. Honeywell
Mk 46 Mod 5; anti-submarine; active/passive homing to 11 km
(5.9 nm) at 40 kts; warhead 44 kg.
A/S mortars: 1 Bofors 375 mm twin-barrelled trainable ❻; auto-
matic loading; range 3600 m.
Countermeasures: Decoys: 2 Loral Hycor SRBOC 6-barrelled Mk
36 for chaff and IR flares.
US Prairie Masker; blade rate suppression.
ESM: Elsag Mk 1000 (part of Deneb system); intercept.
ECM: Ceselsa Canopus; jammer.
Combat data systems: SEWACO action data automation; Link
11 being fitted. Saturn SATCOM ❼.
Fire control: Signaal WM 22/41 or WM 25; GM 101.

Radars: Air/surface search: Signaal DA 05/2 ❽; E/F band; range
137 km *(75 nm)* for 2 m² target.
Navigation: Signaal ZW 06 ❾; I band.
Fire control: Signaal WM 22/41 or WM 25 system ❿; I/J band;
range 46 km *(25 nm)*.
Sonars: Raytheon 1160B; hull-mounted; active search and
attack; medium frequency. VDS may be added.

Programmes: Officially rated as Corvettes. *Diana* (tenth of the
name) originates with the galley *Diana* of 1570. Infanta Elena
and Cristina are the daughters of King Juan Carlos. Approval
for second four ships given on 21 May 1976. First four ordered
7 December 1973 (83 per cent Spanish ship construction
components) and four more from Bazán, Ferrol on 25 May
1976.
Modernisation: The 40 mm gun aft of the mainmast was
planned to be replaced by Meroka with associated fire-control

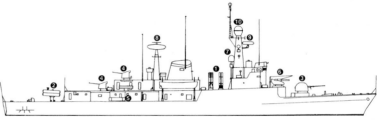

DESCUBIERTA   *(Scale 1 : 900), Ian Sturton*

radars but this update may be shelved. SRBOC chaff launchers
fitted and EW equipment updated. Link 11 being added.
WM 25 fire-control system may be updated in four of the class
by 1995.
Structure: Original Portuguese 'João Coutinho' design by Comodoro de Oliveira PN developed by Blohm & Voss and considerably modified by Bazán including use of Y-shaped funnel.
Harpoon fitted between bridge and funnel. Noise reduction
measures include Masker fitted to shafts, propellers (five types
tested) under trial for four years, auxiliary gas-turbine generator
fitted on upper deck for use during passive sonar search, all
main and auxiliary diesels sound-mounted. Fully stabilised.
Automatic computerised engine and alternator control; two
independent engine rooms; normal running on two diesels.
Operational: All based at Cartagena, forming 21st Squadron.
Sales: F 37 and F 38 sold to Egypt prior to completion. One to
Morocco in 1983.

CAZADORA   *3/1993, A Campanera i Rovira*

5 BALEARES (F 70) CLASS

Name	No
BALEARES	F 71
ANDALUCÍA	F 72
CATALUÑA	F 73
ASTURIAS	F 74
EXTREMADURA	F 75

Builders	Laid down	Launched	Commissioned
Bazán, Ferrol	31 Oct 1968	20 Aug 1970	24 Sep 1973
Bazán, Ferrol	2 July 1969	30 Mar 1971	23 May 1974
Bazán, Ferrol	20 Aug 1970	3 Nov 1971	16 Jan 1975
Bazán, Ferrol	30 Mar 1971	13 May 1972	2 Dec 1975
Bazán, Ferrol	3 Nov 1971	21 Nov 1972	10 Nov 1976

Displacement, tons: 3350 standard; 4177 full load
Dimensions, feet (metres): 438 × 46.9 × 15.4; 25.6 (sonar)
(133.6 × 14.3 × 4.7; 7.8)
Main machinery: 2 Combustion Engineering V2M boilers; 1200
psi *(84.4 kg/cm sq)*; 950°F *(510°C)*; 1 Westinghouse turbine;
35 000 hp(m) *(25.7 MW)*; 1 shaft
Speed, knots: 28. **Range, miles:** 4500 at 20 kts
Complement: 256 (15 officers)

Missiles: SSM: 8 McDonnell Douglas Harpoon (4 normally carried) ❶; active radar homing to 130 km *(70 nm)* at 0.9 Mach;
warhead 227 kg.
SAM: 16 GDC Pomona Standard SM-1MR; Mk 22 Mod 0
launcher ❷; command guidance; semi-active radar homing to
46 km *(25 nm)* at 2 Mach.
A/S: Honeywell ASROC Mk 112 octuple launcher ❸; 8 reloads;
inertial guidance to 1.6-10 km *(1-5.4 nm)*; payload Mk 46
torpedo.
Guns: 1 FMC 5 in *(127 mm)*/54 Mk 42 Mod 9 ❹; dual purpose;
85° elevation; 20-40 rounds/minute to 24 km *(13 nm)* anti-
surface; 14 km *(7.7 nm)* anti-aircraft; weight of shell 32 kg;
600 rounds in magazine.
2 Bazán 20 mm/120 12-barrelled Meroka ❺; 85° elevation;
3600 rounds/minute combined to 2 km.
Torpedoes: 4—324 mm US Mk 32 fixed tubes (fitted internally
and angled at 45 degrees) ❻. Honeywell Mk 46 Mod 5; anti-
submarine; active/passive homing to 11 km *(5.9 nm)* at 40 kts;
warhead 44 kg.
2—484 mm US Mk 25 stern tubes ❼. Westinghouse Mk 37;
anti-submarine; wire-guided; active/passive homing to 8 km
(4.4 nm) at 24 kts; warhead 150 kg. Total of 41 torpedoes of all
types carried.
Countermeasures: Decoys: 4 Loral Hycor SRBOC Mk 36 6-bar-
relled chaff launchers.
ESM: Ceselsa Deneb; intercept.
ECM: Ceselsa Canopus; jammer.
Combat data systems: Tritan 1 action data automation; Link 11.
Saturn SATCOM ❽.
Fire control: Mk 68 GFCS (2 channels of fire). Mk 74 missile sys-
tem with Mk 73 director. Mk 114 torpedo control.
Radars: Air search: Hughes SPS 52A ❾; 3D; E/F band; range
439 km *(240 nm)*.
Surface search: Raytheon SPS 10 ❿; G band.
Navigation: Raytheon Marine Pathfinder; I/J band.
Fire control: Western Electric SPG 53B ⓫; I/J band (for Mk 68).
Raytheon SPG 51C ⓬; G/I band (for Mk 73).
Selenia RAN 12L ⓭; I band (for Meroka). 2 Sperry VPS 2 ⓮
(for Meroka).
Tacan: SRN 15A.
Sonars: Raytheon SQS 56 (DE 1160); hull-mounted; active
search and attack; medium frequency.
EDO SQS 35V; VDS; active search and attack; medium
frequency.

Programmes: This class resulted from a very close co-operation
between Spain and the USA. Programme was approved 17
November 1964, technical support agreement with USA being
signed 31 March 1966. US Navy supplied weapons and sen-

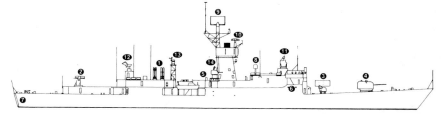

BALEARES *(Scale 1 : 1200), Ian Sturton*

ANDALUCÍA *7/1993, Camil Busquets i Vilanova*

sors. Major hull sections, turbines and gearboxes made at El
Ferrol, superstructures at Alicante, boilers, distilling plants and
propellers at Cadiz.
Modernisation: The mid-life update programme was done in two
stages; all had completed the first stage by the end of 1987
and *Asturias* was the first to be fully modernised in 1988; *Extremadura* completed in May 1989, *Cataluña* in early 1990,
Baleares in July 1990 and *Andalucía* in February 1991.

Changes included the fitting of two Meroka 20 mm CIWS, Link
11, Tritan data control, Deneb passive EW systems, four Mk 36
SRBOC chaff launchers and replacing SQS 23 with DE 1160
sonar.
Structure: Generally similar to US Navy's Knox class although
they differ in the missile system, Mk 25 torpedo tubes and lack
of helicopter facilities.
Operational: All based at Ferrol, forming the 31st Squadron.

EXTREMADURA *5/1991, H M Steele*

SHIPBORNE AIRCRAFT

Numbers/Type: 11 BAe/McDonnell Douglas EAV-8B Bravo (Harrier II).
Operational speed: 562 kts *(1041 km/h)*.
Service ceiling: Not available.
Range: 480 nm *(889 km)*.
Role/Weapon systems: Delivered in 1987-88 for the new aircraft carrier. The plan is to update them to AV-8B Harrier Plus standard with APG-65 radar plus FLIR in 1996-98. Deliveries of 8 new AV-8B planned from January 1996. Sensors: ECM; ALQ 164. Weapons: Strike; 2 × 25 mm GAU-12/U cannon, 2 or 4 × AIM-9L Sidewinder, 2 or 4 × AGM-65E Maverick; up to 16 GP bombs. AMRAAM and Harpoon in updated aircraft.

BRAVO   5/1992, F Gámez

Numbers/Type: 7/2 BAe/McDonnell Douglas AV-8S/TAV 8S Matador (Harrier).
Operational speed: 640 kts *(1186 km/h)*.
Service ceiling: 51 200 ft *(15 600 m)*.
Range: 800 nm *(1480 km)*.
Role/Weapon systems: AV-8S supplied via US and formed for strike/reconnaissance role with one squadron. Sensors: None. Weapons: Strike; 2 × 30 mm Aden cannon, 2 × AIM-9 Sidewinder or 20 mm/127 mm rockets and 'iron' bombs.

MATADOR   8/1991, Camil Busquets i Vilanova

Numbers/Type: 9 Sikorsky SH-3D/G Sea King.
Operational speed: 118 kts *(219 km/h)*.
Service ceiling: 14 700 ft *(4480 m)*.
Range: 542 nm *(1005 km)*.
Role/Weapon systems: Medium ASW helicopter from aircraft carrier; surface search and SAR are secondary roles. Modernisation in 1989 included new sonars, Doppler radars and IFF. Sensors: APS-124 search radar, Bendix AQS-13F dipping sonar, sonobuoys. Weapons: ASW; 4 × Mk 46 torpedoes or depth bombs. ASV; 4 Aerospatiale AS 12 wire-guided missiles.

SEA KING   4/1992, Diego Quevedo

Numbers/Type: 3 Sikorsky SH-3D Sea King AEW.
Operational speed: 110 kts *(204 km/h)*.
Service ceiling: 14 700 ft *(4480 m)*.
Range: 542 nm *(1005 km)*.
Role/Weapon systems: Three Sea King helicopters were taken in hand in 1986 for conversion to AEW role to provide organic cover; first entered service August 1987. Three more may be converted in due course. Sensors: Thorn-EMI Searchwater radar, ESM. Weapons: Unarmed.

SEA KING AEW   5/1993, Camil Busquets i Vilanova

Numbers/Type: 6 Sikorsky SH-70L Seahawk (LAMPS III).
Operational speed: 135 kts *(249 km/h)*.
Service ceiling: 10 000 ft *(3050 m)*.
Range: 600 nm *(1110 km)*.
Role/Weapon systems: ASW helicopter; delivery in 1988-89 for new FFG 7 frigates. Four more to be acquired in due course. Sensors: Search radar, sonobuoys, ECM/ESM. Weapons: ASW; 2 × Mk 46 torpedoes or depth bombs. ASV; ASM being considered.

SEAHAWK   7/1992, Camil Busquets i Vilanova

Numbers/Type: 10 Agusta AB 212ASW.
Operational speed: 106 kts *(196 km/h)*.
Service ceiling: 14 200 ft *(4330 m)*.
Range: 230 nm *(426 km)*.
Role/Weapon systems: ASW and surface search; four are equipped for Fleet ECM support and six for Assault operations with the Amphibious Brigade. Sensors: Selenia search radar, Bendix dipping sonar, Elmer ECM. Weapons: ASW; 2 × Mk 46 torpedoes or 4 × depth bombs. ASV; 4 × Aerospatiale AS 12 wire-guided missiles.

AB 212   3/1993, Diego Quevedo

Numbers/Type: 10 Hughes 500MD/ASW.
Operational speed: 110 kts *(204 km/h)*.
Service ceiling: 10 000 ft *(3050 m)*.
Range: 203 nm *(376 km)*.
Role/Weapon systems: Weapons carrier helicopter for ASW operations, with MAD detection capability; used for training; secondary role is SAR and surface search. Sensors: Some have search radar, MAD. Weapons: ASW; 1 × Mk 46 torpedo or depth bomb.

HUGHES 500   5/1992, A Campanera i Rovira

LAND-BASED MARITIME AIRCRAFT (FRONT LINE)

Numbers/Type: 14 Aerospatiale AS 332 Super Puma.
Operational speed: 151 kts *(279 km/h)*.
Service ceiling: 15 090 ft *(4600 m)*.
Range: 335 nm *(620 km)*.
Role/Weapon systems: Limited search and SAR helicopter operated by Air Force. Sensors: Search radar. Weapons: Unarmed.

Numbers/Type: 9 CASA C-212 Aviocar.
Operational speed: 190 kts *(353 km/h)*.
Service ceiling: 24 000 ft *(7315 m)*.
Range: 1650 nm *(3055 km)*.
Role/Weapon systems: Mediterranean and Atlantic surveillance is carried out by detached flights for the Air Force; SAR is secondary role. Sensors: APS-128 radar, MAD, sonobuoys and ESM. Weapons: ASW; Mk 46 torpedoes or depth bombs. ASV; 2 × rockets or machine gun pods.

Numbers/Type: (6) CASA/Nurtanio CN-235
Operational speed: 240 kts *(445 km/h)*.
Service ceiling: 26 600 ft *(8110 m)*.
Range: 669 nm *(1240 km)*.
Role/Weapon systems: Air Force operated; 20 of the type used for transport tasks. Three maritime patrol versions are planned for delivery in 1997/98. Medium-range maritime patrol for surface surveillance and possible ASV/ASW; Sensors: Search radar: Litton AN/APS 504; MAD; acoustic processors; sonobuoys. Weapons suite to be selected.

Numbers/Type: 3 Fokker F27 Maritime.
Operational speed: 250 kts *(463 km/h)*.
Service ceiling: 29 500 ft *(8990 m)*.
Range: 2700 nm *(5000 km)*.
Role/Weapon systems: Canaries and offshore patrol by Air Force. To be replaced by CN-235 in 1997/98. Sensors: APS-504 search radar, cameras. Weapons: ASW; torpedoes or depth bombs. ASV; possible conversion for missiles under consideration.

Numbers/Type: 2/5 Lockheed P-3A/B Orion.
Operational speed: 410 kts *(760 km/h)*.
Service ceiling: 28 300 ft *(8625 m)*.
Range: 4000 nm *(7410 km)*.
Role/Weapon systems: Air Force operation for long-range MR/ASW; P-3A supplemented in 1988 by P-3B Orions from Norway after Lockheed modernisation. All to be further upgraded with APS 134 radar, FLIR, ALR 66 V(3) ESM and AQS 81 MAD by 1995. Sensors: Search radar, MAD, ECM/ESM, 87 × sonobuoys. Weapons: ASW; 8 × torpedoes or depth bombs internally; 10 × underwing stations. ASV; 4 × Harpoon or 127 mm rockets.

PATROL FORCES

Note: The BES-50 surface effect ship project was cancelled in 1993.

4 SERVIOLA CLASS (OFFSHORE PATROL VESSELS)

Name	No	Builders	Laid down	Launched	Commissioned
SERVIOLA	P 71	Bazán, Ferrol	17 Oct 1989	10 May 1990	22 Mar 1991
CENTINELA	P 72	Bazán, Ferrol	12 Dec 1989	30 Mar 1990	24 Sep 1991
VIGIA	P 73	Bazán, Ferrol	30 Oct 1990	12 Apr 1991	24 Mar 1992
ATALAYA	P 74	Bazán, Ferrol	14 Dec 1990	22 Nov 1991	29 June 1992

Displacement, tons: 836 standard; 1106 full load
Dimensions, feet (metres): 225.4; 206.7 pp × 34 × 11 *(68.7; 63 × 10.4 × 3.4)*
Main machinery: 2 MTU-Bazán 16V 956 TB91 diesels; 7500 hp(m) *(5.5 MW)* sustained; 2 shafts
Speed, knots: 19. **Range, miles:** 8000 at 12 kts
Complement: 42 (8 officers) plus 6 spare berths

Guns: 1 US 3 in *(76 mm)*/50 Mk 27; 85° elevation; 20 rounds/minute to 12 km *(6.6 nm)*; weight of shell 6 kg (see *Structure*). 2—12.7 mm MGs.
Fire control: Bazán Alcor optronic director. Hispano mini combat system.
Radars: Surface search: Racal Decca 2459; I band.
Navigation: Racal Decca ARPA 2690 BT; I band.

Helicopters: 1 AB-212.

Programmes: Project B215 ordered from Bazán, Ferrol in late 1988. Patrulleros de Altura have replaced the Atrevida class. The larger Milano design was rejected as being too expensive.
Structure: A modified Halcón class design similar to ships produced for Argentina and Mexico. Full helicopter facilities enabling operation in up to Sea State 4 using non-retractable stabilisers. Three firefighting pumps. The guns are old stock refurbished but could be replaced by an OTO Melara 76 mm/62 or a Bofors 40 mm/70 Model 600. Other equipment fits could include four Harpoon SSM, Meroka CIWS, Sea Sparrow SAM or a Bofors 375 mm ASW rocket launcher.
Operational: For EEZ patrol only. May carry some female crew. *Vigia* based at Cadiz, *Serviola* and *Atalaya* at Ferrol and *Centinela* at Las Palmas.

CENTINELA   *7/1993, Diego Quevedo*

1 CORMORAN CLASS (FAST ATTACK CRAFT—GUN)

Name	No	Builders	Commissioned
CORMORAN	P 41 (ex-*P 53*)	Bazán, San Fernando	27 Oct 1989

Displacement, tons: 374 full load
Dimensions, feet (metres): 185.7 × 24.7 × 6.5 *(56.6 × 7.5 × 2)*
Main machinery: 3 MTU-Bazán 16V 956 TB91 diesels; 11 250 hp(m) *(8.27 MW)* sustained; 3 shafts
Speed, knots: 34
Complement: 32 (5 officers)
Guns: 1 Bofors 40/70 SP 48; 1 Oerlikon 20 mm.
Fire control: Alcor C modular system.
Radars: Surface search: I band.

Comment: Launched as a private venture and demonstrator in October 1985; taken over by the Navy in October 1989 but not purchased, and may be reclaimed by Bazán if a buyer is found. The design is able to carry SSMs and a 76 mm/62 gun but has commissioned with a second-hand Bofors taken from a deleted ship. Based at Cadiz and is used as a testbed as well as for Straits patrols. More being built for sale.

4 CONEJERA CLASS (COASTAL PATROL CRAFT)

Name	No	Builders	Commissioned
CONEJERA	P 31	Bazán, Ferrol	31 Dec 1981
DRAGONERA	P 32	Bazán, Ferrol	31 Dec 1981
ESPALMADOR	P 33	Bazán, Ferrol	10 May 1982
ALCANADA	P 34	Bazán, Ferrol	10 May 1982

Displacement, tons: 85 full load
Dimensions, feet (metres): 106.6 × 17.4 × 4.6 *(32.2 × 5.3 × 1.4)*
Main machinery: 2 MTU-Bazán MA 16V 362 SB80 diesels; 2450 hp(m) *(1.8 MW)*; 2 shafts
Speed, knots: 25. **Range, miles:** 1200 at 15 kts
Complement: 12
Guns: 1 Oerlikon 20 mm Mk 10. 1—12.7 mm MG.

Comment: Ordered in 1978, funded jointly by the Navy and the Ministry of Commerce. Naval manned.

CORMORAN   *4/1992, van Ginderen Collection*

ESPALMADOR   *12/1993, Diego Quevedo*

1 PESCALONSO CLASS (LARGE PATROL CRAFT)

Name	No	Builders	Commissioned
CHILREU (ex-Pescalonso 2)	P 61	Gijon, Asturias	30 Mar 1992

Displacement, tons: 1157 full load
Dimensions, feet (metres): 222.4 × 36.1 × 15.4 (67.8 × 11 × 4.7)
Main machinery: 1 MAK 6M-453K diesel; 2460 hp(m) (1.81 MW) sustained; 1 shaft
Speed, knots: 13. **Range, miles:** 1500 at 12 kts
Complement: 25
Guns: 1—12.7 mm MG.

Comment: Launched 2 May 1988 and purchased by the Fisheries Department for the Navy to use as a Fishery Protection vessel based at Ferrol. Former stern ramp trawler. Inmarsat fitted.

CHILREU   3/1994, Diego Quevedo

6 BARCELÓ CLASS (FAST ATTACK CRAFT—GUN)

Name	No	Builders	Commissioned
BARCELÓ	P 11	Lürssen, Vegesack	20 Mar 1976
LAYA	P 12	Bazán, La Carraca	23 Dec 1976
JAVIER QUIROGA	P 13	Bazán, La Carraca	4 Apr 1977
ORDÓÑEZ	P 14	Bazán, La Carraca	7 June 1977
ACEVEDO	P 15	Bazán, La Carraca	14 July 1977
CÁNDIDO PÉREZ	P 16	Bazán, La Carraca	25 Nov 1977

Displacement, tons: 134 full load
Dimensions, feet (metres): 118.7 × 19 × 6.2 (36.2 × 5.8 × 1.9)
Main machinery: 2 MTU-Bazán MD 16V 538 TB90 diesels; 6000 hp(m) (4.41 MW) sustained; 2 shafts
Speed, knots: 36. **Range, miles:** 1200 at 17 kts
Complement: 19 (3 officers)
Guns: 1 Breda 40 mm/70. 1 Oerlikon 20 mm/85. 2—12.7 mm MGs.
Torpedoes: Fitted for 2—21 in (533 mm) tubes.
Fire control: CSEE optical director.
Radars: Surface search: Raytheon 1220/6XB; I/J band.

Comment: Ordered 5 December 1973. All manned by the Navy although the cost is being borne by the Ministry of Commerce. Of Lürssen TNC 36 design. Reported as able to take two or four surface-to-surface missiles instead of 20 mm gun and torpedo tubes. All may be transferred to the Guardia Civil del Mar in due course.

ORDÓÑEZ   9/1993, Diego Quevedo

10 ANAGA CLASS (LARGE PATROL CRAFT)

Name	No	Builders	Commissioned
ANAGA	P 21	Bazán, La Carraca	14 Oct 1980
TAGOMAGO	P 22	Bazán, La Carraca	30 Jan 1981
MAROLA	P 23	Bazán, La Carraca	4 June 1981
MOURO	P 24	Bazán, La Carraca	14 July 1981
GROSA	P 25	Bazán, La Carraca	15 Sep 1981
MEDAS	P 26	Bazán, La Carraca	16 Oct 1981
IZARO	P 27	Bazán, La Carraca	9 Dec 1981
TABARCA	P 28	Bazán, La Carraca	30 Dec 1981
DEVA	P 29	Bazán, La Carraca	3 June 1982
BERGANTIN	P 30	Bazán, La Carraca	28 July 1982

Displacement, tons: 296.5 standard; 350 full load
Dimensions, feet (metres): 145.6 × 21.6 × 8.2 (44.4 × 6.6 × 2.5)
Main machinery: 1 MTU-Bazán 16V 956 SB90 diesel; 4000 hp(m) (2.94 MW) sustained; 1 shaft; cp prop
Speed, knots: 22. **Range, miles:** 4000 at 13 kts
Complement: 25 (3 officers)
Guns: 1 FMC 3 in (76 mm)/50 Mk 22. 1 Oerlikon 20 mm Mk 10. 2—7.62 mm MGs.
Radars: Surface search: 1 Racal Decca 1226; I band.
Navigation: Sperry; I band.

Comment: Ordered from Bazán, Cádiz on 22 July 1978. For fishery and EEZ patrol duties. Rescue and firefighting capability.

MEDAS   7/1993, Diego Quevedo

2 TORALLA CLASS (COASTAL PATROL CRAFT)

Name	No	Builders	Commissioned
TORALLA	P 81	Viudes, Barcelona	27 Feb 1987
FORMENTOR	P 82	Viudes, Barcelona	23 June 1988

Displacement, tons: 56 standard; 77 full load
Dimensions, feet (metres): 93.5 × 21.3 × 5.9 (28.5 × 6.5 × 1.8)
Main machinery: 2 MTU-Bazán 8V 396 TB93 diesels; 2100 hp(m) (1.54 MW) sustained; 2 shafts
Speed, knots: 20. **Range, miles:** 1000 at 12 kts
Complement: 13
Guns: 1 Browning 12.7 mm MG.
Radars: Surface search: Racal Decca RM 1070; I band.
Navigation: Racal Decca RM 270; I band.

Comment: Wooden hull with GRP sheath.

TORALLA   2/1993, Diego Quevedo

2 P 101 CLASS (COASTAL PATROL CRAFT)

P 104   P 114

Displacement, tons: 18.5 standard; 20.8 full load
Dimensions, feet (metres): 44.9 × 14.4 × 4.3 (13.7 × 4.4 × 1.3)
Main machinery: 2 Baudouin-Interdiesel DNP-350; 768 hp(m) (564 kW); 2 shafts
Speed, knots: 23.3. **Range, miles:** 430 at 18 kts
Complement: 6
Guns: 1—12.7 mm MG.
Radars: Surface search: Decca 110; I band.

Comment: Ordered under the programme agreed 13 May 1977, funded jointly by the Navy and the Ministry of Commerce. Built to the Aresa LVC 160 design by Aresa, Arenys de Mar, Barcelona. GRP hull. 11 of the class transferred to harbour auxiliary duties with Y numbers, the remainder paid off in 1993.

P 101 class (old number)   3/1993, Diego Quevedo

1 INSHORE/RIVER PATROL LAUNCH

Name	No	Builders	Commissioned
CABO FRADERA	P 201	Bazán, La Carraca	25 Feb 1963

Displacement, tons: 21
Dimensions, feet (metres): 58.3 × 13.8 × 3 (17.8 × 4.2 × 0.9)
Speed, knots: 10
Complement: 9
Guns: 1—7.62 mm MG

Comment: Based at Tuy on River Minho for border patrol with Portugal.

CABO FRADERA   1987, Royal Spanish Navy

1 P 202 CLASS (INSHORE PATROL CRAFT)

P 221

Displacement, tons: 4.8 full load
Dimensions, feet (metres): 29.2 × 10.2 × 2.3 *(8.9 × 3.1 × 0.7)*
Main machinery: 2 Ebro MH 58 diesels; 180 hp(m) *(132 kW)* sustained; 2 shafts
Speed, knots: 18. **Range, miles:** 120 at 18 kts
Complement: 4
Guns: 1—7.62 mm MG.
Radars: Navigation: Decca 60 for 10 craft based in northern ports.

Comment: A class of 30 craft ordered from Rodman, Vigo under the programme agreed 13 May 1977, funded jointly by the Navy and the Ministry of Commerce. Five transferred to harbour auxiliaries, the remainder paid off in 1993. *P 221* serves on the River Minho.

AMPHIBIOUS FORCES

0 + 2 NEWPORT CLASS

Name	No	Builders	Commissioned
— (ex-*Barnstable County*	— (ex-1197)	National Steel	27 May 1972

Displacement, tons: 4975 light; 8450 full load
Dimensions, feet (metres): 522.3 (hull) × 69.5 × 17.5 (aft) *(159.2 × 21.2 × 5.3)*
Main machinery: 6 ARCO 16-251 diesels; 16 500 hp *(12.3 MW)* sustained; 2 shafts; cp props; bow thruster
Speed, knots: 20. **Range, miles:** 2500 at 14 kts
Complement: 257 (13 officers)
Military lift: 400 troops; (20 officers) 500 tons vehicles; 3 LCVPs and 1 LCPL on davits.

Guns: 4 USN 3 in *(76 mm)*/50 (2 twin); Mk 33; 1 General Electric/General Dynamics 20 mm Vulcan Phalanx Mk 15.
Radars: Surface search: Raytheon SPS 10F; G band.
Navigation: Marconi LN 66; I band.

Helicopters: Platform only.

Programmes: First one to be transferred from the US at the end of June 1994 to replace *Velasco*. The second will probably be acquired in late 1994.
Structure: The 3 in guns may be removed on transfer. The ramp is supported by twin derrick arms. A ramp just forward of the superstructure connects the lower tank deck with the main deck and a vehicle passage through the superstructure provides access to the parking area amidships. A stern gate to the tank deck permits unloading of amphibious tractors into the water, or unloading of other vehicles into an LCU or on to a pier. Vehicle stowage covers 19 000 sq ft. Length over derrick arms is 562 ft *(171.3 m)*; full load draught is 11.5 ft forward and 17.5 ft aft. Bow thruster fitted to hold position offshore while unloading amphibious tractors.

0 + 1 (1) AMPHIBIOUS TRANSPORT SHIP (LPD)

Displacement, tons: 12 000 full load
Dimensions, feet (metres): 492.1 × 82 × 19.3 *(150 × 25 × 5.9)*
Main machinery: 4 diesels (possible diesel-electric); 2 shafts
Speed, knots: 20. **Range, miles:** 6000 at 14 kts
Complement: 115 plus 12 spare
Military lift: 600 fully equipped troops or 170 APCs or 33 MBTs. 3 LCVPs and 2 LCUs/LCMs or 6 LCVPs in docking well
Guns: 2 Meroka CIWS. 4 Oerlikon 20 mm.
Helicopters: 6 NH-90 or 4 EH-101.

Comment: Originally started as a national project by the Netherlands. In 1990 the ATS was seen as a possible solution to fulfil the requirements for a new LPD. Joint project definition study announced in July 1991. The ship will be able to transport a fully equipped battalion of 600 marines providing a built-in dock for landing craft and a helicopter flight deck for debarkation in offshore conditions. Alternatively the ship can also be used as a general logistic support ship for both military and civil operations, including environmental and disaster relief tasks. Construction is planned to start in July 1994 for commissioning in mid-1998. No dates are available for the second of class.

AMPHIBIOUS TRANSPORT SHIP   *(not to scale), Ian Sturton*

3 EDIC CLASS (LCTs)

A 06-A 08

Displacement, tons: 279 standard; 665 full load
Dimensions, feet (metres): 193.5 × 39 × 4.3 *(59 × 11.9 × 1.3)*
Main machinery: 2 MTU-Bazán MA 6 R 362 SB70 diesels; 1120 hp(m) *(823 kW)*; 2 shafts
Speed, knots: 9.5. **Range, miles:** 1500 at 9 kts
Complement: 23
Military lift: 300 tons; 35 troops
Guns: 2—12.7 mm MGs. 1—81 mm mortar.
Radars: Navigation: Decca; I band.

Comment: Built by Bazán, La Carraca to the French EDIC design and commissioned in December 1966. Rated as logistic craft.

A 07   *7/1993, Diego Quevedo*

2 PAUL REVERE CLASS (ATTACK TRANSPORTS)

Name	No	Builders	Commissioned
CASTILLA (ex-*Diamond Mariner*, ex-USS *Paul Revere* LPA 248)	L 21 (ex-TA 12)	New York SB	3 Sep 1958
ARAGÓN (ex-*Prairie Mariner*, ex-USS *Francis Marion* LPA 249)	L 22	New York SB	6 July 1961

Displacement, tons: 10 709 light; 16 315 (L 21), 16 573 (L 22) full load
Dimensions, feet (metres): 563.5 × 76 × 27 *(171.8 × 23.1 × 8.2)*
Main machinery: 2 Foster-Wheeler boilers; 600 psi *(42.3 kg/cm sq)*; 870°F *(467°C)*; 1 GE turbine; 22 000 hp *(16.4 MW)*; 1 shaft
Speed, knots: 22. **Range, miles:** 17 000 at 14 kts
Complement: 610 (L 21), 660 (L 22) (35 officers)
Military lift: 1657 troops; 7 LCM 6s (161-167 for L 21 and 261-267 for L 22); 5 LCVPs; 3 LCPs

Guns: 8 US 3 in *(76 mm)*/50 (4 twin); 85° elevation; 50 rounds/minute to 12.8 km *(7 nm)*; weight of shell 6 kg.
Countermeasures: Decoys: Loral Hycor SRBOC Mk 36 chaff launcher.
ESM: WLR1; radar intercept. ECM: ULQ 6; jammer.
Radars: Air search: RCA SPS 12 (L 21); D band; range 119 km *(65 nm)*.
Lockheed SPS 40 (L 22); E/F band; range 320 km *(175 nm)*.
Surface search: Raytheon SPS 10; G band.
Fire control: Four SPG 50 or SPG 34; I/J band.

Helicopters: Platform for 1 AS 332 Super Puma type.

Programmes: Originally C4-S-1 cargo vessels converted to APAs. L 21 by Todd Shipyard, San Pedro and L 22 by Bethlehem, Baltimore. Designated LPAs in 1969. L 21 transferred from US 17 January 1980 by sale, L 22 11 July 1980.
Operational: *Aragón* is the Flagship for Amphibious Command. SATCOM fitted.

CASTILLA   *10/1993, Diego Quevedo*

2 TERREBONNE PARISH CLASS (LSTs)

Name	No	Builders	Commissioned
VELASCO (ex-USS *Terrebonne Parish* LST 1156)	L 11	Bath Iron Works	21 Nov 1952
MARTIN ALVAREZ (ex-USS *Wexford County* LST 1168)	L 12	Christy Corporation	15 June 1954

Displacement, tons: 2590 standard; 5800 full load
Dimensions, feet (metres): 384 × 55 × 17 *(117.1 × 16.8 × 5.2)*
Main machinery: 4 General Motors 16-278A diesels; 6000 hp *(4.48 MW)*; 2 shafts
Speed, knots: 15. **Range, miles:** 15 000 at 9 kts
Complement: 153 (395 troops)
Military lift: 395 troops; 10 Mk 48 tanks or 17 LVTPs; 3 LCVPs; 1 LCP

Guns: 6 US 3 in *(76 mm)*/50 (3 twin).
Fire control: 2 Mk 63 GFCS.
Radars: Surface search: Racal Decca TM 1229; I band.
Navigation: Decca; I band.
Fire control: Two Western Electric SPG 34; I/J band.

Programmes: Both transferred from US on 29 October 1971. Purchased on 17 May 1978. To be replaced by two ex-US Newport class in 1994/95.

VELASCO   *10/1993, Diego Quevedo*

2 LCUs

L 71 (ex-*LCU 11*, ex-*LCU 1*, ex-*LCU 1471*)   **L 72** (ex-*LCU 12*, ex-*LCU 2*, ex-*LCU 1491*)

Displacement, tons: 354 full load
Dimensions, feet (metres): 119.7 × 31.5 × 5.2 *(36.5 × 9.6 × 1.6)*
Main machinery: 3 Gray Marine 64 YTL diesels; 675 hp *(504 kW)*; 3 shafts
Speed, knots: 7.6
Complement: 14
Military lift: 160 tons

Comment: Transferred from US June 1972. Purchased August 1976.

L 71   *1990, Royal Spanish Navy*

8 LCM 8

L 81-86 (ex-*LCM 81-86*, ex-*E 81-86*)   **L 87-88**

Displacement, tons: 115-120 full load
Dimensions, feet (metres): 74.5 × 21.7 × 5.9 *(22.7 × 6.6 × 1.8)*
Main machinery: 4 GM 6-71 diesels; 696 hp *(519 kW)* sustained; 2 shafts
Speed, knots: 11
Complement: 5

Comment: First six ordered from Oxnard, California in 1974. Assembled in Spain. Commissioned in July-September 1975. Two more built by Bazán, San Fernando, and completed in early 1989.

L 82   *10/1989, Camil Busquets i Vilanova*

43 LANDING CRAFT

Comment: Apart from those used for divers there are 14 LCM 6, 20 LCVP and 9 LCP. Ten of the LCM 6, eight of the LCVPs and most of the LCPs were built in Spanish Shipyards 1986-88.

LCM L 162   *10/1993, Diego Quevedo*

1 HOVERCRAFT

VCA 36

Displacement, tons: 36 full load
Dimensions, feet (metres): 82.7 × 37.4 × 31.2 (height) *(25.2 × 11.4 × 9.5)*
Main machinery: 2 Textron-Lycoming TF-25 gas-turbines; 5000 hp *(3.73 MW)* sustained
Speed, knots: 60. **Range, miles:** 145 at 45 kts
Complement: 3
Military lift: 14 tons or 70 troops and 3 Land Rovers or 1 Scorpion light tank
Sonars: French helicopter type for trials; VDS; high frequency.

Comment: Built by Chaconsa, Murcia as an evolution of the VCA 3 design. Operational in 1988. More may be ordered in due course to fulfill tactical and logistic requirements.

VCA 36   *5/1992, A Campanera i Rovira*

MINE WARFARE FORCES

0 + 4 CME CLASS (MINEHUNTERS)

M 51-M 54

Displacement, tons: 530 full load
Dimensions, feet (metres): 177.2 oa; 167.3 wl × 35.1 × 7.2 *(54; 51 × 10.7 × 2.2)*
Main machinery: 2 MTU-Bazán 6V 396 TB83 diesels; 1523 hp(m) *(1.12 MW)*; 2 motors (for hunting); 200 kW; 2 Voith Schneider props; 2 side thrusters; 150 hp(m) *(110 kW)*
Speed, knots: 14; 7 (hunting). **Range, miles:** 2000 at 12 kts
Complement: 40 (7 officers)
Guns: 1 Oerlikon 20 mm GAM-B01.
Combat data systems: FABA/GEC/Marconi Nautis.
Radars: Navigation: I band.
Sonars: Side scanning; active; high frequency.
  VDS; active; high frequency.

Comment: On 4 July 1989 a technology transfer contract was signed with Vosper Thornycroft to allow Bazán to design a new MCM vessel based on the Sandown class. The order for four of the class was authorised on 7 May 1993, and an agreement signed on 26 November 1993 between DCN and Bazán provides for training in GRP technology. The first of class to be laid down in 1995 for delivery in 1998. Minehunting system will be by FABA-Bazán with Inisel. The ships will have two SAES ROVs and either the GEC/Marconi 2093 sonar or the SQQ 32 developed for the US Osprey class. Final requirement is for eight of the class. CME (Contra Minas Español).

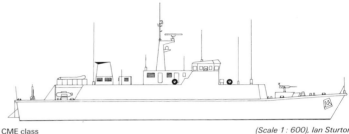

CME class   *(Scale 1 : 600), Ian Sturton*

8 ADJUTANT, REDWING and MSC 268 CLASSES
(MINESWEEPERS—COASTAL)

Name	No	Builders	Commissioned
JÚCAR (ex-*MSC 220*)	M 21	Bellingham SY	22 June 1956
EBRO (ex-*MSC 269*)	M 22	Bellingham SY	19 Dec 1958
DUERO (ex-*Spoonbill* MSC 202)	M 23	Tampa Marine Corporation	16 June 1959
TAJO (ex-*MSC 287*)	M 24	Tampa Marine Corporation	9 July 1959
GENIL (ex-*MSC 279*)	M 25	Tacoma, Seattle	11 Sep 1959
ODIEL (ex-*MSC 288*)	M 26	Tampa Marine Corporation	9 Oct 1959
SIL (ex-*Redwing* MSC 200)	M 27	Tampa Marine Corporation	16 Jan 1959
MIÑO (ex-*MSC 266*)	M 28	Adams YY, Mass	25 Oct 1956

Displacement, tons: 355 standard; 384 full load
Dimensions, feet (metres): 144 × 28 × 8.2 *(43.9 × 8.5 × 2.5)*
Main machinery: 2 GM 8-268A diesels; 880 hp *(656 kW)*; 2 shafts
Speed, knots: 14. **Range, miles:** 2700 at 10 kts
Complement: 39 (3 officers)
Guns: 2 Oerlikon 20 mm (twin).
Radars: Navigation: Decca TM 626 or RM 914; I band.
Sonars: UQS 1; active minehunting; high frequency.

Comment: Transferred from US. Wooden hulled. Two sub-types: M 22, M 24, M 25 and M 26 with no mainmast but crane abreast the funnel. M 21, M 23, M 27 and M 28 have derrick on mainmast. Three others of the class transferred to Patrol Ship duties in 1980 and deleted in 1993.

GENIL   *3/1993, Diego Quevedo*

MIÑO   *3/1993, Diego Quevedo*

4 GUADALETE (AGGRESSIVE) CLASS (MINESWEEPERS—OCEAN)

Name	No	Builders	Commissioned
GUADALETE (ex-USS *Dynamic* MSO 432)	M 41	Colbert BW, Stockton, Calif	15 Dec 1953
GUADALMEDINA (ex-USS *Pivot* MSO 463)	M 42	Wilmington BW, Calif	12 July 1954
GUADALQUIVIR (ex-USS *Persistant* MSO 491)	M 43	Tacoma, Washington	3 Feb 1956
GUADIANA (ex-USS *Vigor* MSO 473)	M 44	Burgess Boat Co, Manitowoc	8 Nov 1954

Displacement, tons: 817-853 full load
Dimensions, feet (metres): 172.5 × 35 × 14.1 *(52.6 × 10.7 × 4.3)*
Main machinery: 4 Packard ID-1700 diesels; 2280 hp *(1.7 MW)*; 2 shafts; cp props
Speed, knots: 14. **Range, miles:** 3000 at 10 kts
Complement: 74 (6 officers)
Guns: 2 Oerlikon 20 mm (twin).
Countermeasures: Pluto ROVs in some.
Radars: Surface search: Raytheon SPS 5C; G/H band; range 37 km *(20 nm)*.
Navigation: Decca; I band.
Sonars: General Electric SQQ 14; VDS; active minehunting; high frequency.

Comment: The first three were transferred from US and commissioned on 1 July 1971. The fourth ship was delivered 4 April 1972. All purchased August 1974. Modernisation completed in 1984-86 to extend service lives. At least two Pluto ROVs acquired in 1989 in order to gain experience while the new MCMVs are being built.

GUADALQUIVIR   *3/1993, Diego Quevedo*

SURVEY AND RESEARCH SHIPS

1 DARSS CLASS (RESEARCH SHIP)

Name	No	Builders	Launched
ALERTA (ex-*Jasmund*)	A 111	Peenewerft, Wolgast	27 Feb 1982

Displacement, tons: 2292 full load
Dimensions, feet (metres): 250.3 × 39.7 × 13.8 *(76.3 × 12.1 × 4.2)*
Main machinery: 1 Kolomna Type 40-DM diesel; 2200 hp(m) *(1.6 MW)* sustained; 1 shaft; cp prop
Speed, knots: 12. **Range, miles:** 1000 at 12 kts
Complement: 60
Guns: Fitted for 3 twin 25 mm/70.
Radars: Navigation: I band.

Comment: Former GDR depot ship converted to an AGI, with additional accommodation replacing much of the storage capacity. Was to have transferred to Ecuador in 1991 but the sale was cancelled. Commissioned in the Spanish Navy on 6 December 1992 and sailed from Wilhelmshaven for a refit at Las Palmas prior to being based at Cartagena and used as an AGI and trials equipment ship.

ALERTA   *7/1993, Diego Quevedo*

1 RESEARCH SHIP

Name	No	Builders	Commissioned
HESPÉRIDES (ex-*Mar Antártico*)	A 33	Bazán, Cartagena	16 May 1991

Displacement, tons: 2738 full load
Dimensions, feet (metres): 270.7; 255.2 × 46.9 × 14.8 *(82.5; 77.8 × 14.3 × 4.5)*
Main machinery: Diesel-electric; 4 MAN-Bazán 14V20/27 diesels; 6860 hp(m) *(5 MW)* sustained; 4 generators; 2 AEG motors; 3800 hp(m) *(2.8 MW)*; 1 shaft; bow and stern thrusters; 350 hp(m) *(257 kW)* each
Speed, knots: 15. **Range, miles:** 12 000 at 13 kts
Complement: 39 (9 officers) plus 30 scientists
Radars: Surface search: Racal/Hispano ARPA 2690; I band.
Navigation: Racal 2690 ACS; F band.
Helicopters: AB 212 or similar.

Comment: Ordered in July 1988 from Bazán, Cartagena, by the Ministry of Education and Science. Laid down in 1989, launched 12 March 1990. Has 330 sq m of laboratories, Simbad ice sonar, navigation radars and GPS. Dome in keel houses several sensors. Ice strengthened hull capable of breaking first year ice up to 45 cm at 5 kts. The main task is to support the Spanish base at Livingston Island, Antarctica replacing the tug *Las Palmas*. Manned and operated by the Navy. Has a red hull, foremast and funnels and a telescopic hangar.

HESPÉRIDES   *9/1993, F Gámez*

4 CASTOR CLASS (SURVEY SHIPS)

Name	No	Builders	Commissioned
CASTOR	A 21 (ex-H 4)	Bazán, La Carraca	10 Nov 1966
POLLUX	A 22 (ex-H 5)	Bazán, La Carraca	6 Dec 1966
ANTARES	A 23	Bazán, La Carraca	21 Nov 1974
RIGEL	A 24	Bazán, La Carraca	21 Nov 1974

Displacement, tons: 327 standard; 355 full load
Dimensions, feet (metres): 125.9 × 24.9 × 10.2 *(38.4 × 7.6 × 3.1)*
Main machinery: 1 Sulzer 4TD36 diesel; 720 hp(m) *(530 kW)*; 1 shaft
Speed, knots: 11.5. **Range, miles:** 3620 at 8 kts
Complement: 36 (4 officers)
Radars: Navigation: Raytheon 1620; I/J band.

Comment: Fitted with Raydist, Omega and digital presentation of data. A 21 and 22 have gaps in the gunwhale aft for Oropesa sweep. In A 23 and 24 this is a full run to the stern.

ANTARES   *10/1993, Diego Quevedo*

2 MALASPINA CLASS (SURVEY SHIPS)

Name	No	Builders	Commissioned
MALASPINA	A 31	Bazán, La Carraca	21 Feb 1975
TOFIÑO	A 32	Bazán, La Carraca	23 Apr 1975

Displacement, tons: 820 standard; 1090 full load
Dimensions, feet (metres): 188.9 × 38.4 × 12.8 *(57.6 × 11.7 × 3.9)*
Main machinery: 2 San Carlos MWM TbRHS-345-61 diesels; 3600 hp(m) *(2.64 MW)*; 2 shafts; cp props
Speed, knots: 15. **Range, miles:** 4000 at 12 kts; 3140 at 14.5 kts
Complement: 63 (9 officers)
Guns: 2 Oerlikon 20 mm.
Radars: Navigation: Raytheon 1220/6XB; I/J band.

Comment: Ordered mid-1972. Both named after their immediate predecessors. Developed from British Bulldog class. Fitted with two Atlas DESO-10 AN 1021 (280-1400 m) echo-sounders, retractable Burnett 538-2 sonar for deep sounding, Egg Mark B side-scan sonar, Raydist DR-S navigation system, Hewlett Packard 2100A computer inserted into Magnavox Transit satellite navigation system, active rudder with fixed pitch auxiliary propeller. *Malaspina* used for a NATO evaluation of a Ship's Laser Inertial Navigation System (SLINS) produced by British Aerospace.

TOFIÑO   *8/1992, F Gámez*

AUXILIARIES

Note: *Campeón* is a civilian tanker owned by CAMPSA and chartered as required. Fitted for one beam and one stern RAS station. 14 862 grt, 166 m in length and with a top speed of 14.5 kts.

0 + 1 AOR 90 (ZUIDERKRUIS) CLASS (FLEET LOGISTIC TANKER)

Name	No	Builders	Commissioned
PATIÑO	A 14	Bazán, Ferrol	June 1995

Displacement, tons: 5762 light; 17 045 full load
Dimensions, feet (metres): 544.6 × 72.2 × 26.2 *(166 × 22 × 8)*
Main machinery: Diesel-electric; 2 Bazán MAN 16V40/45 diesels; 24 000 hp(m) *(17.6 MW)* sustained; 1 motor; 1 shaft; cp prop
Speed, knots: 20. **Range, miles:** 13 440 at 20 kts
Complement: 136 plus 24 aircrew plus 20 spare
Cargo capacity: 6815 tons dieso; 1660 tons aviation fuel; 500 tons solids
Guns: 2 Bazán 20 mm/120 Meroka CIWS. 2 Oerlikon 20 mm/90.
Countermeasures: Decoys: 4 chaff launchers.
ESM/ECM: Aldebaran intercept and jammer.
Radars: 2 navigation/helo control; I band.
Helicopters: 3 SH-3D Sea King size.

Comment: The Bazán design AP 21 was rejected in favour of this joint Netherlands/Spain design based on *Zuiderkruis*. Ordered on 26 December 1991. Laid down 1 July 1993 which is two years later than planned. Scheduled launch June 1994. She will replace the discarded *Teide* as a carrier group support ship. Two supply stations each side for both liquids and solids. Stern refuelling. One Vertrep supply station, and workshops for aircraft maintenance. Medical facilities. Built to merchant ship standards with military NBC. Accommodation for up to 50 female crew members.

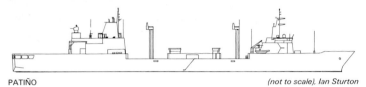
PATIÑO   *(not to scale), Ian Sturton*

1 TRANSPORT SHIP

Name	No	Builders	Commissioned
CONTRAMAESTRE CASADO	A 01	Eriksberg-Göteborg, Sweden	15 Dec 1982
(ex-*Thanasis-K*, ex-*Fortuna Reefer*,			
ex-*Bonzo*, ex-*Bajamar*,			
ex-*Leeward Islands*)			

Displacement, tons: 5300 full load
Dimensions, feet (metres): 343.4 × 46.9 × 29.2 *(104.7 × 14.3 × 8.9)*
Main machinery: 1 Burmeister & Wain diesel; 3600 hp(m) *(2.65 MW)*; 1 shaft
Speed, knots: 16. **Range, miles:** 8000 at 15 kts
Complement: 72
Guns: 2 Oerlikon 20 mm.

Comment: Built in the 1950s. Impounded as smuggler. Delivered after conversion 6 December 1983. Has a helicopter deck.

CONTRAMAESTRE CASADO   *9/1993, Diego Quevedo*

1 FLEET TANKER

Name	No	Builders	Commissioned
MARQUÉS DE LA ENSENADA	A 11	Bazán, Ferrol	3 June 1991
(ex-*Mar del Norte*)			

Displacement, tons: 13 380 full load
Dimensions, feet (metres): 403.9 oa; 377.3 wl × 64 × 25.9 *(123.1; 115 × 19.5 × 7.9)*
Main machinery: 1 MAN-Bazán 18V40/50A; 11 247 hp(m) *(8.27 MW)* sustained; 1 shaft
Speed, knots: 16. **Range, miles:** 10 000 at 15 kts
Complement: 80 (11 officers)
Cargo capacity: 7498 tons dieso; 1746 tons JP-5; 120 tons deck cargo
Guns: 2—7.62 mm MGs.
Radars: Surface search: Racal Decca 2459; I/F band.
Navigation: Racal Decca ARPA 2690/9; I band.
Helicopters: 1 AB 212 or similar.

Comment: Ordered 30 December 1988. Laid down 16 November 1989 and launched 3 October 1990. The deletion of the *Teide* left a serious deficiency in the Fleet's at sea replenishment capability which is to be restored in due course by the new Zuiderkruis type of logistic tanker. In addition, and as a stop gap, this tanker was built at one third of the cost of the larger support ship. Two Vertrep stations and a platform for a Sea King size helicopter. Replenishment stations on both sides and one astern. Provision for Meroka CIWS behind the bridge and four chaff launchers as well as ESM. Has a small hospital. Served with distinction in the Adriatic in 1993.

MARQUÉS DE LA ENSENADA   *10/1993*

10 HARBOUR TANKERS

No	Displacement, tons	Dimensions metres	Builders	Commissioned
Y 231	524	34 × 7 × 2.9	Bazán, Cádiz	1981
Y 232	830	42.8 × 8.4 × 3.1	Bazán, Cádiz	1981
Y 235	510	37.8 × 6.6 × 3	Bazán, Ferrol	1959
Y 236	200	28 × 5.2 × 1.9	Bazán, Cádiz	1959
Y 237	344	34.3 × 6.2 × 2.5	Bazán, Cádiz	1965
Y 251	200	28 × 5.2 × 1.9	Bazán, Ferrol	1959
Y 252	337	34.3 × 6.2 × 2.5	Bazán, Cádiz	1965
Y 253	337	34.3 × 6.2 × 2.5	Bazán, Cádiz	1965
Y 254	214.7	24.5 × 5.5 × 2.2	Bazán, Cádiz	1981
Y 255	524	34 × 7 × 2.9	Bazán, Cádiz	1981

Y 236   *11/1993, Diego Quevedo*

4 BOOM DEFENCE VESSELS

Y 361-362   Y 364-365

Displacement, tons: 53 standard
Dimensions, feet (metres): 73.1 × 28.5 × 2.6 *(22.3 × 8.7 × 0.8)*

Comment: Details given are for *Y 361-362* which are net laying barges, *Y 364-365* are tugs for the barges.

2 LOGISTIC SUPPORT SHIPS

Name	No	Builders	Commissioned
MAR CARIBE (ex-*Amatista*)	A 101	Duro Felguera, Gijon	24 Mar 1975
MAR ROJO (ex-*Amapola*)	A 102	Duro Felguera, Gijon	24 Mar 1975

Displacement, tons: 1860 full load
Dimensions, feet (metres): 176.4 × 38.8 × 14.8 *(53.8 × 11.8 × 4.5)*
Main machinery: 2 Echevarria-Burmeister & Wain 18V23HU diesels; 4860 hp(m) *(3.57 MW)*; 2 shafts; bow thruster
Speed, knots: 13.5. **Range, miles:** 6000 at 10 kts
Complement: 44

Comment: Two offshore oil rig support tugs were acquired and commissioned into the Navy 14 December 1988. Bollard pull, 80 tons. *Mar Rojo* converted as a diver support vessel. She has a dynamic positioning system and carries a sidescan mine detection high frequency sonar as well as a semi-autonomous remote-controlled DSRV. The control cable restricts operations to within 75 m of an auxiliary diving unit. The DSRV is launched and recovered by a hydraulic arm. *Mar Caribe* works with Amphibious Forces.

MAR ROJO   *9/1993, Diego Quevedo*

1 WATER TANKER

FOGONERO BAÑOBRE A 64 (ex-*AA 23*, ex-*A 11*)

Displacement, tons: 575 full load
Dimensions, feet (metres): 146.9 × 24.9 × 9.8 *(44.8 × 7.6 × 3)*
Main machinery: 1 diesel; 700 hp(m) *(514 kW)*; 1 shaft
Speed, knots: 9. **Range, miles:** 1000 at 8 kts
Complement: 17
Cargo capacity: 350 tons

Comment: Built at Bazán, La Carraca. Commissioned 24 January 1963. Ocean-going. Two others of the class paid off in December 1993.

WATER TANKER (old number)   *3/1993, Diego Quevedo*

1 WATER TANKER

CONTRAMAESTRE CASTELLÓ A 61 (ex-*AA 06*, ex-*A 6*)

Displacement, tons: 1811 full load
Dimensions, feet (metres): 210.3 × 31.5 × 15.7 *(64.1 × 9.6 × 4.8)*
Main machinery: 1 boiler; 1 reciprocating engine; 800 ihp(m) *(588 kW)*; 1 shaft
Speed, knots: 9
Complement: 27
Cargo capacity: 1000 tons
Guns: 2—12.7 mm MGs.

Comment: Commissioned 30 January 1952. Ocean-going.

CONTRAMAESTRE CASTELLÓ   *7/1993, Diego Quevedo*

1 WATER TANKER

MARINERO JARANOA A 65 (ex-*AA 31*)

Displacement, tons: 527 full load
Dimensions, feet (metres): 123 × 23 × 9.8 *(37.5 × 7 × 3)*
Main machinery: 1 diesel; 600 hp(m) *(441 kW)*; 1 shaft
Speed, knots: 10.8
Complement: 13
Cargo capacity: 300 tons

Comment: Built by Bazán, Cádiz. Similar to Y 231 and Y 255 (harbour tankers). Commissioned 16 March 1981.

MARINERO JARANOA   *1987, Royal Spanish Navy*

1 WATER TANKER

CONDESTABLE ZARAGOZA A 66 (ex-*AA 41*)

Displacement, tons: 892 full load
Dimensions, feet (metres): 152.2 × 27.6 × 11.2 *(46.4 × 8.4 × 3.4)*
Main machinery: 1 diesel; 700 hp(m) *(515 kW)*; 1 shaft
Speed, knots: 10.8
Complement: 16
Cargo capacity: 600 tons

Comment: Built by Bazán, Cádiz. Commissioned 16 October 1981. Similar to Y 232 oil tanker.

CONDESTABLE ZARAGOZA   *1990, Royal Spanish Navy*

3 WATER BOATS

Y 271-273 (ex-*YA 01-03*, ex-*AB 01-03*)

Displacement, tons: 320 (Y 271-2); 344 (Y 273)
Dimensions, feet (metres): 112.5 × 20.3 × 8.2 *(34.3 × 6.2 × 2.5)*
Main machinery: 1 diesel; 280 hp(m) *(206 kW)*; 1 shaft
Speed, knots: 9.7
Complement: 8
Cargo capacity: 200 tons

Comment: Harbour water-boats. Commissioned 1959. Similar to tankers Y 237, 252 and 253.

2 DIVING SUPPORT VESSELS

NEREIDA Y 562 (ex-*YBZ 11*)   **PROSERPINA** Y 563 (ex-*YBZ 12*)

Displacement, tons: 103.5
Dimensions, feet (metres): 70.5 × 19.2 × 9.5 *(21.5 × 5.9 × 2.9)*
Main machinery: 1 Sulzer diesel; 200 hp(m) *(147 kW)*; 1 shaft
Speed, knots: 9

Comment: Built by Bazán, Cartagena. Frogmen support craft. There is also an unpropelled barge Y 565.

PROSERPINA   *2/1993, Diego Quevedo*

40+ HARBOUR CRAFT

Y 501-513	Y 517-518	Y 538-540	Y 572-578
Y 515	Y 529-535	Y 570-571	Y 580-584

Displacement, tons: 8-13.7
Speed, knots: 7-17

Comment: Some used as divers boats, others as harbour ferries. Five are former patrol craft of the P 101 and P 202 class.

Y 584   *6/1993, Diego Quevedo*

2 MINE TRANSPORT CRAFT

Y 372   Y 373

Displacement, tons: 178 full load
Dimensions, feet (metres): 101.4 × 21.7 × 9.8 *(30.9 × 6.6 × 3)*
Speed, knots: 7
Complement: 8
Mines: 50.

Comment: Built by Bazán 1961. Transports torpedoes and mines and, in emergency, can act as a minelayer.

40 BARGES

Comment: Have Y numbers. Four in 200 series carry fuel, 31 in 300 for ammunition and general stores, five in 400 for anti-pollution. Four deleted in 1991 and replaced by Y 421-425. Three deleted in 1992.

Y 222 (fuel)   *9/1993, Diego Quevedo*

Y 365 (ammunition)   *2/1993, Diego Quevedo*

4 FLOATING CRANES

Y 382-384   Y 385

Displacement, tons: 490 (Y 384); 470 (Y 382-3); 272 (Y 385)
Dimensions, feet (metres): 73.8 × 45.9 × 9.8 *(22.5 × 14 × 3)* (Y 382-4)
62.3 × 38.4 × 7.9 *(19 × 11.7 × 2.4)* (Y 385)
Military lift: 30 tons (Y 382-4); 15 tons (Y 385)

Comment: Based at Cartagena, Ferrol and La Carraca. Completed 1953-56. Y 386 deleted in 1990, Y 381 in 1993.

TRAINING SHIPS

4 SAIL TRAINING SHIPS

Name	No	Builders	Commissioned
JUAN SEBASTIÁN DE ELCANO	A 71	Echevarrieta, Cadiz	28 Feb 1928
AROSA	A 72	—	1 Apr 1981
LA GRACIOSA (ex-*Dejá Vu*)	A 74	—	30 June 1988
GIRALDA	A 75	Morris & Mortimer, Argyll	23 Aug 1993

Displacement, tons: 3420 standard; 3656 full load
Dimensions, feet (metres): 269.2 pp; 308.5 oa × 43.3 × 24.6 *(82; 94.1 × 13.2 × 7.5)*
Main machinery: 1 Deutz MWM RBV 6M diesel; 1500 hp(m) *(1.1 MW)*; 1 shaft
Speed, knots: 8.5. **Range, miles:** 10 000 at 9.5 kts
Complement: 332
Guns: 2—37 mm saluting guns.
Radars: Navigation: Two Decca TM 626; I band.

Comment: Details are for A 71 which is a four masted top-sail schooner—near sister of Chilean *Esmeralda*. Named after the first circumnavigator of the world (1519-22) who succeeded to the command of the expedition led by Magellan after the latter's death. Laid down 24 November 1925. Launched on 5 March 1927. Carries 230 tons oil fuel. Engine replaced in 1992. The other three are a ketch (A 72), a schooner (A 74) (38 tons and 24.5 m in length) used by the Naval School, and a 90 ton ketch (A 75) formerly owned by the father of King Juan Carlos and presented to the Naval school at Pontevedra in 1993. *Giralda* was launched in 1958.

JUAN SEBASTIAN DE ELCANO   *1/1992, F Gámez*

5 TRAINING CRAFT

Name	No	Builders	Commissioned
GUARDIAMARINA BARRUTIA	A 81	Cartagena	14 Sep 1982
GUARDIAMARINA SALAS	A 82	Cartagena	10 May 1983
GUARDIAMARINA GODINEZ	A 83	Cartagena	4 July 1984
GUARDIAMARINA RULL	A 84	Cartagena	11 June 1984
GUARDIAMARINA CHEREGUINI	A 85	Cartagena	11 June 1984

Displacement, tons: 56
Dimensions, feet (metres): 62 × 16.7 × 5.2 *(18.9 × 5.1 × 1.6)*
Speed, knots: 13
Complement: 15; 22 (A 81)
Radars: Navigation: Halcon 948; I band.

Comment: Tenders to Naval School. A 81 has an operations centre.

GUARDIAMARINA BARRUTIA   *1987, Royal Spanish Navy*

TUGS

2 OCEAN TUGS

Name	No	Builders	Commissioned
MAHÓN	A 51	Astilleros Atlántico, Santander	1978
LAS PALMAS	A 52	Astilleros Atlántico, Santander	1978

Displacement, tons: 1437 full load
Dimensions, feet (metres): 134.5 × 38.1 × 18 *(41 × 11.6 × 5.5)*
Main machinery: 2 AESA/Sulzer 16ASV25/30 diesels; 7744 hp(m) *(5.69 MW)*; 2 shafts
Speed, knots: 13. **Range, miles:** 27 000 at 12 kts (A 52)
Complement: 33 (8 officers) plus 45 scientists
Guns: 2—12.7 mm MGs.

Comment: Built for Compania Hispano Americana de Offshore SA as *Circos* (A 51) and *Somiedo*. Commissioned in the Navy 30 July 1981. *Las Palmas* converted in 1988 for Polar Research Ship duties in Antarctica with an ice strengthened bow, an enlarged bridge and two containers aft for laboratories. With the commissioning of *Hesperides*, the ship is based at Las Palmas and is being used as a tug.

MAHÓN   *2/1992, Giorgio Arra*

3 OCEAN TUGS

Name	No	Builders	Commissioned
POSEIDÓN	A 12 (ex-*AS 01*, ex-*RA 6*)	Bazán, La Carraca	8 Aug 1964
CARTAGENA (ex-*Valen*)	A 41 (ex-*RA 1*)	Bazán, Cartagena	9 July 1955
FERROL	A 43 (ex-*AR 45*, ex-*RA 5*)	Bazán, La Carraca	11 Apr 1964

Displacement, tons: 951 standard; 1069 full load
Dimensions, feet (metres): 183.5 × 32.8 × 13.1 *(55.9 × 10 × 4)*
Main machinery: 2 Sulzer diesels; 3200 hp *(2.53 MW)*; 1 shaft; cp prop
Speed, knots: 15. **Range, miles:** 4640 at 14 kts
Complement: 49; 60 (A 12)
Guns: 2 or 4 Oerlikon 20 mm (twin).
Radars: Navigation: Decca TM 626; I band.

Comment: A 12 acts as a frogman support ship and submarine SAR vessel at Cartagena and carries a 300 m/6 h bathyscaphe. Some superstructure differences in all of the class.

CARTAGENA   *1/1994, Diego Quevedo*

2 COASTAL TUGS

Y 116 (ex-*YRR 21*, ex-*71*)   **Y 117** (ex-*YRR 22*, ex-*72*)

Displacement, tons: 422 full load
Dimensions, feet (metres): 91.8 × 26.2 × 12.5 *(28 × 8 × 3.8)*
Main machinery: 1 diesel; 1500 hp *(1.1 MW)*; 1 shaft
Speed, knots: 12.4. **Range, miles:** 3000 at 10 kts

Comment: Built by Bazán, Ferrol. Commissioned 10 April and 1 June 1981 respectively.

Y 116   *10/1992, Camil Busquets i Vilanova*

29 COASTAL and HARBOUR TUGS

No	Displacement tonnes (full load)	HP/speed	Commissioned
Y 111, Y 114	227	800/10	1963
Y 113	217	1400/12	1965
Y 115	216	1500/12	1967
Y 118, Y 121-123	236	1560/14	1989-91
Y 119 (ex-Punta Amer)	260	1750/12	1973
Y 120 (ex-Punta Roca)	260	1750/12	1973
Y 131-135, Y 137-140	70	200/8	1965-67
Y 141-142	229	800/11	1981
Y 143	133	600/10	1961
Y 144-145	195	2030/11	1983
Y 146	173	829/10	1983
Y 147	87	400/10	1987
Y 171-173	10	440/11	1982 (171) 1985 (172-3)

Comment: Y 143 has a troop carrying capability. Y 171-173 are pusher tugs for submarines. Y 118, Y 119-123 have Voith Schneider propulsion.

Y 147   6/1993, Diego Quevedo

POLICE (GUARDIA CIVIL DEL MAR)

Note: Created by Royal decree on 22 February 1991. Bases at La Coruña, Santander, Barcelona, Murcia and Algeciras. Personnel strength 1526 (39 officers). The force has taken over the anti-terrorist role and some general patrol duties as a peacetime paramilitary organisation coming under the Ministry of Defence in war. Order of battle to include:
(a) 11 Coastal Patrol Craft (PA)
(b) 37 Inshore Patrol Craft (PM)
(c) 39 Harbour Patrol Craft (PL)
(d) Light helicopters.
All vessels are to be armed. Full strength will take about five years to achieve.

BO 105   8/1992, F Gámez

12 RODMAN 55 CLASS (INSHORE PATROL CRAFT—PM)

Displacement, tons: 15.7 full load
Dimensions, feet (metres): 54.1 × 12.5 × 2.3 (16.5 × 3.8 × 0.7)
Main machinery: 2 Bazán/MAN D2848-LXE diesels; 1360 hp(m) (1 MW) sustained; 2 Hamilton waterjets
Speed, knots: 40. **Range, miles:** 500 at 35 kts
Complement: 7
Guns: 1—7.62 mm MG.
Radars: Surface search: Ericsson; I band.

Comment: GRP hulls built by Rodman, Vigo. First five in service in 1992, remainder in 1993.

RODMAN 55   7/1993, Diego Quevedo

15 BAZÁN 39 CLASS (INSHORE PATROL CRAFT—PM)

Displacement, tons: 14 full load
Dimensions, feet (metres): 39 × 12.5 × 2.3 (11.9 × 3.8 × 0.7)
Main machinery: 2 Bazán/MAN D2848-LXE diesels; 1360 hp(m) (1 MW) sustained; 2 Hamilton waterjets
Speed, knots: 40. **Range, miles:** 300 at 30 kts
Complement: 4
Guns: 1—7.62 mm MG.
Radars: Surface search: Ericsson.

Comment: GRP hulls built by Bazán and delivered in 1993/94.

BAZÁN 39   7/1993, Camil Busquets i Vilanova

CUSTOMS

Note: All carry ADUANAS on ships' sides. Craft of all types were painted black with a white diagonal stripe in 1990/91. In addition to the listed vessels there are a number of fast boats. Some of the larger vessels are armed with machine guns. There are also four CASA C-212 maritime patrol aircraft and four helicopters.

Name	Displacement tons (full load)	HP/speed	Commissioned
ÁGUILA	80	2700/29	1974
ALBATROS 2 and 3	83	2700/29	1964-69
ALCA 1 and 3	22	2000/45	1987-88
ALCAVARÁN 1-5	85	3920/28	1984-87
ALCOTÁN 2	95	3200/23	—
CÁRABO	57	1350/16	1977
COLIMBO	26	640/20	—
GAVILÁN 1, AGUILUCHO	63	2700/28	1975-76
GAVILÁN 2-4	65	3200/30	1983-87
HALCÓN 2-3	68	3200/28	1980-83
HJ 1, HJ 3-13	20	2000/50	1986
VA 2-5	23	1400/27	1985
CORMORÁN	22	2970/65	1990
CONDOR I	125	5200/30	1991
CONDOR 2	160	1300/15	—
CONDOR 3 (Depot Ship)	1600	2700/14	1991
NEBLÍ (COUGAR CAT (2100)) 1-2	50	3480/42	1993

ALBATROS 3   10/1993, Diego Quevedo

SALVAGE AND ANTI-POLLUTION

Note: A new service under the direction of the Merchant Marine, but may come under a future Coast Guard service in due course. Up to 11 salvage tugs and 11 fast launches (Salvamar). Distinctive red hulls and superstructures with a white diagonal marking on the hull.

SAINT CHARLES   12/1992, Camil Busquets i Vilanova

SRI LANKA

Headquarters' Appointment

Commander of the Navy:
Vice Admiral Damr Samarasekera

Formation

The Royal Ceylon Navy was formed on 9 December 1950 when the Navy Act was proclaimed. Called the Sri Lanka Navy since Republic Day 22 May 1972.

Personnel

(a) 1994: 9900 (750 officers)
(b) Voluntary service
(c) SLVNF: 1020 (102 officers)
(d) Naval reservists: 100 (12 officers)

General

The Tamil insurgency in Sri Lanka had a major impact on the naval programme. The main area of maritime importance is the Palk Strait between India and the primarily Tamil area of northern Sri Lanka. This area has many small creeks—the main requirement is the support of shallow draught fast craft, a very different task from EEZ patrols.

Bases

Naval Base at Trincomalee was expanded in 1988-89 programme and expanded again in 1993.
Other bases at Karainagar, Colombo, Welisara, Tangalle, and Kalpitiya.
There are four Area Commands—North, South, East and West.

Prefix to Ships' Names

SLNS. Pennant numbers changed on 1 November 1987.

Strength of the Fleet

Type	Active	Building
Command Ships/Tenders	4	—
Fast Attack Craft—Gun	22	(2)
Offshore Patrol Vessels	2	—
Coastal Patrol Craft	23	—
Inshore Patrol Craft	29	(10)
Landing Craft	3	(2)
FPCs	2	—

Mercantile Marine

Lloyd's Register of Shipping:
56 vessels of 293 968 tons gross

DELETIONS

1991	*Balawatha*, P 150	
1992	*Kandula* (sunk)	
1993	*P 464*	

PATROL FORCES

3 ABHEETHA CLASS (COMMAND SHIPS)

Name	No	Builders	Commissioned
ABHEETHA (ex-*Carinia*)	P 714	Chung Wah SB & Eng Co Ltd	9 Aug 1984
EDITHARA (ex-*Francesca*)	P 715	Singapore Slipway Co	9 Aug 1984
WICKRAMA (ex-*Delicia*)	P 716	Chung Wah SB & Eng Co Ltd	9 Aug 1984

Displacement, tons: 2628 full load
Dimensions, feet (metres): 249.7 × 56.1 × 12.5 *(76.1 × 17.1 × 3.8)*
Main machinery: 2 Deutz SBA12M525 diesels; 3000 hp(m) *(2.2 MW)*; 2 shafts
Speed, knots: 12. **Range, miles:** 6000 at 10 kts
Complement: 50
Guns: 2 China 25 mm/60 (twin) Type 61; 85° elevation; 270 rounds/minute to 3 km *(1.6 nm)*; weight of shell 0.34 kg.
8 China 14.5 mm/93 (4 twin) MGs.
Radars: Surface search: Selesmar/Selescan; I band.
Navigation: Furuno; I band.

Comment: Former Ro-Ro ships built 1976-77 and used as command and HQ ships for Light Forces. Classified as Surveillance Command Ships. Dates given are commissioning dates in the Navy. Have a 30 ton crane.

EDITHARA *1992, Sri Lanka Navy*

1 COMMAND SHIP

A 516 (ex-*Kota Rukun*, ex-*Mercury Cove*, ex-*Tjimanuk*)

Displacement, tons: 6300 full load
Dimensions, feet (metres): 326.4 × 51.2 × 22.6 *(99.5 × 15.6 × 6.9)*
Main machinery: 1 NV Werkspoor 6-cyl diesel; 3600 hp(m) *(2.64 MW)*; 1 shaft
Speed, knots: 13. **Range, miles:** 12 000 at 8 kts
Complement: 50
Guns: 1—12.7 mm MG.
Radars: Surface search: Decca 110; I band.
Navigation: Furuno FR 1011; I band.

Comment: Launched in 1959 at Gorinchem Shipyard and acquired from Pacific International Lines in 1986. 3350 grt. Classified as a Command Tender.

A 516 *1986, Sri Lanka Navy*

2 JAYESAGARA CLASS (OFFSHORE PATROL VESSELS)

Name	No	Builders	Commissioned
JAYESAGARA	P 601	Colombo Dockyard	9 Dec 1983
SAGARAWARDENE	P 602	Colombo Dockyard	6 Apr 1984

Displacement, tons: 330 full load
Dimensions, feet (metres): 130.5 × 23 × 7 *(39.8 × 7 × 2.1)*
Main machinery: 2 MAN 8L20/27 diesels; 2180 hp(m) *(1.6 MW)* sustained; 2 shafts
Speed, knots: 15. **Range, miles:** 3000 at 11 kts
Complement: 52 (4 officers)
Guns: 2 China 25 mm/80 (twin). 2 China 14.5 mm (twin) MGs.

Comment: Ordered from Colombo Dockyard on 31 December 1981. P 601 launched 26 May 1983, P 602 launched 20 November 1983.

JAYESAGARA *1993, Sri Lanka Navy*

6 DVORA CLASS (FAST ATTACK CRAFT—GUN)

P 453-P 458

Displacement, tons: 47 full load
Dimensions, feet (metres): 70.8 × 18 × 5.8 *(21.6 × 5.5 × 1.8)*
Main machinery: 2 MTU 12V 331 TC81 diesels; 2605 hp(m) *(1.91 MW)* sustained; 2 shafts
Speed, knots: 36. **Range, miles:** 1200 at 17 kts
Complement: 12
Guns: 2 Oerlikon 20 mm. 2—12.7 mm MGs.
Radars: Surface search: Decca 926; I band.

Comment: First pair transferred from Israel early 1984, next four in October 1986. Built by Israel Aircraft Industries.

P 456 *1992, Sri Lanka Navy*

5 SOORAYA CLASS (FAST ATTACK CRAFT—GUN)

SOORAYA P 310 (ex-P 3140)
WEERAYA P 311 (ex-P 3141)
RANAKAMEE P 312 (ex-P 3142)
JAGATHA P 315 (ex-P 3145)
RAKSHAKA P 316 (ex-P 3146)

Displacement, tons: 113 standard; 131 full load
Dimensions, feet (metres): 127.3 × 17.7 × 5.2 *(38.8 × 5.4 × 1.6)*
Main machinery: 2 Type L12-180 diesels; 2400 hp(m) *(1.76 MW)* (forward); 2 Type L12-180Z; 1820 hp(m) *(1.34 MW)* (aft); 4 shafts
Speed, knots: 29. **Range, miles:** 700 at 16 kts
Complement: 34
Guns: 2 China 37 mm/63 (twin). 4 China 25 mm/80 (2 twin abaft the bridge). 2 China 14.5 mm (twin) MG.
Depth charges: 8.
Radars: Surface search: Skin Head; I band; range 37 km *(20 nm)*.
Navigation: Furuno 825 D; I band.

Comment: Ex-Shanghai II class, the first pair transferred by China in February 1972, the second pair in July 1972, one in December 1972 and two more on 30 November 1980. One deleted in 1991. *Weeraya*, and possibly others, have the alternative gun arrangement of a twin 14.5 mm forward and the 37 mm right aft.

SOORAYA
1992, Sri Lanka Navy

3 + (2) RANA (MOD SHANGHAI II) CLASS
(FAST ATTACK CRAFT—GUN)

RANASURU P 320   **RANAWIRU** P 321   **RANARISI** P 322

Displacement, tons: 150 full load
Dimensions, feet (metres): 134.5 × 17.7 × 5.2 *(41 × 5.4 × 1.6)*
Main machinery: 4 diesels; 4800 hp(m) *(3.53 MW)*; 4 shafts
Speed, knots: 29. **Range, miles:** 750 at 16 kts
Complement: 28 (4 officers)
Guns: 4 China 37 mm/63 (2 twin) Type 76. 4 China 14.5 mm (twin) Type 69.
Radars: Surface search: Racal Decca; I band.

Comment: Acquired from China in September 1991 and commissioned in November 1991. More powerful engines than the Sooraya class; automatic guns and improved habitability. Two more may be acquired.

RANASURU
1992, Sri Lanka Navy

5 SUPER DVORA CLASS (FAST ATTACK CRAFT—GUN)

P 463   P 465-468

Displacement, tons: 54 full load
Dimensions, feet (metres): 73.5 × 18 × 5.8 *(22.4 × 5.5 × 1.8)*
Main machinery: 2 MTU 12V 396 TB93 diesels; 3260 hp(m) *(2.4 MW)* sustained; 2 shafts
Speed, knots: 46. **Range, miles:** 1200 at 17 kts
Complement: 12
Guns: 2 Oerlikon 20 mm. 2—12.7 mm MGs.
Radars: Surface search: Decca 926; I band.

Comment: Ordered from Israel Aircraft Industries in October 1986 and delivered in 1987/88. A more powerful version of the Dvora class. *P 464* was destroyed by Tamil guerrillas on 29 August 1993.

SUPER DVORA (old number)
1992, Sri Lanka Navy

3 SOUTH KOREAN KILLER CLASS (FAST ATTACK CRAFT—GUN)

P 473-P 475

Displacement, tons: 56 full load
Dimensions, feet (metres): 75.5 × 17.7 × 5.9 *(23 × 5.4 × 1.8)*
Main machinery: 2 MTU 396 TB93 diesels; 3260 hp(m) *(2.4 MW)* sustained; 2 shafts
Speed, knots: 40
Complement: 12
Guns: 2 Oerlikon 20 mm. 2—12.7 mm MGs.
Radars: Surface search: Racal Decca; I band.

Comment: Built by Korea SB and Eng, Buson. All commissioned February 1988.

P 473
1992, Sri Lanka Navy

10 COASTAL PATROL CRAFT

P 231-P 235   P 241-P 245

Displacement, tons: 40 full load
Dimensions, feet (metres): 66 × 18 × 7 *(20 × 5.5 × 2.1)*
Main machinery: 2 Detroit 12V-71TA diesels; 840 hp *(626 kW)* sustained; 2 shafts
Speed, knots: 22. **Range, miles:** 1500 at 14 kts
Complement: 10
Guns: 2 Oerlikon 20 mm (24 series). 2—12.7 mm MGs (23 series).

Comment: Ordered from Colombo DY June 1976 (first pair). First six commissioned 1980-81, last five in 1982-83. All craft refitted 1988-89 except *P 236* which was deleted in June 1990.

P 241
1993, Sri Lanka Navy

4 COASTAL PATROL CRAFT

P 201-P 202   P 211   P 214

Displacement, tons: 21 full load
Dimensions, feet (metres): 46.6 × 12.8 × 3.3 *(14.2 × 3.9 × 1)*
Main machinery: 2 Detroit 8V-71TA diesels; 460 hp *(343 kW)*; 2 shafts
Speed, knots: 20. **Range, miles:** 450 at 14 kts
Complement: 6
Guns: 2—12.7 mm MGs.
Radars: Surface search: I band.

Comment: Built by Colombo DY and commissioned in 1982-83 *(P 201-P 202)*, June 1986 *(P 211 and P 214)*.

P 201
1986, Sri Lanka Navy

4 SIMONNEAU SM 500 CLASS (COASTAL PATROL CRAFT)

Displacement, tons: 22 full load
Dimensions, feet (metres): 51.8 × 15.1 × 5.9 *(15.8 × 4.6 × 1.8)*
Main machinery: 2 diesels; 1600 hp(m) *(1.18 MW)*; 2 shafts
Speed, knots: 30
Complement: 6
Guns: 1 Oerlikon 20 mm. 1—7.62 mm MG.
Radars: Surface search: I band.

Comment: Ordered from Simonneau Marine in October 1992. Two built in France, two in Sri Lanka at Colombo dockyard. The plan is to build more in Sri Lanka in due course.

SIMONNEAU SM 500 (old number)   *1992, Simonneau Marine*

5 COASTAL PATROL CRAFT

P 221-P 225 (ex-*P 421-425*)

Displacement, tons: 22 full load
Dimensions, feet (metres): 55.9 × 14.8 × 3.9 *(17 × 4.5 × 1.2)*
Main machinery: 2 Detroit 8V-71TA diesels; 460 hp *(343 kW)*; 2 shafts
Speed, knots: 23. **Range, miles:** 1000 at 12 kts
Complement: 7
Guns: 1—12.7 mm MG.

Comment: Used for general patrol duties. Built by Cheverton Workboats, UK and commissioned in 1977.

P 224   *1992, Sri Lanka Navy*

9 COUGAR CLASS (INSHORE PATROL CRAFT)

P 101-109

Displacement, tons: 7.4 full load
Dimensions, feet (metres): 34.1 × 9.5 × 2.6 *(10.4 × 2.9 × 0.8)*
Main machinery: 2 Sabre diesels; 500 hp *(373 kW)*; 2 shafts
Speed, knots: 30
Complement: 4
Guns: 1—12.7 mm MG.

Comment: First ordered in 1984 for trials, order for remainder placed in 1985. Operate from Command Ships.

P 106   *1992, Sri Lanka Navy*

2 + (10) INSHORE PATROL CRAFT

P 151-152

Displacement, tons: 9 full load
Dimensions, feet (metres): 42.6 × 12.1 × 1.6 *(13 × 3.7 × 0.5)*
Main machinery: 2 Cummins 6BTA5.9-M2; 584 hp *(436 kW)* sustained; 2 waterjets
Speed, knots: 33. **Range, miles:** 330 at 25 kts
Complement: 5
Guns: 1—12.7 mm MG.
Radars: Surface search: I band.

Comment: Built by TAOS Yacht Company, Colombo, and delivered in 1991. Ten more may be acquired.

P 151   *1991, Sri Lanka Navy*

8 INSHORE PATROL CRAFT

P 111-P 123 series

Displacement, tons: 5 full load
Dimensions, feet (metres): 44 × 9.8 × 1.6 *(13.4 × 3 × 0.5)*
Main machinery: 2 Yamaha D 343 diesels; 730 hp(m) *(544 kW)* sustained; 2 shafts
Speed, knots: 26
Complement: 5
Guns: 1—12.7 mm MG.

Comment: Built by Consolidated Marine Engineers, Sri Lanka. First nine delivered in 1988; four more in 1992. Five destroyed by Tamil guerrillas in 1993. Operate from Command Ships.

P 111   *1992, Sri Lanka Navy*

10 INSHORE PATROL CRAFT

P 140-149

Displacement, tons: 3.5 full load
Dimensions, feet (metres): 42 × 8 × 1.6 *(12.8 × 2.4 × 0.5)*
Main machinery: 2 outboard motors; 280 hp *(209 kW)*
Speed, knots: 30
Complement: 4

Comment: Acquired in 1988. Similar to *P 111* but with outboard engines. *P 150* was mined and sunk in August 1991.

P 150   *1989, Sri Lanka Navy*

AMPHIBIOUS FORCES

Note: There are plans for an assault force of Marines in due course. Reports of possible transfers of Russian Alligator or Vydra class landing ships have not been confirmed.

2 LANDING CRAFT (LCM)

Name	No	Builders	Commissioned
PABBATHA	L 838 (ex-A 538)	Vospers, Singapore	21 Dec 1987
RANAGAJA	L 839	Colombo Dockyard	15 Nov 1991
(ex-*Gajasingha*)			

Displacement, tons: 268 full load
Dimensions, feet (metres): 108.3 × 26 × 4.9 *(33 × 8 × 1.5)*
Main machinery: 2 Caterpillar diesels; 1524 hp *(1.14 MW)*; 2 shafts
Speed, knots: 8. **Range, miles:** 1800 at 8 kts
Complement: 12 (2 officers)
Guns: 4 China 14.5 mm (2 twin) *(Ranagaja)*. 2 Oerlikon 20 mm (remainder). 2—12.7 mm MGs.

Comment: Two built in 1983 and acquired in October 1985. Third of the class taken over by the Navy in September 1991. More may be built. *Kandula* sank in October 1992 and was salvaged in mid-December. The plan is to refurbish her, but there must be doubts about the feasibility of doing this successfully after the ship has been under water for two months.

RANAGAJA *10/1991, Sri Lanka Navy*

2 FAST PERSONNEL CARRIERS (FPC)

Name	No	Builders	Commissioned
HANSAYA	A 540 (ex-*Offshore Pioneer*)	Sing Koon Seng, Singapore	20 Dec 1987
LIHINIYA	A 541 (ex-*Offshore Pride*)	Sing Koon Seng, Singapore	20 Dec 1987

Displacement, tons: 154 full load
Dimensions, feet (metres): 98.4 × 36.8 × 7.7 *(30 × 11.2 × 2.3)*
Main machinery: 2 MTU diesels; 2 shafts
Speed, knots: 30
Complement: 12 (2 officers)
Cargo capacity: 60 tons; 120 troops
Guns: 1 Oerlikon 20 mm. 2—12.7 mm MGs.

Comment: Acquired in January 1986 from Aluminium Shipbuilders. Catamaran hulls used for fast transport.

LIHINIYA *1992, Sri Lanka Navy*

1 YUNNAN CLASS (LCU)

L 820

Displacement, tons: 128 full load
Dimensions, feet (metres): 93.8 × 17.7 × 4.6 *(28.6 × 5.4 × 1.4)*
Main machinery: 2 diesels; 600 hp(m) *(441 kW)*; 2 shafts
Speed, knots: 12. **Range, miles:** 500 at 10 kts
Complement: 12 (2 officers)
Military lift: 46 tons
Guns: 4—14.5 mm (2 twin) MGs.

Comment: Acquired from China in May 1991.

L 820 *1992, Sri Lanka Navy*

SUDAN

<table>
<tr><td>Headquarters' Appointment</td><td>Establishment</td><td>General</td></tr>
<tr><td>Commander (Navy):
Brigadier Abbas Al-Sayyid Uthman</td><td>The Navy was established in 1962 to operate on the Red Sea coast and on the River Nile.</td><td>The overall standard of operational efficiency has suffered from lack of maintenance and spare parts, and auxiliaries have drifted into total disrepair. Also reported are an ex-Tanker used for training, a Water Tanker (PB 6) and an unarmed Survey Ship (PB 35). More patrol craft may be acquired from China or Iran.</td></tr>
<tr><td>Personnel</td><td>Bases</td><td>Mercantile Marine</td></tr>
<tr><td>(a) 1994: 500 officers and men
(b) Voluntary service</td><td>Flamingo Bay for Red Sea operations with a separate riverine unit on the Nile based at Khartoum.</td><td>Lloyd's Register of Shipping:
17 vessels of 64 106 tons gross</td></tr>
</table>

PATROL FORCES

2 COASTAL PATROL CRAFT

KADIR (ex-*Shahpar*) 129   KARARI (ex-*Shahram*) 130

Displacement, tons: 70 full load
Dimensions, feet (metres): 75.2 × 16.5 × 6 *(22.9 × 5 × 1.8)*
Main machinery: 2 MTU diesels; 2200 hp(m) *(1.62 MW)*; 2 shafts
Speed, knots: 27
Complement: 19 (3 officers)
Guns: 1 Oerlikon 20 mm.

Comment: Built for Iran by Abeking & Rasmussen in 1970. Transferred to Iranian Coast Guard 1975 and to Sudan later that year. *Sheikan* (128) has been cannibalised for spares but may be refurbished with Iranian assistance. Armaments could also be upgraded.

KADIR *2/1990*

4 KURMUK (TYPE 15) CLASS (INSHORE PATROL CRAFT)

KURMUK 502   QAYSAN 503   RUMBEK 504   MAYOM 505

Displacement, tons: 19.5 full load
Dimensions, feet (metres): 55.4 × 12.8 × 2.3 *(16.9 × 3.9 × 0.7)*
Main machinery: 2 diesels; 330 hp(m) *(243 kW)*; 2 shafts
Speed, knots: 16. **Range, miles:** 160 at 12 kts
Complement: 6
Guns: 1 Oerlikon 20 mm; 2—7.62 mm MGs.
Radars: Surface search: I band.

Comment: Delivered by Yugoslavia on 18 May 1989 for operations on the White Nile.

KURMUK *1989, G Jacobs*

8 ASHOORA I CLASS (INSHORE PATROL CRAFT)

Displacement, tons: 3 full load
Dimensions, feet (metres): 26.6 × 8 × 1.6 *(8.1 × 2.4 × 0.5)*
Main machinery: 2 Yamaha outboards; 400 hp(m) *(294 kW)*
Speed, knots: 42
Complement: 2
Guns: 1—7.62 mm MG.

Comment: Acquired from Iran in 1992. Based at Flamingo Bay.

ASHOORA I   *1992, IRI Marine Industries*

LAND-BASED MARITIME AIRCRAFT

Numbers/Type: 2 CASA C-212 Aviocar.
Operational speed: 190 kts *(353 km/h).*
Service ceiling: 24 000 ft *(7315 m).*
Range: 1650 nm *(3055 km).*
Role/Weapon systems: Limited capability over the Red Sea; no real combat role. Sensors: Search radar. Weapons: Unarmed.

4 SEWART CLASS (INSHORE PATROL CRAFT)

MAROUB 1161	**FIJAB** 1162	**SALAK** 1163	**HALOTE** 1164

Displacement, tons: 9.1 full load
Dimensions, feet (metres): 40 × 12.1 × 3.3 *(12.2 × 3.7 × 1)*
Main machinery: 2 GM diesels; 348 hp *(260 kW)*; 2 shafts
Speed, knots: 31
Complement: 6
Guns: 1—12.7 mm MG.

Comment: Transferred by Iranian Coast Guard in 1975. All were operational in 1993.

AUXILIARIES

7 SUPPLY SHIPS

SOBAT 221	**DINDER** 222	**+ 5**

Displacement, tons: 410 full load
Dimensions, feet (metres): 155.1 × 21 × 7.5 *(47.3 × 6.4 × 2.3)*
Main machinery: 3 Gray Marine diesels; 495 hp *(369 kW)*; 3 shafts
Speed, knots: 9
Complement: 15
Guns: 1 Oerlikon 20 mm. 2—12.7 mm MGs.

Comment: Details given are for the two Yugoslav MFPD class LCTs transferred in 1969. Five similar vessels were delivered from Yugoslavia in 1991 and are based at Kosti. Used for transporting ammunition, petrol and general supplies.

SURINAM

Personnel	Base	Mercantile Marine
1994: 240 officers and men	Paramaribo	*Lloyd's Register of Shipping:* 24 vessels of 12 929 tons gross

PATROL FORCES

Notes: (1) Four ex-German Kondor I class minesweepers were reported as being bought in 1992 but the sale was not confirmed. An option to buy patrol craft from the same source was cancelled.
(2) A new patrol craft is expected from the Netherlands in 1994.

3 LARGE PATROL CRAFT

P 401-P 403 (ex-*S 401-403*)

Displacement, tons: 140 full load
Dimensions, feet (metres): 105 × 21.3 × 5.5 *(32 × 6.5 × 1.7)*
Main machinery: 2 Paxman 12YHCM diesels; 2110 hp *(1.57 MW)*; 2 shafts
Speed, knots: 17.5. **Range, miles:** 1200 at 13.5 kts
Complement: 15
Guns: 2 Bofors 40 mm. 2—7.62 mm MGs.
Radars: Surface search: Decca 110; I band.

Comment: Built by De Vries, Aalsmeer, Netherlands and commissioned in 1976-77. This design has far greater speed and armament potential but Surinam apparently opted for the scaled-down version. Doubtful operational status.

P 403   *1988*

2 COASTAL PATROL CRAFT

C 301   C 303

Displacement, tons: 65
Dimensions, feet (metres): 72.2 × 15.5 × 7.6 *(22 × 4.7 × 2.3)*
Main machinery: 2 Dorman 8JT diesels; 560 hp *(418 kW)*; 2 shafts
Speed, knots: 13.5. **Range, miles:** 650 at 13 kts
Complement: 8
Guns: 1—12.7 mm MG. 2—7.62 mm MGs.
Radars: Surface search: Decca 110; I band.

Comment: Three ordered April 1975 from Schottel, Netherlands. Commissioned in 1976. *C 302* cannibalised for spares. Both in poor condition in early 1994.

C 301   *1980, Surinam Ministry*

3 RIVER PATROL CRAFT

Name	No	Builders	Commissioned
BAHADOER	RP 201	Schottel, Netherlands	Dec 1975
FAJABLOW	RP 202	Schottel, Netherlands	Dec 1975
KORANGON	RP 203	Schottel, Netherlands	Feb 1976

Displacement, tons: 15
Dimensions, feet (metres): 41.4 × 12.5 × 3.6 *(12.6 × 3.8 × 1.1)*
Main machinery: 1 Dorman 8JT diesel; 280 hp *(209 kW)*; 1 shaft
Speed, knots: 14. **Range, miles:** 350 at 10 kts
Complement: 4
Guns: 1—12.7 mm MG.

Comment: Ordered December 1974. Operational status doubtful.

KORANGON   *1980, Surinam Ministry*

2 SURVEY CRAFT

COEROENI   LITANI

Comment: *Coeroeni* of 80 tons launched in 1962; *Litani* of 70 tons launched in 1958. Both craft are owned by the Ministry of Economic Affairs and manned by the Navy.

LAND-BASED MARITIME AIRCRAFT

Numbers/Type: 4 Pilatus Britten-Norman BN-2A Maritime Defender.
Operational speed: 150 kts *(280 km/h).*
Service ceiling: 18 900 ft *(5760 m).*
Range: 1500 nm *(2775 km).*
Role/Weapon systems: Flown by Air Force for coastal patrol. At least two are unserviceable. Sensors: Lightweight search radar. Weapons: Unarmed.

SWEDEN

Headquarters' Appointments

Commander-in-Chief:
  Vice Admiral Peter Nordbeck
Chief of Naval Material Department:
  Rear Admiral Torbjörn Hultman

Senior Commands

Commander-in-Chief of Coastal Fleet:
  Rear Admiral Frank Rosenius
Inspector of Coastal Artillery:
  Brigadier Per Lundbeck

Diplomatic Representation

Defence Attaché in London:
  Commodore Gustaf Taube
Naval Attaché in Moscow:
  Captain Magnus Haglund
Naval Attaché in Washington:
  Captain Bjorn Ljunggren
Defence Attaché in Canberra:
  Commander Nils Bruzelius
Naval Attaché in Bonn:
  Captain Lars Norrsell
Defence Attaché in Paris:
  Captain Carl-Gustaf Dybeck

Pennant Numbers

Numbers are not displayed on major patrol craft.

Organisation

By 1997 there are planned to be 12 submarines, three surface flotillas, three MCMV squadrons and three helicopter squadrons. There are four naval commands: North, East, South and West.

Coastal Artillery

Being reorganised into six amphibious battalions of 800 men in each. Each battalion to have 35 Combatboat 90, 13 Combatboat 90E, four Trossbåt, 26 section vessels and 19 canoes. The plan is to form one battalion per year having started in 1991. There is also to be a heavy coastal missile battery and three mobile battalions by 1997. All Coastal Artillery vessels are fully integrated with the Navy and are therefore not shown as a separate section.

Strength of the Fleet

Type	Active	Building (Planned)
Submarines—Patrol	12	3
Missile Corvettes	6	—
Fast Attack Craft—Missile	28	(4)
Coastal Patrol Craft	9	—
Inshore Patrol Craft	24	3 (11)
Experimental Patrol Craft	1	—
Minelayers	3	—
MCM Support Ship	1	—
Minelayers—Coastal	9	—
Minelayers—Small	22	—
Minesweepers/Hunters—Coastal	10	(4)
Minesweepers—Inshore	14	—
Sonobuoy Craft	4	—
LCMs	21	(4)
LCUs	79	—
LCAs	92	(30)
Mine Transport	1	—
Survey Ships	3	—
Electronic Surveillance Ship	1	—
Transport Ships	2	—
Repair Ship	1	—
Tankers	2	—
Divers Support Ships	3	—
Tugs	18	—
Salvage Ship	1	—
Sail Training Ships	2	—
Icebreakers	7	—
TRVs	3	—

Personnel

(a) 1994: 9000 officers and men of Navy and Coastal Artillery made up of 3000 regulars and 6000 national servicemen (4700 new and the remainder refreshers)
(b) 10-17¼ months' national service

Bases

Muskö (Stockholm), Karlskrona.
Minor bases at Härnösand and Göteborg.

Mercantile Marine

Lloyd's Register of Shipping:
  614 vessels of 2 438 789 tons gross

DELETIONS

Patrol Forces

1992 *Rörö, Arild, Viken, Marstrand*
1993 *Ornö, Svärdet*

Mine Warfare Forces

1992 *Fårösund*
1993 *Fällaren*

Amphibious Forces

1991 *Sleipner* (old)
1992 *Ane, Balder, Loke, Ring*

Auxiliaries

1993 *Belos* (old), *Brännaren, ATB 1, ATB 2, Hebe, Passopp, Fryken, Meranda, Sigrun*

PENNANT LIST

Corvettes		R 135	Västerås	M 33	Viksten	B 03	Svärten
		R 136	Västervik	M 43	Hisingen	B 04	Viggen
K 11	Stockholm	R 137	Umeå	M 44	Blackan		
K 12	Malmö	R 138	Piteå	M 45	Dämman	**Auxiliaries**	
K 21	Göteborg	R 139	Luleå	M 46	Galten		
K 22	Gälve	R 140	Halmstad	M 47	Gillöga	A 201	Orion
K 23	Kalmar	R 141	Strömstad	M 48	Rödlöga	A 212	Ägir
K 24	Sundsvall	R 142	Ystad	M 49	Svartlöga	A 213	Nordanö
		V 05	Öregrund	M 57	Arkö	A 214	Belos III
Patrol Forces		V 06	Slite	M 67	Nämdö	A 229	Eldaren
		V 08	Lysekil	M 68	Blidö	A 237	Minören
P 151	Hugin	V 09	Dalarö	M 71	Landsort	A 241	Urd
P 152	Munin	V 10	Sandhamn	M 72	Arholma	A 246	Hägern
P 153	Magne	V 11	Osthammar	M 73	Koster	A 247	Pelikanen
P 154	Mode	V 53	Tjurkö	M 74	Kullen	A 248	Pingvinen
P 155	Vale	V 54	Sturkö	M 75	Vinga	A 251	Achilles
P 156	Vidar	V 150	Jägaren	M 76	Ven	A 252	Ajax
P 157	Mjölner	61-77	CPC	M 77	Ulvön	A 253	Hermes
P 158	Mysing	SVK 2	Spjutet	MUL 11	Kalvsund	A 261	Utö
P 159	Kaparen	SVK 3	Pilen	MUL 12	Arkosund	A 262	Skredsvik
P 160	Väktaren	SVK 4	Bågen	MUL 13	Kalmarsund	A 263	Galö
P 161	Snapphanen			MUL 14	Alnösund	A 322	Heros
P 162	Spejaren	**Mine Warfare Forces**		MUL 15	Grundsund	A 323	Hercules
P 163	Styrbjörn			MUL 17	Skramsösund	A 324	Hera
P 164	Starkodder	M 02	Älvsborg	MUL 18	Öresund	A 330	Atlas
P 165	Tordön	M 03	Visborg	MUL 19	Barösund	A 343	Sleipner (new)
P 166	Tirfing	M 04	Carlskrona	MUL 20	Furusund	A 701-705	Tugs
R 131	Norrköping	M 20-22	IMS	501-516	Small Minelayers	A 751-756	Tugs
R 132	Nynäshamn	M 24-25	IMS	1879-1884	Small Minelayers	S 01	Gladan
R 133	Norrtälje	M 31	Gåssten	B 01	Ejdern	S 02	Falken
R 134	Varberg	M 32	Norsten	B 02	Krickan		

SUBMARINES

Notes: (1) A rescue vehicle, *Urf (Ubåts Räddnings Farkost)* of 52 tons with a diving depth of 1500 ft *(460 m)* was launched 17 April 1978. Similar to US Navy DSRV she has a capacity for 25 men on each dive.
(2) The last Mala class R-2 two-man craft was scrapped in 1993.

1 MIDGET SUBMARINE

SPIGGEN II

Displacement, tons: 14 dived
Dimensions, feet (metres): 36.1 × 5.6 × 4.6 *(11 × 1.7 × 1.4)*
Main machinery: 1 Volvo Penta diesel; 1 shaft
Speed, knots: 5 dived
Complement: 6

Comment: Launched 19 June 1990. Has an endurance of 14 days and is used as a target for ASW training.

SPIGGEN II

8/1993, Erik Laursen

0 + 3 GOTLAND (A 19) CLASS

Name	No	Builders	Laid down	Launched	Commissioned
GOTLAND	—	Kockums, Malmö	20 Nov 1992	Dec 1994	1997
UPPLAND	—	Kockums, Malmö	14 Jan 1994	Jan 1996	1998
HALLAND	—	Kockums, Malmö	July 1994	Sep 1996	1999

Displacement, tons: 1240 surfaced; 1490 dived
Dimensions, feet (metres): 183.7 × 19.7 × 18.4
 (56 × 6 × 5.6)
Main machinery: Diesel-electric; 2 MTU diesels; 1 Kockums Stirling AIP system; 1 motor; 1 shaft
Speed, knots: 11 surfaced; 20 dived
Complement: 28 (5 officers)

Torpedoes: 4—21 in *(533 mm)* tubes; 12 FFV Type 613.
 2—15.75 in *(400 mm)* tubes; 6 Swedish Ordnance Type 432/451.
Mines: Capability for 48 in an external girdle.
Countermeasures: ESM: Argo 700A; radar warning.
Fire control: CelsiusTech data automation.
Radars: Navigation: I band.
Sonars: Atlas Elektronik CSU-90; hull-mounted; passive search and attack; medium frequency.

Programmes: In October 1986 a research contract was awarded to Kockums for a design to replace the Sjöormen class in the mid-1990s. Ordered on 28 March 1990.
Structure: The design has been developed on the basis of the Type A 17 series but this class will be the first to be built with Air Independent propulsion as part of the design. Details are not yet known but three 75 kW Stirling engines of the type fitted in *Näcken* have been reported, as has one 600 kW V12 version.

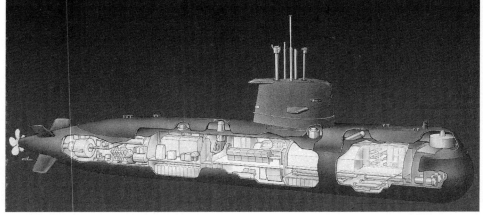

GOTLAND (model)   *1991, Kockums*

4 VÄSTERGÖTLAND (A 17) CLASS

Name	No	Builders	Laid down	Launched	Commissioned
VÄSTERGÖTLAND	—	Kockums, Malmö	10 Jan 1983	17 Sep 1986	27 Nov 1987
HÄLSINGLAND	—	Kockums, Malmö	1 Jan 1984	31 Aug 1987	20 Oct 1988
SÖDERMANLAND	—	Kockums, Malmö	1985	12 Apr 1988	21 Apr 1989
ÖSTERGÖTLAND	—	Kockums, Malmö	1986	9 Dec 1988	10 Jan 1990

Displacement, tons: 1070 surfaced; 1143 dived
Dimensions, feet (metres): 159.1 × 20 × 18.4
 (48.5 × 6.1 × 5.6)
Main machinery: Diesel-electric; 2 Hedemora V12A/15 diesels; 2200 hp(m) *(1.62 MW)*; 1 Jeumont Schneider motor; 1800 hp(m) *(1.32 MW)*; 1 shaft
Speed, knots: 11 surfaced; 20 dived
Complement: 28 (5 officers)

Torpedoes: 6—21 in *(533 mm)* tubes. 12 FFV Type 613; anti-surface; wire-guided; passive homing to 15 km *(8.2 nm)* at 45 kts; warhead 240 kg. Swim-out discharge.
 3—15.75 in *(400 mm)* tubes. 6 FFV Type 431/451; anti-submarine; wire-guided; active/passive homing to 20 km *(10.8 nm)* at 25 kts; warhead 45 kg shaped charge or a small charge anti-intruder version is available.
Mines: Capability for 48 mines in an external girdle.
Countermeasures: ESM: Argo AR-700-S5; radar warning.
Fire control: Ericsson IPS-17 data automation.
Radars: Navigation: Terma; I band.
Sonars: Atlas Elektronik CSU83; hull-mounted; passive search and attack; medium frequency.
 Flank array; passive search; low frequency.

Programmes: Design contract awarded to Kockums, Malmö on 17 April 1978. Contract for construction of these boats signed 8 December 1981. Kockums built midship section and carried

VÄSTERGÖTLAND   *6/1992, Maritime Photographic*

out final assembly while Karlskrona built bow and stern sections. Have replaced the Draken class.
Structure: Single hulled with an X type rudder/after hydroplane design. Reported that SSM were considered but rejected as

non-cost-effective weapons in the context of submarine operations in the Baltic. May be back fitted with Stirling engines in due course. Equipped with Pilkington Optronics CK 38 electro-optic search periscope.

5 SJÖORMEN (A 12) CLASS

Name	No	Builders	Laid down	Launched	Commissioned
SJÖORMEN	—	Kockums, Malmö	1965	25 Jan 1967	31 July 1968
SJÖLEJONET	—	Kockums, Malmö	1966	29 June 1967	16 Dec 1968
SJÖHUNDEN	—	Kockums, Malmö	1966	21 Mar 1968	25 June 1969
SJÖBJÖRNEN	—	Karlskronavarvet	1967	6 Aug 1968	28 Feb 1969
SJÖHÄSTEN	—	Karlskronavarvet	1966	9 Jan 1968	15 Sep 1969

Displacement, tons: 1130 surfaced; 1210 dived
Dimensions, feet (metres): 167.3 × 20 × 19
 (51 × 6.1 × 5.8)
Main machinery: Diesel-electric; 2 Hedemora-Pielstick V12A/A2/15 diesels; 2200 hp(m) *(1.62 MW)*; 1 ASEA motor; 1500 hp(m) *(1.1 MW)*; 1 shaft
Speed, knots: 12 surfaced; 20 dived
Complement: 23 (7 officers)

Torpedoes: 4—21 in *(533 mm)* bow tubes. 10 FFV Type 613;

anti-surface; wire-guided; passive homing to 15 km *(8.2 nm)* at 45 kts; warhead 250 kg.
 2—15.75 in *(400 mm)* tubes. 4 FFV Type 431; anti-submarine; wire-guided; active/passive homing to 20 km *(10.8 nm)* at 25 kts; warhead 45 kg shaped charge.
Mines: Minelaying capability.
Fire control: Ericsson A1 system.
Radars: Navigation: Terma; I band.
Sonars: Plessey Hydra; hull-mounted; passive search and attack; medium frequency.

Modernisation: *Sjölejonet* and *Sjöhunden* modernised with Näcken type electronics to extend life into the late 1990s. All of the class given Plessey sonars (replacing Atlas Elektronik CSU 3) which are similar to RN Type 2074.
Structure: Albacore hull. Twin-decked. Diving depth, 150 m *(492 ft)*.
Operational: Endurance, three weeks. The three unmodernised boats will be replaced in the late 1990s by the Gotland class.

SJÖHÄSTEN   *6/1991, Erik Laursen*

3 NÄCKEN (A 14) CLASS

Name	No	Builders	Laid down	Launched	Commissioned
NÄCKEN	—	Kockums, Malmö	Nov 1972	17 Apr 1978	25 Apr 1980
NAJAD	—	Kockums, Malmö/Karlskronavarvet	Sep 1973	6 Dec 1978	26 June 1981
NEPTUN	—	Kockums, Malmö	Mar 1974	13 Aug 1979	5 Dec 1980

Displacement, tons: 1015 surfaced; 1085 dived
Dimensions, feet (metres): 162.4 (182.1, *Näcken*) × 18.7 × 18 *(49.5 (55.5) × 5.7 × 5.5)*
Main machinery: Diesel-electric; 1 MTU 16V 652 MB80 diesel; 1730 hp(m) *(1.27 MW)*; 2 Stirling V4-275R engines *(Näcken)*; 150 kW; 1 Jeumont Schneider motor; 1800 hp(m) *(1.32 MW)*; 1 shaft
Speed, knots: 12 surfaced; 20 dived
Complement: 27 (5 officers)

Torpedoes: 6—21 in *(533 mm)* tubes. 8 FFV Type 613; anti-surface; wire-guided; passive homing to 15 km *(8.2 nm)* at 45 kts; warhead 250 kg.
2—15.75 in *(400 mm)* tubes. 4 FFV Type 431; anti-submarine; wire-guided; active/passive homing to 20 km *(10.8 nm)* at 25 kts; warhead 45 kg shaped charge.
Mines: Minelaying capability including an external girdle of 48 mines.

Countermeasures: ESM: Argo; radar warning.
Fire control: Ericsson A1 with 2 Censor 932 computers for data processing.
Radars: Navigation: Terma; I band.
Sonars: Thomson Sintra; hull-mounted; passive search and attack; medium frequency.

Modernisation: *Näcken* was taken in hand by Kockums in November 1987 for the installation of a closed-circuit Tillma Stirling diesel which provides non-nuclear propulsion without requiring access to the atmosphere. This involved the ship being lengthened by 6 m and she was relaunched on 6 September 1988. The new section which is neutrally buoyant contains the Stirling generators, two LOX supply tanks and control systems. The other two of the class will not be similarly modified. Work started in 1993 to update all of the class with new fire-control systems, torpedo tube automation and new sonars, to extend service lives into the next century.

Structure: The very high beam to length ratio is notable in this hull design. Has large bow-mounted sonar. Main accommodation space is abaft the control room with machinery spaces right aft. A central computer provides both attack information and data on main machinery. Single periscope. Diving depth 300 m *(984 ft)*.
Operational: The Stirling engine is primarily for slow submerged speed patrolling without much use of battery power. Liquid oxygen (LOX) provides the combustible air. Exhaust products dissolve in water. It is claimed that fully submerged endurance is possible up to 14 days. Trials started on 23 November 1988 and the submarine returned to operational service on 11 April 1989.

NÄCKEN   *8/1993, Per Kornefeldt*

CORVETTES

2 STOCKHOLM CLASS

Name	No	Builders	Laid down	Launched	Commissioned
STOCKHOLM	K 11	Karlskronavarvet	1 Aug 1982	24 Aug 1984	22 Feb 1985
MALMÖ	K 12	Karlskronavarvet	14 Mar 1983	22 Mar 1985	10 May 1985

Displacement, tons: 310 standard; 335 full load
Dimensions, feet (metres): 164 × 22.3 × 6.2 *(50 × 6.8 × 1.9)*
Main machinery: CODAG; 1 GM/Allison 570-KF gas-turbine; 6540 hp(m) *(4.74 MW)* sustained; 2 MTU 16V 396 TB93 diesels; 4200 hp(m) *(3.1 MW)* sustained; 3 shafts
Speed, knots: 32 gas; 20 diesel
Complement: 30 (7 officers)

Missiles: SSM: 8 Saab RBS 15 (4 twin) launchers ❶; inertial guidance; active radar homing to 70 km *(37.8 nm)* at 0.8 Mach; warhead 150 kg.
Guns: 1 Bofors 57 mm/70 Mk 2 ❷; 75° elevation; 220 rounds/minute to 17 km *(9.3 nm)*; weight of shell 2.4 kg.
1 Bofors 40 mm/70 ❸; 85° elevation; 300 rounds/minute to 12.5 km *(6.8 nm)*; weight of shell 0.96 kg.
Torpedoes: 2—21 in *(533 mm)* tubes ❹. FFV Type 613; wire-guided; passive homing to 15 km *(8.2 nm)* at 45 kts; warhead 240 kg. 2-6 can be fitted in lieu of missiles.
4—15.75 in *(400 mm)* tubes; Swedish Ordnance Type 43 or Whitehead Type 422; anti-submarine.
A/S mortars: 4 Saab Elma LLS-920 9-tubed launchers ❺; range 300 m; warhead 4.2 kg shaped charge. IR/chaff decoys.
Depth charges: On mine rails.
Mines: Minelaying capability.
Countermeasures: Decoys: 2 Philips Philax fixed launchers; 4 magazines each holding 36 IR/chaff grenades; fired in groups of nine. A/S mortars have also been adapted to fire IR/chaff decoys.
ESM: Argo Systems AR 700; radar intercept.
ECM: THORN EMI Sceptre XL; jammer.
Combat data systems: Ericsson MARIL 880; data link.
Fire control: Philips 9LV 300 GFCS including a 9LV 100 optronic director ❻.
Radars: Air/surface search: Ericsson Sea Giraffe 50HC ❼; G band.
Navigation: Terma PN 612; I band.
Fire control: Philips 9LV 200 Mk 3 ❽; J band.
Sonars: Simrad SA 950; hull-mounted; active attack.
Thomson Sintra TSM 2642 Salmon ❾; VDS; search; medium frequency.

Programmes: Orders placed in September 1981. Developed from Spica II class.
Operational: Some flexibility in weapon fit depending on mission. The Elma LLS-920 system is designed to surface a submarine even if it does not sink it.

STOCKHOLM   *(Scale 1 : 600), Ian Sturton*

STOCKHOLM   *5/1993, van Ginderen Collection*

4 GÖTEBORG CLASS

Name	No	Builders	Laid down	Launched	Commissioned
GÖTEBORG	K 21	Karlskronavarvet	10 Feb 1986	14 Apr 1989	15 Feb 1990
GÄLVE	K 22	Karlskronavarvet	Sep 1988	23 Mar 1990	1 Feb 1991
KALMAR	K 23	Karlskronavarvet	Sep 1988	1 Nov 1990	1 Sep 1991
SUNDSVALL	K 24	Karlskronavarvet	Mar 1989	29 Nov 1991	7 June 1993

Displacement, tons: 300 standard; 399 full load
Dimensions, feet (metres): 187 × 26.2 × 6.6 *(57 × 8 × 2)*
Main machinery: 3 MTU 16V 396 TB94 diesels; 8700 hp(m)
(6.4 MW) sustained; KaMeWa 80562-6 waterjets
Speed, knots: 32+
Complement: 36 (7 officers) plus 4 spare berths

Missiles: SSM: 8 Saab RBS 15 (4 twin) launchers ❶; inertial guidance; active radar homing to 70 km *(37.8 nm)* at 0.8 Mach;
warhead 150 kg.
Guns: 1 Bofors 57 mm/70 Mk 2 ❷; 75° elevation; 220 rounds/
minute to 17 km *(9.3 nm)*; weight of shell 2.4 kg.
1 Bofors 40 mm/70 (or Bofors Sea Trinity) ❸; 85° elevation;
330 rounds/minute to 12.5 km *(6.8 nm)*; weight of shell
0.96 kg.
Torpedoes: 4—15.75 in *(400 mm)* tubes ❹. Swedish Ordnance
Type 43/45 or Whitehead Type 422; anti-submarine.
A/S mortars: 4 Saab Elma LLS-920 9-tubed launchers ❺; range
300 m; warhead 4.2 kg shaped charge. IR/chaff decoys.
Depth charges: On mine rails.
Mines: Minelaying capability.
Countermeasures: Decoys: 4 Philips Philax fixed launchers; IR
flares and chaff grenades. A/S mortars have also been
adapted to fire IR/chaff decoys.
ESM: Argo Systems AR 700; radar intercept.
ECM: THORN EMI Sceptre XL; jammer.
Combat data systems: CelsiusTech 9LV Mk 3.
Fire control: Two Bofors Electronics 9LV 200 Mk 3 Sea Viking
optronic directors ❼. Bofors Electronics 9LV 450 GFCS. RC1-
400 MFCS. 9AU-300 ASW control system with AQS
928G/SM sonobuoy processor. Bofors 9EW 400 EW control.
Radars: Air/surface search: Ericsson Sea Giraffe 150 HC ❻; G/H
band.
Navigation: Terma PN 612; I-band.
Fire control: Two Bofors Electronics 9GR 400 ❼; I/J band.
Sonars: Thomson Sintra TSM 2643 Salmon ❽; VDS; active
search; medium frequency.
Simrad SA 950; hull-mounted; active attack.

Programmes: Ordered 1 December 1985 as replacements for
Spica I class.
Structure: Efforts have been made to reduce radar and IR signatures. A Bofors Sea Trinity gun has replaced the 40 mm/70 in
one of the class for trials.
Operational: Trials have been done with Atlas Elektronik towed
array.

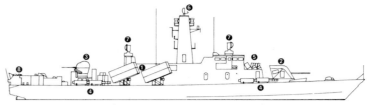

GÖTEBORG

(Scale 1 : 600), Ian Sturton

KALMAR

8/1993, Per Kornefeldt

LAND-BASED MARITIME AIRCRAFT

Numbers/Type: 10 Agusta-Bell 206A JetRanger (HKP-6B).
Operational speed: 115 kts *(213 km/h)*.
Service ceiling: 13 500 ft *(4115 m)*.
Range: 368 nm *(682 km)*.
Role/Weapon systems: Primarily operated in a liaison and training role and for secondary ASW,
SAR and surface search helicopter operations. Weapons: ASW; 4 × Type 11 or depth charges.

Numbers/Type: 7 Boeing 107-II-5/7 Kawasaki KV 107-II. All to HKP-4C/D standard.
Operational speed: 137 kts *(254 km/h)*.
Service ceiling: 8500 ft *(2590 m)*.
Range: 300 nm *(555 km)*.
Role/Weapon systems: ASW and surface search helicopter; updated with new avionics, TM2D
engines, new radar, new sonar, data link for SSM targeting, MARIL 920 combat information system, life prolonged until 2000. Sensors: BEAB Omera radar, Thomson Sintra DUAV-4 dipping
sonar. Weapons: ASW; 6 × Type 11/51 depth charges and/or 2 × Type 42 or Type 43/45
torpedoes.

Numbers/Type: 24 Saab-Scania SH 37 Viggen.
Operational speed: 726 kts *(1345 km/h)*.
Service ceiling: 50 000 ft *(15 240 m)*.
Range: 1080 nm *(1975 km)*.
Role/Weapon systems: Operated by Air Force; to cover the Baltic approaches; peacetime EEZ sur-
veillance assisted by air data camera. Sensors: Ericsson UAP-1023 radar, 1 × recce pod, 1 × cam-
era pod, 1 × ECM pod, 1 × chaff/jammer pod. Weapons: Attack; 2 × Saab RB04 bombs + 2 ×
Saab RB05 ASV missiles. MR; 2 × RB24 air-to-air missiles. Total warload is 6 tons.

Numbers/Type: 1 CASA C-212 Aviocar.
Operational speed: 190 kts *(353 km/h)*.
Service ceiling: 24 000 ft *(7315 m)*.
Range: 1650 nm *(3055 km)*.
Role/Weapon systems: For ASW and surface surveillance. Sensors: Omera radar, Sonobuoys/
Lofar, CDC sonobuoy processor, FLIR, data link. Coastguard variants also in service. Weapons:
ASW; depth charges.

PATROL FORCES

0 + (4) YSM CLASS (FAST ATTACK CRAFT—SES)

Displacement, tons: 350 full load
Dimensions, feet (metres): 180.4 × 45.9 × 9.5 *(55 × 14 × 2.9)*
Main machinery: 2 diesels (drive); 2 diesels (lift); 2 waterjets
Speed, knots: 40+
Missiles: SSM: RBS 15.
SAM: CIWS
Guns: 1 Bofors 57 mm/70 SAK Mk 3.

Comment: The design is based on *Smyge* and it is hoped to start construction within two years. A
smaller YSB type is intended for the MCM role.

1 JÄGAREN CLASS (COASTAL PATROL CRAFT)

Name	No	Builders	Commissioned
JÄGAREN	V 150	Bergens MV, Norway	24 Nov 1972

Displacement, tons: 120 standard; 150 full load
Dimensions, feet (metres): 120 × 20.7 × 5.6 *(36.6 × 6.3 × 1.7)*
Main machinery: 2 Cummins KTA50-M; 2500 hp *(1.87 MW)* sustained; 2 shafts
Speed, knots: 20
Complement: 15
Guns: 1 Bofors 40 mm/70.
Mines: Minelaying capability.
Radars: Surface search.

Comment: The prototype for the Hugin class but was not fitted with missiles, and up to 1988 was
used for training and testing. In 1988 new engines were installed and the craft recommissioned
for patrol duties. Has no torpedo tubes, fire-control radar, ESM or sonar.

YSM (artist's impression)

1993, Royal Swedish Navy

JÄGAREN

8/1991, Maritime Photographic

16 HUGIN CLASS (FAST ATTACK CRAFT—MISSILE)

Name	No	Builders	Commissioned
HUGIN	P 151	Bergens MV, Norway	3 July 1978
MUNIN	P 152	Bergens MV, Norway	3 July 1978
MAGNE	P 153	Bergens MV, Norway	12 Oct 1978
MODE	P 154	Westamarin, Norway	12 Jan 1979
VALE	P 155	Westamarin, Norway	26 Apr 1979
VIDAR	P 156	Westamarin, Norway	10 Aug 1979
MJÖLNER	P 157	Westamarin, Norway	25 Oct 1979
MYSING	P 158	Westamarin, Norway	14 Feb 1980
KAPAREN	P 159	Bergens MV, Norway	7 Aug 1980
VÄKTAREN	P 160	Bergens MV, Norway	19 Sep 1980
SNAPPHANEN	P 161	Bergens MV, Norway	14 Jan 1980
SPEJAREN	P 162	Bergens MV, Norway	21 Mar 1980
STYRBJÖRN	P 163	Bergens MV, Norway	15 June 1980
STARKODDER	P 164	Bergens MV, Norway	24 Aug 1981
TORDÖN	P 165	Bergens MV, Norway	26 Oct 1981
TIRFING	P 166	Bergens MV, Norway	23 Jan 1982

Displacement, tons: 120 standard; 150 or 170 full load (after modernisation)
Dimensions, feet (metres): 120 × 20.7 × 5.6 *(36.6 × 6.3 × 1.7)*
Main machinery: 2 MTU 16V 396 TB94 (after modernisation) or 20V 672 TY90 diesels; 5800 hp(m) *(4.26 MW)* sustained; 2 shafts; 2 hydraulic motors for slow speed propulsion (after modernisation)
Speed, knots: 36
Complement: 22 (3 officers)

Missiles: SSM: 6 Kongsberg Penguin Mk 2; IR homing to 27 km *(14.6 nm)* at 0.8 Mach; warhead 120 kg.
Guns: 1 Bofors 57 mm/70 Mk 1; 75° elevation; 200 rounds/minute to 17 km *(9.3 nm)*; weight of shell 2.4 kg. 57 mm illuminant launchers on either side of mounting.
A/S mortars: 4 Saab Elma 9-tubed launchers; range 300 m; warhead 4.2 kg shaped charge.
Depth charges: 2 racks.
Mines: 24. Mine-rails extend from after end of bridge superstructure with an extension over the stern. Use of these would mean the removal of any missiles.
Countermeasures: Decoys: The A/S mortars can fire IR/chaff decoys.
ESM: Saab Scania EWS 905; radar intercept.
Radars: Surface search: Skanter 16 in Mk 009; I band.
Fire control: Philips 9LV 200 Mk 2; J band.
Sonars: Simrad SA 950 (after modernisation) or SQ 3D/SF; hull-mounted; active attack; high frequency.
Simrad ST 570 VDS (after modernisation); active; high frequency.

Programmes: In the early 1970s it was decided to build fast attack craft similar to the Norwegian Hauk class. Prototype *Jägaren* underwent extensive trials and, on 15 May 1975, an order for a further 16 was placed.
Modernisation: Half life modernisation is being done to eight of the class (P 159-166) between 1991 and 1994. The update includes new engines with improved loiter capability and new sonars including the Simrad Toadfish VDS.
Operational: The VDS can be operated down to 100 m as a dipping sonar, or towed at speeds up to 16 kts. P 153, 155, 157 and 158 are scheduled to pay off in July 1994.

12 NORRKÖPING CLASS (FAST ATTACK CRAFT—MISSILE)

Name	No	Builders	Commissioned
NORRKÖPING	R 131	Karlskronavarvet	11 May 1973
NYNÄSHAMN	R 132	Karlskronavarvet	28 Sep 1973
NORRTÄLJE	R 133	Karlskronavarvet	1 Feb 1974
VARBERG	R 134	Karlskronavarvet	14 June 1974
VÄSTERÅS	R 135	Karlskronavarvet	25 Oct 1974
VÄSTERVIK	R 136	Karlskronavarvet	15 Jan 1975
UMEÅ	R 137	Karlskronavarvet	7 May 1975
PITEÅ	R 138	Karlskronavarvet	12 Sep 1975
LULEÅ	R 139	Karlskronavarvet	28 Nov 1975
HALMSTAD	R 140	Karlskronavarvet	9 Apr 1976
STRÖMSTAD	R 141	Karlskronavarvet	24 Sep 1976
YSTAD	R 142	Karlskronavarvet	10 Jan 1976

Displacement, tons: 190 standard; 230 full load
Dimensions, feet (metres): 143 × 23.3 × 7.4 *(43.6 × 7.1 × 2.4)*
Main machinery: 3 RR Proteus gas-turbines; 12 750 hp *(9.5 MW)* sustained; 3 shafts
Speed, knots: 40.5
Complement: 27 (7 officers)

Missiles: SSM: 8 Saab RBS 15; active radar homing to 70 km *(37.8 nm)* at 0.8 Mach; warhead 150 kg.
Guns: 1 Bofors 57 mm/70 Mk 1; 75° elevation; 200 rounds/minute to 17 km *(9.3 nm)*; weight of shell 2.4 kg. 8 launchers for 57 mm illuminants on side of mounting.
Torpedoes: 6—21 in *(533 mm)* tubes (2-6 can be fitted at the expense of missile armament); Swedish Ordnance Type 613; anti-surface; wire-guided passive homing to 15 km *(8.2 nm)* at 45 kts; warhead 240 kg.
Mines: Minelaying capability.
Countermeasures: Decoys: 2 Philips Philax fixed launchers; IR flares and chaff. A/S mortars can also fire chaff/IR decoys.
ESM: Argo Systems AR 700; radar intercept.
ECM: THORN EMI; jammer.
Combat data systems: MARIL 880 data link.
Radars: Air/surface search: Ericsson Sea Giraffe 50HC; G/H band.
Fire control: Philips 9LV 200 Mk 1; J band.

Modernisation: Programme included missile launchers, new fire-control equipment, modernised electronics and new 57 mm guns. A/S mortars removed. All completed by late 1984. Six of the craft are planned to get new engines, and some weapon systems upgrading including sonobuoy processors AQS 924/928, to keep them in service until 2010.
Structure: Similar to the original Spica class from which they were developed.
Operational: Six of the craft may be fitted with GEC Avionics AQS 924 or the more modern AQS 928 sonobuoy processing equipment.

NORRTÄLJE   *5/1993, Hartmut Ehlers*

MUNIN   *10/1992, van Ginderen Collection*

UMEÅ (with 2 SSM and 4 Torpedoes)   *4/1989, Antonio Moreno*

SNAPPHANEN (with VDS)   *4/1991, Hartmut Ehlers*

STYRBJÖRN   *2/1993, van Ginderen Collection*

VÄSTERVIK   *8/1993, Erik Laursen*

3 DALARÖ CLASS (COASTAL PATROL CRAFT)

Name	No	Builders	Commissioned
DALARÖ	V 09	Djupviksvarvet	21 Sep 1984
SANDHAMN	V 10	Djupviksvarvet	5 Dec 1984
ÖSTHAMMAR	V 11	Djupviksvarvet	1 Mar 1985

Displacement, tons: 50
Dimensions, feet (metres): 76.8 × 16.7 × 3.6 *(23.4 × 5.1 × 1.1)*
Main machinery: 2 MTU 8V 396 TB83 diesels; 2100 hp(m) *(1.54 MW)* sustained; 2 shafts
Speed, knots: 30
Complement: 7 (3 officers)
Guns: 1 Bofors 40 mm/70. 2—7.62 mm MGs.
Mines: Rails fitted.
Radars: Surface search: Terma 610; I band.

Comment: Ordered 28 February 1983 for anti-intruder patrols instead of conversion of further Skanör class. Categorised as part of the Mine Warfare forces. Some variations in the armament carried.

DALARÖ   *5/1993, A Sheldon Duplaix*

17 INSHORE PATROL CRAFT (COASTAL ARTILLERY)

TORSKÄR 61	ÖRSKÄR 66	HOJSKÄR 70	BREDSKÄR 74
VÄDERSKÄR 62	VITASKÄR 67	GETORSKÄR 71	SPRÄNGSKÄR 75
EKESKÄR 63	ALTARSKÄR 68	FLAGGSKÄR 72	HAMNSKÄR 76
SKIFTESKÄR 64	ÄGGSKÄR 69	HÄRADOSKÄR 73	HUVUDSKÄR 77
GRÅSKÄR 65			

Displacement, tons: 30 full load
Dimensions, feet (metres): 69.2 × 15 × 4.3 *(21.1 × 4.6 × 1.3)*
Main machinery: 3 diesels; 3 shafts
Speed, knots: 18 *(61-67)*; 22 *(68-77)*
Guns: 1 Oerlikon 20 mm.
Depth charges: Carried in all of the class.
Radars: Surface search: Decca RM 914; I band.

Comment: These are operated by the Coastal Artillery. The 60 series launched in 1960-61 and 70 series in 1966-67. Modernised in the 1980s with a tripod mast and radar mounted over the bridge. Now called Type 72.

HÄRADOSKÄR (older type)   *8/1990, Gilbert Gyssels*

EKESKÄR (after conversion)   *4/1993, van Ginderen Collection*

3 SKANÖR CLASS (COASTAL PATROL CRAFT)

Name	No	Builders	Recommissioned
ÖREGRUND	V 05 (ex-T 47)	Naval Dockyard, Stockholm	1 Feb 1983
SLITE	V 06 (ex-T 48)	Naval Dockyard, Stockholm	15 Apr 1983
LYSEKIL	V 08 (ex-T 52)	Naval Dockyard, Stockholm	13 June 1983

Displacement, tons: 25 standard
Dimensions, feet (metres): 75.5 × 19.4 × 3.9 *(23 × 5.9 × 1.2)*
Main machinery: 2 MTU 8V 396 TB83 diesels; 2100 hp(m) *(1.54 MW)* sustained; 2 shafts
Speed, knots: 25
Complement: 12
Guns: 1 Bofors 40 mm/70. 1—12 rail 57 mm illuminant launcher.
Mines: Up to 10 (or depth charges).
Radars: Surface search: Skanter 009; I band.

Comment: These craft were originally three of the eight of the T 42 class which first commissioned in 1957-59. Converted having their torpedo tubes removed and their petrol engines replaced by diesels. First two deleted in early 1989, next three in 1992.

LYSEKIL   *8/1989, Erik Laursen*

4 + 3 (5) TAPPER CLASS (COASTAL ARTILLERY)

TAPPER 81	DRISTIG 83	TRYGG 85	HURTIG 87
DJÄRV 82	HÄNDIG 84	MODIG 86	

Displacement, tons: 57 full load
Dimensions, feet (metres): 71.9 × 17.7 × 4.9 *(21.9 × 5.4 × 1.5)*
Main machinery: 2 MWM TBD234V16 diesels; 1812 hp(m) *(1.33 MW)* sustained; 2 shafts
Speed, knots: 25
Complement: 9
Guns: 2—12.7 mm MGs.
A/S mortars: 4 Elma grenade launchers.
Depth charges: 6 on mine rail.
Mines: 1 rail.
Radars: Surface search: 2 Racal Decca; I band.
Sonars: Simrad; hull-mounted; active search; high frequency.

Comment: Seven Type 80 ordered from Djupviksvarvet in early 1992, for delivery between February 1993 and December 1995. Five more to be ordered in 1994. Final total may be 18. A small ROV is carried.

TAPPER   *6/1993, Royal Swedish Navy*

3 SVK CLASS (INSHORE PATROL CRAFT)

SPJUTET SVK 2 (ex-TV 226)	PILEN SVK 3 (ex-TV 230)	BÅGEN SVK 4 (ex-TV 234)

Displacement, tons: 12
Dimensions, feet (metres): 45.9 × 11.1 × 3.3 *(14 × 3.4 × 1)*
Speed, knots: 10
Guns: 1 Oerlikon 20 mm (not always carried).

Comment: *Spjutet* and *Pilen* completed 1954-57. *Bågen* completed 1960 is slightly larger at 15.2 × 3.6 × 1.2 m. All belong to Sjövärnskåren (SVK) which is the Swedish Naval Reserve Association and are used for navigational training.

SVK (old number)   *1989, Royal Swedish Navy*

2 HANO CLASS (COASTAL PATROL CRAFT)

Name	No	Builders	Commissioned
TJURKÖ	V 53	Karlskrona	1953
STURKÖ	V 54	Karlskrona	1953

Displacement, tons: 280 standard
Dimensions, feet (metres): 137.8 × 23 × 9.9 *(42 × 7 × 3)*
Main machinery: 2 Nohab diesels; 910 hp(m) *(669 kW)*; 2 shafts
Speed, knots: 13
Complement: 25
Guns: 2 Bofors 40 mm/70 (not carried).

Comment: Former steel hulled minesweepers converted for patrol duties in 1979. Taken out of service in the late 1980s but restored and disarmed for use as utility craft.

TJURKÖ   *3/1993, van Ginderen Collection*

1 EXPERIMENTAL PATROL CRAFT (SES)

SMYGE

Displacement, tons: 140 full load
Dimensions, feet (metres): 99.7 oa; 88.6 wl × 37.4 × 6.2; 2.3 on cushion *(30.4; 27 × 11.4 × 1.9; 0.7)*
Main machinery: 2 MTU 16V 396 TB94 diesels (drive); 5080 hp(m) *(3.73 MW)* sustained; 2 KaMeWa waterjets
2 Scania DSI14 diesels (lift); 796 hp(m) *(585 kW)* sustained
Speed, knots: 40+
Complement: 14 (6 officers)
Missiles: SSM: 2 RBS 15 retractable mountings.
Guns: 1 Sea Trinity 40 mm CIWS; stealth cupola.
Torpedoes: Type 42; anti-submarine; wire-guided from covered stern tubes.
Mines: Rails or mine countermeasure equipment.
Radars: Air/surface search: Elevating mast.
Sonars: VDS or light towed array.

Comment: A surface effect experimental craft launched 14 March 1991 incorporating a high degree of stealth technology. GRP sandwich construction with Kevlar protection. Evaluation and trials in the period 1991-93 as a basis for the design of future surface warfare and mine countermeasures vessels.

SMYGE   *8/1993, Erik Laursen*

MINE WARFARE FORCES

Note: A transportable COOP system was ordered in 1991. The unit can be shifted from one ship to another and comprises a container, processing module and tactical display, an underwater positioning system, sonar, double Eagle ROV and mine disposal charge and a Type 432 torpedo. Optimised for shallow water surveillance and can be used in conjunction with other MCM systems. The primary role is the detection and destruction of mines.

1 CARLSKRONA CLASS (MINELAYER)

Name	No	Builders	Commissioned
CARLSKRONA	M 04	Karlskronavarvet	11 Jan 1982

Displacement, tons: 3300 standard; 3550 full load
Dimensions, feet (metres): 346.7 × 49.9 × 13.1 *(105.7 × 15.2 × 4)*
Main machinery: 4 Nohab F212 D825 diesels; 10 560 hp(m) *(7.76 MW)*; 2 shafts; cp props
Speed, knots: 20
Complement: 50 plus 136 trainees. Requires 118 as operational minelayer
Guns: 2 Bofors 57 mm/70. 2 Bofors 40 mm/70.
Mines: Can lay 105.
Countermeasures: 2 Philips Philax chaff/IR launchers.
Radars: Air/surface search: Ericsson Sea Giraffe 50HC; G/H band.
Surface search: Raytheon; E/F band.
Fire control: Two Philips 9LV 200 Mk 2; I/J band.
Sonars: Simrad SQ 3D/SF; hull-mounted; active search; high frequency.
Helicopters: Platform only.

Comment: Ordered 25 November 1977, laid down in sections late 1979 and launched 28 June 1980 at the same time as Karlskrona celebrated its tercentenary. Midshipmen's Training Ship as well as a minelayer; also a 'padded' target for exercise torpedoes. Name is an older form of Karlskrona.

CARLSKRONA   *4/1993, S Poynton, RAN*

2 ÄLVSBORG CLASS (MINELAYERS)

Name	No	Builders	Commissioned
ÄLVSBORG	M 02	Karlskronavarvet	6 Apr 1971
VISBORG	M 03	Karlskronavarvet	6 Feb 1976

Displacement, tons: 2500 standard; 2660 full load *(Älvsborg)* 2400 standard; 2650 full load *(Visborg)*
Dimensions, feet (metres): 303.1 × 48.2 × 13.2 *(92.4 × 14.7 × 4)*
Main machinery: 2 Nohab-Polar diesels; 4200 hp(m) *(3.1 MW)*; 1 shaft
Speed, knots: 16
Complement: 95 (accommodation for 205 submariners in *Älvsborg*—158 Admiral's staff in *Visborg*)
Guns: 3 Bofors 40 mm/70.
Mines: 300.
Countermeasures: 2 Philips Philax chaff/IR launchers.
Radars: Surface search: Raytheon; E/F band.
Fire control: Philips 9LV 200 Mk 2; I/J band.
Helicopters: Platform only.

Comment: *Älvsborg* was ordered in 1968 and launched on 11 November 1969; acts as a submarine depot ship. *Visborg*, laid down on 16 October 1973 and launched 22 January 1975 also acts as Command Ship for C-in-C Coastal Fleet. A Bofors Sea Trinity CIWS was to replace one of the 40 mm/70 guns for trials in *Älvsborg* but this was cancelled in 1992.

VISBORG   *8/1992, Maritime Photographic*

ALVSBORG   *1/1993, van Ginderen Collection*

1 MCM SUPPORT SHIP

Name	No	Builders	Commissioned
UTÖ (ex-*Smit Manila*, ex-*Seaford* ex-*Seaforth Challenger*)	A 261	Drypool, Selby	1974

Displacement, tons: 1100 full load
Dimensions, feet (metres): 182.1 × 40.4 × 14.1 *(55.5 × 12.3 × 4.3)*
Main machinery: 1 diesel; 5000 hp(m) *(3.68 MW)*; 1 shaft
Speed, knots: 12
Complement: 32
Guns: 2 Oerlikon 20 mm.

Comment: Ex-supply ship converted by Pan United Ltd, Singapore and recommissioned in April 1989 replacing *Thule*.

UTÖ   *6/1989, van Ginderen Collection*

1 FURUSUND CLASS (COASTAL MINELAYER)

FURUSUND MUL 20

Displacement, tons: 155 standard; 216 full load
Dimensions, feet (metres): 106.9 × 26.9 × 7.5 *(32.6 × 8.2 × 2.3)*
Main machinery: Diesel-electric; 2 Scania GAS 1 diesel generators; 2 motors; 416 hp(m) *(306 kW)*; 2 shafts
Speed, knots: 11.5
Complement: 24
Guns: 1 Oerlikon 20 mm. 2—7.62 mm MGs.
Mines: 22 tons.
Radars: Navigation: Racal Decca 1226; I band.

Comment: Built for Coastal Artillery by ASI Verken, Åmål. *Furusund* launched 16 December 1982, completed 10 October 1983. Plans for three more abandoned.

FURUSUND   1984, Royal Swedish Navy

7 ARKÖSUND CLASS (COASTAL MINELAYERS)

ARKÖSUND MUL 12   **GRUNDSUND** MUL 15   **ÖRESUND** MUL 18
KALMARSUND MUL 13   **SKRAMSÖSUND** MUL 17   **BARÖSUND** MUL 19
ALNÖSUND MUL 14

Displacement, tons: 200 standard; 245 full load
Dimensions, feet (metres): 102.3 × 24.3 × 10.2 *(31.2 × 7.4 × 3.1)*
Main machinery: Diesel-electric; 2 Nohab/Scania diesel generators; 2 motors; 460 hp(m) *(338 kW)*; 2 shafts
Speed, knots: 10.5
Guns: 1 Bofors 40 mm/60; on platform aft of the funnel.
Mines: 26 tons.
Radars: Navigation: Racal Decca 1226; I band.

Comment: All completed by 1954-1957. Operated by Coastal Artillery. One scrapped in 1992 and *Skramsösund* has been reclassified as an auxiliary.

GRUNDSUND   4/1993, van Ginderen Collection

1 COASTAL MINELAYER

KALVSUND MUL 11

Displacement, tons: 200 full load
Dimensions, feet (metres): 98.4 × 23.6 × 11.8 *(30 × 7.2 × 3.6)*
Main machinery: 2 MAN Atlas diesels; 300 hp(m) *(221 kW)*; 2 shafts
Speed, knots: 10
Guns: 2 Oerlikon 20 mm.
Mines: 21 tons.

Comment: Commissioned in 1947. Operated by Coastal Artillery. Reclassified as an auxiliary in 1993.

KALVSUND   4/1993, van Ginderen Collection

6 SMALL MINELAYERS

1879-1884

Displacement, tons: 2.5
Speed, knots: 20

Comment: Ordered from Farösund on 27 November 1982. Completed July 1983-January 1984 for Coastal Artillery. Waterjet propulsion.

16 SMALL MINELAYERS

M 501-516

Displacement, tons: 15
Dimensions, feet (metres): 47.9 × 13.8 × 2.9 *(14.6 × 4.2 × 0.9)*
Main machinery: 2 diesels; 2 shafts
Speed, knots: 14
Complement: 7
Mines: 12.

Comment: Ordered in 1969. Mines are laid from single traps on either beam. Operated by Coastal Artillery.

M 513 (with camouflage net)   4/1993, van Ginderen Collection

7 LANDSORT CLASS (MINEHUNTERS)

Name	No	Builders	Commissioned
LANDSORT	M 71	Karlskronavarvet	19 Apr 1984
ARHOLMA	M 72	Karlskronavarvet	23 Nov 1984
KOSTER	M 73	Karlskronavarvet	30 May 1986
KULLEN	M 74	Karlskronavarvet	28 Nov 1986
VINGA	M 75	Karlskronavarvet	27 Nov 1987
VEN	M 76	Karlskronavarvet	12 Dec 1988
ULVÖN	M 77	Karlskronavarvet	9 Oct 1992

Displacement, tons: 270 standard; 360 full load
Dimensions, feet (metres): 155.8 × 31.5 × 7.3 *(47.5 × 9.6 × 2.2)*
Main machinery: 4 Saab-Scania DSI14 diesels; 1592 hp(m) *(1.17 MW)* sustained; coupled in pairs to 2 Voith Schneider props
Speed, knots: 15. **Range, miles:** 2000 at 12 kts
Complement: 29 (12 officers) plus 4 spare berths

Guns: 1 Bofors 40 mm/70 Mod 48; 85° elevation; 300 rounds/minute to 12.5 km *(6.8 nm)*; weight of shell 0.96 kg. Bofors Sea Trinity CIWS trial carried out in *Vinga* (fitted in place of 40 mm/70).
2—7.62 mm MGs.
A/S mortars: 4 Saab Elma 9-tubed launchers; range 300 m; warhead 4.2 kg shaped charge.
Countermeasures: Decoys: 2 Philips Philax fixed launchers can be carried with 4 magazines each holding 36 grenades; IR/chaff.
MCM: This class is fitted for mechanical sweeps for moored mines as well as magnetic and acoustic sweeps. In addition it is possible to operate 2—15 ton unmanned catamaran magnetic and acoustic sweepers (59 × 20 ft *(18 × 6 m)*); these have SAM numbers. Fitted with 2 Sutec Sea Owl or Double Eagle remote-controlled units with 600 m tether and capable of 350 m depth.
Fire control: Philips 9LV 100 optronic director. Philips 9 MJ 400 minehunting system.
Radars: Navigation: Thomson-CSF Terma; I band.
Sonars: Thomson-CSF TSM-2022; Racal Decca 'Mains' control system; hull-mounted; minehunting; high frequency.

Programmes: The first two of this class ordered in early 1981. Second four in 1984 and the seventh in 1989. *Landsort* launched 2 November 1982, *Arholma* 2 August 1984, *Koster* 16 January 1986, *Kullen* 15 August 1986, *Vinga* 14 August 1987, *Ven* 10 August 1988, and *Ulvön* in 1992. The projected eighth of the class was cancelled.
Structure: The GRP mould for the hull has also been used for the Coast Guard Kbv 171 class.
Operational: The integrated navigation and action data automation system developed by Philips and Racal Decca.
Sales: SAM 3 and SAM 5 sold to the United States Navy in February 1991 and replaced in 1992/93. Four Landsort building for Singapore.

LANDSORT   8/1993, Erik Laursen

SAM 04   8/1993, Per Kornefeldt

3 ARKÖ CLASS (MINESWEEPERS—COASTAL)

Name	No	Builders	Commissioned
ARKÖ	M 57	Karlskronavarvet	1958
NÄMDÖ	M 67	Karlskronavarvet	1964
BLIDÖ	M 68	Hälsingborg	1964

Displacement, tons: 285 standard; 300 full load
Dimensions, feet (metres): 145.6 × 24.6 × 9.9 *(44.4 × 7.5 × 3)*
Main machinery: 2 MTU MB 12V 493 TZ60 diesels; 1360 hp(m) *(1 MW)* sustained; 2 shafts
Speed, knots: 14
Complement: 25
Guns: 1 Bofors 40 mm/70 Mod 48.

Comment: Of wooden construction. There is a small difference in the deck-line between *Arkö* and the remainder. The RBS 70 missiles have been removed.

NÄMDÖ   *8/1990, Gilbert Gyssels*

0 + 4 YSB CLASS (MINESWEEPERS—INSHORE)

Displacement, tons: 175 full load
Dimensions, feet (metres): 118.1 × 19.7 × 7.2 *(36 × 6 × 2.2)*
Main machinery: 2 diesels; 2 shafts
Speed, knots: 12

Comment: Contract awarded to KKV and Erisoft AB on 11 February 1994. To be built by Karlskronavarvet with an Ericsson tactical data system. To be fitted with mechanical, magnetic and acoustic sweeps for minesweeping and side scan and mine avoidance sonars. A ROV with Tritech SE 500 mine classification sonar will also provide a limited minehunting capability. These ships are also to be used for inshore surveillance patrols.

3 GILLÖGA CLASS (MINESWEEPERS—INSHORE)

GILLÖGA M 47	RÖDLÖGA M 48	SVARTLÖGA M 49

Displacement, tons: 110 standard; 135 full load
Dimensions, feet (metres): 72.2 × 21.3 × 11.5 *(22 × 6.5 × 3.5)*
Main machinery: 1 diesel; 380 hp(m) *(279 kW)*; 1 shaft
Speed, knots: 9
Guns: 1 Oerlikon 20 mm.

Comment: Built in 1964. Trawler type.

SVARTLÖGA   *9/1985, Gilbert Gyssels*

4 HISINGEN CLASS (MINESWEEPERS—INSHORE)

HISINGEN M 43	BLACKAN M 44
DÄMMAN M 45	GALTEN M 46

Displacement, tons: 130 standard; 150 full load
Dimensions, feet (metres): 78.7 × 21.3 × 11.5 *(24 × 6.5 × 3.5)*
Main machinery: 1 diesel; 380 hp(m) *(279 kW)*; 1 shaft
Speed, knots: 9
Guns: 1 Oerlikon 20 mm.

Comment: Built in 1960. Trawler type. Now used as diver support ships for mine clearance.

HISINGEN   *7/1993, Erik Laursen*

3 GÅSSTEN CLASS (MINESWEEPERS—INSHORE)

Name	No	Builders	Commissioned
GÅSSTEN	M 31	Knippla Skeppsvarv	16 Nov 1973
NORSTEN	M 32	Hellevikstrands Skeppsvarv	12 Oct 1973
VIKSTEN	M 33	Karlskronavarvet	20 June 1974

Displacement, tons: 120 standard; 135 full load
Dimensions, feet (metres): 78.7 × 21.3 × 11.5 *(24 × 6.5 × 3.5)*
Main machinery: 1 diesel; 460 hp(m) *(338 kW)*; 1 shaft
Speed, knots: 11
Guns: 1 Oerlikon 20 mm.

Comment: Ordered 1972. *Viksten* built of GRP, as a forerunner to new minehunters building at Karlskrona. Others have wooden hulls. These are repeat Hisingen class.

VIKSTEN   *8/1993, van Ginderen Collection*

5 M 15 CLASS (MINESWEEPERS—INSHORE)

M 20	M 21	M 22	M 24	M 25

Displacement, tons: 70 standard
Dimensions, feet (metres): 90.9 × 16.5 × 4.6 *(27.7 × 5 × 1.4)*
Main machinery: 2 diesels; 320 hp(m) *(235 kW)* sustained; 2 shafts
Speed, knots: 12
Complement: 10

Comment: All launched in 1941 and now used as platforms for mine clearance divers. M 20 of this class was re-rated as tender and renamed *Skuld*, but was converted back again in 1993. All five were modernised in 1992/93 and are also used for navigation training. Four others deleted in 1989.

M 15 class   *8/1985, Gunnar Olsen*

4 EJDERN CLASS (SONOBUOY CRAFT)

EJDERN B 01	SVÄRTEN B 03
KRICKAN B 02	VIGGEN B 04

Displacement, tons: 36 full load
Dimensions, feet (metres): 65.6 × 15.7 × 4.3 *(20 × 4.8 × 1.3)*
Main machinery: 2 Volvo Penta TAMD122 diesels; 366 hp(m) *(269 kW)* sustained; 2 shafts
Speed, knots: 15
Complement: 9
Guns: 1—12.7 mm MG.

Comment: Built by Djupviksvarvet and completed in 1991. GRP hulls. Classified as mine warfare vessels. Used for laying and monitoring long sonar arrays.

1 MINE TRANSPORT

MINÖREN A 237

Displacement, tons: 170 full load
Dimensions, feet (metres): 97 × 20.3 × 7.2 *(31.8 × 6.2 × 2.2)*
Main machinery: 2 diesels; 240 hp(m) *(176 kW)*; 2 shafts
Speed, knots: 9
Mines: Have minelaying capability.

Comment: Built in 1940. Mahogany hull. Second of class sold in 1993.

FÄLLAREN   *1987, Royal Swedish Navy*

AMPHIBIOUS FORCES

3 LCMs

Name	No	Builders	Commissioned
BORE	—	Åsigeverken	1967
GRIM	—	Åsigeverken	1961
HEIMDAL	—	Åsigeverken	1967

Displacement, tons: 340 full load
Dimensions, feet (metres): 124 × 28.2 × 8.5 *(37.8 × 8.6 × 2.6)*
Main machinery: 2 diesels; 800 hp(m) *(588 kW)*; 2 shafts
Speed, knots: 12
Military lift: 325 troops
Guns: 2 Oerlikon 20 mm.

Comment: Launched in 1961 *(Grim)* and other two in 1966. Operated by Coastal Artillery and used to transport guns.

BORE   *5/1990, Hartmut Ehlers*

15 LCAs

Displacement, tons: 6 full load
Dimensions, feet (metres): 30.8 × 10.5 × 1.6 *(9.4 × 3.2 × 0.5)*
Speed, knots: 20-25

Comment: Built between 1965 and 1973. Operated by Coastal Artillery. Being replaced by Combatboats.

LCA   *8/1993, Erik Laursen*

77 + 30 COMBATBOAT 90H RAIDING CRAFT
(COASTAL ARTILLERY)

801-877

Displacement, tons: 19 full load
Dimensions, feet (metres): 52.2 × 12.5 × 2.6 *(15.9 × 3.8 × 0.8)*
Main machinery: 2 SAAB Scania DSI14 diesels; 900 hp(m) *(664 kW) (801)*; 1104 hp(m) *(812 kW)* (remainder); 2 Alumina waterjets
Speed, knots: 35
Complement: 3
Military lift: 20 troops plus equipment or 2.8 tons
Missiles: SSM: Rockwell RBS 17 Hellfire; semi-active laser guidance to 5 km *(3 nm)* at 1.0 Mach; warhead 8 kg.
Guns: 3—12.7 mm MGs.
Mines: 4 (or 6 depth charges).
Radars: Navigation: Racal Decca; RD 360 or Furuno 8050; I band.

Comment: The first two are prototypes ordered in January 1988 and built at Dockstavarvet in 1989. 12 more built in 1991/92. 63 more ordered from Dockstavarvet and Gotlands Varv in mid-January 1992, with an option for 30 more which are to be built. The building period for the ordered boats will take up to 1995. This craft has a large hatch forward to aid disembarkation. *802* has a 26° deadrise, *801* and the remainder have 20°. All carry four six-man inflatable rafts. The Aden 30 mm gun fitted in one of the prototypes has been replaced by a standard fit of 3—12.7 mm MGs. The older LCAs are being paid off.

COMBATBOAT 803   *6/1992, Maritime Photographic*

1 LCM

SKAGUL

Displacement, tons: 275 standard
Dimensions, feet (metres): 116.4 × 27.9 × 9.5 *(35.5 × 8.5 × 2.9)*
Main machinery: 2 diesels; 2 shafts
Speed, knots: 11
Military lift: 100 tons

Comment: Built by Hammarbyverken in 1960. A second ship of this type was scrapped in 1991.

SKAGUL   *1981, Royal Swedish Navy*

17 LCMs

603, 604, 606-612, 651-658

Displacement, tons: 55 full load
Dimensions, feet (metres): 68.9 × 19.7 × 4.9 *(21 × 6 × 1.5)*
Main machinery: 2 diesels; 340 hp(m) *(250 kW)*; 2 shafts
Speed, knots: 10
Military lift: 30 tons

Comment: Operated by Navy and Coastal Artillery. Completed from 1980-88. Equipped with Schottel system. Classified as Trossbåt (support boat). Built by Djupviksvarvet.

LCM 610   *8/1993, Erik Laursen*

79 LCUs

210-288

Displacement, tons: 31 full load
Dimensions, feet (metres): 70.2 × 13.8 × 4.2 *(21.4 × 4.2 × 1.3)*
Main machinery: 3 diesels; 600 hp(m) *(441 kW)*; 3 shafts
Speed, knots: 18
Military lift: 40 tons; 40 troops
Guns: 3 to 8—6.5 mm MGs (277-279). 1 Oerlikon 20 mm (remainder).
Mines: Minelaying capability (280-288 only).

Comment: 210-276 completed 1960-76; 277-279 in 1976, 280-284 in 1976-77 and 285-288 in 1986-87.

LCU 244   *8/1993, Erik Laursen*

LCU 255   *4/1993, van Ginderen Collection*

ICEBREAKERS

1 ODEN CLASS

Name	No	Builders	Commissioned
ODEN	—	Gotaverken Arendal, Göteborg	29 Jan 1989

Displacement, tons: 12 900 full load
Dimensions, feet (metres): 352.4 × 102 × 27.9 *(107.4 × 31.1 × 8.5)*
Main machinery: 4 Sulzer ZAL40S8L diesels; 23 940 hp(m) *(17.6 MW)* sustained; 2 shafts; cp props
Speed, knots: 17. **Range, miles:** 30 000 at 13 kts
Complement: 32 plus 17 spare berths
Guns: 4 Bofors 40 mm/70 can be fitted.

Comment: Ordered in February 1987, laid down 19 October 1987, launched 25 August 1988. Can break 1.8 m thick ice at 3 kts. Towing winch aft with a pull of 150 tons. Helicopter platform 73.5 × 57.4 ft *(22.4 × 17.5 m)*. The main hull is only 25 m wide but the full width is at the bow. Also equipped as a minelayer. Second of class may be ordered in due course and is to be called *Thule*.

ODEN   *8/1992, Erik Laursen*

3 ATLE CLASS

Name	No	Builders	Commissioned
ATLE	—	Wärtsilä, Helsinki	21 Oct 1974
FREJ	—	Wärtsilä, Helsinki	30 Sep 1975
YMER	—	Wärtsilä, Helsinki	25 Oct 1977

Displacement, tons: 7900 standard; 9500 full load
Dimensions, feet (metres): 343.1 × 78.1 × 23.9 *(104.6 × 23.8 × 7.3)*
Main machinery: 5 Wärtsilä-Pielstick diesels; 22 000 hp(m) *(16.2 MW)*; 4 Strömberg motors; 22 000 hp(m) *(16.2 MW)*; 4 shafts (2 fwd, 2 aft)
Speed, knots: 19
Complement: 54 (16 officers)
Guns: 4 Bofors 40 mm/70 (not all always embarked).
Helicopters: 2 light.

Comment: Similar to Finnish Urho class.

ATLE and YMER   *8/1992, Maritime Photographic*

Name	No	Builders	Commissioned
TOR	—	Wärtsilä, Crichton-Vulcan Yard, Turku	31 Jan 1964

Displacement, tons: 5290 full load
Dimensions, feet (metres): 277.2 × 66.9 × 20.3 *(84.5 × 20.4 × 6.2)*
Main machinery: Diesel-electric; 4 Wärtsilä diesel generators; 4 motors; 12 000 hp(m) *(8.82 MW)*; 4 shafts (2 fwd, 2 aft)
Speed, knots: 18
Guns: 4 Bofors 40 mm/70 (not all always embarked).
Helicopters: 1 light.

Comment: Towed to Sandvikens Skeppsdocka, Helsingfors, for completion. A near sister to *Tarmo* built for Finland.

TOR   *1986, Royal Swedish Navy*

Name	No	Builders	Commissioned
NJORD	—	Wärtsilä, Helsinki	8 Oct 1969

Displacement, tons: 5150 standard; 5686 full load
Dimensions, feet (metres): 283.8 × 69.5 × 22.6 *(86.5 × 21.2 × 6.9)*
Main machinery: Diesel-electric; 4 Wärtsilä diesel generators; 4 motors; 12 000 hp(m) *(8.82 MW)*; 4 shafts (2 fwd, 2 aft)
Speed, knots: 18
Guns: 4 Bofors 40 mm/70 (not all always embarked).
Helicopters: 1 light.

Comment: Near sister ship of *Tor*.

NJORD   *6/1988, A Sheldon Duplaix*

Name	No	Builders	Commissioned
ALE	—	Wärtsilä, Helsinki	19 Dec 1973

Displacement, tons: 1550
Dimensions, feet (metres): 154.2 × 42.6 × 16.4 *(47 × 13 × 5)*
Main machinery: 2 diesels; 4750 hp(m) *(3.49 MW)*; 2 shafts
Speed, knots: 14
Complement: 32 (8 officers)
Guns: 1 Bofors 40 mm/70 (not embarked).

Comment: Built for operations on Lake Vänern. Also used for surveying.

ALE   *7/1990, A Sheldon Duplaix*

SURVEY SHIPS

Notes: (1) Owned by the National Maritime Administration but manned and operated by the Navy. (2) There is a research ship *Argos*. Civilian manned and owned by the National Board of Fisheries. A second civilian ship *Ocean Surveyor* belongs to the Geological Investigation.

JOHAN NORDENANKAR

Displacement, tons: 2000
Dimensions, feet (metres): 239.5 × 45.9 × 12.5 *(73 × 14 × 3.8)*
Main machinery: 2 diesels; 4000 hp(m) *(2.94 MW)*; 1 shaft
Speed, knots: 15
Complement: 64 (14 officers)
Helicopters: Platform only.

Comment: Ordered from Falkenbergsvarvet in 1977. Commissioned 1 July 1980. Carries eight survey boats.

JOHAN NORDENANKAR   *1993*

NILS STRÖMCRONA

Displacement, tons: 175 standard
Dimensions, feet (metres): 95.1 × 32.8 × 5.2 *(29 × 10 × 1.6)*
Main machinery: 4 Saab Scania DSI14 diesels; 1592 hp(m) *(1.17 MW)* sustained; 2 shafts; bow thrusters
Speed, knots: 12
Complement: 14 (5 officers)

Comment: Completed 28 June 1985. Of catamaran construction—each hull of 3.9 m made of aluminium.

NILS STRÖMCRONA   *9/1993, Erik Laursen*

JACOB HÄGG

Displacement, tons: 131 standard; 160 full load
Dimensions, feet (metres): 119.8 × 24.6 × 5.6 *(36.5 × 7.5 × 1.7)*
Main machinery: 4 Saab Scania DSI14 diesels; 1592 hp(m) *(1.17 MW)* sustained; 2 shafts
Speed, knots: 16
Complement: 13 (5 officers)

Comment: Laid down April 1982. Launched 12 March 1983. Completed 16 May 1983. Aluminium hull.

JACOB HÄGG   *1988, Royal Swedish Navy*

AUXILIARIES

1 DIVER SUPPORT SHIP

SKREDSVIK (ex-*Kbv 172*)   A 262 (ex-*M 70*)

Comment: Details as for Kbv 171 in *Coast Guard* section. Transferred from the Coast Guard in 1991 and used as a Diver Support ship for mine clearance operations after a refit from October 1992 to February 1993. Employed for Command and Control in war.

SKREDSVIK   *8/1993, van Ginderen Collection*

1 TRANSPORT

Name	No	Builders	Commissioned
SLEIPNER (ex-*Ardal*)	A 343	Bergen	1980

Displacement, tons: 1049 full load
Dimensions, feet (metres): 163.1 × 36.1 × 11.5 *(49.7 × 11 × 3.5)*
Main machinery: 1 Normo diesel; 1300 hp(m) *(956 kW)*; 1 shaft
Speed, knots: 12
Cargo capacity: 260 tons

Comment: Acquired in 1992 from a Norwegian Shipping Company.

SLEIPNER   *1993, Royal Swedish Navy*

1 REPAIR SHIP

Name	No	Builders	Commissioned
GALÖ (ex-*Herjolfur*)	A 263	Bergen	1976

Displacement, tons: 1200 full load
Dimensions, feet (metres): 196.9 × 39.4 × 14.4 *(60 × 12 × 4.4)*
Main machinery: 1 Wichman diesel; 2400 hp(m) *(1.76 MW)*; 1 shaft; 2 bow thrusters
Speed, knots: 12

Comment: Built as a ferry for Iceland. Acquired in 1993 as a repair and maintenance ship for patrol craft.

GALÖ   *1993, Royal Swedish Navy*

1 DIVER SUPPORT SHIP

ÄGIR (ex-*Bloom Syrveyor*)   A 212

Displacement, tons: 117 full load
Dimensions, feet (metres): 82 × 24.9 × 6.6 *(25 × 7.6 × 2)*
Main machinery: 2 GM diesels; 2 shafts
Speed, knots: 11

Comment: Built in Norway in 1984. Acquired in 1989.

ÄGIR   *1993, Royal Swedish Navy*

1 DIVER SUPPORT SHIP

NORDANÖ (ex-*Sjojungfrun*)   A 213

Displacement, tons: 148 full load
Dimensions, feet (metres): 80.1 × 24.9 × 8.9 *(24.4 × 7.6 × 2.7)*
Main machinery: 2 Volvo Penta TAMD diesels; 767 hp(m) *(564 kW)*; 2 shafts
Speed, knots: 10

Comment: Launched in 1983 and bought by the Navy in 1992.

NORDANÖ   1993, Royal Swedish Navy

1 SALVAGE SHIP

Name	No	Builders	Recommissioned
BELOS III (ex-*Energy Supporter*)	A 214	De Hoop, Netherlands	Nov 1992

Measurement, tons: 5096 grt
Dimensions, feet (metres): 344.2 × 59.1 × 16.7 *(104.9 × 18 × 5.1)*
Main machinery: 5 MAN 9ASL 25/30 diesel alternators; 8.15 MW; 2 motors; 5110 hp(m) *(3.76 MW)*; 2 shafts
Speed, knots: 14

Comment: Bought from Midland and Scottish Resources in mid-1992 and arrived in Sweden in November 1992. Replaced the previous ship of the same name which paid off in April 1993. Ice strengthened hull and fitted with a helicopter platform.

BELOS III (old name)   1992, Royal Swedish Navy

2 TORPEDO AND MISSILE RECOVERY VESSELS

Name	No	Builders	Commissioned
PELIKANEN	A 247	Djupviksvarvet	26 Sep 1963
PINGVINEN	A 248	Lundevarv-Ooverkstads	14 Mar 1975

Displacement, tons: 191 full load
Dimensions, feet (metres): 108.2 × 19 × 7.2 *(33 × 5.8 × 2.2)*
Main machinery: 2 MTU MB diesels; 1040 hp(m) *(764 kW)*; 2 shafts
Speed, knots: 14

Comment: Torpedo recovery and rocket trials vessels. A 247 has her bridge superstructure forward instead of aft and only has one mast which is abaft the bridge.

PINGVINEN   11/1991, van Ginderen Collection

1 TANKER

Name	No	Builders	Commissioned
ELDAREN (ex-*Brotank*)	A 229	Asiverken, Åmål	1959

Measurement, tons: 320 dwt
Dimensions, feet (metres): 122 × 21.3 × 9.5 *(37.2 × 6.5 × 2.9)*
Main machinery: 1 Volvo-Penta diesel; 300 hp(m) *(220 kW)*; 1 shaft
Speed, knots: 9
Cargo capacity: 300 tons oil fuel; 10 tons water

Comment: Civilian tanker purchased from A F Karlsson in 1980.

ELDAREN   8/1993, Erik Laursen

1 TORPEDO TRANSPORT

HÄGERN A 246

Displacement, tons: 50 standard; 58 full load
Dimensions, feet (metres): 95.1 × 16.4 × 5.9 *(29 × 5 × 1.8)*
Main machinery: 2 diesels; 480 hp(m) *(353 kW)*; 2 shafts
Speed, knots: 10

Comment: Launched in 1951.

HÄGERN   8/1990, Gilbert Gyssels

1 TENDER

URD (ex-*Capella*) A 241

Displacement, tons: 63 standard; 90 full load
Dimensions, feet (metres): 73.8 × 18.3 × 9.2 *(22.5 × 5.6 × 2.8)*
Main machinery: 1 diesel; 200 hp(m) *(147 kW)*; 1 shaft
Speed, knots: 8

Comment: Experimental vessel added to the official list in 1970. Launched in 1929.

2 + (23) COASTAL ARTILLERY SUPPORT VESSEL (TROSSBÄT)

Displacement, tons: 45 full load
Dimensions, feet (metres): 75.5 × 17.7 × 4.6 *(23 × 5.4 × 1.4)*
Main machinery: 2 Saab Scania DSI14 diesels; 796 hp(m) *(586 kW)* sustained; 2 Alumina waterjets
Speed, knots: 15
Complement: 3
Guns: 1 — 12.7 mm MG

Comment: Prototype Trossbät built at Holms Shipyard in 1991 and capable of carrying 15 tons of deck cargo and nine tons internal cargo or 17 troops plus mines. Aluminium hull with a bow ramp. Some ice capability. A second prototype delivered in late 1993 with a view to series production, starting at the end of 1994.

TROSSBÄT   5/1991, Per Kornefeldt

INTELLIGENCE VESSEL (AGI)

1 ELECTRONIC SURVEILLANCE SHIP (AGI)

Name	No	Builders	Commissioned
ORION	A 201	Karlskronavarvet	7 June 1984

Displacement, tons: 1400 full load
Dimensions, feet (metres): 201.1 × 32.8 × 9.8 *(61.3 × 10 × 3)*
Main machinery: 2 Hedemora V8A diesels; 1800 hp(m) *(1.32 MW)* sustained; 2 shafts; cp props
Speed, knots: 15
Complement: 35

Comment: Ordered 23 April 1982. Laid down 28 June 1982. Launched 30 November 1983.

ORION   5/1993, A Sheldon Duplaix

TRAINING SHIPS

2 SAIL TRAINING SHIPS

Name	No	Builders	Commissioned
GLADAN	S 01	Naval Dockyard, Stockholm	1947
FALKEN	S 02	Naval Dockyard, Stockholm	1947

Displacement, tons: 225 standard
Dimensions, feet (metres): 112.8 × 23.6 × 13.8 *(34.4 × 7.2 × 4.2)*
Main machinery: 1 diesel; 120 hp(m) *(88 kW)*; 1 shaft

Comment: Sail training ships. Two masted schooners. Sail area, 512 sq m. Both have had major overhauls in 1986-88 in which all technical systems have been replaced.

FALKEN   7/1990, Maritime Photographic

TUGS

Note: There is also a 35 ton harbour tug *Atlas* A 330. Two of the same class scrapped in 1993.

ACHILLES A 251   **AJAX** A 252

Displacement, tons: 450
Dimensions, feet (metres): 108.2 × 28.9 × 15.1 *(33 × 8.8 × 4.6)*
Main machinery: 1 diesel; 1650 hp(m) *(1.2 MW)*; 1 shaft
Speed, knots: 12

Comment: *Achilles* was launched in 1962 and *Ajax* in 1963. Both are icebreaking tugs.

ACHILLES   4/1991, Hartmut Ehlers

HERMES A 253   **HEROS** A 322

Displacement, tons: 185 standard; 215 full load
Dimensions, feet (metres): 80.5 × 22.6 × 13.1 *(24.5 × 6.9 × 4)*
Main machinery: 1 diesel; 600 hp(m) *(441 kW)*; 1 shaft
Speed, knots: 11

Comment: Launched 1953-57. Icebreaking tugs.

HERMES   8/1993, Per Kornefeldt

HERCULES A 323   **HERA** A 324

Displacement, tons: 127 full load
Dimensions, feet (metres): 65.3 × 21.3 × 12.5 *(19.9 × 6.5 × 3.8)*
Main machinery: 1 diesel; 615 hp(m) *(452 kW)*; 1 shaft
Speed, knots: 10.5

Comment: Launched 1969 and 1971. Icebreaking tugs.

HERA   8/1990, Gilbert Gyssels

A 701-705, 751-756

Displacement, tons: 42 full load
Dimensions, feet (metres): 50.9 × 16.4 × 8.9 *(15.5 × 5 × 2.7)*
Main machinery: 1 diesel; 1 shaft
Speed, knots: 9.5

Comment: Can carry 40 people. Icebreaking tugs. 701-703 used by Coastal Artillery.

A 702   *8/1993, Per Kornefeldt*

COAST GUARD

(KUSTBEVAKNING)

Establishment: Established in 1638, and for 350 years was a part of the Swedish Customs administration. From 1 July 1988 the Coast Guard became an independent civilian authority with a Board supervised by the Ministry of Defence. Organised in four regions with a central Headquarters.

Duties: Responsible for civilian surveillance of Swedish waters, fishery zone and continental shelf. Supervises and enforces fishing regulations, customs, dumping and pollution regulations, environmental protection and traffic regulations. Also concerned with prevention of drug running and forms part of the Swedish search and rescue organisation.

Headquarters Appointments

Director General:
  Leif H Sjöström
Chief of Operations:
  Staffan Kvarnström

Personnel: 1994: 585

Aircraft: One Cessna 337. Three CASA 212. Four B-105 helicopters.

Ships: Tv pennant numbers replaced by Kbv in 1988 but the Kbv is not displayed. Vessels are unarmed and have two distinctive yellow diagonal stripes on blue painted hulls. Superstructures are painted white.

Deletions

1991 *Kbv 172* (sold to Navy)
1992 *Kbv 257* (to Estonia)
1993 *Kbv 244, 249, 250, 256, 260* (all to Latvia), *Kbv 245* (to Lithuania), *Kbv 259, 246* (to Estonia)

1 KBV 181 CLASS

Kbv 181

Displacement, tons: 800 approx
Dimensions, feet (metres): 183.7 × 33.5 × 15.1 *(56 × 10.2 × 4.6)*
Main machinery: 2 diesels; 3755 hp(m) *(2.76 MW)*; 2 shafts
Speed, knots: 16
Complement: 12
Guns: 1 Oerlikon 20 mm (if required).
Radars: Navigation: 2 Racal Decca; I band.
Sonars: Simrad Subsea; active search; high frequency.

Comment: Ordered from Rauma Shipyards in August 1989 and built at Uusikaupunki. Commissioned 30 November 1990. Unarmed in peacetime. Equipped as a Command vessel for SAR and anti-pollution operations. All-steel construction similar to Finnish *Tursas*. Has replaced *Kbv 172*.

Kbv 181   *1992, Swedish Coast Guard*

1 KBV 171 CLASS

Kbv 171

Displacement, tons: 335 standard; 375 full load
Dimensions, feet (metres): 164 × 27.9 × 7.9 *(50 × 8.5 × 2.4)*
Main machinery: 2 Hedemora V16A diesels; 4500 hp(m) *(3.3 MW)*; 2 shafts
Speed, knots: 20. **Range, miles:** 3000 at 12 kts
Complement: 9
Gun: 1 Oerlikon 20 mm (if required).
Mines: Has mining capability.
Radars: Navigation: Two Racal Decca; I band.
Sonars: Simrad Subsea; active search; high frequency.
Helicopters: Platform for 1 light.

Comment: Ordered from Karlskronavarvet in 1978 and completed in 1980. GRP hull identical to Landsort class for the Navy. Sister ship *Kbv 172* replaced by *181* and sold to the Navy as a Diver support ship.

Kbv 171   *7/1993, Erik Laursen*

5 KBV 101 CLASS

Kbv 101-105

Displacement, tons: 50-53 full load
Dimensions, feet (metres): 87.6 × 16.4 × 3.6 *(26.7 × 5 × 1.1)*
Main machinery: 2 Cummins KTA38-M diesels; 2120 hp *(1.56 MW)*; 2 shafts
Speed, knots: 20. **Range, miles:** 1000 at 15 kts
Complement: 8 (accommodation for 16)
Sonars: Hull-mounted; active search; high frequency.

Comment: Built 1969-73 at Djupviksvarvet. Class A cutters. All-welded aluminium hull and upperworks. Equipped for salvage divers. Modernised with new diesels, a new bridge and new electronics completed in 1988.

Kbv 101   *1992, Royal Swedish Navy*

10 KBV 281 CLASS (CLASS B)

Kbv 281-290

Displacement, tons: 36-39 full load
Dimensions, feet (metres): 68.9 × 16.4 × 3 *(21 × 5 × 0.9)*
Main machinery: 2 Cummins KTA38-M diesels; 2120 hp *(1.56 MW)*; 2 shafts
Speed, knots: 27
Complement: 5

Comment: Built by Djupviksvarvet and delivered at one a year from 1979. Last one commissioned 6 December 1990. Aluminium hulls. Four more of a similar design may be ordered for the Navy.

Kbv 286   *7/1993, Erik Laursen*

8 KBV 271 CLASS (CLASS C)

Kbv 271-278

Displacement, tons: 18-20 full load
Dimensions, feet (metres): 63 × 13.1 × 4.3 *(19.2 × 4 × 1.3)*
Main machinery: 2 Volvo Penta TAMD120A diesels; 366 hp(m) *(269 kW)* sustained; 2 shafts
Speed, knots: 22
Complement: 5

Comment: Built 1974-77. Aluminium hulls.

Kbv 274   *1992, Royal Swedish Navy*

12 KBV 301 CLASS

Kbv 301-312

Displacement, tons: 35 full load
Dimensions, feet (metres): 65.6 × 15.1 × 3.6 *(20 × 4.6 × 1.1)*
Main machinery: 2 MTU 183 TE92 diesels; 2000 hp(m) *(1.47 MW)*; 2 KaMeWa waterjets
Speed, knots: 34
Complement: 3
Radars: Navigation: Furuno 7010; I band.

Comment: Building at Karlskronavarvet. First one delivered in May 1993. Up to 15 may be acquired in due course.

Kbv 301   *6/1993, Erik Laursen*

3 KBV 891 CLASS (HOVERCRAFT)

Kbv 891-893

Displacement, tons: 5 full load
Dimensions, feet (metres): 38.4 × 19.4 *(11.7 × 5.9)*
Main machinery: 1 Deutz BFB diesel; 350 hp(m) *(235 kW)*
Speed, knots: 35
Complement: 2
Radars: Navigation: Furuno 7010 D; I band.

Comment: Built by Griffon Hovercraft, Southampton and delivered in 1992/93. Aluminium hulls.

Kbv 891   *4/1992, Swedish Coast Guard*

COAST GUARD PATROL CRAFT (SMALL)

Number	Comment
Kbv 238, 240-243, 247-248 251-255, 258	17 ton aluminium hulls built 1961-72. Class D.
Kbv 314, 317-8, 321, 341 365-6, 368-9, 371-3 381-5, 389, 391-4	Fast patrol craft built 1962-88.
Kbv 602, 661-2, 644-5	'Gemini' type built 1971-88.
Kbv 801, 804-8	Ice craft built 1965-72.

Comment: Kbv 257, 259 and 246 transferred to Estonia in 1992/93. Kbv 244, 249, 250, 256, 260 to Latvia and 245 to Lithuania in 1993/94.

Class D (old number)   *2/1993, G Toremans*

POLLUTION CONTROL CRAFT

Number	Displacement (tons)	Comment
Kbv 041-4 045-51	70-76 235-340	Steel hulled. Class B sea trucks built 1972-1983 by Lunde SY. Complement includes salvage divers. 050 jumboised in 1993.
Kbv 02-03	190-300	Steel hulled support ships. Class A built 1971-76 by Lunde SY. Complement includes salvage divers. Kbv 02 is an older modernised vessel.
Kbv 04	450	Built by Lunde SY in 1978. Carries salvage divers
Kbv 010	400	15 kts. Built by Lunde SY 1985. Sea Truck.
Kbv 020-23	30 (60 Kbv 020)	Aluminium catamaran hulls. Class D.
Kbv 0701-0712	6	Skerry boats. Class E built since 1979.
Kbv 081-099	1	Work boats. GRP on aluminium hulls. Class K built 1971-79.

Kbv 010   *1992, Royal Swedish Navy*

Kbv 022   *6/1992, Per Kornefeldt*

Kbv 048   *3/1992, Per Kornefeldt*

SWITZERLAND

Diplomatic Representation

Defence Attaché in London:
    Major General G de Loës

General

The patrol boats are manned by the Army and split between Lakes Constance, Geneva and Maggiore; one company to each.

Mercantile Marine

Lloyd's Register of Shipping:
    20 vessels of 300 282 tons gross

ARMY

11 AQUARIUS CLASS (Patrouillenboot 80)

ANTARES, AQUARIUS, CASTOR, MARS, ORION, PERSEUS, POLLUX, SATURN, SIRIUS, URANUS, VENUS

Displacement, tons: 5.2
Dimensions, feet (metres): 35.1 × 10.8 × 3 *(10.7 × 3.3 × 0.9)*
Main machinery: 2 Volvo Penta AQ260A petrol engines; 520 hp(m) *(382 kW)* maximum; 2 shafts
Speed, knots: 32.5
Complement: 8
Guns: 2—12.7 mm MGs.
Radars: Surface search: I band.

Comment: Builders Müller AG, Spiez. GRP hulls, wooden superstructure. *Aquarius* commissioned in 1978, *Pollux* in 1984, the remainder in 1981.

MARS   *1991, Aldo Fraccaroli*

SYRIA

Headquarters' Appointments

Commander-in-Chief Navy:
    Vice Admiral Tayyara
Chief of Staff:
    Vice Admiral Kassiem Mahummed Baydoun
Director of Naval Operations:
    Commodore Muhammad Hamud

Personnel

(a) 1994: 4000 officers and men (2500 reserves)
(b) 18 months' national service

Bases

Latakia, Tartous, Al-Mina-al-Bayda, Baniyas

Mercantile Marine

Lloyd's Register of Shipping:
    140 vessels of 208 599 tons gross

SUBMARINES

3 ROMEO CLASS

Displacement, tons: 1475 surfaced; 1830 dived
Dimensions, feet (metres): 251.3 × 22 × 16.1 *(76.6 × 6.7 × 4.9)*
Main machinery: Diesel-electric; 2 Type 37-D diesels; 4000 hp(m) *(2.94 MW)*; 2 motors; 2700 hp(m) *(1.98 MW)*; 2 creep motors; 2 shafts
Speed, knots: 16 surfaced; 13 dived
Range, miles: 9000 at 9 kts surfaced
Complement: 54

Torpedoes: 8—21 in *(533 mm)* (6 bow, 2 stern) tubes. 14 SAET-60; passive homing to 15 km *(8.1 nm)* at 40 kts; warhead 400 kg.
Mines: 28 in lieu of torpedoes.
Countermeasures: ESM: Stop Light; radar warning.
Radars: Surface search: Snoop Tray; I band.
Sonars: Hercules/Feniks; hull-mounted; passive/active search and attack; medium/high frequency.

Programmes: First pair sailed for Tartous in November 1985 and transferred from USSR to Syrian flag after training period in July 1986. Third transferred December 1986. These are unlikely to be new construction and would therefore have been completed about 1961 and badly need replacements.

ROMEO   *1987*

Operational: One ex-Soviet Whiskey class submarine transferred from the Black Sea in November 1985 and acts as an alongside charging platform. All based at Tartous and assessed as non-operational in 1993.

FRIGATES

2 PETYA III CLASS

1/508 (ex-*12*)   **AL HIRASA** 2/508 (ex-*14*)

Displacement, tons: 950 standard; 1180 full load
Dimensions, feet (metres): 268.3 × 29.9 × 9.5 *(81.8 × 9.1 × 2.9)*
Main machinery: CODAG; 2 gas-turbines; 30 000 hp(m) *(22 MW)*; 1 Type 61V-3 diesel; 5400 hp(m) *(3.97 MW)* sustained (centre shaft); 3 shafts
Speed, knots: 32. **Range, miles:** 4870 at 10 kts; 450 at 29 kts
Complement: 98 (8 officers)

Guns: 4—3 in *(76 mm)*/60 (2 twin) ❶; 80° elevation; 90 rounds/minute to 15 km *(8 nm)*; weight of shell 6.8 kg.
Torpedoes: 3—21 in *(533 mm)* (triple) tubes ❷. SAET-40; active/passive homing to 10 km *(5.5 nm)* at 30 kts; warhead 100 kg.
A/S mortars: 4 RBU 2500 16-tubed trainable ❸; range 2500 m; warhead 21 kg.
Depth charges: 2 racks.
Mines: Can carry 22.
Radars: Surface search: Slim Net ❹; E/F band.
Navigation: Don 2; I band.
Fire control: Hawk Screech ❺; I band; range 27 km *(15 nm)*.
IFF: High Pole B. Two Square Head.
Sonars: Hull-mounted; active search and attack; high frequency.

Programmes: Transferred by the USSR in July 1975 and March 1975.
Operational: Based at Tartous.

AL HIRASA   *(Scale 1 : 900), Ian Sturton*

AL HIRASA   *7/1975, MoD*

LAND-BASED MARITIME AIRCRAFT

Numbers/Type: 18/2 Mil Mi-14P Haze A/C.
Operational speed: 124 kts *(230 km/h)*.
Service ceiling: 15 000 ft *(4570 m)*.
Range: 432 nm *(800 km)*.
Role/Weapon systems: Medium-range ASW helicopter. Sensors: Search radar, dipping sonar, MAD, sonobuoys. Weapons: ASW; internally stored torpedoes, depth mines and bombs.

Numbers/Type: 4 Kamov Ka-28 Helix.
Operational speed: 135 kts *(250 km/h)*.
Service ceiling: 19 685 ft *(6000 m)*.
Range: 432 nm *(800 km)*.
Role/Weapon systems: ASW helicopter. All delivered in February 1990. Sensors: Search radar, dipping sonar, sonobuoys, MAD, ECM. Weapons: ASW; 3 torpedoes, depth bombs, mines.

PATROL FORCES

Notes: (1) There is still one ex-Soviet P6 class (No 75) based at Tartous and two Hamelin class 37 m patrol craft based at Latakia.
(2) Second-hand purchase of Nanuchka class is a possibility in due course.
(3) Eight RAIDCO marine craft were acquired in the late 1980s.

4 OSA I (TYPE 205) and 10 OSA II CLASSES
(FAST ATTACK CRAFT—MISSILE)

23-26 (Osa I); **31-40** (Osa II)

Displacement, tons: 210 (245 Osa II) full load
Dimensions, feet (metres): 126.6 × 24.9 × 8.8
(38.6 × 7.6 × 2.7)
Main machinery: 3 Type M 503A diesels; 8025 hp(m) *(5.9 MW)* sustained; 3 shafts (Osa I)
3 Type M 504 diesels; 10 800 hp(m) *(9.94 MW)* sustained; 3 shafts (Osa II)
Speed, knots: 35 (Osa I); 37 (Osa II). **Range, miles:** 400 at 34 kts (Osa I); 500 at 35 kts (Osa II)
Complement: 30

Missiles: SSM: 4 SS-N-2A Styx (Osa I); active radar or IR homing to 46 km *(25 nm)* at 0.9 Mach; warhead 513 kg.
4 SS-N-2C (Osa II); active radar or IR homing to 83 km *(43 nm)* at 0.9 Mach; warhead 513 kg; sea-skimmer at end of run.
Guns: 4—30 mm/65 (2 twin, 1 fwd, 1 aft); 85° elevation; 500 rounds/minute to 5 km *(2.7 nm)*; weight of shell 0.54 kg.
Radars: Surface search: Square Tie; I band; range 73 km *(40 nm)* or limits of radar horizon.
Fire control: Drum Tilt; H/I band.
IFF: Two Square Head. High Pole A or B.

Programmes: Osa I class delivered from USSR as follows: December 1972 (two), October 1973 (three), November 1973 (one), December 1973 (three). Osa II class delivered: September 1978 (one), October 1978 (one), October 1979 (two), November 1979 (two), August 1982 (one), September 1982 (one) and May 1984 (two). Some have already been deleted; more may follow soon.
Structure: Two of the Osa IIs are modified (Nos 39 and 40).
Operational: Osa Is based at Tartous; Osa IIs at Latakia.

OSA II (old number)   *1987*

8 ZHUK (TYPE 1400M) CLASS (COASTAL PATROL CRAFT)

1-8

Displacement, tons: 39 full load
Dimensions, feet (metres): 78.7 × 16.4 × 3.9 *(24 × 5 × 1.2)*
Main machinery: 2 Type M 401B diesels; 2200 hp(m) *(1.6 MW)* sustained; 2 shafts
Speed, knots: 30. **Range, miles:** 1100 at 15 kts
Complement: 11 (3 officers)
Guns: 4—14.5 mm (2 twin) MGs.
Radars: Surface search: Spin Trough; I band.

Comment: Three transferred from USSR in August 1981, three on 25 December 1984 and two more in the late 1980s. All based at Tartous.

ZHUK (Yemen colours)   *1989*

5 KOMAR CLASS (FAST ATTACK CRAFT—MISSILE)

42-46

Displacement, tons: 85 full load
Dimensions, feet (metres): 88.6 × 20.7 × 4.3 *(27 × 6.3 × 1.3)*
Main machinery: 4 Type M 50 diesels; 4400 hp(m) *(3.2 MW)* sustained; 4 shafts
Speed, knots: 37. **Range, miles:** 400 at 30 kts
Complement: 19

Missiles: SSM: 2 SSN-2A Styx; active radar or IR homing to 46 km *(25 nm)* at 0.9 Mach; warhead 513 kg.
Guns: 2—25 mm/80 (twin); 85° elevation; 270 rounds/minute to 3 km *(1.6 nm)*; weight of shell 0.34 kg.
Radars: Surface search: Square Tie; I band.
Fire control: Drum Tilt; H/I band.

Programmes: Acquired from USSR in May 1974. Laid up in 1987 but refitted and operational again in 1990.
Operational: Based at Al-Mina-al-Bayda.

AMPHIBIOUS FORCES

3 POLNOCHNY B CLASS (TYPE 771) (LSM)

1/114   2/114   3/114

Displacement, tons: 760 standard; 834 full load
Dimensions, feet (metres): 246.1 × 31.5 × 7.5 *(75 × 9.6 × 2.3)*
Main machinery: 2 Kolomna Type 40-D diesels; 4400 hp(m) *(3.2 MW)* sustained; 2 shafts
Speed, knots: 19. **Range, miles:** 1500 at 15 kts
Complement: 40
Military lift: 180 troops; 350 tons cargo
Guns: 4—30 mm/65 (2 twin); 85° elevation; 500 rounds/minute to 5 km *(2.7 nm)*; weight of shell 0.54 kg.
2—140 mm rocket launchers; 18 barrels per launcher; range 9 km *(5 nm)*.
Radars: Surface search: Spin Trough; I band.
Fire control: Drum Tilt; I band.

Comment: Built at Northern Shipyard, Gdansk. First transferred from USSR January 1984, two in February 1985 from Black Sea. All based at Tartous.

POLNOCHNY B (Russian colours)   *1988*

MINE WARFARE FORCES

1 NATYA (TYPE 266M) CLASS

642

Displacement, tons: 770 full load
Dimensions, feet (metres): 200.1 × 31.8 × 8.9 *(61 × 9.7 × 2.7)*
Main machinery: 2 Type 504 diesels; 7200 hp(m) *(5.3 MW)* sustained; 2 shafts
Speed, knots: 19. **Range, miles:** 4000 at 10 kts
Complement: 65
Missiles: SAM: 2 SA-N-5 Grail quad launchers; manual aiming; IR homing to 6 km *(3.2 nm)* at 1.5 Mach; altitude to 2500 m *(8000 ft)*; warhead 1.5 kg; 16 missiles.
Guns: 4—30 mm/65 (2 twin). 4—25 mm/80 (2 twin).
A/S mortars: 2 RBU 1200 5-tubed fixed; range 1200 m; warhead 34 kg.
Mines: 10.
Radars: Surface search: Don 2; I band.
Fire control: Drum Tilt; H/I band.

Comment: Arrived in Tartous from USSR in January 1985. Has had sweeping gear removed and acts as a patrol ship. Based at Tartous.

NATYA Class (old number)   *1991*

2 VANYA CLASS (MINESWEEPERS—COASTAL)

KADISIA 775   **YARMUK** 776

Displacement, tons: 200 standard; 250 full load
Dimensions, feet (metres): 131.2 × 23.9 × 5.9 *(40 × 7.3 × 1.8)*
Main machinery: 2 Kolomna Type 9-D-8 diesels; 2000 hp(m) *(1.47 MW)* sustained; 2 shafts
Speed, knots: 16. **Range, miles:** 1400 at 14 kts
Complement: 30
Guns: 2—30 mm/65 (twin).
Mines: Can carry 8.
Radars: Surface search: Don 2; I band.
IFF: Square Head. High Pole B.

Comment: Transferred from USSR January 1973. Probably only one is still operational. Based at Tartous.

1 T 43 CLASS (MINESWEEPER—OCEAN)

HITTIN 504

Displacement, tons: 500 standard; 580 full load
Dimensions, feet (metres): 190.2 × 27.6 × 6.9 *(58 × 8.4 × 2.1)*
Main machinery: 2 Kolomna Type 9-D-8 diesels; 2000 hp(m) *(1.47 MW)* sustained; 2 shafts
Speed, knots: 15. **Range, miles:** 3000 at 10 kts
Complement: 65
Guns: 2—37 mm/63 (twin). 8—14.5 mm MGs (4 twin).
Mines: Can carry 16.
Radars: Surface search: Ball End; E/F band.
Navigation: Don 2; I band.
IFF: Square Head. High Pole A.
Sonars: Stag Ear; hull-mounted; active minehunting; high frequency.

Comment: Two transferred from USSR in 1959. The second of this class was sunk in the Israeli October 1973 war.

T 43 class (Russian colours)   *1985, van Ginderen Collection*

1 SONYA (TYPE 1265) CLASS

532

Displacement, tons: 400 full load
Dimensions, feet (metres): 157.4 × 28.9 × 6.6 *(48 × 8.8 × 2)*
Main machinery: 2 Kolomna Type 9-D-8 diesels; 2000 hp(m) *(1.47 MW)* sustained; 2 shafts
Speed, knots: 15. **Range, miles:** 3000 at 10 kts
Complement: 43
Guns: 2—30 mm/65 (twin) or 2—30 mm/65 AK 630. 2—25 mm/80 (twin).
Mines: 5.
Radars: Surface search: Don 2; I band.
IFF: Two Square Head. One High Pole B.

Comment: Wooden hull. Made passage from USSR in December 1985, transferred January 1986. Based at Tartous.

SONYA (old number)   *4/1992, van Ginderen Collection*

5 YEVGENYA CLASS (MINESWEEPERS—INSHORE)

4/507-8/507

Displacement, tons: 77 standard; 90 full load
Dimensions, feet (metres): 80.7 × 18 × 4.9 *(24.6 × 5.5 × 1.5)*
Main machinery: 2 Type 3-D-12 diesels; 600 hp(m) *(444 kW)*; 2 shafts
Speed, knots: 11. **Range, miles:** 300 at 10 kts
Complement: 10
Guns: 2—14.5 mm (twin) MGs (first pair). 2—25 mm/80 (twin) (second pair).
Radars: Surface search: Spin Trough; I band.
IFF: High Pole.

Comment: First transferred from USSR 1978, two in 1985 and two in 1986. Second pair by Ro-flow from Baltic in February 1985 being new construction with tripod mast. The first two may be non-operational. All based at Tartous.

YEVGENYA (Russian number)   *1991*

AUXILIARIES

1 SEKSTAN CLASS

SR 153

Displacement, tons: 400 full load
Dimensions, feet (metres): 133.8 × 30.5 × 14.1 *(40.8 × 9.3 × 4.3)*
Main machinery: 1 diesel; 400 hp(m) *(2.94 MW)*; 1 shaft
Speed, knots: 11. **Range, miles:** 1000 at 11 kts
Complement: 24
Cargo capacity: 115 tons

Comment: Initially probably belonged to and was used by the Soviet Mediterranean Squadron. At some stage transferred to the Syrian Navy.

1 VIKHR CLASS (TYPE B 98)

Displacement, tons: 2300 full load
Dimensions, feet (metres): 237.2 × 46.9 × 15.1 *(72.3 × 14.3 × 4.6)*
Main machinery: 2 Cegielski-Sulzer 16AV25/30 diesels; 5875 hp(m) *(4.32 MW)*; 2 shafts; cp props; 2 side thrusters; 1006 hp(m) *(740 kW)*
Speed, knots: 16. **Range, miles:** 2500 at 12 kts
Complement: 26 plus 8 salvage team

Comment: Specialist salvage vessel built at North Shipyard, Gdansk in the mid-1980s and delivered from Russia to Syria in May 1992. Ice-strengthened hull. Capable of carrying 50 survivors. Probably civilian manned.

1 POLUCHAT CLASS

Displacement, tons: 70 standard; 100 full load
Dimensions, feet (metres): 97.1 × 19 × 4.8 *(29.6 × 5.8 × 1.5)*
Main machinery: 2 Type M 50 diesels; 2200 hp(m) *(1.6 MW)* sustained; 2 shafts
Speed, knots: 20. **Range, miles:** 1500 at 10 kts
Complement: 15
Guns: 2—14.5 mm (twin) MGs.
Radars: Surface search: Spin Trough; I band.

Comment: Used as divers' base-ship. Transferred from USSR September 1967. Based at Al-Mina-al-Bayda.

POLUCHAT (Russian colours)   *1991, van Ginderen Collection*

3 SURVEY LAUNCHES

Dimensions, feet (metres): 32.2 × 11.2 × 3 *(9.8 × 3.4 × 0.9)*
Main machinery: 2 Volvo Penta diesels; 310 hp(m) *(228 kW)*; 2 shafts
Speed, knots: 25
Complement: 4

Comment: Completed 1986 at Arcor, La Teste, France. GRP hulls.

7 ROTORK SEA TRUCKS

Dimensions, feet (metres): 47.6 × 14.4 × 2.9 *(14.5 × 4.4 × 0.9)*
Main machinery: 2 diesels; 600 hp(m) *(441 kW)*; 2 shafts
Speed, knots: 20
Complement: 8
Guns: 1—7.62 mm MG.

Comment: Light logistic craft delivered in 1980.

TRAINING SHIPS

AL ASSAD

Displacement, tons: 3500 full load
Dimensions, feet (metres): 344.5 × 56.4 × 13.1 *(105 × 17.2 × 4)*
Main machinery: 2 diesels; 2 shafts
Speed, knots: 16. **Range, miles:** 12 500 at 15 kts
Complement: 56 plus 140 cadets

Comment: Built in Polnocny Shipyard, Gdansk and launched 18 February 1987. Delivered in late 1988. Ro-Ro design used as a naval training ship. Unarmed. Based at Latakia.

AL ASSAD   *6/1990, Selçuk Emre*

TAIWAN

REPUBLIC OF CHINA

Headquarters' Appointments

Chief of the General Staff:
Admiral Ho-Chien Liu
Commander-in-Chief:
Admiral Ming-Yao Chuang
Deputy Commander-in-Chief:
Vice Admiral Ling-Ming Tung
Commandant of Marine Corps:
Lieutenant General Kuo-Nan Cheng
Director of Political Warfare:
Vice Admiral Cheng-Ya Chang

Senior Flag Officers

Fleet Commander:
Vice Admiral Chung Ko Hsu
Director of Logistics:
Vice Admiral Te-An Han
Commander of ASW:
Vice Admiral Chieh Lee

Personnel

(a) 1994: 31 500 (and 32 500 reserves) in Navy, 35 000 (and 35 000 reserves) in Marine Corps
(b) 2 years' conscript service

Bases

Tsoying: HQ First Naval District (Southern Taiwan, Pratas and Spratly). Main Base, HQ of Fleet Command, Naval Aviation Group and Marine Corps. Base of southern patrol and transport squadrons. Officers and ratings training, Naval Academy, Naval Shipyard.
Kao-hsiung; Naval Shipyard.
Makung (Pescadores): HQ Second Naval District (Pescadores, Quemoy and Wu Ch'iu). Base for attack squadrons. Naval Shipyard and Training facilities.
Keelung: HQ Third Naval District (Northern Taiwan and Matsu group). Base of northern patrol and transport squadrons. Naval Shipyard.
Minor bases at Suao, Hualien, Tamshui, Hsinchu, Wuchi, Anping and Kenting.

Commands

1. Fleet Commander commands the 151st and 124th destroyer squadrons, the 131st and 146th patrol squadrons, one fast attack squadron, one mine warfare squadron, one amphibious squadron, one helicopter group, and the 256th submarine unit.
2. Logistic Commander commands one support ships squadron and one rescue group.
3. Anti-submarine Warfare (ASW) Command co-ordinates the surface, underwater, and air patrol to hunt down hostile submarines off Taiwan. The TF62 and Amphibious Command were deleted in 1991.
4. A land-based naval anti-ship missile Command is under naval operational control. Equipped with SSM Hsiung Feng II, this Command has forward deployment at off-shore islets of Quemoy, Matsu, WuChiu, and Pescadores along the mainland Chinese coast.

Marine Corps

Two divisions, the 66th and 99th are supported by one amphibious regiment and one logistics regiment. Equipped with M-116, M-733, LARC-5, LVTP5 personnel carriers and LVTH6 armour tractors. Based at Tsoying and in southern Taiwan with detachments at Pratas and Spratly Islands in the South China Sea.

Strength of the Fleet

Type	Active (Reserve)	Building/ Transfer (Planned)
Submarines	4	(8)
Destroyers	16 (6	—
Frigates	11	15 (6)
Corvettes	1	(10)
Fast Attack Craft (Missile)	52	—
Offshore Patrol Craft	22	1 (9)
Coastal Minesweepers/Hunters	13	2 (6)
LSD	2	—
Landing Ships (LST and LSM)	19	—
LCUs	24	1
LCMs	250	—
Minor Landing Craft	150	(5)
Survey Ship	—	1
Combat Support Ship	1	—
Repair Ship	1	—
Transports	6	3
Salvage Ship	1	—
Support Tankers	3	—
Tugs	14	—
Floating Docks	5	—
Customs	13+	(10)
Maritime Police	83	(15)

Maritime Security Police

Comes under the Minister of the Interior but its numerous patrol boats are integrated with the Navy for operational purposes.

Pennant Numbers

Pennant numbers were changed in early 1987.

Mercantile Marine

Lloyd's Register of Shipping:
651 vessels of 6 071 191 tons gross

DELETIONS

Destroyers

1993 *Heng Yang, Yuen Yang*

Frigates

1992 *Wen Shan, Tai Shan*
1993 *Tien Shan, Hua Shan*

Corvettes

1992 *Wu Sheng, Chu Yung*

Patrol Forces

1992 All Coastal Patrol Craft (to Maritime Police)

Amphibious Forces

1993 *Chung Ting, Chung Chi, Chung Lien, Chung Chiang, Chung Shu, Chung Wan*

Mine Warfare Forces

1992 *Yung Ching, Yung Fu*
1993 *Yung Ju, Yung Chi, MSB 12*

Survey Ships

1991 *Lien Chang, Bien Dou*
1992 *Chiu Lien*

Auxiliaries

1992 *Chang Pei*
1993 *Tai Wu, Yung Kang*

PENNANT LIST

Submarines

791	Hai Shih
792	Hai Bao
793	Hai Lung
795	Hai Hu

Destroyers

903	Hua Yang
906	Huei Yang
907	Fu Yang
908	Kwei Yang
909	Chiang Yang
911	Dang Yang
912	Chien Yang
914	Lo Yang
915	Han Yang
917	Nan Yang
918	An Yang
919	Kun Yang
920	Lai Yang
921	Liao Yang
923	Chen Yang
924	Kai Yang
925	Te Yang
926	Shao Yang
927	Yun Yang
928	Cheng Yang
929	Chao Yang
930	Lao Yang

Frigates

827	Tai Yuan
832	Yu Shan
835	Fu Shan
836	Lu Shan
837	Shou Shan
843	Chung Shan
932	Chin Yang
933	Fong Yang
934	Feng Yang
935	—
936	—
937	—
1101	Cheng Kung
1103	Cheng Ho
1105	Chi Kuang (bldg)
1106	Yueh Fei (bldg)
1107	Tzu-I (bldg)
1108	Pan Chao (bldg)
1109	Chang Chien (bldg)
1110	Tien Tan (bldg)

Corvette

867	Ping Jin

Patrol Forces

601	Lung Chiang
602	Sui Chang

Amphibious Forces

191	Chung Cheng
192	Cheng Hai
201	Chung Hai
204	Chung Hsing
205	Chung Chien
208	Chung Shun
210	Chung Yung
216	Chung Kuang
217	Chung Suo
219 (LCC 1)	Kao Hsiung
221	Chung Chuan
222	Chung Sheng
223	Chung Fu
226	Chung Chih
227	Chung Ming
230	Chung Pang
231	Chung Yeh
401	Ho Chi
402	Ho Huei
403	Ho Yao
404	Ho Deng
405	Ho Feng
406	Ho Chao
407	Ho Teng
481	Ho Shun
482	Ho Tsung
484	Ho Chung
485	Ho Chang
486	Ho Cheng
488	Ho Shan
489	Ho Chuan
490	Ho Seng
491	Ho Meng
492	Ho Mou
493	Ho Shou
494	Ho Chun
495	Ho Yung
496	Ho Chien
637	Mei Lo
649	Mei Chin
659	Mei Ping
694	Mei Sung
SB 1	Ho Chie

Mine Warfare Forces

423	Yung Chou
441	Yung Cheng
449	Yung An
462	Yung Sui
469	Yung Lo
476	Yung Shan
479	Yung Nien
485	Yung Jen
488	Yung Hsin

Auxiliaries

507	Hsin Lung
512	Wan Shou
515	Lung Chuan
518	Yun Tai
521	Yu Tai
522	Tai Hu
523	Yuen Feng
524	Ta Hu
525	Wu Kang
530	Wu Yi

Tugs

357	Ta Sueh
367	Ta Teng
395	Ta Peng
542	Ta Han
548	Ta Tung

SUBMARINES

Notes: (1) There are plans to acquire eight patrol submarines in the 1990s. In January 1993 the export of German-built hulls was blocked by the Federal Security Council. France has been similarly discouraged although DCN has tried to sell the Agosta class. In February 1992 the Netherlands Government also refused permission to build in Dutch shipyards but the project was reviewed in 1993 and RDM may be allowed to deliver sections for assembly in Taiwan.
(2) A German-built midget submarine was acquired in 1984 for research. Named *Sea Horse* it has a 52 ton dived displacement, 14.5 × 2.3 m, diesel-electric propulsion generating 80 kW, speed 5 kts and a range of 400 nm surfaced and 35 nm dived. Crew of four plus two divers. A second of class due in 1987 was cancelled by Germany because of protests from China.

2 HAI LUNG CLASS

Name	No
HAI LUNG	793
HAI HU	795

Builders	Laid down	Launched	Commissioned
Wilton Fijenoord, Netherlands	1982	6 Oct 1986	9 Oct 1987
Wilton Fijenoord, Netherlands	1982	20 Dec 1986	9 Apr 1988

Displacement, tons: 2376 surfaced; 2660 dived
Dimensions, feet (metres): 219.6 × 27.6 × 22
(66.9 × 8.4 × 6.7)
Main machinery: Diesel-electric; 3 Bronswerk D-RUB 215-12
diesels; 4050 hp(m) *(3 MW)*; 3 alternators; 2.7 MW; 1 Holec
motor; 5100 hp(m) *(3.74 MW)*; 1 shaft
Speed, knots: 12 surfaced; 20 dived
Range, miles: 10 000 at 9 kts surfaced
Complement: 67 (8 officers)

Torpedoes: 6—21 in *(533 mm)* bow tubes. 28 AEG SUT; dual
purpose; wire-guided; active/passive homing to 12 km
(6.6 nm) at 35 kts; warhead 250 kg.
Countermeasures: ESM: Signaal Rapids; radar warning.
Fire control: Sinbads M Combat System.
Radars: Surface search: Signaal ZW 06; I band.
Sonars: Signaal SIASS-Z; hull-mounted; passive/active intercept
search and attack; low/medium frequency.
Fitted for but not with towed passive array.

Programmes: Order signed with Wilton Fijenoord in September
1981 for these submarines with variations from the standard

HAI LUNG
10/1991, Dr Chien Chung

Netherlands Zwaardvis design. Construction was delayed by
the financial difficulties of the builders but was resumed in
1983. Sea trials of *Hai Lung* in March 1987 and *Hai Hu* in January 1988 and both submarines were shipped out on board a
heavy dock vessel. The names mean *Sea Dragon* and *Sea
Tiger*.

Structure: Two 196-cell batteries. The four horns on the forward
casing are Signaal sonar intercept transducers. Torpedoes
manufactured under licence in Indonesia.
Operational: Hsiung Feng 2 submerged launch SSMs are
planned to be part of the weapons load but a torpedo-launched
version has not yet been developed.

2 GUPPY II CLASS

Name	No
HAI SHIH (ex-USS *Cutlass* SS 478)	791 (ex-SS 91)
HAI BAO (ex-USS *Tusk* SS 426)	792 (ex-SS 92)

Builders	Laid down	Launched	Commissioned
Portsmouth Navy Yard	22 July 1944	5 Nov 1944	17 Mar 1945
Federal SB & DD Co, Kearney, New Jersey	23 Aug 1943	8 July 1945	11 Apr 1946

Displacement, tons: 1870 standard; 2420 dived
Dimensions, feet (metres): 307.5 × 27.2 × 18
(93.7 × 8.3 × 5.5)
Main machinery: Diesel-electric; 3 Fairbanks-Morse diesels;
4500 hp *(3.3 MW)*; 2 Elliott motors; 5400 hp *(4 MW)*; 2 shafts
Speed, knots: 18 surfaced; 15 dived
Range, miles: 8000 at 12 kts surfaced
Complement: 75 (7 officers)

Torpedoes: 10—21 in *(533 mm)* (6 fwd, 4 aft) tubes. AEG SUT;
active/passive homing to 12 km *(6.5 nm)* at 35 kts; 28 km
(15 nm) at 23 kts; warhead 250 kg.
Countermeasures: ESM: WLR-1/3; radar warning.
Radars: Surface search: US SS 2; I band.
Sonars: EDO BQR 2B; hull-mounted; passive search and attack;
medium frequency.
Raytheon/EDO BQS 4C; adds active capability to BQR 2B.
Thomson Sintra DUUG 1B; passive ranging.

Programmes: Originally fleet-type submarines of the US Navy's
Tench class; extensively modernised under the Guppy II pro-
gramme. *Hai Shih* transferred in April 1973 and *Hai Pao* in
October the same year.

HAI SHIH
8/1990, DTM

Structure: Four 126-cell batteries. After 45 years in service diving depth is very limited.

Operational: Used for anti-submarine training exercises. *Hai Shih*
may be paid off in 1994. The torpedoes, acquired from Indonesia, are in poor condition through lack of maintenance.

DESTROYERS

2 ALLEN M SUMNER (WU CHIN I CONVERSION) (FRAM II) CLASS

Name	No
LO YANG (ex-USS *Taussing* DD 746)	914
NAN YANG (ex-USS *John W Thomas* DD 760)	917

Builders	Laid down	Launched	Commissioned
Bethlehem Steel, Staten Island	30 Aug 1943	25 Jan 1944	20 May 1944
Bethlehem Steel, San Francisco	21 Nov 1944	30 Sep 1944	11 Oct 1945

Displacement, tons: 2200 standard; 3320 full load
Dimensions, feet (metres): 376.6 × 40.9 × 19
(114.8 × 12.4 × 5.8)
Main machinery: 4 Babcock & Wilcox boilers; 600 psi
(43.3 kg/cm sq); 850°F *(454°C)*; 2 GE or Westinghouse
geared turbines; 60 000 hp *(45 MW)*; 2 shafts
Speed, knots: 34. **Range, miles:** 1000 at 32 kts
Complement: 275 approx

Missiles: SSM: 5 Hsiung Feng I (1 triple ❶ and 2 single ❷); radar
or optical guidance to 36 km *(19.4 nm)* at 0.7 Mach; warhead
75 kg.
SAM: 1 Sea Chaparral quad launcher ❸; Sidewinder missile; IR
homing to 3 km *(1.6 nm)* supersonic; warhead 5 kg; 16
reloads.
Guns: 2 USN 5 in *(127 mm)*/38 (twin) Mk 38 ❹; 85° elevation;
15 rounds/minute to 17 km *(9.3 nm)*; weight of shell 25 kg.
1 OTO Melara 3 in *(76 mm)*/62 ❺; 85° elevation; 85 rounds/
minute to 16 km *(8.7 nm)*; weight of shell 6 kg.
2 Bofors 40 mm/70 ❻. 4—12.7 mm MGs.
Torpedoes: 6—324 mm US Mk 32 (2 triple) tubes ❼. Honeywell
Mk 46; anti-submarine; active/passive homing to 11 km
(5.9 nm) at 40 kts; warhead 44 kg.
A/S mortars: 2 Hedgehog Mk 10 24-tubed fixed ❽; range
250 m; warhead 13.6 kg.
Countermeasures: Decoys: 4 Kung Fen 6 16-barrelled chaff
launchers.
ESM/ECM: Argo AR 680/681; intercept and jammer.
Fire control: Honeywell H 930 for SSM. Mk 37 GFCS with Koll-
morgen electro-optical sight ❾ for 127 mm.
Radars: Air search: Westinghouse SPS 29 or SPS 37 ❿; B/C
band; range 457 km *(250 nm)*.
Air/surface search: Raytheon SPS 10/SPS 58 ⓫; D band.
Fire control: Two RCA HR 76 ⓬; I/J band (for SSM and guns).
Tacan: SRN-15.
Sonars: EDO SQS 29; hull-mounted; active search and attack;
medium frequency.

Helicopters: 1 McDonnell Douglas 500MD ⓭.

Programmes: Both ships transferred from US 6 May 1974.
Modernisation: Under the Wu Chin I modification programme
the same weapon system changes were made as in the Gearing class.

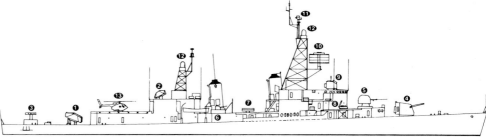

NAN YANG
(Scale 1 : 900), Ian Sturton

NAN YANG
1985, DTM (Raymond Cheung)

Structure: Both ships have latticed masts. *Lo Yang* has the single
SSM launchers on the signal deck on either side of the foremast; its Starboard Bofors abreast the forward funnel and the
Port Bofors abreast the after funnel. *Nan Yang* has both Bofors
abreast the after funnel.

Operational: *Lo Yang* is in poor condition and may be scrapped in
1994.

7 GEARING (WU CHIN I and II CONVERSIONS) (FRAM I and II) CLASS

Name	No	Builders	Laid down	Launched	Commissioned
*FU YANG (ex-USS *Ernest G Small* DD 838) (FRAM II)	907	Bath Iron Works Corporation	30 Jan 1945	14 June 1945	21 Aug 1945
**DANG YANG (ex-USS *Lloyd Thomas* DD 764) (FRAM II)	911	Bethlehem Steel, San Francisco	26 Mar 1944	5 Oct 1945	21 Mar 1947
**HAN YANG (ex-USS *Herbert J Thomas* DD 833)	915	Bath Iron Works Corporation	30 Oct 1944	25 Mar 1945	29 May 1945
**LAI YANG (ex-USS *Leonard F Mason* DD 852)	920	Bethlehem (Quincy)	8 June 1945	4 Jan 1946	28 June 1946
**KAI YANG (ex-USS *Richard B Anderson* DD 786)	924	Todd Pacific SY, Seattle, Washington	1 Dec 1944	7 July 1945	26 Oct 1945
*SHAO YANG (ex-USS *Hawkins* DD 873)	926	Consolidated Steel Corporation	14 May 1944	7 Oct 1944	10 Feb 1945
LAO YANG (ex-USS *Shelton* DD 790)	930	Todd Pacific SY, Seattle, Washington	31 May 1945	8 Mar 1946	21 June 1946

* Wu Chin I   ** Wu Chin II

Displacement, tons: 2425 standard; 3500 approx full load
Dimensions, feet (metres): 390.5 × 41.2 × 19
(119 × 12.6 × 5.8)
Main machinery: 4 Babcock & Wilcox boilers; 600 psi
(43.3 kg/cm sq); 850°F *(454°C)*; 2 GE turbines; 60 000 hp
(45 MW); 2 shafts
Speed, knots: 32.5. **Range, miles:** 5800 at 15 kts
Complement: 275 approx

Missiles: SSM: 5 Hsiung Feng I or II (1 triple ❶, 2 single ❷); radar
   or optical guidance (HFI); inertial guidance and active radar or
   IR homing (HF II) to 36 km *(19.4 nm)* (I) or 60 km *(32.4 nm)* (II)
   at 0.7 Mach (I) and 0.85 Mach (II); warhead 75 kg (not in *Lao
   Yang*).
   1 Sea Chapparal quad launcher ❸; Sidewinder missile; IR homing to 3 km *(1.6 nm)* supersonic; warhead 5 kg; 16 reloads.
A/S: Honeywell ASROC Mk 112 octuple launcher ❹ *(Shao Yang)*;
   inertial guidance to 1.6-10 km *(1-5.4 nm)*; payload Mk 46
   torpedo.
Guns: 2 or 4 USN 5 in *(127 mm)*/38 (1 or 2 twin) Mk 38 ❺; 85°
   elevation; 15 rounds/minute to 17 km *(9.3 nm)*; weight of shell
   25 kg.
   1 OTO Melara 3 in *(76 mm)*/62 ❻; 85° elevation; 85 rounds/
   minute to 16 km *(8.7 nm)*; weight of shell 6 kg.
   2 or 4 Bofors 40 mm/70 (2 single or 2 twin) ❼. 4 or
   6—12.7 mm MGs.
Torpedoes: 6—324 mm US Mk 32 (2 triple) tubes ❽. Honeywell
   Mk 46; anti-submarine; active/passive homing to 11 km
   (5.9 nm) at 40 kts; warhead 44 kg.
Countermeasures: Decoys: 4 Kung Fen 6 16-tubed chaff launchers (mounted abreast after funnel and on the quarterdeck).
   Mk T-6 Fanfare torpedo decoy.
ESM/ECM: ULQ-6 jammers and WLR-1 and WLR-3 passive warn-
   ing receivers or Chang Feng II combined intercept and
   jammers.
Combat data systems: Elbit; action data automation (Wu
   Chin II). SATCOM in some.
Fire control: Honeywell H 930 with 2 RCA HR 76 directors for
   SSM. Mk 37 GFCS with Kollmorgen electro-optical sight ❾ for
   127 mm or IAI Galileo optronic director Mk 114 system (for
   ASROC).
Radars: Air search: Lockheed SPS 40 ❿; E/F band or West-
   inghouse SPS 29 ⓫; B/C band.
   Surface search: Raytheon SPS 10/SPS 58 ⓬; G band or Israeli
   Elta 1040 ⓭ (Wu Chin II).
   Fire control: Western Electric Mk 25 ⓮ or Selenia RTN-10X ⓯
   (Wu Chin II); I/J band.
   Two RCA HR 76 ⓰; I/J band (for SSM and guns).
Tacan: SRN 15.
Sonars: Atlas Elektronik DSQS-21CZ *(Fu Yang* and *Dang Yang)* or
   Raytheon SQS 23H; hull-mounted; active search and attack;
   medium frequency.

Helicopters: 1 McDonnell Douglas 500MD ⓱.

Programmes: *Fu Yang* transferred 5 February 1971; *Dang Yang,*
   12 October 1972; *Han Yang,* 6 May 1974; *Lai Yang,* 20 April
   1973; *Kai Yang,* 10 June 1977 by sale; *Shao Yang,* 10 March
   1978; *Lao Yang* by sale 3 March 1983.
Modernisation: All ships except *Lao Yang* have been
   modernised:
   (a) Wu Chin I: Installation of SSM and Honeywell H 930 Mod 1
   fire-control system with twin lattice masts topped by HR 76
   directors in *Fu Yang* and *Shao Yang*. Developed by Honeywell
   and Chung-Shan Institute. Can track eight targets simultaneously and attack three with a 20 second response time.
   (b) Wu Chin II: *Han Yang, Lai Yang, Kai Yang* and *Dang Yang*
   separately upgraded with the Elbit Naval Tactical Command
   and Control System. Developed by IAI, Israel and Chung-Shan
   Institute. Can track up to 12 targets simultaneously and attack
   three with a 20 second response time. Each ship also received
   an OTO Melara 76 mm gun, two Bofors 40 mm/70 single
   mounts, a quad Sea Chapparal SAM launcher and five (two single and one triple) Hsiung Feng I missile launchers. An
   RTN-10X on a lattice mast and an Officine Galileo optronic
   director replaced the Mk 37 fire-control director on the bridge.
   The SPS-10 surface search radar was replaced by an Elta
   EL-1040. *Dang Yang* is unique in having her OTO Melara in 'A'
   position, triple Hsiung Fengs in 'B' position and a twin 5 in

FU YANG   *(Scale 1 : 1200), Ian Sturton*

SHAO YANG   *(Scale 1 : 1200), Ian Sturton*

DANG YANG   *(Scale 1 : 1200), Ian Sturton*

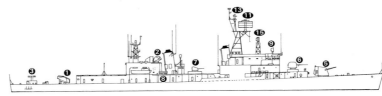

KAI YANG   *(Scale 1 : 1200), Ian Sturton*

KAI YANG   *6/1992, van Ginderen Collection*

mount aft. All the others have a twin 5 in, in 'A', OTO Melara in
'B' and triple Hsiung Fengs aft.
Operational: *Fu Yang* is the Fleet Flagship. *Han Yang* and *Shao
   Yang* are in poor condition with engine problems. *Lao Yang*

should have been given the Wu Chin III conversion but ran
aground in 1987 and so missed the modernisation
programme.

SHAO YANG   *6/1990*

7 GEARING (WU CHIN III CONVERSION) (FRAM I) CLASS

Name	No	Builders	Laid down	Launched	Commissioned
CHIEN YANG (ex-USS *James E Kyes* DD 787)	912	Todd Pacific SY, Seattle, Washington	27 Dec 1944	4 Aug 1945	8 Feb 1946
LIAO YANG (ex-USS *Hanson* DD 832)	921	Bath Iron Works Corporation	7 Oct 1944	11 Mar 1945	11 May 1945
CHEN YANG (ex-USS *Hollister* DD 788)	923	Todd Pacific SY, Seattle, Washington	18 Jan 1945	9 Oct 1945	26 Mar 1946
TE YANG (ex-USS *Sarsfield* DD 837)	925	Bath Iron Works Corporation	15 Jan 1945	27 May 1945	31 July 1945
YUN YANG (ex-USS *Johnston* DD 821)	927	Consolidated Steel Corporation	6 May 1945	19 Oct 1945	10 Oct 1946
SHEN YANG (ex-USS *Power* DD 839)	928	Bath Iron Works Corporation	26 Feb 1945	30 June 1945	13 Sep 1945
CHAO YANG (ex-USS *Hamner* DD 718)	929	Federal SB and DD Co	5 Apr 1945	24 Nov 1945	11 July 1946

Displacement, tons: 2425 standard; 3500 approx full load
Dimensions, feet (metres): 390.5 × 41.2 × 19
(119 × 12.6 × 5.8)
Main machinery: 4 Babcock & Wilcox boilers; 600 psi
(43.3 kg/cm sq); 850°F *(454°C)*; 2 GE turbines; 60 000 hp
(45 MW); 2 shafts
Speed, knots: 32.5. **Range, miles:** 5800 at 15 kts
Complement: 275 approx

Missiles: SAM: 10 General Dynamics Standard SM1-MR (2 triple
❶; 2 twin ❷); command guidance; semi-active radar homing to
46 km *(25 nm)* at 2 Mach.
A/S: Honeywell ASROC Mk 112 octuple launcher ❸; inertial guidance to 1.6-10 km *(1-5.4 nm)*; payload Mk 46 torpedo.
Guns: 1 OTO Melara 3 in *(76 mm)*/62 ❹; 85° elevation; 85
rounds/minute to 16 km *(8.7 nm)*; weight of shell 6 kg.
1 GE/GD 20 mm Vulcan Phalanx Block 1 6-barrelled Mk 15 ❺;
3000 rounds/minute combined to 1.5 km.
2 Bofors 40 mm/70 ❻. 4 or 6—12.7 mm MGs.
Torpedoes: 6—324 mm US Mk 32 (2 triple) tubes ❼. Honeywell
Mk 46; anti-submarine; active/passive homing to 11 km
(5.9 nm) at 40 kts; warhead 44 kg.
Countermeasures: Decoys: 4 Kung Fen 6 16-tubed chaff
launchers ❽.
Mk T-6 Fanfare torpedo decoy.
ESM/ECM: Chang Feng III (Hughes SLQ 17) intercept and
jammers.
Fire control: Honeywell H 930 MFCS Mk 114 system (for
ASROC).
Radars: Air search: Signaal DA-08 (with DA 05 aerial) ❾; E/F
band.
Surface search: Raytheon SPS 10/SPS 58 ❿; G band.
Fire control: Signaal STIR ⓫; I/J band (for Standard and
76 mm).
Westinghouse W-160 ⓬; I band (for Bofors).
Tacan: SRN 15.
Sonars: Raytheon SQS 23 H; hull-mounted; active search and
attack; medium frequency.

Helicopters: 1 McDonnell Douglas 500MD ⓭.

Programmes: *Chien Yang* transferred 18 April 1973; *Liao Yang*,
18 April 1973; *Te Yang* and *Chen Yang*, 1 October 1977 by sale;
Yun Yang, December 1980; *Shen Yang* by sale 27 February
1981; *Chao Yang* by sale 3 March 1983.
Modernisation: All ships converted to area air defence ships
under the Wu Chin III programme. This upgrade involved the
installation of the H 930 Modular Combat System (MCS) with a
Signaal DA-08 air search radar (employing a lightweight
DA-05 antenna) and a Signaal STIR missile control radar directing 10 box-launched Standard SM-1 surface-to-air missiles
(two twin in 'B' position, two triple facing either beam aft). The
system can track 24 targets simultaneously and attack four
with an eight second response time. An OTO Melara 76 mm is
fitted to 'A' position, one Bofors 40 mm/70 is mounted forward of the seaboat on the starboard side, one abaft the
ASROC magazine on the port side and a Mk 15 Block 1 Phalanx
CIWS is aft between two banks of Standard launchers. A Westinghouse W-160 is mounted on a lattice mast on the hangar to

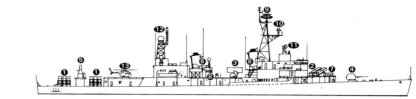

CHIEN YANG

(Scale 1 : 1200), Ian Sturton

CHIEN YANG

6/1993, 92 Wing RAAF

control the Bofors. The amidships ASROC launcher is retained,
its Mk 114 fire-control system is integrated with the H 930
MCS via a digital-analogue interface. The SQS-23 sonar has
also been upgraded to the H standard using a Raytheon solid-
state transmitter. The Chang Feng III EW system was developed jointly by Taiwan's Chung-Shan Institute of Science and

Technology (CSIST) with the assistance of Hughes. The Chang
Feng III employs phased-array antennas which resemble those
of the Hughes SLQ-17, it is capable of both deception and noise
jamming. An eighth ship, *Lao Yang*, was to have been given the
same conversion but missed the programme after a grounding
incident in 1987.

LIAO YANG

6/1993, 92 Wing RAAF

2 ALLEN M SUMNER CLASS

Name	No	Builders	Laid down	Launched	Commissioned
HUA YANG (ex-USS *Bristol* DD 857)	903	Bethlehem Steel, San Pedro	5 May 1944	29 Oct 1944	17 Mar 1945
*HUEI YANG (ex-USS *English* DD 696)	906	Federal SB & DD Co	19 Oct 1943	27 Feb 1944	4 May 1944

* Wu Chin I

Displacement, tons: 2200 standard; 3320 full load
Dimensions, feet (metres): 376.6 × 40.9 × 19
(114.8 × 12.4 × 5.8)
Main machinery: 4 Babcock & Wilcox boilers; 600 psi
(43.3 kg/cm sq); 850°F *(454°C)*; 2 GE or Westinghouse turbines; 60 000 hp *(45 MW)*; 2 shafts
Speed, knots: 34. **Range, miles:** 1000 at 32 kts
Complement: 275

Missiles: SSM: 5 or 6 Hsiung Feng I (2 triple or 1 triple, 2 single in *Huei Yang*) ❶; radar or optical guidance to 36 km *(19.4 nm)* at 0.7 Mach; warhead 75 kg.
SAM: 1 Sea Chapparal quad launcher ❷; Sidewinder missile; IR homing to 3 km *(1.6 nm)* supersonic; warhead 5 kg; 16 reloads.
Guns: 4 USN 5 in *(127 mm)*/38 (2 twin) Mk 38 ❸; 85° elevation; 15 rounds/minute to 17 km *(9.3 nm)*; weight of shell 25 kg.
1 OTO Melara 3 in *(76 mm)*/62 ❹ *(Huei Yang)*.
4 Bofors 40 mm/70 (2 twin) ❺.
Several 20 mm and 12.7 mm MGs. Secondary armament varies.
Torpedoes: 6—324 mm US Mk 32 (2 triple) tubes ❻. Honeywell Mk 46; anti-submarine; active/passive homing to 11 km *(5.9 nm)* at 40 kts; warhead 44 kg.
A/S mortars: 2 Hedgehog Mk 10 24-tubed fixed ❼; range 250 m; warhead 13.6 kg.
Depth charges: 1 rack in some ships; 9 weapons.
Countermeasures: Decoys: 4 Kung Fen 6 16-barrelled chaff launchers.
ECM/ESM: Argo 680/681; intercept and jammer.
Fire control: Galileo optronic director or Honeywell H 930 with two RCA HR 76 directors *(Huei Yang)*.
Radars: Air search: Lockheed SPS 40 ❽; D band; range 146 km *(80 nm)* against fighter aircraft.
Surface search: Raytheon SPS 10 ❾; G band.
Fire control: Selenia RTN 10X ❿; I/J band or two RCA HR 76 *(Huei Yang)* ⓫; I/J band.
Sonars: EDO SQS 29; hull-mounted; active search and attack; medium frequency.

Programmes: *Hua Yang* transferred from US 9 December 1969; *Huei Yang*, 11 August 1970.
Modernisation: Unmodified on transfer. *Hua Yang* had most of its weapons and sensors updated under the Tien Shi (Angel) modification programme. This included the addition of Hsiung Feng SSM and Sea Chapparal SAM. *Huei Yang* was modified under the Wu Chin I programme and has 76 mm OTO Melara guns fitted in 'B' position.
Operational: Two of the class scrapped in 1993; *Hua Yang* is in poor condition and is expected to be scrapped in 1994.

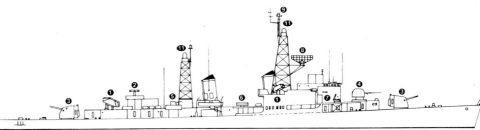

HUA YANG   (Scale 1 : 900), Ian Sturton

HUEI YANG   (Scale 1 : 900), Ian Sturton

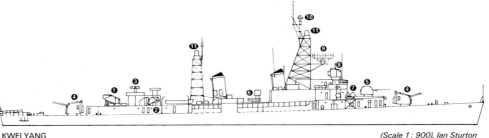

HUEI YANG   1990, Ships of the World

4 FLETCHER CLASS

Name	No	Builders	Laid down	Launched	Commissioned
KWEI YANG (ex-USS *Twining* DD 540)	908	Bethlehem Steel, San Francisco	20 Nov 1942	11 July 1943	1 Dec 1943
CHIANG YANG (ex-USS *Mullany* DD 528)	909	Bethlehem Steel, San Francisco	15 Jan 1942	12 Oct 1942	23 Apr 1943
AN YANG (ex-USS *Kimberly* DD 521)	918	Bethlehem Steel, Staten Island	27 July 1942	4 Feb 1943	22 May 1943
KUN YANG (ex-USS *Yarnall* DD 541)	919	Bethlehem Steel, San Francisco	5 Dec 1942	25 July 1943	30 Dec 1943

Displacement, tons: 2100 standard; 3050 full load
Dimensions, feet (metres): 376.5 × 39.5 × 18
(114.8 × 12 × 5.5)
Main machinery: 4 Babcock & Wilcox boilers; 600 psi
(43.3 kg/cm sq); 850°F *(454°C)*; 2 GE/Allis Chalmers/Westinghouse turbines; 60 000 hp *(45 MW)*; 2 shafts
Speed, knots: 35. **Range, miles:** 3750 at 14 kts
Complement: 261 *(Kwei Yang)*; 279 *(Chiang Yang)*; 270 (remainder)

Missiles: SSM: 5 Hsiung Feng I (1 triple ❶ and 2 single ❷); radar or optical guidance to 36 km *(19.4 nm)* at 0.7 Mach; warhead 75 kg.
SAM: 1 Sea Chapparal quad launcher ❸; Sidewinder missile; IR homing to 3 km *(1.6 nm)* supersonic; warhead 5 kg; 16 reloads.
Guns: 2 USN 5 in *(127 mm)*/38 Mk 30 ❹; 85° elevation; 15 rounds/minute to 17 km *(9.3 nm)*; weight of shell 25 kg. Some may still have 3—5 in *(127 mm)* instead of the 76 mm.
1 OTO Melara 3 in *(76 mm)*/62 ❺; 85° elevation; 85 rounds/minute to 16 km *(8.8 nm)*; weight of shell 6 kg.
Torpedoes: 6—324 mm US Mk 32 (2 triple) tubes ❻. Honeywell Mk 46; anti-submarine; active/passive homing to 11 km *(5.9 nm)* at 40 kts; warhead 44 kg.
A/S mortars: 2 Hedgehog Mk 10 24-tubed fixed ❼; range 250 m; warhead 13.6 kg.
Depth charges: 1 rack.
Mines: 1 rail.
Countermeasures: Decoys: 4 Kung Fen 6 16-barrelled chaff launchers.
ESM/ECM: Argo 680/681; intercept and jammer.
Fire control: Honeywell H 930 for SSM. Mk 37 GFCS with Kollmorgen electro-optical sight ❽ for 127 mm.
Radars: Air search: Lockheed SPS 40 ❾; E/F band.
Air/surface search: Westinghouse SPS 58 ❿; D band.
Fire control: Two RCA HR 76 ⓫; I/J band (for SSM and guns).
Sonars: Atlas Elektronik DSQS-21CZ; hull-mounted; active search and attack; medium frequency.

Programmes: *Kwei Yang* transferred from US 16 August 1971 (sale); *Chiang Yang*, 6 October 1971 (sale); *An Yang*, 2 June 1967; *Kun Yang*, 10 June 1968. *Kun Yang* and *An Yang* purchased 25 January 1974.
Modernisation: Armaments modernised under the Wu Chin I programme. *Kun Yang* can act as a minelayer.
Operational: Because of the state of the hulls, time spent at sea is very limited. All are to be scrapped when the second batch of three Knox class are transferred in 1994/95.

KWEI YANG   (Scale 1 : 900), Ian Sturton

CHIANG YANG   4/1991, DTM

FRIGATES

2 + 4 CHENG KUNG CLASS (KWANG HUA PROJECT) (FLIGHT I)

Name	No	Builders	Laid down	Launched	Commissioned
CHENG KUNG	1101	China SB Corporation, Keelung	7 Jan 1990	5 Oct 1991	7 May 1993
CHENG HO	1103	China SB Corporation, Keelung	21 Dec 1990	15 Oct 1992	21 Apr 1994
CHI KUANG	1105	China SB Corporation, Keelung	4 Oct 1991	27 Sep 1993	Feb 1995
YUEH FEI	1106	China SB Corporation, Keelung	5 Sep 1992	1994	Feb 1996
TZU-I	1107	China SB Corporation, Keelung	Mar 1994	1995	Jan 1997
PAN CHAO	1108	China SB Corporation, Keelung	Jan 1995	1996	Dec 1997

Displacement, tons: 2750 light; 4105 full load
Dimensions, feet (metres): 453 × 45 × 14.8; 24.5 (sonar)
(138.1 × 13.7 × 4.5; 7.5)
Main machinery: 2 GE LM 2500 gas-turbines; 41 000 hp
(30.59 MW) sustained; 1 shaft; cp prop
2 auxiliary retractable props; 650 hp *(484 kW)*
Speed, knots: 29. **Range, miles:** 4500 at 20 kts
Complement: 234 (15 officers) including 19 aircrew

Missiles: SSM: 8 Hsiung Feng II ❶ (2 quad); inertial guidance;
active radar or IR homing to 60 km *(32.4 nm)* at 0.85 Mach;
warhead 75 kg.
SAM: 40 GDC Standard SM1-MR; Mk 13 launcher ❷; command
guidance; semi-active radar homing to 46 km *(25 nm)* at
2 Mach.
Guns: 1 OTO Melara 76 mm/62 Mk 75 ❸; 85° elevation; 85
rounds/minute to 16 km *(8.7 nm)*; weight of shell 6 kg.
4 Bofors 40 mm/70 (2 twin) ❹. 4—12.7 mm MGs.
1 GE/GD 20 mm/76 Vulcan Phalanx 6-barrelled Mk 15 ❺;
3000 rounds/minute combined to 1.5 km.
Torpedoes: 6—324 mm Mk 32 (2 triple) tubes ❻. Honeywell
Mk 46 Mod 5; anti-submarine; active/passive homing to 11 km
(5.9 nm) at 40 kts; warhead 44 kg.
Countermeasures: Decoys: 4 Kung Fen 6 chaff launchers or
locally produced version of RBOC (114 mm).
ESM/ECM: Chang Feng IV (locally produced version of SLQ
32(V)2 with Sidekick); combined radar warning and jammers.
Combat data systems: SYS-2(V)2 action data automation with
UYK 43 computer. Ta Chen link (from *Chi Kuang* onwards).

Fire control: Unisys Mk 92 Mod 6. Mk 13 Mod 4 weapon direc-
tion system. Mk 114 ASW. 2 Mk 24 optical directors. Mk 309
TFCS.
Radars: Air search: Raytheon SPS 49(V)5 ❼; C/D band.
Surface search: ISC Cardion SPS 55 ❽ or Raytheon Chang Bai;
I/J band.
Fire control: USN UD 417 STIR ❾; I/J band.
Unisys Mk 92 Mod 6 ❿; I/J band.
Sonars: Raytheon SQS 56; hull-mounted; active search and
attack; medium frequency.
SQR 18A(V)2; passive towed array or BAe/Thomson Sintra
ATAS active towed array (from *Chi Kuang* onwards).

Helicopters: 2 Sikorsky S-70C(M) ⓫ (only 1 to be embarked).

Programmes: First two ordered 8 May 1989. The first six of the
class are known as Flight I. Named after Chinese generals and
warriors. Reports that the first planned Flight II ship *Chang
Chien* may become a seventh Flight I are not confirmed.
Structure: Similar to the USS *Ingraham*. RAST helicopter haul
down. The area between the mast had to be strengthened to
take the Hsiung Feng II missiles.

CHENG KUNG *(Scale 1 : 1200), Ian Sturton*

CHENG KUNG *4/1993, Chien Chung*

0 + 2 PFG-2 CLASS (KWANG HUA PROJECT) (FLIGHT II)

Name	No	Builders	Laid down	Launched	Commissioned
CHANG CHIEN	1109	China SB Corporation, Keelung	Dec 1995	1997	Nov 1998
TIEN TAN	1110	China SB Corporation, Keelung	June 1996	1998	Oct 1999

Displacement, tons: 4300 full load
Dimensions, feet (metres): 470 × 45 × 14.8; 24.5 (sonar)
(143.3 × 13.7 × 4.5; 7.5)
Main machinery: 2 GE LM 2500 gas-turbines; 41 000 hp
(30.59 MW) sustained; 1 shaft; cp prop; 2 auxiliary props
Speed, knots: 29

Missiles: SSM: 8 Hsiung Feng II (2 quad) ❶.
SAM: Mk 41 VLS ❷; Standard SM-2 (32 or 48 cells).
Guns: 1 OTO Melara 76 mm/62 Mk 75 ❸.
2 GE/GD 20 mm/76 6-barrelled Vulcan Phalanx ❹.
Torpedoes: 6—324 mm Mk 32 (2 triple) tubes ❺; Honeywell Mk
46 Mod 5.
Combat data systems: CSIST. Ta Chen link.
Radars: Air search: GE/RCA ADAR-2N; E/F band; phased
arrays ❻.
Fire control: 2 USN UD 417 STIR ❼.

Helicopters: 1 Sikorsky S-70C(M)1 ❽.

Programmes: Flight II of the PFG-2 class project. If more time is
needed because of revised instructions to potential contractors, *Chang Chien* may become the seventh Flight I ship. The
last four will be Flight III with the emphasis on Fleet area air
defence.

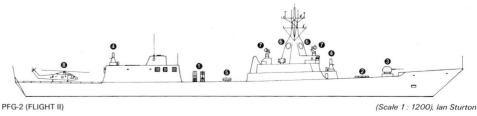

PFG-2 (FLIGHT II) *(Scale 1 : 1200), Ian Sturton*

Structure: Several design and equipment options are not yet
finalised and the details listed could change. Modifications to
Flight I include adding 17 ft to the hull forward of the bridge.
The 76 mm gun mounted in 'A' position. A 32-cell Mk 41 VLS
will replace the Mk 13 launcher and a second Phalanx will be
added on a step forward of the bridge. The starboard hangar
may be replaced by four Mk 41 VLS cells sub-divided into 16
with the Martin Marrietta Quad-pack. The superstructure will
be cut down amidships, the CIC will be moved from the superstructure down into the hull. There will be a backup CIC aft of

the main CIC as survivability measure (made possible by the
modular nature of the combat system). A phased array radar
system similar to the SPY-1 will be fitted, the two competing
are the GE/RCA ADAR-2N and the Raytheon C-MAR. Two
STIRs will provide target illumination. Hughes is offering the
MCS-2000 combat data system while Raytheon has a licensed
produced version of the Plessey Nautis-F. In the break in the
superstructure amidships, eight Hsiung Feng II launchers will
be fitted with options for either Bofors guns or ASW missiles.

1 RUDDEROW, 2 CHARLES LAWRENCE and 3 CROSLEY CLASSES

Name	No	Builders	Laid down	Launched	Commissioned
**TAI YUAN (ex-USS *Ridley* DE 579)	827 (ex-959)	Bethlehem SB Co, Higham, Mass	1943	29 Dec 1943	13 Mar 1944
YU SHAN (ex-USS *Kinzer* APD 91/DE 232)	832 (ex-826)	Charleston Navy Yard, South Carolina	1943	9 Dec 1943	1 Nov 1944
FU SHAN (ex-USS *Truxton* APD 98/DE 282)	835 (ex-838)	Charleston Navy Yard, South Carolina	1943	9 Mar 1944	9 July 1944
*LU SHAN (ex-USS *Bull* APD 78/DE 693)	836 (ex-821)	Defoe SB Co, Bay City, Michigan	1942	25 Mar 1944	12 Aug 1943
SHOU SHAN (ex-USS *Kline* APD 120/DE 687)	837 (ex-893)	Bethlehem, Quincy, Mass	1944	27 June 1944	18 Oct 1944
*CHUNG SHAN (ex-USS *Blessman* APD 48/DE 69)	843 (ex-845)	Bethlehem SB Co, Higham, Mass	1943	19 June 1943	19 Sep 1943

* Charles Lawrence class   ** Rudderow class

Displacement, tons: 1680 standard; 2130 full load
Dimensions, feet (metres): 306 × 37 × 12.6
(93.3 × 11.3 × 3.8)
Main machinery: Turbo-electric; 2 Foster-Wheeler boilers; 435 psi *(30.6 kg/cm sq)*; 750°F *(399°C)*; 2 GE turbo generators; 12 000 hp *(9 MW)*; 2 motors; 2 shafts
Speed, knots: 23.6. **Range, miles:** 5000 at 15 kts
Complement: 200
Military lift: 160 troops, commandos or frogmen

Guns: 4 or 6 Bofors 40 mm/56 (2 or 3 twin); 45° elevation; 160 rounds/minute to 11 km *(5.9 nm)*; weight of shell 0.9 kg. 4—20 mm (2 twin).
Fire control: Mk 51 GFCS.
Radars: Surface search: Raytheon SPS 5 (in most); G/H band; SPS 6C (in *Tai Yuan*); D band.
Navigation: Decca 707 (in some); I band.
Fire control: RCA/GE Mk 26; I/J band.
Sonars: Hull-mounted; active attack; high frequency.

Programmes: *Yu Shan* transferred from US April 1962; *Fu Shan*, March 1966; *Lu Shan*, August 1966; *Shou Shan*, March 1966; *Chung Shan*, July 1967; *Tai Yuan* July 1968. All began as destroyer escorts (DE), but converted during construction or after completion to high-speed transports.
Modernisation: All ships were refitted with a second 5 in gun aft (since removed). One twin 40 mm gun mount forward of bridge and two twin mounts amidships.
Structure: Charles Lawrence class has high bridge; Crosley class has low bridge. Radars and fire-control equipment vary. Davits amidships can hold four LCVP-type landing craft but ships usually carry only one each. Rudderow class (*Tai Yuan*) has a tripod mast and platforms below the bridge for 20 mm guns.
Operational: Sea Chaparral SAM and 5 inch gun systems removed as only the lighter guns are needed for fishery patrol duties. Four paid off in the last two years, but the remainder were all operational in early 1994.

CROSLEY (old number)   8/1993

TAI YUAN   1992, Ships of the World

0 + 6 LA FAYETTE CLASS (KWANG HUA PROJECT II)

Name	No	Builders	Laid down	Launched	Commissioned
—	—	Lorient Dockyard/China SB Corporation	1 Feb 1992	12 Mar 1994	1995

Displacement, tons: 3500 full load
Dimensions, feet (metres): 410.1 × 50.5 × 13.1
(125 × 15.4 × 4)
Main machinery: CODAD; 4 SEMT-Pielstick 12 PA6 V 280 STC diesels; 23 228 hp(m) *(17.08 MW)*; 2 shafts
Speed, knots: 25. **Range, miles:** 7000 at 15 kts
Complement: 134 (15 officers) plus 25 spare

Missiles: SSM: 8 Hsiung Feng II (2 quad); inertial guidance; active radar or IR homing to 60 km *(32.4 nm)* at 0.85 Mach; warhead 75 kg.
SAM: Thomson-CSF Crotale Naval CN2 octuple launcher; command line-of-sight guidance; radar/IR homing to 13 km *(7 nm)* at 3.5 Mach; warhead 14 kg.
Guns: 1 OTO Melara 76 mm/62; 85° elevation; 85 rounds/minute to 16 km *(8.7 nm)*; weight of shell 6 kg.
2 Giat 20F2 20 mm.
Countermeasures: Decoys: 2 CSEE Dagaie chaff launchers.
Combat data systems: Thomson-CSF Tavitac 2000.
Fire control: CSEE Najir optronic director.
Radars: Air/surface search: Thomson-CSF Jupiter; E/F band.
Surface search: Thomson-CSF Triton G; I band.
Fire control: Thomson-CSF Castor IIC; I/J band.
Sonars: BAe/Thomson Sintra ATAS; active towed array.

Helicopters: 1 Sikorsky S-70C(M)1 or Kamen SH-2F.

Programmes: Sale of up to 16 of the class authorised by the French Government in August 1991. Contract for the first six signed with Thomson-CSF in early 1992, being manufactured in France with some weapon assembly by China SB Corporation at Kaohsiung in Taiwan. Second batch of 10 to be built by China SB Corporation if this goes ahead, but latest reports indicate a change to 1500 ton corvettes as a cheaper alternative.

LA FAYETTE (French colours)   10/1993

Structure: Construction details are the same as for the French design but the equipment listed is more uncertain, as is the extent of the work to be done in Taiwan once the hulls have been delivered. Torpedo tubes are probably to be fitted.

Operational: The first of class was reported as doing propulsion sea trials in early 1994. All six are scheduled for delivery by the end of 1996.

3 + 3 (6) KNOX CLASS

Name	No	Builders	Laid down	Launched	Commissioned
CHIN YANG (ex-*Robert E Peary*)	932 (ex-FF 1073)	Lockheed Shipbuilding	20 Dec 1970	23 June 1971	23 Sep 1972
FONG YANG (ex-*Brewton*)	933 (ex-FF 1086)	Avondale Shipyards	2 Oct 1970	24 July 1971	8 July 1972
FENG YANG (ex-*Kirk*)	934 (ex-FF 1087)	Avondale Shipyards	4 Dec 1970	25 Sep 1971	9 Sep 1972
— (ex-*Joseph Hewes*)	935 (ex-FF 1078)	Avondale Shipyards	15 May 1969	7 Mar 1970	22 Apr 1971
— (ex-*Cook*)	936 (ex-FF 1083)	Avondale Shipyards	20 Mar 1970	23 Jan 1971	18 Dec 1971
— (ex-*Barbey*)	937 (ex-FF 1088)	Avondale Shipyards	5 Feb 1971	4 Dec 1971	11 Nov 1972

Displacement, tons: 3011 standard; 3877 (932, 935), 4260 (933, 934) full load

Dimensions, feet (metres): 439.6 × 46.8 × 15; 24.8 (sonar) *(134 × 14.3 × 4.6; 7.8)*

Main machinery: 2 Combustion Engineering/Babcock & Wilcox boilers; 1200 psi *(84.4 kg/cm sq)*; 950°F *(510°C)*; 1 turbine; 35 000 hp *(26 MW)*; 1 shaft

Speed, knots: 27. **Range, miles:** 4000 at 22 kts on 1 boiler

Complement: 288 (17 officers) including aircrew

Missiles: SSM: 8 McDonnell Douglas Harpoon; active radar homing to 130 km *(70 nm)* at 0.9 Mach; warhead 227 kg.
A/S: Honeywell ASROC Mk 16 octuple launcher with reload system (has 2 cells modified to fire Harpoon) ❶; inertial guidance to 1.6-10 km *(1-5.4 nm)*; payload Mk 46 Mod 5 Neartip.

Guns: 1 FMC 5 in *(127 mm)*/54 Mk 42 Mod 9 ❷; 85° elevation; 20-40 rounds/minute to 24 km *(13 nm)* anti-surface; 14 km *(7.7 nm)* anti-aircraft; weight of shell 32 kg.
1 General Electric/General Dynamics 20 mm/76 6-barrelled Mk 15 Vulcan Phalanx ❸; 3000 rounds/minute combined to 1.5 km.

Torpedoes: 4—324 mm Mk 32 (2 twin) fixed tubes ❹. 22 Honeywell Mk 46 Mod 5; anti-submarine; active/passive homing to 11 km *(5.9 nm)* at 40 kts; warhead 44 kg.

Countermeasures: Decoys: 2 Loral Hycor SRBOC 6-barrelled fixed Mk 36 ❺; IR flares and chaff to 4 km *(2.2 nm)*. T Mk-6 Fanfare/SLQ-25 Nixie; torpedo decoy. Prairie Masker hull and blade rate noise suppression.
ESM/ECM: SLQ 32(V)2 ❻; radar warning. Sidekick modification adds jammer and deception system.

Combat data systems: Link 14 receive only. FFISTS (Frigate Integrated Shipboard Tactical System).

Fire control: SWG-1A Harpoon LCS. Mk 68 GFCS. Mk 114 ASW FCS. Mk 1 target designation system. SRQ-4 for LAMPS I.

Radars: Air search: Lockheed SPS 40B ❼; E/F band; range 320 km *(175 nm)*.
Surface search: Raytheon SPS 10 or Norden SPS 67 ❽; G band.
Navigation: Marconi LN 66; I band.
Fire control: Western Electric SPG 53A/D/F ❾; I/J band.
Tacan: SRN 15. IFF: UPX-12.

Sonars: EDO/General Electric SQS 26 CX; bow-mounted; active search and attack; medium frequency.
EDO SQR 18A(V)1; passive towed array.

Helicopters: 1 SH-2F LAMPS I ❿.

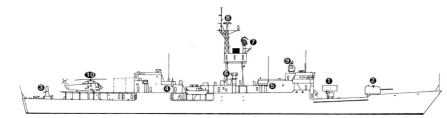

CHIN YANG   *(Scale 1 : 1200), Ian Sturton*

CHIN YANG (alongside *Fong Yang*)   *10/1993, Chien Chung*

Programmes: *Chin Yang* leased on a five year contract from the US on 2 July 1993, *Fong Yang* 23 July 1993 and *Feng Yang* 6 August 1993. All three recommissioned 6 October 1993 in Taiwan. Three more are to be leased in late 1994, and the plan is for further batches of three in both 1995 and 1996.

Structure: ASROC-torpedo reloading capability (note slanting face of bridge structure immediately behind ASROC). Four Mk 32 torpedo tubes are fixed in the midships structure, two to a side, angled out at 45 degrees. The arrangement provides improved loading capability over exposed triple Mk 32 torpedo

tubes. A 4000 lb lightweight anchor is fitted on the port side and an 8000 lb anchor fits into the after section of the sonar.
Operational: Helicopters are to be embarked on the first three by 1995.

FENG YANG (US Colours)   *8/1992, Giorgio Arra*

SHIPBORNE AIRCRAFT

Numbers/Type: 12 Kaman SH-2F/G Seasprite (LAMPS I).
Operational speed: 130 kts *(241 km/h)*.
Service ceiling: 22 500 ft *(6860 m)*.
Range: 367 nm *(679 km)*.
Role/Weapon systems: ASW and OTHT helicopter; transferred in August 1993. In LAMPS I programme, acts as ASW information relay for surface ships. Sensors: LN-66HP radar, ALR-66 ESM, ASN-123 tactical navigation, ASQ-81(V)2 MAD, AAQ-16 night vision system; ARR-57 sonobuoy receivers; 15 sonobuoys. Weapons: ASW; 2 × Mk 46 torpedoes, 8 × Mk 25 smoke markers. ASV; 1 Penguin; 1—7.62 mm MG M60.

Numbers/Type: 10 Hughes 500MD/ASW.
Operational speed: 110 kts *(204 km/h)*.
Service ceiling: 16 000 ft *(4880 m)*.
Range: 203 nm *(376 km)*.
Role/Weapon systems: Short-range ASW helicopter with limited surface search capability. Sensors: Search radar, Texas Instruments MAD. Weapons: ASW; 1 × Mk 46 torpedo or 2 × depth bombs. ASV; Could carry machine gun pods.

HUGHES 500 MD   *1993, Ships of the World*

Numbers/Type: 10 Sikorsky S-70C(M)1.
Operational speed: 145 kts *(269 km/h).*
Service ceiling: 19 000 ft *(5790 m).*
Range: 324 nm *(600 km).*
Role/Weapon systems: Delivered in 1991. This is a variant of the SH-60B and will become sea-borne with the first Cheng Kung and La Fayette class frigates. Another 14 S-70B/C SAR and assault aircraft belong to the Air Force. Sensors: APS 143 search radar; ALR 606 ESM; ARR 84 sonobuoy receiver with ASN 150 data link; dipping sonar. Weapons: ASW; 2 × Mk 46 torpedoes or 2 × Mk 64 depth bombs. ASV; Could carry ASM.

SIKORSKY 70 C(M)   *2/1993, Chien Chung*

LAND-BASED MARITIME AIRCRAFT

Note: Fokker maritime patrol aircraft and A3 fighter bombers may be acquired by the emerging naval air command.

Numbers/Type: 12/20 Grumman S-2E/T (Turbo) Trackers.
Operational speed: 130 kts *(241 km/h).*
Service ceiling: 25 000 ft *(7620 m).*
Range: 1350 nm *(2500 km).*
Role/Weapon systems: Patrol and ASW tasks undertaken by Air Force-manned Trackers, which come under naval control; 20 aircraft updated with turboprop engines and new sensors by mid-1994. Based at Pintung. Seeking long-range MPA as replacement. Sensors: APS 504 search radar, ESM, MAD, AAS 40 FLIR, SSQ-41B, SSQ-47B sonobuoys; AQS 902F sonobuoy processor; ASN 150 data link. Weapons: ASW; 4 × Mk 44 torpedoes, Mk 54 depth charges or Mk 64 depth bombs or mines. ASV; 6 × 127 mm rockets.

TRACKER   *1992, D Hughes*

CORVETTES

Note: Ten 1500 ton corvettes (PCEG) are planned for FY 1995 to be equipped with Hsiung Feng II SSM. First one to be acquired from a Western shipbuilder and the remainder constructed locally.

1 AUK CLASS

Name	No	Builders	Commissioned
PING JIN	867	American SB Co,	16 Nov 1942
(ex-USS *Steady* MSF 118)		Cleveland, Ohio	

Displacement, tons: 890 standard; 1250 full load
Dimensions, feet (metres): 221.2 × 32.2 × 10.8 *(67.4 × 9.8 × 3.3)*
Main machinery: Diesel-electric; 2 GM 12-278A diesels; 2200 hp *(1.64 MW)*; 2 shafts
Speed, knots: 18
Complement: 80
Guns: 4 Bofors 40 mm/56 (2 twin). 4 Oerlikon 20 mm (2 twin).
Radars: Surface search: Raytheon SPS 5; G/H band; range 37 km *(20 nm).*

Comment: Transferred from US March 1968. The last survivor stripped of all heavy armament and used for limited fishery protection duties. Two others of the class became non-operational in 1992.

AUK (old number)   *1980*

PATROL FORCES

Note: All coastal patrol craft were transferred to the Maritime Police on 8 December 1992.

2 LUNG CHIANG CLASS (FAST ATTACK CRAFT—MISSILE)

Name	No	Builders	Commissioned
LUNG CHIANG	601 (ex-PGG 581)	Tacoma Boatbuilding, Wa	15 May 1978
SUI CHIANG	602 (ex-PGG 582)	China SB Corporation, Kaohsiung	1982

Displacement, tons: 218 standard; 275 full load
Dimensions, feet (metres): 164.5 × 23.1 × 9.5 *(50.2 × 7.3 × 2.9)*
Main machinery: CODAG; 3 Avco Lycoming TF-40A gas-turbines; 12 000 hp *(8.95 MW)* sustained; 3 Detroit 12V-149TI diesels; 2736 hp *(2.04 MW)* sustained; 3 shafts; cp props
Speed, knots: 20 kts diesels; 35 kts gas. **Range, miles:** 2700 at 12 kts on 1 diesel; 1900 at 20 kts; 700 at 29 kts
Complement: 41 (5 officers)

Missiles: SSM: 4 Hsiung Feng I; radar or optical guidance to 36 km *(19.4 nm)* at 0.7 Mach; warhead 75 kg.
Guns: 1 OTO Melara 3 in *(76 mm)*/62; 85° elevation; 60 rounds/minute to 16 km *(8.7 nm)*; weight of shell 6 kg.
2 Emerlec 30 mm (twin). 2—12.7 mm MGs.
Countermeasures: Decoys: 4 chaff launchers.
Combat data systems: IPN 10 action data automation.
Fire control: NA 10 Mod 0 GFCS. Honeywell H 930 Mod 2 MFCS (602).
Radars: Surface/air search: Selenia RAN 11 L/X; D/I band; range 82 km *(45 nm).*
Fire control: RCA HR 76; I/J band (for SSM) (602).
Navigation: SPS 58(A); I band.

Programmes: Similar to the US Patrol Ship Multi-Mission Mk 5 (PSMM Mk 5). Second of class was built to an improved design. A much larger number of this class was intended, all to be armed with Harpoon. However, the US ban on export of Harpoon to Taiwan coupled with the high cost and doubts about seaworthiness caused the cancellation of this programme.
Structure: Fin stabilisers were fitted to help correct the poor seakeeping qualities of the design. Hsiung Feng missiles are mounted aft. *Sui Chiang* has a large lattice mast for the HR 76 radar. Both have had engine room fires caused by overheating in GT gearboxes.

LUNG CHIANG   *(not to scale), Ian Sturton*

SUI CHIANG (without armament)   *1982*

50 HAI OU CLASS (FAST ATTACK CRAFT—MISSILE)

FABG 1-3	FABG 5-51

Displacement, tons: 47 full load
Dimensions, feet (metres): 70.8 × 18 × 3.3 *(21.6 × 5.5 × 1)*
Main machinery: 2 MTU 12V 331 TC82 diesels; 2605 hp(m) *(1.92 MW)* sustained; 2 shafts
Speed, knots: 36. **Range, miles:** 700 at 32 kts
Complement: 10

Missiles: SSM: 2 Hsiung Feng I; radar or optical guidance to 36 km *(19.4 nm)* at 0.7 Mach; warhead 75 kg.
Guns: 1 Oerlikon 20 mm. 2—12.7 mm MGs.
Countermeasures: Decoys: 4 Israeli AV2 chaff launchers.
Fire control: Kollmorgen Mk 35 optical director.
Radars: Surface search: Marconi LN 66; I band.
Fire control: RCA R76 C5; I band; range 40 km *(22 nm)* for 1 m² target.

Programmes: This design was developed by Sun Yat Sen Scientific Research Institute from the basic Israeli Dvora plans. Built by China SB Corporation (Tsoying SY), Kaohsiung.
Structure: Aluminium alloy hulls. The first series had a solid mast and the missiles were nearer the stern. Second series changed to a lattice mast and moved the missiles further forward allowing room for 1—20 mm gun right aft.
Operational: The prototype reached 45 kts on trials (probably without 20 mm gun). These craft often carry shoulder-launched SAMs. Based at Makung, Pescadores where they form the Hai Chiao squadron. One task is to provide exercise high-speed targets in shallow waters.

FABG 17   *9/1993, Chien Chung*

0 + 1 (9) KWANG HUA PROJECT III (OFFSHORE PATROL CRAFT)

Comment: Designed by United Ship Design Centre and being built by Lien-Ho shipbuilding company. Laid down 7 August 1993 for launching in October 1994 and delivery in January 1995. This is a 500 ton, 60 m PCG prototype for trials and evaluation before more are ordered.

22 PCL TYPE (OFFSHORE PATROL CRAFT)

PCL 1-22

Displacement, tons: 143 full load
Dimensions, feet (metres): 105 × 29.5 × 5.9 *(32 × 9 × 1.8)*
Main machinery: 3 MTU 12V 396 TB93 diesels; 4890 hp(m) *(3.6 MW)* sustained; 3 shafts
Speed, knots: 40
Complement: 16 (3 officers)
Guns: 1 Bofors 40 mm/60. 2—12.7 mm MGs.
Depth charges: 2 racks.
Radars: Surface search: Decca; I band.
Sonars: Hull-mounted; active search and attack; high frequency.

Comment: Built to Vosper QAF design by China SB Corporation, Kaohsiung in 1987-90. They are used mainly for harbour defence against midget submarines and frogmen and also for Fishery protection tasks.

PCL   *1990, DTM*

AMPHIBIOUS FORCES

Note: Reported that five LCAC are to be acquired from the US.

1 CABILDO and 1 ASHLAND CLASS (LSD)

Name	No	Builders	Commissioned
CHUNG CHENG (ex-*Tung Hai*, ex-USS *White Marsh* LSD 8)	191	Moore Dry Dock, Oakland, California	2 July 1945
CHENG HAI (ex-USS *Fort Marion* LSD 22)	192 (ex-618)	Gulf SB Co, Chickasaw, Alabama	29 Jan 1946

Displacement, tons: 4790 standard; 9078 full load
Dimensions, feet (metres): 457.8 × 72.2 × 18 *(139.6 × 22 × 5.5)*
Main machinery: 2 boilers; 435 psi *(30.6 kg/cm sq)*; 740°F *(393°C)*; 2 turbines; 7000 hp *(5.22 MW)*; 2 shafts
Speed, knots: 15.4. **Range, miles:** 8000 at 15 kts
Complement: 316
Military lift: 3 LCUs or 18 LCMs or 32 LVTs in docking well
Missiles: SAM: 1 Sea Chaparral quadruple launcher.
Guns: 12 Bofors 40 mm/56 (2 quad, 2 twin).
Fire control: US Mk 26 Mod 4.
Radars: Surface search: Raytheon SPS 5; G/H band.
Navigation: Marconi LN 66; I band.

Comment: *Cheng Hai* launched on 22 May 1945, modernised in 1960 and transferred to Taiwan on 15 April 1977. Docking well is 392 × 44 ft with a redundant helicopter platform over well. SAM system fitted forward in 1989. *Chung Cheng* launched 19 July 1943. Converted to serve as a depot ship for patrol craft and landing craft. Transferred from US on 17 November 1960. Paid off in 1990 but back in service in 1993. SAM system fitted in 1992.

CHUNG CHENG   *4/1993, Chien Chung*

1 LST 511-1152 CLASS (FLAGSHIP) (AGC)

Name	No	Builders	Commissioned
KAO HSIUNG (ex-*Chung Hai*, ex-USS *Dukes County* LST 735)	LCC 1 (ex-219, ex-663)	Dravo Corporation, Neville Island, Penn	26 Apr 1944

Displacement, tons: 1653 standard; 3675 full load
Dimensions, feet (metres): 328 × 50 × 14 *(100 × 15.2 × 4.3)*
Main machinery: 2 GM 12-567A diesels; 1800 hp *(1.34 MW)*; 2 shafts
Speed, knots: 11.6. **Range, miles:** 11 200 at 10 kts
Complement: 195
Guns: 10 Bofors 40 mm/56 (5 twin).
Radars: Air search: RCA SPS 12; D band; range 119 km *(65 nm)*.
Surface search: Raytheon SPS 10; G band.

Comment: Launched on 11 March 1944. Transferred from US in May 1957 for service as an LST. Converted to a flagship for amphibious operations and renamed and redesignated (AGC) in 1964. Purchased November 1974. Note lattice mast above bridge structure, modified bridge levels, and antenna mountings on main deck. Redesignated as Command and Control Ship LCC 1.

KAO HSIUNG   *1968*

14 LST 1-510 and 511-1152 CLASSES

Name	No
CHUNG HAI (ex-USS *LST 755*)	201 (ex-697)
CHUNG HSING (ex-USS *LST 557*)	204 (ex-684)
CHUNG CHIEN (ex-USS *LST 716*)	205 (ex-679)
CHUNG SHUN (ex-USS *LST 732*)	208 (ex-624)
CHUNG YUNG (ex-USS *LST 574*)	210 (ex-657)
CHUNG KUANG (ex-USS *LST 503*)	216 (ex-646)
CHUNG SUO (ex-USS *Bradley County* LST 400)	217 (ex-667)
CHUNG CHUAN (ex-*LST 1030*)	221 (ex-651)
CHUNG SHENG (ex-*LST 211*, ex-USS *LSTH 1033*)	222 (ex-686)
CHUNG FU (ex-USS *Iron County* LST 840)	223 (ex-619)
CHUNG CHIH (ex-USS *Sagadahoc County* LST 1091)	226 (ex-655)
CHUNG MING (ex-USS *Sweetwater County* LST 1152)	227 (ex-681)
CHUNG PANG (ex-USS *LST 578*)	230 (ex-629)
CHUNG YEH (ex-USS *Sublette County* LST 1144)	231 (ex-699)

Displacement, tons: 1653 standard; 4080 (3640, 1-510 class) full load
Dimensions, feet (metres): 328 × 50 × 14 *(100 × 15.2 × 4.3)*
Main machinery: 2 GM 12-567A diesels; 1800 hp *(1.34 MW)*; 2 shafts
Speed, knots: 11.6. **Range, miles:** 15 000 at 10 kts
Complement: Varies—100-125 in most ships
Guns: Varies—up to 10 Bofors 40 mm/56 (2 twin, 6 single) with some modernised ships rearmed with 2 USN 3 in *(76 mm)*/50 and 6—40 mm (3 twin).
Several Oerlikon 20 mm (twin or single).
Radars: Navigation: US SO 1, 2 or 8; I band.

Comment: Constructed between 1943 and 1945. These ships have been rebuilt in Taiwan. Six transferred from US in 1946; two in 1947; one in 1948; eight in 1958; one in 1959; two in 1960; one in 1961. Some have davits forward and aft. Pennant numbers have reverted to those used in the 1960s. One deleted in 1990, six more in 1993, and at least half the remainder are to go in the next three years. The midships deck is occasionally used as a helicopter platform.

CHUNG YUNG   *1990, Dr Chien Chung*

4 LSM 1 CLASS

Name	No
MEI LO (ex-USS *LSM 362*)	637 (ex-*LSM 356*)
MEI CHIN (ex-USS *LSM 155*)	649 (ex-*LSM 341*)
MEI PING (ex-USS *LSM 471*)	659 (ex-*LSM 353*)
MEI SUNG (ex-USS *LSM 431*)	694 (ex-*LSM 347*)

Displacement, tons: 1095 full load
Dimensions, feet (metres): 203.5 × 34.2 × 8.3 *(62.1 × 10.4 × 2.5)*
Main machinery: 2 Fairbanks Morse 38D8-1/8-10 diesels; 3540 hp *(2.64 MW)* sustained (637 and 659); 4 GM 16-278A diesels; 3000 hp *(2.24 MW)* (649 and 694); 2 shafts
Speed, knots: 13. **Range, miles:** 2500 at 12 kts
Complement: 65-75
Guns: 2 Bofors 40 mm/56 (twin). 4 or 8 Oerlikon 20 mm (4 single or 4 twin).
Radars: Surface search: SO 8; I band.

Comment: All built in 1945. *Mei Chin* and *Mei Sung* transferred from US 1946, *Mei Ping* in 1956 and *Mei Lo* in 1962. Rebuilt in Taiwan and bear little resemblance to 1970s photographs.

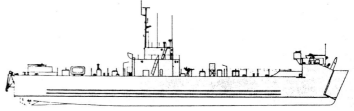

LSM 1 class (modernised)   *1988*

22 LCU 501 and LCU 1466 CLASSES

Name	No	Name	No
HO CHI (ex-*LCU 1212*)	401	HO CHENG (ex-*LCU 1145*)	486
HO HUEI (ex-*LCU 1218*)	402	HO SHAN (ex-*LCU 1596*)	488
HO YAO (ex-*LCU 1244*)	403	HO CHUAN (ex-*LCU 1597*)	489
HO DENG (ex-*LCU 1367*)	404	HO SENG (ex-*LCU 1598*)	490
HO FENG (ex-*LCU 1397*)	405	HO MENG (ex-*LCU 1599*)	491
HO CHAO (ex-*LCU 1429*)	406	HO MOU (ex-*LCU 1600*)	492
HO TENG (ex-*LCU 1452*)	407	HO SHOU (ex-*LCU 1601*)	493
HO SHUN (ex-*LCU 892*)	481	HO CHUN (ex-*LCU 1225*)	494
HO TSUNG (ex-*LCU 1213*)	482	HO YUNG (ex-*LCU 1271*)	495
HO CHUNG (ex-*LCU 849*)	484	HO CHIEN (ex-*LCU 1278*)	496
HO CHANG (ex-*LCU 512*)	485	HO CHIE (ex-*LCU 700*)	SB 1

LCU 501 class (401-486, 494-496, SB 1)

Displacement, tons: 158 light; 309 full load
Dimensions, feet (metres): 119 × 32.7 × 5 *(36.3 × 10 × 1.5)*
Main machinery: 3 GM 6-71 diesels; 522 hp *(390 kW)* sustained; 3 shafts
Speed, knots: 10
Complement: 10-25
Guns: 2 Oerlikon 20 mm. Some also may have 2—12.7 mm MGs.

LCU 1466 class (488-493)

Displacement, tons: 180 light; 360 full load
Dimensions, feet (metres): 119 × 34 × 6 *(36.3 × 10.4 × 1.8)*
Main machinery: 3 Gray Marine 64 YTL diesels; 675 hp *(504 kW)*; 3 shafts
Speed, knots: 10
Complement: 15-25
Guns: 3 Oerlikon 20 mm. Some may also have 2—12.7 mm MGs.

Comment: The LCU 501 series was built in the USA during the Second World War; initially designated LCT(6) series. The six of LCU 1466 series built by Ishikawajima Heavy Industries Co, Tokyo, Japan, for transfer to Taiwan; completed in March 1955. All originally numbered in 200-series; subsequently changed to 400-series.
Transfers: 401-407: November/December 1959 (acquired outright 3 April 1978). SB1, 494-496: January/February 1958. Remainder: 1946-48.

LCU 489   *1991*

2 + 1 TAIWAN TYPE LCU

LCU 497   LCU 498

Comment: Locally built versions of US types.

LCU 498   *10/1992, Chien Chung*

250 LCM 6 CLASS

Displacement, tons: 57 full load
Dimensions, feet (metres): 56.4 × 13.8 × 3.9 *(17.2 × 4.2 × 1.2)*
Main machinery: 2 diesels; 450 hp *(336 kW)*; 2 shafts
Speed, knots: 9
Military lift: 34 tons
Guns: 1—12.7 mm MG.

Comment: Some built in the US, some in Taiwan. 20 were exchanged for torpedoes with Indonesia.

LCM 6   *2/1993, Chien Chung*

150 LCVPs and ASSAULT CRAFT

Comment: Some ex-US, and some built in Taiwan. Most are armed with one or two 7.62 mm MGs. Two transferred to Indonesia in 1988.

TYPE 272   *1989, DTM (Raymond Cheung)*

MINE WARFARE FORCES

Note: Four ex-US Aggressive class may be transferred in 1994/95.

4 + 2 (6) MWV 50 CLASS (MINEHUNTERS—COASTAL)

EXPLORER I-IV

Displacement, tons: 500 full load
Dimensions, feet (metres): 163.1 × 28.5 × 10.2 *(49.7 × 8.7 × 3.1)*
Main machinery: 2 MTU 8V 396 TB93 diesels; 2180 hp(m) *(1.6 MW)* sustained; 2 shafts
Speed, knots: 14
Complement: 45 (5 officers)
Guns: 1 Bofors 40 mm/60.
Radars: Navigation: I band.
Sonars: Simrad SA 950; hull-mounted; active minehunting; high frequency.

Comment: Built for the Chinese Petroleum Corporation by Abeking & Rasmussen at Lemwerder, Germany. First four delivered in 1991 as offshore oil rig support ships and then converted for minehunting in Taiwan. It is reported that Thomson-CSF MCM system is fitted and that a Pluto ROV is carried. Up to eight more of the class may be built with two more reported building in 1993 in Taiwan.

MWV 50   *1990, van Ginderen Collection*

EXPLORER III   *1992, Chien Chung*

9 ADJUTANT and MSC 268 CLASSES
(MINESWEEPERS—COASTAL)

Name	No	Builders	Commissioned
YUNG CHOU (ex-US *MSC 278*)	423 (158)	Tacoma	July 1959
YUNG CHENG (ex-*Maaseik*, ex-US *MSC 78*)	441 (168)	Adams Yacht	July 1953
YUNG AN (ex-US *MSC 123*)	449 (155)	Tacoma	June 1955
YUNG SUI (ex-*Diksmuiden*, ex-US *MSC 65*)	462 (164)	H B Nevins	Feb 1954
YUNG LO (ex-US *MSC 306*)	469 (161)	Dorchester	Apr 1966
YUNG SHAN (ex-*Lier*, ex-US *MSC 63*)	476 (165)	H B Nevins	July 1953
YUNG NIEN (ex-US *MSC 277*)	479 (157)	Tacoma	May 1959
YUNG JEN (ex-*St Niklaas*, ex-US *MSC 64*)	485 (163)	H B Nevins	Feb 1954
YUNG HSIN (ex-US *MSC 302*)	488 (160)	Dorchester	Mar 1965

Displacement, tons: 375 full load
Dimensions, feet (metres): 144 × 27.9 × 8 *(43.9 × 8.5 × 2.4)*
Main machinery: 2 GM 8-268A diesels; 880 hp *(656 kW)*; 2 shafts
Speed, knots: 13. **Range, miles:** 2500 at 12 kts
Complement: 35
Guns: 2 Oerlikon 20 mm (twin).
Radars: Navigation: Decca 707; I band.
Sonars: UQS 1; hull-mounted; minehunting; high frequency.

Comment: Non-magnetic, wood-hulled minesweepers built in the USA specifically for transfer to allied navies. Five transferred from US 1955-1965; four originally built for Belgium and transferred to Taiwan in July 1969. All are of similar design; the ex-Belgian ships have a small boom aft on a pole mast. All refitted 1984-86. Only four of the class have operational sonars, and all are in very poor condition. Several deleted so far.

ADJUTANT class (old number)

AUXILIARIES

1 COMBAT SUPPORT SHIP (AOE)

Name	No	Builders	Launched	Commissioned
WU YI	530	China SB Corporation, Keelung	4 Mar 1989	23 June 1990

Displacement, tons: 7700 light; 17 000 full load
Dimensions, feet (metres): 531.8 × 72.2 × 28 *(162.1 × 22 × 8.6)*
Main machinery: 2 MAN 14-cyl diesels; 25 000 hp(m) *(18.37 MW)*; 2 shafts
Speed, knots: 21. **Range, miles:** 9200 at 10 kts
Cargo capacity: 9300 tons
Missiles: SAM: 1 Sea Chaparral quad launcher.
Guns: 2 Bofors 40 mm/70. 2 Oerlikon 20 mm GAM-CO1.
Countermeasures: Decoys: 2 chaff launchers.
ESM: Radar warning.
Radars: 2 navigation; I band.
Helicopters: Platform for CH-47 or S-70C(M)1.

Comment: Largest unit built so far for the Taiwanese Navy. Design assisted by the United Shipping Design Center in the USA. Beam replenishment rigs on both sides. SAM system on forecastle, 40 mm guns aft of the funnels. Helicopter deck at the stern. Although this is a major step forward in fleet support at sea, more than one of these ships will be needed.

WU YI   6/1993, 92 Wing RAAF

1 AMPHION CLASS (REPAIR SHIP)

Name	No	Builders	Commissioned
YU TAI	521	Tampa Shipbuilding Co, Tampa, Florida	23 Apr 1946
(ex-USS *Cadmus* AR 14)			

Displacement, tons: 7826 standard; 14 490 full load
Dimensions, feet (metres): 492 × 70 × 27.5 *(150.1 × 21.3 × 8.4)*
Main machinery: 2 Foster-Wheeler boilers; 435 psi *(30.6 kg/cm sq)*; 720°F *(382°C)*; 2 Westinghouse turbines; 8560 hp *(6.4 MW)*; 1 shaft
Speed, knots: 16.5
Complement: 920
Guns: 1 USN 5 in *(127 mm)*/38. 6 Bofors 40 mm/56 (3 twin).
Radars: Surface search: Raytheon SPS 5; G/H band; range 37 km *(20 nm)*.

Comment: Transferred from US on 31 January 1974. Fitted with SATCOM and carries up to three LCVPs.

YU TAI   2/1993, Chien Chung

2 YUEN FENG CLASS (ATTACK TRANSPORTS)

Name	No	Builders	Commissioned
YUEN FENG	523	Taiwan Shipbuilding Co, Keelung	1983
—	524	Taiwan Shipbuilding Co, Keelung	1984

Displacement, tons: 4500 full load
Dimensions, feet (metres): 360.9 × 59.1 × 18 *(110 × 18 × 5.5)*
Main machinery: 1 diesel; 1 shaft
Speed, knots: 18
Guns: 1 Bofors 40 mm/70. 2 Oerlikon 20 mm.

Comment: Can carry between 500 and 800 troops in air-conditioned accommodation.

YUEN FENG   10/1993

2 + 3 WU KANG CLASS (ATTACK TRANSPORTS) (AK)

Name	No	Builders	Commissioned
WU KANG	525	China SB Corporation, Keelung	Feb 1985
—	526	China SB Corporation, Keelung	Nov 1988
—	527	China SB Corporation, Keelung	1996
—	528	China SB Corporation, Keelung	1997
—	529	China SB Corporation, Keelung	1999

Displacement, tons: 3040 full load
Dimensions, feet (metres): 331.3 × 55.8 × 16.4 *(101 × 17 × 5)*
Main machinery: 2 diesels; 2 shafts; bow thruster
Speed, knots: 20
Military lift: 1400 troops
Missiles: SAM: 1 Sea Chaparral quad launcher.
Guns: 3 Bofors 40 mm/70.

Comment: First two were built and then the programme stopped. Restarted with the third of class laid down in July 1994. The plan is to build at about one a year to a final total of seven, but this may not be achieved. With a helicopter platform, stern docking facility and davits for four LCVP, the design resembles an LPD. Used mostly for supplying garrisons in offshore islands, and on the Spratley and Pratas islands in the South China Sea. SAM launcher is mounted aft of the foremast. Accommodation is air-conditioned.

WU KANG   1985, DTM

AK 526   10/1992, Dr Chien Chung

2 TAI HU CLASS (TRANSPORTS)

Name	No	Builders	Commissioned
TAI HU (ex-*Ling Yuen*)	522	Taiwan Shipbuilding Co, Keelung	15 Aug 1975
YUN TAI	518	Taiwan Shipbuilding Co, Keelung	1985

Measurement, tons: 2510 dwt; 3040 gross
Dimensions, feet (metres): 328.7 × 47.9 × 16.4 *(100.2 × 14.6 × 5)*
Main machinery: 1—6-cyl diesel; 1 shaft
Complement: 55
Military lift: 500 troops
Guns: 2 Oerlikon 20 mm. 2—12.7 mm MGs.

Comment: Designed by Chinese First Naval Shipyard at Tsoying. *Tai Hu* launched 27 January 1975.

YUN TAI   *7/1985, L J Lamb*

1 JAPANESE TYPE (SUPPORT TANKER)

Name	No	Builders	Commissioned
WAN SHOU	512	Ujina Shipbuilding Co, Hiroshima, Japan	1 Nov 1969

Displacement, tons: 1049 light; 4150 full load
Dimensions, feet (metres): 283.8 × 54 × 18 *(86.5 × 16.5 × 5.5)*
Main machinery: 1 diesel; 2100 hp(m) *(1.54 MW)*; 1 shaft
Speed, knots: 13
Complement: 70
Cargo capacity: 73 600 gal fuel; 62 000 gal water
Guns: 2 Bofors 40 mm/56. 2 Oerlikon 20 mm.

Comment: Employed in resupply of offshore islands.

WAN SHOU   *1984, L J Lamb*

2 PATAPSCO CLASS (SUPPORT TANKERS)

Name	No	Builders	Commissioned
HSIN LUNG (ex-USS *Elkhorn* AOG 7)	507	Cargill, Inc, Savage, Minnesota	12 Feb 1944
LUNG CHUAN (ex-HMNZS *Endeavour*, ex-USS *Namakagon* AOG 53)	515	Cargill, Inc, Savage, Minnesota	10 May 1945

Displacement, tons: 1850 light; 4335 full load
Dimensions, feet (metres): 310.8 × 48.5 × 15.7 *(94.8 × 14.8 × 4.8)*
Main machinery: 2 GM 16-278A diesels; 3000 hp *(2.24 MW)*; 2 shafts
Speed, knots: 14. **Range, miles:** 7000 at 12 kts
Complement: 124
Cargo capacity: 2000 tons
Guns: 1 USN 3 in *(76 mm)*/50. 2 Bofors 40 mm/60.
Radars: Surface search: Raytheon SPS 21; G/H band.

Comment: *Lung Chuan* was launched on 4 November 1944 and transferred from the US to New Zealand on 5 October 1962 for use as an Antarctic resupply ship; strengthened for polar operations and renamed *Endeavour*; returned to the US Navy on 29 June 1971 and retransferred to Taiwan the same date. *Hsin Lung* was launched on 15 May 1943 and was transferred to Taiwan on 1 July 1972. Both transferred by sale 19 May 1976. Third of class scrapped in 1991.

LUNG CHUAN   *2/1988*

1 DIVER CLASS (SALVAGE SHIP)

Name	No	Builders	Commissioned
TA HU (ex-USS *Grapple* ARS 7)	552 (ex-324)	Basalt Rock Co, USA	16 Dec 1943

Displacement, tons: 1557 standard; 1745 full load
Dimensions, feet (metres): 213.5 × 39 × 15 *(65.1 × 11.9 × 4.6)*
Main machinery: Diesel-electric; 4 Cooper Bessemer GSB-8 diesels; 3420 hp *(2.55 MW)*; 2 generators; 2 motors; 2 shafts
Speed, knots: 14. **Range, miles:** 8500 at 13 kts
Complement: 85
Guns: 2 Oerlikon 20 mm.
Radars: Navigation: SPS-53; I band.

Comment: Fitted for salvage, towing and compressed-air diving. Transferred from US 1 December 1977 by sale.

SURVEY AND RESEARCH SHIP

0 + 1 ALLIANCE CLASS

Displacement, tons: 2466 standard; 3180 full load
Dimensions, feet (metres): 305.1 × 49.9 × 16.7 *(93 × 15.2 × 5.1)*
Main machinery: Diesel-electric; 3 MTU/AEG diesel generators; 5712 hp(m) *(4.2 MW)*; 2 AEG motors; 5100 hp(m) *(3.75 MW)*; 2 shafts; bow thruster
Speed, knots: 15. **Range, miles:** 8000 at 12 kts
Complement: 82

Comment: Ordered in June 1993 from Fincantieri and building at Muggiano Shipyard, La Spezia. Almost identical to the NATO vessel. To be delivered in 1995. Designed for oceanography and acoustic research. Facilities include laboratories, position location systems, and overside deployment equipment. Can tow a 20 ton load at 12 kts. Equipment includes a Simrad sidescan sonar EM 1200, deep and shallow echo-sounders, two radars, Navsat and Satcom, a ROV for remote inspection, and a dynamic positioning system with bow thruster and stern positioning propeller. The ship is to be armed after delivery.

ALLIANCE (NATO colours)   *1992*

TUGS

4 CHEROKEE CLASS

Name	No	Builders	Commissioned
TA HAN (ex-USS *Tawakoni*)	ATF 542	United Engineering Co	14 Sep 1944
TA TUNG (ex-USS *Chickasaw*)	ATF 548	United Engineering Co	4 Feb 1943
— (ex-USS *Wenatchee*)	ARS 553	Charleston SB & DD	7 Sep 1944
— (ex-USS *Achomawi*)	ATF 563	United Engineering Co	10 Sep 1944

Displacement, tons: 1235 standard; 1731 full load
Dimensions, feet (metres): 205 × 38.5 × 17 *(62.5 × 11.7 × 5.2)*
Main machinery: Diesel-electric; 4 GM 12-278 diesels; 4400 hp *(3.28 MW)*; 4 generators; 1 motor; 3000 hp *(2.24 MW)*; 1 shaft
Speed, knots: 15. **Range, miles:** 6000 at 14 kts
Complement: 85
Guns: 1 USN 3 in *(76 mm)*/50. Several 12.7 mm MGs.

Comment: *Ta Tung* transferred from US in January 1966 and by sale 19 May 1976, *Ta Han* by sale 1 August 1978. Three more transferred in 1990 but one was immediately cannibalised for spares. *Ta Wan* was sunk as a target in 1988.

ATF 563   *2/1988*

3 SOTOYOMO CLASS

Name	No	Builders	Commissioned
TA SUEH (ex-USS *Tonkawa* ATA 176)	ATA 357	Levingston SB Co, Orange, Texas	19 Aug 1944
TA TENG (ex-USS *Cahokia* ATA 186)	ATA 367	Levingston SB Co, Orange, Texas	24 Nov 1944
TA PENG (ex-USS *Mahopac* ATA 196)	ATA 395	Levingston SB Co, Orange, Texas	21 Dec 1944

Displacement, tons: 435 standard; 860 full load
Dimensions, feet (metres): 143 × 33.9 × 13 *(43.6 × 10.3 × 4)*
Main machinery: Diesel-electric; 2 GM 12-278A diesels; 2200 hp *(1.64 MW)*; 2 generators; 1 motor; 1500 hp *(1.12 MW)*; 1 shaft
Speed, knots: 13
Guns: 1 USN 3 in *(76 mm)*/50. Several 12.7 mm MGs.

Comment: *Ta Sueh* transferred from US in April 1962. *Ta Teng* assigned briefly to US Air Force in 1971 until transferred to Taiwan on 14 April 1972. *Ta Peng* transferred on 1 July 1971. Latter two by sale 19 May 1976. A fourth tug of this class served as a surveying ship but has been scrapped.

7 HARBOUR TUGS

YTL 36-39   YTL 43, 45-46

Comment: Replacements for the old US Army type which were scrapped in 1990/91.

YTL 36   *4/1993, Chien Chung*

5 FLOATING DOCKS

HAY TAN (ex-USN *AFDL 36*) AFDL 1
KIM MEN (ex-USN *AFDL 5*) AFDL 2
HAN JIH (ex-USN *AFDL 34*) AFDL 3

FO WU 5 (ex-USN *ARD 9*) ARD 5
FO WU 6 (ex-USS *Windsor* ARD 22) ARD 6

Comment: Former US Navy floating dry docks. *Hay Tan* transferred in March 1947, *Kim Men* in January 1948, *Han Jih* in July 1959, *Fo Wu 5* in June 1971, *Fo Wu 6* in June 1971. *Fo Wu 6* by sale 19 May 1976 and *Fo Wu 5* on 12 January 1977.

POLICE

Note: The 1000-man 7th Peace Preservation Police Corps, National Police Administration of the Ministry of the Interior, commands two patrol groups of small craft for its police duties of anti-smuggling, anti-insurgency, and fishery protection. The northern group, based at Tamshui, has four squadrons with depots at Hualien, Suao, Keelung, and Hsinchu; the southern group, based at Kaohsiung, has five squadrons with depots at Wuchi, Makung, Anping, and Kenting. Many of these craft were transferred from the Navy on 8 December 1992. In addition, the Police recently requested funds to acquire five 100 ton, 30 kt fast patrol craft to strengthen their anti-smuggling capability. Another 10 units of 300 ton coastal patrol craft will be ordered and constructed elsewhere. A helicopter detachment with SWAT team is planned in FY 1995.

25 LARGE PATROL CRAFT

PP 801-PP 825

Displacement, tons: 100 full load
Dimensions, feet (metres): 90 × 28.6 × 6 *(27.4 × 8.7 × 1.8)*
Main machinery: 2 diesels; 2 shafts
Speed, knots: 30
Guns: 2—12.7 mm MGs (aft).
Radars: Surface search: Decca; I band.

Comment: Types vary but details given are for the seven former naval PBC 5501 class built by China SB Corporation, Kaohsiung 1989-91. These craft were transferred on 8 December 1992.

PP 823   *2/1993, Chien Chung*

31 COASTAL PATROL CRAFT

PP 501-PP 515   PP 601-PP 616

Displacement, tons: 55 full load
Dimensions, feet (metres): 68.9 × 15.7 × 3.3 *(21 × 4.8 × 1)*
Main machinery: 2 Detroit 16V-92TA diesels; 1380 hp *(1.03 MW)* sustained; 2 shafts
Speed, knots: 35
Complement: 8
Guns: 2—12.7 mm MGs.
Radars: Surface search: Decca; I band.

Comment: Types vary but details given are for the 26 former naval PBC 3501 class built at China SB Corporation, Kaohsiung, from 1990 after the first of class had been constructed in Singapore by Vosper QAF. Transferred to the Maritime Police on 8 December 1992.

PP 510 (ex-PBC 3521)   *1991, Chien Chung*

22 RIVER PATROL CRAFT

PP 301-PP 322

Comment: Described as M4 riverine speed boats. Deployed from Tamshui. A further nine craft are used for training.

5 OCEAN FISHERY PROTECTION VESSELS

YU HU 1-5

Comment: Unarmed vessels taken over from the Ministry of Agriculture in April 1993. One is of 800 tons, two of 400 tons, one of 200 tons and one of 100 tons.

CUSTOMS

Notes: (1) Director General De-Ho Jan.
(2) Ten 500 ton patrol vessels authorised in October 1992 for acquisition when funds are available. To be built by Lien-Ho Shipyard, Koahsung in conjunction with a European shipyard.
(3) In addition to the ships listed below, there are large numbers of small harbour launches.

2 TACOMA TYPE (LARGE PATROL CRAFT)

HO HSING   WEI HSING

Displacement, tons: 1795 full load
Dimensions, feet (metres): 270 × 38.1 × 13.1 *(82.3 × 11.6 × 4)*
Main machinery: 2 MTU 16V 1163 TB93 diesels; 13 310 hp(m) *(9.78 MW)* sustained; 2 shafts
Speed, knots: 22. **Range, miles:** 7000 at 16 kts
Complement: 80 (18 officers)

Comment: Built by the China SB Corporation, Keelung, to a Tacoma design and delivered in 1992. Four high-speed interceptor boats are carried on individual davits.

HO HSING   *1992*

2 COASTAL PATROL CRAFT

MOU HSING   FU HSING

Displacement, tons: 917 full load
Dimensions, feet (metres): 214.6 × 31.5 × 10.5 *(65.4 × 9.6 × 3.2)*
Main machinery: 2 MTU 16V 538 TB93 diesels; 7510 hp(m) *(5.52 MW)* sustained; 2 shafts
Speed, knots: 28
Complement: 54

Comment: Ordered from Wilton Fijenoord in September 1986, and commissioned 14 June 1988.

MOU HSING   *5/1988, Wilton Fijenoord*

2 PAO HSING CLASS (COASTAL PATROL CRAFT)

PAO HSING   CHIN HSING

Displacement, tons: 550 full load
Dimensions, feet (metres): 189.6 × 25.6 × 6.9 *(57.8 × 7.8 × 2.1)*
Main machinery: 2 MAN 12V25/30 diesels; 7183 hp(m) *(5.28 MW)* sustained; 2 shafts
Speed, knots: 20
Complement: 40
Guns: 1 Bofors 40 mm/56. 2 Oerlikon 20 mm.

Comment: First delivered 20 May 1980; second 23 May 1985. Built by Keelung yard of China SB Corporation.

CHIN HSING   2/1988

1 HSUN HSING CLASS (COASTAL PATROL CRAFT)

HSUN HSING

Displacement, tons: 264 full load
Dimensions, feet (metres): 146 × 24.6 × 5.8 *(44.5 × 7.5 × 1.7)*
Main machinery: 3 MTU 16V 396 TB93 diesels; 6540 hp(m) *(4.81 MW)* sustained; 3 shafts
Speed, knots: 28. **Range, miles:** 1500 at 20 kts
Guns: 2 Oerlikon 20 mm.

Comment: Built by China SB Corporation and delivered 15 December 1985.

HSUN HSING   1993, Taiwan Customs

1 YUN HSING CLASS (COASTAL PATROL CRAFT)

YUN HSING

Displacement, tons: 964 full load
Dimensions, feet (metres): 213.3 × 32.8 × 9.5 *(65 × 10 × 2.9)*
Main machinery: 2 MAN 12V 25/30 diesels; 7183 hp(m) *(5.28 MW)*; 2 shafts

Comment: Built by China SB Corporation and delivered 28 December 1987.

YUN HSING   6/1988

3 HAI PING CLASS (INSHORE PATROL CRAFT)

HAI PING   HAI AN   HAI CHENG

Displacement, tons: 96 full load
Dimensions, feet (metres): 85.3 × 18.4 × 3.6 *(26 × 5.6 × 1.1)*
Main machinery: 2 MTU 8V 331 TC81 diesels; 1740 hp(m) *(1.28 MW)* sustained; 2 shafts
Speed, knots: 28
Complement: 18

Comment: Built by China SB Corporation, Keelung and delivered 28 February, 18 April and 8 June 1979 respectively.

HAI PING   1989

2 HALTER TYPE (INSHORE PATROL CRAFT)

Displacement, tons: 70 full load
Dimensions, feet (metres): 78.7 × 18.4 × 4.9 *(24 × 5.6 × 1.5)*
Main machinery: 2 Detroit 12V-71TA diesels; 840 hp *(627 kW)* sustained; 2 shafts
Speed, knots: 19

Comment: Purchased in 1977. Steel hulls.

TANZANIA

Senior Appointment

Chief of Navy:
Brigadier Ligate G Sande

General

In 1993 approximately one in four craft was operational, which is an improvement on 1992. There is a small Coastguard Service (KMKM), based on Zanzibar, which uses small boats for anti-smuggling patrols.

Personnel

(a) 1994: 1050
(b) Voluntary service

Bases

Dar Es Salaam, Zanzibar, Mwanza (Lake Victoria). Mtwara (Lake Victoria).

Mercantile Marine

Lloyd's Register of Shipping:
47 vessels of 42 575 tons gross

DELETIONS

1991   *Utafiti, Rafiki, Uhuru*

PATROL FORCES

Note: There is a Police Marine Unit which operates two ex-Chinese Yuchai LSMs. There is also a survey craft TG 5 which is non-operational.

8 SHANGHAI II CLASS (FAST ATTACK CRAFT—GUN)

JW 9861-9868

Displacement, tons: 131 full load
Dimensions, feet (metres): 127.3 × 17.7 × 5.6 *(38.8 × 5.4 × 1.7)*
Main machinery: 2 Type L12-180 diesels; 2400 hp(m) *(1.76 MW)* (forward); 2 Type 12-D-6 diesels; 1820 hp(m) *(1.34 MW)* (aft); 4 shafts
Speed, knots: 30. **Range, miles:** 700 at 16.5 kts
Complement: 34
Guns: 4—37 mm/63 (2 twin). 4—25 mm/80 (2 twin).
Radars: Surface search: Skin Head; I band.

Comment: Six transferred by the People's Republic of China in 1971-72, two more in June 1992. Only the last two are fully operational.

JW 9864   1990

4 HUCHUAN CLASS (FAST ATTACK CRAFT—TORPEDO)

JW 9841-9844

Displacement, tons: 39 standard; 45.8 full load
Dimensions, feet (metres): 71.5 × 20.7 oa × 11.8 (hullborne) *(21.8 × 6.3 × 3.6)*
Main machinery: 3 Type M 50 diesels; 3300 hp(m) *(2.4 MW)* sustained; 3 shafts
Speed, knots: 50. **Range, miles:** 500 at 20 kts
Complement: 11
Guns: 2—14.5 mm (twin) MGs.
Torpedoes: 2—21 in *(533 mm)* tubes.
Radars: Surface search: Skin Head; I band.

Comment: Transferred from China 1975. After a major effort in 1992, these craft were all operational in 1993.

HUCHUAN   1993

4 YULIN CLASS (LAKE PATROL CRAFT)

Displacement, tons: 9.8 full load
Dimensions, feet (metres): 42.6 × 9.5 × 3.5 *(13 × 2.9 × 1.1)*
Main machinery: 1 PRC Type 12150 diesel; 300 hp(m) *(221 kW)*; 1 shaft
Speed, knots: 24
Complement: 10
Guns: 2—14.5 mm (twin) MGs. 2—12.7 mm (twin) MGs.

Comment: Transferred from China late 1966. Based on Victoria Nyanza. One operational in 1993.

5 KIMJIN CLASS (COASTAL PATROL CRAFT)

YU CHAI   SCHALBE   + 3

Displacement, tons: 25 full load
Dimensions, feet (metres): 66.6 × 11 × 5.5 *(20.3 × 3.4 × 1.7)*
Main machinery: 2 Type M 50 diesels; 2200 hp(m) *(1.6 MW)* sustained; 2 shafts
Speed, knots: 42. **Range, miles:** 220 at 20 kts
Complement: 10
Guns: 4—14.5 mm (2 twin) MGs.

Comment: Two delivered from North Korea in September 1987, three more in September 1988. Same type to Nicaragua. One or possibly two operational in 1993.

4 VOSPER THORNYCROFT 75ft TYPE (COASTAL PATROL CRAFT)

Displacement, tons: 70 full load
Dimensions, feet (metres): 75 × 19.5 × 8 *(22.9 × 6 × 2.4)*
Main machinery: 2 diesels; 1840 hp *(1.37 MW)*; 2 shafts
Speed, knots: 24.5. **Range, miles:** 800 at 20 kts
Complement: 11
Guns: 2 Oerlikon 20 mm

Comment: First pair delivered 6 July 1973, second pair 1974. Used for anti-smuggling patrols off Zanzibar.

VOSPER THORNYCROFT 75ft Type   1984, N Overington

THAILAND

Headquarters' Appointments

Commander-in-Chief of the Navy:
    Admiral Prachet Siridej
Deputy Commander-in-Chief:
    Admiral Santiparb Moo-Ming
Assistant Commander-in-Chief:
    Admiral Matra Ampaipast
Chief of Staff:
    Admiral Surawut Maharom
Deputy Chief-of-Staff:
    Vice Admiral Boonplaawd Manuangkaew
Commander-in-Chief, Fleet:
    Admiral Ulan Mongkolnavin
Deputy Commander-in-Chief, Fleet:
    Vice Admiral Chaichit Ratanapol
Chief of Staff, Fleet:
    Vice Admiral Kumron Nutchanart

Diplomatic Representation

Naval Attaché in London:
    Captain Suchart Kolasastraseni
Naval Attaché in Washington:
    Captain Vati Sribhadung
Naval Attaché in Bonn:
    Captain Daweesak Somabha
Naval Attaché in Paris:
    Captain Werapon Waranon
Naval Attaché in Canberra:
    Captain Wichai Juthapakdeeprasert
Naval Attaché in Madrid:
    Captain Amorntep Na-Bangchang

Personnel

(a) 1994: Navy, 62 000 including Naval Air Arm, Marines and Coastal Defence Command
(b) 2 years' national service

Organisation

First naval area command (East Thai Gulf)
Second naval area command (West Thai Gulf)
Third naval area command (Andaman Sea)
First air wing (U-Tapao)
Second air wing (Songkhla)

Bases

Bangkok, Sattahip, Songkhla, Phang-Nga (west coast)

Prefix to Ships' Names

HTMS

Strength of the Fleet

Type	Active	Building (Projected)
Helicopter Carrier	—	1
Frigates	10 + 2	2
Corvettes	5	—
Fast Attack Craft (Missile)	6	—
Fast Attack Craft (Gun)	3	—
Large Patrol Craft	9	—
Coastal Patrol Craft	35	—
River Patrol Craft	60+	—
MCM Support Ship	1	—
Minehunters	2	—
Coastal Minesweepers	3	—
MSBs	5	—
LSTs	6	—
LSMs	2	—
LCG	1	—
LSIL	2	—
Hovercraft	3	—
LCUs	9	—
Landing Craft	40	—
Survey Vessels	5	—
Replenishment Ship	—	1
Oil Tankers	5	—
Water Tanker	1	—
Tugs	6	—
Training Ships	3	—
Marine Police Craft	125	(1)

Marine Corps

Currently consists of two Divisions including an amphibious assault battalion. In 1993 personnel strength is about 20 500, although the establishment figure is 25 000.

Coast Guard

A trial coastal unit of one frigate, eight patrol craft and four aircraft was established on 1 April 1989. The Coast Guard Squadron was officially authorised on 29 September 1992 when the eight patrol craft were increased to 11. Armed Sea Rangers in converted Fishing Vessels are being used to counter pirates. Ships and aircraft are rotated monthly from the Navy.

Coastal Defence Command

This unit was rapidly expanded to the 1992 two Division level after the government charged the RTN with the responsibility of defending the entire Eastern Seaboard Development Project on the east coast of the Gulf of Thailand in 1988. Equipment includes 155 mm and 130 mm guns for coastal defence, 76 mm, 40 mm, 37 mm, 20 mm guns and PL-9B SAM for air defence.

Marine Police

Acts as a Coast Guard in inshore waters with some 62 armed patrol craft and another 63 equipped with small arms only.

Future Plans

Plans to acquire submarines still under consideration. Potential submarine officers have already been trained. A new dockyard will be operational in 1996 at Sattahip, with facilities for large vessels. New batches of patrol craft, LCUs, coastal minesweepers, Bell 212 helicopters and Dornier 228 surveillance aircraft are planned.

Mercantile Marine

Lloyd's Register of Shipping:
    407 vessels of 1 116 457 tons gross

DELETIONS

Patrol Forces

1992   *Sarasin, Phali*
1994   *Tongpliu*

Mine Warfare Forces

1992   *Tadindang*

HELICOPTER CARRIER

0 + 1 CHAKRI NARUEBET CLASS

Name	No	Builders	Laid down	Launched	Commissioned
CHAKRI NARUEBET	911	Bazán, Ferrol	Sep 1994	Feb 1996	July 1997

Displacement, tons: 11 485 full load
Dimensions, feet (metres): 599.1 oa; 538.4 wl × 100.1 oa; 73.8 wl × 20.3
(182.6; 164.1 × 30.5; 22.5 × 6.2)
Flight deck, feet (metres): 572.8 × 100.1 *(174.6 × 30.5)*
Main machinery: CODOG; 2 GE LM 2500 gas-turbines; 44 250 hp *(33 MW)* sustained; 2 MTU 16V 1163 TB83 diesels; 11 780 hp(m) *(8.67 MW)*; 2 shafts; cp props
Speed, knots: 27; 16 (diesels). **Range, miles:** 10 000 at 12 kts
Complement: 455 (62 officers) plus 146 aircrew plus 4 (Royal family)

Missiles: SAM: 1 Mk 41 LCHR 8 cell VLS launcher; Sea Sparrow missiles.
Guns: 4 Vulcan Phalanx CIWS. 2—30 mm.
Countermeasures: Decoys: 4 chaff launchers. ESM/ECM.
Radars: Air search: SPS 52C or SPS 48; E/F band.
Surface search: SPS 64; I band.
Fire control. Aircraft control.
Sonars: Hull-mounted; active search; medium frequency.

Fixed wing aircraft: Up to 12 AV-8B Harrier II type (in due course).
Helicopters: Up to 14 Sea King type; Chinook capable.

Programmes: An initial contract for a 7800 ton vessel with Bremer Vulcan was cancelled on 22 July 1991 and replaced on 27 March 1992 with a government to government contract for a larger ship to be built by Bazán. Fabrication started in October 1993.
Structure: Similar to Spanish *Principe de Asturias*. 12° ski jump and two 20 ton aircraft lifts. Weapon systems still to be confirmed and may be fitted in Thailand after delivery. Hangar can take up 10 Sea Harrier or Sea King sized aircraft.

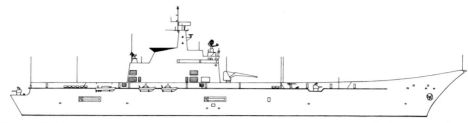

CHAKRI NARUEBET *(Scale 1 : 1500), Ian Sturton*

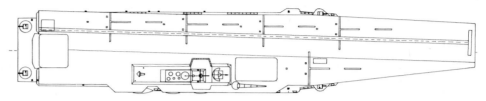

CHAKRI NARUEBET *(Scale 1 : 1500), Ian Sturton*

Operational: Main tasks are SAR co-ordination and EEZ surveillance. Secondary role is air support for all maritime operations.

CHAKRI NARUEBET (model) *1992, Bazán*

FRIGATES

2 TACHIN (TACOMA) CLASS

Name	No	Builders	Laid down	Launched	Commissioned
TACHIN (ex-USS *Glendale* PF 36)	1	Consolidated Steel Corporation, Los Angeles	6 Apr 1943	28 May 1943	1 Oct 1943
PRASAE (ex-USS *Gallup* PF 47)	2	Consolidated Steel Corporation, Los Angeles	18 Aug 1943	17 Sep 1943	29 Feb 1944

Displacement, tons: 1430 standard; 2454 full load
Dimensions, feet (metres): 304 × 37.5 × 12.5
(92.7 × 11.4 × 4.1)
Main machinery: 2 boilers; 2 reciprocating engines; 5500 ihp *(4.1 MW)*; 2 shafts
Speed, knots: 18. **Range, miles:** 7200 at 12 kts; 5400 at 15 kts
Complement: 214 (13 officers)

Guns: 3 USN 3 in *(76 mm)*/50; 85° elevation; 20 rounds/minute to 12 km *(6.6 nm)*; weight of shell 6 kg.
2 Bofors 40 mm/60; 80° elevation; 120 rounds/minute to 10 km *(5.5 nm)*; weight of shell 0.89 kg.
9 Oerlikon 20 mm/70; 800 rounds/minute to 2 km.
Torpedoes: 6—324 mm US Mk 32 (2 triple) tubes; anti-submarine.
A/S mortars: 1 Mk 10 multi-barrelled fixed Hedgehog; range 350 m; warhead 26 kg; 24 rockets.
Depth charges: 8 projectors; 2 racks.
Radars: Air search: Westinghouse SPS 6; D band; range 146 km *(80 nm)* against fighter aircraft.
Surface search: Raytheon SPS 5 *(Tachin)*; G/H band. Raytheon SPS 10 *(Prasae)*; G/H band.
Navigation: Decca; I band.
Fire control: Mk 51; I/J band.
IFF: UPX 12B.
Sonars: EDO SQS 17B; hull-mounted; active search and attack; medium/high frequency.

PRASAE *1/1991, Royal Thai Navy*

Programmes: Delivered from the US on 29 October 1951. The last active survivors of the US equivalent of the British and Canadian River class.

Operational: Used in Training Squadron and in rotation for Coast-guard duties.

0 + 2 NARESUAN CLASS (TYPE 25T) (FFG)

Name	No	Builders	Laid down	Launched	Commissioned
NARESUAN	621	Zhonghua SY, Shanghai	1991	24 July 1993	Oct 1994
TAKSIN	622	Zhonghua SY, Shanghai	1991	May 1994	Sep 1995

Displacement, tons: 2500 standard; 2980 full load
Dimensions, feet (metres): 393.7 × 42.7 × 12.5
(120 × 13 × 3.8)
Main machinery: CODOG; 2 GE LM 2500 gas-turbines; 55 000 hp *(41 MW)* sustained; 2 MTU 20 V 1163 TB83 diesels; 14 730 hp(m) *(10.84 MW)* sustained; 2 shafts; cp props
Speed, knots: 32. **Range, miles:** 4000 at 18 kts
Complement: 150

Missiles: SSM: 8 McDonnell Douglas Harpoon (2 quad) launchers ❶; active radar homing to 130 km *(70 nm)* at 0.9 Mach; warhead 227 kg.
SAM: Mk 41 LCHR 8 cell VLS launcher ❷ Sea Sparrow; semi-active radar homing to 14.6 km *(8 nm)* at 2.5 Mach; warhead 39 kg.
Guns: 1 FMC 5 in *(127 mm)*/54 Mk 45 Mod 2 ❸; 65° elevation; 20 rounds/minute to 23 km *(12.6 nm)*; weight of shell 32 kg. 4 China 37 mm/76 (2 twin) H/PJ 76 A ❹; 85° elevation; 180 rounds/minute to 8.5 km *(4.6 nm)* anti-aircraft; weight of shell 1.42 kg.
Torpedoes: 6—324 mm Mk 32 Mod 5 (2 triple) tubes ❺. Honeywell Mk 46; active/passive homing to 11 km *(5.9 nm)* at 40 kts; warhead 44 kg.
Countermeasures: Decoys: China Type 945 GPJ 26-barrelled launchers ❻; chaff and IR.
ESM/ECM: Mirage EW System.
Fire control: 1 JM-83H Optical Director ❼.
Radars: Air search: Signaal LW 08 ❽; D band.
Surface search: China Type 360 ❾; E/F band.
Navigation: Two Raytheon SPS 64(V)5; I band.
Fire control: Two Signaal STIR ❿; I/J/K band (for SSM and 127 mm).
China 374 G ⓫ (for 37 mm).
Sonars: China SJD-7; hull-mounted; active search and attack; medium frequency.

Helicopters: 1 Kamen SH-2F Seasprite ⓬.

Programmes: Contract signed 21 September 1989 for construction of two ships by the China State SB Corporation (CSSC) with delivery in 1994. US and European weapon systems are to be fitted after delivery in Thailand. By early 1993 the programme had slipped by 12 months but some of this has been recovered.

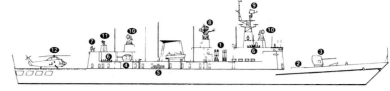

NARESUAN (Scale 1 : 1200), Ian Sturton

NARESUAN 7/1993, Royal Thai Navy

Structure: Jointly designed by the Royal Thai Navy and China State Shipbuilding Corporation (CSSC). This is a new design incorporating much Western machinery and equipment and provides enhanced capabilities by comparison with the four Type 053 class.

NARESUAN (model) 1991, Royal Thai Navy

NARESUAN 9/1993, Hachiro Nakai

4 + (2) CHAO PHRAYA CLASS (TYPES 053 HT and 053 HT (H)) (FFG)

Name	No	Builders	Laid down	Launched	Commissioned
CHAO PHRAYA	455	Hudong SY, Shanghai	1989	24 June 1990	5 Apr 1991
BANGPAKONG	456	Hudong SY, Shanghai	1989	25 July 1990	20 July 1991
KRABURI	457	Hudong SY, Shanghai	1990	28 Dec 1990	16 Jan 1992
SAIBURI	458	Hudong SY, Shanghai	1990	27 Aug 1991	4 Aug 1992

Displacement, tons: 1676 standard; 1924 full load
Dimensions, feet (metres): 338.5 × 37.1 × 10.2
  (103.2 × 11.3 × 3.1)
Main machinery: 4 MTU 20V 1163 TB83 diesels; 29 440 hp(m)
  (21.6 MW) sustained; 2 shafts; cp props
Speed, knots: 30. **Range, miles:** 3500 at 18 kts
Complement: 168 (22 officers)

Missiles: SSM: 8 Ying Ji (Eagle Strike) (C-801) ❶; active radar/IR
  homing to 85 km (45.9 nm) at 0.9 Mach; warhead 165 kg; sea-
  skimmer. This is the extended range version.
SAM: 1 HQ-61 launcher for PL-9 to be fitted in due course.
Guns: 2 (457 and 458) or 4 China 100 mm/56 (1 or 2 twin) ❷;
  85° elevation; 25 rounds/minute to 22 km (12 nm); weight of
  shell 15.9 kg.
  8 China 37 mm/76 (4 twin) H/PJ 76 A ❸; 85° elevation; 180
  rounds/minute to 8.5 km (4.6 nm) anti-aircraft; weight of shell
  1.42 kg.
A/S mortars: 2 RBU 1200 (China Type 86) 5-tubed fixed launch-
  ers ❹; range 1200 m.
Depth charges: 2 BMB racks.
Countermeasures: Decoys: 2 China Type 945 GPJ 26-barrelled
  chaff launchers.
ESM: China Type 923(1); intercept.
ECM: China Type 981(3); jammer.
Combat data systems: China Type ZKJ-3 action data
  automation.
Radars: Air/surface search: China Type 354 Eye Shield ❺;
  E band.
Surface search/fire-control: China Type 352C Square Tie ❻;
  I band (for SSM).
Fire control: China Type 343 Sun Visor ❼; I band (for 100 mm).
  China Type 341 Rice Lamp ❽; I band (for 37 mm).
Navigation: Racal Decca 1290 A/D ARPA; I band.
IFF: Type 651.
Sonars: China Type SJD-5A; hull-mounted; active search and
  attack; medium frequency.

Helicopters: 1 Seahawk or Seasprite (457 and 458) ❾ in due
  course. Bell 212 are embarked as an interim measure.

Programmes: Contract signed 18 July 1988 for four modified
  Jianghu class ships to be built by the China State SB Corporation (CSSC). Two more improved 053 HT (H) type are to be
  built in Thailand. Design work was still being progressed in
  early 1994.
Structure: Thailand would have preferred only the hulls but
  China insisted on full armament. Two of the ships are the Type
  III variant with 100 mm guns, fore and aft, and the other two
  are a variation with a helicopter platform replacing the after
  100 mm gun. German communication equipment fitted.
Operational: On arrival in Thailand each ship was docked to
  make good poor shipbuilding standards, and improve damage
  control capabilities. The ships are mostly used for rotating
  monthly to the Coast Guard, and for training.

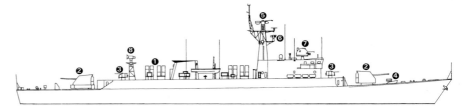

CHAO PHRAYA
(Scale 1 : 900), Ian Sturton

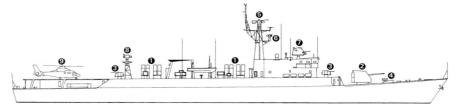

KRABURI
(Scale 1 : 900), Ian Sturton

KRABURI
6/1993, Royal Thai Navy

CHAO PHRAYA
4/1992, 92 Wing RAAF

0 + 2 KNOX CLASS

Name	No	Builders	Laid down	Launched	Commissioned
PHUTTHALOETLA NAPHALAI (ex-*Ouellet*)	462 (ex-FF 1077)	Avondale Shipyards	15 Jan 1969	17 Jan 1970	12 Dec 1970
PHUTTHAYOTFA CHULALOK (ex-*Truett*)	461 (ex-FF 1095)	Avondale Shipyards	27 Apr 1972	3 Feb 1973	1 June 1974

Displacement, tons: 3011 standard; 4260 full load
Dimensions, feet (metres): 439.6 × 46.8 × 15; 24.8 (sonar)
   (134 × 14.3 × 4.6; 7.8)
Main machinery: 2 Combustion Engineering/Babcock & Wilcox
   boilers; 1200 psi *(84.4 kg/cm sq)*; 950°F *(510°C)*; 1 turbine;
   35 000 hp *(26 MW)*; 1 shaft
Speed, knots: 27. **Range, miles:** 4000 at 22 kts on 1 boiler
Complement: 288 (17 officers)

Missiles: SSM: 8 McDonnell Douglas Harpoon; active radar homing to 130 km *(70 nm)* at 0.9 Mach; warhead 227 kg.
A/S: Honeywell ASROC Mk 16 octuple launcher with reload system (has 2 cells modified to fire Harpoon) ❶; inertial guidance
   to 1.6-10 km *(1-5.4 nm)*; payload Mk 46.
Guns: 1 FMC 5 in *(127 mm)*/54 Mk 42 Mod 9 ❷; 85° elevation;
   20-40 rounds/minute to 24 km *(13 nm)* anti-surface; 14 km
   (7.7 nm) anti-aircraft; weight of shell 32 kg.
   1 General Electric/General Dynamics 20 mm/76 6-barrelled
   Mk 15 Vulcan Phalanx ❸; 3000 rounds/minute combined to
   1.5 km.
Torpedoes: 4—324 mm Mk 32 (2 twin) fixed tubes ❹. 22 Honeywell Mk 46; anti-submarine; active/passive homing to 11 km
   (5.9 nm) at 40 kts; warhead 44 kg.
Countermeasures: Decoys: 2 Loral Hycor SRBOC 6-barrelled
   fixed Mk 36 ❺; IR flares and chaff to 4 km *(2.2 nm)*. T Mk-6
   Fanfare/SLQ-25 Nixie; torpedo decoy. Prairie Masker hull and
   blade rate noise suppression.
ESM/ECM: SLQ 32(V)2 ❻; radar warning. Sidekick modification
   adds jammer and deception system.
Combat data systems: Link 14 receive only.
Fire control: SWG-1A Harpoon LCS. Mk 68 GFCS. Mk 114 ASW
   FCS. Mk 1 target designation system. MMS target acquisition
   sight (for mines, small craft and low flying aircraft).
Radars: Air search: Lockheed SPS 40B ❼; E/F band; range
   320 km *(175 nm)*.
Surface search: Raytheon SPS 10 or Norden SPS 67 ❽; G band.
Navigation: Marconi LN 66; I band.
Fire control: Western Electric SPG 53A/D/F ❾; I/J band.
Tacan: SRN 15. IFF: UPX-12.
Sonars: EDO/General Electric SQS 26 CX; bow-mounted; active
   search and attack; medium frequency.
   EDO SQR 18A(V)1; passive towed array; very low frequency.

Helicopters: 1 Seasprite type ❿.

Programmes: The first ship is planned to transfer on lease from
   the US on 30 July 1994 and the second on 19 August 1996.
   Two more may also be acquired in due course.
Structure: Four Mk 32 torpedo tubes are fixed in the midships
   structure, two to a side, angled out at 45°. The arrangement
   provides improved loading capability over exposed triple
   Mk 32 torpedo tubes. A 4000 lb lightweight anchor is fitted on
   the port side and an 8000 lb anchor fits into the after section of
   the sonar dome.

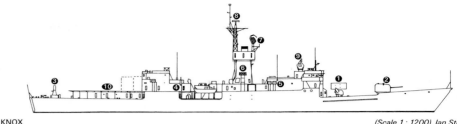

KNOX   *(Scale 1 : 1200), Ian Sturton*

KNOX (US colours)   *9/1993, H M Steele*

Operational: Towed sonar array and helicopter facilities are
   uncertain in early 1994 but the acquisition of these ships adds
   emphasis to the need for a LAMPS I helicopter.

1 YARROW TYPE (TRAINING SHIP)

Name	No	Builders	Laid down	Launched	Commissioned
MAKUT RAJAKUMARN	7	Yarrow (Shipbuilders)	11 Jan 1970	18 Nov 1971	7 May 1973

Displacement, tons: 1650 standard; 1900 full load
Dimensions, feet (metres): 320 × 36 × 18.1
   (97.6 × 11 × 5.5)
Main machinery: CODOG; 1 RR Olympus TM3B gas-turbine;
   22 500 hp *(16.8 MW)* sustained; 1 Crossley-SEMT Pielstick 12
   PC2.2 V 400 diesel; 6000 hp(m) *(4.4 MW)* sustained; 2 shafts
Speed, knots: 26 gas; 18 diesel. **Range, miles:** 5000 at 18 kts;
   1200 at 26 kts
Complement: 140 (16 officers)

Guns: 2 Vickers 4.5 in *(114 mm)*/55 Mk 8 ❶; 55° elevation; 25
   rounds/minute to 22 km *(12 nm)* anti-surface; 6 km *(3.3 nm)*
   anti-aircraft; weight of shell 21 kg.
   2 Bofors 40 mm/60 ❷; 80° elevation; 120 rounds/minute to
   10 km *(5.5 nm)*; weight of shell 0.89 kg.
A/S mortars: 1 Limbo 3-tubed Mk 10 ❸; range 1000 m; warhead
   92 kg.
Depth charges: 1 rack.
Countermeasures: ESM: Racal UA 3; radar warning. FH-4; D/F.
Combat data systems: Signaal Sewaco TH action data
   automation.
Radars: Air/surface search: Signaal DA 05 ❹; E/F band; range
   137 km *(75 nm)* for 2 m² target.
Navigation: Signaal ZW 06; I band.
Fire control: Signaal WM 22 series ❺; I/J band; range 46 km
   (25 nm).
Sonars: Atlas Elektronik DSQS 21C; hull-mounted; active search
   and attack; medium frequency.

Programmes: Ordered on 21 August 1969 as a general-purpose
   frigate.
Modernisation: A severe fire in February 1984 resulted in extensive work including replacement of the Olympus gas-turbine, a
   new ER control room and central electric switchboard. Further
   modifications included the removal of Limbo mortar, Seacat
   SAM system and the installation of new electronics. Plans to fit
   SSM, Sea Sparrow SAM system or CIWS, and torpedo tubes,
   have been shelved, and the Limbo was restored in 1992.
Operational: The ship is largely automated with a consequent
   saving in complement, and has been most successful in service. Has lost its Flagship role to one of the Chinese-built
   frigates and become a training ship.

MAKUT RAJAKUMARN   *(Scale 1 : 900), Ian Sturton*

MAKUT RAJAKUMARN   *5/1993, John Mortimer*

2 TAPI (PF 103) CLASS

Name	No	Builders	Laid down	Launched	Commissioned
TAPI	5	American SB Co, Toledo, Ohio	1 July 1970	17 Oct 1970	19 Nov 1971
KHIRIRAT	6	Norfolk SB & DD Co	18 Feb 1972	2 June 1973	10 Aug 1974

Displacement, tons: 885 standard; 1172 full load
Dimensions, feet (metres): 275 × 33 × 10; 14.1 (sonar)
  (83.8 × 10 × 3; 4.3)
Main machinery: 2 Fairbanks-Morse 38TD8-1/8-9 diesels;
  5250 hp *(3.9 MW)* sustained; 2 shafts
Speed, knots: 20. **Range, miles:** 2400 at 18 kts
Complement: 135 (15 officers)

Guns: 1 OTO Melara 3 in *(76 mm)*/62 compact ❶; 85° elevation;
  85 rounds/minute to 16 km *(8.7 nm)* anti-surface; 12 km
  (6.6 nm) anti-aircraft; weight of shell 6 kg.
  1 Bofors 40 mm/70 ❷; 85° elevation; 300 rounds/minute to
  12.5 km *(6.8 nm)*; weight of shell 0.96 kg.
  2 Oerlikon 20 mm ❸. 2—12.7 mm MGs.
Torpedoes: 6—324 mm US Mk 32 (2 triple) tubes ❹. Honeywell
  Mk 46; anti-submarine; active/passive homing to 11 km
  (5.9 nm) at 40 kts; warhead 44 kg.
Depth charges: 1 rack.
Combat data systems: Signaal Sewaco TH.
Radars: Air/surface search: Signaal LW 04 ❺; E/F band; range
  137 km *(75 nm)* for 2 m² target.
  Surface search: Raytheon SPS 53E ❻; I band.
  Fire control: Signaal WM 22-61 ❼; I/J band; range 46 km
  (25 nm).
IFF: UPX-23.
Sonars: Atlas Elektronik DSQS 21C; hull-mounted; active search
  and attack; medium frequency.

Programmes: *Tapi* was ordered on 27 June 1969. *Khirirat* was
  ordered on 25 June 1971.
Modernisation: *Tapi* completed 1983 and *Khirirat* in 1987. This
  included new gunnery and radars and a slight heightening of
  the funnel. Further modernisation in 1988-89 mainly to external and internal communications.
Structure: Of similar design to the Iranian ships of the Bayandor
  class.

TAPI

(Scale 1 : 900), Ian Sturton

TAPI

6/1993, Royal Thai Navy

1 CANNON CLASS

Name	No	Builders	Laid down	Launched	Commissioned
PIN KLAO (ex-USS *Hemminger* DE 746)	3 (ex-1)	Western Pipe & Steel Co	1943	12 Sep 1943	30 May 1944

Displacement, tons: 1240 standard; 1930 full load
Dimensions, feet (metres): 306 × 36.7 × 14
  (93.3 × 11.2 × 4.3)
Main machinery: Diesel-electric; 4 GM 16-278A diesels;
  6000 hp *(4.5 MW)*; 4 generators; 2 motors; 2 shafts
Speed, knots: 20. **Range, miles:** 10 800 at 12 kts; 6700 at
  19 kts
Complement: 192 (14 officers)

Guns: 3 USN 3 in *(76 mm)*/50 Mk 22; 85° elevation; 20 rounds/
  minute to 12 km *(6.6 nm)*; weight of shell 6 kg.
  6 Bofors 40 mm/60 (3 twin); 80° elevation; 120 rounds/
  minute to 10 km *(5.5 nm)*; weight of shell 0.89 kg.
Torpedoes: 6—324 mm US Mk 32 (2 triple) tubes;
  anti-submarine.
A/S mortars: 1 Hedgehog Mk 10 multi-barrelled fixed; range
  250 m; warhead 13.6 kg; 24 rockets.
Depth charges: 8 projectors; 2 racks.
Countermeasures: ESM: WLR-1; radar warning.
Fire control: Mk 52 radar GFCS for 3 in guns. Mk 63 radar GFCS
  for aft gun only. 2 Mk 51 optical GFCS for 40 mm.
Radars: Air/surface search: Raytheon SPS 5; G/H band.
  Navigation: Raytheon SPS 21; G/H band.
  Fire control: Western Electric Mk 34; I/J band.
  RCA/General Electric Mk 26; I/J band.
IFF: SLR 1.
Sonars: SQS 11; hull-mounted; active attack; high frequency.

Programmes: Transferred from US Navy at New York Navy Ship-
  yard in July 1959 under MDAP and by sale 6 June 1975.
Modernisation: The three 21 in torpedo tubes were removed and
  the four 20 mm guns were replaced by four 40 mm. The six
  A/S torpedo tubes were fitted in 1966.
Operational: Used mostly as an alongside training ship.

PIN KLAO

3/1991, 92 Wing RAAF

SHIPBORNE AIRCRAFT

Notes: (1) Negotiations for SH-2F Seasprite helicopters were still proceeding in early 1994. Kamov
Ka-27 are a possible alternative.
(2) Spanish Harrier AV-8S aircraft are one option for the new carrier in due course.

Numbers/Type: 7 Bell 212.
Operational speed: 100 kts *(185 km/h)*.
Service ceiling: 13 200 ft *(4025 m)*.
Range: 200 nm *(370 km)*.
Role/Weapon systems: Commando assault and general support. Mostly based ashore but oper-
ate from Normed class and frigates. Weapons: Pintle-mounted M60 machine guns.

BELL 212

1993, Royal Thai Navy

Numbers/Type: (6) Sikorsky S-70B Seahawk.
Operational speed: 135 kts *(250 km/h)*.
Service ceiling: 10 000 ft *(3050 m)*.
Range: 600 nm *(1110 km)*.
Role/Weapon systems: Multi-mission helicopters ordered on 28 September 1993 for delivery in
  1997. This is the export model for the SH-60. To be used for patrol, surveillance and SAR.

LAND-BASED MARITIME AIRCRAFT (FRONT LINE)

Notes: (1) In early 1994 negotiations were continuing for up to 30 A7-E Corsair aircraft from the
US Navy.
(2) Cessna transports and UH-1H utility helicopters are in service in the support role.

Numbers/Type: 3/2 Fokker F27 Maritime 200/400.
Operational speed: 250 kts *(463 km/h)*.
Service ceiling: 2500 ft *(7620 m)*.
Range: 2700 nm *(5000 km)*.
Role/Weapon systems: Increased coastal surveillance and response is provided, including ASW
  and ASV action. Sensors: APS-504 search radar, Bendix weather radar, ESM and MAD equip-
  ment. Weapons: ASW; 4 × Mk 46 or Stingray torpedoes or depth bombs or mines. ASV; 2 × Har-
  poon ASM.

Numbers/Type: 3 Lockheed P-3B Orion.
Operational speed: 411 kts *(761 km/h)*.
Service ceiling: 28 300 ft *(8625 m)*.
Range: 4000 nm *(7410 km)*.
Role/Weapon systems: Ordered in 1993 for delivery in 1995/96. Sensors: APS-115 radar, ECM/
  ESM. Weapons: ASW; Mk 46 torpedoes (possibly). ASV; 4 × Harpoon.

Numbers/Type: 4 Bell 214ST.
Operational speed: 130 kts *(241 km/h).*
Service ceiling: 10 000 ft *(3050 m).*
Range: 450 nm *(834 km).*
Role/Weapon systems: VIP and general support duties. Weapons: Pintle-mounted M60 machine guns.

Numbers/Type: 5 Grumman S-2F Tracker.
Operational speed: 130 kts *(241 km/h).*
Service ceiling: 25 000 ft *(7620 m).*
Range: 1350 nm *(2500 km).*
Role/Weapon systems: MR and ASW operations, with limited ASV capability; now being supplemented by F27. Turbo conversion being considered but is unlikely because of airframe condition. Three deleted in 1994. Sensors: Search radar, ESM, MAD. Weapons: ASW; 4 × Mk 46 torpedoes, depth bombs, mines. ASV; 6 × 127 mm rockets.

Numbers/Type: 5 GAF Searchmaster B (Nomad).
Operational speed: 168 kts *(311 km/h).*
Service ceiling: 21 000 ft *(6400 m).*
Range: 730 nm *(1352 km).*
Role/Weapon systems: Short-range MR for EEZ protection and anti-smuggling operations. Sensors: Search radar, cameras. Weapons: Unarmed.

Numbers/Type: 3 Dornier 228.
Operational speed: 200 kts *(370 km/h).*
Service ceiling: 28 000 ft *(8535 m).*
Range: 940 nm *(1740 km).*
Role/Weapon systems: Coastal surveillance and EEZ protection. Acquired in 1991. More of this type are planned.

Numbers/Type: 2 Canadair CL 215.
Operational speed: 206 kts *(382 km/h).*
Service ceiling: 10 000 ft *(3050 m).*
Range: 1125 nm *(2085 km).*
Role/Weapon systems: Used for general purpose transport and SAR.

TRACKER   *1993, Royal Thai Navy*

CL 215   *1993, Royal Thai Navy*

CORVETTES

Note: Two Assad class (ex-Iraq) have been investigated as possible acquisitions.

2 RATTANAKOSIN CLASS

Name	No	Builders	Laid down	Launched	Commissioned
RATTANAKOSIN	1	Tacoma Boatbuilders, Washington	6 Feb 1984	11 Mar 1986	26 Sep 1986
SUKHOTHAI	2	Tacoma Boatbuilders, Washington	26 Mar 1984	20 July 1986	10 June 1987

Displacement, tons: 960 full load
Dimensions, feet (metres): 252 × 31.5 × 8 *(76.8 × 9.6 × 2.4)*
Main machinery: 2 MTU 20V 1163 TB83 diesels; 14 730 hp(m) *(10.83 MW)* sustained; 2 shafts
Speed, knots: 26. **Range, miles:** 3000 at 16 kts
Complement: 87 (15 officers) plus Flag Staff

Missiles: SSM: 8 McDonnell Douglas Harpoon (2 quad) launchers ❶; active radar homing to 130 km *(70 nm)* at 0.9 Mach; warhead 227 kg (84A) or 258 kg (84B/C).
SAM: Selenia Elsag Albatros octuple launcher ❷; 24 Aspide; semi-active radar homing to 13 km *(7 nm)* at 2.5 Mach; height envelope 15-5000 m *(49.2-16 405 ft)*; warhead 30 kg.
Guns: 1 OTO Melara 3 in *(76 mm)*/62 ❸; 85° elevation; 60 rounds/minute to 16 km *(8.7 nm)*; weight of shell 6 kg.
2 Breda 40 mm/70 (twin) ❹; 85° elevation; 300 rounds/minute to 12.5 km *(6.8 nm)*; weight of shell 0.96 kg.
2 Oerlikon 20 mm ❺; 55° elevation; 800 rounds/minute to 2 km.
Torpedoes: 6—324 mm US Mk 32 (2 triple) tubes ❻. MUSL Stingray; active/passive homing to 11 km *(5.9 nm)* at 45 kts; warhead 35 kg (shaped charge); depth to 750 m *(2460 ft)*.
Countermeasures: Decoys: CSEE Dagaie 6 or 10-tubed trainable; IR flares and chaff; H-J band.
ESM: Elettronica; intercept.
Fire control: Signaal Sewaco TH action data automation. Lirod 8 optronic director ❼.

Radars: Air/surface search: Signaal DA 05 ❽; E/F band; range 137 km *(75 nm)* for 2 m² target.
Surface search: Signaal ZW 06 ❾; I band.
Navigation: Decca 1226; I band.
Fire control: Signaal WM 25/41 ❿; I/J band; range 46 km *(25 nm)*.
Sonars: Atlas Elektronik DSQS 21C; hull-mounted; active search and attack; medium frequency.

Programmes: Contract signed with Tacoma on 9 May 1983. Intentions to build a third were overtaken by the Vosper corvettes. First laid down 6 February 1984, launched 11 March 1986; second laid down 26 March 1984, launched 20 July 1986.
Structure: Similar design to missile corvettes built for Saudi Arabia five years earlier. Space for Phalanx aft of the Harpoon launchers.

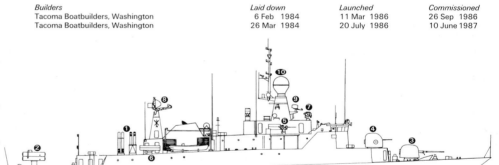

RATTANAKOSIN   *(Scale 1 : 600), Ian Sturton*

RATTANAKOSIN   *1992, Ships of the World*

3 KHAMRONSIN CLASS

Name	No	Builders	Laid down	Launched	Commissioned
KHAMRONSIN	1	Ital Thai Marine, Bangkok	15 Mar 1988	15 Aug 1989	29 July 1992
THAYANCHON	2	Ital Thai Marine, Bangkok	20 Apr 1988	7 Dec 1989	5 Sep 1992
LONGLOM	3	Bangkok Naval Dockyard	15 Mar 1988	8 Aug 1989	2 Oct 1992

Displacement, tons: 475 half load
Dimensions, feet (metres): 203.4 oa; 186 wl × 26.9 × 8.2 *(62; 56.7 × 8.2 × 2.5)*
Main machinery: 2 MTU 12V 1163 TB93; 9980 hp(m) *(7.34 MW)* sustained; 2 KaMeWa cp props
Speed, knots: 25. **Range, miles:** 2500 at 15 kts
Complement: 57 (6 officers)

Guns: 1 OTO Melara 76 mm/62 Mod 7; 85° elevation; 60 rounds/minute to 16 km *(8.7 nm)*; weight of shell 6 kg.
2 Breda 30 mm/70 (twin); 85° elevation; 800 rounds/minute to 12.5 km *(6.8 nm)*; weight of shell 0.37 kg.
Torpedoes: 6 Plessey PMW 49A (2 triple) launchers; MUSL Stingray; active/passive homing to 11 km *(6 nm)* at 45 kts; warhead 35 kg shaped charge.
Combat data systems: Plessey Nautis P action data automation.
Fire control: British Aerospace Sea Archer 1A Mod 2 optronic GFCS.
Radars: Air/surface search: Plessey AWS 4; E/F band; range 101 km *(55 nm)*.
Sonars: Atlas Elektronik DSQS-21C; hull-mounted; active search and attack; medium frequency.

Programmes: Contract signed on 29 September 1987 with Ital Thai Marine of Bangkok for the construction of two ASW corvettes and for technical assistance with a third to be built in Bangkok Naval Dockyard. A fourth of the class with a different superstructure and less armament was ordered by the Police in September 1989. There are no plans for any more of the class.
Structure: The vessels are based on a Vosper Thornycroft Province class 56 m design stretched by increasing the frame spacing along the whole length of the hull. Depth charge racks and mine rails may be added.

KHAMRONSIN   *1991, Royal Thai Navy*

PATROL FORCES

Note: About 150 small patrol boats belong to the Naval Riverine Squadron.

3 RATCHARIT CLASS (FAST ATTACK CRAFT—MISSILE)

Name	No	Builders	Commissioned
RATCHARIT	4	CN Breda (Venezia)	10 Aug 1979
WITTHAYAKHOM	5	CN Breda (Venezia)	12 Nov 1979
UDOMDET	6	CN Breda (Venezia)	21 Feb 1980

Displacement, tons: 235 standard; 270 full load
Dimensions, feet (metres): 163.4 × 24.6 × 7.5 *(49.8 × 7.5 × 2.3)*
Main machinery: 3 MTU MD 20 V 538 TB91 diesels; 11 520 hp(m) *(8.47 MW)* sustained; 3 shafts
Speed, knots: 37. **Range, miles:** 2000 at 15 kts
Complement: 45 (7 officers)

Missiles: SSM: 4 Aerospatiale MM 38 Exocet; inertial cruise; active radar homing to 42 km *(23 nm)* at 0.9 Mach; warhead 165 kg; sea-skimmer.
Guns: 1 OTO Melara 3 in *(76 mm)*/62 compact; 85° elevation; 85 rounds/minute to 16 km *(8.7 nm)* anti-surface; 12 km *(6.6 nm)* anti-aircraft; weight of shell 6 kg.
1 Bofors 40 mm/70; 85° elevation; 300 rounds/minute to 12.5 km *(6.8 nm)*; weight of shell 0.96 kg.
Countermeasures: ESM: Radar warning.
Radars: Surface search: Decca; I band.
Fire control: Signaal WM 25; I/J band; range 46 km *(25 nm)*.

Programmes: Ordered June 1976. *Ratcharit* launched 30 July 1978, *Witthayakhom* 2 September 1978 and *Udomdet* 28 September 1978.
Structure: Standard Breda BMB 230 design.

WITTHAYAKHOM   *6/1993, Royal Thai Navy*

3 CHON BURI CLASS (FAST ATTACK CRAFT—GUN)

Name	No	Builders	Commissioned
CHON BURI	1	CN Breda (Venezia) Mestre	22 Feb 1983
SONGKHLA	2	CN Breda (Venezia) Mestre	15 July 1983
PHUKET	3	CN Breda (Venezia) Mestre	13 Jan 1984

Displacement, tons: 450 full load
Dimensions, feet (metres): 198 × 29 × 15 *(60.4 × 8.8 × 4.5)*
Main machinery: 3 MTU 20V 538 TB92 diesels; 12 795 hp(m) *(9.4 MW)* sustained; 3 shafts; cp props
Speed, knots: 30. **Range, miles:** 2500 at 18 kts; 900 at 30 kts
Complement: 41 (6 officers)
Guns: 2 OTO Melara 3 in *(76 mm)*/62. 2 Breda 40 mm/70 (twin).
Countermeasures: Decoys: 4 Hycor Mk 135 chaff launchers.
ESM: Radar intercept.
Fire control: Lirod 8 optronic director.
Radars: Surface search: Signaal ZW 06; I band.
Fire control: Signaal WM 22/61; I/J band; range 46 km *(25 nm)*.

Comment: Ordered in 1979 (first pair) and 1981. Laid down—*Chon Buri* 15 August 1981 (launched 29 November 1982), *Songkhla* 15 September 1981, *Phuket* 15 December 1981 (launched 3 February 1983). Steel hulls, alloy superstructure. Can be adapted to carry surface-to-surface missiles.

CHON BURI   *1993, Royal Thai Navy*

3 PRABPARAPAK CLASS (FAST ATTACK CRAFT—MISSILE)

Name	No	Builders	Commissioned
PRABPARAPAK	1	Singapore SBEC	28 July 1976
HANHAK SATTRU	2	Singapore SBEC	6 Nov 1976
SUPHAIRIN	3	Singapore SBEC	1 Feb 1977

Displacement, tons: 224 standard; 268 full load
Dimensions, feet (metres): 149 × 24.3 × 7.5 *(45.4 × 7.4 × 2.3)*
Main machinery: 4 MTU 16V 538 TB92 diesels; 13 640 hp(m) *(10 MW)* sustained; 4 shafts
Speed, knots: 40. **Range, miles:** 2000 at 15 kts; 750 at 37 kts
Complement: 41 (5 officers)

Missiles: SSM: 5 IAI Gabriel I (1 triple, 2 single) launchers; radar or optical guidance; semi-active radar homing to 20 km *(10.8 nm)* at 0.7 Mach; warhead 75 kg.
Guns: 1 Bofors 57 mm/70; 75° elevation; 200 rounds/minute to 17 km *(9.3 nm)*; weight of shell 2.4 kg. 8 rocket illuminant launchers on either side of 57 mm gun.
1 Bofors 40 mm/70; 90° elevation; 300 rounds/minute to 12 km *(6.6 nm)*; weight of shell 2.4 kg.
Countermeasures: ESM: Radar intercept.
Radars: Surface search: Kelvin Hughes Type 17; I band.
Fire control: Signaal WM 28/5 series; I/J band.

Programmes: Ordered June 1973. Built under licence from Lürssen. Launch dates—*Prabparapak* 29 July 1975, *Hanhak Sattru* 28 October 1975, *Suphairin* 20 February 1976.
Structure: Same design as Lürssen standard 45 m class built for Singapore. Normally only three Gabriel SSM are carried.

HANHAK SATTRU   *1993, Royal Thai Navy*

6 SATTAHIP (PSMM Mk 5) CLASS (LARGE PATROL CRAFT)

Name	No	Builders	Commissioned
SATTAHIP	4	Ital Thai (Samutprakarn) Ltd	16 Sep 1983
KLONGYAI	5	Ital Thai (Samutprakarn) Ltd	7 May 1984
TAKBAI	6	Ital Thai (Samutprakarn) Ltd	18 July 1984
KANTANG	7	Ital Thai (Samutprakarn) Ltd	14 Oct 1985
THEPHA	8	Ital Thai (Samutprakarn) Ltd	17 Apr 1986
TAIMUANG	9	Ital Thai (Samutprakarn) Ltd	17 Apr 1986

Displacement, tons: 270 standard; 300 full load
Dimensions, feet (metres): 164.5 × 23.9 × 5.9 *(50.1 × 7.3 × 1.8)*
Main machinery: 2 MTU 16V 538 TB92 diesels; 6820 hp(m) *(5 MW)* sustained; 2 shafts
Speed, knots: 22. **Range, miles:** 2500 at 15 kts
Complement: 56
Guns: 1 OTO Melara 3 in *(76 mm)*/62 and 1 Bofors 40 mm/70 (in 4, 5 and 6).
2 USN 3 in *(76 mm)*/50 Mk 26 (in 7, 8 and 9).
2 Oerlikon 20 mm. 2—12.7 mm MGs.
Fire control: NA 18 optronic director (in 4, 5 and 6).
Radars: Surface search: Decca; I band.

Comment: First four ordered 9 September 1981, *Thepha* on 27 December 1983 and *Taimuang* on 31 August 1984. More of this class are planned.

TAKBAI (with OTO Melara gun) *1993, Royal Thai Navy*

TAIMUANG (with US guns) *1993, Royal Thai Navy*

2 PC 461 CLASS (LARGE PATROL CRAFT)

SUKRIP (ex-PC *1218*) PC 5   **LIULOM** (ex-PC *1253*) PC 7

Displacement, tons: 280 standard; 450 full load
Dimensions, feet (metres): 173.7 × 23 × 8.9 *(52.9 × 7 × 2.7)*
Main machinery: 2 diesels; 2880 hp *(2.15 MW)* or 2560 hp *(1.91 MW)* *(Sukrip)*; 2 shafts
Speed, knots: 20. **Range, miles:** 5000 at 10 kts
Complement: 62-71
Guns: 1 USN 3 in *(76 mm)*/50. 1 Bofors 40 mm/60. 5 Oerlikon 20 mm.
Torpedoes: 2—324 mm US Mk 32 tubes; anti-submarine.
A/S mortars: 1 Mk 22 Mousetrap.
Radars: Surface search: Raytheon SPS 35 (1500B) or SPS 21D (PC5); I band.

Comment: Launched in 1941-43 as US PCs. Transferred from US between March 1947 and December 1952. One deleted in 1994.

PC 461 (old number) *1992, Royal Thai Navy*

7 PGM 71 CLASS (LARGE PATROL CRAFT)

T 14-19   T 110

Displacement, tons: 130 standard; 147 full load
Dimensions, feet (metres): 101 × 21 × 6 *(30.8 × 6.4 × 1.9)*
Main machinery: 2 GM diesels; 1800 hp *(1.34 MW)*; 2 shafts
Speed, knots: 18.5. **Range, miles:** 1500 at 10 kts
Complement: 30
Guns: 1 Bofors 40 mm/60. 1 Oerlikon 20 mm. 2—12.7 mm MGs.
In some craft the 20 mm gun has been replaced by an 81 mm mortar/12.7 mm combined mounting aft.
Radars: Surface search: Decca 303 *(T 11 and 12)* or Decca 202 *(remainder)*; I band.

Comment: Built by Peterson Inc between 1966 and 1970. Transferred from US.

T 18 *1992, Royal Thai Navy*

9 T 91 CLASS (COASTAL PATROL CRAFT)

T 91-99

Displacement, tons: 87.5 (T 91), 130 (remainder) standard
Dimensions, feet (metres): 104.3 × 17.5 × 5.5 *(31.8 × 5.3 × 1.7)* (T 91)
118 × 18.7 × 4.9 *(36 × 5.7 × 1.5)* (remainder)
Main machinery: 2 MTU 12V 538 TB81/82 diesels; 3300 hp(m) *(2.43 MW)*/4430 hp(m) *(3.26 MW)* sustained; 2 shafts
Speed, knots: 25. **Range, miles:** 700 at 21 kts
Complement: 21; 23 (T 93-94); 25 (T 99)
Guns: 2 Bofors 40 mm/60. 1—12.7 mm MG (see *Comment*).
Fire control: Sea Archer 1A optronic director (T 99 only).
Radars: Surface search: Raytheon SPS 35 (1500B); I band.

Comment: Built by Royal Thai Naval Dockyard, Bangkok. T 91 commissioned in 1965; T 92-93 in 1973; T 94-98 between 1981 and 1984; T 99 in 1987. T 91 has an extended upperworks and a 20 mm gun in place of the after 40 mm. T 99 has a single Bofors 40/70, one Oerlikon 20 mm and two MGs. There may be other armament variations in the group T 94-98. Major refits from 1983-86 for earlier vessels of the class. More of the class are planned.

T 97 *5/1991, Royal Thai Navy*

12 SWIFT CLASS (COASTAL PATROL CRAFT)

T 21-29   T 210-212

Displacement, tons: 20 standard; 22 full load
Dimensions, feet (metres): 50 × 13 × 3.5 *(15.2 × 4 × 1.1)*
Main machinery: 2 diesels; 480 hp *(358 kW)*; 2 shafts
Speed, knots: 25
Complement: 5
Guns: 2—81 mm mortars. 2—12.7 mm MGs.

Comment: Transferred from US Navy from 1967 to 1975.

T 27 *10/1989, S Tabusa*

14 T 213 CLASS (COASTAL PATROL CRAFT)

T 213-226   T 227-230

Displacement, tons: 35 standard
Dimensions, feet (metres): 64 × 17.5 × 5 *(19.5 × 5.3 × 1.5)*
Main machinery: 2 MTU diesels; 715 hp(m) *(526 kW)*; 2 shafts
Speed, knots: 25
Complement: 8
Guns: 1 Oerlikon 20 mm. 1—81 mm mortar with 12.7 mm MG.

Comment: Built by Ital Thai Marine Ltd. Commissioned—T 213-215, 29 August 1980; T 216-218, 26 March 1981; T 219-223, 16 September 1981; T 224, 19 November 1982; T 225 and T 226, 28 March 1984; T 227-230 in 1990/91. Of alloy construction. Used for fishery patrol and coastal control duties.

T 221 *1992, Royal Thai Navy*

1 HYSUCAT 18 HYDROFOIL (RIVER PATROL CRAFT)

T 231

Displacement, tons: 39
Dimensions, feet (metres): 60 × 21.6 (hull) × 5.9 *(18.3 × 6.6 × 1.6)*
Main machinery: 2 MWM Type diesels; 1640 hp(m) *(1.2 MW)*; 2 shafts
Speed, knots: 36
Complement: 10
Guns: 1 Oerlikon 20 mm.

Comment: Designed by Technautic in association with Lürssen. Ordered in 1984 and started trials in December 1986. GRP hull for hydrofoil-supported catamarans. The Thai Navy was not happy with the trials results and the plan for a class of 12 was cancelled. Gatling gun replaced in 1988 and the associated fire-control equipment removed.

HYSUCAT 231   *11/1988, Trevor Brown*

3 RPC CLASS (RIVER PATROL CRAFT)

Displacement, tons: 13 full load
Dimensions, feet (metres): 35.8 × 10.5 × 3.3 *(10.9 × 3.2 × 1)*
Main machinery: 2 Gray diesels; 450 hp *(335 kW)*; 2 shafts
Speed, knots: 14
Complement: 6
Guns: 4—12.7 mm MGs.

Comment: Transferred from US in 1967. Employed on Mekong River.

RPC class   *1989*

37 PBR Mk II (RIVER PATROL CRAFT)

11-19, 110-132   +5

Displacement, tons: 8 full load
Dimensions, feet (metres): 32.1 × 11.5 × 2.3 *(9.8 × 3.5 × 0.7)*
Main machinery: 2 Detroit diesels; 430 hp *(321 kW)*; 2 Jacuzzi waterjets
Speed, knots: 25. **Range, miles:** 150 at 23 kts
Complement: 4
Guns: 2—12.7 mm (twin) MGs. 2—6.72 mm MGs. 1—60 mm mortar.

Comment: Transferred from US from 1967-73. Employed on Mekong River. Reported to be getting old and maximum speed has been virtually halved. All belong to the Riverine Squadron.

PBR Mk II   *1991, Royal Thai Navy*

91 ASSAULT BOATS (AB)

Displacement, tons: 0.4 full load
Dimensions, feet (metres): 16.4 × 6.2 × 1.3 *(5 × 1.9 × 0.4)*
Speed, knots: 24
Guns: 1—7.62 mm MG.

Comment: Part of the Riverine Squadron with the PBRs and two PCFs.

ASSAULT BOAT   *1991, Royal Thai Navy*

MINE WARFARE FORCES

Note: Purchase of further Lürssen types is unlikely because of cost and reported problems with the minehunting system. Acquisition of inshore minehunters is being considered; possibly eight Chinese Type 312 drones which can be controlled from shore.

1 MCM SUPPORT SHIP

Name	No	Builders	Commissioned
THALANG	1	Bangkok Dock Co Ltd	4 Aug 1980

Displacement, tons: 1000 standard
Dimensions, feet (metres): 185.5 × 33 × 10 *(55.7 × 10 × 3.1)*
Main machinery: 2 MTU diesels; 1310 hp(m) *(963 kW)*; 2 shafts
Speed, knots: 12
Complement: 77
Guns: 1 Bofors 40 mm/70. 2 Oerlikon 20 mm. 2—12.7 mm MGs.
Radars: Surface search: Racal Decca 1226; I band.

Comment: Has minesweeping capability. Two 3 ton cranes provided for change of minesweeping gear in MSCs—four sets carried. Design by Ferrostaal, Essen.

THALANG   *1993, Royal Thai Navy*

2 BANG RACHAN CLASS (MINEHUNTERS/SWEEPERS)

Name	No	Builders	Commissioned
BANG RACHAN	2	Lürssen Vegesack	29 Apr 1987
NONGSARAI	3	Lürssen Vegesack	17 Nov 1987

Displacement, tons: 444 full load
Dimensions, feet (metres): 161.1 × 30.5 × 8.2 *(49.1 × 9.3 × 2.5)*
Main machinery: 2 MTU 12V 396 TB83 diesels; 3120 hp(m) *(2.3 MW)* sustained; 2 shafts; KaMeWa cp props
Auxiliary propulsion; 1 motor
Speed, knots: 17; 7 (electric motor). **Range, miles:** 3100 at 12 kts
Complement: 30
Guns: 3 Oerlikon GAM-BO1 20 mm.
Countermeasures: MCM: MWS 80R minehunting system. Acoustic, magnetic and mechanical sweeps.
2 Gaymarine Pluto 15 remote-controlled submersibles.
Radars: Navigation: 2 Atlas Elektronik 8600 ARPA; I band.
Sonars: Atlas Elektronik DSQS-11H; hull-mounted; minehunting; high frequency.

Comment: First ordered from Lürssen late 1984, arrived Bangkok 22 October 1987. Second ordered 5 August 1985 and arrived in Bangkok May 1988. There have been reports of problems with the minehunting systems, and that more of the class are not being considered. Amagnetic steel frames and deckhouses, wooden hull. Motorola Miniranger MRS III precise navigation system. Draeger decompression chamber.

NONGSARAI   *1993, Royal Thai Navy*

3 BLUEBIRD CLASS (MINESWEEPERS—COASTAL)

Name	No	Builders	Commissioned
LADYA	5	Peterson Builders Inc,	14 Dec 1963
(ex-US *MSC 297*)		Sturgeon Bay, Wisconsin	
BANGKEO	6	Dorchester SB Corporation,	9 July 1965
(ex-US *MSC 303*)		Camden	
DONCHEDI	8	Peterson Builders Inc,	17 Sep 1965
(ex-US *MSC 313*)		Sturgeon Bay, Wisconsin	

Displacement, tons: 317 standard; 384 full load
Dimensions, feet (metres): 145.3 × 27 × 8.5 *(44.3 × 8.2 × 2.6)*
Main machinery: 2 GM 8-268 diesels; 880 hp *(656 kW)*; 2 shafts
Speed, knots: 13. **Range, miles:** 2750 at 12 kts
Complement: 43 (7 officers)
Guns: 2 Oerlikon 20 mm/80 (twin).
Countermeasures: MCM: US Mk 4 (V). Mk 6. US Type Q2 magnetic.
Radars: Navigation: Decca TM 707; I band.
IFF: UPX 5 *(Ladya)*. UPX 12 (rest).
Sonars: UQS 1; hull-mounted; minehunting; high frequency.

Comment: Constructed for Thailand. One paid off in 1992 and the last three are now in limited operational service.

DONCHEDI   *1/1991*

5 MSBs

MLMS 6-10

Displacement, tons: 25 full load
Dimensions, feet (metres): 50.2 × 13.1 × 3 *(15.3 × 4 × 0.9)*
Main machinery: 1 Gray Marine 64 HN9 diesel; 165 hp *(123 kW)*; 1 shaft
Speed, knots: 8
Complement: 10
Guns: 2—7.62 mm MGs.

Comment: Three transferred from US in October 1963 and two in 1964. Wooden hulled, converted from small motor launches. Operated on Chao Phraya river.

AMPHIBIOUS FORCES

2 NORMED CLASS (LSTs)

Name	No	Builders	Commissioned
SICHANG	LST 6	Ital Thai	9 Oct 1987
SURIN	LST 7	Bangkok Dock Co Ltd	16 Dec 1988

Displacement, tons: 3540 standard; 4235 full load
Dimensions, feet (metres): 337.8 × 51.5 × 11.5 *(103 × 15.7 × 3.5)*
Main machinery: 2 MTU 20V 1163 TB82 diesels; 11 000 hp(m) *(8.1 MW)* sustained; 2 shafts
Speed, knots: 16. **Range, miles:** 7000 at 12 kts
Complement: 129
Military lift: 348 troops; 14 tanks or 12 APCs or 850 tons cargo; 3 LCVP; 1 LCPL
Guns: 1 Bofors 40 mm/70. 2 Oerlikon GAM-CO1 20 mm. 2—12.7 mm MGs. 1—81 mm mortar.
Fire control: 2 Sea Archer Mk 1A optronic directors.
Radars: Navigation: Decca; I band.
Helicopters: Platform for 2 Bell 212.

Comment: First ordered 31 August 1984 to a Chantier du Nord (Normed) design. Second ordered to a modified design (possibly 31.2 ft *(9.5 m)* longer and with MWM diesels). The largest naval ships yet built in Thailand. First launched in April 1987, second in early 1988. Have bow doors and a 17 m ramp.

SICHANG   *1/1991*

4 LST 511-1152 CLASS

Name	No	Builders	Commissioned
CHANG	LST 2	Dravo Corporation	29 Dec 1944
(ex-USS *Lincoln County* LST 898)			
PANGAN	LST 3	Chicago Bridge and Iron	7 Apr 1945
(ex-USS *Stark County* LST 1134)		Co, Ill.	
LANTA	LST 4	Chicago Bridge and Iron	9 May 1945
(ex-USS *Stone County* LST 1141)		Co, Ill.	
PRATHONG	LST 5	Jefferson B & M Co, Ind.	13 Sep 1944
(ex-USS *Dodge County* LST 722)			

Displacement, tons: 1650 standard; 3640/4145 full load
Dimensions, feet (metres): 328 × 50 × 14 *(100 × 15.2 × 4.4)*
Main machinery: 2 GM 12-567A diesels; 1800 hp *(1.34 MW)*; 2 shafts
Speed, knots: 11.5. **Range, miles:** 9500 at 9 kts
Complement: 80; 157 (war)
Military lift: 1230 tons max; 815 tons beaching
Guns: 8 Bofors 40 mm/60 (2 twin, 4 single). 2—12.7 mm MGs *(Chang)*. 2 Oerlikon 20 mm/80 (others).
Fire control: 2 Mk 51 GFCS. 2 optical systems.
Radars: Surface search: Raytheon SPS 10 *(Pangan)*; G band.
Navigation: Raytheon; I/J band.

Comment: *Chang* transferred from US in August 1962. *Pangan* 16 May 1966, *Lanta* on 15 August 1973 (by sale 1 March 1979) and *Prathong* on 17 December 1975. *Chang* has a reinforced bow and waterline. *Lanta*, *Prathong* and *Chang* have mobile crane on well deck. All have tripod mast.

PRATHONG   *1/1991*

2 LSM 1 CLASS

Name	No	Builders	Commissioned
KUT (ex-USS *LSM 338*)	LSM 1	Pullman Std Car Co, Chicago	10 Jan 1945
KRAM (ex-USS *LSM 469*)	LSM 3	Brown SB Co, Houston, Texas	17 Mar 1945

Displacement, tons: 743 standard; 1107 full load
Dimensions, feet (metres): 203.5 × 34.5 × 9.9 *(62 × 10.5 × 3)*
Main machinery: 2 Fairbanks-Morse 38D8-1/8-10 diesels; 3540 hp *(2.64 MW)* sustained; 2 shafts
Speed, knots: 12.5. **Range, miles:** 4500 at 12.5 kts
Complement: 91 (6 officers)
Military lift: 452 tons beaching; 50 troops with vehicles
Guns: 2 Bofors 40 mm/60 Mk 3 (twin). 4 Oerlikon 20 mm/70.
Fire control: Mk 51 Mod 2 optical director *(Kram)*.
Radars: Surface search: Raytheon SPS 5 *(Kram)*; G/H band.
Navigation: Raytheon 1500 B; I band.

Comment: Former US landing ships of the LCM, later LSM (Medium Landing Ship) type. *Kram* was transferred to Thailand under MAP at Seattle, Washington, on 25 May 1962, *Kut* in October 1946. One deleted in 1990.

KUT   *1/1991*

2 LSIL 351 CLASS

PRAB LSIL 1   SATAKUT (ex-*LSIL 739*) LSIL 2

Displacement, tons: 230 standard; 399 full load
Dimensions, feet (metres): 157 × 23 × 6 *(47.9 × 7 × 1.8)*
Main machinery: 4 GM diesels; 2320 bhp *(1.73 MW)*; 2 shafts
Speed, knots: 15. **Range, miles:** 5600 at 12.5 kts
Complement: 49 (7 officers)
Military lift: 101 tons or 76 troops
Guns: 1 Bofors 40 mm/60. 4 Oerlikon 20 mm/70.
Radars: Surface search: Raytheon SPS 35 (1500B); I band.

Comment: Built in 1944-45, transferred from US May 1947.

PRAB   *1992, Royal Thai Navy*

1 LCG TYPE

NAKHA (ex-USS *LSSL 102*) LSSL 3

Displacement, tons: 233 standard; 393 full load
Dimensions, feet (metres): 158.1 × 23.6 × 6.2 *(48.2 × 7.2 × 1.9)*
Main machinery: 2 GM diesels; 1320 hp *(985 kW)*; 2 shafts
Speed, knots: 15. **Range, miles:** 5000 at 6 kts
Complement: 60
Guns: 1 USN 3 in *(76 mm)*/50. 4 Bofors 40 mm/60 (2 twin). 4 Oerlikon 20 mm/70 (2 twin).
  6—81 mm mortars. 2—12.7 mm MGs.
Radars: Navigation: Raytheon 1500 B; I band.

Comment: Built by Commercial Ironworks, Oregon in 1945. Transferred from US in 1966. Acquired when Japan returned her to the USA.

NAKHA

4 THONG KAEO CLASS (LCUs)

Name	No	Builders	Commissioned
THONG KAEO	7	Bangkok Dock Co Ltd	23 Dec 1982
THONG LANG	8	Bangkok Dock Co Ltd	19 Apr 1983
WANG NOK	9	Bangkok Dock Co Ltd	16 Sep 1983
WANG NAI	10	Bangkok Dock Co Ltd	11 Nov 1983

Displacement, tons: 193 standard; 396 full load
Dimensions, feet (metres): 134.5 × 29.5 × 6.9 *(41 × 9 × 2.1)*
Main machinery: 2 GM 16V-71 diesels; 1400 hp *(1.04 MW)*; 2 shafts
Speed, knots: 10. **Range, miles:** 1200 at 10 kts
Complement: 31 (3 officers)
Military lift: 3 lorries; 150 tons equipment
Guns: 2 Oerlikon 20 mm. 2—7.62 mm MGs.

Comment: Ordered in 1980. A fifth ship of the class was abandoned. More of the type planned for the mid-1990s.

WANG NAI   *1993, Royal Thai Navy*

5—501 CLASS (LCUs)

MATAPHON LCU 1	**ADANG** LCU 3	**TALIBONG** LCU 6
RAWI LCU 2	**PHETRA** LCU 4	

Displacement, tons: 145 standard; 330 full load
Dimensions, feet (metres): 120.4 × 32 × 4 *(36.7 × 9.8 × 1.2)*
Main machinery: 3 Gray Marine 65 diesels; 675 hp *(503 kW)*; 3 shafts
Speed, knots: 10. **Range, miles:** 650 at 8 kts
Complement: 13
Military lift: 150 tons or 3-4 tanks or 250 troops
Guns: 2 Oerlikon 20 mm/80.

Comment: Transferred from US 1946-47. Employed as transport ferries.

TALIBONG   *8/1991*

12 LCVP

L 51-59, 510-512

Displacement, tons: 12
Main machinery: 1 diesel; 225 hp *(168 kW)*; 1 shaft
Speed, knots: 9
Military lift: 40 troops

Comment: Six transferred from US in 1953, remainder in 1963.

24 LCM 6

14-16, 61-68, 71-78, 81-82, 85-87

Displacement, tons: 56 full load
Dimensions, feet (metres): 56.1 × 14.1 × 3.9 *(17.1 × 4.3 × 1.2)*
Main machinery: 2 Gray Marine 64 HN9 diesels; 330 hp *(264 kW)*; 2 shafts
Speed, knots: 9
Complement: 5
Military lift: 34 tons

Comment: First 21 delivered 1965-69 from US.

LCM 6 (Uruguay colours)   *4/1992, Hartmut Ehlers*

3 GRIFFON 1000 TD HOVERCRAFT

Dimensions, feet (metres): 27.6 × 12.5 *(8.4 × 3.8)*
Main machinery: 1 Deutz BF6L913C diesel; 190 hp(m) *(140 kW)*
Speed, knots: 33. **Range, miles:** 200 at 27 kts
Cargo capacity: 1000 kg plus 9 troops

Comment: Acquired in mid-1990 from Griffon Hovercraft. Although having an obvious amphibious capability they are also to be used for rescue and flood control.

GRIFFON HOVERCRAFT   *1990, Griffon*

4 LCAs

L 40-43

Displacement, tons: 10 full load
Dimensions, feet (metres): 39.4 × 9.8 × 3.3 *(12 × 3 × 1)*
Main machinery: 2 Chrysler diesels; 2 Castoldi Mod 06 waterjets
Speed, knots: 25
Military lift: 35 troops

Comment: Built in Thailand in 1984. Fibreglass hull with bow ramp.

TRAINING SHIPS

1 ALGERINE CLASS

Name	No	Builders	Commissioned
PHOSAMTON (ex-HMS *Minstrel*)	MSF 1	Redfern Construction Co	1945

Displacement, tons: 1040 standard; 1335 full load
Dimensions, feet (metres): 225 × 35.5 × 11.5 *(68.6 × 10.8 × 3.5)*
Main machinery: 2 boilers; 2 reciprocating engines; 2000 ihp *(1.49 MW)*; 2 shafts
Speed, knots: 16. **Range, miles:** 4000 at 10 kts
Complement: 103
Guns: 1 Vickers 4 in *(102 mm)*/45. 1 Bofors 40 mm/60. 2 Oerlikon 20 mm.
Radars: Navigation: Decca Type 974; I band.

Comment: Transferred from UK in April 1947. Received engineering overhaul in 1984. Mine-sweeping gear replaced by a deckhouse to increase training space.

PHOSAMTON   *1/1991, Royal Thai Navy*

Name	No	Builders	Commissioned
MAEKLONG	3	Uraga Dock Co, Japan	June 1937

Displacement, tons: 1400 standard; 2000 full load
Dimensions, feet (metres): 269 × 34 × 10.5 *(82 × 10.4 × 3.2)*
Main machinery: 2 boilers; 2 reciprocating engines; 2500 ihp *(1.87 MW)*; 2 shafts
Speed, knots: 14. **Range, miles:** 8000 at 12 kts
Complement: 155 as training ship
Guns: 4 USN 3 in *(76 mm)*/50. 3 Bofors 40 mm/60. 3 Oerlikon 20 mm.

Comment: The four 18 in torpedo tubes were removed to provide more training space.

MAEKLONG   *1993, Royal Thai Navy*

1 TRAINING SHIP

VISUD SAKORN

Comment: Naval manned and looks like a VIP yacht. Training ship of the Merchant Marine Training Centre, run by the Harbour Department.

VISUD SAKORN   *10/1987*

SURVEY AND RESEARCH SHIPS

Note: There is also a civilian research vessel *Chulab Horn* which completed in 1986.

Name	No	Builders	Commissioned
SUK	—	Bangkok Dock Co Ltd	3 Mar 1982

Displacement, tons: 1450 standard; 1526 full load
Dimensions, feet (metres): 206.3 × 36.1 × 13.4 *(62.9 × 11 × 4.1)*
Main machinery: 2 MTU diesels; 2400 hp(m) *(1.76 MW)*; 2 shafts
Speed, knots: 15
Complement: 86 (20 officers)
Guns: 2 Oerlikon 20 mm. 2—7.62 mm MGs.

Comment: Laid down 27 August 1979, launched 8 September 1981. Designed for oceanographic and survey duties.

SUK   *4/1993, van Ginderen Collection*

Name	No	Builders	Commissioned
CHANTHARA	AGS 11	Lürssen Werft	1961

Displacement, tons: 870 standard; 996 full load
Dimensions, feet (metres): 229.2 × 34.5 × 10 *(69.9 × 10.5 × 3)*
Main machinery: 2 KHD diesels; 1090 hp(m) *(801 kW)*; 2 shafts
Speed, knots: 13.25. **Range, miles:** 10 000 at 10 kts
Complement: 68 (8 officers)
Guns: 1 Bofors 40 mm/60. 1 Oerlikon 20 mm.

Comment: Laid down on 27 September 1960. Launched on 17 December 1960.

CHANTHARA   *1/1991*

Name	No	Builders	Commissioned
SURIYA	—	Bangkok Dock Co Ltd	14 May 1979

Displacement, tons: 690 full load
Dimensions, feet (metres): 177.8 × 33.5 × 10.2 *(54.2 × 10.2 × 3.1)*
Main machinery: 2 MTU diesels; 1310 hp(m) *(963 kW)*; 2 shafts; bow thruster; 135 hp(m) *(99 kW)*
Speed, knots: 12
Complement: 60 (12 officers)
Guns: 2 Oerlikon 20 mm.

Comment: Mostly used to service navigational aids.

SURIYA   *5/1990, 92 Wing RAAF*

2 OCEANOGRAPHIC VESSELS

II   III

Displacement, tons: 90 full load
Dimensions, feet (metres): 91.9 × 18 × 4.9 *(28 × 5.5 × 1.5)*
Main machinery: 1 diesel; 1 shaft
Speed, knots: 12
Complement: 11 (2 officers)

Comment: *II* launched in 1955 by Lürssen, Vegesack and *III* in 1972.

AUXILIARIES

1 REPLENISHMENT TANKER

CHULA   2

Displacement, tons: 2000 full load
Measurement, tons: 960 dwt
Dimensions, feet (metres): 219.8 × 31.2 × 14.4 *(67 × 9.5 × 4.4)*
Main machinery: 2 MTU 12V 396 TC62 diesels; 2400 hp(m) *(1.76 MW)* sustained; 2 shafts
Speed, knots: 14
Complement: 39 (7 officers)
Cargo capacity: 800 tons oil fuel
Guns: 2 Oerlikon 20 mm.
Radars: Navigation: Decca; I band.

Comment: Launched on 24 September 1980 by Singapore Slipway and Engineering Company. Fitted with SATNAV. Replenishment is done by a hose handling crane boom.

CHULA   *1992, Royal Thai Navy*

0 + 1 MODIFIED FUQING (TYPE R22T) CLASS
(REPLENISHMENT SHIP)

Displacement, tons: 22 000 full load
Dimensions, feet (metres): 557.7 × 78.7 × 29.5 *(170 × 24 × 9)*
Main machinery: 2 HD-SEMT Pielstick 16 PC2 6V400; 2 shafts
Speed, knots: 20. **Range, miles:** 10 000 at 15 kts
Complement: 130 plus 53 spare
Cargo capacity: 9000 tons fuel, water, ammunition and stores
Guns: 8—37 mm (4 twin).
Radars: Air/surface search: E/F band.
Navigation: I band.
Fire control: I/J band.
Helicopters: 2 Sea King type.

Comment: Contract signed with China State Shipbuilding Corporation on 29 September 1993. Fabrication to start in December 1994, with planned launch date March 1995 and delivery in September 1996. Two replenishment at sea positions each side and facilities for Vertrep. This ship complements the carrier and the new frigates to give the Navy a full deployment capability.

TYPE R22T (artist's impression) *1993, Royal Thai Navy*

3 HARBOUR TANKERS

PROET YO 9   **CHIK** YO 10   **SAMED** YO 11

Displacement, tons: 360 standard; 485 full load
Dimensions, feet (metres): 122.7 × 19.7 × 8.7 *(37.4 × 6 × 2.7)*
Main machinery: 1 GM 8-268A diesel; 500 hp(m) *(368 kW)*; 1 shaft
Speed, knots: 9
Cargo capacity: 210 tons

Comment: Built by Bangkok Naval Dockyard. *Proet* commissioned 27 January 1967, remainder the same year. All three vessels are identical.

SAMED *8/1991*

1 HARBOUR TANKER

SAMUI (ex-USS *YOG 60*) YO 4

Displacement, tons: 422 standard
Dimensions, feet (metres): 174.5 × 32 × 15 *(53.2 × 9.7 × 4.6)*
Main machinery: 2 diesels; 600 hp *(448 kW)*; 2 shafts
Speed, knots: 8
Complement: 29
Guns: 2 Oerlikon 20 mm.

Comment: Deleted in error in 1990.

SAMUI (alongside CHANG) *8/1991*

1 WATER TANKER

Name	No	Builders	Commissioned
CHUANG	YW 5	Royal Thai Naval Dockyard, Bangkok	1965

Displacement, tons: 305 standard; 485 full load
Dimensions, feet (metres): 136 × 24.6 × 10 *(42 × 7.5 × 3.1)*
Main machinery: 1 GM diesel; 500 hp *(373 kW)*; 1 shaft
Speed, knots: 11
Complement: 29

Comment: Launched on 14 January 1965.

CHUANG *8/1991*

TUGS

2 COASTAL TUGS

SAMAESAN   **RAET**

Displacement, tons: 300 standard
Dimensions, feet (metres): 82 × 27.9 × 7.9 *(25 × 8.5 × 2.4)*
Main machinery: 2 Caterpillar 3512TA diesels; 2350 hp(m) *(1.75 MW)* sustained; 2 Aquamaster US 901 props
Speed, knots: 10
Complement: 6

Comment: Contract signed 23 September 1992 for local construction at Thonburi Naval dockyard. Completed in December 1993.

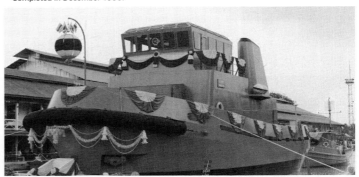

SAMAESAN *1993, Royal Thai Navy*

2 COASTAL TUGS

RIN ATA 5   **RANG** ATA 6

Displacement, tons: 350 standard
Dimensions, feet (metres): 106 × 29.7 × 15.2 *(32.3 × 9 × 4.6)*
Main machinery: 1 MWM TBD441V/12K diesel; 2100 hp(m) *(1.54 MW)*; 1 shaft
Speed, knots: 12. **Range, miles:** 1000 at 10 kts
Complement: 19

Comment: Launched 12 and 14 June 1980 at Singapore Marine Shipyard. Both commissioned 5 March 1981.

RANG *1992, Royal Thai Navy*

2 YTL 422 CLASS

KLUENG BADEN YTL 2   **MARN VICHAI** YTL 3

Displacement, tons: 63 standard
Dimensions, feet (metres): 64.7 × 16.5 × 6 *(19.7 × 5 × 1.8)*
Main machinery: 1 diesel; 240 hp *(179 kW)*; 1 shaft
Speed, knots: 8

Comment: Bought from Canada 1953.

MARN VICHAI   *1992, Royal Thai Navy*

POLICE

1 VOSPER THORNYCROFT TYPE (LARGE PATROL CRAFT)

SRINAKARIN 1804

Displacement, tons: 630 full load
Dimensions, feet (metres): 203.4 × 26.9 × 8.2 *(62 × 8.2 × 2.5)*
Main machinery: 2 Deutz MWM BV16M628 diesels; 9524 hp(m) *(7 MW)* sustained; 2 shafts; KaMeWa cp props
Speed, knots: 25. **Range, miles:** 2500 at 15 kts
Complement: 45
Guns: 1 Oerlikon 30 mm. 2 Oerlikon 20 mm (twin).

Comment: Ordered in September 1989 from Ital Thai Marine. Same hull as the Khamronsin class corvettes for the Navy but much more lightly armed. Delivered in April 1992. Second of class was considered but is not to be built.

SRINAKARIN   *1993, Marine Police*

2 HAMELN TYPE (LARGE PATROL CRAFT)

DAMRONG RACHANUPHAT 1802   **LOPBURI RAMAS** 1803

Displacement, tons: 430 full load
Dimensions, feet (metres): 186 × 26.6 × 8 *(56.7 × 8.1 × 2.4)*
Main machinery: 2 MTU diesels; 4400 hp(m) *(3.23 MW)*; 2 shafts
Speed, knots: 23
Complement: 45
Guns: 1 USN 3 in *(76 mm)*/50. 2 Oerlikon 20 mm (twin).

Comment: Delivered by Schiffwerft Hameln, Germany, on 3 January 1969 and 10 December 1972 respectively.

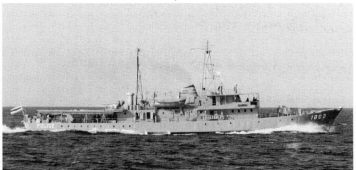

LOPBURI RAMAS   *1993, Marine Police*

2 SUMIDAGAWA TYPE (COASTAL PATROL CRAFT)

CHASANYABADEE 1101   **PHROMYOTHEE** 1103

Displacement, tons: 130 full load
Dimensions, feet (metres): 111.5 × 19 × 9.1 *(34 × 5.8 × 2.8)*
Main machinery: 3 Ikegai diesels; 4050 hp(m) *(2.98 MW)*; 3 shafts
Speed, knots: 32
Complement: 23
Guns: 2—12.7 mm MGs.

Comment: Commissioned in August 1972 and May 1973 respectively.

PHROMYOTHEE   *1990, Marine Police*

1 YOKOHAMA TYPE (COASTAL PATROL CRAFT)

CHAWENGSAK SONGKRAM 1102

Displacement, tons: 190 full load
Dimensions, feet (metres): 116.5 × 23 × 11.5 *(35.5 × 7 × 3.5)*
Main machinery: 4 Ikegai diesels; 5400 hp(m) *(3.79 MW)*; 2 shafts
Speed, knots: 32
Complement: 23
Guns: 2 Oerlikon 20 mm.

Comment: Commissioned 13 April 1973.

CHAWENGSAK SONGKRAM   *1990, Marine Police*

1 ITAL THAI MARINE TYPE (COASTAL PATROL CRAFT)

SRIYANONT 901

Displacement, tons: 52 full load
Dimensions, feet (metres): 90 × 16 × 6.5 *(27.4 × 4.9 × 2)*
Main machinery: 2 Deutz BA16M816 diesels; 2680 hp(m) *(1.97 MW)* sustained; 2 shafts
Speed, knots: 23
Complement: 14
Guns: 1 Oerlikon 20 mm. 2—7.62 mm MGs.

Comment: Commissioned 12 June 1986.

SRIYANONT   *1993, Marine Police*

3 HALTER TYPE (COASTAL PATROL CRAFT)

PHRAONGKAMROP 807   **RAMINTHRA** 809
PICHARNPHOLAKIT 808

Displacement, tons: 34 full load
Dimensions, feet (metres): 65 × 17 × 8.3 *(19.8 × 5.2 × 2.5)*
Main machinery: 3 Detroit 12V-71TA diesels; 1020 hp(m) *(761 kW)* sustained; 3 shafts
Speed, knots: 25
Complement: 14
Guns: 1 Oerlikon 20 mm. 2—7.62 mm MGs.

Comment: Delivered by Halter Marine, New Orleans, and all commissioned on 9 March 1969. Aluminium hulls.

PICHARNPHOLAKIT   *1990, Marine Police*

3 TECHNAUTIC TYPE (COASTAL PATROL CRAFT)

810-812

Displacement, tons: 50 full load
Dimensions, feet (metres): 88.6 × 19.4 × 6.2 *(27 × 5.9 × 1.9)*
Main machinery: 3 Isotta Fraschini diesels; 2500 hp(m) *(1.84 MW)*; 3 hydrojets
Speed, knots: 27
Guns: 1 Oerlikon 20 mm. 2—7.62 mm MGs.

Comment: Delivered by Technautic, Bangkok in 1984.

812   *1990, Marine Police*

5 ITAL THAI MARINE TYPE (COASTAL PATROL CRAFT)

625-629

Displacement, tons: 42 full load
Dimensions, feet (metres): 64 × 17.5 × 5 *(19.5 × 5.3 × 1.5)*
Main machinery: 2 MAN D2842LE diesels; 1350 hp(m) *(992 kW)* sustained; 2 shafts
Speed, knots: 27
Guns: 1—12.7 mm MG.

Comment: Built in Bangkok 1987-90. Aluminium hulls.

ITAL THAI 625   *1990, Marine Police*

17 TECHNAUTIC TYPE (COASTAL PATROL CRAFT)

608-624

Displacement, tons: 30 full load
Dimensions, feet (metres): 60 × 16 × 2.9 *(18.3 × 4.9 × 0.9)*
Main machinery: 2 Isotta Fraschini ID 36 SS 8V diesels; 1760 hp(m) *(1.29 MW)* sustained; 2 hydrojets
Speed, knots: 27
Guns: 1—12.7 mm MG.

Comment: Built from 1983 to 1987 in Bangkok.

TECHNAUTIC 614   *1990, Marine Police*

2 MARSUN TYPE

539-540

Displacement, tons: 30 full load
Dimensions, feet (metres): 57 × 16 × 3 *(17.4 × 4.9 × 0.9)*
Main machinery: 2 Detroit 12V-71TA diesels; 840 hp *(627 kW)* sustained; 2 shafts
Speed, knots: 25
Complement: 8
Guns: 1—12.7 mm MG.

Comment: Built in Thailand. Both commissioned 26 March 1986.

MARSUN 540   *1990, Marine Police*

26 SUMIDAGAWA TYPE (RIVER PATROL CRAFT)

513-538

Displacement, tons: 18 full load
Dimensions, feet (metres): 54.1 × 12.5 × 2.3 *(16.5 × 3.8 × 0.7)*
Main machinery: 2 Cummins diesels; 800 hp *(597 kW)*; 2 shafts
Speed, knots: 23
Guns: 1—12.7 mm MG.

Comment: First 21 built by Sumidagawa, last five by Captain Co, Thailand 1978-79.

SUMIDAGAWA 530   *1990, Marine Police*

24 CAMCRAFT TYPE (RIVER PATROL CRAFT)

415-440

Displacement, tons: 13 full load
Dimensions, feet (metres): 40 × 12 × 3.2 *(12.2 × 3.7 × 1)*
Main machinery: 2 Detroit diesels; 540 hp *(403 kW)*; 2 shafts
Speed, knots: 25

Comment: Delivered by Camcraft, Louisiana. Aluminium hulls.

CAMCRAFT 434   *1990, Marine Police*

38 RIVER PATROL CRAFT

Displacement, tons: 5 full load
Dimensions, feet (metres): 37 × 11 × 6 *(11.3 × 3.4 × 1.8)*
Speed, knots: 25

Comment: Numbers in the 300 series.

RIVER PATROL CRAFT 339   *1990, Marine Police*

TYPHOON BOATS

Comment: Rigid inflatables acquired from Task Force Boats in 1990-91. Two Johnson outboard motors, 450 hp *(336 kW)*; speed 50 kts light or 40 kts with 12 men embarked.

TOGO

Senior Officer	Personnel	Base	Mercantile Marine
Commanding Officer, Navy: Commander Lucien Laval	(a) 1994: 115 (b) Voluntary service	Lome	*Lloyd's Register of Shipping:* 8 vessels of 12 191 tons gross

PATROL FORCES

2 COASTAL PATROL CRAFT

Name	No	Builders	Commissioned
KARA	P 761	Chantiers Navals de l'Esterel, Cannes	1976
MONO	P 762	Chantiers Navals de l'Esterel, Cannes	1976

Displacement, tons: 80 full load
Dimensions, feet (metres): 105 × 19 × 5.3 *(32 × 5.8 × 1.6)*
Main machinery: 2 MTU MB 12V 493 TY60 diesels; 2000 hp(m) *(1.47 MW)* sustained; 2 shafts
Speed, knots: 30. **Range, miles:** 1500 at 15 kts
Complement: 17 (1 officer)
Missiles: SSM: Aerospatiale SS 12M; wire-guided to 5 km *(3 nm)* subsonic; warhead 30 kg.
Guns: 1 Bofors 40 mm/70 (aft). 1 Oerlikon 20 mm.
Radars: Surface search: Decca 916; I band; range 88 km *(48 nm)*.

Comment: Both craft in good condition.

KARA   *1990*

TONGA

Headquarters' Appointments	Base	Mercantile Marine	DELETIONS
Commander Tongan Defence Services: Lieutenant Colonel F Tupou *Commanding Officer, Navy:* HRH Lieutenant Commander Ulukalala Lavaka Ata	Touliki Base, Nuku'alofa (HMNB *Masefield*)	*Lloyd's Register of Shipping:* 14 vessels of 10 666 tons gross	1991 *Tufou, Koula* 1992 *Siliva, Fangailifuka, 'Alo-i-talau*

PATROL FORCES

3 PACIFIC FORUM TYPE (LARGE PATROL CRAFT)

Name	No	Builders	Commissioned
NEIAFU	P 201	Australian Shipbuilding Industries	28 Oct 1989
PANGAI	P 202	Australian Shipbuilding Industries	30 June 1990
SAVEA	P 203	Australian Shipbuilding Industries	23 Mar 1991

Displacement, tons: 162 full load
Dimensions, feet (metres): 103.3 × 26.6 × 6.9 *(31.5 × 8.1 × 2.1)*
Main machinery: 2 Caterpillar 3516TA diesels; 2820 hp *(2.1 MW)* sustained; 2 shafts
Speed, knots: 20. **Range, miles:** 2500 at 12 kts
Complement: 17 (3 officers)
Radars: Surface search: Furuno 1101; I band.

Comment: Part of the Pacific Forum Australia Defence co-operation. First laid down 30 January 1989, second 2 October 1989, third February 1990. Capable of mounting a 20 mm gun or MGs. *Savea* has an oceanographic survey capability.

SAVEA   *10/1991, John Mortimer*

1 LCM

Name	No	Builders	Commissioned
LATE (ex-Australian Army LCM 8 *1057)*	C 315	North Queensland Eng Ltd, Cairns	1 Sep 1982

Displacement, tons: 116 full load
Dimensions, feet (metres): 73.5 × 21 × 3.3 *(22.4 × 6.4 × 1)*
Main machinery: 2 Detroit 12V-71 diesels; 680 hp *(507 kW)* sustained; 2 shafts
Speed, knots: 10. **Range, miles:** 480 at 10 kts
Military lift: 60 tons
Radars: Surface search: Koden MD 305; I band.

Comment: Acquired from the Australian Army.

1 ROYAL YACHT

TITILUPE

Comment: 34 ft *(10.4 m)* long and has a speed of 8 kts. GRP displacement hull. Also used as auxiliary patrol craft.

LATE   *1992, Tonga Maritime Force*

TRINIDAD AND TOBAGO

Headquarters' Appointment

Commanding Officer, Coast Guard:
Commander Anthony Franklin, HBM, ED

General

On 30 June 1989 all former Police craft were handed over to the Coast Guard and renamed. Two survey craft *Meridian* and *Mercator* are civilian manned.

Aircraft

The Coast Guard operates two Cessna 402B and 310R for surveillance. These aircraft can be backed by Air Division helicopters when necessary.

Personnel

(a) 1994: 655 (45 officers)
(b) Voluntary service

Bases

Staubles Bay (HQ)
Hart's Cut, Tobago, Port Fortin (all established in 1989)
Piarco (Air station), Cedros (established in 1992)

Prefix to Ships' Names

TTS

Mercantile Marine

Lloyd's Register of Shipping:
51 vessels of 23 238 tons gross

DELETIONS

1991   *Fort Chacon*
1992   *Buccoo Reef*
1993   *Meridian* (civilian)

COAST GUARD

2 TYPE CG 40 (LARGE PATROL CRAFT)

Name	No	Builders	Commissioned
BARRACUDA	CG 5	Karlskronavarvet	15 June 1980
CASCADURA	CG 6	Karlskronavarvet	15 June 1980

Displacement, tons: 210 full load
Dimensions, feet (metres): 133.2 × 21.9 × 5.2 *(40.6 × 6.7 × 1.6)*
Main machinery: 2 Paxman Valenta 16CM diesels; 6700 hp *(5 MW)* sustained; 2 shafts
Speed, knots: 30. **Range, miles:** 3000 at 15 kts
Complement: 25
Guns: 1 Bofors 40 mm/70. 1 Oerlikon 20 mm.
Radars: Surface search: Racal Decca 1226; I band.

Comment: Ordered in Sweden mid-1978. Laid down early 1979. Fitted with foam-cannon oil pollution equipment and for oceanographic and hydrographic work. Nine spare berths. The hull is similar to Swedish Spica class but with the bridge amidships. One refitted in 1988, the other in 1989.

MORUGA   *1985, Trinidad and Tobago Coast Guard*

CASCADURA   *1/1994, Maritime Photographic*

4 SOUTER WASP 17 METRE CLASS (COASTAL PATROL CRAFT)

Name	No	Builders	Commissioned
PLYMOUTH	CG 27	WA Souter, Cowes	27 Aug 1982
CARONI	CG 28	WA Souter, Cowes	27 Aug 1982
GALEOTA	CG 29	WA Souter, Cowes	27 Aug 1982
MORUGA	CG 30	WA Souter, Cowes	27 Aug 1982

Displacement, tons: 19.3
Dimensions, feet (metres): 55.1 × 13.8 × 4.6 *(16.8 × 4.2 × 1.4)*
Main machinery: 2 GM Stewart and Stevenson 8V-92MTAB diesels; 1470 hp *(1.1 MW)* maximum; 2 shafts
Speed, knots: 32. **Range, miles:** 500 at 18 kts
Complement: 7 (2 officers)
Guns: 1—7.62 mm MG.
Radars: Surface search: Decca 150; I band.

Comment: GRP hulls. There have been reliability problems.

2 WASP 20 METRE CLASS (COASTAL PATROL CRAFT)

Name	No	Builders	Commissioned
KAIRI (ex-*Sea Bird*)	CG 31	WA Souter, Cowes	Dec 1982
MORIAH (ex-*Sea Dog*)	CG 32	WA Souter, Cowes	Dec 1982

Displacement, tons: 32 full load
Dimensions, feet (metres): 65.8 × 16.5 × 5 *(20.1 × 5 × 1.5)*
Main machinery: 2 GM Stewart and Stevenson diesels; 2400 hp *(1.79 MW)*; 2 shafts
Speed, knots: 30. **Range, miles:** 450 at 30 kts
Complement: 6 (2 officers)
Guns: 2—7.62 mm MGs.
Radars: Navigation: Decca 150; I band.

Comment: Ordered late 1981. Aluminium alloy hull. Transferred from the Police in June 1989.

MORIAH   *1989, Trinidad and Tobago Coast Guard*

1 WASP 17 METRE CLASS (COASTAL PATROL CRAFT)

Name	No	Builders	Commissioned
CEDROS (ex-*Sea Erne*)	CG 35	WA Souter, Cowes	1984

Displacement, tons: 19.3 full load
Dimensions, feet (metres): 55.1 × 13.8 × 4.6 *(16.8 × 4.2 × 1.4)*
Main machinery: 2 GM Stewart and Stevenson 8V-92MTAB diesels; 1470 hp *(1.1 MW)* maximum; 2 shafts
Speed, knots: 25
Complement: 7
Radars: Navigation: Decca 150; I band.

Comment: Transferred from Police in June 1989.

CEDROS   *1989, Trinidad and Tobago Coast Guard*

1 SWORD CLASS (COASTAL PATROL CRAFT)

Name	No	Builders	Commissioned
MATELOT (ex-*Sea Skorpion*)	CG 33	SeaArk Marine	May 1979

Displacement, tons: 15.5 full load
Dimensions, feet (metres): 44.9 × 13.4 × 4.3 *(13.7 × 4.1 × 1.3)*
Main machinery: 2 GM diesels; 850 hp *(634 kW)*; 2 shafts
Speed, knots: 28. **Range, miles:** 500 at 20 kts
Complement: 6
Guns: 1—7.62 mm MG.

Comment: Two transferred from the Police in June 1989, one scrapped in 1990.

MATELOT   *1/1994, Maritime Photographic*

1 COASTAL PATROL CRAFT

Name	No	Builders	Commissioned
CARENAGE (ex-*Sea Dragon*)	CG 37	Watercraft, Shoreham	1980

Displacement, tons: 14.9 full load
Dimensions, feet (metres): 45 × 14.1 × 4 *(13.7 × 4.3 × 1.2)*
Main machinery: 2 GM 8V-92 diesels; 606 hp *(452 kW)* sustained; 2 shafts
Speed, knots: 23.5. **Range, miles:** 360 at 18 kts
Complement: 4
Guns: 2—7.62 mm MGs.

Comment: GRP hull. Transferred from Police in June 1989.

CARENAGE   *1989, Trinidad and Tobago Coast Guard*

1 COASTAL SUPPORT CRAFT

SPEYSIDE (ex-*Sea Hawk*) CG 36

Displacement, tons: 12 full load
Dimensions, feet (metres): 36 × 13 × 4 *(10.9 × 3.9 × 1.2)*
Main machinery: 2 GM diesels; 460 hp *(343 kW)*; 2 shafts
Speed, knots: 22. **Range, miles:** 400 at 20 kts

Comment: Built by Tugs and Lighters Ltd, Port of Spain. Transferred from Police in June 1989.

2 BOWEN CLASS (FAST INTERCEPTOR CRAFT)

CG 001   CG 002

Comment: 31 ft fast patrol boats acquired in May 1991. Capable of 40 kts.

CG 001   *1991, Trinidad and Tobago Coast Guard*

3 RHIBs

CG 003-CG 005

Comment: 25 ft fast support craft acquired in August 1993. Twin Johnson outboards give a speed of 45 kts.

CG 004   *1/1994, Maritime Photographic*

8 AUXILIARY VESSELS

NAPARIMA (ex-*CG 26*) A 01	REHAB A 05	RELAY A 08
EL TUCUCHE (ex-*CG 25*) A 02	REDEEM (ex-*Cocrico*) A 06	REVIEW (ex-*Egret*) A 09
REFORM A 04	RECOVER (ex-*Semp*) A 07	

Comment: A variety of craft some of which transferred from Police duties in June 1989 and used for Port Services and other support functions.

REFORM   *1989, Trinidad and Tobago Coast Guard*

TUNISIA

Headquarters' Appointment	Bases	Personnel	Mercantile Marine
Chief of Naval Staff: Capitaine Chadli Cherif	Sfax, Bizerte, La Goulette, Kelibia	(a) 1994: 4500 officers and men (including 700 conscripts) (b) 1 year's national service	*Lloyd's Register of Shipping:* 80 vessels of 269 268 tons gross

FRIGATE

1 SAVAGE CLASS

Name	No	Builders	Laid down	Launched	Commissioned
INKADH (ex-*Président Bourguiba*, ex-USS *Thomas J Gary* DER 326, ex-*DE 326*)	E 7	Consolidated Steel Corporation, Texas	15 June 1943	21 Aug 1943	27 Nov 1943

Displacement, tons: 1200 standard; 1490 full load
Dimensions, feet (metres): 306 × 35 × 14
(93.3 × 10.7 × 4.3)
Main machinery: 4 Fairbanks-Morse 38D8-1/8-10 diesels; 7000 hp *(5.2 MW)* sustained; 2 shafts
Speed, knots: 19. **Range, miles:** 12 000 at 11 kts
Complement: 169

Guns: 2—3 in *(76 mm)*/50; 85° elevation; 20 rounds/minute to 12 km *(6.6 nm)*; weight of shell 6 kg.
2 Oerlikon 20 mm/80; 800 rounds/minute to 2 km.
Torpedoes: 6—324 mm US Mk 32 (2 triple) tubes. Honeywell Mk 44; anti-submarine; active homing to 5.5 km *(3 nm)* at 30 kts; warhead 34 kg.
Fire control: Mk 63 GFCS. Mk 51 Mod 2 GFCS.
Radars: Air search: Westinghouse SPS 29; B/C band; range 457 km *(250 nm)*.
Surface search: Raytheon SPS 10; G band.
Fire control: Western Electric Mk 34; I/J band.
Sonars: EDO SQS 29; hull-mounted; active search and attack; medium/high frequency.

Programmes: Completed as Edsall class DE. Converted to Radar Picket Savage class in 1958. Transferred from US 27 October 1973.
Operational: Used for training but non-operational as a warship and is likely to be replaced by *Salambo* in 1993.

INKADH   *7/1989, van Ginderen Collection*

PATROL FORCES

Note: The three Huludao class expected to be transferred from China, had not arrived by early 1994. It is possible that they may turn out to be replacement Shanghai II class.

3 COMBATTANTE III M CLASS (FAST ATTACK CRAFT—MISSILE)

Name	No	Builders	Commissioned
LA GALITÉ	501	CMN, Cherbourg	27 Feb 1985
TUNIS	502	CMN, Cherbourg	27 Mar 1985
CARTHAGE	503	CMN, Cherbourg	29 Apr 1985

Displacement, tons: 345 standard; 425 full load
Dimensions, feet (metres): 183.7 × 26.9 × 7.2 *(56 × 8.2 × 2.2)*
Main engines: 4 MTU 20V538 TB93 diesels; 18 740 hp(m) *(13.8 MW)* sustained; 4 shafts
Speed, knots: 38.5. **Range, miles:** 700 at 33 kts; 2800 at 10 kts
Complement: 35

Missiles: SSM: 8 Aerospatiale MM 40 Exocet (2 quad) launchers; inertial cruise; active radar homing to 70 km *(40 nm)* at 0.9 Mach; warhead 165 kg; sea-skimmer.
Guns: 1 OTO Melara 3 in *(76 mm)*/62; 85° elevation; 55-65 rounds/minute to 16 km *(8.7 nm)*; weight of shell 6 kg.
2 Breda 40 mm/70 (twin); 85° elevation; 300 rounds/minute to 12.5 km *(6.8 nm)*; weight of shell 0.96 kg.
4 Oerlikon 30 mm/75 (2 twin); 85° elevation; 650 rounds/minute to 10 km *(5.5 nm)*; weight of shell 1 kg or 0.36 kg.
Countermeasures: Decoys: 1 CSEE Dagaie trainable launcher; IR flares and chaff.
ESM: Radar warning.
Combat data systems: Tavitac action data automation.
Fire control: 2 CSEE Naja optronic directors for 30 mm. Thomson-CSF Vega II for SSM, 76 mm and 40 mm.
Radars: Air/surface search: Thomson-CSF Triton S; G band; range 33 km *(18 nm)* for 2 m² target.
Fire control: Thomson-CSF Castor II; I/J band; range 31 km *(17 nm)* for 2 m² target.

Programmes: Ordered in 1981.
Operational: One CSEE Sylosat navigation system.

TUNIS   *6/1992, van Ginderen Collection*

2 + 3 SHANGHAI II CLASS (FAST ATTACK CRAFT—GUN)

GAFSAH P 305   **AMILCAR** P 306

Displacement, tons: 113 standard; 131 full load
Dimensions, feet (metres): 127.3 × 17.7 × 5.6 *(38.8 × 5.4 × 1.7)*
Main machinery: 4 MTU 8V 331 TC92 diesels; 3540 hp(m) *(2.6 MW)* sustained; 4 shafts
Speed, knots: 30. **Range, miles:** 700 at 16.5 kts
Complement: 34
Guns: 4—37 mm/63 (2 twin). 4—25 mm/80 (2 twin).
Radars: Surface search: Skin Head; I band; range 37 km *(20 nm)*.

Comment: Transferred from China 2 April 1977. Two others transferred in 1973, since deleted. Engine change completed December 1984 by the Navy at Socomena shipyards, Bizerte. Three more may be acquired from China in 1994.

SHANGHAI II   *1984*

2 TAZARKA CLASS (FAST ATTACK CRAFT—PATROL)

Name	No	Builders	Commissioned
TAZARKA	P 205	Vosper Thornycroft	27 Oct 1977
MENZEL BOURGUIBA	P 206	Vosper Thornycroft	27 Oct 1977

Displacement, tons: 125 full load
Dimensions, feet (metres): 103 × 19.5 × 5.5 *(31.4 × 5.9 × 1.7)*
Main machinery: 2 MTU diesels; 4000 hp(m) *(2.94 MW)*; 2 shafts
Speed, knots: 27. **Range, miles:** 1500 at 15 kts
Complement: 24
Guns: 2 Oerlikon 20 mm.
Radars: Surface search: Decca 916; I band; range 88 km *(48 nm)*.

Comment: Ordered 9 September 1975. *Tazarka* laid down 23 March 1976 and launched 19 July 1976.

MENZEL BOURGUIBA   *1989*

3 BIZERTE CLASS (LARGE PATROL CRAFT)

Name	No	Builders	Commissioned
BIZERTE	P 301	SFCN, Villeneuve-la-Garenne	10 July 1970
HORRIA (ex-*Liberté*)	P 302	SFCN, Villeneuve-la-Garenne	Oct 1970
MONASTIR	P 304	SFCN, Villeneuve-la-Garenne	25 Mar 1975

Displacement, tons: 250 full load
Dimensions, feet (metres): 157.5 × 23.3 × 7.5 *(48 × 7.1 × 2.3)*
Main machinery: 2 MTU 16V 652 TB81 diesels; 4600 hp(m) *(3.4 MW)* sustained; 2 shafts
Speed, knots: 20. **Range, miles:** 2000 at 16 kts
Complement: 34 (4 officers)
Missiles: SSM: 8 Aerospatiale SS 12M; wire-guided to 5.5 km *(3 nm)* subsonic; warhead 30 kg.
Guns: 2 Bofors 40 mm/70. 2 Oerlikon 20 mm.
Radars: Surface search: Thomson-CSF DRBN 31; I band.

Comment: First pair ordered in 1968, third in August 1973.

BIZERTE *1993, van Ginderen Collection*

4 COASTAL PATROL CRAFT

Name	No	Builders	Commissioned
ISTIKLAL (ex-*VC 11, P 761*)	P 201	Ch Navals de l'Esterel	Apr 1957
JOUMHOURIA	P 202	Ch Navals de l'Esterel	Jan 1961
AL JALA	P 203	Ch Navals de l'Esterel	Nov 1963
REMADA	P 204	Ch Navals de l'Esterel	July 1967

Displacement, tons: 60 standard; 80 full load
Dimensions, feet (metres): 104 × 19 × 5.3 *(31.5 × 5.8 × 1.6)*
Main machinery: 2 MTU MB 12V 493 TY70 diesels; 2200 hp(m) *(1.62 MW)* sustained; 2 shafts
Speed, knots: 30. **Range, miles:** 1500 at 15 kts
Complement: 17 (3 officers)
Guns: 2 Oerlikon 20 mm.

Comment: *Istiklal* transferred from France March 1959. Wooden hulls. Doubtful operational status.

AL JALA *1989*

6 COASTAL PATROL CRAFT

V 101-106

Displacement, tons: 38 full load
Dimensions, feet (metres): 83 × 15.6 × 4.2 *(25 × 4.8 × 1.3)*
Main machinery: 2 Detroit 12V-71TA diesels; 840 hp *(627 kW)* sustained; 2 shafts
Speed, knots: 23. **Range, miles:** 900 at 15 kts
Complement: 11
Guns: 1 Oerlikon 20 mm.

Comment: Built by Chantiers Navals de l'Esterel and commissioned in 1961-63. Two further craft of the same design *(Sabaq el Bahr* T 2 and *Jaouel el Bahr* T 1) but unarmed were transferred to the Fisheries Administration in 1971—same builders. Doubtful operational status.

V 101 *10/1984, van Ginderen Collection*

1 GUESETTE CLASS

Displacement, tons: 8.5 full load
Dimensions, feet (metres): 36.1 × 12.5 × 3.6 *(11 × 3.8 × 1.1)*
Main machinery: 1 Perkins diesel; 1 shaft
Speed, knots: 10
Complement: 6

Comment: French-built survey launch acquired in 1992.

TRAINING/SURVEY SHIPS

1 ROBERT D CONRAD CLASS

Name	No	Builders	Commissioned
N O SALAMBO (ex-*De Steiguer*)	— (ex-T-AGOR 12)	Northwest Iron Works, Portland	28 Feb 1969

Displacement, tons: 1370 full load
Dimensions, feet (metres): 208.9 × 40 × 15.3 *(63.7 × 12.2 × 4.7)*
Main machinery: Diesel-electric; 2 Cummins diesel generators; 1 motor; 1000 hp *(746 kW)*; 1 shaft; bow thruster
Speed, knots: 13. **Range, miles:** 12 000 at 12 kts
Complement: 40
Radars: Navigation: TM 1650/6X; I band.

Comment: Transferred from US on 2 November 1992 and recommissioned on 11 February 1993. Built as an oceanographic research ship. Special features include a 10 ton boom, and a gas turbine for quiet propulsion up to 6 kts. Probably to be used primarily for training replacing *Inkadh.*

N O SALAMBO (old name) *5/1989, Giorgio Arra*

COAST GUARD

4 KONDOR I CLASS

RAS EL BLAD (ex-*Demmin*)　　　RAS AJDIR (ex-*Malchin*)
RAS MAAMOURA (ex-*Templin*)　　RAS ED DREK (ex-*Altentreptow*)

Displacement, tons: 377 full load
Dimensions, feet (metres): 170.3 × 23.3 × 7.2 *(51.9 × 7.1 × 2.2)*
Main machinery: 2 Russki/Kolomna 40-DM; 4408 hp(m) *(3.24 MW)* sustained; 2 shafts
Speed, knots: 20
Complement: 24
Guns: 2—25 mm (twin) can be carried.
Radars: Navigation: I band.

Comment: Former GDR minesweepers built at Peenewerft, Wolgast in 1969-71 and transferred in May 1992. In German service they were fitted with a twin 25 mm gun and a hull-mounted sonar. Ships of the same class acquired by Malta and Guinea Bissau.

RAS MAAMOURA *6/1992, Diego Quevedo*

10 COASTAL PATROL CRAFT

ASSAD BIN FOURAT　　+9

Displacement, tons: 32 full load
Dimensions, feet (metres): 67.3 × 15.4 × 4.3 *(20.5 × 4.7 × 1.3)*
Main machinery: 2 diesels; 1000 hp(m) *(735 kW)*; 2 shafts
Speed, knots: 28. **Range, miles:** 500 at 20 kts
Complement: 8
Guns: 1—12.7 mm MG.

Comment: First one built by Socomena, Bizerte with assistance from South Korea, and completed March 1986. Nine more started building in 1991.

4 INSHORE PATROL CRAFT

GABES　　　　KELIBIA
JERBA　　　　TABARK

Displacement, tons: 12
Dimensions, feet (metres): 42.3 × 12.5 × 3 *(12.9 × 3.8 × 0.9)*
Main machinery: 2 diesels; 800 hp(m) *(588 kW)*; 2 shafts
Speed, knots: 38. **Range, miles:** 250 at 15 kts
Complement: 6
Guns: 2—12.7 mm MGs.

Comment: Built by SBCN, Loctudy in 1988-89.

5 BREMSE CLASS

SBEITLA (ex-G 32)   **UTIQUE** (ex-G 37)   **SELEUTA** (ex-G 39)
BULLARIJIA (ex-G 36)   **UERKOUANE** (ex-G 38)

Displacement, tons: 42 full load
Dimensions, feet (metres): 74.1 × 15.4 × 3.6 *(22.6 × 4.7 × 1.1)*
Main machinery: 2 SKL 6VD 18/5 AL-1 diesels; 944 hp(m) *(694 kW)* sustained; 2 shafts
Speed, knots: 14
Complement: 6
Guns: 2—14.5 mm (twin) MGs can be carried.
Radars: Navigation: TSR 333; I band.

Comment: Built in 1971-72 for the ex-GDR GBK. Transferred in May 1992. Others of the class sold to Malta and Jordan.

UTIQUE (GDR number)   *4/1991, Hartmut Ehlers*

TURKEY

Headquarters' Appointments

Commander-in-Chief, Turkish Naval Forces:
Admiral Vural Bayazit
Chief of Naval Staff:
Vice Admiral Ilhami Erdil

Senior Commands

Fleet Commander (Gölcük):
Admiral Guven Erkaya
Comsarnorth (Istanbul):
Vice Admiral Salim Dervisoglu
Comsarsouth (Izmir):
Vice Admiral Cetin Ersari
Comiststrait (Istanbul):
Rear Admiral Taner Uzunay
Comcanstrait (Çanakkale):
Rear Admiral Orhun Ozdemir
Combasetraining (Karamürsel):
Vice Admiral Aydan Erol
Comeageanzone (Izmir):
Rear Admiral A Yuksel Onel
Commedzone (Mersin):
Rear Admiral Erol Adayener
Comebaseiskenderun (Iskenderun):
Rear Admiral Halil Bolen
Combasegölcük (Gölcük):
Rear Admiral Erdal Baykal
Comblackzone (Ereğli):
Rear Admiral Dogan Haçipoglu
Comseaguard (Coast Guard) (Ankara):
Rear Admiral Niyazi Ulusoy
Comsuracgrup (Gölcük):
Rear Admiral Bulent Alpkaya
Comsabğrup (Gölcük):
Rear Admiral Yalcin Ertuna
Comminesgrup (Gölcük):
Rear Admiral Kemal Tok
Comamphibigrup (Foça-Izmir):
Rear Admiral Aydin Canel
Comfastgrup (Istanbul):
Rear Admiral Atilla Kiyat

Personnel

(a) 1994: 59 800 officers and ratings including 900 Naval Air Arm (reserves 70 000)
(see additional Marines)
(b) 18 months' national service

Bases

Headquarters: Ankara
Main Naval Base: Gölcük
Istanbul, Izmir, Foça, Erdek
Ereğli, Büyükdere, Aksas, Karamürsel (Training), Çanakkale, Iskenderun, Mersin
Dockyards: Gölcük, Taşkizak (Istanbul)

Strength of the Fleet (including Coast Guard)

Type	Active	Building (Planned)
Submarines—Patrol	15	4
Destroyers	8	—
Frigates	12	4 (4)
Fast Attack Craft—Missile	16	5
Fast Attack Craft—Gun	1	—
Large Patrol Craft	23	—
Coastal Patrol Craft	5	—
Minelayer—Large	1	—
Minelayers—Coastal	2	—
Minelayers—Tenders	2	—
Minesweepers/Hunters—Coastal	22	(6)
Minesweepers—Inshore	4	—
Minehunting Tenders	8	—
LSTs	7	1
LCTs	35	2
LCUs	2	—
LCMs	22	—
Survey Vessels	4	—
Depot/Training Ships	4	—
Fleet Replenishment Tanker	1	—
Logistic Support Ship	—	1
Support Tankers	5	—
Harbour Tankers	3	—
Water Tankers	10	(1)
Transports—Large and small	40	—
Salvage Ships	3	—
Boom Defence Vessels	3	—
Net Vessels	2 (5)	—
Tugs	51	—
Coast Guard	58	(24)

Marines

Total: 4000
One brigade of HQ company, three infantry battalions, one artillery battalion, support units.

Coast Guard (Sahil Güvenlik)

Formed in July 1982 from the naval wing of the Jandarma. Prefix J replaced by SG and paint scheme is very light grey with a diagonal stripe forward. About 1000 officers and men. Some craft are permanently based in North Cyprus.

Mercantile Marine

Lloyd's Register of Shipping:
948 vessels of 5 043 840 tons gross

DELETIONS

Destroyers

1992   *Muavenet* (old)
1993   *Adatepe* (old), *Kocatepe* (old), *Zafer* (old)

Patrol Forces

1993   *Mizrak, Kalkan*

Mine Warfare Forces

1993   *Mordogan, Mürefte*

Amphibious Forces

1991   4 EDIC, 8 LCM 8, 7 LCUs
1992   1 LCM 8, 3 LCUs
1993   1 EDIC

Auxiliaries

1992   *Cephane 3, Kanarya, Bekirdere, Gonca, Turgut Alp, Acar*
1993   *C G Hasan* (old), *Onaran, Başaran, AG 1*
1994   *Derya*

PENNANT LIST

Submarines

S 333	Ikinci Inönü
S 335	Burakreis
S 336	Muratreis
S 338	Uluçalireis
S 340	Çerbe
S 341	Çanakkale
S 342	Hizirreis
S 343	Pirireis
S 346	Birinci Inönü
S 347	Atilay
S 348	Saldiray
S 349	Batiray
S 350	Yildiray
S 351	Doğanay
S 352	Dolunay
S 353	Preveze
S 354	Sakarya

Destroyers

D 345	Yücetepe
D 346	Alcitepe
D 347	Anittepe
D 348	Savaştepe
D 349	Kiliç Ali Paşa
D 350	Piyale Paşa
D 351	M Fevzi Çakmak
D 352	Gayret

Frigates

D 358	Berk
D 359	Peyk
D 360	Gelibolu
D 361	Gemlik
F 240	Yavuz
F 241	Turgutreis
F 242	Fatih
F 243	Yildirim
F 244	Barbaros
F 245	Orucreis
F 250	Muavenet
F 251	Adatepe
F 252	Kocatepe
F 253	Zafer
F 254	Trakya
F 255	Akdeniz
F 256	Ege
F 257	Karadeniz

Mine Warfare Forces (Layers)

N 104	Mersin
N 110	Nusret
N 115	Mehmetcik

Mine Warfare Forces (Sweepers)

M 500	Foça
M 501	Fethiye
M 502	Fatsa
M 503	Finike
M 507	Seymen
M 508	Selçuk
M 509	Seyhan
M 510	Samsun
M 511	Sinop
M 512	Surmene
M 513	Seddülbahir
M 514	Silifke
M 515	Saros
M 516	Sigacik
M 517	Sapanca
M 518	Sariyer
M 520	Karamürsel
M 521	Kerempe
M 522	Kilimli
M 523	Kozlu
M 524	Kuşadasi
M 525	Kemer

P 530	Trabzon
P 531	Terme
P 532	Tirebolu
A 601	Tekirdağ
P 312-19	MTB 2-9

Amphibious Forces

L 401	Ertuğrul
L 402	Serdar
NL 120	Bayraktar
NL 121	Sancaktar
NL 122	Çakabey
NL 123	Sarucabey
NL 124	Karamürselbey
NL 125	Osman Gazi

Patrol Forces

P 111	Sultanhisar
P 112	Demirhisar
P 113	Yarhisar
P 114	Akhisar
P 115	Sivrihisar
P 116	Koçhisar
P 140	Girne
P 145	Caner Gönyeli
P 321	Denizkusu
P 322	Atmaca
P 323	Sahin
P 324	Kartal
P 326	Pelikan
P 327	Albatros
P 328	Şimşek
P 329	Kasirga
P 339	Bora
P 340	Dogan
P 341	Marti
P 342	Tayfun
P 343	Volkan
P 344	Rüzgar
P 345	Poyraz
P 346	Gurbet
P 347	Firtina
P 348	Yildiz
P 349	Karayel
P 121-136	AB 21-36
P 141-144	LS 1-4

Auxiliaries

A 570	Taşkizak
A 571	Yüzbaşi Tolunay
A 572	Albay Hakki Burak
A 573	Binbasi Saadettin Gürçan
A 574	Öncü
A 575	Inebolu
A 577	Sokullu Mehmet Paşa
A 578	Darica
A 579	Cezayirli Gazi Hasan Paşa
A 580	Akar
A 583	Akbas
A 584	Kurtaran
A 585	Akin
A 586	Ülkü
A 587	Gazal
A 588	Umur Bey
A 589	Işin
A 590	Yunus
A 591	Sarköy
A 592	Karadeniz Ereglisi
A 593	Eceabat
A 594	Çubuklu
A 596	Ulubat
A 597	Van
A 598	Sögüt
A 599	Önder
A 600	Kavak
P 304	AG 4 (BDV)
P 305	AG 5 (BDV)
P 306	AG 6 (BDV)

SUBMARINES

Note: In addition to those listed below, three old submarines are moored at Gölcük as accommodation ships.

0 + 4 PREVEZE (209) CLASS (TYPE 1400)

Name	No	Builders	Laid down	Launched	Commissioned
PREVEZE	S 353	Gölcük, Kocaeli	12 Sep 1989	22 Oct 1993	July 1994
SAKARYA	S 354	Gölcük, Kocaeli	1 Feb 1990	July 1994	Mar 1995
—	S 355	Gölcük, Kocaeli	July 1994	1997	1998
—	S 356	Gölcük, Kocaeli	July 1994	1998	1999

PREVEZE   11/1993, Selçuk Emre

Displacement, tons: 1454 surfaced; 1586 dived
Dimensions, feet (metres): 203.4 × 20.3 × 18
(62 × 6.2 × 5.5)
Main machinery: Diesel-electric; 4 MTU 12V 396 SB83 diesels;
3800 hp(m) (2.8 MW) sustained; 4 alternators; 1 Siemens
motor; 4000 hp(m) (3.38 MW) sustained; 1 shaft
Speed, knots: 15 surfaced/snorting; 21.5 dived
Range, miles: 8200 at 8 kts surfaced; 400 at 4 kts dived
Complement: 30

Missiles: SSM: McDonnell Douglas Sub Harpoon; active radar
homing to 130 km (70 nm) at 0.9 Mach; warhead 227 kg.
Torpedoes: 8—21 in (533 mm) bow tubes. GEC/Marconi Tigerfish Mk 24 Mod 2; wire-guided; active/passive homing to
13 km (7 nm) at 35 kts active; 29 km (15.7 nm) at 24 kts passive; warhead 134 kg. Total of 14 torpedoes and missiles.
Countermeasures: ESM: Racal Porpoise; radar warning.
Fire control: Atlas Elektronik ISUS 83-2 system.
Radars: Surface search; I band.
Sonars: Atlas Elektronik CSU 83; passive/active search and
attack; medium/high frequency.

Programmes: Order for first two signed in Ankara on 17 November 1987. Being built with HDW assistance. Prefabrication
started in March 1989. An agreement for the second pair has
been made with HDW, and they are to build at Gölcük after the
launch of *Sakarya*.
Structure: Diving depth, 280 m (820 ft). Kollmorgen masts.
Operational: Endurance, 50 days.

6 ATILAY (209) CLASS (TYPE 1200)

Name	No	Builders	Laid down	Launched	Commissioned
ATILAY	S 347	Howaldtswerke, Kiel	1 Dec 1972	23 Oct 1974	23 July 1975
SALDIRAY	S 348	Howaldtswerke, Kiel	2 Jan 1973	14 Feb 1975	21 Oct 1976
BATIRAY	S 349	Howaldtswerke, Kiel	1 June 1975	24 Oct 1977	20 July 1978
YILDIRAY	S 350	Gölcük, Izmit	1 May 1976	20 July 1979	20 July 1981
DOĞANAY	S 351	Gölcük, Izmit	21 Mar 1980	16 Nov 1983	16 Nov 1985
DOLUNAY	S 352	Gölcük, Izmit	9 Mar 1981	22 July 1988	21 July 1989

Displacement, tons: 980 surfaced; 1185 dived
Dimensions, feet (metres): 200.8 × 20.3 × 17.9
(61.2 × 6.2 × 5.5)
Main machinery: Diesel-electric; 4 MTU 12V 493 AZ80 GA31L
diesels; 2400 hp(m) (1.76 MW) sustained; 4 alternators;
1.7 MW; 1 Siemens motor; 4600 hp(m) (3.38 MW) sustained;
1 shaft
Speed, knots: 11 surfaced; 22 dived
Range, miles: 7500 at 8 kts surfaced
Complement: 38 (9 officers)

Torpedoes: 8—21 in (533 mm) tubes. 14 AEG SST 4; wire-
guided; active/passive homing to 28 km (15.3 nm) at 23 kts;

12 km (6.6 nm) at 35 kts; warhead 260 kg. Swim-out
discharge.
Countermeasures: ESM: Thomson-CSF DR 2000; radar
warning.
Fire control: Signaal M8 (S 347-348). Sinbads (remainder).
Radars: Surface search: S 63B; I band.
Sonars: Atlas Elektronik CSU 3; hull-mounted; passive/active
search and attack; medium/high frequency.

Programmes: Designed by Ingenieurkontor, Lübeck for construction by Howaldtswerke, Kiel and sale by Ferrostaal, Essen,
all acting as a consortium. Last three built in Turkey with assistance given by Howaldtswerke.

Modernisation: Fire-control system to be updated starting with
the first pair. Possibly by Atlas Elektronik to Preveze class
standards.
Structure: A single-hull design with two ballast tanks and forward and after trim tanks. Fitted with snort and remote
machinery control. The single screw is slow revving. Very high
capacity batteries with GRP lead-acid cells and battery cooling—by Wilh Hagen. Active and passive sonar, sonar detection
equipment, sound ranging gear and underwater telephone. Fitted with two periscopes, radar and Omega receiver. Fore-
planes retract. Diving depth, 250 m (820 ft).
Operational: Endurance, 50 days.

DOLUNAY   12/1991, Selim San

2 GUPPY III CLASS

Name	No	Builders	Laid down	Launched	Commissioned
ÇANAKKALE (ex-USS *Cobbler* SS 344)	S 341	Electric Boat Co	3 Apr 1944	1 Apr 1945	8 Aug 1945
IKINCI INÖNÜ (ex-USS *Corporal* SS 346)	S 333	Electric Boat Co	27 Apr 1944	10 June 1945	9 Nov 1945

Displacement, tons: 1975 standard; 2450 dived
Dimensions, feet (metres): 326.5 × 27 × 17
(99.5 × 8.2 × 5.2)
Main machinery: Diesel-electric; 4 GM 16-278A diesels;
6000 hp (4.41 MW); 2 motors; 5600 hp (4.2 MW); 2 shafts
Speed, knots: 17.5 surfaced; 15 dived
Range, miles: 10 000 at 10 kts surfaced
Complement: 86 (8 officers)

Torpedoes: 10—21 in (533 mm) (6 bow, 4 stern) tubes; 24 US
Mk 37 torpedoes.
Mines: 40 in lieu of torpedoes.
Radars: Surface search: SS 2A; I band.
Sonars: EDO BQR 2B; hull-mounted; passive search and attack;
medium frequency.
Sperry/Raytheon BQG 4; passive ranging.

Programmes: Transferred from US 21 November 1973.
Operational: Diving probably restricted to periscope depth.

IKINCI INÖNÜ   10/1987, Selim San

5 GUPPY IIA CLASS

Name	No	Builders	Laid down	Launched	Commissioned
BURAKREIS (ex-USS *Seafox* SS 402)	S 335	Portsmouth Navy Yard	2 Nov 1943	28 Mar 1944	13 June 1944
MURATREIS (ex-USS *Razorback* SS 394)	S 336	Portsmouth Navy Yard	9 Sep 1943	27 Jan 1944	3 Apr 1944
ULUÇALIREIS (ex-USS *Thornback* SS 418)	S 338	Portsmouth Navy Yard	5 Apr 1944	7 July 1944	13 Oct 1944
ÇERBE (ex-USS *Trutta* SS 421)	S 340	Portsmouth Navy Yard	22 Dec 1943	22 May 1944	16 Nov 1944
BIRINCI INÖNÜ (ex-USS *Threadfin* SS 410)	S 346	Portsmouth Navy Yard	18 Mar 1944	26 June 1944	30 Aug 1944

Displacement, tons: 1848 surfaced; 2440 dived
Dimensions, feet (metres): 306 × 27 × 17 *(93.2 × 8.2 × 5.2)*
Main machinery: Diesel-electric; 3 Fairbanks-Morse 38D8-1/
8-10 diesels; 4500 hp *(3.4 MW)*; 2 motors; 4800 hp
(3.6 MW); 2 shafts
Speed, knots: 17 surfaced; 14-15 dived
Range, miles: 12 000 at 10 kts surfaced
Complement: 82 (8 officers)

Torpedoes: 10—21 in *(533 mm)* (6 bow, 4 stern) tubes; 24 US
Mk 37 torpedoes.
Mines: 40 in lieu of torpedoes.
Fire control: Mk 106 TFCS.
Radars: Surface search: SS 2A; I band.
Sonars: EDO BQR 2B; hull-mounted; passive search and attack;
medium frequency.
EDO BQS 4; adds active capability to BQR 2B.
Sperry/Raytheon BQG 3; passive ranging.

Programmes: Transfers from US: S 335 December 1970, S 336
17 November 1970, S 340 June 1972, S 338 24 August
1973 and S 346 15 August 1973.
Structure: Çerbe is the only Guppy class submarine still in commission to retain the original low bridge which becomes
unpleasantly wet during surface passages in heavy seas.
Operational: Diving probably restricted to periscope depth.

ÇERBE   *10/1985, Selim San*

BIRINCI INÖNÜ   *3/1993, Selim San*

2 TANG CLASS

Name	No	Builders	Laid down	Launched	Commissioned
HIZIRREIS (ex-USS *Gudgeon* SS 567)	S 342	Portsmouth Navy Yard	20 May 1950	11 June 1952	21 Nov 1952
PIRIREIS (ex-USS *Tang* SS 563)	S 343	Portsmouth Navy Yard	18 Apr 1949	Apr 1951	25 Oct 1951

Displacement, tons: 2100 surfaced; 2700 dived
Dimensions, feet (metres): 287 × 27.3 × 19
(87.4 × 8.3 × 5.8)
Main machinery: Diesel-electric; 3 Fairbanks-Morse 38D8-1/
8-10 diesels; 4500 hp *(3.4 MW)*; 2 motors; 5600 hp
(4.2 MW); 2 shafts
Speed, knots: 16 surfaced; 16 dived
Range, miles: 7600 at 15 kts surfaced

Complement: 87 (8 officers)

Torpedoes: 8—21 in *(533 mm)* (6 fwd, 2 aft) tubes. Westing-
house Mk 37; active/passive homing to 8 km *(4.4 nm)* at
24 kts; warhead 150 kg.
Mines: In lieu of torpedoes.
Fire control: Mk 106 torpedo FCS.
Radars: Surface search: Fairchild BPS 12; I band.

Sonars: EDO BQR 2B; hull-mounted; passive search and attack;
medium frequency.
EDO BQS 4; adds active capability to BQR 2B.
Sperry/Raytheon BQG 4; passive ranging.

Programmes: S 343 transferred by lease from US January
1980—commissioned 21 March 1980. S 342 transferred by
lease 30 September 1983. Both finally purchased in June
1987.

PIRIREIS   *7/1989, Selçuk Emre*

DESTROYERS

6 GEARING (FRAM I) CLASS

Name	No	Builders	Laid down	Launched	Commissioned
YÜCETEPE (ex-USS *Orleck* DD 886)	D 345	Consolidated Steel Corporation	28 Nov 1944	12 May 1945	15 Sep 1945
SAVAŞTEPE (ex-USS *Meredith* DD 890)	D 348	Consolidated Steel Corporation	27 Jan 1945	28 June 1945	31 Dec 1945
KILIÇ ALI PAŞA (ex-USS *Robert H. McCard* DD 822)	D 349	Consolidated Steel Corporation	26 June 1945	9 Nov 1945	26 Oct 1946
PIYALE PAŞA (ex-USS *Fiske* DD 842)	D 350	Bath Iron Works	9 Apr 1945	8 Sep 1945	28 Nov 1945
M FEVZI ÇAKMAK (ex-USS *Charles H Roan* DD 853)	D 351	Bethlehem Steel Corporation, Quincy	27 Sep 1944	15 May 1945	12 Sep 1946
GAYRET (ex-USS *Eversole* DD 789)	D 352	Todd Pacific Shipyard	28 Feb 1945	8 Jan 1946	10 July 1946

Displacement, tons: 2425 standard; 3500 full load
Dimensions, feet (metres): 390.5 × 41.2 × 19
(119 × 12.6 × 5.8)
Main machinery: 4 Babcock & Wilcox boilers; 600 psi
(43.3 kg/cm sq); 850°F *(454°C)*; 2 GE turbines; 60 000 hp
(45 MW); 2 shafts
Speed, knots: 32.5. **Range, miles:** 5800 at 15 kts; 2400 at
25 kts
Complement: 275 (15 officers)

Missiles: SSM: McDonnell Douglas Harpoon ❶ (DD 349-352);
active radar homing to 130 km *(70 nm)* at 0.9 Mach; warhead
227 kg.
A/S: Honeywell ASROC Mk 112 octuple launcher ❷; inertial guidance to 1.6-10 km *(1-5.4 nm)*; payload Mk 46 torpedo.
Guns: 4 USN 5 in *(127 mm)*/38 (2 twin) Mk 38 ❸; 85° elevation;
15 rounds/minute to 17 km *(9.3 nm)*; weight of shell 25 kg. In
A and Y positions in all except D 348 which has them in A
and B.
2 or 4 Oerlikon 35 mm/90 (twin) ❹ (2 twin in D 351-352); 85°
elevation; 550 rounds/minute to 6 km *(3.3 nm)*; weight of
shell 1.55 kg. In B and X positions in D 351-352; remainder
have a single mounting in X position except D 348 which has it
in Y and D 345 in B.
Torpedoes: 6—324 mm US Mk 32 (2 triple) tubes ❺. Honeywell
Mk 46; anti-submarine; active/passive homing to 11 km
(5.9 nm) at 40 kts; warhead 44 kg.
Depth charges: 1 rack (9).
Countermeasures: Decoys: 2 or 4 20-barrelled Breda 105 mm
SCLAR Mk 2 or SRBOC chaff launchers.
ESM: WLR-1 and WLR-3; radar warning.
ECM: ULQ 6; jammer.
Fire control: GFCS Mk 37 for 127 mm. 1 or 2 Mk 51 for 40 mm.
Radars: Air search: Lockheed SPS 40 ❻; E/F band; range
320 km *(175 nm)*.
Surface search: Raytheon SPS 10 ❼; G band.
Navigation: Racal Decca; I band.
Fire control: Western Electric Mk 25 ❽; I/J band.
Sonars: Sangamo SQS 23; hull-mounted; active search and
attack; medium frequency.

Programmes: D 354 is FRAM II conversion—remainder FRAM I.
Transfers from US took place on 27 March 1971 (D 353), 11
July 1973 (D 352) and 21 September 1973 (D 351), D 353 pur-
chased 15 February 1973 and D 354 7 July 1974. D 349 and D
350 leased 5 June 1980, D 348 commissioned in the Turkish
Navy on 20 July 1981. D 345 commissioned 30 March 1983.
Ex-USS *McKean* DD 784 purchased for spares 25 November
1982. D 345, 349 and 350 purchased outright in June 1987.
Modernisation: Plans to install SAM systems in some of the class
have been cancelled.
Structure: All were built with a DASH helicopter platform and
hangar but only D 345 and D 348 retain a flight deck unclut-
tered by guns.

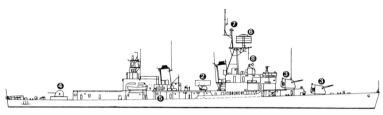

GAYRET
(Scale 1 : 1200), Ian Sturton

SAVASTEPE
(Scale 1 : 1200), Ian Sturton

SAVASTEPE
8/1992, C D Yaylali

KILIÇ ALI PAŞA
8/1993, C D Yaylali

PIYALE PAŞA
8/1993, C D Yaylali

2 CARPENTER (FRAM I) CLASS

Name	No	Builders	Laid down	Launched	Commissioned
ALCITEPE (ex-USS *Robert A Owens* DD 827)	D 346	Bath Iron Works, Maine	29 Oct 1945	15 July 1946	5 Nov 1949
ANITTEPE (ex-USS *Carpenter* DD 825)	D 347	Consolidated Steel, Texas	30 July 1945	30 Dec 1945	15 Dec 1949

Displacement, tons: 2425 standard; 3540 full load
Dimensions, feet (metres): 390.5 × 41 × 20.9
  (119 × 12.5 × 6.4)
Main machinery: 4 Babcock & Wilcox boilers; 600 psi
  (43.3 kg/cm sq); 850°F *(454°C)*; 2 GE turbines; 60 000 hp
  (45 MW); 2 shafts
Speed, knots: 33. **Range, miles:** 6000 at 12 kts
Complement: 275 (15 officers)

Missiles: A/S: Honeywell ASROC Mk 112 octuple launcher ❶;
  inertial guidance to 1.6-10 km *(1-5.4 nm)*; payload Mk 46
  torpedo.
Guns: 2—5 in *(127 mm)*/38 (twin) Mk 38 ❷; 85° elevation; 15
  rounds/minute to 17 km *(9.3 nm)*; weight of shell 25 kg.
  2—3 in *(76 mm)*/50 twin ❸; 85° elevation; 50 rounds/minute
  to 12.8 km *(7 nm)*; weight of shell 6 kg.
  2 Oerlikon 35 mm/90 (twin) ❹; 85° elevation; 550 rounds/
  minute to 6 km *(3.3 nm)*; weight of shell 1.55 kg.
Torpedoes: 6—324 mm US Mk 32 (2 triple) tubes ❺. Honeywell
  Mk 46; anti-submarine; active/passive homing to 11 km
  (5.9 nm) at 40 kts; warhead 44 kg.
Depth charges: 1 rack (9).
Countermeasures: ESM: WLR-1; radar warning.
ECM: ULQ-6; jammer.
Fire control: Mk 56 GFCS. Mk 114 ASW FCS. Mk 1 target desig-
  nation system.
Radars: Air search: Lockheed SPS 40 ❻; E/F band; range
  320 km *(175 nm)*.
  Surface search: Raytheon SPS 10 ❼; G band.
  Fire control: General Electric Mk 35 ❽; I/J band.
Sonars: Sangamo SQS 23; hull-mounted; active search and
  attack; medium frequency.

Helicopters: 1 AB 212ASW ❾.

Programmes: D 347 transferred from US 1981, D 346 in 1982.
  Both purchased outright in June 1987.
Modernisation: Plans to fit a SAM system have been suspended.
Structure: A Gearing design with an ASW bias. Can handle but
  not house AB 212ASW helicopters.

ALCITEPE *(Scale 1 : 1200), Ian Sturton*

ANITTEPE *8/1993, C D Yaylali*

FRIGATES

8 KNOX CLASS

Name	No	Builders	Laid down	Launched	Commissioned
MUAVENET (ex-*Capodanno*)	F 250 (ex-1093)	Avondale Shipyards	12 Oct 1971	21 Oct 1972	17 Nov 1973
ADATEPE (ex-*Fanning*)	F 251 (ex-1076)	Todd Shipyards	7 Dec 1968	24 Jan 1970	23 July 1971
KOCATEPE (ex-*Reasoner*)	F 252 (ex-1063)	Lockheed Shipbuilding	6 Jan 1969	1 Aug 1970	31 July 1971
ZAFER (ex-*Thomas C Hart*)	F 253 (ex-1092)	Avondale Shipyards	8 Oct 1971	12 Aug 1972	28 July 1973
TRAKYA (ex-*McCandless*)	F 254 (ex-1084)	Avondale Shipyards	4 June 1970	20 Mar 1971	18 Mar 1972
AKDENIZ (ex-*Ainsworth*)	F 255 (ex-1090)	Avondale Shipyards	11 June 1971	15 Apr 1972	31 Mar 1973
EGE (ex-*Donald B Beary*)	F 256 (ex-1085)	Avondale Shipyards	24 July 1970	22 May 1971	22 July 1972
KARADENIZ (ex-*Bowen*)	F 257 (ex-1079)	Avondale Shipyards	11 July 1969	2 May 1970	22 May 1971

Displacement, tons: 3011 standard; 4260 full load
Dimensions, feet (metres): 439.6 × 46.8 × 15; 24.8 (sonar)
  (134 × 14.3 × 4.6; 7.8)
Main machinery: 2 Combustion Engineering/Babcock & Wilcox
  boilers; 1200 psi *(84.4 kg/cm sq)*; 950°F *(510°C)*; 1 turbine;
  35 000 hp *(26 MW)*; 1 shaft
Speed, knots: 27. **Range, miles:** 4000 at 22 kts on 1 boiler
Complement: 288 (20 officers)

Missiles: SSM: 8 McDonnell Douglas Harpoon; active radar homing to 130 km *(70 nm)* at 0.9 Mach; warhead 227 kg.
  A/S: Honeywell ASROC Mk 16 octuple launcher with reload system (has 2 cells modified to fire Harpoon) ❶; inertial guidance
  to 1.6-10 km *(1-5.4 nm)*; payload Mk 46 Mod 5 Neartip.
Guns: 1 FMC 5 in *(127 mm)*/54 Mk 42 Mod 9 ❷; 85° elevation;
  20-40 rounds/minute to 24 km *(13 nm)* anti-surface; 14 km
  (7.7 nm) anti-aircraft; weight of shell 32 kg.
  1 General Electric/General Dynamics 20 mm/76 6-barrelled
  Mk 15 Vulcan Phalanx ❸; 3000 rounds/minute combined to
  1.5 km.
Torpedoes: 4—324 mm Mk 32 (2 twin) fixed tubes ❹. 22 Honeywell Mk 46; anti-submarine; active/passive homing to 11 km
  (5.9 nm) at 40 kts; warhead 44 kg.
Countermeasures: Decoys: 2 Loral Hycor SRBOC 6-barrelled
  fixed Mk 36 ❺; IR flares and chaff to 4 km *(2.2 nm)*. T Mk-6
  Fanfare/SLQ-25 Nixie; torpedo decoy. Prairie Masker hull and
  blade rate noise suppression.
ESM/ECM: SLQ 32(V)2 ❻; radar warning. If fitted, Sidekick modi-
  fication adds jammer and deception system.
Combat data systems: Link 14 receive only.
Fire control: SWG-1A Harpoon LCS. Mk 68 GFCS. Mk 114 ASW
  FCS. Mk 1 target designation system. MMS target acquisition
  sight (for mines, small craft and low flying aircraft). SRQ-4 for
  LAMPS I (if acquired).
Radars: Air search: Lockheed SPS 40B ❼; E/F band.
  Surface search: Raytheon SPS 10 or Norden SPS 67 ❽; G band.
  Navigation: Marconi LN 66; I band.
  Fire control: Western Electric SPG 53A/D/F ❾; I/J band.
Tacan: SRN 15. **IFF:** UPX-12.
Sonars: EDO/General Electric SQS 26 CX; bow-mounted; active
  search and attack; medium frequency.
  EDO SQR 18A(V)1; passive towed array; very low frequency.

Helicopters: 1 AB 212ASW ❿; SH-2F LAMPS I (may be
  acquired).

Programmes: In late 1992 the US offered Turkey four of the
  class. A proposal was put to Congress in June 1993 and four
  approved for transfer on a five year lease, plus one more, *Elmer
  Montgomery*, on a grant basis under the Foreign Assistance
  Act. The latter replaced the former destroyer *Muavenet* which
  was scrapped after being hit by a Sea Sparrow missile and is

MUAVENET *(Scale 1 : 1200), Ian Sturton*

ADATEPE *10/1993, Selçuk Emre*

used for spares. A second batch of four is to be transferred in
1994. The first batch all commissioned into the Turkish Navy
on 29 November 1993. The second batch of four is scheduled
for June 1994.
Modernisation: Modified to accommodate the Light Airborne
Multi-Purpose System (LAMPS) and the SH-2F Seasprite anti-
submarine helicopter; hangar and flight deck are enlarged. In
1979 a programme was initiated to fit 3.5 ft bow bulwarks and
spray strakes adding 9.1 tons to a displacement. Sea Sparrow
SAM replaced by Phalanx 1982-88.

Structure: Improved ASROC torpedo reloading capability (note
slanting face of bridge structure immediately behind ASROC).
Four Mk 32 torpedo tubes are fixed in the midships structure,
two to a side, angled out at 45°. The arrangement provides
improved loading capability over exposed triple Mk 32 torpedo
tubes. A 4000 lb lightweight anchor is fitted on the port side
and an 8000 lb anchor fits into the after section of the sonar
dome.
Operational: The purchase of ASW helicopters has been
authorised.

4 YAVUZ CLASS (MEKO 200 TYPE)

Name	No	Builders	Laid down	Launched	Commissioned
YAVUZ	F 240	Blohm & Voss, Hamburg	30 May 1985	7 Nov 1985	17 July 1987
TURGUTREIS (ex-*Turgut*)	F 241	Howaldtswerke, Kiel	20 May 1985	30 May 1986	4 Feb 1988
FATIH	F 242	Gölcük, Izmit	1 Jan 1986	24 Apr 1987	22 July 1988
YILDIRIM	F 243	Gölcük, Izmit	24 Apr 1987	22 July 1988	21 July 1989

Displacement, tons: 2500 standard; 2784 full load
Dimensions, feet (metres): 362.4 × 46.6 × 13.5
  (110.5 × 14.2 × 4.1)
Main machinery: CODAD; 4 MTU 20V 1163 TB93 diesels;
  33 300 hp(m) *(24.5 MW)* sustained; 2 shafts; cp props
Speed, knots: 27. **Range, miles:** 4100 at 18 kts
Complement: 180 (24 officers)

Missiles: SSM: 8 McDonnell Douglas Harpoon (2 quad) launchers **❶**; active radar homing to 130 km *(70 nm)* at 0.9 Mach;
  warhead 227 kg.
  SAM: Raytheon Sea Sparrow Mk 29 Mod 1 octuple launcher **❷**;
  24 Selenia Elsag Aspide; semi-active radar homing to 13 km
  (7 nm) at 2.5 Mach; warhead 39 kg.
Guns: 1 FMC 5 in *(127 mm)*/54 Mk 45 Mod 1 **❸**; 65° elevation;
  20 rounds/minute to 23 km *(12.6 nm)* anti-surface; 15 km
  (8.2 nm) anti-aircraft; weight of shell 32 kg.
  3 Oerlikon-Contraves 25 mm Sea Zenith **❹**; 4 barrels per
  mounting; 127° elevation; 3400 rounds/minute combined to
  2 km.
Torpedoes: 6—324 mm Mk 32 (2 triple) tubes **❺**. Honeywell Mk
  46; anti-submarine; active/passive homing to 11 km *(5.9 nm)*
  at 40 kts; warhead 44 kg.
Countermeasures: Decoys: 2 Loral Hycor 6-tubed fixed Mk 36
  Mod 1 SRBOC **❻**; IR flares and chaff to 4 km *(2.2 nm)*.
  Nixie SLQ 25; towed torpedo decoy.
  ESM/ECM: Signaal Rapids/Ramses; intercept and jammer.
Combat data systems: Signaal STACOS-TU; action data auto-
  mation; Link 11. WSC 3V(7) SATCOMs.
Fire control: 2 Siemens Albis optronic directors. SWG-1A for
  Harpoon.
Radars: Air search: Signaal DA 08 **❼**; F band.
  Air/surface search: Plessey AWS 6 Dolphin **❽**; G band.
  Fire control: Signaal STIR **❾**; I/J/K band (for SAM); range 140 km
  (76 nm) for 1 m² target.
  Signaal WM 25 **❿**; I/J band (for SSM and 127 mm); range
  46 km *(25 nm)*.
  Two Contraves Seaguard **⓫**; I/J band (for 25 mm).
  Navigation: Racal Decca TM 1226; I band.
  Tacan: URN 25. IFF Mk XII.
Sonars: Raytheon SQS 56 (DE 1160); hull-mounted; active
  search and attack; medium frequency.

Helicopters: 1 AB 212ASW **⓬**.

YAVUZ   *(Scale 1 : 900), Ian Sturton*

YAVUZ   *9/1993, C D Yaylali*

Programmes: Ordered 29 December 1982 with builders and
Thyssen Rheinstahl Technik of Dusseldorf. Meko 200 type
similar to Portuguese frigates. *Turgutreis* was renamed on
14 February 1988. A second batch of two ships is sufficiently
different to merit a separate entry.
Operational: Helicopter has Sea Skua anti-ship missiles.

0 + 4 BARBAROS CLASS (MODIFIED MEKO 200 TYPE)

Name	No	Builders	Laid down	Launched	Commissioned
BARBAROS	F 244	Blohm & Voss, Hamburg	18 Mar 1993	29 Sep 1993	Mar 1995
ORUCREIS	F 245	Gölcük, Kocaeli	Sep 1993	July 1994	Mar 1996
—	F 246	Blohm & Voss, Hamburg	1994	1996	1997
—	F 247	Gölcük, Kocaeli	1994	1997	1998

Displacement, tons: 3350 full load
Dimensions, feet (metres): 382.9 × 48.6 × 14.1
  (116.7 × 14.8 × 4.3)
Main machinery: CODOG; 2 GE LM 2500 gas-turbines;
  60 000 hp *(44.76 MW)* sustained; 2 MTU 16V 1163 TB83 die-
  sels; 11 780 hp(m) *(8.67 MW)* sustained; 2 shafts; cp props
Speed, knots: 32. **Range, miles:** 4100 at 18 kts
Complement: 200 (24 officers)

Missiles: SSM: 8 McDonnell Douglas Harpoon (2 quad) launchers **❶**; active radar homing to 130 km *(70 nm)* at 0.9 Mach;
  warhead 227 kg.
  SAM: Raytheon Sea Sparrow Mk 29 Mod 1 octuple launcher **❷**;
  24 Selenia Elsag Aspide; semi-active radar homing to 13 km
  (7 nm) at 2.5 Mach; warhead 39 kg. To be fitted for but not
  with VLS Mk 41 in F 244 and 245; to be fitted on build in F 246
  and F 247.
Guns: 1 FMC 5 in *(127 mm)*/54 Mk 45 Mod 2 **❸**; 65° elevation;
  20 rounds/minute to 23 km *(12.6 nm)* anti-surface; 15 km
  (8.2 nm) anti-aircraft; weight of shell 32 kg.
  3 Oerlikon-Contraves 25 mm Sea Zenith **❹**; 4 barrels per
  mounting; 127° elevation; 3400 rounds/minute combined to
  2 km.
Torpedoes: 6—324 mm Mk 32 Mod 5 (2 triple) tubes **❺**. Honey-
  well Mk 46; anti-submarine; active/passive homing to 11 km
  (5.9 nm) at 40 kts; warhead 44 kg.
Countermeasures: Decoys: 2 Loral Hycor 6-tubed fixed Mk 36
  Mod 1 SRBOC **❻**; IR flares and chaff to 4 km *(2.2 nm)*.
  Nixie SLQ 25; towed torpedo decoy.
  ESM/ECM: Racal Cutlass/Scorpion; intercept and jammer.
Combat data systems: Thomson-CSF/Signaal STACOS Mod 3;
  Link 11. WSC 3V(7) SATCOMs.
Fire control: 2 Siemens Albis optronic directors.
Radars: Air search: Siemens/Plessey AWS 9 (Type 996) **❼**; 3D;
  E/F band.
  Air/surface search: Plessey AWS 6 Dolphin **❽**; G band.
  Fire control: Signaal STIR **❾**; I/J/K band (for SAM); range 140 km
  (76 nm) for 1 m² target.
  Contraves TMX **❿**; I/J band (for SSM and 127 mm).
  Two Contraves Seaguard **⓫**; I/J band (for 25 mm).
  Navigation: Racal Decca 2690 BT ARPA; I band.
  Tacan: URN 25. IFF Mk XII.
Sonars: Raytheon SQS 56 (DE 1160); hull-mounted; active
  search and attack; medium frequency.

Helicopters: 1 AB 212ASW **⓬**.

Programmes: First pair ordered 19 January 1990, second pair
authorised 14 December 1992 but the order was still waiting
to be implemented in early 1994. Programme started 5
November 1991 with construction commencing in June 1992
in Germany.

BARBAROS   *(Scale 1 : 900), Ian Sturton*

BARBAROS   *4/1994, M. Nitz*

Structure: An improvement on the Yavuz class. Mk 29 Sea Sparrow launchers fitted in the first two, while the second pair will
have Mk 41 VLS, which will then be retrofitted in the first two in
due course. The ships have CODOG propulsion for a higher top
speed. Other differences with *Yavuz* include a full command
system, improved radars, and a citadel for NBCD protection.
Operational: Helicopter has Sea Skua anti-ship missiles. The first
pair will probably be used as Flagships.

2 KÖLN CLASS

Name	No	Builders	Laid down	Launched	Commissioned
GELIBOLU (ex-*Gazi Osman Pasa*) (ex-*Karlsruhe* F 223)	D 360	HC Stulcken Sohn, Hamburg	15 Dec 1958	24 Oct 1959	15 Dec 1962
GEMLIK (ex-*Braunschweig* F 225, ex-*Emden* F 221)	D 361	HC Stulcken Sohn, Hamburg	28 July 1960	3 Feb 1962	16 June 1964

Displacement, tons: 2100 standard; 2700 full load
Dimensions, feet (metres): 360.5 × 36.1 × 16.7 (sonar)
(109.9 × 11 × 5.1)
Main machinery: CODAG; 2 Brown Boveri gas-turbines;
24 000 hp(m) *(17.7 MW)*; 4 MAN 16-cyl diesels; 12 000 hp(m)
(8.8 MW); 2 shafts; cp props
Speed, knots: 28; 18 diesels. **Range, miles:** 920 at 28 kts; 3000
at 18 kts
Complement: 210 (17 officers)

Guns: 2 Creusot Loire 3.9 in *(100 mm)*/55 Mod 53 ❶; 80° elev-
ation; 60-80 rounds/minute to 17 km *(9.3 nm)*; weight of shell
13.5 kg.
6 Bofors 40 mm/70 (2 twin ❷, 2 single ❸); 85° elevation to
12 km *(6.6 nm)*; weight of shell 0.96 kg.
Torpedoes: 4—21 in *(533 mm)* tubes ❹; anti-submarine.
A/S mortars: 2 Bofors 375 mm 4-tubed trainable ❺; range
1600 m or 3600 m depending on weapon; 72 carried.
Depth charges: 2 racks (12).
Mines: Can carry 80.
Countermeasures: Decoys: 2 multi-barrelled chaff launchers.
ESM: Radar intercept.
Radars: Air/surface search: Signaal DA 08 ❻; F band; range
204 km *(110 nm)* for 2 m² target.
Navigation: Kelvin Hughes; I band.
Fire control: Two Signaal M 44 ❼; I/J band (for 100 mm).
Signaal M 45 ❽; I/J band (for 40 mm).
Sonars: PAE/CWE; hull-mounted; active search and attack;
high/medium frequency.

Programmes: First two transferred by West German Navy. *Gelibolu* commissioned 28 March 1983; *Gemlik*, 23 September
1983. The last two of this class, ex-FGN *Lübeck* and *Braunschweig* were also bought in December 1988 and June 1989
respectively to be used to provide spares for the other two. In
1992 *Braunschweig* replaced *Emden* taking the same name
and pennant number.
Operational: An engine fire in *Gemlik* in 1989 led to speculation
that she might be replaced by one of the others, but this did not
happen until after a second fire in 1991. These ships are notoriously short of fresh water distilling capacity which limits operational range without water tanker support.

GELIBOLU   *(Scale 1 : 1200), Ian Sturton*

GELIBOLU   *9/1993, Selim San*

2 BERK CLASS

Name	No	Builders	Laid down	Launched	Commissioned
BERK	D 358	Gölcük Naval Yard	9 Mar 1967	25 June 1971	12 July 1972
PEYK	D 359	Gölcük Naval Yard	18 Jan 1968	7 June 1972	24 July 1975

Displacement, tons: 1450 standard; 1950 full load
Dimensions, feet (metres): 311.7 × 38.7 × 18.1
(95 × 11.8 × 5.5)
Main machinery: 4 Fiat-Tosi Type 3-016-RSS diesels; 24 00
hp(m) *(17.7 MW)*; 1 shaft
Speed, knots: 25

Guns: 4 USN 3 in *(76 mm)*/50 (2 twin) ❶; 85° elevation; 50
rounds/minute to 12.8 km *(7 nm)*; weight of shell 6 kg.
Torpedoes: 6—324 mm US Mk 32 (2 triple) tubes ❷. Honeywell
Mk 46; anti-submarine; active/passive homing to 11 km
(5.9 nm) at 40 kts; warhead 44 kg.
A/S mortars: 2 Mk 11 Hedgehog 24-rocket launchers ❸; range
250 m; warhead 13.6 kg.
Depth charges: 1 rack.
Countermeasures: ESM: WLR 1; radar warning.
Fire control: 2 Mk 63 GFCS.
Radars: Air search: Lockheed SPS 40 ❹; E/F band; range
320 km *(175 nm)*.
Surface search: Raytheon SPS 10 ❺; G band.
Navigation: Racal Decca; I band.
Fire control: Two Western Electric Mk 34 ❻; I/J band (for guns).

BERK   *(Scale 1 : 900), Ian Sturton*

Sonars: Sangamo SQS 29/31 series; hull-mounted; active
search and attack; high frequency.

Helicopters: Platform only for AB 212ASW ❼.

Programmes: First major warships built in Turkey. Both are
named after famous ships of the Ottoman Navy.
Structure: Of modified US Claud Jones design (now Indonesian
Samadikun class).

BERK   *1/1989, Hartmut Ehlers*

SHIPBORNE AIRCRAFT

Note: The purchase of four medium size ASW helicopters was authorised in 1993.

Numbers/Type: 14 Agusta AB 212ASW.
Operational speed: 106 kts *(196 km/h).*
Service ceiling: 14 200 ft *(4330 m).*
Range: 230 nm *(426 km).*
Role/Weapon systems: ASV/ASW helicopter with recently updated systems. Sensors: Ferranti Sea Spray Mk 3 radar, ECM/ESM, MAD, Bendix ASQ-18 dipping sonar. Weapons: ASW; 2 × Mk 46 or 244/S torpedoes. AVS; 2 × Sea Skua missiles.

AB 212   *1988, Turkish Navy*

LAND-BASED MARITIME AIRCRAFT

Note: The plan was to acquire P3 Orion aircraft from the US in 1993/94, but this may be overtaken by the cheaper option of CASA CN-235M aircraft.

Numbers/Type: 14 Grumman S-2E Tracker.
Operational speed: 130 kts *(241 km/h).*
Service ceiling: 2500 ft *(7620 m).*
Range: 1350 nm *(2500 km).*
Role/Weapon systems: Air Force manned for ASW and MR operations in Black and Mediterranean Seas; updated in past but in need of replacement. All aircraft were grounded in August 1993. Sensors: Search radar, ESM, MAD. Weapons: ASW; 4 × Mk 46 torpedoes, depth bombs or mines. ASV; 6 × 127 mm rockets.

PATROL FORCES

0 + 5 YILDIZ CLASS (FAST ATTACK CRAFT—MISSILE)

Name	No	Builders	Commissioned
YILDIZ	P 348	Taskizak Yard, Istanbul	July 1994
KARAYEL	P 349	Taskizak Yard, Istanbul	1995
—	P 350	Taskizak Yard, Istanbul	1996
—	P 351	Taskizak Yard, Istanbul	1997
—	P 352	Taskizak Yard, Istanbul	1998

Displacement, tons: 436 full load
Dimensions, feet (metres): 190.6 × 25 × 8.8 *(58.1 × 7.6 × 2.7)*
Main machinery: 4 MTU 16V 956 TB92 diesels; 17 700 hp(m) *(13 MW)* sustained; 4 shafts
Speed, knots: 38. **Range, miles:** 1050 at 30 kts
Complement: 45 (6 officers)

Missiles: SSM: 8 McDonnell Douglas Harpoon (2 quad) launchers; active radar homing to 130 km *(70 nm)* at 0.9 Mach; warhead 227 kg.
Guns: 1 OTO Melara 3 in *(76 mm)*/62 compact; 85° elevation; 85 rounds/minute to 16 km *(8.7 nm)* anti-surface; 12 km *(6.6 nm)* anti-aircraft; weight of shell 6 kg.
2 Oerlikon 35 mm/90 (twin); 85° elevation; 550 rounds/minute to 6 km *(3.3 nm)*; weight of shell 1.55 kg.
Countermeasures: Decoys: 2 SRBOC chaff launchers.
ESM/ECM: Racal Cutlass.
Combat data systems: Signaal/Thomson-CSF TACTICOS.
Fire control: LIOD optronic director; Vesta helo data link.
Radars: Surface search: Siemens Plessey AW 6 Dolphin; G band.
Fire control: Oerlikon/Contraves TMX; I/J band.

Programmes: First pair ordered in June 1991. Three more authorised in early 1993, contract signed in May 1993 subject to confirmation.
Structure: Dogan class hull with much improved weapon systems.

YILDIZ (model)   *1991, C D Yaylali*

8 DOGAN CLASS (FAST ATTACK CRAFT—MISSILE)

Name	No	Builders	Commissioned
DOĞAN	P 340	Lürssen, Vegesack	15 June 1977
MARTI	P 341	Taşkizak Yard, Istanbul	28 July 1978
TAYFUN	P 342	Taşkizak Yard, Istanbul	19 July 1979
VOLKAN	P 343	Taşkizak Yard, Istanbul	25 July 1980
RÜZGAR	P 344	Taşkizak Yard, Istanbul	17 Dec 1984
POYRAZ	P 345	Taşkizak Yard, Istanbul	7 Feb 1986
GURBET	P 346	Taşkizak Yard, Istanbul	22 July 1988
FIRTINA	P 347	Taşkizak Yard, Istanbul	23 Oct 1988

Displacement, tons: 436 full load
Dimensions, feet (metres): 190.6 × 25 × 8.8 *(58.1 × 7.6 × 2.7)*
Main machinery: 4 MTU 16V 956 TB92 diesels; 17 700 hp(m) *(13 MW)* sustained; 4 shafts
Speed, knots: 38. **Range, miles:** 1050 at 30 kts
Complement: 38 (5 officers)

Missiles: SSM: 8 McDonnell Douglas Harpoon (2 quad) launchers; active radar homing to 130 km *(70 nm)* at 0.9 Mach; warhead 227 kg.
Guns: 1 OTO Melara 3 in *(76 mm)*/62 compact; 85° elevation; 85 rounds/minute to 16 km *(8.7 nm)* anti-surface; 12 km *(6.6 nm)* anti-aircraft; weight of shell 6 kg.
2 Oerlikon 35 mm/90 (twin); 85° elevation; 550 rounds/minute to 6 km *(3.3 nm)*; weight of shell 1.55 kg.
Countermeasures: Decoys: 2 multi-barrelled chaff launchers.
ESM: MEL Susie; radar warning.
Radars: Surface search: Racal Decca 1226; I band.
Fire control: Signaal WM 28/41; I/J band; range 46 km *(25 nm)*.

Programmes: First ordered 3 August 1973 to a Lürssen FPB 57 design. Successor class being built using the same hull and propulsion.
Structure: Aluminium superstructure; steel hulls.

FIRTINA   *3/1993, Selim San*

8 KARTAL CLASS (FAST ATTACK CRAFT—MISSILE)

Name	No	Builders	Commissioned
DENIZKUSU	P 321 (ex-*P 336*)	Lürssen, Vegesack	1967
ATMACA	P 322 (ex-*P 335*)	Lürssen, Vegesack	1967
SAHIN	P 323 (ex-*P 334*)	Lürssen, Vegesack	1967
KARTAL	P 324 (ex-*P 333*)	Lürssen, Vegesack	1967
PELIKAN	P 326	Lürssen, Vegesack	1968
ALBATROS	P 327 (ex-*P 325*)	Lürssen, Vegesack	1968
ŞIMŞEK	P 328 (ex-*P 332*)	Lürssen, Vegesack	1968
KASIRGA	P 329 (ex-*P 338*)	Lürssen, Vegesack	1967

Displacement, tons: 160 standard; 190 full load
Dimensions, feet (metres): 139.4 × 23 × 7.9 *(42.5 × 7 × 2.4)*
Main machinery: 4 MTU MD 16V 538 TB90 diesels; 12 000 hp(m) *(8.82 MW)* sustained; 4 shafts
Speed, knots: 42. **Range, miles:** 500 at 40 kts
Complement: 39

Missiles: SSM: 2 or 4 Kongsberg Penguin Mk 2; IR homing to 27 km *(14.6 nm)* at 0.8 Mach; warhead 120 kg.
Guns: 2 Bofors 40 mm/70; 90° elevation; 300 rounds/minute to 12 km *(6.6 nm)*; weight of shell 0.96 kg.
Torpedoes: 2—21 in *(533 mm)* tubes; anti-surface.
Mines: Can carry 4.
Radars: Surface search: Racal Decca 1226; I band.

Structure: Similar design to the Jaguar class.
Operational: *Meltem* sunk in collision with Soviet naval training ship *Khasan* in Bosphorus in 1985. Subsequently salvaged but beyond repair.

ALBATROS   *1/1989, Hartmut Ehlers*

1 GIRNE CLASS (FAST ATTACK CRAFT—GUN)

Name	No	Builders	Commissioned
GIRNE	P 140	Taşkizak Naval Yard	30 July 1976

Displacement, tons: 341 standard; 399 full load
Dimensions, feet (metres): 190.6 × 24.9 × 9.2 *(58.1 × 7.6 × 2.8)*
Main machinery: 2 MTU 16V 956 SB90 diesels; 8000 hp(m) *(5.9 MW)* sustained; 2 shafts
Speed, knots: 36. **Range, miles:** 4200 at 16 kts
Complement: 54 (6 officers)
Guns: 2 Bofors 40 mm/70. 2 Oerlikon 20 mm.
A/S mortars: 2 Mk 20 Mousetrap 4-rocket launchers; range 200 m; warhead 50 kg.
Depth charges: 2 projectors; 2 racks.
Fire control: CSEE Naja optronic director.
Radars: Surface search: Racal Decca; I band.
Sonars: MS 25; hull-mounted; active attack; high frequency.

Comment: Unsuccessful prototype of an ASW patrol boat on a Lürssen 57 hull.

GIRNE   *1988, Turkish Navy*

1 ASHEVILLE CLASS (LARGE PATROL CRAFT)

Name	No	Builders	Commissioned
BORA (ex-USS *Surprise* PG 97)	P 339	Petersons, Wisconsin	17 Oct 1969

Displacement, tons: 225 standard; 245 full load
Dimensions, feet (metres): 164.5 × 23.8 × 9.5 *(50.1 × 7.3 × 2.9)*
Main machinery: CODAG; 1 GE LM 1500 gas-turbine; 13 300 hp *(9.92 MW)*; 2 Cummins VT12-875M diesels; 1450 hp *(1.08 MW)*; 2 shafts
Speed, knots: 40 gas; 16 diesels. **Range, miles:** 320 at 38 kts
Complement: 37 (5 officers)
Guns: 1 USN 3 in *(76 mm)*/50 Mk 34; 85° elevation; 50 rounds/minute to 12.8 km *(7 nm)*; weight of shell 6 kg.
1 Bofors 40 mm/56 Mk 10. 4—12.7 mm (2 twin) MGs.
Fire control: Mk 63 GFCS.
Radars: Surface search: Sperry SPS 53; I/J band.
Fire control: Western Electric SPG 50; I/J band.

Comment: This vessel belongs to the largest Patrol Type built by the US Navy since the Second World War and the first of that Navy to have gas-turbines. Transferred from US on 28 February 1973 on loan and purchased outright in June 1987.

BORA   *8/1988, Selçuk Emre*

12 LARGE PATROL CRAFT

AB 25-AB 36   P 125-P 136   *(ex-P 1225-P 1236)*

Displacement, tons: 170 full load
Dimensions, feet (metres): 132 × 21 × 5.5 *(40.2 × 6.4 × 1.7)*
Main machinery: 4 SACM-AGO V16CSHR diesels; 9600 hp(m) *(7.06 MW)*; 2 cruise diesels; 300 hp(m) *(220 kW)*; 2 shafts
Speed, knots: 22
Complement: 31 (3 officers)
Guns: 1 or 2 Bofors 40 mm/70 (in some).
1 Oerlikon 20 mm (in those with 1—40 mm). 2—12.7 mm MGs.
A/S mortars: 1 Mk 20 Mousetrap 4-rocket launcher; range 200 m; warhead 50 kg.
Depth charges: 1 rack.
Sonars: Hull-mounted; active search and attack; high frequency.

Comment: Built at Taşkizak Naval Yard and commissioned between 1967 and 1970. Pennant numbers changed in 1991.

AB 31   *5/1993*

6 HISAR (PC 1638) CLASS (LARGE PATROL CRAFT)

Name	No	Builders	Commissioned
SULTANHISAR (ex-*PC 1638*)	P 111	Gunderson Bros Engineering Co, Portland, Oregon	May 1964
DEMIRHISAR (ex-*PC 1639*)	P 112	Gunderson Bros Engineering Co, Portland, Oregon	Apr 1965
YARHISAR (ex-*PC 1640*)	P 113	Gunderson Bros Engineering Co, Portland, Oregon	Sep 1964
AKHISAR (ex-*PC 1641*)	P 114	Gunderson Bros Engineering Co, Portland, Oregon	Dec 1964
SIVRIHISAR (ex-*PC 1642*)	P 115	Gunderson Bros Engineering Co, Portland, Oregon	June 1965
KOÇHISAR (ex-*PC 1643*)	P 116	Gölcük Dockyard, Turkey	July 1965

Displacement, tons: 325 standard; 477 full load
Dimensions, feet (metres): 173.7 × 23 × 10.2 *(53 × 7 × 3.1)*
Main machinery: 2 Fairbanks-Morse diesels; 2800 hp *(2.09 MW)*; 2 shafts
Speed, knots: 19. **Range, miles:** 6000 at 10 kts
Complement: 31 (3 officers)
Guns: 1 Bofors 40 mm/60. 4 Oerlikon 20 mm (2 twin).
A/S mortars: 1 Hedgehog Mk 15 trainable 24-rocket launcher; range 250 m; warhead 13.6 kg.
Depth charges: 4 projectors; 1 rack (9).
Radars: Surface search: Decca 707; I band.
Sonars: EDO SQS 17A; hull-mounted; active attack; high frequency.

Comment: Transferred from the US on build.

YARHISAR   *1/1990, Selim San*

4 PGM 71 CLASS (LARGE PATROL CRAFT)

AB 21-AB 24 (ex-*PGM 104-PGM 108*)   P 121-P 124   *(ex-P 1221-P 1224)*

Displacement, tons: 130 standard; 147 full load
Dimensions, feet (metres): 101 × 21 × 7 *(30.8 × 6.4 × 2.1)*
Main machinery: GM diesels; 2 shafts
Speed, knots: 18.5. **Range, miles:** 1500 at 10 kts
Complement: 15
Guns: 1 Bofors 40 mm/60. 4 Oerlikon 20 mm (2 twin). 1—7.62 mm MG.
A/S mortars: 2 Mk 22 Mousetrap 8-rocket launchers; range 200 m; warhead 50 kg.
Depth charges: 2 racks (4).
Radars: Surface search: Raytheon; I band.
Sonars: EDO SQS 17A; hull-mounted; active attack; high frequency.

Comment: Built by Peterson, Sturgeon Bay and commissioned 1967-68. Transferred from US almost immediately after completion. Pennant numbers changed in 1991.

AB 21   *4/1993, Turkish Navy*

1 COASTAL PATROL CRAFT

CANER GÖNYELI   P 145

Displacement, tons: 56 full load
Dimensions, feet (metres): 87.6 × 15.4 × 5.6 *(26.7 × 4.7 × 1.7)*
Main machinery: 2 diesels; 1250 hp(m) *(918 kW)*; 2 shafts
Speed, knots: 19
Complement: 14 (1 officer)
Guns: 2 Oerlikon 20 mm.

Comment: Based in North Cyprus. Similar to KW 15 class in the Coast Guard. Built in 1976.

CANER GÖNYELI   *1990, Turkish Navy*

4 COAST GUARD TYPE (COASTAL PATROL CRAFT)

LS 1-LS 4   P 141-P 144   (ex-P 1209-P 1212)

Displacement, tons: 63 full load
Dimensions, feet (metres): 83 × 14 × 5 *(25.3 × 4.3 × 1.6)*
Main machinery: 2 Cummins diesels; 1100 hp *(820 kW)*; 2 shafts
Speed, knots: 13
Complement: 17 (3 officers)
Guns: 1 Oerlikon 20 mm.
A/S mortars: 2 Mk 20 Mousetrap 8-rocket launchers; range 200 m; warhead 50 kg.
Radars: Surface search: I band.
Sonars: Hull-mounted; active attack; high frequency.

Comment: Transferred from USCG on 25 June 1953. All built by US Coast Guard Yard, Curtis Bay, Maryland. Pennant numbers changed in 1991.

LS 1   *1992, Turkish Navy*

MINE WARFARE FORCES

Note: Minelayers: see *Bayraktar, Sancaktar, Çakabey, Sarucabey* and *Karamürselbey* under Amphibious Forces.

1 MINELAYER

Name	No	Builders	Commissioned
NUSRET	N 110 (ex-N 108)	Frederikshavn Dockyard, Denmark	16 Sep 1964

Displacement, tons: 1880 standard
Dimensions, feet (metres): 252.7 × 41 × 11 *(77 × 12.6 × 3.4)*
Main machinery: 2 GM EMD 16-567 diesels; 2800 hp *(2.1 MW)*; 2 shafts; cp props
Speed, knots: 18
Complement: 153 (13 officers)
Guns: 4 USN 3 in *(76 mm)* (2 twin) Mk 33; 85° elevation; 50 rounds/minute to 12.8 km *(7 nm)*; weight of shell 6 kg.
Mines: 400.
Fire control: 2 Mk 63 GFCS.
Radars: Air/surface search: Selenia RAN 7S; E/F band; range 165 km *(90 nm)*.
Navigation: I band.
Fire control: Western Electric Mk 34; I/J band.

Comment: Laid down in 1962, launched in 1964. Similar to Danish Falster class.

NUSRET   *1986, Selçuk Emre*

1 MODIFIED LSM 1 CLASS (COASTAL MINELAYERS)

Name	No	Builders	Commissioned
MERSIN (ex-US *LSM 494*, ex-*MMC 13*)	N 104	Brown SB Co, Texas	8 May 1945

Displacement, tons: 743 standard; 1100 full load
Dimensions, feet (metres): 203.2 × 34.5 × 8.5 *(61.9 × 10.5 × 2.6)*
Main machinery: 2 GM 16-278A diesels; 3000 hp *(2.24 MW)*; 2 shafts
Speed, knots: 12. **Range, miles:** 2500 at 12 kts
Complement: 89 (8 officers)
Guns: 6 Bofors 40 mm/60 (3 twin). 6 Oerlikon 20 mm.
Mines: 400.

Comment: Ex-US Landing Ship Medium. Launched in 1945, converted into coastal minelayer by the US Navy in 1952 and taken over by the Turkish Navy in October 1952 under MAP.

MERSIN   *1993, Turkish Navy*

1 YMP TYPE (COASTAL MINELAYER)

Name	No	Builders	Commissioned
MEHMETCIK (ex-US *YMP 3*)	N 115	Higgins Inc, New Orleans	1958

Displacement, tons: 540 full load
Dimensions, feet (metres): 130 × 35 × 6 *(39.6 × 10.7 × 1.9)*
Main machinery: 2 GM 6-71 diesels; 348 hp *(260 kW)* sustained; 2 shafts
Speed, knots: 10
Complement: 31 (3 officers)

Comment: Former US motor mine planter. Steel hulled. Transferred under MAP in 1958. For harbour defence. Soon to be deleted.

MEHMETCIK   *9/1991, Erik Laursen*

2 MINELAYER TENDERS

SAMANDIRA 1 Y 131 (ex-Y 1148)   **SAMANDIRA 2** Y 132 (ex-Y 1149)

Displacement, tons: 72 full load
Dimensions, feet (metres): 64.3 × 18.7 × 5.9 *(19.6 × 5.7 × 1.8)*
Main machinery: 1 Gray Marine 64 HN9 diesel; 225 hp *(168 kW)*; 1 shaft
Speed, knots: 10
Complement: 8

Comment: Acquired in 1959. Used for laying and recovering mine distribution boxes.

SAMANDIRA 2   *9/1991, Erik Laursen*

12 ADJUTANT, MSC 268 and MSC 294 CLASSES
(MINESWEEPERS—COASTAL)

SEYMEN (ex-*MSC 131*) M 507	**SEDDULBAHIR** (ex-*MSC 272*) M 513
SELÇUK (ex-*MSC 124*) M 508	**SILIFKE** (ex-USS *MSC 304*) M 514
SEYHAN (ex-*MSC 142*) M 509	**SAROS** (ex-USS *MSC 305*) M 515
SAMSUN (ex-USS *MSC 268*) M 510	**SIGACIK** (ex-USS *MSC 311*) M 516
SINOP (ex-USS *MSC 270*) M 511	**SAPANCA** (ex-USS *MSC 312*) M 517
SURMENE (ex-USS *MSC 271*) M 512	**SARIYER** (ex-USS *MSC 315*) M 518

Displacement, tons: 320 standard; 370 full load
Dimensions, feet (metres): 141 × 26 × 8.3 *(43 × 8 × 2.6)*
Main machinery: 4 GM 6-71 diesels; 696 hp *(519 kW)* sustained; 2 shafts (MSC 268 class)
2 Waukesha L 1616 diesels; 1200 hp *(895 kW)*; 2 shafts (MSC 294 class)
Speed, knots: 14. **Range, miles:** 2500 at 10 kts
Complement: 38 (4 officers)
Guns: 2 Oerlikon 20 mm (twin).
Radars: Navigation: Decca; I band.
Sonars: UQS-1D; hull-mounted mine search; high frequency.

Comment: Built 1955-59 (M 507-M 513) and 1965-67 (M 514-M 518). Transferred from US on 19 November 1970, 24 March 1970, 24 March 1970, 30 September 1958, February 1959, 27 February 1959, May 1959, September 1965, February 1965, June 1965, 26 July 1965, 8 September 1967, respectively. M 508 and M 509 were transferred from France (via the USA) and M 507 from Belgium (via the USA). Height of funnels and bridge arrangements vary.

SELÇUK   *7/1991, Selim San*

0 + (6) MINEHUNTERS/SWEEPERS

Displacement, tons: 600 full load
Main machinery: MTU or Paxman diesels; Voith Schneider props
Guns: Oerlikon 35 mm.
Fire control: Signaal optronic director.
Radars: Navigation: I band.
Sonars: Simrad; active; high frequency.

Comment: Tenders originally called for in 1991. Final bids were delayed to July 1993, with orders expected in mid-1994. Most of the details shown are speculative, based on former statements of intent. The cheapest solution may be to buy Tripartite minehunters second hand.

4 TRABZON (MCB) CLASS (MINESWEEPERS/PATROL VESSELS)

TRABZON (ex-HMCS *Gaspe*)
P 530 (ex-M 530)
TERME (ex-HMCS *Trinity*)
P 531 (ex-M 531)

TIREBOLU (ex-HMCS *Comax*)
P 532 (ex-M 532)
TEKIRDAG (ex-HMCS *Ungava*)
A 601 (ex-M 533)

Displacement, tons: 370 standard; 470 full load
Dimensions, feet (metres): 164 × 30.2 × 9.2 *(50 × 9.2 × 2.8)*
Main machinery: 2 GM 12-278A diesels; 2200 hp *(1.64 MW)*; 2 shafts
Speed, knots: 15. **Range, miles:** 4500 at 11 kts
Complement: 35 (4 officers)
Guns: 1 Bofors 40 mm/60. 2—12.7 mm MGs.

Comment: Transferred from Canada on 19 May 1958. Built by Davie SB Co 1951-53. Of similar type to British Ton class. *Tekirdag* has been fitted with ECM pods abaft mast. Pennant numbers changed in 1991 reflecting use of three as patrol ships and one as an auxiliary.

TEKIRDAG   *6/1993, Selim San*

6 VEGESACK CLASS (MINESWEEPERS—COASTAL)

Name	No	Builders	Commissioned
KARAMÜRSEL (ex-*Worms* M 1253)	M 520	Amiot, Cherbourg	30 Apr 1960
KEREMPE (ex-*Detmold* M 1252)	M 521	Amiot, Cherbourg	20 Feb 1960
KILIMLI (ex-*Siegen* M 1254)	M 522	Amiot, Cherbourg	9 July 1960
KOZLU (ex-*Hameln* M 1251)	M 523	Amiot, Cherbourg	15 Oct 1959
KUŞADASI (ex-*Vegesack* M 1250)	M 524	Amiot, Cherbourg	19 Sep 1959
KEMER (ex-*Passau* M 1255)	M 525	Amiot, Cherbourg	15 Oct 1960

Displacement, tons: 362 standard; 378 full load
Dimensions, feet (metres): 155.1 × 28.2 × 9.5 *(47.3 × 8.6 × 2.9)*
Main machinery: 2 MTU MB diesels; 1500 hp(m) *(1.1 MW)*; 2 shafts; cp props
Speed, knots: 15
Complement: 33 (2 officers)
Guns: 2 Oerlikon 20 mm (twin).
Radars: Navigation: Decca; I band.

Comment: Of similar class to French *Mercure*. M 520-524 transferred by West Germany late 1975-early 1976. M 525 transferred 1979 and refitted 1980 at Taşkizak. M 520 converted for trials July 1986-1987.

KARAMÜRSEL   *9/1992, B Sullivan*

4 CAPE CLASS (MINESWEEPERS—INSHORE)

Name	No	Builders	Commissioned
FOÇA (ex-*MSI 15*)	M 500	Peterson, Wisconsin	19 Apr 1968
FETHIYE (ex-*MSI 16*)	M 501	Peterson, Wisconsin	24 Aug 1968
FATSA (ex-*MSI 17*)	M 502	Peterson, Wisconsin	21 Mar 1968
FINIKE (ex-*MSI 18*)	M 503	Peterson, Wisconsin	26 Apr 1968

Displacement, tons: 180 standard; 235 full load
Dimensions, feet (metres): 111.9 × 23.5 × 7.9 *(34 × 7.1 × 2.4)*
Main machinery: 4 GM 6-71 diesels; 696 hp *(520 kW)* sustained; 2 shafts
Speed, knots: 13. **Range, miles:** 900 at 11 kts
Complement: 25 (3 officers)
Guns: 1—12.7 mm MG.

Comment: Built in USA and transferred under MAP at Boston, Massachusetts, August-December 1967.

FATSA   *9/1990, Selim San*

8 MINEHUNTING TENDERS

DALGIÇ 2 (ex-*MTB 2*)	P 312	**MTB 5**	P 315	**MTB 8**	P 318
MTB 3	P 313	**MTB 6**	P 316	**MTB 9**	P 319
MTB 4	P 314	**MTB 7**	P 317		

Displacement, tons: 70 standard
Dimensions, feet (metres): 71.5 × 13.8 × 8.5 *(21.8 × 4.2 × 2.6)*
Main machinery: 2 diesels; 2000 hp(m) *(1.47 MW)*; 2 shafts
Speed, knots: 20
Guns: 1 Oerlikon 20 mm or 1—12.7 mm MG (aft) (in some).

Comment: All launched in 1942. Now employed as minehunting base ships (P 313-319) and diver support craft (P 312).

MTB 9   *9/1991, Erik Laursen*

AMPHIBIOUS FORCES

Note: The prefix 'Ç' for smaller amphibious vessels stands for 'Çikartma Gemisi' (landing vessel) and indicates that the craft are earmarked for national rather than NATO control.

0 + 1 OSMAN GAZI CLASS (LST)

Name	No	Builders	Commissioned
OSMAN GAZI	NL 125	Taşkizak Yard, Istanbul	July 1994

Displacement, tons: 3773 full load
Dimensions, feet (metres): 344.5 × 52.8 × 15.7 *(105 × 16.1 × 4.8)*
Main machinery: 2 MTU 12V 1163 TB73 diesels; 8800 hp(m) *(6.47 MW)*; 2 shafts
Speed, knots: 17. **Range, miles:** 4000 at 15 kts
Military lift: 900 troops; 15 tanks; 4 LCVPs
Guns: 3 Bofors 40 mm/70; 2 Oerlikon 35 mm/90 (twin).
Helicopters: Platform for one large.

Comment: Laid down 7 July 1989, launched 20 July 1990. Full NBCD protection. Equipped with a support weapons co-ordination centre to control amphibious operations. The ship has about a 50 per cent increase in military lift capacity compared with the Sarucabey class. Second of class cancelled in 1991 and *Osman Gazi* has been badly delayed.

OSMAN GAZI   *9/1991, Erik Laursen*

2 LST 512-1152 CLASS (LST/MINELAYER)

Name	No	Commissioned
BAYRAKTAR (ex-FDR *Bottrop*, ex-USS *Saline County* LST 1101)	NL 120 (ex-N-111, ex-A 579, ex-L 403)	26 Jan 1945
SANCAKTAR (ex-FDR *Bochum*, ex-USS *Rice County* LST 1089)	NL 121 (ex-N-112, ex-A 580, ex-L 404)	14 Mar 1945

Displacement, tons: 1653 standard; 4080 full load
Dimensions, feet (metres): 328 × 50 × 14 *(100 × 15.2 × 4.3)*
Main machinery: 2 GM 12-567A diesels; 1800 hp *(1.34 MW)*; 2 shafts; cp props
Speed, knots: 11. **Range, miles:** 15 000 at 9 kts
Complement: 125
Guns: 6 Bofors 40 mm/70 (2 twin, 2 single).
Mines: 4 rails.
Radars: Navigation: Kelvin Hughes; I band.

Comment: Transferred by US to West Germany in 1961 and thence to Turkey on 13 December 1972. Converted into minelayers in West Germany 1962-64. Minelaying gear removed 1974-75 and replaced in 1979. Now dual purpose ships.

BAYRAKTAR   *1990, Turkish Navy*

2 TERREBONNE PARISH CLASS (LSTs)

Name	No	Builders	Commissioned
ERTUĞRUL	L 401	Christy Corporation	15 Dec 1954
(ex-USS *Windham County* LST 1170)			
SERDAR	L 402	Christy Corporation	10 Mar 1954
(ex-USS *Westchester County* LST 1167)			

Displacement, tons: 2590 light; 5800 full load
Dimensions, feet (metres): 384 × 55 × 17 *(117.1 × 16.8 × 5.2)*
Main machinery: 4 GM 16-278A diesels; 6000 hp *(4.48 MW)*; 2 shafts; cp props
Speed, knots: 15
Complement: 116
Military lift: 395 troops; 2200 tons cargo; 4 LCVPs
Guns: 6 USN 3 in *(76 mm)*/50 (3 twin).
Fire control: 2 Mk 63 GFCS.
Radars: Surface search: Raytheon SPS 21; G/H band; range 22 km *(12 nm)*.
Fire control: Two Western Electric Mk 34; I/J band.

Comment: Transferred by USA June 1973 (L 401) and 27 August 1974 (L 402) on loan. Purchased outright in 1988.

ERTUĞRUL   *1990, Turkish Navy*

1 ÇAKABEY CLASS (LST/MINELAYER)

Name	No	Builders	Commissioned
ÇAKABEY	NL 122 (ex-L 405)	Taşkizak Naval Yard	25 July 1980

Displacement, tons: 1600
Dimensions, feet (metres): 253.5 × 39.4 × 7.5 *(77.3 × 12 × 2.3)*
Main machinery: 3 diesels; 4320 hp *(3.2 MW)*; 3 shafts
Speed, knots: 14
Military lift: 400 troops; 9 tanks; 10 jeeps; 2 LCVPs
Guns: 4 Bofors 40 mm/60 (2 twin). 4 Oerlikon 20 mm (2 twin).
Mines: 150 in lieu of amphibious load.
Radars: Navigation: Racal Decca; I band.
Helicopters: Platform only.

Comment: Launched 30 June 1977. Dual purpose minelayer.

ÇAKABEY   *2/1987, Selçuk Emre*

7 EDIC TYPE (LCTs)

Ç 108, 110, 113, 114, 117, 118, 120

Displacement, tons: 580 full load
Dimensions, feet (metres): 186.9 × 39.4 × 4.6 *(57 × 12 × 1.4)*
Main machinery: 3 GM 6-71 diesels; 522 hp *(390 kW)* sustained; 3 shafts
Speed, knots: 8.5. **Range, miles:** 600 at 10 kts
Complement: 15
Military lift: 100 troops; up to 5 tanks
Guns: 2 Oerlikon 20 mm. 2—12.7 mm MGs.

Comment: Built at Gölcük Naval Shipyard 1966-73. French EDIC type. Four scrapped in 1991 and one in 1993.

EDIC Type (old number)   *1987*

2 SARUCABEY CLASS (LST/MINELAYER)

Name	No	Builders	Commissioned
SARUCABEY	NL 123	Taşkizak Naval Yard	26 July 1984
KARAMÜRSELBEY	NL 124	Taşkizak Naval Yard	27 July 1985

Displacement, tons: 2600 full load
Dimensions, feet (metres): 301.8 × 45.9 × 7.5 *(92 × 14 × 2.3)*
Main machinery: 3 diesels; 4320 hp *(3.2 MW)*; 3 shafts
Speed, knots: 14
Military lift: 600 troops; 11 tanks; 12 jeeps; 2 LCVPs
Guns: 3 Bofors 40 mm/70. 4 Oerlikon 20 mm (2 twin).
Mines: 150 in lieu of amphibious lift.
Radars: Navigation: Racal Decca; I band.
Helicopters: Platform only.

Comment: *Sarucabey* is an enlarged Çakabey design more suitable for naval requirements. First one launched 30 July 1981, second 26 July 1984. Dual purpose minelayers.

KARAMÜRSELBEY   *1989, Selçuk Emre*

28 + 2 LCTs

Ç 119, 121-129, 132-135, 137-150

Displacement, tons: 600 full load
Dimensions, feet (metres): 195.5 × 38 × 4.6 *(59.6 × 11.6 × 1.4)*
Main machinery: 3 GM 6-71 diesels; 522 hp *(390 kW)* sustained; 3 shafts (119-138) or 3 MTU diesels; 900 hp(m) *(662 kW)*; 3 shafts (139-150)
Speed, knots: 8.5. **Range, miles:** 600 at 8 kts
Complement: 17 (1 officer)
Military lift: 100 troops; 5 tanks
Guns: 2 Oerlikon 20 mm. 2—12.7 mm MGs.

Comment: Follow-on to the Ç 107 type started building in 1977. Ç 130 and Ç 131 transferred to Libya January 1980 and Ç 136 sunk in 1985. The delivery rate was about two per year from the Taşkizak and Gölcük yards until 1987. Two launched in July 1987 and commissioned in mid-1991. One more completed in 1992 with two others fitting out at Taskizak. Dimensions given are for Ç 139 onwards, earlier craft are 3.6 m shorter and have less freeboard.

Ç 128   *8/1993*

Ç 147   *9/1993, Selçuk Emre*

2 LCUs

Ç 205   Ç 211

Displacement, tons: 320 light; 405 full load
Dimensions, feet (metres): 142 × 28 × 5.7 *(43.3 × 8.5 × 1.7)*
Main machinery: 2 GM 6-71 diesels; 348 hp *(260 kW)* sustained; 2 shafts
Speed, knots: 10
Guns: 2 Oerlikon 20 mm.

Comment: Built by Taşkizak, Istanbul 1965-66. Seven scrapped in 1991, three more in 1992.

Ç 205   *6/1993, Turkish Navy*

22 LCM 8 TYPE

Ç 302-303, 305, 308-309, 312-314, 316, 318-319, 321-331

Displacement, tons: 58 light; 113 full load
Dimensions, feet (metres): 72 × 20.5 × 4.8 *(22 × 6.3 × 1.4)*
Main machinery: 2 GM 6-71 diesels; 348 hp *(260 kW)* sustained; 2 shafts
Speed, knots: 9.5
Complement: 9
Guns: 1—12.7 mm MG.

Comment: Built by Taşkizak, Istanbul in 1965-66. Eight scrapped in 1991, one more in 1992.

Ç 308   *10/1989, Hartmut Ehlers*

SURVEY SHIPS

Name	No	Builders	Commissioned
ÇUBUKLU (ex-*Y 1251*)	A 594	Gölcük	July 1984

Displacement, tons: 680 full load
Dimensions, feet (metres): 132.8 × 31.5 × 10.5 *(40.5 × 9.6 × 3.2)*
Main machinery: 1 MWM diesel; 820 hp(m) *(603 kW)*; 1 shaft; cp prop
Speed, knots: 11
Complement: 31 (5 officers)
Guns: 2 Oerlikon 20 mm.

Comment: Launched 17 November 1983. Qubit advanced integrated navigation and data processing system fitted in 1991.

ÇUBUKLU   *7/1990, Selçuk Emre*

MESAHA 1   Y 35 (ex-*Y 1221*)   MESAHA 2   Y 36 (ex-*Y 1222*)

Displacement, tons: 45 full load
Dimensions, feet (metres): 52.2 × 14.8 × 4.3 *(15.9 × 4.5 × 1.3)*
Main machinery: 2 GM diesels; 330 hp *(246 kW)*; 2 shafts
Speed, knots: 10. **Range, miles:** 600 at 10 kts
Complement: 8

Comment: Built in 1966. Former US Sounding Boats. Similar to Brazil Paraibano class. Pennant numbers changed in 1991.

MESAHA 1   *6/1992, C D Yaylali*

INTELLIGENCE VESSELS (AGI)

Name	No	Builders	Commissioned
YUNUS (ex-*Alster*, ex-*Mellum*)	A 590 (ex-A 50)	Unterweser, Bremen	21 Mar 1961

Displacement, tons: 1497 full load
Dimensions, feet (metres): 275.5 × 34.4 × 18.4 *(84 × 10.5 × 5.6)*
Main machinery: 1 Deutz diesel; 1800 hp(m) *(1.32 MW)*; 1 shaft
Speed, knots: 15
Complement: 90

Comment: Ex-trawler, purchased by West German Navy in 1965. Conversion at Blohm & Voss and commissioned for naval service on 19 October 1971. Transferred in February 1989. Continues to be used as an AGI.

YUNUS   *10/1993, Selim San*

TRAINING SHIPS

2 RHEIN CLASS

Name	No	Builders	Commissioned
SOKULLU MEHMET PAŞA (ex-*Isar*)	A 577	Blohm & Voss	25 Jan 1964
CEZAYIRLI GAZI HASAN PAŞA (ex-*Elbe*)	A 579	Schliekerwerft, Hamburg	17 Apr 1962

Displacement, tons: 2370 standard; 2940 full load
Dimensions, feet (metres): 322.1 × 38.8 × 14.4 *(98.2 × 11.8 × 4.4)*
Main machinery: 6 MTU MD diesels; 14 400 hp(m) *(10.58 MW)*; 2 shafts
Speed, knots: 20.5. **Range, miles:** 1625 at 15 kts
Complement: 188 (15 officers)
Guns: 2 Creusot Loire 3.9 in *(100 mm)*/55. 4 Bofors 40 mm/60.
Radars: Surface search: Signaal DA 02; E/F band.
Fire control: Two Signaal M 45; I/J band.

Comment: *Ruhr* transferred from Germany 18 July 1975, commissioned in Turkish Navy 16 January 1977. *Isar* transferred 30 September 1982, commissioned 28 March 1983. *Elbe* took *Ruhr*'s place on 15 March 1993, taking over the same name and pennant number. *Main* may also be taken over in 1994.

CEZAYIRLI GAZI HASAN PAŞA   *9/1993, Selim San*

AUXILIARIES

1 FLEET REPLENISHMENT TANKER

Name	No	Builders	Commissioned
AKAR	A 580	Gölcük Naval DY	24 Apr 1987

Displacement, tons: 19 350 full load
Dimensions, feet (metres): 475.9 × 74.8 × 27.6 *(145.1 × 22.8 × 8.4)*
Main machinery: 1 diesel; 6500 hp(m) *(4.78 MW)*; 1 shaft
Speed, knots: 15
Complement: 329
Cargo capacity: 16 000 tons oil fuel
Guns: 2—3 in *(76 mm)*/50 (twin). 2 Bofors 40 mm/70.
Fire control: Mk 63 GFCS.
Radars: Fire control: SPG 34; I band.
Navigation: Decca 1226; I band.
Helicopters: Platform only.

Comment: Launched 17 November 1983. Helicopter flight deck aft. A second ship of the same type is building as a support vessel.

AKAR   *9/1991, Nikolaus Sifferlinger*

2 ANGELN CLASS (DEPOT SHIPS)

Name	No	Builders	Commissioned
ÜLKÜ (ex-Angeln)	A 586	AC de Bretagne	20 Jan 1955
UMUR BEY (ex-Dithmarschen)	A 588	AC de Bretagne	17 Nov 1955

Displacement, tons: 4190 full load
Dimensions, feet (metres): 296.9 × 43.6 × 20.3 *(90.5 × 13.3 × 6.2)*
Main machinery: 2 SEMT-Pielstick diesels; 3000 hp(m) *(2.2 MW)*; 1 shaft
Speed, knots: 17. **Range, miles:** 3660 at 15 kts
Complement: 57
Cargo capacity: 2670 tons
Guns: 2 Bofors 40 mm/60 (aft). 2 Oerlikon 20 mm.

Comment: Ex-cargo ships bought by West Germany in 1959. Transferred 22 March 1972 and December 1975. A 588 employed as submarine depot ship and A 586 as light forces depot ship.

UMUR BEY 4/1986, Hartmut Ehlers

1 SUPPORT TANKER

Name	No	Builders	Commissioned
TAŞKIZAK	A 570	Taşkizak Naval DY, Istanbul	25 July 1984

Displacement, tons: 1440
Dimensions, feet (metres): 211.9 × 30.8 × 11.5 *(64.6 × 9.4 × 3.5)*
Main machinery: 1 diesel; 1400 hp(m) *(1.03 MW)*; 1 shaft
Speed, knots: 13
Complement: 57
Cargo capacity: 800 tons
Guns: 1 Bofors 40 mm/70. 2 Oerlikon 20 mm.

Comment: Laid down 20 July 1983.

TAŞKIZAK (Dogan class in background) 5/1990, A Sheldon Duplaix

1 SUPPORT TANKER

Name	No	Builders	Commissioned
YÜZBAŞI TOLUNAY	A 571	Taşkizak Naval DY, Istanbul	1951

Displacement, tons: 2500 standard; 3500 full load
Dimensions, feet (metres): 260 × 41 × 19.5 *(79 × 12.4 × 5.9)*
Main machinery: 2 Atlas-Polar diesels; 1920 hp(m) *(1.41 MW)*; 2 shafts
Speed, knots: 14
Guns: 2 Bofors 40 mm/70 (not always embarked).

Comment: Launched on 22 August 1950. Beam and stern replenishment facilities. To be scrapped in 1994.

YÜZBAŞI TOLUNAY 2/1992, C D Yaylali

0 + 1 LOGISTIC SUPPORT SHIP

Name	No	Builders	Commissioned
YARBAY KUDRET GÜNGÖR	—	Sedef Shipyard, Istanbul	Aug 1995

Displacement, tons: 14 000 full load
Dimensions, feet (metres): 475.9 × 74.8 × 24.9 *(145.1 × 22.8 × 7.6)*
Main machinery: 2 diesels; 1 shaft
Speed, knots: 14. **Range, miles:** 6000 at 14 kts
Complement: 202
Cargo capacity: 11 300 tons fuel; 2700 tons water; 80 tons lub oil; 500 m³ dry and refrigerated stores
Guns: To be mounted on bow and bridge wings.
Helicopters: Platform only.

Comment: Similar design to *Akar*. Ordered in February 1993. Laid down 5 November 1993, for completion in 1995. This is the first naval ship to be built at a civilian yard in Turkey.

1 SUPPORT TANKER

Name	No	Builders	Commissioned
ALBAY HAKKI BURAK	A 572	Gölcük Naval DY	1965

Displacement, tons: 3800 full load
Dimensions, feet (metres): 274.7 × 40.2 × 18 *(83.7 × 12.3 × 5.5)*
Main machinery: Diesel-electric; 4 GM 16-567A diesels; 5600 hp *(4.12 MW)*; 4 generators; 2 motors; 4400 hp *(3.28 MW)*; 2 shafts
Speed, knots: 16
Complement: 88
Cargo capacity: 1900 tons oil fuel approx
Guns: 2 Bofors 40 mm/60 (not always fitted).

ALBAY HAKKI BURAK 10/1993, C D Yaylali

1 SUPPORT TANKER

Name	No	Builders	Commissioned
BINBAŞI SAADETTIN GÜRÇAN	A 573	Taşkizak Naval DY, Istanbul	1970

Displacement, tons: 1505 standard; 4460 full load
Dimensions, feet (metres): 294.2 × 38.7 × 17.7 *(89.7 × 11.8 × 5.4)*
Main machinery: Diesel-electric; 4 GM 16-567A diesels; 5600 hp *(4.12 MW)*; 4 generators; 2 motors; 4400 hp *(3.28 MW)*; 2 shafts
Speed, knots: 16
Guns: 1—3 in *(76 mm)*/62. 2 Oerlikon 20 mm.

BINBAŞI SAADETTIN GÜRÇAN 1987, Selçuk Emre

3 HARBOUR TANKERS

H 500, H 501, H 502 Y 140-Y 142 (ex-Y 1231-1233)

Displacement, tons: 300 full load
Dimensions, feet (metres): 110.2 × 27.9 × 5.9 *(33.6 × 8.5 × 1.8)*
Main machinery: 1 diesel; 225 hp(m) *(165 kW)*; 1 shaft
Speed, knots: 11
Cargo capacity: 150 tons

Comment: Sisters of water tankers of Pinar series. Built at Taşkizak in early 1970s. Pennant numbers changed in 1991.

H 501 (old number) 3/1990, Selim San

1 SUPPORT TANKER

Name	No	Builders	Commissioned
INEBOLU (ex-*Bodensee* A 1406, ex-*Unkas*)	A 575	Lindenau, Kiel	26 Mar 1959

Displacement, tons: 1840 full load
Measurement, tons: 1238 dwt
Dimensions, feet (metres): 219.8 × 32.1 × 14.1 *(67 × 9.8 × 4.3)*
Main machinery: 1 MaK diesel; 1050 hp(m) *(772 kW)*; 1 shaft
Speed, knots: 12
Complement: 26
Cargo capacity: 1230 tons
Guns: 2 Oerlikon 20 mm (on bridge).

Comment: Launched 19 November 1955. Of Bodensee class. Transferred September 1977 at Wilhelmshavn, under West German military aid programme. Has replenishment capability.

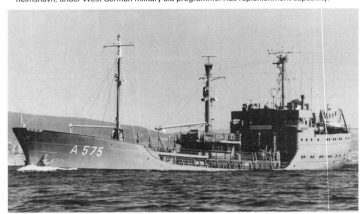

INEBOLU   *4/1986, Hartmut Ehlers*

2 + 1 WATER TANKERS

SÖGÜT (ex-FGR *FW 2*) A 598 (ex-Y 1217)   KAVAK (ex-German *FW 4*) A 600

Displacement, tons: 626 full load
Dimensions, feet (metres): 144.4 × 25.6 × 8.2 *(44.1 × 7.8 × 2.5)*
Main machinery: 1 MWM diesel; 230 hp(m) *(169 kW)*; 1 shaft
Speed, knots: 9.5
Cargo capacity: 340 tons

Comment: *Sögüt* transferred by West Germany 3 December 1975. Pennant number changed in 1991. *Kavak* transferred from Germany 12 April 1991. A third of class *FW 1* is expected to transfer in 1994.

SÖGÜT   *5/1993, Turkish Navy*

2 WATER TANKERS

VAN A 597 (ex-Y 1208)   ULUBAT A 596 (ex-Y 1209)

Displacement, tons: 1200 full load
Dimensions, feet (metres): 174.2 × 29.5 × 9.8 *(53.1 × 9 × 3)*
Main machinery: 1 diesel; 650 hp(m) *(478 kW)*; 1 shaft
Speed, knots: 14
Complement: 39 (3 officers)
Cargo capacity: 700 tons
Guns: 1 Oerlikon 20 mm.

Comment: Two small tankers built in 1968-70 at Gölcük Dockyard. Pennant numbers changed in 1991.

VAN   *9/1993, Selim San*

6 WATER TANKERS

PINAR 1-6   Y 111-Y 116 (ex-Y 1211-Y 1216)

Displacement, tons: 300 full load
Dimensions, feet (metres): 110.2 × 27.9 × 5.9 *(33.6 × 8.5 × 1.8)*
Main machinery: 1 GM diesel; 225 hp *(168 kW)*; 1 shaft
Speed, knots: 11
Cargo capacity: 150 tons

Comment: Built by Taşkizak Naval Yard. Details given for last four, sisters to harbour tankers H 500-502. First pair differ from these particulars and are individually different. *Pinar 1* (launched 1938) of 490 tons displacement with one 240 hp *(179 kW)* diesel, and *Pinar 2* built in 1958 of 1300 tons full load, 167.3 × 27.9 ft *(51 × 8.5 m)*.

PINAR 5 (old number)   *10/1988, Selim San*

1 HARBOUR TANKER

GÖLCÜK Y 50

Displacement, tons: 310 full load
Dimensions, feet (metres): 108.5 × 19.2 × 9.2 *(33.2 × 5.8 × 2.8)*
Main machinery: 1 diesel; 550 hp(m) *(404 kW)*; 1 shaft
Speed, knots: 12

GÖLCÜK   *7/1992, Selçuk Emre*

1 DIVER CLASS (SALVAGE SHIP)

Name	No	Builders	Commissioned
IŞIN (ex-USS *Safeguard* ARS 25)	A 589	Basalt Rock Co, Napa, California	31 Oct 1944

Displacement, tons: 1530 standard; 1970 full load
Dimensions, feet (metres): 213.5 × 41 × 13 *(65.1 × 12.5 × 4)*
Main machinery: Diesel-electric; 4 Cooper-Bessemer GSB-8 diesels; 3420 hp *(2.55 MW)*; 4 generators; 2 motors; 2 shafts
Speed, knots: 14.8
Complement: 110
Guns: 2 Oerlikon 20 mm.

Comment: Transferred from US 28 September 1979 and purchased outright in June 1987.

IŞIN   *5/1990, A Sheldon Duplaix*

1 CHANTICLEER CLASS (SUBMARINE RESCUE SHIP)

Name	No	Builders	Commissioned
AKIN (ex-USS *Greenlet* ASR 10)	A 585	Moore SB & DD Co	29 May 1943

Displacement, tons: 1653 standard; 2321 full load
Dimensions, feet (metres): 251.5 × 44 × 16 *(76.7 × 13.4 × 4.9)*
Main machinery: Diesel-electric; 4 Alco 539 diesels; 3532 hp *(2.63 MW)*; 4 generators; 1 motor; 1 shaft
Speed, knots: 15
Complement: 85
Guns: 1 Bofors 40 mm/60. 4 Oerlikon 20 mm (twin).

Comment: Transferred from US 12 June 1970 and purchased 15 February 1973. Carries a Diving Bell.

AKIN   *9/1991, Erik Laursen*

1 BLUEBIRD CLASS (SUBMARINE RESCUE SHIP)

KURTARAN (ex-USS *Bluebird* ASR 19, ex-*Yurak* AT 165) A 584

Displacement, tons: 1294 standard; 1675 full load
Dimensions, feet (metres): 205 × 38.5 × 11 *(62.5 × 12.2 × 3.5)*
Main machinery: Diesel-electric; 4 GM 12-278A diesels; 4400 hp *(3.28 MW)*; 4 generators; 1 motor; 3000 hp *(2.24 MW)*; 1 shaft
Speed, knots: 16
Complement: 100
Guns: 1 USN 3 in *(76 mm)*/50. 2 Oerlikon 20 mm.

Comment: Former salvage tug adapted as a submarine rescue vessel in 1947. Transferred from the US Navy on 15 August 1950. Carries a Diving Bell.

KURTARAN   *4/1992, C D Yaylali*

1 AMMUNITION TRANSPORT

CEPHANE 2 Y 97 (ex-Y 1195)

Comment: Pennant number changed in 1991.

CEPHANE 2 (old number)   *1980, Stüdyo Oskar, Gölcük*

3 TRANSPORTS

SARKÖY A 591 (ex-Y 1156)   **KARADENIZ EREĞLISI** A 592 (ex-Y 1157)
ECEABAT A 593 (ex-Y 1165)

Displacement, tons: 820 full load
Dimensions, feet (metres): 166.3 × 26.2 × 9.2 *(50.7 × 8 × 2.8)*
Main machinery: 1 diesel; 1440 hp *(1.06 MW)*; 1 shaft
Speed, knots: 10
Cargo capacity: 300 tons
Guns: 1 Oerlikon 20 mm.

Comment: Funnel-aft coaster type. *Sarköy* has a wireless mast at after end of the superstructure. Pennant numbers changed in 1991. Fourth of class *Kanarya* scrapped in 1992.

SARKÖY   *7/1993, C D Yaylali*

2 BARRACK SHIPS

NAŞIT ÖNGEREN (ex-US *APL 47*) Y 38 (ex-Y 1204)
BINBAŞI NETIN SÜLÜS (ex-US *APL 53*) Y 39 (ex-Y 1205)

Comment: Ex-US barrack ships transferred on lease: Y 1204 in October 1972 and Y 1205 on 6 December 1974. Y 1204 based at Ereğli and Y 1205 at Gölcük. Purchased outright June 1987. Pennant numbers changed in 1991.

35 SMALL TRANSPORTS

SALOPA 1-14 Y 21-24 (ex-Y 1031-1044)
LAYTER 1-4 and **6-7** Y 101-104 and Y 106-107
AZIZIYE (ex-Y 1016)
PONTON 1-7 (ex-Y 1061-1067)
ISCI TASITI 1-4 Y 44-47 (ex-Y 1096, Y 1097, Y 1110, Y 1102)
ARSLAN Y 75 (ex-Y 1112)
YAKIT Y 139

Comment: Of varying size and appearance. Pennant numbers changed in 1991.

SALOPA 13   *11/1993, Selim San*

3 BOOM DEFENCE VESSELS

Name	No	Builders	Commissioned
AG 6 (ex-USS *AN 93*, ex-Netherlands *Cerberus* A 895)	P 306	Bethlehem Steel Corporation, Staten Island	10 Nov 1952

Displacement, tons: 780 standard; 855 full load
Dimensions, feet (metres): 165 × 33 × 10 *(50.3 × 10.1 × 3)*
Main machinery: Diesel-electric; 2 GM 8-268A diesels; 880 hp *(656 kW)*; 2 generators; 1 motor; 1 shaft
Speed, knots: 12.8. **Range, miles:** 5200 at 12 kts
Complement: 48
Guns: 1 USN 3 in *(76 mm)*/50. 4 Oerlikon 20 mm.

Comment: Netlayer. Transferred from USA to Netherlands in December 1952. Used first as a boom defence vessel and latterly as salvage and diving tender since 1961 but retained her net-laying capacity. Handed back to US Navy on 17 September 1970 but immediately turned over to the Turkish Navy under grant aid.

AG 6   *5/1990, A Sheldon Duplaix*

Name	No	Builders	Commissioned
AG 5 (ex-*AN 104*)	P 305	Kröger, Rendsburg	5 Feb 1961

Displacement, tons: 680 standard; 960 full load
Dimensions, feet (metres): 173.8 × 35 × 13.5 *(53 × 10.7 × 4.1)*
Main machinery: 1 MAN G7V40/60 diesel; 1470 hp(m) *(1.08 MW)*; 1 shaft
Speed, knots: 12. **Range, miles:** 6500 at 11 kts
Complement: 49
Guns: 1 Bofors 40 mm/60. 3 Oerlikon 20 mm.

Comment: Netlayer P 305 built in US off-shore programme for Turkey.

AG 5   *5/1987, van Ginderen Collection*

Name	No	Builders	Commissioned
AG 4 (ex-USS *Larch*, ex-AN 21)	P 304	American SB Co, Cleveland	13 Dec 1941

Displacement, tons: 560 standard; 805 full load
Dimensions, feet (metres): 163 × 30.5 × 10.5 *(49.7 × 9.3 × 3.2)*
Main machinery: Diesel-electric; 2 diesels; 800 hp *(597 kW)*; 2 generators; 1 motor; 1 shaft
Speed, knots: 12
Complement: 48
Guns: 1—3 in *(76 mm)*. 4 Oerlikon 20 mm.

Comment: Former US netlayer of the Aloe class. Acquired in May 1946.

AG 4   *5/1982, Hartmut Ehlers*

3 NET TENDERS/DAN LAYERS

ŞAMANDIRA MOTORU 11-12   Y 91-Y 92
SM 1 Y 81

Comment: Four more of the class laid up in reserve.

14 UTILITY CRAFT

MAVNA 1-4   (ex-Y 1181-1184)   **MAVNA 7-13**   (ex-Y 1187-1193)
MAVNA 14-16   (ex-Y 1198-1200)

MAVNA 1 (old number)   *1991, van Ginderen Collection*

1 TORPEDO RETRIEVER (TRV)

Ex-TF 107   (ex-Y 873)

Comment: Transferred from Germany 4 September 1989. Built in 1966 of approximately 56 tons.

TRV (old number)   *7/1987, Gilbert Gyssels*

3 TORPEDO RETRIEVERS (TRV)

TORPITO TENDERI Y 95 (ex-Y 1051)   **TAKIP** Y 98 (ex-Y 1052)   **AHMET ERSOY** Y 99
(ex-Y 1102)

TAKIP (old number)   *6/1986, Selçuk Emre*

2 FLAG OFFICERS' YACHTS

HALAS Y 66 (ex-Y 1089)   **GÜL** Y 76 (ex-Y 1103)

Comment: Pennant numbers not displayed.

FLAG OFFICER YACHT   *6/1983, F Örgünsür*

12 FLOATING DOCKS/CRANES

HAVUZ 1 Y 121 (ex-Y 1081) 16 000 tons lift.	**HAVUZ 5** Y 125 (ex-Y 1085) 400 tons lift.
HAVUZ 2 Y 122 (ex-Y 1082) 12 000 tons lift.	**HAVUZ 6** Y 126 (ex-Y 1086) 3000 tons lift.
HAVUZ 3 Y 123 (ex-Y 1083) (ex-US AFDL) 2500 tons lift. 3500 tons lift.	**HAVUZ 7** Y 127 (ex-Y 1087) (ex-US ARD 12)
HAVUZ 4 Y 124 (ex-Y 1084) 4500 tons lift. 700 tons lift.	**HAVUZ 8-10** Y 128-130 (ex-Y 1088-1090)
ALGARNA 3 Y 60 (ex-Y 1021)	**LEVENT** Y 59 (ex-Y 1022)

Comment: *Havuz 7* transferred November 1971 by lease; purchased outright in June 1987. *Algarna* and *Levent* are ex-US floating cranes.

TUGS

1 CHEROKEE CLASS

GAZAL (ex-USS *Sioux* ATF 75) A 587

Displacement, tons: 1235 standard; 1675 full load
Dimensions, feet (metres): 205 × 38.5 × 17 *(62.5 × 11.7 × 5.2)*
Main machinery: Diesel-electric; 4 GM 12-278 diesels; 4400 hp *(3.28 MW)*; 4 generators; 1 motor; 3000 hp *(2.24 MW)*; 1 shaft
Speed, knots: 16. **Range, miles:** 15 000 at 8 kts
Complement: 85
Guns: 1 USN 3 in *(76 mm)*/50. 2 Oerlikon 20 mm.

Comment: Transferred from US 30 October 1972. Purchased 15 August 1973. Can be used for salvage.

GAZAL   *3/1988, Hartmut Ehlers*

1 ARMY TYPE

AKBAŞ A 583 (ex-Y 1119)

Displacement, tons: 971
Dimensions, feet (metres): 146.6 × 33.5 × 14.1 *(44.7 × 10.2 × 4.3)*
Speed, knots: 12
Guns: 2 Oerlikon 20 mm.

Comment: Former US Army vessel based at Gölcük. Pennant number changed in 1991.

AKBAŞ (old number)   *1990, Turkish Navy*

1 OCEAN TUG

DARICA A 578 (ex-Y 1125)

Displacement, tons: 750 full load
Dimensions, feet (metres): 134.2 × 32.2 × 12.8 *(40.9 × 9.8 × 3.9)*
Main machinery: 2 ABC diesels; 4000 hp *(2.94 MW)*; 2 shafts
Speed, knots: 14. **Range, miles:** 2500 at 14 kts

Comment: Built at Taşkizak Naval Yard and commissioned 20 July 1990. Equipped for firefighting and as a torpedo tender. Pennant number changed in 1991.

DARICA (old number)   *1987, Selçuk Emre*

2 COASTAL TUGS

ÖNCÜ A 574 (ex-Y 1120)   **ÖNDER** A 599 (ex-Y 1124)

Displacement, tons: 500
Dimensions, feet (metres): 131.2 × 29.9 × 13.1 *(40 × 9.1 × 4)*
Main machinery: 1 diesel; 1 shaft
Speed, knots: 12
Guns: 2 Oerlikon 20 mm (twin).

Comment: Transferred by USA under MAP. Y 1124 based at Ereğli supporting submarines operating in the Black Sea and towing targets. Y 1120 at Izmir.

ÖNDER (old number)   *10/1989, Hartmut Ehlers*

8 COASTAL/HARBOUR TUGS

Name	No	Displacement, tons/ Speed, knots	Commissioned
SÖNDÜREN	Y 51 (ex-Y 1117)	128/12	1954
KUVVET	Y 53 (ex-Y 1122)	390/10	1962
DOGANARSLAN	Y 52 (ex-Y 1123)	—	1985
ÖZGEN	Y 56 (ex-Y 1128)	—	1987
ATIL	Y 55 (ex-Y 1132)	300/10	1962
ERSEN BAYRAK	Y 64 (ex-Y 1134)	30/9	1946
KUDRET	Y 54 (ex-Y 1229)	128/12	1957
KEPEZ	Y 57	—	1992

DOGANARSLAN (old number)   *10/1989, Hartmut Ehlers*

38 PUSHER TUGS

KATIR 1-38

Comment: From Katir 36, new design.

KATIR 38   *10/1989, Hartmut Ehlers*

COAST GUARD (SAHIL GÜVENLIK)

Notes: (1) Tenders out to local shipyards for fourteen 200 ton and ten 100 ton patrol vessels. All to have 25 mm guns. Orders expected in 1994. The Europatrol 250 craft is a contender.
(2) At least three patrol craft are permanently based in North Cyprus.

8 KW 15 CLASS (LARGE PATROL CRAFT)

SG 12-16, 18-20

Displacement, tons: 70 full load
Dimensions, feet (metres): 94.8 × 15.4 × 4.6 *(28.9 × 4.7 × 1.4)*
Main machinery: 2 MTU diesels; 2000 hp(m) *(1.47 MW)*; 2 shafts
Speed, knots: 25. **Range, miles:** 1500 at 19 kts
Complement: 15
Guns: 1 Bofors 40 mm/60. 2 Oerlikon 20 mm.

Comment: Built by Schweers, Bardenfleth. Commissioned 1961-62.

SG 14   *10/1991, Harald Carstens*

14 LARGE PATROL CRAFT

SG 21-34

Displacement, tons: 170 full load
Dimensions, feet (metres): 132 × 21 × 5.5 *(40.2 × 6.4 × 1.7)*
131.2 × 21.3 × 4.9 *(40 × 6.5 × 1.5)* (SG 30-34)
Main machinery: 2 SACM AGO 195 V16 CSHR diesels; 4800 hp(m) *(3.53 MW)*
2 cruise diesels; 300 hp(m) *(220 kW)*; 2 shafts
Speed, knots: 22
Guns: 1 or 2 Bofors 40 mm/60. 2—12.7 mm MGs.

Comment: SG 21 and 22 built by Gölcük Naval Yard, remainder by Taşkizak Naval Yard. SG 34 commissioned in 1977, remainder 1968-71. SG 30-34 have minor modifications—knuckle at bow, radar stirrup on bridge and MG on superstructure sponsons. These are similar craft to the 12 listed under Light Forces for the Navy.

SG 22   *9/1990, Selçuk Emre*

10 SAR 33 TYPE (LARGE PATROL CRAFT)

SG 61-70

Displacement, tons: 140 standard; 170 full load
Dimensions, feet (metres): 108.3 × 28.3 × 9.7 *(33 × 8.6 × 3)*
Main machinery: 3 SACM AGO 195 V16 CSHR diesels; 7200 hp(m) *(5.29 MW)*; 3 shafts; cp props
Speed, knots: 40. **Range, miles:** 450 at 35 kts; 1000 at 20 kts
Complement: 24
Guns: 1 Bofors 40 mm/60. 2—7.62 mm MGs.
Radars: Surface search: Racal Decca; I band.

Comment: Prototype ordered from Abeking & Rasmussen, Lemwerder in May 1976. The remainder were built at Taşkizak Naval Yard, Istanbul between 1979 and 1981. Fourteen of this class were to have been transferred to Libya but the order was cancelled. Two delivered to Saudi Arabia.

SG 62   *4/1993, van Ginderen Collection*

4 SAR 35 TYPE (LARGE PATROL CRAFT)

SG 71-74

Displacement, tons: 210 full load
Dimensions, feet (metres): 120 × 28.3 × 6.2 *(36.6 × 8.6 × 1.9)*
Main machinery: 3 SACM AGO 195 V16 CSHR diesels; 7200 hp(m) *(5.29 MW)*; 3 shafts
Speed, knots: 40. **Range, miles:** 450 at 35 kts; 1000 at 20 kts
Complement: 24
Guns: 1 Bofors 40 mm/70. 2—7.62 mm MGs.
Radars: Surface search: Racal Decca; I band.

Comment: A slightly enlarged version of SAR 33 Type built by Taşkizak Shipyard between 1985 and 1987.

SG 74   *9/1993, C D Yaylali*

9 + 6 COASTAL PATROL CRAFT

SG 50-56   SG 102-103

Displacement, tons: 25 full load
Dimensions, feet (metres): 47.9 × 11.5 × 3.6 *(14.6 × 3.5 × 1.1)*
Main machinery: 2 diesels; 700 hp(m) *(514 kW)*; 2 shafts
Speed, knots: 18
Complement: 6
Guns: 1—12.7 mm MG or 1 Breda-Oerlikon 25 mm *(SG 102-103)*.

Comment: First four built at Taşkizak Shipyard and commissioned 20 July 1990. Three more laid down in mid-1990 and commissioned in 1991. Six more ordered in 1993 for completion in 1995. *SG 102* and *103* were built for North Cyprus and have been based there since August 1990 and July 1991 respectively. Both these craft were given a heavier gun in 1992.

SG 52   *10/1991, Harald Carstens*

SG 102   *8/1990, Selçuk Emre*

8 COASTAL PATROL CRAFT

SG 41-47, 49

Displacement, tons: 19 full load
Dimensions, feet (metres): 45.9 × 13.8 × 3.6 *(14 × 4.2 × 1.1)*
Main machinery: 2 diesels; 450 hp *(335 kW)*; 2 shafts
Speed, knots: 13
Complement: 5
Guns: 2—7.62 mm (twin) MGs.

Comment: Transferred in the 1950s. Former US Mk 5 45 ft craft built in Second World War. Some have radar on forward edge of bridge, whilst SG 41 has circular scuttles in place of square ports. Similar to Spanish P 231-P 235.

SG 44   *6/1991, Mike Foster*

1 INSHORE PATROL CRAFT

RAIF DENKTAS

Displacement, tons: 10 full load
Dimensions, feet (metres): 38 × 11.5 × 2.4 *(11.6 × 3.5 × 0.7)*
Main machinery: 2 Volvo Aquamatic AQ200F petrol engines; 400 hp(m) *(294 kW)*; 2 shafts
Speed, knots: 28. **Range, miles:** 250 at 25 kts
Complement: 6
Guns: 1—12.7 mm MG.
Radars: Surface search: Raytheon; I band.

Comment: Built by Protekson, Istanbul. Transferred to North Cyprus 23 September 1988. Can be equipped with a rocket launcher.

RAIF DENKTAS (old number)   *9/1988, Selçuk Emre*

2 TRANSPORT CRAFT

SG 104-105

Comment: Small utility craft which sometimes carry two 12.7 mm MGs.

SG 104   *10/1989, Hartmut Ehlers*

2 HARBOUR PATROL CRAFT

SG 1-2

Comment: High-speed patrol boats for anti-smuggling duties.

SG 2   *7/1991, Selim San*

TURKS AND CAICOS

Headquarters' Appointment

Commissioner of Police:
Stanley Williams

General

An Island Police Force funded by the UK Government.

Mercantile Marine

Lloyd's Register of Shipping:
12 vessels of 3685 tons gross

POLICE

Note: There are also four fishery protection launches.

1 DAGGER CLASS (PATROL CRAFT)

SEA HAWK

Displacement, tons: 8
Dimensions, feet (metres): 39.7 × 11.2 × 3.6 *(12.1 × 3.4 × 1.1)*
Main machinery: 2 Perkins T6.3544M diesels; 330 hp *(246 kW)* sustained; 2 shafts
Speed, knots: 24. **Range, miles:** 540 at 20 kts
Guns: 1—7.62 mm MG.

Comment: Completed by Fairey Marine in June 1986. GRP hull.

1 HALMATIC M160 CLASS (PATROL CRAFT)

SEA QUEST

Displacement, tons: 18.5 light
Dimensions, feet (metres): 52.5 × 15.4 × 4.6 *(16 × 4.7 × 1.4)*
Main machinery: 2 Detroit 6V-92TA diesels; 520 hp *(388 kW)* sustained; 2 shafts
Speed, knots: 27. **Range, miles:** 500 at 17 kts
Complement: 8

Comment: Built by Halmatic, Havant and delivered on 22 December 1989. Similar craft acquired by the Virgin Islands, Montserrat and Anguilla. Has a rigid inflatable boat on the stern launched by a gravity davit.

SEA HAWK   *1/1994, Maritime Photographic*

SEA QUEST   *1/1994, Maritime Photographic*

UGANDA

Headquarters' Appointment

Commander, Army Marine Unit:
Captain Saleh Agondoa

Personnel

1994: 400

Bases

HQ: Fort Bell
Entebbe, Sese Isles, Gaba, Jinja, Majinji, Bukakata (all on Lake Victoria).

ARMY

2 KIMJIN CLASS

Displacement, tons: 25 full load
Dimensions, feet (metres): 66.6 × 11 × 5.5 *(20.3 × 3.4 × 1.7)*
Main machinery: 2 diesels; 2400 hp(m) *(1.76 MW)*; 2 shafts
Speed, knots: 42. **Range, miles:** 220 at 20 kts
Complement: 10
Guns: 4—14.5 mm (2 twin) MGs.

Comment: Transferred from North Korea in the early 1980s. One is for use by the President.

6 YUGOSLAV AL8K TYPE

Displacement, tons: 6.3 full load
Dimensions, feet (metres): 36.6 × 12.3 × 1.5 *(11.2 × 3.7 × 0.5)*
Main machinery: 2 diesels; 300 hp(m) *(220 kW)*; 2 shafts
Speed, knots: 25
Complement: 3
Guns: 1—12.7 mm MG.

Comment: Acquired in September 1988. Aluminium hulls. Designed for patrol work on rivers and lakes.

14 GRP PATROL CRAFT

Comment: These are fast motor boats used on the minor lakes and waterways. Some are armed with 7.62 mm MGs.

LAKE PATROL CRAFT   *1989*

UKRAINE

Headquarters' Appointments

Commander of the Navy:
Vice Admiral Vladimir Beskorovainy
Chief of Naval Border Guard:
Rear Admiral Boris Ryabov

Bases

Sevastopol (HQ), Odessa, Nikolayev

Personnel

Planned total of up to 40 000

General

A Maritime Border Guard of some 40 minor Black Sea Fleet units was formed in early 1992. On 21 July a Petya II class light frigate 'defected' from the Russian Navy, and this was immediately followed on 28 July by the commissioning of the *Slavutich*, a second of the Kamchatka class, as the new Flagship of the Navy. On 3 August 1992 a joint agreement signed by Russia and Ukraine, in theory put a stop to further Ukrainian acquisitions by declaring that all Black Sea Fleet units would be jointly operated by the two states until 1995, by which time the division of the Fleet would be agreed. In 1993 other ships, mostly building at Nikolayev, have been claimed, but there is no certainty as to how many of these will become permanent Ukrainian ships, if any.

Mercantile Marine

Lloyd's Register of Shipping:
1124 vessels of 5 264 478 tons gross

Strength of the Fleet in 1994

1 Slava class (CG) *Vilna Ukraina*
2 Krivak III class (FF) *Hetman Dorosenko, Hetman Petr Sagadachny*
1 Grisha V class (FFL) *Lutsk*
1 Petya II class (FFL) *PN 112*
2 Pomornik class (ACV) *Donets,* + 1
1 Kamchatka class (AG) *Slavutich*
1 Malina class (support ship) *PM 16*
1 Mod Altay class (AOR) *Elnya*
1 Elbrus class (rescue ship) *Ayu-Dag*
1 Pozharny I (rescue ship) —

Details for all ships are in the Russia and Associated States section.

UNITED ARAB EMIRATES

Headquarters' Appointments

Commander, Naval Forces:
  Colonel Muhammad Khalfan Al-Muhairi
Deputy Commander, Naval Forces:
  Colonel Suhail Shaheen
Director General, Coast Guard:
  Lieutenant Colonel Abdul Rahman Saleh Shelwah

Personnel

(a) 1994: 2000 (150 officers)
(b) Voluntary service

General

This federation of the former Trucial States (Abu Dhabi, Ajman, Dubai, Fujairah, Ras al Khaimah, Sharjah, Umm al Qaiwan) was formed under a provisional constitution in 1971 with a new constitution coming into effect on 2 December 1976.
Following a decision of the UAE Supreme Defence Council on 6 May 1976 the armed forces of the member states were unified and the organisation of the UAE Armed Forces was furthered by decisions taken on 1 February 1978.

Bases

Taweela (main base) between Abu Dhabi and Dubai.
Dalma and Mina Zayed (Abu Dhabi),
Mina Rashid and Mina Jebel Ali (Dubai),
Mina Saqr (Ras al Khaimah), Mina Sultan (Sharjah),
Khor Fakkan (Sharjah-East Coast).

Mercantile Marine

Lloyd's Register of Shipping:
  286 vessels of 804 374 tons gross

FRIGATES

Note: Statement of Requirement for four frigates of about 2500 tons was put out in mid-1993. The specification included a helicopter, surface-to-surface and surface-to-air missile systems and ASW capability. A second-hand purchase is an alternative, with a new build order for more corvettes.

CORVETTES

2 MURAY JIP (LÜRSSEN 62) CLASS

Name	No	Builders	Commissioned
MURAY JIP	P 6501	Lürssen, Bremen	Nov 1990
DAS	P 6502	Lürssen, Bremen	Jan 1991

Displacement, tons: 630 full load
Dimensions, feet (metres): 206.7 × 30.5 × 8.2 *(63 × 9.3 × 2.5)*
Main machinery: 4 MTU 16V 538 TB92 diesels; 13 640 hp(m) *(10 MW)* sustained; 4 shafts
Speed, knots: 32. **Range, miles:** 4000 at 16 kts
Complement: 43

Missiles: SSM: 4 Aerospatiale MM 40 Exocet; inertial cruise; active radar homing to 70 km *(40 nm)* at 0.9 Mach; warhead 165 kg; sea-skimmer.
 SAM: Thomson-CSF modified Crotale Navale octuple launcher; radar guidance; IR homing to 13 km *(7 nm)* at 2.4 Mach; warhead 14 kg.
Guns: 1 OTO Melara 3 in *(76 mm)*/62 Super Rapid; 85° elevation; 120 rounds/minute to 16 km *(8.7 nm)*; weight of shell 6 kg.
 1 Signaal Goalkeeper with GE 30 mm 7-barrelled; 4200 rounds/minute combined to 2 km.
Countermeasures: Decoys: Dagaie launcher; IR flares and chaff.
ESM/ECM: Racal Cutlass/Cygnus; intercept/jammer.
Radars: Air/surface search: Bofors Ericsson Sea Giraffe 50HC; G band.
 Navigation: Racal Decca 1226; I band.
 Fire control: Bofors Electronic 9LV 331; J band (for gun and SSM).
  Thomson-CSF DRBV 51C; J band (for Crotale).

Helicopters: 1 Aerospatiale Alouette SA 316.

DAS   *4/1991, Harald Carstens*

Programmes: Ordered in late 1986. Similar vessels to Bahrain craft. Delivery in late 1991.
Structure: Lürssen design adapted for the particular conditions of the Gulf. This class has good air defence and a considerable anti-ship capability if the helicopter also carries anti-surface missiles.

MURAY JIP   *6/1990, van Ginderen Collection*

PATROL FORCES

2 MUBARRAZ CLASS (FAST ATTACK CRAFT—MISSILE)

Name	No	Builders	Commissioned
MUBARRAZ	P 4401	Lürssen, Bremen	Aug 1990
MAKASIB	P 4402	Lürssen, Bremen	Aug 1990

Displacement, tons: 260 full load
Dimensions, feet (metres): 147.3 × 23 × 7.2 *(44.9 × 7 × 2.2)*
Main machinery: 2 MTU 20V 538 TB93 diesels; 9370 hp(m) *(6.9 MW)* sustained; 2 shafts
Speed, knots: 40. **Range, miles:** 500 at 38 kts
Complement: 40 (5 officers)

Missiles: SSM: 4 Aerospatiale MM 40 Exocet; inertial cruise; active radar homing to 70 km *(40 nm)* at 0.9 Mach; warhead 165 kg; sea-skimmer.
SAM: 1 Matra Sadral sextuple launcher; Mistral; IR homing to 4 km *(2.2 nm)*; warhead 3 kg.
Guns: 1 OTO Melara 3 in *(76 mm)*/62 Super Rapid; 85° elevation; 120 rounds/minute to 16 km *(8.7 nm)*; weight of shell 6 kg.
Countermeasures: Decoys: Dagaie launchers; IR flares and chaff.
ESM/ECM: Racal Cutlass/Cygnus; intercept/jammer.
Fire control: CSEE Najir optronic director (for SAM).
Radars: Air/surface search: Bofors Ericsson Sea Giraffe 50HC; G band.
Navigation: Racal Decca 1226; I band.
Fire control: Bofors Electronic 9LV 223; J band (for gun and SSM).

Programmes: Ordered in late 1986 from Lürssen Werft at the same time as the two Type 62 vessels.
Structure: This is a modified FPB 38 design, with the first export version of Matra Sadral.

MAKASIB   *9/1990, Foto Flite*

6 ARDHANA CLASS (LARGE PATROL CRAFT)

Name	No	Builders	Commissioned
ARDHANA	P 1101	Vosper Thornycroft	24 June 1975
ZURARA	P 1102	Vosper Thornycroft	14 Aug 1975
MURBAN	P 1103	Vosper Thornycroft	16 Sep 1975
AL GHULLAN	P 1104	Vosper Thornycroft	16 Sep 1975
RADOOM	P 1105	Vosper Thornycroft	1 July 1976
GHANADHAH	P 1106	Vosper Thornycroft	1 July 1976

Displacement, tons: 110 standard; 175 full load
Dimensions, feet (metres): 110 × 21 × 6.6 *(33.5 × 6.4 × 2)*
Main machinery: 2 Paxman 12CM diesels; 5000 hp *(3.73 MW)* sustained; 2 shafts
Speed, knots: 30. **Range, miles:** 1800 at 14 kts
Complement: 26
Guns: 2 Oerlikon/BMARC 30 mm/75 A32 (twin); 85° elevation; 650 rounds/minute to 10 km *(5.5 nm)*; weight of shell 1 kg or 0.36 kg.
1 Oerlikon/BMARC 20 mm/80 A41A; 800 rounds/minute to 2 km.
2—51 mm projectors for illuminants.
Radars: Surface search: Racal Decca TM 1626; I band.

Comment: A class of round bilge steel hull craft. P 1101-2 and P 1105-6 transported by heavy-lift ships. P 1103 and P 1104 were sailed out. Originally operated by Abu Dhabi.

AL GHULLAN   *11/1987*

6 BAN YAS (LÜRSSEN TNC 45) CLASS (FAST ATTACK CRAFT—MISSILE)

Name	No	Builders	Commissioned
BAN YAS	P 4501	Lürssen Vegesack	Nov 1980
MARBAN	P 4502	Lürssen Vegesack	Nov 1980
RODQM	P 4503	Lürssen Vegesack	July 1981
SHAHEEN	P 4504	Lürssen Vegesack	July 1981
SAGAR	P 4505	Lürssen Vegesack	Sep 1981
TARIF	P 4506	Lürssen Vegesack	Sep 1981

Displacement, tons: 260 full load
Dimensions, feet (metres): 147.3 × 23 × 8.2 *(44.9 × 7 × 2.5)*
Main machinery: 4 MTU 16V 538 TB92 diesels; 13 640 hp(m) *(10 MW)* sustained; 4 shafts
Speed, knots: 40. **Range, miles:** 500 at 38 kts
Complement: 40 (5 officers)

Missiles: SSM: 4 Aerospatiale MM 40 Exocet; inertial cruise; active radar homing to 70 km *(40 nm)* at 0.9 Mach; warhead 165 kg; sea-skimmer.
Guns: 1 OTO Melara 3 in *(76 mm)*/62; 85° elevation; 60 rounds/minute to 16 km *(8.7 nm)*; weight of shell 6 kg.
2 Breda 40 mm/70 (twin); 85° elevation; 300 rounds/minute to 12.5 km *(6.8 nm)*; weight of shell 0.96 kg.
2—7.62 mm MGs.
Countermeasures: Decoys: 1 CSEE trainable Dagaie; IR flares and chaff; H-J band.
ESM/ECM: Racal Cutlass/Cygnus; intercept/jammer.
Fire control: 1 CSEE Panda director for 40 mm. PEAB low light USFA IR and TV tracker.
Radars: Surface search: Bofors Ericsson Sea Giraffe 50HC; G band.
Navigation: Racal Decca TM 1226; I band.
Fire control: Philips 9LV 200 Mk 2; J band.

Programmes: Ordered in late 1977. First two shipped in September 1980 and four more in Summer 1981. This class was the first to be fitted with MM40.
Structure: Modified FPB 38 design.

SAGAR   *5/1987*

3 KAWKAB CLASS (COASTAL PATROL CRAFT)

Name	No	Builders	Commissioned
KAWKAB	P 561	Keith Nelson, Bembridge	7 Mar 1969
THOABAN	P 562	Keith Nelson, Bembridge	7 Mar 1969
BANI YAS	P 563	Keith Nelson, Bembridge	27 Dec 1969

Displacement, tons: 32 standard; 38 full load
Dimensions, feet (metres): 57 × 16.5 × 4.5 *(17.4 × 5 × 1.4)*
Main machinery: 2 Caterpillar diesels; 750 hp *(560 kW)*; 2 shafts
Speed, knots: 19. **Range, miles:** 445 at 15 kts
Complement: 11 (2 officers)
Guns: 2 Oerlikon 20 mm.
Radars: Surface search: Racal Decca TM 1626; I band.

Comment: Of glass fibre hull construction. Originally operated by Abu Dhabi.

BANI YAS   *11/1976, UAE Armed Forces*

8 ARCTIC 28 RIBs

Displacement, tons: 4 full load
Dimensions, feet (metres): 27.9 × 9.7 × 2 *(8.5 × 3 × 0.6)*
Main machinery: 2 outboards; 450 hp *(336 kW)*
Speed, knots: 38
Complement: 1 plus 10 troops

Comment: Ordered from Halmatic, Southampton in June 1992 and delivered in mid-1993. GRP hulls. Speed given is fully laden. Used by Special Forces.

ARCTIC 28   *1993, Halmatic*

AUXILIARIES

2 CHEVERTON TYPE (TENDERS)

A 271   **A 272**

Displacement, tons: 3.3 full load
Dimensions, feet (metres): 27 × 9 × 2.7 *(8.2 × 2.7 × 0.8)*
Main machinery: 1 Lister RMW3 diesel; 150 hp *(112 kW)*; 1 shaft
Speed, knots: 8

Comment: Built of GRP. Acquired from Chevertons, Cowes, Isle of Wight in 1975 by Abu Dhabi. A272 has a 2 ton hoist.

3 LSL/LST

AL FEYI L 5401   **JANANAH** L 5402   **DAYYINAH** L 5403

Displacement, tons: 650 full load
Dimensions, feet (metres): 164 × 36.1 × 9.2 *(50 × 11 × 2.8)*
Main machinery: 2 diesels; 1248 hp *(931 kW)*; 2 shafts
Speed, knots: 11. **Range, miles:** 1800 at 11 kts
Complement: 10

Comment: *Al Feyi* built by Siong Huat, Singapore; completed 4 August 1987. The other pair built by Argos Shipyard, Singapore to a similar design and completed in December 1988. Used mostly as transport ships.

1 DIVING TENDER

D 1051

Displacement, tons: 100 full load
Dimensions, feet (metres): 103 × 22.6 × 3.6 *(31.4 × 6.9 × 1.1)*
Main machinery: 2 MTU 12V 396 TB93 diesels; 3260 hp(m) *(2.4 MW)* sustained; 2 waterjets
Speed, knots: 26. **Range, miles:** 390 at 24 kts
Complement: 6

Comment: Ordered from Crestitalia end 1985 for Abu Dhabi and delivered in July 1987. GRP hull. Used primarily for mine clearance but also for diving training, salvage and SAR. Fitted with a decompression chamber and diving bell. Reports of a second of class are not confirmed. Lengthened version of Italian *Alcide Pedretti*.

D 1051   *1987, Crestitalia*

1 LCM

GHAGHA II

Displacement, tons: 100 full load
Dimensions, feet (metres): 131.2 × 32.8 × 3.3 *(40 × 10 × 1)*
Main machinery: 2 diesels; 730 hp *(544 kW)*; 2 shafts
Speed, knots: 9
Complement: 6

Comment: Built by Siong Huat, Singapore; launched 17 April 1987.

1 SUPPORT CRAFT

BARACUDA

Displacement, tons: 1400 full load
Dimensions, feet (metres): 190 × 39.4 × 13.1 *(57.9 × 12 × 4)*
Main machinery: 2 Ruston 12RKC diesels; 6200 hp *(4.6 MW)* sustained; 2 shafts
Speed, knots: 12

Comment: Completed June 1983 by Singapore Slipway Co.

TUGS

ANNAD A 3501

Displacement, tons: 795 full load
Dimensions, feet (metres): 114.8 × 32.2 × 13.8 *(35 × 9.8 × 4.2)*
Main machinery: 2 Caterpillar 3606TA diesels; 4180 hp *(3.12 MW)* sustained; 2 shafts; bow thruster
Speed, knots: 14. **Range, miles:** 2500 at 14 kts
Complement: 14 (3 officers)

Comment: Built by Dunston, Hessle, and completed in April 1989. Bollard pull, 55 tons. Equipped for SAR.

SHIPBORNE AIRCRAFT

Numbers/Type: 6 Aerospatiale SA 316/319S Alouette.
Operational speed: 113 kts *(210 km/h)*.
Service ceiling: 10 500 ft *(3200 m)*.
Range: 290 nm *(540 km)*.
Role/Weapon systems: Reconnaissance and general-purpose helicopters. Most are non-operational. Sensors: radar. Weapons: Could be fitted with ASV weapons.

ALOUETTE   *1992*

LAND-BASED MARITIME AIRCRAFT

Numbers/Type: 8 Aerospatiale AS 535 Cougar.
Operational speed: 150 kts *(280 km/h)*.
Service ceiling: 15 090 ft *(4600 m)*.
Range: 335 nm *(620 km)*.
Role/Weapon systems: Anti-ship and transport helicopter with limited ASV role; utility role widely used. Sensors: Omera ORB 30 radar. Weapons: ASV; 1 × AM 39 Exocet. ASM; depth bombs.

Numbers/Type: 2 Pilatus Britten-Norman Maritime Defender.
Operational speed: 150 kts *(280 km/h)*.
Service ceiling: 18 900 ft *(5760 m)*.
Range: 1500 nm *(2775 km)*.
Role/Weapon systems: Coastal patrol and surveillance aircraft although seldom used in this role. Sensors: Nose-mounted search radar, underwing searchlight. Weapons: Underwing rocket and gun pods.

COAST GUARD

Note: Under control of Minister of Interior. In addition to the vessels listed below there is a number of Customs and Police launches including three Swedish Boghammar 13 m craft of the same type used by Iran and delivered in 1985, two Baglietto police launches acquired in 1988, about 10 elderly Dhafeer and Spear class of 12 and 9 m respectively, and two Halmatic Arun class Pilot craft delivered in 1990/91; some of these launches carry light machine guns.

1 POSILIPO TYPE (COASTAL PATROL CRAFT)

Displacement, tons: 35.5 full load
Dimensions, feet (metres): 64.9 × 19.68 × 3.9 *(19.8 × 6 × 1.2)*
Main machinery: 2 MTU 6V 396 TB93 diesels; 1630 hp(m) *(1.2 MW)* sustained; 2 shafts
Speed, knots: 24
Gun: 1 Oerlikon 20 mm.

Comment: Built by Posilipo, Italy and commissioned on 24 November 1984 in the Abu Dhabi Coast Guard. GRP hull.

5 CAMCRAFT 77 ft (COASTAL PATROL CRAFT)

753-757

Displacement, tons: 70 full load
Dimensions, feet (metres): 76.8 × 18 × 4.9 *(23.4 × 5.5 × 1.5)*
Main machinery: 2 GM 12V-71TA diesels; 840 hp *(627 kW)* sustained; 2 shafts
Speed, knots: 25
Guns: 2 Lawrence Scott 20 mm (not always embarked).

Comment: Completed 1975 by Camcraft, New Orleans. Expected to be paid off in 1994.

CAMCRAFT 757   6/1990

16 CAMCRAFT 65 ft (COASTAL PATROL CRAFT)

Displacement, tons: 50 full load
Dimensions, feet (metres): 65 × 18 × 5 *(19.8 × 5.5 × 1.5)*
Main machinery: 2 MTU 6V 396 TB93 diesels; 1630 hp(m) *(1.2 MW)* sustained; 2 shafts (in 14)
    2 Detroit 8V-92TA diesels; 700 hp *(522 kW)* sustained; 2 shafts (in 2)
Speed, knots: 25
Guns: 1 Oerlikon 20 mm.

Comment: Ordered in 1978.

CAMCRAFT 65 ft   1987, UAE Coast Guard

6 BAGLIETTO GC 23 TYPE (COASTAL PATROL CRAFT)

758   +5

Displacement, tons: 50.7 full load
Dimensions, feet (metres): 78.7 × 18 × 3 *(24 × 5.5 × 0.9)*
Main machinery: 2 MTU 12V 396 TB93 diesels; 3260 hp(m) *(2.4 MW)* sustained; 2 KaMeWa
    waterjets
Speed, knots: 43. **Range, miles:** 700 at 20 kts
Complement: 9
Guns: 1 Oerlikon 20 mm. 2—7.62 mm MGs.

Comment: Built by Baglietto, Varazze. First two completed in March and May 1986, second pair in
    July 1987 and two more in 1988. All were delivered to UAE Coast Guard in Dubai.

BAGLIETTO 758   1987, UAE Coast Guard

2 DIVING TENDERS

Displacement, tons: 8.8
Main machinery: 2 Volvo Penta diesels; 2 shafts
Speed, knots: 11

Comment: FPB 512 Rotork design. Completed May 1981 for Abu Dhabi.

3 BAGLIETTO 59 ft (COASTAL PATROL CRAFT)

501-503

Displacement, tons: 22 full load
Dimensions, feet (metres): 59.4 × 13.9 × 2.3 *(18.1 × 4.3 × 0.7)*
Main machinery: 2 MTU 12V 183 TE92 diesels; 2 shafts
Speed, knots: 40
Complement: 6
Guns: 2—7.62 mm MGs.

Comment: Ordered in 1992 and delivered in late 1993. May be fitted with a larger gun.

BAGLIETTO 503   10/1993, UAE Coast Guard

10 WATERCRAFT 45 ft (COASTAL PATROL CRAFT)

Displacement, tons: 25 full load
Dimensions, feet (metres): 45 × 14.1 × 4.6 *(13.7 × 4.3 × 1.4)*
Main machinery: 2 MAN D2542 diesels; 1300 hp(m) *(956 kW)*; 2 shafts
Speed, knots: 26. **Range, miles:** 380 at 18 kts
Complement: 5
Guns: Mounts for 2—7.62 mm MGs.

Comment: Ordered from Watercraft, UK in February 1982. Delivery in early 1983.

WATERCRAFT 45 ft   1984, UAE Coast Guard

38 HARBOUR PATROL CRAFT

Comment: The latest are 11 Shark 33 built by Shaali Marine, Dubai and delivered in 1993. The
    remainder are a mixture of Baracuda 30 ft and FPB 22 ft classes. All are powered by twin out-
    board engines and most carry a 7.62 mm MG.

SHARK 33   10/1993, UAE Coast Guard

UNITED KINGDOM

Headquarters' Appointments

Chief of the Naval Staff and First Sea Lord:
Admiral Sir Benjamin Bathurst, GCB
Commander-in-Chief, Fleet:
Admiral Sir Hugo White, KCB, CBE
Chief of Naval Personnel and Commander-in-Chief, Naval Home Command:
Vice Admiral Sir Michael Layard, KCB, CBE
Controller of the Navy:
Vice Admiral R Walmsley
Chief of Fleet Support:
Vice Admiral R T Frere
Deputy Commander-in-Chief, Fleet:
Vice Admiral J R Tod
Assistant Chief of the Naval Staff:
Rear Admiral J R Brigstocke

Flag Officers

Flag Officer, Surface Flotilla:
Vice Admiral M C Boyce, OBE
Flag Officer, Submarines:
Rear Admiral R C Lane-Nott
Flag Officer, Naval Aviation:
Rear Admiral I D G Garnett
Commander, UK Task Group:
Rear Admiral M P Gretton
Flag Officer, Sea Training:
Rear Admiral J G Tolhurst
Commander British Forces, Gibraltar:
Rear Admiral J T Sanders, OBE
Flag Officer, Plymouth (South from 4/1995):
Vice Admiral Sir Roy Newman, KCB
Flag Officer, Portsmouth (until 4/1995):
Rear Admiral N E Rankin, CBE
Flag Officer, Scotland, Northern England and Northern Ireland:
Vice Admiral C C Morgan
Hydrographer of the Navy:
Rear Admiral N R Essenhigh
Commodore Minor War Vessels and Diving:
Commodore R C Moore
Commodore Royal Fleet Auxiliaries:
Commodore R M Thorn

Headquarters Royal Marines

Commandant-General, Royal Marines:
Lieutenant General R J Ross, CB, OBE
Major General, Royal Marines:
Major General A M Keeling, CBE

Fleet Disposition

Submarine Flotilla
1st Squadron (*Neptune*, Faslane) 6 Fleet submarines, 4 Strategic submarines
2nd Squadron (*Defiance*, Devonport) 7 Fleet submarines, 4 Patrol submarines

Surface Flotilla
1st Frigate Squadron (Devonport) Type 22 Batch 2
2nd Frigate Squadron (Devonport) Type 22 Batches 1 and 3
3rd Destroyer Squadron (Portsmouth) Type 42
4th Destroyer Squadron (Devonport/Portsmouth) Type 23
5th Destroyer Squadron (Portsmouth) Type 42
6th Frigate Squadron (Devonport) Type 23

MCM Flotilla
1st Squadron (Rosyth), 2nd Squadron (Portsmouth)
3rd Squadron (Rosyth)
Fishery Protection Squadron (Rosyth)

Surveying Flotilla (Devonport)
2 Ocean and 4 Coastal Survey Ships

Diplomatic Representation

Naval Attaché in Athens:
Captain R W Lockyer
Naval Attaché in Beijing:
Captain A B P Armstrong
Naval Attaché in Bonn:
Captain R St J S Bishop
Naval Attaché in Brasilia:
Captain R J Tempest
Naval Adviser in Bridgetown:
Captain R F Shercliffe
Naval Attaché in Cairo:
Commander P G Blanchford
Defence Adviser in Canberra:
Commodore B J Adams
Defence Attaché in Caracas (and Santo Domingo):
Captain R L Perrett
Defence Attaché in Copenhagen:
Commander R Kirkwood
Naval Attaché in The Hague:
Captain H W Rickard
Naval Attaché in Islamabad:
Commander D A Scott
Assistant Defence Adviser in Kuala Lumpur:
Lieutenant Commander C C Williams
Defence Attaché in Lisbon:
Commander R J S Wykes-Sneyd
Naval Attaché in Madrid:
Captain J Gozzard
Naval Attaché in Moscow:
Captain J M Dobson
Naval Adviser in New Delhi:
Captain P N Galloway
Naval Attaché in Oslo:
Commander G S Pearson, OBE
Naval Adviser in Ottawa:
Captain R A Baller
Naval Attaché in Paris:
Captain M A Johnson
Naval Attaché in Riyadh:
Commander J A Barltrop
Naval Attaché in Rome:
Captain K F Read
Defence Attaché in Santiago:
Captain R A Rowley, OBE
Naval Attaché in Tokyo:
Captain A P Masterson-Smith
Naval Attaché in Washington:
Commodore A M Gregory

Personnel (including Royal Marines)

(a) 1 January 1994: 56 420 (RN 49 020; RM 7400)
(b) Volunteer Reserves: RN 3500; RM 1185
(c) Regular Reserves: RN 17 400; RM 2150

Royal Marines Operational Units

HQ 3 Commando Brigade RM; 40 Commando RM; 42 Commando RM; 45 Commando Group (RM/Army); 3 Commando Brigade Air Squadron RM; Commando Logistic Regiment RM (RN/RM/Army); 3 Commando Brigade HQ and Signal Squadron RM including Air Defence Troop RM (Javelin), EW Troop RM, Tactical Air Command Posts RM (3 regular, 1 reserve); 539 Assault Squadron RM (landing craft and raiding craft), including 2 Raiding Troop RMR (raiding craft); Brigade Patrol Troop (reconnaissance); Special Boat Service RM; Comacchio Group RM (security); T Company RMR; 29 Commando Regiment RA (Army); 59 Independent Commando Squadron RE (Army); 289 Commando Battery RA (Volunteers); 131 Independent Squadron RE (Volunteers).

Bases

Northwood (*Warrior*); C-in-C Fleet; FO Submarines
Portsmouth; C-in-C Navhome; HQ Royal Marines; FO Portsmouth (until 4/1995); FO Surface Flotilla
Devonport; FO Plymouth (becomes FO South in 4/1995)
Rosyth; FO Scotland, Northern England and Northern Ireland
Portland; FO Sea Training
Faslane (*Neptune*); Commodore Clyde
Gibraltar; CBF Gibraltar
Hong Kong (*Tamar*); Captain-in-Charge

Strength of the Fleet—1 June 1994

Type	Active (Reserve)	Building (Projected)
SSBNs	4	3
Submarines—Attack	12	(6)
Submarines—Patrol	2 (2)	—
Aircraft Carriers	2 (1)	—
Destroyers	12 (1)	(12)
Frigates	23	4 (3)
Assault Ships (LPDs)	1 (1)	(2)
Helicopter Carrier (LPH)	—	1
LSLs (RFA)	5	—
LCLs (RLC)	2	—
LCRs (RLC)	9	—
LCVPs	21	2
LCUs	12	(4)
Offshore Patrol Vessels	8	—
Large Patrol Craft	5	—
Patrol/Training Craft	28	—
Minehunters/Minesweepers	13	—
Minehunters	5	4 (3)
Minesweepers/Patrol Craft	5	—
Repair/Maintenance Ship (RFA)	1	—
Survey Ships	6	(2)
Antarctic Patrol Ship	1	—
Training Ships	2	—
Royal Yacht	1	—
Large Fleet Tankers (RFA)	2	(3)
Support Tankers (RFA)	4	—
Small Fleet Tankers (RFA)	3	—
Coastal Tankers (RMAS)	4	—
Aviation Training Ship (RFA)	1	—
Fleet Replenishment Ships (RFA)	5	—
SMVs and PMLs	8	—
Trials Ships (RMAS)	2	—
TRVs (RMAS)	5	—
Armament Carriers (RMAS)	2	—
Water Carriers (RMAS)	5	—
Ocean Tugs	3	—
Harbour Tugs	47	—
Range Support Vessels (RMAS)	15	—
Submarine Support Vessels (RMAS)	6	1
Aviation Support Craft (RMAS)	11	—
Tenders (RMAS)	46	—
DG Vessels	1 (1)	—
Sea Cadet Corps Vessels	8	—
Target Vessels	3	—
Royal Logistic Corps	21	—

Mercantile Marine

Lloyd's Register of Shipping:
1532 vessels of 4 116 868 tons gross

Fleet Air Arm Squadrons (see *Shipborne Aircraft* section) on 1 May 1994

	F/W Aircraft	Role	Deployment	Squadron no		F/W Aircraft	Role	Deployment	Squadron no
6	Sea Harrier	FRS 2	*Invincible*	800	11	Sea Harrier			
6	Sea Harrier	FRS 1	*Illustrious/Ark Royal*	801		(FRS 1/2/T4)	Aircrew Training	Yeovilton, *Heron*	899
					13	Jetstream	Aircrew Training	Culdrose, *Seahawk*	750

	Helicopters	Role	Deployment	Squadron no		Helicopters	Role	Deployment	Squadron no
	Sea King AEW 2	Aircrew Training	Culdrose, *Seahawk*	849 HQ	8	Sea King HC 4	Aircrew Training	Yeovilton, *Heron*	707
8	Sea King AEW 2	AEW	*Invincible*	849 A flight	5	Sea King HAS 5	SAR	Culdrose, *Seahawk*	771
	Sea King AEW 2	AEW	*Illustrious/Ark Royal*	849 B flight	6	Sea King HC 4	SAR	Portland, *Osprey*	772
7	Sea King HAS 5/6	ASW	*Invincible*	814	35	Lynx HAS 3	ASUW/ASW	Portland, *Osprey*	815
7	Sea King HAS 5/6	ASW	*Illustrious/Ark Royal*	820	12	Lynx HAS 3	Aircrew Training	Portland, *Osprey*	702
11	Sea King HAS 5/6	ASW	Prestwick, *Gannet*	819	17	Gazelle HT 2	Aircrew Training	Culdrose, *Seahawk*	705
11	Sea King HAS 5/6	Aircrew Training	Culdrose, *Seahawk*	810					
11	Sea King HAS 5	Aircrew Training	Culdrose, *Seahawk*	706					
7	Sea King HC 4	Commando Assault	Yeovilton, *Heron*	845					
8	Sea King HC 4	Commando Assault	Yeovilton, *Heron*	846					

Note: Training and Liaison aircraft not listed under the *Shipborne* or *Land-based Aircraft* sections include Sea Harrier T4N/T4, Gazelle HT 2, Jetstream, Hunter, Falcon 20 (under contract).

DELETIONS

Note: Those ships not shown as sold or broken up are awaiting disposal.

Submarines

1991   *Onyx* (sold), *Odin* (bu), *Onslaught* (bu), *Conqueror, Churchill*
1992   *Swiftsure, Courageous, Otter, Otus* (sold), *Ocelot* (museum), *Osiris* (sold), *Revenge*
1993   *Oracle, Opportune, Opossum*
1994   *Valiant, Upholder, Unseen*

Destroyers

1991   *Bristol* (immobile tender)
1993   *Kent* (sunk)

Frigates

1991   *Danae* (to Ecuador), *Penelope* (to Ecuador), *Arethusa* (sunk), *Cleopatra* (bu), *Minerva* (bu), *Jupiter, Hermione, Charybdis*
1992   *Sirius, Argonaut, Juno, Ariadne* (to Chile)
1993   *Amazon, Ambuscade, Arrow* (all to Pakistan), *Scylla*
1994   *Alacrity, Active, Avenger* (all to Pakistan), *Andromeda*

Mine Warfare Forces

1991   *Gavinton* (bu), *Kirkliston* (bu), *Upton* (sold), *Soberton, Kedleston* (bu)
1992   *Iveston* (SCC), *Kellington* (both reserve)
1993   *Carron, Helmsdale, Ribble, Brinton, Nurton, Sheraton*
1994   *Waveney, Dovey, Helford, Humber*

Patrol Forces

1991   *Sandpiper* (sold), *Peterel* (sold), *Cormorant* (sold), *Hart* (sold)
1992   *Attacker, Hunter, Striker* (all sold to Lebanon), *Sentinel, Fencer* (sold), *Chaser* (sold), *Endurance* (old) (sold)
1993   *Jersey*
1994   *Cygnet*

Amphibious Warfare Forces

1994   *Eden, Forth, Medway* (ex-RLC, all to Belize)

Survey Ship and Craft

1991   *Fawn* (sold), *Yarmouth Navigator* (sold)

Auxiliaries

1991   *Bembridge* (sold), *Lofoten* (sold), *Stalker* (sold), *Garganey* (sold), *Tidespring* (sold), *Challenger* (sold), *Kinbrace, Mandarin, Crystal* (sold), *Torrid* (sold), *Goldeneye* (sold), *Green Rover* (sold to Indonesia)
1992   *Throsk* (sold), *Waterside* (sold) (both to Ecuador), *Regent, Oilstone, Oilfield, Whitehead* (bu), *Watershed, Criccieth, Froxfield, Glencoe, Sultan Venturer* (old)
1993   *Blue Rover* (sold to Portugal), *Olmeda, Alsatian, Pointer, Cricket, Cicala, Fotherby, Dunster*

PENNANT LIST

Note: Numbers are not displayed on Submarines or some RMAS craft.

Aircraft Carriers

R 05	Invincible
R 06	Illustrious
R 07	Ark Royal

Destroyers

D 86	Birmingham
D 87	Newcastle
D 88	Glasgow
D 89	Exeter
D 90	Southampton
D 91	Nottingham
D 92	Liverpool
D 95	Manchester
D 96	Gloucester
D 97	Edinburgh
D 98	York
D 108	Cardiff

Frigates

F 85	Cumberland
F 86	Campbeltown
F 87	Chatham
F 88	Broadsword
F 89	Battleaxe
F 90	Brilliant
F 91	Brazen
F 92	Boxer
F 93	Beaver
F 94	Brave
F 95	London
F 96	Sheffield
F 98	Coventry
F 99	Cornwall
F 229	Lancaster
F 230	Norfolk
F 231	Argyll
F 233	Marlborough
F 234	Iron Duke
F 235	Monmouth
F 236	Montrose
F 237	Westminster
F 238	Northumberland
F 239	Richmond (bldg)
F 240	Somerset (bldg)
F 241	Grafton (bldg)
F 242	Sutherland (bldg)

Amphibious Warfare Forces

—	Ocean
L 10	Fearless
L 11	Intrepid
L 105	Arromanches
L 106	Antwerp
L 107	Andalsnes
L 108	Abbeville
L 109	Akyab
L 110	Aachen
L 111	Arezzo
L 112	Agheila
L 113	Audemer
L 3004	Sir Bedivere
L 3005	Sir Galahad
L 3027	Sir Geraint
L 3036	Sir Percivale

L 3505	Sir Tristram
L 4001	Ardennes
L 4003	Arakan

Mine Warfare Forces

M 29	Brecon
M 30	Ledbury
M 31	Cattistock
M 32	Cottesmore
M 33	Brocklesby
M 34	Middleton
M 35	Dulverton
M 36	Bicester
M 37	Chiddingfold
M 38	Atherstone
M 39	Hurworth
M 40	Berkeley
M 41	Quorn
M 101	Sandown
M 102	Inverness
M 103	Cromer
M 104	Walney
M 105	Bridport
M 1116	Wilton (training)
M 2008	Blackwater
M 2009	Itchen
M 2011	Orwell (training)
M 2013	Spey
M 2014	Arun

Patrol Forces

P 239	Peacock
P 240	Plover
P 241	Starling
P 258	Leeds Castle
P 259	Redpole
P 260	Kingfisher
P 264	Archer
P 265	Dumbarton Castle
P 270	Biter
P 272	Smiter
P 273	Pursuer
P 277	Anglesey
P 278	Alderney
P 279	Blazer
P 280	Dasher
P 291	Puncher
P 292	Charger
P 293	Ranger
P 294	Trumpeter
P 297	Guernsey
P 298	Shetland
P 299	Orkney
P 300	Lindisfarne

Auxiliaries

A 00	Britannia
A 72	Cameron
A 81	Brambleleaf
A 83	Melton
A 84	Menai
A 86	Gleaner
A 87	Meon
A 91	Milford
A 100	Beddgelert
A 107	Messina

A 109	Bayleaf
A 110	Orangeleaf
A 111	Oakleaf
A 112	Felicity
A 114	Magnet
A 115	Lodestone
A 122	Olwen
A 123	Olna
A 124	Olmeda
A 126	Cairn
A 127	Torrent
A 129	Dalmatian
A 130	Roebuck
A 132	Diligence
A 133	Hecla
A 135	Argus
A 138	Herald
A 140	Tornado
A 141	Torch
A 142	Tormentor
A 143	Toreador
A 146	Waterman
A 147	Frances
A 148	Fiona
A 149	Florence
A 150	Genevieve
A 152	Georgina
A 153	Example
A 154	Explorer
A 155	Deerhound
A 156	Daphne
A 157	Loyal Helper
A 158	Supporter
A 159	Loyal Watcher
A 160	Loyal Volunteer
A 161	Loyal Mediator
A 162	Elkhound
A 163	Express
A 164	Goosander
A 165	Pochard
A 166	Kathleen
A 167	Exploit
A 168	Labrador
A 170	Kitty
A 171	Endurance
A 172	Lesley
A 174	Lilah
A 175	Mary
A 177	Edith
A 178	Husky
A 180	Mastiff
A 181	Irene
A 182	Saluki
A 183	Isabel
A 185	Salmoor
A 186	Salmaster
A 187	Salmaid
A 189	Setter
A 190	Joan
A 193	Joyce
A 196	Gwendoline
A 197	Sealyham
A 198	Helen
A 199	Myrtle
A 201	Spaniel
A 202	Nancy
A 205	Norah
A 207	Llandovery
A 208	Lamlash
A 211	Lechlade
A 216	Bee
A 220	Loyal Moderator
A 221	Forceful
A 222	Nimble
A 223	Powerful
A 224	Adept
A 225	Bustler

A 226	Capable
A 227	Careful
A 228	Faithful
A 230	Cockchafer
A 231	Dexterous
A 232	Adamant
A 239	Gnat
A 250	Sheepdog
A 251	Lydford
A 253	Ladybird
A 254	Sultan Venturer
A 269	Grey Rover
A 271	Gold Rover
A 272	Scarab
A 273	Black Rover
A 274	Ettrick
A 277	Elsing
A 285	Auricula
A 308	Ilchester
A 309	Instow
A 311	Ironbridge
A 317	Bulldog
A 318	Ixworth
A 319	Beagle
A 326	Foxhound
A 327	Basset
A 328	Collie
A 330	Corgi
A 344	Impulse
A 345	Impetus
A 348	Felsted
A 353	Elkstone
A 355	Epworth
A 361	Roysterer
A 365	Fulbeck
A 366	Robust
A 367	Newton
A 368	Warden
A 378	Kinterbury
A 381	Cricklade
A 382	Arrochar
A 383	Appleby (SCC)
A 385	Fort Grange
A 386	Fort Austin
A 387	Fort Victoria
A 388	Fort George
A 389	Clovelly
A 394	Fintry
A 402	Grasmere
A 480	Resource
A 488	Cromarty
A 490	Dornoch
A 502	Rollicker
A 1766	Headcorn
A 1767	Hever
A 1768	Harlech
A 1769	Hambledon
A 1770	Loyal Chancellor
A 1771	Loyal Proctor
A 1772	Holmwood
A 1773	Horning
Y 01	Petard
Y 02	Falconet
Y 10	Aberdovey (SCC)
Y 11	Abinger (SCC)
Y 13	Alnmouth (SCC)
Y 17	Waterfall
Y 19	Waterspout
Y 21	Oilpress
Y 23	Oilwell
Y 25	Oilbird
Y 26	Oilman
Y 30	Watercourse
Y 31	Waterfowl
Y 32	Moorhen
Y 33	Moorfowl

SUBMARINES

Strategic Missile Submarines (SSBN)

1 + 3 VANGUARD CLASS (SSBN)

Name	No	Builders	Laid down	Launched	Commissioned
VANGUARD	S 28	Vickers Shipbuilding & Engineering, Barrow-in-Furness	3 Sep 1986	4 Mar 1992	14 Aug 1993
VICTORIOUS	S 29	Vickers Shipbuilding & Engineering, Barrow-in-Furness	3 Dec 1987	29 Sep 1993	Dec 1994
VIGILANT	S 30	Vickers Shipbuilding & Engineering, Barrow-in-Furness	16 Feb 1991	1994	1995
VALIANT	S 31	Vickers Shipbuilding & Engineering, Barrow-in-Furness	1 Feb 1993	1996	1997

VANGUARD   *1993, Racal Electronics*

Displacement, tons: 15 900 dived
Dimensions, feet (metres): 491.8 × 42 × 39.4
(149.9 × 12.8 × 12)
Main machinery: Nuclear; 1 RR PWR 2; 2 GEC turbines; 27 500 hp *(20.5 MW)*; 1 shaft; pump jet propulsor; 1 auxiliary retractable propulsion motor; 2 diesel alternators; 2700 hp *(2 MW)*
Speed, knots: 25 dived
Complement: 135 (14 officers) (2 crews)

Missiles: SLBM: 16 Lockheed Trident 2 (D5) three stage solid fuel rocket; stellar inertial guidance to 12 000 km *(6500 nm)*; thermonuclear warhead of up to 8 MIRV of 100-120 kT; cep 90 m. The D5 can carry up to 12 MIRV but under plans announced in November 1993 each submarine carries a maximum of 96 warheads (of UK manufacture), with a total explosive power no greater than that carried in the Resolution class.
Torpedoes: 4—21 in *(533 mm)* tubes. Marconi Spearfish; dual purpose; wire-guided; active/passive homing to 65 km *(35 nm)* at 60 kts; warhead directed energy. Marconi Tigerfish Mk 24 Mod 2; wire-guided; active/passive homing to 13 km *(7 nm)* at 35 kts active; 29 km *(15.7 nm)* at 24 kts passive; warhead 134 kg.
Countermeasures: Decoys: 2 SSE Mk 10 launchers.
ESM: Racal UAP 3; passive intercept.
Combat data systems: Dowty Sema SMCS.
Fire control: Dowty tactical control system. SAFS 3 FCS.
Radars: Navigation: Kelvin Hughes Type 1007; I band.
Sonars: Marconi/Plessey Type 2054 composite multi-frequency sonar suite includes Marconi/Ferranti Type 2046 towed array, Type 2043 hull-mounted active/passive search and Type 2082 passive intercept and ranging.

Programmes: On 15 July 1980 the government announced its intention to procure from the United States the Trident I weapon system, comprising the C4 ballistic missile and supporting systems for a force of new British missile launching submarines to replace the present Polaris-equipped force in the 1990s. On 11 March 1982 it was announced that the government had opted to procure the improved Trident II weapon system, with the D5 missile, to be deployed in a force of four submarines, in the mid-1990s. *Vanguard* ordered 30 April 1986; *Victorious* 6 October 1987; *Vigilant* 13 November 1990 and the last one 7 July 1992. The original programme anticipated ordering one per year for the first three years so there has been much stretching out of the building programme.
Structure: Refit and recore interval is anticipated at eight to nine years. The outer surface of the submarine is covered with conformal anechoic noise reduction coatings. The limits placed on warhead numbers leaves spare capacity within the Trident system. This capacity is available for a non-strategic warhead variant. Fitted with Pilkington Optronics CK 51 search and CH 91 attack periscopes. The primary operating mode is by TTVC.
Operational: After some early problems there were three successful submerged launched firings of the D5 missile from USS *Tennessee* in December 1989 and the missile was first deployed operationally in March 1990. *Vanguard* started sea trials in October 1992; first operational patrol is planned for late 1994.

Opinion: The intention not to use the full capacity of the Trident system in the present calmer international strategic deterrent climate, opens the door for the development of a number of sub-strategic options if these submarines are to be used to their full potential. At the same time the option remains available to increase the strategic weapon load at some time in the future, should the threat once again merit a greater capability.

The US Navy reported firing a D5 missile in October 1993 to test the feasibility of increasing accuracy by the use of GPS navigational hardware mounted on the missile. This is a step towards the long term aim of developing a conventional kinetic energy weapon. The UK Government has said it has no plans to deploy conventional warheads on Trident.

VANGUARD   *1993, Ships of the World*

2 RESOLUTION CLASS (SSBN)

Name	No	Builders	Laid down	Launched	Commissioned
REPULSE	S 23	Vickers Shipbuilding & Engineering, Barrow-in-Furness	12 Mar 1965	4 Nov 1967	28 Sep 1968
RENOWN	S 26	Cammell Laird, Birkenhead	25 June 1964	25 Feb 1967	15 Nov 1968

Displacement, tons: 7600 surfaced; 8500 dived
Dimensions, feet (metres): 425 × 33 × 30
   (129.5 × 10.1 × 9.1)
Main machinery: Nuclear; 1 RR PWR 1; 2 English Electric turbines; 15 000 hp *(11.2 MW)*; 1 shaft; 2 diesel alternators; 2200 hp *(1.64 MW)*; 1 motor for emergency drive; 1 auxiliary retractable prop
Speed, knots: 20 surfaced; 25 dived
Complement: 143 (13 officers) (2 crews)

Missiles: SLBM: 16 Lockheed Polaris A3 two stage solid fuel rocket; inertial guidance to 4630 km *(2500 nm)*; each missile carries 3 MRV heads each of 200 kT; Chevaline nuclear warheads (fitted in *Renown* 1982, *Repulse* 1986); cep 900 m.
Torpedoes: 6—21 in *(533 mm)* bow tubes. Marconi Tigerfish Mk 24 Mod 2; wire-guided; active/passive homing to 13 km *(7 nm)* at 35 kts active; 29 km *(15.7 nm)* at 24 kts passive; warhead 134 kg.
Countermeasures: Decoys: 2 SSDE launchers.
ESM: MEL UA 11/12; passive intercept.
Combat data systems: Gresham/Dowty DCB data handling system.
Fire control: Dowty tactical control system.
Radars: Navigation: Kelvin Hughes Type 1006; I band.
Sonars: Plessey Type 2001; hull-mounted; active/passive; low frequency.
   BAe Type 2007; hull-mounted; flank array; passive; long range; low frequency.
   Ferranti Type 2046; towed array; passive search; very low frequency.
   Thomson Sintra Type 2019 PARIS or THORN EMI Type 2082; passive intercept and ranging.

Programmes: In February 1963 it was stated that it was intended to order four or five 7000 ton nuclear-powered submarines, each to carry 16 Polaris missiles, and it was planned that the first would be on patrol in 1968. Their hulls and machinery would be of British design. As well as building two submarines Vickers (Shipbuilding) would give lead yard service to the builder of the other two. Four Polaris submarines were in fact ordered in May 1963. The plan to build a fifth Polaris submarine was cancelled on 15 February 1965. Britain's first SSBN, *Resolution,* put to sea on 22 June 1967.
Modernisation: The Chevaline warheads were substituted for the original Polaris missile payloads in a rolling programme between 1982 and 1988. The warhead is similar but it is supported by 'a variety of penetration aids' to overcome antiballistic missile (ABM) defences.
Structure: Fitted with Pilkington Optronics CK 28 search and CH 78 attack opto mechanical periscopes.
Operational: Since early 1969 there has been at least one of these submarines at immediate readiness to fire its intercontinental ballistic missiles. Each submarine, which has accommodation for 19 officers and 135 ratings, is manned on a two-crew basis, in order to get maximum operational time at sea. It has been reported that the Polaris stockpile is some 70 missiles with 45-50 warheads. *Revenge* paid off earlier than expected in May 1992, *Resolution* in June 1994, and the others will decommission sequentially as the Vanguard class enters service.

RENOWN   1993

REPULSE   1992

Attack Submarines (SSN)

Note: As pennant numbers are never displayed and rarely used class lists are in order of completion.

7 + (5) TRAFALGAR CLASS BATCHES 1 and 2 (SSN)

Name	No	Builders	Laid down	Launched	Commissioned
TRAFALGAR	S 107	Vickers Shipbuilding & Engineering, Barrow-in-Furness	25 Apr 1979	1 July 1981	27 May 1983
TURBULENT	S 87	Vickers Shipbuilding & Engineering, Barrow-in-Furness	8 May 1980	1 Dec 1982	28 Apr 1984
TIRELESS	S 88	Vickers Shipbuilding & Engineering, Barrow-in-Furness	6 June 1981	17 Mar 1984	5 Oct 1985
TORBAY	S 90	Vickers Shipbuilding & Engineering, Barrow-in-Furness	3 Dec 1982	8 Mar 1985	7 Feb 1987
TRENCHANT	S 91	Vickers Shipbuilding & Engineering, Barrow-in-Furness	28 Oct 1985	3 Nov 1986	14 Jan 1989
TALENT	S 92	Vickers Shipbuilding & Engineering, Barrow-in-Furness	13 May 1986	15 Apr 1988	12 May 1990
TRIUMPH	S 93	Vickers Shipbuilding & Engineering, Barrow-in-Furness	2 Feb 1987	16 Feb 1991	12 Oct 1991

Displacement, tons: 4700; 5400 (Batch 2) surfaced; 5208; 5900 (Batch 2) dived

Dimensions, feet (metres): 280.1; 293.3 (Batch 2) × 32.1 × 31.2 *(85.4; 89.4 × 9.8 × 9.5)*

Main machinery: Nuclear; 1 RR PWR 1; PWR 2 (Batch 2); 2 GEC turbines; 15 000 hp *(11.2 MW)*; 1 shaft; pump jet propulsor; 2 Paxman diesel alternators; 2800 hp *(2.09 MW)*; 1 motor for emergency drive; 1 auxiliary retractable prop

Speed, knots: 32 dived

Complement: 97 (12 officers)

Missiles: SSM: McDonnell Douglas UGM-84B Sub-Harpoon; active radar homing to 130 km *(70 nm)* at 0.9 Mach; warhead 227 kg.

Torpedoes: 5—21 in *(533 mm)* bow tubes. Marconi Spearfish; wire-guided; active/passive homing to 65 km *(35 nm)* at 60 kts; warhead directed energy. Marconi Tigerfish Mk 24 Mod 2; wire-guided; active/passive homing to 13 km *(7 nm)* at 35 kts active; 29 km *(15.7 nm)* at 24 kts passive; warhead 134 kg; 20 reloads.

Mines: Can be carried in lieu of torpedoes.

Countermeasures: Decoys: 2 SSE Mk 8 launchers. Type 2066 torpedo decoy.

ESM: Racal UAC/CXA (being upgraded to UAP); passive intercept.

Combat data systems: Ferranti/Gresham/Dowty DCB/DCG tactical data handling system. Dowty Sema SMCS after refit.

Fire control: Dowty tactical control system.

Radars: Navigation: Kelvin Hughes Type 1006 or Type 1007; I band.

Sonars: BAe Type 2007 AC or Marconi 2072; hull-mounted; flank array; passive; low frequency.

Plessey Type 2020 or Marconi/Plessey 2074 or Ferranti/Thomson Sintra 2076 (see *Modernisation*); hull-mounted; passive/active search and attack; low frequency.

GEC Avionics Type 2026 or Ferranti Type 2046; towed array; passive search; very low frequency.

Thomson Sintra Type 2019 PARIS or THORN EMI 2082; passive intercept and ranging.

Marconi Type 2077; short range classification; active; high frequency.

Programmes: The first of an improved class of Fleet Submarines. *Trafalgar* ordered 7 April 1977; *Turbulent* 28 July 1978; *Tireless* 5 July 1979; *Torbay* 26 June 1981; *Trenchant* 22 March 1983; *Talent* 10 September 1984; *Triumph* 3 January 1986. An improved version of the class is planned to be ordered in 1995 with an in-service date of 2004, which is some 13 years after the last of the Batch 1s.

Modernisation: Trials have been done on Sonar Type 2057 which has a reelable wet end for the towed array sonar but this may not now be fitted. *Turbulent* has a hump on the after casing under which there is a small winch. Type 1006 radar is to be replaced by Type 1007. All to be updated with Type 2076 sonar systems, integrated with SMCS and countermeasures. From 1995/96 sonar 2076 starts to replace 2074, 2046 and 2082. This update also includes Marconi Type 2077, short range classification sonar. Batch 2 is planned to incorporate the PWR 2 reactor and all those weapon systems improvements going in to Batch 1. Tomahawk cruise missiles are being considered.

Structure: Designed to be considerably quieter than previous

TRIUMPH   1/1993

submarines. The pressure hull and outer surfaces are covered with conformal anechoic noise reduction coatings. Other improvements include speed and endurance. Retractable forward hydroplanes and strengthened fins for under ice operations. Diving depth in excess of 300 m *(985 ft)*. Fitted with

Pilkington Optronics CK 34 search and CH 84 attack optronic periscopes.

Operational: *Trafalgar* was the trials submarine for Spearfish which started full production in 1992. All of the class belong to the Second Submarine Squadron based at Devonport.

TRIUMPH   5/1993, S Poynton, RAN

5 SWIFTSURE CLASS (SSN)

Name	No	Builders	Laid down	Launched	Commissioned
SOVEREIGN	S 108	Vickers Shipbuilding & Engineering, Barrow-in-Furness	18 Sep 1970	17 Feb 1973	11 July 1974
SUPERB	S 109	Vickers Shipbuilding & Engineering, Barrow-in-Furness	16 Mar 1972	30 Nov 1974	13 Nov 1976
SCEPTRE	S 104	Vickers Shipbuilding & Engineering, Barrow-in-Furness	19 Feb 1974	20 Nov 1976	14 Feb 1978
SPARTAN	S 105	Vickers Shipbuilding & Engineering, Barrow-in-Furness	26 Apr 1976	7 Apr 1978	22 Sep 1979
SPLENDID	S 106	Vickers Shipbuilding & Engineering, Barrow-in-Furness	23 Nov 1977	5 Oct 1979	21 Mar 1981

Displacement, tons: 4000 light; 4400 standard; 4900 dived
Dimensions, feet (metres): 272 × 32.3 × 28
 (82.9 × 9.8 × 8.5)
Main machinery: Nuclear; 1 RR PWR 1; 2 GEC turbines;
 15 000 hp *(11.2 MW)*; 1 shaft; pump jet propulsor; 1 Paxman
 diesel alternator; 1900 hp *(1.42 MW)*; 1 motor for emergency
 drive; 1 auxiliary retractable prop
Speed, knots: 30+ dived
Complement: 116 (13 officers)

Missiles: SSM: McDonnell Douglas UGM-84B Sub-Harpoon;
 active radar homing to 130 km *(70 nm)* at 0.9 Mach; warhead
 227 kg.
Torpedoes: 5—21 in *(533 mm)* bow tubes. Marconi Tigerfish
 Mk 24 Mod 2; wire-guided; active/passive homing to 13 km
 (7 nm) at 35 kts active; 29 km *(15.7 nm)* at 24 kts passive;
 warhead 134 kg; 20 reloads. Individual reloading of torpedoes
 in 15 seconds. To be replaced by Spearfish in mid-1990s.
Mines: Can be carried in lieu of torpedoes.
Countermeasures: Decoys: 2 SSE Mk 6 launchers.
ESM: Racal UAC (being upgraded to UAP); passive intercept.
Combat data systems: Ferranti/Gresham/Dowty DCB/DCG tac-
 tical data handling system. Dowty Sema SMCS after refit.
Radars: Navigation: Kelvin Hughes Type 1006; I band.
Sonars: AUWE Type 2001 or Plessey Type 2020 or Marconi/
 Plessey Type 2074; hull-mounted; active/passive search and
 attack; low frequency.
 BAC Type 2007; hull-mounted; flank array; passive; low
 frequency.
 Ferranti Type 2046; towed array; passive search; very low
 frequency.
 Thomson Sintra Type 2019 PARIS; passive intercept and rang-
 ing (to be replaced by 2082 in due course).
 Marconi Type 2077; short range classification (to be fitted);
 active; high frequency.

Programmes: *Sovereign* ordered 16 May 1969; *Superb*, 20 May
 1970; *Sceptre*, 1 Nov 1971; *Spartan*, 7 Feb 1973; *Splendid*,
 26 May 1976.
Modernisation: *Sceptre* finished refit in 1987, *Spartan* in 1989,
 and *Splendid* in 1993, each fitted with a PWR 1 Core Z giving a
 12 year life cycle although refits/refuel cycles will remain at
 eight to nine year intervals. Other improvements include
 acoustic elastomeric tiles, sonar 2020 processing equipment
 and improved decoys. Marconi Type 2077, short range classification sonar is also to be fitted. Others of the class to follow
 some with Marconi/Plessey 2074 sonar instead of 2020 to
 replace Type 2001. Spearfish torpedoes are also to be carried
 in due course.

SUPERB   1991

Structure: Compared with the Valiant class submarines these
 are slightly shorter with a fuller form, the fore-planes set further
 forward, one less torpedo tube and with a deeper diving depth
 and faster. The pressure hull in the Swiftsure class maintains
 its diameter for much greater length than previous classes.
 Control gear by MacTaggart, Scott & Co Ltd for: attack and
 search periscopes, snort induction and exhaust, radar and ESM
 masts, ALK buoy. The forward hydroplanes house within the
 casing. Fitted with Pilkington Optronics CK 33 search and
 CH 83 attack electro-optic periscopes.
Operational: All belong to the First Submarine Squadron based
 at Faslane. As a result of budget cuts *Swiftsure* paid off in 1992
 after less than 20 years' service.

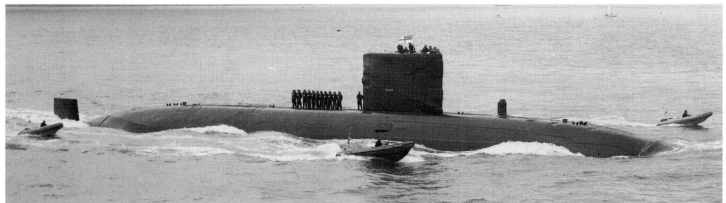

SPARTAN   10/1993, Wright & Logan

SPLENDID   1992

Patrol Submarines (SS)

2 UPHOLDER CLASS (TYPE 2400) (SS)

Name	No	Builders	Start date	Launched	Commissioned
URSULA	S 42	Cammell Laird, Birkenhead (VSEL)	Aug 1987	28 Feb 1991	8 May 1992
UNICORN	S 43	Cammell Laird, Birkenhead (VSEL)	Feb 1989	16 Apr 1992	25 June 1993

Displacement, tons: 2168 surfaced; 2455 dived
Dimensions, feet (metres): 230.6 × 25 × 17.7
(70.3 × 7.6 × 5.5)
Main machinery: Diesel-electric; 2 Paxman Valenta 16SZ die-
sels; 3620 hp *(2.7 MW)* sustained; 2 GEC alternators; 2.8 MW;
1 GEC motor; 5400 hp *(4 MW)*; 1 shaft
Speed, knots: 12 surfaced; 20 dived; 12 snorting.
Range, miles: 8000 at 8 kts snorting
Complement: 47 (7 officers)

Missiles: SSM: McDonnell Douglas UGM-84B Sub-Harpoon;
active radar homing to 130 km *(70 nm)* at 0.9 Mach; warhead
227 kg.
Torpedoes: 6—21 in *(533 mm)* bow tubes. Marconi Tigerfish
Mk 24 Mod 2; wire-guided; active/passive homing to 13 km
(7 nm) at 35 kts active; 29 km *(15.7 nm)* at 24 kts passive;
warhead 134 kg; 12 reloads. Spearfish in due course. Air tur-
bine pump discharge.
Mines: M Mk 5 carried in lieu of torpedoes.
Countermeasures: Decoys: 2 SSE launchers.
ESM: Racal Type UAC or UAP; passive intercept.
Combat data systems: Ferranti-Gresham-Lion DCC tactical data
handling system.
Radars: Navigation: Kelvin Hughes Type 1007; I band.
Sonars: Thomson Sintra Type 2040; hull-mounted; passive
search and intercept; medium frequency.
BAe Type 2007; flank array; passive; low frequency.
GEC Avionics Type 2026 or Type 2046; towed array; passive
search; very low frequency.
Paramax Type 2041; passive ranging.

Programmes: The need for the provision of a new class of non-
nuclear submarines was acknowledged in the late 1970s and
in 1979 the Type 2400 design was first revealed. First boat
ordered from Vickers SEL, 2 November 1983. Further three
ordered on 2 January 1986. Plans for more of the class were
dropped in 1990 as part of a cost cutting exercise.
Modernisation: Sonar suite Type 2076 was to have been fitted
in place of the cancelled Type 2075, but this is likely to be cancelled unless the class is kept in service.
Structure: Single skinned NQ1 high tensile steel hull, tear dropped shape 9:1 ratio, five man lock-out chamber in fin. This is
the first time that the Valenta diesel has been fitted in submarines. Fitted with elastomeric acoustic tiles. Diving depth, greater than 200 m *(650 ft)*. Fitted with Pilkington optronics CK 35
search and CH 85 attack optronic periscopes.
Operational: Endurance, 49 days stores and 90 hours at 3 kts
dived. Problems with the torpedo tube discharge system have
been rectified; *Upholder* in 1992, *Unseen* and *Ursula* in 1993,
Unicorn before commissioning. All based at Devonport as part
of the Second Squadron. First two placed in reserve in April
1994 as a money saving expedient. Second pair to pay off by
the end of the year.

URSULA   *6/1993, van Ginderen Collection*

UNICORN   *9/1993, W Sartori*

UNICORN   *9/1993, Maritime Photographic*

AIRCRAFT CARRIERS
3 INVINCIBLE CLASS (CVSG)

Name	No	Builders	Laid down	Launched	Commissioned
INVINCIBLE	R 05	Vickers Shipbuilding & Engineering, Barrow-in-Furness	20 July 1973	3 May 1977	11 July 1980
ILLUSTRIOUS	R 06	Swan Hunter Shipbuilders, Wallsend	7 Oct 1976	1 Dec 1978	20 June 1982
ARK ROYAL	R 07	Swan Hunter Shipbuilders, Wallsend	14 Dec 1978	2 June 1981	1 Nov 1985

Displacement, tons: 20 600 full load
Dimensions, feet (metres): 685.8 oa; 632 wl × 118 oa; 90 wl × 26 (screws) *(209.1; 192.6 × 36; 27.5 × 8)*
Flight deck, feet (metres): 550 × 44.3 *(167.8 × 13.5)*
Main machinery: COGAG; 4 RR Olympus TM3B gas-turbines; 97 200 hp *(72.5 MW)* sustained; 2 shafts
Speed, knots: 28. **Range, miles:** 7000 at 19 kts
Complement: 685 (60 officers) plus 366 (80 officers) aircrew

Missiles: SAM: British Aerospace Sea Dart twin launcher ❶; radar/semi-active radar guidance to 40 km *(21.5 nm)* at Mach 2; height envelope 100-18 300 m *(328-60 042 ft)*; 36 missiles; limited anti-ship capability.
Guns: 3 General Electric/General Dynamics 20 mm Mk 15 Vulcan Phalanx (R 07) ❷; 6 barrels per launcher; 3000 rounds/minute combined to 1.5 km.
3 Signaal/General Electric 30 mm 7-barrelled Gatling Goalkeeper (R 05 and R 06) ❸; 4200 rounds/minute to 1.5 km.
2 Oerlikon/BMARC 20 mm GAM-BO1 ❹; 55° elevation; 1000 rounds/minute to 2 km.
Countermeasures: Decoys: 8 Sea Gnat 6-barrelled 130 mm dispensers ❺. Prairie Masker noise suppression system.
ESM: MEL UAA 2 or UAF (R 06); intercept.
ECM: THORN EMI Type 675(2); jammer.
Combat data systems: ADAWS 10 (with ADIMP (R 06)) action data automation; Links 10, 11 and 14. US OE-82 VHF SATCOM. SCOT communications ❻; Link 16 in due course. Marisat.

Fire control: GWS 30 Mod 2 for SAM.
Radars: Air search: Marconi/Signaal Type 1022 ❼; D band; range 265 km *(145 nm).*
Surface search: Marconi Type 992R ❽ (R 07); or Plessey Type 996(2) ❾ (R 05 and 06); E/F band.
Navigation: Two Kelvin Hughes Type 1006 (R 05 and 07); Type 1007 (R 06); I band.
Fire control: Two Marconi Type 909 or 909(1) (R 06) ❿; I/J band.
Sonars: Plessey Type 2016; hull-mounted; active search and attack; medium frequency.

Fixed wing aircraft: 9 British Aerospace Sea Harrier FRS 1/2 (see *Shipborne Aircraft* section) ⓫.
Helicopters: Up to 9 Westland Sea King HAS 6 ⓬; 3 Westland Sea King AEW 2.

Programmes: The first of class, the result of many compromises, was ordered from Vickers on 17 April 1973. The order for the second ship was placed on 14 May 1976, the third in December 1978.
Modernisation: In January 1989 R 05 completed a 27 month modernisation which included a 12° ski ramp, space and support facilities for at least 21 aircraft (Sea Harriers, Sea King AEW and ASW helicopters), three Goalkeeper systems, Sonar 2016, Seagnat decoys, 996 radar, Flag and Command facilities to R 07 standards and accommodation for an additional

120 aircrew and Flag Staff. In February 1994 R 06 completed a similar 30 month modernisation to bring her to the same standard, but with additional command and weapon system improvements to those listed for R 05. In addition R 06 has a new main mast, new sponsons for chaff launchers and the starboard side of the forecastle has been roofed in to provide more aircraft parking space with an aircrew briefing room underneath. Ski ramp has been increased to 13°. Plans to fit four lightweight Seawolf launchers were cancelled as an economy measure in 1991. Contract placed in early 1991 to redesign the flight deck lifts.
Structure: The design allows for an open fo'c'sle head and a slightly angled deck which allows the Sea Dart launcher to be set almost amidships. In 1976-77 an amendment was incorporated to allow for the transport and landing of an RM Commando. The forward end of the flight deck (ski-ramp of 12°) allows STOVL aircraft of greater all-up weight to operate more efficiently.
Operational: The role of this class, apart from its primary task of providing a command, control and communications facility, is the operation of both helicopters and STOVL aircraft. Provision has been made for sufficiently large lifts and hangars to accommodate the next generation of both these aircraft. Only two of the class are fully operational at any one time, the third either being in refit, working-up or on stand-by. *Illustrious* replaces *Ark Royal* in February 1995. *Ark Royal* is scheduled for a refit in 1996.

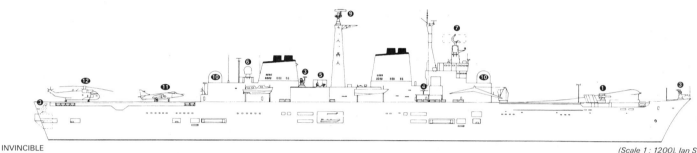

INVINCIBLE

(Scale 1 : 1200), Ian Sturton

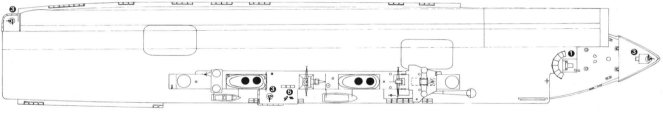

INVINCIBLE

(Scale 1 : 1200), Ian Sturton

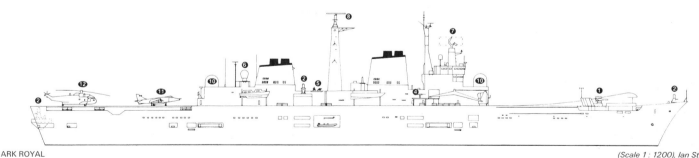

ARK ROYAL

(Scale 1 : 1200), Ian Sturton

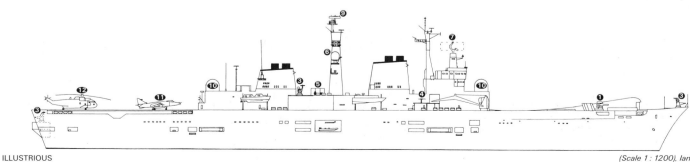

ILLUSTRIOUS

(Scale 1 : 1200), Ian Sturton

ARK ROYAL   *5/1993*

ILLUSTRIOUS   *1/1994*

INVINCIBLE   *11/1992, H M Steele*

DESTROYERS

Note: *Bristol* (D 23) is an immobile tender used for training in Portsmouth Harbour.

12 TYPE 42

Batch 1

Name	No	Builders	Laid down	Launched	Commissioned
BIRMINGHAM	D 86	Cammell Laird, Birkenhead	28 Mar 1972	30 July 1973	3 Dec 1976
NEWCASTLE	D 87	Swan Hunter Shipbuilders, Wallsend-on-Tyne	21 Feb 1973	24 Apr 1975	23 Mar 1978
GLASGOW	D 88	Swan Hunter Shipbuilders, Wallsend-on-Tyne	16 Apr 1974	14 Apr 1976	24 May 1979
CARDIFF	D 108	Vickers Shipbuilding & Engineering, Barrow-in-Furness	6 Nov 1972	22 Feb 1974	24 Sep 1979

Batch 2

Name	No	Builders	Laid down	Launched	Commissioned
EXETER	D 89	Swan Hunter Shipbuilders, Wallsend-on-Tyne	22 July 1976	25 Apr 1978	19 Sep 1980
SOUTHAMPTON	D 90	Vosper Thornycroft, Woolston	21 Oct 1976	29 Jan 1979	31 Oct 1981
NOTTINGHAM	D 91	Vosper Thornycroft, Woolston	6 Feb 1978	18 Feb 1980	14 Apr 1983
LIVERPOOL	D 92	Cammell Laird, Birkenhead	5 July 1978	25 Sep 1980	1 July 1982

Displacement, tons: 3500 standard; 4100 full load
Dimensions, feet (metres): 412 oa; 392 wl × 47 × 19 (screws) *(125; 119.5 × 14.3 × 5.8)*
Main machinery: COGOG; 2 RR Olympus TM3B gas-turbines; 50 000 hp *(37.3 MW)* sustained; 2 RR Tyne RM1C gas-turbines (cruising); 9900 hp *(7.4 MW)* sustained; 2 shafts; cp props
Speed, knots: 29. **Range, miles:** 4000 at 18 kts
Complement: 253 (24 officers) (accommodation for 312)

Missiles: SAM: British Aerospace Sea Dart twin launcher ❶; radar/semi-active radar guidance to 40 km *(21.5 nm)* at 2 Mach; height envelope 100-18 300 m *(328-60 042 ft)*; 22 missiles; limited anti-ship capability.
Guns: 1 Vickers 4.5 in *(114 mm)*/55 Mk 8 ❷; 55° elevation; 25 rounds/minute to 22 km *(11.9 nm)* anti-surface; 6 km *(3.3 nm)* anti-aircraft; weight of shell 21 kg.
2 or 4 Oerlikon/BMARC 20 mm GAM-BO1 ❸ and ❹; 55° elevation; 1000 rounds/minute to 2 km.
2 Oerlikon 20 mm Mk 7A ❹ (in those with only 2 BMARC); 50° elevation; 800 rounds/minute to 2 km; weight of shell 0.24 kg.
2 General Electric/General Dynamics 20 mm Vulcan Phalanx Mk 15 ❺; 6 barrels per launcher; 3000 rounds/minute combined to 1.5 km.
Torpedoes: 6—324 mm Plessey STWS Mk 3 (2 triple) tubes ❻. Fitted for, but not with. Batch 2 may be equipped from 1996.
Countermeasures: Decoys: 4 Sea Gnat 130 mm 6-barrelled launchers ❼; chaff and IR flares. The two after launchers can be replaced by 102 mm barrels.
Graseby Type 182; towed torpedo decoy.
ESM: MEL UAA-2; intercept.
ECM: Type 670 (Batch 1) Type 675(2) (Batch 2); jammer.
Combat data systems: ADAWS 7 action data automation. 2 Marconi SCOT SATCOMs ❽; Links 10, 11 and 14. Marisat. Link 16 in due course.
Fire control: GWS 30 Mod 2 (for SAM); GSA 1 secondary system. Radamec 2100 series optronic surveillance system ❾.

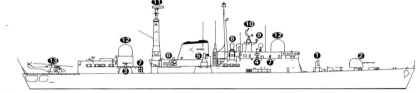

LIVERPOOL (Batch 2)   *(Scale 1 : 1200), Ian Sturton*

NOTTINGHAM   *6/1993, H M Steele*

Radars: Air search: Marconi/Signaal Type 1022 ❿; D band; range 265 km *(145 nm)*.
Surface search: Plessey Type 996 ⓫; E/F band.
Navigation: Kelvin Hughes Type 1006; I band.
Fire control: Two Marconi Type 909 ⓬; or 9091; I/J band.

Sonars: Ferranti Type 2050 or Plessey Type 2016; hull-mounted; active search and attack; medium frequency.
Kelvin Hughes Type 162M; hull-mounted; bottom classification; 50 kHz.

Helicopters: 1 Westland Lynx HAS 3 ⓭.

LIVERPOOL   *2/1993, Maritime Photographic*

CARDIFF   *2/1993, Wright & Logan*

Batch 3

Name	No	Builders	Laid down	Launched	Commissioned
MANCHESTER	D 95	Vickers Shipbuilding & Engineering, Barrow-in-Furness	19 May 1978	24 Nov 1980	16 Dec 1982
GLOUCESTER	D 96	Vosper Thornycroft, Woolston	29 Oct 1979	2 Nov 1982	11 Sep 1985
EDINBURGH	D 97	Cammell Laird, Birkenhead	8 Sep 1980	14 Apr 1983	17 Dec 1985
YORK	D 98	Swan Hunter Shipbuilders, Wallsend-on-Tyne	18 Jan 1980	21 June 1982	9 Aug 1985

Displacement, tons: 3500 standard; 4675 full load
Dimensions, feet (metres): 462.8 oa; 434 wl × 49 × 19 (screws)
(141.1; 132.3 × 14.9 × 5.8)
Main machinery: COGOG; 2 RR Olympus TM3B gas-turbines;
43 000 hp *(32 MW)* sustained; 2 RR Tyne RM1C gas-turbines
(cruising); 10 680 hp *(8 MW)* sustained; 2 shafts; cp props
Speed, knots: 30+. **Range, miles:** 4000 at 18 kts
Complement: 301 (26 officers)

Missiles: SAM: British Aerospace Sea Dart twin launcher ❶;
radar/semi-active radar guidance to 40 km *(21 nm)*; warhead
HE; 22 missiles; limited anti-ship capability.
Guns: 1 Vickers 4.5 in *(114 mm)*/55 Mk 8 ❷; 55° elevation; 25
rounds/minute to 22 km *(11.9 nm)* anti-surface; 6 km *(3.3 nm)*
anti-aircraft; weight of shell 21 kg.
2 Oerlikon/BMARC 20 mm GAM-BO1 ❸; 55° elevation; 1000
rounds/minute to 2 km.
2 Oerlikon 20 mm Mk 7A ❹; 50° elevation; 800 rounds/
minute to 2 km; weight of shell 0.24 kg.
2 BMARC 30 mm ❺ (temporary mountings in D 97).
1 or 2 General Electric/General Dynamics 20 mm Vulcan Phalanx Mk 15 ❻; 6 barrels per launcher; 3000 rounds/minute
combined to 1.5 km. See *Modernisation* comment.
Torpedoes: 6—324 mm STWS Mk 2 (2 triple) tubes ❼. Marconi
Stingray; active/passive homing to 11 km *(5.9 nm)* at 45 kts;
warhead 35 kg.
Countermeasures: 4 Sea Gnat 130 mm 6-barrelled launchers ❽;
chaff and IR flares. The two after launchers can be replaced by
102 mm barrels.
Graseby Type 182; towed torpedo decoy.
ESM: MEL UAA-2; intercept.
ECM: Type 675(2); jammer.
Combat data systems: ADAWS 8 (with ADIMP) action data
automation. Marconi SCOT SATCOM ❾; Links 10, 11 and 14.
Marisat. Link 16 in due course.
Fire control: GWS 30 Mod 2 (for SAM); GSA 1 secondary system.
Radamec 2100 series optronic surveillance system ❿.
Radars: Air search: Marconi/Signaal Type 1022 ⓫; D band;
range 265 km *(145 nm)*.
Air/surface search: Marconi Type 992R or Plessey Type 996 ⓬;
E/F band.
Navigation: Kelvin Hughes Type 1006; I band.
Fire control: Two Marconi Type 909 ⓭ or 909 Mod 1; I/J band.
Sonars: Ferranti Type 2050 or Plessey Type 2016; hull-mounted;
active search and attack.
Kelvin Hughes Type 162M; hull-mounted; bottom classifi-
cation; 50 kHz.

Helicopters: 1 Westland Lynx HAS 3 ⓮.

Batches 1, 2 and 3

Programmes: Designed to provide area air defence for a task
force. In order to provide space for improved weapon systems
and to improve speed and seakeeping a radical change was
made to this class. The completion of later ships was delayed
to allow for some modifications resulting from experience in
the Falklands' campaign (1982).
Modernisation: Vulcan Phalanx replaced 30 mm guns 1987-89.
All have Plessey Type 996 radar in place of Type 992, and Type
909(1) fire-control radars with improved Tx/Rx circuits. STWS
Mk 3 may replace the obsolete Mk 1 in Batch 2. D 97 had a partial conversion completing in 1990 with the Phalanx moved
forward and a protective visor fitted around the bow of the
ship. As a temporary measure 30 mm guns were placed where
Seawolf launchers would have been fitted. That modification
was cancelled in 1991 and D 97 reverts to the standard armament in late 1994. All Batch 2 and 3 ships are having a command system update: D 95 in 1992, D 96 in 1993, D 97 in
1994. Sea Gnat decoy launchers are replacing all other types.
Structure: All have two pairs of stabilisers and twin rudders.
Advantages of gas-turbine propulsion include ability to reach

GLOUCESTER   *(Scale 1 : 1200), Ian Sturton*

EDINBURGH (until late 1994)   *(Scale 1 : 1200), Ian Sturton*

EDINBURGH   *7/1993, Wright & Logan*

MANCHESTER   *9/1993, Hartmut Ehlers*

maximum speed with great rapidity, reduction in space and
weight and 25 per cent reduction in technical manpower. The
stretched Batch 3 have been fitted with a strengthening beam
on each side which increases displacement by 50 tons and
width by 2 feet.

Operational: The helicopter carries the Sea Skua air-to-surface
weapon for use against lightly defended surface ship targets.
Ships may be fitted with DEC laser dazzle sight and additional
decoy flare launchers on operational deployments.

YORK   *8/1993, Maritime Photographic*

14 BROADSWORD CLASS (TYPE 22)

Batch 1

Name	No	Builders	Laid down	Launched	Commissioned
BROADSWORD	F 88	Yarrow Shipbuilders, Glasgow	7 Feb 1975	12 May 1976	3 May 1979
BATTLEAXE	F 89	Yarrow Shipbuilders, Glasgow	4 Feb 1976	18 May 1977	28 Mar 1980
BRILLIANT	F 90	Yarrow Shipbuilders, Glasgow	25 Mar 1977	15 Dec 1978	15 May 1981
BRAZEN	F 91	Yarrow Shipbuilders, Glasgow	18 Aug 1978	4 Mar 1980	2 July 1982

Batch 2

Name	No	Builders	Laid down	Launched	Commissioned
BOXER	F 92	Yarrow Shipbuilders, Glasgow	1 Nov 1979	17 June 1981	14 Jan 1984
BEAVER	F 93	Yarrow Shipbuilders, Glasgow	20 June 1980	8 May 1982	18 Dec 1984
BRAVE	F 94	Yarrow Shipbuilders, Glasgow	24 May 1982	19 Nov 1983	4 July 1986
LONDON (ex-*Bloodhound*)	F 95	Yarrow Shipbuilders, Glasgow	7 Feb 1983	27 Oct 1984	5 June 1987
SHEFFIELD	F 96	Swan Hunter Shipbuilders, Wallsend-on-Tyne	29 Mar 1984	26 Mar 1986	26 July 1988
COVENTRY	F 98	Swan Hunter Shipbuilders, Wallsend-on-Tyne	29 Mar 1984	8 Apr 1986	14 Oct 1988

Displacement, tons: 3500 standard; 4400 full load (Batch 1)
4100 standard; 4800 full load (Batch 2)
Dimensions, feet (metres): 430 oa; 410 wl × 48.5 × 19.9 (screws) *(131.2; 125 × 14.8 × 6)* (Batch 1)
485.8 oa × 48.5 × 21 (screws) *(148.1 × 14.8 × 6.4)* (F 92-93)
480.5 × 48.5 × 21 *(146.5 × 14.8 × 6.4)* (F 94-96 and 98)
Main machinery: COGOG; 2 RR Olympus TM3B gas-turbines; 50 000 hp *(37.3 MW)* sustained or 2 RR Spey SM1C (F 94); 44 000 hp *(32.8 MW)* sustained; 2 RR Tyne RM1C gas turbines; 9900 hp *(7.4 MW)* sustained; 2 shafts; cp props
Speed, knots: 30; 18 on Tynes.
Range, miles: 4500 at 18 kts on Tynes
Complement: 222 (17 officers) plus 65 officers under training (Batch 1)
273 (30 officers) (accommodation for 296) (Batch 2)

Missiles: SSM: 4 Aerospatiale MM 38 Exocet ❶; inertial cruise; active radar homing to 42 km *(23 nm)* at 0.9 Mach; warhead 165 kg; sea-skimmer.
SAM: 2 British Aerospace 6-barrelled Seawolf GWS 25 Mod 0 or Mod 4 (except F 94-96 and 98) ❷; command line-of-sight (CLOS) TV/radar tracking to 5 km *(2.7 nm)* at 2+ Mach; warhead 14 kg; 32 rounds. Being upgraded to Mod 4 with improved radar and optronics.
2 British Aerospace Seawolf GWS 25 Mod 3 (F 94-96 and 98) ❷; has a Type 911 tracker with a second radar channel instead of TV.
Guns: 4 Oerlikon/BMARC GCM-A03 30 mm/75 (2 twin) ❸; 80° elevation; 650 rounds/minute to 10 km *(5.5 nm)*; weight of shell 0.36 kg.
2 Oerlikon/BMARC 20 mm GAM-BO1 ❹; 55° elevation; 1000 rounds/minute to 2 km.
Torpedoes: 6—324 mm Plessey STWS Mk 2 (2 triple) tubes ❺. Marconi Stingray; active/passive homing to 11 km *(5.9 nm)* at 45 kts; warhead 35 kg.
Countermeasures: Decoys: 2 Plessey Shield 12-tubed launchers ❻; IR flares and chaff to 4 km *(2.2 nm)*.
4 Marconi Sea Gnat 6-barrelled fixed launchers.
Graseby Type 182; towed torpedo decoy.
ESM: MEL UAA-2; intercept.
ECM: Type 670; jammers.
Combat data systems: Ferranti CACS 1 (Batch 2); Links 11 and 14; CAAIS (Batch 1); Links 10 and 14 (receive); action data automation. Marconi SCOT SATCOM ❼. Marisat.
Fire control: GWS 25 Mod 0 or 4 (for SAM) (except F 94-96 and 98); GWS 25 Mod 3 (for SAM) (F 94-96 and 98); GWS 50.
Radars: Air/surface search: Marconi Type 967/968 (Type 967M in F 94) ❽; D/E band.
Navigation: Kelvin Hughes Type 1006 or Type 1007; I band.
Fire control: Two Marconi Type 911 or Type 910 (in Mod 0 ships) ❾; I/Ku band (for Seawolf).
Sonars: Plessey Type 2016 or Ferranti/Thomson Sintra Type 2050; hull-mounted; search and attack.
Dowty Type 2031Z (Batch 2 only); towed array; passive search; very low frequency.

Helicopters: 2 Westland Lynx HAS 3 (in all) ❿; or 1 Westland Sea King HAS 5 (or EH 101 Merlin) (F 94-96 and 98).

TYPE 22 (Batch 1)   *(Scale 1 : 1200), Ian Sturton*

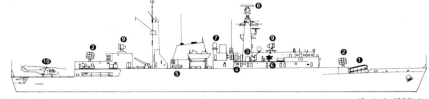

TYPE 22 (Batch 2)   *(Scale 1 : 1200), Ian Sturton*

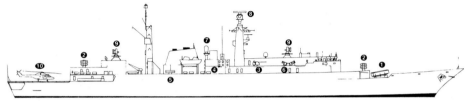

BATTLEAXE   *7/1993, Maritime Photographic*

BEAVER   *1/1993, Maritime Photographic*

Batch 3

Name	No	Builders	Laid down	Launched	Commissioned
CORNWALL	F 99	Yarrow Shipbuilders, Glasgow	14 Dec 1983	14 Oct 1985	23 Apr 1988
CUMBERLAND	F 85	Yarrow Shipbuilders, Glasgow	12 Oct 1984	21 June 1986	10 June 1989
CAMPBELTOWN	F 86	Cammell Laird, Birkenhead	4 Dec 1985	7 Oct 1987	27 May 1989
CHATHAM	F 87	Swan Hunter Shipbuilders, Wallsend-on-Tyne	12 May 1986	20 Jan 1988	4 May 1990

Displacement, tons: 4200 standard; 4900 full load
Dimensions, feet (metres): 485.9 × 48.5 × 21
(148.1 × 14.8 × 6.4)
Main machinery: COGOG; 2 RR Spey SM1A gas-turbines;
29 500 hp *(22 MW)* sustained; 2 RR Tyne RM3C gas-turbines;
10 680 hp *(8 MW)* sustained; 2 shafts; cp props
Speed, knots: 30; 18 on Tynes.
Range, miles: 4500 at 18 kts on Tynes

Complement: 250 (31 officers) (accommodation for 301)

Missiles: SSM: 8 McDonnell Douglas Harpoon Block 1C (2 quad)
launchers ❶; preprogrammed; active radar homing to 130 km
(70 nm) at 0.9 Mach; warhead 227 kg.
SAM: 2 British Aerospace Seawolf GWS 25 Mod 3 ❷; command
line-of-sight (CLOS) with 2 channel radar tracking to 5 km
(2.7 nm) at 2+ Mach; warhead 14 kg.
Guns: 1 Vickers 4.5 in *(114 mm)*/55 Mk 8 ❸; 55° elevation; 25
rounds/minute to 22 km *(11.9 nm)* anti-surface; 6 km *(3.3 nm)*
anti-aircraft; weight of shell 21 kg.
1 Signaal/General Electric 30 mm 7-barrelled Goalkeeper ❹;
4200 rounds/minute combined to 1.5 km.
2 DES/Oerlikon 30 mm/75 ❺; 80° elevation; 650 rounds/
minute to 10 km *(5.5 nm)*; weight of shell 0.36 kg.
Torpedoes: 6—324 mm Plessey STWS Mk 2 (2 triple) tubes ❻.
Marconi Stingray; active/passive homing to 11 km *(5.9 nm)* at
45 kts; warhead 35 kg.
Countermeasures: Decoys: 4 Marconi Sea Gnat 6-barrelled
130 mm fixed launchers ❼; electronic decoy with jammer.
Graseby Type 182; towed torpedo decoy.
ESM: MEL UAA-2; intercept.
ECM: Type 670 or Type 675(2); jammer.
Combat data systems: CACS 5 action data automation; Links 11
and 14. 2 Marconi SCOT SATCOMs ❽. ICS-3 integrated
comms. Marisat.
Fire control: 2 BAe GSA 8A Sea Archer optronic directors with
TV and IR imaging and laser rangefinders ❾. GWS 60. GWS 25
Mod 3 (for SAM).
Radars: Air/surface search: Marconi Type 967/968 ❿; D/E
band.
Navigation: Kelvin Hughes Type 1006 or Type 1007; I band.
Fire control: Two Marconi Type 911 ⓫; I/Ku band (for Seawolf).
Sonars: Plessey Type 2016; hull-mounted; active search and
attack. Being replaced by Ferranti Type 2050.
Dowty Type 2031; towed array; passive search; very low
frequency.

Helicopters: 2 Westland Lynx HAS 3; or 1 Westland Sea King
HAS 5 ⓬ (or EH 101 Merlin).

Batches 1, 2 and 3

Programmes: Originally planned as successors to the Leander
class. Order for the first of class, *Broadsword,* was placed on
8 February 1974.
Modernisation: Rolls Royce Spey SM1C engines (operational in
F 94 in early 1990) give greater power and may be back-fitted
in due course. Seawolf GWS 25 will be progressively upgraded
to Mod 4 standard in all Mod 0 ships. Sonar 2016 is being
replaced by Sonar 2050 and Bofors 40 mm/60 in Batch 1 and
2 have been replaced by Oerlikon 30 mm guns. EW fit is being
updated. CAAIS combat data system in Batch 1 is overdue for
replacement by CACS 1, but the update has been cancelled by
lack of funds.
Structure: Funnel in *Brilliant* and later ships was smoother, slim-
mer and shorter than in first two in build but *Broadsword* and
Battleaxe have been modified and are now the same. Last four
Batch 2 and all Batch 3 have enlarged flight decks to take Sea
King or EH 101 Merlin helicopters. Batch 1 have modified
accommodation to take 65 officers under training.
Operational: This class is primarily designed for ASW operations
and is capable of acting as OTC. Batch 3 have facilities for Flag
and staff. Batch 1 used as training ships. One Lynx normally
embarked for peacetime operations. Ships have been fitted
with DEC laser dazzle device on operational deployments.
Batch 2: 1st Frigate Squadron. Batch 1 and Batch 3: 2nd Frigate Squadron. The first of the class is scheduled to be paid off
in March 1995.

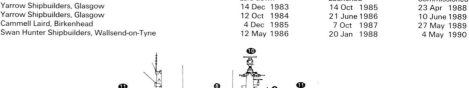
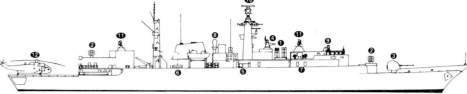

TYPE 22 (Batch 3) *(Scale 1 : 1200), Ian Sturton*

CUMBERLAND *1993, Ships of the World*

CORNWALL *10/1993, 92 Wing RAAF*

FRIGATES

Note: *Andromeda*, the last of the Leander class frigates, is still counted in the strength of the fleet until November 1994. She is in reserve and may be sold off early.

9 + 4 (3) DUKE CLASS (TYPE 23)

Name	No	Builders	Laid down	Launched	Commissioned
NORFOLK	F 230	Yarrow Shipbuilders, Glasgow	14 Dec 1985	10 July 1987	1 June 1990
ARGYLL	F 231	Yarrow Shipbuilders, Glasgow	20 Mar 1987	8 Apr 1989	31 May 1991
LANCASTER	F 229 (ex-F 232)	Yarrow Shipbuilders, Glasgow	18 Dec 1987	24 May 1990	1 May 1992
MARLBOROUGH	F 233	Swan Hunter Shipbuilders, Wallsend-on-Tyne	22 Oct 1987	21 Jan 1989	14 June 1991
IRON DUKE	F 234	Yarrow Shipbuilders, Glasgow	12 Dec 1988	2 Mar 1991	20 May 1993
MONMOUTH	F 235	Yarrow Shipbuilders, Glasgow	1 June 1989	23 Nov 1991	24 Sep 1993
MONTROSE	F 236	Yarrow Shipbuilders, Glasgow	1 Nov 1989	31 July 1992	June 1994
WESTMINSTER	F 237	Swan Hunter Shipbuilders, Wallsend-on-Tyne	18 Jan 1991	4 Feb 1992	13 May 1994
NORTHUMBERLAND	F 238	Swan Hunter Shipbuilders, Wallsend-on-Tyne	4 Apr 1991	4 Apr 1992	Sep 1994
RICHMOND	F 239	Swan Hunter Shipbuilders, Wallsend-on-Tyne	16 Feb 1992	6 Apr 1993	Dec 1994
SOMERSET	F 240	Yarrow Shipbuilders, Glasgow	12 Oct 1992	June 1994	1996
GRAFTON	F 241	Yarrow Shipbuilders, Glasgow	13 May 1993	Dec 1994	1997
SUTHERLAND	F 242	Yarrow Shipbuilders, Glasgow	14 Oct 1993	1996	1997

Displacement, tons: 3500 standard; 4200 full load
Dimensions, feet (metres): 436.2 × 52.8 × 18 (screws); 24 (sonar) *(133 × 16.1 × 5.5; 7.3)*
Main machinery: CODLAG; 2 RR Spey SM1A (F 229-F 236) or SM1C (F 237 onwards) gas-turbines (see *Structure*); 31 100 hp *(23.2 MW)* sustained; 4 Paxman 12CM diesels; 8100 hp *(6 MW)*; 2 GEC motors; 4000 hp *(3 MW)*; 2 shafts
Speed, knots: 28; 15 on diesel-electric.
Range, miles: 7800 miles at 15 kts
Complement: 174 (12 officers) (accommodation for 185 (16 officers))

Missiles: SSM: 8 McDonnell Douglas Harpoon (2 quad) launchers ❶; active radar homing to 130 km *(70 nm)* at 0.9 Mach; warhead 227 kg (84C). 4 normally carried.
SAM: British Aerospace Seawolf GWS 26 Mod 1 VLS ❷; command line-of-sight (CLOS) radar/TV tracking to 6 km *(3.3 nm)* at 2.5 Mach; warhead 14 kg; 32 canisters.
Guns: 1 Vickers 4.5 in *(114 mm)*/55 Mk 8 ❸; 55° elevation; 25 rounds/minute to 22 km *(11.9 nm)* anti-surface; 6 km *(3.3 nm)* anti-aircraft; weight of shell 21 kg.
2 Oerlikon/DES 30 mm/75 Mk 1 ❹; 80° elevation; 650 rounds/minute to 10 km *(5.4 nm)* anti-surface; 3 km *(1.6 nm)* anti-aircraft; weight of shell 0.36 kg.
Torpedoes: 4 Cray Marine 324 mm fixed (2 twin) tubes ❺. Marconi Stingray; active/passive homing to 11 km *(5.9 nm)* at 45 kts; warhead 35 kg (shaped charge); depth to 750 m *(2460 ft)*. Automatic reload in 9 minutes.
Countermeasures: Decoys: 4 Marconi Sea Gnat 6-barrelled 130 mm fixed launchers ❻; for chaff and IR flares.
Type 182; towed torpedo decoy.
ESM: Racal UAF-1 Cutlass ❼; intercept. THORN EMI UAT (F 237 onwards and then retrofit if funds are available).
ECM: Type 675(2) or Racal Scorpion; jammer.
Combat data systems: BAe Sema SSCS action data automation (see *Structure* comment); Links 11, 14 and 16 in due course. Marconi SCOT 1D SATCOMs ❽.
Fire control: BAe GSA 8B/GPEOD optronic director ❾. GWS 60 (for SSM). GWS 26 (for SAM).
Radars: Air/surface search: Plessey Type 996(I) ❿; 3D; E/F band.
Navigation: Kelvin Hughes Type 1007; I band.
Fire control: Two Marconi Type 911 ⓫; I/Ku band.
IFF: 1010/1011.
Sonars: Ferranti/Thomson Sintra Type 2050; bow-mounted; active search and attack.
Dowty Type 2031Z; towed array; passive search; very low frequency. May be replaced by Marconi/Plessey 2057 in due course. One ship to be fitted with Type 2081 active low frequency VDS in due course; others may be back fitted.

Helicopters: 1 Westland Lynx HAS 3 (1 EH 101 Merlin, later) ⓬.

Programmes: The first of this class was ordered from Yarrows on 29 October 1984. Next three in September 1986, with four more out to tender in October 1987 but only three ordered in July 1988. Again four out to tender in late 1988 and only three ordered 19 December 1989. Long lead items for another six ordered in 1990 but contracts were not placed until 23 January 1992 when three more were ordered. The last three are expected to be ordered in 1995.
Planned total total was 23 but is now unlikely to exceed 16. F 229 pennant number changed because 232 was considered unlucky as it is the RN report form number for collisions and groundings.
Structure: Incorporates stealth technology to minimise acoustic, magnetic, radar and IR signatures. The design includes a 7° slope to all vertical surfaces, rounded edges, reduction of IR

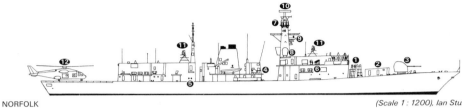

NORFOLK   *(Scale 1 : 1200), Ian Sturton*

MONMOUTH   *4/1993, David Warren*

ARGYLL   *6/1993, H M Steele*

emissions and a hull bubble system to reduce radiated noise. The combined diesel electric and GT propulsion system provides quiet motive power during towed sonar operations. The SM1C engines although capable of 41 MW of power combined are constrained by output into the gearbox. A CIWS gun is not fitted but a possible extension by 7 m at some stage in the building programme would allow one or two Goalkeeper to be carried and increase Seawolf magazine capacity. The first seven ships of the class lack fully automated co-ordination of all weapons and sensors. SSCS software Phase I has been installed in *Westminster* on build and is to be retrofitted in

earlier ships. Subsequent Phases are being fitted on build to all the later ships.
Operational: The ship is capable of carrying out all weapon systems functions without the SSCS Combat Data System. The problem is that in multi-threat situations command speed of response will in theory be much slower. F 233 carrying out a trial of a Dowty track management system (TMS) which uses a form of artificial intelligence. The plan is to base F 233, F 229, F 234, F 237, F 239 and F 241 at Portsmouth (4th Frigate Squadron), with the remainder at Devonport (6th Frigate Squadron) by 1996/97.

MARLBOROUGH   *3/1993, Maritime Photographic*

0 + (12) COMMON NEW GENERATION TYPE (PROJECT HORIZON)

Displacement, tons: 6500 full load
Dimensions, feet (metres): 486.9 × 65.3 × 15.7
(148.4 × 19.9 × 4.8)
Main machinery: CODLAG; 2 gas-turbines; 4 diesels; 2 motors;
2 shafts
Speed, knots: 30. **Range, miles:** 7000 at 18 kts
Complement: 200 plus 35 spare

Missiles: SSM: 8 (2 quad) or VLS ❶; 150-200 km.
SAM: Aster VLS ❷ PAAMS (principal anti-air missile system).
Guns: 1—100/114 mm ❸; anti-surface.
2—30 mm ❹. 2 ILMS (inner layer missile system) ❺.
Torpedoes: 4 (2 twin) fixed launchers ❻.
Countermeasures: Decoys: Chaff/IR flare launchers. Torpedo
defence system.
ESM/ECM ❼.
Combat data systems: Link 16 included. SATCOM ❽.
Radars: Air/surface search: Siemens/Plessey MESAR or Alenia/
Elsag EMPAR ❾.
Surveillance/fire control ❿; multi-function.
Surface search: ⓫.
Sonars: Type 2050; hull-mounted; active search and attack;
medium frequency.

Helicopters: 1 EH 101 Merlin ⓬.

Programmes: Three-nation project for a new AAW ship with

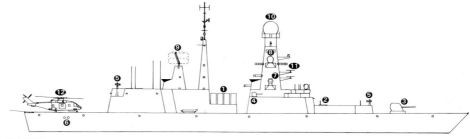

CNG TYPE   *(Scale 1:1200), Ian Sturton*

France and Italy. Joint project office established in 1993. Warship design contract expected in late 1994 for first order in
1996 and an in-service date of 2002.
Structure: Details given are speculative. The drawing is more
recent than the artist's impression.
Opinion: Like all collaborative projects this has strong political
backing because of the theoretical cost savings. The problems
are different numbers of ships required by the three nations,

different operational and industrial priorities, and hidden costs
caused by equipment compromises. The latter increase logistic back-up and training costs if navies are compelled to fit
equipments which are not natural progressions from existing
types. The Netherlands, Germany and Spain are also collaborating for new air defence ships, but have a much less rigid
project structure. This is probably a better model.

CNG TYPE (artist's impression)   *1993*

SHIPBORNE AIRCRAFT

Numbers/Type: 8/41/4 British Aerospace Sea Harrier FRS 1/FRS 2/T4.
Operational speed: 640 kts *(1186 km/h)*.
Service ceiling: 51 200 ft *(15 600 m)*.
Range: 800 nm *(1480 km)*.
Role/Weapon systems: Air defence, reconnaissance and maritime attack; update for 31 aircraft
by 1994 to FRS 2 Standard plus 10 new FRS 2 aircraft. Sensors: Blue Fox or Blue Vixen (FRS 2)
radar, RWR, cameras. IFF Mk II from 1995. Weapons: ASV; 2 × Sea Eagle missiles. Strike; 2 ×
30 mm cannon; 1000 lb bombs; Paveway II laser-guided bombs; BL 755 cluster bombs. AD; 4 ×
AIM-9L Sidewinder or AIM-120 AMRAAM (FRS 2); 2 × 30 mm Aden cannon.

Numbers/Type: 80 Westland Lynx HAS 3/8.
Operational speed: 120 kts *(222 km/h)*.
Service ceiling: 10 000 ft *(3048 m)*.
Range: 320 nm *(593 km)*.
Role/Weapon systems: Primarily anti-surface helicopter with short-range ASW capability;
embarked in all modern RN escorts; Royal Marines operate anti-armour/reconnaissance version
(Lynx AH 1); planned update with centralised tactical system, Sea Owl passive identification sys-
tem and MAD (Lynx HAS 8) to be fitted from 1994. Sensors: Ferranti Sea Spray Mk 1 radar,
'Orange Crop' ESM, chaff and flare dispenser. Weapons: ASW; 2 × Stingray torpedoes or Mk 11
depth bombs. ASV; 4 × Sea Skua missiles; 2—12.7 mm MG pods.

SEA HARRIER FRS 1   *11/1993, H M Steele*

LYNX HAS 3   *1/1994, Maritime Photographic*

SEA HARRIER FRS 2   *1994*

LYNX HAS 8   *1992*

Numbers/Type: 76 Westland Sea King HAS 5/6.
Operational speed: 112 kts *(207 km/h)*.
Service ceiling: 10 000 ft *(3050 m)*.
Range: 500 nm *(925 km)*.
Role/Weapon systems: Embarked and shore-based medium ASW helicopter in front-line and training squadron service; used as active/passive screen force and provides RN's principal airborne ASW assets; Mk 6 entered service in June 1989. Sensors: MEL Sea Searcher radar, 'Orange Crop' ESM, Ferranti 2069 (HAS 6) replacing Type 195M dipping sonar, combined sonar processor AQS 902G-DS Mk 6 replacing 902C. Weapons: ASW; 4 × Stingray torpedoes or Mk 11 depth bombs.

SEA KING HAS 6   *10/1992, Maritime Photographic*

Numbers/Type: 10 Westland Sea King AEW 2.
Operational speed: 110 kts *(204 km/h)*.
Service ceiling: 10 000 ft *(3050 m)*.
Range: 660 nm *(1220 km)*.
Role/Weapon systems: Primarily used for airborne early warning organic to the Fleet, with EW, surface search and OTHT secondary roles; modified from ASW version. Improved radar, IFF Mk II and Link 16 to be fitted from 1995. Sensors: Searchwater AEW radar, 'Orange Crop' ESM, 'Jubilee Guardsmen' IFF. Weapons: Unarmed.

SEA KING AEW 2   *10/1992, Maritime Photographic*

Numbers/Type: 36 Westland Sea King HC4.
Operational speed: 112 kts *(208 km/h)*.
Service ceiling: 10 000 ft *(3050 m)*.
Range: 664 nm *(1230 km)*.
Role/Weapon systems: Commando support and re-supply helicopter; capable of carrying most RM Commando Force equipment underslung. Expected to remain in service to 2010. Sensors: None. Weapons: Can fit 7.62 mm GPMG or similar, missile armament abandoned.

SEA KING HC4   *9/1992, Maritime Photographic*

Numbers/Type: 12 Westland Gazelle AH Mk 1.
Operational speed: 142 kts *(264 km/h)*.
Service ceiling: 9350 ft *(2850 m)*.
Range: 361 nm *(670 km)*.
Role/Weapon systems: Observation with 3 Commando Brigade Air Squadron, Royal Marines. Sensors: None. Weapons: Normally unarmed.

GAZELLE   *1989*

Numbers/Type: 6 Westland Lynx AH Mk 1.
Operational speed: 140 kts *(259 km/h)*.
Service ceiling: 10 600 ft *(3230 m)*.
Range: 340 nm *(630 km)*.
Role/Weapon systems: Military general purpose and anti-tank with 3 Commando Brigade Air Squadron, Royal Marines. Sensors: None. Weapons: Up to 8 Hughes TOW anti-tank missiles.

LYNX AH Mk 1   *1989*

Numbers/Type: 1 Westland/Agusta EH 101 Merlin.
Operational speed: 160 kts *(296 km/h)*.
Service ceiling: 15 000 ft *(4572 m)*.
Range: 550 nm *(1019 km)*.
Role/Weapon systems: Primary anti-submarine role with secondary anti-surface and troop carrying capabilities. Contract for 44 signed 9 October 1991 for delivery from 1996. Sensors: Ferranti Blue Kestrel radar, Ferranti Flash dipping sonar, sonobuoy acoustic processor AQS-903, Racal Orange Reaper ESM, ECM. Weapons: ASW; 4 Stingray torpedoes or Mk 11 depth bombs. ASV; 4 Sea Skua or replacement, capability for guidance of ship-launched SSM.

MERLIN   *1991*

LAND-BASED MARITIME AIRCRAFT (FRONT LINE)

Note: All Air Force manned.

Numbers/Type: 26 Hawker Siddeley Nimrod MR 2/2P.
Operational speed: 500 kts *(926 km/h)*.
Service ceiling: 42 000 ft *(12 800 m)*.
Range: 5000 nm *(9265 km)*.
Role/Weapon systems: Primarily ASW but with ASV, OTHT and control potential at long range from shore bases; peacetime duties include SAR, maritime surveillance. Sensors: THORN EMI Searchwater radar, ECM, ESM, cameras, MAD, sonobuoys, AQS-901 processor. Weapons: ASW; 6.1 tons of Stingray torpedoes or depth bombs or mines. ASV; 4 × Harpoon missiles. Self-defence; 4 × AIM-9L Sidewinder.

Numbers/Type: 7 Boeing E-3D Sentry AEW Mk 1.
Operational speed: 460 kts *(853 km/h)*.
Service ceiling: 36 000 ft *(10 973 m)*.
Range: 870 nm *(1610 km)*.
Role/Weapon systems: Air defence early warning aircraft with secondary role to provide coastal AEW for the Fleet; six hours endurance at the range given above. Sensors: Westinghouse APY-2 surveillance radar, Bendix weather radar, Mk XII IFF, Yellow Gate, ESM, ECM. Weapons: Unarmed.

MINE WARFARE FORCES

13 HUNT CLASS (MINESWEEPERS/MINEHUNTERS—COASTAL)

Name	No	Builders	Commissioned
BRECON	M 29	Vosper Thornycroft, Woolston	21 Mar 1980
LEDBURY	M 30	Vosper Thornycroft, Woolston	11 June 1981
CATTISTOCK	M 31	Vosper Thornycroft, Woolston	16 June 1982
COTTESMORE	M 32	Yarrow Shipbuilders, Glasgow	24 June 1983
BROCKLESBY	M 33	Vosper Thornycroft, Woolston	3 Feb 1983
MIDDLETON	M 34	Yarrow Shipbuilders, Glasgow	15 Aug 1984
DULVERTON	M 35	Vosper Thornycroft, Woolston	4 Nov 1983
BICESTER	M 36	Vosper Thornycroft, Woolston	20 Mar 1986
CHIDDINGFOLD	M 37	Vosper Thornycroft, Woolston	10 Aug 1984
ATHERSTONE	M 38	Vosper Thornycroft, Woolston	30 Jan 1987
HURWORTH	M 39	Vosper Thornycroft, Woolston	2 July 1985
BERKELEY	M 40	Vosper Thornycroft, Woolston	14 Jan 1988
QUORN	M 41	Vosper Thornycroft, Woolston	21 Apr 1989

Displacement, tons: 615 light; 750 full load
Dimensions, feet (metres): 187 wl; 197 oa × 32.8 × 9.5 (keel); 11.2 (screws) *(57; 60 × 10 × 2.9; 3.4)*
Main machinery: 2 Ruston-Paxman 9-59K Deltic diesels; 1900 hp *(1.42 MW)*; 1 Deltic Type 9-55B diesel for pulse generator and auxiliary drive; 780 hp *(582 kW)*; 2 shafts; bow thruster
Speed, knots: 15 diesels; 8 hydraulic drive. **Range, miles:** 1500 at 12 kts
Complement: 45 (6 officers)

Guns: 1 Oerlikon/BMARC 30 mm/75 DS 30B; 65° elevation; 650 rounds/minute to 10 km *(5.4 nm)* anti-surface; 3 km *(1.6 nm)* anti-aircraft; weight of shell 0.36 kg. Replaced Bofors 40 mm.
2 Oerlikon/BMARC 20 mm GAM-CO1 (enhancement); 55° elevation; 900 rounds/minute to 2 km.
2—7.62 mm MGs.
Countermeasures: Decoys: 2 Wallop Barricade Mk III; 6 sets of triple barrels per mounting.
2 Irvin Replica RF; passive decoys.
ESM: MEL Matilda E (enhancement); Marconi Mentor A (in some).
Combat data systems: CAAIS DBA 4 action data automation.
Radars: Navigation: Kelvin Hughes Type 1006; I band.
Sonars: Plessey 193M Mod 1; hull-mounted; minehunting; 100/300 kHz.
Mil Cross mine avoidance sonar; hull-mounted; active; high frequency.
Type 2059 addition to track PAP 104/105.

Programmes: A class of MCM Vessels combining both hunting and sweeping capabilities.
Modernisation: Ten PAP 105 were acquired in 1988-89 to replace the 104s. They have a range of 600 m *(1968 ft)* down to 300 m *(984 ft)* depth and a speed of 6 kts; weight 700 kg. 30 mm gun has replaced the Bofors 40 mm. Racal Mk 53 navigation system ordered in August 1990 for all ships. Mid-life update planned to include VDS sonar, Nautis command system and a replacement PAP or mine disposal UUV. ADI AMASS influence sweep may be included.
Structure: Hulls of GRP.
Operational: Two PAP 104/105 remotely controlled submersibles, MS 14 magnetic loop, Sperry MSSA Mk 1 Towed Acoustic Generator and conventional Mk 8 Oropesa sweeps. For operational deployments fitted with enhanced weapons systems, Inmarsat SATCOMs and some have the SCARAB remote-control floating mine towing device which helps the safe destruction of moored mines once they have been cut from their moorings.

QUORN *10/1993, G Toremans*

DULVERTON *7/1993, H M Steele*

5 RIVER CLASS (MINESWEEPERS/PATROL CRAFT)

Name	No	Builders	Commissioned
BLACKWATER	M 2008	Richards Ltd (GY)	5 July 1985
ITCHEN	M 2009	Richards Ltd (L)	12 Oct 1985
ORWELL	M 2011	Richards Ltd (GY)	27 Nov 1985
SPEY	M 2013	Richards Ltd (L)	4 Apr 1986
ARUN	M 2014	Richards Ltd (L)	29 Aug 1986

Displacement, tons: 890 full load
Dimensions, feet (metres): 156 × 34.5 × 9.5 *(47.5 × 10.5 × 2.9)*
Main machinery: 2 Ruston 6RKC diesels; 3100 hp *(2.3 MW)* sustained; 2 shafts
Speed, knots: 14. **Range, miles:** 4500 at 10 kts
Complement: 30 (7 officers)

Guns: 1 Bofors 40 mm/60 Mk 3; 80° elevation; 120 rounds/minute to 10 km *(5.4 nm)* anti-surface; 3 km *(1.6 nm)* anti-aircraft; weight of shell 0.89 kg.
Radars: Navigation: Two Racal Decca TM 1226C; I band.

Programmes: First ordered 23 September 1982. All built at Lowestoft and Great Yarmouth. Three more planned to be built for Fishery Protection Squadron to replace Ton class but the requirement was cancelled in 1990.
Structure: Steel hulled for deep team sweeping. There have been problems with upper-deck corrosion in some ships. 40 mm guns may be replaced by 30 mm.
Operational: The remainder of a class of 12 built primarily as EDATS wire sweep minesweepers manned by the RNR. Half of the class have paid off after less than 10 years service, as part of a cost cutting exercise, and the remainder are employed in the Northern Ireland Squadron except for *Orwell* which relieves *Wilton* as the BRNC training ship in September 1994.

BLACKWATER *6/1993, Wright & Logan*

5 + 4 (3) SANDOWN CLASS (MINEHUNTERS)

Name	No	Builders	Launched	Commissioned
SANDOWN	M 101	Vosper Thornycroft, Woolston	16 Apr 1988	9 June 1989
INVERNESS	M 102	Vosper Thornycroft, Woolston	27 Feb 1990	24 Jan 1991
CROMER	M 103	Vosper Thornycroft, Woolston	6 Oct 1990	7 Apr 1992
WALNEY	M 104	Vosper Thornycroft, Woolston	25 Nov 1991	20 Feb 1993
BRIDPORT	M 105	Vosper Thornycroft, Woolston	30 July 1992	6 Nov 1993

Displacement, tons: 450 standard; 484 full load
Dimensions, feet (metres): 172.2 × 34.4 × 7.5 *(52.5 × 10.5 × 2.3)*
Main machinery: 2 Paxman Valenta 6RP200E diesels; 1500 hp *(1.12 MW)* sustained; Voith-Schneider propulsion; 2 shafts; 2 Schottel bow thrusters
Speed, knots: 13 diesels; 6.5 electric drive. **Range, miles:** 3000 at 12 kts
Complement: 34 (5 officers) plus 6 spare berths

Guns: 1 Oerlikon/DES 30 mm/75 DS 30B; 65° elevation; 650 rounds/minute to 10 km *(5.4 nm)* anti-surface; 3 km *(1.6 nm)* anti-aircraft; weight of shell 0.36 kg.
Countermeasures: Decoys: 2 Wallop Barricade (to be fitted for deployment).
Combat data systems: Plessey Nautis M action data automation.
Radars: Navigation: Kelvin Hughes Type 1007; I band.
Sonars: Marconi Type 2093; VDS; VLF-VHF multi-function with five arrays; mine search and classification.

Programmes: A class designed for hunting and destroying mines and for operating in deep and exposed waters. Complements the Hunt class. On 9 January 1984 the Vosper Thornycroft design for this class was approved. First one ordered August 1985, laid down 2 February 1987. Four further ships ordered 23 July 1987. A second batch was to have been ordered in 1990 but these were deferred in 1991. Tenders again put out on 1 December 1993 for an order for four in 1994 with an option on three more.
Structure: GRP hull. Combines vectored thrust units with bow thrusters and Remote Control Mine Disposal System (RCMDS). The sonar is deployed from a well in the hull.
Operational: ECA mine disposal system, two PAP 104 Mk 5. These craft can carry two mine wire cutters, a charge of 100 kg and a manipulator with TV/projector. Control cables are either 1000 m (high capacity) or 2000 m (low capacity) and the craft can dive to 300 m at 6 kts with an endurance of 5 × 20 minute missions. Racal Hyperfix. Decca Navigation Mk 21. Allocation: All to 3rd MCM Squadron.
Sales: Three plus an option of three more to Saudi Arabia. Short listed for Australia in early 1993.

BRIDPORT *7/1993, H M Steele*

INVERNESS *5/1993, Wright & Logan*

AMPHIBIOUS WARFARE FORCES

Note: Further amphibious ships and craft covered in RFA and RLC (ex-RCT) sections. These include a Helicopter Support Ship, five LSLs, two LCLs and nine LCTs.

0 + 1 HELICOPTER CARRIER (LPH)

Name	No	Builders	Laid down	Launched	Commissioned
OCEAN	—	Vickers Shipbuilding/Kvaerner Govan	May 1994	June 1996	Sep 1997

OCEAN   *(not to scale), Ian Sturton*

Displacement, tons: 20 000 full load
Dimensions, feet (metres): 666 oa; 633.2 pp × 107 × 21.3
  (203; 193 × 32.6 × 6.6)
Main machinery: 2 diesels; 2 shafts; bow thruster
Speed, knots: 18. **Range, miles:** 8000 at 15 kts
Complement: 255 plus 180 aircrew plus 480 Marines
Military lift: 4 LCVP (on davits); vehicles and equipment for most
  of a marine commando battalion

Guns: 8 Oerlikon/BMARC 30 mm/75 (4 twin) GCM ❶.
  3 Vulcan Phalanx Mk 15 ❷.
Countermeasures: Decoys: 8 Sea Gnat launchers ❸ for chaff/IR
  flares.
  ESM: THORN EMI UAT; intercept.
  ECM: THORN EMI Type 675(2); jammer.
Combat data systems: Ferranti ADAWS 2000; Link 11 and 16
  (in due course); SATCOM ❹; Merlin computer link.
Radars: Air/surface search: Plessey Type 996 ❺; E/F band.
  Surface search: 2 Kelvin Hughes Type 1007 ❻; I band.

Helicopters: 12 Sea King/Merlin.

Programmes: In 1987 five joint venture consortia were invited to
  prepare tenders. Three tenders submitted in July 1989 by
  Swan Hunter/Ferranti International Signal/CAP, Tyne Ship-
  repairers/Sea Containers/Racal Marine Systems, and Vickers
  Shipbuilding and Engineering/Cammel Laird with Three Keys
  Marine. These tenders were then allowed to lapse and a further
  invitation for designs was issued in February 1992. Swan Hunter and VSEL responded in October 1992 and the contract was
  awarded to VSEL on 11 May 1993. The hull is building on the
  Clyde by Kvaerner Govan and will be sailed under its own
  power to Vickers at Barrow for the installation of military
  equipment.
Structure: The hull form is based on the Invincible class with a
  modified superstructure. The deck will be strong enough to
  take Chinook helicopters. Six landing and six parking spots are
  required for the aircraft. Armament to consist of light guns
  only. The combat data system will be compatible with other
  frontline RN ships.
Operational: The LPH will provide a helicopter lift and assault
  capability. The prime role of the vessel will be embarking, supporting and operating a squadron of helicopters (currently
  Westland Sea King HC4) and carrying most of a Royal Marine
  Commando including vehicles, arms and ammunition. A sec-

OCEAN (artist's impression)   *1993, VSEL*

ond of class is preferred to meet the operational requirement
but linkage with the new LPDs gives a single unit more cred-
ibility than it would have without the LPDs. Sea Harriers can be
carried but not supported. Up to 800 marines could be
embarked in an emergency using austere accommodation.

Opinion: This ship survived the latest round of cuts in the Navy
because of the obvious shortcomings of RFA *Argus* which was
trying to perform the role in the Adriatic in 1993. If the navy is
to retain an amphibious warfare capability, replacements for
the elderly LPDs are equally urgent.

0 + (2) ASSAULT SHIPS (LPD(R))

Displacement, tons: 13 500 full load
Dimensions, feet (metres): 551 oa; 507.4 wl × 86.9 × 23
  (168; 154.7 × 26.5 × 7)
Main machinery: Diesel or diesel-electric; 2 shafts
Speed, knots: 18
Complement: 320
Military lift: 300 troops; overload 600 troops; 70 support
  vehicles; 4 LCU (dock); 4 LCVP (davits)

Guns: CIWS supported by portable close range weapons.
Countermeasures: Decoys: 4 Sea Gnat launchers for chaff.
  ESM/ECM.
Combat data systems: ADAWS 2000 or SSCS.
Radars: Air/surface search. Fire-control.

Helicopters: Platform for 2 medium.

Programmes: After surveys had shown that *Intrepid* could not
  again be fully refurbished, a decision was taken in mid-1991 to

LPD(R)   *(Scale 1 : 1500), Ian Sturton*

replace both existing LPDs by similar ships. Project definition
studies by YARD finally completed in early 1994 after a year's
delay caused by attempts to introduce commercial shipbuilding standards without compromising safety. Government
statements indicated an intention to invite tenders for the first
of class in 1993 with a projected in-service date of 1998 but

this has now been delayed to 1994 with an order in 1995 for
completion at the end of the decade. The second would follow
two years later.
Structure: The illustrative design shown in the drawing has
emerged from project definition. Two helicopter landing spots.
Substantial command and control facilities will be included.

LPD(R) (artist's impression)   *1993, BAe Sema YARD*

2 ASSAULT SHIPS (LPD)

Name	No
FEARLESS	L 10
INTREPID	L 11

Builders	Laid down	Launched	Commissioned
Harland & Wolff, Belfast	25 July 1962	19 Dec 1963	25 Nov 1965
John Brown, Clydebank	19 Dec 1962	25 June 1964	11 Mar 1967

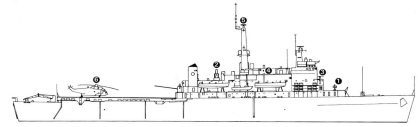

Displacement, tons: 11 060 standard; 12 120 full load; 16 950 dock flooded

Dimensions, feet (metres): 500 wl; 520 oa × 80 × 20.5 (32 flooded) *(152.4; 158.5 × 24.4 × 6.2 (9.8))*

Main machinery: 2 Babcock & Wilcox boilers; 550 psi *(38.66 kg/cm sq)*; 850°F *(454°C)*; 2 English Electric turbines; 22 000 hp *(16.4 MW)*; 2 shafts

Speed, knots: 21. **Range, miles:** 5000 at 20 kts

Complement: 550 (50 officers) plus 22 (3 officers) air group plus 88 (3 officers) RM

Military lift: 380-400 troops; overload 1000 troops; 15 MBTs; 7—3 ton trucks; 20¼ ton trucks (specimen load)
Landing craft: 4 LCU Mk 9 (dock); 4 LCVP Mk 3 (davits)

Missiles: SAM: 2 Shorts Seacat GWS 20 quad launchers ❶; optical guidance to 5 km *(2.7 nm)*.

Guns: 2 GE/GD 20 mm Mk 15 Vulcan Phalanx ❷; 6 barrels per launcher; 3000 rounds/minute combined to 1.5 km.
4 Oerlikon/BMARC 30 mm/75 GCM-AO3 (2 twin) (L 11); 80° elevation; 650 rounds/minute to 10 km *(5.4 nm)* anti-surface; 3 km *(1.6 nm)* anti-aircraft; weight of shell 0.36 kg.
2 Oerlikon/BMARC 20 mm GAM-BO1 ❸; 55° elevation; 1000 rounds/minute to 2 km.

Countermeasures: Decoys: 4 Marconi Sea Gnat 130 mm 6-barrelled fixed launchers for chaff and IR flares ❹.

ESM: Marconi Mentor A; radar warning.

Combat data systems: Plessey Nautis M.

Fire control: GWS 20 optical directors for Seacat.

Radars: Surface search: Plessey Type 994 ❺; E/F band.
Navigation: Kelvin Hughes Type 1006; I band.

Helicopters: Platform for up to 4 Westland Sea King HC 4 ❻.

Programmes: In 1981 their impending deletion was announced. In February 1982 it was reported that they were to be reprieved, a fortunate decision in view of the vital part played by both in the 1982 Falklands' campaign.

Modernisation: *Intrepid* refitted 1984-85. *Fearless* completed a two year refit in November 1990 with two Vulcan Phalanx 20 mm gun mountings and new decoy launchers. *Intrepid* similarly modernised by being fitted for Phalanx and Sea Gnat by December 1993, while still in reserve. Masthead height has been increased by 12 ft.

Structure: The two funnels are staggered across the beam of the ship. Landing craft are floated through the open stern by flooding compartments of the ship and lowering her in the water. They are able to deploy tanks, vehicles and men and have seakeeping qualities much superior to those of tank landing ships as well as greater speed and range. The helicopter platform is also the deckhead of the dock and has two landing spots.

Operational: Each ship is fitted out as a Naval Assault Group/Brigade Headquarters with an Assault Operations Room from which naval and military personnel can mount and control the progress of an assault operation. *Intrepid* is in reserve, although regularly maintained.

FEARLESS

(Scale 1 : 1500), Ian Sturton

FEARLESS

8/1992, H M Steele

FEARLESS

4/1993, Maritime Photographic

12 LCU Mk 9

L 702   L 704-711   L 713-715

Displacement, tons: 89 light; 160 full load
Dimensions, feet (metres): 90.2 × 21.5 × 5 *(27.5 × 6.8 × 1.6)*
Main machinery: 2 Paxman or Dorman diesels; 474 hp *(354 kW)* sustained; 2 shafts; Kort nozzles
Speed, knots: 10. **Range, miles:** 300 at 9 kts
Military lift: 1 MBT or 70 tons of vehicles/stores
Radars: Navigation: I band.

Comment: Operated by the Royal Marines. Four in each LPD. *L 710* is a trials craft for the next generation LCU Mk 10. Fitted in 1993 with two Schottel flush hulled propulsors.

LCU Mk 9   *6/1993, Maritime Photographic*

21 LCVP Mk 4

LCVPs 8031, 8401-8420

Displacement, tons: 10.5 light; 16 full load
Dimensions, feet (metres): 43.8 × 10.9 × 2.8 *(13.4 × 3.3 × 0.8)*
Main machinery: 2 Perkins T6.3544 diesels; 290 hp *(216 kW)*; 2 shafts
Speed, knots: 16 (light). **Range, miles:** 150 at 14 kts
Complement: 3
Military lift: 20 Arctic equipped troops or 5.5 tons

Comment: Built by Souters and McTays. Introduced into service in 1986 as a replacement for the LCVP Mk 3. Fitted with removable arctic canopies across welldeck. Operated by the Royal Marines. *LCVPs 8402, 8409, 8419* and *8420* built for the Royal Logistic Corps. These serve in rotation between the Falklands and UK.

LCVP Mk 4   *8/1992, H M Steele*

4 GRIFFON 2000 TDX(M) (HOVERCRAFT)

Displacement, tons: 6.8 full load
Dimensions, feet (metres): 36.1 × 15.1 *(11 × 4.6)*
Main machinery: 1 Deutz BF8L-513 diesel; 320 hp *(239 kW)*
Speed, knots: 33. **Range, miles:** 300 at 25 kts
Complement: 2
Military lift: 16 troops plus equipment or 2 tons
Guns: 1—7.62 mm MG.
Radars: Navigation: I band.

Comment: Ordered 26 April 1993. First pair delivered 23 November 1993. Aluminium hulls. Capable of being embarked in an LCU. Speed indicated is at sea state 3 with a full load.

GRIFFON 2000   *12/1993, G Hydes*

0 + 2 HALMATIC CRAFT

Comment: 15 m high-speed craft ordered on 3 September 1993. Based on a Fabio Buzzi design with Seatek engines these are low profile, very fast boats for Special Forces. More may be ordered in due course.

3 TYPES OF SMALL CRAFT

Rigid Inflatable Boat Osborne/Halmatic Arctic 22

Comment: Of 1.4 tons and 7.2 m *(23.5 ft)*; twin 140 hp *(104 kW)* or Suzuki outboard motors; 40+ kts; range 30 nm (normal tanks); carry 15 troops or 2475 lbs stores. GRP hull, deck and command console with 20 in diameter neoprene tube.

Rigid Inflatable Boat Osborne/Halmatic Pacific 22

Comment: 2.25 tons and 6.8 m *(22.2 ft)*; Ford Mermaid 4-cyl; turbocharged diesel 155 hp *(115.6 kW)* max; 26 kts; range 85 nm; carry 15 troops or 2475 lbs stores. Construction similar to Arctic 22.

Rigid raiding craft

Comment: RRC Mk 1: 0.87 tons and 5.2 m *(17.2 ft)*; powered by 140 hp *(104 kW)* or Suzuki outboard; 30+ kts fully laden; range 50 nm; carry coxswain plus 8 troops or 2000 lbs. GRP cathedral hull. Being replaced.
RRC Mk 2: 1.31 tons and 6.5 m *(21.3 ft)*; powered by either a single or twin Suzuki 140 hp *(104 kW)* outboard; 30 kts fully laden (50 light); carry 10 troops plus 1500 lbs of equipment or 20 troops. First eight delivered in December 1992, 16 more in 1993. Built by FBM Workboats, Cowes.

PACIFIC 22   *1989*

RRC Mk 2   *1993*

ROYAL YACHT

Name	No	Builders	Laid down	Launched	Commissioned
BRITANNIA	A 00	John Brown, Clydebank	July 1952	16 Apr 1953	14 Jan 1954

Displacement, tons: 3990 light; 4961 full load
Measurement, tons: 5769 gross
Dimensions, feet (metres): 412.2 × 55 × 17 *(125.7 × 16.8 × 5.2)*
Main machinery: 2 boilers; 2 turbines; 12 000 hp *(8.95 MW)*; 2 shafts
Speed, knots: 21; 22.5 trials. **Range, miles:** 2800 at 20 kts; 3200 at 18 kts; 3675 at 14 kts
Complement: 277 (21 officers)
Radars: Navigation: Two Kelvin Hughes Type 1006; I band.

Comment: Designed for use by Her Majesty The Queen in peacetime as the Royal Yacht but can be converted as a medium sized naval hospital ship. Construction conformed to mercantile practice. Fitted with Denny-Brown single fin stabilisers to reduce roll in bad weather from 20 to 6 degrees. To pass under the bridges of the St. Lawrence Seaway when she visited Canada, the top 20 ft of her mainmast and the radio aerial on her foremast were hinged in November 1958 so that they could be lowered as required. 1984 refit included conversion to diesel fuel. SATNAV fitted. Further refit carried out at Devonport 1986-87 which has extended her life by 10-15 years. Oil fuel, 330 tons (510 with auxiliary fuel tanks). Ranges given are without auxiliary fuel tanks. Complement may be reduced to around 225.

BRITANNIA   *5/1993, Camil Busquets i Vilanova*

PATROL FORCES

Note: Four River class minesweepers are used as patrol craft.

1 ANTARCTIC PATROL SHIP

Name	No	Builders	Commissioned
ENDURANCE	A 171	Ulstein Hatlo, Norway	21 Nov 1991
(ex-*Polar Circle*)	(ex-A 176)		

Displacement, tons: 6500 full load
Dimensions, feet (metres): 298.6 × 57.4 × 21.3 *(91 × 17.9 × 6.5)*
Main machinery: 2 Bergen BRM8 diesels, 8160 hp(m) *(6 MW)* sustained; 1 shaft; cp prop; bow and stern thrusters
Speed, knots: 15. **Range, miles:** 6500 at 12 kts
Complement: 112 (15 officers) plus 14 Royal Marines
Radars: Surface search: Furuno; E/F band.
Navigation: Kelvin Hughes Type 1006; I band.
Helicopters: 2 Westland Lynx HAS 3.

Comment: Leased initially in late 1991 and then bought outright in early 1992 as support ship and guard vessel for the British Antarctic Survey. Hull is painted red. Inmarsat and SATCOM fitted. Main machinery is resiliently mounted. Ice-strengthened hull capable of breaking one metre thick ice at 3 kts. Accommodation is to standards previously unknown in the Royal Navy. Name and pennant number changed during refit in mid-1992.

ENDURANCE   *8/1993, W Sartori*

6 ISLAND CLASS (OFFSHORE PATROL VESSELS)

Name	No	Builders	Commissioned
ANGLESEY	P 277	Hall Russell, Aberdeen	1 June 1979
ALDERNEY	P 278	Hall Russell, Aberdeen	6 Oct 1979
GUERNSEY	P 297	Hall Russell, Aberdeen	28 Oct 1977
SHETLAND	P 298	Hall Russell, Aberdeen	14 July 1977
ORKNEY	P 299	Hall Russell, Aberdeen	25 Feb 1977
LINDISFARNE	P 300	Hall Russell, Aberdeen	3 Mar 1978

Displacement, tons: 925 standard; 1260 full load
Dimensions, feet (metres): 176 wl; 195.3 oa × 36 × 15 *(53.7; 59.5 × 11 × 4.5)*
Main machinery: 2 Ruston 12RKC diesels; 5640 hp *(4.21 MW)* sustained; 1 shaft
Speed, knots: 16.5. **Range, miles:** 7000 at 12 kts
Complement: 39

Guns: 1 Bofors 40 mm Mk 3. 1 DES/Oerlikon 30 mm/75 Mk 1 (P 297). 2 FN 7.62 mm MGs.
Countermeasures: ESM: Orange Crop; intercept.
Combat data systems: Racal CANE DEA-1 action data automation.
Radars: Navigation: Kelvin Hughes Type 1006; I band.

Programmes: Order for first five announced 11 February 1975. Order placed 2 July 1975. Two more of class ordered 21 October 1977.
Structure: The earlier ships of this class were retrofitted and the remainder built with enlarged bilge keels to damp down their motion in heavy weather. Fitted with stabilisers and water ballast arrangement.
Operational: Operate as the Offshore Division of the Fishery Protection Squadron. Can carry small RM detachment and two Avon Sea Rider semi-rigid craft with 85 hp motor, for boarding. One paid off in December 1993 and sold to Bangladesh.

GUERNSEY   *9/1993, W Sartori*

1 BIRD and 1 SEAL CLASS (LARGE PATROL CRAFT)

Name	No	Builders	Commissioned
REDPOLE (ex-*Sea Otter*)	P 259	Brooke Marine, Lowestoft	4 Aug 1967
KINGFISHER	P 260	Dunston, Hessle	8 Oct 1975

Displacement, tons: 194 (218, P 259) full load
Dimensions, feet (metres): 120 × 23.6 × 6.5 *(36.6 × 7.2 × 2)*
Main machinery: 2 Paxman 16YJCM diesels; 4200 hp *(3.13 MW)*; 2 shafts
Speed, knots: 21. **Range, miles:** 2000 at 14 kts
Complement: 28 (3 officers, 10 RM)
Guns: 2 FN 7.62 mm MGs.

Comment: *Kingfisher* launched 20 September 1974; *Redpole* transferred by RAF March 1985. Both completed extended refits in 1986. Bird class based on the Seal class RAF rescue launches with some improvement to sea-keeping qualities by cutting down topweight. Both deployed to Northern Ireland. *Redpole* is planned to pay off in July 1994, *Kingfisher* by the end of the year.

KINGFISHER   *8/1993, van Ginderen Collection*

2 CASTLE CLASS (OFFSHORE PATROL VESSELS Mk 2)

Name	No	Builders	Commissioned
LEEDS CASTLE	P 258	Hall Russell, Aberdeen	27 Oct 1981
DUMBARTON CASTLE	P 265	Hall Russell, Aberdeen	26 Mar 1982

Displacement, tons: 1427 full load
Dimensions, feet (metres): 265.7 × 37.7 × 11.8 *(81 × 11.5 × 3.6)*
Main machinery: 2 Ruston 12RKC diesels; 5640 hp *(4.21 MW)* sustained; 2 shafts; cp props
Speed, knots: 19.5. **Range, miles:** 10 000 at 12 kts
Complement: 45 (6 officers) plus austerity accommodation for 25 Royal Marines
Guns: 1 DES/Lawrence Scott Mk 1 30 mm/75; 80° elevation; 650 rounds/minute to 10 km *(5.4 nm)*; weight of shell 0.36 kg.
Mines: Can lay mines.
Countermeasures: Decoys: 2 or 4 Plessey Shield 102 mm 6-tubed chaff launchers.
Combat data systems: Racal CANE DEA-3 action data automation; SATCOM.
Fire control: Radamec 2000 series optronic director.
Radars: Surface search: Plessey Type 944; E/F band.
Navigation: Kelvin Hughes Type 1006; I band.
Helicopters: Platform for operating Sea King or Lynx.

Comment: Started as a private venture. Ordered 8 August 1980. *Leeds Castle* launched 29 October 1980; *Dumbarton Castle* 3 June 1981. Design includes an ability to lay mines. Inmarsat commercial SATCOM terminals fitted. Two Avon Sea Rider high-speed craft are embarked. *Dumbarton Castle* is the South Atlantic patrol ship in to 1994. *Leeds Castle* belongs to the Fishery Protection Squadron Offshore Division.

LEEDS CASTLE   *6/1993, Maritime Photographic*

3 PEACOCK CLASS (LARGE PATROL CRAFT)

Name	No	Builders	Commissioned
PEACOCK	P 239	Hall Russell, Aberdeen	14 July 1984
PLOVER	P 240	Hall Russell, Aberdeen	20 July 1984
STARLING	P 241	Hall Russell, Aberdeen	10 Aug 1984

Displacement, tons: 690 full load
Dimensions, feet (metres): 204.1 × 32.8 × 8.9 *(62.6 × 10 × 2.7)*
Main machinery: 2 Crossley Pielstick 18 PA6 V 280 diesels; 14 000 hp(m) *(10.6 MW)* sustained; 2 shafts; 1 retractable Schottel prop; 181 hp *(135 kW)*
Speed, knots: 25. **Range, miles:** 2500 at 17 kts
Complement: 31 (6 officers) plus 7 spare berths
Guns: 1—3 in *(76 mm)*/62 OTO Melara compact; 85° elevation; 85 rounds/minute to 16 km *(8.6 nm)* anti-surface; 12 km *(6.5 nm)* anti-aircraft; weight of shell 6 kg.
4 FN 7.62 mm MGs.
Fire control: British Aerospace Sea Archer for 76 mm gun.
Radars: Navigation: Kelvin Hughes Type 1006; I band.

Comment: This class replaced the elderly Ton class in Hong Kong, the colony's government paying 75 per cent of the cost. All ordered 30 June 1981. *Peacock* launched 1 December 1982, *Plover* on 12 April 1983, *Starling* on 11 September 1983. All sailed for Hong Kong September 1984-July 1985. Carry two Sea Riders and a Fast Pursuit craft. Have telescopic cranes, loiter drive and replenishment at sea equipment. *Swallow* and *Swift* sold to Ireland 21 November 1988. The remainder is planned to remain in Hong Kong until 1997.

PLOVER   *7/1993, van Ginderen Collection*

14 ARCHER CLASS (TRAINING and PATROL CRAFT)

ARCHER P 264	DASHER P 280	EXAMPLE A 153
BITER P 270	PUNCHER P 291	EXPLORER A 154
SMITER P 272	CHARGER P 292	EXPRESS A 163
PURSUER P 273	RANGER P 293	EXPLOIT A 167
BLAZER P 279	TRUMPETER P 294	

Displacement, tons: 49 full load
Dimensions, feet (metres): 68.2 × 19 × 5.9 *(20.8 × 5.8 × 1.8)*
Main machinery: 2 RR CV 12 M800T; 1590 hp *(1.19 MW)*; 2 shafts
Speed, knots: 22. **Range, miles:** 550 at 15 kts
Complement: 10-14
Guns: 1 Oerlikon 20 mm (can be fitted).
Radars: Navigation: Racal Decca 1216; I band.

Comment: Ordered from Watercraft Ltd, Shoreham. Commissioning dates: *Archer,* August 1985; *Example,* September 1985; *Explorer,* January 1986; *Biter* and *Smiter,* February 1986. The remaining nine were incomplete when Watercraft went into liquidation in 1986 and were towed to Portsmouth for completion by Vosper Thornycroft. Commissioning dates (all 1988): *Pursuer,* February; *Blazer,* March; *Express* and *Dasher,* May; *Charger,* June; *Puncher,* July; *Exploit,* August; *Ranger* and *Trumpeter,* September. Initially allocated for RNR training but underused in that role and now employed: *Ranger* and *Trumpeter* as Gibraltar guard ships; remainder University Naval Units (URNU)—*Puncher* (London), *Blazer* (Southampton), *Smiter* (Glasgow), *Charger* (Liverpool), *Dasher* (Bristol), *Archer* (Aberdeen), *Pursuer* (Sussex) and *Biter* (Manchester and Salford). The four ex-RNXS ships (A 153, 154, 163 and 167) are to be allocated to Universities in 1994. Similar craft building for the Indian Coast Guard.

CHARGER   5/1993, Maritime Photographic

TRAINING SHIPS

1 DARTMOUTH TRAINING SHIP

Name	No	Builders	Commissioned
WILTON	M 1116	Vosper Thornycroft, Woolston	14 July 1973

Displacement, tons: 450 full load
Dimensions, feet (metres): 145 wl; 153 oa × 29.2 × 8.5 *(44.2; 46.3 × 8.9 × 2.5)*
Main machinery: 2 Napier Deltic 18-7A diesels; 3000 hp *(2.24 MW)*; 2 shafts
Speed, knots: 16. **Range, miles:** 2300 at 13 kts
Complement: 37 (5 officers)
Guns: 1 Bofors 40 mm/70 Mk 7; 90° elevation; 300 rounds/minute to 12 km *(6.5 nm)* anti-surface; 4 km *(2.2 nm)* anti-aircraft; weight of shell 0.96 kg.
Radars: Navigation: Kelvin Hughes Type 975; I/J band.
Sonars: Plessey Type 193M; hull-mounted; high frequency.

Comment: The world's first GRP warship. Laid down 7 August 1970 and launched on 18 January 1972. Similar to the Ton class minesweepers and fitted with reconditioned machinery and equipment from the scrapped *Derriton.* Twin active rudders. Used for seamanship and navigation training at the Naval College, Dartmouth. All minesweeping gear removed and a classroom has been built on the stern. Planned to be paid off and relieved by *Orwell* in September 1994.

WILTON   7/1993, Per Kornefeldt

1 NAVIGATION TRAINING VESSEL

NORTHELLA

Measurement, tons: 1535 grt
Dimensions, feet (metres): 226 × 61.7 × 20 *(68.9 × 12.7 × 6.1)*
Main machinery: 1 Mirlees diesel; 3246 hp *(2.39 MW)*; 1 shaft
Speed, knots: 16
Complement: 25

Comment: Having been taken up from trade in April 1982 to act as an auxiliary minesweeper in Falklands campaign (with four others) she was returned to her owners then taken up from trade again in October 1983 to act as target vessel. In 1985 became navigational training ship. Based at Portsmouth and now painted grey. She flies a Blue Ensign and is on charter until 1994 with NP 1020 embarked. Sister ship *Cordella* on charter to the Falkland Islands as a Fishery Patrol ship.

NORTHELLA   2/1993, Maritime Photographic

SURVEY SHIPS

Notes: (1) In addition to the ships listed below some work is done by chartered vessels with Naval Parties embarked. These include *Proud Seahorse* (of MFV type) which operates for the Hydrographer with Naval Party 1016 embarked and *Marine Explorer* with Naval Party 1008. These NPs are to be retained.
(2) The acquisition of two Hydrographic Survey vessels was projected for the mid-1990s. An invitation to tender designs was raised in July 1992 but has since been cancelled. Other possibilities include converted merchant hulls and Fleet Auxiliary status with a Naval Party embarked. The ships could be dual roled as MCMV tenders during deployments abroad. The requirement includes tasking for 320 days a year and the ability to maintain 13 kts in sea state 5.

MARINE EXPLORER   7/1992, van Ginderen Collection

PROUD SEAHORSE   8/1993

1 ROEBUCK CLASS

Name	No	Builders	Commissioned
ROEBUCK	A 130	Brooke Marine, Lowestoft	3 Oct 1986

Displacement, tons: 1059 light, 1431 full load
Dimensions, feet (metres): 210 × 42.6 × 13 *(63.9 × 13 × 4)*
Main machinery: 4 Mirrlees Blackstone ESL8 Mk 1 diesels; 3040 hp *(2.27 MW)*; 2 shafts; cp props
Speed, knots: 15. **Range, miles:** 4000 at 10 kts
Complement: 46 (6 officers)

Comment: Designed for hydrographic surveys to full modern standards on UK continental shelf. Passive tank stabiliser; Hyperfix and transponder position fixing systems; Type 2033BB hull mounted, high definition, sector scanning sonar. Qubit SIPS I integrated navigation and survey system. Air-conditioned. Carries two 9 m surveying motor boats and one 4.5 m RIB. Expected to be sold in 1994-96.

ROEBUCK   9/1993, Hartmut Ehlers

2 BULLDOG CLASS

Name	No	Builders	Commissioned
BULLDOG	A 317	Brooke Marine, Lowestoft	21 Mar 1968
BEAGLE	A 319	Brooke Marine, Lowestoft	9 May 1968

Displacement, tons: 800 standard; 1088 full load
Dimensions, feet (metres): 189 × 36.8 × 12 *(57.6 × 11.2 × 3.7)*
Main machinery: 4 Lister-Blackstone ERS8M diesels; 2640 hp *(1.97 MW)*; 2 shafts; cp props
Speed, knots: 15. **Range, miles:** 4500 at 12 kts
Complement: 42 (5 officers)
Guns: Fitted for 2 Oerlikon 20 mm.

Comment: Originally designed for duty overseas, working in pairs although normally now employed in home waters. Built to commercial standards. Fitted with passive tank stabiliser, precision ranging radar, Hyper Fix system, automatic steering. Qubit SIPS II integrated navigation and survey system fitted in 1990. This allows chart processing in real time as the data is acquired. Air-conditioned throughout. Carry 9 m surveying motor-boat. *Bulldog* completed refit including new radar and UHF in early 1985. *Fox* sold in early 1989 and *Fawn* in 1991. The remaining pair is expected to pay off 1994-96.

BULLDOG   *5/1993, Maritime Photographic*

BEAGLE   *3/1992, J Partington*

Name	No	Builders	Commissioned
GLEANER	A 86	Emsworth Shipyard	5 Dec 1983

Displacement, tons: 22 full load
Dimensions, feet (metres): 48.6 × 15.4 × 4.3 *(14.8 × 4.7 × 1.3)*
Main machinery: 2 RR diesels; 524 hp *(391 kW)*; 1 Perkins 4-236 diesel; 72 hp *(54 kW)*; 3 shafts
Speed, knots: 14 diesels; 7 centre shaft only
Complement: 5 plus 1 spare bunk

Comment: This craft is prefixed HMSML—HM Survey Motor Launch.

GLEANER   *10/1987, W Sartori*

1 HECLA CLASS

Name	No	Builders	Commissioned
HECLA	A 133	Yarrow Shipbuilders, Blythswood	9 June 1965

Displacement, tons: 1915 light; 2733 full load
Measurement, tons: 2898 gross
Dimensions, feet (metres): 260.1 × 49.1 × 15.4 *(79.3 × 15 × 4.7)*
Main machinery: Diesel-electric; 3 Paxman 12YJCZ diesels; 3600 hp *(2.68 MW)* sustained; 3 generators; 1 motor; 2000 hp *(1.49 MW)*; 1 shaft; bow thruster
Speed, knots: 14. **Range, miles:** 12 000 at 11 kts
Complement: 115 (13 officers) plus 6 scientists
Guns: 2 Oerlikon 20 mm (can be fitted).
Radars: Navigation: Kelvin Hughes Type 1006; I band.
Helicopters: 1 Westland Lynx HAS 3.

Comment: The first Royal Navy ship to be designed with a combined oceanographical and hydrographic role. Of merchant ship design and similar in many respects to the Royal Research ship *Discovery*. The fore end of the superstructure incorporates a Land Rover garage and the after end a helicopter hangar with adjacent flight deck. Equipped with chartroom, drawing office and photographic studio; two laboratories, dry and wet; electrical, engineering and shipwright workshops, large storerooms, two 9 m surveying motor-boats and an oceanographic winch. Air-conditioned throughout. Converted in 1990/91 to the same standard as *Herald* for MCM support ship duties with an extended flight deck and a recompression chamber for clearance divers. One of the class sold to Indonesia in 1986, a second paid off in 1990.

HECLA   *10/1991, D & B Teague*

1 IMPROVED HECLA CLASS

Name	No	Builders	Commissioned
HERALD	A 138	Robb Caledon, Leith	31 Oct 1974

Displacement, tons: 2000 standard; 2945 full load
Dimensions, feet (metres): 259.1 × 49.2 × 16 *(79 × 15.4 × 4.9)*
Main machinery: Diesel-electric; 3 Paxman 12YJCZ diesels; 3600 hp *(2.68 MW)* sustained; 3 generators; 1 motor; 2000 hp *(1.49 MW)*; 1 shaft; bow thruster
Speed, knots: 14. **Range, miles:** 12 000 at 11 kts
Complement: 128 (12 officers)
Guns: 2 Oerlikon 20 mm (can be fitted).
Countermeasures: ESM: UAR 1; intercept.
Radars: Navigation: Kelvin Hughes Type 1006; I band.
Helicopters: 1 Westland Lynx HAS 3.

Comment: A later version of the Hecla class design. Laid down 9 November 1972. Launched 4 October 1973. Fitted with Hydroplot Satellite navigation system, computerised data logging, gravimeter, magnetometer, sonars, echo-sounders, an oceanographic winch, passive stabilisation tank and two 35 ft surveying motor-boats. Completed refit in January 1988 with a strengthened and extended flight deck for Lynx. Conducted trials of Scarab remote-controlled mine clearance device. Works in the North Norwegian Sea when not required as an MCM support ship.

HERALD   *4/1993, David Warren*

ROYAL FLEET AUXILIARY SERVICE

Headquarters' Appointment

RFA Type Commander:
Commodore R M Thorn

Personnel

1994: 2050 UK personnel; 33 Hong Kong Chinese

General

The Royal Fleet Auxiliary Service is a civilian-manned fleet under the command of the Commander in Chief Fleet from 1 April 1993. Its main task is to supply warships at sea with fuel, food, stores and ammunition. It also provides aviation platforms, amphibious support for the Navy and Marines and sea transport for Army units. All ships take part in operational sea training. An order in council on 30 November 1989 changed the status of the RFA service to government-owned vessels on non-commercial service.

Ships taken up from Trade (1 April 1994)

The following ships taken up from trade: *Proud Seahorse* and *Marine Explorer* operate in home waters under the Hydrographer; *Northella* in service for navigational training. *Oil Mariner* (supply), *St Brandan* (ferry), *Indomitable* (tug), all operate in the Falkland Islands; *Maersk Ascension* and *Maersk Gannet* as tankers to Ascension Island; *St Angus* as Gulf supply ship.

2 OL CLASS (LARGE FLEET TANKERS) (AO)

Name	No	Builders	Launched	Commissioned
OLWEN	A 122	Hawthorn Leslie, Hebburn-on-Tyne	10 July 1964	21 June 1965
OLNA	A 123	Hawthorn Leslie, Hebburn-on-Tyne	28 July 1965	1 Apr 1966

Displacement, tons: 9367 light; 36 000 full load
Measurement, tons: 25 100 dwt; 18 600 gross
Dimensions, feet (metres): 648 × 84 × 36.4
(197.5 × 25.6 × 11.1)
Main machinery: 2 Babcock & Wilcox boilers; 750 psi
(52.75 kg/cm sq); 950°F (510°C); Pametrada turbines;
26 500 hp (19.77 MW); 1 shaft
Speed, knots: 20
Complement: 95 RFA (accommodation for 40 RN)
Cargo capacity: 16 000 tons diesel; 125 tons lub oil; 2750 tons
Avcat; 375 tons fresh water
Guns: 2 Oerlikon 20 mm. 2—7.62 mm MGs.
Countermeasures: 2 Corvus chaff launchers.
Radars: Surface search and Navigation: 2 Kelvin Hughes; I band.
Helicopters: 2 Westland Sea King HAS 6.

Comment: Designed for underway replenishment both alongside and astern (fuel only) or by helicopter. Specially strengthened for operations in ice, fully air-conditioned. *Olna* has a
transverse bow thrust unit for improved manoeuvrability in
confined waters and an improved design of replenishment-at-
sea systems. Inmarsat SATCOM system fitted. Hangar accommodation for two helicopters port side of funnel.
    Feasibility studies completed in early 1994 for two new
Fleet tankers with planned acceptance dates in 2001. A third is
to be chartered from January 1998.

OLWEN   *6/1993*

1 OAKLEAF CLASS (SUPPORT TANKER) (AOT)

Name	No	Builders	Commissioned	Recommissioned
OAKLEAF (ex-*Oktania*)	A 111	Uddevalla, Sweden	1981	14 Aug 1986

Displacement, tons: 49 648 full load
Measurement, tons: 37 328 dwt
Dimensions, feet (metres): 570 × 105.6 × 36.7
(173.7 × 32.2 × 11.2)
Main machinery: 1 Burmeister & Wain 4L80MCE diesel;
10 800 hp(m) (7.96 MW) sustained; 1 shaft; cp prop; bow and
stern thrusters

Speed, knots: 14
Complement: 36
Cargo capacity: 40 000 cu m fuel
Guns: 2—7.62 mm MGs.
Countermeasures: 2 Plessey Shield chaff launchers can be
fitted.

Comment: Acquired in July 1985 and converted by Falmouth
Ship Repairers to include full RAS rig and extra accommodation. Handed over on completion and renamed. Ice strengthened hull. Marisat fitted.

OAKLEAF   *11/1993, Maritime Photographic*

3 APPLELEAF CLASS (SUPPORT TANKERS) (AOT)

Name	No	Builders	Launched	Commissioned
BRAMBLELEAF (ex-*Hudson Cavalier*)	A 81	Cammell Laird, Birkenhead	22 Jan 1976	3 Mar 1980
BAYLEAF	A 109	Cammell Laird, Birkenhead	27 Oct 1981	26 Mar 1982
ORANGELEAF (ex-*Balder London*, ex-*Hudson Progress*)	A 110	Cammell Laird, Birkenhead	—	2 May 1984

Displacement, tons: 37 747 full load (A 109-110); 40 870
(A 81)
Measurement, tons: 20 761 gross; 11 573 net; 29 999 dwt
Dimensions, feet (metres): 560 × 85 × 36.1
(170.7 × 25.9 × 11)
Main machinery: 2 Pielstick 14 PC2.2 V 400 diesels; 14 000
hp(m) (10.29 MW) sustained; 1 shaft
Speed, knots: 15.5; 16.3 (A 109)
Complement: 60 (20 officers)
Cargo capacity: 22 000 cu m dieso; 3800 cu m Avcat
Guns: 2 Oerlikon 20 mm. 4—7.62 mm MGs.
Countermeasures: Decoys: 2 Vickers Corvus launchers or 2
Plessey Shield launchers.

Comment: *Brambleleaf* chartered in 1979-80 and converted,
completing Autumn 1979. Part of a four-ship order cancelled
by Hudson Fuel and Shipping Co, but completed by the shipbuilders, being the only mercantile order then in hand. *Bayleaf*
built under commercial contract to be chartered by MoD.
Orangeleaf started major refit September 1985 to fit full RAS
capability and extra accommodation. *Appleleaf* sold to Australia in September 1989.

BAYLEAF   *7/1993, Wright & Logan*

3 ROVER CLASS (SMALL FLEET TANKERS) (AOL)

Name	No	Builders	Launched	Commissioned
GREY ROVER	A 269	Swan Hunter Shipbuilders, Wallsend-on-Tyne	17 Apr 1969	10 Apr 1970
GOLD ROVER	A 271	Swan Hunter Shipbuilders, Wallsend-on-Tyne	7 Mar 1973	22 Mar 1974
BLACK ROVER	A 273	Swan Hunter Shipbuilders, Wallsend-on-Tyne	30 Oct 1973	23 Aug 1974

Displacement, tons: 4700 light; 11 522 full load
Measurement, tons: 6692 (A 271, 273), 6822 (A 269) dwt; 7510 gross; 3185 net
Dimensions, feet (metres): 461 × 63 × 24 (140.6 × 19.2 × 7.3)
Main machinery: 2 SEMT-Pielstick 16 PA4 185 diesels; 5344 hp(m) (3.93 MW); 1 shaft; cp prop; bow thruster
Speed, knots: 19. **Range, miles:** 15 000 at 15 kts
Complement: 49 (A 269); 54 (A 271, 273)
Cargo capacity: 6600 tons fuel
Guns: 2 Oerlikon 20 mm. 2—7.62 mm MGs.
Countermeasures: Decoys: 2 Vickers Corvus launchers. 2 Plessey Shield launchers.
1 Graseby Type 182; towed torpedo decoy.
Radars: Navigation: Racal Decca 52690 ARPA; Racal Decca 1690; I band.
Helicopters: Platform for Westland Sea King HAS 5 or HC 4.

Comment: Small fleet tankers designed to replenish HM ships at sea with fuel, fresh water, limited dry cargo and refrigerated stores under all conditions while under way. No hangar but helicopter landing platform is served by a stores lift, to enable stores to be transferred at sea by 'vertical lift'. Capable of HIFR. Siting of SATCOM aerial varies. One employed on training duties at Portland. *Green Rover* sold in 1991 to Indonesia. *Blue Rover* to Portugal in March 1993. *Grey Rover* was also to have been sold in 1993 but will now stay in service until 1997.

GREY ROVER
1/1994, Robert Pabst

2 FORT VICTORIA CLASS (FLEET REPLENISHMENT SHIPS) (AOR(H))

Name	No	Builders	Laid down	Launched	Commissioned
FORT VICTORIA	A 387	Harland & Wolff/Cammell Laird	4 Apr 1988	12 June 1990	June 1994
FORT GEORGE	A 388	Swan Hunter Shipbuilders, Wallsend-on-Tyne	9 Mar 1989	1 Mar 1991	16 July 1993

Displacement, tons: 32 300 full load
Dimensions, feet (metres): 667.7 oa; 607 wl × 99.7 × 32 (203.5; 185 × 30.4 × 9.8)
Main machinery: 2 Crossley SEMT-Pielstick 16 PC2.6 V 400 diesels; 23 904 hp(m) (17.57 MW) sustained; 2 shafts
Speed, knots: 20
Complement: 126 (34 officers) RFA plus 32 (1 officer) RN plus 122 (29 officers) aircrew
Cargo capacity: 12 505 cu m liquids; 6234 cu m solids

Guns: 4 Lawrence Scott 30 mm/75 Mk 1. 2 Signaal 30 mm Goalkeeper may be fitted in due course.
Countermeasures: Decoys: 4 Plessey Shield or 4 Marconi Sea Gnat 6-barrelled chaff/IR launchers. Graseby Type 182; towed torpedo decoy.
ESM: Marconi UAG Mentor; intercept.
Combat data systems: Scot SATCOM.
Radars: Air search: Plessey Type 996; 3D; E/F band.
Navigation: Kelvin Hughes Type 1007; I band.

Helicopters: 5 Westland Sea King/Merlin helicopters.

Programmes: The requirement for these ships is to provide fuel and stores support to the Fleet at sea. *Fort Victoria* ordered 23 April 1986 and *Fort George* on 18 December 1987. *Fort Victoria* delayed by damage during building and entered Cammell Laird Shipyard for post sea trials completion in July 1992. The original plan for six of this class has been progressively eroded and the requirement for more AORs is being reviewed.
Structure: Four dual purpose abeam replenishment rigs for simultaneous transfer of liquids and solids. Stern refuelling. Repair facilities for Merlin helicopters. The plan to fit Seawolf GWS 26 VLS has been abandoned in favour of Goalkeeper CIWS.
Operational: Two helicopter spots. There is a requirement to provide an emergency landing facility for Sea Harriers.

FORT GEORGE
10/1993, W Sartori

FORT VICTORIA
8/1993, Maritime Photographic

2 FORT GRANGE CLASS (FLEET REPLENISHMENT SHIPS) (AFS(H))

Name	No	Builders	Launched	Commissioned
FORT GRANGE	A 385	Scott-Lithgow, Greenock	9 Dec 1976	6 Apr 1978
FORT AUSTIN	A 386	Scott-Lithgow, Greenock	9 Mar 1978	11 May 1979

Displacement, tons: 23 384 full load
Measurement, tons: 8300 dwt
Dimensions, feet (metres): 603 × 79 × 28.2
  (183.9 × 24.1 × 8.6)
Main machinery: 1 Sulzer RND90 diesel; 23 200 hp(m)
  (17.05 MW); 1 shaft; bow thruster
Speed, knots: 22. **Range, miles:** 10 000 at 20 kts
Complement: 127 RFA plus 45 RN plus 36 RNSTS (civilian supply staff)
Cargo capacity: 3500 tons armament, naval and victualling stores in 4 holds of 12 800 cu m
Guns: 2 Oerlikon 20 mm. 4—7.62 mm MGs.
Countermeasures: 2 Vickers Corvus 8-barrelled launchers (upper bridge).
Radars: Navigation: Kelvin Hughes Type 1006; I band.
Helicopters: 4 Westland Sea King.

Comment: Ordered in November 1971. Fitted with a helicopter flight-deck and hangar, thus allowing not only for vertical replenishment but also a base for Force ASW helicopters. ASW stores for helicopters carried on board. Emergency flight deck on the hangar roof. There are six cranes, three of 10 tons lift and three of 5 tons.

FORT AUSTIN   *11/1992, G Toremans*

1 REGENT CLASS (FLEET REPLENISHMENT SHIP) (AFS(H))

Name	No	Builders	Launched	Commissioned
RESOURCE	A 480	Scotts Shipbuilding, Greenock	11 Feb 1966	16 May 1967

Displacement, tons: 13 590 light; 22 890 full load
Measurement, tons: 18 029 gross; 9300 dwt
Dimensions, feet (metres): 640 × 77.2 × 28.5
  (195.1 × 23.5 × 8.7)
Main machinery: 2 Foster-Wheeler boilers; 2 AEI turbines;
  20 000 hp *(14.92 MW);* 1 shaft
Speed, knots: 20. **Range, miles:** 12 000 at 18 kts
Complement: 134 RFA plus 37 RNSTS
Guns: 2 Oerlikon 20 mm (can be fitted). 2—7.62 mm MGs.
Countermeasures: Decoys: 2 Corvus chaff launchers.
Radars: Navigation: Two Kelvin Hughes; I band.

Comment: Ordered on 24 January 1963. Lifts for armaments and stores, seven advanced replenishment rigs and helicopter platforms for transferring loads at sea. A number of the seven holds are temperature controlled to increase cargo storage life. Helicopter not carried but hangar and full flight deck facilities are fitted although the hangar is not big enough for Sea King sized aircraft. Designed from the outset as a Fleet Replenishment Ship. Air-conditioned. *Regent* paid off in December 1992; *Resource* alongside in Split, Croatia throughout 1993 in support of UN operations.

RESOURCE   *6/1992*

1 STENA TYPE (FORWARD REPAIR SHIP)

Name	No	Builders	Commissioned	Recommissioned
DILIGENCE (ex-*Stena Inspector*)	A 132	Oresundsvarvet AB, Landskrona, Sweden	1981	12 Mar 1984

Displacement, tons: 10 765 full load
Measurement, tons: 6550 gross; 4939 dwt
Dimensions, feet (metres): 367.5 × 67.3 × 22.3
  (112 × 20.5 × 6.8)
Flight deck, feet (metres): 83 × 83 *(25.4 × 25.4)*
Main machinery: Diesel-electric; 5 V16 Nohab-Polar diesel generators; 2650 kW; 4 NEBB motors; 6000 hp(m) *(4.41 MW);* 1 shaft; KaMeWa cp prop; 2 KaMeWa bow tunnel thrusters; 3000 hp(m) *(2.2 MW);* 2 azimuth thrusters (aft); 3000 hp(m) *(2.2 MW)*
Speed, knots: 12. **Range, miles:** 5000 at 12 kts
Complement: 41 RFA plus 80 RN (accommodation for 147 plus 55 temporary)
Cargo capacity: Long-jib crane SWL 5 tons; max lift, 40 tons

Guns: 4 Oerlikon 20 mm. 4—7.62 mm MGs.
Countermeasures: Decoys: 4 Plessey Shield 102 mm 6-tubed launchers.

Helicopters: Facilities for up to Boeing Chinook HC 1 (medium lift) size.

Programmes: *Stena Inspector* was designed originally as a Multi-purpose Support Vessel for North Sea oil operations, and completed in January 1981. Chartered on 25 May 1982 for use as a fleet repair ship during the Falklands' campaign. Purchased from Stena (UK) Line in October 1983, and converted for use as Forward Repair Ship in the South Atlantic (Falkland Islands). Conversion by Clyde Dock Engineering Ltd, Govan from 12 November 1983 to 29 February 1984. Naval Party 2010 embarked.
Modernisation: Following items added during conversion: large workshop for hull and machinery repairs (in well-deck); accommodation for naval Junior Rates (new accommodation block); accommodation for crew of conventional submarine (in place of Saturation Diving System); extensive craneage facilities; overside supply of electrical power, water, fuel, steam, air, to ships alongside; large naval store (in place of cement tanks); armament and magazines; Naval Communications System; decompression chamber.
Structure: Four 5 ton anchors for 4-point mooring system. Strengthened for operations in ice (Ice Class 1A). Köngsberg Albatross Positioning System has been retained in full. Uses bow and stern thrusters and main propeller to maintain a selec-ted position to within a few metres, up to Beaufort Force 9. Controlled by Kongsberg KS 500 computers.
Operational: Deployed to the Gulf in August 1987. Back on station in the Falkland Islands in 1989 and then to the Gulf in September 1990, returning to the UK in December 1992 after nearly three years continuous service overseas.

DILIGENCE   *5/1993, Wright & Logan*

1 AVIATION TRAINING SHIP

Name	No
ARGUS (ex-Contender Bezant)	A 135

Builders	Commissioned	Recommissioned
CNR Breda, Venice, Italy	1981	1 June 1988

Displacement, tons: 18 280 standard; 26 421 full load
Measurement, tons: 9965 dwt
Dimensions, feet (metres): 574.5 × 99.7 × 27
(175.1 × 30.4 × 8.2)
Main machinery: 2 Lindholmen SEMT-Pielstick 18 PC2.5 V 400
diesels; 23 400 hp(m) (17.2 MW) sustained; 2 shafts
Speed, knots: 18. **Range, miles:** 20 000 at 19 kts
Complement: 79 RFA plus 39 permanent RN plus 137 RN
aircrew
Cargo capacity: 3300 tons dieso; 1100 tons aviation fuel

Guns: 4 BMARC 30 mm Mk 1. 4—7.62 mm MGs.
Countermeasures: Decoys: 4 Sea Gnat chaff launchers. Graseby
Type 182; torpedo decoy.
ESM: THORN EMI Guardian; radar warning.
Combat data systems: Racal CANE DEB-1 data automation.
Inmarsat SATCOM communications. Marisat.
Radars: Air search: Type 994 MTI; E/F band.
Air/surface search: Kelvin Hughes Type 1006; I band.
Navigation: Racal Decca Type 994; I band.

Fixed wing aircraft: Provision to transport 12 British Aerospace
Sea Harrier FRS 1.
Helicopters: 6 Westland Sea King HAS 5 or similar.

Programmes: Ro-ro container ship whose conversion for her
new task was begun by Harland and Wolff in March 1984 and
completed on 3 March 1988. Purchase price approx £18 million; conversion approx £45 million which included full contractor responsibility for equipment, trials and setting to work.
Relieved Engadine in early 1989.
Structure: Uses former ro-ro deck as hangar with four sliding WT
doors able to operate at a speed of 10 m per minute. Can
replenish other ships underway. One lift port midships, one

ARGUS   11/1993, H M Steele

abaft funnel. Domestic facilities are very limited if she is to be
used in the Command support role. Flight deck is 372.4 ft
(113.5 m) long and has a 5 ft thick concrete layer on its lower
side. First RFA to be fitted with a command system.
Operational: Not as heavily armed as Fort Victoria but similar
'advantage' is being taken of the cost effectiveness of mixed
civilian and naval manning. Deployed to the Gulf in 1990/91 as

a Primary Casualty Receiving Ship (PCRS) with the hangar converted into hospital accommodation. Deployed to the Adriatic
in 1993 as a Helicopter Support Ship. Obvious shortcomings in
this role added impetus to the ordering of a properly designed
LPH. Major fire on 11 January 1994 delayed return to service
after a minor refit.

4 SIR BEDIVERE CLASS (LANDING SHIP LOGISTIC) (LSL)

Name	No	Builders	Laid down	Launched	Commissioned
SIR BEDIVERE	L 3004	Hawthorn Leslie, Hebburn-on-Tyne	Oct 1965	20 July 1966	18 May 1967
SIR GERAINT	L 3027	Alex Stephen, Glasgow	June 1965	26 Jan 1967	12 July 1967
SIR PERCIVALE	L 3036	Hawthorn Leslie, Hebburn-on-Tyne	Apr 1966	4 Oct 1967	23 Mar 1968
SIR TRISTRAM	L 3505	Hawthorn Leslie, Hebburn-on-Tyne	Feb 1966	12 Dec 1966	14 Sep 1967

Displacement, tons: 3270 light; 5674 full load
5800 full load (Sir Tristram)
Dimensions, feet (metres): 412.1; 441.1 (Sir Tristram) × 59.8
× 13 (125.6; 134.4 × 18.2 × 4)
Main machinery: 2 Mirrlees 10-ALSSDM diesels; 9400 hp
(7.01 MW); 2 shafts; bow thruster
Speed, knots: 17. **Range, miles:** 8000 at 15 kts
Complement: 65 (21 officers); 50 (Sir Tristram)
Military lift: 340 troops (534 hard lying); 16 MBTs; 34 mixed
vehicles; 120 tons POL; 30 tons ammunition; 1—20 ton crane;
2—4.5 ton cranes. Sir Tristram has increased capacity for 20
helicopters (11 tank deck and 9 vehicle deck)
Guns: 2 Oerlikon 20 mm. 2—7.62 mm MGs.
Countermeasures: Decoys: 2 Corvus chaff launchers.
Radars: Navigation: Kelvin Hughes Type 1006; I band.
Helicopters: Platforms to operate Gazelle AH 1 or Lynx AH 1/7.

Comment: Fitted for bow and stern loading with drive-through
facilities and deck-to-deck ramps. Facilities provided for
onboard maintenance of vehicles and for laying out pontoon
equipment. Mexeflote self-propelled floating platforms can be
strapped one on each side. Carries 850 tons oil fuel. On 8 June
1982 Sir Tristram was severely damaged off the Falkland
Islands. Tyne Shiprepairers were given a contract to repair and
modify her. This included lengthening by 29 ft, an enlarged
flight deck capable of taking Chinooks and a new bridge. The
aluminium superstructure was replaced by steel and the provision of new communications, an EMR, SATCOM, new navigation systems and helicopter control radar greatly increase
her effectiveness. Completed 9 October 1985. The first three
are to be modernised to the same standard as Sir Tristram with
SLEPs, the first one being scheduled to start in mid-1994 after
a delay of about one year. All deployed to the Gulf in 1991 with
additional 20 mm guns, decoy systems and navigation
equipment.

SIR GERAINT   6/1993

1 SIR GALAHAD CLASS (LSL)

Name	No	Builders	Laid down	Launched	Commissioned
SIR GALAHAD	L 3005	Swan Hunter Shipbuilders, Wallsend-on-Tyne	12 May 1985	13 Dec 1986	25 Nov 1987

Displacement, tons: 8585 full load
Measurement, tons: 3080 dwt
Dimensions, feet (metres): 461 × 64 × 14.1
(140.5 × 19.5 × 4.3)
Main machinery: 2 Mirrlees Blackstone diesels; 13 320 hp
(9.94 MW); 2 shafts; cp props
Speed, knots: 18. **Range, miles:** 13 000 at 15 kts
Complement: 49 (17 officers)
Military lift: 343 troops (537 hard-lying); 18 MBT; 20 mixed
vehicles; ammunition, fuel and stores
Guns: 2 Oerlikon 20 mm GAM-BO3. 2—12.7 mm MGs.
Countermeasures: Decoys: 4 Plessey Shield 102 mm 6-tubed
launchers.
Combat data systems: Racal CANE data automation.
Radars: Navigation: Kelvin Hughes Type 1006; I band.
Helicopters: 1 Westland Sea King HC 4.

Comment: Ordered on 6 September 1984 as a replacement for
Sir Galahad, sunk as a war grave after air attack at Bluff Cove,
Falkland Islands on 8 June 1982. Has bow and stern ramps
with a visor bow gate. One 25 ton crane and three smaller
ones. Mexeflote pontoons can be attached on both sides of the
hull superstructure.

SIR GALAHAD   1/1993, G Toremans

ROYAL MARITIME AUXILIARY SERVICE

3 SAL CLASS (SALVAGE AND MOORING SHIPS)

Name	No	Builders	Commissioned
SALMOOR	A 185	Hall Russell, Aberdeen	12 Nov 1985
SALMASTER	A 186	Hall Russell, Aberdeen	10 Apr 1986
SALMAID	A 187	Hall Russell, Aberdeen	28 Oct 1986

Displacement, tons: 1605 light; 2225 full load
Dimensions, feet (metres): 253 × 48.9 × 12.5 *(77 × 14.9 × 3.8)*
Main machinery: 2 Ruston 8RKC diesels; 4000 hp *(2.98 MW)* sustained; 1 shaft
Speed, knots: 15
Complement: 17 (4 officers) plus 27 spare billets

Comment: Ordered on 23 January 1984. *Salmoor* on Clyde, *Salmaster* at Rosyth, *Salmaid* at Devonport. Lift, 400 tons; 200 tons on horns. Can carry submersibles including LR 5.

SALMAID   *11/1992, Maritime Photograhic*

2 WILD DUCK CLASS (SALVAGE AND MOORING SHIPS)

Name	No	Builders	Commissioned
GOOSANDER	A 164	Robb Caledon, Leith	10 Sep 1973
POCHARD	A 165	Robb Caledon, Leith	11 Dec 1973

Displacement, tons: 692 light; 1648 full load
Dimensions, feet (metres): 197.6 × 40.5 × 13.8 *(60.2 × 12.2 × 4.2)*
Main machinery: 1 Paxman diesel; 750 hp *(560 kW)*; 1 shaft; cp prop
Speed, knots: 10. **Range, miles:** 3000 at 10 kts
Complement: 23

Comment: Capable of laying out and servicing the heaviest moorings used by the Fleet and also maintaining booms for harbour defence. Heavy lifting equipment enables a wide range of salvage operations to be performed, especially in harbour clearance work. The special heavy winches have an ability for tidal lifts over the apron of 200 tons. *Goosander* is based on the Clyde; *Pochard* in reserve at Portsmouth.

GOOSANDER   *1991, RMAS*

3 MOORHEN CLASS (SALVAGE AND MOORING SHIPS)

Name	No	Builders	Commissioned
MOORHEN	Y 32	McTay, Bromborough	Apr 1989
MOORFOWL	Y 33	McTay, Bromborough	May 1989
CAMERON	A 72	Dunston, Hessle	Sep 1991

Displacement, tons: 530 full load
Dimensions, feet (metres): 106 × 37.7 × 6.6 *(32.3 × 11.5 × 2)*
Main machinery: 2 Cummins KT19-M diesels; 730 hp *(545 kW)* sustained; 2 Aquamasters
Speed, knots: 8
Complement: 10 (2 officers)

Comment: Classified as powered mooring lighters. The whole ship can be worked from a 'flying bridge' which is constructed over a through deck. Day mess for five divers. *Moorhen* at Portsmouth, *Moorfowl* at Devonport. *Cameron* works for DRA (Maritime) and is modified as a trials support vessel.

MOORHEN   *7/1993, Maritime Photographic*

4 OILPRESS CLASS (COASTAL TANKERS)

Name	No	Builders	Commissioned
OILPRESS	Y 21	Appledore Ferguson SB	1969
OILWELL	Y 23	Appledore Ferguson SB	1969
OILBIRD	Y 25	Appledore Ferguson SB	1969
OILMAN	Y 26	Appledore Ferguson SB	1969

Displacement, tons: 280 standard; 530 full load
Dimensions, feet (metres): 139.5 × 30 × 8.3 *(42.5 × 9 × 2.5)*
Main machinery: 1 Lister-Blackstone ES6 diesel; 405 hp *(302 kW)*; 1 shaft
Speed, knots: 9
Complement: 8
Cargo capacity: 250 tons dieso

Comment: Ordered on 10 May 1967. Two deleted in 1992.

OILPRESS   *2/1986, A Denholm*

1 TRIALS SHIP

Name	No	Builders	Commissioned
NEWTON	A 367	Scott-Lithgow, Greenock	17 June 1976

Displacement, tons: 3140 light; 4652 full load
Dimensions, feet (metres): 323.5 × 53 × 18.5 *(98.6 × 16 × 5.7)*
Main machinery: Diesel-electric; 3 Mirrlees-Blackstone diesel generators; 4350 hp *(3.25 MW)*; 1 GEC motor; 2040 hp *(1.52 MW)*; Kort nozzle; bow thruster
Speed, knots: 14. **Range, miles:** 5000 at 14 kts
Complement: 64 including 12 scientists

Comment: Passive tank stabilisation. Prime duty sonar propagation trials. Can serve as cable-layer with large cable tanks. Special winch system. Low noise level electric propulsion system. Based at Plymouth.

NEWTON   *1990, van Ginderen Collection*

1 RESEARCH SHIP

Name	No	Builders	Commissioned
COLONEL TEMPLER	—	Hall Russell, Aberdeen	1966

Displacement, tons: 1300 full load
Dimensions, feet (metres): 185.4 × 36 × 18.4 *(56.5 × 11 × 5.6)*
Main machinery: 1 Mirlees KSSMR7 diesel; 1 shaft; bow thruster
Speed, knots: 12.5
Complement: 14 plus 12 scientists

Comment: Built as a stern trawler. Converted in 1980 for use at RAE Farnborough as an acoustic research ship. After a major rebuild in 1992 she is now operated for the Defence Research Agency by the Maritime Systems Department. Carries a 9 m work boat *Quest* Q 26. Well equipped laboratories. Capable of deploying and recovering up to 5 tons of equipment from deck winches and a 5 ton hydraulic A frame.

COLONEL TEMPLER   *6/1993*

1 TRIALS SHIP

Name	No	Builders	Commissioned
AURICULA	A 285	Appledore Ferguson SB	6 Nov 1980

Displacement, tons: 940 light; 1118 full load
Dimensions, feet (metres): 170.5 × 36 × 11.8 *(52 × 11 × 3.6)*
Main machinery: 2 Mirrlees-Blackstone diesels; 1300 hp *(970 kW)*; 2 shafts; bow thruster
Speed, knots: 12
Complement: 32 (7 officers, 10 trials party)

Comment: Sonar trials and experimental ship. Based at Portland and laid up in early 1994.

AURICULA   *1/1992, van Ginderen Collection*

4 TORNADO CLASS (TORPEDO RECOVERY VESSELS)

TORNADO A 140	TORMENTOR A 142
TORCH A 141	TOREADOR A 143

Displacement, tons: 698 full load
Dimensions, feet (metres): 154.5 × 31.3 × 11.3 *(47.1 × 9.6 × 3.4)*
Main machinery: 2 Mirrlees-Blackstone ESL8 MCR diesels; 2200 hp *(1.64 MW)*; 2 shafts
Speed, knots: 14. **Range, miles:** 3000 at 14 kts
Complement: 14

Comment: Ordered from Hall Russell, Aberdeen on 1 July 1977 and launched in 1979-80. *Torch* based at Portland, *Tormentor* at Plymouth, others in the Clyde. *Toreador* may pay off in 1994.

TORMENTOR   *1/1993, Maritime Photographic*

1 TORPEDO RECOVERY VESSEL

Name	No	Builders	Commissioned
TORRENT	A 127	Cleland SB, Wallsend-on-Tyne	10 Sep 1971

Displacement, tons: 550 gross
Dimensions, feet (metres): 162 × 31 × 11.5 *(49.4 × 9.5 × 3.5)*
Main machinery: 2 Paxman diesels; 700 hp *(522 kW)*; 2 shafts
Speed, knots: 10
Complement: 18

Comment: Has a stern ramp for torpedo recovery—can carry 22 torpedoes in hold and 10 on deck. Based at Kyle of Loch Alsh.

TORRENT   *1991, RMAS*

2 ARMAMENT STORE CARRIERS (AKF/ASL)

Name	No	Builders	Commissioned
KINTERBURY	A 378	Appledore Ferguson SB	Nov 1980
ARROCHAR (ex-*St George*)	A 382	Appledore Ferguson SB	July 1981

Displacement, tons: 2207 full load
Measurement, tons: 1150 dwt
Dimensions, feet (metres): 231.2 × 39 × 15 *(70.5 × 11.9 × 4.6)*
Main machinery: 2 Mirrlees-Blackstone diesels; 3000 hp *(2.24 MW)*; 1 shaft
Speed, knots: 14.5. **Range, miles:** 4000 at 11 kts
Complement: 24 (8 officers)

Comment: Carry armament stores in two holds. Internal arrangements of *Arrochar* differ and she is classified as an Armament Ship Logistic (ASL). Twin cranes in the well-deck. *Arrochar* transferred from the RCT on 7 November 1988.

KINTERBURY   *4/1993, Maritime Photographic*

5 WATER CLASS (WATER CARRIERS)

Name	No	Builders	Commissioned
WATERFALL	Y 17	Drypool Engineering & Drydock Co, Hull	1967
WATERSPOUT	Y 19	Drypool Engineering & Drydock Co, Hull	1967
WATERCOURSE	Y 30	Drypool Engineering & Drydock Co, Hull	1974
WATERFOWL	Y 31	Drypool Engineering & Drydock Co, Hull	1974
WATERMAN	A 146	Dunston, Hessle	1978

Measurement, tons: 285 gross
Dimensions, feet (metres): 131.5 × 24.8 × 8 *(40.1 × 7.5 × 2.4)*
Main machinery: 1 Lister-Blackstone ERS8 MCR diesel; 660 hp *(492 kW)*; 1 shaft
Speed, knots: 11
Complement: 8

Comment: Y 19 after deckhouse extended forward. A 146 is a modified ship, having a store-carrying capability and, like Y 31 has a deckhouse forward of the bridge. *Waterfall* based in the Clyde and used as a Salvage Training Vessel. One deleted in 1991 and one in 1992.

WATERCOURSE   *1/1993, Maritime Photographic*

3 OCEAN TUGS

Name	No	Builders	Commissioned
ROYSTERER	A 361	CD Holmes, Beverley, Humberside	26 Apr 1972
ROBUST	A 366	CD Holmes, Beverley, Humberside	6 Apr 1974
ROLLICKER	A 502	CD Holmes, Beverley, Humberside	6 Mar 1973

Displacement, tons: 1630 full load
Dimensions, feet (metres): 178 × 40.3 × 21 *(54.3 × 12.3 × 6.4)*
Main machinery: 2 Mirrlees KMR 6 diesels; 4500 hp *(3.36 MW)*; 2 shafts; cp props
Speed, knots: 15. **Range, miles:** 12 500 at 12 kts
Complement: 28 (salvage party—10 RN officers and ratings)

Comment: Nominal bollard pull, 50 tons. Designed principally for salvage and long-range towage but can be used for general harbour duties, which *Robust* undertakes at Devonport. *Roysterer* based on Clyde, *Rollicker* at Portsmouth.

ROLLICKER   *2/1993, Maritime Photographic*

9 ADEPT CLASS (TUGS)

FORCEFUL A 221	ADEPT A 224	CAREFUL A 227
NIMBLE A 222	BUSTLER A 225	FAITHFUL A 228
POWERFUL A 223	CAPABLE A 226	DEXTEROUS A 231

Displacement, tons: 450
Dimensions, feet (metres): 127.3 × 30.8 × 11.2 *(38.8 × 9.4 × 3.4)*
Main machinery: 2 Ruston 6RKC diesels; 3000 hp *(2.24 MW)* sustained; 2 Voith-Schneider props
Speed, knots: 12
Complement: 10

Comment: 'Twin unit tractor tugs' (TUTT). First four ordered from Richard Dunston (Hessle) on 22 February 1979 and next five on 8 February 1984. Primarily for harbour work with coastal towing capability. Nominal bollard pull, 27.5 tons. *Adept* accepted 28 October 1980, *Bustler* 15 April 1981, *Capable* 11 September 1981, *Careful* 12 March 1982, *Forceful* 18 March 1985, *Nimble* 25 June 1985, *Powerful* 30 October 1985, *Faithful* 21 December 1985, *Dexterous* 23 April 1986. *Adept* at Portland, *Powerful* and *Bustler* at Portsmouth, *Forceful*, *Faithful* and *Careful* at Plymouth, *Nimble* and *Dexterous* at Rosyth, *Capable* at Gibraltar.

BUSTLER   *7/1993, Per Kornefeldt*

16 DOG CLASS (14 TUGS + 2 RANGE TRIALS VESSELS)

CAIRN A 126	MASTIFF A 180	SHEEPDOG A 250
DALMATIAN A 129	SALUKI A 182	FOXHOUND (ex-*Boxer*) A 326
DEERHOUND A 155	SETTER A 189	BASSET (ex-*Beagle*) A 327
ELKHOUND A 162	SEALYHAM A 197	COLLIE A 328
LABRADOR A 168	SPANIEL A 201	CORGI A 330
HUSKY A 178		

Displacement, tons: 248 full load
Dimensions, feet (metres): 94 × 24.5 × 12 *(28.7 × 7.5 × 3.7)*
Main machinery: 2 Lister-Blackstone ERS8 MCR diesels; 1320 hp *(985 kW)*; 2 shafts
Speed, knots: 10. **Range, miles:** 2236 at 10 kts
Complement: 7

Comment: Harbour berthing tugs. *Sealyham* at Gibraltar. Nominal bollard pull, 17.5 tons. Completed 1962-72. *Cairn* and *Collie* operate at Kyle of Loch Alsh as Range trials vessels and have had towing gear removed. Appearance varies considerably, some with mast, some with curved upper-bridge work, some with flat monkey-island. The class needs replacing as a priority. *Corgi* is in reserve at Devonport.

SETTER   *7/1993, Per Kornefeldt*

2 MODIFIED GIRL CLASS (TUGS)

DAPHNE A 156   EDITH A 177

Displacement, tons: 138 standard
Dimensions, feet (metres): 61 × 16.4 × 7.2 *(18.6 × 5 × 2.2)*
Main machinery: 1 diesel; 495 hp *(396 kW)*; 1 shaft
Speed, knots: 10
Complement: 6

Comment: *Edith* at Gibraltar. Both built by Dunstons. Completed 1971-72. Nominal bollard pull, 6.5 tons.

Modified GIRL class   *4/1986, Michael D J Lennon*

12 TRITON CLASS

KATHLEEN A 166	LILAH A 174	ISABEL A 183	MYRTLE A 199
KITTY A 170	MARY A 175	JOAN A 190	NANCY A 202
LESLEY A 172	IRENE A 181	JOYCE A 193	NORAH A 205

Displacement, tons: 107.5 standard
Dimensions, feet (metres): 57.7 × 18 × 7.9 *(17.6 × 5.5 × 2.4)*
Main machinery: 1 diesel; 330 hp *(264 kW)*; 1 shaft
Speed, knots: 7.5
Complement: 4

Comment: All completed by August 1974 by Dunstons. 'Water-tractors' with small wheelhouse and adjoining funnel. Later vessels have masts stepped abaft wheelhouse. Voith-Schneider vertical axis propellers. Nominal bollard pull, 3 tons. Order for two more in 1990 was cancelled.

NORAH   *9/1993, Maritime Photographic*

8 FELICITY CLASS

FELICITY A 112	FLORENCE A 149	GWENDOLINE A 196
FRANCES A 147	GENEVIEVE A 150	HELEN A 198
FIONA A 148	GEORGINA A 152	

Displacement, tons: 144 full load
Dimensions, feet (metres): 70 × 21 × 9.8 *(21.5 × 6.4 × 3)*
Main machinery: 1 Mirrlees-Blackstone ESM8 diesel; 615 hp *(459 kW)*; 1 Voith-Schneider cp prop
Speed, knots: 10
Complement: 4

Comment: First five completed 1973. A 112 built by Dunstons and remainder by Hancocks. A 147, 149 and 150 ordered early 1979 from Richard Dunston (Thorne) and completed by end 1980. Nominal bollard pull, 5.7 tons.

FIONA   *5/1993, Maritime Photographic*

14 RANGE SUPPORT VESSELS

WARDEN A 368

Displacement, tons: 900 full load
Dimensions, feet (metres): 159.4 × 34.4 × 8.2 *(48.6 × 10.5 × 2.5)*
Main machinery: 2 Ruston 8RKC diesels; 4000 hp *(2.98 MW)* sustained; 1 shaft
Speed, knots: 15
Complement: 11 (4 officers)
Radars: Navigation: Racal Decca RM 1250; I band.
Sonars: Dowty 2053; high frequency.

Comment: Built by Richards, Lowestoft and completed in November 1989. In service at Pembroke Dock.

WARDEN   *7/1991, van Ginderen Collection*

FALCONET (ex-*Alfred Herring V C*)
Y 02 (ex-Y 497)

PETARD (ex-*Michael Murphy V C*)
Y 01 (ex-519)

Displacement, tons: 70 full load
Dimensions, feet (metres): 77.7 × 18 × 4.9 *(23.7 × 5.5 × 1.5)*
Main engines: 2 Paxman 8 CM diesels; 2000 hp *(1.49 MW)* sustained; 2 shafts
Speed, knots: 20

Comment: Range Safety Craft built by James and Stone, Brightlingsea. Similar design to Spitfire class. Transferred from the RCT on 30 September 1988. *Falconet* commissioned 1978 serves at the Royal Artillery missile range in the Outer Hebrides; *Petard* commissioned 1983 serves at Pendine range, South Wales.

PETARD   9/1987, Michael D J Lennon

RSC 7713 (ex-*Samuel Morley VC*)
RSC 7821 (ex-*Joseph Hughes GC*)
RSC 8125 (ex-*Sir Paul Travers*)
RSC 8126 (ex-*Sir Cecil Smith*)
RSC 8487 (ex-*Geoffrey Rackman GC*)
RSC 8489 (ex-*Sir Evan Gibb*)

RSC 7820 (ex-*Richard Masters VC*)
RSC 7822 (ex-*James Dalton VC*)
RSC 8128 (ex-*Sir Reginald Kerr*)
RSC 8129 (ex-*Sir Humfrey Gale*)
RSC 8488 (ex-*Walter Cleal GC*)

Displacement, tons: 20.2 full load
Dimensions, feet (metres): 48.2 × 11.5 × 4.3 *(14.7 × 3.5 × 1.3)*
Main machinery: 2 RR C8M 410 or Volvo Penta TAMD-122A diesels; 820 hp *(612 kW)*; 2 shafts
Speed, knots: 22. **Range, miles:** 300 at 20 kts
Complement: 3

Comment: Range Safety Craft of the Honours and Sirs classes, built by Fairey Marine, A R P Whitstable and Halmatic. All completed 1982-86. Transferred from the RCT on 30 September 1988. Another of the class *Sir William Roe* is based in Cyprus and has remained with the Royal Logistic Corps. Based at Whitehaven, Pembroke Dock, Hebrides, Dover, Portland and Kyle of Loch Alsh (7820). Now known only by their pennant numbers. 8124 went aground off Portland in December 1992 and was a write-off. New engines being fitted from 1993.

RSC 7820   6/1991, Maritime Photographic

3 TOWED ARRAY TENDERS

Dimensions, feet (metres): 65.9 × 19.7 × 7.9 *(20.1 × 6 × 2.4)*
Main machinery: 2 Perkins diesels; 400 hp *(298 kW)*; 2 Kort nozzles
Speed, knots: 12
Complement: 8

Comment: Used for transporting clip-on towed arrays from submarine bases at Faslane and Devonport. Naval manned.

TARV   7/1993, Maritime Photographic

2 SUBMARINE BERTHING TUGS

Name	No	Builders	Completed
IMPULSE	A 344	Dunston, Hessle	11 Mar 1993
IMPETUS	A 345	Dunston, Hessle	28 May 1993

Displacement, tons: 530 full load
Dimensions, feet (metres): 106.7 × 34.2 × 11.5 *(32.5 × 10.4 × 3.5)*
Main machinery: 2 W H Allen 8S12 diesels; 3400 hp *(2.54 MW)* sustained; 2 Aquamaster Azimuth thrusters; 1 Jastrom bow thruster
Speed, knots: 12
Complement: 6

Comment: Ordered 28 January 1992 for submarine berthing duties. There are two 10 ton hydraulic winches forward and aft with break capacities of 110 tons. Bollard pull 38.6 tons ahead, 36 tons astern. Fitted with fire fighting and oil pollution equipment. Designed for one man control from the bridge with all round vision and a comprehensive Navaids fit. *Impulse* launched 10 December 1992; *Impetus* 9 February 1993.

IMPULSE (artist's impression)   1992

1 SUBMARINE TENDER

Name	No	Builders	Commissioned
ADAMANT	A 232	FBM, Cowes	18 Jan 1993

Dimensions, feet (metres): 101 × 25.6 × 3.6 *(30.8 × 7.8 × 1.1)*
Main machinery: 2 Cummins KTA-19M2 diesels; 970 hp *(724 kW)* sustained; 2 waterjets
Speed, knots: 23. **Range, miles:** 250 at 22 kts
Complement: 5 plus 36 passengers

Comment: Twin-hulled support ship ordered in 1991 and launched 8 October 1992. Used for personnel and stores transfers in the Firth of Clyde. In addition to the passengers, half a ton of cargo can be carried. Capable of top speed up to sea state 3 and able to transit safely up to sea state 6.

ADAMANT   12/1992, FBM

2 SEAL CLASS (LRRSC) (AVIATION SUPPORT CRAFT)

Name	No	Builders	Commissioned
SEAL	5000	Brooke Marine, Lowestoft	Aug 1967
SEAGULL	5001	Fairmile Construction, Berwick-on-Tweed	1970

Displacement, tons: 159 full load
Dimensions, feet (metres): 120.3 × 23.5 × 6.5 *(36.6 × 7.2 × 2)*
Main machinery: 2 Paxman 16YJCM diesels; 4000 hp *(2.98 MW)* sustained; 2 shafts
Speed, knots: 21
Complement: 9

Comment: Long-range recovery and support craft (LRRSC). All welded steel hull. Aluminium alloy superstructure. Used for weapon recovery, target towing, search and rescue. Both at Invergordon.

SEAL   8/1984, Michael D J Lennon

6 SPITFIRE CLASS (RTTL Mk 3) (AVIATION SUPPORT CRAFT)

Name	No	Builders	Commissioned
SPITFIRE	4000	James and Stone, Brightlingsea	1972
HALIFAX	4003	James and Stone, Brightlingsea	1977
HAMPDEN	4004	James and Stone, Brightlingsea	1980
HURRICANE	4005	James and Stone, Brightlingsea	1980
LANCASTER	4006	James and Stone, Brightlingsea	1981
WELLINGTON	4007	James and Stone, Brightlingsea	1981

Displacement, tons: 70.2 full load
Dimensions, feet (metres): 78.7 × 18 × 4.9 *(24.1 × 5.5 × 1.5)*
Main machinery: 2 Paxman 8YJCM diesels; 2000 hp *(1.49 MW)* sustained; 2 shafts
Speed, knots: 22
Complement: 6

Comment: Rescue target towing launches (RTTL). All welded steel hulls; aluminium alloy superstructure. *Spitfire* has twin funnels, remainder none. Invergordon, *Hurricane*; Great Yarmouth, *Hampden, Lancaster, Wellington*; Plymouth, *Spitfire, Halifax*.

HALIFAX   *9/1993, Hartmut Ehlers*

3 PINNACES 1300 SERIES (AVIATION SUPPORT CRAFT)

1374, 1389, 1392

Displacement, tons: 28.3
Dimensions, feet (metres): 63 × 15.5 × 5 *(19.2 × 4.7 × 1.5)*
Main machinery: 2 RR C6 diesels; 190 hp *(142 kW)*; 2 shafts
Speed, knots: 13
Complement: 5
Guns: 1—12.7 mm MG.

Comment: Hard chine, wooden hulls. Built by Groves and Gutteridge, Robertsons (Dunoon) and Dorset Yacht Co (Poole) in 1955-65. Of 5 ton cargo capacity. *1392* and *1374* at Holyhead; *1389* at Plymouth. Two deleted in 1992.

1389   *9/1993, Hartmut Ehlers*

5 INSECT CLASS (FLEET TENDERS)

BEE A 216	GNAT A 239	SCARAB A 272
COCKCHAFER A 230	LADYBIRD A 253	

Displacement, tons: 475 full load
Dimensions, feet (metres): 111.8 × 28 × 11 *(34.1 × 8.5 × 3.4)*
Main machinery: 1 Lister-Blackstone ERS8 MCR diesel; 660 hp *(492 kW)*; 1 shaft
Speed, knots: 11.3. **Range, miles:** 3000 at 10 kts
Complement: 7

Comment: First two built as stores carriers, two as armament carriers and *Scarab* as mooring vessel capable of lifting 10 tons over the bows. All commissioned between 1970 and 1973. *Gnat* and *Ladybird* operate as armament carriers with a red funnel band. Of 200 ton cargo capacity and 2 ton crane.

BEE   *7/1993, Maritime Photographic*

4 DIVING TENDERS

ILCHESTER A 308	IRONBRIDGE* A 311
INSTOW A 309	IXWORTH* A 318
*RN manned	

Displacement, tons: 143
Dimensions, feet (metres): 80 × 21 × 6.6 *(24.1 × 6.4 × 2)*
Main machinery: 2 Gray Marine diesels; 450 hp *(336 kW)*; 2 shafts
Speed, knots: 12
Complement: 6

Comment: Similar to Clovelly class. Built by Gregson Ltd, Blyth and commissioned in 1974.

INSTOW   *8/1989, Wright & Logan*

8 LOYAL CLASS (FLEET TENDERS)

LOYAL HELPER A 157	LOYAL MEDIATOR A 161
SUPPORTER (ex-*Loyal Supporter*) A 158	LOYAL MODERATOR A 220
LOYAL WATCHER A 159	LOYAL CHANCELLOR A 1770
LOYAL VOLUNTEER A 160	LOYAL PROCTOR A 1771

Displacement, tons: 143
Dimensions, feet (metres): 80 × 21 × 6.6 *(24.1 × 6.4 × 2)*
Main machinery: 1 Lister-Blackstone ERS4 MCR diesel; 320 hp *(239 kW)*; 1 shaft
Speed, knots: 10.5
Complement: 6 (1 officer)

Comment: *Loyal Helper* completed 10 February 1978 and last four later in 1978. (See also Coastal Training Craft). Bases: Portsmouth Command: *Loyal Mediator*. Plymouth Command: *Loyal Moderator* (Pembroke Dock), *Loyal Watcher* (Birkenhead), *Loyal Chancellor* (Plymouth). Scotland Command: *Loyal Volunteer, Loyal Proctor, Supporter* (Belfast), *Loyal Helper* (Rosyth). Former RNXS vessels which may be disposed of in mid-1994, except *Watcher* and *Chancellor* which are earmarked for RN University entry training.

LOYAL CHANCELLOR   *7/1993, Per Kornefeldt*

23 CLOVELLY CLASS (FLEET TENDERS)

CLOVELLY A 389	FINTRY A 394	HORNING A 1773
CRICKLADE A 381	FULBECK A 365	LAMLASH A 208
CROMARTY A 488	GRASMERE A 402	LECHLADE A 211
DORNOCH A 490	HAMBLEDON A 1769	LLANDOVERY A 207
ELKSTONE A 353	HARLECH A 1768	LYDFORD (ex-*Loyal Governor*,
ELSING* A 277	HEADCORN A 1766	ex-*Alert*) A 251
EPWORTH A 355	HEVER A 1767	SULTAN VENTURER* (ex-*Meavy*, ex-*Loyal*
ETTRICK** A 274	HOLMWOOD A 1772	*Factor*, ex-*Vigilant*) A 254
FELSTED A 348		
*RN **RNR		

Displacement, tons: 143 full load
Dimensions, feet (metres): 80 × 21 × 6.6 *(24.4 × 6.4 × 2)*
Main machinery: 1 Lister-Blackstone ERS4 MCR diesel; 320 hp *(239 kW)*; 1 shaft
Speed, knots: 10.3. **Range, miles:** 600 at 10 kts
Complement: 4
Cargo capacity: 36 tons

Comment: All fleet tenders of an improved Aberdovey class commissioned 1970-74. *Elsing* and *Ettrick* at Gibraltar (Royal Navy manned), used for patrol duties. Three based at Falmouth operating with Culdrose helicopters *(Clovelly, Hever, Headcorn)*. Can be used for varying tasks—cargo, passenger, training, diving *(Dornoch)*. *Lydford* at Portland. *Sultan Venturer* replaced the Aberdovey class of the same name in 1992 and serves as a tender to *Sultan*. Listed in alphabetical order.

HAMBLEDON   *9/1993, Maritime Photographic*

5 MANLY CLASS (FLEET TENDERS)

MELTON A 83	**MEON** A 87	**MESSINA** A 107
MENAI A 84	**MILFORD** A 91	

Displacement, tons: 143 full load
Dimensions, feet (metres): 80 × 21 × 6.6 *(24.4 × 6.4 × 2)*
Main machinery: 1 Lister-Blackstone ESR4 MCR diesel; 320 hp *(239 kW)*; 1 shaft
Speed, knots: 10
Complement: 6 (1 officer)

Comment: All built by Richard Dunston, Hessle. Details similar to Clovelly class but with larger deck-house. All completed by early 1983. *Messina*, attached to Royal Marines, Poole for navigational training and remainder RMAS. Three of the class used for training at *Raleigh* have been paid off.

MEON *6/1990, van Ginderen Collection*

1 FBM CATAMARAN CLASS

8837

Displacement, tons: 21 full load
Dimensions, feet (metres): 51.8 × 18 × 4.9 *(15.8 × 5.5 × 1.5)*
Main machinery: 2 Mermaid Turbo 4 diesels; 280 hp *(209 kW)*; 2 shafts
Speed, knots: 13. **Range, miles:** 400 at 10 kts
Complement: 2

Comment: Built by FBM Marine. Can carry 30 passengers or 2 tons stores. First of a new construction type designed to replace some of the older harbour launches.

8837 *8/1993, Maritime Photographic*

3 TARGET VESSELS

BULLSEYE (ex-*Tokio*),   **MAGPIE** (ex-*Hondo*),   **TARGE** (ex-*Erimo*)

Measurement, tons: 273 gross; 91 net
Dimensions, feet (metres): 117.8 × 25.3 × 12.1 *(35.9 × 7.7 × 3.7)*
Main machinery: 1 Mirrlees diesel; 700 hp *(522 kW)*; 1 shaft
Speed, knots: 12
Complement: 2 (on passage only)

Comment: Built by Goole Shipbuilding Co in 1961-62. Side trawlers acquired in June 1982 and January 1984 *(Targe)*. These are employed as radio-controlled targets at Portland. Naval manned.

TARGE *5/1993, Wright & Logan*

2 MAGNET CLASS (DEGAUSSING VESSELS)

MAGNET A 114   **LODESTONE** A 115

Displacement, tons: 955 full load
Dimensions, feet (metres): 179.7 × 37.4 × 9.8 *(54.8 × 11.4 × 3)*
Main machinery: 2 Mirrlees-Blackstone ESL6 MCR diesels; 1650 hp *(1.23 MW)*; 2 shafts
Speed, knots: 14. **Range, miles:** 1750 at 12 kts
Complement: 15

Comment: The pair replaced the three Ham class, *Magnet* based at Portsmouth (in reserve) and *Lodestone* at Greenock. Built by Cleland SB Co Ltd, Wallsend 1979-80.

LODESTONE *2/1993, Maritime Photographic*

5 ABERDOVEY CLASS (AUXILIARY TRAINING VESSELS)

APPLEBY A 383	**ABINGER** Y 11	**BEDDGELERT** A 100
ALNMOUTH Y 13	**ABERDOVEY** Y 10	

Displacement, tons: 117.5 full load
Dimensions, feet (metres): 79.8 × 18 × 5.5 *(24 × 5.5 × 1.7)*
Main machinery: 1 Lister-Blackstone ERS4 MCR diesel; 320 hp *(239 kW)*; 1 shaft
Speed, knots: 10.5. **Range, miles:** 700 at 10 kts
Complement: 3

Comment: Commissioned in the mid-1960s as multipurpose stores carriers (25 tons) or passengers (200). Four of the class have been modified with Sampson posts removed and improved accommodation. These are allocated to Sea Cadet Corps: *Aberdovey* (southern area based at Portsmouth); *Abinger* (eastern area based at Grimsby); *Appleby* (south-west area based at Bristol); *Alnmouth* (north-west area based at Liverpool). *Beddgelert* is a tender to *Caroline* at Belfast.

ABINGER *8/1991, Maurice Bell*

4 SEA CADET CORPS VESSELS

Comment: As well as the Aberdovey class above, there are three MFVs and one ex-IMS used by the SCC: MFV 15 (northern area based at Rosyth); MFV 96 (London); MFV 816 (Gravesend); IMS *Pagham* (Stranraer). All these vessels are in constant use.

MFV *9/1991, Maritime Photographic*

OLIVER TWIST   **URIAH HEEP**

Comment: Ex-RCT General Service Launches of 20 tons. Two RNR tenders—*Oliver Twist* (London); *Uriah Heep* (Bristol).

ARMY (ROYAL LOGISTIC CORPS)

Note: Four LCVPs are listed in the RN section.

2 LANDING CRAFT, LOGISTIC (LCLs) (HMAV)

Name	No	Builders	Commissioned
ARDENNES	L 4001	Brooke Marine, Lowestoft	1977
ARAKAN	L 4003	Brooke Marine, Lowestoft	1978

Displacement, tons: 1146 light; 1733 full load
Dimensions, feet (metres): 236.8 × 49.3 × 15 *(72.2 × 15 × 4.6)*
Main machinery: 2 Mirrlees-Blackstone ESL8 MCR diesels; 2200 hp *(1.64 MW)*; 2 shafts
Speed, knots: 10.3. **Range, miles:** 4000 at 10 kts
Complement: 35 (4 officers) plus 34 troops
Military lift: 350 tons stores or 36 ISO containers; 5 MBTs or 11—8 ton trucks

Comment: Both ordered in October 1974. 150 tons dieso fuel.

ARAKAN   3/1994, van Ginderen Collection

9 RAMPED CRAFT, LOGISTIC (RCLs)

Name	No	Builders	Commissioned
ARROMANCHES	L 105	Brooke Marine, Lowestoft	31 July 1981
ANTWERP	L 106	Brooke Marine, Lowestoft	14 Aug 1981
ANDALSNES	L 107	James and Stone, Brightlingsea	22 May 1984
ABBEVILLE	L 108	James and Stone, Brightlingsea	9 Nov 1984
AKYAB	L 109	James and Stone, Brightlingsea	15 Dec 1984
AACHEN	L 110	James and Stone, Brightlingsea	12 Feb 1987
AREZZO	L 111	James and Stone, Brightlingsea	26 Mar 1987
AGHEILA	L 112	James and Stone, Brightlingsea	12 June 1987
AUDEMER	L 113	James and Stone, Brightlingsea	21 Aug 1987

Displacement, tons: 290 full load
Dimensions, feet (metres): 109.2 × 27.2 × 4.9 *(33.3 × 8.3 × 1.5)*
Main machinery: 2 Dorman 8JTCWM diesels; 504 hp *(376 kW)* sustained; 2 shafts
Speed, knots: 10
Complement: 6 (2 NCOs)

Comment: *Arromanches* and *Antwerp* based in Cyprus; *Andalsnes*, *Abbeville* and *Akyab* in Hong Kong.

AUDEMER   5/1993, Wright & Logan

1—15 METRE RANGE SAFETY CRAFT

SIR WILLIAM ROE 8127

Comment: Built by Halmatic in 1985. Details under RMAS 'Range Support Vessels'. The sole Army survivor of a class of 13 of which 12 were transferred to the RMAS on 30 September 1988. Based in Cyprus.

4 WORK BOATS Mk II

BREAM WB 03		**PERCH** WB 06	
ROACH WB 05		**MILL REEF** WB 08	

Displacement, tons: 19
Dimensions, feet (metres): 47 *(14.3)* long
Speed, knots: 8

Comment: First three built 1966-71; last one built in 1987. Can be handled by LSLs.

PERCH   6/1987, Michael D J Lennon

SCOTTISH FISHERY PROTECTION AGENCY

Notes: (1) In addition to the ships listed below *Scotia* is used for research by the Department of Fisheries.
(2) There are two Cessna Caravan II aircraft with Seaspray 2000 radars.

SULISKER   VIGILANT   NORNA

Displacement, tons: 1566 (1586 *Norna*) full load
Dimensions, feet (metres): 234.3 × 38 × 17.6 *(71.4 × 11.6 × 5.4)*
Main machinery: 2 Ruston 6AT350 diesels; 6000 hp *(4.48 MW)* sustained *(Norna)*; 2 Ruston 12 RK 3 diesels; 5600 hp *(4.18 MW)* sustained; 2 shafts; cp props; bow thruster; 450 hp *(336 kW)*
Speed, knots: 18. **Range, miles:** 7000 at 13 kts
Complement: 15 (6 officers) plus 6 spare bunks

Comment: First pair built by Appledore Ferguson, Port Glasgow. Fitted with helicopter platform. *Sulisker* completed 1981, *Vigilant* completed June 1982. Third ship of this class (although not identical) launched 11 September 1987 by Richards, Lowestoft and completed in June 1988. *Corystes* of this class was built for the Ministry of Agriculture and Fisheries in London.

VIGILANT   1992, SFPA

NORNA   1993, SFPA

WESTRA

Displacement, tons: 778 light; 1285 full load
Measurement, tons: 942 gross
Dimensions, feet (metres): 192.2 × 36.1 × 13.5 *(58.6 × 11 × 4.1)*
Main machinery: 2 British Polar SP112VS-F diesels; 4200 hp *(3.13 MW)*; 1 shaft
Speed, knots: 16.5. **Range, miles:** 10 000 at 12 kts
Complement: 15 (6 officers)

Comment: Built in 1975 by Hall Russell, Aberdeen. Near sister to RN Island class.

WESTRA   *7/1982, van Ginderen Collection*

MOIDART   MORVEN

Displacement, tons: 48 full load
Dimensions, feet (metres): 65 × 18.9 × 5.6 *(19.8 × 5.8 × 1.7)*
Main machinery: 3 Detroit 8V-92TA diesels; 1050 hp *(783 kW)* sustained; 3 shafts
Speed, knots: 18
Complement: 5 (3 officers)

Comment: Cheverton patrol craft completed April 1983. GRP hull.

MOIDART   *1/1984, A Denholm*

SKUA

Displacement, tons: 7.5 full load
Dimensions, feet (metres): 38 × 12.1 × 3.9 *(11.6 × 3.7 × 1.2)*
Main machinery: 2 Sabre 212 diesels; 424 hp *(316 kW)*; 2 shafts
Speed, knots: 24
Complement: 3 (2 officers)

Comment: Pacific 36 class RIB built by Osborne Marine in 1989. Dimensions given include the inflatable flotation collar. Second of class scrapped in 1991.

CUSTOMS

Note: The Customs and Excise (Marine Branch) of HM Treasury operates a considerable number of craft around the UK: two Brooke Marine 33 m craft *(Searcher, Seeker)*; three FBM Marine 26 m craft *(Vigilant, Valiant* and *Venturous)* two Fairey Marine 20 m craft *(Safeguard* and *Swift)*; five Cheverton 8.2 m craft *(Avocet, Bittern, Courser, Diver* and *Egret)*; plus 59 small craft ranging from 4 m Seariders to 10 m harbour launches. None of these vessels is armed. A fourth V class is building at Rosyth and is planned to be in service in 1994.

SEARCHER   *7/1993, Maritime Photographic*

TRINITY HOUSE

Note: A number of vessels of varying types—offshore support craft and lighthouse tenders—may be met throughout the waters of the UK.

THV MERMAID   *7/1993, Maritime Photographic*

SHEFFIELD   *9/1993, H M Steele*

UNITED STATES OF AMERICA

Headquarters' Appointments

Chief of Naval Operations:
Admiral Jeremy M Boorda
Vice Chief of Naval Operations:
Admiral Richard C. Macke
Director, Naval Nuclear Propulsion Programme, Naval Sea Systems Command:
Admiral Bruce DeMars
US Representative to the NATO Military Committee:
Admiral William D Smith
Commander, Military Sealift Command:
Vice Admiral Michael P Kallares
Commander, Naval Air Systems Command:
Vice Admiral William C Bowes
Commander, Naval Sea Systems Command:
Vice Admiral George R Sterner
Commander, Space and Naval Warfare Systems Command:
Rear Admiral Walter H Cantrell

Commanders-in-Chief

Commander-in-Chief, Atlantic Command and NATO Supreme Allied Commander, Atlantic:
Admiral Paul D Miller
Commander-in-Chief, Pacific Command:
Admiral Stanley R. Arthur
Commander-in-Chief, Atlantic Fleet:
Admiral William J. Flanagan Jr
Commander-in-Chief, Pacific Fleet:
Admiral Ronald J. Zlatoper
Commander-in-Chief, Naval Forces, Europe, and NATO Forces, Southern Europe:
Admiral Leighton W Smith Jr
Commander-in Chief, Strategic Command:
Admiral Henry G Chiles Jr
Commander-in-Chief, Central Command:
General Joseph P Hoar (Marines)

Flag Officers (Central Area)

Commander, US Naval Forces, Central Command and Middle East Force:
Vice Admiral John S. Redd

Flag Officers (Atlantic Area)

Commander, Second Fleet, Atlantic Fleet and Striking Fleet, Atlantic:
Vice Admiral Jay L. Johnson
Commander, Naval Surface Force, Atlantic Fleet:
Vice Admiral Philip M Quast
Commander, Sixth Fleet and Striking and Support Forces, Southern Europe:
Vice Admiral Joseph W Prueher
Commander, Submarine Force, Atlantic Fleet and Submarine Allied Command, Atlantic:
Vice Admiral George W Emery
Commander, Naval Air Force, Atlantic Fleet:
Vice Admiral Richard C Allen
Commander, Fleet Air, Keflavik and US Defense Force, Iceland:
Rear Admiral Michael D Haskins
Commander, South Atlantic Force, Atlantic Fleet:
Rear Admiral Wirt R Fladd
Commander, Mine Warfare Command:
Rear Admiral John D Pearson
Commander, Joint Task Force Four:
Rear Admiral George N Gee

Flag Officers (Pacific Area)

Commander, Seventh Fleet, Pacific Fleet:
Vice Admiral Timothy W Wright
Commander, Naval Surface Force, Pacific Fleet:
Vice Admiral David B Robinson
Commander, Third Fleet, Pacific Fleet:
Vice Admiral Jerry L Unruh
Commander, Naval Air Force, Pacific Fleet:
Vice Admiral Robert J Spane
Commander, US Naval Forces, Japan:
Rear Admiral Byron E Tobin
Commander, Submarine Force, Pacific Fleet:
Rear Admiral John M Barr
Commander, US Naval Forces, Korea:
Rear Admiral Edison L Watkins III

Marine Corps

Commandant:
General Carl E Mundy Jr
Assistant Commandant:
General Walter E Boomer
Commander, Fleet Marine Force, Atlantic:
Lieutenant General William M Keys
Commander, Fleet Marine Force, Pacific:
Lieutenant General Henry C Stackpole III

Territorial Seas

On 27 December 1988, the United States claimed territorial seas were extended from three to 12 nautical miles. The USA now exercises sovereignty over waters, seabed and airspace out to 12 nautical miles. This extension also applies to the Commonwealth of Puerto Rico, Guam, American Samoa, the US Virgin Islands, the Commonwealth of the Northern Mariana Islands and any other territory or possession over which the USA exercises sovereignty.

The USA continues to recognise the right of all ships to conduct innocent passage and, in the case of international straits, the right of all ships and aircraft to conduct transit passage through its territorial sea.

Personnel

	1 Jan 1992	1 Jan 1993	1 Jan 1994
Navy			
Officers	72 392	70 777	67 678
Midshipmen	4273	4336	4101
Enlisted	505 174	478 051	444 233
Marine Corps			
Officers	19 753	18 980	18 195
Enlisted	174 287	166 059	158 378

Mercantile Marine

Lloyd's Register of Shipping:
5617 vessels of 14 071 733 tons gross

Strength of the Fleet (1 June 1994)

Type	Active (NRF)	Building (Projected) + Conversion/SLEP	Type	Active	Building (Projected) + Conversion/SLEP
SHIPS OF THE FLEET			**Auxiliary Ships**		
			AD Destroyer Tenders	6	—
Strategic Missile Submarines			AE Ammunition Ships	10	—
SSBN (Ballistic Missile Submarines)	17	4	AFS Combat Stores Ships	2	—
(nuclear-powered)			AGF Miscellaneous Command Ships	2	—
			AGSS Auxiliary Research Submarine	1	—
Attack Submarines			AO Oilers	5	—
SSN Submarines (nuclear-powered)	84	9 (1)	AOE Fast Combat Support Ships	5	3
			AOR Replenishment Oilers	5	—
Aircraft Carriers			ARL Repair Ship Small	1	—
CVN Multipurpose Aircraft Carriers	6	2 (1) + 1	ARS Salvage Ships	7 (2)	—
(nuclear-powered)			AS Submarine Tenders	9	—
CV Multipurpose Aircraft Carriers	5	+ 1	ASR Submarine Rescue Ships	3	—
(conventionally powered)			ATS Salvage and Rescue Ships	3	—
			AVT Training Carrier	1	—
Cruisers					
CGN Guided Missile Cruisers	7	—			
(nuclear-powered)					
CG Guided Missile Cruisers	30	—			
			NAVAL RESERVE FORCE		
Destroyers					
DDG Guided Missile Destroyers	9	24 (3)	FFT Frigates	4	—
DD Destroyers	31	—	FFG Guided Missile Frigates	16	—
			MSO Minesweepers (Ocean)	2	—
Frigates					
FFG Guided Missile Frigates	35 (16)	—			
FF Frigates	— (4)	—			
			MILITARY SEALIFT COMMAND INVENTORY		
Patrol Forces					
PC Coastal Patrol Craft	6	7	**STRATEGIC SEALIFT (Active)**		
Amphibious Warfare Ships			**Ocean Transportation Ships**		
LCC Amphibious Command Ships	2	—	TAO/TAOT Oilers, Tankers	19	—
LHA Amphibious Assault Ships	5	—	Ro-Ro, Freighters, Tankers	As required	—
(general-purpose)					
LHD Amphibious Assault Ships	3	3	**Prepositioning Ships**		
(multipurpose)			TAK/TAKB/TAKF Cargo Ships	9	—
LPD Amphibious Transport Docks	11	(12)	TAOT Tankers	2	—
LPH Amphibious Assault Ships	5	—	TAK Maritime Prepositioning Ships (MPS)	13	—
(helicopter)					
LSD Dock Landing Ships	13	4	**Naval Fleet Auxiliary Force**		
LST Tank Landing Ships	7	—	TAO Oilers	13	5
			TAFS Combat Stores Ships	7	—
Mine Warfare Ships			TATF Fleet Ocean Tugs	7	—
MCM Mine Countermeasures Ships	13	1	TAGOS Ocean Surveillance Ships	14	1
MSO Minesweepers	1 (2)	—	TAK-FBM Fleet Ballistic Missile Ships	1	—
(Ocean)			TAE Ammunition Ship	1	—
MHC Minehunters	1	11			
(Coastal)					

Type	Active	Building	Type	Active	Building
STRATEGIC SEALIFT (Reserve)			**Aviation Support Ships**		
			TAVB Aviation Support Ships (MPS)	2	—
Fast Sealift Ships					
TAKR Fast Sealift Ships (MPS)	8	—	**Hospital Ships**		
			TAH Hospital Ships	2	—
Ready Reserve Force					
TAK/TAKR Cargo Ships (break bulk)	49	—	**SPECIAL MISSION SUPPORT SHIPS**		
TAKR Roll-on/Roll-off Ships	28	—			
TACS Crane Ships	10	—	TAGM Missile Range Instrumentation Ships	2	—
TAKR Heavy Lift Ships	3	—	TAGOR Oceanographic Research Ships	(5 on loan)	3
TAK Barge Carriers	4	—	TAGS Surveying Ships	9	3
TAOT/TAOG Product Carriers	11	—	TAG Navigation Research Ship	1	—
TAP Troop Carriers	2	—	TAG Acoustic Research Ship	1	—
			TARC/TAK Cable Repairing Ships	2	—

Special Notes

To provide similar information to that included in other major navies' Deployment Tables the fleet assignment (abbreviated 'F/S') status of each ship in the US Navy has been included. The assignment appears in a column immediately to the right of the commissioning date. In the case of the Floating Dry Dock section this system is not used. The following abbreviations are used to indicate fleet assignments:

AA	active Atlantic Fleet
Active	active under charter with MSC
AR	in reserve Out of Commission, Atlantic Fleet
ASA	active In Service, Atlantic Fleet
ASR	in reserve Out of Service, Atlantic Fleet
Bldg	building
CONV	ship undergoing conversion
LOAN	ship or craft loaned to another government, or non-government agency, but US Navy retains title or the ship or craft is on the NVR
MAR	in reserve Out of Commission, Atlantic Fleet and laid up in the temporary custody of the Maritime Administration
MPR	same as 'MAR', but applies to the Pacific Fleet
NRF	assigned to the Naval Reserve Force (ships so assigned are listed in a special table for major warships and amphibious ships)
Ord	the contract for the construction of the ship has been let, but actual construction has not yet begun
PA	active Pacific Fleet
PR	in reserve Out of Commission, Pacific Fleet
Proj	the ship is scheduled for construction at some time in the immediate future
PSA	active In Service, Pacific Fleet
PSR	in reserve Out of Service, Pacific Fleet
ROS	reduced Operating Status
TAA	active Military Sealift Command, Atlantic Fleet
TAR	in Ready Reserve, Military Sealift Command, Atlantic Fleet
TPA	active Military Sealift Command, Pacific Fleet
TPR	in Ready Reserve, Military Sealift Command, Pacific Fleet
TWWR	active Military Sealift Command, World-wide Routes

Ship Status Definitions

In Commission: as a rule any ship, except a Service Craft, that is active, is in commission. The ship has a Commanding Officer and flies a commissioning pennant. 'Commissioning date' as used in this section means the date of being 'in commission' rather than 'completion' or 'acceptance into service' as used in some other navies.

In Service: all service craft (dry docks and with classifications that start with 'Y'), with the exception of *Constitution*, that are active, are 'in service'. The ship has an Officer- in-Charge and does not fly a commissioning pennant.

Ships 'in reserve, out of commission' or 'in reserve, out of service' are put in a state of preservation for future service. Depending on the size of the ship or craft, a ship in 'mothballs' usually takes from 30 days to nearly a year to restore to full operational service. The above status definitions do not apply to the Military Sealift Command.

Approved Fiscal Year 1993 Programme

Shipbuilding

		Appropriations (US$ million)
4	Arleigh Burke class DDG (DDG 73-76)	3230
1	Wasp class LHD (LHD 6) (partial funding)	303.1
1	Whidbey Island CV class LSD (LSD 52)	322.6
2	Osprey class MHC (MHC 11-12)	225.3
1	Supply class AOE (AOE 9)	298.1
	Carrier Replacement Programme (Advance Procurement)	829.4
	National Defense Sealift Fund	613.4

Notes: (1) Congress authorised the expenditure of $1200 million for construction of LHD 6, but funded only $303.1 million. The balance of the funding is included in the FY 1994 budget.
(2) The construction of LSD 52 was authorised in the FY 1992 budget, but no funds were provided for construction. This action provides funding for construction.
(3) $500 million was included in the FY 1992 budget for construction of the fourth ship of the AOE-6 class. Subsequently, $300 million of that sum was rescinded, and restored in FY 1993.
(4) Funding for construction of sealift ships is incorporated into the National Defense Sealift Fund which now includes $2.643 million. This fund is controlled by the Department of Defense.

Approved Fiscal Year 1994 Programme

Shipbuilding

		Appropriations (US$ million)
3	Arleigh Burke class DDG (DDG 77-79)	2637.9
1	Wasp class LHD (LHD 6) (completion)	888.6
2	AGOR/TAGS Oceanographic Research Ships	109.5
1	Mine Warfare Command Ship Conversion (MCS(C))	123.6
	Carrier Replacement Programme (Advance Procurement)	1200

Note: The Carrier Replacement funding (for CVN 76) was appropriated in FY 1994 budget but not authorised until February 1994.

Proposed Fiscal Year 1995 Programme

Shipbuilding

		Appropriations (US$ million)
1	Nimitz class (CVN 76)	2447.0
3	Arleigh Burke class (DDG 80-82)	2697.7
1	Kilauea class AE conversion	30.6
1	Mars class AFS conversion	22.8

Notes: (1) The conversions are for AE32 and AFS 6 for MSC service.
(2) SSN 23 is planned for FY 1996 and the New Attack Submarine for FY 1998.

Naval Aviation

US Naval Aviation has scaled down to an active inventory of 4703 aircraft as of 1 January 1994, with approximately 25 per cent of these being operated by the Marine Corps. The principal naval aviation organisations are 11 carrier air wings, 18 maritime patrol squadrons, and three Marine aircraft wings. In addition the Naval Reserve and the Marine Corps Reserve are reducing their Reserve aviation forces to a single combined Air Wing.

Fighter Attack: 22 Naval and 15 Marine Corps squadrons with F/A-18 Hornets. 19 Navy Squadrons for F-14 Tomcats.
Attack: 9 Navy squadrons with A-6E Intruders. 7 Marine squadrons with AV-8B Harriers.
Airborne Early Warning: 12 Navy squadrons with E-2C Hawkeye.
Electronic Warfare: 11 Navy and 4 Marine squadrons with EA-6B Prowler.
Anti-Submarine: 11 Navy squadrons with S-3A/B Viking.
Maritime Patrol: 16 Navy squadrons with P-3C Orion.
Helicopter Anti-Submarine: 22 Navy squadrons with SH-3G/H Sea King, SH-2 LAMPS I, SH-60B and SH-60F LAMPS III.
Helicopter Mine Countermeasures: 2 Navy squadrons with MH-53E Sea Dragons.
Helicopter Support: 7 Navy squadrons with UH-46D/E Sea Knight and CH-53E Super Stallions.
Electronic Reconnaissance: 2 Navy squadrons with EP-3E Orion and 2 with ES-3A Viking.
Communications Relay: 2 Navy squadrons with E-6A Tacamos.
Helicopter Gunship: 6 Marine squadrons with AH-1T/W SuperCobra.
Helicopter Transport: 24 Marine squadrons with CH-46D/E Sea Knight (15), and CH-53D Sea Stallion (3) and CH-53E Super Stallion (6).

Aircraft Procurement Plan FY 1994-96

	94	95	96
AV-8B	4	4*	7*
F/A-18C/D	36	24	24
CH/MH-53E	12	—	—
AH-1W	12	12	9
SH-60B	7	—	—
T-45TS	12	12	12
HH-60H	17	—	—
E-2C	—	4	4

* Remanufactured aircraft
Note: Funding for the first F/A-18E/F is planned for FY 1997.

Naval Special Warfare

SEAL (Sea Air Land) teams are manned at a nominal 10 platoons per team, with 30 platoons on each coast based at Coronado and Norfolk, Virginia. Assigned directly to CinC US Special Operations Command, platoons are allocated to theatre commanders during operational deployments.

Bases

Naval Air Stations and Air Facilities

NAS Adak, AK; NAS Alameda, CA; NAF China Lake, CA; NAF El Centro, CA; NAS Los Alamitos, CA; NAS Miramar; NAS Lemoore, CA; NAS Moffett Field (San Jose), CA; NAS Point Mugu, CA; NAS North Island (San Diego), CA; NAF Andrews, Washington DC; NAS Cecil Field (Jacksonville), FL; NAS Jacksonville, FL; NAS Key West, FL; NAS Whiting Field (Milton), FL; NAS Saufley Field (Pensacola), FL; NAS Pensacola, FL; NAS Mayport, FL; NAS Atlanta (Marietta), GA; NAS Glenview, Ill; NAS Barbers Point (Oahu), HI; NAS New Orleans, LA; NAS Brunswick, ME; NAS Patuxent River, MD; NAS South Weymouth, MA; NAF Detroit, MI; NAS Meridian, MS; NAS Fallon, NV; NAS Lakehurst, NJ; NAF Warminster, PA; NAS Willow Grove, PA; NAS Memphis (Millington), TN; NAS Chase Field (Beeville), TX; NAS Corpus Christi, TX; NAS Dallas, TX; NAS Kingsville, TX; NAS Norfolk, VA; NAS Oceana, VA; NAS Whidbey Island (Oak Harbor), WA; NAF Lajes, Azores; NAS Bermuda; NAS Guantanamo Bay, Cuba; NAF Naples, NAS Sigonella (Sicily), Italy; NAF Atsugi, Japan; NAS Agana, Guam; NAF Okinawa; NAS Diego Garcia.

Naval Stations and Naval Bases (22)

Yokosuka, Japan; Midway Is; Adak, AK; Pearl Harbor, HI; Treasure Is, San Francisco, CA; San Diego, CA; Coronado, San Diego, CA (Amphibs); Long Beach, CA; Mayport, FL; Roosevelt Roads, Puerto Rico; Guantanamo Bay, Cuba; Charleston, SC; Norfolk, VA; Little Creek, Norfolk, VA (Amphibs); Philadelphia, PA; New London, CT (Submarines); Newport, RI; Argentia, Newfoundland; Keflavik, Iceland; Rota, Spain; Naples, Italy; Staten Island, NY.

Strategic Missile Submarine Bases (3)

Charleston, SC; Bangor, WA (West Coast Trident base); Kings Bay, GA (East Coast Trident base)

Navy Yard (1)

Washington, DC (MSC Headquarters) (administration and historical activities).

Naval Shipyards (8)

Pearl Harbor, HI; Puget Sound, Bremerton, WA; Mare Is, Vallejo, CA; Charleston, SC; Norfolk, VA; Philadelphia, PA; Portsmouth, NH (located in Kittery, ME); Long Beach, CA.

Naval Ship Repair Facilities (3)

Yokosuka, Japan; Apra Harbor, Guam; Lumut, Singapore.

Marine Corps Air Stations and Helicopter Facilities (10)

MCAS: Beaufort, SC; El Toro (Santa Ana), CA; Yuma, AZ; Kaneohe Bay, Oahu, HI; Quantico, VA; Cherry Point, NC; Iwakuni, Honshu, Japan; New River (Jacksonville), NC.
MCHF: Tustin, CA; Futema, Okinawa.

Marine Corps Bases (5)

Camp Pendleton, CA; Twentynine Palms, CA; Camp H M Smith (Oahu), HI; Camp Lejeune, NC; Camp Smedley D Butler (Kawasaki), Okinawa, Japan.

CLASSIFICATION OF NAVAL SHIPS AND SERVICE CRAFT

COMBATANT SHIPS

WARSHIPS
Aircraft Carriers:
Aircraft Carrier	CV
Aircraft Carrier	CVN
(nuclear propulsion)	

Surface Combatants:
Guided Missile Cruiser	CG
Guided Missile Cruiser	CGN
(nuclear propulsion)	
Destroyer	DD
Guided Missile Destroyer	DDG
Frigate	FF
Guided Missile Frigate	FFG

Patrol Combatants:
Patrol Combatant Missile	PHM
(hydrofoil)	

Submarines:
Ballistic Missile Submarine	SSBN
(nuclear propulsion)	
Attack Submarine	SSN
(nuclear propulsion)	
Auxiliary Submarine	SSAG

AMPHIBIOUS WARFARE SHIPS
Amphibious Command Ship	LCC
Amphibious Assault Ship	LHA/LHD
(multipurpose)	
Amphibious Cargo Ship	LKA
Amphibious Transport Dock	LPD
Amphibious Assault Ship	LPH
(helicopter)	
Dock Landing Ship	LSD
Logistic Support Vessel (Army)	LSV
Tank Landing Ship	LST

MINE WARFARE SHIPS
Mine Countermeasures Ship	MCM
Minehunter Coastal	MHC
Minesweeper Ocean	MSO
Minesweeping Boats/Drones	MSB/ MSD

AMPHIBIOUS WARFARE CRAFT
Landing Craft, Air Cushion	LCAC
Landing Craft, Mechanised	LCM
Landing Craft, Personnel, Large	LCPL
Landing Craft, Utility	LCU
Landing Craft, Vehicle, Personnel	LCVP
Light Seal Support Craft	LSSC
Amphibious Warping Tug	LWT
Medium Seal Support Craft	MSSC
Swimmer Delivery Vehicle	SDV
Side Loading Warping Tug	SLWT
Special Warfare Craft, Light	SWCL
Special Warfare Craft, Medium	SWCM

PATROL CRAFT
Mini-Armored Troop Carrier	ATC
Patrol Boat (Coastal)	PB(C)
River Patrol Boat	PBR
Patrol Craft	PC
Patrol Craft (fast)	PCF
Patrol Craft (Coastal)	PCC

AUXILIARY SHIPS
Destroyer Tender	AD
Ammunition Ship	AE
Combat Store Ship	AFS
Miscellaneous	AG
Deep Submergence Support Ship	AGDS
Hydrofoil Research Ship	AGEH
Miscellaneous Command Ship	AGF
Missile Range Instrumentation Ship	AGM
Oceanographic Research Ship	AGOR
Ocean Surveillance Ship	AGOS
Patrol Craft Tender	AGP
Surveying Ship	AGS
Auxiliary Research Submarine	AGSS
Hospital Ship	AH
Cargo Ship	AK
Vehicle Cargo Ship	AKR
Auxiliary Lighter	ALS
Oiler	AO
Fast Combat Support Ship	AOE
Gasoline Tanker	AOG
Replenishment Oiler	AOR
Transport Oiler	AOT
Transport	AP
Self-Propelled Barracks Ship	APB
Repair Ship	AR
Cable Repairing Ship	ARC
Repair Ship, Small	ARL
Salvage Ship	ARS
Submarine Tender	AS
Submarine Rescue Ship	ASR
Auxiliary Ocean Tug	ATA
Fleet Ocean Tug	ATF
Salvage and Rescue Ship	ATS
Guided Missile Ship	AVM
Auxiliary Aircraft Landing Training Ship	AVT

SERVICE CRAFT
Large Auxiliary Floating Dry Dock (non self-propelled)	AFDB
Small Auxiliary Floating Dry Dock (non self-propelled)	AFDL
Medium Auxiliary Floating Dry Dock (non self-propelled)	AFDM
Barracks Craft (non self propelled)	APL
Auxiliary Repair Dry Dock (non self-propelled)	ARD
Medium Auxiliary Repair Dry Dock (non self-propelled)	ARDM
Deep Submergence Rescue Vehicle	DSRV
Deep Submergence Vehicle	DSV
Harbour Security Boats	HSB
Unclassified Miscellaneous	IX
Submersible Research Vehicle	NR
Miscellaneous Auxiliary (self-propelled)	YAG
Open Lighter (non self-propelled)	YC
Car Float (non self-propelled)	YCF
Aircraft Transportation Lighter (non self-propelled)	YCV

Floating Crane (non self-propelled)	YD
Diving Tender (non self-propelled)	YDT
Covered Lighter (self-propelled)	YF
Ferry Boat or Launch (self-propelled)	YFB
Yard Floating Dry Dock (non self-propelled)	YFD
Covered Lighter (non self-propelled)	YFN
Large Covered Lighter (non self-propelled)	YFNB
Dry Dock Companion Craft (non self-propelled)	YFND
Lighter (special purpose) (non self-propelled)	YFNX
Floating Power Barge (non self-propelled)	YFP
Refrigerated Covered Lighter (self-propelled)	YFR
Refrigerated Covered Lighter (non self-propelled)	YFRN
Covered Lighter (range tender) (self-propelled)	YFRT
Harbor Utility Craft (self-propelled)	YFU
Garbage Lighter (self-propelled)	YG
Garbage Lighter (non self-propelled)	YGN
Salvage Lift Craft, Heavy (non self-propelled)	YHLC
Dredge (self-propelled)	YM
Salvage Lift Craft, Medium (non self-propelled)	YMLC
Gate Craft (non self-propelled)	YNG
Fuel Oil Barge (self-propelled)	YO
Gasoline Barge (self-propelled)	YOG
Gasoline Barge (non self-propelled)	YOGN
Fuel Oil Barge (non self-propelled)	YON
Oil Storage Barge (non self-propelled)	YOS
Patrol Craft (self-propelled)	YP
Floating Pile Driver (non self-propelled)	YPD
Floating Workshop (non self-propelled)	YR
Repair and Berthing Barge (non self-propelled)	YRB
Repair, Berthing and Messing Barge (non self-propelled)	YRBM
Floating Dry Dock Workshop (hull) (non self-propelled)	YRDH
Floating Dry Dock Workshop (machine) (non self-propelled)	YRDM
Radiological Repair Barge (non self-propelled)	YRR
Salvage Craft Tender (non self-propelled)	YRST
Seaplane Wrecking Derrick (self-propelled)	YSD
Sludge Removal Barge (non self-propelled)	YSR
Large Harbour Tug	YTB
Small Harbour Tug	YTL
Medium Harbour Tug	YTM
Water Barge (self-propelled)	YW
Water Barge (non self-propelled)	YWN

Letter prefixes to classification symbols may be added for further identification. E: prototype ship in an experimental or developmental status. T: assigned to Military Sealift Command. F: being built for a foreign government. X: often added to existing classifications to indicate a new class whose characteristics have not been defined. N: denotes nuclear propulsion when used as last letter of ship symbol.

Classification Of Maritime Administration Ship Designs

The US Maritime Administration is a Division of the US Department of Transportation. All US flag merchant vessels are built under the jurisdiction of the US Maritime Administration and are assigned Maritime Administration design classifications. These classifications consist of three groups of letters and numbers. A number of US Naval Auxiliaries were originally built to Maritime Administration specifications and were acquired during construction or after the ship was completed. It should be noted that the Maritime Administration acts as a 'ship broker' for the US Government and does not build ships for itself. The Maritime Administration generally oversees the operation and administration of the US Merchant Marine.

Merchant Ship Design Classifications

		Length in feet at load water line			
Type		1	2	3	4
C	Cargo	'400	400-450	450-500	500-550
P	Passenger	'500	500-600	600-700	700-800
N	Coastal Cargo	'200	200-250	250-300	300-350
R	Refrigerated Cargo	'400	400-450	450-500	500-550
S	Special (Navy)	'200	200-300	300-400	400-500
T	Tanker	'450	450-500	500-550	550-600

Type of propulsion; number of propellers and passengers

	Single screw		Twin screw	
Passengers	1/12	13+	1/12	13+
Power				
Steam	S	S1	ST	S2
Motor (Diesel)	M	M1	MT	M2
Turbo-Electric	SE	SE1	SET	SE2

Example: C4-S-B1. C4: Cargo Ship between 500 and 550 ft long; S: steam powered; B1: 1st variation ('1') of the original design ('B'). If the third group of letters and numbers read BV1 instead of B1, the translation of the code would be, the 1st variation ('1') of the 22nd modification ('V') of the original design ('B').

Electronic Equipment Classification

The 'AN' nomenclature was designed so that a common designation could be used for Army, Navy and Air Force equipment. The system indicator 'AN' does not mean that the Army, Navy and Air Force use the equipment, but means that the type number was assigned in the 'AN' system.
'AN' nomenclature is assigned to complete sets of equipment and major components of military design; groups of articles of either commercial or military design which are grouped for military purposes; major articles of military design which are not part of or used with a set; and commercial articles when nomenclature will not facilitate military identification and/or procedures.
'AN' nomenclature is not assigned to articles catalogued commercially except as stated above; minor components of military design for which other adequate means of identification are available; small parts such as capacitors and resistors; and articles having other adequate identification in joint military specifications. Nomenclature assignments remain unchanged regardless of later installation and/or application.

Installation

A	Airborne (installed and operated in aircraft).
B	Underwater mobile, submarine.
C	Air transportable (inactivated, do not use).
D	Pilotless carrier.
F	Fixed.
G	Ground, general ground use (includes two or more ground-type installations).
K	Amphibious.
M	Ground, mobile (installed as operating unit in a vehicle which has no function other than transporting the equipment).
P	Pack or portable (animal or man).
S	Water surface craft.
T	Ground, transportable.
U	General utility (includes two or more general installation classes, airborne, shipboard, and ground).
V	Ground, vehicular (installed in vehicle designed for functions other than carrying electronic equipment, etc, such as tanks).
W	Water surface and underwater.

Type of Equipment

A   Invisible light, heat radiation.
B   Pigeon.
C   Carrier.
D   Radiac.
E   Nupac.
F   Photographic.
G   Telegraph or teletype.
I   Interphone and public address.
J   Electromechanical or inertial wire covered.
K   Telemetering.
L   Countermeasures.
M   Meteorological.
N   Sound in air.
P   Radar.
Q   Sonar and underwater sound.
R   Radio.
S   Special types, magnetic, etc, or combinations of types.
T   Telephone (wire).
V   Visual and visible light.
W   Armament (peculiar to armament, not otherwise covered).
X   Facsimile or television.
Y   Data processing.

Purpose

A   Auxiliary assemblies (not complete operating sets used with or part of two or more sets or sets series).
B   Bombing.
C   Communications (receiving and transmitting).
D   Direction finder, reconnaissance and/or surveillance.
E   Ejection and/or release.
G   Fire-control or searchlight directing.
H   Recording and/or reproducing (graphic meteorological and sound).
K   Computing.
L   Searchlight control (inactivated, use G).
M   Maintenance and test assemblies (including tools).
N   Navigational aids (including altimeters, beacons, compasses, racons, depth sounding, approach, and landing).
P   Reproducing (inactivated, do not use).
Q   Special, or combination of purposes.
R   Receiving, passive detecting.
S   Detecting and/or range and bearing, search.
T   Transmitting.
W   Automatic flight or remote control.
X   Identification and recognition.
Example: AN/URD-4A. AN: 'AN' System; U: General Utility; R: Radio; D: Direction Finder, Reconnaissance, and/or Surveillance; 4: Model Number; A: Modification Letter.

Major Commercial Shipyards

Avondale Industries, New Orleans, Louisiana
Avondale Gulfport, Gulfport, Mississippi
Bath Iron Works, Bath, Maine
Bethlehem Steel, Sparrows Point, Maryland
Bollinger Machine Shop and Shipyard, Lockport, Louisiana
Derecktor Shipyards, Middletown, Rhode Island
General Dynamics Corporation, Electric Boat Division, Groton, Connecticut
Halter Marine Inc, Moss Point, Mississippi
Ingalls Shipbuilding, Pascagoula, Mississippi
Intermarine USA, Savannah, Georgia
Marinette Marine, Marinette, Wisconsin
McDermott Shipyards, Morgan City, Louisiana
National Steel & Shipbuilding Company, San Diego, California
Newport News Shipbuilding Company, Newport News, Virginia
Peterson Builders Incorporated, Sturgeon Bay, Wisconsin
Textron Marine Systems, New Orleans, Louisiana

Note: All the above yards have engaged in naval shipbuilding, overhaul, or modernisation except for the General Dynamics/ Electric Boat yard which is engaged only in submarine work. Newport News is the only US shipyard capable of building nuclear-powered aircraft carriers.

Ships Scheduled for Delivery during FY 1994 (21)

Fleet Ballistic Missile Submarine: *Rhode Island* (SSBN 740).
Attack Submarines: *Santa Fe* (SSN 763), *Montpelier* (SSN 765), *Charlotte* (SSN 766), *Hampton* (SSN 767).
Cruiser: *Port Royal* (CG 73).
Guided Missile Destroyers: *Curtis Wilber* (DDG 54), *Stout* (DDG 55), *John S McCain* (DDG 56), *Mischer* (DDG 57), *Laboon* (DDG 58).
Mine Countermeasures Ships: *Dextrous* (MCM 13), *Chief* (MCM 14).
Coastal Minehunter: *Heron* (MHC 52).
Oiler: *Yukon* (TAO 202).
Coastal Patrol Boats: *Monsoon* (PC 4), *Typhoon* (PC 5), *Sirocco* (PC 6), *Squall* (PC 7), *Zephyr* (PC 8), *Chinook* (PC 9).

Ships Scheduled for Delivery during FY 1995 (25)

Fleet Ballistic Missile Submarine: *Maine* (SSBN 741).
Attack Submarines: *Hartford* (SSN 768), *Toledo* (SSN 769), *Tucson* (SSN 770), *Columbia* (SSN 771).
Guided Missile Destroyers: *Russell* (DDG 59), *Paul Hamilton* (DDG 60), *Ramage* (DDG 61), *Fitzgerald* (DDG 62), *Stethem* (DDG 63), *Carney* (DDG 64).
Amphibious Assault Ships: *Boxer* (LHD 4), *Bataan* (LHD 5).
Dock Landing Ships (Cargo Variant): *Harpers Ferry* (LSD 49), *Carter Hall* (LSD 50).
Coastal Minehunters: *Pelican* (MHC 53), *Robin* (MHC 54).
Coastal Patrol Boats: *Firebolt* (PC 10), *Whirlwind* (PC 11), *Thunderbolt* (PC 12), *Shamal* (PC 13).
Combat Support Ships: *Rainier* (AOE 7), *Arctic* (AOE 8).
Ocean Survey Ships: *Pathfinder* (TAGS 60), *Sumner* (TAGS 61).

CONVERSIONS (4):
Vehicle Cargo Ships: (TAKR 295), (TAKR 296), (TAKR 297), (TAKR 298).

Major Warships Taken Out of Service mid-1991 to mid-1994

SSBN
1991   *Lewis and Clark, George C Marshall*
1992   *Alexander Hamilton, Ulysses S Grant, George Washington Carver, Will Rodgers, James Madison, Henry L Stimson*
1993   *Woodrow Wilson, Tecumseh, Benjamin Franklin, Francis Scott Key, Daniel Boone, Casimir Pulaski, John C Calhoun*
1994   *Von Steuben, George Bancroft*

SSN
1991   *Permit, Haddo, Lapon, Guitarro, Sea Devil*
1992   *Tinosa, Guardfish, John Marshall, Haddock, Flasher, Ray, Queenfish*
1993   *Baton Rouge, Richard B Russell, Greenling*
1994   *Sturgeon, Silversides, Gato*

CV
1991   *Lexington*
1992   *Midway*
1993   *Ranger, Forrestal*

BB
1991   *Wisconsin, New Jersey*
1992   *Missouri*

CG/CGN
1993   *Texas, Leahy, Worden, Yarnell, Wainwright, Reeves, Biddle, Gridley*
1994   *Long Beach, Daniels, England, Halsey, Jouett, Horne, Standley, Fox, Sterett*

DDG
1991   *Luce, King, Sampson, Tattnall, William V Pratt, Preble, Lynde McCormick, Robison, Buchanan, Semmes* (to Greece), *Benjamin Stoddert*
1992   *Charles F Adams, Dahlgren, Goldsborough, Waddell* (to Greece), *Berkeley* (to Greece)
1993   *MacDonough, Mahan*

FF/FFG (most of the Knox class is to be leased in 1994/95)
1991   *Roark, Gray, Hepburn, Meyerkord, W S Sims, Lang, Patterson, Bagley, Badger, Blakely, Barbey, Miller, Valdez*
1992   *Knox, Connole, Rathburne, Whipple, Reasoner* (to Turkey), *Stein, Francis Hammond, Vreeland* (to Greece), *Downes, Robert E Peary* (to Taiwan), *Harold E Holt, Trippe* (to Greece), *Paul, Aylwin, Brewton* (to Taiwan), *Pharris, Cook*
1993   *Kirk* (to Taiwan), *Lockwood, Marvin Shields, Fanning* (to Turkey), *Ouellet, Elmer Montgomery* (to Turkey), *Thomas C Hart* (to Turkey), *Capodanno* (to Turkey)
1994   *Moinester, Jesse L Brown, Donald B Beary, Joseph Hughes*

LSD/LPD/LST/LKA/LPH
1991   *Raleigh*
1992   *Vancouver, Barbour County, Newport, Charleston*
1993   *Manitowoc, Sumter, Saint Louis, Iwo Jima, Okinawa, Racine, Schenectedy*
1994   *Peoria, Saginaw, Boulder, Fairfax County, Spartanburg County, Tuscaloosa, Durham, El Paso, Mobile, Fresno*

MSO/MSB
1991   *Adroit, Engage, Enhance, Impervious, Leader*
1992   *Constant, Excel, Fortify*, 7 MSBs
1993   *Exploit, Gallant, Pledge*
1994   *Affray*

PHM
1993   *Pegasus, Hercules, Taurus, Aquila, Aries, Gemini*

Auxiliaries
1991   *Vulcan* (AR), *Fulton* (AS), *Petrel* (ASR), *Florikan* (ASR), *Lynch* (AGOR), *H H Hess* (AGS), *Mississinewa* (AO), *Hassayampa* (AO), *Truckee* (AO), *Navasota* (AO), *Passumpsic* (AO), *Pawcatuck* (AO), *Waccamaw* (AO), *Neptune* (ARC)
1992   *Prairie* (AD), *Concord* (AFS) (to MSC), *Wichita* (AOR), *Preserver* (ARS), *Proteus* (AS), *Pigeon* (ASR), *Paiute* (ATF), *Papago* (ATF), *Vanguard* (AG), *Rigel* (AF), *Destiguer* (AGOR) (to Tunisia), *Thomas Washington* (AGOR) (to Chile), *S P Lee* (AG) (to Mexico), *Adventurous* (AGOS) (to NOAA)
1993   *Mars* (AFS) (to MSC), *Point Loma* (AGDS), *Glover* (AGFF), *Contender* (AGOS), *Chauvenet* (AGS), *Harkness* (AGS), *Marshfield* (AK), *Neosho* (AO), *Kawishiwi* (AO), *Ponchatoula* (AO), *Orion* (AS), *Sierra* (AD), *Haleakala* (AE), *Sylvania* (AFS) (to MSC), *San Diego* (AFS) (to MSC), *San Jose* (AFS) (to MSC), 6 AGOS (to Govt agencies)
1994   *Milwaukee* (AOR), *Yosemite* (AD), *Pyro* (AE), *Jason* (AR), *Conserver* (ARS), *Redstone* (AGM), *Bartlett* (AGOR)

HULL NUMBERS

Note: Ships in reserve not included.

SUBMARINES

Ballistic Missile Submarines

James Madison class
SSBN 634   Stonewall Jackson

Benjamin Franklin class
SSBN 641   Simon Bolivar
SSBN 658   Mariano G Vallejo

Ohio class
SSBN 726   Ohio
SSBN 727   Michigan
SSBN 728   Florida
SSBN 729   Georgia
SSBN 730   Henry M Jackson
SSBN 731   Alabama
SSBN 732   Alaska
SSBN 733   Nevada
SSBN 734   Tennessee
SSBN 735   Pennsylvania

SSBN 736   West Virginia
SSBN 737   Kentucky
SSBN 738   Maryland
SSBN 739   Nebraska
SSBN 740   Rhode Island
SSBN 741   Maine
SSBN 742   Wyoming
SSBN 743   Louisiana

Attack Submarines

Benjamin Franklin class
SSN 642   Kamehameha
SSN 645   James K Polk

Seawolf class
SSN 21   Seawolf
SSN 22   Connecticut

Sturgeon class
SSN 638   Whale
SSN 639   Tautog

SSN 646   Grayling
SSN 647   Pogy
SSN 648   Aspro
SSN 649   Sunfish
SSN 650   Pargo
SSN 652   Puffer
SSN 660   Sand Lance
SSN 662   Gurnard
SSN 663   Hammerhead
SSN 666   Hawkbill
SSN 667   Bergall
SSN 668   Spadefish
SSN 669   Seahorse
SSN 670   Finback
SSN 672   Pintado
SSN 673   Flying Fish
SSN 674   Trepang
SSN 675   Bluefish
SSN 676   Billfish
SSN 677   Drum
SSN 678   Archerfish
SSN 680   William H Bates

SSN 681   Batfish
SSN 682   Tunny
SSN 683   Parche
SSN 684   Cavalla
SSN 686   L Mendel Rivers

Narwhal class
SSN 671   Narwhal

Los Angeles class
SSN 688   Los Angeles
SSN 690   Philadelphia
SSN 691   Memphis
SSN 692   Omaha
SSN 693   Cincinnati
SSN 694   Groton
SSN 695   Birmingham
SSN 696   New York City
SSN 697   Indianapolis
SSN 698   Bremerton
SSN 699   Jacksonville
SSN 700   Dallas

SSN 701   La Jolla
SSN 702   Phoenix
SSN 703   Boston
SSN 704   Baltimore
SSN 705   City of Corpus Christi
SSN 706   Albuquerque
SSN 707   Portsmouth
SSN 708   Minneapolis—Saint Paul
SSN 709   Hyman G Rickover
SSN 710   Augusta
SSN 711   San Francisco
SSN 712   Atlanta
SSN 713   Houston
SSN 714   Norfolk
SSN 715   Buffalo
SSN 716   Salt Lake City
SSN 717   Olympia
SSN 718   Honolulu
SSN 719   Providence
SSN 720   Pittsburgh
SSN 721   Chicago
SSN 722   Key West
SSN 723   Oklahoma City
SSN 724   Louisville
SSN 725   Helena
SSN 750   Newport News
SSN 751   San Juan
SSN 752   Pasadena
SSN 753   Albany
SSN 754   Topeka
SSN 755   Miami
SSN 756   Scranton
SSN 757   Alexandria
SSN 758   Asheville
SSN 759   Jefferson City
SSN 760   Annapolis
SSN 761   Springfield
SSN 762   Columbus
SSN 763   Santa Fe
SSN 764   Boise
SSN 765   Montpelier
SSN 766   Charlotte
SSN 767   Hampton
SSN 768   Hartford
SSN 769   Toledo
SSN 770   Tucson
SSN 771   Columbia
SSN 772   Greeneville
SSN 773   Cheyenne

SURFACE COMBATANTS

Aircraft Carriers

Forrestal class
CV 60   Saratoga
CV 62   Independence

Kitty Hawk class
CV 63   Kitty Hawk
CV 64   Constellation
CV 66   America

John F Kennedy class
CV 67   John F Kennedy

Enterprise class
CVN 65   Enterprise

Nimitz class
CVN 68   Nimitz
CVN 69   Dwight D Eisenhower
CVN 70   Carl Vinson
CVN 71   Theodore Roosevelt
CVN 72   Abraham Lincoln
CVN 73   George Washington
CVN 74   John C Stennis
CVN 75   United States

Cruisers

Leahy class
CG 19   Dale
CG 20   Richmond K Turner

Belknap class
CG 26   Belknap

Ticonderoga class
CG 47   Ticonderoga
CG 48   Yorktown
CG 49   Vincennes
CG 50   Valley Forge
CG 51   Thomas S Gates
CG 52   Bunker Hill
CG 53   Mobile Bay
CG 54   Antietam
CG 55   Leyte Gulf
CG 56   San Jacinto
CG 57   Lake Champlain
CG 58   Philippine Sea
CG 59   Princeton
CG 60   Normandy
CG 61   Monterey
CG 62   Chancellorsville
CG 63   Cowpens
CG 64   Gettysburg
CG 65   Chosin
CG 66   Hue City
CG 67   Shiloh
CG 68   Anzio
CG 69   Vicksburg
CG 70   Lake Erie
CG 71   Cape St George

CG 72   Vella Gulf
CG 73   Port Royal

Bainbridge class
CGN 25   Bainbridge

Truxtun class
CGN 35   Truxtun

California class
CGN 36   California
CGN 37   South Carolina

Virginia class
CGN 38   Virginia
CGN 40   Mississippi
CGN 41   Arkansas

Destroyers

Spruance class
DD 963   Spruance
DD 964   Paul F Foster
DD 965   Kinkaid
DD 966   Hewitt
DD 967   Elliott
DD 968   Arthur W Radford
DD 969   Peterson
DD 970   Caron
DD 971   David R Ray
DD 972   Oldendorf
DD 973   John Young
DD 974   Comte de Grasse
DD 975   O'Brien
DD 976   Merrill
DD 977   Briscoe
DD 978   Stump
DD 979   Conolly
DD 980   Moosbrugger
DD 981   John Hancock
DD 982   Nicholson
DD 983   John Rodgers
DD 984   Leftwich
DD 985   Cushing
DD 986   Harry W Hill
DD 987   O'Bannon
DD 988   Thorn
DD 989   Deyo
DD 990   Ingersoll
DD 991   Fife
DD 992   Fletcher
DD 997   Hayler

Arleigh Burke class
DDG 51   Arleigh Burke
DDG 52   Barry
DDG 53   John Paul Jones
DDG 54   Curtis Wilbur
DDG 55   Stout
DDG 56   John S McCain
DDG 57   Mitscher
DDG 58   Laboon
DDG 59   Russell
DDG 60   Paul Hamilton
DDG 61   Ramage
DDG 62   Fitzgerald
DDG 63   Stethem
DDG 64   Carney
DDG 65   Benfold
DDG 66   Gonzalez
DDG 67   Cole
DDG 68   The Sullivans
DDG 69   Milius
DDG 70   Hopper
DDG 71   Ross
DDG 72   Mahan
DDG 73   Decatur
DDG 74   McFaul
DDG 75   Donald Cook
DDG 76   Higgins

Kidd class
DDG 993   Kidd
DDG 994   Callaghan
DDG 995   Scott
DDG 996   Chandler

Frigates

Knox class
FFT 1079   Bowen
FFT 1084   McCandless
FFT 1090   Ainsworth
FFT 1095   Truett

Oliver Hazard Perry class
FFG 7   Oliver Hazard Perry
FFG 8   McInerney
FFG 9   Wadsworth
FFG 10   Duncan
FFG 11   Clark
FFG 12   George Philip
FFG 13   Samuel Eliot Morison
FFG 14   John H Sides
FFG 15   Estocin
FFG 16   Clifton Sprague
FFG 19   John A Moore
FFG 20   Antrim
FFG 21   Flatley
FFG 22   Fahrion
FFG 23   Lewis B Puller
FFG 24   Jack Williams
FFG 25   Copeland
FFG 26   Gallery
FFG 27   Mahlon S Tisdale
FFG 28   Boone
FFG 29   Stephen W Groves

FFG 30   Reid
FFG 31   Stark
FFG 32   John L Hall
FFG 33   Jarrett
FFG 34   Aubrey Fitch
FFG 36   Underwood
FFG 37   Crommelin
FFG 38   Curts
FFG 39   Doyle
FFG 40   Halyburton
FFG 41   McClusky
FFG 42   Klakring
FFG 43   Thach
FFG 45   De Wert
FFG 46   Rentz
FFG 47   Nicholas
FFG 48   Vandegrift
FFG 49   Robert G Bradley
FFG 50   Taylor
FFG 51   Gary
FFG 52   Carr
FFG 53   Hawes
FFG 54   Ford
FFG 55   Elrod
FFG 56   Simpson
FFG 57   Reuben James
FFG 58   Samuel B Roberts
FFG 59   Kauffman
FFG 60   Rodney M Davis
FFG 61   Ingraham

Coastal Patrol Craft

Cyclone class
PC 1   Cyclone
PC 2   Tempest
PC 3   Hurricane
PC 4   Monsoon
PC 5   Typhoon
PC 6   Sirocco
PC 7   Squall
PC 8   Zephyr
PC 9   Chinook
PC 10   Firebolt
PC 11   Whirlwind
PC 12   Thunderbolt
PC 13   Shamar

AMPHIBIOUS WARFARE SHIPS

Amphibious Assault Ships

Wasp class
LHD 1   Wasp
LHD 2   Essex
LHD 3   Kearsage
LHD 4   Boxer
LHD 5   Bataan
LHD 6   Bonhomme Richard

Tarawa class
LHA 1   Tarawa
LHA 2   Saipan
LHA 3   Belleau Wood
LHA 4   Nassau
LHA 5   Peleliu

Iwo Jima class
LPH 7   Guadalcanal
LPH 9   Guam
LPH 10   Tripoli
LPH 11   New Orleans
LPH 12   Inchon

Amphibious Transport Docks

Austin class
LPD 4   Austin
LPD 5   Ogden
LPD 6   Duluth
LPD 7   Cleveland
LPD 8   Dubuque
LPD 9   Denver
LPD 10   Juneau
LPD 12   Shreveport
LPD 13   Nashville
LPD 14   Trenton
LPD 15   Ponce

Amphibious Cargo Ships

Anchorage class
LSD 36   Anchorage
LSD 37   Portland
LSD 38   Pensacola
LSD 39   Mount Vernon
LSD 40   Fort Fisher

Whidbey Island class
LSD 41   Whidbey Island
LSD 42   Germantown
LSD 43   Fort McHenry
LSD 44   Gunston Hall
LSD 45   Comstock
LSD 46   Tortuga
LSD 47   Rushmore
LSD 48   Ashland
LSD 49   Harpers Ferry
LSD 50   Carter Hall
LSD 51   Oak Hill
LSD 52   Pearl Harbor

Tank Landing Ships

Newport class
LST 1184   Frederick
LST 1186   Cayuga
LST 1189   San Bernardino
LST 1194   La Moure County
LST 1196   Harlan County
LST 1197   Barnstable County
LST 1198   Bristol County

Amphibious Command Ships

Blue Ridge class
LCC 19   Blue Ridge
LCC 20   Mount Whitney

MINE WARFARE SHIPS

Ocean Minesweepers

Aggressive class
MSO 441   Exultant
MSO 455   Implicit
MSO 488   Conquest

Mine Countermeasures Ships

Avenger class
MCM 1   Avenger
MCM 2   Defender
MCM 3   Sentry
MCM 4   Champion
MCM 5   Guardian
MCM 6   Devastator
MCM 7   Patriot
MCM 8   Scout
MCM 9   Pioneer
MCM 10   Warrior
MCM 11   Gladiator
MCM 12   Ardent
MCM 13   Dextrous
MCM 14   Chief

Osprey class
MHC 51   Osprey
MHC 52   Heron
MHC 53   Pelican
MHC 54   Robin
MHC 55   Oriole
MHC 56   Kingfisher
MHC 57   Cormorant
MHC 58   Black Hawk
MHC 59   Falcon
MHC 60   Cardinal
MHC 61   Raven
MHC 62   Shrike

UNDERWAY REPLENISHMENT SHIPS

Ammunition Ships

Suribachi class
AE 21   Suribachi
AE 22   Mauna Kea

Nitro class
AE 23   Nitro

Kilauea class
AE 27   Butte
AE 28   Santa Barbara
AE 29   Mount Hood
AE 32   Flint
AE 33   Shasta
AE 34   Mount Baker
AE 35   Kiska

Combat Stores Ships

Mars class
AFS 3   Niagara Falls
AFS 4   White Plains

Fleet Oilers

Cimarron class
AO 177   Cimarron
AO 178   Monongahela
AO 179   Merrimack
AO 180   Willamette
AO 186   Platte

Fast Combat Support Ships

Sacramento class
AOE 1   Sacramento
AOE 2   Camden
AOE 3   Seattle
AOE 4   Detroit

Supply class
AOE 6   Supply
AOE 7   Rainier
AOE 8   Arctic
AOE 10   Bridge

Replenishment Oilers

Wichita class
AOR 3   Kansas City
AOR 4   Savannah
AOR 5   Wabash
AOR 6   Kalamazoo
AOR 7   Roanoke

MATERIAL SUPPORT SHIPS

Destroyer Tenders

Samuel Gompers class
AD 37   Samuel Gompers
AD 38   Puget Sound

Yellowstone class
AD 41   Yellowstone
AD 42   Acadia
AD 43   Cape Cod
AD 44   Shenandoah

Submarine Tenders

Hunley class
AS 31   Hunley
AS 32   Holland

Simon Lake class
AS 33   Simon Lake
AS 34   Canopus

Spear class
AS 36   L Y Spear
AS 37   Dixon

Emory S Land class
AS 39   Emory S Land
AS 40   Frank Cable
AS 41   McKee

Salvage Ships

Bolster class
ARS 8   Preserver
ARS 38   Bolster
ARS 40   Hoist
ARS 41   Opportune
ARS 42   Reclaimer
ARS 43   Recovery

Safeguard class
ARS 50   Safeguard
ARS 51   Grasp
ARS 52   Salvor
ARS 53   Grapple

Edenton class
ATS 1   Edenton
ATS 2   Beaufort
ATS 3   Brunswick

Submarine Rescue Ships

Chanticleer class
ASR 13   Kittiwake
ASR 15   Sunbird

Pigeon class
ASR 22   Ortolan

SHIPS WITH MISCELLANEOUS MISSIONS

Miscellaneous Flagships

Raleigh and Austin classes
AGF 3   La Salle
AGF 11   Coronado

Auxiliary Research Submarine

Dolphin class
AGSS 555   Dolphin

SHIPS OF THE MILITARY SEALIFT COMMAND

(These ships, when operational, are manned by civilian crews, and carry the prefix 'T' before their normal Hull Numbers)

NAVAL FLEET AUXILIARY FORCE

Fleet Ballistic Missile Support Ship

TAK 286   Vega

Ammunition Ship

TAE 26   Kilauea

Combat Stores Ships

TAFS 1   Mars
TAFS 5   Concord
TAFS 6   San Diego
TAFS 7   San Jose
TAFS 8   Sirius
TAFS 9   Spica
TAFS 10   Saturn

Oilers

Henry J Kaiser class
TAO 187   Henry J Kaiser
TAO 188   Joshua Humphreys
TAO 189   John Lenthall
TAO 190   Andrew J Higgins
TAO 191   Benjamin Isherwood
TAO 192   Henry Eckford
TAO 193   Walter S Diehl
TAO 194   John Ericsson
TAO 195   Leroy Grumman
TAO 196   Kanawha
TAO 197   Pecos
TAO 198   Big Horn
TAO 199   Tippicanoe
TAO 200   Guadalupe
TAO 201   Patuxent
TAO 202   Yukon
TAO 203   Laramie
TAO 204   Rappahannock

Fleet Ocean Tugs

Powhatan class
TATF 166   Powhatan
TATF 167   Narragansett
TATF 168   Catawba
TATF 169   Navajo
TATF 170   Mohawk
TATF 171   Sioux
TATF 172   Apache

Ocean Surveillance Ships

TAGOS 1   Stalwart
TAGOS 6   Persistent
TAGOS 7   Indomitable
TAGOS 8   Prevail
TAGOS 9   Assertive
TAGOS 10   Invincible
TAGOS 11   Audacious
TAGOS 12   Bold
TAGOS 16   Capable
TAGOS 17   Intrepid

Ocean Surveillance Ships (SWATH)

TAGOS 19   Victorious
TAGOS 20   Able
TAGOS 21   Effective
TAGOS 22   Loyal
TAGOS 23   Impeccable

STRATEGIC SEALIFT (Active)

Maritime Prepositioning Ships (MPS)

(These 13 ships are divided into three squadrons and are almost constantly underway. Each squadron contains the equipment and 30 days of supplies for a marine amphibious brigade.)

TAK 3000   Cpl Louis J Hauge Jr
TAK 3001   Pfc William B Baugh
TAK 3002   Pfc James Anderson Jr
TAK 3003   1st Lt Alexander
           Bonnyman
TAK 3004   Pvt Franklin J Phillips
TAK 3005   Sgt Matej Kocak
TAK 3006   Pfc Eugene A Obregon
TAK 3007   Maj Stephen W Pless
TAK 3008   2nd Lt John P Bobo
TAK 3009   Pfc Dewayne T Williams
TAK 3010   1st Lt Baldomero Lopez
TAK 3011   1st Lt Jack Lummus
TAK 3012   Staff Sgt William R Button

Prepositioning (PREPO) Ships

Lash

TAKB 924   Jeb Stuart
TAK 2043   American Kestrel
TAK 2046   Austral Rainbow
TAK 2049   Green Valley
TAK 2064   Green Harbour

Freighters

TAK 322   Buffalo Soldier
TAK 323   American Merlin
TAK 2062   American Cormorant
TAKR 9205   Strong Virginian

Tankers

TAOT 181   Potomac
TAOT 5075   American Osprey
TAOT 1125   Lawrence Gianella

Ocean Transportation Ships

Additional ships come and go as needed to meet MSC commitments. Types of vessel include Ro-Ro, Freighters, Tankers and Combination ships.

Tankers

TAOT 168   Sealift Pacific
TAOT 169   Sealift Arabian Sea
TAOT 170   Sealift South China Sea
TAOT 171   Sealift Indian Ocean
TAOT 172   Sealift Atlantic
TAOT 173   Sealift Mediterranean
TAOT 174   Sealift Caribbean
TAOT 175   Sealift Arctic
TAOT 176   Sealift Antarctic
TAOT 1121   Gus W Darnell
TAOT 1122   Paul Buck
TAOT 1123   Samuel L Cobb
TAOT 1124   Richard G Matthieson

STRATEGIC SEALIFT (Reserve)

Fast Sealift Ships

(These ships are maintained in a high state of readiness for deployment with equipment for a full Army division, but have only skeleton crews except when assigned to specific missions. TAKR 295-299 being converted 1994/95 and names will be changed.)

TAKR 287   Algol
TAKR 288   Bellatrix
TAKR 289   Denebola
TAKR 290   Pollux
TAKR 291   Altair
TAKR 292   Regulus
TAKR 293   Capella
TAKR 294   Antares
TAKR 295   Laura Maersk
TAKR 296   Selandia
TAKR 297   Leise Maersk
TAKR 298   Jutlandia
TAKR 299   Lica Maersk

Aviation Support Ships

TAVB 3   Wright
TAVB 4   Curtiss

Hospital Ships

TAH 19   Mercy
TAH 20   Comfort

SPECIAL MISSION SUPPORT SHIPS

Missile Range Instrumentation Ships

TAGM 22   Range Sentinel
TAGM 23   Observation Island

Oceanographic Research Ships
(Note: Those on loan are not MSC ships)

AGOR 14   Melville (loan)
AGOR 15   Knorr (loan)
AGOR 21   Gyre (loan)
AGOR 22   Moana Wave (loan)
AGOR 23   Thomas G Thompson
           (loan)
AGOR 24   Roger Revelle
TAG 195   Hayes

Surveying Ships

TAGS 26   Silas Bent
TAGS 27   Kane
TAGS 33   Wilkes
TAGS 34   Wyman
TAGS 39   Maury
TAGS 40   Tanner
TAGS 45   Waters
TAGS 51   John McDonnell
TAGS 52   Littlehales
TAGS 60   Pathfinder
TAGS 61   Sumner
TAGS 62   Bowditch

Navigation Research Ship

TAG 194   Vanguard

Cable Repair Ships

TARC 6   Albert J Myer
TARC 7   Zeus

Ready Reserve Force (RRF)

(See pages 826/827)

SUBMARINES

Strategic Missile Submarines (SSBN)

Notes: (1) **Trident:** The Trident fitted SSBN force provides the principle US strategic deterrent. Land and air based systems have been sharply reduced since 1991. The current treaty is the Strategic Arms Reduction Treaty (START). The second treaty resulting from the Washington Summit Agreement of June 1992 is called START II. START limits to eight the number of re-entry bodies (RBs) attributed to each SSBN launch tube associated with the Trident I (C4) and the Trident II (D5) missiles. Under START II the total number of SLBM RBs is limited first to 2160 and then to 1750, with the reductions to be accomplished in two stages. This limit will be achieved by declaring launch tubes aboard SSBNs as attributed with a certain number of RBs. This tube limit must be uniform for each weapon system and/or for each coast. The whole force comes under the US Strategic Command Headquarters at Offutt Air Force Base, Nebraska. Submarines are essentially in constant communications, and speed of

response is equivalent to that of ground-based silos. Trident missile accuracy is as good as ground-based systems and the warhead has a 50 per cent higher yield than the most lethal ICBM. Greater accuracy is being researched using GPS hardware, as are conventional kinetic energy warheads.

(2) **Strategic Cruise Missiles:** A canister version of the Tomahawk SLCM is carried in submarines. This is an underwater-launched weapon with ram-jet propulsion which can deliver nuclear warheads to a range of approximately 2500 km *(1400 nm)*. A shorter range version of the weapon with a conventional warhead has a land attack capability to 900 km *(485 nm)* which is increased by more than 30 per cent in the Block III version approved for production in early 1992. The strategic cruise missile has a low-level, terrain-following flight path over land, much like that of a manned bomber in contrast to the ballistic trajectory of a Polaris/Poseidon/Trident missile. In September 1991 all nu-

clear capable Tomahawks were removed from both submarines and surface ships.

(3) **Names:** When the Polaris submarine programme was initiated, ballistic missile submarines were named after 'distinguished Americans who were known for their devotion to freedom'. Included as 'Americans' were Latin American and Hawaiian leaders, and several Europeans who supported the American fight for independence. In 1976 the SSBN name source was changed to States of the Union, although an exception was made in September 1983 when the selected name of SSBN 730 was changed from *Rhode Island* to *Henry M Jackson*. Jackson was a long time Senator from the State of Washington, a presidential candidate in 1976 and one of the most vigorous and outspoken advocates of a strong national defence.

14 + 4 OHIO CLASS (SSBN)

Name	No	Builders	Launched	Commissioned	F/S
OHIO	SSBN 726	General Dynamics (Electric Boat Div)	7 Apr 1979	11 Nov 1981	PA
MICHIGAN	SSBN 727	General Dynamics (Electric Boat Div)	26 Apr 1980	11 Sep 1982	PA
FLORIDA	SSBN 728	General Dynamics (Electric Boat Div)	14 Nov 1981	18 June 1983	PA
GEORGIA	SSBN 729	General Dynamics (Electric Boat Div)	6 Nov 1982	11 Feb 1984	PA
HENRY M JACKSON	SSBN 730	General Dynamics (Electric Boat Div)	15 Oct 1983	6 Oct 1984	PA
ALABAMA	SSBN 731	General Dynamics (Electric Boat Div)	19 May 1984	25 May 1985	PA
ALASKA	SSBN 732	General Dynamics (Electric Boat Div)	12 Jan 1985	25 Jan 1986	PA
NEVADA	SSBN 733	General Dynamics (Electric Boat Div)	14 Sep 1985	16 Aug 1986	PA
TENNESSEE	SSBN 734	General Dynamics (Electric Boat Div)	13 Dec 1986	17 Dec 1988	AA
PENNSYLVANIA	SSBN 735	General Dynamics (Electric Boat Div)	23 Apr 1988	9 Sep 1989	AA
WEST VIRGINIA	SSBN 736	General Dynamics (Electric Boat Div)	14 Oct 1989	20 Oct 1990	AA
KENTUCKY	SSBN 737	General Dynamics (Electric Boat Div)	11 Aug 1990	13 July 1991	AA
MARYLAND	SSBN 738	General Dynamics (Electric Boat Div)	10 Aug 1991	13 June 1992	AA
NEBRASKA	SSBN 739	General Dynamics (Electric Boat Div)	15 Aug 1992	10 July 1993	AA
RHODE ISLAND	SSBN 740	General Dynamics (Electric Boat Div)	17 July 1993	July 1994	Bldg/AA
MAINE	SSBN 741	General Dynamics (Electric Boat Div)	July 1994	July 1995	Bldg
WYOMING	SSBN 742	General Dynamics (Electric Boat Div)	July 1995	Aug 1996	Bldg
LOUISIANA	SSBN 743	General Dynamics (Electric Boat Div)	Sep 1996	Aug 1997	Bldg

TENNESSEE   4/1993, Giorgio Arra

Displacement, tons: 16 600 surfaced; 18 750 dived
Dimensions, feet (metres): 560 × 42 × 36.4
(170.7 × 12.8 × 11.1)
Main machinery: Nuclear; 1 GE PWR S8G; 2 turbines; 60 000 hp
(44.8 MW); 1 shaft; 1 Magnetek auxiliary prop motor; 325 hp
(242 kW)
Speed, knots: 20+ dived
Complement: 155 (14 officers in first 6, 15 in remainder)

Missiles: SLBM: 24 Lockheed Trident I (C4) (726-733); stellar
inertial guidance to 7400 km *(4000 nm)*; thermonuclear warhead of up to 8 MIRV of 100 kT; CEP 450 m. A limit of 4 may be
imposed under START II.
24 Lockheed Trident II (D5) (734 onwards); stellar inertial guidance to 12 000 km *(6500 nm)*; thermonuclear warheads of up
to 12 MIRVs of either Mk 4 with W76 of 100 kT each, or Mk 5
with W88 of 475 kT each; CEP 90 m. A limit of 8 RVs was set in
1991 under the START counting rules but this may reduce to 4
under START II.
Torpedoes: 4—21 in *(533 mm)* Mk 68 bow tubes. Gould Mk 48;
wire-guided (option); active/passive homing to 50 km
(27 nm)/38 km *(21 nm)* at 40/55 kts; warhead 267 kg; depth
to 900 m *(2950 ft)*.
Countermeasures: Decoys: 8 launchers for Emerson Electric Mk
2; torpedo decoy.
ESM: WLR-8(V)5; intercept. WLR-10; radar warning.
Combat data systems: CCS Mk 2 Mod 3 with UYK 43/UYK 44
computers.
Fire control: Mk 118 digital torpedo fire-control system. Mk 98
missile control system.
Radars: Surface search/navigation/fire-control: BPS 15A; I/J
band.
Sonars: IBM BQQ 6; passive search.
Raytheon BQS 13; spherical array for BQQ 6.
Ametek BQS 15; active/passive for close contacts; high
frequency.
Western Electric BQR 15 (with BQQ 9 signal processor); pas-
sive towed array.
Raytheon BQR 19; active for navigation; high frequency.

Programmes: The 'date laid down' column has been deleted in
this case as being irrelevant because there is a great amount of
prefabrication before the various sections are joined on the
building ways. The lead submarine was contracted to the Electric Boat Division of the General Dynamics Corp (Groton, Connecticut) on 25 July 1974.
Modernisation: WLY-1 acoustic intercept and countermeasures
system is to be fitted in the late 1990s. This is an automatic response system designed for defence against torpedo attack.
Structure: The size of the Trident submarine is dictated primarily
by the 24 vertically launched Trident missiles and the larger
reactor plant to drive the ship. The reactor has a nuclear core
life of about nine years between refuellings. Diving depth is
300 m *(984 ft)*.

Operational: The Extremely Low Frequency (ELF) communications system became operational in 1986 at Michigan and
in 1991 at Wisconsin enabling SSBNs to receive signals at
greater depths and higher speeds than before although the
data rate of ELF is much less than VLF. Each submarine has two
Mk 2 Ship's Inertial Navigation Systems.
Pacific Fleet units with C4 missiles are based at Bangor, Washington, while the D5 submarines in the Atlantic Fleet are based
at King's Bay, Georgia. The base structure permits bringing in
ships of the Ohio class after 70 days at sea, accomplishing
necessary, and sometimes very significant, voyage repairs, and
sending them back to sea in 25 days. That schedule allows
keeping these ships at sea, from commissioning to decommissioning, 66% of the time, including shipyard overhauls. The latter will be at nine year intervals. After two failed tests of the D-5

missile at sea early in 1989, modifications were made leading
to eight successful tests from *Tennessee* and her first operational deployment started in March 1990. The original plan to
retrofit D-5 missiles into the first eight of the class will not go
ahead unless the threat posed by Russian strategic forces is
revived.
In October 1993 *Nebraska* fired a Trident missile to test the
use of GPS hardware for fixing the location of the re-entry
vehicles. This was part of a series of trials leading up to the
possible development of a mid-course guidance package to
produce the pinpoint accuracy required to use the missile for
carrying a conventional kinetic energy payload.

WEST VIRGINIA   3/1993, Giorgio Arra

WEST VIRGINIA   3/1993, Giorgio Arra

5 BENJAMIN FRANKLIN and JAMES MADISON CLASSES (SSBN and SSN)

Name	No	Builders	Laid down	Launched	Commissioned	F/S
STONEWALL JACKSON	SSBN 634	Mare Island Naval Shipyard	4 July 1962	30 Nov 1963	26 Aug 1964	AA
SIMON BOLIVAR	SSBN 641	Newport News Shipbuilding	17 Apr 1963	22 Aug 1964	29 Oct 1965	AA
KAMEHAMEHA*	SSN (ex-SSBN) 642	Mare Island Naval Shipyard	2 May 1963	16 Jan 1965	10 Dec 1965	PA
JAMES K POLK*	SSN (ex-SSBN) 645	General Dynamics (Electric Boat Div)	23 Nov 1963	22 May 1965	16 Apr 1966	AA
MARIANO G VALLEJO	SSBN 658	Mare Island Naval Shipyard	7 July 1964	23 Oct 1965	16 Dec 1966	AA

* SSN conversions

Displacement, tons: 7330 surfaced; 8250 dived
Dimensions, feet (metres): 425 × 33 × 31.5
  (129.5 × 10.1 × 9.6)
Main machinery: Nuclear; 1 Westinghouse PWR S5W; 2 tur-
bines; 15 000 hp *(11.2 MW)*; 1 shaft
  1 Magnetek auxiliary prop motor; 325 hp *(242 kW)*
Speed, knots: 18 surfaced; 25 dived
Complement: 143 (13 officers)

Missiles: SLBM: 16 Lockheed Trident I (C4) (in 3 of the class);
stellar inertial guidance to 7400 km *(4000 nm)*; thermonuclear warhead of up to 8 MIRV of 100 kT; CEP 450 m.
Torpedoes: 4—21 in *(533 mm)* Mk 65 bow tubes. Gould Mk 48;
wire-guided (option); active/passive homing to 50 km
(27 nm)/38 km *(21 nm)* at 40/55 kts; warhead 267 kg; depth
to 900 m *(2950 ft)*.
Countermeasures: Decoys: 8 Emerson Electric Mk 2 launchers;
torpedo decoy.
ESM: WLR-8; intercept. WLR-10; radar warning.
Fire control: Mk 113 Mod 9 torpedo fire-control system. Mk 88
missile control system.
Radars: Surface search/navigation/fire-control: BPS 11A or BPS
15; I/J band.
Sonars: EDO BQR 7; passive search.
  Western Electric; BQR 15; passive towed array.
  Raytheon BQR 19; active for navigation; high frequency.
  Honeywell BQR 21 (Dimus); passive array.
  Raytheon BQS 4; active search and classification.

Programmes: In early 1986, on commissioning of *Alaska* SSBN
732, *Sam Rayburn* had her missile tubes plugged in order to
keep within limits of the SALT agreement and has converted to
a 'moored nuclear reactor training submarine'. Since then the
earlier ships of the class have decommissioned at the rate of
two to three per year, a process which rapidly accelerated from
1991 with all Poseidon submarines withdrawn from operational patrols. *Daniel Webster* has joined *Sam Rayburn* as a
second moored training ship.
Modernisation: The first eight submarines of this class were fitted with the Polaris A-2 missile (1500 nm range) and the next
23 with the Polaris A-3 missile (2500 nm range). All were then
fitted with Poseidon between 1970 and 1977. Between 24
September 1978 and 10 December 1982 twelve were converted to launch Trident I missiles. The conversion included
minor modifications to the launcher and to the ballasting of the
submarine to accommodate the greater weight of the Trident

STONEWALL JACKSON

1/1993, Giorgio Arra

missile as well as extensive modifications to the installed fire-
control, instrumentation and missile checkout subsystems to
support the increased sophistication of the longer range missile. Two of the class *Kamehameha* and *James K Polk* have
been converted to drydock shelters (DDS) SSNs. They are
equipped for special operations, supporting SEALs, one in the
Pacific from late 1993 and the other in the Atlantic from early
1994.

Structure: All have diesel-electric stand-by machinery, snorts,
and 'outboard' auxiliary propeller for emergency use. Diving
depth is approx 300 m *(984 ft)*.
Operational: The two SSN conversions replaced *John Marshall*
and *Sam Houston. Stonewall Jackson* and *Simon Bolivar* are
scheduled to pay off in September 1994.

SIMON BOLIVAR

1/1993, Giorgio Arra

Attack Submarines (SSN)

Notes: (1) **Building programme:** The last remaining diesel-electric submarine paid off in May 1990. The current SSN building programme was thrown into disarray by the proposal to terminate the Seawolf programme, and to advance the design work on the follow-on Centurion or New Attack Submarine (NAS) class. On the basis of money already spent, it was decided in July 1992 to proceed with the second Seawolf and the need to maintain the industrial base has helped so far to save the third of the class. With the last of the Los Angeles hulls scheduled for completion in 1996 and the last Trident submarine in 1997, there is obvious concern over the possible loss of one of the two nuclear submarine building yards.

The New Attack Submarine design is based on a capability of about 75% of Seawolf. Studies have included a modular concept with common propulsion and different weapon systems sections to be decided on build. To control unit costs, size has to be sacrificed, which means compromising on stealth characteristics and weapons capacity. The aim is for 12 (or 20) vertical launch tubes for cruise missiles. Three separate modules might include additional cruise missile tubes, or ballistic missile tubes, or facilities for up to 200 special operations troops. The first of class is scheduled for funding in FY 1998.

(2) **Ancillary programmes:** These include thin-line towed arrays with greatly enhanced detection capability, special hull treatments which improve detection capability against quieter targets, the Mk 48 advanced capability (ADCAP) torpedo, improved Tomahawk missiles, offboard sensors and decoys.
(3) **Deep submergence vehicles:** The Deep Submergence Vehicles (DSV), including the nuclear-propelled *NR-1*, are rated as Service Craft and are listed at the end of the 'Special Vessels' section following the MSC section.
(4) **Swimmer-Seal Delivery Vehicles (SDVs):** About 15 six-man mini submarines are in service for naval commando units. These SDVs have a speed of 6 kts and can be carried by suitably modified SSNs. A new design ASDS (Advanced Swimmer Delivery System) with electric propulsion is out to tender in 1994. These will be dry submersibles capable of carrying four men from a mother submarine to a hostile shore.
(5) **Unmanned Undersea Vehicles (UUVs):** Two prototype surface ship-launched vehicles were built under joint ARPA/Navy UUV programmes. Operational testing of the second vehicle, the Mine Search System (MSS), was completed in 1993. The MSS vehicle is 35 ft long and has a titanium hull with a diameter of 44 in. The payload is housed in an internal pressure hull. The propulsion motor is free flooding and develops 12 hp from two battery sections. MSS operational trials demonstrated the performance of mine detection sonars and the ability of a UUV to survey designated areas with precise navigation.

Another semi-autonomous vehicle is the Advanced Unmanned Search System (AUSS), which was developed by NRaD, San Diego, and is operated by the Navy Supervisor of Salvage. AUSS was designed for search operations to 20 000 ft and is controlled by an acoustic data link from a surface support ship. AUSS is 17 ft long and 31 in in diameter with a graphite epoxy pressure hull weighing 2800 lb. Two main thrusters provide forward and aft propulsion and steering with two vertical thrusters for altitude control. Endurance is 10 hours at 5 kts on silver-zinc batteries. Sensors include a side-looking sonar and a CCD camera which transmits images to the surface via an acoustic data link.

UUVs capable of remote-control from either surface ships or submarines are being researched. Roles are limitless but remote sensing and acoustic deception are two obvious front runners.
(6) **Autonomous Undersea Vehicles (AUVs):** Research work is being done with the aim of producing torpedo-launched remote-controlled vehicles for a range of tasks including surveillance, communications and mine warfare.

0 + 2 (1) SEAWOLF CLASS (SSN)

Name	No	Builders	Start date	Launched	Commissioned
SEAWOLF	SSN 21	General Dynamics (Electric Boat Div)	25 Oct 1989	May 1995	May 1996
CONNECTICUT	SSN 22	General Dynamics (Electric Boat Div)	14 Sep 1992	Mar 1997	Aug 1998

Displacement, tons: 7460 surfaced; 9137 dived
Dimensions, feet (metres): 353 × 42.3 × 35.8 *(107.6 × 12.9 × 10.9)*
Main machinery: Nuclear; 1 GE PWR S6W; 2 turbines; 52 000 hp *(38.8 MW)*; 1 shaft; pumpjet propulsor; 1 Westinghouse secondary propulsion submerged motor
Speed, knots: 35 dived
Complement: 133 (12 officers)

Missiles: SLCM: Up to 45 GDC Tomahawk.
SSM: Tomahawk; Harpoon.
Torpedoes: 8—26 in *(660 mm)* tubes (external measurement is 30 in *(762 mm)*); Mk 48 ADCAP (added capability). Total of about 50 tube-launched missiles and torpedoes.
Mines: In lieu of torpedoes.
Countermeasures: Decoys: torpedo decoys. WLY-1 system in due course.
ESM: WLQ-4(V)1; intercept.
Combat data systems: General Electric BSY-1 system with UYK 44 computers.
Fire control: Raytheon Mk 2 FCS
Radars: Navigation: BPS 16; I band.
Sonars: BQQ 5D suite; TB-16 and TB-23 towed arrays. One surveillance; one tactical.

Programmes: First of class ordered on 9 January 1989; second of class on 3 May 1991. The third was funded initially in FY 1992. In January 1992 it was proposed that funding for the second and third would be rescinded and long-lead work was suspended on 14 February, starting again for *Connecticut* on 17 June. SSN-23 is currently scheduled for funding in FY 1996. Delays in *Seawolf* construction programme have been caused by pressure hull welding problems.
Structure: The modular design has more weapons, a higher tactical speed, better sonars and an ASW mission effectiveness 'three times better than the improved Los Angeles class' according to the Navy. It is estimated that over a billion dollars has been allocated for research and development including the S6W reactor system. Full acoustic cladding fitted. There are no external weapons (as in the improved Los Angeles class). Emphasis has been put on sub-ice capabilities including retractable bow planes. Diving depth, 2000 ft *(610 m)* approx. The torpedo magazine is to be reconfigured in the third of class so that it can be used to accommodate 50 commandos. A larger escape chamber is to be fitted for locking out. These changes may be retrofitted in due course to the first two of the class.
Operational: A quoted 'silent' speed of 20 kts. Other operational advantages include greater manoeuvrability and space for subsequent weapon systems development.

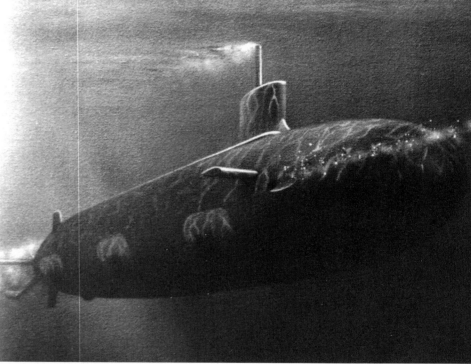

SEAWOLF (artist's impression)   *1989, General Dynamics*

Opinion: This submarine was intended to restore the level of acoustic advantage (in the one to one nuclear submarine engagement against the Russians) which the USN has enjoyed for the last three decades. At the same time the larger capacity of the magazine will enhance overall effectiveness in a number of other roles. The decision to discontinue building this one very expensive design has happened sooner than expected but was the inevitable result of falling defence budgets, technical problems and a much diminished Russian threat.

SEAWOLF (model)   *1989, David Merriman, D & E Miniatures*

29 STURGEON CLASS (SSN)

Name	No	Builders	Laid down	Launched	Commissioned	F/S
WHALE	SSN 638	General Dynamics (Quincy)	27 May 1964	14 Oct 1966	12 Oct 1968	AA
TAUTOG	SSN 639	Ingalls Shipbuilding	27 Jan 1964	15 Apr 1967	17 Aug 1968	PA
GRAYLING	SSN 646	Portsmouth Naval Shipyard	12 May 1964	22 June 1967	11 Oct 1969	AA
POGY	SSN 647	Ingalls Shipbuilding	4 May 1964	3 June 1967	15 May 1971	PA
ASPRO	SSN 648	Ingalls Shipbuilding	23 Nov 1964	29 Nov 1967	20 Feb 1969	PA
SUNFISH	SSN 649	General Dynamics (Quincy)	15 Jan 1965	14 Oct 1966	15 Mar 1969	AA
PARGO	SSN 650	General Dynamics (Electric Boat Div)	3 June 1964	17 Sep 1966	5 Jan 1968	AA
PUFFER	SSN 652	Ingalls Shipbuilding	8 Feb 1965	30 Mar 1968	9 Aug 1969	PA
SAND LANCE	SSN 660	Portsmouth Naval Shipyard	15 Jan 1965	11 Nov 1969	25 Sep 1971	AA
GURNARD	SSN 662	Mare Island Naval Shipyard	22 Dec 1964	20 May 1967	6 Dec 1968	PA
HAMMERHEAD	SSN 663	Newport News Shipbuilding	29 Nov 1965	14 Apr 1967	28 June 1968	AA
HAWKBILL	SSN 666	Mare Island Naval Shipyard	12 Sep 1966	12 Apr 1969	4 Feb 1971	PA
BERGALL	SSN 667	General Dynamics (Electric Boat Div)	16 Apr 1966	17 Feb 1968	13 June 1969	AA
SPADEFISH	SSN 668	Newport News Shipbuilding	21 Dec 1966	15 May 1968	14 Aug 1969	AA
SEAHORSE	SSN 669	General Dynamics (Electric Boat Div)	13 Aug 1966	15 June 1968	19 Sep 1969	AA
FINBACK	SSN 670	Newport News Shipbuilding	26 June 1967	7 Dec 1968	4 Feb 1970	AA
PINTADO	SSN 672	Mare Island Naval Shipyard	27 Oct 1967	16 Aug 1969	11 Sep 1971	PA
FLYING FISH	SSN 673	General Dynamics (Electric Boat Div)	30 June 1967	17 May 1969	29 Apr 1970	AA
TREPANG	SSN 674	General Dynamics (Electric Boat Div)	28 Oct 1967	27 Sep 1969	14 Aug 1970	AA
BLUEFISH	SSN 675	General Dynamics (Electric Boat Div)	13 Mar 1968	10 Jan 1970	8 Jan 1971	AA
BILLFISH	SSN 676	General Dynamics (Electric Boat Div)	20 Sep 1968	1 May 1970	12 Mar 1971	AA
DRUM	SSN 677	Mare Island Naval Shipyard	20 Aug 1968	23 May 1970	15 Apr 1972	PA
ARCHERFISH	SSN 678	General Dynamics (Electric Boat Div)	19 June 1969	16 Jan 1971	17 Dec 1971	AA
WILLIAM H BATES (ex-Redfish)	SSN 680	Ingalls Shipbuilding	4 Aug 1969	11 Dec 1971	5 May 1973	PA
BATFISH	SSN 681	General Dynamics (Electric Boat Div)	9 Feb 1970	9 Oct 1971	1 Sep 1972	AA
TUNNY	SSN 682	Ingalls Shipbuilding	22 May 1970	10 June 1972	26 Jan 1974	PA
PARCHE	SSN 683	Ingalls Shipbuilding	10 Dec 1970	13 Jan 1973	17 Aug 1974	PA
CAVALLA	SSN 684	General Dynamics (Electric Boat Div)	4 June 1970	19 Feb 1972	9 Feb 1973	PA
L MENDEL RIVERS	SSN 686	Newport News Shipbuilding	26 June 1971	2 June 1973	1 Feb 1975	AA

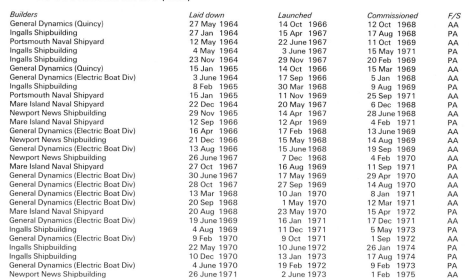

Displacement, tons: 4250; 4460 standard; 4780; 4960 dived (see *Structure*)

Dimensions, feet (metres): 302.2; 292 × 31.8 × 28.9 *(92.1; 89 × 9.7 × 8.8)* (see *Structure*)

Main machinery: Nuclear; 1 Westinghouse PWR S5W; 2 turbines; 15 000 hp *(11.2 MW)*; 1 shaft

Speed, knots: 15 surfaced; 30 dived

Complement: 107 (12 officers)

Missiles: SLCM: GDC Tomahawk (TLAM-N); land attack; Tercom aided inertial navigation system (TAINS) to 2500 km *(1400 nm)* at 0.7 Mach; altitude 15-100 m; nuclear warhead 200 kT; CEP 80 m. There are also two versions (TLAM-C/D) with either a single 454 kg HE warhead or a single warhead with submunitions; range 900 km *(485 nm)*; CEP 10 m.
Nuclear warheads are not normally carried. TLAM-C Block III missiles with increased ranges of more than 30% may be embarked in due course.
SSM: GDC Tomahawk (TASM); anti-ship; inertial guidance; active radar/anti-radiation homing to 460 km *(250 nm)* at 0.7 Mach; warhead 454 kg.
McDonnell Douglas Harpoon; active radar homing to 130 km *(70 nm)* at 0.9 Mach; warhead 227 kg (84A) or 258 kg (84B/C).

Torpedoes: 4—21 in *(533 mm)* Mk 63 tubes midships. Gould Mk 48; wire-guided (option); active/passive homing to 50 km *(27 nm)*/38 km *(21 nm)* at 40/55 kts; warhead 267 kg; depth to 900 m *(2950 ft)*.
Total of 23 weapons, for example 4 Harpoon, 4 Tomahawk and 15 torpedoes. Up to 8 Tomahawk can be carried in most of the class in place of other weapons.

Mines: Mk 67 Mobile and Mk 60 Captor can be carried.

Countermeasures: Decoys: Emerson Electric Mk 2; torpedo decoy launchers.

ESM: WLQ-4; radar warning.

Fire control: Mk 117 torpedo fire-control system.

Radars: Surface search/navigation/fire-control: Sperry BPS 15 or Raytheon BPS 14; I/J band.

Sonars: IBM BQQ 5 (SSN 678 onwards) or Raytheon BQQ 2; passive/active search and attack; low frequency.
EDO BQS 8 or Raytheon BQS 14A; ice detection; high frequency.
Raytheon BQS 13; active/passive array.
BQR 15; towed array; passive search; very low frequency.

ARCHERFISH (with SDV)   *3/1993, Giorgio Arra*

Structure: Sail height is 20 ft 6 in above deck. Sail-mounted diving planes rotate to vertical for breaking through ice when surfacing in arctic regions. SSN 678-684, 686 and 687 are 10 ft longer than remainder of class to accommodate BQQ 5 sonar and electronic gear. Under FY 1982 programme *Cavalla* was converted at Pearl Harbor in August-December 1982 to have a secondary amphibious assault role by carrying a Swimmer Delivery Vehicle (SDV). *Archerfish, Tunny* and *L Mendel Rivers* are similarly equipped. *William H Bates, Hawkbill, Pintado, Billfish* and others have been modified to carry and support the

Navy's Deep Submergence Rescue Vehicles (DSRV). See section on Deep Submergence Vehicles for additional DSRV details. Diving depth is 400 m *(1320 ft)*. Acoustic tiles are fitted and some of the class have anechoic coatings.

Operational: Operational life was expected to be 30 years but many have been decommissioned early and more will follow as a result of defence cutbacks. Subroc phased out in 1990. Nuclear warheads are not carried. *Aspro, Pargo, Gurnard* and *Hammerhead* are scheduled to pay off in September 1994.

GRAYLING   *1/1993, Giorgio Arra*

54 + 7 LOS ANGELES CLASS (SSN)

Name	*No*	*Builders*	*Laid down*	*Launched*	*Commissioned*	*F/S*
LOS ANGELES	SSN 688	Newport News Shipbuilding	8 Jan 1972	6 Apr 1974	13 Nov 1976	PA
PHILADELPHIA	SSN 690	General Dynamics (Electric Boat Div)	12 Aug 1972	19 Oct 1974	25 June 1977	AA
MEMPHIS	SSN 691	Newport News Shipbuilding	23 June 1973	3 Apr 1976	17 Dec 1977	AA
OMAHA	SSN 692	General Dynamics (Electric Boat Div)	27 Jan 1973	21 Feb 1976	11 Mar 1978	PA
CINCINNATI	SSN 693	Newport News Shipbuilding	6 Apr 1974	19 Feb 1977	10 June 1978	AA
GROTON	SSN 694	General Dynamics (Electric Boat Div)	3 Aug 1973	9 Oct 1976	8 July 1978	AA
BIRMINGHAM	SSN 695	Newport News Shipbuilding	26 Apr 1975	29 Oct 1977	16 Dec 1978	AA
NEW YORK CITY	SSN 696	General Dynamics (Electric Boat Div)	15 Dec 1973	18 June 1977	3 Mar 1979	PA
INDIANAPOLIS	SSN 697	General Dynamics (Electric Boat Div)	19 Oct 1974	30 July 1977	5 Jan 1980	PA
BREMERTON	SSN 698	General Dynamics (Electric Boat Div)	8 May 1976	22 July 1978	14 Mar 1981	PA
JACKSONVILLE	SSN 699	General Dynamics (Electric Boat Div)	21 Feb 1976	18 Nov 1978	16 May 1981	AA
DALLAS	SSN 700	General Dynamics (Electric Boat Div)	9 Oct 1976	28 Apr 1979	18 July 1981	AA
LA JOLLA	SSN 701	General Dynamics (Electric Boat Div)	16 Oct 1976	11 Aug 1979	24 Oct 1981	PA
PHOENIX	SSN 702	General Dynamics (Electric Boat Div)	30 July 1977	8 Dec 1979	19 Dec 1981	AA
BOSTON	SSN 703	General Dynamics (Electric Boat Div)	11 Aug 1978	19 Apr 1980	30 Jan 1982	AA
BALTIMORE	SSN 704	General Dynamics (Electric Boat Div)	21 May 1979	13 Dec 1980	24 July 1982	AA
CITY OF CORPUS CHRISTI	SSN 705	General Dynamics (Electric Boat Div)	4 Sep 1979	25 Apr 1981	8 Jan 1983	AA
ALBUQUERQUE	SSN 706	General Dynamics (Electric Boat Div)	27 Dec 1979	13 Mar 1982	21 May 1983	AA
PORTSMOUTH	SSN 707	General Dynamics (Electric Boat Div)	8 May 1980	18 Sep 1982	1 Oct 1983	AA
MINNEAPOLIS-SAINT PAUL	SSN 708	General Dynamics (Electric Boat Div)	30 Jan 1981	19 Mar 1983	10 Mar 1984	AA
HYMAN G RICKOVER	SSN 709	General Dynamics (Electric Boat Div)	24 July 1981	27 Aug 1983	21 July 1984	AA
AUGUSTA	SSN 710	General Dynamics (Electric Boat Div)	1 Apr 1982	21 Jan 1984	19 Jan 1985	AA
SAN FRANCISCO	SSN 711	Newport News Shipbuilding	26 May 1977	27 Oct 1979	24 Apr 1981	PA
ATLANTA	SSN 712	Newport News Shipbuilding	17 Aug 1978	16 Aug 1980	6 Mar 1982	AA
HOUSTON	SSN 713	Newport News Shipbuilding	29 Jan 1979	21 Mar 1981	25 Sep 1982	PA
NORFOLK	SSN 714	Newport News Shipbuilding	1 Aug 1979	31 Oct 1981	21 May 1983	AA
BUFFALO	SSN 715	Newport News Shipbuilding	25 Jan 1980	8 May 1982	5 Nov 1983	PA
SALT LAKE CITY	SSN 716	Newport News Shipbuilding	26 Aug 1980	16 Oct 1982	12 May 1984	AA
OLYMPIA	SSN 717	Newport News Shipbuilding	31 Mar 1981	30 Apr 1983	17 Nov 1984	PA
HONOLULU	SSN 718	Newport News Shipbuilding	10 Nov 1981	24 Sep 1983	6 July 1985	PA
PROVIDENCE	SSN 719	General Dynamics (Electric Boat Div)	14 Oct 1982	4 Aug 1984	27 Aug 1985	AA
PITTSBURGH	SSN 720	General Dynamics (Electric Boat Div)	15 Apr 1983	8 Dec 1984	23 Nov 1985	AA
CHICAGO	SSN 721	Newport News Shipbuilding	5 Jan 1983	13 Oct 1984	27 Sep 1986	PA
KEY WEST	SSN 722	Newport News Shipbuilding	6 July 1983	20 July 1985	12 Sep 1987	AA
OKLAHOMA CITY	SSN 723	Newport News Shipbuilding	4 Jan 1984	2 Nov 1985	9 June 1988	AA
LOUISVILLE	SSN 724	General Dynamics (Electric Boat Div)	16 Sep 1984	14 Dec 1985	8 Nov 1986	AA
HELENA	SSN 725	General Dynamics (Electric Boat Div)	28 Mar 1985	28 June 1986	11 July 1987	PA
NEWPORT NEWS	SSN 750	Newport News Shipbuilding	3 Mar 1984	15 Mar 1986	3 June 1989	AA
SAN JUAN	SSN 751	General Dynamics (Electric Boat Div)	16 Aug 1985	6 Dec 1986	6 Aug 1988	AA
PASADENA	SSN 752	General Dynamics (Electric Boat Div)	20 Dec 1985	12 Sep 1987	11 Feb 1989	PA
ALBANY	SSN 753	Newport News Shipbuilding	22 Apr 1985	13 June 1987	7 Apr 1990	AA
TOPEKA	SSN 754	General Dynamics (Electric Boat Div)	13 May 1986	23 Jan 1988	21 Oct 1989	AA
MIAMI	SSN 755	General Dynamics (Electric Boat Div)	24 Oct 1986	12 Nov 1988	30 June 1990	AA
SCRANTON	SSN 756	Newport News Shipbuilding	29 June 1986	3 July 1989	26 Jan 1991	AA
ALEXANDRIA	SSN 757	General Dynamics (Electric Boat Div)	19 June 1987	23 June 1990	29 June 1991	AA
ASHEVILLE	SSN 758	Newport News Shipbuilding	1 Jan 1987	28 Oct 1989	28 Sep 1991	PA
JEFFERSON CITY	SSN 759	Newport News Shipbuilding	21 Sep 1987	24 Mar 1990	30 Jan 1992	AA
ANNAPOLIS	SSN 760	General Dynamics (Electric Boat Div)	15 June 1988	18 May 1991	11 Apr 1992	AA
SPRINGFIELD	SSN 761	General Dynamics (Electric Boat Div)	29 Jan 1990	4 Jan 1992	9 Jan 1993	PA
COLUMBUS	SSN 762	General Dynamics (Electric Boat Div)	7 Jan 1991	1 Aug 1992	24 July 1993	AA
SANTA FE	SSN 763	General Dynamics (Electric Boat Div)	9 July 1991	12 Dec 1992	8 Jan 1994	AA
BOISE	SSN 764	Newport News Shipbuilding	25 Aug 1988	20 Oct 1990	7 Nov 1992	AA
MONTPELIER	SSN 765	Newport News Shipbuilding	19 May 1989	6 Apr 1991	13 Mar 1993	AA
CHARLOTTE	SSN 766	Newport News Shipbuilding	17 Aug 1990	3 Oct 1992	Aug 1994	Bldg
HAMPTON	SSN 767	Newport News Shipbuilding	2 Mar 1990	28 Sep 1991	6 Nov 1993	AA
HARTFORD	SSN 768	General Dynamics (Electric Boat Div)	27 Apr 1992	4 Dec 1993	Dec 1994	Bldg
TOLEDO	SSN 769	Newport News Shipbuilding	6 May 1991	28 Aug 1993	Feb 1995	Bldg
TUCSON	SSN 770	Newport News Shipbuilding	15 Aug 1991	19 Mar 1994	Aug 1995	Bldg
COLUMBIA	SSN 771	General Dynamics (Electric Boat Div)	24 Apr 1993	Sep 1994	Sep 1995	Bldg
GREENEVILLE	SSN 772	Newport News Shipbuilding	28 Feb 1992	Sep 1994	Feb 1996	Bldg
CHEYENNE	SSN 773	Newport News Shipbuilding	6 July 1992	Apr 1995	Aug 1996	Bldg

Displacement, tons: 6080 standard; 6927 dived
Dimensions, feet (metres): 362 × 33 × 32.3
(110.3 × 10.1 × 9.9)
Main machinery: Nuclear; 1 GE PWR S6G; 2 turbines; 35 000 hp *(26 MW)*; 1 shaft; 1 Magnetek auxiliary prop motor; 325 hp *(242 kW)*
Speed, knots: 32 dived
Complement: 133 (13 officers)

Missiles: SLCM: GDC Tomahawk (TLAM-N); land attack; Tercom aided inertial navigation system (TAINS) to 2500 km *(1400 nm)* at 0.7 Mach; altitude 15-100 m; nuclear warhead 200 kT; CEP 80 m. There are also two versions (TLAM-C/D) with either a single 454 kg HE warhead or a single warhead with submunitions; range 900 km *(485 nm)*; CEP 10 m.
Nuclear warheads are not normally carried. Block III missiles, approved for production in 1992, increases TLAM-C ranges by more than 30%.
SSM: GDC Tomahawk (TASM); anti-ship; inertial guidance; active radar/anti-radiation homing to 460 km *(250 nm)* at 0.7 Mach; warhead 454 kg.
From SSN 719 onwards all are equipped with the Vertical Launch System, which places 12 launch tubes external to the pressure hull behind the BQQ 5 spherical array forward.
McDonnell Douglas Harpoon; active radar homing to 130 km *(70 nm)* at 0.9 Mach; warhead 227 kg.
Torpedoes: 4—21 in *(533 mm)* tubes midships. Gould Mk 48; wire-guided (option); active/passive homing to 50 km *(27 nm)*/38 km *(21 nm)* at 40/55 kts; warhead 267 kg; depth to 900 m *(2950 ft)*. ADCAP first carried in 1990. Air Turbine Pump discharge.
Total of 26 weapons can be tube-launched, for example—8 Tomahawk, 4 Harpoon, 14 torpedoes.
Mines: Can lay Mk 67 Mobile and Mk 60 Captor mines.
Countermeasures: Decoys: Emerson Electric Mk 2; torpedo decoy.
ESM: BRD-7; direction finding. WLR-1H (in 771-773). WLR-8(V)2; intercept. WLR-10; radar warning.
Combat data systems: CCS Mk 1 (being replaced by Mk 2) (688-750) with UYK 7 computers; IBM BSY-1 (751-773) with UYK 43/UYK 44 computers. JOTS, BGIXS and TADIX-A can be fitted.
Fire control: Mk 113 Mod 10 torpedo fire-control system fitted in SSN 688-699 (being replaced by Mk 117) and Mk 117 in later submarines. Mk 81 Mod 3 OTHT.
Radars: Surface search/navigation/fire-control: Sperry BPS 15 A/16; I/J band.
Sonars: IBM BQQ 5A(V)1 (being updated to BQQ 5D/E); passive/active search and attack; low frequency.
BQG 5D wide aperture flank array (SSN 710 and SSN 751 onwards).

SPRINGFIELD *6/1993, Giorgio Arra*

BQR 23/25 (being replaced by TB-23/29 thin line array during overhauls); passive towed array.
Ametek BQS 15; active close-range including ice detection; high frequency.
MIDAS (mine and ice detection avoidance system) (SSN 751 onwards); high frequency.
Raytheon SADS-TG active detection system (being retrofitted).

Programmes: Various major improvement programmes and updating design changes caused programme delays in the late 1980s, not helped by a long strike at the Electric Boat Division. Future commissioning dates are very speculative. From SSN 751 onwards the class is prefixed by an 'I' for 'improved'. Programme terminates at 62 hulls.
Modernisation: Mk 117 TFCS is being back-fitted in earlier submarines of the class. WLY-1 acoustic intercept and countermeasures system will replace WLR 9A/12 acoustic intercept in the late 1990s. EHF communications are being fitted.
Structure: Every effort has been made to improve sound quieting and from SSN 751 onwards the class has acoustic tile cladding to augment the 'mammalian' skin which up to then had been the standard USN outer casing coating. Also from SSN 751 the forward hydro planes are fitted forward instead of on the fin. The planes are retractable mainly for surfacing through ice. The S6G reactor is a modified version of the D2G type fitted in *Bainbridge* and *Truxtun*. The towed sonar array is stowed in a blister on the side of the casing. Reactor core life between refuellings is estimated at 10 years. Diving depth is 450 m *(1475 ft)*. *Memphis* was withdrawn from active service in late 1989 to become an interim research platform for advanced submarine technology. Early trials did not involve major changes to the submarine but tests started in September 1990 for optronic non-hull penetrating masts and a major overhaul will include installation of a large diameter tube for testing UUVs and large torpedoes. An after casing hangar will be fitted for housing larger UUVs and towed arrays. Many other ideas are being evaluated with the main aim of allowing contractors easy access for trials at sea of new equipment. *Augusta* was the trials platform for the BQG-5D wide aperture array passive sonar system. Various staged design improvements have added some 220 tons to the class displacement between 668 and 773.
Operational: Increased emphasis on the ability to operate under the Arctic ice has led to improvements in ice detection sensors, navigation and communications equipment as well as strengthening the sail and placing the sailplanes forward in later units of the class. *Norfolk* fired the first ADCAP torpedo on 23 July 1988 and sank the destroyer *Jonas K Ingram*. Nine of the class took part in the war with Iraq in 1991 and two fired Tomahawk from the eastern Mediterranean. Normally eight Tomahawk missiles are carried internally (in addition to the external tubes in 719 onwards) but this load can be increased depending on the mission. Subroc phased out in 1990. Nuclear weapons disembarked but still available.

SPRINGFIELD   *5/1993, Giorgio Arra*   CITY OF CORPUS CHRISTI   *7/1993, Giorgio Arra*

BOSTON   *6/1993, Giorgio Arra*

PASADENA   *10/1993, S Poynton, RAN*

1 NARWHAL CLASS (SSN)

Name	No	Builders	Laid down	Launched	Commissioned	F/S
NARWHAL	SSN 671	General Dynamics (Electric Boat Div)	17 Jan 1966	9 Sep 1967	12 July 1969	AA

Displacement, tons: 5284 standard; 5830 dived
Dimensions, feet (metres): 314.6 × 37.7 × 27
  (95.9 × 11.5 × 8.2)
Main machinery: Nuclear; 1 GE PWR S5G; 2 turbines; 17 000 hp
  (12.7 MW); 1 shaft
Speed, knots: 20 surfaced; 25 dived
Complement: 129 (13 officers)

Missiles: SSM: 8 GDC Tomahawk (TASM); anti-ship; inertial guidance; active radar/anti-radiation homing to 460 km *(250 nm)*
  at 0.7 Mach; warhead 454 kg. 4 McDonnell Douglas Harpoon;
  active radar homing to 130 km *(70 nm)* at 0.9 Mach; warhead
  227 kg.
Torpedoes: 4—21 in *(533 mm)* tubes midships. Gould Mk 48;
  wire-guided (option); active/passive homing to 50 km
  (27 nm)/38 km *(21 nm)* at 40/55 kts; warhead 227 kg; depth
  to 900 m *(2950 ft)*.
Countermeasures: Decoys: Emerson Electric Mk 2; torpedo
  decoy.
ESM: WLQ-4; radar warning.
Fire control: Mk 117 torpedo fire-control system. Fitted with
  WSC-3 satellite communications transceiver.
Radars: Surface search/navigation/fire-control: Raytheon BPS
  14; I/J band.
Sonars: IBM BQQ 5; passive/active search and attack; low
  frequency.
  EDO BQS 8; upward-looking for ice detection; high frequency.
  Raytheon BQS 14; ice detection; active high frequency.
  TB 23; towed passive array; very low frequency.

Programmes: Authorised in FY 1964.
Structure: *Narwhal* is similar to the Sturgeon class submarines in
  hull design but is fitted with the prototype sea-going S5G natural circulation reactor plant. The natural circulation reactor
  'offers promise of increased reactor plant reliability, simplicity,
  and noise reduction due to the elimination of the need for large
  reactor coolant pumps and associated electrical and control
  equipment by taking maximum advantage of natural convec-
  tion to circulate the reactor coolant.' Also fitted with the experimental TB 23 thin wire towed array which is housed on the
  after casing at the stern.
Operational: To remain in service until late 1990s.

NARWHAL (with TB 23)   *9/1993, Giorgio Arra*

AIRCRAFT CARRIERS

Notes: (1) **Air Wings:** Air wing composition depends on the operational task, and carriers are deploying in one of three configurations. The **Transitional** configuration of 78 total aircraft
includes 20 F-14 Tomcat fighter aircraft, 20 F/A-18 Hornet light
attack, 16 A-6E Intruder medium attack, four EA-6B Prowler elec-
tronic-warfare, four E-2C Hawkeye early-warning/control, six S-3
Viking ASW, and eight SH-3G/60F helicopters. The SH-60F Seahawks are replacing the S-3G/H Sea Kings. The **Power Projection** configuration adds four F/A-18s, bringing the total aboard
to 82. The **50 TACAIR** configuration, to which all air wings are
expected to conform by FY 1997, reduces the number of F-14s
to 20, increases the number of F/A-18s to 36, eliminates all the
A-6Es, adds two S-3s, and reduces the number of helicopters to

five, for a total of 71 aircraft. Marine fighter/attack squadrons are
operating from carriers with Navy squadrons. Budget constraints
and shortages of aircraft may limit numbers embarked. See *Shipborne Aircraft* section for details of aircraft.
(2) **Service Life Extension Programme (SLEP):** The SLEP programme was initiated in 1979. *Saratoga, Independence, Kitty
Hawk* and *Constellation* have completed, but from 1993
extended overhauls have replaced SLEPs. The principal objective
of SLEP was to extend the service life of aircraft carriers an
additional 15 years, providing a reliable, logistically supportable
platform capable of operating all current and future fleet aircraft.
While the major thrust of SLEP was repair and life enhancement,
warfighting improvements are incorporated to keep pace with

the aircraft carrier modernisation baseline. SLEP included complete overhaul of propulsion, auxiliary, and launch systems;
upgrade of aircraft recovery equipment; extensive structure,
tank, and piping repair, and installation of updated sensors,
weapons systems, and electronic suites. On earlier SLEP ships
this included installation of Vulcan Phalanx close-in weapons system (CIWS), NATO Sea Sparrow missile system, SPS 49 radar,
and F/A-18 Hornet capability. In further overhauls, carriers, if already equipped with these systems, are being modernised to current standards incorporating improved NTDS, SPS 48E, TAS
Mk 23 radar, new ASW systems and Raytheon SLQ-32(V)4 combined EW intercept and jammer.

GEORGE WASHINGTON   *9/1993, Giorgio Arra*

1 ENTERPRISE CLASS (CVN)

Name	No	Builders	Laid down	Launched	Commissioned	F/S
ENTERPRISE	CVN 65	Newport News Shipbuilding	4 Feb 1958	24 Sep 1960	25 Nov 1961	Conv

Displacement, tons: 73 502 light; 75 700 standard; 93 970 full load
Dimensions, feet (metres): 1123 × 133 × 39 *(342.3 × 40.5 × 11.9)*
Flight deck, feet (metres): 1088 × 252 *(331.6 × 76.8)*
Main machinery: Nuclear; 8 Westinghouse PWR A2W; 4 Westinghouse turbines; 280 000 hp *(209 MW)*; 4 emergency diesels; 10 720 hp *(8 MW)*; 4 shafts
Speed, knots: 33
Complement: 3215 (171 officers); 2480 aircrew (358 officers); Flag 70 (25 officers)

Missiles: SAM: 3 Raytheon GMLS Mk 29 octuple launchers; NATO Sea Sparrow; semi-active radar homing to 14.6 km *(8 nm)* at 2.5 Mach; warhead 39 kg.
Guns: 3 General Electric/General Dynamics 20 mm Vulcan Phalanx 6-barrelled Mk 15; 3000 rounds/minute (or 4500 in Block 1) combined to 1.5 km.
Countermeasures: Decoys: 4 Loral Hycor SRBOC 6-barrelled fixed Mk 36; IR flares and chaff to 4 km *(2.2 nm)*. SSTDS (Surface Ship Torpedo Defence System). SLQ-36 Nixie (Phase I).
ESM/ECM: SLQ 32(V)4; radar warning; jammer and deception system.
Combat data systems: NTDS/ACDS naval tactical and advanced combat direction systems; Links 4A, 11 and 14. Link 16 in due course. JOTS, POST, CVIC, TESS UMM-1(V)1, SSQ-82. SATCOMS SRR-1, WSC-3 (UHF), WSC-6 (SHF), USC-38 (EHF).
Fire control: 3 Mk 91 Mod 1 MFCS directors (part of NSSMS Mk 57 SAM system).
Radars: Air search: ITT SPS 48E; 3D; E/F band; range 402 km *(220 nm)*.
Raytheon SPS 49(V)5; C/D band; range 457 km *(250 nm)*.
Hughes Mk 23 TAS; D band.
Surface search: Norden SPS 67; G band.
CCA: SPN 41, SPN 43A; SPN 44; 2 SPN 46; J/K/E/F band.
Navigation: Raytheon SPS 64(V)9; Furuno 900; I/J band.
Fire control: Six Mk 95; I/J band (for SAM).
Tacan: URN 25.

Fixed wing aircraft: Transitional air wing includes: 20 F14 Tomcat; 20 F/A-18 Hornet; 4 EA-6B Prowler; 16 A-6E Intruders (includes some KA-6D tankers); 4 E-2C Hawkeye; 6 S-3A/B Viking. Power Projection airwing adds 4 more Hornets. 50 TACAIR airwing adds 12 Hornets and 2 Viking, and removes 14 Tomcat and all Intruders.
Helicopters: 8 SH-3G/H Sea King or SH-60F Seahawk.

Programmes: Authorised in FY 1958 and launched only 31 months after her keel was laid down. Underwent a refit/overhaul at Puget Sound Naval SY, Bremerton, Washington from January 1979 to March 1982. $1.4 billion provided in FY 1990 budget for a 42 month 'complex overhaul' including

ENTERPRISE   *9/1992, Stefan Terzibaschitsch*

refuelling, which is the CVN equivalent of SLEP. This started at Newport News in early 1991 and is scheduled to complete in September 1994.
Modernisation: *Enterprise* was completed without any armament in an effort to hold down construction costs. Space for Terrier missile system was provided. Mk 25 Sea Sparrow BPDMS subsequently was installed in later 1967 and this has been replaced by first two and then three Mk 29 and supplemented with three 20 mm Mk 15 CIWS. A reshaping of the island took place in her 1979-82 refit. This included the removal of the mast and dome (which carried obsolete ECM gear) which were replaced with a mast similar to that of the Nimitz class. The 'billboards' of the SPS 32 and 33 radars were removed and replaced by the antennas of SPS 48C and 49 radars on the new mast. Planned improvements during current overhaul include SPS 48E and Mk 23 TAS air search radars, SPN 46 (vice SPN 42) precision approach and landing radar and improved C³ and EW systems.

Structure: Built to a modified Forrestal class design. *Enterprise* was the world's second nuclear-powered warship (the cruiser *Long Beach* was completed a few months earlier). The first of the eight reactors installed achieved initial criticality on 2 December 1960, shortly after the carrier was launched. After three years of operation during which she steamed more than 207 000 miles, *Enterprise* was refuelled from November 1964 to July 1965. Her second set of cores provided about 300 000 miles steaming. The eight cores initially installed cost $64 million; the second set cost about $20 million. Refuelled again in 1970 the third set of cores lasted for eight years until replaced in 1979-82 overhaul. There are two reactors for each of the ship's four shafts. The eight reactors feed 32 heat exchangers. Aviation facilities include four deck edge lifts, two forward and one each side abaft the island. There are four 295 ft C 13 Mod 1 catapults. Hangars cover 216 000 sq ft with 25 ft deck head. Aviation fuel, 8500 tons.
Operational: 12 days' aviation fuel for intensive flying.

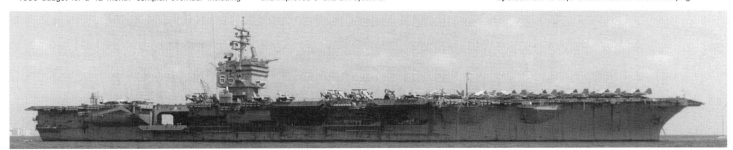

ENTERPRISE   *3/1990, Giorgio Arra*

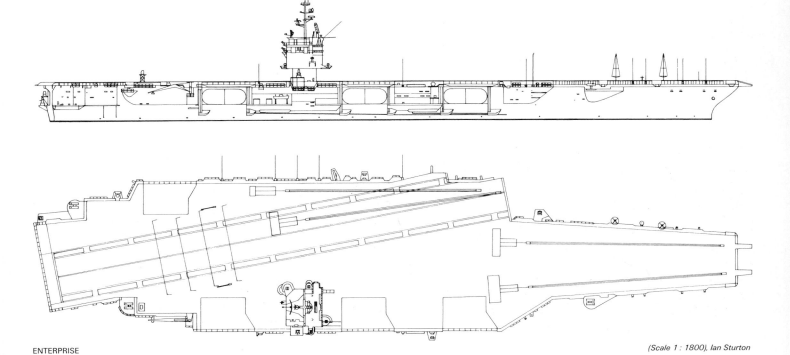

ENTERPRISE   *(Scale 1 : 1800), Ian Sturton*

6 + 2 (1) NIMITZ CLASS (CVN)

Name	No	Builders	Laid down	Launched	Commissioned	F/S
NIMITZ	CVN 68	Newport News Shipbuilding	22 June 1968	13 May 1972	3 May 1975	PA
DWIGHT D EISENHOWER	CVN 69	Newport News Shipbuilding	15 Aug 1970	11 Oct 1975	18 Oct 1977	AA
CARL VINSON	CVN 70	Newport News Shipbuilding	11 Oct 1975	15 Mar 1980	13 Mar 1982	PA
THEODORE ROOSEVELT	CVN 71	Newport News Shipbuilding	13 Oct 1981	27 Oct 1984	25 Oct 1986	AA
ABRAHAM LINCOLN	CVN 72	Newport News Shipbuilding	3 Nov 1984	13 Feb 1988	11 Nov 1989	PA
GEORGE WASHINGTON	CVN 73	Newport News Shipbuilding	25 Aug 1986	21 July 1990	4 July 1992	AA
JOHN C STENNIS	CVN 74	Newport News Shipbuilding	13 Mar 1991	13 Nov 1993	Dec 1995	Bldg
UNITED STATES	CVN 75	Newport News Shipbuilding	29 Nov 1993	Sep 1996	July 1998	Bldg

Displacement, tons: 72 916 (CVN 68-70), 73 973 (CVN 71) light; 91 487 (CVN 68-70), 96 386 (CVN 71), 102 000 (CVN 72-73) full load

Dimensions, feet (metres): 1040 pp; 1092 × 134 × 37 (CVN 68-70); 38.7 (CVN 71); 39 (CVN 72-73) *(317; 332.9 × 40.8 × 11.3; 11.8; 11.9)*

Flight deck, feet (metres): 1092; 779.8 (angled) × 252 *(332.9; 237.7 × 76.8)*

Main machinery: Nuclear; 2 GE PWR A4W/A1G; 4 turbines; 260 000 hp *(194 MW)*; 4 emergency diesels; 10 720 hp *(8 MW)*; 4 shafts

Speed, knots: 30+

Complement: 3184 (203 officers); 2800 aircrew (366 officers); Flag 70 (25 officers)

Missiles: SAM: 3 Raytheon GMLS Mk 29 octuple launchers; NATO Sea Sparrow; semi-active radar homing to 14.6 km *(8 nm)* at 2.5 Mach; warhead 39 kg.

Guns: 4 General Electric/General Dynamics 20 mm Vulcan Phalanx 6-barrelled Mk 15 (3 in CVN 68 and 69); 3000 rounds/minute (or 4500 in Block 1) combined to 1.5 km.

Torpedoes: 6—324 mm Mk 32 (2 triple) tubes; used for anti-wake homing torpedo countermeasures (being fitted).

Countermeasures: Decoys: 4 Loral Hycor SRBOC 6-barrelled fixed Mk 36; IR flares and chaff to 4 km *(2.2 nm)*. SSTDS (torpedo defence system). SLQ 36 Nixie (Phase I).

ESM/ECM: SLQ-32(V)4 (in CVN 73); SLQ 29 (WLR 8 radar warning and SLQ 17AV jammer and deception system). Being replaced by SLQ-32(V)4.

Combat data systems: NTDS/ACDS naval tactical and advanced combat direction systems; Links 4A, 11 and 14. Link 16 in due course. JOTS, POST, CVIC, TESS UMM-1(V)1, SSQ-82. SATCOMS SRR-1, WSC-3 (UHF), WSC-6 (SHF), USC-38 (EHF).

Fire control: 3 Mk 91 Mod 1 MFCS directors (part of the NSSMS Mk 57 SAM system).

Radars: Air search: ITT SPS 48E; 3D; E/F band; range 402 km *(220 nm)*.
Raytheon SPS 49(V)5; C/D band; range 457 km *(250 nm)*.
Hughes Mk 23 TAS; D band.
Surface search: Norden SPS 67V; G band.
CCA: SPN 41, 2 SPN 42 (CVN 68-70), SPN 43B, SPN 44, 2 SPN 46 (CVN 71-73); J/K/E/F band.
Navigation: Raytheon SPS 64(V)9; Furuno 900; I/J band.
Fire control: Six Mk 95; I/J band (for SAM).
Tacan: URN 25.

Fixed wing aircraft: Transitional air wing includes: 20 F14 Tomcat; 20 F/A-18 Hornet; 4 EA-6B Prowler; 16 A-6E Intruders (includes some KA-6D tankers); 4 E-2C Hawkeye; 6 S-3A/B Viking. Power Projection airwing adds 4 more Hornets. 50 TACAIR airwing adds 12 Hornets and 2 Viking, and removes 14 Tomcat and all Intruders.

Helicopters: 8 SH-3G/H Sea King or SH-60F Seahawk.

Programmes: *Nimitz* was authorised in FY 1967, *Dwight D Eisenhower* in FY 1970, *Carl Vinson* in FY 1974, *Theodore Roosevelt* in FY 1980 and *Abraham Lincoln* and *George Washington* in FY 1983. Construction contracts for the last two were awarded in June 1988. The builder is the only US shipyard capable of constructing large, nuclear-propelled surface warships. The FY 1993 ship construction budget included lead items for CVN 76. Some of the funds allocated to the Strategic Sealift programme in FY 1994 may be shifted to CVN 76, while complete funding is sought in FY 1995 budget.

Structure: Damage control measures include sides with system of full and empty compartments (full compartments can contain aviation fuel), approximately 2.5 in Kevlar plating over certain areas of side shell, box protection over magazine and machinery spaces. Aviation facilities include four lifts, two at the forward end of the flight deck, one to starboard abaft the island and one to port at the stern. There are four steam catapults (C13-1) and four (or three) Mk 7 Mod 3 arrester wires. Launch rate is one every 20 seconds. The hangar can hold less than half the full aircraft complement, deckhead is 25.6 ft. Aviation fuel, 9000 tons. Tactical Flag Command Centre for Flagship role. Mk 32 triple torpedo tubes are being fitted on each quarter as part of the defence against wake homing torpedoes.

Operational: Multi-mission role of 'attack/ASW'. From CVN 70 onwards ships have an A/S control centre and A/S facilities; CVN 68 and 69 will be back fitted. Endurance of 16 days for aviation fuel (steady flying). 13 years' theoretical life for nuclear reactors (CVN 68-70); 15 years' (CVN 71-75); 800 000 to 1 million miles between refuelling. Trials started in December 1992 in CVN 71 with 600 Marines embarked, including six CH-53D and four UH-1N helicopters, which displaced two squadrons of fixed wing aircraft. Other variations of this 'Adaptive Joint Force Packaging' are being tried but the concept is controversial and is being reviewed.

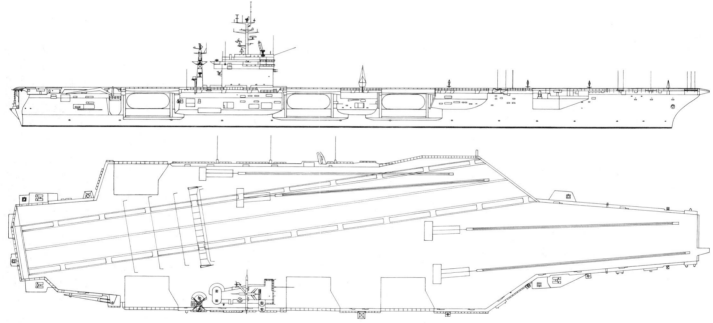

CARL VINSON

(Scale 1 : 1800), Ian Sturton

GEORGE WASHINGTON

9/1993, Giorgio Arra

GEORGE WASHINGTON *10/1993, A Sheldon Duplaix*

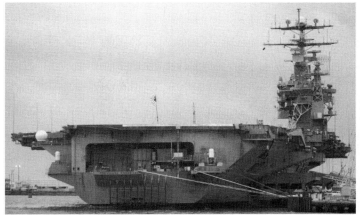

THEODORE ROOSEVELT *10/1993, A Sheldon Duplaix*

GEORGE WASHINGTON *9/1993, Giorgio Arra*

NIMITZ *6/1993, 92 Wing RAAF*

4 KITTY HAWK and JOHN F KENNEDY CLASSES (CV)

Name	No	Builders	Laid down	Launched	Commissioned	F/S
KITTY HAWK	CV 63	New York Shipbuilding	27 Dec 1956	21 May 1960	29 Apr 1961	PA
CONSTELLATION	CV 64	New York Naval Shipyard	14 Sep 1957	8 Oct 1960	27 Oct 1961	PA
AMERICA	CV 66	Newport News Shipbuilding	9 Jan 1961	1 Feb 1964	23 Jan 1965	AA
JOHN F KENNEDY	CV 67	Newport News Shipbuilding	22 Oct 1964	27 May 1967	7 Sep 1968	Conv

Displacement, tons: 60 100 standard; 81 123 full load (CV 63)
   60 100 standard; 81 773 full load (CV 64)
   60 300 standard; 79 724 full load (CV 66)
   61 000 standard; 80 941 full load (CV 67)
Dimensions, feet (metres): 1062.5 (CV 63); 1072.5 (CV 64);
   1047.5 (CV 66); 1052 (CV 67) × 130 × 37.4
   (323.6; 326.9; 319.3; 320.6 × 39.6 × 11.4)
Flight deck, feet (metres): 1046 × 252 *(318.8 × 76.8)*
Main machinery: 8 Foster-Wheeler boilers; 1200 psi
   (83.4 kg/cm sq); 950°F *(510°C)*; 4 Westinghouse turbines;
   280 000 hp *(209 MW)*; 4 shafts
Speed, knots: 32. **Range, miles:** 4000 at 30 kts; 12 000 at
   20 kts
Complement: 2930 (155 officers); aircrew 2480 (320 officers)
   (except CV 67); Flag 70 (25 officers)

Missiles: SAM: 3 Raytheon GMLS Mk 29 octuple launchers;
   NATO Sea Sparrow; semi-active radar homing to 14.6 km
   (8 nm) at 2.5 Mach; warhead 39 kg.
Guns: 3 General Electric/General Dynamics 20 mm Vulcan
   Phalanx 6-barrelled Mk 15; 3000 rounds/minute (or 4500 in
   Block 1) combined to 1.5 km.
Countermeasures: Decoys: 4 Loral Hycor SRBOC 6-barrelled
   fixed Mk 36; IR flares and chaff to 4 km *(2.2 nm)*. SSTDS (Sur-
   face Ship Torpedo Defence System). SLQ-36 Nixie (Phase I).
   ESM/ECM: SLQ-32(V)4 (in CV 63 and 64). SLQ 29 (WLR 8 and
   SLQ 17) in CV 66; WLR 3, WLR 11; combined radar warning,
   jammer and deception system.
Combat data systems: NTDS/ACDS naval tactical and
   advanced combat direction systems (see *Modernisation*);
   Links 4A, 11 and 14. Link 16 in due course. JOTS, POST, CVIC,
   TESS UMM-1(V)1, SSQ-82. SATCOMS SRR-1, WSC-3 (UHF),
   WSC-6 (SHF), USC-38 (EHF).
Fire control: 3 Mk 91 MFCS directors (part of NSSMS Mk 57
   SAM system).
Radars: Air search: ITT SPS 48C/E; 3D; E/F band; range 402 km
   (220 nm).
   Raytheon SPS 49(V)5; C/D band; range 457 km *(250 nm)*.
   Hughes Mk 23 TAS; D band.
   Surface search: Raytheon SPS 10F or Norden SPS 67; G band.
   CCA: SPN 41, SPN 43A; SPN 44; 2 SPN 46; J/K/E/F band.
   Navigation: Raytheon SPN 64(V)9; Furuno 900; I band.
   Fire control: 6 Mk 95; I/J band (for SAM).
   Tacan: URN 25.
Sonars: Fitted for SQS 23 (CV 66-67).

Fixed wing aircraft: Transitional air wing includes: 20 F14 Tomcat; 20 F/A-18 Hornet; 4 EA-6B Prowler; 16 A-6E Intruders
   (includes some KA-6D tankers); 4 E-2C Hawkeye; 6 S-3A/B
   Viking. Power Projection airwing adds 4 more Hornets. 50
   TACAIR airwing adds 12 Hornets and 2 Viking, and removes
   14 Tomcat and all Intruders.
Helicopters: 8 SH-3G/H Sea King or SH-60F Seahawk.

Programmes: *Kitty Hawk* was authorised in FY 1956, *Constel-
   lation* in FY 1957, *America* in FY 1961, and *John F Kennedy* in
   FY 1963.
Modernisation: Service Life Extension Programme (SLEP): *Kitty
   Hawk* completed in February 1991 and *Constellation* in
   December 1992. A 'complex overhaul' of *Kennedy* was funded
   in FY 1991 and started in September 1993. On completion in
   1996, *Kennedy* is to become the reserve and training carrier.
   ACDS Block 1 trials are being done in *Constellation*. The first
   full fit is scheduled for 1996.
Structure: These ships were built to an improved Forrestal
   design and are easily recognised by their island structure being
   set farther aft than the superstructure in the four Forrestal class
   ships. They have two deck-edge lifts forward of the superstructure, a third lift aft of the structure, and the port-side lift on the
   after quarter. This arrangement considerably improves flight
   deck operations. Four C13 steam catapults (with one C13-1 in
   America and *Kennedy*) and four arrester wires. *John F Kennedy*

KENNEDY

9/1992, Maritime Photographic

and *America* have stern anchors as well as bow anchors
because of their planned bow sonar domes. All have a small
radar mast abaft the island. The island is painted black

between flight deck and bridge to mask jet exhaust stains.
Aviation fuel of 5882 tons are carried.
Operational: *America* is scheduled to pay off in 1996.

KENNEDY

9/1992, Maritime Photographic

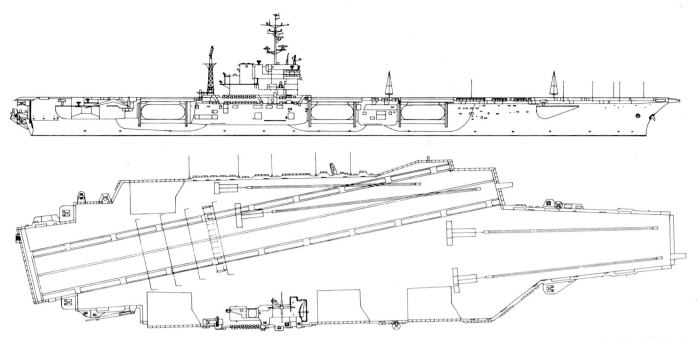

AMERICA   *(Scale 1 : 1800), Ian Sturton*

AMERICA   *9/1991, Maritime Photographic*

AMERICA   *10/1991, H M Steele*

2 FORRESTAL CLASS (CV)

Name	No	Builders	Laid down	Launched	Commissioned	F/S
SARATOGA	CV 60	New York Naval Shipyard	16 Dec 1952	8 Oct 1955	14 Apr 1956	AA
INDEPENDENCE	CV 62	New York Naval Shipyard	1 July 1955	6 June 1958	10 Jan 1959	PA

Displacement, tons: 59 060 (CV 60), 60 000 (CV 62) standard; 80 383 (CV 60), 80 643 (CV 62) full load
Dimensions, feet (metres): 1063 (CV 60); 1071 (CV 62) × 130 × 37 *(324; 326.4 × 39.6 × 11.3)*
Flight deck, feet (metres): 1047 × 250.3 (CV 60); 270 (CV 62) *(319.1 × 76.3; 82.3)*
Main machinery: 8 Babcock & Wilcox boilers; 1200 psi *(83.4 kg/cm sq)*; 950°F *(510°C)*; 4 Westinghouse turbines; 280 000 hp *(209 MW)*; 4 shafts
Speed, knots: 33. **Range, miles:** 8000 at 20 kts; 4000 at 30 kts
Complement: 2900 (154 officers); aircrew 2279 (329 officers); Flag 70 (25 officers)

Missiles: SAM: 3 Raytheon GMLS Mk 29 octuple launchers; NATO Sea Sparrow; semi-active radar homing to 14.6 km *(8 nm)* at 2.5 Mach; warhead 39 kg.
Guns: 3 General Electric/General Dynamics 20 mm Vulcan Phalanx 6-barrelled Mk 15; 3000 rounds/minute (or 4500 in Block 1) combined to 1.5 km.
Countermeasures: Decoys: 4 Loral Hycor SRBOC 6-barrelled fixed Mk 36; IR flares and chaff to 4 km *(2.2 nm)*. SSTDS (Surface Ship Torpedo Defence System). SLQ-36 Nixie (Phase I).
ESM/ECM: SLQ-32(V)3 (CV 62). SLQ-32(V)4 (CV 60); combined radar warning, jammer and deception systems.
Combat data systems: NTDS/ACDS naval tactical and advanced combat direction systems; Links 4A, 11 and 14. Link

16 in due course. JOTS, POST, CVIC, TESS UMM-1(V)1, SSQ-82. SATCOMS SRR-1, WSC-3 (UHF), WSC-6 (SHF), USC-38 (EHF).
Fire control: 3 Mk 91 Mod 3 MFCS directors (part of NSSMS Mk 57 SAM system).
Radars: Air search: ITT SPS 48C; 3D; E/F band; range 402 km *(220 nm)*.
Raytheon SPS 49(V)5; C/D band; range 457 km *(250 nm)*. Hughes Mk 23 TAS; D band.
Surface search: Norden SPS 67; G band.
CCA: SPN 41, 2 SPN 42, SPN 43A, SPN 44; J/K/E/F band.
Navigation: Raytheon SPN 64(V)9; I band.
Fire control: 4 or 6 Mk 95 (for SAM); I/J band.
Tacan: URN 25.

Fixed wing aircraft: Transitional air wing includes: 20 F14 Tomcat; 20 F/A-18 Hornet; 4 EA-6B Prowler; 16 A-6E Intruders (includes some KA-6D tankers); 4 E-2C Hawkeye; 6 S-3A/B Viking. Power Projection airwing adds 4 more Hornets. 50 TACAIR airwing adds 12 Hornets and 2 Viking, and removes 14 Tomcat and all Intruders.
Helicopters: 8 SH-3H Sea King or SH-60F Seahawk.

Programmes: *Saratoga* authorised in FY 1953 and *Independence* in FY 1955.

Modernisation: Service Life Extension Programme (SLEP): The Navy's aircraft carrier Service Life Extension Programme (SLEP) began with ships of the *Forrestal* class. *Saratoga* from October 1980 to February 1983, and *Independence* April 1985 to May 1988. Two Mk 25 BPDMS launchers fitted in *Independence* in 1973 with the subsequent removal of all 5 in guns, *Saratoga* in 1974. These have been replaced by three Mk 29 GMLS launchers during SLEP.
Structure: The Forrestal class ships were the first aircraft carriers designed and built specifically to operate jet-propelled aircraft. Redesigned early in construction to incorporate British-developed angled flight deck and steam catapults. These were the first US aircraft carriers built with an enclosed bow area to improve seaworthiness. Other features include armoured flight deck and advanced underwater protection and internal compartmentation to reduce effects of conventional and nuclear attack. Mast configurations differ. Funnel height of *Independence* increased by 10 ft in 1980. Aviation facilities include four 72 × 50 ft *(21.9 × 15.2 m)* lifts with capacity of 99 000 lb (45 tons), four steam catapults (2 C7 and 2 C 11 in CV 60 and 4 C 13 in CV 62) and four arrester wires. Aviation fuel, 5500 tons.
Operational: *Independence* is based in Yokosuka, Japan. *Saratoga* is scheduled to pay off in August 1994.

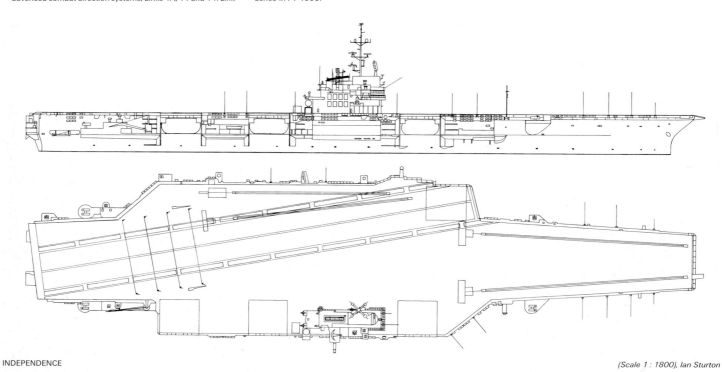

INDEPENDENCE

(Scale 1 : 1800), Ian Sturton

INDEPENDENCE

2/1993, Hachiro Nakai

INDEPENDENCE

CRUISERS

Notes: (1) Two ships of the Virginia class, two of the California class, and Kidd class destroyers, received the New Threat Upgrade (NTU) modernisation between FY 1986 and FY 1994. This included Standard SM-2 missiles where appropriate, updated air/surface search and fire-control radars, improved weapons direction and missile fire-control systems and the SYS-2 Integrated Automatic Target Detection and Tracking system (IADT). Where appropriate Mk 10 and Mk 26 missile launchers are also being converted from analog to digital systems.

(2) Navstar GPS (SRN-24) is being fitted in all major warships. As well as being an incomparable aid to navigation, this system has marked implications in combat data exchange and third party targeting for long-range weapon systems.

3 VIRGINIA CLASS: GUIDED MISSILE CRUISERS (CGN)

Name	No	Builders	Laid down	Launched	Commissioned	F/S
VIRGINIA	CGN 38	Newport News Shipbuilding	19 Aug 1972	14 Dec 1974	11 Sep 1976	AA
MISSISSIPPI	CGN 40	Newport News Shipbuilding	22 Feb 1975	31 July 1976	5 Aug 1978	AA
ARKANSAS	CGN 41	Newport News Shipbuilding	17 Jan 1977	21 Oct 1978	18 Oct 1980	PA

Displacement, tons: 8623 light; 11 300 full load
Dimensions, feet (metres): 585 × 63 × 31.5 (sonar)
(178.3 × 19.2 × 9.6)
Main machinery: Nuclear; 2 GE PWR D2G; 2 turbines;
70 000 hp *(52 MW)*; 2 shafts
Speed, knots: 30+
Complement: 558-624 (38-45 officers)

Missiles: SLCM/SSM: 8 GDC Tomahawk (2 quad) ❶; combination of (a) land attack; TAINS (Tercom aided navigation system) to 2500 km *(1400 nm)* at 0.7 Mach; altitude 15-100 m *(49.2-328.1 ft)*; warhead nuclear 200 kT (TLAM-N); CEP 80 m; or warhead 454 kg (TLAM-C) or submunitions (TLAM-D); range 1300 km *(700 nm)*; CEP 10 m. Nuclear warheads are not normally carried. Range increased by over 30% in TLAM-C Batch III which started production in 1992.
(b) anti-ship (TASM); inertial guidance; active radar and anti-radiation homing to 460 km *(250 nm)* at 0.7 Mach; warhead 454 kg.
8 McDonnell Douglas Harpoon (2 quad) ❷; active radar homing to 130 km *(70 nm)* at 0.9 Mach; warhead 227 kg.
SAM: GDC Standard SM-2MR; command/inertial guidance; semi-active radar homing to 73 km *(40 nm)* at 2 Mach.
A/S: Honeywell ASROC; inertial guidance to 1.6-10 km *(1-5.4 nm)*; payload Mk 46 Mod 5 Neartip or Mk 50 in due course. SAM and A/S missiles are fired from 2 twin GMLS Mk 26 launchers supplied by a total of 68 weapons ❸.
Guns: 2 FMC 5 in *(127 mm)*/54 Mk 45 Mod 0 ❹; 65° elevation; 20 rounds/minute to 23 km *(12.6 nm)* anti-surface; 15 km *(8.2 nm)* anti-aircraft; weight of shell 32 kg.
2 General Electric/General Dynamics 20 mm Vulcan Phalanx 6-barrelled Mk 15 ❺; 3000 rounds/minute (or 4500 in Block 1) combined to 1.5 kg.
4—12.7 mm MGs.
Torpedoes: 6—324 mm Mk 32 (2 triple) tubes ❻. Honeywell Mk 46 Mod 5; anti-submarine; active/passive homing to 11 km *(5.9 nm)* at 40 kts; warhead 44 kg. Being replaced by Mk 50 from 1994.
Countermeasures: Decoys: 4 Loral Hycor SRBOC 6-barrelled fixed Mk 36 ❼; IR flares and chaff to 4 km *(2.2 nm)*. T Mk 6 Fanfare or SLQ-26 Nixie; torpedo decoy system.
ESM/ECM: SLQ 32V(3); combined radar warning, jammer and deception system. OUTBOARD II.
Combat data systems: NTDS with Links 4A, 11, 14 and 16 in due course. SATCOM ❽ SRR-1; WSC-3 (UHF); USC 38 (EHF).
Fire control: SWG-2 Tomahawk WCS. SWG-1A Harpoon LCS. 1 Mk 74 MFCS. 1 digital Mk 116 ASW FCS. 1 Mk 86 Mod 5 GFCS for forward missile channel and gun fire. SYS-2(V)1 IADT.
Radars: Air search: ITT SPS 48C or 48D/E (NTU) ❾; 3D; E/F band; range 402 km *(220 nm)*.
Lockheed SPS 40B or Raytheon SPS 49(V)5 (NTU) ❿; C/D band.
Surface search: ISC Cardion SPS 55 ⓫; I/J band.
Navigation: Raytheon SPS 64(V)9; I/J band.
Fire control: Two SPG 51D ⓬; G/I band.
SPG 60D ⓭; I/J band. SPQ 9A ⓮; I/J band.
Tacan: URN 25. IFF Mk XII AIMS UPX 29.
Sonars: EDO/GE SQS 53A; bow-mounted; active search and attack; medium frequency. Based on SQS 26 but with digital computers.

Programmes: *Virginia* was authorised in FY 1970, *Mississippi* in FY 1972, and *Arkansas* in FY 1975. Originally classified as guided missile frigates (DLGN); subsequently reclassified as guided missile cruisers (CGN) on 30 June 1975.

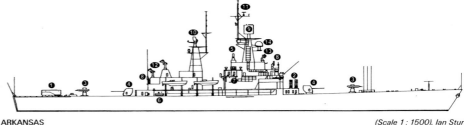

ARKANSAS   *(Scale 1 : 1500), Ian Sturton*

MISSISSIPPI   *10/1993, Giorgio Arra*

Modernisation: Standard SM-1MR replaced by SM-2MR using Block II missiles to counter current and projected anti-ship cruise missile threats at extended ranges in the presence of severe enemy electronic countermeasures. Production systems were deployed in all guided missile cruisers and in DDG 993 class destroyers in FY 1988. The initial phase of fleet introduction of SM-2 in a Tartar ship was completed in May 1986 in *Virginia*. Tomahawk fitted in two armoured box launchers in all of the class at the expense of the helicopter capability. *Mississippi* and *Arkansas* have completed NTU. This included upgrading the Mk 74 MFCS and SPG 51D radars, improving the Mk 26 launchers, replacing SPS 40B radar by Raytheon SPS 49 and improving SPS 48, plus IADT SYS-2(V)2 (Integrated Automatic Detection and Track). Plans to fit *Virginia* were shelved in 1993, and the fourth of class paid off in mid-1993.
Structure: The principal differences between the Virginia and California classes are the provision of improvements to anti-air warfare capability, electronic warfare equipment, and antisubmarine fire-control system. The deletion of the separate ASROC Mk 16 launcher permitted the Virginia class to be 11 ft shorter.
Operational: To save money on refuelling, *Texas* was paid off in 1993 and *Virginia* follows in September 1994.

ARKANSAS   *3/1994, Hachiro Nakai*

2 CALIFORNIA CLASS: GUIDED MISSILE CRUISERS (CGN)

Name	No	Builders	Laid down	Launched	Commissioned	F/S
CALIFORNIA	CGN 36	Newport News Shipbuilding	23 Jan 1970	22 Sep 1971	16 Feb 1974	PA
SOUTH CAROLINA	CGN 37	Newport News Shipbuilding	1 Dec 1970	1 July 1972	25 Jan 1975	AA

Displacement, tons: 8706 light; 9561 standard; 10 450 full load (9473, CGN 37)
Dimensions, feet (metres): 596 × 61 × 31.5 (sonar) *(181.7 × 18.6 × 9.6)*
Main machinery: Nuclear; 2 GE PWR D2G; 2 turbines; 70 000 hp *(52 MW)*; 2 shafts
Speed, knots: 30+
Complement: 603 (44 officers)

Missiles: SSM: 8 McDonnell Douglas Harpoon (2 quad) launchers ❶; active radar homing to 130 km *(70 nm)* at 0.9 Mach; warhead 227 kg.
SAM: 80 GDC Standard SM-2MR; 2 Mk 13 Mod 7 launchers ❷; command/inertial guidance; semi-active radar homing to 73 km *(40 nm)* at 2 Mach.
A/S: Honeywell ASROC Mk 16 octuple launcher ❸; inertial guidance to 1.6-10 km *(1-5.4 nm)*; Mk 46 Mod 5 Neartip/Mk 50; 24 weapons carried.
Guns: 2 FMC 5 in *(127 mm)*/54 Mk 45 Mod 0 ❹; 65° elevation; 20 rounds/minute to 23 km *(12.6 nm)* anti-surface; 15 km *(8.2 nm)* anti-aircraft; weight of shell 32 kg.
2 General Electric/General Dynamics 20 mm Vulcan Phalanx 6-barrelled Mk 15 ❺; 3000 rounds/minute (or 4500 in Block 1) combined to 1.5 km.
4—12.7 mm MGs.
Torpedoes: 4—324 mm Mk 32 (2 twin) fixed tubes. Honeywell Mk 46 Mod 5; anti-submarine; active/passive homing to 11 km *(5.9 nm)* at 40 kts; warhead 44 kg.
Countermeasures: Decoys: 4 Loral Hycor SRBOC 6-barrelled fixed Mk 36; IR flares and chaff to 4 km *(2.2 nm)*. SLQ-25; torpedo decoy system.
ESM/ECM: SLQ 32(V)3; combined radar warning, jammer and deception system. OUTBOARD.
Combat data systems: NTDS with Links 4A, 11, 14 and 16 in due course. SATCOM SRR-1, WSC-3 (UHF), USC 38 (EHF).
Fire control: SWG-1A Harpoon LCS. 2 Mk 74 MFCS Mod 2.1 Mk 86 Mod 3 GFCS. 1 Mk 14 weapon direction system. 1 Mk 114 ASW FCS. SYS-2(V)2 IADT.
Radars: Air search: ITT SPS 48E ❻; 3D; E/F band; range 402 km *(220 nm)*.
Raytheon SPS 49(V)5 ❼; C/D band.
Surface search: Norden SPS 67 ❽; G band.
Navigation: Marconi LN 66; I/J band.
Fire control: Four SPG 51D ❾; G/I band.
SPG 60D ❿; I/J band. SPQ 9A ⓫; I/J band.
Tacan: URN 25.
Sonars: EDO/GE SQS 26 CX; bow-mounted; active search and attack; medium frequency.

Helicopters: Platform only.

Programmes: *California* was authorised in FY 1967 and *South Carolina* in FY 1968. Originally classified as guided missile destroyers (DLGN); subsequently reclassified as guided missile cruisers (CGN) on 30 June 1975.

Modernisation: It was planned to fit Tomahawk missiles but the project was cancelled due to topweight constraints. Both have completed the New Threat Upgrade modernisation. This included Standard SM-2 missiles, upgrading the Mk 74 MFCS and SPG 51D radars, replacing SPS 40B radar by SPS 49, upgrading SPS 48 radar, fitting the Mk 14 weapon direction system and the SYS(V)2 IADT.

Structure: Harpoon missiles are in two quadruple sets with the midships launcher facing to starboard and the aft launcher to port.
Operational: Both are scheduled to pay off in 1998/99.

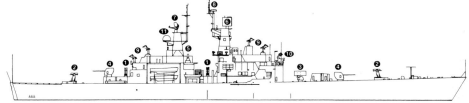

CALIFORNIA *(Scale 1 : 1500), Ian Sturton*

SOUTH CAROLINA *3/1991, Giorgio Arra*

1 TRUXTUN CLASS: GUIDED MISSILE CRUISER (CGN)

Name	No	Builders	Laid down	Launched	Commissioned	F/S
TRUXTUN	CGN 35	New York Shipbuilding	17 June 1963	19 Dec 1964	27 May 1967	PA

Displacement, tons: 8322 light; 9127 full load
Dimensions, feet (metres): 564 × 58 × 31 (sonar) *(171.9 × 17.7 × 9.4)*
Main machinery: Nuclear; 2 GE PWR D2G; 2 turbines; 70 000 hp *(52 MW)*; 2 shafts
Speed, knots: 30
Complement: 561 (39 officers); Flag 18 (6 officers)

Missiles: SSM: 8 McDonnell Douglas Harpoon (2 quad) launchers ❶; active radar homing to 130 km *(70 nm)* at 0.9 Mach; warhead 227 kg.
SAM: 40 GDC Standard SM-2ER Block 2; command/inertial guidance; semi-active radar homing to 137 km *(75 nm)* at 2.5 Mach.
A/S: 20 Honeywell ASROC; inertial guidance to 1.6-10 km *(1-5.4 nm)*; payload Mk 46 Mod 5 Neartip. 1 twin Mk 10 Mod 16 launcher for SAM and ASROC ❷.
Guns: 1 FMC 5 in *(127 mm)*/54 Mk 42 Mod 10 ❸; 85° elevation; 20-40 rounds/minute to 24 km *(13.1 nm)* anti-surface; 14 km *(7.7 nm)* anti-aircraft; weight of shell 32 kg.
2 General Electric/General Dynamics 20 mm Vulcan Phalanx 6-barrelled Mk 15 ❹; 3000 rounds/minute (or 4500 in Block 1) combined to 1.5 km.
4—12.7 mm MGs.
Torpedoes: 4—324 mm Mk 32 (2 twin) fixed tubes. Honeywell Mk 46 Mod 5; anti-submarine; active/passive homing to 11 km *(5.9 nm)* at 40 kts; warhead 44 kg.
Countermeasures: Decoys: 4 Loral Hycor SRBOC 6-barrelled fixed Mk 36; IR flares and chaff to 4 km *(2.2 nm)*. SLQ-25 Nixie; towed torpedo decoy.
ESM/ECM: SLQ 32(V)3; combined radar warning, jammer and deception system. WLR-1; radar warning.
Combat data systems: NTDS with Links 4A, 11 and 14. SATCOM SRR-1, WSC-3 (UHF).
Fire control: SWG-1A Harpoon LCS. 2 Mk 76 Mod 6 MFCS. 1 Mk 68 GFCS. 1 Mk 14 weapon direction system. Mk 111 ASW FCS. SYS-2(V)2 IADT.
Radars: Air search: ITT SPS 48E ❺; 3D; E/F band; range 402 km *(220 nm)*.
Raytheon SPS 49(V)5 ❻; C/D band; range 457 km *(250 nm)*.
Surface search: Norden SPS 67 ❼; G band.
Navigation: Marconi LN 66; I band.
Fire control: SPG 53F ❽; I/J band. Two SPG 55C ❾; G/H band.
Tacan: URN 25. IFF Mk 12 AIMS.
Sonars: EDO/GE SQS 26 AXR; bow-mounted; active search and attack; medium frequency.

Helicopters: 1 SH-2G Sea Sprite ❿.

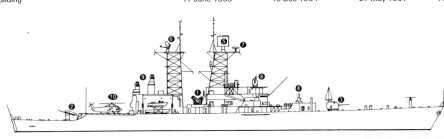

TRUXTUN *(Scale 1 : 1500), Ian Sturton*

TRUXTUN *6/1990, G Salmeri, RAN*

Programmes: *Truxtun* was the US Navy's fourth nuclear-powered surface warship. The Navy had requested seven oil-burning frigates in the FY 1962 shipbuilding programme; Congress authorised seven ships, but stipulated that one ship must be nuclear-powered. Originally classified as a guided missile frigate (DLGN); subsequently reclassified as a guided missile cruiser (CGN) on 30 June 1975. *Truxtun* is the fifth ship to be named after Commodore Thomas Truxtun *(sic)* who commanded the frigate *Constellation* (38 guns) in her successful encounter with the French frigate *L'Insurgente* (44) in 1799.
Structure: Although the *Truxtun* design is adapted from the Belknap class, the nuclear ship's gun-missile launcher arrangement is reversed from the non-nuclear ships.
Operational: Now planned to be paid off in FY 1995.

27 TICONDEROGA CLASS: GUIDED MISSILE CRUISERS (CG—AEGIS)

Name	No	Builder/Programme	Laid down	Launched	Commissioned	F/S
TICONDEROGA	CG 47 (ex-DDG 47)	Ingalls Shipbuilding	21 Jan 1980	25 Apr 1981	22 Jan 1983	AA
YORKTOWN	CG 48	Ingalls Shipbuilding	19 Oct 1981	17 Jan 1983	4 July 1984	AA
VINCENNES	CG 49	Ingalls Shipbuilding	20 Oct 1982	14 Jan 1984	6 July 1985	PA
VALLEY FORGE	CG 50	Ingalls Shipbuilding	14 Apr 1983	23 June 1984	18 Jan 1986	PA
THOMAS S GATES	CG 51	Bath Iron Works	31 Aug 1984	14 Dec 1985	22 Aug 1987	PA
BUNKER HILL	CG 52	Ingalls Shipbuilding	11 Jan 1984	11 Mar 1985	20 Sep 1986	PA
MOBILE BAY	CG 53	Ingalls Shipbuilding	6 June 1984	22 Aug 1985	21 Feb 1987	PA
ANTIETAM	CG 54	Ingalls Shipbuilding	15 Nov 1984	14 Feb 1986	6 June 1987	PA
LEYTE GULF	CG 55	Ingalls Shipbuilding	18 Mar 1985	20 June 1986	26 Sep 1987	AA
SAN JACINTO	CG 56	Ingalls Shipbuilding	24 July 1985	14 Nov 1986	23 Jan 1988	AA
LAKE CHAMPLAIN	CG 57	Ingalls Shipbuilding	3 Mar 1986	3 Apr 1987	12 Aug 1988	PA
PHILIPPINE SEA	CG 58	Bath Iron Works	8 May 1986	12 July 1987	18 Mar 1989	AA
PRINCETON	CG 59	Ingalls Shipbuilding	15 Oct 1986	2 Oct 1987	11 Feb 1989	PA
NORMANDY	CG 60	Bath Iron Works	7 Apr 1987	19 Mar 1988	9 Dec 1989	AA
MONTEREY	CG 61	Bath Iron Works	19 Aug 1987	23 Oct 1988	16 June 1990	AA
CHANCELLORSVILLE	CG 62	Ingalls Shipbuilding	24 June 1987	15 July 1988	4 Nov 1989	PA
COWPENS	CG 63	Bath Iron Works	23 Dec 1987	11 Mar 1989	9 Mar 1991	AA
GETTYSBURG	CG 64	Bath Iron Works	17 Aug 1988	22 July 1989	22 June 1991	AA
CHOSIN	CG 65	Ingalls Shipbuilding	22 July 1988	1 Sep 1989	12 Jan 1991	PA
HUE CITY	CG 66	Ingalls Shipbuilding	20 Feb 1989	1 June 1990	14 Sep 1991	AA
SHILOH	CG 67	Bath Iron Works	1 Aug 1989	8 Sep 1990	2 July 1992	PA
ANZIO	CG 68	Ingalls Shipbuilding	21 Aug 1989	2 Nov 1990	2 May 1992	AA
VICKSBURG	CG 69	Ingalls Shipbuilding	30 May 1990	2 Aug 1991	14 Nov 1992	AA
LAKE ERIE	CG 70	Bath Iron Works	6 Mar 1990	13 July 1991	24 July 1993	PA
CAPE ST GEORGE	CG 71	Ingalls Shipbuilding	19 Nov 1990	10 Jan 1992	12 June 1993	AA
VELLA GULF	CG 72	Ingalls Shipbuilding	22 Apr 1991	13 June 1992	18 Sep 1993	AA
PORT ROYAL	CG 73	Ingalls Shipbuilding	18 Oct 1991	20 Nov 1992	July 1994	PA

Displacement, tons: 7015 light; 9590 (CG 47-48); 9407 (CG 49-51); 9466 (remainder) full load

Dimensions, feet (metres): 567 × 55 × 31 (sonar)
(172.8 × 16.8 × 9.5)

Main machinery: 4 GE LM 2500 gas-turbines; 86 000 hp *(64.16 MW)* sustained; 2 shafts; cp props

Speed, knots: 30+. **Range, miles:** 6000 at 20 kts

Complement: 358 (24 officers); accommodation for 405 total

Missiles: SLCM/SSM: GDC Tomahawk (CG 52 onwards); combination of (a) land attack; TAINS (Tercom aided navigation system) to 2500 km *(1400 nm)* at 0.7 Mach; altitude 15-100 m *(49.2-328.1 ft)*; warhead nuclear 200 kT (TLAM-N); or warhead 454 kg or 317 kg (Block II) (TLAM-C) or submunitions (TLAM-D); range 1300 km *(700 nm)*; CEP 10 m. Nuclear warheads are not normally carried. Range increased by 30% in TLAM-C Block III which started production in 1992 and is GPS fitted.
(b) anti-ship (TASM); inertial guidance; active radar and anti-radiation homing to 460 km *(250 nm)* at 0.7 Mach; warhead 454 kg.
8 McDonnell Douglas Harpoon (2 quad) ❶; active radar homing to 130 km *(70 nm)* at 0.9 Mach; warhead 227 kg. Extended range SLAM can be fired from modified Harpoon canisters.

SAM: 68 (CG 47-51); 122 (CG 52 onwards) GDC Standard SM-2MR; command/inertial guidance; semi-active radar homing to 73 km *(40 nm)* at 2 Mach.

A/S: 20 Honeywell ASROC; inertial guidance to 1.6-10 km *(1-5.4 nm)*; payload Mk 46 Mod 5 Neartip/Mk 50.
SAM and A/S missiles are fired from 2 twin Mk 26 Mod 5 launchers ❷ (CG 47-51) and 2 Mk 41 Mod 0 vertical launchers ❸ (61 missiles per launcher) (CG 52 onwards). Tomahawk is carried in CG 52 onwards with 8 missiles in each VLS launcher and 12 in the magazines. Vertical launch ASROC to be back fitted when available increasing the range to 16.6 km *(9 nm)*.

Guns: 2 FMC 5 in *(127 mm)*/54 Mk 45 (Mod 0 (CG 47-50); Mod 1 (CG 51 onwards)) ❹; 65° elevation; 20 rounds/minute to 23 km *(12.6 nm)* anti-surface; weight of shell 32 kg.
2 General Electric/General Dynamics 20 mm/76 Vulcan Phalanx 6-barrelled Mk 15 ❺; 3000 rounds/minute (4500 in Block 1) combined to 1.5 km.
4—12.7 mm MGs.

Torpedoes: 6—324 mm Mk 32 (2 triple) tubes (fitted in the ship's side aft) ❻. 36 Honeywell Mk 46 Mod 5; anti-submarine; active/passive homing to 11 km *(5.9 nm)* at 40 kts; warhead 44 kg. Being replaced by Mk 50 from 1994.

Countermeasures: Decoys: 4 or 6 Loral Hycor SRBOC 6-barrelled fixed Mk 36 ❼; IR flares and chaff to 4 km *(2.2 nm)*. SLQ-25 Nixie; towed torpedo decoy.
ESM/ECM: Raytheon SLQ 32V(3) ❽; combined radar warning, jammer and deception system.

Combat data systems: NTDS with Links 4A, 11, 14 and 16 in due course. SATCOM SRR-1, WSC-3 (UHF), USC-38 (EHF). UYK 7 and 20 computers (CG 47-58); UYK 43/44 (CG 59 onwards). SQQ 28 for LAMPS sonobuoy data link ❾.

Fire control: SWG-3 Tomahawk WCS. SWG-1A Harpoon LCS. Aegis Mk 7 Mod 2 multi-target tracking with Mk 99 MFCS (includes 4 Mk 80 illuminator directors); has at least 12 channels of fire. Singer Librascope Mk 116 Mod 6 (53B) or 7 (53C) FCS for ASW. Lockheed Mk 86 Mod 9 GFCS.

Radars: Air search/fire-control: RCA SPY 1A phased arrays ❿; 3D; E/F band (CG 47-58).
Raytheon SPY 1B phased arrays ⓫; 3D; E/F band (CG 59 on).
Air search: Raytheon SPS 49(V)7 ⓬; C/D band; range 457 km *(250 nm)*.
Surface search: ISC Cardion SPS 55 ⓭; I/J band.
Navigation: Raytheon SPS 64(V)9; I band.
Fire control: Lockheed SPQ 9A ⓮; I/J band; range 37 km *(20 nm)*.
Four Raytheon/RCA SPG 62 ⓯; I/J band.
Tacan: URN 25. IFF Mk XII AIMS UPX-29.

Sonars: General Electric/Hughes SQS 53A/B (CG 47-55); bow-mounted; active search and attack; medium frequency.
Gould SQR 19 (CG 54-55); passive towed array (TACTAS).
Gould/Raytheon SQQ 89(V)3 (CG 56 onwards); combines hull-mounted active SQS 53B (CG 56-67) or SQS 53C (CG 68-73) and passive towed array SQR 19.

Helicopters: 2 SH-60B Seahawk LAMPS III ⓰; 2 SH-2F LAMPS I (CG 47-48) ⓱.

Programmes: Last five approved in the FY 1988 ship construction budget. That decision stemmed from the delays being encountered in the construction of *Arleigh Burke*, and the

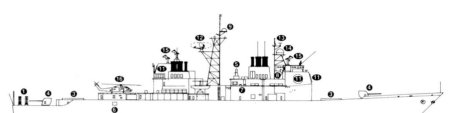
BUNKER HILL   *(Scale 1 : 1500), Ian Sturton*

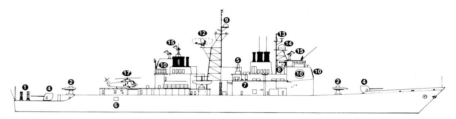
TICONDEROGA   *(Scale 1 : 1500), Ian Sturton*

CAPE ST GEORGE   *8/1993, Giorgio Arra*

realisation that the Navy was in no position at that time to award further contracts for construction of more DDG 51s.

Modernisation: Long Range Improvement Programme: In order to include the latest in technology in these ships, four baselines were planned and five have evolved. *Ticonderoga*, equipped with LAMPS I, represents Baseline O. Baseline I starts with *Vincennes* equipped with LAMPS III, RAST haul-down flight deck system and Block 2 Standard missiles. Baseline II, beginning with *Bunker Hill*, adds Tomahawk, and the Vertical Launch System. Baseline III starting with *San Jacinto* adds the SQQ 89 sonar. Baseline IV, beginning with *Princeton* (CG 59), incorporates the advanced AN/SPY 1B radar on UYQ-21 displays and includes the upgraded computers UYK-43/44. According to the Navy, this method of upgrading ship capabilities provides the best available combat system to the fleet while reducing operation and support costs. *Lake Champlain* fired the first SLAM missile from a Harpoon canister in June 1990; the extended range SSM was controlled in terminal flight by a LAMPS III helicopter. A Standard missile is being developed to provide defence against ballistic missiles.

Structure: The Ticonderoga class design is a modification of the Spruance class. The same basic hull is used, with the same gas-turbine propulsion plant although the overall length is slightly increased. The design includes Kevlar armour to protect vital spaces. No stabilisers. *Vincennes* and later ships have a lighter tripod mainmast vice the square quadruped of the first two.

Operational: *Yorktown* provided the air-intercept support for Navy fighters intercepting the Egyptian airliner carrying the hijackers of the cruise ship *Achille Lauro* from Egypt to Tunisia. In March and April of 1986, *Yorktown* and *Vincennes* were focal points of the successful operations in the Gulf of Sidra which led to the sinking of two Libyan patrol boats and of the strike by carrier-based Navy aircraft and shore-based F-111s against Libyan missile sites and other targets. *Vincennes* was again in the news with the misidentification and shooting down of an airliner during a surface engagement with Iranian gunboats in 1988. The report of that incident describes the Aegis system as having performed as designed, and the sensor data collected was accurate but 'it should be appreciated that Aegis is not capable of identifying the type of aircraft being tracked. Ships of the class were again active in directing the air defence of the northern Gulf during the Iraq war in early 1991. *Princeton* was damaged by a mine; repairs were completed in December 1991. Seven of the class fired Tomahawk missiles and others of the class fired again in January and June 1993 at targets in Iraq. Aegis's major advantages are the extended range of its sensors, its fast reaction time, the capacity to track many targets at once, its ability to send this information automatically to other units, and its data displays which combine sensor information with other inputs. Because of its long-range radar, it gives operators additional time to react, to gather data, and to make considered judgements. Operating close to land, these advantages can be eroded. A combination of Aegis and an upgraded Standard missile is to give the first naval defence against ballistic missiles. Two of the class are based at Yokosuka, Japan.

MOBILE BAY   *6/1993, Vic Jeffery, RAN*

CAPE ST GEORGE   *8/1993, Giorgio Arra*

COWPENS   *10/1993, Giorgio Arra*

VALLEY FORGE   *1/1993, van Ginderen Collection*

VALLEY FORGE   *6/1993, John Mortimer*

1 BAINBRIDGE CLASS: GUIDED MISSILE CRUISER (CGN)

Name	No	Builders	Laid down	Launched	Commissioned	F/S
BAINBRIDGE	CGN 25	Bethlehem Steel	15 May 1959	15 Apr 1961	6 Oct 1962	AA

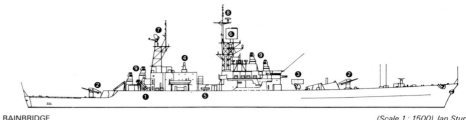

BAINBRIDGE   (Scale 1 : 1500), Ian Sturton

Displacement, tons: 7804 light; 8592 full load
Dimensions, feet (metres): 565 × 57.9 × 31.2 (sonar)
(172.3 × 17.6 × 9.5)
Main machinery: Nuclear; 2 GE PWR D2G; 2 turbines;
70 000 hp (52 MW); 2 shafts
Speed, knots: 30
Complement: 558 (42 officers); Flag 18 (6 officers)

Missiles: SSM: 8 McDonnell Douglas Harpoon (2 quad) launchers ❶; active radar homing to 130 km (70 nm) at 0.9 Mach;
warhead 227 kg.
SAM: 80 GDC Standard SM-2ER; 2 twin Mk 10 launchers (Mod
13 fwd, Mod 14 aft) ❷; command/inertial guidance; semi-
active radar homing to 137 km (75 nm) at 2.5 Mach.
A/S: Honeywell ASROC Mk 16 octuple launcher ❸; inertial guidance to 1.6-10 km (1-5.4 nm); payload Mk 46 Mod 5 Neartip.
Guns: 2 General Electric/General Dynamics 20 mm Vulcan Phalanx 6-barrelled Mk 15 ❹; 3000 rounds/minute (or 4500 in
Block 1) combined to 1.5 km.
4—12.7 mm MGs.
Torpedoes: 6—324 mm Mk 32 (2 triple) tubes ❺. Honeywell
Mk 46; anti-submarine; active/passive homing to 11 km
(5.9 nm) at 40 kts; warhead 44 kg.
Countermeasures: Decoys: 4 Loral Hycor SRBOC 6-barrelled
fixed Mk 36; IR flares and chaff to 4 km (2.2 nm). T-Mk 6-Fan-
fare; towed torpedo decoy.
ESM/ECM: SLQ 32V(3); combined radar warning, jammer and
deception system. WLR-1; radar warning.
Combat data systems: NTDS with Links 4A, 11 and 14. SATCOM
SRR-1, WSC-3 (UHF).
Fire control: SWG-1A Harpoon LCS. 2 Mk 76 MFCS. 1 Mk 14
weapons direction system. Mk 111 ASW FCS.
Radars: Air search: ITT SPS 48C ❻; 3D; E/F band; range 402 km
(220 nm).
Raytheon SPS 49(V)5 ❼; C/D band; range 457 km (250 nm).
Surface search: Norden SPS 67 ❽; G band.
Fire control: Four Sperry SPG 55C ❾; G/H band; range 51 km
(28 nm).
Navigation: Raytheon SPS 64(V)9; I band.
Tacan: URN 25. IFF Mk XV.
Sonars: Sperry SQQ 23; bow-mounted; active search and attack;
medium frequency.
·BQR-20A sonar receiver.

Helicopters: Platform for Sea King but no hangar.

Programmes: *Bainbridge* was the US Navy's third nuclear-
powered surface warship (after the cruiser *Long Beach* and the
aircraft carrier *Enterprise*). Authorised in FY 1959. Originally
classified as a guided missile frigate (DLGN); reclassified as a
guided missile cruiser (CGN) on 30 June 1975.
Modernisation: *Bainbridge* underwent an Anti-Air Warfare
(AAW) modernisation at the Puget Sound Naval Shipyard from
30 June 1974 to 24 September 1976. The ship was fitted with
the Naval Tactical Data System (NTDS) and improved guid-

BAINBRIDGE   9/1993, Maritime Photographic

ance capability for missiles. Four 3 in twin gun mountings were
removed. Further improvements during 1983/85 refit, including Phalanx 20 mm, upgrading of SAM, SRBOC fit and replacement radars and ESM.

Operational: Now planned to be paid off in FY 1995 although she
may cease to be operational some time before then.

1 BELKNAP CLASS: GUIDED MISSILE CRUISERS (CG)

Name	No	Builders	Laid down	Launched	Commissioned	F/S
BELKNAP	CG 26	Bath Iron Works	5 Feb 1962	20 July 1963	7 Nov 1964	AA

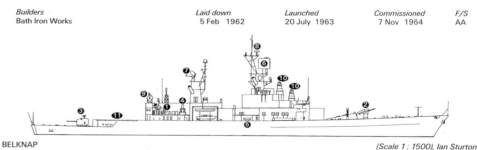

BELKNAP   (Scale 1 : 1500), Ian Sturton

Displacement, tons: 6570 standard; 8575 full load
Dimensions, feet (metres): 547 × 54.8 × 28.8 (sonar)
(166.7 × 16.7 × 8.8)
Main machinery: 4 Combustion Engineering boilers; 1200 psi
(84.4 kg/cm sq); 950°F (510°C); 2 GE turbines; 85 000 hp
(63 MW); 2 shafts
Speed, knots: 32.5. **Range, miles:** 8000 at 14 kts; 2500 at
30 kts
Complement: 479 (26 officers); Flag 111 (30 officers)

Missiles: SSM: 8 McDonnell Douglas Harpoon (2 quad) launchers ❶; active radar homing to 130 km (70 nm) at 0.9 Mach;
warhead 227 kg.
SAM: 40 GDC Standard SM-2ER; combined/inertial guidance;
semi-active radar homing to 137 km (75 nm) at 2.5 Mach.
A/S: 20 Honeywell ASROC; inertial guidance to 1.6-10 km (1-
5.4 nm); payload Mk 46 Mod 5 Neartip/Mk 50. 1 twin Mk 10
Mod 15 launcher for SAM and ASROC ❷.
Guns: 1 FMC 5 in (127 mm)/54 Mk 42 Mod 10 ❸; 85° elevation;
20-40 rounds/minute to 24 km (13.1 nm) anti-surface; 14 km
(7.7 nm) anti-aircraft; weight of shell 32 kg.
2 General Electric/General Dynamics 20 mm Vulcan Phalanx
6-barrelled Mk 15 ❹; 3000 rounds/minute (4500 in Block 1)
combined to 1.5 km.
Torpedoes: 6—324 mm Mk 32 (2 triple) tubes ❺. 18 Honeywell
Mk 46 Mod 5; anti-submarine; active/passive homing to 11 km
(5.9 nm) at 40 kts; warhead 44 kg.
Countermeasures: Decoys: 4 Loral Hycor SRBOC 6-barrelled
fixed Mk 36; IR flares and chaff to 4 km (2.2 nm). SLQ 25 Nixie;
torpedo decoy.
ESM/ECM: SLQ 32(V)3; combined radar warning, jammer and
deception system.
Combat data systems: NTDS with Links 4A, 11, 14 and 16 in due
course. SATCOM SRR-1, WSC-3 (UHF); WSC-6 (SHF), USC-38
(EHF).
Fire control: SWG-1 Harpoon LCS. 2 Mk 76 Mod 9 MFCS. Mk 68
GFCS. Mk 7 weapon direction system. Mk 116 ASW fire-
control system.
Radars: Air search: ITT SPS 48C ❻; 3D; E/F band; range 402 km
(220 nm).
Raytheon SPS 49(V)3/5 ❼; C/D band.
Surface search: Norden SPS 67 ❽; G band.
Navigation: Marconi LN 66; I band.
Fire control: Western Electric SPG 53F ❾; I/J band.
Two Sperry/RCA SPG 55D ❿; G/H band; range 51 km
(28 nm) (for Standard).

Tacan: URN 25. IFF Mk XII AIMS UPX-29.
Sonars: General Electric/Hughes SQS 53C; bow-mounted;
active search and attack; medium/low frequency.

Helicopters: Platform for 1 medium ⓫.

Modernisation: Severely damaged in a collision with the carrier
John F Kennedy (CV 67) on 22 November 1975 near Sicily.
Repair and modernisation included Flag accommodation in

BELKNAP   11/1991, French Navy

front of the bridge and the hangar converted for additional
accommodation. Recommissioned 10 May 1980. Tactical Flag
Command Centre fitted in 1983-85. This ship was not given
the New Threat Upgrade (NTU) modernisation.

Operational: Sixth Fleet Flagship. The only one of the class to survive the slaughter at the end of 1993/early 1994 when the
other eight were paid off in a bid to rid the Navy of 1200 psi
steam propulsion plants.

2 LEAHY CLASS: GUIDED MISSILE CRUISERS (CG)

Name	No	Builders	Laid down	Launched	Commissioned	F/S
DALE	CG 19	New York Shipbuilding	6 Sep 1960	28 July 1962	23 Nov 1963	AA
RICHMOND K TURNER	CG 20	New York Shipbuilding	9 Jan 1961	6 Apr 1963	13 June 1964	AA

Displacement, tons: 4650 light; 5670 standard; 8203 full load
Dimensions, feet (metres): 533 × 54.9 × 24.8 (sonar)
(162.5 × 16.6 × 7.6)
Main machinery: 4 Babcock & Wilcox boilers; 1200 psi
(84.4 kg/cm sq); 950°F *(510°C)*; 2 GE turbines; 85 000 hp
(63 MW); 2 shafts
Speed, knots: 32.7. **Range, miles:** 8000 at 20 kts; 2500 at
30 kts
Complement: 423 (26 officers); Flag 18 (6 officers)

Missiles: SSM: 8 McDonnell Douglas Harpoon (2 quad) launchers ❶; active radar homing to 130 km *(70 nm)* at 0.9 Mach;
warhead 227 kg.
SAM: 80 GDC Standard SM-2ER; 2 twin Mk 10 launchers (Mod
13 fwd, Mod 14 aft) ❷; command/inertial guidance; semi-
active radar homing to 137 km *(75 nm)* at 2.5 Mach.
Guns: 2 General Electric/General Dynamics 20 mm Vulcan
Phalanx 6-barrelled Mk 15 ❸; 3000 rounds/minute (4500 in
Block 1) combined to 1.5 km.
4—12.7 mm MGs.
Countermeasures: Decoys: 6 Loral Hycor SRBOC 6-barrelled
fixed Mk 36; IR flares and chaff to 4 km *(2.2 nm)*. T-Mk 6 Fan-
fare/SLQ 25 Nixie; towed torpedo decoy. NATO Sea Gnat.
SSQ-95 AEB. SLQ 39/49 chaff buoy/expendables.
ESM/ECM: SLQ 32(V)3; combined radar warning, jammer and
deception system.
Combat data systems: NTDS with Links 4A, 11, 14. SATCOM
SRR-1, WSC-3 (UHF).
Fire control: SWG-1A Harpoon LCS. Mk 76 MFCS. Mk 14
weapon direction system. SYS-2(V)2 IADT.
Radars: Air search: ITT SPS 48 E ❹; 3D; E/F band; range 402 km
(220 nm).
Raytheon SPS 49(V)3/5 ❺; C/D band; range 457 km
(250 nm).
Surface search: Raytheon SPS 10F or Norden SPS 67 ❻; G band.
Navigation: Raytheon SPS 64(V)9; I band.
Fire control: Four Sperry/RCA SPG 55C ❼; G/H band; range
51 km *(28 nm)*.
Tacan: URN 25. IFF Mk XV.

Helicopters: Platform only with limited facilities.

Modernisation: Modernised between 1967 and 1972 to
improve their Anti-Air Warfare (AAW) capabilities. 76 mm
guns were removed and superstructure enlarged to provide
space for additional electronic equipment, including NTDS;
improved Tacan fitted and improved guidance system for SAM
missiles installed, and larger ship's service turbo generators
provided. New Threat Upgrade modernisation completed
1987-91; this included SPS 48E radar, updating the Mk 10
launchers and Mk 76 MFCS and improving the SPG 55 fire-
control radars.
Operational: All ASW equipment removed. Last pair scheduled
to pay off in September 1994.

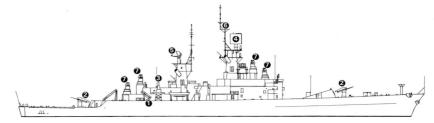

DALE   *(Scale 1 : 1500), Ian Sturton*

LEAHY class (old number) (no ASROC)   *10/1993, Giorgio Arra*

DESTROYERS

Note: One Forrest Sherman class *Decatur* (DDG 31) refurbished with a full ship self-defence system to act as a live target. All systems will be operated by remote-control.
Testing is scheduled to start in late 1994.

0 + 1 (3) ARLEIGH BURKE CLASS (FLIGHT IIA): GUIDED MISSILE DESTROYERS (AEGIS) (DDG)

Displacement, tons: 9217 full load
Dimensions, feet (metres): 509.5 × 66.9 × 20.7; 32.7 (sonar)
(155.3 × 20.4 × 6.3; 9.9)
Main machinery: 4 GE LM 2500-30 gas-turbines; 105 000 hp
(78.33 MW) sustained; 2 shafts; cp props
Speed, knots: 32. **Range, miles:** 4400 at 20 kts
Complement: 380 (32 officers)

Missiles: SLCM/SSM: Tomahawk.
SAM: Standard SM-2ER (Block IV).
Evolved Sea Sparrow CIWS.
A/S: ASROC.
2 Vertical Launch Systems for Tomahawk, Standard, Sea Spar-
row and ASROC. 32 cells forward, 64 cells aft ❶.
Guns: 1—5 in *(127 mm)*/54 ❷.
Torpedoes: 6—324 mm Mk 32 (2 triple) tubes ❸.
Countermeasures: Decoys: 2 chaff launchers ❹.
ESM/ECM: SLQ 32(V)3 ❺; intercept and jammer.
Combat data systems: Includes JTIDS, Tactical Information Ex-
change System (TADIX B) and Tactical Data Information Link
(TADIL J).
Radars: Air search/fire-control: SPY 1D phased arrays ❻ with
Track Initiation Processor.
Surface search: SPS 67(V) ❼.
Fire control: 3 SPG 62 ❽.
Sonars: SQS 53C; hull-mounted; active search and attack;
medium frequency.
Kingfisher; hull-mounted mine detection; active; high
frequency.

ARLEIGH BURKE FLIGHT IIA   *(Scale 1 : 1500), Ian Sturton*

Helicopters: 2 SH-60B/F LAMPS III ❾.

Programmes: First ship of this revised Arleigh Burke class design
is DDG 79 which was authorised in the FY 1994 budget. Funding for three more sought in FY 1995.
Structure: The upgrade from Flight II includes two hangars for
embarked helicopters and an extended transom to increase
the size of a RAST fitted flight deck at the expense of SQR 19
TACTAS. Vertical launchers are increased at each end by three

cells and will be able to fire the agile Evolved Sea Sparrow
missile which replaces Phalanx. Harpoon may be fitted for, but
not with. Other changes include the Kingfisher minehunting
sonar, a reconfiguration of the SPY-1D arrays and the inclusion
of a Track Initiation Processor in the Aegis radar system. Use of
fibre optic technology should reduce weight and improve
reliability. The line drawing shows the ship as configured in
early 1993, no doubt there are more changes to come. The At
Sea Missile Handling System has been deleted.

5 + 23 ARLEIGH BURKE CLASS (FLIGHTS I and II): GUIDED MISSILE DESTROYERS (AEGIS) (DDG)

Name	No	Builders	Laid down	Launched	Commissioned	F/S
ARLEIGH BURKE	DDG 51	Bath Iron Works	6 Dec 1988	16 Sep 1989	4 July 1991	AA
BARRY (ex-*John Barry*)	DDG 52	Ingalls Shipbuilding	26 Feb 1990	10 May 1991	12 Dec 1992	AA
JOHN PAUL JONES	DDG 53	Bath Iron Works	8 Aug 1990	26 Oct 1991	18 Dec 1993	PA
CURTIS WILBUR	DDG 54	Bath Iron Works	12 Mar 1992	16 May 1992	19 Mar 1994	PA
STOUT	DDG 55	Ingalls Shipbuilding	13 Sep 1991	16 Oct 1992	Aug 1994	Bldg
JOHN S McCAIN	DDG 56	Bath Iron Works	3 Sep 1991	26 Sep 1992	June 1994	PA
MITSCHER	DDG 57	Ingalls Shipbuilding	12 Feb 1992	7 May 1993	Sep 1994	Bldg
LABOON	DDG 58	Bath Iron Works	23 Mar 1992	2 Feb 1993	Aug 1994	Bldg
RUSSELL	DDG 59	Ingalls Shipbuilding	27 July 1992	20 Oct 1993	Jan 1995	Bldg
PAUL HAMILTON	DDG 60	Bath Iron Works	25 Aug 1992	24 July 1993	Dec 1994	Bldg
RAMAGE	DDG 61	Ingalls Shipbuilding	4 Jan 1993	12 Feb 1994	Apr 1995	Bldg
FITZGERALD	DDG 62	Bath Iron Works	9 Feb 1993	11 Dec 1993	May 1995	Bldg
STETHEM	DDG 63	Ingalls Shipbuilding	11 May 1993	June 1994	July 1995	Bldg
CARNEY	DDG 64	Bath Iron Works	3 Aug 1993	June 1994	Oct 1995	Bldg
BENFOLD	DDG 65	Ingalls Shipbuilding	27 Sep 1993	Nov 1994	Dec 1995	Bldg
GONZALEZ	DDG 66	Bath Iron Works	11 Jan 1994	Nov 1994	Apr 1996	Bldg
COLE	DDG 67	Ingalls Shipbuilding	28 Feb 1994	Apr 1995	June 1996	Bldg
THE SULLIVANS	DDG 68	Bath Iron Works	July 1994	May 1995	Aug 1996	Ord
MILIUS	DDG 69	Ingalls Shipbuilding	Aug 1994	Sep 1995	Oct 1996	Ord
HOPPER	DDG 70	Bath Iron Works	Nov 1994	Oct 1995	Jan 1997	Ord
ROSS	DDG 71	Ingalls Shipbuilding	Jan 1995	Feb 1996	Apr 1997	Ord
MAHAN	DDG 72	Bath Iron Works	Apr 1995	Mar 1996	Aug 1997	Ord
DECATUR	DDG 73	Bath Iron Works	Oct 1995	Aug 1996	Nov 1997	Ord
McFAUL	DDG 74	Ingalls Shipbuilding	Dec 1995	Jan 1997	Mar 1998	Ord
DONALD COOK	DDG 75	Bath Iron Works	Mar 1996	Jan 1997	May 1998	Ord
HIGGINS	DDG 76	Bath Iron Works	Aug 1996	June 1997	Oct 1998	Ord
	DDG 77-78	Authorised FY 1994	—	—	—	Proj

Displacement, tons: 8422; 9033 (from DDG 72) full load
Dimensions, feet (metres): 504.5 × 66.9 × 20.7; 32.7 (sonar) *(153.8 × 20.4 × 6.3; 9.9)*
Main machinery: 4 GE LM 2500 gas-turbines; 105 000 hp *(78.33 MW)* sustained; 2 shafts; cp props
Speed, knots: 32. **Range, miles:** 4400 at 20 kts
Complement: 303 (23 officers) plus 38 spare

Missiles: SLCM/SSM: 56 GDC Tomahawk; combination of (a) land attack; TAINS (Tercom aided navigation system) to 2500 km *(1400 nm)* at 0.7 Mach; altitude 15-100 m *(49.2-328.1 ft)*; warhead nuclear 200 kT (TLAM-N); CEP 80 m; or warhead 454 kg or 317 kg (Block II) (TLAM-C) or submunitions (TLAM-D); range 1300 km *(700 nm)*; CEP 10 m. Nuclear warheads not normally carried. Range increased by 30% in TLAM-C Block III which started production in 1992.
(b) anti-ship (TASM); inertial guidance; active radar and anti-radiation; homing to 460 km *(250 nm)* at 0.7 Mach; warhead 454 kg.
8 McDonnell Douglas Harpoon (2 quad) ❶; active radar homing to 130 km *(70 nm)* at 0.9 Mach; warhead 227 kg.
SAM: GDC Standard SM-2MR Block 4; command/inertial guidance; semi-active radar homing to 73 km *(40 nm)* at 2 Mach. Extended range from DDG 72 onwards.
A/S: Honeywell ASROC; inertial guidance to 1.6-16.6 km *(1-9 nm)*; payload Mk 46 Mod 5 Neartip/Mk 50.
2 Martin Marietta Mk 41 (Mod 0 forward, Mod 1 aft) Vertical Launch Systems (VLS) for Tomahawk, Standard and ASROC ❷; 2 magazines; 29 missiles fwd, 61 aft. Mod 2 from DDG 59 onwards.
Guns: 1 FMC 5 in *(127 mm)*/54 Mk 45 Mod 1 or 2 ❸; 65° elevation; 20 rounds/minute to 23 km *(12.6 nm)*; weight of shell 32 kg. No anti-aircraft capability.
2 General Electric/General Dynamics 20 mm Vulcan Phalanx 6-barrelled Mk 15 ❹; 3000 rounds/minute (4500 in Block 1) combined to 1.5 km.
Torpedoes: 6—324 mm Mk 32 Mod 14 (2 triple) tubes ❺. Honeywell Mk 46 Mod 5; anti-submarine; active/passive homing to 11 km *(5.9 nm)* at 40 kts; warhead 44 kg. Some Mk 50 may be carried from 1994.
Countermeasures: Decoys: 2 Loral Hycor SRBOC 6-barrelled fixed Mk 36 Mod 12 ❻; IR flares and chaff to 4 km *(2.2 nm)*. SLQ 25 Nixie; torpedo decoy. NATO Sea Gnat. SLQ-95 AEB. SLQ-39 chaff buoy.
ESM/ECM: Raytheon SLQ 32(V)2 ❼ or SLQ 32(V)3 (from DDG 72); radar warning. Sidekick modification adds jammer and deception system to (V)2. Combat DF (from DDG 72).
Combat data systems: NTDS Mod 5 with Links 4A, 11, 14 and 16 (from DDG 72). SATCOM SRR-1, WSC-3 (UHF), USC-38 (EHF) (from 1992). SQQ 28 for LAMPS processor data link. TADIX B Tactical Information Exchange System (from DDG 72).
Fire control: SWG-3 Tomahawk WCS. SWG-1A Harpoon LCS. Aegis multi-target tracking with Mk 99 Mod 3 MFCS and three Mk 80 illuminators. GWS 34 Mod 0 GFCS (includes Mk 160 Mod 4 computing system and Kollmorgen optronic sight). Singer Librascope Mk 116 Mod 7 FCS for ASW. SAR-8 IR surveillance system to be fitted in due course.
Radars: Air search/fire-control: RCA SPY 1D phased arrays ❽; 3D; E/F band.
Surface search: Norden SPS 67(V)3 ❾; G band.
Navigation: Raytheon SPS 64(V)9; I band.
Fire control: Three Raytheon/RCA SPG 62 ❿; I/J band.
Tacan: URN 25 ⓫. IFF Mk XII AIMS UPX-29.
Sonars: Gould/Raytheon/GE SQQ 89(V)6; combines SQS 53C; bow-mounted; active search and attack with SQR 19 passive towed array (TACTAS) (and SRQ-4 LAMPS III shipboard terminal); medium frequency.

Helicopters: Platform and facilities to fuel and rearm LAMPS III SH 60B/F helicopters ⓬.

Programmes: Designed as replacements for the Adams and Coontz classes of guided missile destroyers. First ship authorised in FY 1985. Order rate is projected at three or four per year up to a total of 49. The first 21 are Flight 1 and the next seven are Flight II. See separate entry for Flight IIA.
Structure: The ship, except for the aluminium funnels, is constructed of steel. 70 tons of Kevlar armour provided to protect vital spaces. This is the first class of US Navy warship designed with a 'collective protection system for defense against the fallout associated with NBC Warfare'. The ship's crew are protected by double air-locked hatches, fewer accesses to the weatherdecks and positive pressurisation of the interior of the ship to keep out contaminants. All incoming air is filtered and more reliance placed on recirculating air inside the ship. All

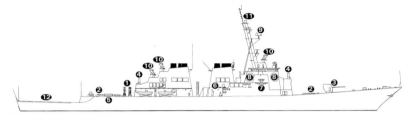

ARLEIGH BURKE   *(Scale 1 : 1500), Ian Sturton*

STOUT   *1/1994, Ingalls Shipbuilding*

BARRY   *11/1993, Maritime Photographic*

accommodation compartments have sprinkler systems. Stealth technology includes angled surfaces and rounded edges to reduce radar signature and IR signature suppression. The Ops room is below the waterline and electronics are EMP hardened. The original upright mast design has been changed possibly to increase separation between electronic systems and the forward funnel. Differences in Flight II starting with DDG 72 include Link 16, SLQ 32(V)3 EW suite, extended range SAM missiles and improved tactical information exchange systems.

Opinion: The obvious deficiency in a ship of this size is the lack of its own helicopter and this has been recognised in the bringing forward of modifications proposed for later ships of the class. Regardless of attempts at role specialisation the modern warship's usage over its full life means that the ubiquitous helicopter receives more operational tasking than any other weapon system.

4 KIDD CLASS: GUIDED MISSILE DESTROYERS (DDG)

Name	No	Builders	Laid down	Launched	Commissioned	F/S
KIDD (ex-Iranian *Kouroosh*)	DDG 993 (ex-US DD 993)	Ingalls Shipbuilding	26 June 1978	11 Aug 1979	27 June 1981	AA
CALLAGHAN (ex-Iranian *Daryush*)	DDG 994 (ex-US DD 994)	Ingalls Shipbuilding	23 Oct 1978	1 Dec 1979	29 Aug 1981	PA
SCOTT (ex-Iranian *Nader*)	DDG 995 (ex-US DD 995, ex-US DD 996)	Ingalls Shipbuilding	12 Feb 1979	1 Mar 1980	24 Oct 1981	AA
CHANDLER (ex-Iranian *Anoushirvan*)	DDG 996 (ex-US DD 996, ex-US DD 998)	Ingalls Shipbuilding	7 May 1979	24 May 1980	13 Mar 1982	PA

Displacement, tons: 6950 light; 9574 full load
Dimensions, feet (metres): 563.3 × 55 × 20; 33 sonar
(171.7 × 16.8 × 6.2; 10)
Main machinery: 4 GE LM 2500 gas-turbines; 86 000 hp
(64.16 MW) sustained; 2 shafts
Speed, knots: 33. **Range, miles:** 3300 at 30 kts; 6000 at 20 kts;
8000 at 17 kts
Complement: 339 (20 officers)

Missiles: SSM: 8 McDonnell Douglas Harpoon (2 quad) launchers ❶; active radar homing to 130 km *(70 nm)* at 0.9 Mach;
warhead 227 kg.
SAM: 52 GDC Standard SM-2MR; command/inertial guidance;
semi-active radar homing to 73 km *(40 nm)* at 2 Mach.
A/S: 16 Honeywell ASROC; inertial guidance to 1.6-10 km *(1-
5.4 nm)*; payload Mk 46 Mod 5 Neartip/Mk 50. 2 twin Mk 26
(Mod 3 and Mod 4) launchers for Standard and ASROC ❷;
missiles are split between 2 magazines.
Guns: 2 FMC 5 in *(127 mm)*/54 Mk 45 Mod 0 ❸; 65° elevation;
20 rounds/minute to 23 km *(12.6 nm)*; weight of shell 32 kg
plus SALGP (Semi-Active Laser-Guided Projectiles).
2 General Electric/General Dynamics 20 mm Vulcan Phalanx
6-barrelled Mk 15 ❹; 3000 rounds/minute (4500 in Block 1)
combined to 1.5 km.
4—12.7 mm MGs.
Torpedoes: 6—324 mm Mk 32 (2 triple) tubes ❺. Honeywell
Mk 46 Mod 5; anti-submarine; active/passive homing to
11 km *(5.9 nm)* at 40 kts; warhead 44 kg. Torpedoes fired from
inside the hull under the hangar.
Countermeasures: Decoys: 4 Loral Hycor SRBOC 6-barrelled
fixed Mk 36; IR flares and chaff to 4 km *(2.2 nm)*. SLQ 25 Nixie;
torpedo decoy.
ESM/ECM: SLQ 32(V)2; radar warning. Sidekick modification
adds jammer and deception system.
Combat data systems: NTDS with Links 4A, 11, 14 and 16 in due
course. SATCOM SRR-1, WSC-3 (UHF); USC-38 (EHF).
Fire control: SWG-1A Harpoon LCS. 2 Mk 74 MFCS. Mk 86 Mod
5 GFCS. Mk 116 FCS for ASW. Mk 14 WDS. SYS 2(V)2 IADT.
SRQ-4 for LAMPS III. 4 SYR 3393 for SAM mid-course
guidance.
Radars: Air search: ITT SPS 48E ❻; 3D; E/F band; range 402 km
(220 nm).
Raytheon SPS 49(V)5 ❼; C/D band.
Surface search: ISC Cardion SPS 55 ❽; I/J band.
Navigation: Raytheon SPS 64; I/J band.
Fire control: Two SPG 51D ❾, 1 SPG 60 ❿, 1 SPQ 9A ⓫; G/I/J
band.
Tacan: URN 25. IFF Mk XII AIMS UPX-29.
Sonars: General Electric/Hughes SQS 53A; bow-mounted;
search and attack; medium frequency. To receive SQS 53C on
completion of evaluation.
Gould SQR 19 (TACTAS); passive towed array (may be fitted).

Helicopters: 2 SH-2F LAMPS I ⓬ or 1 SH-60 LAMPS III.

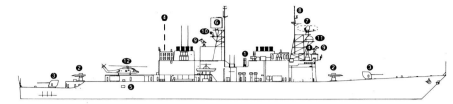

SCOTT   *(Scale 1 : 1500), Ian Sturton*

CALLAGHAN   *6/1992, A Campanera i Rovira*

Programmes: On 25 July 1979 the US Navy took over the con-
tracts of four destroyers originally ordered by the Iranian
Government in 1974.
Modernisation: Between 1988 and 1990 all received the New
Threat Upgrade modernisation with updated Mk 74 MFCS for
SM-2MR and SPG 51D radars, SPS 49(V)5 and Mk 14 weapon
direction system.

Structure: The modular concept has been used extensively to
facilitate construction and modernisation. Displacement is
well over design because of the addition of Kevlar armour.
Excellent air conditioning because of original Iranian requirements. NTU led to a rearrangement of the mainmast and repo-
sitioning of SPS 48 and the SPG 60 aerials, in order to make
room for the SPS 49.

Operational: These ships are optimised for general warfare
instead of anti-submarine warfare as are the Spruance class,
and the ability to fire SM-2MR allows them to support Aegis
cruisers, if necessary allowing Aegis to control the missiles.
The addition of SPS 49 markedly improves air picture compil-
ation capability.

SCOTT   *9/1993, G Toremans*

31 SPRUANCE CLASS: DESTROYERS (DD)

Name	No	Builders	Laid down	Launched	Commissioned	F/S
SPRUANCE	DD 963	Ingalls Shipbuilding	17 Nov 1972	10 Nov 1973	20 Sep 1975	AA
PAUL F FOSTER	DD 964	Ingalls Shipbuilding	6 Feb 1973	23 Feb 1974	21 Feb 1976	PA
KINKAID	DD 965	Ingalls Shipbuilding	19 Apr 1973	25 May 1974	10 July 1976	PA
HEWITT	DD 966	Ingalls Shipbuilding	23 July 1973	24 Aug 1974	25 Sep 1976	PA
ELLIOTT	DD 967	Ingalls Shipbuilding	15 Oct 1973	19 Dec 1974	22 Jan 1976	AA
ARTHUR W RADFORD	DD 968	Ingalls Shipbuilding	14 Jan 1974	1 Mar 1975	16 Apr 1977	AA
PETERSON	DD 969	Ingalls Shipbuilding	29 Apr 1974	21 June 1975	9 July 1977	AA
CARON	DD 970	Ingalls Shipbuilding	1 July 1974	24 June 1975	1 Oct 1977	AA
DAVID R RAY	DD 971	Ingalls Shipbuilding	23 Sep 1974	23 Aug 1975	19 Nov 1977	PA
OLDENDORF	DD 972	Ingalls Shipbuilding	27 Dec 1974	21 Oct 1975	4 Mar 1978	PA
JOHN YOUNG	DD 973	Ingalls Shipbuilding	17 Feb 1975	7 Feb 1976	20 May 1978	PA
COMTE DE GRASSE	DD 974	Ingalls Shipbuilding	4 Apr 1975	26 Mar 1976	5 Aug 1978	AA
O'BRIEN	DD 975	Ingalls Shipbuilding	9 May 1975	8 July 1976	3 Dec 1977	PA
MERRILL	DD 976	Ingalls Shipbuilding	16 June 1975	1 Sep 1976	11 Mar 1978	PA
BRISCOE	DD 977	Ingalls Shipbuilding	21 July 1975	15 Dec 1976	3 June 1978	AA
STUMP	DD 978	Ingalls Shipbuilding	25 Aug 1975	29 Jan 1977	19 Aug 1978	AA
CONOLLY	DD 979	Ingalls Shipbuilding	29 Sep 1975	19 Feb 1977	14 Oct 1978	AA
MOOSBRUGGER	DD 980	Ingalls Shipbuilding	3 Nov 1975	23 July 1977	16 Dec 1978	AA
JOHN HANCOCK	DD 981	Ingalls Shipbuilding	16 Jan 1976	29 Oct 1977	1 Mar 1979	AA
NICHOLSON	DD 982	Ingalls Shipbuilding	20 Feb 1976	11 Nov 1977	12 May 1979	AA
JOHN RODGERS	DD 983	Ingalls Shipbuilding	12 Aug 1976	25 Feb 1978	14 July 1979	AA
LEFTWICH	DD 984	Ingalls Shipbuilding	12 Nov 1976	8 Apr 1978	25 Aug 1979	PA
CUSHING	DD 985	Ingalls Shipbuilding	27 Dec 1976	17 June 1978	21 Sep 1979	PA
HARRY W HILL	DD 986	Ingalls Shipbuilding	3 Jan 1977	10 Aug 1978	17 Nov 1979	PA
O'BANNON	DD 987	Ingalls Shipbuilding	21 Feb 1977	25 Sep 1978	15 Dec 1979	AA
THORN	DD 988	Ingalls Shipbuilding	29 Aug 1977	14 Nov 1978	16 Feb 1980	AA
DEYO	DD 989	Ingalls Shipbuilding	14 Oct 1977	27 Jan 1979	22 Mar 1980	AA
INGERSOLL	DD 990	Ingalls Shipbuilding	5 Dec 1977	10 Mar 1979	12 Apr 1980	PA
FIFE	DD 991	Ingalls Shipbuilding	6 Mar 1978	1 May 1979	31 May 1980	PA
FLETCHER	DD 992	Ingalls Shipbuilding	24 Apr 1978	16 June 1979	12 July 1980	PA
HAYLER	DD 997	Ingalls Shipbuilding	20 Oct 1980	27 Mar 1982	5 Mar 1983	AA

Displacement, tons: 5770 light; 8040 full load
Dimensions, feet (metres): 563.2 × 55.1 × 19; 29 (sonar)
(171.7 × 16.8 × 5.8; 8.8)
Main machinery: 4 GE LM 2500 gas-turbines; 86 000 hp
(64.16 MW) sustained; 2 shafts; cp props
Speed, knots: 33. **Range, miles:** 6000 at 20 kts
Complement: 319-339 (20 officers)

Missiles: SLCM/SSM: GDC Tomahawk ❶; combination of (a) land attack; TAINS (Tercom aided navigational system) to 2500 km *(1400 nm)* at 0.7 Mach; altitude 15-100 m *(49.2-328.1 ft)*; warhead nuclear 200 kT (TLAM-N); CEP 80 m; or warhead 454 kg or 317 kg (Block II) (TLAM-C) or submunitions (TLAM-D); range 1300 km *(700 nm)*; CEP 10 m. Nuclear warheads not normally carried. Range increased by 30% in TLAM-C Batch III which started production in 1992.
(b) anti-ship (TASM); active radar/anti-radiation homing to 460 km *(250 nm)* at 0.7 Mach; warhead 454 kg.
8 fitted on the forecastle in 2 Mk 44 armoured box launchers in DD 974, 976, 979, 983-984, 989-990. Remainder being fitted with the Mk 41 Mod 0 VLS ❷ with one 61 missile magazine combining 45 Tomahawk and ASROC in some.
8 McDonnell Douglas Harpoon (2 quad) ❸; active radar homing to 130 km *(70 nm)* at 0.9 Mach; warhead 227 kg.
SAM: Raytheon GMLS Mk 29 octuple launcher ❹; 24 Sea Sparrow; semi-active radar homing to 14.6 km *(8 nm)* at 2.5 Mach; warhead 39 kg.
GDC RAM quadruple launcher (DD 971); passive IR/antiradiation homing to 9.6 km *(5.2 nm)* at 2 Mach; warhead 9.1 kg. To be fitted in others from 1994. Fitted starboard side right aft.
A/S: 24 Honeywell ASROC Mk 16 octuple launcher with Mk 112 reload system ❺ (not in VLS fitted ships; VLS ASROC in *Elliott* and some other VLS ships); inertial guidance to 1.6-10 km *(1-5.5 nm)*; payload Mk 46 Mod 5 Neartip/Mk 50. VLS ASROC has a range of 16.6 km *(9 nm)*.
Guns: 2 FMC 5 in *(127 mm)*/54 Mk 45 Mod 0/1 ❻; 65° elevation; 20 rounds/minute to 23 km *(12.6 nm)* anti-surface; 15 km *(8.2 nm)* anti-aircraft; weight of shell 32 kg. SALGP (Semi-Active Laser-Guided Projectile).
2 General Electric/General Dynamics 20 mm/76 6-barrelled Mk 15 Vulcan Phalanx ❼; 3000 rounds/minute (4500 in Batch 1) combined to 1.5 km.
4—12.7 mm MGs.
Torpedoes: 6—324 mm Mk 32 (2 triple) tubes ❽. 14 Honeywell Mk 46; anti-submarine; active/passive homing to 11 km *(5.9 nm)* at 40 kts; warhead 44 kg. Being replaced by Mk 50. The tubes are inside the superstructure to facilitate maintenance and reloading. Torpedoes are fired through side ports.
Countermeasures: Decoys: 4 Loral Hycor SRBOC 6-barrelled fixed Mk 36 ❾; IR flares and chaff to 4 km *(2.2 nm)*. SLQ 39 chaff buoy.
SLQ 25 Nixie; torpedo decoy. Prairie/Masker hull/blade rate noise suppression system.
ESM/ECM: SLQ 32(V)2 ❿; radar warning. Sidekick modification adds jammer and deception system. WLR-1 (in some). OUT-BOARD (in some).
Combat data systems: NTDS with Links 11 and 14. SATCOMS ⓫ SRR-1, WSC-3 (UHF), USC-38 (EHF) (in some). SQQ 28 for LAMPS data link.
Fire control: SWG-3 Tomahawk WCS. SWG-1A Harpoon LCS. Mk 116 Mod 7 FCS ASW. Mk 86 Mod 3 GFCS. Mk 91 MFCS. SRQ-4 LAMPS III. SAR-8 IR director (DD 965).

MERRILL (with box Tomahawk)

1/1994, van Ginderen Collection

Radars: Air search: Lockheed SPS 40B/C/D (not in DD 997) ⓬; E/F band; range 320 km *(175 nm)*.
Raytheon SPS 49V (DD 997); C/D band; range 457 km *(250 nm)*.
Hughes Mk 23 TAS; D band.
Surface search: ISC Cardion SPS 55 ⓭; I/J band.
Navigation: Marconi LN 66 or SPS 53; I band. Raytheon SPS 64(V)9 to be fitted.
Fire control: Lockheed SPG 60 ⓮; I/J band.
Lockheed SPQ 9A ⓯; I/J band; range 37 km *(20 nm)*.
Raytheon Mk 95 ⓰; I/J band (for SAM).
Tacan: URN 20 or URN 25 (D 997). IFF Mk XII AIMS UPX-25.
Sonars: SQQ 89(V)6 including GE/Hughes SQS 53B/C; bow-mounted; active search and attack; medium frequency; and Gould SQR 19 (TACTAS); passive towed array. All except DDs 988-990 have the full SQQ 89 system.

Helicopters: 1 SH-60B LAMPS III ⓱ or 1 SH-2F LAMPS I.

Programmes: Funds approved between FY 1970 and FY 1978.
Modernisation: Beginning with FY 1986 overhauls, major improvements have been made. These include the installation of VLS, upgrading of EW to SLQ 32V(2) plus sidekick; LAMPS III and the recovery, assist, secure and traverse system (RAST), the Halon 1301 firefighting system and anti-missile and target acquisition systems. VLS Mk 41 ships are capable of launching Standard SM-2MR for control by Aegis fitted vessels. Seventeen of the class converted to VLS by early 1994 and seven more are scheduled to receive it, the last one in FY 1995. The remainder will not be upgraded and may be paid off early. One of the class is being used to test the development model of RAIDS (rapid anti-ship missile integrated defence system). 11 of the class are to have helicopters fitted with ASV missiles by the end of 1995.
Structure: Extensive use of the modular concept has been used to facilitate construction and block modernisation. There is a high level of automation. These were the first large US warships to employ gas-turbine propulsion and advanced self-noise reduction features. Kevlar internal coating in all vital spaces.
Operational: Three of the class are based at Yokosuka, Japan. Eleven took part in the war with Iraq in 1991. *Fife* with 58 firings was the most prolific launcher of Tomahawk missiles. Three of the class again fired missiles into Iraq in January 1993.

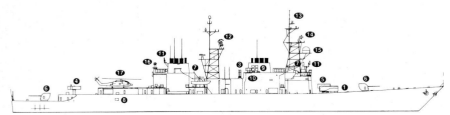

MERRILL

(Scale 1 : 1500), Ian Sturton

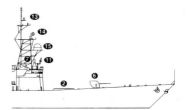

SPRUANCE

(Scale 1 : 1500), Ian Sturton

O'BRIEN (with VLS)   *10/1991, Giorgio Arra*

HEWITT   *10/1993, 92 Wing RAAF*

FRIGATES

51 OLIVER HAZARD PERRY CLASS: GUIDED MISSILE FRIGATES (FFG)

Name	No	Builders	Laid down	Launched	Commissioned	F/S
OLIVER HAZARD PERRY	FFG 7 (ex-PF 109)	Bath Iron Works	12 June 1975	25 Sep 1976	17 Dec 1977	NRF
McINERNEY	FFG 8	Bath Iron Works	7 Nov 1977	4 Nov 1978	19 Nov 1979	AA
WADSWORTH	FFG 9	Todd Shipyards, San Pedro	13 July 1977	29 July 1978	28 Feb 1980	NRF
DUNCAN	FFG 10	Todd Shipyards, Seattle	29 Apr 1977	1 Mar 1978	15 May 1980	NRF
CLARK	FFG 11	Bath Iron Works	17 July 1978	24 Mar 1979	9 May 1980	NRF
GEORGE PHILIP	FFG 12	Todd Shipyards, San Pedro	14 Dec 1977	16 Dec 1978	10 Oct 1980	NRF
SAMUEL ELIOT MORISON	FFG 13	Bath Iron Works	4 Dec 1978	14 July 1979	11 Oct 1980	NRF
JOHN H SIDES	FFG 14	Todd Shipyards, San Pedro	7 Aug 1978	19 May 1979	30 May 1981	NRF
ESTOCIN	FFG 15	Bath Iron Works	2 Apr 1979	3 Nov 1979	10 Jan 1981	NRF
CLIFTON SPRAGUE	FFG 16	Bath Iron Works	30 Sep 1979	16 Feb 1980	21 Mar 1981	NRF
JOHN A MOORE	FFG 19	Todd Shipyards, San Pedro	19 Dec 1978	20 Oct 1979	14 Nov 1981	NRF
ANTRIM	FFG 20	Todd Shipyards, Seattle	21 June 1978	27 Mar 1979	26 Sep 1981	NRF
FLATLEY	FFG 21	Bath Iron Works	13 Nov 1979	15 May 1980	20 June 1981	NRF
FAHRION	FFG 22	Todd Shipyards, Seattle	1 Dec 1978	24 Aug 1979	16 Jan 1982	NRF
LEWIS B PULLER	FFG 23	Todd Shipyards, San Pedro	23 May 1979	15 Mar 1980	17 Apr 1982	NRF
JACK WILLIAMS	FFG 24	Bath Iron Works	25 Feb 1980	30 Aug 1980	19 Sep 1981	AA
COPELAND	FFG 25	Todd Shipyards, San Pedro	24 Oct 1979	26 July 1980	7 Aug 1982	NRF
GALLERY	FFG 26	Bath Iron Works	17 May 1980	20 Dec 1980	5 Dec 1981	AA
MAHLON S TISDALE	FFG 27	Todd Shipyards, San Pedro	19 Mar 1980	7 Feb 1981	27 Nov 1982	NRF
BOONE	FFG 28	Todd Shipyards, Seattle	27 Mar 1979	16 Jan 1980	15 May 1982	AA
STEPHEN W GROVES	FFG 29	Bath Iron Works	16 Sep 1980	4 Apr 1981	17 Apr 1982	AA
REID	FFG 30	Todd Shipyards, San Pedro	8 Oct 1980	27 June 1981	19 Feb 1983	PA
STARK	FFG 31	Todd Shipyards, Seattle	24 Aug 1979	30 May 1980	23 Oct 1982	AA
JOHN L HALL	FFG 32	Bath Iron Works	5 Jan 1981	24 July 1981	26 June 1982	AA
JARRETT	FFG 33	Todd Shipyards, San Pedro	11 Feb 1981	17 Oct 1981	2 July 1983	PA
AUBREY FITCH	FFG 34	Bath Iron Works	10 Apr 1981	17 Oct 1981	9 Oct 1982	AA
UNDERWOOD	FFG 36	Bath Iron Works	3 Aug 1981	6 Feb 1982	29 Jan 1983	AA
CROMMELIN	FFG 37	Todd Shipyards, Seattle	30 May 1980	1 July 1981	18 June 1983	PA
CURTS	FFG 38	Todd Shipyards, San Pedro	1 July 1981	6 Mar 1982	8 Oct 1983	PA
DOYLE	FFG 39	Bath Iron Works	16 Nov 1981	22 May 1982	21 May 1983	AA
HALYBURTON	FFG 40	Todd Shipyards, Seattle	26 Sep 1980	15 Oct 1981	7 Jan 1984	AA
McCLUSKY	FFG 41	Todd Shipyards, San Pedro	21 Oct 1981	18 Sep 1982	10 Dec 1983	PA
KLAKRING	FFG 42	Bath Iron Works	19 Feb 1982	18 Sep 1982	20 Aug 1983	AA
THACH	FFG 43	Todd Shipyards, San Pedro	10 Mar 1982	18 Dec 1982	17 Mar 1984	PA
De WERT	FFG 45	Bath Iron Works	14 June 1982	18 Dec 1982	19 Nov 1983	AA
RENTZ	FFG 46	Todd Shipyards, San Pedro	18 Sep 1982	16 July 1983	30 June 1984	PA
NICHOLAS	FFG 47	Bath Iron Works	27 Sep 1982	23 Apr 1983	10 Mar 1984	AA
VANDEGRIFT	FFG 48	Todd Shipyards, Seattle	13 Oct 1981	15 Oct 1982	24 Nov 1984	PA
ROBERT G BRADLEY	FFG 49	Bath Iron Works	28 Dec 1982	13 Aug 1983	11 Aug 1984	AA
TAYLOR	FFG 50	Bath Iron Works	5 May 1983	5 Nov 1983	1 Dec 1984	AA
GARY	FFG 51	Todd Shipyards, San Pedro	18 Dec 1982	19 Nov 1983	17 Nov 1984	PA
CARR	FFG 52	Todd Shipyards, Seattle	26 Mar 1982	26 Feb 1983	27 July 1985	AA
HAWES	FFG 53	Bath Iron Works	22 Aug 1983	18 Feb 1984	9 Feb 1985	AA
FORD	FFG 54	Todd Shipyards, San Pedro	16 July 1983	23 June 1984	29 June 1985	PA
ELROD	FFG 55	Bath Iron Works	21 Nov 1983	12 May 1984	18 May 1985	AA
SIMPSON	FFG 56	Bath Iron Works	27 Feb 1984	21 Aug 1984	10 Aug 1985	AA
REUBEN JAMES	FFG 57	Todd Shipyards, San Pedro	19 Nov 1983	8 Feb 1985	22 Mar 1986	AA
SAMUEL B ROBERTS	FFG 58	Bath Iron Works	21 May 1984	8 Dec 1984	12 Apr 1986	AA
KAUFFMAN	FFG 59	Bath Iron Works	8 Apr 1985	29 Mar 1986	28 Feb 1987	AA
RODNEY M DAVIS	FFG 60	Todd Shipyards, San Pedro	8 Feb 1985	11 Jan 1986	9 May 1987	PA
INGRAHAM	FFG 61	Todd Shipyards, San Pedro	30 Mar 1987	25 June 1988	5 Aug 1989	PA

Displacement, tons: 2750 light; 3638; 4100 (FFG 8, 36-61) full load
Dimensions, feet (metres): 445; 453 (FFG 8, 36-61) × 45 × 14.8; 24.5 (sonar) *(135.6; 138.1 × 13.7 × 4.5; 7.5)*
Main machinery: 2 GE LM 2500 gas-turbines; 41 000 hp *(30.59 MW)* sustained; 1 shaft; cp prop
2 auxiliary retractable props; 650 hp *(484 kW)*
Speed, knots: 29. **Range, miles:** 4500 at 20 kts
Complement: 206 (13 officers) including 19 aircrew

Missiles: SSM: 4 McDonnell Douglas Harpoon; active radar homing to 130 km *(70 nm)* at 0.9 Mach; warhead 227 kg.
SAM: 36 GDC Standard SM-1MR; command guidance; semi-active radar homing to 46 km *(25 nm)* at 2 Mach.
1 Mk 13 Mod 4 launcher for both SSM and SAM missiles ❶.
Guns: 1 OTO Melara 3 in *(76 mm)*/62 Mk 75 ❷; 85° elevation; 85 rounds/minute to 16 km *(8.7 nm)* anti-surface; 12 km *(6.6 nm)* anti-aircraft; weight of shell 6 kg.
1 General Electric/General Dynamics 20 mm/76 6-barrelled Mk 15 Vulcan Phalanx ❸; 3000 rounds/minute (4500 in Block 1) combined to 1.5 km.
4—12.7 mm MGs. McDonnell Douglas 25 mm Mk 38 guns can be fitted.
Torpedoes: 6—324 mm Mk 32 (2 triple) tubes ❹. 24 Honeywell Mk 46 Mod 5 (or Mk 50); anti-submarine; active/passive homing to 11 km *(5.9 nm)* at 40 kts; warhead 44 kg.
Countermeasures: Decoys: 2 Loral Hycor SRBOC 6-barrelled fixed Mk 36 ❺; IR flares and chaff to 4 km *(2.2 nm)*.
T—Mk-6 Fanfare/SLQ-25 Nixie; torpedo decoy.
ESM/ECM: SLQ 32(V)2 ❻; radar warning. Sidekick modification adds jammer and deception system.
Combat data systems: NTDS with Link 11 and 14. Link 14 only (NRF ships). SATCOM ❼ SRR-1, WSC-3 (UHF). SQQ 28 for LAMPS data link.
Fire control: SWG-1 Harpoon LCS. Mk 92 (Mod 4 or Mod 6 (FFG 61 and during modernisation in 11 others of the class)), WCS with CAS (Combined Antenna System). The Mk 92 is the US version of the Signaal WM-28 system. Mk 13 weapon direction system. 2 Mk 24 optical directors. SYS 2(V) IADT (FFG 61 and in 11 others of the class - see *Modernisation*). SRQ-4 for LAMPS III, SKR-4A for LAMPS I.
Radars: Air search: Raytheon SPS 49(V)4 or 5 (FFG 61 and during modernisation of others) ❽; C/D band; range 457 km *(250 nm)*.
Surface search: ISC Cardion SPS 55 ❾; I band.
Fire control: Lockheed STIR (modified SPG 60) ❿; I/J band; range 110 km *(60 nm)*.
Sperry Mk 92 (Signaal WM 28) ⓫; I/J band.
Tacan: URN 25. IFF Mk XII AIMS UPX-29.
Sonars: Raytheon SQS 56 or SQS 53B; hull-mounted; active search and attack; medium frequency.
Gould SQR 19; passive towed array. A few SQR 18A still fitted to ships assigned to the NRF.
SQQ 89(V)2 (SQS 53B and SQR 19) (in FFG 36-61 and retrofitted in all except 14 NRF ships by 1994).

Helicopters: 2 SH-2G LAMPS I (NRF ships) or 2 SH-60B LAMPS III ⓬. Canadair CL 227 (FFG 48) (see *Operational*).

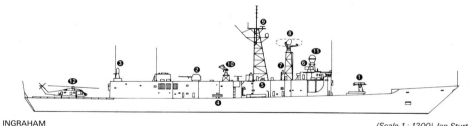

INGRAHAM
(Scale 1 : 1200), Ian Sturton

McINERNEY
10/1993, Maritime Photographic

Programmes: They are follow-on ships to the large number of frigates (formerly DE) built in the 1960s and early 1970s, with the later ships emphasising anti-ship/aircraft/missile capabilities while the previous classes were oriented primarily against submarines (eg, larger SQS 26 sonar and ASROC). The lead ship (FFG 7) was authorised in FY 1973. On 31 January 1984 the first of this class transferred to the Naval Reserve Force. Since then 15 more have transferred. NRF ships have about 75 reservists in their complement.
Modernisation: To accommodate the helicopter landing system (RAST), the overall length of the ship was increased by 8 ft *(2.4 m)* by increasing the angle of the ship's transom, between the waterline and the fantail, from virtually straight up to a 45° angle outwards. LAMPS III support facilities and RAST were fitted in all ships authorised from FFG 36 onwards, during construction and have been back fitted to all except NRF ships. The remainder can operate this aircraft without landing facilities. *Ingraham* has much improved Combat Data and Fire Control equipment which was retrofitted in FFG 36, 48, 50, 51 and 57 in 1993/94 and is scheduled for 47, 53, 54, 55, 52 and 59 in 1994/95. SQS 56 is being modified for mine detection.
Structure: The original single hangar has been changed to two adjacent hangars. Provided with 19 mm Kevlar armour protection over vital spaces. 25 mm guns can be fitted for some operational deployments.

Operational: Ships of this class were the first Navy experience in implementing a design-to-cost acquisition concept. Many of their limitations were manifest during the intense fires which resulted from *Stark* (FFG 31) being struck by two Exocet missiles in the Persian Gulf 17 May 1987. Since then there have been many improvements in firefighting and damage control doctrine and procedures and equipment to deal with residual missile propellant-induced fires. *Stark* was once again operational in August 1988. On 14 April 1988, *Samuel B Roberts* (FFG 58), was mined in the Gulf. *Roberts* was able to reach Bahrain using the auxiliary propulsion motor. She was repaired at Bath Iron Works returning to the fleet in November 1989. Fourteen ships of the class were active in the war with Iraq in 1991. *Vandegrift* is the trials ship for the Canadair CL-227 Sea Sentinel MAVUS II unmanned rotary wing air vehicle. This machine can carry either TV or IR cameras, or an ECM decoy system or a communications relay. Other payloads include synthetic aperture radar or Elint and Sigint equipment. The MAVUS II is carried in the starboard hangar. Trials are being conducted in the Caribbean in conjunction with the US Coast Guard.
Sales: Australia has bought four of the class and has built two more. Spain has four completed and is building two more. Taiwan is building six or seven.

ELROD

1/1994, Maritime Photographic

JARRETT

1/1993, 92 Wing RAAF

4 KNOX CLASS: FRIGATES (FFT)

Name	No	Builders	Laid down	Launched	Commissioned	F/S
BOWEN	FFT 1079	Avondale Shipyards	11 July 1969	2 May 1970	22 May 1971	NRF
McCANDLESS	FFT 1084	Avondale Shipyards	4 June 1970	20 Mar 1971	18 Mar 1972	NRF
AINSWORTH	FFT 1090	Avondale Shipyards	11 June 1971	15 Apr 1972	31 Mar 1973	NRF
TRUETT	FFT 1095	Avondale Shipyards	27 Apr 1972	3 Feb 1973	1 June 1974	NRF

Displacement, tons: 3011 standard; 4260 full load
Dimensions, feet (metres): 439.6 × 46.8 × 15; 24.8 (sonar) *(134 × 14.3 × 4.6; 7.8)*
Main machinery: 2 Combustion Engineering/Babcock & Wilcox boilers; 1200 psi *(84.4 kg/cm sq)*; 950°F *(510°C)*; 1 turbine; 35 000 hp *(26 MW)*; 1 shaft
Speed, knots: 27. **Range, miles:** 4000 at 22 kts on 1 boiler
Complement: 288 (17 officers)

Missiles: SSM: 8 McDonnell Douglas Harpoon; active radar homing to 130 km *(70 nm)* at 0.9 Mach; warhead 227 kg.
A/S: Honeywell ASROC Mk 16 octuple launcher with reload system (has 2 cells modified to fire Harpoon) ❶; inertial guidance to 1.6-10 km *(1-5.4 nm)*; payload Mk 46 Mod 5 Neartip.
Guns: 1 FMC 5 in *(127 mm)*/54 Mk 42 Mod 9 ❷; 85° elevation; 20-40 rounds/minute to 24 km *(13 nm)* anti-surface; 14 km *(7.7 nm)* anti-aircraft; weight of shell 32 kg.
1 General Electric/General Dynamics 20 mm/76 6-barrelled Mk 15 Vulcan Phalanx ❸; 3000 rounds/minute combined to 1.5 km.
Torpedoes: 4—324 mm Mk 32 (2 twin) fixed tubes ❹. 22 Honeywell Mk 46 Mod 5; anti-submarine; active/passive homing to 11 km *(5.9 nm)* at 40 kts; warhead 44 kg.
Countermeasures: Decoys: 2 Loral Hycor SRBOC 6-barrelled fixed Mk 36 ❺; IR flares and chaff to 4 km *(2.2 nm)*. T Mk-6 Fanfare/SLQ-25 Nixie; torpedo decoy. Prairie Masker hull and blade rate noise suppression.
ESM/ECM: SLQ 32(V)2 ❻; radar warning. Sidekick modification adds jammer and deception system.
Combat data systems: Link 14 receive only. SATCOM ❼ SRR-1, WSC-3 (UHF). FFISTS (Frigate Integrated Shipboard Tactical Systems) (see *Modernisation*).
Fire control: SWG-1A Harpoon LCS. Mk 68 GFCS. Mk 114 ASW FCS. Mk 1 target designation system. MMS target acquisition sight (for mines, small craft and low flying aircraft). SRQ-4 for LAMPS I.
Radars: Air search: Lockheed SPS 40B ❽; E/F band; range 320 km *(175 nm)*.
Surface search: Raytheon SPS 10 or Norden SPS 67 ❾; G band.
Navigation: Marconi LN 66; I band.
Fire control: Western Electric SPG 53A/D/F ❿; I/J band.
Tacan: SRN 15. IFF: UPX-12.
Sonars: EDO/General Electric SQS 26 CX; bow-mounted; active search and attack; medium frequency.
EDO SQR 18A(V)1; passive towed array; very low frequency.

Helicopters: 1 SH-2F LAMPS I ⓫.

Programmes: These last four are all scheduled to pay off by the end of FY 1994, and be transferred on lease (see *Sales*). FFT denotes training platform.

KNOX class

(Scale 1 : 1200), Ian Sturton

BOWEN

9/1992, Maritime Photographic

Sales: Three to Greece in mid-1992; two to Taiwan in mid-1992 and one in mid-1993; four to Turkey in late 1993. Proposed transfers in 1994 include four to Brazil, two to Egypt, two to Spain, three to Taiwan, four to Thailand, four to Turkey and two to Venezuela.

Major Combatant Naval Reserve Force Training Ships

Name/Hull No	NRF Homeport	Assignment	Name/Hull No	NRF Homeport	Assignment
OLIVER HAZARD PERRY (FFG 7)	New York, NY	May 1984	ANTRIM (FFG 20)	Mobile, AL	Jan 1987
WADSWORTH (FFG 9)	Long Beach, CA	June 1985	FLATLEY (FFG 21)	Mobile, AL	Nov 1987
DUNCAN (FFG 10)	Long Beach, CA	Jan 1984	FAHRION (FFG 22)	Charleston, SC	Sep 1988
CLARK (FFG 11)	Boston, MA	Sep 1985	LEWIS B PULLER (FFG 23)	Long Beach, CA	June 1987
GEORGE PHILIP (FFG 12)	Long Beach, CA	Jan 1986	COPELAND (FFG 25)	San Diego, CA	July 1988
SAMUEL ELIOT MORISON (FFG 13)	Charleston, SC	June 1986	MAHLON S TISDALE (FFG 27)	San Diego, CA	July 1988
JOHN H SIDES (FFG 14)	Long Beach, CA	Aug 1986	BOWEN (FFT 1079) (until 9/1994)	New York, NY	Dec 1991
ESTOCIN (FFG 15)	Newport, RI	Sep 1986	McCANDLESS (FFT 1084) (until 8/1994)	Ingleside, TX	Dec 1991
CLIFTON SPRAGUE (FFG 16)	New York, NY	Aug 1984	AINSWORTH (FFT 1090) (until 8/1994)	New York, NY	Dec 1991
JOHN A MOORE (FFG 19)	Long Beach, CA	Jan 1987	TRUETT (FFT 1095) (until 7/1994)	Ingleside, TX	Dec 1991

SHIPBORNE AIRCRAFT (FRONT LINE)

Notes: (1) Numbers given are for 1 January 1994.
(2) Development aircraft types which have been cancelled include the General Dynamics A-12 stealth advanced tactical aircraft (ATA), and the Lockheed P-7A MPA. The Boeing/Bell Textron MV-22A Osprey tilt rotor aircraft has so far survived several attempts at cancellation and continues development into 1994.

Numbers/Type: 327/36/304/107 McDonnell Douglas F/A-18A/B/C/D Hornet.
Operational speed: 1032 kts *(1910 km/h)*.
Service ceiling: 50 000 ft *(15 240 m)*.
Range: 1000 nm *(1850 km)*.
Role/Weapon systems: Strike interdictor for USN/USMC air groups; total procurement of about 800 expected. Some are used for EW support with ALQ-167 jammers. Sensors: ESM: ALR 67, ALQ 165 ASPJ (18C/D), APG-65 or APG-73 radar, AAS-38 FLIR, ASQ-173 tracker. Weapons: ASV; 4 × Harpoon or SLAM missiles. Strike; up to 7.7 tons of bombs. AD; 1 × 20 mm Vulcan cannon, 9 × AIM-7/AIM-9 missiles. Typical ASV load might include 20 mm gun, 7.7 ton bombs, 2 AIM-9 missiles. Typical AAW load might include 20 mm gun, 4 AIM-7, 2 AIM-9 missiles. 18C/D includes AIM-120 AMRAAM and AGM-65 Maverick capability.

Numbers/Type: 11/338 Grumman KA-6D/A-6E Intruder.
Operational speed: 560 kts *(1037 km/h)*.
Service ceiling: 42 400 ft *(12 925 m)*.
Range: 2818 nm *(5222 km)*.
Role/Weapon systems: All weather strike and armed reconnaissance role; updating programme cancelled in mid-1993. KA-6D is the tanker version. Sensors: APQ-148 or 156 search/attack radar, ALR 67 ESM, RWR, ECM. Weapons: ASV; 24 × Harpoon and nuclear weapons, 12 × Mk 36 mines. Strike; up to 8.2 tons of underwing stores. Self-defence; 4 × AIM-9 Sidewinder or 2 AIM-120 AMRAAM or 2 AIM-7M Sparrow. Systems Weapons Improvements Programme (SWIP) included AGM-88 HARM and AGM-65 Maverick missiles.

HORNET

8/1993, Hachiro Nakai

INTRUDER

1990, US Navy

Numbers/Type: 360/69/62 Grumman F-14A/B/D Tomcat.
Operational speed: 1342 kts *(2485 km/h).*
Service ceiling: 56 000 ft *(17 070 m).*
Range: 1735 nm *(3220 km).*
Role/Weapon systems: Standard fleet fighter aircraft for long-range air defence of task groups; undergoing phased improvements; F-14D flew in early 1988 with in-service date of 1990. Sensors: AWG-9 or APG-71 (D type) radar, ALQ-126 jammer, ASN-92 nav or ASN-139 (D type), ALR-45 or ALR-67 (D type) RWR; IRST and JTIDS (Link 16) (D type). Weapons: AD; 1 × 20 mm cannon, 6 × AIM-54 Phoenix; AGM-88 HARM and AGM-84 Harpoon/SLAM being added. CAP; 1 × 20 mm cannon, 4 × Phoenix, 2 × AIM-7M, 2 × AIM-9M. Recce; 1 × 20 mm cannon, 2 × AIM-7M, 2 × AIM-9M.

TOMCAT   *9/1992, Maritime Photographic*

TOMCAT   *1989*

Numbers/Type: 187/1/24 McDonnell Douglas/British Aerospace AV-8B/AV-8B Plus/TAV-8B Harrier II.
Operational speed: 562 kts *(1041 km/h).*
Service ceiling: 50 000 ft *(15 240 m).*
Range: 800 nm *(1480 km).*
Role/Weapon systems: Close support for USMC operational from 1985. A total of 28 AV-8B Plus delivery scheduled to start in June 1993. Sensors: FLIR, laser designator and ECM; ALR-67 ESM; APG-65 radar (AV-8B Plus). Weapons: Strike; up to 4.2 tons of 'iron' bombs or Paveway II LGM, AGM-62 Walleye or AGM-65 Maverick. Self-defence; 1 × GAU-12/U 25 mm cannon and 4 × AIM-9L Sidewinder.

HARRIER II   *1/1991, Ingalls Shipbuilding*

Numbers/Type: 35 McDonnell Douglas A-4M Skyhawk.
Operational speed: 560 kts *(1038 km/h).*
Service ceiling: 45 000 ft *(13 780 m).*
Range: 1060 nm *(1963 km).*
Role/Weapon systems: Ageing but important strike potential for USMC maintained for reserves; about 150 training versions in service. Sensors: Attack radar, ECM. Weapons: Strike; up to 1.6 tons fuselage and 3 tons underwing. AD; 2 × 20 mm cannon, 4 × AIM-7 or 9s.

SKYHAWK   *1989, Hughes Aircraft*

Numbers/Type: 40/100/16 Lockheed S-3A/3B/ES-3A Viking.
Operational speed: 450 kts *(834 km/h).*
Service ceiling: 35 000 ft *(10 670 m).*
Range: 2000 nm *(3706 km).*
Role/Weapon systems: Standard ASW/ASV aircraft; works in concert with towed array escorts; possible replacement from 1996 by Osprey tilt-rotor; first S-3B flew in 1987; conversion to B type at the rate of about 30 a year to complete in 1994; 16 converted to ELINT configuration (ES-3A), replaced obsolete EA-3B for combined EW and targeting. First one flew in January 1992, last one delivered September 1993. Link 11 fitted. Sensors: APS-137(V)1 radar; APN-200 radar, FLIR, MAD, ASQ-81(V)1, 60 × sonobuoys; ESM: ALR-76; ECM ALE 47; ALE 39 chaff. Weapons: ASW; 4 × Mk 54 depth charges, 4 × Mk 46/Mk 50 torpedoes. ASV; 2 × Harpoon Block 1C; mines.

VIKING   *1987, US Navy*

Numbers/Type: 130 Grumman EA-6B Prowler.
Operational speed: 566 kts *(1048 km/h).*
Service ceiling: 41 200 ft *(12 550 m).*
Range: 955 nm *(1769 km).*
Role/Weapon systems: EW and jamming aircraft to accompanying strikes and armed reconnaissance; being uprated to ADVCAP with new engines and ECM. Sensors: APS-130 radar; ALQ-99F, ALQ-149 (ADVCAP) jammers. Weapons: AGM-88 HARM anti-radiation missile capable.

PROWLER   *8/1993, Hachiro Nakai*

Numbers/Type: 119 Grumman E-2C Hawkeye.
Operational speed: 323 kts *(598 km/h)*.
Service ceiling: 30 800 ft *(9390 m)*.
Range: 1000 nm *(1850 km)*.
Role/Weapon systems: Used for direction of AD and strike operations; last production delivery planned for mid-1994. Sensors: ESM: ALR-73 PDS, ALQ-108; Airborne tactical data system with Links 4A and 11, APS-125/138/145 radar. Weapons: Unarmed.

HAWKEYE   *1989, US Navy*

Numbers/Type: 141/67 Sikorsky SH-60B/F Seahawk (LAMPS III).
Operational speed: 135 kts *(250 km/h)*.
Service ceiling: 10 000 ft *(3050 m)*.
Range: 600 nm *(1110 km)*.
Role/Weapon systems: LAMPS III air vehicle for medium-range ASW and for ASV; planned at a rate of about 12 each per year; SH-60B operated from DDH and FFH class escorts; non-autonomous; SH-60F is derived CV model to replace Sea King; entered service 1989. Block II upgrade to include Inverse Synthetic Aperture Radar (ISAR) plus tactical data transfer and SLAM terminal guidance. Sensors: APS-124 search radar, FLIR, ASQ-811(V) MAD, 25 sonobuoys (Difar or Dicass (60F)), LLTV. AQS-13F dipping sonar (60F) (to be replaced by ALFS in due course); ALQ-142/156 ESM, ALQ-144 ECM. ALE-39 chaff and flare dispenser; Link 11. Weapons: ASW; 2/3 × Mk 46/Mk 50 torpedoes or depth bombs. ASV; 1 × Penguin Mk 2 Mod 7 missile (in 28 aircraft for Oliver Perry frigates from 1992); 1—7.62 mm MG M60; AGM-114 Hellfire (possibly).

SEAHAWK   *10/1993, Maritime Photographic*

Numbers/Type: 64/24 Kaman SH-2F/G Seasprite (LAMPS I).
Operational speed: 130 kts *(241 km/h)*.
Service ceiling: 22 500 ft *(6860 m)*.
Range: 367 nm *(679 km)*.
Role/Weapon systems: ASW and OTHT helicopter; second production run ended in 1987; in LAMPS I programme, acts as ASW information relay for surface ships. Six SH-2G were new build, 14 more converted by 1993 with improved engines, avionics and sensor processing. 30 more to be converted in due course. Most of the SH-2F are to retire with the Knox class in 1994. Sensors: LN-66HP radar, ALR-66 ESM, ALE-39 ECM, ASN-150 tactical nav, ASQ-81(V)2 MAD, AAQ-16 FLIR; AAR 47 IR threat detection; ARR-57 sonobuoy receivers; 15 sonobuoys. For the Gulf War in 1991, additional EW equipment included AAQ-34 FLIR, ALE-37 chaff, ALQ 144 IR counter, plus DLQ 3B video data link. A DEMON mine detection system was also fitted. Weapons: ASW: 2 × Mk 46/Mk 50 torpedoes, 8 × Mk 25 smoke markers, 1 depth bomb. ASV: 1 Penguin; 1—7.62 mm MG M60.

SEASPRITE 2G   *1993, Kamen*

Numbers/Type: 17/111 Sikorsky SH-3G/H Sea King.
Operational speed: 144 kts *(267 km/h)*.
Service ceiling: 12 200 ft *(3720 m)*.
Range: 630 nm *(1166 km)*.
Role/Weapon systems: Carrier battle group inner zone ASW; also used for liaison and SAR tasks. Being replaced by SH-60F. Sensors: AN/APS-24 search radar, Bendix AQS-13 dipping sonar, Texas Instruments ASQ-81(V)2 MAD, 25 sonobuoys. Weapons: ASW; 2 × Mk 46/Mk 50 torpedoes or depth bombs or mines.

SEA KING   *9/1992, Maritime Photographic*

Numbers/Type: 47/28/241 Boeing HH-46D/CH-46D/E/UH-46D/E Sea Knight.
Operational speed: 137 kts *(254 km/h)*.
Service ceiling: 8500 ft *(2590 m)*.
Range: 180 nm *(338 km)*.
Role/Weapon systems: Support/assault (USMC) for 18 Marines and resupply (USN) helicopter respectively. Can lift 1.3 tons or 4.5 tons in a cargo net or sling. Sensors: None. Weapons: Unarmed.

SEA KNIGHT CH-46   *10/1992, Maritime Photographic*

Numbers/Type: 128 Sikorsky CH-53E Super Stallion.
Operational speed: 170 kts *(315 km/h)*.
Service ceiling: 18 500 ft *(5640 m)*.
Range: 230 nm *(425 km)*.
Role/Weapon systems: Uprated, three-engined version of Sea Stallion with support (USN) and transport (USMC) roles. Total of about 200 aircraft planned. Carries 56 Marines. Sensors: None. Weapons: Up to 3 × 12.7 mm machine guns.

SUPER STALLION   *1990, US Navy*

Numbers/Type: 76 Sikorsky CH-53D Sea Stallion.
Operational speed: 150 kts *(278 km/h)*.
Service ceiling: 21 000 ft *(6400 m)*.
Range: 540 nm *(1000 km)*.
Role/Weapon systems: Assault, support and transport helicopters; can carry 38 Marines. Sensors: None. Weapons: Up to 3 × 12.7 mm machine guns.

SEA DRAGON MCM SLEDGE   *7/1992, Jürg Kürsener*

SEA STALLION   *11/1991, A Campanera i Rovira*

Numbers/Type: 132 Bell AH-1W Super Cobra.
Operational speed: 149 kts *(277 km/h)*.
Service ceiling: 12 200 ft *(3718 m)*.
Range: 317 nm *(587 km)*.
Role/Weapon systems: Close support helicopter; uprated and improved version, with own air defence capability; being procured at about 12 a year. Sensors: NTS (laser and FLIR nightsight) to be retrofitted from 1993 at the rate of 24 aircraft per year. Weapons: Strike/assault; 1 or 3 × 20 mm cannon, 8 × TOW or Hellfire missiles, gun and grenade pods. Self-defence; 2 × AIM-9L Sidewinder missiles.

Numbers/Type: 29 Sikorsky MH-53E Sea Dragon.
Operational speed: 170 kts *(315 km/h)*.
Service ceiling: 18 500 ft *(5640 m)*.
Range: 1000 nm *(1850 km)*.
Role/Weapon systems: Three-engined AMCM helicopter similar to Super Stallion; total of about 60 planned; tows ALQ-166 MCM sweep equipment; self-deployed if necessary. Sensors: AQS-14 or AQS-20 dipping sonar being fitted. Weapons: 2 × 12.7 mm guns for self-defence.

SUPER COBRA   *1984, Bell Helicopters*

Numbers/Type: 109 Bell UH-1N Iroquois. Twin Huey
Operational speed: 110 kts *(204 km/h)*.
Service ceiling: 15 000 ft *(4570 m)*.
Range: 250 nm *(463 km)*.
Role/Weapon systems: Support and logistics helicopter for USMC operations afloat and ashore. Can carry 16 Marines. Sensors: None. Weapons: Can be armed with 7.62 mm machine guns.

SEA DRAGON   *1991*   TWIN HUEY   *1990, Bell Helicopters*

LAND-BASED MARITIME AIRCRAFT (FRONT LINE)

Numbers/Type: 257 Lockheed P-3C Orion.
Operational speed: 411 kts *(761 km/h)*.
Service ceiling: 28 300 ft *(8625 m)*.
Range: 4000 nm *(7410 km)*.
Role/Weapon systems: 144 in operational squadrons deployed worldwide in support of US Naval operations; primarily ASW; update III conversions to 138 airframes. Remainder of P-3Bs (75) have been allocated to the Naval Reserves. Sensors: APS-115 search radar or APS 137(V)5 to be fitted in 68 aircraft from 1995, ASQ-81 MAD, up to 100 × sonobuoys, AAR-36 FLIR, cameras, AXR-13 LLTV, ALR 66 or ALQ 78 ESM. Weapons: ASW; 4 × Mk 44/46/50 torpedoes or 2 × Mk 101 nuclear depth bombs (not carried). ASV; 4 × Harpoon, 6 × Mk 55/56 mines.

Numbers/Type: 12 Lockheed EP-3E Orion.
Operational speed: 411 kts *(761 km/h)*.
Service ceiling: 28 300 ft *(8625 m)*.
Range: 4000 nm *(7410 km)*.
Role/Weapon systems: Electronic warfare and intelligence gathering aircraft. Sensors: EW equipment including AN/ALR-60, AN/ALQ-76, AN/ALQ-78, AN/ALQ-108 and AN/ASQ-114. Weapons: Unarmed.

Numbers/Type: 16 Boeing E-6A Hermes/TACAMO.
Operational speed: 455 kts *(842 km/h)*.
Service ceiling: 42 000 ft *(12 800 m)*.
Range: 6350 nm *(11 760 km/h)*.
Role/Weapon systems: First flew in February 1987 and has replaced EC-130Q. EMP hardened against nuclear bursts. Sensors: Supports Trident Fleet radio communications. Weapons: Unarmed.

TACAMO   *1989, Boeing*

AMPHIBIOUS WARFARE FORCES

Notes: (1) Additional capacity is provided by the maritime pre-positioning ships (see listing at end of *Military Sealift Command* section) which are either new construction or conversions of relatively new commercial ships. One squadron is maintained on station in the Atlantic, a second at Guam, and a third at Diego Garcia. Each carries equipment to support a Marine Expeditionary Force. Ships of the latter two squadrons were the first to arrive at Saudi

Arabian ports after the build-up of US forces in the Middle East was ordered in late 1990. The Diego Garcia squadron was also involved in late 1992 providing equipment for US forces in Somalia and that support continued throughout 1993. Also in 1993, and into 1994, there is a constant presence in the Adriatic in indirect support of UN operations in Bosnia.

(2) **Minesweeping:** Several of the larger amphibious ships have been used as operating bases for minesweeping helicopters in the absence of a 'mother ship' for such aircraft. *Inchon* is planned to become a dedicated support ship by 1996.

2 BLUE RIDGE CLASS: AMPHIBIOUS COMMAND SHIPS (LCC)

Name	No	Builders	Laid down	Launched	Commissioned	F/S
BLUE RIDGE	LCC 19	Philadelphia Naval Shipyard	27 Feb 1967	4 Jan 1969	14 Nov 1970	PA
MOUNT WHITNEY	LCC 20	Newport News Shipbuilding	8 Jan 1969	8 Jan 1970	16 Jan 1971	AA

Displacement, tons: 16 790 light; 18 372 full load *(Blue Ridge)* 16 100 light; 18 646 full load *(Mount Whitney)*
Dimensions, feet (metres): 636.5 × 107.9 × 28.9 *(194 × 32.9 × 8.8)*
Main machinery: 2 Foster-Wheeler boilers; 600 psi *(42.3 kg/cm sq)*; 870°F *(467°C)*; 1 GE turbine; 22 000 hp *(16.4 MW)*; 1 shaft
Speed, knots: 23. **Range, miles:** 13 000 at 16 kts
Complement: 821 (43 officers); Flag 170-190.
Military lift: 700 troops; 3 LCPs; 2 LCVPs

Missiles: SAM: 2 Raytheon GMLS Mk 25 Mod 1 octuple launchers ❶; 16 Sea Sparrow; semi-active radar homing to 14.6 km *(8 nm)* at 2.5 Mach; warhead 39 kg.
Guns: 4 USN 3 in *(76 mm)*/50 (2 twin) Mk 33 ❷; 85° elevation; 50 rounds/minute to 12.8 km *(7 nm)*; weight of shell 6 kg. Antennas and their supports severely restrict firing arcs of guns, which are seldom embarked.
2 General Electric/General Dynamics 20 mm/76 6-barrelled Vulcan Phalanx Mk 15 ❸; 3000 rounds/minute (4500 in Block 1) combined to 1.5 km.
Countermeasures: Decoys: 4 Loral Hycor SRBOC 6-barrelled fixed Mk 36; IR flares and chaff to 4 km *(2.2 nm)*. SLQ-25 Nixie; torpedo decoy.
ESM/ECM: SLQ 32(V)3; combined radar intercept, jammer and deception system.
Combat data systems: NTDS with Links 4A, 11, 14 and 16 in due course. Amphibious Command Information System (ACIS), and Naval Intelligence Processing System (NIPS). SATCOMS ❹; SSR-1, WSC-3 (UHF), WSC-6 (SHF), USC-38 (EHF) (from 1992), SMQ-6 receiver.
Fire control: 2 Mk 115 MFCS. No GFCS.
Radars: Air search: ITT SPS 48C ❺; 3D; E/F band; range 402 km *(220 nm)*.
Lockheed SPS 40C ❻; E/F band; range 320 km *(175 nm)*.
Hughes Mk 23 TAS; D band (to be fitted).
Surface search: Raytheon SPS 65(V)1 ❼; G band.
Navigation: Marconi LN 66; Raytheon SPS 64(V)9; I band.
Fire control: Two Mk 51; I/J band (for SAM).
Tacan: URN 20/25. IFF: Mk XII AIMS UPX-29.

Helicopters: 1 utility can be carried.

Programmes: Authorised in FY 1965 and 1966. Originally designated Amphibious Force Flagships (AGC); redesignated Amphibious Command Ships (LCC) on 1 January 1969.

BLUE RIDGE   *(Scale 1 : 1800), Ian Sturton*

MOUNT WHITNEY   *9/1993, Antonio Moreno*

Modernisation: Modernisation completed FY 1987 although the Mk 23 TAS radar may be fitted in due course.
Structure: General hull design and machinery arrangement are similar to the Iwo Jima class assault ships.
Operational: These are large amphibious force command ships of post-Second World War design. They can provide integrated

command and control facilities for sea, air and land commanders in amphibious operations. The main guns are seldom embarked. *Blue Ridge* is the Seventh Fleet flagship, based at Yokosuka, Japan. *Mount Whitney* serves as flagship Second Fleet, based at Norfolk, Virginia.

BLUE RIDGE   *4/1993, Hachiro Nakai*

0 + (12) LPD 17 MULTI-PURPOSE AMPHIBIOUS SHIPS

Displacement, tons: 23 000 full load
Dimensions, feet (metres): 699 × 103 × 21 *(213.1 × 31.4 × 6.4)*
Main machinery: 4 diesels; 40 000 hp *(29.84 MW)*; 2 shafts
Speed, knots: 22
Complement: 495
Military lift: 750 troops; 2 LCACs

Missiles: SAM: 2 GDC RAM launchers.
Guns: 3 GE/GD Mk 15 Vulcan Phalanx.
Countermeasures: ESM/ECM: SLQ 32(V)3; intercept and jammer.
Radars: Air search: Raytheon SPS 49; C/D band.
Hughes Mk 23 TAS; D band.

Helicopters: 1 CH-53 Sea Stallion.

Programmes: The LPD 17 (ex-LX) programme was approved by the Defense Acquisition Board on 11 January 1993. The ship has entered the preliminary design phase. It is intended to replace four classes of amphibious ships: LPD 4s, LSTs, LKAs

LPD 17   *(Scale 1 : 1800), Ian Sturton*

and LSD 36s. The lead-ship contract award is planned for FY 1996 with delivery in FY 2002. In 1998, and in each year thereafter, two ship contracts are to be awarded. With the exception of the first ship, it is anticipated that 55-60 months will be required between contract award and delivery. Twelve ships are planned with the last one scheduled to complete in 2007.
Structure: LPD 17 will be a Panama Canal-capable ship able to control and support landing forces disembarking either via surface craft such as LCACs or by VTOL aircraft, principally

helicopters. The ship design supports a lift capability of 25 000 sq ft of deck space for vehicles, 25 000 cu ft of cargo below decks, 750 embarked Marines, 2 LCACs, and 2 CH-53 helicopters, with a hangar able to support 1 CH-53. It will not have the flag configuration of LPDs or the heavy over-the-side lift capability of LKAs. There will be a crane on board for support of boat operations. The ship will lack the capability to offload over a beach. Otherwise, it will have most of the capabilities of the four classes of ships it is replacing.

3 + 3 WASP CLASS: AMPHIBIOUS ASSAULT SHIP (multipurpose) (LHD)

Name	No	Builders	Laid down	Launched	Commissioned	F/S
WASP	LHD 1	Ingalls Shipbuilding	30 May 1985	4 Aug 1987	29 July 1989	AA
ESSEX	LHD 2	Ingalls Shipbuilding	20 Mar 1989	4 Jan 1991	17 Oct 1992	PA
KEARSARGE	LHD 3	Ingalls Shipbuilding	6 Feb 1990	26 Mar 1992	16 Oct 1993	AA
BOXER	LHD 4	Ingalls Shipbuilding	8 Apr 1991	13 Aug 1993	Dec 1994	Bldg/PA
BATAAN	LHD 5	Ingalls Shipbuilding	Apr 1994	Mar 1996	May 1997	Bldg
BONHOMME RICHARD	LHD 6	Ingalls Shipbuilding	Apr 1995	Mar 1997	May 1998	Bldg

Displacement, tons: 28 233 light; 40 532 full load
Dimensions, feet (metres): 844 oa; 788 wl × 140.1 oa; 106 wl × 26.6 *(257.3; 240.2 × 42.7; 32.3 × 8.1)*
Flight deck, feet (metres): 819 × 106 *(249.6 × 32.3)*
Main machinery: 2 Combustion Engineering boilers; 600 psi *(42.3 kg/cm sq)*; 900°F *(482°C)*; 2 Westinghouse turbines; 70 000 hp *(52.2 MW)*; 2 shafts
Speed, knots: 22. **Range, miles:** 9500 at 18 kts
Complement: 1077 (98 officers)
Military lift: 1870 troops; 12 LCM 6s or 3 LCACs; 1232 tons aviation fuel; 4 LCPL

Missiles: SAM: 2 Raytheon GMLS Mk 29 octuple launchers ❶; 16 Sea Sparrow; semi-active radar homing to 14.6 km *(8 nm)* at 2.5 Mach; warhead 39 kg. 1 launcher located aft, on a transom that overhangs the stern, and a second on a raised deck forward of the superstructure.
Guns: 3 General Electric/General Dynamics 20 mm 6-barrelled Vulcan Phalanx Mk 15 ❷; 3000 rounds/minute (4500 in Batch 1) combined to 1.5 km. One fitted on each quarter and one aft of the NSSMS launcher on the island.
8—12.7 mm MGs.
Countermeasures: Decoys: 4 or 6 Loral Hycor SRBOC 6-barrelled fixed Mk 36; IR flares and chaff to 4 km *(2.2 nm)*.
SLQ 25 Nixie; acoustic torpedo decoy system. NATO Sea Gnat. SLQ-49 chaff buoys. AEB SSQ-95.

ESM/ECM: SLQ 32(V)3; combined radar warning, jammer and deception system.
Combat data systems: Integrated Tactical Amphibious Warfare Data System (ITAWDS) and Marine Tactical Amphibious C² System (MTACCS). Links 4A, 11 (modified), 14 and 16 in due course. SATCOMS ❸ SSR-1, WSC-3 (UHF), USC-38 (EHF) (from 1992). SMQ-11 Metsat.
Fire control: 2 Mk 91 MFCS. SYS-2(V)3 IADT.
Radars: Air search: Hughes SPS 52C ❹ (LHD 1); 3D; E/F band; range 439 km *(240 nm)*.
ITT SPS 48E (except LHD 1); 3D; E/F band; range 402 km *(220 nm)*.
Raytheon SPS 49(V)9 ❺; C/D band; range 457 km *(250 nm)*. Hughes Mk 23 TAS ❻; D band.
Surface search: Norden SPS 67 ❼; G band.
Navigation: SPS 64(V)9; I band.
CCA: SPN 35A and SPN 43B.
Fire control: Two Mk 95; I/J band.
Tacan: URN 25. IFF: CIS Mk XV UPX-29.

Fixed wing aircraft: 6-8 AV-8B Harriers or up to 20 in secondary role.
Helicopters: Capacity for 42 CH-46E Sea Knight but has the capability to support: AH-1W Super Cobra, CH-53E Super Stallion, CH-53D Sea Stallion, UH-1N Twin Huey, AH-1T Sea Cobra, and SH-60B Seahawk helicopters.

Programmes: Fifth of the class ordered 20 December 1991. Although an LHD was not included in the FY 1993 budget, Congress took the unusual action of authorising the expenditure of $1.2 billion for a sixth, but allocating only $300 million in funding, enough to get it under a construction contract. The balance of the funding was provided in FY 1994. Plans to include a seventh of class in FY 1995 budget have been shelved.
Structure: Two aircraft elevators, one to starboard and aft of the 'island' and one to port amidships; both fold for Panama canal transits. The well deck is 267 × 50 ft and can accommodate up to three Amphibious Air-Cushion Vehicles (LCAC). The flight deck has nine helicopter landing spots. Cargo capacity is 101 000 cu ft total with an additional 20 000 sq ft to accommodate vehicles. Vehicle storage is available for five M1 tanks, 25 LAVs, eight M 198 guns, 68 trucks, 10 logistic vehicles and several service vehicles. The bridge is two decks lower than that of an LHA, command, control and communication spaces having been moved inside the hull to avoid 'cheap kill' damage. Fitted with a 600-bed capacity hospital and six operating rooms. HY-100 steel covers the flight deck. Nine 32 ft monorail trains each carrying 6000 lbs, deliver material to the well deck at 6.8 mph.
Operational: A typical complement of aircraft would be a mix of 30 helicopters and six to eight Harriers (AV-8B). In the secondary role as a sea control ship the most likely mix is 20 AV-8B Harriers and four to six SH-60B Seahawk helicopters.

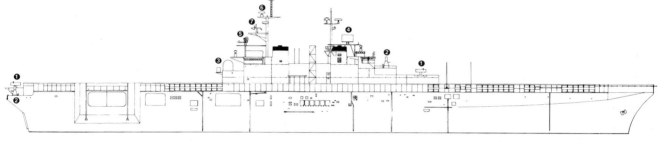

WASP   *(Scale 1 : 1500), Ian Sturton*

KEARSARGE   *8/1993, Ingalls Shipbuilding*

KEARSARGE   *8/1993, Ingalls Shipbuilding*

WASP   *7/1993, van Ginderen Collection*

5 TARAWA CLASS: AMPHIBIOUS ASSAULT SHIPS (multipurpose) (LHA)

Name	No	Builders	Erection of First Module	Launched	Commissioned	F/S
TARAWA	LHA 1	Ingalls Shipbuilding	15 Nov 1971	1 Dec 1973	29 May 1976	PA
SAIPAN	LHA 2	Ingalls Shipbuilding	21 July 1972	18 July 1974	15 Oct 1977	AA
BELLEAU WOOD	LHA 3	Ingalls Shipbuilding	5 Mar 1973	11 Apr 1977	23 Sep 1978	PA
NASSAU	LHA 4	Ingalls Shipbuilding	13 Aug 1973	21 Jan 1978	28 July 1979	AA
PELELIU (ex-Da Nang)	LHA 5	Ingalls Shipbuilding	12 Nov 1976	25 Nov 1978	3 May 1980	PA

Displacement, tons: 39 967 full load
Dimensions, feet (metres): 834 × 131.9 × 25.9
(254.2 × 40.2 × 7.9)
Flight deck, feet (metres): 820 × 118.1 *(250 × 36)*
Main machinery: 2 Combustion Engineering boilers; 600 psi
(42.3 kg/cm sq); 900°F *(482°C)*; 2 Westinghouse turbines;
70 000 hp *(52.2 MW)*; 2 shafts; bow thruster; 900 hp
(670 kW)
Speed, knots: 24. **Range, miles:** 10 000 at 20 kts
Complement: 930 (56 officers)
Military lift: 1703 troops; 4 LCU 1610 type or 2 LCU and 2 LCM 8
or 17 LCM 6 or 45 LVT tractors; 1200 tons aviation fuel. 1
LCAC may be embarked. 4 LCPL

Missiles: SAM: 2 GDC RAM ❶; 21 rounds per launcher; passive
IR/anti-radiation homing to 9.6 km *(5.2 nm)* at 2 Mach; warhead 9.1 kg (being fitted).
Guns: 2 FMC 5 in *(127 mm)*/54 Mk 45 Mod 1 ❷; 65° elevation;
20 rounds/minute to 23 km *(12.6 nm)* anti-surface; 15 km
(8.2 nm) anti-aircraft; weight of shell 32 kg.
6 Mk 242 25 mm automatic cannons.
2 General Electric/General Dynamics 20 mm/76 6-barrelled
Vulcan Phalanx Mk 15 ❸; 3000 rounds/minute (4500 in Block
1) combined to 1.5 km.
Countermeasures: Decoys: 4 Loral Hycor SRBOC 6-barrelled
fixed Mk 36; IR flares and chaff to 4 km *(2.2 nm)*.
SLQ 25 Nixie; acoustic torpedo decoy system. NATO Sea Gnat.
SLQ-49 chaff buoys. AEB SSQ-95.
ESM/ECM: SLQ 32V(3); combined radar intercept, jammer and
deception system.
Combat data systems: Integrated Tactical Amphibious Warfare
Data System (ITAWDS) to provide computerised support in
control of helicopters and aircraft, shipboard weapons and sen-
sors, navigation, landing craft control, and electronic warfare.
Links 4A, 11, 14 and 16 in due course. SATCOM SRR-1, WSC-3
(UHF), USC-38 (EHF) (LHA 2 and 4). SMQ-11 Metsat.
Fire control: Mk 86 Mod 4 GFCS. 2 optronic directors.
Radars: Air search: Hughes SPS 52C ❹; 3D; E/F band; range
439 km *(240 nm)*.
Lockheed SPS 40B/C/D ❺; E/F band; range 320 km
(175 nm).
Hughes Mk 23 TAS; D band.
Surface search: Raytheon SPS 67 ❻; G band.

TARAWA   *4/1993, Hachiro Nakai*

Navigation: Raytheon SPS 64(V)9; I band.
CCA: SPN 35A; SPN 43B.
Fire control: Lockheed SPG 60 ❼; I/J band.
Lockheed SPQ 9A ❽; I/J band; range 37 km *(20 nm)*.
Tacan: URN 25. IFF: CIS Mk XV.

Fixed wing aircraft: Harrier AV-8B VSTOL aircraft in place of
some helicopters as required.
Helicopters: 19 CH-53D Sea Stallion or 26 CH-46D/E Sea
Knight.

Programmes: Originally intended to be a class of nine ships.
LHA1 was authorised in FY 1969, LHA 2 and LHA 3 in FY 1970
and LHA 4 and LHA 5 in FY 1971.
Modernisation: Two Vulcan Phalanx CIWS replaced the GMLS
Mk 25 Sea Sparrow launchers. Programme completed in early
1991. RAM launchers being fitted, first in LHA 5 in 1993, second in LHA 3 in 1994. One launcher is above the bridge offset
to port, and the other on the starboard side at the after end of
the flight deck. Mk 23 TAS target acquisition radar fitted in
LHA 3 and 5 in 1992, LHA 4 in 1993 and the last pair in 1994.

Structure: Beneath the full-length flight deck are two half-length
hangar decks, the two being connected by an elevator amidships on the port side and a stern lift; beneath the after elevator
is a floodable docking well measuring 268 ft in length and
78 ft in width which is capable of accommodating four LCU
1610 type landing craft. Also included is a large garage for
trucks and AFVs and troop berthing for a reinforced battalion.
33 730 sq ft available for vehicles and 116 900 cu ft for palletted stores. Extensive medical facilities including operating
rooms, X-ray room, hospital ward, isolation ward, laboratories,
pharmacy, dental operating room and medical store rooms.
Operational: The flight deck can operate a maximum of nine
CH-53D Sea Stallion or 12 CH-46D/E Sea Knight helicopters or
a mix of these and other helicopters. With some additional
modifications, ships of this class can effectively operate AV-8B
aircraft. The normal mix of aircraft allows for six AV-8Bs. The
optimum aircraft configuration for this class is dependent upon
assigned missions. Unmanned Reconnaissance Vehicles
(URVs) can be operated. *Belleau Wood* is based at Sasebo,
Japan.

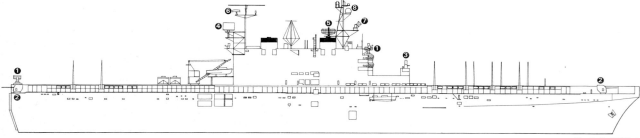

PELELIU   *(Scale 1 : 1500), Ian Sturton*

TARAWA   *6/1991, 92 Wing RAAF*

5 IWO JIMA CLASS: AMPHIBIOUS ASSAULT SHIPS (LPH)

Name	No	Builders	Laid down	Launched	Commissioned	F/S
GUADALCANAL	LPH 7	Philadelphia Naval Shipyard	1 Sep 1961	16 Mar 1963	20 July 1963	AA
GUAM	LPH 9	Philadelphia Naval Shipyard	15 Nov 1962	22 Aug 1964	16 Jan 1965	AA
TRIPOLI	LPH 10	Ingalls Shipbuilding	15 June 1964	31 July 1965	6 Aug 1966	PA
NEW ORLEANS	LPH 11	Philadelphia Naval Shipyard	1 Mar 1966	3 Feb 1968	16 Nov 1968	PA
INCHON	LPH 12	Ingalls Shipbuilding	8 Apr 1968	24 May 1969	20 June 1970	AA

Displacement, tons: 11 250 light; 18 798 full load
Dimensions, feet (metres): 602.3 × 104 × 31.7
(183.7 × 31.7 × 9.7)
Flight deck, feet (metres): 602.3 × 104 *(183.7 × 31.7)*
Main machinery: 2 Babcock & Wilcox/Combustion Engineering
boilers; 600 psi *(42.3 kg/cm sq)*; 900°F *(482°C)*; 1 De Laval/
GE/Westinghouse turbine; 23 000 hp *(17.2 MW)*; 1 shaft
Speed, knots: 23. **Range, miles:** 10 000 at 20 kts
Complement: 902 (52 officers)
Military lift: 1562 troops (158 officers); 1500 tons aviation fuel;
2 LCPL

Missiles: SAM: 2 Raytheon GMLS Mk 25 octuple launchers ❶;
Sea Sparrow; semi-active radar homing to 14.6 km *(8 nm)* at
2.5 Mach; warhead 39 kg. 1 launcher forward of island structure and 1 on the port quarter.
Guns: 4 USN 3 in *(76 mm)*/50 (2 twin) Mk 33 ❷; 85° elevation;
50 rounds/minute to 12.8 km *(7 nm)*; weight of shell 6 kg.
2 General Electric/General Dynamics 20 mm 6-barrelled Vul-
can Phalanx Mk 15 ❸; 3000 rounds/minute (4500 in Batch 1)
combined to 1.5 km.
Up to 8—12.7 mm MGs.
Countermeasures: Decoys: 4 Loral Hycor SRBOC 6-barrelled
fixed Mk 36; IR flares and chaff to 4 km *(2.2 nm)*.
ESM/ECM: SLQ 32(V)3; combined radar warning, jammer and
deception system.
Combat data systems: SATCOM ❹ SRR-1, WSC-3 (UHF).
Fire control: Mk 115 MFCS. 2 Mk 71 directors.
Radars: Air search: Westinghouse SPS 65 ❺; 3D; D band.
Lockheed SPS 40 ❻; E/F band; range 320 km *(175 nm)*.
Surface search: Raytheon SPS 10 ❼; G band.
CCA: SPN 35 and SPN 43.
Navigation: Marconi LN 66; I band.
Fire control: Two Mk 51; I/J band.
Tacan: URN 25. IFF: Mk XII UPX-29.

Fixed wing aircraft: 4 AV-8B Harriers in place of some
helicopters.
Helicopters: Capacity for 20 CH-46D/E Sea Knight or 11 CH-53D
Sea Stallion.

Programmes: *Guam* was modified late in 1971 and began operations in January 1972 as an interim sea control ship; she
reverted to the amphibious role in 1974 but kept 12 AV-8As on
board. All are being replaced by the Wasp class. The first two
paid off in 1992 and 1993 respectively.
Modernisation: Plans to convert *Inchon* to a Mine Countermeasures Command, Control and Support Ship (MCS) are
expected to be put in hand in mid-1994. The crew will increase
to 1420 (113 officers) including an embarked staff. The main
guns and SPS 65 radar are to be removed, and close range
armament upgraded to include 25 mm guns. Up to 8 MCMV
will be able to tie up alongside. Hangar space will be provided
for 8 MH-53E Sea Stallion helicopters. Workshop spaces will
be much improved and new cranes fitted on the upper deck.
Structure: Two deck-edge lifts, one to port opposite the bridge
and one to starboard aft of island. Full hangars are provided; no
arresting wires or catapults. Two small elevators carry cargo
from holds to flight deck. Stowage of 4300 sq ft for vehicles
and 37 400 cu ft for palletted stores. Fitted with extensive
medical facilities including operating room, X-ray room, hospital ward, isolation ward, laboratory, pharmacy, dental operating room, and medical store rooms.
Operational: The flight decks provide for simultaneous take off or
landing of seven CH-46 Sea Knight or four CH-53 Sea Stallion
helicopters during normal operations. Can operate AV-8Bs following modifications to refine day/night capability. Each LPH
can carry a Marine battalion landing team, its guns, vehicles,
and equipment, plus a reinforced squadron of transport helicopters and various support personnel. All have been used on
many occasions as platforms for airborne minesweeping oper-

IWO JIMA   *(Scale 1 : 1500), Ian Sturton*

TRIPOLI   *10/1991, Giorgio Arra*

ations. *Tripoli* was damaged by a mine in the Gulf in 1991 but
was operational again within a few weeks. She was the principal support ship for the Somalian operation in December 1992.

Inchon is planned to be converted to a mine warfare command
and support ship by 1996 and is to be based at Ingleside,
Texas. *Guadalcanal* is to pay off in September 1994.

TRIPOLI   *10/1993, Giorgio Arra*

11 AUSTIN CLASS: AMPHIBIOUS TRANSPORT DOCKS (LPD)

Name	No	Builders	Laid down	Launched	Commissioned	F/S
AUSTIN	LPD 4	New York Naval Shipyard	4 Feb 1963	27 June 1964	6 Feb 1965	AA
OGDEN	LPD 5	New York Naval Shipyard	4 Feb 1963	27 June 1964	19 June 1965	PA
DULUTH	LPD 6	New York Naval Shipyard	18 Dec 1963	14 Aug 1965	18 Dec 1965	PA
CLEVELAND	LPD 7	Ingalls Shipbuilding	30 Nov 1964	7 May 1966	21 Apr 1967	PA
DUBUQUE	LPD 8	Ingalls Shipbuilding	25 Jan 1965	6 Aug 1966	1 Sep 1967	PA
DENVER	LPD 9	Lockheed SB & Construction Co	7 Feb 1964	23 Jan 1965	26 Oct 1968	PA
JUNEAU	LPD 10	Lockheed SB & Construction Co	23 Jan 1965	12 Feb 1966	12 July 1969	PA
SHREVEPORT	LPD 12	Lockheed SB & Construction Co	27 Dec 1965	25 Oct 1966	12 Dec 1970	AA
NASHVILLE	LPD 13	Lockheed SB & Construction Co	14 Mar 1966	7 Oct 1967	14 Feb 1970	AA
TRENTON	LPD 14	Lockheed SB & Construction Co	8 Aug 1966	3 Aug 1968	6 Mar 1971	AA
PONCE	LPD 15	Lockheed SB & Construction Co	31 Oct 1966	20 May 1970	10 July 1971	AA

Displacement, tons: 9130 light; 16 500-17 244 full load
Dimensions, feet (metres): 570 × 100 (84 hull) × 23 *(173.8 × 30.5 (25.6) × 7)*
Main machinery: 2 Foster-Wheeler boilers (Babcock & Wilcox in LPD 5 and 12); 600 psi *(42.3 kg/cm sq)*; 870°F *(467°C)*; 2 De Laval turbines; 24 000 hp *(18 MW)*; 2 shafts
Speed, knots: 21. **Range, miles:** 7700 at 20 kts.
Complement: 420 (24 officers); Flag 90 (in LPD 7-13)
Military lift: 930 troops (840 only in LPD 7-13); 9 LCM 6s or 4 LCM 8s or 2 LCAC or 20 LVTs. 4 LCPL/LCVP

Guns: 2 or 4 USN 3 in *(76 mm)*/50 (1 or 2 twin) Mk 33 ❶; 85° elevation; 50 rounds/minute to 12.8 km *(7 nm)*; weight of shell 6 kg. Local control only. Not carried in most of the class.
2 General Electric/General Dynamics 20 mm/76 6-barrelled Vulcan Phalanx Mk 15 ❷; 3000 rounds/minute (4500 in Block 1) combined to 1.5 km. Being fitted in FY 1988-93 during maintenance periods.
Countermeasures: Decoys: 4 Loral Hycor SRBOC 6-barrelled Mk 36; IR flares and chaff to 4 km *(2.2 nm)*.
ESM: SLQ 32(V)1; intercept. May be updated to (V)2.
Combat data systems: SATCOM SRR-1, WSC-3 (UHF).
Radars: Air search: Lockheed SPS 40B/C ❸; E/F band; range 320 km *(175 nm)*.
Surface search: Raytheon SPS 10F or Norden SPS 67 ❹; G band.
Navigation: Marconi LN 66; I band.
Tacan: URN 25. IFF: Mk XII UPX-29.

Helicopters: Up to 6 CH-46D/E Sea Knight can be carried. Hangar for only 1 light (not in LPD 4).

Programmes: LPD 4-6 were authorised in the FY 1962 new construction programme, LPD 7-10 in FY 1963, LPD 12 and 13 in FY 1964, LPD 14 and LPD 15 in FY 1965. LPD 16 was cancelled.
Modernisation: Planned SLEPs cancelled. Modernisation being carried out in normal maintenance periods from FY 1987. This includes fitting two Phalanx, SPS 67 radar replacing SPS 10 and updating EW capability. Most of the 3 in guns have been removed.
Structure: Enlarged versions of the earlier Raleigh class (now paid off). LPD 7-13 have an additional bridge and are fitted as flagships. One small telescopic hangar. There are structural variations in the positions of guns and electronic equipment in different ships of the class. Flight deck is 168 ft *(51.2 m)* in length. Well deck 394 × 50 ft *(120.1 × 15.2 m)*. This design is the model for the LX class to start building in the mid-1990s.
Operational: A typical operational load might include one Seahawk, two Sea Knight, two Twin Huey, four Sea Cobra helicopters and one patrol boat armed with two 20 mm guns. Eight of the class were involved in the war with Iraq in 1991. Pioneer UAV trials in LPD 9 in 1993/94.

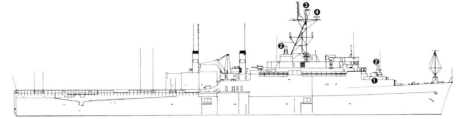

NASHVILLE

(Scale 1 : 1500), Ian Sturton

TRENTON

10/1993, A Sheldon Duplaix

DENVER

4/1993, Hachiro Nakai

8 WHIDBEY ISLAND and 0 + 4 HARPERS FERRY CLASSES: DOCK LANDING SHIPS (LSD and LSD-CV)

Name	No	Builders	Laid down	Launched	Commissioned	F/S
WHIDBEY ISLAND	LSD 41	Lockheed SB & Construction Co	4 Aug 1981	10 June 1983	9 Feb 1985	AA
GERMANTOWN	LSD 42	Lockheed SB & Construction Co	5 Aug 1982	29 June 1984	8 Feb 1986	PA
FORT McHENRY	LSD 43	Lockheed SB & Construction Co	10 June 1983	1 Feb 1986	8 Aug 1987	PA
GUNSTON HALL	LSD 44	Avondale Industries	26 May 1986	27 June 1987	22 Apr 1989	AA
COMSTOCK	LSD 45	Avondale Industries	27 Oct 1986	16 Jan 1988	3 Feb 1990	PA
TORTUGA	LSD 46	Avondale Industries	23 Mar 1987	15 Sep 1988	17 Nov 1990	AA
RUSHMORE	LSD 47	Avondale Industries	9 Nov 1987	6 May 1989	1 June 1991	PA
ASHLAND	LSD 48	Avondale Industries	4 Apr 1988	11 Nov 1989	9 May 1992	AA
HARPERS FERRY	LSD 49	Avondale Industries	15 Apr 1991	16 Jan 1993	Nov 1994	Bldg
CARTER HALL	LSD 50	Avondale Industries	11 Nov 1991	2 Oct 1993	July 1995	Bldg
OAK HILL	LSD 51	Avondale Industries	21 Sep 1992	26 Mar 1994	Mar 1996	Bldg
PEARL HARBOR	LSD 52	Avondale Industries	Dec 1994	July 1996	May 1998	Bldg

Displacement, tons: 11 125 light; 15 726 (LSD 41-48), 16 740 (LSD 49 onwards) full load
Dimensions, feet (metres): 609 × 84 × 20.5
 (185.6 × 25.6 × 6.3)
Main machinery: 4 Colt SEMT-Pielstick 16 PC2.5 V 400 diesels; 37 440 hp(m) *(27.5 MW)* sustained; 2 shafts; cp props
Speed, knots: 22. **Range, miles:** 8000 at 18 kts
Complement: 340 (21 officers)
Military lift: 450 troops; 2 (CV) or 4 LCACs (Amphibious Air Cushion Vehicles), or 9 (CV) or 21 LCM 6, or 1 (CV) or 3 LCUs, or 64 LVTs. 2 LCPL
Cargo capacity: 5000 cu ft for marine cargo, 12 500 sq ft for vehicles (including four preloaded LCACs in the well deck). The 'cargo version' has 67 600 cu ft for marine cargo, 20 200 sq ft for vehicles but only two LCACs. Aviation fuel, 90 tons.

Missiles: 1 GDC RAM; passive IR/anti-radiation homing to 9.6 km *(5.2 nm)* at 2 Mach; warhead 9.1 kg. Fitted in LSD 41 for SSDS trials.
Guns: 2 General Electric/General Dynamics 20 mm/76 6-barrelled Vulcan Phalanx Mk 15 ❶; 3000 rounds/minute (4500 in Block 1) combined to 1.5 km.
 2 Mk 68 Mod 1 20 mm. 8—12.7 mm MGs. 2 Mk 88 25 mm Bushmaster (LSD 47 and 48 vice the 20 mm guns).
Countermeasures: Decoys: 4 Loral Hycor SRBOC 6-barrelled Mk 36; IR flares and chaff to 4 km *(2.2 nm)*.
ESM: SLQ 32(V)1; intercept. May be updated to (V)2.
Combat data systems: SATCOM SRR-1, WSC-3 (UHF). SSDS (in LSD 41) (see *Modernisation*).
Fire control: SAR-81R optronic director (in LSD 41).
Radars: Air search: Raytheon SPS 49V ❷; C/D band.
Surface search: Norden SPS 67V ❸; G band.
Navigation: Raytheon SPS 64(V)9; I/J band.
Tacan: URN 25. IFF: Mk XII UPX-29.

Helicopters: Platform only for 2 CH-53 series Stallion.

Programmes: Originally it was planned to construct six ships of this class as replacements for the Thomaston class LSDs. Eventually, the level of Whidbey Island class ships was established at eight, with five additional cargo-carrying variants of that class to be built to provide increased cargo-carrying capability. The first cargo variant, LSD 49, was authorised and funded in the FY 1988 budget; LSD 50 in FY 1989 and LSD 51

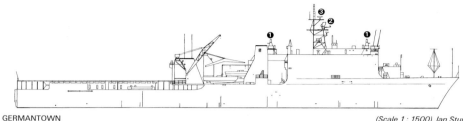

GERMANTOWN   *(Scale 1 : 1500), Ian Sturton*

COMSTOCK   *4/1993, Hachiro Nakai*

in FY 1991. The fourth was authorised in FY 1992 but not ordered until 12 October 1993.
Modernisation: The SSDS (ship self-defence system) was fitted in LSD 41 for trials starting in 1993. The system integrates and controls SPS 49, SLQ-32, SLQ-49, DLS Mks 36 and 50, Sea Gnat and a number of other systems including CIWS. Four SSDS alternatives are being defined based on the extent of overall integration. The aim is to improve response times to anti-ship missiles. Trials continue into 1995. The aim is to improve response times to anti-ship cruise missiles in non-Aegis ships.

Structure: Based on the earlier Anchorage class. One 60 and one 20 ton crane. Well deck measures 440 × 50 ft *(134.1 × 15.2 m)* in the LSD but is shorter in the Cargo Variant (CV). The cargo version is a minimum modification to the LSD 41 design. Changes in that design include additional air-conditioning, piping and hull structure; the forward Phalanx is lower down and there is only one crane. There is approximately 90% commonality between the two ships.
Operational: LSD 42 is based at Sasebo.

5 ANCHORAGE CLASS: DOCK LANDING SHIPS (LSD)

Name	No	Builders	Laid down	Launched	Commissioned	F/S
ANCHORAGE	LSD 36	Ingalls Shipbuilding	13 Mar 1967	5 May 1968	15 Mar 1969	PA
PORTLAND	LSD 37	General Dynamics, Quincy	21 Sep 1967	20 Dec 1969	3 Oct 1970	AA
PENSACOLA	LSD 38	General Dynamics, Quincy	12 Mar 1969	11 July 1970	27 Mar 1971	AA
MOUNT VERNON	LSD 39	General Dynamics, Quincy	29 Jan 1970	17 Apr 1971	13 May 1972	PA
FORT FISHER	LSD 40	General Dynamics, Quincy	15 July 1970	22 Apr 1972	9 Dec 1972	PA

Displacement, tons: 8600 light; 13 700 full load
Dimensions, feet (metres): 553.3 × 84 × 20
 (168.6 × 25.6 × 6)
Main machinery: 2 Foster-Wheeler boilers (Combustion Engineering in LSD 36); 600 psi *(42.3 kg/cm sq)*; 870°F *(467°C)*; 2 De Laval turbines; 24 000 hp *(18 MW)*; 2 shafts
Speed, knots: 22. **Range, miles:** 14 800 at 12 kts
Complement: 374 (24 officers)
Military lift: 366 troops (18 officers); 3 LCUs or 3 LCACs or 18 LCM 6 or 9 LCM 8 or 50 LVTs; 1 LCM 6 on deck; 2 LCPLs and 1 LCVP on davits. Aviation fuel, 90 tons

ANCHORAGE   *(Scale 1 : 1500), Ian Sturton*

Guns: 2 or 4 USN 3 in *(76 mm)*/50 (2 twin) Mk 33 ❶; 85° elevation; 50 rounds/minute to 12.8 km *(7 nm)*; weight of shell 6 kg. Local control only. Most are not fitted.
 2 General Electric/General Dynamics 20 mm/76 6-barrelled Vulcan Phalanx Mk 15 ❷; 3000 rounds/minute combined to 1.5 km.
Countermeasures: Decoys: 4 Loral Hycor SRBOC 6-barrelled Mk 36; IR flares and chaff to 4 km *(2.2 nm)*.
ESM: SLQ 32(V)1; intercept. May be updated to (V)2.
Combat data systems: SATCOM SRR-1, WSC-3 (UHF).
Radars: Air search: Lockheed SPS 40 ❸; E/F band; range 320 km *(175 nm)*.
Surface search: Raytheon SPS 10 ❹; G band.
Navigation: Marconi LN 66; I band.

Helicopters: Platform only.

Structure: Helicopter platform aft with docking well partially open; helicopter platform can be removed. Docking well approximately 430 × 50 ft *(131.1 × 15.2 m)*. Two 50 ton capacity cranes. 3 in guns are being removed.
Operational: Four of the class were involved in the war with Iraq in 1991.

FORT FISHER   *10/1993, Giorgio Arra*

7 NEWPORT CLASS: TANK LANDING SHIPS (LST)

Name	No	Builders	Laid down	Launched	Commissioned	F/S
FREDERICK	LST 1184	National Steel & Shipbuilding Co	13 Apr 1968	8 Mar 1969	11 Apr 1970	PA
CAYUGA	LST 1186	National Steel & Shipbuilding Co	28 Sep 1968	12 July 1969	8 Aug 1970	PA
SAN BERNARDINO	LST 1189	National Steel & Shipbuilding Co	12 July 1969	28 Mar 1970	27 Mar 1971	PA
LA MOURE COUNTY	LST 1194	National Steel & Shipbuilding Co	22 May 1970	13 Feb 1971	18 Dec 1971	AA
HARLAN COUNTY	LST 1196	National Steel & Shipbuilding Co	7 Nov 1970	24 July 1971	8 Apr 1972	AA
BARNSTABLE COUNTY	LST 1197	National Steel & Shipbuilding Co	19 Dec 1970	2 Oct 1971	27 May 1972	AA
BRISTOL COUNTY	LST 1198	National Steel & Shipbuilding Co	13 Feb 1971	4 Dec 1971	5 Aug 1972	PA

Displacement, tons: 4975 light; 8450 full load
Dimensions, feet (metres): 522.3 (hull) × 69.5 × 17.5 (aft)
(159.2 × 21.2 × 5.3)
Main machinery: 6 ALCO 16-251 diesels; 16 500 hp (12.3 MW)
sustained; 2 shafts; cp props; bow thruster
Speed, knots: 20. **Range, miles:** 2500 at 14 kts
Complement: 257 (13 officers)
Military lift: 400 troops (20 officers); 500 tons vehicles; 3 LCVPs
and 1 LCPL on davits

Guns: 4 USN 3 in (76 mm)/50 (2 twin) Mk 33; 85° elevation; 50
rounds/minute to 12.8 km (7 nm); weight of shell 6 kg. Local
control only. Not all are fitted.
1 General Electric/General Dynamics 20 mm Vulcan Phalanx
Mk 15.
Combat data systems: SATCOM SRR-1, WSC-3 (UHF).
Radars: Surface search: Raytheon SPS 67; G band.
Navigation: Marconi LN 66 or Raytheon CRP 3100 Pathfinder
(LST 1194); I/J band.

Helicopters: Platform only.

Modernisation: Phalanx CIWS is fitted on the bridge roof.
Structure: The hull form required to achieve 20 kts would not
permit bow doors, thus these ships unload by a 112 ft ramp
over their bow. The ramp is supported by twin derrick arms. A
ramp just forward of the superstructure connects the lower
tank deck with the main deck and a vehicle passage through
the superstructure provides access to the parking area amidships. A stern gate to the tank deck permits unloading of
amphibious tractors into the water, or unloading of other
vehicles into an LCU or on to a pier. Vehicle stowage covers
19 000 sq ft. Length over derrick arms is 562 ft (171.3 m); full
load draught is 11.5 ft forward and 17.5 ft aft. Bow thruster fitted to hold position offshore while unloading amphibious tractors. The 3 in guns are being removed.
Operational: They operate with 20 knot amphibious squadrons
to transport tanks, other heavy vehicles, engineering equipment, and supplies which cannot be readily landed by helicopters or landing craft. ESM equipment fitted in some. Fourteen
of the class were involved in the war with Iraq in 1991. Of these
last seven at least three are scheduled to pay off by September
1994.
Sales: Two may be leased to Australia and two to Spain in
mid-1994. Other countries are also interested.

HARLAN COUNTY   4/1993, Giorgio Arra

HARLAN COUNTY (with Mexeflotes)   2/1992, F Sadek

5 + 1 FRANK S BESSON CLASS: LOGISTIC SUPPORT VESSELS (LSV-ARMY)

Name	No	Builders	Completed
GENERAL FRANK S BESSON JR	LSV 1	Moss Point Marine, MS	18 Dec 1987
CW 3 HAROLD C CLINGER	LSV 2	Moss Point Marine, MS	20 Feb 1988
GENERAL BREHON B SOMERVELL	LSV 3	Moss Point Marine, MS	2 Apr 1988
LT GENERAL WILLIAM B BUNKER	LSV 4	Moss Point Marine, MS	18 May 1988
MAJOR GENERAL CHARLES P GROSS	LSV 5	Moss Point Marine, MS	30 Apr 1991
—	LSV 6	Moss Point Marine, MS	Dec 1994

Displacement, tons: 4265 full load
Dimensions, feet (metres): 272.8 × 60 × 12 (83.1 × 18.3 × 3.7)
Main machinery: 2 GM EMD 16-645E2 diesels; 3900 hp (2.9 MW) sustained; 2 shafts
Speed, knots: 11.6. **Range, miles:** 6000 at 11 kts
Complement: 30 (6 officers)
Military lift: 2280 tons of vehicles, containers or general cargo

Comment: Army owned Ro-ro design with 10 500 sq ft of deck space for cargo. Capable of beaching with 4 ft over the ramp on a 1:30 offshore gradient with a payload of 900 tons of cargo. Two
modified ships of the class built for the Philippines Navy in 1993/94.

35 LCU 2001 CLASS: UTILITY LANDING CRAFT (LCU-ARMY)

LCU 2001-2035

Displacement, tons: 1102 full load
Dimensions, feet (metres): 173.8 × 42 × 8.5 (53 × 12.8 × 2.6)
Main machinery: 2 Cummins KTA50-M diesels; 2500 hp (1.87 MW) sustained; 2 shafts; bow
thruster
Speed, knots: 11.5. **Range, miles:** 4500 at 11.5 kts
Complement: 13 (2 officers)
Military lift: 350 tons
Radars: Navigation: Two Raytheon SPS 64; I band.

Comment: Order placed with Lockheed by US Army 11 June 1986 for 25 craft with an option on
15 more but only 35 were built. First one completed 21 February 1990 by Moss Point Marine.
The 2001 series have names, some of which duplicate naval ships. These are the first LCUs to
have been built to an Army specification.

GENERAL FRANK S BESSON   1988, Giorgio Arra

LCU 2006   7/1990, Giorgio Arra

72 + 19 LANDING CRAFT AIR-CUSHION (LCAC)

Displacement, tons: 87.2 light; 170-182 full load
Dimensions, feet (metres): 88 oa (on cushion) (81 between hard structures) × 47 beam (on cushion) (43 beam hard structure) × 2.9 draught (off cushion) *(26.8 (24.7) × 14.3 (13.1) × 0.9)*
Main machinery: 4 Avco-Lycoming TF-40B gas-turbines; 2 for propulsion and 2 for lift; 16 000 hp *(12 MW)* sustained; 2 shrouded reversible pitch airscrews (propulsion); 4 double entry fans, centrifugal or mixed flow (lift)
Speed, knots: 40 (loaded). **Range, miles:** 300 at 35 kts; 200 at 40 kts
Complement: 5
Military lift: 24 troops; 1 MBT or 60-75 tons

Guns: 2—12.7 mm MGs.
Radars: Navigation: Marconi LN 66; I band.

Programmes: Being built by Textron Marine Systems and Avondale Gulfport, the latter yard having been purchased from Lockheed Shipbuilding. 33 funded FY 1982-86, 15 in FY 1989, 12 in each of FY 1990 and 1991. In FY 1992 Congress authorised 12 but then provided funds for 24 although only the 12 authorised are to be built. Subsequently seven more were included in FY 1993 for a total of 91. The last one should complete in early 1997.
Structure: Incorporates the best attributes of the JEFF(A) and JEFF(B) learned from over five years of testing the two prototypes. Bow ramp 28.8 ft, stern ramp 15 ft. Cargo space capacity is 1809 sq ft. Noise and dust levels are high and if disabled the craft is not easy to tow. Spray suppressors have been added to the skirt to reduce interference with the driver's vision.
Operational: Ship classes capable of carrying the LCAC are Wasp (three), Tarawa (one), Anchorage (four), Austin (two), Whidbey (four) and Modified Whidbey (two). MCMV role is being evaluated as a secondary priority using unmanned craft. According to the USMC the craft can cross 70 per cent of the world's coastlines compared to about 15 per cent for conventional landing craft. Some limitations in very rough seas. Shore bases on each coast at Little Creek, Virginia and Camp Pendleton, California. Some were used in the Gulf in 1991 to recapture an Iraq-held island which belonged to Kuwait. They were also used for relief operations in Bangladesh, and in landing Marines in Somalia in December 1992. Performance and reliability have exceeded expectations.

LCAC 34   *9/1992, Stefan Terzibaschitsch*

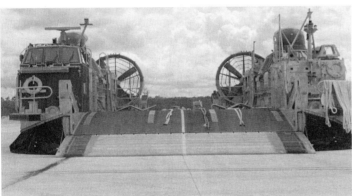

LCAC 38   *9/1992, Stefan Terzibaschitsch*

55 LCU 1600 CLASS: UTILITY LANDING CRAFT
(LCU-ARMY (15) and NAVY (40))

Displacement, tons: 200 light; 375 (437, LCU 1680-81) full load
Dimensions, feet (metres): 134.9 × 29 × 6.1 *(41.1 × 8.8 × 1.9)*
Main machinery: 4 Detroit 6-71 diesels; 696 hp *(519 kW)* sustained; 2 shafts; Kort nozzles
2 Detroit 12V-71 diesels (LCU 1621, 1680-1681); 680 hp *(508 kW)* sustained; 2 shafts; Kort nozzles
Speed, knots: 11. **Range, miles:** 1200 at 8 kts
Complement: 14 (2 officers)
Military lift: 170 tons; 3 M103 (64 tons) or M48 (48 tons) tanks or 350 troops
Guns: 2—12.7 mm MGs.
Radars: Navigation: LN 66 or SPS-53; I band.

Comment: Improved steel hulled landing craft, larger than previous series. Versatile craft used for a variety of tasks. Pennant numbers are in the 1600 series. Most were built between the mid-1960s and mid-1980s. There are no plans for more of this type. At least three converted as ASDV 1-3, 1 and 3 based in San Diego and 2 in Little Creek. LCU 1641 carries a chute over a cutaway stern and is used as a mine recovery tender at Charleston, South Carolina.

LCU 1663   *4/1993, Giorgio Arra*

102 MECHANISED LANDING CRAFT: LCM 8 TYPE

Displacement, tons: 105 full load (aluminium)
Dimensions, feet (metres): 73.7 × 21 × 5.2 *(22.5 × 6.4 × 1.6)*
Main machinery: 2 Detroit 6-71 diesels; 348 hp *(260 kW)* sustained or 2 Detroit 12V-71 diesels; 680 hp *(508 kW)* sustained; 2 shafts
Speed, knots: 12. **Range, miles:** 190 at 9 kts full load
Complement: 5
Military lift: 180 tons or 1 M48 or 1 M60 tank or 200 troops

Comment: Naval craft are Mk 7 all-aluminium new construction types for use in amphibious ships. The last 12 were built in 1993/94. 125 similar craft are used by the Army including some older welded steel types which can only lift 60 tons.

LCM 8   *9/1991, Giorgio Arra*

72 MECHANISED LANDING CRAFT: LCM 6 TYPE

Displacement, tons: 64 full load
Dimensions, feet (metres): 56.2 × 14 × 3.9 *(17.1 × 4.3 × 1.2)*
Main machinery: 2 Detroit 6-71 diesels; 348 hp *(260 kW)* sustained or 2 Detroit 8V-71 diesels; 460 hp *(344 kW)* sustained; 2 shafts
Speed, knots: 9. **Range, miles:** 130 at 9 kts
Complement: 5
Military lift: 34 tons or 80 troops

Comment: Welded-steel construction. Used for various utility tasks.

LCM 6   *9/1986, Giorgio Arra*

167 LANDING CRAFT PERSONNEL (LCPL)

Displacement, tons: 11 full load
Dimensions, feet (metres): 36 × 12.1 × 3.8 *(11 × 3.7 × 1.2)*
Main machinery: 1 GM 8V-71TI diesel; 425 hp *(317 kW)* sustained; 1 shaft
Speed, knots: 20. **Range, miles:** 150 at 20 kts
Complement: 3
Military lift: 17 troops

Comment: There are 12 Mk 11, 140 Mk 12 and 15 Mk 13. Details given are for eight Mk 13 of GRP construction, ordered from Bollinger Shipyard in FY 1989 and delivered in 1991, and seven from Peterson Builders ordered in October 1992 and delivered in 1993/94. Some have navigation radar. For use as control craft and carried aboard LHA, LPD, LSD and LST classes.

LCPL   *4/1991, Bollinger*

PATROL FORCES

Notes: (1) There are large numbers of RIBs in service.
(2) The six Pegasus class hydrofoils (PHM) were all placed in reserve in 1993 as being too expensive to operate.

6 + 7 CYCLONE CLASS (COASTAL PATROL CRAFT) (PC)

Name	No	Builders	Commissioned
CYCLONE	PC 1	Bollinger, Lockport	7 Aug 1993
TEMPEST	PC 2	Bollinger, Lockport	21 Aug 1993
HURRICANE	PC 3	Bollinger, Lockport	15 Oct 1993
MONSOON	PC 4	Bollinger, Lockport	22 Jan 1994
TYPHOON	PC 5	Bollinger, Lockport	12 Feb 1994
SIROCCO	PC 6	Bollinger, Lockport	11 June 1994
SQUALL	PC 7	Bollinger, Lockport	Aug 1994
ZEPHYR	PC 8	Bollinger, Lockport	Oct 1994
CHINOOK	PC 9	Bollinger, Lockport	Dec 1994
FIREBOLT	PC 10	Bollinger, Lockport	Mar 1995
WHIRLWIND	PC 11	Bollinger, Lockport	May 1995
THUNDERBOLT	PC 12	Bollinger, Lockport	June 1995
SHAMAR	PC 13	Bollinger, Lockport	Aug 1995

Displacement, tons: 328 full load
Dimensions, feet (metres): 170.6 × 24.9 × 7.2 *(52 × 7.6 × 2.2)*
Main machinery: 4 Paxman Valenta 16RP200CM diesels; 13 400 hp *(10 MW)* sustained; 4 shafts
Speed, knots: 35. **Range, miles:** 2500 at 12 kts
Complement: 28 (4 officers) plus 8 Marines or SEALs
Missiles: SAM: 1 sextuple Stinger mounting.
Guns: 2—25 mm Mk 38. 2—12.7 mm MGs. 2—7.62 mm MGs. 2—40 mm Mk 19 grenade launchers (MGs and grenade launchers are interchangeable).
Countermeasures: Decoys: 2 Mk 52 sextuple chaff launchers.
ESM: APR-39; radar warning.
Fire control: Marconi VISTAR IM 405 IR system.
Radars: Surface search: Sperry RASCAR; I band.
Navigation: Raytheon SPS 64(V)9; I band.
Sonars: Wesmar; hull-mounted; active; high frequency.

Comment: Contract awarded for eight in August 1990 and five more in July 1991. Building at Bollinger Shipyard, Louisiana. The design is based on the Vosper Thornycroft Ramadan class modified to meet US Navy requirements. Shoulder-launched Stinger SAM may be carried. The craft have a slow speed loiter capability. The plan is to operate them in pairs with a 12 man maintenance team in two trucks ashore. Based at Norfolk, VA and San Diego, CA. A stabilised weapons platform system is being developed for Stinger or Hellfire. Two SEAL raiding craft and one RIB are carried. Swimmers can be 'launched' from a platform at the stern.

CYCLONE   *7/1993, Giorgio Arra*

1 SEA STALKER Mk V SOC

Displacement, tons: 50 full load
Dimensions, feet (metres): 74.3 × 18 × 5.6 *(22.6 × 5.5 × 1.7)*
Main machinery: 2 MTU 16V 396 TE94 diesels; 7000 hp(m) *(5.15 MW)*; 2 shafts
1 Sabre diesel; 350 hp *(261 kW)*; 1 Hamilton waterjet
Speed, knots: 53. **Range, miles:** 500 at 47 kts
Complement: 8

Comment: Ordered in August 1993 for delivery and trials in 1994. Built by Peterson, Sturgeon Bay and based on the Cougar Marine Cat 2100 already in service with the Spanish Customs. The waterjet provides loiter propulsion. The hull is an asymmetrical catamaran. MGs and a radar are part of the equipment. The craft is designed for transport by road or by C5 aircraft.

SEA STALKER   *2/1994, Peterson Builders*

2 XFPB Mk V SOC

Displacement, tons: 52 full load
Dimensions, feet (metres): 82 × 18 × 4.3 *(25 × 5.5 × 1.3)*
Main machinery: 3 MTU 8V 396 or Detroit diesels; 13 500 hp(m) *(9.92 MW)*; 3 waterjets or 3 shafts
Speed, knots: 50
Complement: 9

Comment: Ordered in August 1993 for delivery and trials in 1994. Built by Halter Marine to the Italian XFPB design delivered to the Mexican Navy as the Isla Coronado class. One has a Kevlar composite hull with Detroit diesels and propellers, the other has an aluminium hull with MTU engines and waterjet propulsors. Both are road or air transportable.

XFPB (Mexican colours)   *1993, Mexican Navy*

14 PATROL BOATS—Mk III (11) and Mk IV (3) Series (PB)

Displacement, tons: 31.5 light; 41.25 full load
Dimensions, feet (metres): 65 × 18 × 5.9 *(19.8 × 5.5 × 1.8)*
Main machinery: 3 Detroit 8V-71 diesels; 690 hp *(515 kW)* sustained (Mk III); 3 Detroit 8V-92; 909 hp *(670 kW)* sustained (Mk IV); 3 shafts
Speed, knots: 28. **Range, miles:** 450 at 26 kts
Complement: 9 (1 officer)
Guns: 2—25 mm Mk 38. 2—12.7 mm MGs. 1—81 mm mortar. 1—40 mm Mk 19 grenade launcher.

Comment: The PB series was developed as replacements for the Swift type inshore patrol craft (PCF). Mk III built by Peterson, Wisconsin in the mid-1970s and Mk IV by Atlantic Marine, Florida in 1985-86. The Mk III design has the pilot house offset to starboard to provide space on port side for installation of additional weapons. Armaments can vary with combinations of guns, MGs and mortars. Used by the Special Boat Units. Active in the Gulf, one of them being involved with the capture of the *Iran Ajr* minelayer on 22 September 1987. Two delivered to Columbia in 1990. The three Mk IV are extended by 3 ft in length, based in Panama and may be transferred.

PB Mk III   *4/1991, Giorgio Arra*

30 RIVER PATROL BOATS Mk II Series (PBR)

Displacement, tons: 8.9 full load
Dimensions, feet (metres): 32 × 11 × 2.6 *(9.8 × 3.4 × 0.8)*
Main machinery: 2 GM 6V-53 diesels; 296 hp *(221 kW)*; 2 Jacuzzi waterjets
Speed, knots: 24. **Range, miles:** 150 at 22 kts
Complement: 4 or 5
Guns: 3—12.7 mm MGs (twin mount fwd, single aft). 1—40 mm Mk 19 grenade launcher. 1—60 mm mortar (in some boats).
Radars: Navigation: Raytheon 1900; I band.

Comment: Fibreglass hull river patrol boats. Approximately 500 built 1967-73; most transferred to South Vietnam and some to Thailand. Used for Reserve training.

PBR Mk II   *10/1993, Giorgio Arra*

0 + 10 (15) COASTAL PATROL CRAFT

Comment: 42 ft craft ordered from Peterson Builders in 1993. Aluminium hulls with twin MTU diesels and waterjet propulsion. Each has a 12.7 mm MG aft and a search radar. When completed these craft are to be distributed through the FMS system.

7 STINGER CLASS (RIVER PATROL BOATS)

Displacement, tons: 7.4 full load
Dimensions, feet (metres): 35 × 9.3 × 2.2 *(10.6 × 2.8 × 0.6)*
Main machinery: 2 Cummins 6BTA5.9-M2 diesels; 600 hp *(448 kW)* maximum; 2 Hamilton waterjets
Speed, knots: 38. **Range, miles:** 250 at 26 kts
Complement: 4
Military lift: 10 troops
Guns: 2 or 4—12.7 mm MGs (2 single or 2 twin) or 2—40 mm Mk 19 grenade launchers; 2—7.62 mm MGs.
Radars: Navigation: Raytheon 1900; I band.

Comment: Riverine assault craft ordered for the Marines from SeaArk Marine 5 May 1990 and delivered less than three months later on 1 August 1990. Aluminium hulls which can be transported by road each on its own trailer. Being evaluated in transport, fire support and reconnaissance roles.

MINI ATC   *1987, Giorgio Arra*

STINGER   *7/1990, SeaArk*

22 MINI ARMOURED TROOP CARRIERS (ATC)

Displacement, tons: 14.8 full load
Dimensions, feet (metres): 36 × 12.7 × 3.5 *(11 × 3.9 × 1.1)*
Main machinery: 2 GM 8V-53 diesels; 566 hp *(422 kW)*; 2 Jacuzzi 14YS waterjets
Speed, knots: 28. **Range, miles:** 37 at 28 kts
Complement: 2
Military lift: 20 troops
Guns: 4—12.7 mm MGs. 1—40 mm Mk 19 grenade launcher.

Comment: Built by Sewart, Louisiana 1972-73. A small troop carrier for riverine and SEAL operations; aluminium hull; ceramic armour. Draught 1 ft when under way at high speed. Used by Special Boat Forces of the NRF.

85 PORT SECURITY CRAFT

Displacement, tons: 3.9 full load
Dimensions, feet (metres): 24 × 8 × 3.3 *(7.3 × 2.4 × 1)*
Main machinery: 1 Volvo Penta AQAD41A diesel; 200 hp(m) *(149 kW)* maximum; Type 290 outdrive
Speed, knots: 22
Complement: 2
Guns: 1—7.62 mm MG.

Comment: Built by Peterson, Wisconsin and delivered between 29 February 1988 and 12 May 1989 in batches of 50, 25 and 10. Used for protecting naval installations, ports, harbours and anchorages. In addition there are large numbers of other small craft used in similar roles.

PORT SECURITY CRAFT   *1/1988, Peterson*

MINE WARFARE FORCES

Notes: (1) The use of LCACs for MCM duties is being evaluated. (2) There are no surface minelayers. Mining is done by carrier-based aircraft, land-based patrol aircraft and submarines. US Air Force B-52s also have a minelaying capability.
(3) NRF ships are manned by composite active/reserve crews. Some of the Osprey class are to be allocated in due course.

(4) Two SAM unmanned sweepers (*Gerry* (SAM 03) and *Peggy* (SAM 05)) were acquired from Sweden in February 1991 and are still being evaluated. Details under Swedish Landsort class.
(5) MH-53E Sea Stallion helicopters are deployed in amphibious assault ships for mine countermeasures operations.

(6) The LPH *Inchon* is to be converted as a Command and Support Ship by 1996 (see Iwo Jima class).

13 + 1 AVENGER CLASS: MINE COUNTERMEASURES VESSELS (MCM)

Name	No	Builders	Laid down	Launched	Commissioned	F/S
AVENGER	MCM 1	Peterson Builders Inc	3 June 1983	15 June 1985	12 Sep 1987	AA
DEFENDER	MCM 2	Marinette Marine Corp	1 Dec 1983	4 Apr 1987	30 Sep 1989	AA
SENTRY	MCM 3	Peterson Builders Inc	8 Oct 1984	20 Sep 1986	2 Sep 1989	AA
CHAMPION	MCM 4	Marinette Marine Corp	28 June 1984	15 Apr 1989	31 Jan 1991	AA
GUARDIAN	MCM 5	Peterson Builders Inc	8 May 1985	20 June 1987	16 Dec 1989	AA
DEVASTATOR	MCM 6	Peterson Builders Inc	9 Feb 1987	11 June 1988	6 Oct 1990	AA
PATRIOT	MCM 7	Marinette Marine Corp	31 Mar 1987	15 May 1990	18 Oct 1991	AA
SCOUT	MCM 8	Peterson Builders Inc	8 June 1987	20 May 1989	15 Dec 1990	AA
PIONEER	MCM 9	Peterson Builders Inc	5 June 1989	25 Aug 1990	7 Dec 1992	AA
WARRIOR	MCM 10	Peterson Builders Inc	25 Sep 1989	8 Dec 1990	3 Apr 1993	AA
GLADIATOR	MCM 11	Peterson Builders Inc	7 July 1990	29 June 1991	18 Sep 1993	AA
ARDENT	MCM 12	Peterson Builders Inc	22 Oct 1990	16 Nov 1991	18 Feb 1994	AA
DEXTROUS	MCM 13	Peterson Builders Inc	11 Mar 1991	20 June 1992	July 1994	AA
CHIEF	MCM 14	Peterson Builders Inc	19 Aug 1991	12 June 1993	Sep 1994	Bldg/AA

Displacement, tons: 1312 full load
Dimensions, feet (metres): 224 × 39 × 12.2 *(68.3 × 11.9 × 3.7)*
Main machinery: 4 Waukesha L-1616 diesels (MCM 1-2) or 4 Isotta Fraschini ID 36 SS 6V AM diesels (MCM 3 onwards); 2400 hp(m) *(1.76 MW)* sustained; 2 Hansome Electric motors; 400 hp(m) *(294 kW)* for hovering; 2 shafts; 1 Omnithruster hydrojet; 350 hp *(257 kW)*
Speed, knots: 13.5
Complement: 81 (6 officers)

Guns: 2—12.7 mm Mk 26 MGs.
Countermeasures: MCM: 2 SLQ-48; Honeywell ROV mine neutralisation system, capable of 6 kts (1500 m cable with cutter and countermining charge). SLQ 37(V)2; magnetic/acoustic influence sweep equipment. Oropesa Type 0 Size 1; mechanical sweep. EDO ALQ 166 magnetic minesweeping vehicle.
Combat data systems: SATCOM SRR-1; WSC-3 (UHF). GEC/ Marconi Nautis M in last two ships (and to be fitted in all), includes Paramax SYQ 13 command system and SSN 2 PINS.
Radars: Surface search: ISC Cardion SPS 55; I/J band.
Sonars: General Electric SQQ 30 or Raytheon/Thomson Sintra SQQ 32 (in MCM 10 onwards and being retrofitted); VDS; active minehunting; high frequency.

Programmes: The contract for the prototype MCM was awarded in June 1982; MCM 2 in May 1983; MCM 3-5 in December 1983; MCM 6-8 in August 1986. MCM 9 was funded in the FY 1985 programme and MCM 10-11 in the FY 1986 programme; however, contracts for their construction were not awarded until January 1989. The last three were funded in FY 1990.
Structure: The hull is constructed of oak, Douglas fir and Alaskan cedar, with a thin coating of fibreglass on the outside, to permit taking advantage of wood's low magnetic signature. A prob-

PATRIOT   *5/1993, Giorgio Arra*

lem of engine rotation on the Waukesha diesels in MCM 1-2 was resolved; however, those engines have been replaced in the rest of the class by low magnetic engines manufactured by Isotta-Fraschini of Milan, Italy. Fitted with SSN2(V) precise integrated navigation system (PINS).

Operational: *Avenger* fitted with the SQQ 32 for Gulf operations in 1991 and all of the class are being retrofitted. All are to be based at Ingleside, Texas.

1 + 11 OSPREY CLASS (MINEHUNTERS COASTAL) (MHC)

Name	No	Builders	Launched		Commissioned		F/S
OSPREY	MHC 51	Intermarine, Savannah	23 Mar	1991	20 Nov	1993	AA
HERON	MHC 52	Intermarine, Savannah	21 Mar	1992	Aug	1994	Bldg
PELICAN	MHC 53	Avondale Industries	24 Oct	1992	Aug	1994	Bldg
ROBIN	MHC 54	Avondale Industries	31 Mar	1993	Mar	1995	Bldg
ORIOLE	MHC 55	Intermarine, Savannah	22 May	1993	Feb	1995	Bldg
KINGFISHER	MHC 56	Avondale Industries	23 Apr	1994	Sep	1995	Bldg
CORMORANT	MHC 57	Avondale Industries	Oct	1994	Mar	1996	Bldg
BLACK HAWK	MHC 58	Intermarine, Savannah	Aug	1994	Aug	1995	Bldg
FALCON	MHC 59	Intermarine, Savannah	Jan	1995	Feb	1996	Bldg
CARDINAL	MHC 60	Intermarine, Savannah	July	1995	Aug	1996	Bldg
RAVEN	MHC 61	Intermarine, Savannah	Jan	1996	Feb	1997	Bldg
SHRIKE	MHC 62	Intermarine, Savannah	Aug	1996	Aug	1997	Bldg

Displacement, tons: 889 full load
Dimensions, feet (metres): 188 × 35.9 × 9.5
(57.3 × 11 × 2.9)
Main machinery: 2 Isotta Fraschini ID 36 SS 8V AM diesels;
1600 hp(m) *(1.18 MW)* sustained; 2 Voith Schneider props;
2 hydraulic motors; 360 hp(m) *(265 kW)*
Speed, knots: 12. **Range, miles:** 1500 at 12 kts
Complement: 51 (4 officers)

Guns: 2—12.7 mm MGs.
Countermeasures: MCM: SLQ 53 deep sweep from 1995. Both
mechanical and modular influence sweep systems being
developed independently of ship construction programme.
SLQ-48 ROV mine neutralisation system (with 1070 m cable).
Combat data systems: Unisys SYQ 13 and SYQ 109; integrated
combat and machinery control system.
Radars: Navigation: Raytheon SPS 64; I band.
Sonars: Raytheon/Thomson Sintra SQQ 32; VDS; active mine-
hunting; high frequency.

Programmes: A project to construct 17 MSH was cancelled in
mid-1986 because the design, based on a surface effect ship,
failed shock testing. A design contract for Lerici class mine
hunters was then awarded in August 1986 followed by a construction contract in May 1987 for the lead ship of the class.
Intermarine SpA established Intermarine USA and purchased
Sayler Marine Corporation in Savannah, Georgia. On 2 October
1989 Avondale, Gulfport was named as the second construction source. Plans for a lengthened version have been shelved.
Engine modifications in *Osprey* have delayed completion.
Structure: Construction is of monocoque GRP throughout hull,
with frames eliminated. Main machinery is mounted on GRP
cradles and provided with acoustic enclosures. SQQ 32 is
deployed from a central well forward. Fitted with Voith cyc-
loidal propellers which eliminate need for forward thrust diving
station keeping. SYQ 13 navigation command system.

OSPREY   8/1993, Intermarine USA

3 AGGRESSIVE CLASS: OCEAN MINESWEEPERS (MSO)

Name	No	Builders	Commissioned
EXULTANT	MSO 441	Higgins, New Orleans	22 June 1954
IMPLICIT	MSO 455	Wilmington Boat	10 Mar 1954
CONQUEST	MSO 488	Martinac, Tacoma	20 July 1955

Displacement, tons: 720 standard; 780 full load
Dimensions, feet (metres): 172.5 × 35.1 × 14.1 *(52.6 × 10.7 × 4.3)*
Main machinery: 4 Packard ID-1700 (MSO 455) or Waukesha (MSO 441 and 488) diesels;
2280 hp *(1.7 MW)*; 2 shafts; cp props
Speed, knots: 14. **Range, miles:** 3000 at 10 kts
Complement: 86 (7 officers); 39 (3 officers) plus 47 (4 officers) reserves in NRF ships
Guns: 2—12.7 mm MGs.
Combat data systems: SATCOM SRR-1.
Radars: Navigation: Sperry SPS 53L; I/J band.
Sonars: General Electric SQQ 14; VDS; active minehunting; high frequency.

Comment: These last three are scheduled to pay off by July 1994. All are fitted with mechanical,
acoustic and magnetic sweeps and can carry a ROV. Deletion has been delayed by problems
with the Osprey class programme. MSO 455 and 488 are NRF ships. Four of the class may be
transferred to Taiwan in 1994/95.

CONQUEST   10/1993, Giorgio Arra

HARBOUR DEFENCE PROJECT (COOP)

10 YP 654 CLASS + 3 HATTERAS and WESTPORT CLASS

Displacement, tons: 68 full load
Dimensions, feet (metres): 80.4 × 18.8 × 5.3 *(24.5 × 5.7 × 1.6)*
Main machinery: 4 GM diesels; 660 hp *(492 kW)*; 2 shafts
Speed, knots: 13. **Range, miles:** 400 at 12 kts
Complement: 9
Radars: Navigation: Raytheon 1220; I band.

Comment: Details given are for the YP class. The COOP programme came into being at a time
when USN mine warfare assets were at a low point, and it was expected that the use of converted patrol boats, craft captured from drug smugglers, and fishing boats could provide a useful
mine countermeasures force in and around US harbours. It was estimated that the force might
number in excess of 80 craft dispersed in 22 ports. Unfortunately, few of the captured drug
smuggling boats proved usable and enhancing the capabilities of patrol craft (YPs) and fishing
boats proved to be difficult. Also the Navy embarked upon a major construction programme of
mine countermeasures vessels, and as a result the COOP programme was sharply reduced from
the original concept. The Navy had planned to eliminate the programme at the end of FY 1992,
but Congress provided funding in both FY 1993 and FY 1994 for its continued operation. The
Navy is considering several options for the programme's future, including operations involving
ordnance, shipping channel surveys and mine detection. In early 1994, there were 13 COOP
units sharing 16 ports on the east coast, west coast, Hawaii and the Gulf of Mexico. Four crews
comprised of nine Reservists each are assigned to each craft.

CT 6   4/1991, Giorgio Arra

AUXILIARIES

Notes: (1) The Auxiliary Ships of the US Navy are usually divided into two broad categories, underway replenishment ships (UNREP) and fleet support ships. UNREP ships carry out the direct support of deployed forces in the forward area of operations.

Most US Navy replenishment ships are fitted with helicopter platforms to allow the transfer of supplies by vertical replenishment (VERTREP). Helicopters are carried specifically for this purpose by the ammunition ships (AE), the combat store ships (AFS), the fast combat support ships (AOE), and replenishment oilers (AOR). Carrier-based helicopters are sometimes employed in this role.

Planned UNREP ship force levels are declining as warship numbers reduce. The current plan is to be able to provide support in two major regional crises simultaneously. This plan is based on the availability of some storage depots on foreign territory, and the use of Military Sealift Ships to carry fuels, munitions, and the stores from the USA or overseas sources for transfer to UNREP ships in overseas areas. Some 16 to 18 UNREP ships are normally forward deployed in the Mediterranean, Western Pacific and Indian Ocean areas in support of the 6th and 7th Fleets, respectively. During the build up to the war with Iraq in 1991, more than 30 ships were involved.

Fleet support ships provide primarily maintenance and related towing and salvage services at advanced bases and at ports in the USA. These ships normally do not provide fuel, munitions, or other supplies except when ships are alongside for maintenance. Most fleet support ships operate from bases in the USA.

(2) Some underway replenishment ships and fleet support ships are Navy manned and armed, but an increasing number are operated by the Military Sealift Command (MSC) with civilian crews and unarmed. The latter ships have T-prefix before their designations and are listed in the next section.

6 YELLOWSTONE and SAMUEL GOMPERS CLASSES: DESTROYER TENDERS (AD)

Name	No	Builders	Commissioned	F/S
SAMUEL GOMPERS	AD 37	Puget Sound SY, Bremerton	1 July 1967	PA
PUGET SOUND	AD 38	Puget Sound SY, Bremerton	27 Apr 1968	AA
YELLOWSTONE	AD 41	National Steel & Shipbuilding Co	31 May 1980	AA
ACADIA	AD 42	National Steel & Shipbuilding Co	6 June 1981	PA
CAPE COD	AD 43	National Steel & Shipbuilding Co	17 Apr 1982	PA
SHENANDOAH	AD 44	National Steel & Shipbuilding Co	17 Dec 1983	AA

Displacement, tons: 20 500 (20 224, AD 41-44) full load
Dimensions, feet (metres): 644 × 85 × 22.5 *(196.3 × 25.9 × 6.9)* (AD 37-38)
641.8 × 85 × 22.5 *(195.6 × 25.9 × 6.9)* (AD 41-44)
Main machinery: 2 Combustion Engineering boilers; 620 psi *(43.6 kg/cm sq)*; 860°F *(462°C)*;
1 De Laval turbine; 20 000 hp *(14.9 MW)*; 1 shaft
Speed, knots: 20
Complement: 1681 including 4 officers and 96 enlisted women
Guns: 4—20 mm Mk 67 (AD 37-38). 2—20 mm Mk 67 (AD 41-44).
2—40 mm Mk 14 MGs. 2—40 mm saluting guns (AD 37-38).
Radars: Surface search: Raytheon SPS 10; G band.
Navigation: Marconi LN 66; I band.
Helicopters: Platform for 1 utility.

Comment: The first US destroyer tenders of post-Second World War design. Also have facilities for servicing nuclear power plants. Services can be provided simultaneously to six guided-missile destroyers moored alongside. Basic hull design similar to LY Spear and Simon Lake submarine tenders. Two 30 ton capacity cranes. *Puget Sound* has a hangar. All have WSC-3 (UHF) SATCOM.

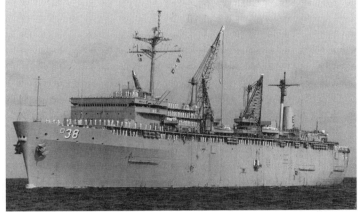

PUGET SOUND   *4/1993, Giorgio Arra*

1 DOLPHIN CLASS (AGSS)

Name	No	Builders	Commissioned	F/S
DOLPHIN	AGSS 555	Portsmouth Naval Shipyard	17 Aug 1968	PA

Displacement, tons: 800 standard; 930 full load
Dimensions, feet (metres): 152 × 19.3 × 18 *(46.3 × 5.9 × 5.5)*
Main machinery: Diesel-electric; 2 Detroit 12V-71 diesels; 840 hp *(616 kW)* sustained; 2 generators; 1 motor; 1 shaft
Fitted with 330 cell silver-zinc battery
Speed, knots: 15+ dived
Complement: 37 (4 officers) plus 4-7 scientists
Radars: Navigation: Sperry SPS 53 portable; I/J band.
Sonars: Ametek BQS 15; active close-range detection; high frequency.
EDO BQR 2; passive search; low frequency.
Acoustic arrays towed at up to 4000 ft astern.

Comment: Authorised in FY 1961; laid down 9 November 1962 and launched 8 June 1968 after delays caused by changes in mission. Has a constant diameter cylindrical pressure hull approximately 15 ft in outer diameter closed at both ends with hemispherical heads. Pressure hull fabricated of HY-80 steel with aluminium and fibreglass used in secondary structures to reduce weight. No conventional hydroplanes are mounted, improved rudder design and other features provide manoeuvring control and hovering capability. Fitted for deep-ocean sonar and oceanographic research. She is highly automated and has three computer-operated systems, a safety system, hovering system, and one that is classified. The digital-computer submarine safety system monitors equipment and provides data on closed-circuit television screens; malfunctions in equipment set off an alarm and if they are not corrected within the prescribed time the system, unless overridden by an operator, automatically brings the submarine to the surface. There are several research stations for scientists and she is fitted to take water samples down to her operating depth. Assigned to Submarine Development Group 1 at San Diego. Designed for deep diving operations. Submerged endurance is approximately 24 hours with an at-sea endurance of 14 days.

7 KILAUEA CLASS: AMMUNITION SHIPS (AE)

Name	No	Builders	Commissioned	F/S
BUTTE	AE 27	General Dynamics, Quincy	14 Dec 1968	AA
SANTA BARBARA	AE 28	Bethlehem Steel	11 July 1970	AA
MOUNT HOOD	AE 29	Bethlehem Steel	1 May 1971	PA
FLINT	AE 32	Ingalls Shipbuilding	20 Nov 1971	PA
SHASTA	AE 33	Ingalls Shipbuilding	26 Feb 1972	PA
MOUNT BAKER	AE 34	Ingalls Shipbuilding	22 July 1972	AA
KISKA	AE 35	Ingalls Shipbuilding	16 Dec 1972	PA

Displacement, tons: 9340 light; 19 940 full load
Dimensions, feet (metres): 564 × 81 × 28 *(171.9 × 24.7 × 8.5)*
Main machinery: 3 Foster-Wheeler boilers; 600 psi *(42.3 kg/cm sq)*; 870°F *(467°C)*; 1 GE turbine;
22 000 hp *(16.4 MW)*; 1 shaft
Speed, knots: 20. **Range, miles:** 10 000 at 18 kts
Complement: 383 (17 officers)
Guns: 4 USN 3 in *(76 mm)*/50 (2 twin) Mk 33. Twin closed mounts forward and twin open mounts aft, between funnel and after booms. Local control only. Being removed.
2 General Electric/General Dynamics 20 mm Vulcan Phalanx.
Countermeasures: Decoys: 2 Loral Hycor SRBOC 6-barrelled Mk 36; IR flares and chaff.
ESM: SLQ 32(V)1; intercept.
Radars: Surface search: Raytheon SPS 10F; G band.
Navigation: Marconi LN 66; I band.
Tacan: URN 25.
Helicopters: 2 UH-46E Sea Knight (cargo normally embarked).

Comment: FAST replenishment system. Vulcan Phalanx is now fitted in all. Another of the class, *Kilauea*, disarmed and transferred to MSC 1 October 1980 and is renumbered TAE 26. 3 in guns are being removed. *Flint* is being converted for MSC service in FY 1995 with five others to follow in FY 1996-98.

SHASTA   *10/1993, Giorgio Arra*

3 SURIBACHI and NITRO CLASSES: AMMUNITION SHIPS (AE)

Name	No	Builders	Commissioned	F/S
SURIBACHI	AE 21	Bethlehem Steel	17 Nov 1956	AA
MAUNA KEA	AE 22	Bethlehem Steel	30 Mar 1957	PA
NITRO	AE 23	Bethlehem Steel	1 May 1959	AA

Displacement, tons: 7470 light; 10 000 standard; 15 500 full load (AE 21-22) 15 900 standard;
16 083 full load (AE 23)
Dimensions, feet (metres): 502 × 72 × 29 *(153 × 21.9 × 8.8)* (AE 21-22)
512 × 72 × 29 *(156.1 × 21.9 × 8.8)* (AE 23)
Main machinery: 2 Combustion Engineering boilers; 625 psi *(43.9 kg/cm sq)*; 850°F *(454°C)*;
1 Bethlehem turbine; 16 000 hp *(11.9 MW)*; 1 shaft
Speed, knots: 20.6; 18 (AE 21-22)
Complement: 312 (18 officers)
Guns: 4 USN 3 in *(76 mm)*/50 (2 twin) Mk 33. Local control only.
Countermeasures: Decoys: 2 Loral Hycor SRBOC 6-barrelled Mk 36; IR flares and chaff (not in all).
ESM: SLQ 32(V)1; intercept (not in all).
Radars: Surface search: Raytheon SPS 10; G band.
Navigation: Marconi LN 66; I band.
Helicopters: Platform only.

Comment: All were modernised in 1960s; fitted with high-speed transfer equipment, three holds configured for stowage of missiles and helicopter platform fitted aft (two after twin 3 in gun mounts removed). Arrangements of twin 3 in gun mounts differ, some ships have them in tandem and others side-by-side. *Mauna Kea* fitted with mine rails for trials in 1984. 3 in guns may be removed.

SURIBACHI   *10/1993, Wright & Logan*

2 MARS CLASS: COMBAT STORE SHIPS (AFS)

Name	No	Builders	Commissioned	F/S
NIAGARA FALLS	AFS 3	National Steel & Shipbuilding Co	29 Apr 1967	PA
WHITE PLAINS	AFS 4	National Steel & Shipbuilding Co	23 Nov 1968	PA

Displacement, tons: 9200 light; 15 900-18 663 full load
Dimensions, feet (metres): 581 × 79 × 24 *(177.1 × 24.1 × 7.3)*
Main machinery: 3 Babcock & Wilcox boilers; 580 psi *(40.8 kg/cm sq)*; 825°F *(440°C)*; 1 De Laval turbine (Westinghouse in AFS 6); 22 000 hp *(16.4 MW)*; 1 shaft
Speed, knots: 20. **Range, miles:** 10 000 at 18 kts
Complement: 428 (25 officers)
Cargo capacity: 2625 tons dry stores; 1300 tons refrigerated stores (varies with specific loadings)
Guns: 4 USN 3 in *(76 mm)*/50 (2 twin) Mk 33. Local control only.
   2 General Electric/General Dynamics 20 mm Vulcan Phalanx Mk 15.
Countermeasures: Decoys: 2 Loral Hycor SRBOC 6-barrelled Mk 36; IR flares and chaff to 4 km *(2.2 nm)*.
ESM: SLQ 32(V)1; intercept.
Radars: Surface search: Raytheon SPS 10 series; G band.
Navigation: Marconi LN 66.
Tacan: URN 25.
Helicopters: 2 UH-46E Sea Knight normally assigned.

Comment: 'M' frames replace conventional king posts and booms, which are equipped with automatic tensioning devices. Armament has been modified. As well as the provisions listed above these ships carry comprehensive inventories of aviation and spare parts of all types for the Fleet. Phalanx placements vary in different ships of the class. Both grounded at Guam in a typhoon in August 1992. Four of the class were disarmed and transferred to the MSC on 15 October 1992, 1 February 1993, 11 August 1993 and 2 November 1993 respectively. AFS 3 is scheduled to follow in September 1994. AFS 4 decommissions in 1995.

MARS class (old number)   5/1993, S Poynton, RAN

1 CONVERTED RALEIGH CLASS: MISCELLANEOUS COMMAND SHIP (AGF)

Name	No	Builders	Commissioned	F/S
LA SALLE	AGF 3 (ex-LPD 3)	New York Naval Shipyard	22 Feb 1964	AA

Displacement, tons: 9670 light; 14 650 full load
Dimensions, feet (metres): 519.7 × 84 × 21 *(158.4 × 25.6 × 6.4)*
Main machinery: 2 Babcock & Wilcox boilers; 600 psi *(42.2 kg/cm sq)*; 870°F *(467°C)*; 2 De Laval turbines; 24 000 hp *(17.9 MW)*; 2 shafts
Speed, knots: 20. **Range, miles:** 9600 at 16 kts
Complement: 440 (25 officers) plus 59 Flag Staff (12 officers)
Guns: 4 USN 3 in *(76 mm)*/50 (2 twin) Mk 33. Local control only. May not be carried.
   2 General Electric/General Dynamics 20 mm Vulcan Phalanx Mk 15.
   2—25 mm Mk 38. 2—40 mm saluting guns.
Countermeasures: Decoys: 4 Loral Hycor SRBOC Mk 36; chaff and IR flares.
ESM: SLQ 32(V)2; WLR-1; intercept.
Radars: Air search: Lockheed SPS 40; E/F band; range 320 km *(175 nm)*.
   Surface search: Raytheon SPS 10D; G band.
Navigation: Marconi LN 66; I band.
Tacan: URN 25.
Helicopters: 1 light.

Comment: A former amphibious transport dock (LPD) of the Raleigh class. Authorised in FY 1961. She served as an amphibious ship until 1972 and still retains an amphibious assault capability. Converted in 1972 at Philadelphia Navy Yard. Flag command and communications facilities installed; additional air-conditioning fitted; painted white to help retard heat of Persian Gulf area. Helicopter hangar installed on the port side of the flight deck. Deck landing spots for heavy helicopters. Reclassified as a flagship and designated AGF 3 on 1 July 1972 keeping previous '3' hull number. Has served as flagship for the US Commander, Middle East Force, operating in the Persian Gulf, Arabian Sea and Indian Ocean. A comprehensive communications fit includes WSC-6. Refitted again in 1993/94.

LA SALLE   1983, Giorgio Arra

1 CONVERTED AUSTIN CLASS: MISCELLANEOUS COMMAND SHIP (AGF)

Name	No	Builders	Commissioned	F/S
CORONADO	AGF 11 (ex-LPD 11)	Lockheed SB & Construction Co	23 May 1970	PA

Displacement, tons: 11 482 light; 16 912 full load
Dimensions, feet (metres): 570 × 100 × 23 *(173.8 × 30.5 × 7)*
Main machinery: 2 Foster-Wheeler boilers; 600 psi *(42.2 kg/cm sq)*; 870°F *(467°C)*; 2 De Laval turbines; 24 000 hp *(17.9 MW)*; 2 shafts
Speed, knots: 21. **Range, miles:** 7700 at 20 kts
Complement: 516 (25 officers) plus 120 Flag Staff
Guns: 2 USN 3 in *(76 mm)*/50 (twin) Mk 33. Local control only. May not be fitted.
   2 General Electric/General Dynamics 20 mm Vulcan Phalanx Mk 15. 2—12.7 mm MGs.
Countermeasures: Decoys: 4 Loral Hycor SRBOC 6-barrelled Mk 36; IR flares and chaff.
ESM: SLQ 32V(2); WLR-1; intercept.
Radars: Air search: Lockheed SPS 40C; E/F band; range 320 km *(175 nm)*.
   Surface search: Raytheon SPS 10F; G band.
Navigation: Marconi LN 66; I band.
Tacan: URN 25.
Helicopters: 2 Light.

Comment: A former LPD of the Austin class. Authorised in FY 1964. She retains an amphibious assault capability. Converted in late 1980 as a temporary replacement for *La Salle* (AGF 3), as flagship, US Commander, Middle East Force, so *La Salle* could be overhauled. When *Coronado* was relieved by *La Salle* in early 1983, it was planned for her to be reconverted back to an LPD. Due to the shortage of fleet flagships, however, she will continue in the flagship role for the foreseeable future. When relieved by *Belknap* as Sixth Fleet flagship in July 1986, she deployed to the Pacific to become the flagship of the Third Fleet then in Hawaii. She is now based at San Diego. Comprehensive communications fit includes WSC-6 on a lattice mast fitted in 1987. At the same time a sponson built out over the port side increased the overall width of the ship by some 15 ft. 3 in guns removed.

CORONADO   4/1993, Hachiro Nakai

5 JUMBOISED CIMARRON CLASS: OILERS (AO)

Name	No	Builders	Commissioned	F/S
CIMARRON	AO 177	Avondale Shipyards	10 Jan 1981	PA
MONONGAHELA	AO 178	Avondale Shipyards	5 Sep 1981	AA
MERRIMACK	AO 179	Avondale Shipyards	14 Nov 1981	AA
WILLAMETTE	AO 180	Avondale Shipyards	18 Dec 1982	PA
PLATTE	AO 186	Avondale Shipyards	16 Apr 1983	AA

Displacement, tons: 8210 light; 37 870 full load
Dimensions, feet (metres): 708.5 × 88 × 35 *(216 × 26.8 × 10.7)*
Main machinery: 2 Combustion Engineering boilers; 600 psi *(42.2 kg/cm sq)*; 850°F *(454°C)*; 1 turbine; 24 000 hp *(17.9 MW)*; 1 shaft
Speed, knots: 19
Complement: 135 (12 officers) plus 90 spare berths
Cargo capacity: 180 000 barrels of fuel
Guns: 2 General Electric/General Dynamics 20 mm Vulcan Phalanx Mk 15.
Countermeasures: Decoys: Loral Hycor SRBOC 6-barrelled Mk 36; IR flares and chaff to 4 km *(2.2 nm)*.
SLQ Nixie; towed torpedo decoy.
ESM: SLQ 32(V)1; intercept.
Radars: Surface search: ISC Cardion SPS 55 (AO 177-179); I/J band.
   Raytheon SPS 10B (AO 180 and 186); G band.
Navigation: Marconi LN 66; I band.
Helicopters: Platform only.

Comment: Significantly smaller than the previous Neosho class (now in MSC), these ships were originally 'sized' to provide two complete refuellings of a fossil-fuelled aircraft carrier and six to eight accompanying destroyers. All five ships of the class have been 'jumboised', thus increasing their capacities from 120 000 bbls to 180 000 bbls and improving underway replenishment capabilities. Funding for the first 'jumboisation' was provided in FY 1987, second in FY 1988, third and fourth in FY 1989, and fifth in FY 1990. All completed with new mid-body sections by the end of 1992. The class may be transferred to the MSC in due course.

PLATTE   10/1993, A Sheldon Duplaix

1 + 3 SUPPLY CLASS: FAST COMBAT SUPPORT SHIPS (AOE)

Name	No	Builders	Commissioned	F/S
SUPPLY	AOE 6	National Steel & Shipbuilding Co	26 Feb 1994	AA
RAINIER	AOE 7	National Steel & Shipbuilding Co	Nov 1994	Bldg
ARCTIC	AOE 8	National Steel & Shipbuilding Co	Aug 1995	Bldg
BRIDGE	AOE 10	National Steel & Shipbuilding Co	Nov 1997	Bldg

Displacement, tons: 19 700 light; 48 800 full load
Dimensions, feet (metres): 753.7 × 107 × 38 *(229.7 × 32.6 × 11.6)*
Main machinery: 4 GE LM 2500 gas-turbines; 105 000 hp *(78.33 MW)* sustained; 2 shafts
Speed, knots: 25
Complement: Accommodation for 667 (40 officers)
Cargo capacity: 156 000 barrels of fuel; 1800 tons ammunition; 400 tons refrigerated cargo; 250 tons general cargo; 20 000 gallons water
Missiles: SAM: Raytheon GMLS Mk 29 octuple launcher; NATO Sea Sparrow.
Guns: 2 General Electric/General Dynamics 20 mm Vulcan Phalanx Mk 15. 2 Hughes 25 mm Mk 88. 4—12.7 mm MGs.
Countermeasures: Decoys: 4 Loral Hycor SRBOC 6-barrelled Mk 36; IR flares and chaff. Nixie torpedo decoy.
ESM/ECM: SLQ 32(V)3; combined intercept and jammer.
Fire control: Mk 91 MFCS.
Radars: Air search: Hughes Mk 23 TAS; D band.
Air/surface search: Norden SPS 67; G band.
Navigation: Raytheon SPS 64(V)9; I band.
Fire control: 2 Raytheon Mk 95; I/J band.
Tacan: URN 25.
Helicopters: 3 UH-46E Sea Knight.

Comment: To augment underway replenishment capability. Construction of *Supply* started in June 1988 and the second and third in August 1989 and July 1990 respectively. Funds for fourth of class were rescinded in FY 1992 but restored in FY 1993. The aim was one ship per carrier air group but by 1994 there were no plans to build more. *Supply* was launched on 6 October 1990 and started sea trials in March 1993. *Rainier* launched 28 September 1991, *Arctic* 30 October 1993. The ships have six RAS stations, four 10 ton cargo booms and two Vertrep positions.

SUPPLY   *2/1993, National Steel & Shipbuilding Company*

RAINIER   *7/1993, van Ginderen Collection*

4 SAFEGUARD CLASS: SALVAGE SHIPS (ARS)

Name	No	Builders	Commissioned	F/S
SAFEGUARD	ARS 50	Peterson Builders Inc	16 Aug 1985	PA
GRASP	ARS 51	Peterson Builders Inc	14 Dec 1985	AA
SALVOR	ARS 52	Peterson Builders Inc	14 June 1986	PA
GRAPPLE	ARS 53	Peterson Builders Inc	15 Nov 1986	AA

Displacement, tons: 2880 full load
Dimensions, feet (metres): 255 × 51 × 17 *(77.7 × 15.5 × 5.2)*
Main machinery: 4 Caterpillar diesels; 4200 hp *(3.13 MW)*; 2 shafts; cp Kort nozzle props; bow thruster; 500 hp *(373 kW)*
Speed, knots: 14. **Range, miles:** 8000 at 12 kts
Complement: 90 (6 officers)
Guns: 2 Oerlikon 20 mm Mk 67.
Radars: Navigation: ISC Cardion SPS 55; I/J band.

Comment: Prototype approved in FY 1981, two in FY 1982 and one in FY 1983. The procurement of the fifth ARS was dropped on instructions from Congress. *Safeguard* launched 12 November 1983, *Grasp* 21 April 1984, *Salvor* 28 July 1984 and *Grapple* 8 December 1984. This class is essentially an updated Bolster class ARS which required only a moderate amount of development effort, primarily to satisfy new standards of habitability, galley, messing, medical and storeroom areas. The design follows conventional commercial and Navy design criteria. Equipped with recompression chamber. Bollard pull, 65.5 tons. Using beach extraction equipment the pull increases to 360 tons. 150 ton deadlift.

GRASP   *3/1993, Giorgio Arra*

5 BOLSTER CLASS: SALVAGE SHIPS (ARS)

Name	No	Builders	Commissioned	F/S
BOLSTER	ARS 38	Basalt Rock Co, Napa, CA	1 May 1945	NRF
HOIST	ARS 40	Basalt Rock Co, Napa, CA	21 July 1945	AA
OPPORTUNE	ARS 41	Basalt Rock Co, Napa, CA	5 Oct 1945	AA
RECLAIMER	ARS 42	Basalt Rock Co, Napa, CA	20 Dec 1945	NRF
RECOVERY	ARS 43	Basalt Rock Co, Napa, CA	15 May 1946	AA

Displacement, tons: 1530 standard; 2045 full load
Dimensions, feet (metres): 213.5 × 44 (41, ARS 38) × 13 *(65.1 × 13.4 (12.5) × 4)*
Main machinery: Diesel-electric; 4 Cooper-Bessemer GSB-8 diesels; 2736 hp *(2.04 MW)* sustained; 4 generators; or 2 Caterpillar D 399 in ARS 38, 39, 42; 2250 hp *(1.67 MW)* sustained; 2 generators; 2 shafts
Speed, knots: 14.8. **Range, miles:** 9000 at 14 kts; 20 000 at 7 kts
Complement: 103 (6 officers)
Guns: 2 Oerlikon 20 mm Mk 68 (Mk 67 in ARS 39 and 41).
Radars: Surface search: Raytheon SPS 10; G band or Sperry SPS 53; I/J band.
Navigation: Marconi LN 66; I band.

Comment: Equipped with compressed air diving equipment and 10 ton and 20 ton booms. Bollard pull 30 tons. All have SATCOM receivers. All scheduled to pay off in September 1994.

HOIST   *4/1993, Giorgio Arra*

2 SIMON LAKE CLASS: SUBMARINE TENDERS (AS)

Name	No	Builders	Commissioned	F/S
SIMON LAKE	AS 33	Puget Sound Naval Shipyard	7 Nov 1964	AA
CANOPUS	AS 34	Ingalls Shipbuilding	4 Nov 1965	AA

Displacement, tons: 19 934 (AS 33); 21 089 (AS 34) full load
Dimensions, feet (metres): 643.7 × 85 × 30 *(196.2 × 25.9 × 9.1)*
Main machinery: 2 Combustion Engineering boilers; 620 psi *(43.6 kg/cm sq)*; 860°F *(462°C)*; 1 De Laval turbine; 20 000 hp *(14.9 MW)*; 1 shaft
Speed, knots: 20. **Range, miles:** 7600 at 18 kts
Complement: 915 (58 officers) (AS 33); 660 (56 officers) (AS 34)
Guns: 4—20 mm Mk 67.
Radars: Surface search: Raytheon SPS 10; G band.
Navigation: Marconi LN 66; I band.
Helicopters: Platform only.

Comment: Designed to service fleet ballistic missile submarines (SSBN), with three submarines alongside being supported simultaneously. Carry two 30 ton cranes and four 5 ton mobile cranes. Capable of handling all existing submarine ballistic missiles. 3 in guns removed.

CANOPUS   *10/1993, A Sheldon Duplaix*

4 SACRAMENTO CLASS: FAST COMBAT SUPPORT SHIPS (AOE)

Name	No	Builders	Commissioned	F/S
SACRAMENTO	AOE 1	Puget Sound SY	14 Mar 1964	PA
CAMDEN	AOE 2	New York Shipbuilding	1 Apr 1967	PA
SEATTLE	AOE 3	Puget Sound SY	5 Apr 1969	AA
DETROIT	AOE 4	Puget Sound SY	28 Mar 1970	AA

Displacement, tons: 19 200 light; 51 400-53 600 full load
Dimensions, feet (metres): 793 × 107 × 39.3 *(241.7 × 32.6 × 12)*
Main machinery: 4 Combustion Engineering boilers; 600 psi *(42.2 kg/cm sq)*; 900°F *(480°C)*; 2 GE turbines; 100 000 hp *(76.4 MW)*; 2 shafts
Speed, knots: 26. **Range, miles:** 6000 at 25 kts; 10 000 at 17 kts
Complement: 601 (24 officers)
Cargo capacity: 177 000 barrels of fuel; 2150 tons munitions; 500 tons dry stores; 250 tons refrigerated stores
Missiles: SAM: Raytheon NATO Sea Sparrow Mk 29 octuple launcher.
Guns: 2 General Electric/General Dynamics 20 mm Vulcan Phalanx Mk 15. 4—12.7 mm MGs.
Countermeasures: Decoys: Loral Hycor SRBOC 6-barrelled Mk 36; IR flares and chaff to 4 km *(2.2 nm)*.
ESM/ECM: SLQ 32(V)3; combined intercept and jammer.
Fire control: Mk 91 Mod 1 MFCS.
Radars: Air search: Lockheed SPS 40 series, Westinghouse SPS 58A (AOE 1 and 2), SPS 58A only (AOE 4); E/F and D band (SPS 58). Hughes Mk 23 TAS (AOE 3); D band.
Surface search: Raytheon SPS 10F; G band.
Navigation: Marconi LN 66; I band.
Fire control: 2 Raytheon Mk 95; I/J band (for SAM).
Tacan: URN 25.
Helicopters: 2 UH-46E Sea Knight normally assigned.

Comment: Designed to provide rapid replenishment at sea of petroleum, munitions, provisions, and fleet freight. Fitted with large hangar for vertical replenishment operations (VERTREP). These ships can be distinguished from the smaller Wichita class replenishment oilers by their larger superstructures and funnel, helicopter deck at lower level, and hangar structure aft of funnel. *Camden* used as the trials ship for improved replenishment at sea equipment.

SEATTLE   *12/1993, Maritime Photographic*

5 WICHITA CLASS: REPLENISHMENT OILERS (AOR)

Name	No	Builders	Commissioned	F/S
KANSAS CITY	AOR 3	General Dynamics, Quincy	6 June 1970	PA
SAVANNAH	AOR 4	General Dynamics, Quincy	5 Dec 1970	AA
WABASH	AOR 5	General Dynamics, Quincy	20 Nov 1971	PA
KALAMAZOO	AOR 6	General Dynamics, Quincy	11 Aug 1973	AA
ROANOKE	AOR 7	National Steel & Shipbuilding Co	30 Oct 1976	PA

Displacement, tons: 13 000 light; 41 350 full load
Dimensions, feet (metres): 659 × 96 × 33.3 *(200.9 × 29.3 × 10.2)*
Main machinery: 3 Foster-Wheeler boilers; 615 psi *(43.3 kg/cm sq)*; 851°F *(454°C)*; 2 GE turbines; 32 000 hp *(23.9 MW)*; 2 shafts
Speed, knots: 20. **Range, miles:** 6500 at 19 kts; 10 000 at 16 kts
Complement: 454 (20 officers)
Cargo capacity: 160 000 barrels of fuel; 600 tons munitions; 200 tons dry stores; 100 tons refrigerated stores
Missiles: SAM: Raytheon NATO Sea Sparrow Mk 29 octuple launcher.
Guns: 2 General Electric/General Dynamics 20 mm Vulcan Phalanx Mk 15. 2 or 4 Oerlikon 20 mm may also be carried.
Countermeasures: Decoys: 4 Loral Hycor SRBOC 6-barrelled Mk 36; IR flares and chaff to 4 km *(2.2 nm)*.
ESM/ECM: SLQ 32(V)3 (being fitted to replace WLR 6).
Fire control: 1 Mk 91 MFCS.
Radars: Air search: Hughes Mk 23 TAS; D band.
Surface search: Raytheon SPS 10F; G band.
Navigation: Marconi LN 66; I band.
Fire control: 2 Mk 76; I/J band. Raytheon Mk 95; I/J band.
Tacan: URN 25 or SRN 15.
Helicopters: 2 UH-46E Sea Knight can be embarked.

Comment: Designed to provide rapid replenishment at sea of petroleum and munitions with a limited capacity for provision and fleet freight. Fitted with helicopter platform and internal arrangement for vertical replenishment operations (VERTREP). Hangars were added after the main gun armament was removed. One of the class paid off in 1993 and a second in early 1994. *Wabash* is scheduled to pay off in September 1994.

WABASH   *8/1992, Hachiro Nakai*

5 L Y SPEAR and EMORY S LAND CLASS: SUBMARINE TENDERS (AS)

Name	No	Builders	Commissioned	F/S
L Y SPEAR	AS 36	General Dynamics, Quincy	28 Feb 1970	AA
DIXON	AS 37	General Dynamics, Quincy	7 Aug 1971	PA
EMORY S LAND	AS 39	Lockheed SB & Construction Co	7 July 1979	AA
FRANK CABLE	AS 40	Lockheed SB & Construction Co	5 Feb 1980	AA
McKEE	AS 41	Lockheed SB & Construction Co	15 Aug 1981	PA

Displacement, tons: 13 000 standard (13 840, later ships); 22 640 (AS 36 and AS 37); 23 493 (AS 39-41) full load
Dimensions, feet (metres): 643.8 × 85 × 28.5 *(196.2 × 25.9 × 8.7)*
Main machinery: 2 Foster-Wheeler boilers; 620 psi *(43.6 kg/cm sq)*; 860°F *(462°C)*; 1 GE turbine; 20 000 hp *(14.9 MW)*; 1 shaft
Speed, knots: 20. **Range, miles:** 10 000 at 12 kts
Complement: 535 (52 officers) plus Flag Staff 69 (25 officers) (AS 39-41)
Guns: 4 Oerlikon 20 mm Mk 67.
Radars: Navigation: Raytheon SPS 10 (AS 36, 37); G band.
ISC Cardion SPS 55 (others); I/J band.
Helicopters: Platform only.

Comment: The first US submarine tenders designed specifically for servicing nuclear-propelled attack submarines. Basic hull design similar to Samuel Gompers and Simon Lake classes tenders. Each ship can simultaneously provide services to four submarines moored alongside. AS 39 and later ships (Emory S Land class) are especially configured to support SSN 688 class submarines. Carry one 30 ton crane and two 5 ton mobile cranes. Have a 23 bed sick bay.

EMORY S LAND   *10/1993, A Sheldon Duplaix*

2 HUNLEY CLASS: SUBMARINE TENDERS (AS)

Name	No	Builders	Commissioned	F/S
HUNLEY	AS 31	Newport News Shipbuilding	16 June 1962	AA
HOLLAND	AS 32	Ingalls Shipbuilding	7 Sep 1963	PA

Displacement, tons: 10 500 standard; 19 820 full load
Dimensions, feet (metres): 599 × 83 × 27 *(182.6 × 25.3 × 8.2)*
Main machinery: Diesel-electric; 6 Fairbanks-Morse 38D-1/8-12 diesel generators; 8.7 MW sustained; 1 motor; 1 shaft
Speed, knots: 19. **Range, miles:** 10 000 at 12 kts
Complement: 612/658 (54 officers)
Guns: 4 Oerlikon 20 mm Mk 68.
Radars: Surface search: Raytheon SPS 10; G band.
Navigation: Marconi LN 66; I band.
Helicopters: Platform only.

Comment: The first US submarine tenders of post-Second World War construction; they are designed to provide repair and supply services to fleet ballistic missile submarines (SSBN). Have 52 separate workshops to provide complete support. Both ships originally fitted with a 32 ton capacity hammerhead crane; subsequently refitted with two amidships cranes as in Simon Lake class. Capable of handling all existing submarine ballistic missiles. *Hunley* is to pay off by September 1994.

HOLLAND   *8/1992, Giorgio Arra*

1 PIGEON CLASS: SUBMARINE RESCUE SHIP (ASR)

Name	No	Builders	Commissioned	F/S
ORTOLAN	ASR 22	Alabama DD & SB Co, Mobile	14 July 1973	AA

Displacement, tons: 3411 standard; 4570 full load
Dimensions, feet (metres): 251 × 86 (see *Comment*) × 21.3 *(76.5 × 26.2 × 6.5)*
Main machinery: 4 Alco diesels; 6000 hp *(4.48 MW)*; 2 shafts; 2 bow thrusters to be fitted
Speed, knots: 15. **Range, miles:** 8500 at 13 kts
Complement: 195 (9 officers); includes 24 (4 officers) for the submersibles; Flag 14 (4 officers)
Guns: 2 Oerlikon 20 mm Mk 68.
Radars: Surface search: Sperry SPS 53; I/J band.
Navigation: Marconi LN 66; I band.
Sonars: SQQ-25; hull-mounted; precision 3D system for tracking submersibles; high frequency.
Helicopters: Platform only.

Comment: Tasks include (1) surface support for the Deep Submergence Rescue Vehicles (DSRV), (2) rescue employing the existing McCann rescue chamber, (3) major deep-sea diving support and (4) operational control for salvage operations. Capable of transporting, servicing, lowering, and raising two Deep Submergence Rescue Vehicles (DSRV) (see section on Deep Submergence Vehicles). Designed with catamaran hull, the first ocean-going catamaran ship to be built for the US Navy with the exception of TAG *Hayes* of the MSC, since Robert Fulton's steam gunboat *Demologos* of 1812. Each of the twin hulls is 251 ft long and 26 ft wide. The well between the hulls is 34 ft across, giving the ASR a maximum beam of 86 ft. The Mk II Deep Diving System supports conventional or saturation divers operating at depths to 850 ft. The system consists of two recompression chambers and two personnel transfer capsules to transport divers between the ship and ocean floor. Fitted for helium-oxygen diving. One of the class decommissioned in FY 1993.

ORTOLAN   *3/1993, Giorgio Arra*

3 EDENTON CLASS: SALVAGE AND RESCUE SHIPS (ATS)

Name	No	Builders	Commissioned	F/S
EDENTON	ATS 1	Brooke Marine, Lowestoft, England	23 Jan 1971	AA
BEAUFORT	ATS 2	Brooke Marine, Lowestoft, England	22 Jan 1972	PA
BRUNSWICK	ATS 3	Brooke Marine, Lowestoft, England	19 Dec 1972	PA

Displacement, tons: 2929 full load
Dimensions, feet (metres): 282.6 × 50 × 15.1 *(86.1 × 15.2 × 4.6)*
Main machinery: 4 Paxman 12YJCM diesels; 6000 hp *(4.48 MW)* sustained; 2 shafts; cp props; bow thruster
Speed, knots: 16. **Range, miles:** 10 000 at 13 kts
Complement: 129 (7 officers)
Guns: 2 Oerlikon 20 mm Mk 68 (ATS 2 and 3). 2 Oerlikon 20 mm (twin) Mk 24 (ATS 1).
Radars: Navigation: Sperry SPS 53; I/J band.

Comment: Capable of (1) ocean towing, (2) supporting diver operations to depths of 850 ft, (3) lifting submerged objects weighing as much as 600 000 lb from a depth of 120 ft by static tidal lift or 30 000 lb by dynamic lift, (4) fighting ship fires. Fitted with 10 ton capacity crane forward and 20 ton capacity crane aft. ATS 1 was authorised in FY 1966; ATS 2 and ATS 3 in FY 1967. Three follow-on ships of this class were cancelled. Classification changed from salvage tug (ATS) to salvage and rescue ship (ATS) on 16 February 1971. Can carry the air-transportable Mk 1 Deep Diving System which can support four divers working in two-man shifts at depths to 850 ft. The system consists of a double-chamber recompression chamber and a personnel transfer capsule to transport divers between the ship and ocean floor. The ships' organic diving capability is compressed air only.

BEAUFORT   *6/1991, 92 Wing RAAF*

2 CHANTICLEER CLASS: SUBMARINE RESCUE SHIPS (ASR)

Name	No	Builders	Commissioned	F/S
KITTIWAKE	ASR 13	Savannah Machine & Foundry Co	18 July 1946	AA
SUNBIRD	ASR 15	Savannah Machine & Foundry Co	28 Jan 1947	AA

Displacement, tons: 1653 standard; 2320 full load
Dimensions, feet (metres): 251.5 × 44 × 16 *(76.7 × 13.4 × 4.9)*
Main machinery: Diesel-electric; 4 GM diesels; 3000 hp *(2.24 MW)*; 4 generators; 1 motor; 1 shaft
Speed, knots: 15
Complement: 103 (7 officers)
Guns: 2 Oerlikon 20 mm Mk 68.
Radars: Surface search: Sperry SPS 53; I/J band.

Comment: Equipped with powerful pumps, heavy air compressors, and rescue chambers for submarine salvage and rescue operations. Fitted for helium-oxygen diving. Underwater communications equipped. Former US Navy submarine rescue ships also transferred to the navies of Brazil and Turkey. Both scheduled to pay off in September 1994.

SUNBIRD   *5/1993, Giorgio Arra*

FLOATING DRY DOCKS

Comment: The US Navy operates a number of floating dry docks to supplement dry dock facilities at major naval activities, to support fleet ballistic missile submarines (SSBN) at advanced bases, and to provide repair capabilities in forward combat areas.
   The larger floating dry docks are made sectional to facilitate movement overseas and to render them self docking. The ARD-type docks have the forward end of their docking well closed by a structure resembling the bow of a ship to facilitate towing. Berthing facilities, repair shops, and machinery are housed in sides of larger docks. None is self-propelled.
   Each section of the AFDB docks has a lifting capacity of about 10 000 tons and is 256 × 80 ft, with wing walls 83 ft high; the wing walls, which contain compartments, fold down when the sections are towed.

LARGE AUXILIARY FLOATING DRY DOCKS (AFDB)

Name/No	Completed	Capacity (tons)	Construction*	Status
ARTISAN (AFDB 1)	1943	36 000	Steel (4)	Pearl Harbor (B-E), inactive
AFDB 2	1944	36 000	Steel (10)	Pearl Harbor (B-E), inactive
MACHINIST (AFDB 8)	1979	32 000	Steel (1)	Hawaii, inactive until 1996

* Figures in brackets indicate the number of sections of each dock remaining.

AFDB   *6/1990, van Ginderen collection*

YARD FLOATING DRY DOCKS (YFD)

Name/No	Completed	Capacity (tons)	Construction	Status
YFD 54	1943	5000	Wood	Commercial lease, Todd Pacific SY, Seattle, WA
YFD 69	1945	15 000	Steel (3)	Commercial lease, Port of Portland, OR
YFD 70	1945	15 000	Steel (3)	Commercial lease, Todd Pacific SY, Seattle, WA
YFD 83 (ex-AFDL 31)	1943	1000	Steel	US Coast Guard loan since Jan 1947

MEDIUM AUXILIARY FLOATING DRY DOCKS (AFDM)

Name/No	Completed	Capacity (tons)	Construction	Status
AFDM 2 (ex-YFD 4)	1942	12 000	Steel (3)	Commercial lease, Halter Marine, Beaumont, TX
AFDM 3 (ex-YFD 6)	1943	12 000	Steel (3)	Commercial lease, Bender SY, Mobile, AL
RESOURCEFUL (AFDM 5) (ex-YFD 21)	1943	17 200	Steel (3)	Active, Guam
COMPETENT (AFDM 6) (ex-YFD 62)	1944	10 000	Steel (3)	Active, Pearl Harbor
SUSTAIN (AFDM 7) (ex-YFD 63)	1945	13 500	Steel (3)	Active, Norfolk, VA. Two sections in reserve at James River
RICHLAND (AFDM 8) (ex-YFD 64)	1944	16 000	Steel (3)	Active, Guam, Marianas
RESOLUTE (AFDM 10)	1945	10 000	Steel (3)	Active, Norfolk, VA
STEADFAST (AFDM 14) (ex-YFD 71)	1945	9700	Steel (3)	Active, San Diego, CA

STEADFAST   9/1992, Stefan Terzibaschitsch

SMALL AUXILIARY FLOATING DRY DOCKS (AFDL)

Name/No	Completed	Capacity (tons)	Construction	Status
DYNAMIC (AFDL 6)	1944	950	Steel	Little Creek, VA
ADEPT (AFDL 23)	1944	1770	Steel	Commercial lease, Ingleside, TX
RELIANCE (AFDL 47)	1946	7000	Steel	Commercial lease, Deytens, SC

Sales: AFDL 1 to Dominican Republic; 4, Brazil; 5, Taiwan; 11, Kampuchea; 20, Philippines; 22, Vietnam; 24, Philippines; 26, Paraguay; 28, Mexico; 33, Peru; 34 and 36, Taiwan; 39, Brazil; 44, Philippines.

DYNAMIC   6/1986, Giorgio Arra

AUXILIARY REPAIR DRY DOCKS and MEDIUM AUXILIARY REPAIR DRY DOCKS (ARD and ARDM)

Name/No	Completed	Capacity (tons)	Construction	Status
WATERFORD (ARD 5)	1942	4500	Steel	New London, CT
SAN ONOFRE (ARD 30)	1944	4500	Steel	San Diego, CA
OAK RIDGE (ARDM 1) (ex-ARD 19)	1944	7500	Steel	Kings Bay, GA
ENDURANCE (ARDM 3) (ex-ARD 18)	1944	5600	Steel	Charleston, SC
SHIPPINGPORT (ARDM 4)	1979	7800	Steel	New London, CT
ARCO (ARDM 5)	1986	7800	Steel	San Diego, CA

Sales: ARD 2 to Mexico; 6, Pakistan; 8, Peru; 9, Taiwan; 11, Mexico; 12, Turkey; 13, Venezuela; 14, Brazil; 15, Mexico; 17, Ecuador; 22 *(Windsor)*, Taiwan; 23, Argentina; 24, Ecuador; 25, Chile; 28, Colombia; 29, Iran; 32, Chile.

SAN ONOFRE   9/1992, Stefan Terzibaschitsch

UNCLASSIFIED MISCELLANEOUS (IX)

Notes: (1) In addition to the vessels listed below it is planned to use one of the ex-Forrest Sherman class, *Decatur* as a Self Defense testing-ship, including high energy laser trials, starting in 1995.
(2) IX 502, 503, 504, 507 and 510 are barrack ships of mid-1940s vintage.
(3) IX 512 and 516 are decommissioned SSBNs used for propulsion plant training and IX 509 is a research barge.
(4) IX 513 *(Empress II)* was taken out of service in 1993.

Name	No	Under Way	F/S
CONSTITUTION	— (ex-IX 21)	22 July 1798	AA

Displacement, tons: 2200
Dimensions, feet (metres): 175.2 × 45 × 20 *(53.4 × 13.7 × 6.1)*
Speed, knots: 12 under sail
Complement: 49 (2 officers)

Comment: The oldest ship remaining on the Navy List. *Constitution* is one of the six frigates authorised by act of Congress on 27 March 1794. After rehabilitation was formerly placed in commission 1 July 1931. Served as Flagship of the First Naval District until 1 October 1977 when she was transferred to the control of the Director of Naval History, Department of the Navy. She is usually taken out every year into Boston Harbor and 'turned around' so her masts and spars will weather evenly. Overhauled at the former Boston Naval Shipyard from April 1973 to early 1975 to 'spruce her up' for the American Bicentennial. Entered dry dock again at the Charles Town Navy Yard, Boston, in July 1992 for inspection. Preservation activities started on 21 October 1992, the 196th birthday of the US Navy. The ship will stay in dry dock until December 1995, and is expected to be fully rigged and operational in March 1996. Repairs are being conducted by the Navy through the Naval Historical Center Detachment, Boston. The ship is open for public tours throughout the dry docking period. The scope of the current overhaul has been broadened to include the re-installation of key structural supports. Laser, ultrasonic and X-ray testing is being utilised to plan repairs.

CONSTITUTION   7/1992, van Ginderen Collection

IX 506 (ex-YFU 82)

Displacement, tons: 375 full load
Dimensions, feet (metres): 119 × 34 × 6 *(36.3 × 10.4 × 1.8)*
Main machinery: 4 GM 6-71 diesels; 696 hp *(519 kW)* sustained; 2 shafts
Speed, knots: 10
Complement: 12 (2 officers)

Comment: Reclassified 1 April 1978 for Naval Oceanographic Systems Center and fitted with a triple 324 mm torpedo tube mounting in the bows.

IX 506   5/1986, Giorgio Arra

Name	No	Builders	Commissioned	F/S
ORCA	IX 508 (ex-LCU 1618)	Gunderson Bros, Portland	1959	PSA

Comment: For general characteristics, see under LCU 1610 class in the *Amphibious Warfare* section. Conversion and overhaul in 1977 included installation of a bow thruster, a bridge and pilot house, and a hangar type enclosed storage area in the well deck, for the support of the Center's recovery vehicles CURV I and CURV II and installation of a crane. Reclassified as IX on 1 December 1979. Assigned to the Naval Command, Control, and Ocean Surveillance Center. Is being used for range support of test and evaluation programmes and is expected to be in service at least until 1995.

ORCA   *4/1988, Giorgio Arra*

Name	Builders	Commissioned
IX 514 (ex-*YFU 79*)	Pacific Coast Eng, Alameda	1968

Displacement, tons: 380 full load
Dimensions, feet (metres): 125 × 36 × 7.5 *(38.1 × 10.9 × 2.3)*
Main machinery: 4 GM 6-71 diesels; 696 hp *(519 kW)* sustained; 2 shafts
Speed, knots: 8

Comment: Harbour utility craft converted in 1986 with a flight deck covering two thirds of the vessel and a new bridge and flight control position at the forward end. Used for basic helicopter flight training at Pensacola, Florida.

1 SURFACE EFFECT SHIP (SES)

Name	Builders	Commissioned
IX 515 (SES-200) (ex-USCG *Dorado*)	Bell Halter, New Orleans	Feb 1979

Displacement, tons: 243 full load
Dimensions, feet (metres): 159.1 × 42.6 × 6; 3 on cushion *(48.5 × 13 × 1.8; 0.9)*
Main machinery: 2 MTU 16V 396 TB94 diesels (propulsion); 5800 hp(m) *(4.26 MW)* sustained; 2 KaMeWa waterjets
2 MTU 6V 396 TB83 diesels (lift); 1560 hp(m) *(1.15 MW)* sustained
Speed, knots: 45. **Range, miles:** 2950 at 30 kts
Complement: 22 (2 officers)

Comment: Transferred to Coast Guard operational control for joint Navy/Coast Guard trials, she was commissioned as USCG *Dorado* (WSES 1). After the conclusion of successful trials, which led to the Coast Guard ordering three more for duty in the Caribbean Sea (see Coast Guard Sea Bird class for details), she was decommissioned on 15 December 1981 and returned to the Navy. After 10 months (December 1981 to August 1982) modification at the Bell-Halter yard, New Orleans, which included the addition of a 50 ft *(15.2 m)* mid-section, she was returned to service 24 September 1982. The mid-section was added to increase the cushion length-to-beam ratio which leads to higher speeds. From January-June 1986, IX 515, carried out a series of trials in European waters in conjunction with NATO navies and in August-September 1986 in Canadian waters. In 1990 she was fitted with more powerful MTU diesels driving KaMeWa waterjets and new lift engines.
The IX 515 is a water-borne, air-supported craft with catamaran-style rigid sidewalls. It uses a cushion of air trapped between the sidewalls and flexible bow and stern seals to lift a large part of the hull clear of the water to reduce drag. A portion of the sidewall remains in the water to aid in stability and manoeuvrability. Modifications to the advanced ride control system were made in 1988 and 1989. Under operational control of Carderock Division, Naval Surface Warfare Center (formerly David Taylor Research Center), and based at Special Trials Unit Detachment, Naval Air Station, Patuxent River, MD. Will continue to serve as a high performance test platform for Navy HM&E and weapon system development programmes, and as operational demonstrator for an advanced naval vehicle hullform.

IX 515   *2/1990, Giorgio Arra*

MINOR AUXILIARIES

Note: As of January 1994, the US Navy had 987 active and 51 inactive service craft, primarily small craft, on the US Naval Vessel Register. A majority of them provide services to the fleet in various harbours and ports. Others are ocean-going ships such as *Elk River* that provide services to the fleet in the research area. Only the self-propelled craft and relics are listed in the Register. The non self-propelled craft, such as floating cranes and dredgers are not included. Most of the service craft are rated as 'active, in service', but a few are rated as 'in commission'.

Name	No	Builders	Commissioned	F/S
MONOB I	YAG 61 (ex-IX 309, ex-YW 87)	Zenith Dredge Co	Nov 1943	ASA

Displacement, tons: 440 light; 1390 full load
Dimensions, feet (metres): 191.9 × 33.1 × 15.7 *(58.5 × 10.1 × 4.8)*
Main machinery: 1 Caterpillar D 398 diesel; 850 hp *(634 kW)*; 1 shaft
Speed, knots: 9

Comment: *Monob I* is a mobile listening barge converted from a self-propelled water barge. Built in 1943 and completed conversion for acoustic research in May 1969. Conducts research for the Naval Mine Defence Laboratory, Panama City, Florida. Designation changed from IX 309 to YAG 61 on 1 July 1970. Planned to be replaced in 1995/96.

MONOB I   *7/1988, Giorgio Arra*

Name	No	Builders	Commissioned	F/S
DEER ISLAND	YAG 62	Halter Marine	1962	ASA

Displacement, tons: 400 full load
Dimensions, feet (metres): 120.1 × 27.9 × 6.9 *(36.6 × 8.5 × 2.1)*
Speed, knots: 10
Complement: 20

Comment: Acquired for use in tests in sound quieting for surface vessels. Based at Port Everglades, Florida. Put on the Naval Vessel Register on 15 March 1982. Planned to be replaced by TAG and TAGOS ships.

DEER ISLAND   *5/1992, Giorgio Arra*

3 FERRYBOATS (YFB)

YFB 83   **YFB 88**   **YFB 89**

Comment: 390 ton ferryboats built in the late 1960s and used to transport personnel and vehicles in large harbours; self-propelled. Three others are inactive.

11 DIVING TENDERS (YDT)

Comment: Tenders used to support shallow-water diving operations. Of 1940s vintage are *Phoebus* YDT 14 (ex-YF 294), and *Suitland* YDT 15 (ex-YF 336). There is also a non self-propelled vessel *Tom O'Malley* YDT 16 (ex-YFNB 43). More recent acquisitions include eight Peterson Dive Boats with portable standardised diving systems delivered between November 1989 and August 1990. The boats are 50 ft in length, displace some 42 tons and are capable of 9 knots on two diesels. The Diving Module has its own diesel generator.

DIVING TENDER   *11/1990, Peterson Builders*

2 HARBOUR UTILITY CRAFT LCU TYPE (YFU)

YFU 83   YFU 91 (ex-LCU 1608)

Comment: Former utility landing craft employed primarily as harbour and coastal cargo craft (see section on Landing Craft for basic characteristics).

YFU 83   *11/1993, Maritime Photographic*

8 FUEL OIL BARGES (YO)

YO 47, 129, 203, 220, 223-225, 230

Comment: Small liquid fuel carriers intended to fuel ships where no pierside fuelling facilities are available, self-propelled; *47* is in reserve. In addition there are 51 non self-propelled (YON).

YO 203   *9/1992, Stefan Terzibaschitsch*

5 GASOLINE BARGES (YOG)

YOG 58, 78, 88, 93, 196

Comment: Similar to the fuel barges (YO), but carry about 950 tons of gasoline and aviation fuels; self-propelled. *YOG 58* and *93* are in reserve. In addition there are 12 non-self-propelled (YOGN).

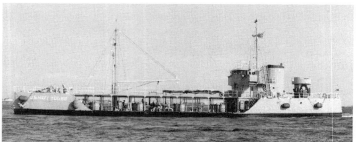

YOG 88   *4/1988, Giorgio Arra*

4 TORPEDO TRIALS CRAFT (YTT)

CAPE FLATTERY YTT 9	**DISCOVERY BAY** YTT 11
BATTLE POINT YTT 10	**AGATE PASS** YTT 12

Displacement, tons: 1168 full load
Dimensions, feet (metres): 186.5 × 40 × 10.5 *(56.9 × 12.2 × 3.2)*
Main machinery: 1 Cummins KTA50-M diesel; 1250 hp *(932 kW)* sustained; 1 shaft; 1 bow thruster; 400 hp *(298 kW)*; 2 stern thrusters; 600 hp *(448 kW)*
Speed, knots: 11. **Range, miles:** 1000 at 10 kts
Complement: 31 plus 9 spare berths

Comment: Built by McDermott Shipyard, Morgan City, and delivered in 1990-91. Fitted with two 21 in Mk 59 and three (one triple) 12.75 in Mk 32 Mod 5 torpedo tubes. These vessels have replaced the YFRT covered lighters for torpedo trials and development. Underwater recovery vessels SORD 4, TROV and CURV.

CAPE FLATTERY   *1990, McDermott Shipyard*

20 TORPEDO RETRIEVERS (TR and TWR)

Comment: Four different types spread around the Fleet bases and at AUTEC.

TWR 1   *6/1989, Giorgio Arra*

TWR 821   *3/1992, Giorgio Arra*

TWR 3   *4/1991, Giorgio Arra*

27 PATROL CRAFT (YP)

YP 678-705

Displacement, tons: 167 full load
Dimensions, feet (metres): 108 × 24 × 5.9 *(32.9 × 7.3 × 1.8)*
Main machinery: 2 Detroit 12V-71 diesels; 680 hp *(507 kW)* sustained; 2 shafts
Speed, knots: 13.3. **Range, miles:** 1500 at 12 kts
Complement: 6 (2 officers) plus 24 midshipmen
Radars: Navigation: I band.

Comment: Built in the 1980s by Peterson Builders and Marinette Marine, both in Wisconsin. Used for instruction in seamanship and navigation at the US Naval Academy, Annapolis, MD, and Naval Officer Candidate School and Surface Warfare Officers School, both at Newport, RI. Some earlier versions converted for mine countermeasures operations and assigned to the COOP project.

YP 680   6/1993, Giorgio Arra

TUGS

76 LARGE HARBOUR TUGS (YTB)

EDENSHAW	YTB 752	OPELIKA	YTB 798
OSHKOSH	YTB 757	NATCHITOCHES	YTB 799
PADUCAH	YTB 758	PALATKA	YTB 801
BOGALUSA	YTB 759	CHERAW	YTB 802
NATICK	YTB 760	NANTICOKE	YTB 803
OTTUMWA	YTB 761	AHOSKIE	YTB 804
TUSCUMBIA	YTB 762	OCALA	YTB 805
MUSKEGON	YTB 763	TUSKEGEE	YTB 806
MISHAWAKA	YTB 764	MASSAPEQUA	YTB 807
OKMULGEE	YTB 765	WENATCHEE	YTB 808
WAPAKONETA	YTB 766	AGAWAM	YTB 809
APALACHICOLA	YTB 767	ANOKA	YTB 810
ARCATA	YTB 768	HOUMA	YTB 811
CHESANING	YTB 769	ACCONAC	YTB 812
DAHLONEGA	YTB 770	POUGHKEEPSIE	YTB 813
KEOKUK	YTB 771	WAXAHATCHIE	YTB 814
NASHUA	YTB 774	NEODESHA	YTB 815
WAUWATOSA	YTB 775	CAMPTI	YTB 816
WEEHAWKEN	YTB 776	HYANNIS	YTB 817
NOGALES	YTB 777	MECOSTA	YTB 818
APOPKA	YTB 778	IUKA	YTB 819
MANHATTAN	YTB 779	WANAMASSA	YTB 820
SAUGUS	YTB 780	TONTOGANY	YTB 821
NIANTIC	YTB 781	PAWHUSKA	YTB 822
MANISTEE	YTB 782	CANONCHET	YTB 823
REDWING	YTB 783	SANTAQUIN	YTB 824
KALISPELL	YTB 784	WATHENA	YTB 825
WINNEMUCCA	YTB 785	WASHTUCNA	YTB 826
KITTANNING	YTB 787	CHETEK	YTB 827
WAPATO	YTB 788	CATAHECASSA	YTB 828
TOMAHAWK	YTB 789	METACOM	YTB 829
MENOMINEE	YTB 790	PUSHMATAHA	YTB 830
MARINETTE	YTB 791	DEKANAWIDA	YTB 831
ANTIGO	YTB 792	PETALESHARO	YTB 832
PIQUA	YTB 793	SHABONEE	YTB 833
MANDAN	YTB 794	NEWGAGON	YTB 834
KETCHIKAN	YTB 795	SKENANDOA	YTB 835
SACO	YTB 796	POKAGON	YTB 836
TAMAQUA	YTB 797		

Displacement, tons: 356 full load
Dimensions, feet (metres): 109 × 30 × 13.8 *(33.2 × 9.1 × 4.2)*
Main machinery: 2 Fairbanks-Morse 38D8-1/8-12 diesels; 7000 hp *(5.2 MW)* sustained; 2 shafts
Speed, knots: 12. **Range, miles:** 2000 at 12 kts
Complement: 10-12

Comment: Built between 1959 and 1975. Two transferred to Saudi Arabia in 1975. In future tugs will be provided by contractors and numbers are being reduced.

WAPATO   12/1993, Maritime Photographic

RESEARCH SHIPS

Notes: (1) There are many naval associated research vessels which are civilian manned and not carried on the US Naval Vessel Register. In addition civilian ships are leased for short periods to support a particular research project or trial. Some of those recently employed include *RSB-1* (missile booster recovery), *Acoustic Pioneer* and *Acoustic Explorer* (acoustic research), *Seacon* (missile retriever) and *Erline* (hydrographic research).
(2) The ex-GDR Tarantul class *Hiddensee* is operated by Dynacorp with a crew of 12.

SEACON (missile retriever)   5/1993, Giorgio Arra

ACOUSTIC PIONEER   2/1993, Giorgio Arra

BEAGLE   3/1992, J Partington

3 ASHEVILLE CLASS

ATHENA (ex-*Chehalis*)   **ATHENA II** (ex-*Grand Rapids*)   **LAUREN** (ex-*Douglas*)

Displacement, tons: 245 full load
Dimensions, feet (metres): 164.5 × 23.8 × 9.5 *(50.1 × 7.3 × 2.9)*
Main machinery: CODOG; 1 GE LM 1500 gas-turbine; 12 500 hp *(9.3 MW)*; 2 Cummins VT12-875 diesels; 1450 hp *(1.07 MW)*; 2 shafts
Speed, knots: 16. **Range, miles:** 1700 at 16 kts
Complement: 22

Comment: All built 1969-71. Work for the Ships Research and Development centre, Carderock. Disarmed except *Lauren* which has maintained its military appearance.

ATHENA II   6/1993, Giorgio Arra

LAUREN   11/1991, Giorgio Arra

SEA SHADOW

Displacement, tons: 560 full load
Dimensions, feet (metres): 160 × 70 × 14 *(48.8 × 21.3 × 4.3)*
Main machinery: Diesel-electric; 2 shafts
Speed, knots: 13
Complement: 4

Comment: Built by Lockheed in 1983/84. Testing started in 1985 but the ship was then laid up until April 1993 when testing resumed off Santa Cruz island, southern California. There is a stealth ship prototype of SWATH design with sides angled at 45° to minimise the radar cross section. Operated by Lockheed for testing all aspects of stealth technology.

SEA SHADOW   *1993, Lockheed*

MILITARY SEALIFT COMMAND (MSC)

Notes: (1) The US Navy's Military Sealift Command has the responsibility for providing sealift for all components of the Department of Defense. In 1990-91, the US response to the Iraqi invasion of Kuwait resulted in MSC having to use almost all of its available and usable sealift and support ship assets to move military equipment to the Middle East and to provide maintenance and medical support to US forces transported to that area.

This mobilisation and supply effort included the activation of all eight fast sealift ships (former SL-7s) and 79 of the 96 ships in the Ready Reserve Force at the time of the invasion, including all 17 Ro-Ros in the RRF. It required the movement of two Maritime Prepositioning Ship squadrons (nine ships loaded with equipment for two Marine Expeditionary Brigades) from Guam and Diego Garcia to Saudi Arabia and of the Afloat Prepositioning Force (12 ships loaded with equipment for the Army and the Air Force). Later the third Maritime Prepositioning Ship squadron was moved from the Atlantic to the combat area. The two hospital ships were sailed immediately to the Middle East, as were the two aviation support ships. With usable MSC assets exhausted, MSC began chartering ships, both US flag and foreign, and by the end of 1991 a total of 127 US flag and 293 foreign ships had been chartered. At the start of the war with Iraq on 17 January 1991, MSC had delivered 1.7 million short tons of cargo to Saudi Arabia, had another half million tons under way, and had delivered 3.9 million tons of POL. In all, more than 2.5 million short tons of cargo and 6.1 million tons of POL were moved to the Middle East.

To meet manning requirements for all of the ships activated more than 3000 merchant seamen were hired by the Maritime Administration at MSC's request. Difficulties were encountered in finding enough qualified personnel to man the steam propulsion plants which were predominant in the RRF.

This operation focused attention on a number of basic US sealift problems:
(a) There was a shortage of Ro-Ros, the types of ships most needed to handle military rolling stock.
(b) Over the years, insufficient funds had been made available to properly maintain RRF ships and have them ready for emergencies. As a consequence, many could not be activated.
(c) There are not enough fast sealift ships available. The United States only has eight, and seven of these (one broke down on its initial voyage) were operated at a tempo that caused maintenance problems. Those seven ships carried nine per cent of the cargo moved to and from the Middle East. Six of the class were again active in late 1992/93 to move equipment and supplies to Somalia.
(2) In January 1992, a Mobility Requirements Study calling for DoD to acquire at least 20 large medium-speed (24 kts) roll-on/roll-off ships was submitted to Congress. These were defined as having 35 302 m² of total capacity, with 27 870 m² available for prepositioning. $1.8 billion already had been appropriated for construction and conversion of such ships. The funding was increased by another $600 million which was included in the FY 1993 defence budget. Contracts for the detailed design and conversion of five ships awarded to National Steel and Shipbuilding (three ships) and Newport News Shipbuilding (two ships) on 30 July 1993. The five ships to be converted are foreign-built. On 2 and 15 September 1993 contracts for detailed design and construction of one lead ship and five additional ships were awarded to National Steel and to Avondale Industries.
(3) Other MSC ships such as ocean surveillance vessels, research ships, and scientific support ships continue their routine operations. At the beginning of 1994 a total of 15 ships was assigned to special mission support, and 43 to MSC's fleet auxiliary force.
(4) MSC headquarters are in the Washington Navy Yard. The organisation is commanded by a vice admiral, and its four principal area commands by captains.
(5) No ship of the Military Sealift Command is armed in peacetime.
(6) Military Sealift Command nucleus ships are assigned standard US Navy hull designations with the added prefix 'T'. Funnels have black, grey, blue and gold horizontal bands.
(7) On 1 October 1987, the transportation elements of the three services were merged into the US Transportation Command, a unified command with headquarters at Scott AFB, Illinois, and reporting directly to the Joint Chiefs of Staff. Commander USTRANSCOM (Military Sealift Command, Military Airlift Command, and Military Traffic Management Command) has exercised fiscal and operational control of all three components since mid-1992.

1 KILAUEA CLASS: AMMUNITION SHIP (AE)

Name	No	Commissioned	F/S
KILAUEA	T-AE 26	10 Aug 1968	TPA

Comment: Transferred to MSC for activation and operation 1 October 1980. Ship underwent a civilian modification (CIVMOD) overhaul from which extensive superstructure work was accomplished in the living spaces. All gear from station seven was removed. Main armament was taken out. *Kilauea* has 7 UNREP stations operational: 4 port, 3 stbd and has been outfitted with a commercial type satellite navigation system. For particulars refer to Kilauea class in Auxiliaries section. Complement is 120 civilians and 67 naval personnel (for communications equipment and helicopter handling). Six others of the class are planned to transfer starting with *Flint* in FY 1995.

KILAUEA   *10/1989, L/S P Steele RAN*

4 MARS CLASS: COMBAT STORE SHIPS (AFS)

Name	No	Builders	Commissioned	F/S
CONCORD	T-AFS 5	National Steel & Shipbuilding Co	27 Nov 1968	TPA
MARS	T-AFS 1	National Steel & Shipbuilding Co	21 Dec 1963	TPA
SAN DIEGO	T-AFS 6	National Steel & Shipbuilding Co	24 May 1969	TAA
SAN JOSE	T-AFS 7	National Steel & Shipbuilding Co	23 Oct 1970	TAA

Displacement, tons: 9200 light; 15 900-18 663 full load
Dimensions, feet (metres): 581 × 79 × 24 *(177.1 × 24.1 × 7.3)*
Main machinery: 3 Babcock & Wilcox boilers; 580 psi *(40.8 kg/cm sq)*; 825°F *(440°C)*; 1 De Laval turbine (Westinghouse in AFS 6); 22 000 hp *(16.4 MW)*; 1 shaft
Speed, knots: 20. **Range, miles:** 10 000 at 18 kts
Complement: 135
Cargo capacity: 2625 tons dry stores; 1300 tons refrigerated stores (varies with specific loadings)
Radars: Surface search: Raytheon SPS 10 series; G band.
Navigation: Marconi LN 66.
Tacan: URN 25.
Helicopters: 2 UH-46E Sea Knight normally assigned.

Comment: *Concord* transferred to MSC on 15 October 1992 after disarming and conversion to a civilian crew. *Mars* followed on 1 February 1993, *San Diego* on 11 August 1993 and *San Jose* on 2 November 1993. *Niagara Falls* is scheduled for transfer in September 1994. All are planned to have accommodation improvements and stores lifts installed in the late 1990s. Four more of the class are scheduled to be similarly converted. These ships carry comprehensive inventories of aviation spare parts as well as the cargo listed above.

CONCORD   *10/1992, A Sheldon Duplaix*

1 HAYES CLASS: ACOUSTIC RESEARCH SHIP (AG)

Name	No	Builders	Completed	F/S
HAYES	T-AG 195 (ex-AGOR 16)	Todd Shipyards, Seattle	21 July 1971	TAA

Displacement, tons: 4037 full load
Dimensions, feet (metres): 256.5 × 75 (see *Comment*) × 22 *(78.2 × 22.9 × 6.7)*
Main machinery: Diesel-electric; 2 Caterpillar 3516TA diesels; 3620 hp *(2.7 MW)* sustained; 2 generators; 2 Westinghouse motors; 2400 hp *(1.79 MW)*; 2 auxiliary diesels (for creep speed); 330 hp *(246 kW)*; 2 shafts; cp props
Speed, knots: 10. **Range, miles:** 2000 at 10 kts
Complement: 74 (10 officers) including scientists
Radars: Navigation: Raytheon TM 1650/6X and TM 1660/12S; I band.

Comment: *Hayes* is one of two classes of US naval ships to have a catamaran hull, the other being the ASR 21 class submarine rescue ship. Laid down 12 November 1969; launched 2 July 1970. To Ready Reserve 10 June 1983 and transferred to James River (Maritime Administration) for lay-up in 1984 having been too costly to operate. Under FY 1986 programme being converted to Acoustic Research Ship (AG) in place of *Monob I* (YAG 61); reclassified T-AG 195 and completed in early 1992 after five years work in two shipyards. Mission is to transport, deploy and retrieve acoustic arrays, to conduct acoustic surveys in support of the submarine noise reduction programme and to carry out acoustic testing. Catamaran hull design provides large deck working area, centre well for operating equipment at great depths, and removes laboratory areas from main propulsion machinery. Each hull is 246 ft long and 24 ft wide (maximum). There are three 36 in diameter instrument wells in addition to the main centre well.

HAYES   *2/1992*

3 SIRIUS (LYNESS) CLASS: COMBAT STORES SHIP (AFS)

Name	No	Builders	Commissioned	F/S
SIRIUS (ex-RFA *Lyness*)	T-AFS 8	Swan Hunter & Wigham Richardson Ltd, Wallsend-on-Tyne	22 Dec 1966	TAA
SPICA (ex-RFA *Tarbatness*)	T-AFS 9	Swan Hunter & Wigham Richardson Ltd, Wallsend-on-Tyne	21 Mar 1967	TPA
SATURN (ex-RFA *Stromness*)	T-AFS 10	Swan Hunter & Wigham Richardson Ltd, Wallsend-on-Tyne	10 Aug 1967	TAA

Displacement, tons: 9010 light; 16 792 full load
Measurement, tons: 7782 dwt; 12 359 gross; 4744 net
Dimensions, feet (metres): 524 × 72 × 22 *(159.7 × 22 × 6.7)*
Main machinery: 1 Wallsend-Sulzer 8RD76 diesel; 11 520 hp *(8.59 MW)*; 1 shaft
Speed, knots: 18. **Range, miles:** 12 000 at 16 kts
Complement: 116 (with a Navy contingent of 18 (1 officer))
Cargo capacity: 8313 cu m dry; 3921 cu m frozen
Helicopters: 2 UH-46E Sea Knight.

Comment: Lifts and mobile appliances for handling stores internally, and a new replenishment at sea system and a helicopter landing platform for transferring loads at sea. A feature of the ship is the use of closed-circuit television to monitor the movement of stores. Air-conditioned. After a period of charter *Sirius* was purchased from the UK on 1 March 1982, *Spica* on 30 September 1982 and *Saturn* on 1 October 1983.

SIRIUS *9/1993, G Toremans*

1 CONVERTED COMPASS ISLAND CLASS: MISSILE RANGE INSTRUMENTATION SHIP (AGM)

Name	No	Builders	Commissioned	F/S
OBSERVATION ISLAND (ex-*Empire State Mariner*)	T-AGM 23 (ex-AG 154, ex-YAG 57)	New York Shipbuilding	5 Dec 1958	TPA

Displacement, tons: 13 060 light; 17 015 full load
Dimensions, feet (metres): 564 × 76 × 25 *(171.6 × 23.2 × 7.6)*
Main machinery: 2 Foster-Wheeler boilers; 600 psi *(42.3 kg/cm sq)*; 875°F *(467°C)*; 1 GE turbine; 19 250 hp *(14.36 MW)*; 1 shaft
Speed, knots: 20. **Range, miles:** 17 000 at 15 kts
Complement: 143 civilian (20 officers, 60-65 technicians)
Missiles: SLBM: She fired the first ship-launched Polaris missile at sea on 27 August 1959. Refitted to fire the improved Poseidon missile in 1969 and launched the first Poseidon test missile fired afloat on 16 December 1969.
Radars: Navigation: Raytheon 1650/9X and 1660/12S; I band.

Comment: Built as a Mariner class merchant ship (C4-S-A1 type); launched on 15 August 1953; acquired by the Navy on 10 September 1956 for use as a Fleet Ballistic Missile (FBM) test ship. Converted at Norfolk Naval Shipyard. In reserve from September 1972. On 18 August 1977, *Observation Island* was reacquired by the US Navy from the Maritime Administration and transferred to the Military Sealift Command. Reclassified AGM 23 on 1 May 1979. Converted to Missile Range Instrumentation Ship from July 1979-April 1981 at Maryland SB and DD Co to carry an Air Force shipborne phased-array radar system (Cobra Judy) for collection of data on foreign ballistic missile tests. Operated by the Navy for the US Air Force Intelligence command, Patrick Air Force Base, Florida.

OBSERVATION ISLAND *5/1993, Giorgio Arra*

1 CONVERTED HASKELL CLASS: MISSILE RANGE INSTRUMENTATION SHIP (AGM)

Name	No	Builders	Commissioned	F/S
RANGE SENTINEL (ex-*Sherburne*)	T-AGM 22 (ex-APA 205)	Permanente Metals Corp, Richmond, CA	20 Sep 1944	TAA

Displacement, tons: 8853 light; 12 170 full load
Dimensions, feet (metres): 455 × 62 × 26 *(138.7 × 18.9 × 7.9)*
Main machinery: 2 Combustion Engineering boilers; 525 psi *(37 kg/cm sq)*; 750°F *(399°C)*; 1 Westinghouse turbine; 8500 hp *(6.34 MW)*; 1 shaft
Speed, knots: 17.7. **Range, miles:** 12 000 at 15 kts
Complement: 81 civilian (15 officers, 12 technical personnel); 43 naval (3 officers)
Radars: Navigation: Raytheon TM 1650/6X and TM 1660/12S; I band.

Comment: Former attack transport (APA) converted specifically to serve as a range instrumentation ship in support of the Fleet Ballistic Missile (FBM) programme. Maritime Administration VC2-S-AP5 type. Reclassified AGM 22 on 16 April 1969 and renamed *Range Sentinel* on 26 April 1971. In Maritime Administration reserve from 1 October 1958 until 22 October 1969. Converted from October 1969 to October 1971; placed in service as T-AGM 22 on 14 October 1971. Has telemetry and missile tracking equipment.

RANGE SENTINEL *4/1993, Giorgio Arra*

1 CONVERTED MISSION CLASS: NAVIGATION RESEARCH SHIP (AG)

Name	No	Builders	Completed	F/S
VANGUARD (ex-*Muscle Shoals*, ex-*Mission San Fernando*)	T-AG 194 (ex-AGM 19, ex-AO 122)	Marine Ship Corp, Sausalito, CA	29 Feb 1944	TAA

Displacement, tons: 13 882 light; 24 710 full load
Dimensions, feet (metres): 595 × 75 × 25 *(181.4 × 22.9 × 7.6)*
Main machinery: Turbo-electric; 2 Babcock & Wilcox boilers; 600 psi *(42.3 kg/cm sq)*; 825°F *(440°C)*; Westinghouse turbo-generators; 10 000 hp *(7.46 MW)*; 1 motor; 1 shaft
Speed, knots: 14. **Range, miles:** 25 000 at 13 kts
Complement: 45 plus 18 scientists plus 141 spare
Radars: Navigation: Raytheon TM 1650/9X and TM 1660/12S; I band.

Comment: *Vanguard* supports sponsor programmes in navigation research by providing a platform for testing fleet ballistic missile guidance and missile systems. Reclassified as AG 194 in September 1980. Is under operational control of Director, Strategic Systems Program.

VANGUARD *4/1993, Giorgio Arra*

2 GYRE CLASS: OCEANOGRAPHIC RESEARCH SHIPS (AGOR)

Name	No	Builders	Completed	F/S
GYRE	AGOR 21	Halter Marine	14 Nov 1973	Loan
MOANA WAVE	AGOR 22	Halter Marine	16 Jan 1974	Loan

Displacement, tons: 1427 (AGOR 21), 1853 (AGOR 22) full load
Dimensions, feet (metres): 174 × 36 × 13 *(53 × 11 × 4)* (AGOR 21)
210 × 36 × 13 *(64 × 11 × 4)* (AGOR 22)
Main machinery: 2 Caterpillar diesels; 1700 hp *(1.27 MW)*; 2 shafts; cp props; bow thruster; 150 hp *(112 kW)*
Speed, knots: 11.5. **Range, miles:** 12 000 at 10 kts
Complement: 13 plus 19 scientists

Comment: Based on a commercial ship design. Open deck aft provides space for equipment vans to permit rapid change of mission capabilities. Single hard-chine hulls. *Moana Wave* was lengthened in 1984 and fitted with a laboratory at the stern. They are assigned for operation to Texas A & M University and the University of Hawaii, respectively and are not MSC ships.

MOANA WAVE *1991, van Ginderen Collection*

2 MELVILLE CLASS: OCEANOGRAPHIC RESEARCH SHIPS (AGOR)

Name	No	Builders	Completed	F/S
MELVILLE	AGOR 14	Defoe SB Co, Bay City, MI	27 Aug 1969	Loan
KNORR	AGOR 15	Defoe SB Co, Bay City, MI	14 Jan 1970	Loan

Displacement, tons: 2670 full load
Dimensions, feet (metres): 278.9 × 46.3 × 15.1 *(85 × 14.1 × 4.6)*
Main machinery: Diesel-electric; 4 diesel generators; 3 motors; 3000 hp *(2.24 MW)*; 3 shafts (2 aft, 1 fwd)
Speed, knots: 14. **Range, miles:** 12 000 at 12 kts
Complement: 58 (9 officers) plus 33 scientists

Comment: *Melville* operated by Scripps Institution of Oceanography and *Knorr* by Woods Hole Oceanography Institution for the Office of Naval Research, under technical control of the Oceanographer of the Navy. These ships are not part of the MSC. Fitted with internal wells for lowering equipment, underwater lights and observation ports. Facilities for handling small research submersibles. Problems with the propulsion system have led to major modifications including electric drive (vice the original mechanical) and the insertion of a 34 ft central section increasing the displacement from the original 1915 tons and allowing better accommodation and improved laboratory spaces. The forward propeller is retractable. These ships are highly manoeuvrable for precise position keeping.

MELVILLE   *1986, Giorgio Arra*

4 VICTORIOUS CLASS: OCEAN SURVEILLANCE SHIPS (AGOS)

Name	No	Builders	Completed	F/S
VICTORIOUS	T-AGOS 19	McDermott Marine	5 Sep 1991	TPA
ABLE	T-AGOS 20	McDermott Marine	22 July 1992	TAA
EFFECTIVE	T-AGOS 21	McDermott Marine	27 Jan 1993	TPA
LOYAL	T-AGOS 22	McDermott Marine	1 July 1993	TAA

Displacement, tons: 3396 full load
Dimensions, feet (metres): 234.5 × 93.6 × 24.8 *(71.5 × 28.5 × 7.6)*
Main machinery: Diesel-electric; 4 Caterpillar 3512TA diesels; 5440 hp *(4 MW)* sustained; 2 GE motors; 3200 hp *(2.39 MW)*; 2 shafts; 2 bow thrusters; 2400 hp *(1.79 MW)*
Speed, knots: 16; 3 when towing
Complement: 34 (22 civilian, 12 Navy)
Radars: Navigation: Two Raytheon; I band.
Sonars: UQQ 2 SURTASS and LFA; towed array; passive/active surveillance.

Comment: All of SWATH design because of its greater stability at slow speeds in high latitudes under adverse weather conditions. A contract for the first SWATH ship, T-AGOS 19, was awarded in November 1986, and options for the next three were exercised in October 1988. Same WSC-6 communications, links and operating procedures as the Stalwart class. T-AGOS 20 is conducting trials with a Reduced Diameter Array (RDA) with an enhanced signal processor. The Low Frequency Active component is producing both mono and bistatic performance against submerged diesel submarines in shallow water. Short thin-line twin arrays are also being developed.

VICTORIOUS   *8/1992, P Campbell*

ABLE   *9/1992, Stefan Terzibaschitsch*

1 + 3 THOMAS G THOMPSON CLASS: OCEANOGRAPHIC RESEARCH SHIPS (AGOR)

Name	No	Builders	In Service	F/S
THOMAS G THOMPSON (ex-*Ewing*)	AGOR-23	Halter Marine	July 1992	Loan
ROGER REVELLE	AGOR-24	Halter Marine	Dec 1996	Bldg
—	AGOR-25	Halter Marine	1997	Bldg
—	—	Halter Marine	1997	Bldg/ NOAA

Displacement, tons: 3251 full load
Dimensions, feet (metres): 274 oa; 246.8 wl × 52.5 × 19 *(83.5; 75.2 × 16 × 5.6)*
Main machinery: Diesel-electric; 6 diesel generators; 6.65 MW (3 × 1.5 MW and 3 × 715 kW); 2 motors; 6000 hp *(4.48 MW)*; 2 shafts; bow thruster; 1140 hp *(850 kW)*
Speed, knots: 15. **Range, miles:** 8000 at 12 kts
Complement: 20 plus 30 scientists plus 20 spare berths
Sonars: Atlas Elektronik Hydrographic.

Comment: *Thomas G Thompson* is the first of a new class of oceanographic research vessels capable of operating worldwide in all seasons and suitable for use by navy laboratories, contractors and academic institutions; laid down 23 March 1989, launched 27 July 1990 and delivered 8 July 1991. Dynamic positioning system enables station to be held within 300 ft of a point. 4000 sq ft of laboratories. Loaned to the University of Washington and sponsored by the Chief of Naval Research, these ships are not part of the MSC. Ships in this series may be of different hull designs and will be able to meet changing oceanographic requirements for general, year-round, worldwide research. This will include launching, towing and recovering a variety of equipment. The ships will also be involved in hydrographic data collection. The second ship of the class was authorised in FY 1992, ordered 11 January 1993 from Trinity Marine and will be delivered in May 1996. The third and fourth were ordered from Trinity Marine in early 1994. AGOR-25 will be operated by the Woods Hole Oceanographic Institution and the fourth of class by NOAA.

THOMAS G THOMPSON   *1992, Halter Marine*

10 STALWART CLASS: OCEAN SURVEILLANCE SHIPS (AGOS)

Name	No	Laid down	Completed	F/S
STALWART	T-AGOS 1	3 Apr 1982	9 Nov 1984	TAA
PERSISTENT	T-AGOS 6	22 Oct 1984	14 Aug 1985	TAA
INDOMITABLE	T-AGOS 7	26 Jan 1985	26 Nov 1985	TAA
PREVAIL	T-AGOS 8	13 Mar 1985	5 Mar 1986	TAA
ASSERTIVE	T-AGOS 9	30 July 1985	12 Sep 1986	TPA
INVINCIBLE	T-AGOS 10	8 Nov 1985	30 Jan 1987	TAA
AUDACIOUS (ex-*Dauntless*)	T-AGOS 11	29 Feb 1986	18 June 1989	TPA
BOLD (ex-*Vigorous*)	T-AGOS 12	13 June 1988	20 Oct 1989	TAA
CAPABLE	T-AGOS 16	17 Oct 1987	8 July 1989	TAA
TENACIOUS (ex-*Intrepid*)	T-AGOS 17	26 Feb 1988	8 Nov 1989	TPA

Displacement, tons: 2262 full load
Dimensions, feet (metres): 224 × 43 × 14.9 *(68.3 × 13.1 × 4.5)*
Main machinery: Diesel-electric; 4 Caterpillar D 398B diesel generators; 3200 hp *(2.39 MW)*; 2 motors; 1600 hp *(1.2 MW)*; 2 shafts; bow thruster; 550 hp *(410 kW)*
Speed, knots: 11; 3 when towing. **Range, miles:** 4000 at 11 kts; 6450 at 3 kts
Complement: 30-33 (9 officers) (21 civilian manning, 9-12 Navy contingent)
Radars: Navigation: Two Raytheon; I band.
Sonars: UQQ2 SURTASS; towed array; passive surveillance (in five of the class).

Comment: This programme completed after several rocky years stemming from the financial difficulties of Tacoma Boatbuilding Co, which built the first eight ships but initially was unable to complete T-AGOS 9-12 before filing for bankruptcy. Halter Marine built T-AGOS 13-18. The ships are operated and maintained by civilian contractors. SURTASS is a linear array of 8575 ft *(2614 m)* deployed on a 6000 ft *(1829 m)* tow cable and neutrally buoyant. The array can operate at depths between 500 and 1500 ft. Information from the array is relayed via WSC-6 (SHF) SATCOM link to shore. SURTASS patrols are of 60-90 days duration which even with passive tank stabilisation is a long time to wallow around at 3 kts. Three of the ships have been converted for utilisation in the drug interdiction campaign. Four are involved in Atlantic undersea surveillance, and one in similar operations in the Pacific. One is involved in research and development activity in the Pacific, and another is in a reduced operating status. Six others of the class have been transferred to other government agencies including two to the Coast Guard. All 16 could be converted back to SURTASS operations if required.

BOLD   *10/1992, Giorgio Arra*

0 + 1 IMPECCABLE CLASS: OCEAN SURVEILLANCE SHIP (AGOS)

Name	No	Builders	Completed	F/S
IMPECCABLE	T-AGOS 23	Tampa Shipyard	1995	Bldg

Displacement, tons: 5370 full load
Dimensions, feet (metres): 281.5 × 95.8 × 26 *(85.8 × 29.2 × 7.9)*
Main machinery: Diesel-electric; 3 GM EMD 12-645F7B diesel generators; 5.48 MW *(60 Hz)* sustained; 2 Westinghouse motors; 5000 hp *(3.73 MW)*; 2 shafts; 2 omni-thruster hydrojets; 1800 hp *(1.34 MW)*
Speed, knots: 12; 3 when towing
Complement: 45 (26 civilian, 19 Navy)

Comment: Hull form based on that of *Victorious*. Acoustic systems should include an active low frequency towed array, which has a series of modules each of which houses two high powered transducers. These can be used with either mono or bistatic receivers. First of the class included in FY 1990 budget but a contract was not awarded until March 1991. Laid down 2 February 1993. Ship was 60 per cent complete when shipyard encountered difficulties that led to termination in October 1993 of the contract for completion of two Kaiser class oilers. Work also stopped on *Impeccable*, and the construction contract was also cancelled. A decision with regard to her future status is to be made. A second ship of the class will not now be procured, as the demand for ships of this type has declined sharply.

IMPECCABLE (artist's impression)   1991, Tampa Shipyard

4 SILAS BENT and WILKES CLASSES: SURVEYING SHIPS (AGS)

Name	No	Builders	Completed	F/S
SILAS BENT	T-AGS 26	American SB Co, Lorain	23 July 1965	TPA
KANE	T-AGS 27	Christy Corp, Sturgeon Bay	19 May 1967	TAA
WILKES	T-AGS 33	Defoe SB Co, Bay City, MI	28 June 1971	TPA
WYMAN	T-AGS 34	Defoe SB Co, Bay City, MI	3 Nov 1971	TAA

Displacement, tons: 2550-2843 full load
Dimensions, feet (metres): 285.3 × 48 × 15.1 *(87 × 14.6 × 4.6)*
Main machinery: Diesel-electric; 2 Alco diesel generators; 1 Westinghouse/GE motor; 3600 hp *(2.69 MW)*; 1 shaft; bow thruster; 350 hp *(261 kW)*
Speed, knots: 15. **Range, miles:** 8000 at 13 kts
Complement: 37 (12 officers) plus 28 scientists
Radars: Navigation: RM 1650/9X and TM 1660/12S *(Silas Bent)*; I band.

Comment: Designed specifically for surveying operations. Bow propulsion unit for precise manoeuvrability and station keeping. All ships in commission operated for the Oceanographer of the Navy under technical control of the Naval Oceanographic Office.

WYMAN   3/1991, Giorgio Arra

2 MAURY CLASS: SURVEYING SHIPS (AGS)

Name	No	Builders	Completed	F/S
MAURY	T-AGS 39	Bethlehem Steel	31 Mar 1989	TAA
TANNER	T-AGS 40	Bethlehem Steel	27 Aug 1990	TAA

Displacement, tons: 16 074 full load
Dimensions, feet (metres): 500; 462.1 wl × 72 × 30 *(152.4; 140.8 × 22 × 9.1)*
Main machinery: 2 Transamerica De Laval R5-V16 Enterprise diesels; 27 240 hp *(20.4 MW)* sustained; 1 shaft
Speed, knots: 20. **Range, miles:** 12 000 at 20 kts
Complement: 108 (56 civilian, 52 Navy) plus 20 scientists

Comment: The first such ships to be constructed in many years. Both ordered 25 June 1985. *Maury* laid down 29 July 1986 and *Tanner* 22 October 1986. They have replaced *Bowditch* (T-AGS 21) and *Dutton* (T-AGS 22) and are operated by MSC for the Oceanographer of the Navy under technical control of the Naval Oceanographic Office. Fitted with SQN-17 bottom topography survey system and other acoustic systems including 2 BQN-3 narrow-beam for surveying purposes. In-service dates delayed by main machinery installation problems. Almost half the displacement is water ballast to provide sufficient draft for the sonar. *Tanner* may be paid off in 1994.

MAURY   3/1994, Hachiro Nakai

1 WATERS CLASS: SURVEYING SHIP (AGS)

Name	No	Builders	Completed	F/S
WATERS	T-AGS 45	Avondale Industries	26 May 1993	TPA

Displacement, tons: 12 208 full load
Dimensions, feet (metres): 455 × 68.9 × 21 *(138.7 × 21 × 6.4)*
Main machinery: Diesel-electric; 5 GM EMD diesels; 2 Westinghouse motors; 6800 hp *(15.07 MW)*; 2 shafts
Speed, knots: 12. **Range, miles:** 6500 at 12 kts
Complement: 89 (37 officers) plus 6 spare

Comment: Ordered 4 April 1990. Laid down 16 May 1991 and launched 6 June 1992. Carries out oceanographic and acoustic surveys in support of the Integrated Underwater Surveillance System. The ship carries a remote-controlled submersible operated from a centreline moonpool.

WATERS   8/1993, Giorgio Arra

2 JOHN McDONNELL CLASS: SURVEYING SHIPS (AGS)

Name	No	Builders	Completed	F/S
JOHN McDONNELL	T-AGS 51	Halter Marine	16 Dec 1991	TAA
LITTLEHALES	T-AGS 52	Halter Marine	1 Jan 1992	TAA

Displacement, tons: 2054 full load
Dimensions, feet (metres): 208 × 45 × 14 *(63.4 × 13.7 × 4.3)*
Main machinery: 1 GM EMD 12-645E6 diesel; 2550 hp *(1.9 MW)* sustained; 1 auxiliary diesel; 230 hp *(172 kW)*; 1 shaft
Speed, knots: 12. **Range, miles:** 13 800 at 12 kts
Complement: 22 plus 11 scientists

Comment: Laid down on 3 August 1989 and 25 October 1989 respectively. *McDonnell* launched 15 August 1990, *Littlehales* 14 February 1991. Have replaced *Chauvenet* and *Harkness*. Carry 34 ft survey launches for data collection in coastal regions with depths between 10 and 600 m and in deep water to 4000 m. A small diesel is used for propulsion at towing speeds of up to 6 kts.

JOHN McDONNELL   1/1992, Halter Marine

0 + 3 PATHFINDER CLASS: SURVEYING SHIPS (AGS)

Name	No	Builders	Completed
PATHFINDER	T-AGS 60	Halter Marine	Oct 1994
SUMNER	T-AGS 61	Halter Marine	Apr 1995
BOWDITCH	T-AGS 62	Halter Marine	Nov 1995

Displacement, tons: 4762 full load
Dimensions, feet (metres): 328.5 × 58 × 18 *(100.1 × 17.7 × 5.5)*
Main machinery: Diesel-electric; 6 diesel generators; 2 motors; 6000 hp *(4.48 MW)*; 2 shafts; bow thruster
Speed, knots: 16. **Range, miles:** 12 000 at 12 kts
Complement: 60

Comment: Contract awarded in January 1991 for two ships with an option for a third which was taken up on 29 May 1992. *Pathfinder* laid down 20 January 1993 and launched 7 October 1993. Replacements for Robert D Conrad class, all of which have been paid off or leased to other countries. *Sumner* may be equipped for Arctic operations.

PATHFINDER (artist's impression)   *1992, Trinity Marine*

2 MERCY CLASS: HOSPITAL SHIPS (AH)

Name	No	Builders	Completed	F/S
MERCY (ex-SS *Worth*)	T-AH 19	National Steel & Shipbuilding Co	1976	ROS
COMFORT (ex-SS *Rose City*)	T-AH 20	National Steel & Shipbuilding Co	1976	ROS

Displacement, tons: 69 360 full load
Measurement, tons: 54 367 gross; 35 958 net
Dimensions, feet (metres): 894 × 105.6 × 32.8 *(272.6 × 32.2 × 10)*
Main machinery: 2 boilers; 2 GE turbines; 24 500 hp *(18.3 MW)*; 2 shafts
Speed, knots: 16.5. **Range, miles:** 12 500 at 15 kts
Complement: 68 civilian crew; 820 naval medical staff; 372 naval support staff; 15 naval communications staff
Radars: Navigation: SPS 67; I band.
Tacan: URN 25.
Helicopters: Platform only.

Comment: Plans to convert SS *United States* were dropped in favour of converting these two San Clemente class tankers. Contracts awarded to National Steel & Shipbuilding in 1983. Conversion of T-AH 19 was begun in 1984 and that of T-AH 20 in 1985. *Mercy* was commissioned 19 December 1986; *Comfort* on 30 November 1987. *Mercy* berthed at Oakland, CA, in a reduced operating status; *Comfort* at Baltimore. Each ship has 1000 beds, 12 operating theatres, laboratories, pharmacies, dental, radiology and optometry departments, physical-therapy and burn-care units and radiological services. Both deployed in the Gulf in 1990-91 with full medical staffs mostly drawn from naval hospitals on both US coasts.

MERCY   *3/1991, 92 Wing RAAF*

3 MAERSK CLASS (AKR)

Name	No	Completed	F/S
LAURA MAERSK	T-AKR 295	1980	Conv
LEISE MAERSK	T-AKR 297	1981	Conv
LICA MAERSK	T-AKR 299	1981	Conv

Measurement, tons: 54 298 grt
Dimensions, feet (metres): 885.3 × 105.6 × 34.3 *(269.8 × 32.2 × 10.5)*
Main machinery: 1 Burmeister & Wain 12L90 GFCA diesel; 46 653 hp(m) *(34.29 MW)*; 1 shaft
Speed, knots: 24. **Range, miles:** 18 500 at 24 kts
Complement: 40 plus 50 troops
Cargo capacity: 263 232 sq ft plus 50 932 sq ft deck cargo

Comment: Contract given to National Steel & Shipbuilding on 30 July 1993. All to be converted with a stern slewing ramp, side accesses and improved craneage. To be renamed before entering service. Conversion started for *Laura* 15 January 1994, *Leise* 15 April 1994 and *Lica* is scheduled for mid-1994. All should complete in 1995/96.

1 CONVERTED C3-S-33a TYPE: CARGO SHIP (AK)

Name	No	Completed	F/S
VEGA (ex-SS *Bay*, ex-*Mormacbay*)	T-AK 286	14 Oct 1960	TAA

Displacement, tons: 15 404 full load
Measurement, tons: 6590 gross
Dimensions, feet (metres): 483.3 × 68 × 28.5 *(147.2 × 20.7 × 8.7)*
Main machinery: 2 Combustion Engineering boilers; 615 psi *(43.3 kg/cm sq)*; 850°F *(457°C)*; 1 GE turbine; 12 100 hp *(9 MW)*; 1 shaft
Speed, knots: 19. **Range, miles:** 14 000 at 18 kts
Complement: 67 plus 7 man naval contingent

Comment: Built by Sun Shipbuilding and Drydock Co, Chester, Pennsylvania for the MooreMcCormack Lines. *Vega* was acquired in October 1981 and was converted to an FBM Support Ship. Capable of carrying 16 Trident missiles; equipped with eight 10-ton capacity booms, four 5-ton capacity booms and one 75-ton capacity boom. Deployed with MSC Atlantic Fleet in July 1983. Scheduled to pay off in 1994.

VEGA   *1986, Giorgio Arra*

0 + 12 BOB HOPE CLASS (AK)

Name	No	Builders	Completed
—	T-AKR 300	Avondale Industries	Nov 1997
—	T-AKR 301	National Steel & Shipbuilding Co	Nov 1997

Measurement, tons: 62 644 grt
Dimensions, feet (metres): 951.4 × 106 × 37 *(290 × 32.3 × 11.3)*
Main machinery: 4 diesels; 65 160 hp *(48.6 MW)*; 2 gas-turbines; 64 000 hp *(47.7 MW)*; 2 shafts
Speed, knots: 24. **Range, miles:** 12 000 at 24 kts
Complement: 40 plus 50 troops
Cargo capacity: 397 413 sq ft

Comment: Contracts given on 2 and 15 September to each shipyard for one ship followed by an option on five more. Ro-Ro type ships with stern ramps and side access. Construction is expected to start in October 1994 after a slight delay caused by a challenge from two other shipbuilders to the award of these contracts.

T-AKR 300 (artist's impression)   *Avondale/National Steel*

5—T 5 TYPE: TRANSPORT OILERS (AOT)

Name	No	Builders	Commissioned
GUS W DARNELL	T-AOT 1121	American SB Co, Tampa, FL	11 Sep 1985
PAUL BUCK	T-AOT 1122	American SB Co, Tampa, FL	11 Sep 1985
SAMUEL L COBB	T-AOT 1123	American SB Co, Tampa, FL	15 Nov 1985
RICHARD G MATTHIESON	T-AOT 1124	American SB Co, Tampa, FL	18 Feb 1986
LAWRENCE H GIANELLA	T-AOT 1125	American SB Co, Tampa, FL	22 Apr 1986

Displacement, tons: 39 000 full load
Dimensions, feet (metres): 615 × 90 × 34 *(187.5 × 27.4 × 10.4)*
Main machinery: 1 Sulzer 5RTA76 diesel; 18 400 hp(m) *(13.52 MW)* sustained; 1 shaft
Speed, knots: 16. **Range, miles:** 12 000 at 16 kts
Complement: 23 (9 officers)
Cargo capacity: 238 400 barrels of oil fuel

Comment: Built for Ocean Carriers Inc, Houston, Texas specifically for long-term time charter to the Military Sealift Command (20 years) as Ocean Transportation ships. The last two are able to rig underway replenishment gear. *Lawrence H Gianella* transferred to the RRF in 1992.

LAWRENCE H GIANELLA (RRF)   *1/1993, van Ginderen Collection*

2 SELANDIA CLASS (AKR)

Name	No	Completed	F/S
SELANDIA	T-AKR 296	1972	Conv
JUTLANDIA	T-AKR 298	1972	Conv

Measurement, tons: 55 422 grt
Dimensions, feet (metres): 949.3 × 105.8 × 36.3 *(289.4 × 32.2 × 11.9)*
Main machinery: 1 Burmeister & Wain 12K84EF diesel; 26 000 hp(m) *(19.11 MW)*; 2 Burmeister & Wain 9K84EF diesels; 39 000 hp(m) *(28.66 MW)*; 3 shafts (centre cp prop)
Speed, knots: 22. **Range, miles:** 27 000 at 22 kts
Complement: 40 plus 50 troops
Cargo capacity: 292 128 sq ft plus 47 085 sq ft deck cargo

Comment: Contract given to Newport News Shipbuilding on 30 July 1993. Both to be converted with a stern slewing ramp, side accesses and improved craneage. To be renamed before entering service. Conversion started for *Selandia* on 31 October 1993 and *Jutlandia* in early 1994. Both should complete in 1995/96.

13 + 5 HENRY J KAISER CLASS: OILERS (AO)

Name	No	Builders	Laid down	Completed	F/S
HENRY J KAISER	T-AO 187	Avondale	22 Aug 1984	19 Dec 1986	TAA
JOSHUA HUMPHREYS	T-AO 188	Avondale	17 Dec 1984	2 Apr 1987	TAA
JOHN LENTHALL	T-AO 189	Avondale	15 July 1985	2 June 1987	TAA
ANDREW J HIGGINS	T-AO 190	Avondale	21 Nov 1985	20 Oct 1987	TPA
BENJAMIN ISHERWOOD	T-AO 191	Penn Ship/ Tampa	12 July 1986	—	Bldg/PSR
HENRY ECKFORD	T-AO 192	Penn Ship/ Tampa	22 Jan 1987	—	Bldg/PSR
WALTER S DIEHL	T-AO 193	Avondale	8 July 1986	13 Sep 1988	TPA
JOHN ERICSSON	T-AO 194	Avondale	15 Mar 1989	18 Mar 1991	TPA
LEROY GRUMMAN	T-AO 195	Avondale	7 June 1987	2 Aug 1989	TAA
KANAWHA	T-AO 196	Avondale	13 July 1989	6 Dec 1991	TAA
PECOS	T-AO 197	Avondale	17 Feb 1988	6 July 1990	TPA
BIG HORN	T-AO 198	Avondale	9 Oct 1989	31 July 1992	TAA
TIPPECANOE	T-AO 199	Avondale	19 Nov 1990	26 Mar 1993	TPA
GUADALUPE	T-AO 200	Avondale	9 July 1990	26 Oct 1992	TPA
PATUXENT	T-AO 201	Avondale	16 Oct 1991	June 1995	Bldg/TAA
YUKON	T-AO 202	Avondale	13 May 1991	11 Dec 1993	TPA
LARAMIE	T-AO 203	Avondale	Oct 1994	June 1996	Bldg/TAA
RAPPAHANNOCK	T-AO 204	Avondale	29 June 1992	Nov 1995	Bldg/TPA

Displacement, tons: 40 700 full load
Dimensions, feet (metres): 677.5 × 97.5 × 35 *(206.5 × 29.7 × 10.7)*
Main machinery: 2 Colt-Pielstick 10 PC4.2 V 570 diesels; 34 422 hp(m) *(24.3 MW)* sustained; 2 shafts
Speed, knots: 20. **Range, miles:** 6000 at 18 kts
Complement: 95 civilian (20 officers); 21 naval (1 officer)
Cargo capacity: 180 000 barrels of fuel oil
Guns: 1 Vulcan Phalanx CIWS (fitted for).
Countermeasures: Decoys: SLQ-25 Nixie; towed torpedo decoy.
Helicopters: Platform only.

Comment: Construction was delayed initially by design difficulties, and by excessive vibration at high speeds and other problems encountered in the first ship of the class. The ships are fitted for Vulcan Phalanx CIWS. There are stations on both sides for underway replenishment of fuel and solids. Fitted with integrated electrical auxiliary propulsion. T-AOs 201, 203 and 204 have been delayed by the decision to fit double hulls to meet the requirements of the Oil Pollution Act of 1990. This modification increases construction time from 32 to 42 months and reduces cargo capacity by 15 per cent. T-AOs 191 and 192 were transferred from Penn Ship (when the yard became bankrupt) to Tampa. Tampa's contract was also cancelled on 30 August 1993, with both vessels still incomplete. In October 1993 they were towed away and made inactive.

GUADALUPE   *4/1993, Hachiro Nakai*

ANDREW J HIGGINS   *6/1993, Vic Jeffery, RAN*

9 SEALIFT CLASS: TRANSPORT OILERS (AOT, ex-AO)

Name	No	Builders	Completed	F/S
SEALIFT PACIFIC	T-AOT 168	Todd Shipyards	14 Aug 1974	TWWR
SEALIFT ARABIAN SEA	T-AOT 169	Todd Shipyards	6 May 1975	TWWR
SEALIFT CHINA SEA	T-AOT 170	Todd Shipyards	9 May 1975	TWWR
SEALIFT INDIAN OCEAN	T-AOT 171	Todd Shipyards	29 Aug 1975	TWWR
SEALIFT ATLANTIC	T-AOT 172	Bath Iron Works	26 Aug 1974	TWWR
SEALIFT MEDITERRANEAN	T-AOT 173	Bath Iron Works	6 Nov 1974	TWWR
SEALIFT CARIBBEAN	T-AOT 174	Bath Iron Works	10 Feb 1975	TWWR
SEALIFT ARCTIC	T-AOT 175	Bath Iron Works	22 May 1975	TWWR
SEALIFT ANTARCTIC	T-AOT 176	Bath Iron Works	1 Aug 1975	TWWR

Displacement, tons: 34 100 full load
Measurement, tons: 27 300 dwt
Dimensions, feet (metres): 587 × 84 × 34.6 *(178.9 × 25.6 × 10.6)*
Main machinery: 2 Colt-Pielstick 14 PC2 V 400 diesels; 14 000 hp(m) *(10.3 MW)* sustained; 1 shaft; cp prop; bow thruster
Speed, knots: 16. **Range, miles:** 7500 at 16 kts
Complement: 24 (9 officers) plus 2 Maritime Academy cadets
Cargo capacity: 185 000 barrels of oil fuel

Comment: Built specially for long term-charter by the Military Sealift Command. Operated for MSC as Ocean Transportation Ships under charter by Marine Transport Lines Inc. Automated engine room. All reclassified T-AOT on 30 September 1978.

SEALIFT PACIFIC   *12/1993, Diego Quevedo*

7 POWHATAN CLASS: FLEET OCEAN TUGS (ATF)

Name	No	Laid down	Completed	F/S
POWHATAN	T-ATF 166	30 Sep 1976	15 June 1979	TAA
NARRAGANSETT	T-ATF 167	5 May 1977	9 Nov 1979	TPA
CATAWBA	T-ATF 168	14 Dec 1977	28 May 1980	TPA
NAVAJO	T-ATF 169	14 Dec 1977	13 June 1980	TPA
MOHAWK	T-ATF 170	22 Mar 1979	16 Oct 1980	TAA
SIOUX	T-ATF 171	22 Mar 1979	1 May 1981	TPA
APACHE	T-ATF 172	22 Mar 1979	30 July 1981	TAA

Displacement, tons: 2260 full load
Dimensions, feet (metres): 240.2 × 42 × 15 *(73.2 × 12.8 × 4.6)*
Main machinery: 2 GM EMD 20-645F7B diesels; 5.73 MW sustained; 2 shafts; Kort nozzles (except in *Powhatan* and one other); cp props; bow thruster; 300 hp *(224 kW)*
Speed, knots: 14.5. **Range, miles:** 10 000 at 13 kts
Complement: 23 (17 civilians, 6 naval communications technicians)
Guns: Space provided to fit 2—20 mm and 2—12.7 mm MGs in war.

Comment: Built at Marinette Marine Corp, Wisconsin patterned after commercial off-shore supply ship design. Originally intended as successors to the Cherokee and Abnaki class ATFs. However, procurement was halted at seven ships with no more planned. All transferred to MSC upon completion. 10 ton capacity crane and a bollard pull of at least 54 tons. A 'deck grid' is fitted aft which contains 1 in bolt receptacles spaced 24 in apart. This allows for the bolting down of a wide variety of portable equipment. There are two GPH fire-pumps supplying three fire monitors with up to 2200 gallons of foam per minute. A deep module can be embarked to support naval salvage teams.

NAVAJO   *6/1993, Giorgio Arra*

MISCELLANEOUS OCEAN TRANSPORTATION SHIPS

Note: In addition to the AOTs listed in the Sealift and T Type classes, there are a number of ships of varying types under charter to the MSC. Numbers and names are constantly changing.

1 ZEUS CLASS: CABLE REPAIRING SHIP (ARC)

Name	No	Builders	Completed	F/S
ZEUS	T-ARC 7	National Steel & Shipbuilding Co	19 Mar 1984	TPA

Displacement, tons: 8370 light; 14 157 full load
Dimensions, feet (metres): 502.5 × 73 × 25 *(153.2 × 22.3 × 7.6)*
Main machinery: Diesel-electric; 5 GM EMD 20-645F7B diesel generators; 14.32 MW sustained; 2 motors; 2 shafts; cp props; bow thrusters (forward and aft)
Speed, knots: 15.8. **Range, miles:** 10 000 at 15 kts
Complement: 126 (88 civilians, 6 Navy, 32 scientists)

Comment: Ordered 7 August 1979. Remotely manned engineering room controlled from the bridge.

ZEUS   *2/1993, Giorgio Arra*

1 NEPTUNE CLASS: CABLE REPAIRING SHIP (ARC)

Name	No	Builders	Commissioned	F/S
ALBERT J MYER	T-ARC 6	Pusey & Jones Corp, Wilmington, DE	13 May 1963	TPA

Displacement, tons: 8500 full load
Dimensions, feet (metres): 369 × 47 × 27 *(112.5 × 14.3 × 8.2)*
Main machinery: Diesel-electric; 4 GE diesel generators; 2 motors; 4000 hp *(2.98 MW)*; 2 shafts
Speed, knots: 14. **Range, miles:** 10 000 at 13 kts
Complement: 92 civilian (16 officers, 18 scientists)
Radars: Navigation: RM 1650/6X *(Myer)*; I band.

Comment: Built as an S3-S2-BP1 type cable ship for the Maritime Administration. *Albert J Myer* acquired from US Army on 18 September 1963. Fitted with electric cable handling machinery (in place of steam equipment) and precision navigation equipment. Rebuilt at Bethlehem Steel Co, Key Highway Division, Baltimore from March 1978 to May 1980. Modernisation included stripping the superstructure down to the main deck, gutting the hull, replacing the entire propulsion system, the wiring and piping and replacing the decks and superstructure with aluminium where possible. Sister ship *Neptune* in reserve from October 1991. Scheduled to pay off in 1994.

ALBERT J MYER   *4/1990, Giorgio Arra*

AUXILIARY SEALIFT SHIPS: READY RESERVE FORCE (RRF)

Note: Due to the lack of sealift capability within both the US Navy and US Merchant Marine, a programme was initiated in the early 1980s to create a Ready Reserve Force (RRF) of ships that could be made available quickly for military sealift operations without disrupting routine commerce. Now included in the RRF are auxiliary crane ships, roll-on/roll-off, break bulk, heavy lift, barge carriers, POL product tankers, and troopships. Most of these are normally maintained in a laid-up status at three national storage sites: James River, VA (East); Beaumont, TX (Gulf); and Suisun Bay, CA (West). However, in 1993 more than half the force was either at sea or dispersed among 17 other ports. The responsibility for maintenance and upkeep was transferred from the Military Sealift Command to the Maritime Administration in FY 1989, but they remain under operational control of MSC. More than three-quarters of the force was employed during Desert Shield/Storm in 1990/91, transporting equipment to the Middle East before and during the war, and returning it to the United States at the conclusion of hostilities. MSC added 12 Ro-Ros in 1993 by purchase through MARAD. The long-range goal for the RRF is 140 ships by 1999. RRF ships have red, white and blue funnel markings. All have had additional navigation and communications equipment fitted.

49 BREAK BULK SHIPS

CAPE CATAWBA TAK 5074	**BANNER** TAK 5008
LAKE TAK 5016	**DEL MONTE** TAK 5049
PRIDE TAK 5017	**DEL VALLE** TAK 5050
SCAN TAK 5018	**DEL VIENTO** TAK 5026
SOUTHERN CROSS TAK 285	**COURIER** TAK 5019
CAPE CANAVERAL TAK 5040	**PIONEER COMMANDER** TAK 2016
CAPE CANSO TAK 5037	**PIONEER CONTRACTOR** TAK 2018
CAPE CHALMERS TAK 5036	**PIONEER CRUSADER** TAK 2019
CAPE COD TAK 5041	**BUYER** TAK 2033
CAPE CLEAR TAK 5039	**CAPE JOHN** TAK 5022
CAPE CARTHAGE TAK 5042	**CAPE JACOB** TAK 5029
CAPE CATOCHE TAK 5043	**CAPE GIBSON** TAK 5051
CAPE JOHNSON TAK 5075	**CAPE GIRARDEAU** TAK 2039
CAPE JUBY TAK 5077	**NORTHERN LIGHT** TAKR 284
CAPE ALAVA TAK 5012	**AGENT** TAK 5015
CAPE ALEXANDER TAK 5010	**AMBASSADOR** TAK 5007
CAPE ANN TAK 5009	**CAPE BON** TAK 5059
CAPE ARCHWAY TAK 5011	**ADVENTURER** TAK 5005
CAPE AVINOF TAK 5013	**AIDE** TAK 5006
CAPE NOME TAK 1014	**CAPE BORDA** TAK 5058
GULF BANKER TAK 5044	**CAPE BOVER** TAK 5057
GULF FARMER TAK 5045	**CAPE BLANCO** TAK 5060
GULF MERCHANT TAK 5046	**CAPE BRETON** TAKR 5056
GULF TRADER TAK 2036	**CAPE ISLAND** —
CAPE ISABEL —	

GULF TRADER   *4/1992, 92 Wing RAAF*

10 AUXILIARY CRANE SHIPS

KEYSTONE STATE TACS 1	**CORNHUSKER STATE** TACS 6
GEM STATE TACS 2	**DIAMOND STATE** TACS 7
GRAND CANYON STATE TACS 3	**EQUALITY STATE** TACS 8
GOPHER STATE TACS 4	**GREEN MOUNTAIN STATE** TACS 9
FLICKERTAIL STATE TACS 5	**BEAVER STATE** TACS 10

Comment: See *MPS* section for details. *Gopher State* is activated as an Army prepositioning ship and stationed at Diego Garcia.

28 RO-RO SHIPS

ADM WM H CALLAGHAN TAKR 1001	**COMET** TAKR 7
CAPE HENRY* TAKR 5067	**METEOR** TAKR 9
CAPE HORN* TAKR 5068	**CAPE WASHINGTON*** (ex-*Hual Transporter*)
CAPE HUDSON* TAKR 5066	(TAKR 9961)
CAPE DOMINGO TAKR 5053	**CAPE WRATH*** (ex-*Hual Trader*) (TAKR 9962)
CAPE DIAMOND TAKR 5055	**CAPE TEXAS** (ex-*Lyra*)
CAPE DECISION* TAKR 5054	**CAPE TRINITY** (ex-*Santos*)
CAPE DOUGLAS* TAKR 5052	**CAPE TAYLOR** (ex-*Cygnus*)
CAPE DUCATO TAKR 5051	**CAPE RACE** (ex-*G&C Admiral*)
CAPE EDMONT TAKR 5069	**CAPE RISE** (ex-*Saudi Riyadh*)
CAPE LAMBERT TAKR 5077	**CAPE RAY** (ex-*Saudi Makkah*)
CAPE LOBOS TAKR 5078	**CAPE VICTORY** (ex-*Merzario Britania*)
CAPE INSCRIPTION TAKR 5076	**CAPE VINCENT** (ex-*Taabo Italia*)
CAPE ISABEL TAKR 5062	**CAPE ORLANDO** (ex-*American Eagle*)
	CAPE ISLAND (ex-*Mercury*)

Comment: Ships marked * were activated to serve as Army prepositioning ships and were based at either Diego Garcia or Saipan by April 1994.

CAPE HENRY   *2/1994, van Ginderen Collection*

11 PRODUCT TANKERS

MOUNT WASHINGTON TAOT 169	**ALATNA** TAOG 81
PETERSBURG TAOT 9101	**CHATTAHOOCHEE** TAOG 82
SHOSHONE TAOT 151	**AMERICAN EXPLORER** TAOT 165
CHESAPEAKE TAOT 5084	**MISSION BUENAVENTURA** TAOT 1012
NODAWAY TAOG 78	**MISSION CAPISTRANO** TAOT 5005
	MOUNT VERNON TAOT 5083

9 MISCELLANEOUS SHIPS

Barge carriers
CAPE FAREWELL TAK 5073
CAPE FLATTERY TAK 5070
CAPE FLORIDA TAK 5071
AUSTRAL LIGHTNING
TAK 5061

Troopships
EMPIRE STATE TAP 1001
PATRIOT STATE TAP 1000

Heavy lift ships
CAPE MOHICAN TAKR 5065
CAPE MAY TAKR 5063
CAPE MENDOCINO TAKR 5064

PATRIOT STATE   2/1993, Giorgio Arra

AFLOAT PREPOSITIONING FORCE (PREPO)

Notes: (1) In order to improve US capability to deploy its forces rapidly to any area of conflict, and especially to South-West Asia, and to enhance the readiness of existing forces, the Carter Administration created a force comprising elements of all three services and named it the Rapid Deployment Joint Task Force (RDJTF). Initially composed of seven Military Sealift Command ships, it was first deployed to Diego Garcia in July 1980. For a time it was expanded to 17 ships; it carried tactical equipment, ammunition, POL, and supplies to sustain combat operations until reinforcements could be shipped from the USA. Thirteen ships were converted or built as part of the Maritime Prepositioning Ship programme (MPS) (see following section), and one five-ship squadron of MPS ships was based at Diego Garcia in 1985. On 7 August 1990, the PREPO force consisted of 11 ships. All 11 of these were deployed to Saudi Arabia in 1990 when the military reinforcement began and were among the first arrivals in the build-up of American forces.
(2) The PREPO ships carry Army, Navy and Air Force equipment and supplies. Commander, Maritime Prepositioning Squadron Two controls MPS and PREPO ships at Diego Garcia. Commander, MSC Mediterranean controls *Buffalo Soldier* (TAK 322) and *American Merlin* (TAK 323). In addition, a tanker shuttles in and out of the force. In 1993, this ship was the *Lawrence H Gianella* (TAOT 1125).
(3) In early 1994, the 11 ships listed below were deployed.

2 LASH TYPE: CARGO SHIPS, BARGE (AKB)

Name	No	Builders	Completed	F/S
GREEN VALLEY	T-AK 2049	Avondale Shipyards	Feb 1975	PREPO
GREEN HARBOR	T-AK 2064	Avondale Shipyards	Feb 1974	PREPO

Displacement, tons: 62 314 full load
Measurement, tons: 32 278 gross; 46 152 dwt
Dimensions, feet (metres): 893.3 × 100 × 60 *(272.3 × 30.5 × 18.3)*
Main machinery: 2 Combustion Engineering boilers; 1100 psi *(77.3 kg/cm sq)*; 2 De Laval turbines; 32 000 hp *(23.9 MW)*; 1 shaft
Speed, knots: 22. **Range, miles:** 15 000 at 20 kts
Complement: 32
Cargo capacity: 1 691 500 cu ft (in 85 bales)

Comment: *Green Valley* acquired on 31 January 1992 and *Green Harbor* 20 October 1985, both for Army PREPO. Stationed at Diego Garcia. Owned and operated by Central Gulf Lines.

GREEN VALLEY   7/1991, van Ginderen Collection

2 LASH TYPE: CARGO SHIPS, BARGE (AKB)

Name	No	Builders	Completed	F/S
AUSTRAL RAINBOW (ex-*China Bear*)	TAK 2046	Avondale Shipyards	1972	PREPO
AMERICAN KESTREL	TAK 2043	Avondale Shipyards	1974	PREPO

Measurement, tons: 26 406 gross; 39 277 dwt
Dimensions, feet (metres): 820 × 100 × 40.7 *(249.9 × 30.4 × 12.4)*
Speed, knots: 19+
Complement: 33
Cargo capacity: 1 663 248 cu ft (77 bales)

Comment: *Austral Rainbow* re-acquired 26 May 1987. Owned and operated by Central Gulf Lines and stationed at Diego Garcia. *American Kestrel* acquired 20 June 1988. Both for Air Force PREPO. Owned by Kestrel Shipbuilding and operated by Osprey Ship Management. Stationed at Diego Garcia.

AUSTRAL RAINBOW   1992, MSC

1 FLOAT-ON/FLOAT-OFF TYPE CARGO SHIP, SEMI-SUBMERSIBLE (AKF)

Name	No	Builders	Completed	F/S
AMERICAN CORMORANT (ex-*Ferncarrier*)	T-AK 2062	Eriksbergs Mekaniska Verkstads AB	Sep 1974	PREPO

Displacement, tons: 69 555 full load
Measurement, tons: 10 196 gross; 47 230 dwt
Dimensions, feet (metres): 738 × 135 × 35.1 *(225 × 41.1 × 10.7)*
Main machinery: 1 Eriksberg/Burmeister & Wain 10K84EF diesel; 19 900 hp(m) *(14.6 MW)*; 1 shaft; 2 thrusters; 3000 hp(m) *(2.2 MW)*
Speed, knots: 16. **Range, miles:** 23 700 at 13 kts
Complement: 21
Cargo capacity: 10 000 barrels of fuel; 44 000 tons deck cargo

Comment: Converted in 1982. Acquired on time charter 25 November 1985 for Army. Owned by Cormorant Shipholding and operated by Osprey Ship Management. Cargo includes Army watercraft and port support equipment. Rated as a heavy lift ship and stationed at Diego Garcia.

AMERICAN CORMORANT   10/1993, van Ginderen Collection

1 TANKER TYPE: TRANSPORT OILER (AOT)

Name	No	Builders	Commissioned	F/S
POTOMAC	TAOT 181	Sun Shipbuilding	Jan 1957	PREPO

Displacement, tons: 34 700 full load
Dimensions, feet (metres): 614.5 × 83.5 × 33.7 *(187.3 × 25.5 × 10.3)*
Main machinery: 2 boilers; 2 turbines; 20 460 hp *(15.3 MW)*; 2 shafts
Speed, knots: 18
Complement: 49
Cargo capacity: 1 069 700 cu ft liquids; 30 400 cu ft solids

Comment: Acquired in 1991. Operated by American Foreign Shipping and owned by MARAD.

1 LASH TYPE: CARGO SHIP, BARGE (AKB)

Name	No	Builders	Completed	F/S
JEB STUART (ex-*Atlantic Forest*)	TAKB 924	Sumitomo Shipbuilding	1969	PREPO

Displacement, tons: 66 629 full load
Dimensions, feet (metres): 857 × 106 × 40 *(261.2 × 32.3 × 12.2)*
Speed, knots: 17
Complement: 27
Cargo capacity: 1 683 191 cu ft

Comment: Acquired 8 December 1992 for Army PREPO and assigned to Diego Garcia. Owned and operated by Waterman Steamship Company.

2 RO-RO CONTAINERS: CARGO SHIPS (AK)

Name	No	Builders	Completed	F/S
AMERICAN MERLIN (ex-*CGM Utrillo*)	TAK 323	Chantiers Navigation de la Ciotat	1978	MED PREPO
BUFFALO SOLDIER (ex-*CGM Monet*)	TAK 322	Chantiers Navigation de la Ciotat	1978	MED PREPO

Displacement, tons: 40 357 full load
Dimensions, feet (metres): 670 × 87 × 34.5 *(204.2 × 26.5 × 10.5)*
Speed, knots: 16
Complement: 23
Cargo capacity: 1 517 447 cu ft

Comment: Reflagged French Government Line ships. *American Merlin* owned by American Automar and operated by Osprey Ship Management. *Buffalo Soldier* owned and operated by Red River Shipping. Both for Air Force PREPO.

1 RO-RO CONTAINER: CARGO SHIP (AK)

Name	No	Builders	Completed	F/S
STRONG VIRGINIAN (ex-*Saint Magnus*)	—	Bremer-Vegesach, Germany	1984	PREPO

Displacement, tons: 31 390 full load
Dimensions, feet (metres): 512 × 105 × 29.6 *(156.1 × 32 × 9)*
Speed, knots: 16.5
Complement: 33
Cargo capacity: 855 859 cu ft

Comment: Reflagged Antigua/Barbuda flag with heavy lift capability. Stationed at Diego Garcia with Navy fleet hospital aboard. Owned and operated by Van Ommeren Shipping Inc.

1 TANKER TYPE: TRANSPORT OILER (AOT)

Name	No	Builders	Completed	F/S
AMERICAN OSPREY	TAOT 5075	Bethlehem Steel	1958	PREPO

Displacement, tons: 44 840 full load
Dimensions, feet (metres): 661.1 × 89.9 × 36.1 *(201.5 × 27.4 × 11)*
Main machinery: 2 Combustion Engineering boilers; 2 Bethlehem turbines; 15 000 hp *(11.19 MW)*; 1 shaft
Speed, knots: 17. **Range, miles:** 14 000 at 17 kts
Complement: 37
Cargo capacity: 268 000 bbls fuel oil

Comment: Acquired by MARAD in 1984 and operated by American Foreign Steamship. Ship has been fitted with the Offshore Petroleum Discharge System.

AMERICAN OSPREY   *11/1993, 92 Wing RAAF*

MARITIME PREPOSITIONING SHIP (MPS) PROGRAMME

Notes: (1) The Navy has been able to achieve a notable increase in its lift capability by the construction of five ships and the conversion of eight others. These are now divided into three squadrons, each of which contains the equipment for one Marine Expeditionary Brigade (MEB). Lift capability can also be augmented by the eight Algol class fast logistics ships. These amphibious elements are supported by two maintenance aviation support ships, nine crane ships and two hospital ships. The maintenance aviation support ships and the hospital ships are maintained in a reduced operating status and the crane ships as a part of the Ready Reserve Force.
(2) With the ending of Marine Expeditionary Brigades (MEB), each MPS squadron supports a Marine Expeditionary Force (MEF) up to brigade level. Assignments are flexible and reinforcements come from all sources.
(3) Strictly speaking, only the 13 AKs are MPS ships but it is convenient to place the details of fast sealift ships, aviation support ships and crane ships in this section.
(4) MPS Squadron 1 in Western Atlantic, 2 in Diego Garcia, and 3 in Guam/Saipan.

3 SGT MATEJ KOCAK CLASS: VEHICLE CARGO SHIPS (AK)

Name	No	Builders	Completed	F/S
SGT MATEJ KOCAK (ex-SS *John B Waterman*)	T-AK 3005	Pennsylvania SB Co, Chester, PA	Mar 1981	Sqn 1
PFC EUGENE A OBREGON (ex-SS *Thomas Heywood*)	T-AK 3006	Pennsylvania SB Co, Chester, PA	Nov 1982	Sqn 1
MAJ STEPHEN W PLESS (ex-SS *Charles Carroll*)	T-AK 3007	General Dynamics Corp, Quincy, MA	Mar 1983	Sqn 1

Displacement, tons: 48 754 full load
Dimensions, feet (metres): 821 × 105.6 × 32.3 *(250.2 × 32.2 × 9.8)*
Main machinery: 2 boilers; 2 GE turbines; 30 000 hp *(22.4 MW)*; 1 shaft
Speed, knots: 20. **Range, miles:** 13 000 at 20 kts
Complement: 29 plus 10 technicians
Cargo capacity: Containers, 532; Ro-ro, 152 236 sq ft; JP-5 bbls, 20 290; DF-2 bbls, 12 355; Mogas bbls, 3717; stable water, 2189; cranes, 2 twin 50 ton and 1—30 ton gantry
Helicopters: Platform only.

Comment: Converted from three Waterman Line ships by National Steel and Shipbuilding, San Diego. Delivery dates T-AK 3005, 1 October 1984; T-AK 3006, 16 January 1985; T-AK 3007, 15 May 1985. Conversion work included the addition of 157 ft *(47.9 m)* amidships.

MATEJ KOCAK   *6/1991, Giorgio Arra*

5 CPL LOUIS J HAUGE, JR CLASS: VEHICLE CARGO SHIPS (AK)

Name	No	Builders	Completed	F/S
CPL LOUIS J HAUGE, JR (ex-MV *Estelle Maersk*)	T-AK 3000	Odense Staalskibsvaerft A/S, Lindo	Oct 1979	Sqn 2
PFC WILLIAM B BAUGH (ex-MV *Eleo Maersk*)	T-AK 3001	Odense Staalskibsvaerft A/S, Lindo	Apr 1979	Sqn 2
PFC JAMES ANDERSON, JR (ex-MV *Emma Maersk*)	T-AK 3002	Odense Staalskibsvaerft A/S, Lindo	July 1979	Sqn 2
1st LT ALEX BONNYMAN (ex-MV *Emilie Maersk*)	T-AK 3003	Odense Staalskibsvaerft A/S, Lindo	Jan 1980	Sqn 2
PVT FRANKLIN J PHILLIPS (ex-Pvt *Harry Fisher*, ex-MV *Evelyn Maersk*)	T-AK 3004	Odense Staalskibsvaerft A/S, Lindo	Apr 1980	Sqn 2

Displacement, tons: 46 552 full load
Dimensions, feet (metres): 755 × 90 × 37.1 *(230 × 27.4 × 11.3)*
Main machinery: 1 Sulzer 7RND76M diesel; 16 800 hp(m) *(12.35 MW)*; 1 shaft
Speed, knots: 17.5. **Range, miles:** 10 800 at 16 kts
Complement: 27 plus 10 technicians
Cargo capacity: Containers, 361; Ro-ro, 121 595 sq ft; JP-5 bbls, 17 128; DF-2 bbls, 10 642; Mogas bbls, 3865; stable water, 2022; cranes, 3 twin 30 ton; 92 831 cu ft breakbulk
Helicopters: Platform only.

Comment: Converted from five Maersk Line ships by Bethlehem Steel, Sparrow Point, MD; T-AK 3000, 3002 and 3004 delivered 7 September 1984, 26 March 1985 and 24 September 1985 respectively and by Bethlehem Steel, Beaumont, TX; T-AK 3001 and 3003 delivered 12 September 1985 and 30 October 1985 respectively. Conversion work included the addition of 157 ft *(47.9 m)* amidships.

LOUIS J HAUGE   *1/1991, van Ginderen Collection*

5 2nd LT JOHN P BOBO CLASS: VEHICLE CARGO SHIPS (AK)

Name	No	Builders	Completed	F/S
2nd LT JOHN P BOBO	T-AK 3008	General Dynamics, Quincy	14 Feb 1985	Sqn 1
PFC DEWAYNE T WILLIAMS	T-AK 3009	General Dynamics, Quincy	6 June 1985	Sqn 3
1st LT BALDOMERO LOPEZ	T-AK 3010	General Dynamics, Quincy	20 Nov 1985	Sqn 3
1st LT JACK LUMMUS	T-AK 3011	General Dynamics, Quincy	6 Mar 1986	Sqn 3
SGT WILLIAM R BUTTON	T-AK 3012	General Dynamics, Quincy	27 May 1986	Sqn 3

Displacement, tons: 44 330 full load
Dimensions, feet (metres): 675.2 × 105.5 × 29.6 *(205.8 × 32.2 × 9)*
Main machinery: 2 Stork Werkspoor 16TM410 diesels; 27 000 hp(m) *(19.84 MW)* sustained; 1 shaft; bow thruster; 1000 hp *(746 kW)*
Speed, knots: 18. **Range, miles:** 12 840 at 18 kts
Complement: 30 plus 10 technicians
Cargo capacity: Containers, 530; Ro-ro, 152 185 sq ft; JP-5 bbls, 20 776; DF-2 bbls, 13 334; Mogas bbls, 4880; stable water, 2357; cranes, 1 single and 2 twin 39 ton
Helicopters: Platform only.

Comment: Operated by American Overseas Marine on a long charter. Each squadron supports a Marine Expeditionary Force.

PFC DEWAYNE T WILLIAMS   *9/1993, Giorgio Arra*

2 T-AVB 3 CLASS:
MAINTENANCE AVIATION/SUPPORT SHIPS (AVB)

Name	No	Builders	Completed	F/S
WRIGHT (ex-SS *Young America*)	T-AVB 3	Ingalls Shipbuilding	1970	ROS
CURTISS (ex-SS *Great Republic*)	T-AVB 4	Ingalls Shipbuilding	1969	ROS

Displacement, tons: 23 872 full load
Measurement, tons: 11 757 gross; 6850 net; 15 946 dwt
Dimensions, feet (metres): 602 × 90.2 × 29.8 *(183.5 × 27.5 × 9.1)*
Main machinery: 2 Combustion Engineering boilers; 2 GE turbines; 30 000 hp *(22.4 MW)*; 1 shaft
Speed, knots: 23. **Range, miles:** 9000 at 22 kts
Complement: 41 crew and 1 Aircraft Maintenance Detachment totalling 366 men

Comment: To further reinforce the capabilities of the Maritime Prepositioning Ship programme, conversion of two ro-ro ships into maintenance aviation support ships was approved in FY 1985 and FY 1986. *Wright* was completed 14 May 1986, *Curtiss* 18 August 1987. Both conversions took place at Todd Shipyards, Galveston, Texas. Each ship has side ports and three decks aft of the bridge superstructure and has the capability to load the vans and equipment of a Marine Aviation Intermediate Maintenance Activity. The ships' mission is to service aircraft until their containerised units can be offloaded. They can then revert to a standard sealift role if required. Maritime Administration hull design is C5-S-78a. They are operated by American Overseas Marine and maintained in a reduced operating status.

WRIGHT   *10/1991, 92 Wing RAAF*

10 KEYSTONE STATE CLASS: AUXILIARY CRANE SHIPS (ACS)

Name	No	Builders	Conversion Completed
KEYSTONE STATE (ex-SS *President Harrison*)	T-ACS 1	Defoe SB Co, Bay City	1984
GEM STATE (ex-SS *President Monroe*)	T-ACS 2	Defoe SB Co, Bay City	1985
GRAND CANYON STATE (ex-SS *President Polk*)	T-ACS 3	Dillingham S R, Portland	1986
GOPHER STATE (ex-*Export Leader*)	T-ACS 4	Norshipco, Norfolk	Oct 1987
FLICKERTAIL STATE (ex-*Export Lightning*)	T-ACS 5	Norshipco, Norfolk	Dec 1987
CORNHUSKER STATE (ex-*Staghound*)	T-ACS 6	Norshipco, Norfolk	Mar 1988
DIAMOND STATE (ex-*President Truman*)	T-ACS 7	Tampa SY	Jan 1989
EQUALITY STATE (ex-*American Banker*)	T-ACS 8	Tampa SY	May 1989
GREEN MOUNTAIN STATE (ex-*American Altair*)	T-ACS 9	Norshipco, Norfolk	Sep 1990
BEAVER STATE (ex-*American Draco*)	T-ACS 10	Norshipco, Norfolk	1993

Displacement, tons: 31 500 full load
Dimensions, feet (metres): 668.6 × 76.1 × 33.5 *(203.8 × 23.2 × 10.2)*
Main machinery: 2 boilers; 2 GE turbines; 19 250 hp *(14.4 MW)*; 1 shaft
Speed, knots: 20. **Range, miles:** 13 000 at 20 kts
Complement: 89
Cargo capacity: 300+ standard containers

Comment: Auxiliary crane ships are container ships to which have been added up to three twin boom pedestal cranes which will lift containerised or other cargo from itself or adjacent vessels and deposit it on a pier or into lighterage. Since a significant portion of the US merchant fleet is composed of non-self sustaining container ships lacking integral cranes, thus needing a fully developed port to unload, a requirement exists for crane ships that can unload others in areas of the world which have very simple, damaged or no developed port facilities. Funds provided in the FY 1988 budget for conversion of T-ACS 9 and 10 were transferred to other Navy SCN accounts. Funding for T-ACS 9 was then taken from Maritime Administration budgets. The 10th ship on which work had stopped in 1991 because of shortage of funds, was finally completed in 1993. There are minor dimensional differences between some of the class. Five of the ships were deployed to the Gulf in 1990-91 but the excellent Saudi harbour facilities meant that dockside cranes were available to unload cargoes, so their particular talents were not required other than as standard cargo ships. T-ACS 4 was activated to serve as a temporary Army PREPO ship at Diego Garcia in early 1994.

GOPHER STATE   *2/1994, van Ginderen Collection*

8 ALGOL CLASS: VEHICLE CARGO SHIPS (AKR)

Name	No	Builders	Delivered
ALGOL (ex-SS *Sea-Land Exchange*)	T-AKR 287	Rotterdamsche DD Mij NV, Rotterdam	7 May 1973
BELLATRIX (ex-SS *Sea-Land Trade*)	T-AKR 288	Rheinstahl Nordseewerke, Emden, West Germany	6 Apr 1973
DENEBOLA (ex-SS *Sea-Land Resource*)	T-AKR 289	Rotterdamsche DD Mij NV, Rotterdam	4 Dec 1973
POLLUX (ex-SS *Sea-Land Market*)	T-AKR 290	A G Weser, Bremen, West Germany	20 Sep 1973
ALTAIR (ex-SS *Sea-Land Finance*)	T-AKR 291	Rheinstahl Nordseewerke, Emden, West Germany	17 Sep 1973
REGULUS (ex-SS *Sea-Land Commerce*)	T-AKR 292	A G Weser, Bremen, West Germany	30 Mar 1973
CAPELLA (ex-SS *Sea-Land McLean*)	T-AKR 293	Rotterdamsche DD Mij NV, Rotterdam	4 Oct 1972
ANTARES (ex-SS *Sea-Land Galloway*)	T-AKR 294	A G Weser, Bremen, West Germany	27 Sep 1972

Displacement, tons: 55 355 full load
Measurement, tons: 25 389 net; 27 051-28 095 dwt
Dimensions, feet (metres): 946.2 × 106 × 34.8 *(288.4 × 32.3 × 10.6)*
Main machinery: 2 Foster-Wheeler boilers; 875 psi *(61.6 kg/cm sq)*; 950°F *(510°C)*; 2 GE MST-19 steam turbines; 120 000 hp *(89.5 MW)*; 2 shafts
Speed, knots: 30. **Range, miles:** 12 200 at 27 kts
Complement: 42 (as merchant ship); 24 (minimum)
Helicopters: Platform only.

Comment: All originally built as container-ships for Sea-Land Services Inc, Port Elizabeth, New Jersey but reported as using too much fuel to be cost effective as merchant ships. Six ships of this class were approved for acquisition in FY 1981 and the remaining two in FY 1982. The purchase price included 4000 containers and 800 container chassis for use in container ship configuration. All eight converted to Vehicle Cargo Ships (AKR). Conversion included the addition of roll-on/roll-off features. The area between the forward and after superstructures allows for a helicopter flight deck and hangar. The capacities are as follows: (square feet) enclosed roll-on/roll-off and helo hangar 114 000—128 000, flight deck 32 000 and light vehicle roll-on/roll-off aft 17 500. In addition to one roll-on/roll-off ramp port and starboard, twin 35-ton pedestal cranes are installed between the deckhouses and twin 50-ton cranes are installed aft to facilitate lift-on/lift-off cargo operations. 93 per cent of an army mechanised division can be lifted using all eight ships.
Seven of the class (*Antares* broke down) moved some nine per cent of all cargo transported between the US and Saudi Arabia during and after the war with Iraq and six were activated for the Somalian operation in December 1992. All are based in Atlantic and Gulf of Mexico ports. These ships are to be augmented by 12 new construction and five converted Ro-Ro ships capable of 24 knots and cheaper to build and maintain.

REGULUS   *6/1993, van Ginderen Collection*

BELLATRIX   *10/1993, van Ginderen Collection*

DEEP SUBMERGENCE VEHICLES

(Included in US Naval Vessel Register)

Note: The US Navy acquired its first deep submergence vehicle with the purchase in 1958 of the bathyscope *Trieste*, designed and constructed by Professor Auguste Piccard.
Trieste reached a record depth of 35 800 ft *(10 910 m)* in the Challenger Deep off the Marianas on 23 January 1960, being piloted by Lieutenant Don Walsh, USN, and Jacques Piccard (son of Auguste). Rebuilt and designated *Trieste II*. Transferred to Naval museum of Underwater Warfare, Keyport Washington.
After the loss of *Thresher* (SSN 593) in 1963 the US Navy initiated an extensive deep submergence programme that led to construction of two Deep Submergence Rescue Vehicles (DSRV).
Several of these deep submergence vehicles and other craft and support ships are operated by Submarine Development Group One at San Diego, California. The Group is a major operational command that includes advanced diving equipment; divers trained in 'saturation' techniques; the DSVs *Turtle, Sea Cliff*, DSRV-1, DSRV-2; the submarine *Dolphin* (AGSS 555) and several submarine rescue ships. Two unmanned vessels CURV (Cable Controlled Underwater Remote Vehicle) Super Scorpios made test dives to 5000 ft *(1524 m)* and ATV (Advanced Tethered Vehicle) to 20 000 ft *(1800 m)* in late 1990. There are no plans to build any more deep submergence vehicles.

1 NUCLEAR-POWERED OCEAN ENGINEERING AND RESEARCH VEHICLE

Name	Builders	In service	F/S
NR 1	General Dynamics (Electric Boat Div)	27 Oct 1969	ASA

Displacement, tons: 380 surfaced; 700 dived
Dimensions, feet (metres): 147 × 12.4 × 14.6 *(44.8 × 3.8 × 4.5)*
Main machinery: Nuclear; 1 PWR; 1 turbo-alternator; 2 motors (external to the hull); 2 props; 4 ducted thrusters (2 vertical, 2 horizontal)
Complement: 13 (3 officers, 2 scientists)

Comment: NR 1 was built primarily to serve as a test platform for a small nuclear propulsion plant; however, the craft additionally provides an advanced deep submergence ocean engineering and research capability. She was the only Naval deep submergence vehicle to be used in the recovery of the wreckage of the space shuttle *Challenger* January-April 1986. Laid down on 10 June 1967; launched on 25 January 1969. Commanded by an officer-in-charge vice commanding officer. First nuclear-propelled service craft. Overhauled and refuelled in 1993. Refitted with a new bow which extended her length by 9.6 ft, and new sonars and cameras. The fin and rudder are painted red.
The NR 1 is fitted with wheels beneath the hull to permit 'bottom crawling' and she is fitted with external lights, external television cameras, a remote-controlled manipulator, and various recovery devices. No periscopes, but fixed television mast. Diving depth, 2475 ft *(754 m)*. A surface 'mother' ship is required to support her.

NR 1   *9/1993, Giorgio Arra*

2 DEEP SUBMERGENCE RESCUE VEHICLES

Name	No	Builders	In service	F/S
MYSTIC	DSRV 1	Lockheed Missiles and Space Co,	7 Aug 1971	PSA
AVALON	DSRV 2	Sunnyvale, CA	28 July 1972	ASA

Displacement, tons: 30 surfaced; 38 dived
Dimensions, feet (metres): 49.2 × 8 *(15 × 2.4)*
Main machinery: Electric motors; silver/zinc batteries; 1 prop (movable control shroud); 4 ducted thrusters (2 fwd, 2 aft)
Speed, knots: 4. **Range, miles:** 24 at 3 kts
Complement: 4 (pilot, co-pilot, 2 rescue sphere operators) plus 24 rescued men
Sonars: Search and navigational sonar, and closed-circuit television (supplemented by optical devices) are installed in the DSRV to determine the exact location of a disabled submarine within a given area and for pinpointing the submarine's escape hatches. Side-looking sonar can be fitted for search missions.

Comment: The DSRV is intended to provide a quick-reaction world-wide, all-weather capability for the rescue of survivors in a disabled submarine. Transportable by road, aircraft (in C141 and C 5 jet cargo aircraft), surface ship (*Ortolan* (ASR 22) submarine rescue ship), and specially modified SSNs.
The carrying submarine will launch and recover the DSRV while submerged and, if necessary, while under ice. A total of six DSRVs were planned, but only two were funded. They alternate their duties every two months.
The outer hull is constructed of formed fibreglass. Within this outer hull are three interconnected spheres which form the main pressure capsule. Each sphere is 7.5 ft in diameter and is constructed of HY-140 steel. The forward sphere contains the vehicle's control equipment and is manned by the pilot and co-pilot, the centre and after spheres accommodate 24 passengers and a third crewman. Under the DSRV's centre sphere is a hemispherical protrusion or 'skirt' which seals over the disabled submarine's hatch. During the mating operation the skirt is pumped dry to enable personnel to transfer. Operating depth, 1525 m *(5000 ft)*. Names are not 'official'. Both have been upgraded with modern electronics and navigation systems.

AVALON   *12/1985, Giorgio Arra*

2 DEEP SUBMERGENCE VEHICLES: MODIFIED ALVIN TYPE

Name	No	Builders	F/S
TURTLE (ex-*Autec II*)	DSV 3	General Dynamics (Electric Boat Div)	PA
SEA CLIFF (ex-*Autec I*)	DSV 4	General Dynamics (Electric Boat Div)	PSA

Displacement, tons: 26 full load
Dimensions, feet (metres): 26 × 10 *(7.9 × 3.1)* (DSV 3); 31 × 12 *(9.5 × 3.7)* (DSV 4)
Main machinery: Electric motors; 1 prop (trainable); 2 thrusters (trainable)
Speed, knots: 2.5. **Range, miles:** 24 at 2 kts
Complement: 3 (pilot, co-pilot, observer)

Comment: Intended for deep submergence research and work tasks. Launched on 11 December 1968 and placed in service on 1 June 1971. In 1979-80 *Turtle* was overhauled and upgraded for operations to 10 000 feet. In 1983-84 *Sea Cliff* provided with titanium sphere giving a depth capability of 20 000 feet. *Sea Cliff* reached a depth of 20 000 feet 10 March 1985. Both vessels have been upgraded with improved cameras, lighting and navigation systems. Twin-arm manipulator fitted. Silver/zinc batteries. Operating depth 3050 m *(10 000 ft)* for DSV 3 and 6100 m *(20 000 ft)* for DSV 4.

TURTLE   *7/1988, W Donko*

1 DEEP SUBMERGENCE VEHICLE: ALVIN TYPE

Name	No	Builders	F/S
ALVIN	DSV 2	General Mills Inc, Minneapolis	PSA

Displacement, tons: 18 full load
Dimensions, feet (metres): 26.5 × 8.5 *(8.1 × 2.6)*
Main machinery: 6 brushless DC motors; 6 thrusters; 2 vertical-motion thrusters (located near the centre of gravity); 2 horizontally (near stern) (1 directed athwartships, 1 directed longitudinally); 2 on rotatable shaft near stern for vertical or longitudinal motion
Speed, knots: 2. **Range, miles:** 3 at 0.5 kt
Complement: 3 (1 pilot, 2 observers)

Comment: *Alvin* was built for operation by the Woods Hole Oceanographic Institution for the Office of Naval Research. Original configuration had an operating depth of 6000 ft. Named for Allyn C Vine of Woods Hole Oceanographic Institution. *Alvin* accidentally sank in 5051 ft of water on 16 October 1968; subsequently raised in August 1969; refurbished 1970-71 in original configuration. Placed in service on Navy List 1 June 1971. Subsequently refitted with titanium pressure sphere to provide increased depth capability and again operational in November 1973. Currently leased to Wood's Hole. She has two banks of lead acid batteries, 120V DC system with 47 kWh capacity. Operating depth, 4000 m *(13 120 ft)*.

1 MOTHER SHIP

LANEY CHOUEST

Measurement, tons: 497 grt
Dimensions, feet (metres): 233.9 × 49.9 × 14.1 *(71.3 × 15.2 × 4.3)*
Main machinery: 3 GM EMD 16-710G7 diesels; 9210 hp *(6.87 MW)*; 3 shafts
Speed, knots: 16
Complement: 24

Comment: Acts as the mother ship to the DSVs.

LANEY CHOUEST (tender)   *5/1991, Stefan Terzibaschitsch*

COAST GUARD

Senior Officers

Commandant:
  Admiral Robert E Kramek
Vice-Commandant:
  Vice Admiral Arthur E Henn
Chief of Staff:
  Vice Admiral Kent H Williams
Commander, Atlantic Area:
  Vice Admiral James L Loy
Commander, Pacific Area:
  Vice Admiral Richard D Herr

Establishment

The United States Coast Guard was established by an Act of Congress approved 28 January 1915, which consolidated the Revenue Cutter Service (founded in 1790) and the Life Saving Service (founded in 1848). The act of establishment stated the Coast Guard "shall be a military service and a branch of the armed forces of the USA at all times. The Coast Guard shall be a service in the Treasury Department except when operating as a service in the Navy".
Congress further legislated that in time of national emergency or when the President so directs, the Coast Guard operates as a part of the Navy. Some ships of the Coast Guard did operate as a part of the Navy during the First and Second World Wars and the Vietnam War.
The Lighthouse Service (founded in 1789) was transferred to the Coast Guard on 1 July 1939 and the Bureau of Navigation and Steamboat Inspection on 28 February 1942.
The Coast Guard was transferred to the newly established Department of Transportation on 1 April 1967.

Personnel

1 Jan 1994: 5877 officers, 1546 warrant officers,
30 450 enlisted men, 892 cadets,
160 Public Health Service personnel,
8000 reserves (1000 officers).

Missions

The current missions of the Coast Guard are to (1) enforce or assist in the enforcement of applicable Federal laws upon the high seas and waters subject to the jurisdiction of the USA including environmental protection; (2) administer all Federal laws regarding safety of life and property on the high seas and on waters subject to the jurisdiction of the USA, except those laws specifically entrusted to other Federal agencies; (3) develop, establish, maintain, operate, and conduct aids to maritime navigation, ocean stations, icebreaking activities, oceanographic research, and rescue facilities; and (4) maintain a state of readiness to function as a specialised service in the Navy when so directed by the President.

Cutter Strength

All Coast Guard vessels over 65 ft in length and that have adequate crew accommodation are referred to as 'cutters'. All names are preceded by USCG. The first two digits of the hull number for all Coast Guard vessels under 100 ft in length indicates the approximate length overall.
Approximately 2000 standard and non-standard boats are in service ranging in size from 11 ft skiffs to 55 ft aids-to-navigation craft.

Category/Classification		Active	Building
Cutters			
WHEC	High Endurance Cutters	12	—
WMEC	Medium Endurance Cutters	34	—
Icebreakers			
WAGB	Icebreakers	3	1
WTGB	Icebreaking Tugs	9	—
Patrol Forces			
WPB	Patrol Craft, Large	90	—

Training Cutter

WIX	Training Cutter	1	—

Buoy Tenders

WLB	Buoy Tenders, Seagoing	27	1 (4)
WLM	Buoy Tenders, Coastal	11	1 (13)
WLI	Buoy Tenders, Inland	6	—
WLR	Buoy Tenders, River	18	—

Construction Tenders

WLIC	Construction Tenders, Inland	16	—

Harbour Tugs

WYTL	Harbour Tugs, Small	14	—
SAR Craft		1450+	—

DELETIONS

Medium Endurance Cutters

1991 *Chilula, Cherokee*
1993 *Tamarao*

Patrol Forces

1991 *Cape Hatteras* (Mexico), *Point Hope* (Costa Rica), *Point Verde* (Mexico), *Point Herron* (Mexico), *Point Roberts, Point Judith* (Venezuela), *Point Barrow* (Panama), *Point Charles, Point Knoll* (Venezuela)
1992 *Point Thatcher, Point Brown, Point Harris*
1993 *Point Lookout*
1994 *Sea Hawk, Shearwater, Petrel* (all in reserve)

Tenders

1991 *Fir, Salvia*
1993 *Blackhaw*

HIGH ENDURANCE CUTTERS

12 HAMILTON and HERO CLASSES (WHEC)

Name	No	Builders	Laid down	Launched	Commissioned	F/S
HAMILTON	WHEC 715	Avondale Shipyards	Jan 1965	18 Dec 1965	20 Feb 1967	PA
DALLAS	WHEC 716	Avondale Shipyards	7 Feb 1966	1 Oct 1966	1 Oct 1967	AA
MELLON	WHEC 717	Avondale Shipyards	25 July 1966	11 Feb 1967	22 Dec 1967	PA
CHASE	WHEC 718	Avondale Shipyards	27 Oct 1966	20 May 1967	1 Mar 1968	PA
BOUTWELL	WHEC 719	Avondale Shipyards	5 Dec 1966	17 June 1967	14 June 1968	PA
SHERMAN	WHEC 720	Avondale Shipyards	23 Jan 1967	23 Sep 1967	23 Aug 1968	PA
GALLATIN	WHEC 721	Avondale Shipyards	27 Feb 1967	18 Nov 1967	20 Dec 1968	AA
MORGENTHAU	WHEC 722	Avondale Shipyards	17 July 1967	10 Feb 1968	14 Feb 1969	PA
RUSH	WHEC 723	Avondale Shipyards	23 Oct 1967	16 Nov 1968	3 July 1969	PA
MUNRO	WHEC 724	Avondale Shipyards	18 Feb 1970	5 Dec 1970	10 Sep 1971	PA
JARVIS	WHEC 725	Avondale Shipyards	9 Sep 1970	24 Apr 1971	30 Dec 1971	PA
MIDGETT	WHEC 726	Avondale Shipyards	5 Apr 1971	4 Sep 1971	17 Mar 1972	PA

Displacement, tons: 3050 full load
Dimensions, feet (metres): 378 × 42.8 × 20
  (115.2 × 13.1 × 6.1)
Flight deck, feet (metres): 88 × 40 *(26.8 × 12.2)*
Main machinery: CODOG; 2 Pratt & Whitney FT4A-6 gas turbines; 36 000 hp *(26.86 MW)*; 2 Fairbanks-Morse 38TD8-1/8-12 diesels; 7000 hp *(5.22 MW)* sustained; 2 shafts; cp props; retractable bow propulsor; 350 hp *(261 kW)*
Speed, knots: 29. **Range, miles:** 14 000 at 11 kts diesels; 2400 at 29 kts gas
Complement: 179 (21 officers)

Guns: 1 OTO Melara 3 in *(76 mm)*/62 Mk 75 Compact ❶; 85° elevation; 85 rounds/minute to 16 km *(8.7 nm)* anti-surface; 12 km *(6.6 nm)* anti-aircraft; weight of shell 6 kg.
  2 McDonnell Douglas 25 mm/87 Mk 38. 4—12.7 mm MGs.
  1 GE/GD 20 mm Vulcan Phalanx 6 barrelled Mk 15 ❷; 3000 rounds/minute combined to 1.5 km.
Countermeasures: Decoys: 2 Loral Hycor SRBOC 6-barrelled fixed Mk 36; IR flares and chaff.
  ESM: WLR-1C, WLR-3; radar warning.
Combat data systems: SCCS (to be fitted to all by 1996) includes OTCIXS satellite link.
Fire control: Mk 92 Mod 1 GFCS.
Radars: Air search: Lockheed SPS 40B ❸; D/E band.
  Surface search: Raytheon SPS 64(V)6 ❹; I band.
  Fire control: Sperry Mk 92 ❺; I/J band.
  Tacan: URN 25.

Helicopters: 1 HH-65A or 1 HH-60J ❻.

Programmes: In the Autumn of 1977 *Gallatin* and *Morgenthau* were the first of the Coast Guard ships to have women assigned as permanent members of the crew.
Modernisation: FRAM programme for all 12 ships in this class from October 1985 to October 1992. Work included standardising the engineering plants, improving the clutching systems, replacing SPS 29 air-search radar with SPS 40 radar and replacing the Mk 56 fire-control system and 5 in/38 gun mount with the Mk 92 system and a single 76 mm OTO Melara Compact gun. In addition Harpoon and Phalanx CIWS fitted to five of the class by 1992 and CIWS to all by late 1993. The flight deck and other aircraft facilities upgraded to handle a Jay Hawk helicopter including a telescopic hangar. URN 25 Tacan added along with the SQR 4 and SQR 17 sonobuoy receiving set and passive acoustic analysis systems. SRBOC chaff launchers were also fitted but not improved ESM which has

GALLATIN

(Scale 1 : 1200), Ian Sturton

GALATIN

5/1993, Erik Laursen

been shelved. All missiles, torpedo tubes, sonar and ASW equipment removed in 1993/94. 25 mm Mk 38 guns replaced the 20 mm Mk 67. Shipboard Command and Control System (SCCS) is to be fitted to all of the class by 1996.
Structure: These ships have clipper bows, twin funnels enclosing a helicopter hangar, helicopter platform aft. All are fitted with elaborate communications equipment. Superstructure is largely of aluminium construction. Bridge control of manoeuv-

ring is by aircraft-type joystick rather than wheel. Engine and propeller pitch consoles are located in wheelhouse and at bridge wing stations as well as engine room control booth.
Operational: Ten of the class are based in the Pacific, leaving only two on the East Coast. The removal of SSMs and all ASW equipment sensibly refocuses these ships on Coast Guard roles.

MEDIUM ENDURANCE CUTTERS
13 FAMOUS CUTTER CLASS (WMEC)

Name	No	Builders	Laid down	Launched	Commissioned	F/S
BEAR	WMEC 901	Tacoma Boatbuilding Co	23 Aug 1979	25 Sep 1980	4 Feb 1983	AA
TAMPA	WMEC 902	Tacoma Boatbuilding Co	3 Apr 1980	19 Mar 1981	16 Mar 1984	AA
HARRIET LANE	WMEC 903	Tacoma Boatbuilding Co	15 Oct 1980	6 Feb 1982	20 Sep 1984	AA
NORTHLAND	WMEC 904	Tacoma Boatbuilding Co	9 Apr 1981	7 May 1982	17 Dec 1984	AA
SPENCER	WMEC 905	Robert E Derecktor Corp	26 June 1982	17 Apr 1984	28 June 1986	AA
SENECA	WMEC 906	Robert E Derecktor Corp	16 Sep 1982	17 Apr 1984	4 May 1987	AA
ESCANABA	WMEC 907	Robert E Derecktor Corp	1 Apr 1983	6 Feb 1985	27 Aug 1987	AA
TAHOMA	WMEC 908	Robert E Derecktor Corp	28 June 1983	6 Feb 1985	6 Apr 1988	AA
CAMPBELL	WMEC 909	Robert E Derecktor Corp	10 Aug 1984	29 Apr 1986	19 Aug 1988	AA
THETIS	WMEC 910	Robert E Derecktor Corp	24 Aug 1984	29 Apr 1986	30 June 1989	AA
FORWARD	WMEC 911	Robert E Derecktor Corp	11 July 1986	22 Aug 1987	4 Aug 1990	AA
LEGARE	WMEC 912	Robert E Derecktor Corp	11 July 1986	22 Aug 1987	4 Aug 1990	AA
MOHAWK	WMEC 913	Robert E Derecktor Corp	15 Mar 1987	5 May 1988	20 Mar 1991	AA

Displacement, tons: 1780 full load
Dimensions, feet (metres): 270 × 38 × 13.5
   (82.3 × 11.6 × 4.1)
Main machinery: 2 Alco 18V-251 diesels; 7290 hp *(5.44 MW)*
   sustained; 2 shafts; cp props
Speed, knots: 19.5. **Range, miles:** 9500 at 13 kts, 3850 at
   19.5 kts
Complement: 100 (14 officers) plus 16 aircrew

Guns: 1 OTO Melara 3 in *(76 mm)*/62 Mk 75 ❶; 85° elevation;
   85 rounds/minute to 16 km *(8.7 nm)* anti-surface; 12 km
   (6.6 nm) anti-aircraft; weight of shell 6 kg.
   2—12.7 mm MGs and/or 2—40 mm Mk 19 grenade launchers
   ❷.
Countermeasures: Decoys: 2 Loral Hycor SRBOC 6-barrelled
   fixed Mk 36; IR flares and chaff.
   ESM/ECM: SLQ 32(V)2; radar intercept.
Combat data systems: Sperry COMDAC. OTCIXS satellite link
   (being fitted).
Radars: Surface search: Raytheon SPS 64(V) ❸; I band.
   Fire control: Sperry Mk 92 Mod 1 ❹; I/J band.
   Tacan: URN 25.

Helicopters: 1 HH-65A ❺ or HH-60J.

Programmes: This class has replaced the Campbell class and
   other medium and high endurance cutters. The contract for

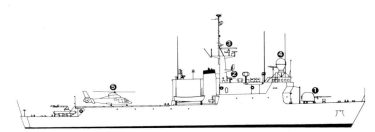

BEAR

(Scale 1 : 900), Ian Sturton

construction of WMEC 905-913 was originally awarded to
Tacoma Boatbuilding Co on 29 August 1980. However, under
lawsuit from the Robert E Derecktor Corp, Middletown, Rhode
Island, the contract to Tacoma was determined by a US District
Court to be invalid and was awarded to Robert E Derecktor
Corp on 15 January 1981.
Modernisation: OTCIXS satellite link being fitted from 1992.
Structure: They are the only medium endurance cutters with a
   helicopter hangar (which is telescopic) and the first cutters

with automated command and control centre. Fin stabilisers
fitted. *Thetis* has been fitted with the French DCN Talon landing and hold down helicopter system, which in due course is to
be retrofitted to all helicopter capable cutters. Plans to fit SSM
and/or CIWS have been abandoned as has towed array sonar.
Operational: Bases are at Portsmouth, New Bedford, Key West
and Boston. Reported to be very lively in heavy seas perhaps
because the length to beam ratio is unusually small for ships
required to operate in Atlantic conditions.

FORWARD

3/1993, Giorgio Arra

3 DIVER CLASS (WMEC)

Name	No	Builders	USN Comm.	F/S
ACUSHNET	WMEC 167	Basalt Rock Co,	5 Feb 1944	PA
(ex-USS *Shackle*)	(ex-WAGO 167,	Napa, CA		
	ex-WAT 167, ex-ARS 9)			
YOCONA	WMEC 168	Basalt Rock Co,	3 Nov 1944	PA
(ex-USS *Seize*)	(ex-WAT 168, ex-ARS 26)	Napa, CA		
ESCAPE	WMEC 6	Basalt Rock Co,	20 Nov 1943	AA
	(ex-ARS 6)	Napa, CA		

Displacement, tons: 1557 standard; 1745 full load
Dimensions, feet (metres): 213.5 × 39 × 15 *(65.1 × 11.9 × 4.6)*
Main machinery: 4 Cooper-Bessemer GSB-8 *(Yocona)*, 4 Caterpillar D 399 diesels; 4500 hp
   (3.36 MW) sustained *(Escape)*, 4 Fairbanks-Morse *(Acushnet)* diesels; 3000 hp *(2.24 MW)*;
   2 shafts
Speed, knots: 15.5. **Range, miles:** 9000 at 15 kts
Complement: 64 (7 officers) *(Acushnet)*; 72 (7 officers) *(Yocona)*
Radars: Navigation: 2 Raytheon SPS 64; I band.

Comment: Large, steel-hulled salvage ships transferred from the Navy to the Coast Guard and
   employed in tug and oceanographic duties. *Acushnet* modified for handling environmental data
   buoys and reclassified WAGO in 1968 and reclassified WMEC in 1980; *Yocona* reverted to
   WMEC in 1968. *Escape* transferred on loan from USN on 4 December 1980. Refitted at Curtis
   Bay Yard in 1980-81. Major renovation work completed on *Acushnet* in 1983 will enable her to
   continue operating through 1997. Plans to replace *Yocona* have been delayed.

ACUSHNET

10/1993, Giorgio Arra

16 RELIANCE CLASS (WMEC)

Name	No	Builders	Commissioned	MMA completion	F/S
RELIANCE	WMEC 615	Todd Shipyards	20 June 1964	Jan 1989	AA (Newcastle)
DILIGENCE	WMEC 616	Todd Shipyards	26 Aug 1964	Mar 1992	AA (Wilmington)
VIGILANT	WMEC 617	Todd Shipyards	3 Oct 1964	Aug 1990	AA (Cape Canaveral)
ACTIVE	WMEC 618	Christy Corp	17 Sep 1966	Feb 1987	PA (Port Angeles)
CONFIDENCE	WMEC 619	Coast Guard Yard, Baltimore	19 Feb 1966	June 1988	AA (Cape Canaveral)
RESOLUTE	WMEC 620	Coast Guard Yard, Baltimore	8 Dec 1966	Mar 1996	AA (New London)
VALIANT	WMEC 621	American Shipbuilding Co	28 Oct 1967	July 1993	AA (Miami)
COURAGEOUS	WMEC 622	American Shipbuilding Co	10 Apr 1968	Mar 1990	AA (Panama City)
STEADFAST	WMEC 623	American Shipbuilding Co	25 Sep 1968	Jan 1994	PA (Astoria)
DAUNTLESS	WMEC 624	American Shipbuilding Co	10 June 1968	Mar 1995	MMA/AA (Galveston)
VENTUROUS	WMEC 625	American Shipbuilding Co	16 Aug 1968	Sep 1995	MMA/PA (St Petersburg)
DEPENDABLE	WMEC 626	American Shipbuilding Co	22 Nov 1968	Nov 1996	AA (Corpus Christi)
VIGOROUS	WMEC 627	American Shipbuilding Co	2 May 1969	Jan 1993	AA (Cape May)
DURABLE	WMEC 628	Coast Guard Yard, Baltimore	8 Dec 1967	Jan 1989	AA (St Petersburg)
DECISIVE	WMEC 629	Coast Guard Yard, Baltimore	23 Aug 1968	Mar 1997	AA (St Petersburg)
ALERT	WMEC 630	Coast Guard Yard, Baltimore	4 Aug 1969	Aug 1994	AA (Astoria)

Displacement, tons: 950 standard; 1007 (1129 after MMA) full load (WMEC 620-630)
970 (1110 after MMA) full load (WMEC 618, 619)
Dimensions, feet (metres): 210.5 × 34 × 10.5
(64.2 × 10.4 × 3.2)
Main machinery: 2 Alco 16V-251 diesels; 6480 hp *(4.83 MW)* sustained; 2 shafts; cp props
Speed, knots: 18. **Range, miles:** 6100 at 14 kts; 2700 at 18 kts
Complement: 74 (12 officers)

Guns: 1 McDonnell Douglas 25 mm/87 Mk 38; 55° elevation; 200 rounds/minute to 6.8 km *(3.4 nm)*. 2—12.7 mm MGs.
Radars: Surface search: 2 Raytheon SPS 64(V); I band.

Helicopters: 1 HH-65A embarked as required.

Modernisation: All 16 cutters have undergone or will undergo a Major Maintenance Availability (MMA) which takes approximately 18 months. The exhausts for main engines, ship service generators and boilers are run in a new vertical funnel which reduces flight deck size. Scheduled completion dates are listed above but future dates are at best only estimates. 76 mm guns have been replaced by 25 mm Mk 38.
Structure: Designed for search and rescue duties. Design features include 360 degree visibility from bridge; helicopter flight deck (no hangar); and engine exhaust vent at stern in place of conventional funnel which is being built during MMA. Capable of towing ships up to 10 000 tons. Air-conditioned throughout except engine room; high degree of habitability.
Operational: Normally operate within 500 miles of the coast. All these cutters are active with the exception of those decommissioned for an MMA. Primary roles are SAR, law-enforcement and defence operations.

DAUNTLESS (before MMA)   10/1992, Giorgio Arra

RELIANCE (after MMA)   5/1993, Giorgio Arra

1 STORIS CLASS (WMEC)

Name	No	Builders	Commissioned	F/S
STORIS (ex-*Eskimo*)	WMEC 38 (ex-WAGB 38, ex-WAGL 38)	Toledo Shipbuilding Co, Ohio	30 Sep 1942	PA

Displacement, tons: 1715 standard; 1925 full load
Dimensions, feet (metres): 230 × 43 × 15 *(70.1 × 13.1 × 4.6)*
Main machinery: Diesel-electric; 3 GM EMD diesel generators; 1 motor; 3000 hp *(2.24 MW)*; 1 shaft
Speed, knots: 14. **Range, miles:** 22 000 at 8 kts; 12 000 at 14 kts
Complement: 106 (10 officers)
Guns: 1 McDonnell Douglas 25 mm/87 Mk 38.
Radars: Navigation: Raytheon SPS 64; I band.

Comment: Laid down on 14 July 1941; launched on 4 April 1942 as ice patrol tender. Strengthened for ice navigation and sometimes employed as icebreaker. Employed in Alaskan service for search, rescue and law enforcement. *Storis* completed a major maintenance availability in June 1986, during which her main engines were replaced with EMD diesels and her living quarters expanded. Gun changed in 1994.

STORIS   *1983, USCG*

1 + 1 STALWART CLASS

Name	No	Builders	Commissioned
VINDICATOR	—	Tacoma Boat	20 Nov 1984

Displacement, tons: 2262 full load
Dimensions, feet (metres): 224 × 43 × 14.9 *(68.3 × 13.1 × 4.5)*
Main machinery: Diesel-electric; 4 Caterpillar D 398B diesel generators; 3200 hp *(2.39 MW)*; 2 motors 1600 hp *(1.2 MW)*; 2 shafts; bow thruster; 550 hp *(410 kW)*
Speed, knots: 11; 3 when towing **Range, miles:** 4000 at 11 kts; 6450 at 3 kts
Complement: 30-33 (9 officers)
Radars: Navigation: Two Raytheon; I band.
Sonars: UQQ2 SURTASS; towed array; passive surveillance.

Comment: Transferred from the MSC in early 1994. Planned conversion in FY 1995 with a second of class. Details given are for the ship in naval service.

AEROSTAT SHIPS

5 AEROSTAT SHIPS (ARMY)

Name	Builders	Completed	F/S
ATLANTIC SENTRY	Steiner Marine, AL	1986	AA (Key West)
CARIBBEAN SENTRY	Halter Marine, LA	1987	AA (Key West)
GULF SENTRY	Halter Marine, LA	1984	AA (Miami)
PACIFIC SENTRY	Halter Marine, LA	1983	AA (Miami)
WINDWARD SENTRY	McDermott, LA	1979	AA (Key West)

Displacement, tons: 2140 full load
Dimensions, feet (metres): 192 × 44 × 15.1 *(58.5 × 13.4 × 4.6)*
Main machinery: 2 GM EMD 16-645E6 diesels; 3900 hp *(2.91 MW)*; 2 shafts
Speed, knots: 12. **Range, miles:** 7000 at 10 kts
Complement: 10 civilian plus 9 Army

Comment: There are some minor differences between these ships which have been either purchased or leased between April 1987 and November 1989. Each consists of a Mobile Aerostat Platform (MAP) with installed mooring system, a helium-filled aerostat with APS-143(V)2 or APS 128 attached radar, and radar, communications, and computer consoles in the MAP operations centre. Their mission is to provide continuous traffic-surveillance information to other law-enforcement units for the purpose of interdicting drug-trafficking and alien vessels. SBAs normally work in conjunction with Coast Guard cutters and patrol boats but successful operations have also been conducted with other US and foreign naval resources. They are operated throughout the Caribbean Sea, the Gulf of Mexico, and the Straits of Florida, and particularly in choke points between major islands where target vessels must pass. The aerostats are 109 ft long and 37 ft in diameter; their operational altitude is zero to 2500 ft. The first system was first tested and evaluated in 1984. Four of the five systems are operational at any given time. At sea endurance is 31 days. Transferred to the Army in 1992 and strictly speaking do not belong in this section.

CARIBBEAN SENTRY with AEROSTAT   *1/1990, Giorgio Arra*

SHIPBORNE AIRCRAFT

Numbers/Type: 96 Aerospatiale HH 65A Dolphin.
Operational speed: 165 kts *(300 km/h)*.
Service ceiling: 11 810 ft *(3600 m)*.
Range: 400 nm *(741 km)*.
Role/Weapon systems: Short-range rescue and recovery (SRR) helicopter. 80 aircraft are operational. Sensors: Bendix RDR 1500 radar and Collins mission management system. Weapons: Unarmed.

DOLPHIN   *1989, USCG*

Numbers/Type: 36 Sikorsky HH-60J Jay Hawk.
Operational speed: 180 kts *(333 km/h)*.
Service ceiling: 17 200 ft *(5240 m)*.
Range: 350 nm *(648 km)*.
Role/Weapon systems: Coast Guard version of Seahawk, first flew in 1988, replacing HH-3F in MRR role. Total of 40 ordered, all to be delivered by 1995. Sensors: Bendix weather/search radar. Weapons: Unarmed.

JAY HAWK   *1992, Sikorsky*

LAND-BASED MARITIME AIRCRAFT (FRONT LINE)

Note: In February 1993 there were in addition three CH-3Es on loan from the Air Force and two RG-8A single-engined reconnaissance aircraft. Four P-3B Orions are used for AEW by US Customs.

Numbers/Type: 25/7/9 AMD-BA HU-25A/B/C Guardian Falcon.
Operational speed: 420 kts *(774 km/h)*.
Service ceiling: 42 000 ft *(12 800 m)*.
Range: 1940 nm *(3594 km)*.
Role/Weapon systems: Medium-range maritime reconnaissance role. 27 are operational. Sensors: Weather/search radar. Weapons: Unarmed.

Numbers/Type: 30 Lockheed HC-130H.
Operational speed: 325 kts *(602 km/h)*.
Service ceiling: 33 000 ft *(10 060 m)*.
Range: 4250 nm *(7876 km)*.
Role/Weapon systems: Long-range maritime reconnaissance role; further orders expected. 25 are operational. Sensors: Weather/search radar: APS 137. Weapons: Unarmed.

Numbers/Type: 2 Schweitzer R6-8A Condor.
Operational speed: 138 kts *(256 km/h)*.
Service ceiling: 18 000 ft *(5490 m)*.
Range: 600 nm *(1108 km)*.
Role/Weapon systems: Short-range maritime reconnaissance. Sensors: AAQ-15 FLIR. Weapons: Unarmed.

ICEBREAKERS

0 + 1 HEALY CLASS (WAGB)

Name	No	Builders	Commissioned
HEALY	WAGB 20	Avondale Industries	1997

Displacement, tons: 15 332 full load
Dimensions, feet (metres): 420 oa; 397.8 wl × 82 × 32 *(128; 121.2 × 25 × 9.8)*
Main machinery: Diesel-electric; 4 diesels; 40 000 hp *(29.84 MW)*; 4 alternators; 2 motors; 30 000 hp *(22.38 MW)*; 2 shafts; bow thruster; 2000 hp *(1.49 MW)*
Speed, knots: 12.5. **Range, miles:** 16 000 at 12.5 kts
Complement: 75
Helicopters: 2 HH-65A.

Comment: In response to the 1984 Interagency Polar Icebreaker Requirements Study and Congressional mandate, approval was given for the construction of a new icebreaker as a replacement for two Wind class which were then decommissioned in 1988. However, no action was taken to provide funds for the new ship until Congress included it in the Navy's FY 1991 ship construction budget and after further delays the ship was ordered 15 July 1993. Icebreaking capability of not less than 8 ft at 3 kts.

HEALY *(not to scale), Ian Sturton*

2 POLAR CLASS (WAGB)

Name	No	Builders	Commissioned	F/S
POLAR STAR	WAGB 10	Lockheed SB & Construction Co	19 Jan 1976	PA
POLAR SEA	WAGB 11	Lockheed SB & Construction Co	23 Feb 1978	PA

Displacement, tons: 13 190 full load
Dimensions, feet (metres): 399 × 86 × 32 *(121.6 × 26.2 × 9.8)*
Main machinery: CODOG; diesel-electric (AC/DC); 6 Alco 16V-251F/Westinghouse AC diesel generators; 21 000 hp *(15.66 MW)* sustained; 3 Westinghouse DC motors; 18 000 hp *(13.42 MW)* sustained; 3 Pratt & Whitney FT4A-12 gas-turbines; 60 000 hp *(44.76 MW)* sustained; 3 Philadelphia 75 VMGS gears; 60 000 hp *(44.76 MW)* sustained; 3 shafts; cp props
Speed, knots: 18. **Range, miles:** 28 275 at 13 kts
Complement: 142 (15 officers) plus 33 scientists and 12 aircrew
Guns: 2—12.7 mm MGs.
Radars: Navigation: Raytheon SPS 64; I band.
Helicopters: 2 HH-65A.

Comment: These ships are the first icebreakers built for US service since *Glacier* was constructed two decades earlier. Both are based at Seattle, WA. At a continuous speed of 3 kts, they can break ice 6 ft *(1.8 m)* thick, and by ramming can break 21 ft *(6.4 m)* pack. Conventional icebreaker hull form with 'White' cutaway bow configuration and well-rounded body sections to prevent being trapped in ice. The ice belt is 1.75 in *(44.45 mm)* thick supported by framing at 16in *(0.4 m)* centres. Three heeling systems assist icebreaking and ship extraction. Two 15 ton capacity cranes fitted aft; one 3 ton capacity crane fitted forward. Two over-the-side oceanographic winches, one over-the-stern trawl/core winch. Deck fixtures for scientific research vans, and research laboratories provided for arctic and oceanographic research. Between 1986-92, science facilities were upgraded including habitability, lab spaces and winch capabilities.

POLAR SEA *12/1993, van Ginderen Collection*

1 MACKINAW CLASS (WAGB)

Name	No	Builders	Commissioned	F/S
MACKINAW	WAGB 83	Toledo Shipbuilding Co, Ohio	20 Dec 1944	GLA

Displacement, tons: 5252
Dimensions, feet (metres): 290 × 74 × 19 *(88.4 × 22.6 × 5.8)*
Main machinery: Diesel-electric; 6 Fairbanks-Morse 38D8-1/8-12 diesel generators; 8.7 MW sustained; Elliot electric drive; 10 000 hp *(7.46 MW)*; 3 shafts (1 fwd, 2 aft)
Speed, knots: 18.7. **Range, miles:** 41 000 at 11.5 kts; 10 000 at 18.7 kts
Complement: 74 (8 officers)
Radars: Navigation: Raytheon SPS 64; I band.

Comment: Specially designed and constructed for service as icebreaker on the Great Lakes. Equipped with two 5 ton capacity cranes. Clear area for helicopter is provided on the quarterdeck, the aircraft being called for from shore Coast Guard station. Scheduled to be paid off in FY 1988 as a means of helping the Coast Guard cope with severe budget cuts but pressure from members of Congress from states bordering the Great Lakes, where *Mackinaw* operates, resulted in her being placed in an 'In Commission, Special' status. Operational again in Spring 1988. A safety and survivability overhaul is being done around operations from 1992-94. Scheduled for decommissioning in December 1994 after 50 years service.

MACKINAW *1983, USCG*

9 BAY CLASS (TUGS—WGTB)

Name	No	Laid down	Commissioned	F/S
KATMAI BAY	WTGB 101	7 Nov 1977	8 Jan 1979	GLA
BRISTOL BAY	WTGB 102	13 Feb 1978	5 Apr 1979	GLA
MOBILE BAY	WTGB 103	13 Feb 1978	6 May 1979	GLA
BISCAYNE BAY	WTGB 104	29 Aug 1978	8 Dec 1979	GLA
NEAH BAY	WTGB 105	6 Aug 1979	18 Aug 1980	GLA
MORRO BAY	WTGB 106	6 Aug 1979	25 Jan 1981	AA
PENOBSCOT BAY	WTGB 107	24 July 1983	4 Sep 1984	AA
THUNDER BAY	WTGB 108	20 July 1984	29 Dec 1985	AA
STURGEON BAY	WTGB 109	9 July 1986	20 Aug 1988	AA

Displacement, tons: 662 full load
Dimensions, feet (metres): 140 × 37.6 × 12.5 *(42.7 × 11.4 × 3.8)*
Main machinery: Diesel-electric; 2 Fairbanks-Morse 38D8-1/8-10 diesel generators; 2.4 MW sustained; Westinghouse electric drive; 2500 hp *(1.87 MW)*; 1 shaft
Speed, knots: 14.7. **Range, miles:** 4000 at 12 kts
Complement: 17 (3 officers)
Radars: Navigation: Raytheon SPS 64; I band.

Comment: The size, manoeuvrability and other operational characteristics of these vessels are tailored for operations in harbours and other restricted waters and for fulfilling present and anticipated multi-mission requirements. All units are ice-strengthened for operation on the Great Lakes, coastal waters and in rivers and can break 24 in of ice continuously and up to 8 ft by ramming. A self contained portable bubbler van and system reduces hull friction. First six built at Tacoma Boatbuilding, Tacoma. WTGB 107-109 built in Tacoma by Bay City Marine, San Diego. *Bristol Bay* and *Mobile Bay* have had their bows reinforced to push the two aids-to-navigation barges on the Great Lakes.

PENOBSCOT BAY *6/1991, Giorgio Arra*

SEAGOING TENDERS

0 + 1 (4) JUNIPER CLASS (BUOY TENDERS—WLB)

Name	No	Builders	Commissioned
JUNIPER	WLB 601	Marinette Marine	1995

Displacement, tons: 2032 full load
Dimensions, feet (metres): 225 × 46 × 13 *(68.6 × 14 × 4)*
Main machinery: 2 diesels; 6200 hp *(4.6 MW)*; 1 shaft; bow and stern thrusters
Speed, knots: 15. **Range, miles:** 6000 at 12 kts
Complement: 40 (6 officers)
Guns: 1—25 mm/87 Mk 38.
Radars: Surface search: I band.

Comment: In January 1993, the Coast Guard awarded Marinette Marine of Marinette, WI, a contract to construct the first of a new class of seagoing buoy tenders, with an option for four more. Construction of the first of class started in 1994, with delivery in 1995. Capable of breaking 14 in of ice at 3 kts or a minimum of 3 ft by ramming. Main hoist can lift 20 tons, secondary 5 tons. The class is named after the first *Juniper*, which was built in 1940 and decommissioned in 1975.

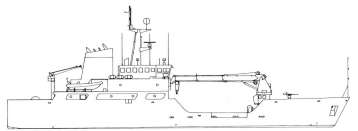

JUNIPER *(not to scale), Ian Sturton*

27 BALSAM CLASS (BUOY TENDERS—WLB)

Name	No	Launched	F/S	Name	No	Launched	F/S
A Series				C Series			
COWSLIP	WLB 277	1942	AA	BASSWOOD	WLB 388	1944	PA
GENTIAN	WLB 290	1942	AA	BITTERSWEET	WLB 389	1944	AA
LAUREL	WLB 291	1942	AA	BRAMBLE	WLB 392	1944	GLA
SORREL	WLB 296	1943	AA	FIREBUSH	WLB 393	1944	PA
CITRUS	WMEC 300	1943	PA	HORNBEAM	WLB 394	1944	AA
CONIFER	WLB 301	1943	PA	IRIS	WLB 395	1944	PA
MADRONA	WLB 302	1943	AA	MALLOW	WLB 396	1944	PA
				MARIPOSA	WLB 397	1944	PA
B Series				SASSAFRAS	WLB 401	1944	PA
IRONWOOD	WLB 297	1943	PA	SEDGE	WLB 402	1944	PA
BUTTONWOOD	WLB 306	1943	PA	SPAR	WLB 403	1944	AA
PLANETREE	WLB 307	1943	PA	SUNDEW	WLB 404	1944	GLA
PAPAW	WLB 308	1943	AR	SWEETBRIER	WLB 405	1944	PA
SWEETGUM	WLB 309	1943	AR	ACACIA	WLB 406	1944	GLA
				WOODRUSH	WLB 407	1944	PA

Displacement, tons: 757 standard; 1034 full load
Dimensions, feet (metres): 180 × 37 × 12 *(54.9 × 11.3 × 3.8)*
Main machinery: Diesel-electric; 2 diesels; 1402 hp *(1.06 MW)* or 1800 hp *(1.34 MW)* (404); 1 motor; 1200 hp *(895 kW)*; 1 shaft; bow thruster (except in 388, 395 and 396)
Speed, knots: 13
Complement: 53 (6 officers)
Guns: 2—12.7 mm MGs (except 392, 406 and 404).
Radars: Navigation: Raytheon SPS 64; I band.

Comment: Seagoing buoy tenders. *Ironwood* built by Coast Guard Yard at Curtis Bay, Maryland; others by Marine Iron & Shipbuilding Co, Duluth, Minnesota, or Zenith Dredge Co, Duluth, Minnesota. Completed 1943-45. All have 20 ton capacity booms.
Modernisation and Service Life Extension Programmes: *Cowslip, Gentian, Conifer, Sorrel, Madrona, Laurel, Papaw, Sweetgum* and *Buttonwood* have completed an 18 month SLEP. Work included replacement of main engines, improvement of electronics, navigation and weight-handling systems, and improved habitability. *Ironwood, Bittersweet, Bramble, Firebush, Hornbeam, Mariposa, Sassafras, Sedge, Spar, Sundew, Sweetbrier, Acacia* and *Woodrush* all underwent major renovation in the mid- to late 1970s which was not as extensive as the current SLEPs. However, in the 1988-91 period all of these cutters received same main engines as those installed in cutters receiving SLEP. The last 20 mm guns removed in 1993. *Sundew's* main engines are the same as the others but are 'ungoverned' because of her icebreaking capability.

MARIPOSA 4/1993, Giorgio Arra

PATROL CRAFT

Notes: (1) Heritage class programme cancelled on 25 November 1991. The first of class *Leopold* was not completed. The cause of the cancellation was attributed to changing requirements and availability of more ships as a result of former USSR decline. It was also reported that there were concerns about the design. A smaller patrol craft is now being considered.
(2) The three Seabird class SES ships were placed in reserve on 31 January 1994.

41 POINT CLASS (WPB)

Name	No	F/S	Name	No	F/S
A Series			POINT HANNON	82355	AA
POINT SWIFT	82312	AA	POINT FRANCIS	82356	AA
			POINT HURON	82357	AA
C Series			POINT STUART	82358	PA
POINT HIGHLAND	82333	AA	POINT STEELE	82359	AA
POINT LEDGE	82334	PA	POINT WINSLOW	82360	PA
POINT COUNTESS	82335	PA	POINT NOWELL	82363	AA
POINT GLASS	82336	AA	POINT WHITEHORN	82364	AA
POINT DIVIDE	82337	PA	POINT TURNER	82365	AA
POINT BRIDGE	82338	PA	POINT LOBOS	82366	AA
POINT CHICO	82339	PA	POINT WARDE	82368	AA
POINT BATAN	82340	AA	POINT HEYER	82369	PA
POINT BAKER	82342	AA	POINT RICHMOND	82370	PA
POINT WELLS	82343	AA			
POINT ESTERO	82344	AA	D Series		
POINT ARENA	82346	AA	POINT BARNES	82371	AA
POINT BONITA	82347	AA	POINT BROWER	82372	PA
POINT SPENCER	82349	AA	POINT CAMDEN	82373	PA
POINT FRANKLIN	82350	AA	POINT CARREW	82374	PA
POINT BENNETT	82351	PA	POINT DORAN	82375	PA
POINT SAL	82352	AA	POINT HOBART	82377	PA
POINT MONROE	82353	AA	POINT JACKSON	82378	AA
POINT EVANS	82354	PA	POINT MARTIN	82379	AA

Displacement, tons: 67 (A series); 66 (C series); 69 (D series) full load
Dimensions, feet (metres): 83 × 17.2 × 5.8 *(25.3 × 5.2 × 1.8)*
Main machinery: 2 Cummins or Caterpillar diesels; 1600 hp *(1.19 MW)*; 2 shafts
Speed, knots: 23.5; 22.6 (D series). **Range, miles:** 1500 at 8 kts; 1200 at 8 kts (D series)
Complement: 10 (1 officer)
Guns: 2—12.7 mm MGs.
Radars: Navigation: Raytheon SPS 64; I band.

Comment: Steel-hulled craft with aluminium superstructures designed for patrol and search and rescue. A series built 1960-61; C series in 1961-67, and D series in 1970. Some of the cutters operate with an officer assigned, the rest with all-enlisted crews. Twenty-six of the 'A' and 'B' series were transferred to South Vietnam in 1969-70. Some of the remaining cutters are being re-engined with Caterpillar engines. Some of the class are now in service with navies of Costa Rica, Panama, Mexico and Venezuela.

POINT DIVIDE 10/1993, Giorgio Arra

49 ISLAND CLASS (WPB)

Name	No	Home Port	Commissioned
FARALLON	WPB 1301	Miami, FL	15 Nov 1985
MANITOU	WPB 1302	Miami, FL	24 Jan 1986
MATAGORDA	WPB 1303	Miami, FL	28 Feb 1986
MAUI	WPB 1304	Miami, FL	24 Mar 1986
MONHEGAN	WPB 1305	Roosevelt Roads, PR	11 Apr 1986
NUNIVAK	WPB 1306	Roosevelt Roads, PR	2 May 1986
OCRACOKE	WPB 1307	Roosevelt Roads, PR	23 May 1986
VASHON	WPB 1308	Roosevelt Roads, PR	13 June 1986
AQUIDNECK	WPB 1309	Portsmouth, VA	25 July 1986
MUSTANG	WPB 1310	Seward, AK	29 Aug 1986
NAUSHON	WPB 1311	Ketchikan, AK	3 Oct 1986
SANIBEL	WPB 1312	Rockland, ME	14 Nov 1986
EDISTO	WPB 1313	Crescent City, CA	7 Jan 1987
SAPELO	WPB 1314	Eureka, CA	24 Feb 1987
MATINICUS	WPB 1315	Cape May, NJ	16 Apr 1987
NANTUCKET	WPB 1316	Roosevelt Roads, PR	4 June 1987
ATTU	WPB 1317	San Juan, PR	6 Feb 1988
BARANOF	WPB 1318	Miami, FL	12 Mar 1988
CHANDELEUR	WPB 1319	Miami, FL	16 Apr 1988
CHINCOTEAGUE	WPB 1320	Mobile, AL	21 May 1988
CUSHING	WPB 1321	Mobile, AL	25 June 1988
CUTTYHUNK	WPB 1322	Port Angeles, WA	30 July 1988
DRUMMOND	WPB 1323	Port Canaveral, FL	3 Sep 1988
KEY LARGO	WPB 1324	Savannah, GA	8 Oct 1988
METOMPKIN	WPB 1325	Charleston, SC	12 Nov 1988
MONOMOY	WPB 1326	Woods Hole, MA	17 Dec 1988
ORCAS	WPB 1327	Coos Bay, OR	21 Jan 1989
PADRE	WPB 1328	Key West, FL	25 Feb 1989
SITKINAK	WPB 1329	Key West, FL	1 Apr 1989
TYBEE	WPB 1330	San Diego, CA	5 May 1989
WASHINGTON	WPB 1331	Honolulu, HI	9 June 1989
WRANGELL	WPB 1332	Sandy Hook, NJ	9 July 1989
ADAK	WPB 1333	Sandy Hook, NJ	18 Aug 1989
LIBERTY	WPB 1334	Auke Bay, AK	22 Sep 1989
ANACAPA	WPB 1335	Petersburg, AK	27 Oct 1989
KISKA	WPB 1336	Hilo, HI	1 Dec 1989
ASSATEAGUE	WPB 1337	Honolulu, HI	5 Jan 1990
GRAND ISLE	WPB 1338	Gloucester, MA	19 Feb 1991
KEY BISCAYNE	WPB 1339	Corpus Christi, TX	12 Mar 1991
JEFFERSON ISLAND	WPB 1340	South Portland, ME	9 Apr 1991
KODIAK ISLAND	WPB 1341	Panama City, FL	14 May 1991
LONG ISLAND	WPB 1342	Monterey, CA	18 June 1991
BAINBRIDGE ISLAND	WPB 1343	Sandy Hook, NJ	23 July 1991
BLOCK ISLAND	WPB 1344	Atlantic Beach, NC	27 Aug 1991
STATEN ISLAND	WPB 1345	Atlantic Beach, NC	1 Oct 1991
ROANOKE ISLAND	WPB 1346	Homer, AK	5 Nov 1991
PEA ISLAND	WPB 1347	Mayport, FL	10 Dec 1991
KNIGHT ISLAND	WPB 1348	Freeport, TX	14 Jan 1992
GALVESTON ISLAND	WPB 1349	Apra Harbor, Guam	25 Feb 1992

Displacement, tons: 168 (A series); 154 (B and C series) full load
Dimensions, feet (metres): 110 × 21 × 7.3 *(33.5 × 6.4 × 2.2)*
Main machinery: 2 Paxman Valenta 16RP 200M diesels (A and B series); 5800 hp *(4.3 MW)*; 2 Caterpillar 3516 diesels (C series); 5400 hp *(4.03 MW)*; 2 shafts
Speed, knots: 29. **Range, miles:** 3928 at 10 kts
Complement: 16 (2 officers)
Guns: 1 McDonnell Douglas 25 mm/87 Mk 38. 2—12.7 mm M60 MGs.
Radars: Navigation: Raytheon SPS 64V; I band.

Comment: All built by the Bollinger Machine Shop and Shipyard at Lockport, Louisiana. The design is based upon the 110 ft patrol craft built by Vosper Thornycroft, UK, which are currently serving in Venezuela, Qatar, Abu Dhabi and Singapore, but modified to meet Coast Guard needs. Vosper Thornycroft supplied design support, stabilisers, propellers, and steering gear. All are having 25 mm Mk 38 guns installed. Batches: A 1301-1316, B 1317-1337, C 1338-1349. Batch C had their allocated names changed prior to completion in 1991/92.

TYBEE 6/1993, Giorgio Arra

COASTAL TENDERS

0 + 1 (13) KEEPER CLASS (BUOY TENDERS—WLM)

Name	No	Builders	Commissioned
IDA LEWIS	WLM 650	Marinette Marine	1996

Displacement, tons: 845 full load
Dimensions, feet (metres): 175 × 36 × 7.9 (53.3 × 11 × 2.4)
Main machinery: 2 diesels; 3420 hp (2.55 MW); 2 Z-drives; bow thruster
Speed, knots: 12. **Range, miles:** 2000 at 10 kts
Complement: 18 (1 officer)
Radars: Surface search: I band.

Comment: Contract awarded 24 June 1993 for first of class with an option for 13 more. Capable of breaking 9 in of ice at 3 kts or 18 in by ramming. Named after Lighthouse Keepers for the Lighthouse Service, one of the predecessors of the modern Coast Guard. The ship is a scaled down model of the Juniper class for coastal service. Main hoist to lift 10 tons, secondary 3.75 tons. The ship will also be able to skim and recover surface oil pollution.

5 RED CLASS (BUOY TENDERS—WLM)

Name	No	Launched	F/S	Name	No	Launched	F/S
RED WOOD	WLM 685	1964	AA	RED CEDAR	WLM 688	1970	AA
RED BEECH	WLM 686	1964	AA	RED OAK	WLM 689	1971	AA
RED BIRCH	WLM 687	1965	AA				

Displacement, tons: 471 standard; 536 full load
Dimensions, feet (metres): 157 × 33 × 6 (47.9 × 10.1 × 1.8)
Main machinery: 2 diesels; 1800 hp (1.34 MW); 2 shafts; cp props; bow thruster
Speed, knots: 12.8. **Range, miles:** 2248 at 11.6 kts
Complement: 31 (4 officers)

Comment: All built by Coast Guard Yard, Curtis Bay, Maryland. Steel hulls strengthened for light icebreaking. Steering and engine controls on each bridge wing as well as in pilot house. Living spaces are air-conditioned. Fitted with 10 ton capacity boom.

RED OAK   8/1987, van Ginderen Collection

6 WHITE SUMAC CLASS (BUOY TENDERS—WLM)

Name	No	F/S	Name	No	F/S
WHITE SUMAC	WLM 540	AA	WHITE HEATH	WLM 545	AA
WHITE LUPINE	WLM 546	AA	WHITE HOLLY	WLM 543	AA
WHITE PINE	WLM 547	AA	WHITE SAGE	WLM 544	AA

Displacement, tons: 435 standard; 485 full load
Dimensions, feet (metres): 133 × 31 × 9 (40.5 × 9.5 × 2.7)
Main machinery: 2 Caterpillar diesels; 600 hp (448 kW); 2 shafts
Speed, knots: 9.8
Complement: 24 (1 officer)

Comment: All launched in 1943. All six ships are former US Navy YFs, adapted for the Coast Guard. Fitted with 10 ton capacity boom.

WHITE SUMAC   1/1992, Giorgio Arra

BUOY TENDERS (INLAND—WLI)

Name	No	F/S	Name	No	F/S
BLUEBELL	WLI 313	PA	BUCKTHORN	WLI 642	GLA

Displacement, tons: 226 (174 Bluebell) full load
Dimensions, feet (metres): 100 × 24 × 5 (30.5 × 7.3 × 1.5) (Buckthorn draught 4 (1.2))
Main machinery: 2 Caterpillar diesels; 600 hp (448 kW); 2 shafts
Speed, knots: 11.9; 10.5 (Bluebell)
Complement: 14 (1 officer)

Comment: Bluebell completed 1945, and Buckthorn in 1963.

BUCKTHORN   2/1989, van Ginderen Collection

Name	No	F/S	Name	No	F/S
BLACKBERRY	WLI 65303	AA	BAYBERRY	WLI 65400	PA
CHOKEBERRY	WLI 65304	AA	ELDERBERRY	WLI 65401	PA

Displacement, tons: 68 full load
Dimensions, feet (metres): 65 × 17 × 4 (19.8 × 5.2 × 1.2)
Main machinery: 1 or 2 (Bayberry and Elderberry) GM diesels; 1 or 2 shafts
Speed, knots: 11
Complement: 9

Comment: First two completed in 1946, second two in 1954.

BAYBERRY   1983, USCG

BUOY TENDERS (RIVER) (WLR)

Notes: (1) All are based on rivers of USA especially the Mississippi and the Missouri and its tributaries.
(2) Two ATON (aids to navigation) barges completed in 1991/92 by Marinette Marine. For use on the Great Lakes in conjunction with icebreaker tugs Bristol Bay and Mobile Bay.

ATON I and Icebreaker Tug (WGTB)   1991, Marinette Marine

KANKAKEE WLR 75500   **GREENBRIAR** WLR 75501

Displacement, tons: 161 full load
Dimensions, feet (metres): 75.1 × 24 × 4.9 (22.9 × 7.3 × 1.5)
Main machinery: 2 Caterpillar 3412T diesels; 1006 hp (750 kW) sustained; 2 shafts
Speed, knots: 12. **Range, miles:** 600 at 12 kts
Complement: 13

Comment: Kankakee completed by Avondale 27 February 1990, and Greenbriar 12 April 1990. Have replaced Dogwood and Lantana. More of the class are planned.

SUMAC WLR 311

Displacement, tons: 423 full load
Dimensions, feet (metres): 115 × 30 × 6 (35.1 × 9.1 × 1.8)
Main machinery: 3 Caterpillar D 379 diesels; 1644 hp (1.23 MW); 3 shafts
Speed, knots: 10.6
Complement: 13

Comment: Built in 1943. Scheduled for replacement.

GASCONADE	WLR 75401		KICKAPOO	WLR 75406	
MUSKINGUM	WLR 75402		KANAWHA	WLR 75407	
WYACONDA	WLR 75403		PATOKA	WLR 75408	
CHIPPEWA	WLR 75404		CHENA	WLR 75409	
CHEYENNE	WLR 75405				

Displacement, tons: 150 full load
Dimensions, feet (metres): 75 × 22 × 4 *(22.9 × 6.7 × 1.2)*
Main machinery: 2 Caterpillar diesels; 660 hp *(492 kW)*; 2 shafts
Speed, knots: 10.8
Complement: 12

Comment: Built 1964-71.

Buoy Tender   *6/1991, Giorgio Arra*

OUACHITA	WLR 65501		SCIOTO	WLR 65504
CIMARRON	WLR 65502		OSAGE	WLR 65505
OBION	WLR 65503		SANGAMON	WLR 65506

Displacement, tons: 146 full load
Dimensions, feet (metres): 65.6 × 21 × 5 *(20 × 6.4 × 1.5)*
Main machinery: 2 Caterpillar diesels; 660 hp *(492 kW)*; 2 shafts
Speed, knots: 12.5
Complement: 10

Comment: Built in 1960-62.

SAIL TRAINING CUTTER

1 EAGLE CLASS (WIX)

Name	No	Builders	F/S
EAGLE (ex-*Horst Wessel*)	WIX 327	Blohm & Voss, Hamburg	AA

Displacement, tons: 1784 full load
Dimensions, feet (metres): 231 wl; 293.6 oa × 39.4 × 16.1 *(70.4; 89.5 × 12 × 4.9)*
Main machinery: 1 Caterpillar D 399 auxiliary diesel; 1125 hp *(839 kW)* sustained; 1 shaft
Speed, knots: 10.5; 18 sail. **Range, miles:** 5450 at 7.5 kts diesel only
Complement: 245 (19 officers, 180 cadets)
Radars: Navigation: Raytheon SPS 64; I band.

Comment: Former German training ship. Launched on 13 June 1936. Taken by the USA as part of reparations after the Second World War for employment in US Coast Guard Practice Squadron. Taken over at Bremerhaven in January 1946; arrived at home port of New London, Connecticut, in July 1946. (Sister ship *Albert Leo Schlageter* was also taken by the USA in 1945 but was sold to Brazil in 1948 and re-sold to Portugal in 1962. Another ship of similar design, *Gorch Fock*, transferred to the USSR in 1946 and survives as *Tovarisch*). *Eagle* was extensively overhauled 1981-82. When the Coast Guard added the orange-and-blue marking stripes to cutters in the 1960s *Eagle* was exempted because of their effect on her graceful lines; however, in early 1976 the stripes and words 'Coast Guard' were added in time for the July 1976 Operation Sail in New York harbour. During the Coast Guard's year-long bicentennial celebration, which ended 4 August 1990, *Eagle* visited each of the 10 ports where the original revenue cutters were home-ported: Baltimore, MD; New London, CT; Washington, NC; Savannah, GA; Philadelphia, PA; Newburyport, MA; Portsmouth, NH; Charleston, SC; New York, NY; and Hampton, VA.
Fore and main masts 150.3 ft *(45.8 m)*; mizzen 132 ft *(40.2 m)*; sail area, 25 351 sq ft.

EAGLE and CONDOR (the old and the new)   *1991*

CONSTRUCTION TENDERS (INLAND) (WLIC)

Note: All, although operating on inland waters, are administered by the Atlantic Area.

4 PAMLICO CLASS

Name	No	F/S	Name	No	F/S
PAMLICO	WLIC 800	AA	KENNEBEC	WLIC 802	AA
HUDSON	WLIC 801	AA	SAGINAW	WLIC 803	AA

Displacement, tons: 459 full load
Dimensions, feet (metres): 160.9 × 30 × 4 *(49 × 9.1 × 1.2)*
Main machinery: 2 Caterpillar diesels; 1000 hp *(746 kW)*; 2 shafts
Speed, knots: 11.5
Complement: 15 (1 officer)

Comment: Completed in 1976 at the Coast Guard Yard, Curtis Bay, Maryland. These ships maintain structures and buoys in bay areas along the Atlantic and Gulf coasts.

HUDSON   *12/1989, Giorgio Arra*

3 COSMOS CLASS

Name	No	F/S	Name	No	F/S
RAMBLER	WLIC 298	AA	PRIMROSE	WLIC 316	AA
SMILAX	WLIC 315	AA			

Displacement, tons: 178 full load
Dimensions, feet (metres): 100 × 24 × 5 *(30.5 × 7.3 × 1.5)*
Main machinery: 2 Caterpillar D 353 diesels; 425 hp *(317 kW)* sustained; 2 shafts
Speed, knots: 10.5
Complement: 15 (1 officer)

Comment: Completed in 1944. *Primrose* fitted with pile driver. Primary areas of operation are intercoastal waters from Virginia to Georgia. All have 5000 lb cranes.

PRIMROSE   *7/1990, van Ginderen Collection*

9 ANVIL/CLAMP CLASSES

Name	No	F/S	Name	No	F/S	Name	No	F/S
ANVIL	WLIC 75301	AA	MALLET	WLIC 75304	AA	WEDGE	WLIC 75307	AA
HAMMER	WLIC 75302	AA	VISE	WLIC 75305	AA	HATCHET	WLIC 75309	AA
SLEDGE	WLIC 75303	AA	CLAMP	WLIC 75306	AA	AXE	WLIC 75310	AA

Displacement, tons: 140 full load
Dimensions, feet (metres): 75 (76—WLIC 75306-75310) × 22 × 4 *(22.9 (23.2) × 6.7 × 1.2)*
Main machinery: 2 Caterpillar diesels; 660 hp *(492 kW)*; 2 shafts
Speed, knots: 10
Complement: 13 (1 officer in *Mallet, Sledge* and *Vise*)

Comment: Completed 1962-65. Primary areas of operation are intercoastal waters from Texas to New Jersey.

SLEDGE   *7/1988, W Donko*

HARBOUR TUGS

14 65 ft CLASS (WYTL)

CAPSTAN WYTL 65601	**CATENARY** WYTL 65606	**LINE** WYTL 65611
CHOCK WYTL 65602	**BRIDLE** WYTL 65607	**WIRE** WYTL 65612
SWIVEL WYTL 65603	**PENDANT** WYTL 65608	**BOLLARD** WYTL 65614
TACKLE WYTL 65604	**SHACKLE** WYTL 65609	**CLEAT** WYTL 65615
TOWLINE WYTL 65605	**HAWSER** WYTL 65610	

Displacement, tons: 72 full load
Dimensions, feet (metres): 65 × 19 × 7 *(19.8 × 5.8 × 2.1)*
Main machinery: 1 diesel; 400 hp *(298 kW)* or 1 Caterpillar 3412 TA diesel (65601-65606);
  475 hp *(637 kW)* sustained; 1 shaft
Speed, knots: 10
Complement: 10

Comment: Built from 1961 to 1967. All active in the Atlantic Fleet. First six re-engined in 1993/94.

41 ft UTILITY CRAFT   *10/1993, Giorgio Arra*

6 + (90) MOTOR LIFEBOATS

Displacement, tons: 20 full load
Dimensions, feet (metres): 47.9 × 14 × 1.8 *(14.6 × 4.3 × 0.5)*
Main machinery: 2 diesels; 850 hp *(634 kW)* sustained; 2 shafts
Speed, knots: 25. **Range, miles:** 200 at 25 kts
Complement: 4

Comment: Built by Textron Marine, New Orleans. The prototype completed trials in mid-1991. Five production boats delivered by early 1994. Final numbers will be up to 100 to replace the ageing fleet of 44 ft lifeboats. Aluminium hulls, self-righting with a 9000 lb bollard pull and a towing capability of 150 tons. Primarily a lifeboat but it has a multi-mission capability.

HAWSER   *5/1993, Giorgio Arra*

1450 + RESCUE AND UTILITY CRAFT

Note: There is a large number of utility craft of several different types.

FERRY   *6/1990, Giorgio Arra*

MOTOR LIFEBOAT   *1993, US Coast Guard*

NATIONAL OCEANIC AND ATMOSPHERIC ADMINISTRATION (NOAA)

Command

Director, NOAA Corps Operations:
  Rear Admiral Sigmund R Petersen
Director, Charting and Geodetic Services:
  Rear Admiral J Austin Yeager
Deputy Director, NOAA Corps Operations:
  Rear Admiral William L Stubblefield
Director, Atlantic Marine Center:
  Rear Admiral Freddie L Jeffries
Director, Pacific Marine Center:
  Rear Admiral John C Albright
Director Aircraft Operations Center:
  Rear Admiral Francis D Moran

Establishment

The Survey of the Coast was established by an act of the US Congress on February 10, 1807. In 1834 the organisation was renamed the US Coast Survey, and in 1878, the Coast and Geodetic Survey was established to provide a pool of sea-going scientists and engineers to command and operate the vessels of the Coast and Geodetic Survey, lead field parties, and manage research and engineering programmes. The Coast and Geodetic Survey was made a component of the Environmental Science Services Administration in the US Department of Commerce on July 13, 1965. In October 1970, the Environmental Science Services Administration was reorganised and renamed the National Oceanic and Atmospheric Administration (NOAA). The Coast and Geodetic Survey was incorporated into NOAA as the National Ocean Survey, with its jurisdiction expanded to include functions of the US Lake Survey (formerly a part of the US Army Corps of

MT MITCHELL   *9/1992, Stefan Terzibaschitsch*

Engineers), the US Coast Guard's national Data Buoy Development Project, and the US Navy's National Oceanographic Instrumentation Center. The Commissioned Officer Corps was renamed the NOAA Corps.

Missions

The office of NOAA Corps Operations is responsible to the US Department of Commerce. NOAA's research vessels conduct operations in hydrography, bathymetry, oceanography, atmospheric research, fisheries surveys and research, and related programmes in living and non-living marine resources. Larger research vessels operate in international waters; smaller vessels operate primarily in Atlantic and Pacific coastal waters, in the Gulfs of Mexico and Alaska, and in the US Lakes. The Office of NOAA also conducts diving operations and operates fixed-wing and rotary-wing aircraft for reconnaissance, oceanographic and atmospheric research, and to support aerial mapping and charting.

NOAA is the largest component of the US Department of Commerce, with a diverse set of responsibilities in environmental science. These responsibilities include the Office of NOAA Corps Operations, the National Ocean Service, the National Weather Service, the National Marine Fisheries Service, the National Environmental Satellite, Data, and Information Service, and the Office of Oceanic and Atmospheric Research.

Ships

The following ships may be met with at sea. All are painted white with two-tone blue bands on the funnels and buff masts. The plan is to replace and modernise up to 17 ships by the end of the decade. AGOR 26 was ordered in early 1994 (see MSC section).
Oceanographic Survey Ships: *Researcher, Oceanographer, Surveyor, Malcolm Baldrige.*
Hydrographic Survey Ships: *Fairweather, Rainier, Mt. Mitchell.*
Coastal Survey Ships: *McArthur, Davidson, Whiting, Pierce.*
Coastal Vessels: *Rude, Heck, Ferrel.*
Fisheries Assessment: *Millar Freeman, Oregon II, Chapman, Albatros IV, Townsend Cromwell, David Jorden, Delaware II, John N Cobb, Murre II*
Three Stalwart class TAGOS ships were acquired in 1992/93.

WHITING   *9/1992, Stefan Terzibaschitsch*

Personnel

The National Ocean Survey has approximately 400 commissioned officers and 12 000 civil service personnel. NOAA commissioned officers frequently serve with the military and may be transferred for hostilities.

Bases

Major: Norfolk, VA and Seattle, WA.
Minor: Woods Hole, MA; Pascagoula, MS; Miami, FL; La Jolla, CA; Honolulu, HI.

ADVENTUROUS   *9/1992, Maritime Photographic*

URUGUAY

Headquarters' Appointment

Commander-in-Chief of the Navy:
  Vice Admiral James Coates

Diplomatic Representation

Naval Attaché in London:
  Captain Julian Valdez

Personnel

(a) 1994: 4590 (including 500 naval infantry, 300 naval air and 2000 Coast Guard)
(b) Voluntary service

Prefectura Naval (PNN)

Established in 1981 primarily for harbour security and coastline guard duties. In 1991 it was integrated with the Navy but some patrol craft still retain Prefectura markings.

Bases

Montevideo: Main naval base with two dry docks and a slipway at Punta Lobos
La Paloma: Naval station Ernesto Motto
Paysandu: River base

Marines

Cuerpo de Fusileros Navales consisting of 500 men in three units plus a command company of 100.

Prefix to Ships' Names

ROU

Mercantile Marine

Lloyd's Register of Shipping:
  96 vessels of 149 317 tons gross

DELETIONS

Frigate

1991   *18 de Julio*

Auxiliary

1991   *Vanguardia* (old)

FRIGATES

3 COMMANDANT RIVIÈRE CLASS

Name	No	Builders	Laid down	Launched	Commissioned	Recommissioned
URUGUAY (ex-*Commandant Bourdais*)	1	Lorient Naval Dockyard	Apr 1959	15 Apr 1961	10 Mar 1962	20 Aug 1990
GENERAL ARTIGAS (ex-*Victor Schoelcher*)	2	Lorient Naval Dockyard	Oct 1957	11 Oct 1958	15 Oct 1962	9 Jan 1989
MONTEVIDEO (ex-*Amiral Charner*)	3 (ex-4)	Lorient Naval Dockyard	Nov 1958	12 Mar 1960	14 Dec 1962	28 Jan 1991

Displacement, tons: 1750 standard; 2250 full load
Dimensions, feet (metres): 336.9 × 38.4 × 14.1
 (102.7 × 11.7 × 4.3)
Main machinery: 4 SEMT-Pielstick 12 PC series diesels;
 16 000 hp(m) *(11.8 MW)*; 2 shafts
Speed, knots: 25. **Range, miles:** 7500 at 15 kts
Complement: 159 (9 officers)

Missiles: SSM: 4 Aerospatiale MM 38 Exocet ❶; active radar
 homing to 42 km *(23 nm)* at 0.9 Mach; warhead 165 kg;
 sea-skimmer.
Guns: 2 DCN 3.9 in *(100 mm)*/55 Mod 1953 automatic ❷; dual
 purpose; 80° elevation; 60 rounds/minute to 17 km *(9 nm)*
 anti-surface; 8 km *(4.4 nm)* anti-aircraft; weight of shell
 13.5 kg.
 2 Hispano Suiza 30 mm/70 ❸; 83° elevation; 600 rounds/
 minute to 8.5 km *(4.8 nm)* anti-aircraft.
Torpedoes: 6—21.7 in *(550 mm)* (2 triple) tubes ❹ ECAN L3; anti-
 submarine; active homing to 5.5 km *(3 nm)* at 25 kts; warhead
 200 kg; depth to 300 m *(985 ft)*.
A/S mortars: 1 Mortier 305 mm 4-barrelled launcher ❺; automatic loading; range 2700 m; warhead 227 kg.

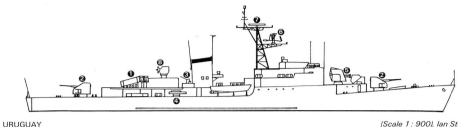

URUGUAY   *(Scale 1 : 900), Ian Sturton*

Countermeasures: ESM: ARBR 16; radar warning.
Fire control: C T Analogique. Sagem DMAA optical director.
Radars: Air/surface search: Thomson-CSF DRBV 22A ❻; D band.
Navigation: Racal Decca 1226 ❼; I band.
Fire control: Thomson-CSF DRBC 32C ❽; I band.
Sonars: EDO SQS 17; hull-mounted; active search; medium
 frequency.
 Thomson Sintra DUBA 3; active attack; high frequency.

Programmes: First one bought from France through SOFMA on
 30 September 1988, second pair 14 March 1990. All refitted
 before transfer.
Structure: Exocet and Dagaie removed before transfer but SSM
 casings were retained and missiles restored in 1991/92.
Operational: Can carry a Flag Officer and staff. In French service
 this class sometimes embarked up to 80 soldiers and two
 LCPs.

URUGUAY   *11/1993, Miguel A Soro*

MONTEVIDEO   *3/1992*

LAND-BASED MARITIME AIRCRAFT (FRONT LINE)

Note: In addition there are also four helicopters (one Sikorsky SH-34I, one Bell 47G and two West-land Wessex) and three fixed wing aircraft (three Cessna C-182).

Numbers/Type: 1/1/2 Beechcraft Super King Air 200T/T34B/T34C.
Operational speed: 282 kts *(523 km/h).*
Service ceiling: 35 000 ft *(10 670 m).*
Range: 2030 nm *(3756 km).*
Role/Weapon systems: Used for coastal patrol and protection operations, as well as transport. Sensors: Search radar. Weapons: Unarmed.

Numbers/Type: 3 Grumman S-3G Tracker.
Operational speed: 130 kts *(241 km/h).*
Service ceiling: 25 000 ft *(7620 m).*
Range: 1350 nm *(2500 km).*
Role/Weapon systems: ASW and surface search with recently improved systems. Sensors: Search radar, MAD, sonobuoys. Weapons: ASW; torpedoes, depth bombs or mines. ASV; rockets underwing.

PATROL FORCES

3 VIGILANTE CLASS (LARGE PATROL CRAFT)

Name	No	Builders	Commissioned
15 de NOVIEMBRE	5	CMN, Cherbourg	25 Mar 1981
25 de AGOSTO	6	CMN, Cherbourg	25 Mar 1981
COMODORO COÉ	7	CMN, Cherbourg	25 Mar 1981

Displacement, tons: 190 full load
Dimensions, feet (metres): 137 × 22.4 × 5.2 *(41.8 × 6.8 × 1.6)*
Main machinery: 2 MTU 12V 538 TB91 diesels; 4600 hp(m) *(3.4 MW)* sustained; 2 shafts
Speed, knots: 28. **Range, miles:** 2400 at 15 kts
Complement: 28 (5 officers)
Gun: 1 Bofors 40 mm/70.
Fire control: CSEE Naja optronic director.
Radars: Surface search: Racal Decca TM 1226C; I band.

Comment: Ordered in 1979. Steel hull. First launched 16 October 1980, second 11 December 1980 and third 27 January 1981. Offered for sale in 1992 but remaining in the Navy until sold. Venezuela showed an interest in 1993 but the sale was not confirmed.

25 de AGOSTO (with the rest of the class)   *4/1993*

2 CAPE CLASS (LARGE PATROL CRAFT)

Name	No	Builders	Commissioned
COLONIA (ex-*Cape Higgon*)	10	Coast Guard Yard, Curtis Bay	14 Oct 1953
RIO NEGRO (ex-*Cape Horn*)	11	Coast Guard Yard, Curtis Bay	3 Sep 1958

Displacement, tons: 98 standard; 148 full load
Dimensions, feet (metres): 95 × 20.2 × 6.6 *(28.9 × 6.2 × 2)*
Main machinery: 2 GM 16V-149TI diesels; 2322 hp *(1.73 MW)* sustained; 2 shafts
Speed, knots: 20. **Range, miles:** 2500 at 10 kts
Complement: 14 (1 officer)
Guns: 2—12.7 mm MGs.
Radars: Navigation: Raytheon SPS 64; I band

Comment: Designed for port security and search and rescue. Steel hulled. During modernisation in 1974 received new engines, electronics, and deck equipment, had superstructure modified or replaced, and had habitability improved. Transferred from the US Coast Guard in January 1990. Both based at Paysandu.

COLONIA   *1/1990, Giorgio Arra*

1 LARGE PATROL CRAFT

Name	No	Builders	Commissioned
SALTO	14 (ex-GS 24, ex-PR 2)	Cantieri Navali Riuniti, Ancona	1936

Displacement, tons: 150 standard; 180 full load
Dimensions, feet (metres): 137 × 18 × 10 *(41.8 × 5.5 × 3.1)*
Main machinery: 2 GM diesels; 1000 hp *(746 kW)*; 2 shafts
Speed, knots: 17. **Range, miles:** 4000 at 10 kts
Complement: 26
Guns: 1 Bofors 40 mm/70.

Comment: She also acts as a survey vessel. Based at Paysandu.

SALTO   *1988, Uruguayan Navy*

1 COASTAL PATROL CRAFT

Name	No	Builders	Commissioned
PAYSANDU	12 (ex-PR 12)	Sewart, USA	1968

Displacement, tons: 60 full load
Dimensions, feet (metres): 83 × 18 × 6 *(25.3 × 5.5 × 1.8)*
Main machinery: 2 GM 16V-71 diesels; 811 hp *(605 kW)* sustained; 2 shafts
Speed, knots: 22. **Range, miles:** 800 at 20 kts
Complement: 8
Guns: 3—12.7 mm MGs.
Radars: Surface search: Raytheon 1500B; I band.

Comment: Formerly incorrectly listed under Coast Guard. Based at Paysandu.

3 COASTGUARD PATROL CRAFT

70-72

Displacement, tons: 90 full load
Dimensions, feet (metres): 72.2 × 16.4 × 5.9 *(22 × 5 × 1.8)*
Main machinery: 2 GM diesels; 400 hp *(298 kW)*; 2 shafts
Speed, knots: 12
Complement: 8

Comment: The Prefectura is part of the Navy but these patrol craft retain Prefectura markings.

70   *11/1993, F Murillo*

MINE WARFARE FORCES

4 KONDOR II CLASS (MINESWEEPERS—COASTAL)

Name	No	Builders	Recommissioned
TEMERARIO (ex-*Riesa*)	31	Peenewerft, Wolgast	11 Oct 1991
VALIENTE (ex-*Eilenburg*)	32	Peenewerft, Wolgast	11 Oct 1991
FORTUNA (ex-*Bernau*)	33	Peenewerft, Wolgast	11 Oct 1991
AUDAZ (ex-*Eisleben*)	34	Peenewerft, Wolgast	11 Oct 1991

Displacement, tons: 310 full load
Dimensions, feet (metres): 186 × 24.6 × 7.9 *(56.7 × 7.5 × 2.4)*
Main machinery: 2 Russki/Kolomna Type 40-DM diesels; 4408 hp(m) *(3.24 MW)* sustained; 2 shafts; cp props
Speed, knots: 17
Complement: 31 (6 officers)
Guns: 1 Bofors 40 mm/60.
Mines: 2 rails.
Radars: Surface search: TSR 333; I band.

Comment: Built between 1970 and 1978 and belonged to the former GDR Navy. Transferred in October 1991 without armament. Minesweeping gear retained including MSG-3 variable depth sweep device.

FORTUNA   *10/1993, F Murillo*

RESEARCH SHIP

1 AUK CLASS

Name	No	Builders	Commissioned
COMANDANTE PEDRO CAMPBELL	24 (ex-4, ex-MS 31,	Defoe B & M	9 Nov 1942
(ex-USS *Chickadee*, MSF 59)	ex-MSF 1)	Works	

Displacement, tons: 1090 standard; 1250 full load
Dimensions, feet (metres): 221.2 × 32.2 × 10.8 *(67.5 × 9.8 × 3.3)*
Main machinery: Diesel-electric; 4 Alco 539 diesels; 3532 hp *(2.63 MW)*; 4 generators; 2 motors; 2 shafts
Speed, knots: 18. **Range, miles:** 4300 at 10 kts
Complement: 105

Comment: Former US fleet minesweeper. Launched on 20 July 1942. Transferred on loan and commissioned at San Diego on 18 August 1966. Purchased 15 August 1976. Sweeping gear removed and classified as a corvette. Refitted again at Montevideo naval yard in 1988-89 and then recommissioned for Antarctic service without armament. Now classified as a 'Buque Cientifico' and has a red hull. To be relieved by *Vanguardia* and may be scrapped in 1994.

COMANDANTE PEDRO CAMPBELL   *4/1992, Hartmut Ehlers*

TRAINING SHIPS

1 SAIL TRAINING SHIP

Name	No	Builders	Commissioned
CAPITAN MIRANDA	20 (ex-GS 10)	Sociedad Espanola de Construccion Naval, Matagorda, Cadiz	1930

Displacement, tons: 516 standard; 527 full load
Dimensions, feet (metres): 179 × 26 × 10.5 *(54.6 × 7.9 × 3.2)*
Main machinery: 1 GM diesel; 600 hp *(448 kW)*; 1 shaft
Speed, knots: 11
Complement: 49

Comment: Originally a diesel-driven survey ship with pronounced clipper bow. Converted for service as a three-masted schooner, commissioning as cadet training ship in 1978.

CAPITAN MIRANDA   *4/1992, Giorgio Ghiglione*

AUXILIARIES

1 PIAST CLASS (TYPE 570) (SALVAGE SHIP)

Name	No	Builders	Commissioned
VANGUARDIA	26 (ex-A 441)	Northern Shipyard, Gdansk	1977
(ex-*Otto Von Guericke*)			

Displacement, tons: 1732 full load
Dimensions, feet (metres): 240 × 39.4 × 13.1 *(73.2 × 12 × 4)*
Main machinery: 2 Zgoda diesels; 3800 hp(m) *(2.79 MW)*; 2 shafts
Speed, knots: 16. **Range, miles:** 3000 at 12 kts
Radars: Navigation: TSR 333; I band.

Comment: Acquired from Germany in October 1991 and sailed from Rostock in January 1992 after a refit at Neptun-Warnow Werft. Carries extensive towing and firefighting equipment plus a diving bell forward of the bridge. Armed with four 25 mm twin guns when in service with the former GDR Navy.

VANGUARDIA   *10/1991, Reinhard Kramer*

1 COHOES CLASS (SALVAGE SHIP)

Name	No	Builders	Commissioned
HURACAN	25 (ex-AM 25,	Commercial Ironworks,	24 Aug 1945
(ex-USS *Nahant* AN 83)	ex-BT 30)	Portland, Oregon	

Displacement, tons: 650 standard; 855 full load
Dimensions, feet (metres): 168.5 × 33.8 × 11.7 *(51.4 × 10.3 × 3.6)*
Main machinery: Diesel-electric; 2 Busch-Sulzer 539 diesels; 1500 hp *(1.12 MW)*; 2 generators; 1 motor; 1 shaft
Speed, knots: 11.5
Complement: 48
Guns: 3 Oerlikon 20 mm.

Comment: Former US netlayer, transferred 15 October 1968 for salvage services carrying divers and underwater swimmers. In 1954 diving equipment and a recompression chamber were installed. Commissioned in Uruguayan Navy 7 April 1969.

HURACAN   *1987, Uruguayan Navy*

1 TANKER

Name	No	Builders	Commissioned
PRESIDENTE RIVERA	—	Uddevallavarvet AB	2 July 1981
(ex-M/V *Viking Harrier*)			

Measurement, tons: 42 235 gross; 87 325 dwt
Dimensions, feet (metres): 750 × 139.1 × 44.3 *(228.6 × 42.4 × 13.5)*
Main machinery: 1 MAN Burmeister & Wain diesel; 15 800 hp(m) *(11.6 MW)*; 1 shaft
Speed, knots: 15

Comment: Purchased in September 1987 and handed over in January 1988. Chartered to ANCAP (state oil company). Offered for sale in 1992.

PRESIDENTE RIVERA   *2/1991, van Ginderen Collection*

1 SOTOYOMO CLASS (SUPPORT SHIP)

Name	No	Builders	Commissioned
SAN JOSÉ	22 (ex-USS ATA 122,	Levingstone SB Co	10 June 1943
(ex-*Lautaro*)	ex-62)		

Displacement, tons: 860 full load
Dimensions, feet (metres): 143 × 33.9 × 13 *(43.6 × 10.3 × 4)*
Main machinery: Diesel-electric; 2 GM 12-278A diesels; 2200 hp *(1.64 MW)*; 2 generators; 1 motor; 1500 hp *(1.12 MW)*; 1 shaft
Speed, knots: 13. **Range, miles:** 16 500 at 12 kts
Complement: 49 (3 officers)
Guns: 1 USN 3 in *(76 mm)*/50 Mk 26.
Radars: Navigation: Decca 505; I band.

Comment: Originally an ocean rescue tug in USN service but was reclassified as a patrol vessel on transfer to the Chilean Navy. Paid off in 1990 and recommissioned in the Uruguay Navy on 17 May 1991.

SAN JOSÉ   5/1991, Uruguayan Navy

1 BUOY TENDER

SIRIUS 21

Displacement, tons: 290 full load
Dimensions, feet (metres): 115.1 × 32.8 × 5.9 *(35.1 × 10 × 1.8)*
Main machinery: 2 Detroit 12V-71TA diesels; 840 hp *(626 kW)* sustained; 2 shafts
Speed, knots: 11
Complement: 15

Comment: Buoy tender built at Montevideo Naval Yard and completed in 1988. Endurance, five days.

SIRIUS   4/1992, Hartmut Ehlers

4 LCM 6 CLASS

LD 40-43

Displacement, tons: 24 light; 57 full load
Dimensions, feet (metres): 56.1 × 14.1 × 3.9 *(17.1 × 4.3 × 1.2)*
Main machinery: 2 Gray Marine 64 HN9 diesels; 330 hp *(264 kW)*; 2 shafts
Speed, knots: 9. **Range, miles:** 130 at 9 kts
Complement: 5
Military lift: 30 tons

Comment: Transferred on lease from US October 1972. *LD 43* is subordinate to the Fleet Air Arm Flying School at Lago del Sauce.

LD 41   4/1992, Hartmut Ehlers

2 LCVPs

LD 44-45

Displacement, tons: 15 full load
Dimensions, feet (metres): 46.5 × 11.6 × 2.7 *(14.1 × 3.5 × 0.8)*
Main machinery: 1 GM 4-71 diesel; 115 hp *(86 kW)* sustained; 1 shaft
Speed, knots: 9. **Range, miles:** 580 at 9 kts
Military lift: 10 tons

Comment: Built at Naval Shipyard, Montevideo and completed 1980.

LD 45   4/1992, Hartmut Ehlers

TUG

BANCO ORTIZ (ex-*Zingst*, ex-*Elbe*)   27 (ex-7, ex-Y 1655)

Displacement, tons: 261 full load
Dimensions, feet (metres): 100 × 26.6 × 10.8 *(30.5 × 8.1 × 3.3)*
Main machinery: 1 R6 DV 148 diesel; 1 shaft
Speed, knots: 10

Comment: Ex-GDR Type 270 coastal tug acquired in October 1991.

BANCO ORTIZ   4/1993

VANUATU

Senior Officer	General	Mercantile Marine

Senior Officer

Commissioner of Police:
   W D Saul

General

Originally the New Hebrides. Achieved independence on 30 July 1980, having previously been under Franco-British condominium. The Marine Police are based at Vita (capital) on Efate Island.

Mercantile Marine

Lloyd's Register of Shipping:
   283 vessels of 1 945 731 tons gross

POLICE

1 PACIFIC FORUM PATROL CRAFT

Name	No	Builders	Commissioned
TUKORO	—	Australian Shipbuilding Industries	13 June 1987

Displacement, tons: 165 full load
Dimensions, feet (metres): 103.3 × 26.6 × 6.9 *(31.5 × 8.1 × 2.1)*
Main machinery: 2 Caterpillar 3516TA diesels; 4400 hp *(3.28 MW)* sustained; 2 shafts
Speed, knots: 18. **Range, miles:** 2500 at 12 kts
Complement: 18 (3 officers)
Guns: Can carry 1—20 mm and 2—12.7 mm MGs, but will probably remain unarmed.
Radars: Navigation: Furuno 1011; I band.

Comment: Under the Defence Co-operation Programme Australia has provided one Patrol Craft to the Vanuatu Government. Training and operational and technical assistance is also given by the Royal Australian Navy. Ordered 13 September 1985.

TUKORO   *10/1991, Guy Toremans*

VENEZUELA

Headquarters' Appointments

Commander General of the Navy (Chief of Naval Operations):
Vice Admiral Julian Mauco Quintana
Deputy Chief of Naval Operations:
Vice Admiral Carlos Augusto Ramos Flores
Chief of Naval Staff:
Vice Admiral Rafael Huizi Clavier
Chief of Coast Guard:
Rear Admiral Jesus E Briceno Garcia

Diplomatic Representation

Naval Attaché in London:
Captain N A Eljuri

Personnel

(a) 1994: 14 800 officers and men including 5200 Marine Corps
(b) 2 years national service

Marines

Two operational Commands—Western and Eastern. The Marines consist of four Battalion Groups—UTC 1 *Libertador Simón Bolívar,* at Maiquetía; UTC 2 *General Rafael Urdaneta,* at Puerto Cabello; UTC 3 *Mariscal José Antonio de Sucre,* at Carúpano and UTC 4 *General Francisco de Miranda,* at Punto Fijo—the existing battalions having been redesignated 'Unidades Tácticas de Combate'; an Amphibious Vehicles Unit—the Unidad de Tanques Anfíbios *Capitán de Corbeta Miguel Ponce Lugo,* a Mixed Artillery Group, an Engineer Unit; a Signals Unit; a Transport Unit and one regiment of Naval Police. There is also the Comando Ribereno de Infantería de Marina *General Frank Rísquez Irribaren,* a paracommando unit and a unit of frogmen commandos.

Coast Guard

Formed in August 1982 as a para-naval force under the command of a Rear Admiral. With headquarters at La Guaira its primary task is the surveillance of the 200 mile Exclusive Economic Zone. Naval control.

National Guard

The Fuerzas Armadas de Cooperacion, generally known as the National Guard, is a paramilitary organisation, currently 17 000 strong. It is concerned, among other things, with customs and internal security—the Maritime Wing operates Coastal and Inshore Patrol Craft.

Bases

Caracas: Main HQ. La Carlota Naval Air Station.
Puerto Cabello: Contralmirante Agustin Armario Main Naval Base, Naval Air Station Command, Naval Schools and Dockyard.
Punto Fijo: Mariscal Falcón Base for Fast Attack Craft.
La Guaira: Small Naval Base (Naval Academy).
Maracaibo: Teniente de Navio Pedro Lucas Urribarri Base for Coast Guard Squadron.
La Banquilla: Secondary Coast Guard Base.
La Tortuga, Los Testigos Islands and Aves de Sotavento: Minor Coast Guard Bases.
Ciudad Bolivar (Orinoco River): HQ Fluvial Command.

Fleet Organisation

The fleet is split into 'Type' squadrons—all the frigates together (except GC 11 and 12) and the same for submarines, light and amphibious forces. Service Craft Squadron composed of T 44 and BE 11, and Coast Guard Squadron includes GC 11 and 12, RA 33 and BO 11. The Fast Attack Squadron of the Constitución class is subordinate to the Fleet Command. There is also a River Forces (Fluvial) Command subordinate to the Marines.

New Construction

Long-term plans include two further submarines, four MCM vessels, two LSMs and a replenishment tanker. Current financial problems and political instability continue to cause delays in construction and modernisation programmes.

Mercantile Marine

Lloyd's Register of Shipping:
251 vessels of 970 539 tons gross

Strength of the Fleet

Type	Active	Building (Planned)
Submarines, Patrol	2	—
Frigates	6	2
Fast Attack Craft—Missile/Gun	6	—
LSTs	4	—
LCUs	2	—
LCVPs	12	—
Transport	1	—
Survey Ships	3	—
Coast Guard Craft	30	(16)
Sail Training Ship	1	—

DELETION

Amphibious Forces

1993 *Amazonas*

SUBMARINES

2 CABALO (209) CLASS (TYPE 1300)

Name	No	Builders	Laid down	Launched	Commissioned
SÁBALO	S 31 (ex-S 21)	Howaldtswerke, Kiel	2 May 1973	1 July 1975	6 Aug 1976
CARIBE	S 32 (ex-S 22)	Howaldtswerke, Kiel	1 Aug 1973	6 Nov 1975	11 Mar 1977

Displacement, tons: 1285 surfaced; 1600 dived
Dimensions, feet (metres): 200.1 × 20.3 × 18 *(61.2 × 6.2 × 5.5)*
Main machinery: Diesel-electric; 4 MTU 12V 493 AZ80 GA31L diesels; 2400 hp(m) *(1.76 MW)* sustained; 4 alternators; 1.7 MW; 1 Siemens motor; 4600 hp(m) *(3.38 MW)* sustained; 1 shaft
Speed, knots: 10 surfaced; 22 dived
Range, miles: 7500 at 10 kts surfaced
Complement: 33 (5 officers)

Torpedoes: 8—21 in *(533 mm)* bow tubes. Combination of (a) AEG SST 4; anti-surface; wire-guided; active/passive homing to 12 km *(6.6 nm)* at 35 kts or 28 km *(15.3 nm)* at 23 kts; warhead 260 kg and (b) Westinghouse Mk 37; anti-submarine; wire-guided; active/passive homing to 8 km *(4.4 nm)* at 24 kts; warhead 150 kg. 14 torpedoes carried. Swim-out discharge.
Countermeasures: ESM: Radar warning.
Fire control: Atlas Elektronik TFCS.
Radars: Navigation: Terma Scanter Mil; I band.
Sonars: Atlas Elektronik CSU 3-32; hull-mounted; passive/active search and attack; medium frequency.
Thomson Sintra DUUX 2; passive ranging.

Programmes: Type 209, IK81 designed by Ingenieurkontor Lübeck for construction by Howaldtswerke, Kiel and sale by Ferrostaal, Essen, all acting as a consortium. Both refitted at

SABALO   *1/1994, Maritime Photographic*

Kiel in 1981 and 1984 respectively. There are plans for two more of the class.
Modernisation: Carried out by HDW at Kiel. *Sabalo* started in April 1990 and left in late 1992 without fully completing the refit. *Caribe* still docked in Kiel throughout 1993 awaiting payment. The hull is slightly lengthened and new engines, fire control, sonar and attack periscopes fitted.

Structure: A single-hull design with two main ballast tanks and forward and after trim tanks. The additional length is due to the new sonar dome similar to German Type 206 system. Fitted with snort and remote machinery control. Slow revving single screw. Very high capacity batteries with GRP lead-acid cells and battery-cooling. Diving depth 250 m *(820 ft)*.
Operational: Endurance, 50 days patrol.

FRIGATES

6 MODIFIED LUPO CLASS

Name	No	Builders	Laid down	Launched	Commissioned
MARISCAL SUCRE	F 21	Fincantieri, Riva Trigoso	19 Nov 1976	28 Sep 1978	10 May 1980
ALMIRANTE BRIÓN	F 22	Fincantieri, Riva Trigoso	June 1977	22 Feb 1979	7 Mar 1981
GENERAL URDANETA	F 23	Fincantieri, Riva Trigoso	23 Jan 1978	23 Mar 1979	8 Aug 1981
GENERAL SOUBLETTE	F 24	Fincantieri, Riva Trigoso	26 Aug 1978	4 Jan 1980	5 Dec 1981
GENERAL SALOM	F 25	Fincantieri, Riva Trigoso	7 Nov 1978	13 Jan 1980	3 Apr 1982
ALMIRANTE GARCIA (ex-*José Felix Ribas*)	F 26	Fincantieri, Riva Trigoso	21 Aug 1979	4 Oct 1980	30 July 1982

Displacement, tons: 2208 standard; 2520 full load
Dimensions, feet (metres): 371.3 × 37.1 × 12.1
  (113.2 × 11.3 × 3.7)
Main machinery: CODOG; 2 Fiat/GE LM 2500 gas-turbines;
  50 000 hp *(37.3 MW)* sustained; 2 GMT A230.20M diesels;
  8000 hp(m) *(5.97 MW)* sustained; 2 shafts; cp props
Speed, knots: 35; 21 on diesels. **Range, miles:** 5000 at 15 kts
Complement: 185

Missiles: SSM: 8 OTO Melara/Matra Otomat Teseo Mk 2 TG1 ❶;
  active radar homing to 80 km *(43.2 nm)* at 0.9 Mach; warhead
  210 kg; sea-skimmer for last 4 km *(2.2 nm)*.
  SAM: Selenia Elsag Albatros octuple launcher ❷; 8 Aspide; semi-
  active radar homing to 13 km *(7 nm)* at 2.5 Mach; height envelope 15-5000 m *(49.2-16 405 ft)*; warhead 30 kg.
Guns: 1 OTO Melara 5 in *(127 mm)*/54 ❸; 85° elevation; 45
  rounds/minute to 16 km *(8.7 nm)*; weight of shell 32 kg.
  4 Breda 40 mm/70 (2 twin) ❹; 85° elevation; 300 rounds/
  minute to 12.5 km *(6.8 nm)*; weight of shell 0.96 kg.
Torpedoes: 6—324 mm ILAS 3 (2 triple) tubes ❺. Whitehead
  A 244S; anti-submarine; active/passive homing to 7 km
  (3.8 nm) at 33 kts; warhead 34 kg (shaped charge).
Countermeasures: Decoys: 2 Breda 105 mm SCLAR 20-bar-
  relled trainable ❻; chaff to 5 km *(2.7 nm)*; illuminants to 12 km
  (6.6 nm). Can be used for HE bombardment.
ESM/ECM: Elisra; intercept/jammer.
Fire control: Selenia IPN 10 action data automation. 2 Elsag NA
  10 MFCS. 2 Dardo GFCS for 40 mm.
Radars: Air/surface search: Selenia RAN 10S ❼; E/F band; range
  155 km *(85 nm)*.
  Surface search: SMA SPQ/2F; I band; range 73 km *(40 nm)*.
  Fire control: Two Selenia Orion 10XP ❽; I/J band.
  Two Selenia RTN 20X ❾; I/J band; range 15 km *(8 nm)* (for
  Dardo).
Tacan: SRN 15A.
Sonars: EDO SQS 29 (Mod 610E); hull-mounted; active search
  and attack; medium frequency.

Helicopters: 1 AB 212ASW ❿.

Programmes: All ordered on 24 October 1975. Similar to ships in
  the Italian and Peruvian navies.
Modernisation: The first two of the class were scheduled to start
  a refit by Litton's Ingalls Shipyard in September 1992 but this
  had still not started by early 1994, although contracts were
  reported as being near completion. New communications, EW
  and data link equipment to be fitted. The helicopter is also to be
  upgraded.
Structure: Fixed hangar means no space for Aspide reloads.
  Fully stabilised.

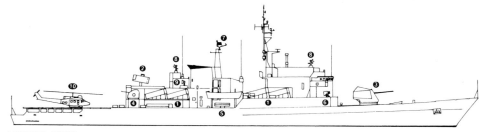

MARISCAL SUCRE   (Scale 1 : 900), Ian Sturton

GENERAL SOUBLETTE   1/1994, Maritime Photographic

ALMIRANTE BRIÓN   1/1994, Maritime Photographic

0 + 2 KNOX CLASS

Name	No	Builders	Laid down	Launched	Commissioned
— (ex-*Roark*)	— (ex-FF 1053)	Todd Shipyards, Seattle	2 Feb 1966	24 Apr 1967	22 Nov 1969
— (ex-*Gray*)	— (ex-FF 1054)	Todd Shipyards, Seattle	19 Nov 1966	3 Nov 1967	4 Apr 1970

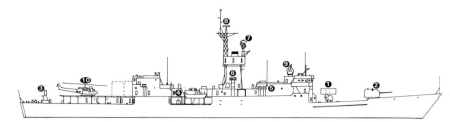

KNOX

(Scale 1 : 1200), Ian Sturton

Displacement, tons: 3011 standard; 4260 full load
Dimensions, feet (metres): 439.6 × 46.8 × 15; 24.8 (sonar) (134 × 14.3 × 4.6; 7.8)
Main machinery: 2 Combustion Engineering/Babcock & Wilcox boilers; 1200 psi (84.4 kg/cm sq); 950°F (510°C); 1 turbine; 35 000 hp (26 MW); 1 shaft
Speed, knots: 27. **Range, miles:** 4000 at 22 kts on 1 boiler
Complement: 288 (17 officers)

Missiles: SSM: 8 McDonnell Douglas Harpoon; active radar homing to 130 km (70 nm) at 0.9 Mach; warhead 227 kg. May be fitted.
A/S: Honeywell ASROC Mk 16 octuple launcher with reload system (has 2 cells modified to fire Harpoon) ❶; inertial guidance to 1.6-10 km (1-5.4 nm); payload Mk 46.
Guns: 1 FMC 5 in (127 mm)/54 Mk 42 Mod 9 ❷; 85° elevation; 20-40 rounds/minute to 24 km (13 nm) anti-surface; 14 km (7.7 nm) anti-aircraft; weight of shell 32 kg.
1 General Electric/General Dynamics 20 mm/76 6-barrelled Mk 15 Vulcan Phalanx ❸; 3000 rounds/minute combined to 1.5 km.
Torpedoes: 4—324 mm Mk 32 (2 twin) fixed tubes ❹. 22 Honeywell Mk 46; anti-submarine; active/passive homing to 11 km (5.9 nm) at 40 kts; warhead 44 kg.
Countermeasures: Decoys: 2 Loral Hycor SRBOC 6-barrelled fixed Mk 36 ❺; IR flares and chaff to 4 km (2.2 nm). T Mk-6 Fanfare/SLQ-25 Nixie; torpedo decoy. Prairie Masker hull and blade rate noise suppression.
ESM/ECM: SLQ 32(V)2 ❻; radar warning. Sidekick modification adds jammer and deception system.

Combat data systems: Link 14 receive only.
Fire control: SWG-1A Harpoon LCS. Mk 68 GFCS. Mk 114 ASW FCS. Mk 1 target designation system.
Radars: Air search: Lockheed SPS 40B ❼; E/F band; range 320 km (175 nm).
Surface search: Raytheon SPS 10 or Norden SPS 67 ❽; G band.
Navigation: Marconi LN 66; I band.
Fire control: Western Electric SPG 53A/D ❾; I/J band.
Tacan: SRN 15. IFF: UPX-12.
Sonars: EDO/General Electric SQS 26 CX; bow-mounted; active search and attack; medium frequency.
EDO SQR 18A(V)1; passive towed array; very low frequency.

Helicopters: 1 AB 212ASW ❿.

Programmes: Lease agreed from US in December 1993 subject to approval by Congress. Transfer planned for mid-1994. Ships of this class have been transferred to Greece, Taiwan and Turkey and transfers are planned for Brazil, Egypt, Morocco, Oman, Spain and Thailand in 1994/95.
Modernisation: Vulcan Phalanx replaced Sea Sparrow SAM in the mid-1980s.
Structure: Four torpedo tubes are fixed in the midship superstructure, two to a side, angled out at 45°. A lightweight anchor is fitted on the port side and an 8000 lb anchor fits in to the after section of the sonar dome.
Operational: The ship carried a medium helicopter in USN service. The transfer of Harpoon is not confirmed.

SHIPBORNE AIRCRAFT

Numbers/Type: 5 Agusta AB 212ASW.
Operational speed: 106 kts (196 km/h).
Service ceiling: 14 200 ft (4330 m).
Range: 230 nm (426 km).
Role/Weapon systems: ASW helicopter with secondary ASV role; has ECM/EW potential. Sensors: APS-705 search radar, Bendix ASQ-18A dipping sonar. Weapons: ASW; 2 × Mk 46 or A244/S torpedoes or depth bombs. ASV; 2 × Marte anti-ship missiles.

AB 212ASW

1/1994, Maritime Photographic

LAND-BASED MARITIME AIRCRAFT

Numbers/Type: 1 CASA C-212 S 3 Aviocar.
Operational speed: 190 kts (353 km/h).
Service ceiling: 24 000 ft (7315 m).
Range: 1650 nm (3055 km).
Role/Weapon systems: Medium-range MR and coastal protection aircraft; limited armed action. Eight additional aircraft reported ordered in mid-1990 to replace the Trackers and to provide two Communications aircraft. Sensors: APS-128 radar. Weapons: ASW; depth bombs. ASV; gun and rocket pods.

Numbers/Type: 6 Grumman S-2E Tracker.
Operational speed: 130 kts (241 km/h).
Service ceiling: 25 000 ft (7620 m).
Range: 1350 nm (2500 km).
Role/Weapon systems: ASW, surface search and armed MR in Caribbean Sea. Plans to update engines have been abandoned. Sensors: Search radar, MAD, 32 × sonobuoys. Weapons: ASW; internally carried torpedoes, depth bombs and/or mines. ASV; 6 × 127 mm rockets.

Numbers/Type: 3 Agusta ASH-3H Sea King.
Operational speed: 120 kts (222 km/h).
Service ceiling: 12 200 ft (3720 m).
Range: 630 nm (1165 km).
Role/Weapon systems: Medium ASW support. Sensors: Selenia MM/APS-705 chin-mounted search radar, limited ESM. Weapons: ASW, 4 × Mk 46 or A244/S torpedoes or 4 × depth bombs, or combination. ASV; 2 × Marte anti-ship missiles.

AMPHIBIOUS FORCES

Note: In addition there are 11 LCVPs built in 1976.

2 LCUs

Name	No	Builders	Commissioned
MARGARITA	T 71	Swiftships Inc, Morgan City	Jan 1984
LA ORCHILA	T 72	Swiftships Inc, Morgan City	May 1984

Displacement, tons: 390 full load
Dimensions, feet (metres): 129.9 × 36.1 × 5.9 (39.6 × 11 × 1.8)
Main machinery: 2 Detroit 16V-149 diesels; 1800 hp (1.34 MW) sustained; 2 shafts
Speed, knots: 13. **Range, miles:** 1500 at 10 kts
Complement: 26 (4 officers)
Military lift: 150 tons cargo; 100 tons fuel
Guns: 3—12.7 mm MGs.

Comment: Both serve in River Command. Reported that four or more are planned in due course. Have a 15 ton crane.

4 CAPANA (ALLIGATOR) CLASS (LSTs)

Name	No	Builders	Commissioned
CAPANA	T 61	Korea Tacoma Marine	24 July 1984
ESEQUIBO	T 62	Korea Tacoma Marine	24 July 1984
GOAJIRA	T 63	Korea Tacoma Marine	20 Nov 1984
LOS LLANOS	T 64	Korea Tacoma Marine	20 Nov 1984

Displacement, tons: 4070 full load
Dimensions, feet (metres): 343.8 × 50.5 × 9.8 (104.8 × 15.4 × 3)
Main machinery: 2 diesels; 7200 hp(m) (5.3 MW); 2 shafts
Speed, knots: 14. **Range, miles:** 5600 at 11 kts
Complement: 117 (13 officers)
Cargo capacity: 202 troops; 1600 tons cargo; 4 LCVPs
Guns: 2 Breda 40 mm/70 (twin). 2 Oerlikon 20 mm GAM-BO1.
Fire control: Selenia NA 18/V; optronic director.
Helicopters: Platform only.

Comment: Ordered in August 1982. Version III of Korea Tacoma Alligator type. Each has a 50 ton tank turntable and a lift between decks. Similar to Indonesian LSTs. *Goajira* was out of service from June 1987 to May 1993 after a serious fire.

MARGARITA (with MANAURE alongside)

1989, Venezuelan Navy

ESEQUIBO

11/1993, Maritime Photographic

PATROL FORCES

Note: Plans for new patrol craft have been delayed.

6 CONSTITUCIÓN CLASS (FAST ATTACK CRAFT—MISSILE AND GUN)

Name	No	Builders	Laid down	Launched	Commissioned
CONSTITUCIÓN	PC 11	Vosper Thornycroft	Jan 1973	1 June 1973	16 Aug 1974
FEDERACIÓN	PC 12	Vosper Thornycroft	Aug 1973	26 Feb 1974	25 Mar 1975
INDEPENDENCIA	PC 13	Vosper Thornycroft	Feb 1973	24 July 1973	20 Sep 1974
LIBERTAD	PC 14	Vosper Thornycroft	Sep 1973	5 Mar 1974	12 June 1975
PATRIA	PC 15	Vosper Thornycroft	Mar 1973	27 Sep 1973	9 Jan 1975
VICTORIA	PC 16	Vosper Thornycroft	Mar 1974	3 Sep 1974	22 Sep 1975

Displacement, tons: 170 full load
Dimensions, feet (metres): 121 × 23.3 × 6 *(36.9 × 7.1 × 1.8)*
Main machinery: 2 MTU MD 16V 538 TB90 diesels; 6000 hp(m)
(4.4 MW) sustained; 2 shafts
Speed, knots: 31. **Range, miles:** 1350 at 16 kts
Complement: 20 (4 officers)

Missiles: SSM: 2 OTO Melara/Matra Otomat Teseo Mk 2 TG1
(Federación, Libertad and *Victoria)*; active radar homing to
80 km *(43.2 nm)* at 0.9 Mach; warhead 210 kg; sea-skimmer.
Guns: 1 OTO Melara 3 in *(76 mm)*/62 compact *(Constitución,
Independencia* and *Patria)*; 85° elevation; 85 rounds/minute to
16 km *(8.7 nm)*; weight of shell 6 kg.
1 Breda 30 mm/70 *(Federación, Libertad* and *Victoria)*; 85°
elevation; 800 rounds/minute; weight of shell 0.37 kg.
Fire control: Elsag NA 10 Mod 1 GFCS (gunships). Alenia Elsag
Medusa optronic director (missile ships).
Radars: Surface search: SPQ 2D.
Fire control: Selenia RTN 10X (in 76 mm ships); I/J band.

Programmes: Transferred from the Navy in 1983 to the Coast
Guard but now back again with Fleet Command.
Modernisation: All were to have been modernised with the three
gun FACs being fitted with Harpoon SSM in place of the
76 mm and Harpoon replacing Otomat in the other three. This
update was cancelled in 1993. Single Breda 30 mm guns were
acquired in 1989 and have replaced the 40 mm guns in the
missile craft.

FEDERACIÓN (with Otomat)   *7/1990, Venezuelan Navy*

CONSTITUCIÓN (with 76 mm gun)   *7/1990, Venezuelan Navy*

SURVEY SHIPS

1 SURVEY AND RESEARCH SHIP

Name	No	Builders	Commissioned
PUNTA BRAVA	BO 11	Bazán, Cartagena	14 Mar 1991

Displacement, tons: 1170 full load
Dimensions, feet (metres): 202.4 × 39 × 12.1 *(61.7 × 11.9 × 3.7)*
Main machinery: 2 Bazán-MAN 7L20/27 diesels; 2500 hp(m) *(1.84 MW)*; 2 shafts
Speed, knots: 13. **Range, miles:** 8000 at 13 kts
Complement: 49 (6 officers) plus 6 scientists
Radars: Navigation: ARPA; I band.

Comment: Ordered in September 1988 and launched 9 March 1990. Developed from the Spanish
Malaspina class. A multipurpose ship for oceanography, marine resource evaluation, geophysical and biological research. Equipped with Qubit hydrographic system. Carries two survey
launches. EW equipment is to be fitted. Coast Guard markings from April 1993.

2 SURVEY CRAFT

Name	No	Builders	Commissioned
GABRIELA (ex-*Peninsula de Araya*)	LH 11 (ex-P 119)	Abeking & Rasmussen, Lemwerder	5 Feb 1974
LELY (ex-*Peninsula de Paraguana*)	LH 12 (ex-P 121)	Abeking & Rasmussen, Lemwerder	7 Feb 1974

Displacement, tons: 90 full load
Dimensions, feet (metres): 88.6 × 18.4 × 4.9 *(27 × 5.6 × 1.5)*
Main machinery: 2 MTU diesels; 2300 hp(m) *(1.69 MW)*; 2 shafts
Speed, knots: 20
Complement: 9 (1 officer)

Comment: LH 12 laid down 28 May 1973, launched 12 December 1973 and LH 11 laid down
10 March 1973, launched 29 November 1973. Acquired in September 1986 from the Instituto
de Canalizaciones.

PUNTA BRAVA   *1/1994, Maritime Photographic*

GABRIELA (alongside *Alcatraz* PG 32)   *1/1994, Maritime Photographic*

AUXILIARIES

Note: A fleet tanker is to be acquired as soon as possible.

1 LOGISTIC SUPPORT SHIP

Name	No	Builders	Commissioned
PUERTO CABELLO	T 44	Drammen Slip & Verk,	1972
(ex-M/V *Sierra Nevada*)		Drammen	

Displacement, tons: 13 500 full load
Measurement, tons: 6682 gross; 9218 dwt
Dimensions, feet (metres): 461.3 × 59 × 29.5 *(140.6 × 18 × 9)*
Main machinery: 1 Sulzer diesel; 13 200 hp(m) *(9.7 MW)*; 1 shaft
Speed, knots: 22.5

Comment: Commissioned in the Navy 22 May 1986. Former refrigerated cargo ship.

PUERTO CABELLO   *5/1991, Giorgio Arra*

TRAINING SHIP

1 SAIL TRAINING SHIP

Name	No	Builders	Commissioned
SIMON BOLIVAR	BE 11	A T Celaya, Bilbao	6 Aug 1980

Displacement, tons: 1260 full load
Measurement, tons: 934 gross
Dimensions, feet (metres): 270.6 × 34.8 × 14.4 *(82.5 × 10.6 × 4.4)*
Main machinery: 1 Detroit 12V-149T diesel; 875 hp *(652 kW)* sustained; 1 shaft
Speed, knots: 10
Complement: 195 (17 officers, 76 ratings, 18 midshipwomen, 84 midshipmen)

Comment: Ordered in 1978. Launched 21 November 1979. Three-masted barque; near sister to *Guayas* (Ecuador). Sail area (23 sails), 1650 m². Highest mast, 131.2 ft *(40 m)*.

SIMON BOLIVAR   *1/1994, Maritime Photographic*

COAST GUARD

Note: Plans for new offshore patrol ships have been delayed by lack of funds. Three Vigilante class patrol craft were to have been acquired from Uruguay, but this sale has not been confirmed.

1 CHEROKEE CLASS

Name	No	Builders	Commissioned
MIGUEL RODRIGUEZ	RA 33	Charleston SB and DD Co	9 Nov 1945
(ex-USS *Salinan* ATF 161)	(ex-R 23)		

Displacement, tons: 1235 standard; 1675 full load
Dimensions, feet (metres): 205 × 38.5 × 17 *(62.5 × 11.7 × 5.2)*
Main machinery: Diesel-electric; 4 GM 16-278A diesels; 4400 hp *(3.28 MW)*; 4 generators; 1 motor; 3000 hp *(2.24 MW)*; 1 shaft
Speed, knots: 15. **Range, miles:** 7000 at 15 kts.
Complement: 85
Guns: 1 USN 3 in *(76 mm)*/50 *(Felipe Larrazábal)*.
Radars: Navigation: Sperry SPS 53; I/J band.

Comment: Acquired from US on 1 September 1978. Last of a class of three.

MIGUEL RODRIGUEZ   *8/1992, Hartmut Ehlers*

2 ALMIRANTE CLEMENTE CLASS

Name	No	Builders	Commissioned
ALMIRANTE CLEMENTE	GC 11	Ansaldo, Leghorn	1956
GENERAL JOSÉ TRINIDAD MORAN	GC 12	Ansaldo, Leghorn	1956

Displacement, tons: 1300 standard; 1500 full load
Dimensions, feet (metres): 325.1 × 35.5 × 12.2 *(99.1 × 10.8 × 3.7)*
Main machinery: 2 GMT 16-645E7C diesels; 6080 hp(m) *(4.47 MW)* sustained; 2 shafts
Speed, knots: 22. **Range, miles:** 3500 at 15 kts
Complement: 162 (12 officers)

Guns: 2 OTO Melara 3 in *(76 mm)*/62 compact; 85° elevation; 85 rounds/minute to 16 km *(8.7 nm)*; weight of shell 6 kg.
  2 Breda 40 mm/70 (twin); 85° elevation; 300 rounds/minute to 12.5 km *(6.8 nm)*; weight of shell 0.96 kg.
Torpedoes: 6—324 mm ILAS 3 (2 triple) tubes. Whitehead A 244S; anti-submarine; active/passive homing to 7 km *(3.8 nm)* at 33 kts; warhead 34 kg (shaped charge).
Fire control: Elsag NA 10 GFCS.
Radars: Air search: Plessey AWS 4; D band.
  Surface search: Racal Decca 1226; I band.
  Fire control: Selenia RTN 10X; I/J band; range 40 km *(22 nm)*.
Sonars: Plessey PMS 26; hull-mounted; active search and attack; 10 kHz.

Programmes: Survivors of a class of six ordered in 1953. Both laid down 5 May 1954 and launched 12 December 1954.
Modernisation: Both ships were refitted by Cammell Laird/Plessey group in April 1968. 4 in guns replaced by 76 mm OTO Melara compact. Both refitted again in Italy in 1983-85, prior to transfer to Coast Guard duties.
Structure: Fitted with Denny-Brown fin stabilisers and air-conditioned throughout the living and command spaces.
Operational: Navigation, SATNAV fitted. Oil fuel, 350 tons.

ALMIRANTE CLEMENTE   *1989, Venezuelan Navy*

2 POINT CLASS

PETREL (ex-*Point Knoll*) PG 31   ALCATRAZ (ex-*Point Judith*) PG 32

Displacement, tons: 66 full load
Dimensions, feet (metres): 83 × 17.2 × 5.8 *(25.3 × 5.2 × 1.8)*
Main machinery: 2 Caterpillar diesels; 1600 hp *(1.19 MW)*; 2 shafts
Speed, knots: 23.5. **Range, miles:** 1500 at 8 kts
Complement: 10 (1 officer)

Comment: *Petrel* transferred from USCG on 11 September 1991, and *Alcatraz* on 20 December 1991. The 12.7 mm MGs in US service may be upgraded. Eight more of the class may be acquired.

POINT class (USCG colours)   *1988, Giorgio Arra*

2 UTILITY CRAFT

LOS TAQUES LG 11   **LOS CAYOS** LG 12

Comment: Former trawlers; displacement, 300 tons. Commissioned 15 May 1981 and 17 July 1984 respectively. Used for salvage and SAR tasks.

LOS CAYOS   *1989, Venezuelan Navy*

6 RIVER CRAFT

ANACOCO LF 11   **ATURES** LF 13   **EL AMPARO** LA 01
MANAIPO LF 12   **MAIPURES** LF 14   **YOPITO** LC 01

Comment: *El Amparo* is an ambulance launch similar to PF 31.

7 INSHORE PATROL CRAFT

POLARIS LG 21   **RIGEL** LG 23   **ANTARES** LG 25   **ALTAIR** LG 27
SPICA LG 22   **ALDEBARAN** LG 24   **CANOPUS** LG 26

Displacement, tons: 5 full load
Dimensions, feet (metres): 32.8 × 8.5 × 2.6 *(10 × 2.6 × 0.8)*
Main machinery: 2 diesels; 400 hp(m) *(294 kW)*; 2 shafts
Speed, knots: 45. **Range, miles:** 140 at 45 kts
Complement: 4

Comment: Acquired in 1987 from Cougar Marine, Hamble.

8 RIVER PATROL CRAFT

Name	No	Displacement (tons)	Speed (kts)
MANAURE	PF 21	18	15
MARA	PF 22	18	15
GUAICAIPURO	PF 23	14	15
TAMANACO	PF 24	14	15
TEREPAIMA	PF 31	3	45
TIUNA	PF 32	3	45
YARACUY	PF 33	3	45
SOROCAIMA	PF 34	3	45

Comment: All have a complement of five and are armed with one 12.7 mm MG.

MANAURE   *1989, Venezuelan Navy*

4 + 16 INSHORE PATROL BOATS

CONSTANCIA LRG 001   **HONESTIDAD** LRG 003
PERSEVERANCIA LRG 002   **TENACIDAD** LRG 004

Comment: First three speed boat type with GRP hulls delivered from a local shipyard in December 1991. Fourth completed in August 1993. Up to 20 may be built.

NATIONAL GUARD

(FUERZAS ARMADAS DE COOPERACION)

Note: Up to about 100 patrol craft in total including River Launches and undecked District Craft. Less than half were operational in early 1994.

22 ITALIAN TYPE A (COASTAL PATROL CRAFT)

Name	No	Name	No
RIO ORINOCO	A 7414	RIO CAPANAPARO	A 7425
RIO CUYUNI	A 7415	RIO YURUARI	A 7426
RIO VENTUARI	A 7416	RIO CAURA	A 7427
RIO CAPARO	A 7417	RIO MOTATAN	A 7628
RIO TOCUYO	A 7418	RIO GRITA	A 7629
RIO VENAMO	A 7419	RIO YURUAN	A 7630
RIO LIMON	A 7420	RIO BOCONO	A 7631
RIO SAN JUAN	A 7421	RIO NEVERI	A 7632
RIO TURBIO	A 7422	RIO CARONI	A 7633
RIO TORBES	A 7423	RIO GUANARE	A 7634
RIO ESCALANTE	A 7424	RIO GUAINIA	A 7635

Italian built (A 7414, A 7416-A 7424)

Displacement, tons: 48 full load
Dimensions, feet (metres): 75.4 × 19 × 8.5 *(23 × 5.8 × 2.6)*
Main machinery: 2 MTU 12V 493 TY70 diesels; 2200 hp(m) *(1.62 MW)* sustained; 2 shafts
Speed, knots: 30. **Range, miles:** 500 at 25 kts
Complement: 8
Guns: 1—12.7 mm MG.
Radars: Navigation: FR 24; I band.

Comment: First ordered in May 1973 from INMA, La Spezia and delivered from 1974 onwards.

Venezuelan built (A 7415, A 7425-A 7635)

Displacement, tons: 43 full load
Dimensions, feet (metres): 76.8 × 16.1 × 10.2 *(23.4 × 4.9 × 3.1)*
Main machinery: 2 GM 12V 92 TI diesels; 2040 hp *(1.52 kW)* sustained; 2 shafts
Speed, knots: 30. **Range, miles:** 1000 at 25 kts
Complement: 12
Guns: 1—12.7 mm MG.
Radars: Navigation: FR 711; I band.

Comment: Ordered from Dianca, Puerto Cabello.

RIO GUANARE   *1989*

2 VENEZUELAN TYPE

RIO ALTAGRACIA A 6704   **RIO MANZANARES** A 6705

Dimensions, feet (metres): 49.2 × 12.5 × 6.2 *(15 × 3.8 × 1.9)*
Main machinery: 1 Type 4B-316 diesel; 1 shaft
Speed, knots: 12. **Range, miles:** 140 at 12 kts
Complement: 6
Radars: Navigation: FR 10; I band.

12 PUNTA CLASS

Name	No	Name	No
PUNTA BARIMA	A 8201	PUNTA MACOYA	A 8307
PUNTA MOSQUITO	A 8202	PUNTA MORON	A 8308
PUNTA MULATOS	A 8203	PUNTA UNARE	A 8309
PUNTA PERRET	A 8204	PUNTA BALLENA	A 8310
PUNTA CARDON	A 8205	PUNTA MACURO	A 8311
PUNTA PLAYA	A 8206	PUNTA MARIUSA	A 8312

Displacement, tons: 15 full load
Dimensions, feet (metres): 43 × 13.4 × 3.9 *(13.1 × 4.1 × 1.2)*
Main machinery: 2 Detroit 12V-92TA diesels; 1020 hp *(761 kW)* sustained; 2 shafts
Speed, knots: 28. **Range, miles:** 390 at 25 kts
Complement: 4
Guns: 2—12.7 mm MGs.
Radars: Navigation: Raytheon; I band.

Comment: Ordered 24 January 1984. Built by Bertram Yacht, Miami, Florida. Aluminium hulls. Completed from July-December 1984.

PUNTA class (alongside RIO GUANARE)   *1989*

12 PROTECTOR CLASS

Name	No	Name	No
RIO ARAUCA II	B 8421	RIO SARARE	B 8427
RIO CATATUMBO II	B 8422	RIO URIBANTE	B 8428
RIO APURE II	B 8423	RIO SINARUCO	B 8429
RIO NEGRO II	B 8424	RIO ICABARU	B 8430
RIO META II	B 8425	RIO GUARICO II	B 8431
RIO PORTUGUESA II	B 8426	RIO YARACUY	B 8432

Displacement, tons: 15 full load
Dimensions, feet (metres): 43.6 × 14.8 × 3.9 *(13.3 × 4.5 × 1.2)*
Main machinery: 2 Detroit 8V-92TA diesels; 750 hp *(560 kW)* sustained; 2 shafts
Speed, knots: 28. **Range, miles:** 600 at 25 kts
Complement: 4
Guns: 2—12.7 mm MGs.

Comment: Built by SeaArk Marine, Monticello and commissioned in 1987.

PROTECTOR class   *1987, SeaArk*

10 LAGO CLASS (RIVER PATROL CRAFT)

Name	No	Name	No
LAGO 1	A 6901	RIO CHAMA	A 7919
LAGO 2	A 6902	RIO CARIBE	A 7920
LAGO 3	A 6903	RIO TUY	A 7921
LAGO 4	A 6904	MANATI	A 7929
RIO CABRIALES	A 7918	GOAIGOAZA	A 8223

Displacement, tons: 1.5 full load
Dimensions, feet (metres): 20.7 × 7.9 × 1 *(6.3 × 2.4 × 0.3)*
Main machinery: 2 Evinrude outboard petrol engines; 230 hp *(172 kW)*
Speed, knots: 30. **Range, miles:** 120 at 15 kts
Complement: 4
Guns: 1—12.7 mm MG.
Radars: Navigation: FR 10.

Comment: Built by SeaArk Marine, Monticello. All delivered 6 August 1984. The last pair are classi-fied as Yachts.

15 SEA ARK TYPE (RIVER PATROL CRAFT)

Displacement, tons: 0.5
Dimensions, feet (metres): 18 × 6.9 × 0.7 *(5.5 × 2.1 × 0.2)*
Main machinery: 1 OMC outboard
Speed, knots: 30. **Range, miles:** 75 at 15 kts
Complement: 4
Guns: 1—12.7 mm MG.

Comment: Ordered from SeaArk Marine, Monticello. Completed May-August 1984. Aluminium hull.

VIETNAM

Headquarters' Appointment

Chief of Naval Forces:
Vice Admiral Hoang Hau Thai

Personnel

(a) 1994: 9000 regulars
(b) Additional conscripts on three to four year term (about 3000)
(c) 27 000 naval infantry

Strength of the Fleet

From 1978 to 1990 the USSR transferred a number of ships and craft as well as providing fuel in return for the use of Cam-Ranh Bay naval base. From 1 January 1991 the relationship became formal with further transfers only available at market prices. Many of the ex-US naval ships have now been deleted either by sale or scrap. The resultant order of battle is now composed of vessels most of which can lay some claim to operational avail-ability. There are many others still alongside in naval bases either as hulks or providing spares for the operational units.

Bases

Cam Ranh Bay, Cân Tho, Hai Phong, Hue, Da Nang, Hanoi.

Pennant numbers

Appear to change frequently.

Mercantile Marine

Lloyd's Register of Shipping:
333 vessels of 728 307 tons gross

FRIGATES

5 PETYA CLASS

HQ 09,11 (Type III)   HQ 13, 15, 17 (Type II)

Displacement, tons: 950 standard; 1180 full load
Dimensions, feet (metres): 268.3 × 29.9 × 9.5 *(81.8 × 9.1 × 2.9)*
Main machinery: CODAG; 2 gas-turbines; 30 000 hp(m) *(22 MW)*; 1 Type 61V-3 diesel; 5400 hp(m) *(3.97 MW)* sustained; centre shaft; 3 shafts
Speed, knots: 32. **Range, miles:** 4870 at 10 kts; 450 at 29 kts
Complement: 98

Guns: 4 USSR 3 in *(76 mm)*/60 (2 twin); 80° elevation; 90 rounds/minute to 15 km *(8 nm)*; weight of shell 6.8 kg.
Torpedoes: 3—21 in *(533 mm)* (triple) tubes (Petya III). SAET-60; passive homing up to 15 km *(8.1 nm)* at 40 kts; warhead 400 kg.
10—16 in *(406 mm)* (2 quin) tubes (Petya II). SAET-40; active/passive homing up to 10 km *(5.5 nm)* at 30 kts; warhead 100 kg.
A/S mortars: 4 RBU 6000 12-tubed trainable (Petya II); range 6000 m; warhead 31 kg.
4 RBU 2500 16-tubed trainable (Petya III); range 2500 m; warhead 21 kg.
Depth charges: 2 racks.
Mines: Can carry 22.
Countermeasures: ESM: 2 Watch Dog; radar warning.
Radars: Air/surface search: Strut Curve; F band; range 110 km *(60 nm)* for 2 m² target.
Navigation: Don 2; I band.
Fire control: Hawk Screech; I band.
IFF: High Pole B. Two Square Head.
Sonars: Hull-mounted; active attack; high frequency.

Programmes: Two Petya III (export version) transferred from USSR in December 1978 and three Petya IIs, two in December 1983 and one in December 1984.
Structure: The Petya IIIs have the same hulls as the Petya IIs but are fitted with one triple 21 in *(533 mm)* torpedo launcher in place of the two 16 in *(406 mm)* quintuple tubes and have four RBU 2500s in place of two RBU 6000s.

1 SAVAGE CLASS

Name	No	Builders	Commissioned
DAI KY (ex-*Tran Khanh Du*, ex-USS *Forster* DER 334)	HQ 03	Consolidated Steel Corporation, Orange, Texas	25 Jan 1944

Displacement, tons: 1590 standard; 1850 full load
Dimensions, feet (metres): 306 × 36.6 × 14 *(93.3 × 11.2 × 4.3)*
Main machinery: 4 Fairbanks-Morse 38D8-1/8-10 diesels; 7080 hp *(5.28 MW)* sustained; 2 shafts
Speed, knots: 21. **Range, miles:** 10 000 at 15 kts
Complement: 170 approx

Missiles: SAM: 2 SA-N-5 Grail quad launchers; manual aiming; IR homing to 6 km *(3.2 nm)* at 1.5 Mach; altitude to 2500 m *(8000 ft)*; warhead 1.5 kg.
Guns: 2 USN 3 in *(76 mm)*/50; 85° elevation; 20 rounds/minute to 12 km *(6.6 nm)*; weight of shell 6 kg.
Torpedoes: 6—324 mm US Mk 32 (2 triple) tubes.
A/S mortars: 1 Mk 15 Hedgehog; range 250 m; warhead 13.6 kg.
Depth charges: 1 rack.
Fire control: Mk 63 GFCS (fwd). Mk 51 GFCS (aft).
Radars: Air search: Westinghouse SPS 28; B/C band.
Surface search: Raytheon SPS 10; G band.
Fire control: Western Electric Mk 34; I/J band.
Sonars: SQS 29; hull-mounted; active attack; high frequency.

Programmes: Former US Navy destroyer escort of the FMR design group. Transferred to South Vietnamese Navy on 25 September 1971. Was in overhaul at time of occupation of South Viet-nam and was written off by the USN as 'Transferred to Vietnam' 30 April 1975.
Operational: Used as a training ship.

HQ 17   *10/1993, 92 Wing RAAF*

SAVAGE (Tunisian colours)   *1989, van Ginderen Collection*

1 BARNEGAT CLASS

Name	No	Builders	Commissioned
PHAM NGU LAO	HQ 01	Lake Washington SY	28 Jan 1943
(ex-USCG *Absecon* WHEC 374,			
ex-*WAVP 23*)			

Displacement, tons: 1766 standard; 2800 full load
Dimensions, feet (metres): 310.8 × 41.1 × 13.5 *(94.7 × 12.5 × 4.1)*
Main machinery: 2 Fairbanks-Morse 38D8-1/8-10 diesels; 3540 hp *(2.64 MW)* sustained; 2 shafts
Speed, knots: 18. **Range, miles:** 20 000 at 12 kts
Complement: 200 approx

Missiles: SSM: 2 SS-N-2A Styx; active radar or IR homing to 46 km *(25 nm)* at 0.9 Mach; warhead 513 kg.
SAM: 2 SA-N-5 Grail quad launchers; manual aiming; IR homing to 6 km *(3.2 nm)* at 1.5 Mach; altitude to 2500 m *(8000 ft)*; warhead 1.5 kg.
Guns: 1 USN 5 in *(127 mm)*/38; 85° elevation; 15 rounds/minute to 17 km *(9.3 nm)*; weight of shell 25 kg.
3—37 mm/63. 4—25 mm (2 twin).
2—81 mm mortars.
Radars: Surface search: Raytheon SPS 21; G/H band; range 22 km *(12 nm)*.
Fire control: RCA/GE Mk 26; I/J band.

Programmes: Last of a group built as seaplane tenders for the US Navy. Transferred to US Coast Guard in 1948, initially on loan designated WAVP and then on permanent transfer, subsequently redesignated as high endurance cutter (WHEC). Transferred from US Coast Guard to South Vietnamese Navy in 1971.
Modernisation: SSMs mounted aft and close range armament fitted in the mid-1980s.

BARNEGAT (Italian colours)   *1991, van Ginderen Collection*

CORVETTES

2 ADMIRABLE CLASS

Name	No	Launched
— (ex-USS *Prowess* IX 305, ex-MSF 280, ex-*Ha Hoi*)	HQ 07	17 Feb 1944
— (ex-USS *Sentry*, ex-MSF 299)	HQ 13	30 May 1944

Displacement, tons: 650 standard; 945 full load
Dimensions, feet (metres): 184.5 × 33 × 9.75 *(56.3 × 10 × 3)*
Main machinery: 2 Cooper-Bessemer GSB-8 diesels; 1710 hp *(1.28 MW)*; 2 shafts
Speed, knots: 14
Complement: 80 approx
Guns: 2 China 57 mm/70 (twin). 2—37 mm/63. Up to 8 Oerlikon 20 mm (4 twin).
Radars: Surface search: Sperry SPS 53; I band.

Comment: Former US Navy minesweepers. Built by Gulf SB Corp, Chicasaw, Alabama. Transferred to South Vietnam in 1970. Minesweeping equipment has been removed. Written off by the USN as 'Transferred to Vietnam' 30 April 1975. One employed in patrol and escort roles. Second ship probably non-operational.

ADMIRABLE (Dominican Republic colours)   *1990, Hartmut Ehlers*

LAND-BASED MARITIME AIRCRAFT

Numbers/Type: 5 Mil Mi-4 Hound B.
Operational speed: 113 kts *(210 km/h)*.
Service ceiling: 18 000 ft *(5500 m)*.
Range: 216 nm *(400 km)*.
Role/Weapon systems: Limited value ASW helicopter with primary support and assault roles. Sensors: Possible search radar and sonobuoys. Weapons: 4 × torpedoes or mines, light machine guns.

Numbers/Type: 3 Kamov Ka-27/Ka-29 Helix A.
Operational speed: 135 kts *(250 km/h)*.
Service ceiling: 19 685 ft *(6000 m)*.
Range: 432 nm *(800 km)*.
Role/Weapon systems: ASW helicopter; successor to Hormone with greater ASW potential. Sensors: Search radar, dipping sonar, MAD, ECM. Weapons: ASW; 3 × torpedoes, depth bombs or mines.

Numbers/Type: 4 Kamov Ka-25 Hormone A.
Operational speed: 119 kts *(220 km/h)*.
Service ceiling: 11 500 ft *(3500 m)*.
Range: 350 nm *(650 km)*.
Role/Weapon systems: Sensors: Search radar, dipping sonar, MAD, ECM, EW equipment and search radar. Weapons: ASW; 2 × torpedoes, depth bombs. ASV; 2 or 4 × missiles or rocket launchers.

Numbers/Type: 4 Beriev Be-12 Mail.
Operational speed: 328 kts *(608 km/h)*.
Service ceiling: 37 000 ft *(11 280 m)*.
Range: 4050 nm *(7500 km)*.
Role/Weapon systems: Long-range ASW/MR amphibian. Sensors: Search/weather radar, MAD, EW. Weapons: ASW; 5 tons of depth bombs, mines or torpedoes. ASV; limited missile and rocket armament.

PATROL FORCES

Note: In addition to the craft listed below there are eight ex-Chinese Shanghai II class and 14 ex-Chinese Shantou class of doubtful operational status.

8 OSA II CLASS (FAST ATTACK CRAFT—MISSILE)

116-123

Displacement, tons: 245 full load
Dimensions, feet (metres): 126.6 × 24.9 × 8.8 *(38.6 × 7.6 × 2.7)*
Main machinery: 3 Type M 504 diesels; 10 800 hp(m) *(7.94 MW)* sustained; 3 shafts
Speed, knots: 37. **Range, miles:** 500 at 35 kts
Complement: 30
Missiles: SSM: 4 SS-N-2B Styx; active radar or IR homing to 46 km *(25 nm)* at 0.9 Mach; warhead 513 kg.
Guns: 4 USSR 30 mm/65 (2 twin); 85° elevation; 500 rounds/minute to 5 km *(2.7 nm)*; weight of shell 0.54 kg.
Radars: Surface search: Square Tie; I band.
Fire control: Drum Tilt; H/I band.
IFF: High Pole. Two Square Head.

Comment: Transferred from USSR: two in October 1979, two in September 1980, two in November 1980 and two in February 1981.

OSA II (Russian number)   *1987, G Jacobs*

16 SHERSHEN CLASS (FAST ATTACK CRAFT—TORPEDO)

Displacement, tons: 145 standard; 170 full load
Dimensions, feet (metres): 113.8 × 22 × 4.9 *(34.7 × 6.7 × 1.5)*
Main machinery: 3 Type 503A diesels; 8025 hp(m) *(5.9 MW)* sustained; 3 shafts
Speed, knots: 45. **Range, miles:** 850 at 30 kts; 460 at 42 kts
Complement: 23
Missiles: SAM: 1 SA-N-5 Grail quad launcher; manual aiming; IR homing to 6 km *(3.2 nm)* at 1.5 Mach; altitude to 2500 m *(8000 ft)*; warhead 1.5 kg.
Guns: 4 USSR 30 mm/65 (2 twin); 85° elevation; 500 rounds/minute to 5 km *(2.7 nm)*; weight of shell 0.54 kg.
Torpedoes: 4—21 in *(533 mm)* tubes (not in all).
Depth charges: 2 racks (12).
Mines: Can carry 6.
Radars: Surface search: Pot Drum; H/I band.
Fire control: Drum Tilt; H/I band.
IFF: High Pole A. Square Head.

Comment: Transferred from USSR: two in 1973, two in April 1979 (without torpedo tubes), two in September 1979, two in August 1980, two in October 1980, two in January 1983 and four in June 1983.

SHERSHEN   *1987*

5 TURYA CLASS (FAST ATTACK CRAFT—TORPEDO, HYDROFOIL)

Displacement, tons: 190 standard; 250 full load
Dimensions, feet (metres): 129.9 × 29.9 (41 over foils) × 5.9 (13.1 over foils)
(39.6 × 7.6 (12.5) × 1.8 (4))
Main machinery: 3 Type M 504 diesels; 10 800 hp(m) *(7.94 MW)* sustained; 3 shafts
Speed, knots: 40. **Range, miles:** 600 at 35 kts foilborne; 1450 at 14 kts hullborne
Complement: 30
Guns: 2 USSR 57 mm/70 (twin, aft); 90° elevation; 120 rounds/minute to 8 km *(4.4 nm)*; weight
    of shell 2.8 kg.
    2 USSR 25 mm/80 (twin, fwd); 85° elevation; 270 rounds/minute to 3 km *(1.6 nm)*; weight of
    shell 0.34 kg.
Torpedoes: 4—21 in *(533 mm)* tubes (not in all).
Depth charges: 2 racks.
Radars: Surface search: Pot Drum; H/I band.
Fire control: Muff Cob; G/H band.
IFF: High Pole B. Square Head.
Sonars: Helicopter (not in all); VDS; high frequency.

Comment: Transferred from USSR: two in mid-1984, one in late 1984 and two in January 1986.
    Two of the five do not have torpedo tubes or sonar.

TURYA (without torpedo tubes)   1988

8 SO 1 CLASS (LARGE PATROL CRAFT)

Displacement, tons: 170 standard; 215 full load
Dimensions, feet (metres): 137.8 × 19.7 × 5.9 *(42 × 6 × 1.8)*
Main machinery: 3 Kolomna Type 40-D diesels; 6600 hp(m) *(4.8 MW)* sustained; 3 shafts
Speed, knots: 28. **Range, miles:** 1100 at 13 kts; 350 at 28 kts
Complement: 31
Guns: 4 USSR 25 mm/80 (2 twin); 85° elevation; 270 rounds/minute to 3 km *(1.6 nm)*; weight of
    shell 0.34 kg.
A/S mortars: 4 RBU 1200 5-tubed fixed; range 1200 m; warhead 34 kg.
Depth charges: 2 racks (24).
Mines: 10.
Radars: Surface search: Pot Head; I band.
IFF: High Pole A. Dead Duck.

Comment: Transferred from USSR: two in March 1980, two in September 1980, two in May
    1981, and two in September 1983. Four more of this class were transferred in 1960-63 but
    have been deleted.

SO 1   1984

11 ZHUK (TYPE 1400M) CLASS (FAST ATTACK CRAFT—PATROL)

Displacement, tons: 39 full load
Dimensions, feet (metres): 78.7 × 16.4 × 3.9 *(24 × 5 × 1.2)*
Main machinery: 2 Type M 401B diesels; 2200 hp(m) *(1.6 MW)* sustained; 2 shafts
Speed, knots: 30. **Range, miles:** 1100 at 15 kts
Complement: 11 (3 officers)
Guns: 4—14.5 mm (2 twin) MGs.

Comment: Transferred: three in 1978, three in November 1979, three in February 1986, two in
    January 1990 and three in August 1990. So far three have been deleted, a further four are of
    doubtful operational status.

ZHUK   10/1993, 92 Wing RAAF

3 PGM 71 CLASS (LARGE PATROL CRAFT)

Displacement, tons: 142 full load
Dimensions, feet (metres): 101 × 21.3 × 7.5 *(30.8 × 6.5 × 2.3)*
Main machinery: 2 GM 6-71 diesels; 1392 hp *(1.04 MW)* sustained; 2 shafts
Speed, knots: 17. **Range, miles:** 1000 at 17 kts
Complement: 30
Guns: 1 Bofors 40 mm/56. 4 Oerlikon 20 mm.

Comment: Ten transferred from US to South Vietnam 1963-67. Three deleted in 1988-89, four
    more in 1990-91. Probably non-operational.

2 PO 2 CLASS (COASTAL PATROL CRAFT)

Displacement, tons: 55 full load
Dimensions, feet (metres): 82 × 16.7 × 5.6 *(25 × 5.1 × 1.7)*
Main machinery: 1 Type 3-D-12 diesel; 300 hp(m) *(220 kW)* sustained; 1 shaft
Speed, knots: 12
Complement: 8
Guns: 2 USSR 25 mm/80.

Comment: Two transferred from USSR in 1977, two in February 1980, one in October 1981, one
    in 1982 and four in 1983. Four deleted 1983-84, four more in 1986-87. Probably
    non-operational.

PO 2   1990

2 POLUCHAT CLASS (COASTAL PATROL CRAFT)

Displacement, tons: 100 full load
Dimensions, feet (metres): 97.1 × 19 × 4.8 *(29.6 × 5.8 × 1.5)*
Main machinery: 2 Type M 50 diesels; 2200 hp(m) *(1.6 MW)* sustained; 2 shafts
Speed, knots: 20. **Range, miles:** 1500 at 10 kts
Complement: 15
Guns: 2—12.7 mm MGs.
Radars: Navigation: Spin Trough; I band.

Comment: Both transferred from USSR in January 1990. Can be used as torpedo recovery vessels.

POLUCHAT (Russian colours)   7/1993, Hartmut Ehlers

RIVER PATROL CRAFT

Comment: There are large numbers of river patrol boats, mostly armed with MGs.

RIVER CRAFT   1991, B Lemachko

AMPHIBIOUS FORCES

3 POLNOCHNY CLASS (TYPE 771) (LSM)

HQ 511   **HQ 512**   **HQ 513**

Displacement, tons: 760 standard; 834 full load
Dimensions, feet (metres): 246.1 × 31.5 × 7.5 *(75 × 9.6 × 2.3)*
Main machinery: 3 Kolomna Type 40-D diesels; 4400 hp(m) *(3.2 MW)* sustained; 3 shafts
Speed, knots: 19
Complement: 40
Guns: 2 or 4 USSR 30 mm/65 (1 or 2 twin). 2—140 mm rocket launchers.
Radars: Surface search: Don 2 or Spin Trough; I band.
Fire control: Drum Tilt; H/I band.

Comment: Transfers from USSR: one in May 1979 (B), one in November 1979 (A) and one in February 1980 (B). Details as for Polnochny B class.

POLNOCHNY B   *1989*

1 LST 1-510 and 2 LST 511-1152 CLASSES

QUI NONH (ex-USS *Bulloch County* LST 509)	HQ 502
VUNG TAU (ex-USS *Cochino County* LST 603)	HQ 503
DA NANG (ex-USS *Maricopa County* LST 938)	HQ 505

Displacement, tons: 2366 beaching; 4080 full load
Dimensions, feet (metres): 328 × 50 × 14 *(100 × 15.2 × 4.3)*
Main machinery: 2 GM 12-567A diesels; 1800 hp *(1.34 MW)*; 2 shafts
Speed, knots: 11. **Range, miles:** 6000 at 10 kts
Complement: 110

Comment: Built in 1943-44. Transferred from US to South Vietnam in mid-1960s.

DA NANG   *1988, G Jacobs*

12 T 4 CLASS (LCUs)

Displacement, tons: 93 full load
Dimensions, feet (metres): 65.3 × 18.4 × 4.6 *(19.9 × 5.6 × 1.4)*
Main machinery: 2 diesels; 316 hp(m) *(232 kW)*; 2 shafts
Speed, knots: 10
Complement: 4

Comment: Transfers from USSR: ten in 1967, five in 1969, all of which were probably sunk. Twelve more in 1979.

22 LANDING CRAFT (LCM and LCU)

Comment: It is reported that at the beginning of 1994 there were still some five LCUs, 14 LCM 8 and LCM 6, and three LCVPs remaining of the 180 minor landing craft left behind by the US in 1975.

MINE WARFARE FORCES

2 LIENYUN CLASS (MINESWEEPERS—COASTAL)

Displacement, tons: 400 full load
Dimensions, feet (metres): 131.2 × 26.2 × 11.5 *(40 × 8 × 3.5)*
Main machinery: 1 diesel; 400 hp(m) *(294 kW)*; 1 shaft
Speed, knots: 8
Guns: 2—12.7 mm MGs.

Comment: Acquired from China. Trawler type with a minesweeping winch and davits aft.

2 YURKA CLASS (MINESWEEPER—OCEAN)

HQ 851   **HQ 852**

Displacement, tons: 460 full load
Dimensions, feet (metres): 171.9 × 30.8 × 8.5 *(52.4 × 9.4 × 2.6)*
Main machinery: 2 Type M 503 diesels; 5350 hp(m) *(3.91 MW)* sustained; 2 shafts
Speed, knots: 17. **Range, miles:** 1500 at 12 kts
Complement: 60
Guns: 4 USSR 30 mm/65 (2 twin); 500 rounds/minute to 5 km *(2.7 nm)*; weight of shell 0.54 kg.
Mines: 10.
Radars: Surface search: Don 2; I band.
Fire control: Drum Tilt; H/I band.
Sonars: Stag Ear; hull-mounted; active minehunting; high frequency.

Comment: Transferred from USSR December 1979. Steel-hulled, built in early 1970s.

YURKA (Russian colours)   *1991, van Ginderen Collection*

4 SONYA CLASS (MINESWEEPER/HUNTER—COASTAL)

Displacement, tons: 400 full load
Dimensions, feet (metres): 157.4 × 28.9 × 6.6 *(48 × 8.8 × 2)*
Main machinery: 2 Kolomna 9-D-8 diesels; 2000 hp(m) *(1.47 MW)* sustained; 2 shafts
Speed, knots: 15. **Range, miles:** 3000 at 10 kts
Complement: 43
Guns: 2 USSR 30 mm/65 AK 630. 2—25 mm/80 (twin).
Mines: 5.
Radars: Surface search: Don 2; I band.

Comment: First one transferred from USSR 16 February 1987, second in February 1988, third in July 1989, fourth in March 1990.

SONYA   *11/1991, G Jacobs*

2 YEVGENYA CLASS (MINEHUNTER—INSHORE)

Displacement, tons: 90 full load
Dimensions, feet (metres): 80.7 × 18 × 4.9 *(24.6 × 5.5 × 1.5)*
Main machinery: 2 Type 3-D-12 diesels; 600 hp(m) *(440 kW)* sustained; 2 shafts
Speed, knots: 11. **Range, miles:** 300 at 10 kts
Complement: 10
Guns: 2 USSR 25 mm/80 (twin).
Radars: Surface search: Spin Trough; I band.

Comment: First transferred from USSR in October 1979; two in December 1986. One deleted in 1990.

YEVGENYA   *1993, B Lemachko*

5 K 8 CLASS (MINESWEEPING BOATS)

Displacement, tons: 26 full load
Dimensions, feet (metres): 55.4 × 10.5 × 2.6 *(16.9 × 3.2 × 0.8)*
Main machinery: 2 Type 3-D-6 diesels; 300 hp(m) *(220 kW)* sustained; 2 shafts
Speed, knots: 18
Complement: 6
Guns: 2—14.5 mm (twin) MGs.

Comment: Transferred from USSR in October 1980.

SURVEY SHIP

1 KAMENKA (TYPE 870) CLASS (SURVEY SHIP)

Displacement, tons: 705 full load
Dimensions, feet (metres): 175.5 × 29.8 × 8.5 *(53.5 × 9.1 × 2.6)*
Main machinery: 2 diesels; 1800 hp(m) *(1.32 MW)*; 2 shafts; cp props
Speed, knots: 14. **Range, miles:** 4000 at 10 kts
Complement: 25
Radars: Navigation: Don 2; I band.

Comment: Transferred from USSR December 1979. Built at Northern Shipyard, Gdansk in 1971.

KAMENKA (Russian colours)   *1984*

AUXILIARIES

Notes: (1) In addition to the vessels listed below there are two YOG 5 fuel lighters, two floating cranes and two ex-Soviet unarmed Nyryat 2 diving tenders.
(2) A diving support vessel *(Hai Son)* of 881 tons and 50 m in length was completed by Korea Tacoma, Masan in March 1990. This ship may not be naval.

12 SL CLASS TRANSPORTS AND 4 TANKERS

Comment: These are ships of between 200 and 550 tons used for coastal transport having been left over from the Vietnam war. Most were delivered from China in the late 1960s. The tankers have a cargo capacity of 400 tons of fuel oil. All are armed with 12.7 mm MGs.

HQ 671 (SL class)   *12/1988, G Jacobs*

2 FLOATING DOCKS

Comment: One has a lift capacity of 8500 tons. Transferred from USSR August 1983. Second one *(Khersson)* has a lift capacity of 4500 tons and was supplied in 1988.

VIRGIN ISLANDS

Headquarters' Appointment	**Base**	**Mercantile Marine**
Commissioner of Police: Vernon E Malone	Road Town, Tortola	*Lloyd's Register of Shipping:* 2 vessels of 469 tons gross

POLICE

1 HALMATIC M 140 PATROL CRAFT

ST URSULA

Displacement, tons: 17 full load
Dimensions, feet (metres): 50.6 × 12.8 × 3.9 *(15.4 × 3.9 × 1.2)*
Main machinery: 2 Detroit 6V-92TA diesels; 520 hp *(388 kW)* sustained; 2 shafts
Speed, knots: 23. **Range, miles:** 300 at 20 kts
Complement: 6
Guns: 2—7.62 mm MG.

Comment: Built by Halmatic with funds provided by the UK and commissioned 4 July 1988. Large davit aft for rapid launch and recovery of a rigid inflatable boat.

ST URSULA   *10/1993, Maritime Photographic*

2 SEA RIDER DINGHIES

Comment: Model SR5M, built by Avon, with 70 hp *(52 kW)* Yamaha and 65 hp *(48.5 kW)* Evinrude outboard engines. Acquired in 1986.

US BORDER PATROL

1 DAUNTLESS CLASS

PB 1

Displacement, tons: 13 full load
Dimensions, feet (metres): 40 × 14 × 4.3 *(12.2 × 4.3 × 1.3)*
Main machinery: 3 Cummins diesels; 900 hp *(671 kW)*; 3 Hamilton waterjets
Speed, knots: 32
Complement: 5
Guns: 1—7.62 mm MG.
Radars: Surface search: Raytheon; I band.

Comment: Built by SeaArk Marine, Monticello and delivered in January 1994. This craft is similar to those in service in Jamaica and is used by the US Border Patrol to assist in the prevention of illegal immigration to Puerto Rico and the Virgin Islands.

DAUNTLESS   *1/1994, SeaArk Marine*

WESTERN SAMOA

General

After 48 years of New Zealand occupation, mandate and trustee-ship, Western Samoa achieved independence in 1962.

Base

Apia

Mercantile Marine

Lloyd's Register of Shipping:
7 vessels of 6253 tons gross

PATROL FORCES

1 PACIFIC FORUM PATROL CRAFT

Name	No	Builders	Commissioned
NAFANUA	—	Australian Shipbuilding Industries	5 Mar 1988

Displacement, tons: 165 full load
Dimensions, feet (metres): 103.3 × 26.6 × 6.9 *(31.5 × 8.1 × 2.1)*
Main machinery: 2 Caterpillar 3516TA diesels; 4400 hp *(3.28 MW)* sustained; 2 shafts
Speed, knots: 20. **Range, miles:** 2500 at 12 kts
Complement: 17 (3 officers)
Guns: Can carry 1 Oerlikon 20 mm and 2—7.62 mm MGs.
Radars: Surface search: Furuno 1011; I band.

Comment: Under the Defence Co-operation Programme Australia has provided a number of these craft to Pacific islands. Training, operational and technical assistance is provided by the Royal Australian Navy. Ordered 3 October 1985.

1 LCU

LADY SAMOA II

Comment: Built by Yokohama Yacht Co and launched 28 July 1988.

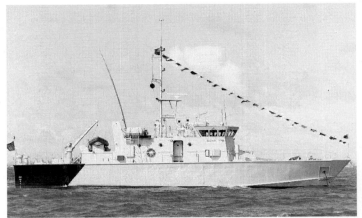

NAFANUA   *10/1991, John Mortimer*

YEMEN

General

In May 1990 the north and south Yemen republics were again reunited. Many ships of the Ethiopian Navy took refuge in Yemeni ports during 1991. An agreement was reached in mid-1992 to return these ships.

Headquarters' Appointments

Commander Naval Forces:
  Colonel Ali Qasim Talib
Chief of Staff
  Colonel Abdul Karim Muharram

Personnel

(a) 1994: 2500 (including 500 Marines)
(b) 2 years' national service

Bases

Main: Aden, Hodeida
Secondary: Mukalla, Perim, Socotra

Mercantile Marine

Lloyd's Register of Shipping:
  40 vessels of 24 261 tons gross

DELETIONS

Patrol Forces

1992/93   *Osa 116,* 1 Zhuk

Amphibious Forces

1993   *Al Wudia* (unserviceable)

Mine Warfare Forces

1992   1 Natya (returned to Ethiopia), 1 Sonya (returned to Ethiopia)

Auxiliaries

1991   1 Oskol II (returned to Russia)

PATROL FORCES

Notes: (1) Two ex-Soviet Mol class occasionally reported, but both belong to Ethiopia.
(2) Two ex-Soviet SO 1 class *(402* and *619)* may still be just operational.

2 TARANTUL I CLASS (TYPE 1241) (MISSILE CORVETTE)

971   976

Displacement, tons: 385 standard; 580 full load
Dimensions, feet (metres): 184.1 × 37.7 × 8.2 *(56.1 × 11.5 × 2.5)*
Main machinery: COGOG; 2 Nikolayev Type DR 77 gas-turbines; 16 016 hp(m) *(11.77 MW)* sustained; 2 Nikolayev Type DR 76 gas-turbines with reversible gearboxes; 4993 hp(m) *(3.67 MW)* sustained; 2 shafts
Speed, knots: 36. **Range, miles:** 400 at 36 kts; 2000 at 20 kts
Complement: 50

Missiles: SSM: 4 SS-N-2C Styx (2 twin) launchers; active radar or IR homing to 83 km *(45 nm)* at 0.9 Mach; warhead 513 kg; sea-skimmer at end of run.
SAM: SA-N-5 Grail quad launcher; manual aiming; IR homing to 10 km *(5.4 nm)* at 1.5 Mach; altitude to 2500 m *(8000 ft)*; warhead 1.1 kg.
Guns: 1—3 in *(76 mm)*/60; 85° elevation; 120 rounds/minute to 7 km *(3.8 nm)*; weight of shell 7 kg.
2—30 mm/65 AK 630; 6 barrels per mounting; 3000 rounds/minute to 2 km.
Countermeasures: Decoys: 2—16-barrelled chaff launchers.
ESM: 2 receivers.
Fire control: Hood Wink optronic director.
Radars: Air/surface search: Plank Shave (also for missile control); E band.
Navigation: Spin Trough; I band.
Fire control: Bass Tilt; H/I band.
IFF: Square Head. High Pole.

Programmes: First one delivered from USSR in November 1990, second in January 1991. This is the standard export version.

5 OSA II CLASS (FAST ATTACK CRAFT—MISSILE)

117   118   121   122   129

Displacement, tons: 245 full load
Dimensions, feet (metres): 126.6 × 24.9 × 8.8 *(38.6 × 7.6 × 2.7)*
Main machinery: 3 Type M 504 diesels; 10 800 hp(m) *(7.94 MW)* sustained; 3 shafts
Speed, knots: 37. **Range, miles:** 500 at 35 kts
Complement: 30
Missiles: SSM: 4 SS-N-2B Styx; active radar or IR homing to 46 km *(25 nm)* at 0.9 Mach; warhead 513 kg.
Guns: 4 USSR 30 mm/65 (2 twin); 85° elevation; 500 rounds/minute to 5 km *(2.7 nm)*; weight of shell 0.54 kg.
Radars: Surface search: Square Tie; I band.
Fire control: Drum Tilt; H/I band.

Comment: Transferred from USSR: one in February 1979, one in March 1979, two in January 1980, one in December 1980, one in January 1982, one on 24 February 1983 and one in September 1983. Three have been deleted so far, although at least one of these is used for spares.

TARANTUL 971   *11/1993*

OSA 121   *11/1993*

3 BROADSWORD CLASS (COASTAL PATROL CRAFT)

26 SEPTEMBER 141   **RAMADAN** 142   **SANA'A** 143

Displacement, tons: 90.5 standard; 110 full load
Dimensions, feet (metres): 105 × 20.4 × 6.3 *(32 × 6.2 × 1.9)*
Main machinery: 2 GM 16V-149TI diesels; 2322 hp *(1.73 MW)* sustained; 2 shafts
Speed, knots: 32
Complement: 14
Guns: 2 USSR 25 mm/80 (twin). 2—14.5 mm (twin) MGs. 2—12.7 mm MGs.
Radars: Surface search: Decca 914; I band.

Comment: Acquired in 1978 from Halter Marine, New Orleans. Guns added after delivery. Probably non-operational.

RAMADAN   *1987*

4 ZHUK CLASS (TYPE 1400M) (FAST ATTACK CRAFT—PATROL)

202   **203**   **303**   **304**

Displacement, tons: 39 full load
Dimensions, feet (metres): 78.7 × 16.4 × 3.9 *(24 × 5 × 1.2)*
Main machinery: 2 Type M 401B diesels; 2200 hp(m) *(1.6 MW)* sustained; 2 shafts
Speed, knots: 30. **Range, miles:** 1100 at 15 kts
Complement: 11 (3 officers)
Guns: 4—14.5 mm (2 twin) MGs.
Radars: Surface search: Spin Trough; I band.

Comment: Two delivered from USSR in December 1984 and three in January 1987. One has been cannibalised for spares.

ZHUK   *3/1990*

AMPHIBIOUS FORCES

1 POLNOCHNY A CLASS (TYPE 770) (LCT)

SIRA 137

Displacement, tons: 750 standard; 800 full load
Dimensions, feet (metres): 239.3 × 27.9 × 5.8 *(73 × 8.5 × 1.8)*
Main machinery: 2 Kolomna Type 40-D diesels; 4400 hp(m) *(3.2 MW)* sustained; 2 shafts
Speed, knots: 19. **Range, miles:** 1000 at 18 kts
Complement: 40
Military lift: 100 troops; 6 tanks
Guns: 2 USSR 30 mm/65 (twin). 2—18-barrelled 140 mm rocket launchers.

Comment: Transferred from USSR in August 1973 (two) and July 1977. *138* burnt out in March 1986, and 136 was unserviceable by 1993.

SIRA   *7/1986, van Ginderen Collection*

1 ROPUCHA I (TYPE 775) CLASS (LST)

139

Displacement, tons: 4080 full load
Dimensions, feet (metres): 369.1 × 49.2 × 12.1 *(112.5 × 15 × 3.7)*
Main machinery: 2 Zgoda-Sulzer 16ZVB40/48 diesels; 19 230 hp(m) *(14.14 MW)* sustained; 2 shafts
Speed, knots: 17.5. **Range, miles:** 3500 at 16 kts; 6000 at 12 kts
Complement: 98
Military lift: 10 MBT plus 190 troops or 24 AFVs plus 170 troops or mines
Missiles: SAM: 4 SA-N-5 Grail quad launchers; manual aiming; IR homing to 6 km *(3.2 nm)* at 1.5 Mach; altitude to 2500 m *(8000 ft)*; warhead 1.5 kg; 32 missiles.
Guns: 4—57 mm/80 (2 twin); 85° elevation; 120 rounds/minute to 6 km *(3.3 nm)*; weight of shell 2.8 kg.
2—122 mm BM-21 (naval). 2 × 20-barrelled rocket launchers; range 9 km *(5 nm)*.
Mines: 92 contact type.
Fire control: 2 Squeeze Box optronic directors.
Radars: Air/surface search: Strut Curve; F band.
Navigation: Don 2 or Kivach; I band.
Fire control: Muff Cob; G/H band.
IFF: Two High Pole A or Salt Pot A.

Comment: Acquired from USSR in 1979 having been built at Gdansk, Poland. Returned to the Baltic for a refit in 1991 but was back in Aden by early 1993. The ship is a Ro-Ro design with a tank deck running the whole length of the ship. This is the only Ropucha in service outside the Russian Navy.

ROPUCHA 139   *11/1993*

2 ONDATRA CLASS (LCUs)

13   **14**

Displacement, tons: 145 full load
Dimensions, feet (metres): 78.7 × 16.4 × 4.9 *(24 × 5 × 1.5)*
Main machinery: 1 diesel; 300 hp(m) *(221 kW)*; 1 shaft
Speed, knots: 10. **Range, miles:** 500 at 5 kts
Complement: 4
Military lift: 1 MBT

Comment: Transferred from USSR January 1983. Both operational.

ONDATRA 14   *1990*

2 T 4 CLASS (LCVP)

134   **135**

Displacement, tons: 70 full load
Dimensions, feet (metres): 62.3 × 14 × 3.3 *(19 × 4.3 × 1)*
Main machinery: 2 diesels; 316 hp(m) *(232 kW)*; 2 shafts
Speed, knots: 10. **Range, miles:** 1500 at 10 kts
Complement: 4

Comment: Three transferred from USSR in November 1970 and two in December 1981. First three deleted.

MINE WARFARE FORCES

1 NATYA CLASS (MINESWEEPERS—OCEAN)

201

Displacement, tons: 770 full load
Dimensions, feet (metres): 200.1 × 31.8 × 8.9 *(61 × 9.7 × 2.7)*
Main machinery: 2 Type M 504 diesels; 7200 hp(m) *(5.3 MW)* sustained; 2 shafts
Speed, knots: 19. **Range, miles:** 4000 at 10 kts
Complement: 65
Guns: 4—30 mm/65 (2 twin); 85° elevation; 500 rounds/minute to 5 km *(2.7 nm)*; weight of shell 0.54 kg.
    4—25 mm/80 (2 twin); 270 rounds/minute to 3 km *(1.6 nm)*; weight of shell 0.34 kg.
A/S mortars: 2 RBU 1200 five-tubed fixed launchers; range 1200 m; warhead 34 kg.
Mines: 10
Radars: Surface search: Don 2; I band.
Sonars: Hull-mounted; active minehunting; high frequency.

Comment: Transferred from USSR in February 1991. A second of class was delivered to Ethiopia in October 1991 but sheltered in Aden for a time in 1992.

NATYA (Ethiopian colours)   *10/1991, Foto Flite*

6 YEVGENYA CLASS (MINEHUNTERS—INSHORE)

11   12   15   +3

Displacement, tons: 77 standard; 90 full load
Dimensions, feet (metres): 80.7 × 18 × 4.9 *(24.6 × 5.5 × 1.5)*
Main machinery: 2 Type 3-D-12 diesels; 600 hp(m) *(440 kW)* sustained; 2 shafts
Speed, knots: 11. **Range, miles:** 300 at 10 kts
Complement: 10
Guns: 2—25 mm/80 (twin) or 2—14.5 mm (twin) MGs.
Radars: Navigation: Spin Trough; I band.
IFF: High Pole.
Sonars: Small transducer lifted over stern on crane.

Comment: GRP hulls. Two transferred from USSR in May 1982, third in November 1987, and three more in March 1990.

YEVGENYA (Russian colours)   *7/1993, Hartmut Ehlers*

AUXILIARIES

Notes: (1) A 4500 ton Floating Dock was provided by the USSR.

(2) A 14 m Hydrographic craft acquired from Cougar Marine in 1988.

2 TOPLIVO CLASS (TANKERS)

135   140

Displacement, tons: 1029 full load
Dimensions, feet (metres): 176.2 × 31.8 × 10.5 *(53.7 × 9.7 × 3.2)*
Main machinery: 1 6DR 30/50-5 diesel; 600 hp(m) *(441 kW)*; 1 shaft
Speed, knots: 10.5. **Range, miles:** 400 at 7 kts
Complement: 23
Cargo capacity: 500 tons
Radars: Navigation: Don; I band.

Comment: Two small harbour tankers acquired in the early 1980s. *135* carries water, *140* oil.

TOPLIVO   *1990, van Ginderen Collection*

2 SHABWAH CLASS (TUGS)

SHABWAH   AL MAHRAH

Comment: 225 grt; built by McTay Marine, Bromborough and launched 14 November 1986 and 6 January 1987. Both delivered in May 1987.

YUGOSLAVIA

Headquarters' Appointments

Commander-in-Chief:
    Rear Admiral Dojcilo Isakovic
Fleet Commander:
    Rear Admiral Milan Zec

Personnel

1994: 6000 (4500 conscripts)

General

In spite of losing most of its former major naval facilities to Croatia, the Federal (Serbia and Montenegro) Navy is still about 80 per cent operational. The command is now almost wholly Serbian and bases in the Bay of Cattaro, although lacking an adequate support infrastructure, have been improved. Up to early 1994, international forces have only been threatened if they enter territorial waters.

Bases and Organisation

Headquarters: Kumbor
Main bases: Tivat, Bar

Mercantile Marine

Lloyd's Register of Shipping:
    9 vessels of 2351 tons gross

Strength of the Fleet

Type	Active
Submarines—Patrol	5
Midget Submarines	5
Frigates	4
Fast Attack Craft—Missile	10
Fast Attack Craft—Torpedo	4
Fast Attack Craft—Patrol	6
River Patrol Craft	21
Minehunters/sweepers	2
River Minesweepers	19
LCTs/Minelayers	5
LCUs/LCVPs	18
Training Ships	2
Survey Craft	3
HQ Ships	2
Tankers	3

DELETIONS

Midget Submarines

1991   *Soca* (Croatia)

Corvettes

1992   *Mornar, Borač*

Patrol Forces

1990   *Marijan, Mitar Acev* (Croatia), *Topcider, Streljko*
1991   *Vlado Cvetkovic* (Croatia), *Velimir Skorpik* (Croatia), *Partizan III* (Croatia), *Biokovo, Cer* (Croatia), *Kozolo* (Croatia)
1992   *Vlado Bagat, Petar Drapšin, Franč Rozman-Stane, Pionir, Partizan, Jadran, Partizan II, Napredak, Kornat, Crvena Zvezda, Koprivnik, Mukos, Kalnik* (Type 131), *Velebit* (Type 131), *Granicar* (Type 131), *Rudnik* (Type 131), *Romanija* (Type 131)
1993   *Kamenar* (Type 131), *Kozuf* (Type 131)

Mine Warfare Forces

1990   *RML 318*
1991   *Iz* (Croatia), *Vukov Klanac* (Croatia)
1992   *Olib, Gradac, RML 308*
1993   *M 117-121*

Amphibious Warfare Forces

1990   *DTM 213, 215, 217, 221, 226, 228, 234, 237*
1991   3 MFPD-3 Type (Croatia), *DSM 501* (Croatia), 4 Type 21 (Croatia), 2 Type 11 (Croatia), 3 Type 22 (Croatia), *DTM 233, DJC 629*
1992   *DJC 607, DJC 611*

Auxiliaries and Survey Ships

1990   *PH 123, PR 36, BH 1, BH 2, CH 2*
1991   *Andrija Mohorovicic* (Croatia), *Spasilac* (Croatia), *PN 25* (Croatia), *PO 51* (Croatia), *Meduza* PT 71 (Croatia), *LR 71, LR 73* (Croatia), *Lubin, Ugor*

SUBMARINES

2 SAVA CLASS (PATROL SUBMARINES)

Name	No
SAVA	831
DRAVA	832

Builders	Laid down	Launched	Commissioned
S and DE Factory, Split	1975	1977	1978
S and DE Factory, Split	1978	1980	1981

Displacement, tons: 830 surfaced; 960 dived
Dimensions, feet (metres): 182.7 × 23.6 × 16.7
(55.7 × 7.2 × 5.1)
Main machinery: Diesel-electric; 2 Sulzer diesels; 1600 hp(m)
(1.18 MW); 2 generators; 1 MW; 1 motor; 1560 hp(m)
(1.15 MW); 1 shaft
Speed, knots: 10 surfaced; 16 dived
Complement: 27

Torpedoes: 6—21 in *(533 mm)* bow tubes. 10 TEST-71ME;
active/passive homing to 15 km *(8.1 nm)* at 40 kts; warhead
205 kg.
Mines: 20 in lieu of torpedoes.
Countermeasures: ESM: Stop Light; radar warning.
Radars: Surface search: Snoop Group; I band.
Sonars: Atlas Elektronik PRS3; hull-mounted; passive ranging;
medium frequency.

Structure: An improved version of the Heroj class. Diving depth,
300 m *(980 ft)*. Probably built with USSR electronic equipment
and armament. Possible Thomson Sintra active/passive sonar
and unconfirmed reports of Swedish torpedoes. One operational in early 1994, the second in refit at Tivat.

DRAVA
1988, Yugoslav Navy

3 HEROJ CLASS (PATROL SUBMARINES)

Name	No
HEROJ	821
JUNAK	822
USKOK	823

Builders	Laid down	Launched	Commissioned
Uljanik Shipyard, Pula	1964	1967	1968
S and DE Factory, Split	1965	1968	1969
Uljanik Shipyard, Pula	1966	1969	1970

Displacement, tons: 1170 surfaced; 1350 dived
Dimensions, feet (metres): 210 × 23.6 × 16.7
(64 × 7.2 × 5.1)
Main machinery: Diesel-electric; 2 Sulzer diesels; 1600 hp(m)
(1.18 MW); 2 generators; 1 MW; 1 motor; 1560 hp(m)
(1.15 MW); 1 shaft
Speed, knots: 10 surfaced; 16 dived
Range, miles: 4100 at 10 kts dived and snorting
Complement: 35

Torpedoes: 6—21 in *(533 mm)* bow tubes. 10 SET-65E; active/
passive homing to 15 km *(8.1 nm)* at 40 kts; warhead 205 kg.
Mines: 20 in lieu of torpedoes.
Countermeasures: ESM: Stop Light; radar warning.
Radars: Surface search: Snoop Group; I band.
Sonars: Atlas Elektronik PRS3; hull-mounted; passive ranging;
medium frequency.

Structure: Have mainly USSR electronic equipment and armament. Diving depth 300 m *(980 ft)*.
Operational: Two operational in early 1994, with one in reserve
providing spares.

HEROJ
1982

5 UNA CLASS (MIDGET SUBMARINES)

TISA 911	ZETA 913	VARDAR 916
UNA 912	KUPA 915	

Displacement, tons: 76 surfaced; 88 dived
Dimensions, feet (metres): 61.7 × 9 × 8.2 *(18.8 × 2.7 × 2.5)*
Main machinery: 2 motors; 68 hp(m) *(50 kW)*; 1 shaft
Speed, knots: 6 surfaced; 8 dived
Range, miles: 200 at 4 kts
Complement: 6
Sonars: Atlas Elektronik; passive/active search; high frequency.

Comment: Building yard, Split. First of class commissioned May
1985; last two in 1989. Exit/re-entry capability with mining
capacity. Can carry six combat swimmers, plus four Swimmer
Delivery Vehicles (SDV) and limpet mines. Diving depth: 105 m
(345 ft). Batteries can only be charged from shore or from a
depot ship. *Soca 914* to Croatia in 1991.

UNA
1987

4 R-2 MALA CLASS (TWO-MAN SWIMMER DELIVERY VEHICLES)

Displacement, tons: 1.4
Dimensions, feet (metres): 16.1 × 4.6 × 4.3 *(4.9 × 1.4 × 1.3)*
Main machinery: 1 motor; 4.5 hp(m) *(3.3 kW)*; 1 shaft
Speed, knots: 4.4
Range, miles: 18 at 4.4 kts; 23 at 3.7 kts
Complement: 2
Mines: 250 kg of limpet mines.

Comment: This is a free-flood craft with the main motor, battery,
navigation-pod and electronic equipment housed in separate
watertight cylinders. Instrumentation includes aircraft type
gyro-compass, magnetic compass, depth gauge (with 0-100 m
scale), echo sounder, sonar and two searchlights. Constructed
of light aluminium and plexiglass, it is fitted with fore and after-

hydroplanes, the tail being a conventional cruciform with a
single rudder abaft the screw. Large perspex windows give a
good all-round view. Operating depth, 60 m *(196.9 ft)*, maximum. A number of these craft have been sold to Russia. Six
transferred to Libya. Sweden has also taken delivery of both
two and one-man versions of this type.

Note: Yugoslavia also reported to operate a number of R-1 'wet
chariots'. Can be transported in submarine torpedo tubes.
Crewed by one man. Propulsion 1 kW electric motor; 24 v silver-zinc batteries. Normal operating depth 60 m *(196.9 ft)*.
Range 6 nm at 3 kts. Weight 145 kg. Dimensions 12.2 × 3.45
× 0.8 ft *(3.72 × 1.05 × 0.26 m)*.

R-2 with Swedish NACKEN
12/1988, Gilbert Gyssels

FRIGATES

2 SPLIT (KONI) and 2 KOTOR CLASSES

SPLIT 31	KOTOR 33
KOPAR 32	PULA 34

Displacement, tons: 1700 standard; 1900 full load
Dimensions, feet (metres): 317.3 × 42 × 13.7
(96.7 × 12.8 × 4.2)
Main machinery: CODAG; 1 gas-turbine; 18 000 hp(m)
(13.2 MW); 2 Russki B-68 diesels; 15 820 hp(m) *(11.63 MW)*
sustained (31 and 32); 2 SEMT-Pielstick 12 PA6 V 280 diesels;
9600 hp(m) *(7.1 MW)* sustained (33 and 34); 3 shafts
Speed, knots: 27 gas; 22 diesel. **Range, miles:** 1800 at 14 kts
Complement: 110

Missiles: SSM: 4 SS-N-2C Styx ❶; active radar or IR homing to
83 km *(45 nm)* at 0.9 Mach; warhead 513 kg; sea-skimmer at
end of run. May be replaced by RBS-15 in due course.
SAM: SA-N-4 Gecko twin launcher ❷; semi-active radar homing
to 15 km *(8 nm)* at 2.5 Mach; height envelope 9-3048 m
(29.5-10 000 ft); warhead 50 kg.
Guns: 4 USSR 3 in *(76 mm)*/60 (2 twin) (1 mounting only in VPB
33 and 34) ❸; 80° elevation; 90 rounds/minute to 15 km
(8 nm); weight of shell 6.8 kg.
4 USSR 30 mm/65 (2 twin) ❹; 85° elevation; 500 rounds/
minute to 5 km *(2.7 nm)*; weight of shell 0.54 kg.
Torpedoes: 6—324 mm (2 triple) tubes ❺ (VPB 33 and 34 only).
Whitehead A 244; anti-submarine; active passive homing to
6 km *(3.3 nm)* at 30 kts; warhead 34 kg. There is doubt about
whether these tubes are still fitted.
A/S mortars: 2 RBU 6000 12-barrelled trainable ❻; range
6000 m; warhead 31 kg.
Mines: Can lay mines.
Countermeasures: Decoys: 2 Wallop Barricade double layer
chaff launchers.
Radars: Air/surface search: Strut Curve ❼; F band; range 110 km
(60 nm) for 2 m² target.
Navigation: Don 2 (VPB 31 and 32); I band. Palm Frond (VPB 33
and 34); I band.
Fire control: Owl Screech ❽; G band (VPB 31 and 32). PEAB
9LV200 ❾; I band (VPB 33 and 34) (for 76 mm and SSM).
Drum Tilt ❿; H/I band (for 30 mm).
Pop Group ⓫; F/H/I band (for SAM).
IFF: High Pole; two Square Head.
Sonars: Hull-mounted; active search and attack; medium
frequency.

Programmes: First two transferred from the USSR 10 March
1980 and 5 December 1982. Second pair built under licence
in Uljanic and Tito SYs, respectively. Both completed in
mid-1988. Type name, VPB (Veliki Patrolni Brod). Original
names have been retained.
Structure: Although the hulls are identical to the Koni class there
are some equipment, and considerable structural differences
between the USSR and Yugoslav-built ships. The two ex-USSR
ships have the SS-N-2C missiles aft of midships and facing aft.
The second pair have the same missiles level with the forward
end of the bridge facing forward. The Yugoslav-built ships
probably have the same gas-turbine engines as the other pair
but there are different diesels. Two triple torpedo tubes replace
the after 76 mm gun mounting and there is a different arrangement of the bridge superstructure which is similar to the training frigates sold to Iraq and Indonesia.

KOPAR   *(Scale 1 : 900), Ian Sturton*

SPLIT   *11/1992*

KOTOR   *(Scale 1 : 900), Ian Sturton*

Operational: In spite of damage to one of the class in 1991, three
were operational in early 1994 with the fourth providing
spares.

KOTOR   *1989, Yugoslav Navy*

LAND-BASED MARITIME AIRCRAFT

Notes: (1) Operational numbers of aircraft are uncertain but they include about 10 Mi-14 Haze.
(2) The Air Force has a naval brigade with about 50 Galeb/Jastreb fighter bombers, 15 Orao reconnaissance, and four CL-215 amphibians.

Numbers/Type: 8 Kamov Ka-25 Hormone A.
Operational speed: 104 kts *(193 km/h)*.
Service ceiling: 11 500 ft *(3500 m)*.
Range: 217 nm *(400 km)*.
Role/Weapon systems: ASW within Yugoslavian waters in support of submarine flotilla. Sensors:
Search radar, MAD, dipping sonar, sonobuoys. Weapons: ASW; 2 × torpedoes or depth bombs.
ASV; 4 × locally produced wire-guided missiles.

Numbers/Type: 10 Mil Mi-8 Hip C.
Operational speed: 112 kts *(225 km/h)*.
Service ceiling: 14 760 ft *(4500 m)*.
Range: 251 nm *(465 km)*.
Role/Weapon systems: Coastal patrol and support helicopter for harbour protection and coastal
patrol; supported by air force Aerospatiale SA 341/2 Gazelles from time to time. Sensors: Cam-
eras only. Weapons: Self-defence; 1 × 27 mm cannon. Strike; up to 192 × 68 mm rockets or gun
pods, 6 × locally produced wire-guided missiles.

Numbers/Type: 12 Kamov Ka-28 Helix A.
Operational speed: 110 kts *(204 km/h)*.
Service ceiling: 12 000 ft *(3658 m)*.
Range: 270 nm *(500 km)*.
Role/Weapon systems: ASW within territorial waters, to supplement and replace Ka-25. Sensors:
Search radar, MAD, dipping sonar, sonobuoys. Weapons: ASW only; 2 × torpedoes or depth
bombs.

PATROL FORCES

5 KONČAR CLASS (TYPE 240) (FAST ATTACK CRAFT—MISSILE)

Name	No	Builders	Commissioned
RADE KONČAR	401	Tito SY, Kraljevica	Apr 1977
RAMIZ SADIKU	403	Tito SY, Kraljevica	Aug 1978
HASAN ZAHIROVIČ-LACA	404	Tito SY, Kraljevica	Dec 1978
ORCE NIKOLOV	405	Tito SY, Kraljevica	Aug 1979
ANTE BANINA	406	Tito SY, Kraljevica	Nov 1980

Displacement, tons: 242 full load
Dimensions, feet (metres): 147.6 × 27.6 × 8.2 *(45 × 8.4 × 2.5)*
Main machinery: CODAG; 2 RR Proteus gas-turbines; 7200 hp *(5.37 MW)* sustained; 2 MTU 20V 538 TB92 diesels; 8530 hp(m) *(6.27 MW)* sustained; 4 shafts
Speed, knots: 39. **Range, miles:** 500 at 35 kts; 880 at 23 kts (diesels)
Complement: 30 (5 officers)

Missiles: SSM: 2 SS-N-2B Styx; active radar or IR homing to 46 km *(25 nm)* at 0.9 Mach; warhead 513 kg. May be replaced by RBS-15 in due course.
Guns: 1 or 2 Bofors 57 mm/70; 75° elevation; 200 rounds/minute to 17 km *(9.3 nm)*; weight of shell 2.4 kg.
128 mm rocket launcher for illuminants.
2—30 mm/65 (twin) may be fitted in place of the after 57 mm.
Countermeasures: Wallop Barricade double layer chaff launcher.
Fire control: PEAB 9LV 209 GFCS.
Radars: Surface search: Decca 1226; I band.
Fire control: Philips TAB; I/J band.

Programmes: Type name, Raketna Topovnjaca.
Structure: Aluminium superstructure. Designed by the Naval Shipping Institute in Zagreb based on Swedish Spica class with bridge amidships like Malaysian boats. The after 57 mm gun is replaced by a twin 30 mm mounting in some of the class.
Operational: 402 was taken by Croatia in 1991 and one of these five was either badly damaged or sunk. Probably only three of the class were operational in early 1994.

RADE KONČAR   1986

HASAN ZAHIROVIČ-LACA   11/1992

4 SHERSHEN CLASS (TYPE 201)
(FAST ATTACK CRAFT—TORPEDO)

PROLETER 213   **IVAN** 215   **BIOKOVAC** 218   **PIONIR II** 224

Displacement, tons: 145 standard; 170 full load
Dimensions, feet (metres): 113.8 × 22.3 × 4.9 *(34.7 × 6.7 × 1.5)*
Main machinery: 3 Type M 503A diesels; 8025 hp(m) *(5.9 MW)* sustained; 3 shafts
Speed, knots: 45. **Range, miles:** 850 at 30 kts
Complement: 23
Guns: 4 USSR 30 mm/65 (2 twin); 85° elevation; 500 rounds/minute to 5 km *(2.7 nm)*; weight of shell 0.54 kg.
Torpedoes: 4—21 in *(533 mm)* tubes. SAET-60; passive homing to 15 km *(8.1 nm)* at 40 kts; warhead 400 kg.
Mines: 6.
Radars: Surface search: Pot Head; I band.
Fire control: Drum Tilt; H/I band.
IFF: High Pole. Square Head.

Comment: Some acquired from USSR. Remainder built under licence by Tito Shipyard, Kraljevica between 1966 and 1971. Named after partisan craft of the Second World War. Type name, Torpedni Čamac. One more held by Croatia; a second was captured but damaged beyond repair. Eight others paid off by 1993.

SHERSHEN (old number)   1988, Yugoslav Navy

5 OSA I CLASS (TYPE 205) (FAST ATTACK CRAFT—MISSILE)

STEVAN FILIPOVIĆ STEVA 304	**JOSIP MAŽAR SOSA** 307
ŽIKICA JOVANOVIĆ-ŠPANAC 305	**KARLO ROJC** 308
NIKOLA MARTINOVIĆ 306	

Displacement, tons: 171 standard; 210 full load
Dimensions, feet (metres): 126.6 × 24.9 × 8.8 *(38.6 × 7.6 × 2.7)*
Main machinery: 3 Type M 503A diesels; 8025 hp(m) *(5.9 MW)* sustained; 3 shafts
Speed, knots: 35. **Range, miles:** 400 at 34 kts
Complement: 30 (4 officers)

Missiles: SSM: 4 SS-N-2A Styx; active radar or IR homing to 46 km *(25 nm)* at 0.9 Mach; warhead 513 kg.
Guns: 4 USSR 30 mm/65 (2 twin); 85° elevation; 500 rounds/minute to 5 km *(2.7 nm)*; weight of shell 0.54 kg.
Radars: Surface search: Square Tie; I band.
Fire control: Drum Tilt; H/I band.
IFF: High Pole. 2 Square Head.

Programmes: Transferred from USSR in the late 1960s. Named after war heroes. Type name, Raketni Čamac.
Operational: Two more of the class held by Croatia. Three others cannibalised for spares.

OSA I (old number)   1982, Yugoslav Navy

6 MIRNA CLASS (TYPE 140) (FAST ATTACK CRAFT—PATROL)

POHORJE 172	**GRMEČ** 175	**KOSMAJ** 178
UČKA 174	**FRUŠKA GORA** 177	**ZELENGORA** 179

Displacement, tons: 120 full load
Dimensions, feet (metres): 104.9 × 22 × 7.5 *(32 × 6.7 × 2.3)*
Main machinery: 2 SEMT-Pielstick 12 PA4 200 VGDS diesels; 5292 hp(m) *(3.89 MW)* sustained; 2 shafts
Speed, knots: 30. **Range, miles:** 400 at 20 kts
Complement: 19 (3 officers)
Missiles: SAM: 1 SA-N-5 Grail quad mounting; manual aiming; IR homing to 6 km *(3.2 nm)* at 1.5 Mach; altitude to 2500 m *(8000 ft)*; warhead 1.5 kg.
Guns: 1 Bofors 40 mm/70. 1 Oerlikon 20 mm. 2—128 mm illuminant launchers.
Depth charges: 8 rails.

Comment: Builders, Kraljevica Yard. Commissioned 1981-85. A most unusual feature of this design is the fitting of an electric outboard motor giving a speed of up to 6 kts. One sunk possibly by a limpet mine in November 1991. Two held by Croatia. Two more paid off by 1993.

POHORJE   1988, Yugoslav Navy

6 TYPE 20 (RIVER PATROL CRAFT)

PC 211-216

Displacement, tons: 55 standard
Dimensions, feet (metres): 71.5 × 17 × 3.9 *(21.8 × 5.3 × 1.2)*
Main machinery: 2 diesels; 1156 hp(m) *(850 kW)*; 2 shafts
Speed, knots: 16. **Range, miles:** 200 at 15 kts
Complement: 10
Guns: 2 Oerlikon 20 mm.
Radars: Surface search: Decca 110; I band.

Comment: Completed since 1984. Steel hull with GRP superstructure.

TYPE 20   *1988, Yugoslav Navy*

4 BOTICA CLASS (TYPE 16) (RIVER PATROL CRAFT)

PC 303-306

Displacement, tons: 23 full load
Dimensions, feet (metres): 55.8 × 11.8 × 2.8 *(17 × 3.6 × 0.8)*
Main machinery: 2 diesels; 464 hp(m) *(340 kW)*; 2 shafts
Speed, knots: 15
Complement: 7
Military lift: 3 tons
Guns: 1 Oerlikon 20 mm. 7—7.62 mm MGs.
Radars: Surface search: Decca 110; I band.

Comment: Can carry up to 30 troops. These remaining four were all operational in early 1994.

TYPE 16 (model)   *1988, Yugoslav Navy*

11 TYPE 15 (RIVER PATROL CRAFT)

Displacement, tons: 19.5 full load
Dimensions, feet (metres): 55.4 × 12.8 × 2.3 *(16.9 × 3.9 × 0.7)*
Main machinery: 2 diesels; 330 hp(m) *(242 kW)*; 2 shafts
Speed, knots: 16. **Range, miles:** 160 at 12 kts
Complement: 6
Guns: 1 Oerlikon 20 mm; 2—7.62 mm MGs.
Radars: Surface search: Racal Decca 110; I band.

Comment: Built in Yugoslavia in the late 1980s for use in shallow water. Steel hulls with GRP super-structure. Four air-conditioned craft were delivered to Sudan on 18 May 1989. One deleted so far.

TYPE 15   *1989, Yugoslav Navy*

AMPHIBIOUS FORCES

6 TYPE 21 (LCUs)

DJC 604-606, 608-610

Displacement, tons: 32 full load
Dimensions, feet (metres): 69.9 × 15.7 × 5.2 *(21.3 × 4.8 × 1.6)*
Main machinery: 1 diesel; 1450 hp(m) *(1.07 MW)*; 1 shaft
Speed, knots: 23. **Range, miles:** 320 at 22 kts
Complement: 6
Military lift: 6 tons
Guns: 1—20 mm M71.

Comment: The survivors of a class of 30 built between 1976 and 1979. Four held by Croatia in 1991. Others sunk or scrapped.

DJC 607   *1989, Yugoslav Navy*

1 SILBA CLASS (LCT/MINELAYER)

Name	No	Builders	Commissioned
SILBA	DBM 241	Brodosplit Shipyard, Split	1990

Displacement, tons: 880 full load
Dimensions, feet (metres): 163.1 oa; 144 wl × 33.5 × 8.5 *(49.7; 43.9 × 10.2 × 2.6)*
Main machinery: 2 Alpha 10V23L-VO diesels; 3100 hp(m) *(2.28 MW)* sustained; 2 shafts; cp props
Speed, knots: 12. **Range, miles:** 1200 at 12 kts
Complement: 33 (3 officers)
Military lift: 460 tons or 6 medium tanks or 7 APCs or 4—130 mm guns plus towing vehicles or 300 troops with equipment
Missiles: SAM: 1 SA-N-5 Grail quad mounting.
Guns: 4—30 mm/65 (2 twin) AK 230.
  4—20 mm M75 (quad). 2—128 mm illuminant launchers.
Mines: 94 Type SAG-1.
Radars: Surface search: I band.

Comment: Ro-Ro design with bow and stern ramps. Can be used for minelaying, transporting weapons or equipment and troops. A second of class was launched in July 1992 for the Croatian Navy.

SILBA   *1990, Yugoslav Navy*

8 TYPE 22 (LCUs)

DJC 621, 625-628, 630-632

Displacement, tons: 48 full load
Dimensions, feet (metres): 73.2 × 15.7 × 3.3 *(22.3 × 4.8 × 1)*
Main engines: 2 MTU diesels; 1740 hp(m) *(1.28 MW)*; 2 waterjets
Speed, knots: 35. **Range, miles:** 320 at 22 kts
Complement: 8
Military lift: 40 troops or 15 tons cargo
Guns: 2—20 mm M71.
Radars: Navigation: Decca 101; I band.

Comment: Built of polyester and glass fibre. Last one completed in 1987. Three held by Croatia.

DJC 627   *1989, Yugoslav Navy*

2 MFPD-3 TYPE + 2 DSM 501 TYPE (LCTs/MINELAYERS)

DTM 229   DTM 232   DSM 513   DSM 514

Displacement, tons: 410 full load
Dimensions, feet (metres): 155.1 × 21 × 7.5 *(47.3 × 6.4 × 2.3)*
Main machinery: 3 Gray Marine 64 HN9 diesels; 495 hp *(369 kW)*; 3 shafts
Speed, knots: 9
Complement: 15
Military lift: 200 troops or 3 heavy tanks
Guns: 2—20 mm (twin).
Mines: Can carry 100.

Comment: Unlike other tank landing craft in that the centre part of the bow drops to form a ramp
down which the tanks go ashore, the vertical section of the bow being articulated to form outer
end of ramp. Built in Yugoslavia. Can also act as minelayers. Two sold to Sudan in 1969. DTM
(Desantni Tenkonosac/Minopolagac means landing ship tank/minelayer). Four of the class
acquired by Croatia in 1991, several others deleted.

MFPD-3 TYPE   1989, Yugoslav Navy

4 TYPE 11 (LCVP)

DJC 614, 616-618

Displacement, tons: 10 full load
Dimensions, feet (metres): 37 × 10.2 × 1.6 *(11.3 × 3.1 × 0.5)*
Main machinery: 2 diesels; 2 waterjets
Speed, knots: 23. **Range, miles:** 100 at 15 kts
Complement: 2
Military lift: 4.8 tons of equipment or troops
Guns: 1—7.62 mm MG.
Radars: Navigation: I band.

Comment: GRP construction building from 1986. Many sunk or damaged.

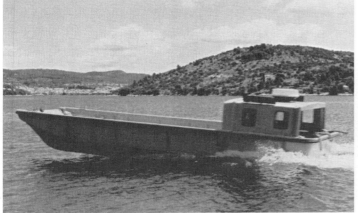

LCVP TYPE 11   1990, Yugoslav Navy

MINE WARFARE FORCES

2 HAM CLASS (MINESWEEPERS—INSHORE)

MLJ M 141   **BRSEČ** M 142

Displacement, tons: 120 standard; 159 full load
Dimensions, feet (metres): 106.5 × 21.3 × 5.5 *(32.5 × 6.5 × 1.7)*
Main machinery: 2 Paxman YHAXM diesels; 1100 hp *(821 kW)*; 2 shafts
Speed, knots: 14. **Range, miles:** 2000 at 9 kts
Complement: 22
Guns: 2 Oerlikon 20 mm (twin).

Comment: Built in Yugoslavia 1964-66 under the US Military Aid Programme. Wooden hulls. One
more acquired by Croatia in 1991.

HAM (old number)   1988, Yugoslav Navy

2 VUKOV KLANAC CLASS (MINESWEEPERS/HUNTERS)

Name	No	Builders	Commissioned
PODGORA (ex-*Smeli*)	M 152 (ex-D 26)	A Normand, France	Sep 1957
BLITVENICA* (ex-*Slobodni*)	M 153 (ex-D 27)	A Normand, France	Sep 1957

*Hunter

Displacement, tons: 365 standard; 424 full load
Dimensions, feet (metres): 152 × 28 × 8.2 *(46.4 × 8.6 × 2.5)*
Main machinery: 2 SEMT-Pielstick PA1 175 diesels; 1620 hp(m) *(1.19 MW)*; 2 shafts
Speed, knots: 15. **Range, miles:** 3000 at 10 kts
Complement: 40
Guns: 2 Oerlikon 20 mm.
Countermeasures: MCMV: PAP 104 (minehunter); remote-controlled submersibles.
Radars: Navigation: Thomson-CSF DRBN 30; I band.
Sonars: Plessey Type 193M (minehunter); hull-mounted; active minehunting; high frequency.

Comment: Built to a British design as US 'off-shore' orders. *Blitvenica* converted to minehunter in
1980-81. Decca Hi-fix. One more acquired by Croatia in 1991. *Gradac* was scrapped in 1993.

BLITVENICA   1988, Yugoslav Navy

7 NESTIN CLASS (RIVER MINESWEEPERS)

Name	No	Builders	Commissioned
NESTIN	M 331	Brodotehnika, Belgrade	20 Dec 1975
MOTAJICA	M 332	Brodotehnika, Belgrade	18 Dec 1976
BELEGIŠ	M 333	Brodotehnika, Belgrade	1976
BOCUT	M 334	Brodotehnika, Belgrade	1979
VUČEDOL	M 335	Brodotehnika, Belgrade	1979
DJERDAR	M 336	Brodotehnika, Belgrade	1980
PANONSKO MORE	M 337	Brodotehnika, Belgrade	1980

Displacement, tons: 65 full load
Dimensions, feet (metres): 88.6 × 21.7 × 5.2 *(27 × 6.3 × 1.6)*
Main machinery: 2 diesels; 520 hp(m) *(382 kW)*; 2 shafts
Speed, knots: 15. **Range, miles:** 860 at 11 kts
Complement: 17
Guns: 5 Hispano 20 mm (triple fwd, 2 single aft).
Mines: 24 can be carried.
Countermeasures: MCMV: Magnetic, acoustic and explosive sweeping gear.
Radars: Surface search: Racal Decca 1226; I band.

Comment: Eight transferred to Hungary and three to Iraq.

MOTAJICA   1982, Yugoslav Navy

5 TYPE M 301 CLASS (RIVER MINESWEEPERS)

RML 319-323

Displacement, tons: 38
Speed, knots: 12
Guns: 2 Oerlikon 20 mm.
Radars: Surface search: Racal Decca; I band.

Comment: All launched in 1951-53. Serve on the Danube. Have minelaying capability. Several
scrapped.

M 301 TYPE   1982, Yugoslav Navy

TRAINING SHIPS

Note: In addition to *Galeb*, the sail training ship *Jadran* (ex-*Marco Polo*), previously thought to have been deleted in 1992, is still in service. She was launched in 1932 and has a sail area of 8600 sq ft (800 m²) and an auxiliary 375 hp diesel. Crew of 150 when at sea.

1 GALEB CLASS (AX)

Name	No	Builders	Commissioned
GALEB (ex-*Kuchuk*, ex-*Ramb III*, ex-German *Kiebitz*)	M 11	Ansaldo, Genoa	1939

Displacement, tons: 5182 standard
Measurement, tons: 3667 gross
Dimensions, feet (metres): 384.8 × 51.2 × 18.4 *(117.3 × 15.6 × 5.6)*
Main machinery: 2 Burmeister & Wain diesels; 7200 hp(m) *(5.29 MW)*; 2 shafts
Speed, knots: 17. **Range, miles:** 20 000 at 16 kts
Guns: 4—40 mm/56.
Mines: Capacity not known.

Comment: Ex-Italian. Launched 6 March 1938. Sunk as an auxiliary cruiser in 1944, refloated and reconstructed in 1952. Serves as Fleet Flagship, Presidential Yacht and training ship. Former armament was four 3.5 in, four 40 mm and 24—20 mm (six quadruple) guns but these guns were landed in the mid-1960s and replacements only mounted several years later. Classified as a minelayer. Operational in early 1993.

GALEB   *7/1989, A Sheldon Duplaix*

SURVEY SHIPS

3 SURVEY CRAFT

Comment: *BH 11* and *BH 12* of 70 tons, complement 12; and *CH 1* of 4.5 tons, complement 3. All other craft deleted.

AUXILIARIES

1 KOZARA CLASS (HEADQUARTERS SHIP)

KOZARA PB 34 (ex-PB 30)

Displacement, tons: 695 full load
Dimensions, feet (metres): 219.8 × 31.2 × 4.6 *(67 × 9.5 × 1.4)*
Main machinery: 2 Deutz RV6M545 diesels; 800 hp(m) *(588 kW)*; 2 shafts
Speed, knots: 12

Comment: Former Presidential Yacht on Danube. Built in Austria in 1940. Acts as Flagship of the river flotilla.

KOZARA (old number)   *1982, Yugoslav Navy*

2 HARBOUR TANKERS

PN 26   PN 27

Displacement, tons: 430 full load
Dimensions, feet (metres): 151 × 23.6 × 10.2 *(46 × 7.2 × 3.1)*
Main machinery: 1 diesel; 300 hp(m) *(220 kW)*; 1 shaft
Speed, knots: 7

Comment: Built at Split in mid-1950s. The last survivors of the class. One more held by Croatia.

1 VIS CLASS (HEADQUARTERS SHIP)

VIS PB 35 (ex-PB 25)

Displacement, tons: 680 full load
Dimensions, feet (metres): 187 × 27.9 × 11.5 *(57 × 8.5 × 3.5)*
Main machinery: 2 diesels; 2000 hp(m) *(1.47 MW)*; 2 shafts
Speed, knots: 17
Guns: 1 Bofors 40 mm/60. 2 Oerlikon 20 mm.

Comment: Built in 1956. Serves as the Command ship of the Federal Navy. Design based on the former yacht *Jadranka*.

VIS   *1987*

1 LUBIN CLASS (AKL)

KIT PO 93

Displacement, tons: 860 full load
Dimensions, feet (metres): 190.9 × 36 × 9.2 *(58.2 × 11 × 2.8)*
Main machinery: 2 diesels; 3500 hp(m) *(2.57 MW)*; 2 shafts; cp props
Speed, knots: 16. **Range, miles:** 1500 at 16 kts.
Complement: 43
Military lift: 150 troops; 6 tanks
Guns: 1 Bofors 40 mm/70. 4—20 mm M75 (quad). 128 mm rocket launcher for illuminants.

Comment: Fitted with bow doors and two upper-deck cranes. Roll-on/roll-off cargo ship built in the 1980s and employed by the Navy usually as ammunition transport. PO (Pomocni Oruzar or auxiliary ammunition ship). Two others deleted in 1991.

KIT   *1987, Yugoslav Navy*

1 WATER TANKER

ALGA PV 17

Displacement, tons: 600 full load
Dimensions, feet (metres): 144.4 × 25.6 × 10.5 *(44 × 7.8 × 3.2)*
Main machinery: 1 diesel; 350 hp(m) *(257 kW)*; 1 shaft
Speed, knots: 8
Cargo capacity: 380 tons
Guns: 1 Bofors 40 mm/60. 1—20 mm M71.

Comment: Incorrectly reported as acquired by Croatia in 1991.

ALGA   *10/1990, Eric Grove*

4 PT 82 CLASS (AKL)

PT 82   PT 83   PT 86   PT 87

Displacement, tons: 58 full load
Dimensions, feet (metres): 67.3 × 14.8 × 3.7 *(20.5 × 4.5 × 1.4)*
Main machinery: 2 diesels; 304 hp(m) *(223 kW)*; 2 shafts
Speed, knots: 12. **Range, miles:** 400 at 10 kts
Complement: 6
Cargo capacity: 15 tons or 70 troops with equipment
Guns: 2—20 mm M71 (can be fitted).

Comment: Completed in 1987. General-purpose transport craft.

PT 83   *1989, Yugoslav Navy*

1 PT 71 TYPE (TRANSPORT)

JASTOG PT 72

Displacement, tons: 310 standard; 428 full load
Dimensions, feet (metres): 152.2 × 23.6 × 17.1 *(46.4 × 7.2 × 5.2)*
Main machinery: 1 Burmeister & Wain diesel; 300 hp(m) *(220 kW)*; 1 shaft
Speed, knots: 7

Comment: Built in 1953. Second of class acquired by Croatia in 1991.

JASTOG   *1982, Yugoslav Navy*

1 SABAC CLASS (DEGAUSSING VESSEL)

RSRB 36

Displacement, tons: 110 standard
Dimensions, feet (metres): 105.6 × 23.3 × 3.9 *(32.2 × 7.1 × 1.2)*
Main machinery: 1 diesel; 528 hp(m) *(388 kW)*; 1 shaft
Speed, knots: 10. **Range, miles:** 660 at 10 kts
Complement: 20
Guns: 2—20 mm M71.

Comment: Used to degauss River vessels up to a length of 50 m.

36   *1987, Yugoslav Navy*

TENDERS

Displacement, tons: 51 full load
Dimensions, feet (metres): 69 × 14.8 × 4.6 *(21 × 4.5 × 1.4)*
Main machinery: 2 diesels; 304 hp(m) *(224 kW)*; 2 shafts
Speed, knots: 12. **Range, miles:** 400 at 10 kts
Guns: 2—20 mm M71 can be carried.
Radars: Navigation: Decca; I band.

Comment: A number of tenders similar to PT 82 class which, as transports, can carry up to 130 people or 15 tons of cargo and also act as diving tenders.

TENDER   *10/1990, Eric Grove*

2 PRESIDENTIAL YACHTS (SUPPLY CRAFT)

Comment: Former Presidential Yachts used as supply craft and naval manned.

SUPPLY CRAFT   *1990, Florian Jentsch*

TUGS

Note: In addition there are two harbour tugs LR 72 and LR 77. Two others acquired by Croatia in 1991.

3 COASTAL TUGS

PR 37, 38, 48

Displacement, tons: 550 full load
Dimensions, feet (metres): 105 × 26.2 × 16.4 *(32 × 8 × 5)*
Speed, knots: 11

Comment: Built at Split in 1950s. Type name, PR (Pomorski Remorker).

COASTAL TUG   *1988, Yugoslav Navy*

ZAIRE

Personnel

(a)   1994: 1500 officers and men (including 600 marines)
(b)   Voluntary service

Bases

Matadi, Boma, Banana

Mercantile Marine

Lloyd's Register of Shipping:
   27 vessels of 14 917 tons gross

PATROL FORCES

Note: Six TB 40 and 20 TB 11PA patrol craft were ordered from North Korea in 1989 but none has been delivered due to lack of funds.

2 SHANGHAI II CLASS (FAST ATTACK CRAFT—GUN)

106   +1

Displacement, tons: 113 standard; 131 full load
Dimensions, feet (metres): 127.3 × 17.7 × 5.6 *(38.8 × 5.4 × 1.7)*
Main machinery: 2 Type L12-180 diesels; 2400 hp(m) *(1.76 MW)* forward; 2 Type L12-180Z diesels; 1820 hp(m) *(1.34 MW)* aft; 4 shafts
Speed, knots: 30. **Range, miles:** 700 at 17 kts
Complement: 34
Guns: 4—37 mm/65 (2 twin). 4—25 mm/80 (2 twin).

Comment: First four delivered from China in 1976-78. All were thought to be beyond repair by 1985 but two of the four were patched up and two replacements were delivered in February 1987. Two sunk at moorings in mid-1990.

SHANGHAI II 106   *1988, Gilbert Gyssels*

4 SWIFTSHIPS (COASTAL PATROL CRAFT)

KIALA   LUADIA   KANITSHA   MBOKO

Displacement, tons: 19 full load
Dimensions, feet (metres): 51.2 × 13.5 × 3.6 *(15.6 × 4.1 × 1.1)*
Main machinery: 2 GM 12V-71 diesels; 680 hp *(507 kW)* sustained; 2 shafts
Speed, knots: 25. **Range, miles:** 400 at 24 kts
Complement: 12
Guns: 6—12.7 mm MGs.

Comment: Built by Swiftships, Morgan City, in 1971. Doubtful operational status and two have already been deleted.

6 ARCOA 25 CLASS (PATROL CRAFT)

Displacement, tons: 2 full load
Dimensions, feet (metres): 24.6 × 9.8 × 2.6 *(7.5 × 3 × 0.8)*
Main machinery: 2 Baudouin diesels; 320 hp(m) *(235 kW)*; 2 shafts
Speed, knots: 30

Comment: Twenty-nine ordered in 1974 in France and delivered by Arcoa. MG mountings forward and aft. Fourteen more delivered 1980-81. Eight were still serviceable at the end of 1990 but this had reduced to six by 1994.

Indexes

COUNTRY ABBREVIATIONS

Alb	Albania			Kir	Kiribati	SA	South Africa
Alg	Algeria	DR	Dominican Republic	Kwt	Kuwait	Sab	Sabah
Ana	Anguilla	Ecu	Ecuador	Lat	Latvia	SAr	Saudi Arabia
Ang	Angola	Egy	Egypt	Lbr	Liberia	Sen	Senegal
Ant	Antigua and Barbuda	ElS	El Salvador	Lby	Libya	Sey	Seychelles
Arg	Argentina	EqG	Equatorial Guinea	Leb	Lebanon	Sin	Singapore
Aus	Austria	Est	Estonia	Lit	Lithuania	SL	Sierra Leone
Aust	Australia	Eth	Ethiopia and Eritrea	Mad	Madagascar	Sol	Solomon Islands
Az	Azerbaijan	Fae	Faeroes	Mex	Mexico	Spn	Spain
Ban	Bangladesh	Fij	Fiji	MI	Marshall Islands	Sri	Sri Lanka
Bar	Barbados	Fl	Falkland Islands	Mic	Micronesia	StK	St Kitts
Bdi	Burundi	Fin	Finland	Mld	Maldive Islands	StL	St Lucia
Bel	Belgium	Fra	France	Mlt	Malta	StV	St Vincent and the Grenadines
Ben	Benin	Gab	Gabon	Mlw	Malawi	Sud	Sudan
Bhm	Bahamas	Gam	The Gambia	Mly	Malaysia	Sur	Surinam
Bhr	Bahrain	GB	Guinea-Bissau	Mns	Montserrat	Swe	Sweden
Blz	Belize	Ger	Germany	Mor	Morocco	Swi	Switzerland
Bmd	Bermuda	Geo	Georgia	Moz	Mozambique	Syr	Syria
Bol	Bolivia	Gha	Ghana	Mrt	Mauritius	Tan	Tanzania
Bru	Brunei	Gn	Guinea	Mtn	Mauritania	TC	Turks and Caicos
Brz	Brazil	Gra	Grenada	Nam	Namibia	Tld	Thailand
Bul	Bulgaria	Gre	Greece	NATO	NATO	Tog	Togo
Bur	Burma	Gua	Guatemala	Nic	Nicaragua	Ton	Tonga
Cam	Cameroon	Guy	Guyana	Nig	Nigeria	TT	Trinidad and Tobago
Can	Canada	Hai	Haiti	Nld	Netherlands	Tun	Tunisia
Chi	Chile	HK	Hong Kong	Nor	Norway	Tur	Turkey
CI	Cook Islands	Hon	Honduras	NZ	New Zealand	UAE	United Arab Emirates
Cmb	Cambodia	Hun	Hungary	Omn	Oman	Uga	Uganda
Col	Colombia	IC	Ivory Coast	Pak	Pakistan	UK	United Kingdom
Com	Comoro Islands	Ice	Iceland	Pan	Panama	Ukr	Ukraine
Con	Congo	Ind	India	Par	Paraguay	Uru	Uruguay
CPR	China, People's Republic	Indo	Indonesia	Per	Peru	USA	United States of America
CpV	Cape Verde	Iran	Iran	Plp	Philippines	Van	Vanuatu
CR	Costa Rica	Iraq	Iraq	PNG	Papua New Guinea	Ven	Venezuela
Cro	Croatia	Ire	Ireland	Pol	Poland	VI	Virgin Islands
Cub	Cuba	Isr	Israel	Por	Portugal	Vtn	Vietnam
Cypr	Cyprus (Republic)	Ita	Italy	Qat	Qatar	WS	Western Samoa
Den	Denmark	Jam	Jamaica	RoC	Taiwan	Yem	Yemen
Dji	Djibouti	Jor	Jordan	RoK	Korea, Republic (South)	Yug	Yugoslavia
Dom	Dominica	Jpn	Japan	Rom	Romania	Zai	Zaire
DPRK	Korea, Democratic	Ken	Kenya	Rus	Russia and Associated States		
	People's Republic (North)						

Named Ships

† denotes secondary reference is in text or note.

Class Index

† denotes reference is in text or note.

Aircraft by Countries

FLOREAL
Ocean Capable Patrol Vessel

Photo Daniel Riffet

6 units for the French Navy.

CHANTIERS DE L'ATLANTIQUE

GEC ALSTHOM

CHANTIERS DE L'ATLANTIQUE / S.A.
38, Avenue Kléber / 75116 Paris / France
Tel. (33-1) 47 55 27 54 / Telex: 645 043 SHIPYAR / Fax: (33-1) 47 55 27 77